Angling Times Fishooked

The Ultimate "where to fish guide"
for UK and Irish Freshwater Fisheries

Coarse, Game and Combination Fisheries
UK & Irish Tackle Shops, UK & Irish Associations,
Clubs and Important Angling Addresses

Also available on CD-ROM
Updated daily on www.fishooked.com

The next generation directories

Angling Times Fishooked

Publisher: HCC Publishing Ltd
Publishing Director: Howard Cox
Advertising Manager: Neil Stokes
Data Research Manager: Claire Thorpe
Design & Production: Lucy Hibbert
Editor: Julian Grattidge
Editorial Programmer: Matthew Corne

ISBN: 1-903897-10-6

Further Information:

Emails: information@fishooked.co.uk
contactus@hccpublishing.co.uk

Website: www.fishooked.com

Address: Meaford Power Station, Meaford, Stone, Staffordshire, ST15 0UU.

Tel: 0870 7420042 (From outside the UK +441782 371173)
Fax: 0870 7541667 (From outside the UK +441782 371166)

Foreword

Having been a keen angling all rounder for many years and like many others, I am fully aware how locating new waters can be fraught with difficulty.

For many years I would spend each close season scouring over Ordnance Survey maps with my angling companions, looking for blobs of water, noting their location, then setting out in the car to investigate further. On all but a handful of occasions these trips proved fruitless. At best you would get there only to realise that the place did not live up to initial expectations, at worst you would get chased across some farmers yard by an overprotective dog before you even got a glimpse of water!

...but now at last there is Angling Times's "Fishooked"!

A clear, concise, and informative next-generation directory with details on over 8,800 freshwater locations throughout the UK and Ireland.

Whatever your fondness, specimen, pleasure, match, or fly, **Fishooked** provides usable information on name, location, water type, coarse or game, facilities, allowances, price, fish types, and even size of fish present. All the information you could need to help you bank the fish of your dreams!

With over 3,000 freshwater locations added to this second edition, along with detailed information on tackle suppliers, manufacturers, clubs and associations, **Fishooked** remains the most comprehensive work of its kind. As a testament to the popularity of **Fishooked** the largest selling fishing publication **"Angling Times"** has agreed to put its prestigious brand name in partnership with **Fishooked**. Over 500,000 anglers read this vital weekly read and therefore **Fishooked** is destined to be the leading "where to fish" guide for the UK and Ireland.

Whatever you are looking for, 30lb carp in Kent, holiday waters in Ireland, or game waters in Gloucestershire...**Fishooked** has the lot!

In addition to this hard copy format, **Fishooked** is also available as a powerful interactive CD-ROM, containing additional venue information, photographs, maps and diagrams, even details on the nearest pub!

Purchasing **Fishooked** in either form also allows membership to the **www.fishooked.com** website, giving access to a whole host of 'fishy' information updated on a daily basis. **The CD and website give you a million extra ways to locate the fishery of your choice.**

Julian Grattidge
Editor and Specimen all-rounder
(Coarse and Game)

Background

When the bites dry up and the alarms fall silent we often think about fishing a new venue, if you're really lucky it's the opposite way around, you've emptied the lake, set a new club record and its time to move on, either way, how do you go about locating a new venue that's right for you?

A quick trip around any lake is enough to tell you that every angler is different, some want to pleasure fish, some want to catch specimens, some want to catch big carp, whilst others are sick of the sight of them, for others its game fish they are after, and that's just the species! What about night-fishing, facilities, prices, syndicate or day ticket, all are important factors when trying to find the venue that's right for you.

This has been the age-old problem with the majority of conventional angling directories. They don't provide the enquirer with the information they want, in the way that they want it. Most directories set out with good intentions, however, as the modern angler becomes more discerning, sophisticated, and even demanding, these 'one-dimensional' directories tend to leave the enquirer "short-changed" and invariably frustrated.

With years of expertise in market research, database management, publishing, and perhaps most importantly angling, the team at HCC knew what was needed. A truly 'searchable' directory, structured in such a way that any angler, no matter what their fishing requirements, would be able to pick up the book and find 'useable' information, presented in a structured manner that was easy on the eye.

Since its launch, Fishooked has received great acclaim from pleasure anglers and professionals alike, with many angling industry specialists referring to it as 'the greatest work of its kind'.

Welcome to Fishooked one of the Next Generation Directories from HCC Publishing.

Fishooked is available as truly interactive searchable CD-ROM and is updated daily on the internet site www.fishooked.com. These unique electronic publications allow millions of ways for anglers to locate a fishery. However due to popular demand we have also produced this handy sized hardcopy directory that leads the way in locating information by more than just "location" or "fishery name". At last there is a way to find fisheries by the way "you" want to find them.

Fishooked Directory

Obviously there are limitations in the number of indices (index sections) to locate a fishery of choice without the concomitant massive increase in the physical size of the book. We have chosen the 12 most popular search routes that anglers use to find a fishery. Just look at the contents page to see how Fishooked allows comprehensive searches even in a hard copy format such as this directory. But, If you wish to carry out a much more intensive interrogation of the Fishooked database then subscribe to the CD and/or the website www.fishooked.com.

Your Involvement in Fishooked

We welcome your input; in fact we positively encourage your comments about any inaccuracies that may be apparent. We also welcome your recommendations about fisheries not currently covered in Fishooked. So let's hear your constructive criticism. It is our aim to continue and to improve the most comprehensive source of information about UK & Irish Fisheries currently available to you. So complete the enclosed forms or write to us about the fisheries included or not included in Fishooked.

Data issue points to be aware of whilst using Fishooked.

1. Information given by fisheries is usually obtained using sophisticated "data collection" questionnaires. If you would like to receive one please contact us by telephone 08707 420042 or send in the application form located at the end of of Section 14. You can also email us using information@fishooked.co.uk.

2. Where fisheries are repeated or there are duplicated names for a river, shows that there is more than one section of that water or fishery, fishable, and that it may be leased or owned by another body. For similar reasoning some fisheries may have duplicated information with minor changes such as telephone numbers or contact details being the only things that are different. We made an editorial decision to repeat some entries with minor changes to help with clarity. In some sections, notably the tabular sections, duplicate names (e.g. Thames) will be listed together with an identity code number that can be cross-referenced with section 1.

3. London is listed as a county (we know it is not). Sub-areas of London have been recognised as a locality and are entered when they are known (e.g. Camden, Waterloo etc).

4. Some areas of information are incomplete due to lack of any co-operation by a fishery manager. That person, for unclear reasoning, prefers that you do not know more than they want to divulge.

5. In certain sections some names have been shortened to enable a uniform layout, but remain recognisable.

6. Abbreviations used in Fishooked:

a. C.Scotland: Central Scotland	b. AC: Angling Club
c. AA: Angling Association	d. S Yorks: South Yorkshire
e. WN: Water Name	f. WT: Water Type
g. FT: Fishery Type	h. F.Size: Fishery size in acres
i. W.Size:Water size in acres	j. Nr.Rd: Nearest Road
k. (T): Telephone number	l. (F): Fax number
m. (E): E-mail address	n. (M): Mobile
o. (W): Web address	
p. £Fr: Where free fishing is available	

7. The most recognised part of a water name is written first (e.g. Henley) and the water name (e.g. River Thames) if any, is written in brackets

8. All telephone numbers have been corrected to the British telecom recommended layout, including international numbers (any changes to numbers after publication is in the hands of BT). Don't forget that the international code for the UK is +44 and Ireland is +353

9. Some Irish waters are best contacted through the regional fisheries board for their area. If you need to know more details about individual waters please contact them or visit their websites. Many of the regional fishery boards are listed in section 14

10. All prices listed are in UK pounds. Irish Punts have been converted to UK pounds at the time of publishing.

11. Please note that Eire (Ireland) does not have postcodes, if the address is very minimal for the fishery and there isn't a contact number, a letter to the address will be the best way to contact them.

12. 'Unspecified' water type means that the type of water was not divulged to us in our validations and data collection.

13. The section listing where free fishing is available should be checked before venturing out on a visit. These change frequently.

14. The Reference Number shown at the end of each fishery entry (e.g. Ref: FH645) in Section 1 is a cross reference with Sections 6,7,8,9,10,11 and 12. If there is more than one fishery with an identical name in these sections, then this unique reference number will help guide you to the fishery of your choice back in Section 1.

Rod Licences

Here is the text supplied on the Environments Agency's website regarding fishing licenses in England and Wales. Government enforced licenses are not required in Scotland. In Ireland there are regional variations to licensing and it is advisable that you contact the Fishery direct as to what is currently required.

All monies collected from rod licences by the Environment Agency are invested directly into fisheries activities (enforcement, monitoring, disease detection, research and development, fish rearing and management, fish runs and habitat maintenance and fish rescue among other activities).

Did you know that anyone aged 12 years or over who fishes for salmon, trout, freshwater fish or eels in England and Wales must have an Environment Agency Rod Fishing Licence?

A background to rod licensing in England and Wales

Before 1992 and the introduction of the single national rod licence, the National Rivers Authority (NRA) issued some 87 different regional rod licences. Of these 46 were migratory salmon id licences of one type or another.

The NRA inherited this confused mixture of licence types and duties from the 10 independent Water Authorities, which in part, formed the NRA in September 1989. There were considerable difficulties maintaining such a varied range of licences and the system was not in keeping with the culture of a National organisation. The major problems were:

Licences were not transferable between Regions, and some anglers had to buy several a year.

Duties were inconsistent, for example in 1991, a Northumbria full annual salmon and migratory trout licence cost £55, whereas the same licence for the North West cost £31.20, and an Anglian all species licence cost £7.50.

Administration costs were duplicated across 10 Regions.

In 1992 the NRA, following extensive public consultation, introduced a single national rod licence for all species. Concessions were offered to senior citizens, juniors and some disabled anglers at a little over half price.

April 1993 saw the introduction of a seven-day licence, priced, like the concessionary licence at a little over half price. Following further extensive consultation the NRA in 1994 introduced a new two-tier licence replacing the single licence for all species.

The two tiers were the salmon and sea trout licence and the non-migratory trout and coarse fish licence. At the same time, the seven-day licence was extended to cover 8 days and a new one-day licence was introduced. This range of categories (full, concessionary, eight-day and one-day) for the two types of licence have remained unchanged since.

In 1994/95, licences were made available from 17,500 Post offices for the first time. Prior to this some 2,500 outlets sold the licence.

The Environment Agency introduced a telephone sales line for full licences and junior concessionary licences in 1999 and this service is still available by telephoning 0870 1662 662 (for debit and credit card users)

The most recent service and licence, which the Environment Agency launched in April 2000, is the Beginner's licence, to help encourage new anglers into the sport.

Rod fishing licence prices 2001/02 - vailid from 01 April 2001

Category	Non Migratory Trout & Coarse Fish	Salmon & Sea Trout
Full	£20.00	£59.00
Junior	£5.00	£29.50
8-day	£6.50	£16.50
1-day	£2.50	£5.50

Concessionary Licences
You are eligible for a concessionary licence if:

- You are aged 12 to 16 inclusive
- You are aged 65 years or over
- You receive:
  1. Long-term incapacity benefit
  2. Short-term incapacity benefit (at the higher rate)
  3. Severe disablement allowance
  4. A war pension which includes unemployability supplement

Where can I buy my Licence?

Rod Fishing Licences are available from:

- Every Post Office in England and Wales.
- The Telesales Service: 0870 1662 662
  (for full and junior concessionary licences)
- The Internet: http://www.environment-agency.gov.uk/

UK Freshwater Fish Records

British Record Fish Committee, Head Office, Level 5, Hamlyn House, Mardle Way, Buckfastleigh, TQ11 0NS.

Tel:01364 644643 Fax: 01364 644486 email - ho@nfsa.org.uk.

GAME FISH RECORDS - OCTOBER 2001

Species	(lbs-ozs-drms)			(kilo grms)	Date	Captor and Location
Charr, Arctic (N)	9	8	0	4.309	1995	W. Fairbairn, Loch Arkaig, Inverness, Scotland.
Grayling (N)	4	3	0	1.899	1989	S.R. Lanigan, River Frome, Dorset.
Salmon, Atlantic (N)	64	0	0	29.029	1922	Miss G.W. Ballatine, River Tay, Scotland.
Trout, American Brook (C)	8	3	0	3.713	1998	E. Holland, Fontburn Reservoir, Northumberland
Trout, Brown (N)	30	9	0	13.863	2000	K. Oliver, Loch Awe, Argyll, Scotland.
Trout Brown (C)	28	1	0	12.729	1995	D. Taylor, Dever Springs Trout, Fishery, Hants.
Trout, Rainbow (C)	36	14	8	16.740	1995	C. White, Dever Springs Trout Fishery, Hants.
Trout Rainbow (R)	24	1	4	10.921	1998	J. Hammond, Hanningfield Reservoir, Essex
Trout, Sea (N)	28	5	4	12.850	1992	J.Farrent, Calshot Spit, River Test,

COARSE FISH RECORDS - OCTOBER 2001

Species	(lbs-ozs-drms)			(kilo grms)	Date	Captor and Location
Barbel	19	0	0	8.618	2001	T. Gibson, Great Ouse, Buckinghamshire.
Bitterling				21 grms	1998	D. Flack, Barway Lake, Cambridgeshire.
Bleak		4	9	.129	1998	D. Flack, River Lark, Cambridgeshire.
Bream (Common Bronze)	18	08	0	8.392	2001	K. Walker, Bawburgh Lakes, Norwich.
Bream, Silver		15	0	.425	1988	D.E. Flack, Grime Spring, Lakenheath, Suffolk.
Bullhead (Miller's Thumb)	1	0		.028	1983	R. Johnson, Bramley & Green Rvr,Nr.Guildford, Surrey.
Carp	59	12	0	27.103	2001	T. Glebioska, Conningbrook Lake, Ashford, Kent.
Carp, Crucian	4	8	0	2.041	2000	J. Allen, RMC Summer Pit, Yately, Hants.
Carp, Grass	36	08	0	16.585	2001	C. Nash, Church Lake, Horton, Berkshire.
Catfish, Bullhead,Black	1	3	0	.540	2001	K.Clements, Lake Meadows, Essex.
Catfish, Wels	62	0	0	28.123	1997	R. Garner, Withy Pool, Henlow, Beds. *
Chub	8	10	0	3.912	1994	P. Smith, River Tees, Blackwell, Co. Durham.
Dace	1	4	4	.574	1960	J. L. Gasson, Little Ouse, Thetford, Norfolk.
Eel	11	2	0	5.046	1978	Master S. Terry, Kingfisher Lake,Nr. Ringwood, Hants.
Goldfish, Brown	5	11	8	2.594	1994	D. Lewis, 6 acre Surrey still water pond.
Gudgeon		5	0	.141	1990	D.H. Hull, Rvr Nadder, Sutton Mandeville, Wiltshire.
Minnow			13.5	.024	1998	J. Sawyer, Whitworth Lake, Spennymoor.
Orfe, Golden	8	5	0	3.770	2000	M. Wilkinson, Lymm Vale, Cheshire.
Perch	5	9	0	2.523	1985	J. Shayler, from a Private Lake, Kent.
Pike	46	13	0	21.234	1992	R. Lewis, Llandegfedd, Wales.
Walleye (Pikeperch)	11	12	0	5.329	1934	F. Adams, The Delph, Welney, Norfolk.
Zander (Pikeperch)	19	5	8	8 774	1998	D. Lavender, Fen Water, Cambs.
Pumpkinseed		4	9	.129	1987	D.L. Wallis, Whessoe Pond, Darlington, Co. Durham.
Roach	4	3	0	1.899	1990	R.N. Clarke, Dorset Stour.
Rudd	4	10	0	2.097	2001	S. Parry, Co. Armagh, Northern Ireland.
Ruffe		5	4	.148	1980	R.J. Jenkins, West View Farm, Cumbria, Private Lake.
Schelly (Skelly)	2	1	9	.950	1986	S.M. Barrie, Haweswater Reservoir, Cumbria.
Stickleback, 3-spined				7 grms	1998	D. Flack, High Flyer Lake, Ely, Cambs.
Tench	15	3	6	6.899	2001	D.Ward,Stilwater,Surrey (Subjest to.F.C).

*LISTCLOSED23rdOCTOBER,2000,Nofurtherclaimsconsidered.
(N) Natural (C) Cultivated (R) ResidenT

Claiming a British Record

Issued by the BRITISH RECORD (rod-caught) FISH COMMITTEE, Head Office, Level 5, Hamlyn House, Mardle Way, Buckfastleigh, TQ11 0NS.

PROCEDURE

1. (a) The claimant should contact the Committee Secretary by telephone.
   (b) Advice will then be given concerning preservation, identification and claims procedure.

2. Claims must be confirmed promptly in writing to the Secretary stating:
   (a) The species of fish, the weight and if a game fish whether a natural or cultivated fish or in the case of the Rainbow Trout whether a cultivated, resident or wild fish,

   (b) The date and place of capture, the tackle used, and in the case of sea fish whether shore or boat caught.

   (c) The names and addresses of witnesses, preferably two, both as to the capture by the claimant and the weight, who will be required to sign the forms supporting the claim. (If no witnesses to the capture are available, the claimant must verify his claim by affidavit).

   (d) Photographs of the fish must be made available which should be good quality and preferably in colour. They should include shots of the angler, holding the fish in a normal manner, or in the case of a very large fish, standing alongside it, and also the fish lying on the ground on or next to, an identifiable object.

3. No claim will be accepted unless the Committee is satisfied as to species, method of capture and weight. The Committee reserves the right to reject any claim if not satisfied on any matter, which the Committee may think in the particular circumstances to be material. The Committee requires a high degree of proof in order to safeguard the integrity of the list. As a high degree of proof is required rejection of a claim imports no reflection on the bona fides of the claimant. All costs of submitting a claim must be met by the claimant.

   Chairman: Mr. R.W. Page, Secretary: Mr. D. Rowe
   Scientific, Adviser: Mr. A. Wheeler

METHODS OF CAPTURE

(a) Claims can only be accepted in respect of fish which are caught by fair angling with rod and line. Fair angling is defined by the fish taking the baited hook or lure into its mouth, and must be in accord with the rules of the respective angling discipline Coarse, Game or Sea.

(b) Fish must be caught on rod and line with any legal hook or lure and hooked and played by one person only. Assistance to land the fish (i.e. gaffing, netting) is permitted provided the helper does no touch any part of the tackle other than the leader.

5. WEIGHT.

(a) The fish must be weighed on land using scales or steel yards which can be tested on behalf of the Committee. Where possible commercial or trade scales which are checked regularly by the Weights and Measures Department should be used. The sensitivity of the scales should be appropriate to the size of the fish, i.e. small fish should be weighed on finely graduated scales and the weight claimed for the fish should be to a division of weight (ounce, dram, gramme) not less than the smallest division shown on the scales.

(b) A Weights and Measures Certificate must be produced certifying the accuracy of the scales used and indicating testing at the claimed weight.

(c) In the case of species weighing less than one pound the claimed weight must be submitted in grammes.

(d) The weight must be verified by two independent witnesses who, for example, should not be relations of the claimant .

6. (a)The Committee is required from time to time to consider claims for fish of species which cannot be determined to its satisfaction without inspection. For this reason and others, claimants are strongly advised not to liberate or otherwise dispose of a fish for which it is intended to enter a claim until an inspection of the body, dead or alive, has been made by a representative of the committee and permission given for disposal.

   (b)While claimants should recognise that failure to produce the fish for inspection may prove prejudicial to the acceptance of a claim, the Committee does not bind itself to reject a claim solely because inspection has not been made.

   (c) All carriage costs incurred in production of the fish for inspection by the committee must be borne by the claimant.

7. Claims can be made for species not included in the Committee Record Fish List.

8. The Committee will issue at regular intervals its list of British Record (rod-caught)Fish.

9. No fish caught out of season shall be accepted as a new record.

10. A fish for which a record is claimed must be normal and not obviously suffering from any disease by which the weight could be enhanced.

11. All species of freshwater fish listed in the 1995-1996 Record List are regarded as native or as established aliens and a Section 30 Consent(under the Salmon and Freshwater Fisheries Act 1975) will not normally be required, unless the established alien specie has not previously been caught in the water of capture.

    In the case of a specie which is an established alien not known to have been caught in the water of capture before or is a specie for which no previous record has been awarded, the Committee reserves the right to request the production of a Section 30 Consent and a MAFF Consent to introduce a non-native species of fish (under the Wildlife and Countryside Act 1981).

    The possibility of freshwater fish close to, or above the British Record Weight being imported into the UK and claimed as a British Record has been considered by the Committee which is of the mind that such claims should not be considered.

PROTECTED FISHES.

The following are rare or threatened species in Great Britain and are protected under the provisions of the Wildlife and Countryside Act(1981) and later Orders. This protection results in it being an offence to capture any of these fishes intentionally. Anglers who believe that they may have captured a specimen of any of these species are advised to unhook and release the fish unharmed as soon as possible after capture.

Allis shad Alosa alosa
Burbot Lota lota
Schelly, powan or gwyniad Coregonus lavaretus
Sturgeon Acipenser sturio
Vendace Coregonus albula

No claims for records for these species will be entertained by the BRFC. (The entries for Allis shad and Schelly in the List of Records are given as historical records only).

IF YOU CATCH A RECORD FISH

If an angler catches a potential British record fish he/she should make the claim in the first instance to the BRFC Secretariat at 51A Queen Street, Newton Abbot, Devon, TQ12 2Q]. (Tel/24 hour answer phone 01626331330; fax also). The Secretariat will advise accordingly and, where appropriate, forward to the claimant or his/her agent, the necessary claim forms. Once completed the forms should be returned to the Secretariat who will forward them to the respective discipline for their consideration and endorsement. The claim will then be brought to the next BRFC meeting, which takes place as and when necessary but normally in April and October. The representatives of the disciplines are as follows:- STA; NFA/NASA; NFSA.

Medium sized fish can be preserved for considerable periods by refrigeration (deep freeze), or immersion in formalin. If a fish is to be sent by post or rail it is best immersed in a solution of one tablespoon of formalin (40% solution of formaldehyde) to a pint of water. For despatch, the fish should be wrapped in a cloth wrung out in the solution, placed in a plastic bag sealed as far as possible, and wrapped in stout brown paper; please enclose the name and address of the sender and whether the fish should be returned - if so the postage. The fish should be weighed before being placed in preserving liquids."

Contents

A-Z UK & Irish Fisheries

SECTION 1

This main section of the directory can be used to locate a Fishery you know, or a Fishery you may have chosen using other sections of this book.

What information can I find?

Address, useful contact details, fishery profile (water name, water type, fishery/water sizes), nearest road or rail station, and free fishing. Use the unique reference no. to identify a fishery in sections 6, 7, 8, 9, 10, 11 & 12 eg. FH1867.

Angling Times Fishooked Directory

A1 PITS

A1 Pits, South Muskham, Newark, **NOTTINGHAMSHIRE**, NG, **England**.
Contact/s: Lesley.
(T) 01636 612108
Profile: FT: Coarse; **WN:** Trent; **WT:** Combination (Still & Moving). **Location: Nr. Rd:** A1; **Main Rd:** A616.
Ref: FH0001

ABBEY FISHERY

Abbey Fishery, Penvale Lodges, Horshoe Pass Rd, Llangollen, **DENBIGHSHIRE**, LL20 8DD, **Wales**.
Contact/s: Mr David Penman (Manager).
(T) 01978 860266 **(F)** 01978 860266
Profile: FT: Game; **WN:** Eglwseg; **WT:** Pond (Still & Moving) **W. Size:** 1600 Metres.
Location: Nr. Rd: Horshoe Pass Road; **Main Rd:** A542; **Rail:** Ruabon.
Ref: FH0002

ABBEY LAKES

Abbey Lakes, Orrell, Skelmersdale, **LANCASHIRE**, WN8, **England**.
Contact/s: Mr Neil Jupp (Club Secretary), Lymm Angling Club, PO Box 350, Warrington, Cheshire, WA2 9FB.
(T) 01925 411744
Profile: FT: Coarse; **WN:** Abbey; **WT:** Lake (Still) **W. Size:** 2 Acres. **Location: Nr. Rd:** A577 to Skelmersdale; **Main Rd:** M58 or A577 intersection.
Ref: FH0003

ABBEY WATERS

Abbey Waters, Attleborough, **NORFOLK**, **England**.
(W) www.fisheries.co.uk/barford/index.htm
Contact/s: Ms Sarah Thomson (Manager), Barford Lakes Fishery, Common Farm, Chapel St, Barford, NR9 4AB.
(T) 01603 759624 **(F)** 01603 758111
(E) barfordlakes@barfordlakes.force9.co.uk
Profile: FT: Coarse; **WN:** Abbey; **WT:** Lake (Still); **F. Size:** 1 Acre; **W. Size:** 1 Acre.
Location: Rail: Attleborough.
Ref: FH0004

ABBEYCOURT LAKE

Abbeycourt Lake, 85 Bank St, Sandling, Maidstone, **KENT**, ME1, **England**.
Contact/s: Mr Rob Earl (Manager), Maidstone Angling Ctre, 15 Perryfield St, Maidstone, Kent, ME14 2SY.
(T) 01622 677326 **(F)** 01622 752021
Profile: FT: Coarse; **WN:** Abbeycourt; **WT:** Lake (Still).
Ref: FH0005

ABBIE POND

Abbie Pond, Amotherby, Malton, **YORKSHIRE (NORTH)**, YO17, **England**.
Contact/s: Mr John Jackson (Secretary).
(T) 01653 693606
Profile: FT: Coarse; **WN:** Abbie; **WT:** Pond (Still).
Ref: FH0006

ABBOTS HALL

Abbots Hall, Ingworth, Norwich, **NORFOLK**, NR11, **England**.
Contact/s: Mr Simon Dodsworth, The National Trust, Blickling, Norwich, Norfolk, NR11 6NF.
(T) 01263 733471or738000 **(F)** 01263 734924
Profile: FT: Game; **WN:** Abbots Hall; **WT:** Canal (Still).
Ref: FH0007

ABBOTS POOL

Abbots Pool, Abbots Leigh, Bristol, BS, **England**.
Contact/s: Manager, Bristol Angling Ctre, 12 Doncaster Rd, Southmead, Bristol, BS10 5PL.
(T) 01179 500201 **(F)** 01179 592799
Manager, Avon Angling Ctre, 348 Whitewell Rd, Bristol, Somerset, BS5 7BP.
(T) 01179 517250
Manager, S Shipp Tackle Shop, 7 Victoria St, Staple Hill, Bristol, BS16 5JP.
(T) 01179 566985
Manager, Scotts Tackle Shop, 42 Soundwell Rd, Bristol, Somerset, BS16 4QP.
(T) 01179 567371
Manager, Fish and Field Tackle Shop, 60 Broad St, Chipping Sodbury, Bristol, BS37 6AG.
(T) 01454 314034
Profile: FT: Coarse; **WN:** Abbots; **WT:** Pond (Still).
Ref: FH0008

ABBOTS SALFORD PARK

Abbots Salford Park, Abbots Salford, Evesham, **WORCESTERSHIRE**, WR11 5UT, **England**.
Contact/s: Ms Sandra Rogers.
(T) 01386 870244
Profile: FT: Coarse; **WN:** Abbots Salford Park; **WT:** Pond (Still) **W. Size:** 1600 Metres.
Location: Main Rd: B469.
Ref: FH0009

ABBOTTS COURT

Abbotts Court, Rochester, **KENT**, ME3, **England**.
Contact/s: Mrs A Thomas, 23 Everest Drive, Hoo, Rochester, Kent, ME3 9AN.
Profile: FT: Coarse; **WN:** Abbotts Court; **WT:** Gravel Pit (Still).
Ref: FH0010

ABBOTTS WORTHY

Abbotts Worthy, Orvis, Vermont House, Unit 30A, North Way, Andover, **HAMPSHIRE**, SP10 5RW, **England**.
Contact/s: Ms Judith Thornton (Fishing Administrator).
(T) 01264 349519 **(F)** 01264 349505
Profile: FT: Game; **WN:** Itchen; **WT:** River (Moving). **Location: Nr. Rd:** B3047; **Main Rd:** A33; **Rail:** Winchester.
Ref: FH0011

ABBROOK POND

Abbrook Pond, Abbrook, Kingsteignton, Newton Abbot, **DEVON**, TQ1, **England**.
Contact/s: Manager, Exeter Angling Ctre, Smythen St, Exeter, Devon, EX1 1BN.
(T) 01392 435591or436404 **(F)** 01392 433855
Mr Barry Lucas (Hon Secretary), Mayfield, Gorwyn Lane, Cheriton Bishop, Exeter, EX6 6JL.
(T) 01647 24566
Mr Dave Cornish.
(T) 01392 256770
Profile: FT: Coarse; **WN:** Abbrook; **WT:** Gravel Pit (Still) **W. Size:** 4 Acres. **Location: Nr. Rd:** Kingsteignton to Chudleigh road; **Main Rd:** B3193.
Ref: FH0012

ABERDEEN BOX POOL

Aberdeen Box Pool Limited, 5 Albert Quay, Aberdeen, **ABERDEENSHIRE**, AB1 2QA, **Scotland**.
Contact/s: Manager, Caley Fisheries Limited, 5a Albert Quay, Aberdeen, Aberdeenshire, AB11 5QA.
(T) 01224 593786
Profile: FT: Coarse; **WN:** Aberdeen Box; **WT:** Pool (Still).
Ref: FH0013

ABERFELDY ASSOCIATION BEAT

Aberfeldy Association Beat, Aberfeldy, **PERTH AND KINROSS**, PH15, **Scotland**.
(W) www.fishingnet.com/beats/aberfeldy
Contact/s: Mr G MacDougall (Secretary), 60 Moness Cres, Aberfeldy, Perth and Kinross, PH15.
Profile: FT: Combination; **WN:** Aberfeldy Association Beat; **WT:** Pool (Still).
Ref: FH0014

ABERNANT FARM FISHERY

Abernant Farm Fishery, Pontrhydyfen, Port Talbot, **NEATH PORT TALBOT**, SA13, **Wales**.
Contact/s: Mr David Price (Owner).
(T) 01639 633082
Profile: FT: Game; **WN:** Abernant Farm Fishery; **WT:** River (Moving).
Ref: FH0015

ABINGDON PARK LAKE

Abingdon Park Lake, Northampton, **NORTHAMPTONSHIRE**, NN, **England**.
Contact/s: Fishery Manager.
(T) 01604 31814
Profile: FT: Coarse; **WN:** Abingdon; **WT:** Lake (Still).
Ref: FH0016

ABNEY PARK

Abney Park, Cheadle Hulme, **CHESHIRE**, SK8, **England**.
Contact/s: Ranger, Etherow Country Park, George St, Compstall, Stockport, SK6 5JD.
(T) 0161 4276937 **(F)** 0161 4273643
Profile: FT: Coarse; **WN:** Abney Park; **WT:** Lake (Still). **Location: Nr. Rd:** Manchester Road; **Main Rd:** B5095 north, Cheadle Village.
Ref: FH0017

ABY POND

Aby Pond, Bridge Farm, Belleau, Alford, **LINCOLNSHIRE**, LN13 0BP, **England**.
Contact/s: Mr A Harrop.
(T) 01507 480225 **(F)** 01507 480749
Profile: FT: Coarse; **WN:** Aby; **WT:** Pond (Still).
Ref: FH0018

ACKERS PIT

Ackers Pit, Acker's Lane, Stockton Heath, Warrington, **CHESHIRE**, WA4, **England**.
(W) www.warrington-anglers.org.uk
Contact/s: Mr Frank Lythgoe (Secretary), Warrington Angling Association, 52 Parker St, Warrington, Lancashire.
(T) 01928 716238 **(F)** 01928 713898
(E) info@warrington-anglers.org.uk
Profile: FT: Coarse; **WN:** Acker's; **WT:** Gravel Pit (Still). **Location: Nr. Rd:** Acker's Lane; **Main Rd:** A49 or A56.
Ref: FH0019

ACKTON POND

Ackton Pond, Pontefract, **YORKSHIRE (WEST)**, WF7, **England**.
Contact/s: Mr Paul Griffith.
(T) 01977 798484
Profile: FT: Coarse; **WN:** Ackton; **WT:** Pond (Still) **W. Size:** 2 Acres. **Location: Nr. Rd:** B6133; **Main Rd:** M62 junction 32.
Ref: FH0020

ACLAUREEN (LOUGH)

Aclaureen (Lough), Claremorris, **COUNTY GALWAY**, **Ireland**.
Contact/s: Mr Danny Goldrick (Angling Officer), The Western Regional Fisheries Board, Weir Lodge, Earl's Island, Galway City, County Galway.
(T) 091 563118 **(F)** 091 566335
(E) wrfb@iol.ie
Profile: FT: Coarse; **WN:** Aclaureen; **WT:** Lough (Still) **W. Size:** 10 Acres.
Ref: FH0021

ACLE (RIVER)

River Acle, Acle, Norwich, **NORFOLK**, NR13, **England**.
Contact/s: Fisheries Manager, East Norwich Inn Ltd, 47 Old Rd, Acle, Norwich, Norfolk N13 3QN.
(T) 01493 751112 **(F)** 01493 751109
Profile: FT: Coarse; **WN:** Acle; **WT:** River (Moving). **Location: Main Rd:** A47. **£Fr**
Ref: FH0022

ACR FISHERIES

Acr Fisheries, Evesbatch, Worcester, **WORCESTERSHIRE**, WR, **England**.
Profile: FT: Coarse; **WN:** Acr Fisheries; **WT:** Lake (Still). **Location: Nr. Rd:** B4220; **Main Rd:** A4103, South West of Worcester.
Ref: FH0023

ACREKNOWE RESERVOIR

Acreknowe Reservoir, Hawick, **SCOTTISH BORDERS**, TD9, **Scotland**.
Contact/s: **Mr Penman** (Manager), Pet Store, 1 Union St, Hawick, Scottish Borders, TD9 9LF.
(T) 01450 373543 **(F)** 01450 373543
Mr Eric Stewart (Secretary/Treasurer), Hawick Angling Club, 5 Sandbed, Hawick, Scottish Borders, TD9 0HE.
(T) 01450 373771
Profile: **FT:** Game; **WN:** Acreknowe; **WT:** Reservoir (Still) **W. Size:** 14 Acres.
Location: **Main Rd:** A7; **Rail:** Carlisle.
Ref: FH0024

ACTON BURNELL

Acton Burnell, Shifnal, **SHROPSHIRE**, **England**.
Contact/s: **Mr Rob Hales** (Fisheries Manager), Middle Farm House, Church Lane, Sheriffhales, Shifnal, Shropshire TF11 3RD.
Profile: **FT:** Coarse; **WN:** Lower Lake & Top Pool; **WT:** Lake (Still).
Ref: FH0025

ADAMS POOL

Adams Pool, Alcester, **WARWICKSHIRE**, B50, **England**.
Contact/s: **Mr Ron Griffiths** (Fishery Controller), 22 Cooper Cl, Stoke Heath, Bromsgrove, Warwickshire.
(T) 01527 835534 **(F)** 01527 576403 **(M)** 07798 585014
Profile: **FT:** Coarse; **WN:** Adam's; **WT:** Pond (Still) **W. Size:** 2 Acres. Location: **Nr. Rd:** A435; **Rail:** Redditch.
Ref: FH0026

ADLESTROP LAKE

Adlestrop Lake, Adlerstrop, Stow On The Wold, **GLOUCESTERSHIRE**, GL54 0YN, **England**.
(W) www.macs-tackle.co.uk
Contact/s: **Mr Bill McKenzie** (Club Secretary), Macs Tackle, Bourton On The Water, Gloucestershire, GL54 2EP.
(T) 01451 821719
(E) williampmac@netscapeonline.co.uk
Mr Malcolm Smith (Match Secretary), 2 Ward Rd, Northleach, Gloucestershire, GL54 3RL.
(T) 01451 860173 **(M)** 07760 101083
Profile: **FT:** Coarse; **WN:** Adlestrop; **WT:** Lake (Still) **W. Size:** 5 Acres. Location: **Nr. Rd:** A436; **Main Rd:** A429 (Fosse Way); **Rail:** Moreton In Marsh.
Ref: FH0027

ADLINGTON RESERVOIR

Adlington Reservoir, Bolton, **LANCASHIRE**, WA5, **England**.
Contact/s: **Mr Roy Rhodes** (Conservation, Access and Recreation Manager), Rivington Water Treatment Works, Bolton Rd, Horwich, Bolton, BL6 7RN.
(T) 01204 664300
Profile: **FT:** Game; **WN:** Adlington; **WT:** Reservoir (Still).
Ref: FH0028

ADMIRALS WALK LAKE

Admirals Walk Lake, Conker Lane, Hoddesdon, **HERTFORDSHIRE**, EN11, **England**.
Contact/s: **Mr Gary Smith** (Information Officer), Lee Valley Park Information Ctre, Abbey Gardens, Waltham Abbey, Essex, EN9 1XQ.
(T) 01992 702200
Mr Krizim Seltham (Angling Manager), Lee Valley Regional Park Authority, Myddleton House, Bulls Cross, Enfield, EN2 9HG.
(T) 01992 709832
(E) garysmith@leevalleypark.org.uk
Profile: **FT:** Coarse; **WN:** Admirals Walk; **WT:** Gravel Pit (Still) **W. Size:** 25 Acres.
Location: **Nr. Rd:** Admirals Walk; **Main Rd:** A10; **Rail:** Broxbourne.
Ref: FH0029

ADUR (RIVER)

River Adur, Streatham Bridge, Henfield, **SUSSEX (WEST)**, BN5, **England**.
Contact/s: **Mr A C Carr** (Membership Secretary), Badgers Oak, 28 Lucastes Lane, Haywards Heath, RH12 1RL.
(T) 01444 450597
Profile: **FT:** Combination; **WN:** Adur; **WT:** River (Moving) **W. Size:** 11200 Metres.
Location: **Nr. Rd:** Streatham Bridge to Upper Adur.
Ref: FH0030

ADUR (RIVER)

River Adur, Bramber, Steyning, **SUSSEX (WEST)**, BN44, **England**.
Contact/s: Fisheries Contact, Hyde Square News, Hyde Sq, Upper Beeding, Sussex (West).
Profile: **FT:** Combination; **WN:** Adur; **WT:** River (Moving) **W. Size:** 4800 Metres.
Location: **Nr. Rd:** Bramber Bridge to Streatham Old Railway.
Ref: FH0031

ADUR (RIVER)

River Adur, Henfield, **SUSSEX (WEST)**, BN5, **England**.
Contact/s: Manager, Prime Angling, 74 Brighton Rd, Worthing, Sussex (West), BN11 2EN.
(T) 01903 527050or821594
Mr Ken Dunman (Manager), Tackle Shop, 2 Marine Pl, Worthing, Brighton, BN11 3DN.
(T) 01903 239802
Profile: **FT:** Coarse; **WN:** Adur; **WT:** River (Moving).
Ref: FH0032

ADUR (RIVER)

River Adur, Upper Beeding, Steyning, **SUSSEX (WEST)**, BN44, **England**.
(W) www.calpac.bizland.com
Contact/s: **Mr Colin Trafford** (General Secretary).
(T) 020 82242617
Mrs Diane Wheeler (Secretary), 314 Old Lodge Lane, Purley, Surrey, CR8 4AQ.
(T) 020 86602766
Profile: **FT:** Coarse; **WN:** Adur; **WT:** River (Moving) **W. Size:** 2400 Metres. Location: **Main Rd:** A283 to Bamber.
Ref: FH0033

ADUR (RIVER)

River Adur, Shermanbury Pl, Shermanbury, Henfield, **SUSSEX (WEST)**, BN5, **England**.
Contact/s: **Mr Tony Carr** (Secretary).
(T) 01444 450597
Profile: **FT:** Combination; **WN:** Adur; **WT:** Combination (Still & Moving) **W. Size:** 2400 Metres. Location: **Main Rd:** Shermanbury.
Ref: FH0034

AERON (RIVER)

River Aeron, Aberaeron, **CEREDIGION**, SA46, **Wales**.
Contact/s: **Mr Nigel Davis** (Secretary), Wenallt, 16 Belle Vue Trce, Aberaeron, Carmarthenshire, SA46 0HB.
(T) 01545 571013
Profile: **FT:** Game; **WN:** Aeron; **WT:** River (Moving).
Ref: FH0035

AFAN STREAM

Afan Stream, Aberavon, Port Talbot, **NEATH PORT TALBOT**, SA12, **Wales**.
Contact/s: **Mr M Reynolds** (Secretary), Afan Valley Angling Club, 8 Newlands, Baglan, Neath Port Talbot.
Profile: **FT:** Game; **WN:** Afan; **WT:** Stream (Moving). Location: **Nr. Rd:** Aberavon to Cymmer.
Ref: FH0036

AFON LLYFNI (RIVER)

River Afon Llyfni, Pontllyfni, Caernarfon, **GWYNEDD**, LL55, **Wales**.
Contact/s: **Mr Huw P Hughes** (Hon Secretary), Seiont, Gwyrfai and Llyfni Anglers Society, Llugwy, Ystad Eryri, Bethel, Caernarfon, LL55 1BX.
(T) 01248 670666
(E) huw.hughes@lineone.net
Profile: **FT:** Game; **WN:** Llyfni; **WT:** River (Moving) **W. Size:** 9000 Metres. Location: **Nr. Rd:** Pontllyfni to South of Penygroes; **Main Rd:** A499 or A487; **Rail:** Bangor.
Ref: FH0037

AFON SEIONT (RIVER)

River Afon Seiont, Caernarfon, **GWYNEDD**, LL55, **Wales**.
Contact/s: **Mr Huw P Hughes** (Hon Secretary), Seiont, Gwyrfai and Llyfni Anglers Society, Llugwy, Ystad Eryri, Bethel, Caernarfon, LL55 1BX.
(T) 01248 670666
(E) huw.hughes@lineone.net
Profile: **FT:** Game; **WN:** Seiont; **WT:** River (Moving) **W. Size:** 32000 Metres. Location: **Nr. Rd:** Caernarfon to Pen-y-llyn; **Main Rd:** A4086; **Rail:** Bangor.
Ref: FH0038

AGIVEY (RIVER)

River Agivey, Garvagh, Coleraine, **COUNTY LONDONDERRY**, BT51, **Northern Ireland**.
Contact/s: **Mr Albert Atkins** (Manager), 67 Coleraine Rd, Garvagh, County Londonderry.
(T) 028 70358555
Profile: **FT:** Game; **WN:** Agivey; **WT:** River (Moving) **W. Size:** 36800 Metres.
Ref: FH0039

AILLBRACK LOUGH

Aillbrack Lough, Aillbrack, **COUNTY CLARE**, **Ireland**.
Contact/s: **Mr Kevin Duffy** (Manager).
(T) 065 7071061
Profile: **FT:** Game; **WN:** Aillbrack; **WT:** Lough (Still) **W. Size:** 20 Acres.
Ref: FH0040

AIRA BECK

Aira Beck, Ullswater, Penrith, **CUMBRIA**, CA11, **England**.
Profile: **FT:** Game; **WN:** Aira beck; **WT:** River (Moving). Location: **Main Rd:** A595 west.
£Fr
Ref: FH0041

AIRE (RIVER)

River Aire, Birkin, Beal, Goole, **HUMBERSIDE**, DN14, **England**.
Contact/s: Fishery Manager.
(T) 01977 512655
Mr Bill Baxter.
(T) 01977 514250
Profile: **FT:** Coarse; **WN:** Aire; **WT:** River (Moving). Location: **Main Rd:** M62 then A645.
Ref: FH0042

AIRE (RIVER)

River Aire, Shipley, **YORKSHIRE (WEST)**, BD, **England**.
Contact/s: **Mr W M Troman** (President), 7 Hall Royd, Shipley, Yorkshire (West), BD18 3ED.
(T) 01274 583088
Profile: **FT:** Combination; **WN:** Aire; **WT:** Combination (Still & Moving) **W. Size:** 4800 Metres. Location: **Nr. Rd:** A650; **Main Rd:** A650; **Rail:** Saltaire.
Ref: FH0043

AIRE (RIVER)

River Aire, Keighley, **YORKSHIRE (WEST)**, BD2, **England**.
Contact/s: **Mr Dennis Freeman** (Secretary), Keighley Angling Club, 62 Eelhomle View St, Beechcliffe, Keighley, West Yorkshire, BD20 6AY.
(T) 01535 663695
Profile: **FT:** Combination; **WN:** Aire; **WT:** River (Moving) **W. Size:** 22400 Metres.
Location: **Rail:** Keighley.
Ref: FH0044

AIRE (RIVER)

River Aire, Kildwick, Keighley, **YORKSHIRE (WEST)**, BD20, **England**.
Contact/s: **Mr Nigel Bower** (Secretary), K and L Tackle, 131 Mornington St, Keighley, Yorkshire (West), BD21 2EB.
(T) 01535 667574 **(F)** 01535 661805
Profile: **FT:** Combination; **WN:** Aire; **WT:** River (Moving) **W. Size:** 4800 Metres.
Location: **Nr. Rd:** Skipton to Cross Hills; **Main Rd:** A629 from Skipton to Kildwick.
Ref: FH0045

AIRE (RIVER)

River Aire, Hunslet, Stourton, Leeds, **YORKSHIRE (WEST)**, LS, **England**.
Contact/s: Area Manager, Environment Agency, Ridings Area Office, Phoenix House, Global Avenue, Leeds, LS11 8PG.
(T) 0113 2440191or2314834 **(F)** 0113 2134609
Profile: **FT:** Coarse; **WN:** Aire; **WT:** River (Moving). **Location:** **Nr. Rd:** B6481; **Main Rd:** M1.
Ref: FH0046

AIRE AND CALDER CANAL

Aire And Calder Canal, Great Heck, Goole, **HUMBERSIDE**, DN14, **England**.
Contact/s: **Mr Les Rogers** (Secretary), Goole and District Angling Association, 39 Clifton Gardens, Goole, Humberside (North), DN14 6AR.
(T) 01405 769096
Profile: **FT:** Coarse; **WN:** Aire and Calder; **WT:** Canal (Still) **W. Size:** 16000 Metres.
Location: **Nr. Rd:** Great Heck to Goole; **Main Rd:** M62; **Rail:** Goole.
Ref: FH0047

AIRE AND CALDER CANAL

Aire And Calder Navigation, Fleet Lane, Oulton, **YORKSHIRE (WEST)**, **England**.
Contact/s: **Mr Barry Wright** (Match Secretary).
(T) 01977 559022
Profile: **FT:** Coarse; **WN:** Aire and Calder; **WT:** Canal (Still). **Location:** **Nr. Rd:** Fleet Lane; **Main Rd:** A639; **Rail:** Castleford.
Ref: FH0048

AKERMOOR LOCH

Akermoor Loch, Hawick, **SCOTTISH BORDERS**, TD9, **Scotland**.
Contact/s: **Mr Penman** (Manager), Pet Store, 1 Union St, Hawick, Scottish Borders, TD9 9LF.
(T) 01450 373543 **(F)** 01450 373543
Mr Eric Stewart (Secretary/Treasurer), Hawick Angling Club, 5 Sandbed, Hawick, Scottish Borders, TD9 0HE.
(T) 01450 373771
Profile: **FT:** Game; **WN:** Akermoor; **WT:** Loch (Still) **W. Size:** 11 Acres. **Location:** **Main Rd:** A7; **Rail:** Carlisle.
Ref: FH0049

ALBERT BRIDGE

Albert Bridge, Windsor, **BERKSHIRE**, SL4, **England**.
Contact/s: **Mr Alan Beaven** (Secretary), Old Windsor Angling Club, 88 St Andrew's Way, Slough, Berkshire, SL1 5LJ.
(T) 01628 602537
Profile: **FT:** Coarse; **WN:** Thames; **WT:** River (Moving) **W. Size:** 500 Metres. **Location:** **Nr. Rd:** B3021; **Main Rd:** A308.
Ref: FH0050

ALBRIGHTON MOAT PROJECT

Albrighton Moat Project, Blue House Lane, Albrighton, Wolverhampton, **STAFFORDSHIRE**, WV7 3FL, **England**.
Contact/s: **Mr Jukes**, Albrighton Moat Project, Blue House Lane, Albrighton, Wolverhampton, WV3FL.
(T) 01902 372441 **(F)** 01902 374117
Profile: **FT:** Coarse; **WN:** Albrighton; **WT:** Moat (Still) **W. Size:** 4 Acres. **Location:** **Main Rd:** A41; **Rail:** Wolverhampton.
Ref: FH0051

ALBURY ESTATE FISHERIES

Albury Estate Fisheries, The Estate Office, Weston Yard, Albury, Guildford, **SURREY**, GU5 9AF, **England**.
(W) www.alburyestate.com
Contact/s: **Mr Tony Hern** (Manager), Albury Estate Fisheries, The Estate Office, Weston Yard, Guildford, GU5 9AF.
(T) 01483 202323 **(F)** 01483 203235 **(M)** 07976 810737
(E) tonyhern@lineone.net
Profile: **FT:** Game; **WN:** Albury Estate Fisheries; **WT:** Combination (Still & Moving); **F. Size:** 3000 Acres; **W. Size:** 16 Acres.
Location: **Nr. Rd:** A248; **Main Rd:** A248; **Rail:** Chilworth.
Ref: FH0052

ALBYNS LAKE

Albyns Lake, Hornchurch County Park, South Hornchurch, Hornchurch, **ESSEX**, RM12, **England**.
Contact/s:
(T) 01708 521721
Profile: **FT:** Coarse; **WN:** Albyn's; **WT:** Lake (Still) **W. Size:** 2 Acres. **Location:** **Nr. Rd:** Abbs Cross Lane; **Main Rd:** A13, A125.
Ref: FH0053

ALDAMORE POOL

Aldamore Pool, Sudbury, Ashbourne, **DERBYSHIRE**, DE6, **England**.
Profile: **FT:** Coarse; **WN:** Aldamore Pool; **WT:** Lake (Still) **W. Size:** 5 Acres. **Location:** **Main Rd:** A50.
Ref: FH0054

ALDE (RIVER)

River Alde, Aldeburgh, **SUFFOLK**, IP15, **England**.
Profile: **FT:** Combination; **WN:** Alde; **WT:** River (Moving). **Location:** **Main Rd:** A12, A1094.
Ref: FH0055

ALDE (RIVER)

River Alde, Snape, Saxmundham, **SUFFOLK**, IP17, **England**.
Profile: **FT:** Coarse; **WN:** Alde; **WT:** River (Moving).
Ref: FH0056

ALDEBY HALL FARM PITS

Aldeby Hall Farm Pits, Aldeby, Beccles, **SUFFOLK**, NR34 0AJ, **England**.
Contact/s: Fishery Manager.
(T) 01502 677648
Profile: **FT:** Coarse; **WN:** Aldeby; **WT:** Gravel Pit (Still).
Ref: FH0057

ALDENHAM RESERVOIR

Aldenham Reservoir, Aldenham Country Park, Dagger Lane, Elstree, Borehamwood, **HERTFORDSHIRE**, WD6, **England**.
Mr Eric Barnes (Park Manager), Hertfordshire County Council, Park Office, Dagger Lane, Elstree, WD6 3AT.
(T) 020 89534978 **(M)** 07974 272750
Mr Martin Hartup (Fishery Manager).
(T) 020 89539602
Profile: **FT:** Coarse; **WN:** Aldenham; **WT:** Lake (Still); **F. Size:** 165 Acres; **W. Size:** 60 Acres. **Location:** **Nr. Rd:** Aldenham Road; **Main Rd:** M1, junction 5; **Rail:** Borehamwood.
Ref: FH0058

ALDER LAKE

Alder Lake, Alder Farm, Lewdon, Okehampton, **DEVON**, EX20 4PJ, **England**.
Contact/s: **Mr Bob Westlake**.
(T) 01566 783444 **(F)** 01566 783483
Profile: **FT:** Combination; **WN:** Alder Lake; **WT:** Lake (Still) **W. Size:** 4 Acres. **Location:** **Nr. Rd:** West Devon Drive; **Main Rd:** A30; **Rail:** Plymouth.
Ref: FH0059

ALDERBROOK LAKE

Alderbrook Lake, Alderbrook Farm, Cranleigh, **SURREY**, GU6, **England**.
Contact/s: **Mr Nick Bamford** (Publicity Officer), Cranleigh Angling Club, 20 High St, Cranleigh, Surrey, GU6 8AE.
(T) 01483 274566
Mrs Sue Buxton, 5 Ginger's Cl, Cranleigh, Surrey, GU6 7JL.
Profile: **FT:** Coarse; **WN:** Alderbrook; **WT:** Pond (Still). **Location:** **Nr. Rd:** Horseshoe Lane; **Main Rd:** B2128 to Guildford.
Ref: FH0060

ALDERMASTON

Aldermaston, Paices Hill, Aldermaston, Reading, **BERKSHIRE**, RG7, **England**.
Contact/s: **Mr Patrick Todd** (Estate Manager), Wasing Estate Farm Office, Wasing Park, Aldermaston, Reading, RG7 4NG.
(T) 0118 9714140 **(F)** 0118 9713251
Profile: **FT:** Coarse; **WN:** Aldermaston; **WT:** Lake (Still) **W. Size:** 1 Acre. **Location:** **Nr. Rd:** A340 to Aldermaston; **Main Rd:** M4 at Theale.
Ref: FH0061

ALDERS FARM TROUT FISHERY

Alders Farm Trout Fishery, Ivy Lane, Great Brickhill, Milton Keynes, **BUCKINGHAMSHIRE**, MK17 9AH, **England**.
Mr Richard Wostrope (Owner).
(T) 01525 261713 **(F)** 01525 261713
Profile: **FT:** Combination; **WN:** Alders Farm Trout Fishery; **WT:** Pond (Still) **W. Size:** 11 Acres. **Location:** **Nr. Rd:** Ivy Lane; **Main Rd:** A5; **Rail:** Leighton Buzzard.
Ref: FH0062

ALDERS LAKE

Alders Lake, Sessay, Thirsk, **YORKSHIRE (NORTH)**, YO7, **England**.
Contact/s: **Mr David Kay** (Fishery Manager).
(T) 01845 501321
Profile: **FT:** Coarse; **WN:** Alders; **WT:** Lake (Still).
Ref: FH0063

ALDERS LAKES

Alders Lakes, Castle Way, Larkfield, **KENT**, **England**.
(W) www.aldersfishing.co.uk
Contact/s: **Mrs Babbage** (Club Secretary), 116 Crampton Road, Sevenoaks, Kent. TN14 5DZ..
(T) 01732 461964
Profile: **FT:** Coarse; **WN:** Big Lake, Trout Lake, Ford Lake, Castle Lake; **WT:** Lake (Still); **F. Size:** 40 Acres. **Location:** **Nr. Rd:** A228; **Rail:** New Hythe.
Ref: FH0064

ALDERSONS LAKES

Aldersons Lakes, Needham Market, Ipswich, **SUFFOLK**, IP2, **England**.
Contact/s: **Mr George Alderson** (Secretary), Gipping APS, 19 Clover Cl, Needham Market, Ipswich, Suffolk IP2 0PW.
(T) 01473 602828
Profile: **FT:** Coarse; **WN:** Aldersons; **WT:** Lake (Still) **W. Size:** 8 Acres. **Location:** **Nr. Rd:** Bamford to Stowmarket; **Main Rd:** Needham Market; **Rail:** Stowmarket.
Ref: FH0065

ALDERWOOD PONDS

Alderwood Ponds, Horsham Rd, Steyning, **SUSSEX (WEST)**, BN44, **England**.
Contact/s: **Mr David Holmes**, Highview, Bayards, Horsham Rd, Steyning, BN44 3AA.
(T) 01903 816377 **(F)** 01903 816377
Profile: **FT:** Coarse; **WN:** Alderwood; **WT:** Pond (Still) **W. Size:** 2 Acres. **Location:** **Nr. Rd:** B2135, Steyning to Ashurst; **Main Rd:** B283; **Rail:** Shoreham-by-Sea.
Ref: FH0066

ALDWARK BRIDGE

Aldwark Bridge, Aldward, York, **YORKSHIRE**

(NORTH), YO1, **England**.
Contact/s: **Mr John Lane** (Secretary), York and District Angling Association, 39 Lowfields Drive, Acomb, York, YO2 3DQ.
(T) 01904 783178
Profile: **FT:** Coarse; **WN:** Aldwark; **WT:** River (Moving) **W. Size:** 4800 Metres.
Ref: FH0067

ALDWINCLE PITS

Aldwincle Pits, Thrapston, Kettering, **NORTHAMPTONSHIRE**, NN14, **England**.
Contact/s: Fishery Manager.
(T) 01536 517665
Profile: **FT:** Coarse; **WN:** Aldwincle; **WT:** Gravel Pit (Still).
Ref: FH0068

ALED (RIVER)

River Aled, Llansannan, Denbigh, **CONWY**, LL16, **Wales**.
Contact/s: **Mr W J P Staines** (Hon Secretary), Delamere, Coed Esgob Lane, St Asaph.
(T) 01745 583926
Profile: **FT:** Game; **WN:** Aled; **WT:** River (Moving) **W. Size:** 2400 Metres. Location: **Nr. Rd:** A544.
Ref: FH0069

ALEMOOR RESERVOIR

Alemoor Reservoir, Roverton, Hawick, **SCOTTISH BORDERS**, TD9, **Scotland**.
Contact/s: **Mr Eric Stewart** (Secretary/Treasurer), Hawick Angling Club, 5 Sandbed, Hawick, Scottish Borders, TD9 0HE.
(T) 01450 373771
Profile: **FT:** Game; **WN:** Alemoor; **WT:** Reservoir (Still) **W. Size:** 40 Acres.
Location: **Nr. Rd:** B711; **Main Rd:** A7; **Rail:** Carlisle.
Ref: FH0070

ALEXANDRA PALACE LAKE

Alexandra Palace Lake, Alexandra Park, Finchley, London, **LONDON (GREATER)**, NW, **England**.
Contact/s: **Mr John Lee**.
(T) 020 88898266
Profile: **FT:** Coarse; **WN:** Alexandra Palace; **WT:** Pool (Still). Location: **Nr. Rd:** Muswell Hill to Bridge Road; **Main Rd:** Priory Road.
Ref: FH0071

ALEXANDRA PARK

Alexandra Park, Oldham, **MANCHESTER (GREATER)**, OL, **England**.
Contact/s: Fishery Manager.
(T) 0161 6787626
Profile: **FT:** Coarse; **WN:** Alexandra; **WT:** Lake (Still) **W. Size:** 3 Acres. Location: **Nr. Rd:** King's Road; **Main Rd:** M62 junction 20, A627, Queens Road.
Ref: FH0072

ALEXANDRA PARK LAKE

Alexandra Park Lake, Alexandra Palace, Haringey, London, **LONDON (GREATER)**, N, **England**.
Contact/s: Fishery Manager.
(T) 020 88818809
Profile: **FT:** Coarse; **WN:** Alexandra Park; **WT:** Lake (Still). Location: **Main Rd:** A10, A105. **£Fr**
Ref: FH0073

ALEXANDRA PARK WATERS

Alexandra Park Waters, St Helens Rd, Hastings, **SUSSEX (EAST)**, TN34, **England**.
Contact/s: **Mr Peter Maclean** (Hon Secretary), 37 Collier Rd, Hastings, Sussex (East), TN34 3JR.
(T) 01424 715218
Profile: **FT:** Coarse; **WN:** Buckshole; **WT:** Reservoir (Still) **W. Size:** 5 Acres. Location: **Nr. Rd:** St Helens Road; **Main Rd:** A21; **Rail:** Hastings.
Ref: FH0074

ALFORD ROAD FISHERIES

Alford Road Fisheries, Cranleigh, **SURREY**, GU6, **England**.
Contact/s: **Mr Robbie Gainger** (Secretary), Rudwick Angling Society, 32 Glebe Rd, Cranleigh, Surrey, GU6 7AS.
(T) 01483 275944
Profile: **FT:** Coarse; **WN:** Alford Road Fisheries; **WT:** Lake (Still).
Ref: FH0075

ALLANDALE TARN

Allandale Tarn, Allandale Hall, Gavieside, West Calder, **LOTHIAN (WEST)**, EH55 8PT, **Scotland**.
Contact/s: **Mrs Margo Allan** (Owner).
(T) 01506 873073 **(F)** 01506 873073
Profile: **FT:** Game; **WN:** Allandale; **WT:** Tarn (Still); **F. Size:** 25 Acres; **W. Size:** 3 Acres.
Location: **Nr. Rd:** A71; **Main Rd:** A71; **Rail:** West Calder.
Ref: FH0076

ALLARD FISHERIES

Allard Fisheries, Beechpark, Cahercalla, Ennis, **COUNTY CLARE**, **Ireland**.
Contact/s: **Mr James Allard**.
(T) 065 6824367
Profile: **FT:** Combination; **WN:** Allard Fisheries; **WT:** Combination (Still & Moving); **F. Size:** 100 Acres; **W. Size:** 45 Acres.
Location: **Nr. Rd:** Inagh; **Main Rd:** M18; **Rail:** Ennis.
Ref: FH0077

ALLESTREE LAKE

Allestree Park Lake, Allestree Park, Allestree, Derby, **DERBYSHIRE**, DE, **England**.
Contact/s: **Mr Allan Martin** (Head Ranger).
(T) 01332 367800
Profile: **FT:** Coarse; **WN:** Allestree; **WT:** Lake (Still) **W. Size:** 12 Acres. Location: **Nr. Rd:** Main Avenue; **Main Rd:** A6; **Rail:** Derby.
Ref: FH0078

ALLHALLOWS LEISURE PARK

Allhallows Leisure Park, Leisure Park, Allhallows-on-Sea, Rochester, **KENT**, ME3 9QD, **England**.
Contact/s: **Mr Graham Plant** (Manager).
(T) 01634 270385
Profile: **FT:** Coarse; **WN:** Allhallows Leisure Park; **WT:** Lake (Still). Location: **Nr. Rd:** Leisure Park.
Ref: FH0079

ALLSMOOR POND

Allsmoor Pond, Calfridus Way, Bullbrook, Bracknell, **BERKSHIRE**, RG12 7QW, **England**.
Contact/s: **Mr Nigel Smith** (Senior Ranger).
(T) 01344 354441
Profile: **FT:** Coarse; **WN:** Allsmoor; **WT:** Pond (Still). Location: **Nr. Rd:** Calfridus Way; **Main Rd:** A322.
Ref: FH0080

ALLTAMI CLAY PITS

Alltami Clay Pits, Mold, **FLINTSHIRE**, CH7, **Wales**.
Contact/s: **Lionell Everton** (Manager), Lionels Tackle Shop, Ash Gr, Pentre Lane, Buckley, CH7 3PA.
(T) 01244 543191
Mr Jim Howard (Secretary).
(T) 01244 661468
Mr Roger Millard (Chairman).
(T) 01352 732972
Profile: **FT:** Coarse; **WN:** Alltami Clay; **WT:** Gravel Pit (Still). Location: **Nr. Rd:** A494.
Ref: FH0081

ALMOND (RIVER)

River Almond, Cramond, South Queensferry, **LOTHIAN (WEST)**, EH30, **Scotland**.
Contact/s: **Mr Craig Campbell** (Secretary), Cramond Angling Club, 2 Canmore St, South Queensferry, EH30 9ND.
Profile: **FT:** Game; **WN:** Almond; **WT:** River (Moving).
Ref: FH0082

ALMOND (RIVER)

River Almond, Auchnafree, Dunkeld, **PERTH AND KINROSS**, PH8, **Scotland**.
(W) www.fishingnet.com/beats/almond/auchnafree.htm
Contact/s: Manager, Auchnafree Lodge, Amulee, Dunkeld, Perth and Kinross, PH8 0EH.
(T) 01350 725233 **(F)** 01350 725277
Profile: **FT:** Combination; **WN:** Almond; **WT:** River (Moving).
Ref: FH0083

ALMOND (RIVER)

River Almond, Perth, **PERTH AND KINROSS**, PH, **Scotland**.
(W) www.fishingnet.com/beats/almond/almond
Contact/s: **Mrs S Woods** (Secretary), Mansfield Estates, Scone Palace, Scone, Perth and Kinross, PH2 6BD.
(T) 01738 522308
Profile: **FT:** Game; **WN:** Almond; **WT:** River (Moving).
Ref: FH0084

ALN (RIVER)

River Aln, Alnwick, **NORTHUMBERLAND**, NE66, **England**.
Contact/s: **Mr Alan Lawson** (Secretary), White House, Alnwick, Northumberland, NE66 2LN.
(T) 01665 579272 **(F)** 01665 579272 **(M)** 07901 614856
Profile: **FT:** Game; **WN:** Aln; **WT:** River (Moving) **W. Size:** 5000 Metres. Location: **Nr. Rd:** B1340, A1068; **Main Rd:** A1; **Rail:** Alnmouth.
Ref: FH0085

ALTMORE FISHERIES

Altmore Fisheries, 32 Altmore Rd, Pomeroy, Dungannon, **COUNTY TYRONE**, BT70 2UN, **Northern Ireland**.
Contact/s: **Ms Ann Hurl** (Fisheries Manager).
(T) 028 87758977
Profile: **FT:** Game; **WN:** Altmore Fisheries; **WT:** Lake (Still) **W. Size:** 3 Acres. Location: **Nr. Rd:** Altmore Road; **Main Rd:** A4.
Ref: FH0086

ALTON MANOR FARM

Alton Manor Farm, Idridgehay, Wirksworth, Matlock, **DERBYSHIRE**, DE4, **England**.
Contact/s: **Mr Stephen Jones** (Manager).
(T) 01629 822318
Profile: **FT:** Game; **WN:** Alton Manor Farm; **WT:** Lake (Still).
Ref: FH0087

ALTON WATER RESERVOIR

Alton Water Reservoir, Holbrook Rd, Ipswich, **SUFFOLK**, IP9 2, **England**.
Contact/s: **Mr Simon Waters** (Warden), Anglian Water Services Ltd, Holbrook Rd, Strutton, Ipswich, IP9 2RY.
(T) 01473 589105 **(F)** 01473 589113 **(M)** 07802 646698
Profile: **FT:** Coarse; **WN:** Alton Water; **WT:** Reservoir (Still) **W. Size:** 300 Acres.
Location: **Nr. Rd:** Holbrook Road; **Main Rd:** A137; **Rail:** Ipswich.
Ref: FH0088

ALVASTON LAKE

Elvaston Castle Country Park, Main Rd, Elvaston, Nr Alvaston, Derby, **DERBYSHIRE**, DE, **England**.
Contact/s: **Mr Allan Martin** (Head Ranger).
(T) 01332 367800
Profile: **FT:** Coarse; **WN:** Alvaston; **WT:** Lake (Still) **W. Size:** 5 Acres. Location: **Nr. Rd:** Main Road; **Main Rd:** B5010; **Rail:** Derby.
Ref: FH0089

ALVECHURCH FISHERIES

Alvechurch Fisheries, Little Stannell's, Bittell Rd, Barnt Green, Birmingham, **MIDLANDS (WEST)**, B45 8LT, **England**.

Contact/s: **Mr Mark Gittins** (Owner).
(T) 0121 4454274
Profile: **FT:** Coarse; **WN:** Alvechurch Fisheries; **WT:** Pool (Still); **F. Size:** 7 Acres; **W. Size:** 2 Acres. **Location:** **Nr. Rd:** Bittell Road; **Main Rd:** A441; **Rail:** Barnet Green.
Ref: FH0090

ALVINGHAM FISHERIES
Alvingham Fisheries, Riverside Ponds, Lock Rd, Louth, **LINCOLNSHIRE**, LN11 7EU, **England**.
Contact/s: Fishery Manager.
(T) 01507 327012
Profile: **FT:** Coarse; **WN:** Alvingham Fisheries; **WT:** Lake (Still).
Ref: FH0091

ALWEN (RIVER)
River Alwen, Corwen, **DENBIGHSHIRE**, LL21, **Wales**.
Contact/s: **Mr David Scutter** (Manager), Llyn Brenig Visitors Ctre, Cerrigdrudion, Corwen, Conwy, LL21 9TT.
(T) 01490 420463 **(F)** 01490 420694
(E) llyn.brenig@hyder.com
Profile: **FT:** Game; **WN:** Alwen; **WT:** River (Moving). **Location:** **Nr. Rd:** B4501 Denbigh to Cerrigydrudion; **Main Rd:** A5.
Ref: FH0092

ALWEN RESERVOIR
Alwen Reservoir, Corwen, **DENBIGHSHIRE**, LL21, **Wales**.
Contact/s: **Mr David Scutter**, Llyn Brenig Visitors Ctre, Cerrigdrudion, Corwen, Conwy, LL21 9TT.
(T) 01490 420463 **(F)** 01490 420694
(E) llyn.brenig@hyder.com
Profile: **FT:** Game; **WN:** Alwen; **WT:** Reservoir (Still) **W. Size:** 368 Acres. **Location:** **Nr. Rd:** B4501.
Ref: FH0093

ALYN (RIVER)
River Alyn, Pont-Y-Capel, Wrexham, LL12, **Wales**.
Contact/s: **Mr A Pickles** (Secretary), Griffin Angling Club, Green Pastures, Pont-y-Capel, Gresford, Wrexham.
(T) 01978 852655
Profile: **FT:** Game; **WN:** Alyn; **WT:** River (Moving) **W. Size:** 923 Metres. **Location:** **Nr. Rd:** Llay New Road Bridget o Pont-Y-Capel Bridge.
Ref: FH0094

ALYN (RIVER)
River Alyn, Hope, Wrexham, LL12, **Wales**.
Contact/s: **Mrs E Lewis** (Hon Secretary), Bronwlfa, Hawarden Rd, Caergwrle, Wrexham.
Profile: **FT:** Game; **WN:** Alyn; **WT:** River (Moving) **W. Size:** 4000 Metres. **Location:** **Nr. Rd:** Hope to Caergwrle.
Ref: FH0095

ALYN (RIVER)
River Alyn, Rossett, Wrexham, LL12, **Wales**.
Contact/s: **Mr Brian Harper** (Secretary), 7 Hawthorn Rd, Marford, Wrexham.
(T) 01978 854514
Profile: **FT:** Game; **WN:** Alyn; **WT:** River (Moving) **W. Size:** 3200 Metres. **Location:** **Nr. Rd:** Gresford Sewage Works; **Main Rd:** Wrexham By-pass; **Rail:** Wrexham.
Ref: FH0096

ALYN (RIVER)
River Alyn, Llanferres, Mold, **FLINTSHIRE**, CH7, **Wales**.
Contact/s: **Mr A G R Brown** (Secretary), Northern Anglers, 10 Dale Rd, Golbourne, Warrington, WA3 3PN.
(T) 01942 726917
Profile: **FT:** Game; **WN:** Alyn; **WT:** River (Moving). **Location:** **Nr. Rd:** Mold to Ruthin Road; **Main Rd:** A494.
Ref: FH0097

ALYN (RIVER)
River Alyn, Pont-Y-Delyn, Mold, **FLINTSHIRE**, CH7, **Wales**.
Contact/s: **Mr J Tattum** (Hon Secretary), Llys Athro, Kings St, Leeswood, Mold, CH7 4SB.
(T) 01352 770213
Mr Martin Stark (Area Manager), Environment Agency, Sapphire East, 550 Streetsbrook Rd, Solihull, B91 1QT.
(T) 0121 7112324 **(F)** 0121 7115824
Profile: **FT:** Game; **WN:** Alyn; **WT:** River (Moving). **Location:** **Nr. Rd:** Druid Inn to Pont-Y-Delyn.
Ref: FH0098

AMALWHIDDEN FARM
Amalwhidden Farm, Nancledra, Penzance, **CORNWALL**, TR20, **England**.
Contact/s: **Mr Brian Cooks**.
(T) 01736 796961
Profile: **FT:** Coarse; **WN:** Amalwhidden Farm; **WT:** Pool (Still) **W. Size:** 1 Acre. **Location:** **Nr. Rd:** Nancledra to Towednack; **Main Rd:** B3311.
Ref: FH0099

AMERDEN POOL
Amerden Pool, Bury Hill, Maidenhead, **BERKSHIRE**, SL6, **England**.
Contact/s: **Buzz** (Manager), Boyer Leisure Ltd, Heron's Point Tackle Shop, Farlow's Lake, Ford Lane, Iver SL0 9LL.
(T) 01753 630302 or 01895 444707 **(F)** 01753 630302
(E) info@boyer.co.uk
Profile: **FT:** Coarse; **WN:** Farlows; **WT:** Lake (Still) **W. Size:** 34 Acres. **Location:** **Nr. Rd:** Bury Hill; **Main Rd:** A4, Bath Road; **Rail:** Taplow.
Ref: FH0100

AMHERST LODGE FISHERY
Amherst Lodge Fishery, Uplyme, Lyme Regis, **DORSET**, DT7 3XH, **England**.
(W) www.amherstlodge.com
Contact/s: **Mr B Stansfield** (Owner).
(T) 01297 442773
Profile: **FT:** Game; **WN:** Amherst Lodge Fishery; **WT:** Lake (Still); **F. Size:** 37 Acres; **W. Size:** 5 Acres. **Location:** **Nr. Rd:** B3165, Cathle Lane; **Main Rd:** A35; **Rail:** Axminster.
Ref: FH0101

AMPTHILL RESERVOIR
Ampthill Reservoir, Kempston, Ampthill, Bedford, **BEDFORDSHIRE**, MK42, **England**.
Contact/s: Fishery Manager.
(T) 01525 405984
Manager, Dixon Bros, 95 Travistock St, Bedford, Bedfordshire, MK40 2RR.
(T) 01234 267145/01525405984.
Profile: **FT:** Coarse; **WN:** Ampthill; **WT:** Reservoir (Still).
Ref: FH0102

AMULREE BEAT
Amulree Beat, Dunkeld, **PERTH AND KINROSS**, PH8, **Scotland**.
(W) www.fishingnet.com/beats/braan/amulree81.htm
Contact/s: **Mrs Diana MacDonald** (Permit Contact).
Mrs Vicky Hammer (Owner), Kettles of Dunkeld, 15-17 Atholl St, Dunkeld, Perth and Kinross, PH8 0AR.
(T) 01350 727556
Profile: **FT:** Game; **WN:** Amulree Beat; **WT:** Pool (Still).
Ref: FH0103

AMWELL LAKES
Amwell Lakes, High St, Stanstead Abbotts, Ware, **HERTFORDSHIRE**, SG12, **England**.
(W) www.rmcangling.co.uk
Contact/s: **Mr Ian Welch** (Angling Manager), RMC Angling, The Square, Lightwater, Surrey, GU18 5SS.
(T) 01276 453300 **(F)** 01276 456611
(E) info@rmcangling.co.uk
Profile: **FT:** Coarse; **WN:** Amwell; **WT:** Lake (Still) **W. Size:** 8 Acres. **Location:** **Nr. Rd:** High Street, off the A414; **Main Rd:** A10; **Rail:** St Margarets.
Ref: FH0104

ANCHOR MEADOWS FISHERY
Anchor Meadows Fishery, The Bungalow, Evesham, **WORCESTERSHIRE**, WR11, **England**.
Contact/s: Fishery Manager.
(T) 01386 48065
Profile: **FT:** Coarse; **WN:** Avon (Harvington to Anchor Meadows); **WT:** River (Moving) **W. Size:** 500 Metres.
Ref: FH0105

ANGLERS ELDORADO
Anglers Eldorado, The Gables, Winsford, Halwill Junction, Hatherleigh, Beaworthy, **DEVON**, EX21 5XT, **England**.
Contact/s: **Mr Zyg Gregorek** (Owner).
(T) 01409 221559 **(F)** 01409 221593
Profile: **FT:** Coarse; **WN:** Anglers Eldorado; **WT:** Lake (Still); **F. Size:** 20 Acres; **W. Size:** 10 Acres. **Location:** **Nr. Rd:** B3218 to Halwill; **Main Rd:** A30; **Rail:** Exeter.
Ref: FH0106

ANGLERS PARADISE
Anglers Paradise, Loreto Rd, Killarney, **COUNTY KERRY**, **Ireland**.
Profile: **FT:** Game; **WN:** Anglers Paradise; **WT:** Loch (Still).
Ref: FH0107

ANGLERS PARADISE
Anglers Paradise, Angler's Paradise Holidays, The Gables, Winsford, Halwill Junction, Beaworthy, **DEVON**, EX21 5XT, **England**.
(W) www.anglers-paradise.co.uk
Contact/s: **Mr Zyg Gregorek**.
(T) 01409 221559 **(F)** 01409 221593
Profile: **FT:** Coarse; **WN:** Anglers Paradise; **WT:** Lake (Still); **F. Size:** 170 Acres; **W. Size:** 20 Acres. **Location:** **Main Rd:** A30, Okehampton; **Rail:** Exeter.
Ref: FH0108

ANGLERS SHANGRILA
Anglers Shangrila, The Gables, Winsford, Halwill Junction, Hatherleigh, Beaworthy, **DEVON**, EX21 5XT, **England**.
Contact/s: **Mr Zyg Gregorek**, The Gables, Winsfold, Halwill Juction, Devon, EX21 5XT.
(T) 01409 221559 **(F)** 01409 221593
Profile: **FT:** Coarse; **WN:** Anglers Shangrila; **WT:** Lake (Still); **F. Size:** 15 Acres; **W. Size:** 10 Acres. **Location:** **Main Rd:** A30 to Okehampton; **Rail:** Exeter.
Ref: FH0109

ANGLEZARKE RESERVOIR
Anglezarke Reservoir, Wigan, **LANCASHIRE**, WA5, **England**.
Contact/s: **Mr Roy Rhodes** (Conservation, Access and Recreation Manager), Rivington Water Treatment Works, Bolton Rd, Horwich, Bolton, BL6 7RN.
(T) 01204 664300
Profile: **FT:** Game; **WN:** Anglezarke; **WT:** Reservoir (Still).
Ref: FH0110

ANKER (RIVER)
River Anker, Polesworth, Tamworth, **STAFFORDSHIRE**, B78, **England**.
Contact/s: **Mr John Hyde** (Secretary), Coventry and District Angling Club, 111 Lord Litton Avenue, Stoke, Coventry, CV2 5JT.
(T) 024 76418893
Mr John Williams (Secretary), Birmingham Anglers Association, 100 Icknield Port Rd, Rotton Park, Birmingham, B16 0AP.
(T) 0121 4549111
Profile: **FT:** Coarse; **WN:** Anker; **WT:** River (Moving).
Ref: FH0111

ANNAGINNY STILL WATER FISHERY
Annaginny Still Water Trout And Coarse Fishery, 40B Annaginny Rd, Newmills, Dungannon, **COUNTY TYRONE**, BT71 4DZ, **Northern Ireland**.

KEY: **(w):** Web address **(T):** Telephone number **(F):** Fax Number **(M):** Mobile Number **(E):** E-mail Address
F. Size: Fishery Size **FT:** Fisherytype **WN:** WaterName/s **WT:** WaterType **W. Size:** Water Size **£Free:** Free Fishing

Contact/s: **Mr Alan Abraham** (Fishery Manager).
(T) 028 87747808or8650afterhours **(F)** 028 87747808 **(M)** 07730 133934
Profile: **FT:** Combination; **WN:** Annaginny Still Water Trout And Coarse Fishery; **WT:** Lake (Still) **W. Size:** 12 Acres. **Location:** **Nr. Rd:** Annaginny Road; **Main Rd:** A29; **Rail:** Portadown.
Ref: FH0112

ANNAN (RIVER)

River Annan, Warmanbie Hotel, Warmanbie Stretch, Annan, **DUMFRIES AND GALLOWAY**, DG12 5LL, **Scotland**.
(W) www.warmanbie.co.uk
Contact/s: **Mr Billy** (Head Chef).
(T) 01461 204015 **(F)** 01461 204015
(E) info@warmanbie.co.uk
Mr Rod Duncan.
(T) 01461 204015 **(F)** 01461 204015
Profile: **FT:** Game; **WN:** Annan; **WT:** River (Moving) **W. Size:** 750 Metres. **Location:** **Nr. Rd:** B722; **Main Rd:** A75; **Rail:** Annan.
£Fr
Ref: FH0113

ANNAN (RIVER)

River Annan, Hoddom And Kinmount Estate, Estate Office, Hoddom, Lockerbie, **DUMFRIES AND GALLOWAY**, DG11, **Scotland**.
Contact/s: **D Graham** (Bailiff), Hoddom and Kinmount Estates, Hoddom Estate Office, Lockerbie, Dumfries and Galloway, DG11 1BE.
(T) 01576 300417 **(M)** 07711 681507
Mr A Dickson (Hon Secretary), Upper Annandale Angling Association, Braehead, Woodford, Maffot, Dumfries and Galloway DG10 9PL.
(T) 01683 300592
Profile: **FT:** Game; **WN:** Annan; **WT:** River (Moving).
Ref: FH0114

ANNAS (RIVER)

River Annas, Bootle Village, Millom, **CUMBRIA**, LA19, **England**.
Contact/s: **Mr D J Dixon** (Secretary), 1 Churchill Drive, Millom, Cumbria, LA18 5DD.
(T) 01229 774241
Profile: **FT:** Game; **WN:** Annass; **WT:** River (Moving). **Location:** **Nr. Rd:** B Road; **Main Rd:** A595 to Bootle; **Rail:** Bootle.
Ref: FH0115

ANNAS STREAM

Annas Stream, Bootle, Millom, **CUMBRIA**, LA19, **England**.
Contact/s: **Mr D J Dixon** (Secretary), 1 Churchill Drive, Millom, Cumbria, LA18 5DD.
(T) 01229 774241
Profile: **FT:** Game; **WN:** Annas; **WT:** Stream (Moving).
Ref: FH0116

ANTON (RIVER)

River Anton, Rooksbury Mill, Rooksbury Rd, Andover, **HAMPSHIRE**, SP10, **England**.
Contact/s: **Mr** (Fishery Manager).
(T) 01264 352921
Profile: **FT:** Game; **WN:** Anton; **WT:** River (Moving). **Location:** **Nr. Rd:** Rooksbury Road.
Ref: FH0117

ANTON LAKE

Anton Lake, Andover, **HAMPSHIRE**, SP10, **England**.
Contact/s: Manager, Challis Tackle, 60 Mylen Rd, Andover, Hampshire, SP10 3HA.
(T) 01264 361103
Profile: **FT:** Coarse; **WN:** Anton Lake; **WT:** Lake (Still). **Location:** **Main Rd:** A3093.
Ref: FH0118

ANTROBUS LAKES

Antrobus Lakes, Antrobus Golf Course, Antrobus, Lymm, **CHESHIRE**, WA13, **England**.
Contact/s: **Mr Neil Jupp** (Club Secretary), Lymm Angling Club, PO Box 350, Warrington, Cheshire, WA2 9FB.
(T) 01925 411774
Profile: **FT:** Coarse; **WN:** Antrobus; **WT:** Lake (Still). **Location:** **Main Rd:** A559.
Ref: FH0119

APEX LAKE

Apex Lake, Highbridge, Burnham-on-Sea, **SOMERSET**, TA8, **England**.
Contact/s: **Mr Rf Newton** (Hon Treasurer).
(T) 01275 856107
Mr S Bonwick (Secretary), 13 Tennyson Avenue, Clevedon, Somerset, BS21 7OQ.
(T) 01275 791933
Profile: **FT:** Coarse; **WN:** Apex; **WT:** Lake (Still). **Location:** **Nr. Rd:** Burnham-on-Sea; **Main Rd:** M5, junction 22, A38.
Ref: FH0120

APLEY POOLS

Apley Pool, Lee Gomory, Telford, **SHROPSHIRE**, TF, **England**.
Contact/s: **Mr Malcolm Kelly** (Nfa Disability Officer, West Midlands Region), 14 Sycamore Cl, Wellington, Telford, Shropshire, TF1 3NH.
(T) 01952 244272
Mr Stan Harris (Secretary), Telford Angling Association, 73 Burnside, Brookside, Telford, TF3 1DA.
(T) 01952 590605
Profile: **FT:** Coarse; **WN:** Apley; **WT:** Pool (Still) **W. Size:** 5 Acres. **Location:** **Nr. Rd:** A442; **Main Rd:** M54, junction 6.
Ref: FH0121

APPERLEY POOLS

Apperley Pools, Apperley, Tewkesbury, **GLOUCESTERSHIRE**, GL20, **England**.
Contact/s: **Mr John Williams** (Secretary), Birmingham Anglers Association, 100 Icknield Port Rd, Rotton Park, Birmingham, B16 0AP.
(T) 0121 4549111
Profile: **FT:** Coarse; **WN:** Apperley; **WT:** Lake (Still) **W. Size:** 4 Acres. **Location:** **Nr. Rd:** A38 Gloucester Road; **Main Rd:** M5, junction 5, A46.
Ref: FH0122

APPLETON RESERVOIR

Appleton Reservoir, Warrington, **CHESHIRE**, WA, **England**.
Contact/s: **Mr Frank Lythgoe** (Secretary), Warrington Angling Association, 52 Parker St, Warrington, Lancashire.
(T) 01928 716238 **(F)** 01928 713898
(E) info@warrington-anglers.org.uk
Profile: **FT:** Combination; **WN:** Appleton; **WT:** Reservoir (Still).
Ref: FH0123

AQUALATE MERE

Aqualate Mere, Aqualate Estate, Newport, **SHROPSHIRE**, TF10, **England**.
Contact/s: **Mr Albert Perkins** (Hon Secretary), 63 Fowlers Lane, Light Oaks, Stoke-on-Trent, Staffordshire, ST2 7NB.
Mr John Davey (Bailiff), Hotel Rudyard, Lake Rd, Rudyard, Leek, ST13 8RN.
(T) 01538 306280 **(F)** 01538 306280
Ms Liz Hayes (Manager).
(T) 01625 251262
Profile: **FT:** Coarse; **WN:** Aqualate; **WT:** Lake (Still) **W. Size:** 180 Acres. **Location:** **Main Rd:** A518.
Ref: FH0124

ARA (RIVER)

River Ara, Tipperary Town, **COUNTY TIPPERARY**, **Ireland**.
Contact/s: **Mr John Evans**, 52-53 Main St, Tipperary, County Tipperary.
(T) 062 51124
Profile: **FT:** Game; **WN:** Ara River; **WT:** River (Moving) **W. Size:** 10500 Metres. **Location:** **Nr. Rd:** Waterford to Limerick Road; **Rail:** Tipperary.
Ref: FH0125

ARDAN GRANGE ANGLING

Ardan Grange Guest House And Angling Centre, Ardan Grange, Milltown, Belturbet, **COUNTY CAVAN**, **Ireland**.
Contact/s: **Mr Peter May**.
(T) 049 9522639 **(F)** 049 9522639
Profile: **FT:** Combination; **WN:** Ardan; **WT:** Lake (Still).
Ref: FH0126

ARDENCOTE

Ardencote Manor Hotel And Country Club, Lye Green Rd, Claverdon, Warwick, **WARWICKSHIRE**, CV35 8LS, **England**.
Contact/s: **Mr Allan Clark** (Manager), Ardencote Manor Hotel and Country Club, Star Lane, Claverdon, Warwick, CV35 8LS.
(T) 01926 843111
Profile: **FT:** Game; **WN:** Ardencote; **WT:** Lake (Still); **F. Size:** 40 Acres; **W. Size:** 3 Acres. **Location:** **Nr. Rd:** A4189 Warwick to Henley Road; **Main Rd:** M40.
Ref: FH0127

ARDGOWAN TROUT FISHERY

Ardgowan Trout Fishery, Cornalees Bridge, Greenock, **INVERCLYDE**, PA16 1LX, **Scotland**.
(W) www.trout-fishery.co.uk
Contact/s: **Mr David Moffat** (Managing Director), 19 Cardwell Rd, Govrock, PA19 1UG.
(T) 01475 522492
(E) enquires@trout-fishery.co.uk
Profile: **FT:** Game; **WN:** Ardgowan; **WT:** Loch (Still) **W. Size:** 37 Acres. **Location:** **Main Rd:** A78; **Rail:** Inverkip.
Ref: FH0128

ARDINGLY RESERVOIR

Ardingly Reservoir, The Lodge, Ardingly, Haywards Heath, **SUSSEX (WEST)**, RH17 6SQ, **England**.
(W) www.ardinglyactivitycentre.co.uk
Contact/s: **Mr Wes Horton** (Bailiff).
(T) 01444 892549 **(F)** 01444 891088
(E) sales@ardinglyactivitycentre.co.uk
Profile: **FT:** Coarse; **WN:** Ardingly; **WT:** Reservoir (Still) **W. Size:** 198 Acres. **Location:** **Nr. Rd:** B2028; **Main Rd:** B2028; **Rail:** Haywards Heath.
Ref: FH0129

ARDLEIGH RESERVOIR

Ardleigh Reservoir, The Fishing Lodge, Clover Way, Ardleigh, Colchester, **ESSEX**, CO7 7PT, **England**.
Contact/s: **Mr Barry T Bartholomew**.
(T) 01206 230642
Mr Jeremy Holyman (Bailiff).
(T) 01206 230642 **(F)** 01206 230464
Profile: **FT:** Coarse; **WN:** Ardleigh; **WT:** Reservoir (Still) **W. Size:** 145 Acres. **Location:** **Nr. Rd:** Clover Way; **Main Rd:** A137; **Rail:** Manningtree or Colchester.
Ref: FH0130

ARDTORNISH ESTATE LOCHS

Ardtornish Estate Lochs, Ardtornish Estate Office, Movern, Oban, **ARGYLL AND BUTE**, PA34, **Scotland**.
Profile: **FT:** Game; **WN:** Ardtornish; **WT:** Loch (Still).
Ref: FH0131

ARENA LAKE

Arena Lake, Thurrock, Grays, **ESSEX**, RM17, **England**.
Contact/s: **Mr Chris Osmon**. **(M)** 07973 217902
Profile: **FT:** Coarse; **WN:** Arena Lake; **WT:** Gravel Pit (Still) **W. Size:** 10 Acres. **Location:** **Main Rd:** M25 Dartford Tunnel then A13.
Ref: FH0132

ARGAE LAKE

Argae Lake, Moss Valley Park, Wrexham, LL, **Wales**.
Profile: **FT:** Coarse; **WN:** Argae; **WT:** Lake (Still) **W. Size:** 4 Acres.
Ref: FH0133

ARGAL RESERVOIR

Argal Reservoir, Trevera, Penryn, **CORNWALL**, **England**.
Contact/s: South West Lakes Trust.
(T) 01837 871565
Profile: **FT:** Coarse; **WN:** Argal; **WT:** Reservoir (Still) **W. Size:** 65 Acres.
Location: **Main Rd:** A39; **Rail:** Penryn.
Ref: FH0134

ARKSEY STATION POND

Arksey Station Pond, Station Rd, Bentley, Doncaster, **YORKSHIRE (SOUTH)**, **England**.
Contact/s: .
(T) 01302 822293
Profile: **FT:** Coarse; **WN:** Arksey Station Pond; **WT:** Lake (Still); **F. Size:** 3 Acres; **W. Size:** 2 Acres. **Location:** **Nr. Rd:** Station Road; **Main Rd:** A638.
Ref: FH0135

ARLESEY LAKE

Arlesey Lake, Etonbury Farm, Stotfold Rd, Arlesey, **BEDFORDSHIRE**, SG16 6XB, **England**.
Contact/s: **Mr D Beatham** (Owner).
(T) 01462 731709
Profile: **FT:** Coarse; **WN:** Arlesey; **WT:** Lake (Still) **W. Size:** 12 Acres. **Location:** **Main Rd:** A507.
Ref: FH0136

ARLINGTON TROUT FISHERY

Arlington Trout Fishery, Arlington Reservoir, Berwick, Polegate, **SUSSEX (EAST)**, BN26 6TF, **England**.
Contact/s: **Ms Emma Goddard** (Environment Coordinator).
(T) 01323 870810 **(F)** 01323 871153 **(M)** 07802 757526
(E) egoddard@saur.co.uk
Profile: **FT:** Game; **WN:** Arlington; **WT:** Reservoir (Still) **W. Size:** 120 Acres.
Location: **Nr. Rd:** B2108; **Main Rd:** A27; **Rail:** Berwick.
Ref: FH0137

ARMIGERS FARM

Armigers Farm, Thaxted, Dunmow, **ESSEX**, CM6, **England**.
(W) www.bdac.co.uk
Contact/s: **Mr Derek Howard** (Hon Treasurer), Billericay and District Angling Club, 4 Long Meadow Drive, Wickford, Essex, SS11 8AX.
(T) 01268 734468
Profile: **FT:** Coarse; **WN:** Armigers Farm; **WT:** Lake (Still); **F. Size:** 7 Acres; **W. Size:** 6 Acres. **Location:** **Main Rd:** B1051; **Rail:** Elsenham.
Ref: FH0138

ARMSTRONG FISHERY

Armstrong Fishery, Ballina Rd, Foxford, **COUNTY MAYO**, **Ireland**.
Contact/s: **Mr George Armstrong**.
(T) 021 502555
Profile: **FT:** Game; **WT:** River (Moving).
Ref: FH0139

ARNFIELD RESERVOIR

Arnfield Reservoir, Tintwistle, Glossop, **DERBYSHIRE**, SK13 1HP, **England**.
Contact/s: **Mr Peter Sharples** (Conservation, Access and Recreation Manager), North West Water Ltd, Woodhead Rd, Tintwhistle, Hadfield via Hyde, SK14 7HR.
(T) 01457 864187
Mr S Cuthbert (Fishery Manager).
(T) 01457 856269 **(M)** 07831 518284
Profile: **FT:** Coarse; **WN:** Arnfield; **WT:** Reservoir (Still) **W. Size:** 40 Acres.
Ref: FH0140

ARROW VALLEY LAKE

Arrow Valley Lake, Battens Drive, South Meons Moat, Redditch, **WORCESTERSHIRE**, B98, **England**.
Contact/s: **Mr Adrian Collingwood**.
(T) 01527 464000 **(F)** 01527 464000
Mr Richard Davidson.
(T) 01527 464000 **(F)** 01527 464000
Profile: **FT:** Coarse; **WN:** Arrow Valley; **WT:** Lake (Still) **W. Size:** 30 Acres. **Location:** **Nr. Rd:** Battens Drive; **Main Rd:** A448, A435.
Ref: FH0141

ARROWE PARK LAKE

Arrowe Park Lake, Arrowe Park Rd, Wirral, **MERSEYSIDE**, CH49 5LW, **England**.
Profile: **FT:** Coarse; **WN:** Arrowe; **WT:** Lake (Still). **Location:** **Nr. Rd:** Greasby to Irby.
Ref: FH0142

ARTRO (RIVER)

River Artro, Cwm-Yr-Afon, Llandysul, **CEREDIGION**, SA44, **Wales**.
Contact/s: **Mr P G Cozens** (Hon Secretary), Awelfryn, Llanbedr, Gwynedd, LL45 2HL.
(T) 01341 23226
Profile: **FT:** Game; **WN:** Artro; **WT:** River (Moving) **W. Size:** 6400 Metres. **Location:** **Nr. Rd:** Cwm-yr-Afon to estuary.
Ref: FH0143

ARUN (RIVER)

River Arun, Slinfold, Rudgwick, Horsham, **SUSSEX (WEST)**, RH12, **England**.
Contact/s: Manager, Prime Angling, 74 Brighton Rd, Worthing, Sussex (West), BN11 2EN.
(T) 01903 527050
Mr Glue (Match Secretary).
(T) 01483 273082
Profile: **FT:** Coarse; **WN:** Arun; **WT:** River (Moving). **Location:** **Nr. Rd:** Slinfold to Gibbons Mill.
Ref: FH0144

ARUN (RIVER)

River Arun, Littlehampton, **SUSSEX (WEST)**, BN16, **England**.
Contact/s: Secretary, Littlehampton and District Angling Club, Arun View Hotel, Littlehampton, Sussex (West).
Profile: **FT:** Combination; **WN:** Arun; **WT:** River (Moving).
Ref: FH0145

ARUN (RIVER)

River Arun, Arundel, **SUSSEX (WEST)**, BN18, **England**.
Contact/s: Manager, Tropicana Of Littlehampton, 5-6 Pier Rd, Littlehampton, Sussex (West), BN17 5BA.
(T) 01903 715190
Profile: **FT:** Coarse; **WN:** Arun; **WT:** River (Moving). **Location:** **Nr. Rd:** Arundel town.
Ref: FH0146

ARUN (RIVER)

River Arun, Bognor Regis, **SUSSEX (WEST)**, PO21, **England**.
Contact/s: **Mrs C Luffman**, Chichester and District Angling Society, 17 Arun Rd, Bognor Regis, Sussex (West), PO21 5PD.
(T) 01243 867673
Profile: **FT:** Coarse; **WN:** Arun; **WT:** River (Moving).
Ref: FH0147

ARUN (RIVER)

River Arun, Hardham, Pulborough, **SUSSEX (WEST)**, RH20, **England**.
Contact/s: **Mr Ash Girdler**, 3 Chase Plain Cottages, Portsmouth Rd, Hindhead, Surrey, GU26 6BZ.
(T) 01428 607768
Profile: **FT:** Combination; **WN:** Arun; **WT:** River (Moving) **W. Size:** 2200 Metres. **Location:** **Nr. Rd:** Hardham Village; **Main Rd:** A29 to Chichester.
Ref: FH0148

ARUN (RIVER)

River Arun, South Dean, Tillington, Petworth, **SUSSEX (WEST)**, GU28 0RE, **England**.
Contact/s: **Mr Richard Etherington** (Owner), South Dean, Tillington, Petworth, GU28 0RE.
(T) 01798 343111
Profile: **FT:** Combination; **WN:** Arun; **WT:** Tributary (Moving) **W. Size:** 8800 Metres.
Ref: FH0149

ARUN (RIVER)

River Arun, Amberley, Arundel, **SUSSEX (WEST)**, BN18, **England**.
(W) www.calpac.bizland.com
Contact/s: **Mr Colin Trafford** (General Secretary).
(T) 020 82242617
Profile: **FT:** Coarse; **WN:** Arun; **WT:** River (Moving). **Location:** **Nr. Rd:** Houghton Bridge to South Stoke; **Main Rd:** A29, B2139; **Rail:** Houghton.
Ref: FH0150

ARUN (RIVER)

River Arun, Swan Meadow, Pulborough, **SUSSEX (WEST)**, RH20, **England**.
(W) www.calpac.bizland.com
Contact/s: **Mr Colin Trafford** (General Secretary).
(T) 020 82242617
Mrs Diane Wheeler (Secretary), 314 Old Lodge Lane, Purley, Surrey, CR8 4AQ.
(T) 020 86602766
Profile: **FT:** Coarse; **WN:** Arun; **WT:** River (Moving) **W. Size:** 1200 Metres. **Location:** **Nr. Rd:** Swan Meadow; **Main Rd:** A29 from Billingshurst.
Ref: FH0151

ARUN (RIVER)

River Arun, Greatham Bridge, Coldwaltham, Pulborough, **SUSSEX (WEST)**, GU29, **England**.
Contact/s: **Mr C Boxall** (Treasurer), Rother Angling Club, Innisfree, Ashfield Rd, Midhurst, West Sussex, GU29 9SX.
(T) 01730 813885
Profile: **FT:** Coarse; **WN:** Arun; **WT:** River (Moving) **W. Size:** 700 Metres. **Location:** **Nr. Rd:** Watersfield to Greatham Road; **Main Rd:** A29; **Rail:** Pulborough.
Ref: FH0152

ARUN (RIVER)

River Arun, Buck Green, Rudgwick, Horsham, **SUSSEX (WEST)**, RH12, **England**.
Contact/s: **Mr B D Smith** (Secretary), Southern Anglers, 3 Cheriton Cl, Havant, Hamptonshire, PO9 4PU.
Profile: **FT:** Coarse; **WN:** Arun; **WT:** River (Moving) **W. Size:** 800 Metres. **Location:** **Nr. Rd:** Bucks Green.
Ref: FH0153

ASCOTT PONDS

Ascott Ponds, Faceby, Middlesbrough, **CLEVELAND**, TS9, **England**.
Contact/s: **Mr Dermot Speight** (Secretary).
(T) 01642 881694
Profile: **FT:** Coarse; **WN:** Ascott; **WT:** Pool (Still) **W. Size:** 4 Acres. **Location:** **Nr. Rd:** Middlesborough to Thirsk; **Main Rd:** A19, to Stokesley.
Ref: FH0154

ASHBOURNE TROUT FISHERY

Ashbourne Trout Fishery, Penhurst Lane, Penhurst, Battle, **SUSSEX (EAST)**, TN33 9QR, **England**.
Contact/s: **Mr Alex Webb**.
(T) 01424 892288
Profile: **FT:** Game; **WN:** Ashbourne Trout Fishery; **WT:** River (Moving).
Ref: FH0155

ASHBY CANAL

Ashby Canal, Nuneaton, **WARWICKSHIRE**, CV10, **England**.
Contact/s: Secretary.
(T) 01455 890264
Profile: **FT:** Coarse; **WN:** Ashby; **WT:** Canal (Still).
Ref: FH0156

ASHBY CANAL

Ashby Canal, Higham On The Hill, Nuneaton, **WARWICKSHIRE**, CV13 6, **England**.
Contact/s: Manager, British Waterways, Fradley Junction, Alreswas, Burton-on-Trent, DE13 7DN.
(T) 01283 790236
Profile: FT: Coarse; WN: Ashby; WT: Canal (Still).
Ref: FH0157

ASHBY PARK FISHERIES

Ashby Park Fisheries, West Ashby, Horncastle, **LINCOLNSHIRE**, LN9 5PP, **England**.
Contact/s: Mr Robin Francis.
(T) 01507 527966
Profile: FT: Coarse; WN: Ashby Park; WT: Lake (Still); F. Size: 52 Acres; W. Size: 15 Acres. Location: Nr. Rd: A158; Main Rd: A158 north to Lincoln.
Ref: FH0158

ASHCOMBE FISHERY

Ashcombe Fishery, Ashcombe, Dawlish, **DEVON**, EX7 0QD, **England**.
Contact/s: Mr Ian Staples (Owner), Ashcombe Training and Activites, Ashcombe, Dawlish, Devon, EX7 0QD.
(T) 01626 866766
Profile: FT: Coarse; WN: Ashcombe Fishery; WT: Pond (Still) W. Size: 3 Acres. Location: Main Rd: A3192 to Exeter; Rail: Teignmouth.
Ref: FH0159

ASHELDHAM FISHERY

Asheldham Fishery, Hall Rd, Asheldham, Southminster, **ESSEX**, CM0, **England**.
(W) www.bdac.co.uk
Contact/s: Mr Derek Howard (Hon Treasurer), Billericay and District Angling Club, 4 Long Meadow Drive, Wickford, Essex, SS11 8AX.
(T) 01268 734468
Profile: FT: Coarse; WN: Asheldham Fishery; WT: Gravel Pit (Still); F. Size: 5 Acres; W. Size: 4 Acres. Location: Nr. Rd: Hall Road; Main Rd: B1021; Rail: Southminster.
Ref: FH0160

ASHENHURST LAKES

Ashenhurst Lakes, Blackely, Manchester, **MANCHESTER (GREATER)**, M2, **England**.
Contact/s: Secretary, Broughton Angling Club, 23 Hill Field, Oadby, Leicester, LE2 4RN.
Mr G Guy (Membership Secretary), Broughton Angling Club, 27 Geralds Rd, Salford, M6 6DW.
Profile: FT: Coarse; WN: Ashenhurst; WT: Lake (Still) W. Size: 2 Acres. Location: Nr. Rd: Blackely.
Ref: FH0161

ASHGROVE LAKE

Ashgrove Lake, Lake Lane, Egginton, Derby, **DERBYSHIRE**, DE65, **England**.
Contact/s: Mr John Fearn.
(T) 01889 563070
Profile: FT: Coarse; WN: Ashgrove; WT: Lake (Still) W. Size: 2 Acres. Location: Nr. Rd: Ashgrove Lane; Main Rd: A5132 to Hilton.
Ref: FH0162

ASHLEY (RIVER)

River Ashley, Bollington, Macclesfield, **CHESHIRE**, SK10, **England**.
Profile: FT: Combination; WN: Ashley; WT: River (Moving) W. Size: 1600 Metres.
Ref: FH0163

ASHLEY POOL

Ashley Pool, Ashley Hall, Ashley Rd, Hale, Altrincham, **CHESHIRE**, **England**.
(W) www.baymalton-anglingclub.org
Contact/s: Mr Stewart Godber (Club Secretary), 38 Edenfield Rd, Mobberley, Cheshire, WA16 7HE.
(T) 01565 872582
Profile: FT: Coarse; WN: Ashley; WT: Pool (Still); F. Size: 1 Acre; W. Size: 1 Acre. Location: Nr. Rd: Ashley Road; Main Rd: A556 (T); Rail: Ashley.
Ref: FH0164

ASHLEY POOLS

Ashley Pools, Ashley, Loggerheads, **STAFFORDSHIRE**, **England**.
(W) www.fentondas.co.uk
Contact/s: Mr C Yates (Club Secretary), The Puzzles, 5 Gatley Gr, Meir Park, Stoke-on-Trent, Staffordshire ST3 7SH.
(T) 01782 396913
Profile: FT: Coarse; WN: Ashley; WT: Pool (Still). Location: Main Rd: A53; Rail: Stableford.
Ref: FH0165

ASHMEAD LAKES

Ashmead Lakes, Stonetam, Ash, Martock, **SOMERSET**, TA12 6PP, **England**.
Contact/s: Fishery Manager.
(T) 01935 823319
Profile: FT: Coarse; WN: Ashmead; WT: Lake (Still). Location: Nr. Rd: Stonetam.
Ref: FH0166

ASHMERE FISHERIES

Ashmere Fisheries, Felix Lane, Shepperton, London, **LONDON (GREATER)**, TW17 8NN, **England**.
Contact/s: Mrs Jean Howman (Owner).
(T) 01932 225445 (F) 01932 253793
Profile: FT: Game; WN: Ashmere; WT: Gravel Pit (Still) W. Size: 20 Acres. Location: Nr. Rd: B375; Main Rd: A244; Rail: Walton-on-Thames.
Ref: FH0167

ASHPERTON MOAT

Ashperton Moat, Ashperton Village, Hereford, **HEREFORDSHIRE**, HR, **England**.
Profile: FT: Coarse; WN: Ashperton; WT: Moat (Still) W. Size: 1 Acre. Location: Nr. Rd: A417 to Leominster; Main Rd: A438.
Ref: FH0168

ASHRIDGE MANOR

Ashridge Manor, Wokingham, **BERKSHIRE**, RG40, **England**.
Contact/s: Mr Kevin Hiscock (Match Secretary), Bracknell Angling Ctre, 2a Fowlers Lane, Bracknell, Berkshire, RG42 1XP.
(T) 01344 425130
Mr Vic Fletcher.
(T) 0118 9892651or01189770730
Profile: FT: Coarse; WN: Ashridge Manor; WT: Lake (Still).
Ref: FH0169

ASHTON CANAL

Ashton Canal, Abbey Lake Public House, Orrell, Wigan, **LANCASHIRE**, WN5, **England**.
Profile: FT: Coarse; WN: Ashton; WT: Canal (Still). Location: Nr. Rd: A5777 to Orrell; Main Rd: M6, junction 26.
Ref: FH0170

ASHTON KEYNES POOL

Ashton Keynes Pool, Ashton Keynes, Cirencester, **GLOUCESTERSHIRE**, GL7, **England**.
Contact/s: Mr Ray Daffon (Secretary), South Cerney Angling Club, Broadway Lane, South Cerney, Cirencester, GL7 5UH.
(T) 01285 861876 (M) 07775 970643
Profile: FT: Coarse; WN: Ashton Keynes Pool; WT: Lake (Still).
Ref: FH0171

ASHVALE FISHERIES

Ashvale Fisheries, Wimbledon, London, **LONDON (GREATER)**, SW19, **England**.
Contact/s: Mr Adrian Bewley (Manager), Ashvale Fisheries, 69 Fortescue Rd, Wimbledon, London, SW19 2EA.
(T) 020 82873892
Profile: FT: Game; WN: Ashvale Fisheries; WT: Lake (Still). Location: Nr. Rd: Fortescue Road. £Fr
Ref: FH0172

ASKERN LAKE

Askern Lake, Askern, Doncaster, **YORKSHIRE (SOUTH)**, DN, **England**.
Contact/s: Area Manager, Environment Agency, Ridings Area Office, Phoenix House, Global Avenue, Leeds, LS11 8PG.
(T) 0113 2440191or2314834 (F) 0113 2134609
Mr P Billington.
(T) 01302 737360
Profile: FT: Coarse; WN: Askern; WT: Lake (Still). Location: Nr. Rd: A19 in town centre.
Ref: FH0173

ASSAROE LAKE

Assaroe Lake, Knader, Ballyshannon, **COUNTY DONEGAL**, **Ireland**.
Contact/s: Mr J Weeney.
(T) 072 51165
Profile: FT: Combination; WN: Erne; WT: River (Moving); F. Size: 100 Acres; W. Size: 100 Acres. Location: Nr. Rd: Belleek Road; Rail: Sugo.
Ref: FH0174

ASTBURY FALLS FISH FARM

Astbury Falls Fish Farm, Astbury Lane, Bridgnorth, **MIDLANDS (WEST)**, WV1, **England**.
Contact/s: Mr David Holyhead.
(T) 01746 766797
Profile: FT: Combination; WN: Astbury Falls Fish Farm; WT: Lake (Still) W. Size: 1 Acre.
Ref: FH0175

ASTBURY MERE

Astbury Mere, Astbury Mere Country Park, Astbury, Congleton, **CHESHIRE**, **England**.
Contact/s: Alison (Water Sport Centre Manager).
(T) 01260 297172
Profile: FT: Coarse; WN: Astbury Mere; WT: Pit (Still); F. Size: 100 Acres; W. Size: 50 Acres. Location: Nr. Rd: A34 at Astbury; Main Rd: A34; Rail: Congleton.
Ref: FH0176

ASTLE POOL

Astle Pool, Astle Hall, Chelford, Knutsford, **CHESHIRE**, WA16, **England**.
Contact/s: Mr Frank Lythgoe (Secretary), Warrington Angling Association, 52 Parker St, Warrington, Lancashire.
(T) 01928 716238 (F) 01928 713898
(E) info@warrington-anglers.org.uk
Profile: FT: Coarse; WN: Astle; WT: Pool (Still) W. Size: 5 Acres. Location: Nr. Rd: Peover Lane; Main Rd: A537.
Ref: FH0177

ASTWOOD FISHERY

Astwood Fishery, Droitwich, **WORCESTERSHIRE**, WR9, **England**.
Contact/s: Secretary, Droitwich and District AS, c/o Talbot Hotel, 19 High St, Droitwich, WR9 8EJ.
(T) 01905 773331
Mr Frank Kean (Fishery Manager).
(T) 01905 770092
Profile: FT: Coarse; WN: Astwood Fishery; WT: Pool (Still) W. Size: 2 Acres.
Ref: FH0178

ATHERSLEY MEMORIAL LAKE

Athersley Memorial Lake, Athersley, Barnsley, **YORKSHIRE (SOUTH)**, S7, **England**.
Contact/s: Area Manager, Environment Agency, Ridings Area Office, Phoenix House, Global Avenue, Leeds, LS11 8PG.
(T) 0113 2440191or2314834 (F) 0113 2134609
Mr Nigel Labdon.
(T) 01226 774529
Profile: FT: Coarse; WN: Athersley Memorial; WT: Lake (Still). Location: Nr. Rd: Athersley.
Ref: FH0179

ATHRY FISHERY

Athry Fishery, The Zetland Hotel, Cashel, **COUNTY TIPPERARY**, **Ireland**.
Contact/s: **Mr John Prendergast**.
(T) 095 31111
Profile: **FT:** Game; **WN:** Ballynahinch; **WT:** River (Moving).
Ref: FH0180

ATKINSONS TARN COARSE FISHERY

Atkinsons Tarn Coarse Fishery, Windermere, **CUMBRIA**, LA23, **England**.
Contact/s: **Mr Chris Sodo** (Hon Treasurer), Windermere, Ambleside and District Angling Association, Ecclerigg Court, Ecclerigg, Windermere, LA23 1LQ.
(T) 01539 445083
Profile: **FT:** Combination; **WN:** Atkinsons; **WT:** Tarn (Still) **W. Size:** 1 Acre. **Location:** **Nr. Rd:** B284 Kendal to Bowness; **Main Rd:** A591 or A6.
Ref: FH0181

ATTENBOROUGH GRAVEL PITS

Attenborough Gravel Pits, Beeston, Nottingham, **NOTTINGHAMSHIRE**, NG9, **England**.
Contact/s: **Mr Trevor Lowe** (Bailiff).
(T) 0115 9733245
Profile: **FT:** Coarse; **WN:** Attenborough; **WT:** Gravel Pit (Still) **W. Size:** 24 Acres.
Ref: FH0182

ATTENBOROUGH SOUTH

Attenborough South, Chertsey, **SURREY**, KT16, **England**.
Contact/s: Manager, Wotsits Tackle, Arklow House Farm, Rotten Row, Theddlethorpe, LN12 1NX.
(T) 08707 441014
Profile: **FT:** Coarse; **WN:** Attenborough South; **WT:** Gravel Pit (Still).
Ref: FH0183

AUCHESSON BEAT

Auchesson Beat, Crianlarich, **STIRLING**, FK20, **Scotland**.
(W) www.fishingnet.com/beats/dochart/auchesson.htm
Contact/s: Manager, Auchesson House, Crianlarich, Perth and Kinross, FK20 8QS.
Profile: **FT:** Combination; **WN:** Auchesson Beat; **WT:** Pool (Still).
Ref: FH0184

AVALLON HOLIDAY PARK

Avallon Holiday Park, North Petherwin, Launceston, **CORNWALL**, PL15 8NX, **England**.
Contact/s: Fishery Manager.
(T) 01502 501501
Profile: **FT:** Coarse; **WN:** Avallon; **WT:** Lake (Still).
Ref: FH0185

AVALON FISHERIES

Avalon Fisheries, Shapwick Rd, Westhay, Glastonbury, **SOMERSET**, BA6, **England**.
Contact/s: **Mr Allan Tedder**, 7 Coronation Rd, Bridgwater, Somerset, TA6 7DS.
(T) 01278 456429 **(M)** 07966 363413
Profile: **FT:** Coarse; **WN:** Avalon Fisheries; **WT:** Lake (Still); **F. Size:** 25 Acres; **W. Size:** 10 Acres. **Location:** **Nr. Rd:** Willows Garden Centre, B3151; **Main Rd:** A39; **Rail:** Bridgwater.
Ref: FH0186

AVELEY LAKES

Aveley Lakes, Romford Rd, Aveley, Romford, **ESSEX**, RM, **England**.
Profile: **FT:** Coarse; **WN:** Aveley; **WT:** Lake (Still). **Location:** **Nr. Rd:** Romford Road; **Main Rd:** M25, junction 30.
Ref: FH0187

AVETON GIFFORD STREAM

Aveton Gifford Stream, Aveton Gifford, Kingsbridge, **DEVON**, TQ7, **England**.
Contact/s: Manager, Loddiswell Post Office, Loddiswell, Kingsbridge, Devon, TQ7 4QH.
(T) 01548 550329
Mr P O'Neil, 55 Church St, Kingsbridge, Devon.
Profile: **FT:** Game; **WN:** Aveton Gifford; **WT:** Stream (Moving).
Ref: FH0188

AVIELOCHAN

Avielochan, Lochside, Inverness, **HIGHLAND**, IV, **Scotland**.
Contact/s: **Mrs G A McDonald** (Ticket Sales).
(T) 01479 810847
Profile: **FT:** Game; **WN:** Avielochan; **WT:** Loch (Still).
Ref: FH0189

AVINGTON TROUT FISHERIES

Avington Trout Fisheries, Avington, Winchester, **HAMPSHIRE**, SO21 1BZ, **England**.
Contact/s: Manager, The Rod Box, London Rd, King's Worthy, Winchester, SO23 7QN.
(T) 01962 883600
Mr Howard Holland.
(T) 01962 779312
Profile: **FT:** Game; **WN:** Itchen; **WT:** Combination (Still & Moving) **W. Size:** 4 Acres.
Ref: FH0190

AVON (BRISTOL) (RIVER)

River Bristol Avon, Chequers Weir, Bristol, BS, **England**.
Contact/s: **Mr Bob Taylor** (Secretary), 27 Flaxpits Lane, Winterbourne, Bristol, BS36 1LA.
(T) 01454 773990
Profile: **FT:** Coarse; **WN:** Bristol Avon (Chequers Weir to Netham); **WT:** River (Moving) **W. Size:** 4800 Metres. **Location:** **Rail:** Temple Meads. **£Fr**
Ref: FH0191

AVON (BRISTOL) (RIVER)

River Bristol Avon, The Trees, Saltford, Bristol, BS31 3, **England**.
Contact/s: **Mr Dave Crookes** (Secretary), 25 Otago Trce, Larkhall, Bath, Somerset, BA1 6SX.
(T) 01225 427164
Profile: **FT:** Coarse; **WN:** Bristol Avon; **WT:** River (Moving).
Ref: FH0192

AVON (BRISTOL) (RIVER)

River Bristol Avon, Grosvenor, Bath, **SOMERSET**, BA3, **England**.
Contact/s: **Mr Jeff Parker** (Secretary), Bristol, Bath and Wilts Amalgamation, 16 Lansdown View, Kingswood, Bristol, BS15 4AW.
(T) 01179 672977
Profile: **FT:** Coarse; **WN:** Bristol Avon; **WT:** River (Moving). **Location:** **Main Rd:** A46.
Ref: FH0193

AVON (BRISTOL) (RIVER)

River Bristol Avon, Queen's Field, Melksham, **WILTSHIRE**, SN12, **England**.
Contact/s: **Mr Jeff Parker** (Secretary), Bristol, Bath and Wilts Amalgamation, 16 Lansdown View, Kingswood, Bristol, BS15 4AW.
(T) 01179 672977
Profile: **FT:** Coarse; **WN:** Bristol Avon (Lacock to Queen's Field Farm); **WT:** River (Moving). **Location:** **Main Rd:** A350.
Ref: FH0194

AVON (BRISTOL) (RIVER)

River Bristol Avon, Bristol Avon At Sutton Benger, Sutton Benger, Chippenham, **WILTSHIRE**, SN15, **England**.
Contact/s: **Mr Peter Gilbert** (Chairman), 31 Havelock St, Swindon, Wiltshire, SN1 1SD.
(T) 01793 535396 **(F)** 01793 535396
Profile: **FT:** Coarse; **WN:** Bristol Avon; **WT:** River (Moving) **W. Size:** 3000 Metres. **Location:** **Nr. Rd:** Sutton Lane; **Main Rd:** Swindon to Chippenham.
Ref: FH0195

AVON (BRISTOL) (RIVER)

River Bristol Avon, Monkton Park, Chippenham, **WILTSHIRE**, SN15, **England**.
Contact/s: **Mr Rob Bullock** (Manager), Rob's Tackle, 22 Marshfield Rd, Chippenham, Wiltshire, SN15 1JX.
(T) 01249 659210 **(F)** 01249 659210
Profile: **FT:** Coarse; **WN:** Bristol Avon; **WT:** River (Moving). **Location:** **Main Rd:** A420.
Ref: FH0196

AVON (BRISTOL) (RIVER)

River Bristol Avon, Conigre, Melksham, **WILTSHIRE**, SN12, **England**.
Contact/s: **Mr Jim Escott** (Secretary), 56 Addison Rd, Melksham, Avon, SN12 6LL.
(T) 01225 708814
Profile: **FT:** Coarse; **WN:** Bristol Avon; **WT:** River (Moving). **Location:** **Nr. Rd:** A350; **Main Rd:** Melksham to Trowbridge.
Ref: FH0197

AVON (BRISTOL) (RIVER)

River Bristol Avon, Kellaway's, West Tytherley, Salisbury, **WILTSHIRE**, SP5, **England**.
Contact/s: **Mr Rob Bullock** (Manager), Rob's Tackle, 19 New Rd, Chippenham, Wiltshire, SN15 1JX.
(T) 01249 659210 **(F)** 01249 659210
Mr Shaun Wilkins.
(T) 01249 461590
Profile: **FT:** Coarse; **WN:** Bristol Avon; **WT:** River (Moving) **W. Size:** 2400 Metres. **Location:** **Nr. Rd:** Sutton Benger to Avon; **Main Rd:** East Tytherton.
Ref: FH0198

AVON (BRISTOL) (RIVER)

River Bristol Avon, Lacock Abbey, Lacock, Chippenham, **WILTSHIRE**, SN15, **England**.
Contact/s: **Mr Jeff Parker** (Secretary), Bristol, Bath and Wilts Amalgamation, 16 Lansdown View, Kingswood, Bristol, BS15 4AW.
(T) 01179 672977
Profile: **FT:** Coarse; **WN:** Bristol Avon (Reybridge to Lacock Bridge); **WT:** River (Moving) **W. Size:** 1200 Metres. **Location:** **Nr. Rd:** Chippenham to Melksham; **Main Rd:** A350.
Ref: FH0199

AVON (BRISTOL) (RIVER)

River Bristol Avon, Beanacre Dump, Beanacre, Melksham, **WILTSHIRE**, SN12, **England**.
Contact/s: **Mr Jim Escott** (Secretary), 56 Addison Rd, Melksham, Avon, SN12 6LL.
(T) 01225 708814
Profile: **FT:** Coarse; **WN:** Bristol Avon; **WT:** River (Moving) **W. Size:** 2700 Metres. **Location:** **Nr. Rd:** A350 to Trowbridge; **Main Rd:** Scotland Road.
Ref: FH0200

AVON (BRISTOL) (RIVER)

River Bristol Avon, Seagry, Christian Malford, Chippenham, **WILTSHIRE**, SN15, **England**.
Contact/s: **Mr Jeff Parker** (Secretary), Bristol, Bath and Wilts Amalgamation, 16 Lansdown View, Kingswood, Bristol, BS15 4AW.
(T) 01179 672977
Profile: **FT:** Coarse; **WN:** Bristol Avon (Seagry to Christian Malford); **WT:** River (Moving). **Location:** **Nr. Rd:** B4069; **Main Rd:** M4, junction 17.
Ref: FH0201

AVON (RIVER)

River Avon, Keynsham, Bristol, BS31, **England**.
Contact/s: **Mr Findaly** (Owner), Keynsham Pet and Garden Ctre, 5 Bath Hill, Keynsham, Bristol, BS31 1EB.
(T) 01179 862366
Mrs Findaly (Owner).

KEY: **(w)**: Web address **(T)**: Telephone number **(F)**: Fax Number **(M)**: Mobile Number **(E)**: E-mail Address
F. Size: Fishery Size **FT:** Fisherytype **WN:** WaterName/s **WT:** WaterType **W. Size:** Water Size **£Fr**: Free Fishing

Profile: **FT:** Coarse; **WN:** Avon (Compton Dando to Wollard); **WT:** River (Moving).
Location: **Nr. Rd:** Compton Dando to Wollard.
Ref: FH0202

AVON (RIVER)

River Avon, Thurlestone, Kingsbridge, **DEVON**, TQ7, **England**.
Profile: **FT:** Game; **WN:** Avon; **WT:** River (Moving) **W. Size:** 35200 Metres.
Ref: FH0203

AVON (RIVER)

River Avon, Christchurch, **DORSET**, BH23, **England**.
Contact/s: **Mr R J Andrews** (Club Secretary), Christchurch Angling Club, 4 Marley Cl, New Milton, BH25 5LL.
(T) 01425 638502
Profile: **FT:** Combination; **WN:** Avon (Fordingbridge to Christchurch); **WT:** River (Moving).
Ref: FH0204

AVON (RIVER)

River Avon, Staverton, Cheltenham, **GLOUCESTERSHIRE**, GL51, **England**.
Contact/s: **Mr P O'Callaghan** (Secretary), 4 Fitzmaurice Cl, Bradford-on-Avon, Wiltshire, BA15 1UE.
(T) 01225 863163
Mr R Edwards (Secretary), Avon Angling Club, 56 Addison Rd, Melksham, Wiltshire, SN12 8DR.
(T) 01225 763835
Profile: **FT:** Coarse; **WN:** Avon (Staverton and Bradford-on-Avon); **WT:** River (Moving) **W. Size:** 11200 Metres.
Ref: FH0205

AVON (RIVER)

River Avon, Breamore, Ringwood, **HAMPSHIRE**, BH24, **England**.
Contact/s: **Mr Rod Smith** (Secretary), Avon Dairy Farm, The Bridges, Ringwood, BH24 2BA.
(T) 01425 472642
Profile: **FT:** Combination; **WN:** Avon; **WT:** River (Moving) **W. Size:** 2400 Metres.
Ref: FH0206

AVON (RIVER)

River Avon, Larkhall, **LANARKSHIRE (SOUTH)**, ML9, **Scotland**.
Contact/s: **Mr P Brooks** (Secretary), 3 The Neuk, Stonehouse, Larkhall, Lanarkshire, ML9 3HP.
Profile: **FT:** Game; **WN:** Avon; **WT:** River (Moving) **W. Size:** 22400 Metres. **Location:** **Nr. Rd:** Strathven Road; **Main Rd:** Stonehouse to Larkhall.
Ref: FH0207

AVON (RIVER)

River Avon, Bretford, Coventry, **MIDLANDS (WEST)**, CV, **England**.
Contact/s: **Mr John Hyde** (Secretary), Coventry and District Angling Club, 111 Lord Litton Avenue, Stoke, Coventry, CV2 5JT.
(T) 024 76418893
Profile: **FT:** Coarse; **WN:** Avon; **WT:** River (Moving).
Ref: FH0208

AVON (RIVER)

River Avon, Castle Bridge, Warwick, **MIDLANDS (WEST)**, CV3, **England**.
Contact/s: **Mr T Butler** (Manager), Baileys of Warwick, 30 Emscote Rd, Warwick, Warwickshire, CV34 4PP.
(T) 01926 491984 **(F)** 01926 411264
Profile: **FT:** Coarse; **WN:** Avon; **WT:** River (Moving).
Ref: FH0209

AVON (RIVER)

River Avon, Bath, **SOMERSET**, BA, **England**.
Contact/s: Secretary, Bath Angling Association, 37 Broad St, Bath, Somerset, BA1 5LT.
Profile: **FT:** Combination; **WN:** Avon (Bathampton to City Weirs); **WT:** River (Moving).
Ref: FH0210

AVON (RIVER)

River Avon, Midford Brook, Midford, Bath, **SOMERSET**, BA2, **England**.
Profile: **FT:** Game; **WN:** Avon; **WT:** River (Moving).
Ref: FH0211

AVON (RIVER)

River Avon, Frome, **SOMERSET**, BA11, **England**.
Contact/s: Manager, Frome Angling Ctre, 11 Church St, Frome, Somerset, BA11 1PW.
(T) 01373 467143 **(F)** 01373 452919
Profile: **FT:** Coarse; **WN:** Avon; **WT:** River (Moving) **W. Size:** 19200 Metres.
Ref: FH0212

AVON (RIVER)

River Avon, Seven Meadows And Stannless, Stratford-upon-Avon, **WARWICKSHIRE**, CV37, **England**.
Contact/s: **Mr Craig Cleeve**, The Craig Cleeve House Hotel, 67-69 Shipston Rd, Stratford-upon-Avon, Warwickshire, CV37 7LW.
(T) 01789 296573 **(F)** 01789 299452
Mr Ken Waldenmar (Secretary), Stratford-upon-Avon Angling Club, Park Farm, Compton Verney, Combrook, Kineton, Warwickshire.
(T) 01789 720603
Profile: **FT:** Coarse; **WN:** Avon (Lucy's Mill Bridge to Stannels Bridge); **WT:** River (Moving) **W. Size:** 1600 Metres.
Ref: FH0213

AVON (RIVER)

River Avon, Rugby, **WARWICKSHIRE**, CV, **England**.
Contact/s: **Mr A.S. Churchward** (Fisheries Manager), Environment Agency, Lower Severn Area Office, Riversmeet House, Newtown Industrial Estate, Tewkesbury GL20 8JG.
(T) 01684 850951 **(F)** 01684 293599
Profile: **FT:** Coarse; **WN:** Avon; **WT:** River (Moving) **W. Size:** 640 Metres. **Location:** **Nr. Rd:** B4112, Newbold Road; **Main Rd:** A426, Liecester Road. **£Fr**
Ref: FH0214

AVON (RIVER)

River Avon, Lucy's Mill, Stratford-upon-Avon, **WARWICKSHIRE**, CV37, **England**.
Contact/s: Fishery Manager.
(T) 01926 424491
Profile: **FT:** Coarse; **WN:** Avon; **WT:** River (Moving).
Ref: FH0215

AVON (RIVER)

River Avon, Chippenham, **WILTSHIRE**, SN, **England**.
Contact/s: **Mr Brian Duffield** (Secretary), 95 Malmesbury Rd, Chippenham, Wiltshire.
(T) 01249 655575
(E) brian.dufield@barclays.net
Profile: **FT:** Coarse; **WN:** Avon; **WT:** Combination (Still & Moving). **Location:** **Nr. Rd:** A4; **Main Rd:** A429; **Rail:** Chippenham.
Ref: FH0216

AVON (RIVER)

River Avon, Chippenham, **WILTSHIRE**, SN15, **England**.
Contact/s: **Mr T Moulton** (Secretary), 70 Perry's Lane, Wroughton, Swindon, Wiltshire, SN4 9AP.
(T) 01793 813155
Profile: **FT:** Coarse; **WN:** Avon; **WT:** River (Moving).
Ref: FH0217

AVON (RIVER)

River Avon, Melksham, **WILTSHIRE**, SN12, **England**.
Contact/s: **Mr Rob Bullock** (Manager), Rob's Tackle, 19 New Rd, Chippenham, Wiltshire, SN15 1JX.
(T) 01249 659210 **(F)** 01249 659210
Profile: **FT:** Coarse; **WN:** Avon; **WT:** River (Moving) **W. Size:** 5600 Metres. **Location:** **Nr. Rd:** Beanacre to Whaddon; **Main Rd:** High Street.
Ref: FH0218

AVON (RIVER)

River Avon, Nadder, Wilton, Salisbury, **WILTSHIRE**, SP2, **England**.
Contact/s: **Mr B Ricketts** (Secretary), 26 St Martians Cl, Barford St Martin, Sailsbury, Wiltshire, SP3 4AX.
Profile: **FT:** Coarse; **WN:** Avon; **WT:** River (Moving) **W. Size:** 4800 Metres.
Ref: FH0219

AVON (RIVER)

River Avon, Salisbury, **WILTSHIRE**, SP, **England**.
Contact/s: **Mr Ron Hillier** (Secretary), 29 New Zealand Avenue, Salisbury, Wiltshire, SP2 7JX.
(T) 01722 321164
Profile: **FT:** Coarse; **WN:** Avon; **WT:** River (Moving). **Location:** **Rail:** Salisbury.
Ref: FH0220

AVON (RIVER)

River Avon, Steeple Langford, Wilton, Salisbury, **WILTSHIRE**, SP2, **England**.
Profile: **FT:** Game; **WN:** Avon (Steeple Langford to Quidhampton); **WT:** River (Moving) **W. Size:** 9600 Metres.
Ref: FH0221

AVON (RIVER)

River Avon, Maiden Bradley, Longleat Estate, Warminster, **WILTSHIRE**, BA12, **England**.
Contact/s: Bailiff, Parkhill Cottage, Longleat Estate, Warminster, Wiltshire.
Profile: **FT:** Coarse; **WN:** Avon; **WT:** River (Moving) **W. Size:** 3200 Metres.
Ref: FH0222

AVON (RIVER)

River Avon, Twyford Farm, Evesham Country Centre, Evesham, **WORCESTERSHIRE**, WR11, **England**.
Contact/s: **Mr Stuart Gottfried. (M)** 07973 147323
Profile: **FT:** Coarse; **WN:** Avon; **WT:** Combination (Still & Moving) **W. Size:** 2 Acres.
Ref: FH0223

AVON (RIVER)

River Avon, Common Rd, Evesham, **WORCESTERSHIRE**, WR11, **England**.
Contact/s: **Mr C Thompson** (Chairman).
(T) 01386 458800
Profile: **FT:** Coarse; **WN:** Avon; **WT:** River (Moving).
Ref: FH0224

AVON (RIVER)

River Avon, Pensham, Pershore, **WORCESTERSHIRE**, WR10, **England**.
Contact/s: **Mr Dave Beresford** (Manager), Allans Fishing Tackle, 26-30 Malvern Rd, Worcester, Worcestershire, WR2 4LG.
(T) 01905 422107 **(F)** 01905 422107
Mr John Wells (Chairman), Worcester and District United Angling Association, Poplar Cottages, Poplar Rd, Whichenford, WR6 6YF.
(T) 01886 888459
Profile: **FT:** Coarse; **WN:** Avon; **WT:** River (Moving) **W. Size:** 1000 Metres.
Ref: FH0225

AVON DAM

Avon Dam, Totnes, **DEVON**, TQ9, **England**.
Contact/s: **Mr Chris Hall** (Manager).
(T) 01837 871565 **(F)** 01837 871534
Profile: **FT:** Coarse; **WN:** Avon; **WT:** Mill Dam (Still).
Ref: FH0227

AVON RIVER FISHERIES

River Avon Fisheries Bickton, Bickton Manor, Bickton, Fordingbridge, **HAMPSHIRE**, SP6 2HA, **England**.
Contact/s: J A C Sykes.
(T) 01425 652236
Profile: **FT:** Combination; **WN:** Hampshire Avon; **WT:** River (Moving); **F. Size:** 500 Acres; **W. Size:** 4000 Metres. **Location:** **Nr. Rd:** A338; **Rail:** Salisbury.
Ref: FH0228

AVON SPRINGS FISHERY

Avon Springs Fishery, Recreation Rd, Durrington, Salisbury, **WILTSHIRE**, SP4 8HH, **England**.
(W) www.fishingfly.co.uk
Contact/s: **Mr Barrie Bawden** (Owner).
(T) 01980 653557 **(F)** 01980 655267 **(M)** 07774 801401
(E) barrie@fishingfly.co.uk
Profile: **FT:** Game; **WN:** Avon Springs Fishery; **WT:** Combination (Still & Moving); **F. Size:** 21 Acres; **W. Size:** 8 Acres. **Location:** **Nr. Rd:** A345; **Main Rd:** A303; **Rail:** Salisbury.
Ref: FH0229

AVON TYRRELL LAKES

Avon Tyrrell Lakes, Avon Tyrrell Activity Ctre, Youth Clubs Uk, Bransgore, Christchurch, **DORSET**, BH23 8EE, **England**.
(W) www.avontyrrell.org.uk
Contact/s: **Mr Dave Clark** (Estate Warden).
(T) 01425 672347 **(F)** 01425 673883 **(M)** 07961 358452
(E) info@avontyrrell.org.uk
Profile: **FT:** Coarse; **WN:** Avon Tyrrell; **WT:** Lake (Still); **F. Size:** 50 Acres; **W. Size:** 2 Acres. **Location:** **Nr. Rd:** Private track, Between A31 and A35; **Main Rd:** A35; **Rail:** New Milton.
Ref: FH0230

AWBRIDGE DANES LAKE

Awbridge Danes Lake, Romsey, **HAMPSHIRE**, SO51, **England**.
Contact/s: **Mr John Burns**.
(T) 01794 341537
Profile: **FT:** Coarse; **WN:** Awbridge Danes; **WT:** Lake (Still) **W. Size:** 10 Acres. **Location:** **Nr. Rd:** Danes Road; **Main Rd:** A27.
Ref: FH0231

AXE (RIVER)

River Axe, Old Wardour, Axminster, **DEVON**, EX13, **England**.
Profile: **FT:** Game; **WN:** Axe; **WT:** River (Moving).
Ref: FH0233

AXE (RIVER)

River Axe, Higher Cownhayne Farm, Colyton, **DEVON**, EX13 6HD, **England**.
Contact/s: **Mrs E Pady** (owner).
(T) 01297 552267
Profile: **FT:** Game; **WN:** Axe; **WT:** River (Moving).
Ref: FH0234

AYCLIFFE LAKE

Aycliffe Lake, Aycliffe, Newton Aycliffe, **COUNTY DURHAM**, DL, **England**.
Contact/s: **Mr Stuart Newbury** (Fishery Manager), 4 Trafford Cl, Darlington, DL1 2SS.
(T) 01325 369672
Profile: **FT:** Coarse; **WN:** Aycliffe; **WT:** Lake (Still) **W. Size:** 2 Acres. **Location:** **Main Rd:** B6444.
Ref: FH0235

AYLESBURY ARM CANAL

Aylesbury Arm Canal, Marsworth To Aston Clinton, Tring, **HERTFORDSHIRE**, HP23, **England**.
(W) www.tringanglers.club24.co.uk
Contact/s: **Mr Stuart Riddle** (Secretary), The Tring Anglers, PO Box 1947, Tring, Hertfordshire, HP23 5LZ.
(T) 01442 826148
Profile: **FT:** Coarse; **WN:** Aylesbury Arm Canal; **WT:** Canal (Still).
Ref: FH0236

AYLESBURY ARM CANAL

Aylesbury Arm Canal, Aylesbury, **HERTFORDSHIRE**, HP1, **England**.
Contact/s: **Mr John MacDonald**.
(T) 01296 429983
Profile: **FT:** Coarse; **WN:** Aylesbury Arm Canal; **WT:** Canal (Still).
Ref: FH0237

AYR (RIVER)

River Ayr, Ayr, **AYRSHIRE (SOUTH)**, KA, **Scotland**.
Contact/s: Manager, Gamesport of Ayr, 60 Sandgate, Ayr, Ayrshire (East), KA7 1BX.
(T) 01292 263822 **(F)** 01292 263822
Profile: **FT:** Game; **WN:** Ayr; **WT:** River (Moving).
Ref: FH0238

BABINGLEY (RIVER)

River Babingley, Babingley, King's Lynn, **NORFOLK**, PE31, **England**.
Contact/s: **Mr Mick Grief** (Secretary), King's Lynn Angling Association, 67 Peckover Way, South Woonton, King's Lynn, PE30 3UE.
(T) 01553 671545
Profile: **FT:** Coarse; **WN:** Babingley; **WT:** River (Moving) **W. Size:** 14400 Metres. **Location:** **Rail:** North Wootton.
Ref: FH0239

BACHE POOL

Bache Pool, Oakley Hall, Loggerheads, Market Drayton, **SHROPSHIRE**, **England**.
Contact/s: **Mr John Turner** (Hon Secretary), Prince Albert Angling Society, 15 Pexhill Drive, Macclesfield, Cheshire, SK10 3LP.
(T) 01625 422010
Profile: **FT:** Coarse; **WN:** Bache Pool; **WT:** Clay Pit (Still) **W. Size:** 1 Acre. **Location:** **Main Rd:** B5415; **Rail:** Whitchurch.
Ref: FH0240

BACKHILL FISHERY

Backhill Fishery, Gamrie, Macduff, **ABERDEENSHIRE**, AB44, **Scotland**.
Profile: **FT:** Game; **WN:** Backhill Fishery; **WT:** River (Moving).
Ref: FH0241

BACKWATER

Backwater, Medmenham, Marlow, **BUCKINGHAMSHIRE**, SL7, **England**.
Contact/s: **Mr J Woodhouse** (Secretary), Marlow Angling Club, Conifers, Ash Rd, High Wycombe, Buckinghamshire, HP12 4SW.
(T) 01494 523988
Profile: **FT:** Coarse; **WN:** Backwater; **WT:** River (Moving).
Ref: FH0242

BACON FACTORY POND

Bacon Factory Pond, Sherburn-In-Elmet, Tadcaster, **YORKSHIRE (NORTH)**, LS24, **England**.
Contact/s: **Mr Robert Howgate** (Secretary), Wheatsheaf Angling Club, 4 Sprigfield Rd, Sherburn in Elmet, Leeds, LS25 6BD.
(T) 01977 684772
Profile: **FT:** Coarse; **WN:** Bacon Factory; **WT:** Pond (Still) **W. Size:** 2 Acres. **Location:** **Nr. Rd:** B1222; **Main Rd:** A63.
Ref: FH0243

BADDILEY RESERVOIR

Baddiley Reservoir, Mere House, Nr. Wenbury Heath, Nantwich, **CHESHIRE**, **England**.
Contact/s: **Mr John Turner** (Hon Secretary), Prince Albert Angling Society, 15 Pexhill Drive, Macclesfield, Cheshire, SK10 3LP.
(T) 01625 422010
Profile: **FT:** Game; **WN:** Baddiley Reservoir; **WT:** Reservoir (Still); **F. Size:** 6 Acres; **W. Size:** 5 Acres. **Location:** **Main Rd:** A534; **Rail:** Nantwich.
Ref: FH0244

BADEN HALL FISHERY

Baden Hall Fishery, Baden Hall Farm, Eccleshall, Stafford, **STAFFORDSHIRE**, ST21 6LG, **England**.
(W) www.badenhall.com
Mr James Goucher (Owner), Baden Hall, Eccleshall, Staffordshire. St21 6LG.
(T) 01785 850313 **(F)** 01785 851650
(E) enquiries@badenhall.com
Profile: **FT:** Coarse; **WN:** Baden Hall Fishery; **WT:** Pool (Still); **F. Size:** 30 Acres. **Location:** **Nr. Rd:** Eccleshall to Swynnerton Road; **Main Rd:** M6, junction 14; **Rail:** Stafford.
Ref: FH0245

BADHAM FARM LAKE

Badham Farm Lake, St Keyne, Liskeard, **CORNWALL**, PL14 4RW, **England**.
Contact/s: **Mr Robert Brown**.
(T) 01579 343572
Mrs Joyce Brown.
(T) 01579 343572
Profile: **FT:** Coarse; **WN:** Badham Farm; **WT:** Lake (Still) **W. Size:** 1 Acre.
Ref: FH0246

BADSHOT LEA

Badshot Lea, Badshot Lea Rd, Farnham, **SURREY**, GU10, **England**.
Contact/s: **Mr Mick Borra** (Secretary), The Creel, 36 Station Rd, Aldershot, Hampshire, GU11 1HT.
(T) 01252 320871
Profile: **FT:** Coarse; **WN:** Badshot Lea; **WT:** Lake (Still).
Ref: FH0247

BAFFINS POND

Baffins Pond, Copnor, Portsmouth, **HAMPSHIRE**, PO2 7NL, **England**.
Contact/s: **Mr R G Snook** (Secretary), 86 Carnarvon Rd, Copnor, Portsmouth, Hampshire, PO2 7NL.
(T) 023 92662986
Profile: **FT:** Coarse; **WN:** Baffins; **WT:** Pond (Still).
Ref: FH0248

BAGWOOD LAKE

Bagwood Lake, Woodlands Lane, Bristol, BS32 4JY, **England**.
Contact/s: **Paul** (Manager), Woodlands Golf and Country Club, Woodlands Land, Bradley Stoke, Bristol, BS32 4JY.
(T) 01454 201856
Profile: **FT:** Coarse; **WN:** Bagwood; **WT:** Lake (Still). **Location:** **Nr. Rd:** Woodlands Lane.
Ref: FH0249

BAILEY (RIVER)

River Bailey, Roxburgh, Kelso, **SCOTTISH BORDERS**, TD5, **Scotland**.
Contact/s: Manager, Bailey Mill Farm Holidays and Trekking Ctre, Bailey Mill, Newcastleton, Scottish Borders, TD9 0TR.
(T) 01697 748617
Profile: **FT:** Game; **WN:** Bailey; **WT:** River (Moving) **W. Size:** 8000 Metres. **Location:** **Rail:** Carlisle.
Ref: FH0250

BAILIEBORO LAKES

Bailieboro Lakes, Bailieborough, **COUNTY CAVAN**, **Ireland**.
Contact/s: **Mr Pat McCabe** (Secretary), Virginia Coarse Angling Club, Rahardrum, Virginia, County Cavan, Ireland.
(T) 042 9694352or498547649 **(F)** 042 9666318
Profile: **FT:** Coarse; **WN:** Bailieboro Lakes; **WT:** Lake (Still).
Ref: FH0251

BAIN (RIVER)

River Bain, Bainbridge, Leyburn, **YORKSHIRE**

(NORTH), DL8, **England**.
Contact/s: **Mr Peter Bennet**.
(T) 01748 824894
Profile: **FT:** Coarse; **WN:** Bain; **WT:** River (Moving).
Ref: FH0252

BAKE FISHING LAKES

Bake Fishing Lakes, Trerulefoot, Saltash, **CORNWALL**, PL12 5BL, **England**.
Contact/s: **Mr Chris Bond**.
(T) 01503 240304 **(F)** 01503 240882 **(M)** 07798 585836
Mr Tony Lister (Fishery Manager), Broadmoor Farm, Stoketon, Saltash, Cornwall, PL12 4SA.
(T) 01752 849027 **(F)** 01503 240882 **(M)** 07798 585836
(E) tony.lister@bakelakes.co.uk
Ms Alison Bond.
(T) 01503 240304 **(F)** 01503 240882 **(M)** 07798 585836
Profile: **FT:** Combination; **WN:** Bake; **WT:** Lake (Still); **F. Size:** 25 Acres; **W. Size:** 15 Acres. **Location:** **Nr. Rd:** Bake Lane; **Main Rd:** A38, A374; **Rail:** St Germans.
Ref: FH0253

BAKERS FARM

Bakers Farm, Moortown, Torrington, **DEVON**, EX38 7ES, **England**.
Contact/s: **Mr C G Ridd** (Owner).
(T) 01805 623260
Profile: **FT:** Coarse; **WN:** Bakers Farm; **WT:** Lake (Still) **W. Size:** 1 Acre.
Ref: FH0254

BAKERS LAKE

Bakers Lake, Stowmarket, **SUFFOLK**, IP14, **England**.
Contact/s: Fishery Manager.
(T) 01473 728179
Profile: **FT:** Coarse; **WN:** Bakers; **WT:** Lake (Still).
Ref: FH0255

BALCOMBE LAKE

Balcombe Lake, Balcombe, Haywards Heath, **SUSSEX (WEST)**, RH17, **England**.
Contact/s: **Mr J Kenward** (Secretary), Haywards Heath and District Angling Society, 60 Franklyn Rd, Haywards Heath, Sussex (West), RH16 4DH.
(T) 01444 452572
Profile: **FT:** Coarse; **WN:** Balcombe; **WT:** Lake (Still).
Ref: FH0256

BALGRAVE RESERVOIR

Balgrave Reservoir, Newton Mearns, Glasgow, **GLASGOW (CITY OF)**, G, **Scotland**.
Profile: **FT:** Game; **WN:** Balgrave; **WT:** Reservoir (Still).
Ref: FH0257

BALL GROVE LAKE

Ball Grove Lake, Ball Grove Pinic Site, Winewall, Colne, **LANCASHIRE**, BB8, **England**.
(W) www.pearce81.freeserve.co.uk
Contact/s: **Mr Terry Hartley** (Outdoor Recreation Officer), Pendle Leisure Services, Crown Way, Colne, Lancashire, BB8 8NP.
(T) 01282 661230 **(F)** 01282 661137 **(M)** 07718 601881
(E) plc@leisureinpendle.co.uk
Profile: **FT:** Coarse; **WN:** Ball Grove; **WT:** Pond (Still) **W. Size:** 1 Acre. **Location:** **Nr. Rd:** A6068; **Main Rd:** A6068; **Rail:** Colne.
Ref: FH0258

BALLAST PIT

Ballast Pit, Haysden Country Park, Lower Haysden Rd, Tonbridge, **KENT**, TN1, **England**.
Contact/s: **Mr Alex Heggie** (Membership Secretary), Little Lucy's Farmhouse, Lower St, Hildenborough, Tonbridge, TN11 8PT.
(T) 01732 832352 **(F)** 01732 832352
Mr Tom Creasey (Hon Secretary), 3 Invicta Flats, Great Brooms Rd, Tunbridge Wells, Kent, TN4 9DD.
(T) 01892 520520
Profile: **FT:** Coarse; **WN:** Ballast Pit; **WT:** Lake (Still) **W. Size:** 8 Acres. **Location:** **Nr. Rd:** Lower Haysden Road; **Main Rd:** A26, Quarryhill; **Rail:** Tonbridge.
Ref: FH0259

BALLECHIN BEAT

Ballechin Beat, Pitlochry, **PERTH AND KINROSS**, PH, **Scotland**.
(W) www.fishingnet.com/beats/ballechin
Contact/s: **Ms Em Honeyman** (Manager), Wade Newsagents, 31 Bank St, Aberfeldy, Perth and Kinross, PH15 2BB.
(T) 01887 820397
Profile: **FT:** Combination; **WN:** Ballechin Beat; **WT:** Pool (Still).
Ref: FH0260

BALLINAFID LAKE

Ballinafid Lake, Mullingar, **COUNTY WESTMEATH**, **Ireland**.
Profile: **FT:** Coarse; **WN:** Ballinafid; **WT:** Lake (Still). **Location:** **Nr. Rd:** N4 Mullingar to Longford Road.
Ref: FH0261

BALLINAKILL LAKE

Ballinakill Lake, Kilkenny, **COUNTY KILKENNY**, **Ireland**.
Contact/s: **Mr Matt Doyle**, Grandtown, Ballacolla, Portlaoise, County Laois, Ireland.
Profile: **FT:** Coarse; **WN:** Ballinakill; **WT:** Lake (Still).
Ref: FH0262

BALLINAMALLARD (RIVER)

River Ballinamallard, Ballinamallard, Enniskillen, **COUNTY FERMANAGH**, BT94, **Northern Ireland**.
Contact/s: **Mr Hugh Mannix**, Brookville, Ballinamallard, County Fermanagh.
(T) 028 66388183after6pm
W Bradford, 6 Barragh Rd, Ballinamallard, County Fermanagh.
(T) 028 66388474after6pm
Profile: **FT:** Game; **WN:** Ballinamallard; **WT:** River (Moving) **W. Size:** 8000 Metres.
Ref: FH0263

BALLINAROONE LODGE FISHERY

Ballinaroone Lodge Fishery, Ballinaroone Lodge, Ballyduff, Waterford, **COUNTY WATERFORD**, **Ireland**.
Contact/s: Fishery Manager.
(T) 058 59370
Profile: **FT:** Game; **WN:** Ballinaroone Lodge Fishery; **WT:** Lough (Still).
Ref: FH0264

BALLINCOLLIG RESERVOIR

Ballincollig Reservoir, Ballincollig Village, Cork, **COUNTY CORK**, **Ireland**.
Profile: **FT:** Coarse; **WN:** Ballincollig; **WT:** Reservoir (Still) **W. Size:** 8 Acres.
Ref: FH0265

BALLINDERRY (RIVER)

River Ballinderry, Coagh, Cookstown, **COUNTY TYRONE**, BT80, **Northern Ireland**.
Contact/s: Manager, Mace Shop, 3 Main St, Coagh, Cookstown, BT80 0ED.
(T) 028 86736559
Mr David Hagan (Manager).
(T) 028 86737055
Mr Leo Cassidy (Assistant Secretary), 18 Spring Rd, Ballinderry Bridge, Cookstown, County Tyrone, BT80 0BD.
(T) 028 86748779
Profile: **FT:** Game; **WN:** Ballinderry; **WT:** River (Moving) **W. Size:** 3200 Metres.
Ref: FH0266

BALLINDERRY (RIVER)

River Ballinderry, Cookstown, **COUNTY TYRONE**, BT80, **Northern Ireland**.
Contact/s: **Mr Jim Devlin** (Secretary), 175 Spring Rd, Ballinderry Bridge, Cookstown, County Tyrone, BT80 0BD.
(T) 028 86744511
Mr Leo Cassidy (Assistant Secretary), 18 Spring Rd, Ballinderry Bridge, Cookstown, County Tyrone, BT80 0BD.
(T) 028 86748779
Profile: **FT:** Game; **WN:** Ballinderry; **WT:** River (Moving) **W. Size:** 4800 Metres.
Ref: FH0267

BALLINDERRY (RIVER)

River Ballinderry, Cookstown, **COUNTY TYRONE**, BT80, **Northern Ireland**.
Contact/s: **Mr Robin Black** (Secretary), 24 Chetnutt Gr, Lower Kildress Rd, Cookstown, County Tyrone, BT80 9RN.
(T) 028 86763809
Profile: **FT:** Game; **WN:** Ballinderry; **WT:** River (Moving) **W. Size:** 1600 Metres.
Ref: FH0268

BALLINDERRY (RIVER)

River Ballinderry, Cookstown, **COUNTY TYRONE**, BT80, **Northern Ireland**.
Contact/s: **Mr Stanley Aspinall** (Manager), 2 Rathbeg, Cookstown, County Tyrone.
(T) 028 79665905
Profile: **FT:** Game; **WN:** Ballinderry; **WT:** River (Moving) **W. Size:** 3200 Metres.
Ref: FH0269

BALLINDOOLY LOUGH AND POND

Ballindooly Lough And Pond, Moycullen, **COUNTY GALWAY**, **Ireland**.
Contact/s: **Mr Danny Goldrick** (Angling Officer), The Western Regional Fisheries Board, Weir Lodge, Earl's Island, Galway City, County Galway.
(T) 091 563118 **(F)** 091 566335
(E) wrfb@iol.ie
Profile: **FT:** Coarse; **WN:** Ballindooly; **WT:** Lough (Still) **W. Size:** 25 Acres.
Ref: FH0270

BALLO RESERVOIR

Ballo Reservoir, Glenrothes, **FIFE**, KY7, **Scotland**.
Contact/s: **Mr Robert Watson**.
(T) 0131 4402047
Profile: **FT:** Game; **WN:** Ballo; **WT:** Reservoir (Still).
Ref: FH0271

BALLS GREEN LAKES

Balls Green Lakes, Hartfield, **SUSSEX (EAST)**, TN7 4, **England**.
(W) www.calpac.bizland.com
Contact/s: **Mr Colin Trafford** (General Secretary).
(T) 020 82242617
Mrs Diane Wheeler (Membership Secretary), 314 Old Lodge Lane, Purley, Surrey, CR8 4AQ.
(T) 020 86602766
Profile: **FT:** Coarse; **WN:** Balls Green; **WT:** Pond (Still) **W. Size:** 2 Acres. **Location:** **Main Rd:** A264.
Ref: FH0272

BALLY GRANGE FISHERY

Bally Grange Fishery, Carrowdore, Newtownards, **COUNTY DOWN**, BT22 2, **Northern Ireland**.
Contact/s: **Mr Peter Calvert** (Manager).
(T) 028 91788883
Profile: **FT:** Game; **WN:** Bally Grange; **WT:** Lake (Still) **W. Size:** 1 Acre.
Ref: FH0273

BALLYGAWLEY (RIVER)

River Ballygawley, Ballygawley, Aughnacloy, **COUNTY TYRONE**, BT696, **Northern Ireland**.
Contact/s: **Mrs Liz Salter** (Manager), Aughnacloy Development Association, The McCreedy Mill Centre, Aughnacloy, County Tyrone, BT69 6AL.
(T) 028 85557002
Profile: **FT:** Game; **WN:** Ballygawley; **WT:** River (Moving).
Ref: FH0274

BALLYLOUGH

Ballylough, Castlewellan, **COUNTY DOWN**, BT31, **Northern Ireland**.
Contact/s: Mr J L Harty, 22 Larchfield Park, Newcastle, County Down.
(T) 028 43726017after5.30pm
Profile: FT: Game; WN: Ballylough; WT: Lake (Still) W. Size: 22 Acres.
Ref: FH0275

BALLYMAQUIRK FISHERY

Ballymaquirk Fishery And Lodge, Greybrook House, Waterfall, **COUNTY CORK**, **Ireland**.
Contact/s: Mr George Armstrong.
(T) 021 502555
Profile: FT: Game; WN: Ballymaquirk; WT: Reservoir (Still).
Ref: FH0276

BALLYMASCANLON (RIVER)

River Ballymascanlon, Dundalk Bay, Dundalk, **COUNTY LOUTH**, **Ireland**.
Contact/s: Secretary, Dundalk Brown Trout Angling Club, 3 Mill Rd, Forkhill, Newry, BT35 95J.
Mr John Clarke (Club Secretary).
(T) 028 3088 8378
Profile: FT: Game; WN: Ballymascanlon (Dundalk Bay-Northern Island Border; WT: River (Moving) W. Size: 9600 Metres.
Location: Rail: Dundalk.
Ref: FH0277

BALLYNAHINCH CASTLE FISHERY

Ballynahinch Castle Fishery, Ballynahinch Castle Hotel, Ballynahinch, Recess, **COUNTY GALWAY**, **Ireland**.
Contact/s: Mr Patrick O'Flatherty (Fishery Manager).
(T) 095 31006 (F) 095 31085
Profile: FT: Game; WN: Ballynahinch; WT: Combination (Still & Moving) W. Size: 4000 Metres.
Ref: FH0278

BALLYNAHINCH FISHERY

Top Waters Ballynahinch Fishery, Tullaboy House, Maam Cross, **COUNTY GALWAY**, **Ireland**.
Contact/s: Mr L Lyons-Joyce.
(T) 091 552305
Profile: FT: Game; WN: Ballynahinch; WT: River (Moving).
Ref: FH4877

BALLYSHUNNOCK

Ballyshunnock, Waterford, **COUNTY WATERFORD**, **Ireland**.
Contact/s: Manager, Carrolls Cross Inn, Carrolls Cross, Kilmacthomas, County Waterford, Ireland.
(T) 051 294328
Profile: FT: Game; WN: Ballyshunnock; WT: Reservoir (Still) W. Size: 70 Acres.
Ref: FH0279

BALVAIG (RIVER)

River Balvaig, Balquhidder, Lochearnhead, **STIRLING**, FK19, **Scotland**.
Contact/s: Manager, Craigruie Sporting Estate, Balquhidder, Lochearnhead, Perth and Kinross, FK19 8PQ.
Profile: FT: Game; WN: Balvaig; WT: River (Moving).
Ref: FH0280

BANDON (RIVER)

River Bandon, Dunmanway, **COUNTY CORK**, **Ireland**.
Contact/s: Mr P MacCarthy (Secretary), Dunmanway Salmon and Trout Angling Association, Yew Tree Bar, Dunmanway, County Cork, Ireland.
Profile: FT: Game; WN: Bandon; WT: River (Moving) W. Size: 12800 Metres.
Ref: FH0281

BANDON (RIVER)

River Bandon, Bandon, **COUNTY CORK**, **Ireland**.
Contact/s: Mr Mj O'Regan (Secretary), Oliver Plunkett St, Bandon, County Cork, Ireland.
(T) 023 41674
Profile: FT: Game; WN: Bandon; WT: River (Moving) W. Size: 11200 Metres.
Ref: FH0282

BANDON (RIVER)

River Bandon, Kicoleman Fishery, Enniskeane, **COUNTY CORK**, **Ireland**.
Contact/s: Manager.
(T) 023 47279 (F) 023 47408
Profile: FT: Game; WN: Bandon; WT: River (Moving).
Ref: FH0283

BANDON (RIVER)

River Bandon, Ballineen Bridge, Ballineen, **COUNTY CORK**, **Ireland**.
Contact/s: Mr Tom Fehilly (Secretary), Bridge St, Ballineen, County Cork, Ireland.
Profile: FT: Game; WN: Bandon; WT: River (Moving) W. Size: 6400 Metres.
Ref: FH0284

BANK END COARSE FISHERIES

Bank End Coarse Fisheries, Ninescores Farm, Finningley, Doncaster, **YORKSHIRE (SOUTH)**, DN9 3DY, **Scotland**.
Contact/s: Mr Andrew McCallum (Owner/Fishery Manager).
(T) 01302 770224
Profile: FT: Coarse; WN: Bank End Coarse Fisheries; WT: Lake (Still); F. Size: 12 Acres; W. Size: 10 Acres. **Location:** Nr. Rd: Ninescores Lane; Main Rd: B1396; Rail: Doncaster.
Ref: FH0285

BANK HOUSE FLY FISHERY

Bank House Fly Fishery, Low Mill, Caton, Lancaster, **LANCASHIRE**, LA2 9HX, **England**.
Contact/s: Mrs Jan Dobson (Manager).
(T) 01524 770412 (M) 07779 989465
Profile: FT: Game; WN: Bank House Fly Fishery; WT: Pond (Still); F. Size: 2 Acres; W. Size: 2 Acres. **Location:** Nr. Rd: A683; Main Rd: M6, junction 34; Rail: Lancaster.
£Fr
Ref: FH0286

BANKES POOL

Bankes Pool, Great Witley, Stourport-on-Severn, **WORCESTERSHIRE**, DY13, **England**.
Profile: FT: Coarse; WN: Bankes; WT: Pond (Still). **Location:** Main Rd: A451, A443 North of Worcester.
Ref: FH0287

BANKS (THE)

Banks (The), Rugby, **WARWICKSHIRE**, CV, **England**.
Contact/s: Mr Richard Bubb.
(T) 01788 579521
Profile: FT: Coarse; WN: The Banks; WT: Canal (Still). **Location:** Nr. Rd: M45; Main Rd: Rugby.
Ref: FH0288

BANKS POND

Banks Pond, Old Hutton, Kendal, **CUMBRIA**, LA, **England**.
Contact/s: Mr Tony Ryan, 8 Hayfell Rise, Kendal, Cumbria.
Profile: FT: Coarse; WN: Banks; WT: Pond (Still). **Location:** Nr. Rd: B6254; Main Rd: M6, just off.
Ref: FH0289

BANN (LOWER) (RIVER)

River Lower Bann, Agivey- Drumaheglis, Ballymena, **COUNTY ANTRIM**, BT44, **Northern Ireland**.
Contact/s: Manager, Bann System Ltd, Dundarave, Bushmills, BT57 8ST.
(T) 028 25821301
Manager, Bannvalley Guns and Tackle, 18 Main St, Portglenone, Ballymena, BT44 8AB.
(T) 028 25821383 (F) 028 25821383
Profile: FT: Game; WN: Bann Lower; WT: River (Moving).
Ref: FH0290

BANN (LOWER) (RIVER)

River Lower Bann, Gilmore's Shore, Ballymena, **COUNTY ANTRIM**, BT44, **Northern Ireland**.
Contact/s: Manager, Bann System Ltd, Dundarave, Bushmills, BT57 8ST.
(T) 028 25821301
Manager, Bannvalley Guns and Tackle, 18 Main St, Portglenone, Ballymena, BT44 8AB.
(T) 028 25821383 (F) 028 25821383
Profile: FT: Coarse; WN: Lower Bann; WT: River (Moving).
Ref: FH0291

BANN (LOWER) (RIVER)

River Lower Bann, Kilrea, Coleraine, **COUNTY LONDONDERRY**, BT51, **Northern Ireland**.
Contact/s: Manager, Donaghy Brothers, 34 Maghera St, Kilrea, Colerine, BT51 5QN.
(T) 028 29540001
Profile: FT: Game; WN: Lower Bann; WT: River (Moving) W. Size: 400 Metres.
Ref: FH0292

BANN (LWR) NAVIGATIONAL CANAL

River Lower Bann Navigational Canal, Movanagher, **COUNTY ANTRIM**, BT, **Northern Ireland**.
Contact/s: Mr Albert Atkins, 67 Coleraine Rd, Garvagh, County Londonderry.
(T) 028 25558555
Mr J Hamilton (Manager), O'Rorke McDonald and Tweed, 37-39 Church St, Antrim, County Antrim, BT41 4BD.
(T) 028 94463108 (F) 028 94465592
Profile: FT: Coarse; WN: Lower Bann Navigational; WT: Canal (Still). **Location:** Nr. Rd: B64.
Ref: FH0293

BANN (LWR) NAVIGATIONAL CANAL

River Lower Bann Navigational Canal, Toomebridge, Antrim, **COUNTY ANTRIM**, BT41, **Northern Ireland**.
Contact/s: Mr Albert Atkins, 67 Coleraine Rd, Garvagh, County Londonderry.
(T) 028 25558555
Mr J Hamilton (Manager), O'Rorke McDonald and Tweed, 37-39 Church St, Antrim, County Antrim, BT41 4BD.
(T) 028 94463108 (F) 028 94465592
Profile: FT: Coarse; WN: Lower Bann Navigational; WT: Canal (Still). **Location:** Main Rd: A6.
Ref: FH0294

BANN (LWR) NAVIGATIONAL CANAL

River Lower Bann Navigational Canal, Portna, **COUNTY ANTRIM**, BT, **Northern Ireland**.
Contact/s: Mr Albert Atkins, 67 Coleraine Rd, Garvagh, County Londonderry.
(T) 028 25558555
Mr J Hamilton (Manager), O'Rorke McDonald and Tweed, 37-39 Church St, Antrim, County Antrim, BT41 4BD.
(T) 028 94463108 (F) 028 94465592
Profile: FT: Coarse; WN: Lower Bann Navigational; WT: Canal (Still). **Location:** Main Rd: A54.
Ref: FH0295

BANN (UPPER) (RIVER)

River Upper Bann, Gilford, Craigavon, **COUNTY ARMAGH**, BT63, **Northern Ireland**.
Contact/s: Manager, Spar Shop, 40-44 Mill St, Gilford, Craigavon, BT63 6HQ.
(T) 028 38831087
Mr Mervyn Magee, 11 Station Rd, Scarva, Craigavon, County Armagh, BT63 6JY.
(T) 028 38831529
Profile: FT: Game; WN: Upper Bann; WT: River (Moving) W. Size: 11200 Metres.
Ref: FH0296

BANN (UPPER) (RIVER)

River Upper Bann, Banbridge, **COUNTY DOWN**, BT32, **Northern Ireland**.
Contact/s: Manager, Anglers Rest, 42

Aughnacloy Rd, Katesbridge, Banbridge, BT32 5QG.
(T) 028 40671515
Mr James Coburn (Manager), Coburn's and Son Limited, 32 Scarva St, Banbridge, County Down, BT32 3DD.
(T) 028 40662207
Profile: **FT:** Game; **WN:** Upper Bann; **WT:** River (Moving) **W. Size:** 16000 Metres.
Ref: FH0297

BANN (UPPER) (RIVER)

River Upper Bann, Rathfriland, **COUNTY DOWN**, BT34, **Northern Ireland**.
Contact/s: **Mr John Dougan**, 33 Newry Rd, Rathfriland, County Down.
(T) 028 40638943
Mr Willie Downey, 19 Warrenview Park, Rathfriland, County Down.
(T) 028 40630077
R Graham (Manager), 11 Downpatrick St, Rathfriland, Newry, BT34 5DG.
(T) 028 40638179
Profile: **FT:** Game; **WN:** Upper Bann; **WT:** River (Moving) **W. Size:** 24000 Metres.
Ref: FH0298

BANN (UPPER) AND TRIBUTARIES

Upper Bann And Tributaries, Hilltown, Newry, **COUNTY DOWN**, BT34, **Northern Ireland**.
Contact/s: Manager, Downshire Arms Hotel, Main St, Hilltown, Newry, BT34 5UH.
(T) 028 40638899
Francie Brogan.
(T) 028 43771228
Profile: **FT:** Game; **WN:** Upper Bann; **WT:** River (Moving) **W. Size:** 19200 Metres.
Ref: FH0299

BANNISTER HALL FARM

Bannister Hall Farm, Mere Brow, Preston, **LANCASHIRE**, PR4, **England**.
Contact/s: Fishery Manager.
(T) 01704 821474
Profile: **FT:** Coarse; **WN:** Bannister Hall Farm; **WT:** Pool (Still). **Location:** **Nr. Rd:** A565 Tarleton to Southport; **Main Rd:** Mere Brow.
Ref: FH0300

BANWY (RIVER)

River Banwy, Neuadd, Bridge Farm, Caereinion, Welshpool, **POWYS**, SY21, **Wales**.
Contact/s: **Mr P Hulme** (Secretary), Montgomeryshire Angling Association, 306 Heol-y-Coleg, Vaynor Estate, Newtown, SY16 1RA.
(T) 01938 553867
Profile: **FT:** Game; **WN:** Banwy; **WT:** River (Moving).
Ref: FH0301

BARBON BECK

Barbon Beck, Barbon, Carnforth, **CUMBRIA**, LA6 2, **England**.
Contact/s: **Mr D E Halton** (Secretary), Kirby Lonsdale D Angling Association, Wennington Rd, Wray, Lancashire, LA2 8QH.
Profile: **FT:** Coarse; **WN:** Barbon Beck; **WT:** Stream (Moving).
Ref: FH0302

BARCOMBE RESERVOIR

Barcombe Reservoir, Barcombe Water Treatment Works, Barcombe, Lewes, **SUSSEX (EAST)**, BN8 5BY, **England**.
Contact/s: Manager.
(T) 01273 814819 (F) 01273 814069
Ms Emma Goddard (Environment Coordinator).
(T) 01323 870810 (F) 01323 871153 (M) 07802 757526
(E) egoddard@southeastwater.co.uk
Profile: **FT:** Game; **WN:** Barcombe; **WT:** Reservoir (Still) **W. Size:** 40 Acres.
Location: **Nr. Rd:** Lewes to Uckfield, sign posted; **Main Rd:** A26; **Rail:** Lewes.
Ref: FH0303

BARDEN LAKE

Barden Lake, Haysden Country Park, Tonbridge, **KENT**, TN1, **England**.
Contact/s: **Mr Alex Heggie** (Membership Secretary), Little Lucy's Farmhouse, Lower St, Hildenborough, Tonbridge, TN11 8PT.
(T) 01732 832352 (F) 01732 832352
Mr J Anscombe (Fisheries Manager).
(T) 01732 355959
Profile: **FT:** Coarse; **WN:** Barden; **WT:** Lake (Still) **W. Size:** 22 Acres. **Location:** **Nr. Rd:** Lower Haysden Road; **Main Rd:** A26.
Ref: FH0304

BARFORD LAKES FISHERY

Barford Lakes Fishery, Common Farm, Chapel St, Barford, Norwich, **NORFOLK**, NR9 4AB, **England**.
(W) www.fisheries.co.uk/barford/index.htm
Contact/s: **Ms Sarah Thomson** (Manager), Barford Lakes Fishery, Common Farm, Chapel St, Barford, NR9 4AB.
(T) 01603 759624 (F) 01603 758111
(E) barfordlakes@barfordlakes.force9.co.uk
Profile: **FT:** Coarse; **WN:** Pleasure Lake, Match Lake, & Top Lake; **WT:** Lake (Still); **F. Size:** 5 Acres. **Location:** **Nr. Rd:** B1108 to Watton; **Main Rd:** A47; **Rail:** Thorpe Station, Norwich.
Ref: FH0305

BARHAM A PIT

Barham A Pit, Claydon, Ipswich, **SUFFOLK**, IP6, **England**.
Contact/s: **Mr Norman Bickers**, Breakaway Tackle, 376 Bramford Rd, Ipswich, Suffolk, IP1 5AY.
(T) 01473 741393 (F) 01473 462482
(E) norman@breakaway-tackle.co.uk
Profile: **FT:** Coarse; **WN:** Barham A; **WT:** Gravel Pit (Still).
Ref: FH0306

BARHAM B PIT

Barham B Pit, Pesthouse Lane, Barham, Ipswich, **SUFFOLK**, **England**.
(W) www.gippingaps.co.uk
Contact/s: **Mr G Alderson** (Club Secretary), 37 Heatherhayes, Ipswich, IP2 9SL.
(T) 01473 602828
Profile: **FT:** Coarse; **WN:** B Pit; **WT:** Pit (Still); **F. Size:** 30 Acres; **W. Size:** 20 Acres. **Location:** **Nr. Rd:** Pesthouse Lane; **Main Rd:** A14; **Rail:** Claydon.
Ref: FH0307

BARKERS LAKE

Barkers Lake, Ringstead, Kettering, **NORTHAMPTONSHIRE**, NN14, **England**.
Contact/s: **Mr R Blenkharn** (Secretary), 66 Redland Drive, Kingsthorpe, Northampton, NN10 8TU.
Profile: **FT:** Coarse; **WN:** Barker's; **WT:** Lake (Still); **F. Size:** 25 Acres.
Ref: FH0308

BARLE (RIVER)

River Barle, Tarr Steps Hotel, Hawkridge, Dulverton, **SOMERSET**, TA22 9PY, **England**.
Contact/s: **Mr Shaun Blackmore**.
(T) 01643 851293 (F) 01643 851218
Profile: **FT:** Game; **WN:** Barle; **WT:** River (Moving) **W. Size:** 4500 Metres. **Location:** **Rail:** Tiverton Parkway.
Ref: FH0309

BARLEYLANDS RESERVOIR

Barleylands Reservoir, Barleylands Farm, Crays Hill, Billericay, **ESSEX**, CM1, **England**.
(W) www.bdac.co.uk
Contact/s: **Mr Derek Howard** (Hon Treasurer), Billericay and District Angling Club, 4 Long Meadow Drive, Wickford, Essex, SS11 8AX.
(T) 01268 734468
Profile: **FT:** Coarse; **WN:** Barleylands; **WT:** Reservoir (Still); **F. Size:** 6 Acres; **W. Size:** 5 Acres. **Location:** **Nr. Rd:** A129; **Main Rd:** A129, Billericay to Wickford; **Rail:** Wickford.
Ref: FH0310

BARLOW COMMON NATURE RESERVE

Barlow Common Nature Reserve, Barlow Rd, Barlow, Selby, **YORKSHIRE (NORTH)**, YO8, **England**.
Contact/s: , Selby District Council, Civic Ctre, Portholme Rd, Selby, North Yorkshire YO8 4SB.
(T) 01757 705101
Ms Lorraine Pearey (Assistant Countryside Manager).
(T) 01757 617110
Ms Rachel Stanhope (Countryside Officer).
(T) 01757 617110
Profile: **FT:** Coarse; **WN:** The Mere; **WT:** Lake (Still) **W. Size:** 4 Acres. **Location:** **Nr. Rd:** Barlow Road; **Main Rd:** A1041; **Rail:** Selby.
Ref: FH0311

BARLOW FISHERIES

Barlow Fisheries, Barlow, Chesterfield, **DERBYSHIRE**, S43, **England**.
Contact/s: **Mr Rex Ward**.
(T) 0114 2890543
Profile: **FT:** Combination; **WN:** Barlow Fisheries; **WT:** Lake (Still). **Location:** **Nr. Rd:** Fork right after the church, continue downwards until the end; **Main Rd:** B6051 from Chesterfield to Barlow. **£Fr**
Ref: FH0312

BARN LAKE

Barn Lake, Longtown, Carlisle, **CUMBRIA**, CA, **England**.
Contact/s: **Mr Phillip Nicholls** (Manager), Barn Lake, Longtown, Carlisle.
(T) 01228 791108
Profile: **FT:** Coarse; **WN:** Barn Lake; **WT:** Gravel Pit (Still) **W. Size:** 10 Acres.
Location: **Nr. Rd:** Longtown.
Ref: FH0313

BARNATTIN RESERVOIR

Barnattin Reservoir, Drogheda, **COUNTY LOUTH**, **Ireland**.
Contact/s: **Mr John Murphy** (Secretary).
(T) 077 1034078
Profile: **FT:** Game; **WN:** Barnattin; **WT:** Reservoir (Still).
Ref: FH0314

BARNCROFT

Barncroft, Killin, **STIRLING**, FK21, **Scotland**.
(W) www.fishingnet.com/beats/dochart/barncroft.htm
Contact/s: **Mr G D Coyne** (Gamekeeper), Auchlyne Keeper's Cottage, Auchlyne Estate, Glendochart, Killin, Perth and Kinross.
(T) 01567 820487
Profile: **FT:** Combination; **WN:** Dochart; **WT:** River (Moving).
Ref: FH0315

BARNES TROUT LAKES

Barnes Lakes, Bankside, Standlake, Witney, Oxford, **OXFORDSHIRE**, OX8 7QB, **England**.
Contact/s: **Mr John Barnes** (Manager).
(T) 01865 300343
Profile: **FT:** Combination; **WN:** Barnes Lake; **WT:** Lake (Still) **W. Size:** 74 Acres.
Location: **Nr. Rd:** A415; **Main Rd:** A40; **Rail:** Oxford.
Ref: FH0316

BARNINGHAM HALL LAKE

Barningham Hall Lake, Matlaske, Norwich, **NORFOLK**, NR11, **England**.
Contact/s: **Mr R Westgate** (Fishery Manager), Wroxham and District Angling Club, 31 The Paddocks, Old Catton, Norwich, NR6 7HF.
(T) 01603 401062 (F) 01603 897122 (M) 07885 644262
(E) robert.westgate@virgin.net
Profile: **FT:** Coarse; **WN:** Barningham Pool; **WT:** Lake (Still) **W. Size:** 6 Acres. **Location:**

Nr. Rd: Norwich to Cromor; **Main Rd:** A140; **Rail:** Cromor.
Ref: FH0317

BARNSFOLD WATERS

Barnsfold Waters, Barns Lane, Goosnargh, Preston, **LANCASHIRE**, PR3 2NJ, **England**.
Contact/s: **Mr J F Casson** (Owner).
(T) 01995 61583 **(F)** 01995 61583
Profile: **FT:** Game; **WN:** Barnsfold Waters; **WT:** Reservoir (Still) **W. Size:** 23 Acres.
Location: **Nr. Rd:** Barns Lane; **Main Rd:** A6; **Rail:** Preston.
Ref: FH0318

BARNSLEY CANAL

Barnsley Canal, Twibel St, Barnsley, **YORKSHIRE (SOUTH)**, S7, **England**.
Contact/s: **Mr Brian Megraw**, Tackle Box, 7 Doncaster Rd, Barnsley, Yorkshire (South), S70 1TH.
(T) 01226 247131
Profile: **FT:** Coarse; **WN:** Barnsley Canal; **WT:** Canal (Still). **Location:** **Main Rd:** A628.
Ref: FH0319

BARNWELL COUNTRY PARK

Barnwell Country Park, Barnwell Rd, Oundle, Peterborough, **CAMBRIDGESHIRE**, PE8 5PE, **England**.
Contact/s: **Mr Chris Soans** (Country Park Officer).
(T) 01832 273435 **(F)** 01832 274779
Profile: **FT:** Coarse; **WN:** Barnwell Country Park; **WT:** Gravel Pit (Still) **W. Size:** 8 Acres.
Location: **Nr. Rd:** Old A605 Road; **Main Rd:** A605; **Rail:** Peterborough. **£Fr**
Ref: FH0320

BARNWELL PIT

Barnwell Pit, Newmarket Rd, Cambridge, **CAMBRIDGESHIRE**, CB, **England**.
Contact/s: Fishery Manager.
(T) 01223 420308
Profile: **FT:** Coarse; **WN:** Barnwell; **WT:** Gravel Pit (Still). **Location:** **Nr. Rd:** Newmarket Road; **Main Rd:** A14.
Ref: FH0321

BARONS PONDS (NEW SITE)

Barons Ponds (New Site), Flying Bull Inn, Rake, Liss, **HAMPSHIRE**, GU33, **England**.
Contact/s: Manager, Tackle Up, 151 Fleet Rd, Fleet, Hampshire, GU13 8PD.
(T) 01252 614066
Mr Peter Archer, Petersfield Angling Ctre, 34 Dragon St, Petersfield, Hampshire, GU31 4JJ.
(T) 01730 266999 **(F)** 01730 266999
Profile: **FT:** Coarse; **WN:** Barons; **WT:** Lake (Still). **Location:** **Nr. Rd:** A3.
Ref: FH0322

BARONSCOURT LAKES

Baronscourt Lakes, Baronscourt Leisure Pursuits, Golf Course Rd, Newtownstewart, Omagh, **COUNTY TYRONE**, BT78 4LF, **Northern Ireland**.
Contact/s: Manager.
(T) 028 81661013 **(F)** 028 81661900
Mr David Campbell (Manager), Mourne Valley Tackle, 50 Main St, Newtownsteward, Omagh, County Tyrone, BT78 4AA.
(T) 028 81661543
Profile: **FT:** Coarse; **WN:** Baronscourt Lakes; **WT:** Lake (Still). **Location:** **Nr. Rd:** Golf Course Road.
Ref: FH0323

BARRETTS FARM FISHERY

Barretts Farm Fishery, Salt Pit Lane, Mawdsley, Ormskirk, **LANCASHIRE**, L40, **England**.
Contact/s: **Mrs Cowburn**.
(T) 01257 450484
Profile: **FT:** Coarse; **WN:** Barretts Farm Fishery; **WT:** Pond (Still). **Location:** **Nr. Rd:** Salt Pit Lane; **Main Rd:** B5250 to Eccleston.
Ref: FH0324

BARROW (RIVER)

River Barrow, Graighuenamanagh, **COUNTY CARLOW**, **Ireland**.
Contact/s: **Mr J Butler**, 7 Fairview, Tinnahinch, Graighuenamanagh, County Carlow, Ireland.
Profile: **FT:** Coarse; **WN:** Barrow; **WT:** River (Moving).
Ref: FH0325

BARROW (RIVER)

River Barrow, Athy, **COUNTY KILDARE**, **Ireland**.
Contact/s: Manager, Griffin Hawe Limited, 22 Duke St, Athy, County Kildare, Ireland.
(T) 050 731221 **(F)** 050 733885
(E) griffinhawe@tinet.ie
Profile: **FT:** Game; **WN:** Barrow; **WT:** River (Moving).
Ref: FH0326

BARROW (RIVER)

River Barrow, Portarlington, **COUNTY LAOIS**, **Ireland**.
Contact/s: **Ms Patsy Farrell**, Portarlington Angling Club, White Hart Lane, Kilmalogue, Portarlington, County Offaly.
(T) 050 243003
Profile: **FT:** Game; **WN:** Barrow; **WT:** River (Moving) **W. Size:** 10000 Metres. **Location:** **Nr. Rd:** Monasterevin to Portarlington; **Main Rd:** N7 Dublin to Cork; **Rail:** Portarlington.
Ref: FH0327

BARROW (UPPER) (RIVER)

Barrow (Upper) (River), Portarlington, **COUNTY LAOIS**, **Ireland**.
Contact/s: **Mr Pat Maher** (Secretary), Portarlington Angling Club, Inchacooley, Monasterevin, County Laois, Ireland.
Profile: **FT:** Game; **WN:** Upper Barrow; **WT:** River (Moving) **W. Size:** 9600 Metres.
Ref: FH0328

BARROW RESERVOIRS

Barrow Reservoirs, Barrow Gurney, Bristol, **SOMERSET**, BS40 8XH, **England**.
Contact/s: **Mr Bob Handford**, Bristol Water Plc, Woodford Lodge, Chew Stoke, Bristol, BS40 8XH.
(T) 01275 332339 **(F)** 01275 331377
(E) bob.handford@bristolwater.co.uk
S Taylor, Bristol Water Plc, Woodford Lodge, Chew Stoke, Bristol, BS40 8XH.
(T) 01275 332339 **(F)** 01275 331377
Profile: **FT:** Game; **WN:** Barrow; **WT:** Reservoir (Still) **W. Size:** 125 Acres.
Location: **Nr. Rd:** A38; **Main Rd:** A38; **Rail:** Bristol.
Ref: FH0329

BARROWFORD RESERVOIR

Barrowford Reservoir, Nelson, **LANCASHIRE**, BB9, **England**.
Contact/s: **Mr Griffiths** (Fishery Manager).
(T) 01606 723800
Profile: **FT:** Coarse; **WN:** Barrowford; **WT:** Reservoir (Still).
Ref: FH0330

BARROW-IN-FURNESS RESERVOIR

Barrow-In-Furness Reservoir, Barrow-In-Furness, **CUMBRIA**, LA, **England**.
Profile: **FT:** Coarse; **WN:** Barrow-in-Furness; **WT:** Reservoir (Still).
Ref: FH0331

BARRY RESERVOIR

Barry Reservoir, Dinas Powys, **GLAMORGAN (VALE OF)**, CF64, **Wales**.
Contact/s: **P Mason**, 8 Denys Cl, Dinas Powys, Glamorgan (Vale of).
Profile: **FT:** Coarse; **WN:** Barry; **WT:** Reservoir (Still).
Ref: FH0332

BARSCOBE LOCH

Barscobe Loch, Barscobe, Dalry, Castle Douglas, **DUMFRIES AND GALLOWAY**, DG7, **Scotland**.
Contact/s: **Ms S Stewart**, Castle Cottage, Barscobe, Balmaclellen, Castle Douglas, DG7 3QG.
(T) 01644 4202094
Profile: **FT:** Game; **WN:** Barscobe; **WT:** Loch (Still).
Ref: FH0333

BARSHAM DRAIN

Barsham Drain, Bungay Rd, Beccles, **SUFFOLK**, NR34, **England**.
Contact/s: **Mr Arthur Crane** (Secretary), 27 Rigbourne Hill, Beccles, Suffolk, NR34 9JG.
(T) 01502 716716
Profile: **FT:** Coarse; **WN:** Barsham; **WT:** River (Moving). **Location:** **Nr. Rd:** Bungay Road.
Ref: FH0334

BARTLES LODGE

Bartles Lodge, Elsing, Dereham, **NORFOLK**, NR20 3EA, **England**.
Contact/s: **Mr David Bartlett** (Owner).
(T) 01362 637177
Profile: **FT:** Coarse; **WN:** Bartles Lodge; **WT:** Lake (Still) **W. Size:** 2 Acres. **Location:** **Nr. Rd:** Church Lane; **Main Rd:** A1067.
Ref: FH0335

BARTLEY MILL FISHERY

Bartley Mill Fishery, Bells Yew Green, Lamberhurst, Tunbridge Wells, **KENT**, TN3 8BH, **England**.
Contact/s: Fishery Manager.
(T) 01892 891403
Profile: **FT:** Combination; **WN:** Bartley Mill Fishery; **WT:** Lake (Still).
Ref: FH0336

BARTON BROADS LAKE

Barton Broads Lake, Maltkiln Lane, Barton-upon-Humber, **LINCOLNSHIRE (NORTH)**, DN18, **England**.
Contact/s: **Mr Barry Rudge**, Barrys Fishing Lakes, 25 Westfield Avenue, Goole, DN14 6JY.
(T) 01405 720231office **(F)** 01405 720490
Mr Kirk Rudge.
(T) 01405 720231office **(F)** 01405 720490
Profile: **FT:** Coarse; **WN:** Barton Broads; **WT:** Lake (Still); **F. Size:** 14 Acres; **W. Size:** 8 Acres. **Location:** **Nr. Rd:** Waterside Road; **Main Rd:** A15; **Rail:** Barton.
Ref: FH0337

BARTON COURT FISHERY

Barton Court Fishery, East Lodge, Kintbury, Hungerford, **BERKSHIRE**, RG17 9SA, **England**.
(W) www.riverkennet.co.uk
Contact/s: **Mr Bob Bailey**.
(T) 01488 658905 **(F)** 01488 658094 **(M)** 07860 252717
(E) info@riverkennet.co.uk
Profile: **FT:** Combination; **WN:** Kennet; **WT:** River (Moving) **W. Size:** 5775 Metres.
Location: **Nr. Rd:** A4; **Main Rd:** A4; **Rail:** Kintbury.
Ref: FH0338

BARWAY LAKE

Barway Lake, Barway, Ely, **CAMBRIDGESHIRE**, CB7, **England**.
Contact/s: **Mr P Randall**.
(T) 01353 720052
Profile: **FT:** Coarse; **WN:** Barway; **WT:** Lake (Still) **W. Size:** 5 Acres.
Ref: FH0339

BASFORD COARSE FISHERY

Basford Coarse Fishery, Turners Croft, Basford Green, Leek, **STAFFORDSHIRE**, ST13 7ER, **England**.
Contact/s: **Mr Smith** (Owner).
Profile: **FT:** Coarse; **WN:** Basford Coarse Fishery; **WT:** Pool (Still); **F. Size:** 10 Acres; **W. Size:** 3 Acres. **Location:** **Nr. Rd:** Station Road; **Main Rd:** A520; **Rail:** Stoke on Trent.
Ref: FH0340

BASINGSTOKE CANAL

Basingstoke Canal, Greywell Tunnel To Ash Wharf, Basingstoke, **HAMPSHIRE**, RG24 9HE, **England**.
Contact/s: **Mr Andre Grandjean** (Manager).
(T) 01256 412680
R Jenkins (Secretary), BC Angling Association, 26 Tintern Cl, Basingstoke, RG24 9HE.
Profile: **FT:** Coarse; **WN:** Basingstoke; **WT:** Canal (Still) **W. Size:** 24000 Metres.
Location: **Nr. Rd:** B3008; **Main Rd:** A31.
Ref: FH0341

BASINGSTOKE CANAL

Basingstoke Canal, Odiham, Hook, **HAMPSHIRE**, RG29, **England**.
Contact/s: **Mr Andre Grandjean** (Secretary).
(T) 01256 412680
Profile: **FT:** Coarse; **WN:** Basingstoke; **WT:** Canal (Still).
Ref: FH0342

BASON BRIDGE

Bason Bridge, Brue, Basonbridge, Highbridge, **SOMERSET**, TA9, **England**.
Profile: **FT:** Coarse; **WN:** Brue; **WT:** River (Moving). Location: **Nr. Rd:** Milk Factory.
Ref: FH0343

BASSENTHWAITE LAKE

Bassenthwaite Lake, Leconfield Estates Company, Keswick, **CUMBRIA**, CA12, **England**.
Contact/s: Fisheries Manager, NPA Office, Blencathra Ctre.
(T) 01768 779633
Profile: **FT:** Combination; **WN:** Bassenthwaite; **WT:** Lake (Still) **W. Size:** 14 Acres. Location: **Nr. Rd:** A66 North of Keswick and B5291.
Ref: FH0344

BASTON FEN FISHERY

Baston Fen Fishery, Baston, Bourne, **LINCOLNSHIRE**, PE10, **England**.
Contact/s: Fishery Manager.
(T) 01778 560607
Profile: **FT:** Coarse; **WN:** Baston Fen Fishery; **WT:** Lake (Still).
Ref: FH0345

BATCHWORTH LAKE

Batchworth Lake, Rickmansworth, **HERTFORDSHIRE**, HA5, **England**.
Contact/s: **Mr L Dalton** (Secretary), Uxbridge Rovers Angling and Conservation Society, PO Box 253, Harrow, Middlesex, HA3 8XN.
(T) 01814 281739
Profile: **FT:** Coarse; **WN:** Batchworth; **WT:** Lake (Still). Location: **Nr. Rd:** Riverside Drive; **Main Rd:** A404.
Ref: FH0346

BAWBURGH LAKES

Bawburgh Lakes, Bawburgh, Norwich, **NORFOLK**, NR, **England**.
Mr Chris Turnbull (Head Bailiff), 35 Rose Valley, Norwich, NR2 2PX.
(T) 01603 630187
Profile: **FT:** Coarse; **WN:** Bawburgh; **WT:** Gravel Pit (Still); **F. Size:** 120 Acres; **W. Size:** 80 Acres. Location: **Nr. Rd:** New Road; **Main Rd:** B1108 to Watton.
Ref: FH0348

BAXTERS GARDEN FARM LAKE

Baxters Garden Farm Lake, Hinckley, **LEICESTERSHIRE**, LE10, **England**.
Contact/s: Manager.
(T) 01455 291193
Profile: **FT:** Coarse; **WN:** Baxters; **WT:** Lake (Still) **W. Size:** 2 Acres.
Ref: FH0349

BAYLIAU FISHERY

Bayliau Fishery, River Teifi, Lampeter, **CEREDIGION**, SA48, **Wales**.
(W) www.fishing-in-wales.co.uk/llandysul-aa/beat2a
Contact/s: **Mr Artie Jones** (Hon Secretary), Llandysul Angling Association, Glas-y-Dorlan, Llyn-y-Fran Rd, Llandysul, SA44 4JW.
(T) 01559 362317
Profile: **FT:** Game; **WN:** Teifi; **WT:** River (Moving) **W. Size:** 2400 Metres. Location: **Nr. Rd:** B4343 Cwmann to Llanfair Clydogau.
Ref: FH0350

BAYLIS POOLS

Baylis Pools, Shifnal, **SHROPSHIRE**, TF11, **England**.
Contact/s: **Ms Mabel Baylis** (Owner).
(T) 01952 460530
Profile: **FT:** Coarse; **WN:** Baylis; **WT:** Pool (Still) **W. Size:** 10 Acres. Location: **Main Rd:** M54, junction 4.
Ref: FH0351

BAYSTONE BANK RESERVIOR

Baystone Bank Reservior, Millom, **CUMBRIA**, LA, **England**.
Contact/s: **Mr D J Dixon** (Secretary), Millom and District Angling Association, 1 Churchill Drive, Millom, Cumbria, LA18 5DD.
(T) 01229 774241
Profile: **FT:** Game; **WN:** Baystone Bank; **WT:** Reservoir (Still) **W. Size:** 5 Acres. Location: **Nr. Rd:** A595; **Main Rd:** A595.
Ref: FH0352

BEACONS FISHERY

Beacons Fishery, Merthyr, Brecon, **POWYS**, LD3, **Wales**.
Contact/s: Fishery Manager.
(T) 01443 450577
Profile: **FT:** Game; **WN:** Beacons Fishery; **WT:** River (Moving).
Ref: FH0353

BEACONS RESERVOIRS

Beacons Reservoirs, Hammden Limited, Sluvad, New Inn, Pontypool, **TORFAEN**, NP4 0TA, **Wales**.
Contact/s: **Mr C Hatch** (Area Manager), Hamdden Ltd, Sluvad Treatment Works, Llandegfedd Reservoir, New Inn, Pontypool, Gwent NP4 0TA.
(T) 01495 769281 **(F)** 01495 769283
Profile: **FT:** Game; **WN:** Beacons; **WT:** Reservoir (Still) **W. Size:** 52 Acres.
Ref: FH0354

BEAL EASE FISHERY

Beal Ease Fishery, Foxford, **COUNTY MAYO**, **Ireland**.
Contact/s: **Mrs Mary Gannon**, Post Office, Foxford, County Mayo, Ireland.
Profile: **FT:** Game; **WT:** River (Moving).
Ref: FH0355

BEAMISH LAKE FLY FISHERY

Beamish Lake Fly Fishery, South Causey Hotel, Beamish Burn Rd, Stanley, **COUNTY DURHAM**, DH9 0LS, **England**.
Contact/s: **Mr Ricky Haugh** (Fishery Manager).
(T) 01207 235555 **(M)** 07930 803336
Profile: **FT:** Game; **WN:** Beamish; **WT:** Lake (Still).
Ref: FH0356

BEAULY (RIVER)

River Beauly, Inverness, **HIGHLAND**, IV, **Scotland**.
Contact/s: **Mr J Grahams**, 37 Castle Streey, Inverness, Highland, Scotland. **(M)** 04632 33178
Profile: **FT:** Game; **WN:** Beauly; **WT:** River (Moving).
Ref: FH0357

BEAUMONT FISHERIES

Beaumont Fisheries, Station Town, Wingate, **COUNTY DURHAM**, TS28 5LZ, **England**.
(W) www.beaumontfisheries.com
Contact/s: **Mr Alan Levington** (Manager).
(T) 01429 838274 **(F)** 01429 838274 **(M)** 07973 265008
(E) alan@beaumontfisheries.com
Profile: **FT:** Coarse; **WN:** Beaumont Fisheries; **WT:** Clay Pit (Still) **W. Size:** 3 Acres. Location: **Nr. Rd:** B1280; **Main Rd:** A181; **Rail:** Durham.
Ref: FH0358

BEAVER FARM FISHERY

Beaver Farm Fishery, Eastbourne Rd, Newchapel, Lingfield, **SURREY**, RH7 6HL, **England**.
(W) www.calpac.bizland.com
Contact/s: **Mr Jeff Wheeler**.
Mr Paul Freeman (Fishery Manager), Beaver Farm, Eastbourne Road, Newchapel, Lingfield, Surrey. RH7 6HL..
(T) 01342 835608 **(M)** 07710 656041
Profile: **FT:** Coarse; **WN:** Beaver Farm Fishery; **WT:** Combination (Still & Moving); **F. Size:** 49 Acres; **W. Size:** 16 Acres.
Location: **Nr. Rd:** A22; **Main Rd:** A22, B2028; **Rail:** Lingfield, East Grinstead.
Ref: FH0359

BECCLES QUAY

Beccles Quay, Beccles, **SUFFOLK**, NR34, **England**.
Contact/s: **Mr Arthur Crane** (Secretary), 27 Rigbourne Hill, Beccles, Suffolk, NR34 9JG.
(T) 01502 716716
Profile: **FT:** Coarse; **WN:** Beccles; **WT:** River (Moving).
Ref: FH0360

BECKERINGS RESERVOIR

Beckerings Park Farm Reservoir, Flitwick, Steppingley, Bedford, **BEDFORDSHIRE**, MK45, **England**.
Contact/s: **Mr G Buss** (Secretary), 1 Easthill Rd, Houghton Regis, Dunstable, Bedfordshire, LU5 5EQ.
(T) 01582 28114
Profile: **FT:** Coarse; **WN:** Beckerings Park Farm; **WT:** Reservoir (Still) **W. Size:** 5 Acres.
Location: **Main Rd:** A418.
Ref: FH0361

BEDALE BECK

Bedale Beck, Leeming Bar, Northallerton, **YORKSHIRE (NORTH)**, DL7, **England**.
(W) www.rmcangling.co.uk
Contact/s: **Mr Barry Hignett** (Secretary), Ferryhill and District Angling Club, 74 Grasmere Rd, Garden Farm Estate, Chester-le-Street, County Durham.
(T) 0191 3883557
Profile: **FT:** Coarse; **WN:** Bedale Beck; **WT:** Stream (Moving) **W. Size:** 2400 Metres.
Location: **Main Rd:** A1.
Ref: FH0362

BEDFONT LAKE

Bedfont Lake, Bedfont Rd, Bedfont, Feltham, London, **LONDON (GREATER)**, TW14, **England**.
Contact/s: **Mr Gordon Davis** (Manager), Boyer Leisure Ltd, Heron's Point Tackle Shop, Farlow's Lake, Ford Lane, Iver SL0 9LL.
(T) 01753 630302 or 01895444707 **(F)** 01753 630302
(E) info@boyer.co.uk
Profile: **FT:** Coarse; **WN:** Bedfont; **WT:** Lake (Still) **W. Size:** 9 Acres. Location: **Nr. Rd:** B137, Ashford to Feltham; **Main Rd:** A30; **Rail:** Feltham.
Ref: FH0363

BEDFORD BOATING LAKE

Bedford Boating Lake, Bedford Embankment, Bedford, **BUCKINGHAMSHIRE**, MK4, **England**.
Profile: **FT:** Coarse; **WN:** Bedford Boating Lake; **WT:** Lake (Still) **W. Size:** 2 Acres.
Ref: FH0364

BEDFORDS PARK LAKE

Bedfords Park Lake, Havering, Romford, **ESSEX**, RM4, **England**.

Contact/s: Mr Paul Curry.
(T) 01708 723246
Profile: FT: Coarse; WN: Bedfords Park; WT: Lake (Still) W. Size: 2 Acres. Location: Nr. Rd: Lower Bedfords Road; Main Rd: A12 to B175.
Ref: FH0365

BEECHES BROOK FISHERY

Beeches Brook Fishery, Forest Rd, Burley, Ringwood, **HAMPSHIRE**, BH24 4DQ, **England**.
Contact/s: Mr John Grant.
(T) 01425 402373
Profile: FT: Coarse; WN: Beeches Brook; WT: Lake (Still). Location: Main Rd: Forest Road.
Ref: FH0366

BEECHES POOL

Beeches Pool, Woodlands Farm, Beech Rd, Ironbridge, Telford, **SHROPSHIRE**, TF8 7PA, **England**.
Contact/s: Mr Chris Allaen (Manager), Woodlands Farm, Beech Rd, Ironbridge, Shropshire, TF8 7PA.
(T) 01952 432741
Profile: FT: Coarse; WN: Beeches; WT: Pool (Still); F. Size: 2 Acres; W. Size: 1 Acre. Location: Nr. Rd: Beech Road; Main Rd: B4373; Rail: Telford.
Ref: FH0367

BEECRAIGS LOCH

Beecraigs Loch, Park Ctre, Linlithgow, **LOTHIAN (WEST)**, EH49, **Scotland**.
Contact/s: Mr Jim Mckenna (Fishery Manager).
(T) 01506 844516
Profile: FT: Game; WN: Beecraigs; WT: Loch (Still).
Ref: FH0368

BEEDOMS FISHERY

Beedoms Fishery, Carcroft, Doncaster, **YORKSHIRE (SOUTH)**, DN6, **England**.
Contact/s: Mr M A Beedom, 1 Martindale Walk, Carcroft, Doncaster, South Yorkshire DN6 8BX.
(T) 01302 330749
Profile: FT: Coarse; WN: Beedoms Fishery; WT: Lake (Still).
Ref: FH0369

BEEFOLD LODGE

Beefold Lodge, Atherton, Manchester, **MANCHESTER (GREATER)**, M46, **England**.
Contact/s: Fishery Manager.
(T) 01942 670890
Profile: FT: Coarse; WN: Beefold Lodge; WT: Lake (Still).
Ref: FH0370

BEEHIVE FARM WOODLANDS LAKES

Beehive Farm Woodlands Lakes, Rosliston, Swadlincote, **DERBYSHIRE**, DE12 8HZ, **England**.
Contact/s: Mr Alistair Chapman (Partner).
(T) 01283 769980 (F) 01283 761467
Profile: FT: Coarse; WN: Bontany Bay and Horseshoe; WT: Lake (Still); F. Size: 46 Acres; W. Size: 5 Acres. Location: Nr. Rd: Bothanybay Lane; Main Rd: A38, M42, A444; Rail: Tamworth.
Ref: FH0371

BEGUEILIN LAKE

Begueilin Lake, Tynycornel Hotel, Talyllyn, Brecon, **POWYS**, LD3, **Wales**.
Contact/s: Hotel Manager, Tyn-y-Cornel Hotel, Talyllyn, Tywyn, Gwynedd, LL36 9AJ.
(T) 01654 782282
Profile: FT: Game; WN: Begueilin; WT: Lake (Still).
Ref: FH0372

BEIRTON LAKES

Beirton Lakes, Oxford, **OXFORDSHIRE**, OX, **England**.
Contact/s: Mr Derek Rudge (Fishery Manager). (M) 07836 755344
Profile: FT: Coarse; WN: Beirton Lakes; WT: Lake (Still).
Ref: FH0373

BELA STREAM

Bela Stream, Milnthorpe, **CUMBRIA**, LA7, **England**.
Profile: FT: Game; WN: Bela; WT: Stream (Moving).
Ref: FH0374

BELFREY COARSE FISHERY

Belfrey Coarse Fishery, Broad Farm, Hellingly, Hailsham, **SUSSEX (EAST)**, BN27, **England**.
Contact/s: Mr Stewart Ellery (Manager), 81 Howlett Drive, Hailsham, Sussex (East), BN27 1QW.
(T) 01323 441130 (M) 07977 565763
Profile: FT: Coarse; WN: Belfrey; WT: Pond (Still) W. Size: 2 Acres. Location: Nr. Rd: A262; Main Rd: North Street; Rail: Polegate.
Ref: FH0375

BELL WEIR LOCK

Bell Weir Lock, Riverside, Egham, **SURREY**, TW20 0AA, **England**.
Contact/s: Fishery Contact.
(T) 01784 432333
Recreational Manager, The Environment Agency, Kings Meadow Rd, Reading, Berkshire, RG1 8DQ.
(T) 0118 9535000 (F) 0118 9500388
Profile: FT: Combination; WN: Thames; WT: Lock (Still). Location: Main Rd: A308.
Ref: FH0376

BELLBROOK VALLEY

Bellbrook Valley Trout Fishery, Bellbrook Farm, Oakford, Tiverton, **DEVON**, EX16 9EX, **England**.
Contact/s: Mr Mike Pusey (Owner).
(T) 01398 351292
Profile: FT: Game; WN: Bellbrook Valley Trout Fishery; WT: Lake (Still); F. Size: 22 Acres; W. Size: 5 Acres. Location: Nr. Rd: Spurway to Stoodleigh; Main Rd: A361; Rail: Tiverton Parkway.
Ref: FH0377

BELLEAU BRIDGE FARM LAKE

Belleau Bridge Farm Lake, Alford, Louth, **LINCOLNSHIRE**, LN11, **England**.
Contact/s: Mr Harrop.
(T) 01507 480225
Profile: FT: Coarse; WN: Belleau Bridge Farm; WT: Lake (Still).
Ref: FH0378

BELLFLASK TROUT FISHERY

Bellflask Trout Fishery, Bellflask House, East Tanfield, Wath, Ripon, **YORKSHIRE (NORTH)**, HG4 5LW, **England**.
Contact/s: Mr Brian Moorland (Manager).
(T) 01677 470716
Profile: FT: Game; WN: Bellflask Trout Fishery; WT: Lake (Still) W. Size: 10 Acres. Location: Main Rd: A1.
Ref: FH0379

BELLS YARD LAKE

Bells Yard Lake, Horncastle, **LINCOLNSHIRE**, LN9, **England**.
Contact/s: Fishery Manager.
(T) 01507 527277
Profile: FT: Coarse; WN: Bells Yard; WT: Lake (Still).
Ref: FH0380

BELMONT POOL

Belmont Pool, Northwich, **CHESHIRE**, CW9, **England**.
Contact/s: Mr Neil Jupp (Club Secretary), Lymm Angling Club, PO Box 350, Warrington, Cheshire, WA2 9FB.
(T) 01925 411774
Profile: FT: Coarse; WN: Belmont; WT: Pool (Still) W. Size: 1 Acre. Location: Nr. Rd: Pole Lane; Main Rd: A559.
Ref: FH0381

BELPER POND

Belper Pond, Wyver Lane, Belper, **DERBYSHIRE**, DE56, **England**.
Contact/s: Mr P Smith (Secretary), 11 Lander Lane, Belper, Derbyshire.
Profile: FT: Coarse; WN: Belper; WT: Pool (Still) W. Size: 3 Acres. Location: Nr. Rd: Wyver Lane.
Ref: FH0382

BELVOIR CASTLE

Belvoir Castle, Estate Office, Grantham, **LINCOLNSHIRE**, NG32 1PD, **England**.
Contact/s: Mr Don Wells (Manager), Belvoir Estate, Estate Office, Belvoir Castle, Belvoir, Grantham, NG32 1PD.
(T) 01476 870262 (F) 01476 870443
Profile: FT: Coarse; WN: Belvoir and Knipton; WT: Combination (Still) W. Size: 47 Acres. Location: Nr. Rd: Melton Mowbray to Grantham; Main Rd: A607, A52.
Ref: FH0383

BENNETTS POOL

Bennetts Pool, Hucks Farm Fishery, Willow Rd, Martley, Worcester, **WORCESTERSHIRE**, WR6 6PS, **England**.
Contact/s: Mr K Fidoe (Manager).
(T) 01886 821374
Profile: FT: Coarse; WN: Bennets; WT: Pool (Still).
Ref: FH0384

BENS LAKE

Bens Lake, Drake House, Bishop's Green, Newbury, **BERKSHIRE**, RG20 4HT, **England**.
Contact/s: Mr Ben Drake (Owner).
(T) 01635 268447
Profile: FT: Coarse; WN: Bens; WT: Lake (Still). Location: Nr. Rd: A339 Bishop's Green Road; Main Rd: A34.
Ref: FH0385

BENSON LOCK

Benson Lock, Preston Crowmarsh, Benson, Wallingford, **OXFORDSHIRE**, OX10, **England**.
Contact/s: Recreational Manager, The Environment Agency, Kings Meadow Rd, Reading, Berkshire, RG1 8DQ.
(T) 0118 9535000 (F) 0118 9500388
Profile: FT: Combination; WN: Thames; WT: Lock (Still). Location: Main Rd: A423 to Preston Crowmarsh.
Ref: FH0386

BENTHALL LAKE

Benthall Lake, Broseley, **SHROPSHIRE**, TF12 5, **England**.
Contact/s: Mr Mick Tuff (Secretary), Dawley Angling Society, 68 Coronation St, Madley, Telford, TF7 5EH.
(T) 01952 590348
Profile: FT: Coarse; WN: Benthall; WT: Lake (Still).
Ref: FH0387

BENTHAM STREAM

Bentham Stream, River Wenning, Clapham, Lancaster, **LANCASHIRE**, LA2 8DR, **England**.
Contact/s: Secretary, Bentham Angling Association, Estate Office, Clapham via Lancaster, Yorkshire (North), LA2 8DR.
(T) 01524 251302 (F) 01524 251466
Profile: FT: Game; WN: Bentham; WT: Stream (Moving) W. Size: 8000 Metres.
Ref: FH0388

BENTHAM TROUT FISHERY

Bentham Trout Fishery, Low Mill, Bentham, Lancaster, **LANCASHIRE**, LA2, **England**.
Contact/s: Fishery Manager.
(T) 01524 261305
Profile: FT: Game; WN: Wenning; WT: River (Moving).
Ref: FH0389

BENTLEY TROUT POOL

Bentley Trout Pool, John St, Utkinton, Tarporley, **CHESHIRE**, CW6 0, **England**.
Contact/s: Mr Neil Jupp (Club Secretary), Lymm Angling Club, PO Box 350, Warrington,

Cheshire, WA2 9FB.
(T) 01925 411774
Profile: FT: Game; WN: Bentley; WT: Pool (Still). Location: Nr. Rd: John Street; Main Rd: A54, B5152.
Ref: FH0390

BERKELEY FARM

Berkeley Farm, Boys Hill, Sherborne, **DORSET**, DT9 5PJ, **England**.
Contact/s: Mrs Vickery, Berkeley Farm, Boys Hill, Sherborne, Dorset, DT9 5PJ.
(T) 01963 210269
Profile: FT: Coarse; WN: Berkeley Farm; WT: Pond (Still).
Ref: FH0391

BERRYNARBOR MILL POND

Berrynarbor Mill Pond, Berrynarbor, Ilfracombe, **DEVON**, EX34, **England**.
Contact/s: Mr Brian Malin (Manager), Mill Park Coarse Fishing Lake, Berrynarbor, Ilfracombe, Devon, EX34 9SH.
(T) 01271 882647 (F) 01271 882667
Profile: FT: Coarse; WN: Berrynarbor Mill; WT: Pond (Still) W. Size: 3 Acres. Location: Nr. Rd: A339; Main Rd: M5.
Ref: FH0392

BERWICK PONDS

Berwick Ponds, Rainham, **ESSEX**, RM13, **England**.
Contact/s: Mr Mike Prior.
(T) 07932 150089 (M) 07768 124462
Profile: FT: Coarse; WN: Berwick; WT: Pond (Still) W. Size: 14 Acres. Location: Nr. Rd: Berwick Road; Main Rd: A13, Upminster Road North.
Ref: FH0393

BESSY BECK TROUT FARM

Bessy Beck Trout Farm, Newbiggin-on-Lune, Kirkby Stephen, **CUMBRIA**, CA17 4LY, **England**.
Contact/s: Mr Simon Norman - Ballantyne (Owner).
(T) 01539 623303 (F) 01539 623303
Profile: FT: Game; WN: Bessy Beck; WT: Lake (Still); F. Size: 4 Acres; W. Size: 3 Acres. Location: Nr. Rd: A685; Main Rd: A685; Rail: Kirby Stephen.
Ref: FH0394

BESTWOOD POND

Bestwood Pond, Nottingham, **NOTTINGHAMSHIRE**, NG, **England**.
Contact/s: W Belshaw, Nottingham and District Federation of Angling Societies, 17 Spring Green, Clifton Estate, Nottingham, Nottinghamshire.
(T) 0115 9216645
Profile: FT: Coarse; WN: Bestwood Pond; WT: Pond (Still).
Ref: FH0395

BETLEY MERE

Betley Court Farm, Betley, Crewe, **CHESHIRE**, CW3 9BH, **England**.
Contact/s: Mr Chris Manifold (Syndicate Manager), 18 Francis St, Crewe, Cheshire, CW2 6HF.
(T) 01270 580076
Profile: FT: Coarse; WN: Betley Mere; WT: Mere (Still); F. Size: 50 Acres; W. Size: 30 Acres. Location: Nr. Rd: A531; Main Rd: A531; Rail: Nantwich.
Ref: FH0396

BETULA WATERS

Betula Waters, Ledbury, **HEREFORDSHIRE**, HR8, **England**.
Contact/s: Mr James Sansoni.
(T) 0121 4303129
Profile: FT: Coarse; WN: Betula; WT: Lake (Still) W. Size: 2 Acres.
Ref: FH0397

BEVERLEY AND BARMSTON DRAIN

Beverley And Barmston Drain, Hempholme To Hull, Brandesburton, Driffield, **HUMBERSIDE**, YO25, **England**.
Contact/s: Area Manager, Environment Agency, Ridings Area Office, Phoenix House, Global Avenue, Leeds, LS11 8PG.
(T) 0113 2440191or2314834 (F) 0113 2134609
Fishery Manager.
(T) 0113 2312100
Profile: FT: Coarse; WN: Beverley and Barmston Drain; WT: Drain (Moving). Location: Nr. Rd: Hempholme to Hull.
Ref: FH0398

BEVERLEY BECK

Beverley Beck, Hull, **HUMBERSIDE**, HU, **England**.
Contact/s: Mr Brian Rushworth (Secretary).
(T) 01482 882655
Profile: FT: Coarse; WN: Beverley Beck; WT: Stream (Moving) W. Size: 1600 Metres.
Ref: FH0399

BEVERLEY CANAL

Beverley Canal, Beverley, **HUMBERSIDE**, HU17, **England**.
Contact/s: Area Manager, Environment Agency, Ridings Area Office, Phoenix House, Global Avenue, Leeds, LS11 8PG.
(T) 0113 2440191or2314834 (F) 0113 2134609
Mr Paul Caygill (Secretary), Hull and District Anglers Association, 17 Linley Cl, Leven, Beverley, HU17 5NP.
(T) 01964 542677
Profile: FT: Coarse; WN: Beverley; WT: Canal (Still).
Ref: FH0400

BEVERN STREAM

Bevern Stream, Barcombe, Lewes, **SUSSEX (EAST)**, BN8, **England**.
Contact/s: Mr John Goodrick (Hon Secretary), Ouse Angling Preservation Society, 'Applegarth', School Lane, Barcombe, BN8 5DT.
(T) 01273 400380
Profile: FT: Coarse; WN: Bevern; WT: Stream (Moving) W. Size: 800 Metres. Location: Rail: Lewes.
Ref: FH0401

BEWDLEY POOL

Bewdley Pool, Bewdley, Kidderminster, **WORCESTERSHIRE**, DY, **England**.
Profile: FT: Coarse; WN: Bewdley; WT: Pond (Still). Location: Main Rd: A442, A448.
Ref: FH0402

BEWL WATER

Bewl Water, Bewl Water Fishing Lodge, Bewl Water, Lamberhurst, **KENT**, TN3 8JH, **England**.
Contact/s: Mr Howard Makenzie (Manager).
(T) 01892 890352 (F) 01892 890232
Profile: FT: Game; WN: Bewl Water; WT: Reservoir (Still); F. Size: 1480 Acres; W. Size: 770 Acres. Location: Nr. Rd: Beel Bridge Lane; Main Rd: A21; Rail: Wadhurst.
£Fr
Ref: FH0403

BICKERLEY MILLSTREAM

Bickerley Millstream, Ringwood, **HAMPSHIRE**, BH24, **England**.
Contact/s: Mr Kevin Grozier (Permit Secretary), 15 Greenfinch Walk, Hightown, Ringwood, Hampshire, BH24 3RJ.
(T) 01425 471466 (F) 01425 471466
Profile: FT: Coarse; WN: Bickerley Millstream; WT: River (Moving) W. Size: 1600 Metres. Location: Main Rd: B3347.
Ref: FH0404

BICKERSHAW WATERS

Bickershaw Waters, Bickershaw, Wigan, **LANCASHIRE**, WN2, **England**.
Contact/s: Fishery Manager.
(T) 01942 604388
Profile: FT: Coarse; WN: Bickershaw Waters; WT: Lake (Still).
Ref: FH0405

BICKERTON FARM FISHERY

Bickerton Farm Fishery, Kellaton, Hallsands, Kingsbridge, **DEVON**, TQ7 2EU, **England**.
Contact/s: Mr Graham Tolchard (Owner).
(T) 01548 511220
Profile: FT: Coarse; WN: Bickerton Farm Fishery; WT: Pond (Still). Location: Main Rd: A79.
Ref: FH0406

BIDDENDEN LAKE

Biddenden Lake, Bettenham Manor, Biddenden, Tenterden, **KENT**, TN30, **England**.
Contact/s: J Hampshire.
Profile: FT: Coarse; WN: Biddenden; WT: Lake (Still).
Ref: FH0407

BIDDLESTONE LAKE

Biddlestone Lake, Glewstone, Whitchurch, Ross-on-Wye, **HEREFORDSHIRE**, HR9, **England**.
Contact/s: Mr Brian Powell (Red Banks Pools Manager), Three Counties Fisheries, Field Cottage, Ryton, Dymock, Gloucestershire, GL18 2DH.
(T) 01531 890455
Profile: FT: Coarse; WN: Biddlestone; WT: Lake (Still) W. Size: 2 Acres. Location: Nr. Rd: Biddlestone; Main Rd: A4137.
Ref: FH0408

BIDDULPH GRANGE

Biddulph Grange Country Park, Biddulph Grange, Biddulph, Stoke-on-Trent, **STAFFORDSHIRE**, **England**.
Contact/s: Park Ranger, Rangers Office, Biddulph Grange Country Park, Biddulph Grange, Biddulph, Staffordshire.
(T) 01782 522447
Profile: FT: Coarse; WN: Biddulph Grange; WT: Lake (Still); F. Size: 10 Acres; W. Size: 5 Acres. Location: Nr. Rd: Grange Road; Main Rd: Congleton Road (A527); Rail: Congleton.
Ref: FH0409

BIERTON FISHING LAKES

Bierton Fishing Lakes, Brick Kiln Lane, Bierton, Aylesbury, **HERTFORDSHIRE**, HP1, **England**.
Contact/s: Mr Derek Rudge, 9 Firs Court, Aylesbury Rd, Bierton, Aylesbury, Buckinghamshire, HP22 5AY.
(T) 01296 426036 (F) 01296 426036 (M) 07836 755344
(E) lrugde@hotmail.com
Profile: FT: Coarse; WN: Bierton; WT: Lake (Still). Location: Nr. Rd: A418; Main Rd: A418; Rail: Aylesbury.
Ref: FH0410

BIG HOLE PIT

Big Hole Pit, Rawcliffe, Goole, **HUMBERSIDE**, DN14, **England**.
Contact/s: Mr Les Rogers (Secretary), Goole and District Angling Association, 39 Clifton Gardens, Goole, Humberside (North), DN14 6AR.
(T) 01405 769096
Profile: FT: Coarse; WN: Big Hole Pit; WT: Clay Pit (Still) W. Size: 4 Acres. Location: Nr. Rd: A614; Main Rd: M62, junction 36; Rail: Goole.
Ref: FH0411

BIG WATERS

Big Waters, Seaton Burn, Newcastle Upon Tyne, **TYNE AND WEAR**, NE, **England**.
Contact/s: Mr Gary Rutherford (Secretary), 21 Blagdon Trce, Seaton Burn, Newcastle-upon-Tyne, NE13 6EY.
(T) 0191 2366703
Profile: FT: Coarse; WN: Big Waters; WT: Lake (Still) W. Size: 20 Acres. Location: Main Rd: A1, North of Newcastle.
Ref: FH0412

BIGGIN LAKE
Biggin Lake, Oundle, Peterborough, **CAMBRIDGESHIRE**, PE8, **England**.
Contact/s: Fishery Manager.
(T) 01536 523084
Profile: **FT:** Coarse; **WN:** Biggin; **WT:** Lake (Still).
Ref: FH0413

BIGLAND HALL LAKE
Bigland Hall Lake, Bigland Hall Estate, Blackbarrow, Haverthwaite, Ulverston, **CUMBRIA**, LA12 8PB, **England**.
Profile: **FT:** Coarse; **WN:** Bigland; **WT:** Lake (Still) **W. Size:** 13 Acres. **Location:** **Nr. Rd:** A590 Kendal to Barrow Road; **Main Rd:** A6.
Ref: FH0414

BILCOMBES POND
Bilcombes Pond, Fawley, Southampton, **HAMPSHIRE**, **England**.
Contact/s: **Mr Brian Tillman** (Manager), The Ruffs, Chapel Lane, Blackfield, Southampton, SO45 1YX.
(T) 023 80891617 **(F)** 023 80891616
(E) brian@mfcfishery.f9.co.uk
Profile: **FT:** Coarse; **WN:** Bilcombes; **WT:** Pond (Still); **F. Size:** 10 Acres; **W. Size:** 8 Acres. **Location:** **Main Rd:** A326.
Ref: FH0415

BILLABONG PARK
Billabong Water Sports And Caravan Park, Hempholme Bridge, Brandesburton, Driffield, **HUMBERSIDE**, YO25 8NA, **England**.
Contact/s: **Mrs L Caddy** (Owner).
(T) 01964 543631
Profile: **FT:** Combination; **WN:** Billabong Water Sports And Caravan Park; **WT:** Gravel Pit (Still) **W. Size:** 11 Acres. **Location:** **Nr. Rd:** A165.
Ref: FH0416

BILLET LANE
Billet Lane, Iver, **BUCKINGHAMSHIRE**, SL0, **England**.
Contact/s: **Mr L Dalton** (Secretary), Uxbridge Rovers Angling and Conservation Society, PO Box 253, Harrow, Middlesex, HA3 8XN.
(T) 01814 281739
Profile: **FT:** Coarse; **WN:** Billet Lane; **WT:** Reservoir (Still). **Location:** **Nr. Rd:** Billet Lane; **Main Rd:** M25, B470.
Ref: FH0417

BILLING AQUADROME
Billing Aquadrome, Northampton, **NORTHAMPTONSHIRE**, NN, **England**.
Contact/s: Fishery Manager.
(T) 01602 408181
Profile: **FT:** Coarse; **WN:** Billing Aquadrome; **WT:** Lake (Still).
Ref: FH0418

BILLING DAM
Billing Dam, Rawdon, Leeds, **YORKSHIRE (WEST)**, LS19, **England**.
Contact/s: **Mr Anthony Aldridge** (Manager), 3 Larkfield Mount, Rawdon, Yorkshire (West).
(T) 0113 2505951
Profile: **FT:** Game; **WN:** Billing; **WT:** Mill Dam (Still).
Ref: FH0419

BILLINGE GREEN
Billinge Green, Davenham, Northwich, **CHESHIRE**, CW9, **England**.
Contact/s: Secretary, Northwich Angling Association, PO Box 18, Northwich, CW9 5SE.
Profile: **FT:** Coarse; **WN:** Billinge Green; **WT:** Pond (Still). **Location:** **Main Rd:** A556.
Ref: FH0420

BILLINGFORD PIT
Billingford Pit, Billingford, East Dereham, **NORFOLK**, **England**.
Contact/s: **Mr David Appleby** (Club Secretary), 6 Rump Cl, Swanton Morley, Dereham, Norfolk, NR20 4NH.
(T) 01362 637591
Profile: **FT:** Coarse; **WN:** Billingford; **WT:** Lake (Still). **Location:** **Main Rd:** B1145; **Rail:** Norwich.
Ref: FH0421

BILLINGSMOOR FARM
Billingsmoor Farm, Butterleigh, Cullompton, **DEVON**, EX15, **England**.
Contact/s: **Mr Dave Warren**.
(T) 01884 32320
Mr John Berry (Manager).
(T) 01884 32320
Profile: **FT:** Coarse; **WN:** Billingsmoor Farm; **WT:** Pond (Still); **F. Size:** 12 Acres; **W. Size:** 3 Acres. **Location:** **Main Rd:** M5.
Ref: FH0422

BILLS POOL
Bills Pool, St Erth, Hayle, **CORNWALL**, TR27, **England**.
Contact/s: **Mr Bill Knott**.
(T) 01736 763721
Profile: **FT:** Coarse; **WN:** Bill's; **WT:** Pool (Still). **Location:** **Main Rd:** A30 to Marazion; **Rail:** St Erth.
Ref: FH0423

BILNEY LAKES
Bilney Lakes, Lakeside Fisheries, East Bilney, Dereham, **NORFOLK**, NR20 4AL, **England**.
Contact/s: **Mr Tony Fell**.
(T) 01362 861015
Profile: **FT:** Coarse; **WN:** Bilney Lakes; **WT:** Lake (Still) **W. Size:** 6 Acres. **Location:** **Nr. Rd:** B1146; **Main Rd:** A47; **Rail:** Dereham.
Ref: FH0424

BIRCH GROVE
Birch Grove, Baschurch, Shrewsbury, **SHROPSHIRE**, **England**.
Contact/s: **Mrs Mary Paisley**.
(T) 0114 2580812
Profile: **FT:** Coarse; **WN:** Birch Grove; **WT:** Lake (Still); **F. Size:** 6 Acres; **W. Size:** 4 Acres. **Location:** **Rail:** Shrewsbury.
Ref: FH0425

BIRCHDEN FARM FISHERY
Birchden Farm Fishery, Eridge Rd, Groombridge, Tunbridge Wells, **KENT**, TN3 9NR, **England**.
Contact/s: **Mr Colin Vicary** (Bailiff).
(T) 01892 862940
Mr Stephen Barnes (Owner).
(T) 01892 862940 **(M)** 07881 550751
Profile: **FT:** Coarse; **WN:** Birchden Farm Fishery; **WT:** Pond (Still); **F. Size:** 4 Acres; **W. Size:** 2 Acres. **Location:** **Nr. Rd:** Eridge Road; **Main Rd:** A264, B2110; **Rail:** Eridge.
Ref: FH0426

BIRCHMERE
Birchmere, Thamesmead, Woolwich, London, **LONDON (GREATER)**, **England**.
Contact/s: .
(T) 020 83102750
Profile: **FT:** Coarse; **WN:** Birchmere; **WT:** Mere (Still).
Ref: FH0427

BIRDS GREEN
Birds Green, Fyfield, Ongar, **ESSEX**, CM5, **England**.
Contact/s: Fishery Manager.
(T) 01277 899645
Profile: **FT:** Coarse; **WN:** Birds Green; **WT:** Lake (Still). **Location:** **Nr. Rd:** B184; **Main Rd:** Chipping Ongar.
Ref: FH0428

BIRKACRE LODGES
Birkacre Lodges, Coppull, Chorley, **LANCASHIRE**, PR, **England**.
(W) www.wiganaa.f9.co.uk
Contact/s: **Mr Gerry Wilson** (Hon Secretary), Wigan and District Angling Association, 11 Guildford Avenue, Chorley, Lancashire, PR6 8TG.
(T) 01257 265905
(E) gerry@wiganna.freeserve.co.uk
Profile: **FT:** Coarse; **WN:** Birkacre Lodges; **WT:** Lake (Still) **W. Size:** 4 Acres. **Location:** **Nr. Rd:** B5251; **Main Rd:** M61, junction 8, M6.
Ref: FH0429

BIRKDALE FISHERY
Birkdale Fishery, Terrington, Malton, **YORKSHIRE (NORTH)**, YO17, **England**.
Contact/s: **Mr Gibson** (Fishery Manager).
(T) 01653 648301
Profile: **FT:** Coarse; **WN:** Birkdale Fishery; **WT:** Lake (Still). **Location:** **Main Rd:** Terrington.
Ref: FH0430

BIRKENHEAD LOWER PARK LAKE
Birkenhead Lower Park Lake, Conway St, Birkenhead, **MERSEYSIDE**, CH, **England**.
Contact/s: Manager, The Wirral Angling Centre, 207 Church Rd, Birkenhead, Merseyside, CH42 0LD.
(T) 0151 6447554
Mr Joey Waterhouse (Bailiff).
(T) 0151 6450549
Profile: **FT:** Coarse; **WN:** Birkenhead Lower; **WT:** Lake (Still). **Location:** **Nr. Rd:** Conway Street; **Main Rd:** A553.
Ref: FH0431

BIRMINGHAM TO WORCESTER CANAL
Birmingham To Worcester Canal, Broseley, **SHROPSHIRE**, TF12 5, **England**.
(W) www.easyweb.easynet.co.uk
Contact/s: **Mr Mick Tuff** (Secretary), Dawley Angling Society, 68 Coronation St, Madley, Telford, TF7 5EH.
(T) 01952 590348
Profile: **FT:** Coarse; **WN:** Birmingham to Worcester; **WT:** Canal (Still).
Ref: FH0432

BIRMINGHAM TO WORCESTER CANAL
Birmingham To Worcester Canal, Worcester, **WORCESTERSHIRE**, WR2, **England**.
(W) www.easyweb.easynet.co.uk
Contact/s: **Mr Dave Beresford** (Manager), Allans Fishing Tackle, 26-30 Malvern Rd, Worcester, Worcestershire, WR2 4LG.
(T) 01905 422107 **(F)** 01905 422107
Mr John Wells (Chairman), Worcester and District United Angling Association, Poplar Cottages, Poplar Rd, Whichenford, WR6 6YF.
(T) 01886 888459
Profile: **FT:** Coarse; **WN:** Worcester; **WT:** Canal (Still) **W. Size:** 2400 Metres.
Ref: FH0433

BIRMINGHAM TO WORCESTER CANAL
Birmingham To Worcester Canal, Stoke Prior, Stoke Works, Wychbold, Bromsgrove, **WORCESTERSHIRE**, B60, **England**.
(W) www.easyweb.easynet.co.uk
Contact/s: **Mr John Williams** (Secretary), Birmingham Anglers Association, 100 Icknield Port Rd, Rotton Park, Birmingham, B16 0AP.
(T) 0121 4549111
Profile: **FT:** Coarse; **WN:** Birmingham and Worcester; **WT:** Canal (Still). **Location:** **Nr. Rd:** Stoke Pound Bridge to Shernal Green; **Main Rd:** M5 or A38.
Ref: FH0434

BISHOPS BOWL LAKES
Bishops Bowl Lakes, Station Rd, Bishops Itchington, Leamington Spa, **WARWICKSHIRE**, CV33 0SR, **England**.
Contact/s: **Mr Rob Kerr**.
(T) 01926 613344
Profile: **FT:** Coarse; **WN:** Bishop, Blue, Walworth, Dinosaur Dip, & Mere Lakes; **WT:** Pool (Still); **F. Size:** 200 Acres. **Location:** **Nr. Rd:** Bishops Itchington; **Main Rd:** M40, junction 12, B4451 to Southam.
Ref: FH0435

BISHOPS GREEN FARM LAKE
Bishops Green Farm Lake, Bishops Green, Newbury, **BERKSHIRE**, RG20 4JP, **England**.
Contact/s: **Mr N H Smith** (Owner).
(T) 01635 268365 **(F)** 01635 268365

Profile: **FT:** Coarse; **WN:** Bishops Green Farm; **WT:** Lake (Still) **W. Size:** 1 Acre.
Location: **Nr. Rd:** A339 to Ecchinswell, just off; **Main Rd:** A339; **Rail:** Newbury or Thatcham.
Ref: FH0436

BISS (RIVER)

River Biss, Trowbridge, **WILTSHIRE**, BA14, **England**.
Contact/s: **Mr P O'Callaghan** (Secretary), 4 Fitzmaurice Cl, Bradford-on-Avon, Wiltshire, BA15 1UE.
(T) 01225 863163
Profile: **FT:** Coarse; **WN:** Biss; **WT:** River (Moving) **W. Size:** 1600 Metres.
Ref: FH0437

BITTERWELL LAKE

Bitterwell Lake, The Chalet, Bram Hill, Coalpit Heath, Bristol, BS17 2UF, **England**.
Contact/s: **Mrs Mary Reid** (Caretaker).
(T) 01454 778960 **(F)** 01454 778960
Profile: **FT:** Coarse; **WN:** Avon; **WT:** Lake (Still); **F. Size:** 3 Acres; **W. Size:** 2 Acres.
Location: **Nr. Rd:** Ram Hill; **Main Rd:** Westerleigh Road; **Rail:** Parkway Filton.
Ref: FH0438

BLACK BECK (RIVER)

River Black Beck, Millom, **MANCHESTER (GREATER)**, LA1, **England**.
Contact/s: **Mr D J Dixon** (Secretary), 1 Churchill Drive, Millom, Cumbria, LA18 5DD.
(T) 01229 774241
Profile: **FT:** Game; **WN:** Black Beck; **WT:** River (Moving). **Location:** **Nr. Rd:** A5093; **Main Rd:** A5093.
Ref: FH0439

BLACK ESK RESERVOIR

Black Esk Reservoir, Lockerbie, **DUMFRIES AND GALLOWAY**, DG11, **Scotland**.
Contact/s: **J Crowson**, Sandyford Cottage, Boreland, Lockerbie, Dumfries and Galloway.
(T) 01576 6287
Profile: **FT:** Game; **WN:** Black Esk; **WT:** Reservoir (Still). **Location:** **Nr. Rd:** B723 Lockerbie to Eskdalemuir.
Ref: FH0440

BLACK HILL POOLS

Black Hill Pools, Warwick Rd, High Cl, Near Snitterfield, Stratford-upon-Avon, **WARWICKSHIRE**, **England**.
Contact/s: **Mr Arthur Deeming** (Match Secretary).
(T) 01926 429171
Profile: **FT:** Coarse; **WN:** Black Hill Pools**WT:** Lake. **Location:** **Nr. Rd:** Warwick Road (A439); **Rail:** Stratford-upon-Avon.
Ref: FH0441

BLACK LAKE

Black Lake, Lindow Common, Wilmslow, **CHESHIRE**, SK9, **England**.
Profile: **FT:** Coarse; **WN:** Black; **WT:** Lake (Still). **Location:** **Nr. Rd:** Racecourse Road; **Main Rd:** Altrincham Road, A538.
Ref: FH0442

BLACK LAKE

Black Lake, Fulford, Meirheath, Stoke-on-Trent, **STAFFORDSHIRE**, **England**.
(W) www.fentondas.co.uk
Contact/s: **Mr C Yates** (Club Secretary), The Puzzles, 5 Gatley Gr, Meir Park, Stoke-on-Trent, Staffordshire ST3 7SH.
(T) 01782 396913
Profile: **FT:** Coarse; **WN:** Black Lake; **WT:** Lake (Still). **Location:** **Main Rd:** B5066; **Rail:** Blythe Bridge.
Ref: FH0443

BLACK LOCH

Black Loch, Wigtown, Newton Stewart, **DUMFRIES AND GALLOWAY**, DG8, **Scotland**.
Contact/s: **Mr Jim Stewart** (Owner), Fordbank Hotel, Wigtown, Dumfries and Galloway.
(T) 01988 402346
Profile: **FT:** Game; **WN:** Black; **WT:** Loch (Still).
Ref: FH0444

BLACK MONK TROUT LAKES

Black Monk Trout Lakes, Lenchwick, Evesham, **WORCESTERSHIRE**, WR11 4TG, **England**.
Contact/s: **Mr Hywel Morgan**.
(T) 01386 870180
Profile: **FT:** Game; **WN:** Black Monk; **WT:** Lake (Still); **F. Size:** 10 Acres.
Ref: FH0445

BLACK MOSS RESERVOIR

Black Moss Reservoir, Saddleworth, Oldham, **MANCHESTER (GREATER)**, OL3, **England**.
Contact/s: **Mr Griffiths** (Fishery Manager).
(T) 01606 723800
Profile: **FT:** Coarse; **WN:** Black Moss; **WT:** Reservoir (Still).
Ref: FH0446

BLACK PARK

Black Park, Iver, **BUCKINGHAMSHIRE**, SL0, **England**.
Contact/s: Fishery Manager.
(T) 01753 511060
Profile: **FT:** Coarse; **WN:** Black Park; **WT:** Lake (Still) **W. Size:** 7 Acres. **Location:** **Nr. Rd:** Town Centre. **£Fr**
Ref: FH0447

BLACKADDER WATER

Blackadder Water, Bladder Mount, Duns, **SCOTTISH BORDERS**, TD, **Scotland**.
Contact/s: **Mr R B Harrower**.
(T) 01890 81264
Profile: **FT:** Game; **WN:** Blackadder; **WT:** Loch (Still).
Ref: FH0448

BLACKBURN FARM TROUT FISHERY

Blackburn Farm Trout Fishery, Blackburn Farm, Hawes, **YORKSHIRE (NORTH)**, DL8 3NX, **England**.
Contact/s: **Mr H Moore** (Owner).
(T) 01969 667524
Profile: **FT:** Game; **WN:** Blackburn Farm Trout Fishery; **WT:** Lake (Still).
Ref: FH0449

BLACKLAND LAKES

Blackland Lakes Holiday And Leisure Centre, Stockley Lane, Calne, **WILTSHIRE**, SN11 0NQ, **England**.
(W) www.blacklandlakes.co.uk
Contact/s: **Mr John Walden** (Owner).
(T) 01249 813672 **(F)** 01249 811346
Profile: **FT:** Coarse; **WN:** Blackland; **WT:** Lake (Still); **F. Size:** 30 Acres; **W. Size:** 2 Acres. **Location:** **Nr. Rd:** Stockley Lane; **Main Rd:** A4; **Rail:** Chippenham.
Ref: FH0450

BLACKLEACH RESERVOIR

Blackleach Reservoir, Walkden, Worsley, Manchester, **MANCHESTER (GREATER)**, M28, **England**.
Contact/s: **Mr Bob Fearnhead** (Secretary), Farnworth and District Angling Association, 3 Windmill Rd, Walkden, Manchester (Greater), M28 3RP.
(T) 0161 7994242
Profile: **FT:** Coarse; **WN:** Blackleach; **WT:** Reservoir (Still) **W. Size:** 10 Acres.
Location: **Nr. Rd:** Bolton Road North; **Main Rd:** Bolton Road North; **Rail:** Walkden.
Ref: FH0451

BLACKMORE WOOD

Blackmore Wood, Green St, Ingatestone, **ESSEX**, CM4, **England**.
Contact/s: **Mr Sid Hibbert** (Secretary), Basildon and District Angling Society, 15 Culverdown, Basildon, Essex, SS14 2AL.
(T) 01268 287798
Profile: **FT:** Coarse; **WN:** Blackmore Wood; **WT:** Lake (Still) **W. Size:** 6 Acres. **Location:** **Nr. Rd:** Green Street; **Main Rd:** A12, B1002 to Heybridge.
Ref: FH0452

BLACKMOSS RESERVOIR

Blackmoss Reservoir, Pendle, Nelson, **LANCASHIRE**, BB9, **England**.
Contact/s: **Mr R Hudson** (Secretary), 61 Barnoldswick Rd, Higherford, Nelson, Lancashire, BB9 6BQ.
Mr Roy Rhodes (Conservation, Access and Recreation Manager), Rivington Water Treatment Works, Bolton Rd, Horwich, Bolton, BL6 7RN.
(T) 01204 664300
Profile: **FT:** Game; **WN:** Blackmoss; **WT:** Reservoir (Still).
Ref: FH0453

BLACKSHAW FARM LAKES

Blackshaw Farm Lakes, Blackshaw Moor, Leek, **STAFFORDSHIRE**, ST13, **England**.
Contact/s: **Mr John Turner** (Hon Secretary), Prince Albert Angling Society, 15 Pexhill Drive, Macclesfield, Cheshire, SK10 3LP.
(T) 01625 422010
Profile: **FT:** Coarse; **WN:** Blackshaw Farm; **WT:** Lake (Still) **W. Size:** 4 Acres. **Location:** **Nr. Rd:** Tittesworth Road; **Main Rd:** A53; **Rail:** Stoke-On-Trent.
Ref: FH0454

BLACKTON RESERVOIR

Blackton Reservoir, Romaldkirk, Barnard Castle, **COUNTY DURHAM**, DL12, **England**.
Contact/s: **Mr Paul Russell**, Northumbrian Water Ltd, Head Office, Recreation Department, Abbey Rd, Durham DH1 5FJ.
(T) 0191 3832222 **(F)** 0191 3841920
Profile: **FT:** Game; **WN:** Blackton; **WT:** Reservoir (Still).
Ref: FH0455

BLACKWATER (RIVER)

River Blackwater, Armagh, **COUNTY ARMAGH**, BT60, **Northern Ireland**.
Contact/s: **Cathal Doyle** (Secretary), Armagh Fisheries Ltd, 6 Knockamell Park, Armagh, County Armagh, BT61 7HJ.
(T) 028 37522068after6pm
Dessie Cartmill (Manager), Armagh Fisheries Ltd, G I Stores, 5 Dobbin St, Armagh, County Armagh.
(T) 028 37522335 **(F)** 028 37522335
Profile: **FT:** Combination; **WN:** Blackwater; **WT:** River (Moving).
Ref: FH0456

BLACKWATER (RIVER)

River Blackwater, Fermoy, **COUNTY CORK**, **Ireland**.
Contact/s: **Mr John Mulvihill** (Competition Secretary and Live Bait), 3 Casement Row, Fermoy, County Cork, Ireland.
(T) 025 32425
Profile: **FT:** Coarse; **WN:** Blackwater; **WT:** River (Moving).
Ref: FH0457

BLACKWATER (RIVER)

River Blackwater, Cappoquin, **COUNTY CORK**, **Ireland**.
Contact/s: **Mr Michael Penruddock** (Manager), Lismore Estate Office, Lismore Castle, Lismore, County Waterford, Ireland.
(T) 058 54424
Profile: **FT:** Game; **WN:** Blackwater; **WT:** River (Moving).
Ref: FH0458

BLACKWATER (RIVER)

River Blackwater, Conna, **COUNTY CORK**, **Ireland**.
Contact/s: **Mrs McCarthy**, Elgin Cottage, Ballyduff, County Waterford, Ireland.
(T) 058 60255
Profile: **FT:** Game; **WN:** Blackwater; **WT:** River (Moving).
Ref: FH0459

BLACKWATER (RIVER)

River Blackwater, Fermoy, **COUNTY CORK**, **Ireland**.
Contact/s: **Mr Brian Toomey** (Manager), Toomeys Sports Shop and Fishing Tackle, 18 McCurtain St, Fermoy, County Cork, Ireland.
(T) 025 31101
Profile: **FT:** Combination; **WN:** Blackwater; **WT:** River (Moving).
Ref: FH0460

BLACKWATER (RIVER)

River Blackwater, Mallow, **COUNTY CORK**, **Ireland**.
Contact/s: **Mr Pat Hayes** (Secretary), Mallow Trout Anglers, The Spa, Mallow, County Cork, Ireland.
Profile: **FT:** Combination; **WN:** Blackwater; **WT:** River (Moving) **W. Size:** 6400 Metres.
Ref: FH0461

BLACKWATER (RIVER)

River Blackwater, Conna, **COUNTY CORK**, **Ireland**.
Contact/s: **Mrs Merrie Green**, Ballyvolane House, Castlelyons, County Cork, Ireland.
Profile: **FT:** Game; **WN:** Blackwater; **WT:** River (Moving).
Ref: FH0462

BLACKWATER (RIVER)

River Blackwater, Fermoy, **COUNTY CORK**, **Ireland**.
Contact/s: **Mrs Merrie Green** (Manager), Ballyvolane House, Castlelyons, County Cork, Ireland.
(T) 025 36349
Profile: **FT:** Game; **WN:** Blackwater; **WT:** River (Moving) **W. Size:** 16000 Metres.
Ref: FH0463

BLACKWATER (RIVER)

River Blackwater, Careysville Fishery, Careysville House, Fermoy, **COUNTY CORK**, **Ireland**.
Contact/s: **Mr Michael Penruddock** (Manager).
(T) 025 31094or5854424 **(F)** 058 54896
Profile: **FT:** Game; **WN:** Blackwater; **WT:** River (Moving).
Ref: FH0464

BLACKWATER (RIVER)

Blackwater (River), Cappoquin, **COUNTY CORK**, **Ireland**.
Contact/s: Manager, Tight Lines Tackle and Gift Shop, Main St, Cappoquin, County Cork, Ireland.
Profile: **FT:** Game; **WN:** Blackwater; **WT:** River (Moving) **W. Size:** 6400 Metres.
Ref: FH0465

BLACKWATER (RIVER)

Blackwater (River), Kilmacow, **COUNTY KILKENNY**, **Ireland**.
Contact/s: Manager, Hook Line and Sinker, 31 Rose Inn St, Kilkenny, County Kilkenny, Ireland.
(T) 056 71699
Profile: **FT:** Game; **WN:** Blackwater; **WT:** River (Moving).
Ref: FH0466

BLACKWATER (RIVER)

River Blackwater, Clogher, **COUNTY TYRONE**, BT76, **Northern Ireland**.
Contact/s: **Mr Seamus McGirr** (Manager), 2 Richmond Drive, Clogher, County Tyrone, BT76 0AD.
(T) 028 85548293or85548279
Profile: **FT:** Game; **WN:** Blackwater; **WT:** River (Moving) **W. Size:** 35200 Metres.
Ref: FH0467

BLACKWATER (RIVER)

Blackwater (River), Portlaw Clodiagh, **COUNTY WATERFORD**, **Ireland**.
Contact/s: Manager, Shoot'n and Fish'n, 26a Ballybricken, Waterford, County Waterford, Ireland.
(T) 051 878087
Profile: **FT:** Game; **WN:** Blackwater; **WT:** River (Moving).
Ref: FH0468

BLACKWATER (RIVER)

River Blackwater, Upper Ballyduff, **COUNTY WATERFORD**, **Ireland**.
Contact/s: **Mr Emon Bolger** (Secretary), Ballyduff Trout Fish Angling Association, Post Office, Ballyduff, County Waterford, Ireland.
Profile: **FT:** Game; **WN:** Blackwater; **WT:** River (Moving) **W. Size:** 9600 Metres.
Ref: FH0469

BLACKWATER (RIVER)

River Blackwater, Lismore, **COUNTY WATERFORD**, **Ireland**.
Contact/s: **Mr B Hogan** (Secretary), Lismore Salmon Angling Association, Main St, Lismore, County Waterford, Ireland.
Mr Michael Penruddock (Manager), Lismore Estate Office, Lismore Castle, Lismore, County Waterford, Ireland.
(T) 058 54424
Profile: **FT:** Game; **WN:** Blackwater; **WT:** River (Moving) **W. Size:** 2400 Metres.
Ref: FH0470

BLACKWATER (RIVER)

River Blackwater, Tallow, **COUNTY WATERFORD**, **Ireland**.
Contact/s: **Mr Alan Sivyer**, Bride View Bar, Tallow Bridge, Tallow, County Waterford, Ireland.
(T) 058 56522
Profile: **FT:** Combination; **WN:** Blackwater; **WT:** River (Moving) **W. Size:** 7200 Metres.
Location: **Nr. Rd:** Mogeely.
Ref: FH0471

BLACKWATER (RIVER)

River Blackwater, Lismore, **COUNTY WATERFORD**, **Ireland**.
Contact/s: **Mr Michael Penruddock** (Manager), Lismore Estate Office, Lismore Castle, Lismore, County Waterford, Ireland.
(T) 058 54424
Profile: **FT:** Game; **WN:** Blackwater; **WT:** River (Moving) **W. Size:** 2120 Metres.
Ref: FH0472

BLACKWATER (RIVER)

River Blackwater, Coggeshall, Colchester, **ESSEX**, CO6, **England**.
Contact/s: **Mr M K Turner** (Secretary), Colchester Angling Preservation Society, 29 Lodge Rd, Braintree, Essex, CO2 8PX.
Profile: **FT:** Coarse; **WN:** Blackwater; **WT:** River (Moving).
Ref: FH0473

BLACKWATER (RIVER)

River Blackwater, Braintree, **ESSEX**, CM7, **England**.
Contact/s: **Mr Clack** (Secretary).
(T) 01376 44201
Profile: **FT:** Coarse; **WN:** Blackwater; **WT:** River (Moving).
Ref: FH0474

BLACKWATER (RIVER)

River Blackwater, Back Lake, Appleford Bridge, Chelmsford, **ESSEX**, CM, **England**.
Profile: **FT:** Coarse; **WN:** Blackwater; **WT:** River (Moving) **W. Size:** 24000 Metres.
Ref: FH0475

BLACKWATER (RIVER)

River Blackwater, Maldon, **ESSEX**, CM9, **England**.
Profile: **FT:** Coarse; **WN:** River Blackwater; **WT:** Combination (Still & Moving).
Ref: FH0476

BLACKWATER (RIVER)

River Blackwater, Blue Mills, Witham, **ESSEX**, CM8, **England**.
(W) www.bdac.co.uk
Contact/s: **Mr Derek Howard** (Hon Treasurer), Billericay and District Angling Club, 4 Long Meadow Drive, Wickford, Essex, SS11 8AX.
(T) 01268 734468
Profile: **FT:** Coarse; **WN:** Blackwater; **WT:** River (Moving) **W. Size:** 900 Metres.
Location: **Main Rd:** A12, B1018; **Rail:** Witham.
Ref: FH0477

BLACKWATER (RIVER)

River Blackwater, Braintree, Witham, **ESSEX**, CM8, **England**.
Profile: **FT:** Coarse; **WN:** Blackwater; **WT:** River (Moving) **W. Size:** 12200 Metres.
Location: **Nr. Rd:** Witham to Braintree.
Ref: FH0478

BLACKWATER FISHERY

Blackwater Fishery, Kenmare, Kerry, **COUNTY KERRY**, **Ireland**.
Contact/s: **Mrs Merrie Green** (Manager), Ballyvolane House, Castlelyons, County Cork, Ireland.
(T) 025 36349
Profile: **FT:** Game; **WN:** Blackwater; **WT:** River (Moving).
Ref: FH0479

BLACKWATER FLY FISHING

Blackwater Fly Fishing, Ghillie Cottage, Kilbarry Stud, Fermoy, **COUNTY CORK**, **Ireland**.
Contact/s: **Mr Doug Lock**.
(T) 025 32720 **(F)** 025 33000
Profile: **FT:** Game; **WN:** Blackwater; **WT:** River (Moving). Location: **Nr. Rd:** Ghillie Cottage; **Main Rd:** Kilbarry Stud.
Ref: FH0480

BLACKWATER LODGE

Blackwater Lodge Hotel And Fishery, Upper Ballyduff, **COUNTY WATERFORD**, **Ireland**.
Contact/s: **Mr Ian Powell**.
(T) 058 60235 **(F)** 058 60162
(E) bwlodge@indigo.ie
Profile: **FT:** Combination; **WN:** Munster Blackwater; **WT:** River (Moving) **W. Size:** 64000 Metres.
Ref: FH0481

BLACKWATER SALMON FISHERY

Blackwater Salmon Fishery, Ballyvonlane House, Castlelyons, **COUNTY CORK**, **Ireland**.
Contact/s: **Mrs Merrie Green** (Manager), Ballyvolane House, Castlelyons, County Cork, Ireland.
(T) 025 36349
Profile: **FT:** Game; **WN:** Blackwater; **WT:** Combination (Still & Moving).
Ref: FH0482

BLACKWOOD POOL

Blackwood Pool, Bagnall Rd, Bagnall, Stoke-on-Trent, **STAFFORDSHIRE**, ST9, **England**.
Contact/s: **Mr Julian Grattidge**, 60 Begars Lane, Leek, Staffordshire, ST13 8JR.
(T) 01538 386435
(E) julian.grattidge@btinternet.com
Mr Sean Lawlor (Club Secretary).
(T) 01782 504567
Profile: **FT:** Coarse; **WN:** Blackwood Pool; **WT:** Pool (Still); **F. Size:** 2 Acres; **W. Size:** 1 Acre. Location: **Nr. Rd:** Milton to Bagnall/Werrington; **Main Rd:** A53; **Rail:** Stoke-On-Trent.
Ref: FH0483

BLACKWOOL TROUT FISHERY

Blackwool Trout Fishery, Blackwool Farm, Colhook Common, Petworth, **SUSSEX (WEST)**, GU28 9ND, **England**.
(W) www.blackwoolfarm.co.uk
Contact/s: **C Savage** (Manager).
(T) 01428 707258 **(F)** 01428 707255
(E) enquires@blackwoolfarm.co.uk
Mr Taff Baker (Manager). **(M)** 07867 978264
Profile: **FT:** Game; **WN:** Blackwool Trout Fishery; **WT:** Lake (Still); **F. Size:** 106 Acres; **W. Size:** 2 Acres. Location: **Nr. Rd:** A283; **Main Rd:** A283; **Rail:** Haselmere.
Ref: FH0484

BLADNOCH (RIVER)

River Bladnoch, Creebridge House Hotel, Newton Stewart, **DUMFRIES AND GALLOWAY**, DG8 6NP, **Scotland**.
Contact/s: **Mr Tony Dickinson** (Manager), Galloway Guns and Tackle, 36a Arthur St, Newton Stewart, Dumfries and Galloway, DG8 6DE.
(T) 01671 403404 **(F)** 01671 403404
Profile: **FT:** Combination; **WN:** Bladnoch; **WT:** River (Moving).
Ref: FH0485

BLADON LAKE

Bladon Lake, Woodstock, **OXFORDSHIRE**, OX20, **England**.
Contact/s: **Mrs Barbara Cornet** (Fishery Manager).
(T) 01993 811432 **(F)** 01993 813108
Profile: **FT:** Coarse; **WN:** Bladon Lake; **WT:** Lake (Still).
Ref: FH0486

BLAGDON LAKE

Blagdon Lake, Blagdon, Bristol, **SOMERSET**, **England**.
(W) www.bristolwater.co.uk
Contact/s: **Mr Bob Handford**, Bristol Water Plc, Woodford Lodge, Chew Stoke, Bristol, BS40 8XH.
(T) 01275 332339 **(F)** 01275 331377
(E) bob.hanford@bristolwater.co.uk
Profile: **FT:** Game; **WN:** Blagdon; **WT:** Lake (Still); **F. Size:** 480 Acres; **W. Size:** 440 Acres. **Location:** **Nr. Rd:** A368; **Main Rd:** A38, A370; **Rail:** Bristol.
Ref: FH0487

BLAIRMORE FISHERY

Blairmore Fishery, Blairmore Farm, Balfron Station, Glasgow, **STIRLING**, G63 0NQ, **Scotland**.
Contact/s: **Mr A McAllister**.
(T) 01360 660217
Profile: **FT:** Game; **WN:** Blairmore Fishery; **WT:** River (Moving). **Location:** **Main Rd:** A81.
Ref: FH0488

BLAKEMERE

Blakemere, Sandiway, Ellesmere, Northwich, **CHESHIRE**, CW8, **England**.
Profile: **FT:** Coarse; **WN:** Blakemere; **WT:** Lake (Still) **W. Size:** 7 Acres.
Ref: FH0489

BLAKEMERE

Blakemere, Whitchurch, **SHROPSHIRE**, SY13, **England**.
Profile: **FT:** Coarse; **WN:** Blakemere; **WT:** Lake (Still).
Ref: FH0490

BLAKEWELL FISHERIES

Blakewell Fisheries, Blakewell Lane, Muddiford, Barnstaple, **DEVON**, EX31 4ET, **England**.
Contact/s: **Mr John Nickell** (Owner).
(T) 01271 344533 **(F)** 01271 374267
Mr Richard Nickell (Owner).
(T) 01271 344533 **(F)** 01271 374267
Profile: **FT:** Game; **WN:** Blakewell Fisheries; **WT:** Lake (Still). **Location:** **Nr. Rd:** Blakewell Lane; **Main Rd:** Muddiford.
Ref: FH0491

BLASFORD HILL FISHERIES

Blasford Hill Fisheries, Little Waltham, Chelmsford, **ESSEX**, CM3, **England**.
Contact/s: **Mr Chris Peachey - Edwards** (Owner), Glenroy, Blasford Hill, Little Waltham, Chelmsford, CM3 3PL.
(T) 01245 362772 **(F)** 01245 357689 **(M)** 07860 110303
Profile: **FT:** Coarse; **WN:** Chelmer; **WT:** Combination (Still & Moving); **F. Size:** 20 Acres; **W. Size:** 6 Acres. **Location:** **Nr. Rd:** B1008; **Rail:** Chelmsford.
Ref: FH0492

BLASHFORD LAKES

Blashford Lakes, Ivy Lane, Christchurch, **DORSET**, BH23, **England**.
Contact/s: Customer Services, Wessex Water, Billing Ctre, Clevedon Walk, Nailsea, Bristol, BS48 1WW.
(T) 01179 290611 **(F)** 01275 810519
Mr R J Andrews (Club Secretary), Christchurch Angling Club, 4 Marley Cl, New Milton, BH25 5LL.
(T) 01425 638502
Profile: **FT:** Coarse; **WN:** Blashford; **WT:** Lake (Still). **Location:** **Nr. Rd:** Ivy Lane; **Main Rd:** A338.
Ref: FH0493

BLEA TARN

Blea Tarn, Blea Tarn Farmhouse, Langdale, Scarborough, **YORKSHIRE (NORTH)**, YO13, **England**.
Contact/s: **Mrs Myers**.
Profile: **FT:** Combination; **WN:** Blea; **WT:** Tarn (Still).
Ref: FH0494

BLELHAM TARN

Blelham Tarn, Wray, Hawkshead, Ambleside, **CUMBRIA**, LA22, **England**.
Contact/s: Fishery Manager.
(T) 01539 433203
Mr Chris Sodo (Hon Treasurer), Windermere, Ambleside and District Angling Association, Ecclerigg Court, Ecclerigg, Windermere, LA23 1LQ.
(T) 01539 445083
Profile: **FT:** Combination; **WN:** Blelham; **WT:** Lake (Still) **W. Size:** 25 Acres.
Location: **Main Rd:** B5286 from Ambleside to Hawkshead; **Rail:** Windermere.
Ref: FH0495

BLENCARN LAKE

Blencarn Lake, Blencarn Hall, Penrith, **CUMBRIA**, CA10 1TX, **England**.
Contact/s: **Mr J Stampter**.
(T) 01768 88284
Profile: **FT:** Game; **WN:** Blencarn; **WT:** Lake (Still) **W. Size:** 15 Acres. **Location:** **Nr. Rd:** A686; **Main Rd:** M6, junction 40.
Ref: FH0496

BLENHEIM LAKE

Blenheim Lake, Estate Office, Blenheim Palace, Woodstock, **OXFORDSHIRE**, OX20 1PS, **England**.
Contact/s: **Mrs Barbara Cornet** (Fishery Manager).
(T) 01993 811432 **(F)** 01993 813108
Profile: **FT:** Coarse; **WN:** Blenheim; **WT:** Lake (Still).
Ref: FH0497

BLENHEIM LODGE HOTEL

Blenheim Lodge Hotel, Brantfell Rd, Bowness-on-Windermere, Windermere, **CUMBRIA**, LA23 3AE, **England**.
Contact/s: Hotel Manager.
(T) 01539 443440
Profile: **FT:** Coarse; **WN:** Windermere; **WT:** Lake (Still).
Ref: FH0498

BLESSINGBOURNE LAKE

Blessingbourne Lake, Blessingbourne, Fivemiletown, **COUNTY TYRONE**, BT75, **Northern Ireland**.
Contact/s: Fishery Manager.
(T) 028 66521221
Profile: **FT:** Coarse; **WN:** Blessingbourne Lake; **WT:** Lake (Still).
Ref: FH0499

BLICKLING PARK LAKE

Blickling Park Lake, 1 Park Gates, Aylsham, Blickling, Norwich, **NORFOLK**, NR11 6NJ, **England**.
Contact/s: **Mr Dave Cooper** (Bailiff).
(T) 01263 734181
Profile: **FT:** Coarse; **WN:** Blickling; **WT:** Lake (Still) **W. Size:** 25 Acres. **Location:** **Nr. Rd:** Aylesham to Itteringham; **Main Rd:** B1354.
Ref: FH0500

BLITHE (RIVER)

Blithe (River), Uttoxeter, **STAFFORDSHIRE**, **England**.
(W) www.fentondas.co.uk
Contact/s: **Mr C Yates** (Club Secretary), The Puzzles, 5 Gatley Gr, Meir Park, Stoke-on-Trent, Staffordshire ST3 7SH.
(T) 01782 396913
Profile: **FT:** Combination; **WN:** Blithe; **WT:** River (Moving). **Location:** **Rail:** Uttoxeter.
Ref: FH0501

BLITHFIELD RESERVOIR

Blithfield Reservoir, Abbots Bromley, Rugeley, **STAFFORDSHIRE**, WS15, **England**.
Contact/s: **Mr Mike Ray** (Fishery Manager), Blithfield Anglers Limited, Reservoir Rd, Near Rugeley, Staffordshire, WS15 3DU.
(T) 01283 840284
Profile: **FT:** Game; **WN:** Blithfield; **WT:** Reservoir (Still) **W. Size:** 800 Acres.
Ref: FH0502

BLOCK FEN COMPLEX

Block Fen Complex, Lakes A And B, Mepal, Ely, **CAMBRIDGESHIRE**, CB6, **England**.
Contact/s: Manager, Arbury Angling Ctre, 48 Arbury Court, Cambridge, Cambridgeshire, CB4 2JQ.
(T) 01223 300216
Profile: **FT:** Coarse; **WN:** Block Fen Complex; **WT:** Pit (Still). **Location:** **Nr. Rd:** A142; **Main Rd:** A10.
Ref: FH0503

BLUE LAGOON

Blue Lagoon, Arlesey, **HERTFORDSHIRE**, SG1, **England**.
Profile: **FT:** Coarse; **WN:** Blue Lagoon; **WT:** Gravel Pit (Still) **W. Size:** 30 Acres.
Location: **Nr. Rd:** Bedfordshire Border.
Ref: FH0504

BLUE LAGOON

Blue Lagoon, Broomfleet, Hull, **HUMBERSIDE**, HU, **England**.
Contact/s: **Mr Bill Brame** (Secretary), Hull and District Angler's Association, PO Box 188, Hull, HU9 1AN.
Mr Dave Harold (Fisheries Information Officer), 33 Jipdane Orchard Park, Hull, Yorkshire (East), HU6 9EE.
(T) 01482 809832
Profile: **FT:** Coarse; **WN:** Blue Lagoon; **WT:** Lake (Still); **F. Size:** 3 Acres; **W. Size:** 2 Acres. **Location:** **Main Rd:** B1230; **Rail:** Broomfleet.
Ref: FH0505

BLUE LAGOON

Blue Lagoon, Northampton, **NORTHAMPTONSHIRE**, NN, **England**.
Contact/s: Fishery Manager.
(T) 01604 757589
Profile: **FT:** Coarse; **WN:** Blue; **WT:** Lake (Still).
Ref: FH0506

BLUE LAGOON LAKE

Blue Lagoon Lake, Bobbin Lodge Hill, Chartham, Canterbury, **KENT**, **England**.
(W) www.midkentfish.demon.co.uk
Contact/s: **Mr Chris Logsdon** (Fisheries Manager), Mid Kent Fisheries, Chilham Water Mill, Mill Lane, Chilham, CT4 8EE.
(T) 01227 730668
(E) chilham@midkentfisheries.co.uk
Profile: **FT:** Coarse; **WN:** Blue Lagoon; **WT:** Lake (Still); **F. Size:** 30 Acres; **W. Size:** 5 Acres. **Location:** **Main Rd:** A28; **Rail:** Chartham.
Ref: FH0507

BLUE LAKE

Blue Lake, Waun-Y-Pound Industrial Estate, Ebbw Vale, **BLAENAU GWENT**, NP23, **Wales**.
Contact/s: **J Williams** (Manager), 38

Bethcar St, Ebbw Vale, Gwent NP23 6HQ.
(T) 01495 305353
Mr Ray Satterley (Match Secretary).
(T) 01495 307613
Profile: FT: Coarse; **WN:** Blue; **WT:** Lake (Still) **W. Size:** 4 Acres. **Location: Nr. Rd:** B4486; **Main Rd:** A465.
Ref: FH0508

BLUE LAKE

Blue Lake, South Tawton, Okehampton, **DEVON**, EX20, **England**.
Contact/s: Mr Andy Spencer.
(T) 024 76422248
Mr Brad Green.
(T) 024 76465403
Profile: FT: Coarse; **WN:** Blue Lake; **WT:** Gravel Pit (Still). **Location: Main Rd:** A30 to Okehampton.
Ref: FH0509

BLUE POOL

Blue Pool, Randley Avenue, Telford, **SHROPSHIRE**, TF, **England**.
Contact/s: Mr Malcolm Kelly (Nfa Disability Officer, West Midlands Region), 14 Sycamore Cl, Wellington, Telford, Shropshire, TF1 3NH.
(T) 01952 244272
Profile: FT: Coarse; **WN:** Blue; **WT:** Pool (Still). **Location: Nr. Rd:** St Quentin roundabout; **Main Rd:** M54, junction 4.
Ref: FH0510

BLUE WATERS

Blue Waters, Woolpit, Bury St Edmunds, **SUFFOLK**, IP30, **England**.
Contact/s: Mr Baker.
(T) 01359 240293
Profile: FT: Coarse; **WN:** Blue Waters; **WT:** Gravel Pit (Still) **W. Size:** 2 Acres. **Location: Nr. Rd:** Bury St Edmunds to Stowmarket; **Main Rd:** A14 to Woolpit.
Ref: FH0511

BLUEBELL FISHING PONDS

Bluebell Fishing Ponds, Maidstone, **KENT**, ME1, **England**.
Contact/s: Mr Rob Earl (Manager), Maidstone Angling Ctre, 15 Perryfield St, Maidstone, Kent, ME14 2SY.
(T) 01622 677326 **(F)** 01622 752021
Profile: FT: Coarse; **WN:** Bluebell; **WT:** Pond (Still) **W. Size:** 2 Acres. **Location: Nr. Rd:** A229; **Main Rd:** M20.
Ref: FH0512

BLUEBELL LAKE

Bluebell Lake, Tansor, Oundle, Peterborough, **CAMBRIDGESHIRE**, PE8 5HN, **England**.
(W) www.fisheries.co.uk/bluebell
Mr Tony Bridgefoot (Owner), Bluebell Lake, Tansor, Oundle, Peterborough, Cambridgeshire, PE8 5HN.
(T) 01832 226042 **(M)** 07702 641926
Profile: FT: Coarse; **WN:** Bluebell Lake; **WT:** Gravel Pit (Still); **F. Size:** 108 Acres; **W. Size:** 40 Acres. **Location: Nr. Rd:** Tansor to Fotheringhay; **Main Rd:** A605; **Rail:** Peterborough.
Ref: FH0513

BLUNDELLS FARM FISHERY

Blundells Farm Fishery, Rixton, Warrington, **CHESHIRE**, WA3, **England**.
Contact/s: Mr John Blundell (Farmer), Mosside Farm, Prospect Lane, Rixton, Warrington, WA3 6EJ.
(T) 0161 7752124
Profile: FT: Coarse; **WN:** Blundells Farm Fishery; **WT:** Lake (Still) **W. Size:** 4 Acres. **Location: Nr. Rd:** A57; **Main Rd:** M6, junction 21.
Ref: FH0514

BLUNHAM PITS

Blunham Pits, Maperton Lodge, Station Rd, Raunds, Wellingborough, **NORTHAMPTONSHIRE**, NN9, **England**.
Contact/s: Mr Twell.
Mr G Palmer (Club Secretary).
(T) 01234 823959 / 0123023959
Profile: FT: Coarse; **WN:** Blunham Pits; **WT:** Combination (Still & Moving) **W. Size:** 7 Acres. **Location: Nr. Rd:** Station Road; **Main Rd:** A1.
Ref: FH0515

BLUNTS AND CANTS MERES

Blunts And Cants Meres, Crouchmans Farm Rd, Ulting, Hatfield Peverel, Chelmsford, **ESSEX**, CM, **England**.
(W) www.chelmsfordaa.freeserve.co.uk
Contact/s: Mr Frank Wright (Membership Secretary), Chelmsford Angling Association, 61 Readers Court, Great Baddow, Chelmsford, CM2 8EX.
(T) 01245 474246or264832
(E) frank@chelmsfordaa.freeserve.co.uk
Ms Irene Lewis (Secretary), 60 Delamere Rd, Chelmsford, CM1 2TG.
(T) 01245 264832
Profile: FT: Combination; **WN:** Chelmer Blackwater; **WT:** Combination (Still & Moving); **F. Size:** 6 Acres; **W. Size:** 6 Acres. **Location: Nr. Rd:** Couches Farm Road; **Main Rd:** The Street; **Rail:** Hatfield Peverell.
Ref: FH0516

BLYTHE (RIVER)

Blythe (River), Somers Road, Meriden, Coventry, **MIDLANDS (WEST)**, CV7, **England**.
Contact/s: Mr John Burchell (Manager), Packington Fisheries, Maxstoke Lane, Meriden, Coventry, CV7 7HR.
(T) 01676 523833or522754 **(F)** 01676 522754
Profile: FT: Coarse; **WN:** Blythe; **WT:** River (Moving); **F. Size:** 80 Acres; **W. Size:** 1200 Metres. **Location: Nr. Rd:** Hampton Lane; **Main Rd:** A45; **Rail:** Birmingham International.
Ref: FH0517

BLYTHE WATERS

Blythe Waters, Hampton Rd, Knowle, Solihull, **MIDLANDS (WEST)**, B92 0JL, **England**.
Contact/s: Mr B M Fisher.
(T) 01675 442108
Mr Graham Young (Fishery Manager).
(T) 0121 6242599
Profile: FT: Coarse; **WN:** Blythe; **WT:** Lake (Still). **Location: Nr. Rd:** Hampton Road; **Main Rd:** M42, junction 5, A4141 to Knowle; **Rail:** Hampton-in-Arden.
Ref: FH0518

BOAT POND

Boat Pond, Highlands Rd, Beaufort Hill, Ebbw Vale, **BLAENAU GWENT**, NP23, **Wales**.
Contact/s: Secretary, Ebbw Vale Welfare Angling Club, 53 Bethcar St, Ebbw Vale.
(T) 01495 301392
Profile: FT: Coarse; **WN:** Boat; **WT:** Pond (Still) **W. Size:** 4 Acres. **Location: Nr. Rd:** A465.
Ref: FH0519

BOATSIDE FARM

Boatside Farm, Aberedw, Builth Wells, **POWYS**, LD2, **Wales**.
Contact/s: Mr Bill Hawkins (Information Contact), 89 Rosemary Crescent West, Goldthorn Park, Wolverhampton, WV4 5AN.
(T) 01902 334086
Profile: FT: Game; **WN:** Wye; **WT:** River (Moving) **W. Size:** 800 Metres.
Ref: FH0520

BODDINGTON RESERVOIR

Boddington Reservoir, Upper Boddington Village, Byfield, Daventry, **NORTHAMPTONSHIRE**, NN11, **England**.
Contact/s: Mr John Ellis (Manager).
(T) 01923 208717 **(F)** 01923 208787
Profile: FT: Coarse; **WN:** Boddington; **WT:** Reservoir (Still) **W. Size:** 65 Acres. **Location: Nr. Rd:** Boddington to Byfield; **Main Rd:** A361.
Ref: FH0521

BODIDRIS GAME FISHERY

Bodidris Game Fishery, Rhydtalog Moor, Rhydtalog, Wrexham, LL11 3BF, **Wales**.
Contact/s: Mr Dave Penman.
(T) 01978 790527
Profile: FT: Game; **WN:** Bodidris Game Fishery; **WT:** Lake (Still).
Ref: FH0522

BOG GROVE

Bog Grove, Totham, Maldon, **ESSEX**, CM9, **England**.
Contact/s: Terry Lazell (Secretary), Maldon Angling Society, 14 Barn View Rd, Coggleshall, Essex, CO6 1RF.
(T) 01376 563937
Profile: FT: Coarse; **WN:** Bog Grove; **WT:** Lake (Still) **W. Size:** 2 Acres. **Location: Main Rd:** A12, North East of Chelmsford.
Ref: FH0523

BOGGART HOLE CLOUGH

Boggart Hole Clough, Blackley Park, Manchester, **MANCHESTER (GREATER)**, M, **England**.
Contact/s: Area Manager, Manchester City Council, Town Hall, Albert Sq, Manchester, M60 2AF.
(T) 0161 7409970
Manager.
(T) 0161 2052519
Manager.
(T) 0161 7407985
Profile: FT: Coarse; **WN:** Boggart Hole Clough; **WT:** Lake (Still). **Location: Nr. Rd:** Charleston Road; **Main Rd:** M66, B6393, A6104.
Ref: FH0524

BOGNIE & MOUNTBLAIRY FISHING

Bognie And Mountblairy Fishing, Huntly, **ABERDEENSHIRE**, AB54, **Scotland**.
Contact/s: Mrs J McRae (Manager), BMF Group, Estate Office, Frendraught House, Forgue, Huntly, AB54 6EB.
(T) 01464 871331 **(F)** 01464 871333
Profile: FT: Game; **WN:** Deveron; **WT:** River (Moving) **W. Size:** 8046 Metres. **Location: Main Rd:** B9121; **Rail:** Huntly.
Ref: FH0525

BOHERBAUN (RIVER)

River Boherbaun, Athy, **COUNTY KILDARE**, **Ireland**.
Contact/s: Manager, Griffin Hawe Limited, 22 Duke St, Athy, County Kildare, Ireland.
(T) 050 731221 **(F)** 050 733885
(E) griffinhawe@tinet.ie
Profile: FT: Game; **WN:** Boherbaun; **WT:** River (Moving).
Ref: FH0526

BOJO FISHERIES

Bojo Fisheries, Barretts Park Farm, Heathfield, **SUSSEX (EAST)**, TN21 8QS, **England**.
Contact/s: Mr R Leeves.
(T) 01435 863668
Profile: FT: Coarse; **WN:** Bojo Fisheries; **WT:** Lake (Still).
Ref: FH0527

BOLAM LAKE COUNTRY PARK

Bolam Lake Country Park, Site Office, Belsay, Newcastle Upon Tyne, **TYNE AND WEAR**, NE20, **England**.
Contact/s: Mr F Povey (Manager), Northumberland County Council, County Hall, Morpeth, Northumberland, NE61 2EF.
(T) 01661 881234
Profile: FT: Coarse; **WN:** Bolam; **WT:** Lake (Still) **W. Size:** 20 Acres. **Location: Nr. Rd:** C155; **Main Rd:** A696; **Rail:** Morpeth.
Ref: FH0528

BOLDERMERE

Boldermere, Wisley, Woking, **SURREY**, GU23, **England**.
Contact/s: Mr Alan Tanner.
(T) 01483 575801
Profile: FT: Coarse; **WN:** Boldermere; **WT:**

Lake (Still). **Location:** **Nr. Rd:** Old Lane; **Main Rd:** A3 to Guildford.
Ref: FH0529

BOLDINGS POOLS

Boldings Pools, Astley Abbotts, Bridgnorth, **SHROPSHIRE**, WV16 4SS, **England**.
(W) www.boldings-pools.co.uk
Contact/s: **Mr Ed Turner** (Manager).
(T) 01746 763255 **(F)** 01746 763255
Mr Mark Turner (Fishery Manager).
(T) 01746 763255 **(F)** 01746 763255
(E) mark@boldings-pools.co.uk
Mrs Sue Turner (Fishery Manager).
(T) 01746 763255 **(F)** 01746 763255
Profile: **FT:** Combination; **WN:** Boldings Pool; **WT:** Pool (Still) **W. Size:** 20 Acres. **Location:** **Nr. Rd:** Stanley Lane; **Main Rd:** B4373; **Rail:** Telford.
Ref: FH0530

BOLEBROOK CASTLE

Bolebrook Castle, East Grinstead, **SUSSEX (WEST)**, RH19, **England**.
Contact/s: **Mr Adrian Bewley** (Manager), Ashvale Fisheries, 69 Fortescue Rd, Wimbledon, London, SW19 2EA.
(T) 020 82873892
Profile: **FT:** Coarse; **WN:** Bolebrook Castle; **WT:** Lake (Still) **W. Size:** 3 Acres.
Ref: FH0531

BOLESWORTH CASTLE

Bolesworth Castle, Tattenhall, Chester, **CHESHIRE**, CH, **England**.
Contact/s: **Mr Albert Perkins** (Hon Secretary), 63 Fowlers Lane, Light Oaks, Stoke-on-Trent, Staffordshire, ST2 7NB.
Ms Liz Hayes (Manager).
(T) 01625 251262
Profile: **FT:** Coarse; **WN:** Bolesworth; **WT:** Lake (Still); **F. Size:** 20 Acres; **W. Size:** 8 Acres. **Location:** **Nr. Rd:** Whitchurch to Chester; **Main Rd:** A41; **Rail:** Chester.
Ref: FH0532

BOLFRACKS BEAT

Bolfracks Beat, Kenmore, Aberfeldy, **PERTH AND KINROSS**, PH15, **Scotland**.
(W) www.fishingnet.com/beats/bolfracks
Contact/s: **Mr Paul Fishlock** (Salmon Permit Contact), Taymouth Castle, 2 The Square, Kenmore, Perth and Kinross, PH15 2HH.
(T) 01887 830765 **(F)** 01887 830830
Profile: **FT:** Game; **WN:** Bolfracks, Dalrawer, Neils, Haugh and Home Farm; **WT:** Pool (Still).
Ref: FH0533

BOLINGEY LAKE

Bolingey Lake, Penwartha Rd, Bolingey, Perranporth, **CORNWALL**, TR6 0DH, **England**.
Contact/s: **John**.
(T) 01872 572388
Mr Mike Gorman.
(T) 01872 572388
Profile: **FT:** Coarse; **WN:** Bolingey; **WT:** Lake (Still) **W. Size:** 5 Acres. **Location:** **Nr. Rd:** B3285; **Main Rd:** Perranporth.
Ref: FH0534

BOLLIN (RIVER)

River Bollin, Cinder, Knutsford, **CHESHIRE**, WA16, **England**.
Contact/s: **Mr Neil Jupp** (Club Secretary), Lymm Angling Club, PO Box 350, Warrington, Cheshire, WA2 9FB.
(T) 01925 411744
Profile: **FT:** Combination; **WN:** Bollin; **WT:** River (Moving). **Location:** **Nr. Rd:** A6144; **Main Rd:** A50 to Knutsford.
Ref: FH0535

BOLLIN (RIVER)

River Bollin, Reddish, Knutsford, **CHESHIRE**, WA16, **England**.
Contact/s: **Mr Neil Jupp** (Club Secretary), Lymm Angling Club, PO Box 350, Warrington, Cheshire, WA2 9FB.
(T) 01925 411744
Profile: **FT:** Combination; **WN:** Bollin; **WT:** River (Moving). **Location:** **Nr. Rd:** A6144; **Main Rd:** A50 to Knutsford.
Ref: FH0536

BOLLIN (RIVER)

River Bollin, Mill, Knutsford, **CHESHIRE**, WA16, **England**.
Contact/s: **Mr Neil Jupp** (Club Secretary), Lymm Angling Club, PO Box 350, Warrington, Cheshire, WA2 9FB.
(T) 01925 411744
Profile: **FT:** Combination; **WN:** Bollin; **WT:** River (Moving). **Location:** **Nr. Rd:** A6144; **Main Rd:** A50 to Knutsford.
Ref: FH0537

BOLLINHURST RESERVOIR

Bollinhurst Reservoir, Disley, Stockport, **MANCHESTER (GREATER)**, SK12 2, **England**.
Contact/s: **Mr G Heywood** (Secretary), 10 Marlett Avenue, Disley, Stockport.
Mr Roy Rhodes (Conservation, Access and Recreation Manager), Rivington Water Treatment Works, Bolton Rd, Horwich, Bolton, BL6 7RN.
(T) 01204 664300
Profile: **FT:** Combination; **WN:** Bollinhurst; **WT:** Reservoir (Still).
Ref: FH0538

BOLTON ABBEY FISHERIES

Bolton Abbey Fisheries, The Estate Office, Bolton Abbey, Skipton, **YORKSHIRE (NORTH)**, BD23 6EX, **England**.
Contact/s: , The Trustees of the Chatsworth Settlement, Bolton Abbey, Skipton, Yorkshire (North), BD23 6EX.
(T) 01756 710227 **(F)** 01756 710535
Mr Charles Hoyle (River Bailiff).
(T) 01756 710391
Profile: **FT:** Game; **WN:** Wharfe; **WT:** River (Moving) **W. Size:** 9000 Metres. **Location:** **Nr. Rd:** B6160; **Main Rd:** A59; **Rail:** Ilkley or Skipton.
Ref: FH0539

BOLTON CANAL

Bolton Canal, Nob End, Bolton, **LANCASHIRE**, BL, **England**.
Contact/s: **Mr Terence A McKee** (Secretary), Bolton and District Angling Association, 1 Lever Edge Lane, Bolton, Lancashire, BL3 3BU.
(T) 01204 393726
Profile: **FT:** Coarse; **WN:** Bolton; **WT:** Canal (Still) **W. Size:** 1600 Metres. **Location:** **Nr. Rd:** A6053, Hall Lane to Nob End; **Main Rd:** M61, junction 3.
Ref: FH0540

BONEHILL MILL

Bonehill Mill, Lichfield St, Fazeley, Tamworth, **STAFFORDSHIRE**, B78 3QQ, **England**.
Contact/s: Fishery Manager.
(T) 01827 288482
Profile: **FT:** Coarse; **WN:** Bonehill Mill; **WT:** Lake (Still). **Location:** **Nr. Rd:** Lichfield Street; **Main Rd:** Fazeley.
Ref: FH0541

BONTNEWYDD FISHERY

Bontnewydd Fishery, Betws Garmon, Caernarfon, **GWYNEDD**, LL54, **Wales**.
Contact/s: **G J M Wills** (Secretary), Bryn Mafon, Caethro, Caernarfon.
(T) 01286 673379
Profile: **FT:** Game; **WN:** Bontnewydd Fishery; **WT:** River (Moving).
Ref: FH0542

BOOTON CLAY PIT

Booton Clay Pit, Reepham Rd, Booton, Norwich, **NORFOLK**, NR10, **England**.
Contact/s: Secretary, Cawston Angling Club, 27 Holman Cl, Aylsham, Norfolk.
Mr Stephen Brownsell (Chairman).
(T) 01263 732263 or 01263732433
Profile: **FT:** Coarse; **WT:** Gravel Pit (Still) **W. Size:** 2 Acres. **Location:** **Nr. Rd:** Reepham Road; **Main Rd:** A140, Holt to Norwich; **Rail:** Norwich.
Ref: FH0543

BORDE HILL GARDEN LAKES

Borde Hill Gardens, Haywards Heath, **SUSSEX (WEST)**, RH17, **England**.
Contact/s: **Mr Robin Southon**.
(T) 01444 412561
Profile: **FT:** Coarse; **WN:** Borde Hill Gardens; **WT:** Lake (Still); **F. Size:** 200 Acres; **W. Size:** 6 Acres. **Location:** **Nr. Rd:** Balcombe; **Main Rd:** A272; **Rail:** Haywards Heath.
Ref: FH0544

BORDEAUX PIT

Bordeaux Pit, Little Chesterford, Saffron Walden, **ESSEX**, CB1, **England**.
Contact/s: **Mr N Roberts** (Manager).
(T) 01223 836773
Profile: **FT:** Coarse; **WN:** Bordeaux; **WT:** Gravel Pit (Still) **W. Size:** 3 Acres. **Location:** **Nr. Rd:** B1383; **Main Rd:** M11; **Rail:** Great Chesterford.
Ref: FH0545

BORDER FISHERIES

Border Fisheries, Betley, Crewe, **CHESHIRE**, CW, **England**.
Contact/s: **Mr Mick Glover**.
(T) 01270 820812
Profile: **FT:** Coarse; **WN:** Border Fisheries; **WT:** Pool (Still) **W. Size:** 7 Acres. **Location:** **Nr. Rd:** Signposted; **Main Rd:** M6, junction 16, take A500 then A531.
Ref: FH0546

BORE VALLEY LAKES

Bore Valley Lakes, Saxthorpe Rd, Aylsham, Norwich, **NORFOLK**, NR11, **England**.
Contact/s: **Mr Michael Smith** (Manager).
(T) 01263 576666or587666
Profile: **FT:** Coarse; **WN:** Bore Valley; **WT:** Lake (Still).
Ref: FH0547

BOREHAM FISHERY

Boreham Fishery, Waltham Rd, Boreham, Chelmsford, **ESSEX**, CM, **England**.
(W) www.rmcangling.co.uk
Contact/s: **Mr Ian Welch** (Angling Manager), RMC Angling, The Square, Lightwater, Surrey, GU18 5SS.
(T) 01276 453300 **(F)** 01276 456611
(E) info@rmcangling.co.uk
Profile: **FT:** Coarse; **WN:** A1; **WT:** Gravel Pit (Still) **W. Size:** 1 Acre. **Location:** **Nr. Rd:** Wallaces Farm Road; **Main Rd:** A131, A12.
Ref: FH0548

BOREHAM MERES

Boreham Meres, Waltham Rd, Boreham, Chelmsford, **ESSEX**, CM3, **England**.
(W) www.chelmsfordaa.freeserve.co.uk
Contact/s: **Mr Frank Wright** (Membership Secretary), Chelmsford Angling Association, 61 Readers Court, Great Baddow, Chelmsford, CM2 8EX.
(T) 01245 474246or264832
(E) frank@chelmsfordaa.freeserve.co.uk
Profile: **FT:** Coarse; **WN:** Boreham Mere; **WT:** Lake (Still); **F. Size:** 18 Acres; **W. Size:** 6 Acres. **Location:** **Nr. Rd:** Waltham Road; **Main Rd:** A12; **Rail:** Hatfield Peverell.
Ref: FH0549

BORELAND

Boreland, Glenlochay, Killin, **STIRLING**, FK21, **Scotland**.
(W) www.fishingnet.com/beats/lochy/boreland.htm
Contact/s: Manager, Keeper's Cottage, Borland Estate, Glenlochay, Killin, Perth and Kinross.
(T) 01567 820562
Profile: **FT:** Combination; **WN:** Lochay; **WT:** River (Moving).
Ref: FH0550

BORINGWHEEL TROUT FISHERY

Boringwheel Trout Fishery, Boringwheel

House, Cackle St, Nutley, Uckfield, **SUSSEX (EAST)**, TN22 3DU, **England**.
Contact/s: Manager.
(T) 01825 712629
Profile: FT: Game; **WN:** Boringwheel Trout Fishery; **WT:** Lake (Still) **W. Size:** 6 Acres.
Location: Nr. Rd: Cackle Street.
Ref: FH0551

BORRANS RESERVOIR

Borrans Reservoir, High Borrans, Outdoor Pursuit Ctre, Windermere, **CUMBRIA**, LA23, **England**.
Contact/s: Fisheries Manager, North Tynside M.B.C., Educational Department, High Borrans, Outdoor Pursuit Ctre, Windermere.
Mr Roy Rhodes (Conservation, Access and Recreation Manager), Rivington Water Treatment Works, Bolton Rd, Horwich, Bolton, BL6 7RN.
(T) 01204 664300
Profile: FT: Game; **WN:** Borrans; **WT:** Reservoir (Still). **Location: Nr. Rd:** High Borrans.
Ref: FH0552

BORROWDALE FISHERIES

Borrowdale Fisheries, The Cottage, Seathwaite, Keswick, **CUMBRIA**, CA12 5XJ, **England**.
Contact/s: Mr Stan Edmondson (Manager), Troutdale Cottage, Borrowdale, Keswick, Cumbria.
(T) 01768 777293 **(F)** 01768 777293
Profile: FT: Coarse; **WN:** Borrowdale Fisheries; **WT:** Pool (Still). **Location: Nr. Rd:** Keswick to Borrowdale; **Main Rd:** A66, M6; **Rail:** Penrith.
Ref: FH0553

BORROWPIT LAKE

Borrowpit Lake, Tamworth, **STAFFORDSHIRE**, B77, **England**.
Contact/s: Mr Fred Limm (Manager).
(T) 01827 58098
Profile: FT: Coarse; **WN:** Borrow Pit; **WT:** Pool (Still) **W. Size:** 20 Acres.
Ref: FH0554

BORWICK LAKE

Borwick Lake, Kellet Lane, Carnforth, **CUMBRIA**, LA6, **England**.
Contact/s: Mr Terry Coates.
(T) 01524 720844
Profile: FT: Coarse; **WN:** Borwick; **WT:** Lake (Still). **Location: Nr. Rd:** Kellet Lane; **Main Rd:** B6254.
Ref: FH0555

BOSCATHNOE RESERVOIR

Boscathnoe Reservoir, Penzance, **CORNWALL**, TR, **England**.
Contact/s: Mr Chris Bird (Manager), Newtown Angling Ctre, Newtown, Germoe, Penzance, TR20 9AE.
(T) 01736 763721 **(F)** 01736 763721
Mr Reg England (Manager), Peninsula Coarse Fisheries, St Cleer Depot, Lewdown, Okehampton, Devon EX20 4QT.
(T) 01837 871565 **(F)** 01837 871534
Profile: FT: Coarse; **WN:** Boscathnoe; **WT:** Reservoir (Still) **W. Size:** 4 Acres.
Ref: FH0556

BOSLEY RESERVOIR

Bosley Reservoir, Fishing Station, Bosley, Macclesfield, **CHESHIRE**, SK11, **England**.
Contact/s: Mr John Turner (Hon Secretary), Prince Albert Angling Society, 15 Pexhill Drive, Macclesfield, Cheshire, SK10 3LP.
(T) 01625 422010
Profile: FT: Coarse; **WN:** Bosley; **WT:** Reservoir (Still) **W. Size:** 90 Acres.
Location: Nr. Rd: A54 Bosley to Buxton; **Rail:** Macclesfield.
Ref: FH0557

BOSMERE LAKE

Bosmere Lake, Needham Market, Ipswich, **SUFFOLK**, IP6, **England**.
Contact/s: Fishery Manager.
(T) 01473 728179
Profile: FT: Coarse; **WN:** Bosmere; **WT:** Lake (Still).
Ref: FH0558

BOSTON SPA

Boston Spa, Boston Spa, Wetherby, **YORKSHIRE (WEST)**, LS23, **England**.
Contact/s: Mr A Waddington (Secretary), Boston Spa Angling Club, The Cottage, 17 The Village, Thorpe Arch, Wetherby LS23 7AR.
Profile: FT: Combination; **WN:** Boston; **WT:** Lake (Still).
Ref: FH0559

BOSWORTH & FRIEZELAND

Bosworth Water Trust And Friezeland Pools, Market Bosworth, Nuneaton, **WARWICKSHIRE**, CV13, **England**.
Contact/s: Mr Nigel Riley.
(T) 01455 291912
Profile: FT: Coarse; **WN:** Bosworth Water Trust And Friezeland Pools; **WT:** Lake (Still).
Location: Nr. Rd: Leicester to Market Bosworth; **Main Rd:** B585.
Ref: FH0561

BOSWORTH PARK LAKE

Bosworth Park Lake, Nuneaton, **WARWICKSHIRE**, CV10, **England**.
Contact/s: Manager, Bosworth Battlefield Centre and Country Park, Ambion Lane, Sutton Cheney, Nuneaton, Warwickshire, CV13 0AD.
(T) 01455 290429
Profile: FT: Coarse; **WN:** Bosworth; **WT:** Lake (Still) **W. Size:** 2 Acres.
Ref: FH0560

BOTTOMS DAM

Bottoms Dam, Holmbridge, Holmfirth, Huddersfield, **YORKSHIRE (WEST)**, HD7 1PR, **England**.
Contact/s: Mr D Rushforth (Membership Secretary), 122 Longwood Gate, Longwood, Huddersfield, Yorkshire (West), HD3 4US.
(T) 01484 651028
Mr N Blacker (Bailiff), 49 Towenend Rd, Wooldale, Huddersfield.
(T) 01484 686894
Profile: FT: Combination; **WN:** Bottoms Dam; **WT:** Lake (Still) **W. Size:** 2 Acres.
Location: Nr. Rd: A6024 to Holmbridge; **Main Rd:** A616 Woodhead Road to Holmfirth.
Ref: FH0562

BOTTOMS RESERVOIR

Bottoms Reservoir, Langley, Macclesfield, **CHESHIRE**, SK22, **England**.
Contact/s: Mr D Blackburn (Secretary), Woodhead Rd, Tintwistle, Hyde, Cheshire, SK14 7HS.
(T) 01457 864566
Mr Peter Sharples (Conservation, Access and Recreation Manager), North West Water Ltd, Woodhead Rd, Tintwistle, Hadfield via Hyde, SK14 7HR.
(T) 01457 864187
Profile: FT: Coarse; **WN:** Bottoms; **WT:** Reservoir (Still); **F. Size:** 10 Acres; **W. Size:** 5 Acres. **Location: Nr. Rd:** Clarke Lane; **Main Rd:** A52; **Rail:** Macclesfield.
Ref: FH0563

BOUGH BEECH RESERVOIR

Bough Beech Reservoir, Honeycroft Farm, Three Elm Lane, Golden Green, Tonbridge, **KENT**, TN11 0BS, **England**.
Contact/s: Mr Ken Crow, Honey Croft Lane, 3 Elm Lane, Golden Green, Tonbridge, TN11 0BS.
(T) 01732 851544
Profile: FT: Combination; **WN:** Bough Beech; **WT:** Reservoir (Still) **W. Size:** 280 Acres.
Location: Main Rd: A21, A26; **Rail:** Chiddingstone.
Ref: FH0564

BOULTHAM PARK LAKE

Boultham Park Lake, Rookery Lane, Lincoln, **LINCOLNSHIRE**, LN, **England**.
Contact/s: Mr Colin Parker (Secretary), Lincoln and District Angling Association, 4 Pottergate Cl, Waddington, Lincoln, LN5 9LY.
(T) 01522 720777
Mr Frank Butler (Chairman).
(T) 01522 534174
Profile: FT: Coarse; **WN:** Boultham Park; **WT:** Lake (Still) **W. Size:** 4 Acres. **Location: Nr. Rd:** Rookery Lane; **Main Rd:** A1434 or A46; **Rail:** Lincoln.
Ref: FH0565

BOUNDARY WATER PARK

Boundary Water Park, Holmes Chapel, Knutsford, **CHESHIRE**, WA16, **England**.
Contact/s: Mr Stewart Godber, 38 Edenfield Rd, Mobberley, Knutsford, Cheshire, WA16 7HE.
(T) 01565 872582
Profile: FT: Coarse; **WN:** Boundary; **WT:** Lake (Still) **W. Size:** 16 Acres. **Location: Nr. Rd:** Homles Chapel north to Knutsford; **Main Rd:** A50. **£Fr=**
Ref: FH0566

BOURTON FISHERIES

Bourton Fisheries, Manor Farm, 2 Glynswood Rd, Buckingham, **BUCKINGHAMSHIRE**, MK18 1JF, **England**.
Contact/s: Mr Stewart Martin (Secretary).
(T) 01280 817107 **(F)** 01280 817107
(E) stewartm@exl.co.uk
Profile: FT: Coarse; **WN:** Upper Great Ouse; **WT:** River (Moving) **W. Size:** 3500 Metres.
Location: Nr. Rd: Buckingham to Deanshanger; **Main Rd:** A422; **Rail:** Milton Keynes.
Ref: FH0567

BOURTON-ON-THE-WATER PIT NO1

Bourton-On-The-Water Gravel Pit No1, Rissington Rd, Bourton-on-the-Water, Cheltenham, **GLOUCESTERSHIRE**, GL54 2BN, **England**.
(W) www.macs-tackle.co.uk
Contact/s: Mr Bill McKenzie (Club Secretary), Mac's Tackle, Unit 1 The Industrial Estate, Bourton-On-The-Water, Gloucestershire.
(T) 01451 822207
(E) williampmac@netscapeonline.co.uk
Mr Malcolm Smth (Match Secretary), 2 Ward Rd, Northleach, Near Cheltenham, Gloucestershire, GL54 3RL.
(T) 01451 860173 **(M)** 07760 101083
Profile: FT: Coarse; **WN:** Bourton-On-The-Water No1; **WT:** Gravel Pit (Still) **W. Size:** 12 Acres. **Location: Nr. Rd:** Rissington Road; **Main Rd:** A429; **Rail:** Moreton In Marsh.
Ref: FH0568

BOVINGTON MERE 1

Bovington 1, Wickham Bishop Rd, Hatfield Peverel, Chelmsford, **ESSEX**, **England**.
(W) www.c-a-p-s.co.uk
Contact/s: Mr Paul Masters (Secretary), CAPS Membership, 17 Azalea Court, Sycamore Rd, Colchester Essex, CO4 3NU.
(T) 01376 512255
(E) secretary@c-a-p-s.co.uk
Profile: FT: Coarse; **WN:** Bovington 1; **WT:** Gravel Pit (Still); **F. Size:** 10 Acres; **W. Size:** 3 Acres. **Location: Nr. Rd:** Wickham Bishop Road; **Main Rd:** A12; **Rail:** Hatfield Peverel.
Ref: FH0569

BOVINGTON MERE 2

Bovington 2, Wickham Bishop Rd, Hatfield Peverel, Chelmsford, **ESSEX**, **England**.
(W) www.c-a-p-s.co.uk
Contact/s: Mr Paul Masters (Secretary), CAPS Membership, 17 Azalea Court, Sycamore Rd, Colchester Essex, CO4 3NU.
(T) 01376 512255
(E) secretary@c-a-p-s.co.uk
Profile: FT: Coarse; **WN:** Bovington 2; **WT:** Gravel Pit (Still); **F. Size:** 10 Acres; **W. Size:** 5 Acres. **Location: Nr. Rd:** Wickham Bishop Road; **Main Rd:** A12; **Rail:** Hatfield Peverel.
Ref: FH0570

BOWDEN SPRINGS FISHERY

Bowden Springs Fishery, Caribber Mill, Linlithgow, **LOTHIAN (WEST)**, EH49, **Scotland**.
Contact/s: **Mr Meiry Henderson**.
(T) 01506 847269
Mr Patrick Forsyth (Fishery Manager).
(T) 01506 847269
Profile: **FT:** Game; **WN:** Bowden Springs Fishery; **WT:** Reservoir (Still).
Ref: FH0571

BOWKER LAKES

Bowker Lakes, Crumpsall, Manchester, **MANCHESTER (GREATER)**, M, **England**.
Profile: **FT:** Coarse; **WN:** Bowker; **WT:** Lake (Still). Location: **Main Rd:** A665 North of Manchester.
Ref: FH0572

BOWLERS CANAL

Bowlers Canal, Olney, **BUCKINGHAMSHIRE**, MK46, **England**.
Contact/s: **Mr Kv Osborne** (Secretary), Milton Keynes Angling Association, 11 Gilpin Way, Olney, Buckinghamshire, MK46 4DN.
(T) 01234 713144
Profile: **FT:** Coarse; **WN:** Bowlers; **WT:** Canal (Still).
Ref: FH0573

BOWMANS LAKES

Bowmans Lakes, Bowmansgreen Farm, London Colney, St Albans, **HERTFORDSHIRE**, AL2, **England**.
Contact/s: **Mr Ben Tucker** (Manager), 10-11 Pleasant Pl, West Hyde, Rickmansworth, Hertfordshire, WD3 2XZ.
(T) 01895 824455 **(M)** 07973 453711
Profile: **FT:** Coarse; **WN:** Bowmans Lakes; **WT:** Gravel Pit (Still); **F. Size:** 60 Acres; **W. Size:** 42 Acres. Location: **Nr. Rd:** Coursers Road, A414; **Main Rd:** M25, junction 22,; **Rail:** Radlett.
Ref: FH0574

BOWOOD LAKE

Bowood Lake, Bowood Estate, Calne, **WILTSHIRE**, SN11 0LZ, **England**.
Contact/s: **Mrs Christine Jennings** (Fishery Manager).
(T) 01249 812102
Profile: **FT:** Coarse; **WN:** Bowood; **WT:** Lake (Still). Location: **Main Rd:** A4.
Ref: FH0575

BOWYERS WATER

Bowyers Water, Trinity Lane, Waltham Cross, **HERTFORDSHIRE**, EN, **England**.
Contact/s: Information Officer, Lee Valley Park Information Ctre, Abbey Gardens, Waltham Abbey, Essex, EN9 1XQ.
(T) 01992 702200
Ms Krizim Seltham (Angling Manager), Lee Valley Regional Park Authority, Myddleton House, Bulls Cross, Enfield, EN2 9HG.
(T) 01992 709832
(E) garysmith@leevalleypark.org.uk
Profile: **FT:** Coarse; **WN:** Bowyers Water; **WT:** Gravel Pit (Still) **W. Size:** 35 Acres. Location: **Nr. Rd:** B176; **Main Rd:** A10, M25 junction 25; **Rail:** Cheshunt.
Ref: FH0576

BOXERS LAKE

Boxers Lake, Lonsdale Drive, Enfield, London, **LONDON (GREATER)**, EN2, **England**.
Contact/s: **Mr Ron Sears** (Head Bailiff), 37 Rowantree Rd, Enfield, Middlesex, EN2 8PY.
(T) 020 83664538
Mrs Sue Davey (Fishery Manager).
(T) 020 83516717
Profile: **FT:** Coarse; **WN:** Boxers; **WT:** Lake (Still) **W. Size:** 4 Acres. Location: **Nr. Rd:** Bramley Road; **Main Rd:** A110; **Rail:** Enfield Chase.
Ref: FH0577

BOXMOOR TROUT FISHERY

Boxmoor Trout Fishery, 81 Marlowes, Hemel Hempstead, **HERTFORDSHIRE**, HP, **England**.
Contact/s: **Mr R Hands**, 23 Sebright Rd, Boxmoor, Hemel Hempstead.
(T) 01442 393381
Profile: **FT:** Game; **WN:** Boxmoor Trout Fishery; **WT:** Lake (Still) **W. Size:** 3 Acres.
Ref: FH0578

BOYLE (RIVER)

River Boyle, Boyle, **COUNTY ROSCOMMON**, **Ireland**.
Contact/s: Manager, Boyle Tourist Office, King House, Boyle, County Roscommon, Ireland.
(T) 079 62145
Mr Jas Cogan (Secretary), Kilcolman Rd, Ballaghaderren, County Roscommon, Ireland.
(T) 090 760077
Profile: **FT:** Combination; **WN:** Boyle; **WT:** River (Moving).
Ref: FH0579

BOYNE (RIVER)

River Boyne, Oldbridge, Drogheda, **COUNTY LOUTH**, **Ireland**.
Contact/s: **Mr John Murphy** (Secretary).
(T) 077 1034078
Profile: **FT:** Game; **WN:** Boyne; **WT:** River (Moving).
Ref: FH0580

BOYNE (RIVER)

River Boyne, Navan, **COUNTY MEATH**, **Ireland**.
Contact/s: Manager, Sportsden, Trimgate St, Navan, County Meath, Ireland.
(T) 046 21130
Profile: **FT:** Game; **WN:** Boyne; **WT:** River (Moving) **W. Size:** 16000 Metres.
Ref: FH0581

BOYNE (RIVER)

River Boyne, Slane, **COUNTY MEATH**, **Ireland**.
Contact/s: **Mr Ray Foster** (Secretary).
(T) 01 8315406
Profile: **FT:** Game; **WN:** Boyne; **WT:** River (Moving).
Ref: FH0582

BOYNE (RIVER)

River Boyne, Kells, **COUNTY MEATH**, **Ireland**.
Contact/s: **Mr John Flynn** (Secretary), Kells Angling Association, Old School House, Kells, County Meath, Ireland.
Mr Tom Murray (Manager), Shooting and Fishing Shop, Carrick St, Kells, County Meath, Ireland.
Profile: **FT:** Game; **WN:** Boyne; **WT:** River (Moving) **W. Size:** 24000 Metres.
Ref: FH0583

BRAAN (RIVER)

River Braan, Dunkeld, **PERTH AND KINROSS**, PH8, **Scotland**.
Contact/s: **Mr Archie Steele** (Secretary), Dunkeld and Birnam Angling Association, 21 Willow Bank, Birnam, Perth and Kinross.
(T) 01350 727428
Profile: **FT:** Game; **WN:** Braan; **WT:** River (Moving) **W. Size:** 19200 Metres. Location: **Nr. Rd:** A822; **Main Rd:** A9; **Rail:** Birnam.
Ref: FH0584

BRACK LOCH

Brack Loch, Dalry, Castle Douglas, **DUMFRIES AND GALLOWAY**, DG7, **Scotland**.
Contact/s: **Mr Alan Decent** (Secretary), Milton Park Hotel, Dalry, Castle Douglas, Dumfries and Galloway, DG7 3SR.
(T) 01644 430286
Profile: **FT:** Game; **WN:** Brack; **WT:** Loch (Still). Location: **Main Rd:** A702.
Ref: FH0585

BRACKHILL LAKE

Brackhill Lake, Earith, Huntingdon, **CAMBRIDGESHIRE**, PE17, **England**.
Profile: **FT:** Coarse; **WN:** Brackhill Lake; **WT:** Gravel Pit (Still).
Ref: FH0586

BRADFORD RESERVOIR

Bradford Reservoir, Melville St, Burnden, Bolton, **LANCASHIRE**, BL, **England**.
Contact/s: **Mr Terence A McKee** (Secretary), Bolton and District Angling Association, 1 Lever Edge Lane, Bolton, Lancashire, BL3 3BU.
(T) 01204 393726
Profile: **FT:** Coarse; **WN:** Bradford; **WT:** Reservoir (Still) **W. Size:** 3 Acres. Location: **Nr. Rd:** Melville Street; **Main Rd:** B6536.
Ref: FH0587

BRADING LAKE

Brading Lake, Brading, Sandown, **ISLE OF WIGHT**, PO36, **England**.
Contact/s: **Mr Graham Redfern**.
(T) 01983 406132 **(F)** 01983 408923
Profile: **FT:** Coarse; **WN:** Brading; **WT:** Lake (Still).
Ref: FH0588

BRADLEYS PIT

Bradleys Pit, South Cerney, Cirencester, **GLOUCESTERSHIRE**, GL7, **England**.
Profile: **FT:** Coarse; **WN:** Bradleys; **WT:** Gravel Pit (Still) **W. Size:** 115 Acres. Location: **Main Rd:** A417 or A429.
Ref: FH0589

BRADMOOR LAKES

Bradmoor Lakes, Narborough, King's Lynn, **NORFOLK**, PE32, **England**.
Profile: **FT:** Coarse; **WN:** Bradmoor; **WT:** Lake (Still).
Ref: FH0590

BRADSHAW HALL FISHERIES

Bradshaw Hall Fisheries, Bradshaw Hall Fold, Bradshaw Rd, Bolton, **LANCASHIRE**, BL2 4JH, **England**.
Contact/s: **Mr John Kelly** (Owner).
(T) 01204 307197 **(F)** 01204 303515
Profile: **FT:** Coarse; **WN:** Bradshaw Hall Fisheries; **WT:** Reservoir (Still) **W. Size:** 3 Acres. Location: **Nr. Rd:** Bradshaw Hall Road; **Main Rd:** A676 from Bolton to Burnley.
Ref: FH0591

BRAES SALMON STATION

Braes Salmon Station, Camustinivaig, Portree, **HIGHLAND**, IV51 9LQ, **Scotland**.
Contact/s: Fishery Manager.
(T) 01478 650318
Profile: **FT:** Game; **WN:** Braes Salmon Station; **WT:** River (Moving).
Ref: FH0592

BRAFFERTON COARSE FISHERY

Brafferton Coarse Fishery, Boroughbridge Rd, Helperby, York, **YORKSHIRE (NORTH)**, YO61 2PD, **England**.
Contact/s: **Mr Mark Faulkner**.
(T) 01423 360402 **(F)** 01423 360402 **(M)** 07710 784016
Profile: **FT:** Coarse; **WN:** Brafferton Pond; **WT:** Lake (Still) **W. Size:** 5 Acres. Location: **Nr. Rd:** Boroughbridge Road; **Main Rd:** A19; **Rail:** Thirsk.
Ref: FH0593

BRAGGS WOOD TROUT FISHERY

Braggs Wood Trout Fishery, Braggs Wood Water, Braggs Hill, Boynton, Launceston, **CORNWALL**, PL15 9RG, **England**.
Contact/s: **Mr Peter Horrell** (Manager).
(T) 01566 776474
Profile: **FT:** Game; **WN:** Braggs Wood; **WT:** Lake (Still) **W. Size:** 1 Acre. Location: **Nr. Rd:** Launceston to Holsworthy.
Ref: FH0594

BRAID (RIVER)

River Braid, Ballymena, **COUNTY ANTRIM**, BT42, **Northern Ireland**.
Contact/s: Manager, McNeill's Hardware, Main St, Broughshane, Ballymena, County Antrim.

(T) 028 2561629
Mr Billy Erwin, Whinsmoor Park, Broughshane, Ballymena, County Antrim.
(T) 028 25861433
Mr Peter Morgan, 5 Ashfield, Broughshane, Ballymena, County Antrim.
(T) 028 25861187
Mr Stephen Coulter, 50 The Knockans, Broughshane, Ballymena, County Antrim, BT43 7LQ.
(T) 028 25861616
Profile: **FT:** Game; **WN:** Braid; **WT:** River (Moving) **W. Size:** 14400 Metres.
Ref: FH0595

BRAKE MILL POOL

Brake Mill Pool, Stakenbridge Lane, Hagley, Worcester, **WORCESTERSHIRE**, WR, **England**.
Contact/s: **Mr Mal Storey**, Mal Storey Angling Ctre, 129 Sutton Rd, Kidderminster, Worcestershire, DY11 6QR.
(T) 01562 745221
Profile: **FT:** Coarse; **WN:** Brake Mill; **WT:** Lake (Still) **W. Size:** 2 Acres. **Location:** **Nr. Rd:** Birmingham to Kidderminster (A456).
Ref: FH0596

BRAMCOTE MAINS FISHERY

Bramcote Mains Fishery, Bulkington, Bedworth, **WARWICKSHIRE**, CV12, **England**.
Contact/s: Manager, Saxmundham Angling Ctre, Rear of Market Pl, Saxmundham, Suffolk, IP17 1AH.
(T) 01728 603443
Mr David Elgin (Manager).
(T) 01455 220441
Profile: **FT:** Coarse; **WN:** Bramcote Mains Fishery; **WT:** Lake (Still). **Location:** **Nr. Rd:** B4109; **Main Rd:** M69.
Ref: FH0597

BRAMPTON CANAL

Brampton Canal, Brampton, Wombwell, Barnsley, **YORKSHIRE (SOUTH)**, **England**.
Contact/s: **Mr Tony Eaton** (Club Secretary), 60 Walton St, Gawber, Barnsley, S75 2PD.
(T) 01226 203090 (M) 07979 970201
Profile: **FT:** Coarse; **WN:** Brampton; **WT:** Canal (Still). **Location:** **Nr. Rd:** A633; **Rail:** Wombwell.
Ref: FH0598

BRANDES BURTON 3 AND 4

Brandes Burton 3 And 4, Brandesburton, Hull, **HUMBERSIDE**, HU, **England**.
Contact/s: **Mr Dave Harold** (Fisheries Information Officer), 33 Jipdane Orchard Park, Hull, Yorkshire (East), HU6 9EE.
(T) 01428 809832
Profile: **FT:** Coarse; **WN:** Brandes Burton; **WT:** Lake (Still) **W. Size:** 8 Acres. **Location:** **Nr. Rd:** A165; **Main Rd:** A1035.
Ref: FH0599

BRANDESBURTON

Brandesburton, Hempholme Lane, Brandesburton, Driffield, **HUMBERSIDE**, YO25, **England**.
Contact/s: **Mr Bill Brame** (Secretary), Hull and District Angler's Association, PO Box 188, Hull, HU9 1AN.
Mr Paul Caygill (Secretary), Hull and District Anglers Association, 17 Linley Cl, Leven, Beverley, HU17 5NP.
(T) 01964 542677
Profile: **FT:** Coarse; **WN:** Brandesburton No.2; **WT:** Lake (Still); **F. Size:** 12 Acres; **W. Size:** 11 Acres. **Location:** **Nr. Rd:** Hempholme Lane; **Main Rd:** A165, A1035.
Ref: FH0600

BRANSFORD GAME FISHERY

Bransford Game Fishery, Hill End Farm, Station Rd, Bransford, Worcester, **WORCESTERSHIRE**, WR6 5JJ, **England**.
Contact/s: **Mr Ron Taylor**.
(T) 01905 830548
Profile: **FT:** Game; **WN:** Bransford Game Fishery; **WT:** Combination (Still & Moving) **W. Size:** 4 Acres. **Location:** **Nr. Rd:** Station Road; **Main Rd:** A449; **Rail:** Malvern Link.
Ref: FH0601

BRANTRY LOUGH

Brantry Lough, Benburb, Dungannon, **COUNTY TYRONE**, BT71 7, **Northern Ireland**.
Contact/s: **Mrs Liz Salter** (Manager), Aughnacloy Development Association, The McCreedy Mill Centre, Aughnacloy, County Tyrone, BT69 6AL.
(T) 028 85557002
Profile: **FT:** Game; **WN:** Brantry; **WT:** Lough (Still) **W. Size:** 60 Acres. **Location:** **Nr. Rd:** B45; **Main Rd:** B128.
Ref: FH0602

BRASSIDE POND

Brasside Pond, Newton Hall, Brasside, Durham, **COUNTY DURHAM**, DH, **England**.
Contact/s: **Mr John Hall** (Secretary), 21 Northumbria Pl, Stanley, County Durham, DH9 0UB.
(T) 01207 232401
Mr Steve Wilkinson (Manager).
(T) 0191 3839010
Profile: **FT:** Coarse; **WN:** Brasside Pond; **WT:** Lake (Still) **W. Size:** 4 Acres. **Location:** **Nr. Rd:** Franklin Prison; **Main Rd:** A167 to Chester-le-Street.
Ref: FH0603

BRATHAY (RIVER)

River Brathay, Clappersgate, Ambleside, **CUMBRIA**, LA22, **England**.
Contact/s: **Mr Chris Sodo** (Hon Treasurer), Windermere, Ambleside and District Angling Association, Ecclerigg Court, Ecclerigg, Windermere, LA23 1LQ.
(T) 01539 445083
Mrs Vera Carlson (Owner), Carlsons Fishing Tackle, 64/66 Kirkland, Kendal, Cumbria, LA9 5AP.
(T) 01539 724867
Profile: **FT:** Game; **WN:** Brathay; **WT:** River (Moving). **Location:** **Nr. Rd:** A593; **Main Rd:** A591.
Ref: FH0604

BRAXTED HALL ESTATE

Braxted Hall Estate, Braxted Lane, Witham, **ESSEX**, CM8, **England**.
Contact/s: **Mr Frank Wright** (Membership Secretary), Chelmsford Angling Association, 61 Readers Court, Great Baddow, Chelmsford, CM2 8EX.
(T) 01245 474246or264832
(E) frank@chelmsfordaa.freeserve.co.uk
Profile: **FT:** Coarse; **WN:** Braxted Hall Estate; **WT:** Lake (Still); **F. Size:** 28 Acres; **W. Size:** 14 Acres. **Location:** **Nr. Rd:** Braxted Lane; **Main Rd:** A12 to Witham; **Rail:** Witham.
Ref: FH0605

BRAY LAKE

Bray Lake, Maidenhead, **BERKSHIRE**, SL6, **England**.
Contact/s: **Mr G Hoing**.
(T) 01628 522405
Profile: **FT:** Game; **WN:** Bray; **WT:** Lake (Still).
Ref: FH0606

BRAY LOCK

Bray Lock, Amerden Lane, Bray, Maidenhead, **BERKSHIRE**, SL6 0EE, **England**.
Contact/s: Recreational Manager, The Environment Agency, Kings Meadow Rd, Reading, Berkshire, RG1 8DQ.
(T) 0118 9535000 (F) 0118 9500388
Mr Cheshire (Lock Keeper).
(T) 01628 621650
Profile: **FT:** Combination; **WN:** Bray; **WT:** Lock (Still) **W. Size:** 40 Metres. **Location:** **Nr. Rd:** Amerden Lane; **Main Rd:** A4; **Rail:** Taplow.
Ref: FH0607

BRAYTON POND

Brayton Pond, Home Farm, Brayton, Aspatria, Carlisle, **CUMBRIA**, CA5, **England**.
Contact/s: **Mr R H Ward**.
(T) 01697 320262
Profile: **FT:** Coarse; **WN:** Brayton; **WT:** Pond (Still) **W. Size:** 8 Acres. **Location:** **Main Rd:** A596.
Ref: FH0608

BREAKAWAY PIT

Breakaway Pit, Melton Brick'kiln Farm, Melton, Woodbridge, **SUFFOLK**, IP12, **England**.
Contact/s: **Mr Norman Bickers** (Owner), Breakaway Tackle, 376 Bramford Rd, Ipswich, Suffolk, IP1 5AY.
(T) 01473 741393 (F) 01473 462482
(E) norman@breakaway-tackle.co.uk
Profile: **FT:** Coarse; **WN:** Breakaway; **WT:** Gravel Pit (Still) **W. Size:** 5 Acres. **Location:** **Nr. Rd:** A1; **Main Rd:** Claydon interchange.
Ref: FH0609

BREAKWATER PARK

Breakwater Park, Off Newry St, Holyhead, **ISLE OF ANGLESEY**, **Wales**.
Contact/s: **Ray Swales** (Club Secretary), 36 Trem-y-mor, Rhosneiger, Isle of Anglesey, LL64 5QR.
(T) 01407 810136
(E) swales24@hotmail.com
Profile: **FT:** Coarse; **WN:** Breakwater Park; **WT:** Pool (Still); **F. Size:** 2 Acres; **W. Size:** 2 Acres. **Location:** **Nr. Rd:** Newry Road; **Main Rd:** A5 (T); **Rail:** Holyhead.
Ref: FH0610

BREAM HOLE

Bream Hole, Marsh Lane, Nantwich, **CHESHIRE**, CW5, **England**.
Contact/s: Manager, Mohmar Bait Farm, Hack Green, Baddington, Nantwich, CW5 8AL.
(T) 01270 627419
Profile: **FT:** Coarse; **WN:** Bream Hole; **WT:** Canal (Still). **Location:** **Main Rd:** A534, Wrexham Road.
Ref: FH0611

BREDONS HARDWICK

Bredons Hardwick, Tewkesbury, **GLOUCESTERSHIRE**, GL20, **England**.
Contact/s: Manager, The Royal Hop Pole Hotel, Church St, Tewesbury, Gloucestershire, GL20 5RT.
(T) 01684 293236
Profile: **FT:** Coarse; **WN:** Bredons Hardwick; **WT:** Gravel Pit (Still) **W. Size:** 10 Acres. **Location:** **Nr. Rd:** A38; **Main Rd:** A46, M5, M50.
Ref: FH0612

BREEDOGE LOUGH

Breedoge Lough, Ballaghaderren, **COUNTY ROSCOMMON**, **Ireland**.
Contact/s: Manager, Boyle Tourist Office, King House, Boyle, County Roscommon, Ireland.
(T) 079 62145
Mr Jas Cogan (Secretary), Kilcolman Rd, Ballaghaderren, County Roscommon, Ireland.
(T) 090 760077
Profile: **FT:** Game; **WN:** Breedoge; **WT:** Lough (Still).
Ref: FH0613

BRENIG RESERVOIR

Brenig Reservoir, Visitor Ctre, Cerrig-Y-Drudion, Corwen, **DENBIGHSHIRE**, LL21 9TT, **Wales**.
Contact/s: **Mr Dwr Cymrn**, Llyn Brenig Visitors Ctre, Cerrigdrudion, Corwen, Conwy, LL21 9TT.
(T) 01490 420463 (F) 01490 420694
(E) llyn.brenig@hyder.com
Profile: **FT:** Game; **WN:** Brenig; **WT:** Reservoir (Still).
Ref: FH0614

BRENKLEY POND

Brenkley Pond, Newcastle Upon Tyne, **TYNE AND WEAR**, NE, **England**.
Contact/s: Alan.

(T) 01670 827831
Mr Albert Robson (Membership Secretary), Wansbeck and Cramlington Angling Club, 10 Second Avenue, Ashington, Northumberland, NE63 0BJ.
(T) 01670 819647
Profile: **FT:** Coarse; **WN:** Brenkley; **WT:** Pond (Still).
Ref: FH0615

BRERETON HEATH COUNTRY PARK

Brereton Heath Country Park, Davenport Lane, Davenport, Congleton, **CHESHIRE**, CW12 4SU, **England**.
Profile: **FT:** Coarse; **WN:** Brereton Heath Country Park; **WT:** Gravel Pit (Still) **W. Size:** 14 Acres. **Location:** **Main Rd:** A54.
Ref: FH0616

BRERTON QUARRY

Brerton Quarry, Middlewich, **CHESHIRE**, CW10, **England**.
Contact/s: Secretary.
(T) 01477 534115
Dave, Dave's of Middlewich, Lewin St, Middlewich, Cheshire, CW10 9AX.
(T) 01606 833853 (F) 01606 737469
Profile: **FT:** Coarse; **WN:** Brerton; **WT:** Gravel Pit (Still). **Location:** **Main Rd:** A54.
Ref: FH0617

BRIARCROFT FISHERY

Briarcroft Fishery, Rawcliffe Rd, St Michaels-on-Wyre, Preston, **LANCASHIRE**, PR3 0UH, **England**.
Contact/s: **Mr Ashcroft**.
(T) 01995 679289
Profile: **FT:** Coarse; **WN:** Briarcroft; **WT:** Lake (Still). **Location:** **Nr. Rd:** Rawcliffe Road; **Main Rd:** A586.
Ref: FH0618

BRIARWOOD FISHERY

Briarwood Fishery, Harlington, Ampthill, Bedford, **BEDFORDSHIRE**, MK45, **England**.
Contact/s: Fishery Manager.
Profile: **FT:** Coarse; **WN:** Briarwood Fishery; **WT:** Lake (Still) **W. Size:** 2 Acres. **Location:** **Nr. Rd:** Harlington; **Main Rd:** A5120.
Ref: FH0619

BRICK FARM LAKE

Brick Farm Lake, Windmill Hill, Herstmonceux, Hailsham, **SUSSEX (EAST)**, BN27 4RS, **England**.
Contact/s: **Mr Gary Martin** (Manager).
(T) 01323 832615
Profile: **FT:** Game; **WN:** Brick Farm; **WT:** Clay Pit (Still) **W. Size:** 2 Acres. **Location:** **Nr. Rd:** Windmill Hill; **Main Rd:** A271; **Rail:** Polegate.
Ref: FH0620

BRICKHOUSE FARM FISHERIES

Brickhouse Farm Fisheries, Doddinghurst Rd, Pilgrims Hatch, Brentwood, **ESSEX**, CM15 0SG, **England**.
Contact/s: . **(M)** 07713 952999
Mr Dennis Oliver (Manager).
(T) 01277 261405 (F) 01227 201958
Mr Richard Bennett (Owner).
(T) 07759 875376
Profile: **FT:** Combination; **WN:** Brickhouse Farm Fisheries; **WT:** Lake (Still). **Location:** **Nr. Rd:** Doddinghurst Road; **Main Rd:** M25, junction 28, then A1023.
Ref: FH0621

BRICKYARD FARM LAKE

Brickyard Farm Lake, Brickyard Farm, High St, Amotherby, Malton, **YORKSHIRE (NORTH)**, YO17 6TL, **England**.
Contact/s: **Mr John Jackson** (Secretary).
(T) 01653 693606
Profile: **FT:** Coarse; **WN:** Brickyard; **WT:** Lake (Still) **W. Size:** 4 Acres. **Location:** **Nr. Rd:** B1257 Malton to Barton-le-Street; **Main Rd:** Amotherby.
Ref: FH0622

BRICKYARD FISHERY

Brickyard Fishery, South Rd, South Somercoates, Louth, **LINCOLNSHIRE**, LN11 7PY, **England**.
Contact/s: **Mrs Mary Cartwright** (Owner).
(T) 01507 358331 (F) 01507 358331
Profile: **FT:** Coarse; **WN:** Brickyard Fishery; **WT:** Clay Pit (Still) **W. Size:** 4 Acres. **Location:** **Nr. Rd:** South Road; **Main Rd:** A1031.
Ref: FH0623

BRICKYARD FISHERY

Brickyard Fishery, Hutton Moor, Ripon, **YORKSHIRE (NORTH)**, HG4, **England**.
Contact/s: **Ms Susanne Scawthorn**, Brickyard Cottage, Hutton Moor, Ripon, HG4 5MA.
(T) 01765 640666
Profile: **FT:** Coarse; **WN:** Brickyard Fishery; **WT:** Lake (Still). **Location:** **Main Rd:** A61.
Ref: FH0624

BRICKYARD LAKE

Brickyard Lake, 26 Eastwood Rd, Bexhill-on-Sea, **SUSSEX (EAST)**, TN39 3PS, **England**.
Contact/s: **Mr George Allen** (Owner), Rowallen Fisheries, 26 Eastwood Rd, Bexhill on Sea, Sussex (East), TN39 3PS.
(T) 01424 217239
Profile: **FT:** Coarse; **WN:** Brickyard; **WT:** Lake (Still).
Ref: FH0625

BRICKYARD POND

Brickyard Pond, Broomfleet Village, Brough, **HUMBERSIDE**, HU15, **England**.
Mr Dave Harold (Fisheries Information Officer), 33 Jipdane Orchard Park, Hull, Yorkshire (East), HU6 9EE.
(T) 01482 809832
Profile: **FT:** Coarse; **WN:** Brickyard Pond; **WT:** Lake (Still); **F. Size:** 10 Acres; **W. Size:** 6 Acres. **Location:** **Main Rd:** B1230.
Ref: FH0626

BRICKYARD POND

Brickyard Pond, Buckminster, Grantham, **LINCOLNSHIRE**, NG33, **England**.
Contact/s: Fishery Manager.
(T) 01476 565728
Profile: **FT:** Coarse; **WN:** Brickyard; **WT:** Pond (Still).
Ref: FH0627

BRICKYARD PONDS

Brickyard Ponds, Bolton-upon-Dearne, Rotherham, **YORKSHIRE (SOUTH)**, S63, **England**.
Contact/s: Fishery Manager.
(T) 01709 893131
Profile: **FT:** Coarse; **WN:** Brickyard; **WT:** Pond (Still).
Ref: FH0628

BRIDGE FARM FISHERIES

Bridge Farm Fisheries, Beeston, East Dereham, **NORFOLK**, **England**.
Profile: **FT:** Coarse; **WN:** Bridge Farm Fisheries; **WT:** Lake (Still). **Location:** **Main Rd:** A47; **Rail:** East Dereham.
Ref: FH0629

BRIDGE FARM RESERVOIRS

Bridge Farm Reservoirs, Wickham Market, Woodbridge, **SUFFOLK**, IP, **England**.
Contact/s: Fishery Manager.
(T) 01473 603443
Mr Chris Johnson.
(T) 01473 737671
Mr Dave Smith.
(T) 01473 623228
Profile: **FT:** Coarse; **WN:** Bridge Farm; **WT:** Reservoir (Still). **Location:** **Nr. Rd:** B1078; **Main Rd:** Ipswich, A12 to B1078 to Wickham Market.
Ref: FH0630

BRIDGE INN FISHERY

Bridge Lake, 2 Fakenham Rd, Lenwade, **NORFOLK**, NR9 5SE, **England**.
(W) www.lenwade-bridge.com
Contact/s: **Mr Darren Emmett** (Owner), The Bridge Public House, 2 Fakenham Rd, Lenwade, Norfolk, NR9 5SE.
(T) 01603 872248
(E) redl2000@aol.uk
Mrs Clare Emmett (Owner), The Bridge Public House, 2 Fakenham Rd, Lenwade, Norfolk, NR9 5SE.
(T) 01603 872248
(E) redl2000@aol.uk
Profile: **FT:** Coarse; **WN:** Bridge Lake; **WT:** Gravel Pit (Still); **F. Size:** 5 Acres; **W. Size:** 5 Acres. **Location:** **Nr. Rd:** A1067; **Main Rd:** A1067; **Rail:** Norwich. **£Fr**
Ref: FH0631

BRIDGE OF WEIR

Bridge Of Weir, Bridge Of Weir, **RENFREWSHIRE**, PA11, **Scotland**.
Contact/s: Hon Secretary, Duncans Paper Shop, Main St, Bridge of Weir, Renfrewshire PA11.
Profile: **FT:** Game; **WN:** Bridge of Weir; **WT:** River (Moving).
Ref: FH0632

BRIDGE POOL

Bridge Pool, Patshull Park, Burnhill Green, Wolverhampton, **MIDLANDS (WEST)**, WV, **England**.
Profile: **FT:** Coarse; **WN:** Bridge; **WT:** Pool (Still). **Location:** **Nr. Rd:** Patshull Park; **Main Rd:** Burnhill Green.
Ref: FH0633

BRIDGEWATER CANAL

Bridgewater Canal, Runcorn, **CHESHIRE**, WA, **England**.
Contact/s: **Mr Dave Forbes** (Sceretary), Halton Joint Anglers' Association, 132 Edinburgh Rd, Hough Green, Widnes, WA8 8BB.
(T) 0151 4245594
Profile: **FT:** Coarse; **WN:** Bridgewater; **WT:** Canal (Still) **W. Size:** 11200 Metres. **Location:** **Nr. Rd:** High Street; **Main Rd:** M56 junction 12, A557, B5155; **Rail:** Runcorn. **£Fr**
Ref: FH0634

BRIDGEWATER CANAL

Bridgewater Canal, Dane Rd, Sale, **CHESHIRE**, M33, **England**.
Contact/s: **Mr A G R Brown** (Secretary), Northern Anglers, 10 Dale Rd, Golbourne, Warrington, WA3 3PN.
(T) 01942 726917
Mr Brian Wade, Trafford Angling Supplies, 38 Moss Rd, Stretford, Manchester, M32 0AY.
(T) 0161 8641211
Mr Frank Pennington. **(M)** 07770 652433
Profile: **FT:** Coarse; **WN:** Bridgewater; **WT:** Canal (Still). **Location:** **Nr. Rd:** Dane Road; **Main Rd:** M63, junction 8; **Rail:** Sale.
Ref: FH0635

BRIDGEWATER CANAL

Bridgewater Canal, Moore, Warrington, **CHESHIRE**, WA4, **England**.
Contact/s: **Mr Frank Lythgoe** (Secretary), Warrington Angling Association, 52 Parker St, Warrington, Lancashire.
(T) 01928 716238 (F) 01928 713898
(E) info@warrington-anglers.org.uk
Profile: **FT:** Coarse; **WN:** Bridgewater; **WT:** Canal (Still) **W. Size:** 25600 Metres. **Location:** **Nr. Rd:** Daresbury to Warrington; **Main Rd:** M56, junction 11.
Ref: FH0636

BRIDGEWATER CANAL

Bridgewater Canal, Broadheath Bridge, Statham, Warrington, **CHESHIRE**, WA, **England**.
Contact/s: **Mr Frank Lythgoe** (Secretary), Warrington Angling Association, 52 Parker St, Warrington, Lancashire.
(T) 01928 716238 (F) 01928 713898
(E) info@warrington-anglers.org.uk

Profile: **FT:** Coarse; **WN:** Bridgewater; **WT:** Canal (Still).
Ref: FH0637

BRIDGEWATER CANAL

Bridgewater Canal, Trafford, Manchester, **MANCHESTER (GREATER)**, M26, **England**.
Contact/s: **Mr Brian Wade**, Trafford Angling Supplies, 38 Moss Rd, Stretford, Manchester, M32 0AY.
(T) 0161 8641211
Profile: **FT:** Coarse; **WN:** Bridgewater; **WT:** Canal (Still). **Location:** **Nr. Rd:** Waters Meet to Trafford Road; **Main Rd:** A5063.
Ref: FH0638

BRIDGEWATER CANAL

Bridgewater Canal, Kraft Arm, Stretford, Manchester, **MANCHESTER (GREATER)**, M, **England**.
Contact/s: **Mr Brian Wade**, Trafford Angling Supplies, 38 Moss Rd, Stretford, Manchester, M32 0AY.
(T) 0161 8641211
Profile: **FT:** Coarse; **WN:** Bridgewater; **WT:** Canal (Still).
Ref: FH0639

BRIDGEWATER FISHERY

Bridgewater Fishery, 93 Windmill Rd, Donaghadee, **COUNTY DOWN**, BT21 0NQ, **Northern Ireland**.
Contact/s: Fishery Manager.
(T) 028 91883348
Profile: **FT:** Game; **WN:** Bridgewater Fishery
Ref: FH0640

BRIGHAM (RIVER)

River Brigham, Brigham, Cockermouth, **CUMBRIA**, CA13, **England**.
Profile: **FT:** Coarse; **WN:** Brigham; **WT:** River (Moving).
Ref: FH0641

BRIGHOUSE

Brighouse, Halifax, **YORKSHIRE (WEST)**, HX, **England**.
Contact/s: **Mr D B Arnett**, 49 Templars Way, Bradford.
Mr D Noble (Secretary), Brighouse Angling Association, 1a Church Lane, Brighouse, Yorkshire (West), HD6 1AT.
(T) 01484 717034
Profile: **FT:** Coarse; **WN:** Calder; **WT:** River (Moving) **W. Size:** 22400 Metres.
Ref: FH0642

BRIGHOUSE POOL

Brighouse Pool, Mobberley, Knutsford, **CHESHIRE**, **England**.
(W) www.baymalton-anglingclub.org
Contact/s: **Mr Stewart Godber** (Club Secretary), 38 Edenfield Rd, Mobberley, Cheshire, WA16 7HE.
(T) 01565 872582
Profile: **FT:** Coarse; **WN:** Brighouse; **WT:** Pool (Still); **F. Size:** 1 Acre; **W. Size:** 1 Acre. **Location:** **Main Rd:** B5085; **Rail:** Mobberley Station.
Ref: FH0643

BRIMPTON LAKE

Brimpton Lake, Brimpton Village, Reading, **BERKSHIRE**, RG7, **England**.
Contact/s: **Mr Bill Brown-Lee** (Secretary), Reading and District Angling Association, 47 Calbourne Drive, Calcot, Reading, Berkshire, RG3 7DB.
(T) 0118 9417368
Profile: **FT:** Coarse; **WN:** Brimpton; **WT:** Lake (Still).
Ref: FH0644

BRINSCALL LODGE

Brinscall Lodge, Brinscall, Chorley, **LANCASHIRE**, PR6, **England**.
Contact/s: **Mr Bernard Wren** (Secretary), 1 Belmont Cl, Brinscall, Chorley, Lancashire, PR6 8SX.
(T) 01254 830935
Mr D Hough, 1 Lodge Bank, Brinscall, Chorley, Lancashire.
Profile: **FT:** Coarse; **WN:** Brinscall; **WT:** Lake (Still).
Ref: FH0645

BRISTOL AVON

Avon (Bristol), Swineford, Bristol, BS, **England**.
Contact/s: **Mr Jeff Parker** (Secretary), Bristol, Bath and Wilts Amalgamation, 16 Lansdown View, Kingswood, Bristol, BS15 4AW.
(T) 01179 672977
Profile: **FT:** Coarse; **WN:** Bristol Avon; **WT:** River (Moving).
Ref: FH0646

BRISTOL AVON

Avon (Bristol), Bath, **SOMERSET**, BA, **England**.
(W) www.weststackle.com
Contact/s: **Mr Steve** (Manager), Wests Tackle, 32 Roundstone St, Trowbridge, Wiltshire, BA14 8DE.
(T) 01225 755472 (F) 01225 755472
(E) steve@weststackle.com
Profile: **FT:** Coarse; **WN:** Bristol Avon; **WT:** River (Moving) **W. Size:** 10000 Metres.
Location: **Nr. Rd:** A350; **Main Rd:** A350; **Rail:** Bath.
Ref: FH0647

BRISTOL AVON

Avon (Bristol), Bath, **SOMERSET**, BA, **England**.
(W) www.weststackle.com
Contact/s: **Mr Steve** (Manager), Wests Tackle, 32 Roundstone St, Trowbridge, Wiltshire, BA14 8DE.
(T) 01225 755472 (F) 01225 755472
(E) steve@weststackle.com
Profile: **FT:** Coarse; **WN:** Bristol Avon; **WT:** River (Moving) **W. Size:** 2500 Metres.
Location: **Nr. Rd:** A350; **Main Rd:** A350; **Rail:** Bath.
Ref: FH0648

BRISTOL AVON

Avon (Bristol), Bath, **SOMERSET**, BA3, **England**.
(W) www.weststackle.com
Contact/s: **Mr Steve** (Manager), Wests Tackle, 32 Roundstone St, Trowbridge, Wiltshire, BA14 8DE.
(T) 01225 755472 (F) 01225 755472
(E) steve@weststackle.com
Profile: **FT:** Coarse; **WN:** Bristol Avon; **WT:** River (Moving) **W. Size:** 1000 Metres.
Location: **Nr. Rd:** A350; **Main Rd:** A350; **Rail:** Bath.
Ref: FH0649

BRISTOL AVON

Avon (Bristol), Bradford-on-Avon, **WILTSHIRE**, BA15, **England**.
(W) www.weststackle.com
Contact/s: **Mr Steve** (Manager), Wests Tackle, 32 Roundstone St, Trowbridge, Wiltshire, BA14 8DE.
(T) 01225 755472 (F) 01225 755472
(E) steve@weststackle.com
Profile: **FT:** Coarse; **WN:** Bristol Avon; **WT:** River (Moving) **W. Size:** 5000 Metres.
Location: **Nr. Rd:** A350; **Main Rd:** A350; **Rail:** Bath.
Ref: FH0650

BRISTOL AVON

Avon (Bristol), Holt To Melksham, Melksham, **WILTSHIRE**, SN12, **England**.
(W) www.weststackle.com
Contact/s: **Mr R Edwards** (Secretary), Avon Angling Club, 56 Addison Rd, Melksham, Wiltshire, SN12 8DR.
(T) 01225 763835
Mr Steve Ince (Manager), Wests Tackle, 32 Roundstone St, Trowbridge, Wiltshire, BA14 8DE.
(T) 01225 755472 (F) 01225 755472
(E) steve@weststackle.com
Profile: **FT:** Coarse; **WN:** Bristol Avon; **WT:** River (Moving) **W. Size:** 3200 Metres.
Location: **Main Rd:** B3107.
Ref: FH0651

BRISTOL AVON

Avon (Bristol), Christian Malford, Chippenham, **WILTSHIRE**, SN15, **England**.
Profile: **FT:** Coarse; **WN:** Avon; **WT:** River (Moving).
Ref: FH0652

BRISTOL AVON

Avon (Bristol), Queenfield Farm, Laycock, Chippenham, **WILTSHIRE**, SN15, **England**.
Contact/s: **Mr Jeff Parker** (Secretary), Bristol, Bath and Wilts Amalgamation, 16 Lansdown View, Kingswood, Bristol, BS15 4AW.
(T) 01179 672977
Profile: **FT:** Coarse; **WN:** Bristol Avon; **WT:** River (Moving).
Ref: FH0653

BRISTOL AVON

Avon (Bristol), Seagry Mill, Seagry, Chippenham, **WILTSHIRE**, SN15, **England**.
Profile: **FT:** Coarse; **WN:** Avon; **WT:** River (Moving).
Ref: FH0654

BRISTOL DOCKS

Bristol Docks, Bristol, BS, **England**.
Contact/s: Manager, Avon Angling Ctre, 348 Whitewell Rd, Bristol, Somerset, BS5 7BP.
(T) 01179 517250
Mr Bob Taylor (Secretary), 27 Flaxpits Lane, Winterbourne, Bristol, BS36 1LA.
(T) 01454 773990
Profile: **FT:** Coarse; **WN:** Bristol Docks; **WT:** Combination (Still) **W. Size:** 19200 Metres.
Ref: FH0655

BRIT (RIVER)

River Brit, Bridport, **DORSET**, DT6, **England**.
Contact/s: Manager, Civil Service Sports Council, 7-8 Buckingham Pl, Bellfield Rd, High Wycombe, HP13 5HW.
Profile: **FT:** Game; **WN:** Brit; **WT:** River (Moving).
Ref: FH0656

BRITFORD FISHERY

Britford Fishery, Humberts, 8 Rollestone St, Britford, Salisbury, **WILTSHIRE**, SP5, **England**.
Profile: **FT:** Combination; **WN:** Avon; **WT:** Lake (Still).
Ref: FH0657

BRITTENS POND

Brittens Pond, Salt Box Road, Jacobs Well, Guildford, **SURREY**, GU3, **England**.
Contact/s: **Mr Alan Tanner**.
(T) 01483 575801
Profile: **FT:** Coarse; **WN:** Brittens; **WT:** Pond (Still) **W. Size:** 3 Acres. **Location:** **Nr. Rd:** Salt Box Road; **Main Rd:** A322, Lightwater to Guilford.
Ref: FH0658

BRITTON COURT FARM

Britton Court Farm, Hackington Rd, Tyler Hill, Canterbury, **KENT**, CT2 9NG, **England**.
Contact/s: **Mr David Laugharne** (Owner).
(T) 01227 760574 o r764555
Profile: **FT:** Game; **WN:** Britton Court Farm; **WT:** Lake (Still) **W. Size:** 4 Acres. **Location:** **Nr. Rd:** Tyler Hill; **Main Rd:** Chesterfield Road to Whitstable and Tankerton.
Ref: FH0659

BRO TYWI FISHERIES

Bro Tywi Fisheries, Byrbwll Farm, Croesyceiliog, Carmarthen, **CARMARTHENSHIRE**, SA32 8DR, **Wales**.
Contact/s: **Mr Albert Rees** (Owner).
(T) 01267 235687
Profile: **FT:** Combination; **WN:** Bro Tywi Fisheries; **WT:** Reservoir (Still). **Location:** **Nr. Rd:** Bribwell Farm.
Ref: FH0660

BROAD ACRES LAKE

Broad Acres, Forest Lane, Hanbury, Bromsgrove, **WORCESTERSHIRE**, B60, **England**.
Contact/s: Fishery Manager.
(T) 01527 821880
Profile: **FT:** Coarse; **WN:** Broad Acres; **WT:** Lake (Still) **W. Size:** 3 Acres. **Location:** **Nr. Rd:** B4091 to Hanbury; **Main Rd:** A38.
Ref: FH0661

BROAD COLNEY LAKES

Broad Colney Lakes, Shenley Lane, London Colney, St Albans, **HERTFORDSHIRE**, AL2, **England**.
(W) www.badac.co.uk
Contact/s: **Mr D Porter** (Secretary), Barnet and District Angling Club, 72 Rivington Cres, Mill Hill, London, NW7 2LF.
(T) 020 84401303
Profile: **FT:** Coarse; **WN:** Broad Colney; **WT:** Lake (Still) **W. Size:** 30 Acres. **Location:** **Nr. Rd:** Shenley Lane.
Ref: FH0662

BROAD GREEN AND TUFNELL MERE

Broad Green And Tufnell Mere, Larks Lane, Broads Green, Great Waltham, Chelmsford, **ESSEX**, CM3, **England**.
(W) www.chelmsfordaa.freeserve.co.uk
Contact/s: **Mr Frank Wright** (Membership Secretary), Chelmsford Angling Association, 61 Readers Court, Great Baddow, Chelmsford, CM2 8EX.
(T) 01245 474246or264832
(E) frank@chelmsfordaa.freeserve.co.uk
Profile: **FT:** Coarse; **WN:** Broad Green and Tufnell Mere; **WT:** Combination (Still); **F. Size:** 19 Acres; **W. Size:** 18 Acres. **Location:** **Nr. Rd:** Larks Lane; **Main Rd:** B1008; **Rail:** Chelmsford.
Ref: FH0663

BROADLANDS LAKES

Broadlands Lakes, Ringwood, **HAMPSHIRE**, **England**.
Contact/s: **Mr Gerry Or Steve** (Owner).
(T) 023 80869881
Profile: **FT:** Coarse; **WN:** Broadlands; **WT:** Lake (Still); **F. Size:** 86 Acres; **W. Size:** 28 Acres. **Location:** **Nr. Rd:** Hill Street; **Main Rd:** A36; **Rail:** Totton.
Ref: FH0664

BROADLANDS MAIN LAKE

Broadlands Main Lake, Romsey, **HAMPSHIRE**, SO51, **England**.
Contact/s: **Mr Steve Whitfield**.
(T) 023 80869881
Profile: **FT:** Coarse; **WN:** Broadlands; **WT:** Lake (Still). **Location:** **Nr. Rd:** Hill Street; **Main Rd:** A36.
Ref: FH0665

BROADWATER LAKE

Broadwater Lake, Godalming, **SURREY**, GU, **England**.
Contact/s: **A Johnson**, 86 Peper Harrow Rd, Godalming, Surrey.
Profile: **FT:** Coarse; **WN:** Broadwater; **WT:** Lake (Still).
Ref: FH0666

BROCKAMIN POOLS

Brockamin Pools, Brockamin, Worcester, **WORCESTERSHIRE**, WR2, **England**.
Contact/s: **Mr Dave Beresford** (Manager), Allans Fishing Tackle, 26-30 Malvern Rd, Worcester, Worcestershire, WR2 4LG.
(T) 01905 422407 **(F)** 01905 422107
Profile: **FT:** Coarse; **WN:** Brockamin; **WT:** Pool (Still). **Location:** **Nr. Rd:** Dingle road; **Main Rd:** A4103.
Ref: FH0667

BROCKHILL COUNTRY PARK

Brockhill Country Park, Saltwood, Hythe, **KENT**, CT21, **England**.
Contact/s: Fishery Manager.
(T) 01303 262013
Profile: **FT:** Coarse; **WN:** Brockhill Country Park; **WT:** Lake (Still).
Ref: FH0668

BROCKHILL FARM TROUT POOLS

Brockhill Farm Trout Pools, Brockhill Lane, Tardebigge, Redditch, **WORCESTERSHIRE**, B97 6RB, **England**.
Contact/s: **Mr Keith Tolley** (Manager).
(T) 01527 69953
Profile: **FT:** Game; **WN:** Brockhill Farm Trout Pools; **WT:** Lake (Still) **W. Size:** 3 Acres.
Ref: FH0669

BROCKHURST MOAT

Brockhurst Moat, Portsmouth, **HAMPSHIRE**, PO2, **England**.
Contact/s: **Mr R G Snook** (Secretary), 86 Carnarvon Rd, Copnor, Portsmouth, Hampshire, PO2 7NL.
(T) 023 92662986
Profile: **FT:** Coarse; **WN:** Brockhurst; **WT:** Moat (Still). **Location:** **Nr. Rd:** Carnarvon Road.
Ref: FH0670

BROCKTON GRANGE

Brockton Grange, Brockton, Much Wenlock, **SHROPSHIRE**, TF13, **England**.
Profile: **FT:** Coarse; **WN:** Brockton Grange; **WT:** Lake (Still). **Location:** **Nr. Rd:** Brockton.
Ref: FH0671

BROGBOROUGH NO.1 PIT

Brogborough No.1 Pit, Brogborough, Bedford, **BEDFORDSHIRE**, MK43, **England**.
Contact/s: **Mr Paul Woodward** (Secretary).
(T) 01525 405385
Mr Steve Barnett (Secretary).
(T) 01525 876993
Profile: **FT:** Coarse; **WN:** Brogborough No.1; **WT:** Gravel Pit (Still) **W. Size:** 350 Acres.
Ref: FH0672

BROHLY (LOUGH)

Lough Brohly, Ballina, **COUNTY MAYO**, **Ireland**.
Contact/s: Angling Officer, North Western Regional Fisheries Board, Ardnaree House, Abbey St, Ballina, County Mayo.
(T) 096 22623 **(F)** 096 70543
Profile: **FT:** Game; **WN:** Brohly; **WT:** Lough (Still) **W. Size:** 820 Acres.
Ref: FH0673

BROKEN BREA FISHERY

Broken Brea, Easby, Richmond, **YORKSHIRE (NORTH)**, DL10 7EY, **England**.
(W) www.brokenbrea.com
Contact/s: **Mr Chris Keay** (Manager). **(F)** 01748 850619
Mr Clive Simpson (Accommodation Manager).
(T) 01748 825647 **(F)** 01748 850619
Profile: **FT:** Coarse; **WN:** Broken Brea; **WT:** Lake (Still); **F. Size:** 12 Acres; **W. Size:** 8 Acres. **Location:** **Nr. Rd:** B6217; **Main Rd:** Brompton-on-Swale to Richmond; **Rail:** Darlington.
Ref: FH0674

BRON EIFION FISHERIES

Bron Eifion Fisheries, Criccieth, Pwllheli, **GWYNEDD**, LL53, **Wales**.
Contact/s: Manager, Central Buildings, High St, Porthmadog, Gwynedd, LL49 9LR.
(T) 01766 512464or523287
Profile: **FT:** Game; **WN:** Bron Eifion Fisheries; **WT:** Lake (Still); **F. Size:** 40 Acres; **W. Size:** 6 Acres.
Ref: FH0675

BROOK BANK POOL

Brook Bank Pool, Goostrey, Holmes Chapel, **CHESHIRE**, **England**.
(W) www.baymalton-anglingclub.org
Contact/s: **Mr Stewart Godber** (Club Secretary), 38 Edenfield Rd, Mobberley, Cheshire, WA16 7HE.
(T) 01565 872582
Profile: **FT:** Coarse; **WN:** Brook Bank Pool; **WT:** Pool (Still); **F. Size:** 2 Acres; **W. Size:** 1 Acre. **Location:** **Main Rd:** A535; **Rail:** Goostrey Station.
Ref: FH0676

BROOK FARM TROUT FISHERY

Brook Farm Trout Fishery, Brook Farm, Cranham, Gloucester, **GLOUCESTERSHIRE**, GL4 8HZ, **England**.
Contact/s: **Mr Peter Turnham**.
(T) 01452 813162
Ms Carol Turnham (Owner).
(T) 01452 813162 **(F)** 01452 813075
Profile: **FT:** Game; **WN:** Brook Farm Trout Fishery; **WT:** Lake (Still). **Location:** **Main Rd:** A46; **Rail:** Gloucester.
Ref: FH0677

BROOK MEADOW FISHERY

Brook Meadow Fishery, Sibbertoft, Market Harborough, **LEICESTERSHIRE**, LE16 9UJ, **England**.
Contact/s: **Mr M Hart**.
(T) 01858 880886 **(F)** 01858 880886
Mrs J Hart (Owner).
(T) 01858 882886
Profile: **FT:** Coarse; **WN:** Brook Meadow Fishery; **WT:** Lake (Still). **Location:** **Nr. Rd:** Sibbertoft.
Ref: FH0678

BROOKFIELD FISHERY

Brookfield Fishery, Ynsybwl, Pontypridd, **RHONDDA CYNON TAFF**, CF37 3NR, **Wales**.
Contact/s: **Mr Brian Davies** (Fishery Manager).
(T) 01443 790388
Profile: **FT:** Game; **WN:** Brookfield Fishery; **WT:** Lake (Still).
Ref: FH0679

BROOKFIELD LAKE

Brookfield Lake, Cheshunt, Waltham Cross, **HERTFORDSHIRE**, EN, **England**.
Contact/s: Manager, Simpsons of Turnford, Nunsbury Drive, Broxbourne, Hertfordshire, EN10 6AQ.
(T) 01992 468799 **(F)** 01992 466227
Profile: **FT:** Coarse; **WN:** Brookfield; **WT:** Lake (Still).
Ref: FH0680

BROOKFOOT LAKE

Brookfoot Lake, Bridghouse, Halifax, **YORKSHIRE (WEST)**, HX, **England**.
Contact/s: **M Riley**, Brighouse Angling Association, 30 Ravenstone Drive, West Vale, Greetland, Halifax, West Yorkshire HX.
(T) 01484 711063
Mr D Noble (Secretary), Brighouse Angling Association, 1a Church Lane, Brighouse, Yorkshire (West), HD6 1AT.
(T) 01484 717034
Mr David Finnigan (Manager), 32 Crowtrees Lane, Rastrick, Halifax, Yorkshire (West).
(T) 01422 373223or01484722310
Profile: **FT:** Coarse; **WN:** Brookfoot; **WT:** Lake (Still).
Ref: FH0681

BROOKHALL FISHERY

Brookhall Lake, Tiptree, Colchester, **ESSEX**, CO5, **England**.
Contact/s: **Betty Hooper** (Manager), Penyghent, Post Office Corner, Stutton, Ipswich, Suffolk, IP9 2TJ.
(T) 07939 259651
Profile: **FT:** Coarse; **WN:** Brookhall; **WT:** Lake (Still); **F. Size:** 4 Acres; **W. Size:** 4 Acres. **Location:** **Main Rd:** A12.
Ref: FH0682

BROOKLANDS

Brooklands, Ings Lane, Brompton, Scarborough, **YORKSHIRE (NORTH)**, YO13 9DS, **England**.
Contact/s: **Mrs Richie**.
(T) 01944 710395

Profile: **FT:** Coarse; **WN:** Brooklands; **WT:** Lake (Still) **W. Size:** 1 Acre. **Location:** **Nr. Rd:** Ings Lane; **Main Rd:** A64; **Rail:** Scarborough.
Ref: FH0683

BROOKLANDS LAKE

Brooklands Lake, Princes Rd, Dartford, **KENT**, DA, **England**.
Contact/s: **Mr Alan Kirknick** (Ticket Sales), Dartford and District APS, 2 Walnut Tree Avenue, Dartford, DA11 1LJ.
(T) 01322 270397
Mr Geoff Hough (Owner), Dartford Angling Ctre, 84 Lowfield St, Dartford, Kent, DA1 1HS.
(T) 01322 228532
Profile: **FT:** Coarse; **WN:** Brooklands; **WT:** Lake (Still) **W. Size:** 20 Acres. **Location:** **Nr. Rd:** Princess Road or Powder Mill Lane; **Main Rd:** M25, junction 1b, A225; **Rail:** Dartford.
Ref: FH0684

BROOKSBY COLLEGE

Brooksby College, Brooksby, Melton Mowbray, **LEICESTERSHIRE**, LE14 2LJ, **England**.
Contact/s: Fishery Manager.
(T) 01664 434291
Profile: **FT:** Coarse; **WN:** Brooksby College; **WT:** Pond (Still).
Ref: FH0685

BROOKSIDE FISHERIES

Brookside Fisheries, Church Lane, Betley, Crewe, **CHESHIRE**, CW3 9AY, **England**.
Contact/s: **Mr Dave Barratt** (Owner).
(T) 01270 820528 **(F)** 01270 820528
Profile: **FT:** Coarse; **WN:** Brookside Fisheries; **WT:** Combination (Still & Moving) **W. Size:** 4 Acres. **Location:** **Nr. Rd:** Church Lane; **Main Rd:** A51, M6 junction 16; **Rail:** Crewe.
Ref: FH0686

BROOKSIDE LAKES

Brookside Lakes, Higher Whitley, Stretton, Warrington, **CHESHIRE**, WA4, **England**.
Contact/s: **Mr Mike Timmis**.
(T) 01925 730893
Profile: **FT:** Coarse; **WN:** Brookside; **WT:** Lake (Still). **Location:** **Nr. Rd:** M56 junction 10 to Northwich; **Main Rd:** A49.
Ref: FH0687

BROOM

Broom, Shefford, Stanford, **BEDFORDSHIRE**, SG18, **England**.
Contact/s: **Mr J Leath** (Secretary), Shefford and District Angling Association, 3 Ivel Cl, Shefford, Bedfordshire, SG17 5JX.
(T) 01462 812323
Profile: **FT:** Coarse; **WN:** Broom; **WT:** Lake (Still) **W. Size:** 8 Acres. **Location:** **Nr. Rd:** A658.
Ref: FH0688

BROOM FISHERIES

Broom Fisheries, Newbie, Annan, **DUMFRIES AND GALLOWAY**, DG12 5FP, **Scotland**.
(W) www.broomfisheries.co.uk
Contact/s: **Mr John Wright** (Fishery Manager), Broom Fisheries, Newbie, Annan, Dumfries and Galloway, Scotland. DG12 5PF..
(T) 01461 700209 **(M)** 07850 157668
(E) info@broomfisheries.co.uk
Profile: **FT:** Combination; **WN:** Broom Fisheries; **WT:** Loch (Still); **F. Size:** 200 Acres; **W. Size:** 7 Acres. **Location:** **Nr. Rd:** Situated off the Newbie Road; **Main Rd:** A75; **Rail:** Annan.
Ref: FH0689

BROOM OF MOY

Broom Of Moy, Jaj Monro, South St, Elgin, **MORAY**, IV30, **Scotland**.
Contact/s: Manager, Fishing Tackle Shop, 97d High St, Forres, Moray, IV36 1AA.
(T) 01309 672936
Mr J Fraser (Hon Secretary).
Profile: **FT:** Game; **WN:** Findhorn; **WT:** River (Moving) **W. Size:** 2750 Metres.
Ref: FH0690

BROOMBANKS PITS

Broombanks Pits, Sittingbourne, **KENT**, ME10, **England**.
Contact/s: Secretary, Sittingbourne Angling Club, 2 Chapel House, Shakespeare Rd, Sittingbourne, Kent ME.
Profile: **FT:** Coarse; **WN:** Broombanks; **WT:** Gravel Pit (Still).
Ref: FH0691

BROOME FISHERIES

Broome Fisheries, Syston, Leicester, **LEICESTERSHIRE**, LE7, **England**.
Contact/s: **Mr A Smith** (Secretary), 10 Londs Avenue, Leicester, Leicestershire, LE4 2HY.
(T) 0116 2357210
Mr G Taylor (Membership Secretary), Broome Angling Society, 100 New Romney Cres, Leicester.
(T) 0116 2417018
Profile: **FT:** Coarse; **WN:** Broome Fisheries; **WT:** Lake (Still) **W. Size:** 2 Acres. **Location:** **Nr. Rd:** Meadow Lane; **Main Rd:** A46 North of Leicester; **Rail:** Leicester.
Ref: FH0692

BROOME PITS

Broome Pits, Yarmouth Rd, Broome, Bungay, **SUFFOLK**, NR35, **England**.
Contact/s: **Mr B Garrye** (Bailiff).
(T) 01986 855188
Mr Ian Gosling (Hon Secretary), Bungay Cherry Tree Angling Club, 37 St Marys Trce, Flixton Rd, Bungay, NR35 1DN.
(T) 01986 892982
Profile: **FT:** Coarse; **WN:** Broome; **WT:** Gravel Pit (Still) **W. Size:** 25 Acres. **Location:** **Nr. Rd:** Yarmouth Road; **Main Rd:** A143, Bury.
Ref: FH0693

BROOMFLEET PONDS

Broomfleet Ponds, Newport, Brough, **HUMBERSIDE**, HU15, **England**.
Contact/s: Fishery Manager.
(T) 0113 2312100
Profile: **FT:** Coarse; **WN:** Broomfleet; **WT:** Pond (Still).
Ref: FH0694

BROOMHAM FISHERY

Broomham Fishery, White Hart Pub, Catsfield, Battle, **SUSSEX (EAST)**, TN33, **England**.
Contact/s: **Mr Peter Maclean** (Hon Secretary), 37 Collier Rd, Hastings, Sussex (East), TN34 3JR.
(T) 01424 715218
Profile: **FT:** Coarse; **WN:** Broomham; **WT:** Lake (Still) **W. Size:** 6 Acres. **Location:** **Nr. Rd:** A271; **Main Rd:** A21 to Hastings.
Ref: FH0695

BROOMWOOD LAKE

Broomwood Lake, St. Paul's Cray, Orpington, **LONDON (GREATER)**, **England**.
Contact/s: .
(T) 01689 835510
Profile: **FT:** Coarse; **WN:** Broomwood; **WT:** Lake (Still); **F. Size:** 5 Acres; **W. Size:** 4 Acres. **Location:** **Nr. Rd:** Brooks way; **Main Rd:** A224 Sevenoaks Way.
Ref: FH0696

BROSNA (TRIBUTARY)

Brosna (Tributary), Inland Fisheries Trust, Dublin, **COUNTY DUBLIN**, **Ireland**.
Profile: **FT:** Game; **WN:** Brosna; **WT:** Tributary (Moving).
Ref: FH0698

BROWNES POND

Brownes Pond, Elmwood Avenue, Bridgwater, **SOMERSET**, TA, **England**.
Contact/s: **Mr Phil Dodds** (Owner).
(T) 01278 444145
Profile: **FT:** Coarse; **WN:** Brownes; **WT:** Pond (Still) **W. Size:** 2 Acres. **Location:** **Nr. Rd:** Elmwood Avenue; **Main Rd:** A38,Taunton Road.
Ref: FH0699

BROWNEY (RIVER)

River Browney, Croxdale, Durham, **COUNTY DURHAM**, DH6, **England**.
Contact/s: **Mr Barry Hignett** (Secretary), Ferryhill and District Angling Club, 74 Grasmere Rd, Garden Farm Estate, Chester-le-Street, County Durham.
(T) 0191 3883557
Profile: **FT:** Combination; **WN:** Browney; **WT:** River (Moving) **W. Size:** 1600 Metres.
Ref: FH0700

BROWNHILL RESERVOIR

Brownhill Reservoir, Colne, **LANCASHIRE**, BB8, **England**.
Profile: **FT:** Game; **WN:** Brownhill; **WT:** Reservoir (Still). **Location:** **Nr. Rd:** Colne and Foulridge.
Ref: FH0701

BROWNING CUDMORE FISHERY

Browning Cudmore Fishery, Pleck Lane, Whitmore, Newcastle-under-Lyme, **STAFFORDSHIRE**, ST5 5HW, **England**.
Contact/s: **Mr C M Brewster** (Managing Director).
(T) 01782 680919 **(F)** 01782 680490
Mr Douglas Simcock.
(T) 01782 680919 **(F)** 01782 680490
Mr E Cavenage-Mainwaring.
Profile: **FT:** Coarse; **WN:** Browning Cudmore Fishery; **WT:** Combination (Still); **F. Size:** 800 Acres; **W. Size:** 40 Acres. **Location:** **Nr. Rd:** Three Mile Lane; **Main Rd:** A53; **Rail:** Stoke-on-Trent.
Ref: FH0702

BROWNLEES POND

Brownlees Pond, Cromwell Avenue, Warrington, **CHESHIRE**, **England**.
(W) www.pohas.moonfruit.com
Contact/s: **Mr Joe Worsley** (Club Secretary), 54, Shackleton Close, Old Hall, Warrington, WA5 9QE.
(T) 01925 413750
(E) joseph.worsley@btinternet.com
Profile: **FT:** Coarse; **WN:** Brownlee's Pond; **WT:** Pond (Still); **F. Size:** 1 Acre; **W. Size:** 1 Acre. **Location:** **Nr. Rd:** Cromwell Avenue; **Main Rd:** A57; **Rail:** Warrington.
Ref: FH0703

BROWNWICH POND

Brownwich Pond, Copnor, Portsmouth, **HAMPSHIRE**, PO2 7NL, **England**.
Contact/s: **Mr R G Snook** (Secretary), 86 Carnarvon Rd, Copnor, Portsmouth, Hampshire, PO2 7NL.
(T) 023 92662986
Profile: **FT:** Coarse; **WN:** Brownwich Pond; **WT:** Lake (Still). **Location:** **Nr. Rd:** Carnarvon Road.
Ref: FH0704

BROXBOURNE

Broxbourne, Meadgate Lane, Broxbourne, Hoddesdon, **HERTFORDSHIRE**, EN11, **England**.
Profile: **FT:** Coarse; **WN:** Broxbourne; **WT:** Gravel Pit (Still) **W. Size:** 126 Acres. **Location:** **Nr. Rd:** A1170; **Main Rd:** A10, North of the M25.
Ref: FH0705

BROXBOURNE MEADOWS FISHERY

Broxbourne Meadows Fishery, Enfield, London, **LONDON (GREATER)**, EN2, **England**.
Contact/s: **Mr Gary Smith** (Information Officer), Lee Valley Park Information Ctre, Abbey Gardens, Waltham Abbey, Essex, EN9 1XQ.
(T) 01992 702200
Mr Krizim Seltham (Angling Manager), Lee Valley Regional Park Authority, Myddleton House, Bulls Cross, Enfield, EN2 9HG.
(T) 01992 709832
(E) garysmith@leevalleypark.org.uk
Profile: **FT:** Coarse; **WN:** Lynch; **WT:** River

(Moving).
Ref: FH0706

BRUE (RIVER)

River Brue, Highbridge, **SOMERSET**, TA9, **England**.
Contact/s: **Mr S Bonwick** (Secretary), 13 Tennyson Avenue, Clevedon, Somerset, BS21 7QQ.
(T) 01275 791933
Profile: **FT:** Coarse; **WN:** Brue; **WT:** River (Moving). **Location:** **Main Rd:** M5 then A38.
Ref: FH0707

BRUE (RIVER)

River Brue, Street, **SOMERSET**, BA16, **England**.
Contact/s: **Mr Gf Miller** (Secretary), 22 Benedict St, Glastonbury, Somerset, BA6.
Mr Nick Hughes (Manager), Street Angling Ctre, 160 High St, St, Somerset, BA16 0NH.
(T) 01458 447830 **(F)** 01458 447830
Profile: **FT:** Combination; **WN:** Brue; **WT:** River (Moving).
Ref: FH0708

BRUN CLOUGH RESERVOIR

Brun Clough Reservoir, Saddleworth, Oldham, **MANCHESTER (GREATER)**, OL3, **England**.
Contact/s: Fishery Manager.
(T) 01457 875500
Profile: **FT:** Coarse; **WN:** Brun Clough; **WT:** Reservoir (Still).
Ref: FH0709

BRUNTIS LOCH

Bruntis Loch, Newton Stewart, **DUMFRIES AND GALLOWAY**, DG8, **Scotland**.
Contact/s: **Mr Tony Dickinson** (Managing Director).
(T) 01671 403604
Profile: **FT:** Game; **WN:** Bruntis; **WT:** Loch (Still). **Location:** **Main Rd:** A75.
Ref: FH0710

BRYAN HEY RESERVOIR

Bryan Hey Reservoir, Scout Rd, Horrocks Fold, Bolton, **LANCASHIRE**, BL, **England**.
Contact/s: Fishery Manager.
(T) 01257 404151
Mr Wilf Brooks, 13 Conrad Cl, Worsley Mesnes, Wigan, WN3 5UA.
(T) 01942 239578
Profile: **FT:** Coarse; **WN:** Bryan Hey; **WT:** Reservoir (Still) **W. Size:** 2 Acres. **Location:** **Nr. Rd:** Scout Road; **Main Rd:** Bolton.
Ref: FH0711

BRYN FLASH

Bryn Flash, Wigan, **LANCASHIRE**, WN, **England**.
(W) www.wiganaa.f9.co.uk
Contact/s: **Mr Gerry Wilson** (Hon Secretary), Wigan and District Angling Association, 11 Guildford Avenue, Chorley, Lancashire, PR6 8TG.
(T) 01257 265905
(E) gerry@wiganna.freeserve.co.uk
Profile: **FT:** Coarse; **WN:** Bryn Flash; **WT:** Lake (Still) **W. Size:** 1 Acre. **Location:** **Main Rd:** M6, A49, A573.
Ref: FH0712

BRYNHAWC FISHERY

Brynhawc Fishery, Maesycrugiau, Pencader, **CARMARTHENSHIRE**, SA39, **Wales**.
(W) www.fishing-in-wales.co.uk/llandysul-aa/beat8
Contact/s: **Mr Artie Jones** (Hon Secretary), Llandysul Angling Association, Glas-y-Dorlan, Llyn-y-Fran Rd, Llandysul, SA44 4JW.
(T) 01559 362317
Profile: **FT:** Game; **WN:** Teifi; **WT:** River (Moving).
Ref: FH0713

BUBWITH (RIVER)

River Bubwith, Bubwith, Selby, **YORKSHIRE (NORTH)**, YO8, **England**.
Contact/s: **Mr Mike Redman** (Manager), 2 Meadowfield, Breighton Rd, Bubwith, YO8 7DZ.
(T) 01757 288891
Profile: **FT:** Coarse; **WN:** Bubwith; **WT:** River (Moving) **W. Size:** 6400 Metres.
Ref: FH0714

BUCCLEUCH ESTATES

Buccleuch Estates Ltd, The Estate Office, Bowhill, Selkirk, **SCOTTISH BORDERS**, TD7 5ES, **Scotland**.
Contact/s: **Mrs J Crosbie** (Per The Factor Ghillie).
(T) 01750 20753or32334 **(F)** 01750 22172
(E) jcrosbie@buccleuch.com
Profile: **FT:** Game; **WN:** Buccleuch Estates Ltd; **WT:** Lake (Still) **W. Size:** 10 Acres.
Ref: FH0715

BUCHAN PARK FISHERIES

Buchan Park Fisheries, Crawley, **CORNWALL**, RH10, **England**.
Contact/s: **Mr Kicholls** (Secretary), 24 Rillside, Furnace Green, Crawley, Sussex (West), RH10.
Profile: **FT:** Coarse; **WN:** Buchan Park Fisheries; **WT:** Lake (Still).
Ref: FH0716

BUCKENHAM PITS

Buckenham Pits, Ickburgh, Thetford, **NORFOLK**, IP26, **England**.
Contact/s: Fishery Manager.
(T) 01824 878400
Profile: **FT:** Coarse; **WN:** Buckenham; **WT:** Gravel Pit (Still).
Ref: FH0717

BUCKLEY TRAP POOL

Buckley Trap Pool, Ewloe Pl, Buckley, **FLINTSHIRE**, CH7, **Wales**.
Contact/s: Fishery Manager.
(T) 01244 543191
Profile: **FT:** Coarse; **WN:** Buckley Trap Pool; **WT:** Lake (Still); **F. Size:** 7 Acres; **W. Size:** 4 Acres. **Location:** **Nr. Rd:** Ewloe Place; **Main Rd:** A494; **Rail:** Ellesmere Port.
Ref: FH0718

BUCKLEY WOOD RESERVOIR

Buckley Wood Reservoir, Rochdale, **MANCHESTER (GREATER)**, OL, **England**.
Contact/s: **Mr R Pealin** (Secretary), 732 Whitworth Rd, Rochdale, Lancashire.
Mr Roy Rhodes (Conservation, Access and Recreation Manager), Rivington Water Treatment Works, Bolton Rd, Horwich, Bolton, BL6 7RN.
(T) 01204 664300
Profile: **FT:** Coarse; **WN:** Buckley Wood; **WT:** Reservoir (Still).
Ref: FH0719

BUCKMINSTER PARK LAKE

Buckminster Park Lake, Buckminster, Grantham, **LINCOLNSHIRE**, NG33 5SD, **England**.
Contact/s: Area Manager, Buckminster Management Ltd, Estate Office, Buckminster, Grantham, NG33 5SD.
(T) 01476 860471
Profile: **FT:** Combination; **WN:** Buckminster; **WT:** Lake (Still).
Ref: FH0720

BUDE CANAL

Bude Canal, Bude, **CORNWALL**, EX23, **England**.
Contact/s: **Mr Dick Turner**, 2 Pathfields, Bude, EX23 8DW.
(T) 01288 353162
Mr P Braund.
(T) 01752 232804
Profile: **FT:** Coarse; **WN:** Bude; **WT:** Canal (Still) **W. Size:** 1800 Metres.
Ref: FH0721

BUDWORTH MERE

Budworth Mere, Warrington Rd, Great Budworth, Northwich, **CHESHIRE**, CW9, **England**.
Contact/s: **Mr J Clitheroe** (Secretary), Northwich Angling Association, PO Box 18, Northwich, Cheshire, CW9 5SE.
(T) 01606 75132
Profile: **FT:** Coarse; **WN:** Budworth Mere; **WT:** Lake (Still) **W. Size:** 50 Acres. **Location:** **Main Rd:** B5075.
Ref: FH0722

BUITTLE RESERVOIR

Buittle Reservoir, Dalbeattie, **DUMFRIES AND GALLOWAY**, DG5, **Scotland**.
Contact/s: **Mr John Moran** (Secretary), Dalbeattie Angling Association, 12 Church Cres, Dalbeattie, Dumfries and Galloway, DG5 4BA.
(T) 01556 610026 **(M)** 07778 140569
Profile: **FT:** Game; **WN:** Buittle; **WT:** Reservoir (Still) **W. Size:** 11 Acres. **Location:** **Nr. Rd:** A711; **Main Rd:** A75; **Rail:** Dumfries.
Ref: FH0723

BULL FISHERY

Bull Fishery, Halesowen, **MIDLANDS (WEST)**, B63, **England**.
Contact/s: **Mr Norman Edwards**. **(M)** 07778 218363
Profile: **FT:** Coarse; **WN:** Bull Fishery; **WT:** Pool (Still).
Ref: FH0724

BULL HOLE

Bull Hole, Barnby Dun, Doncaster, **YORKSHIRE (SOUTH)**, DN3, **England**.
Contact/s: **Mr Vinnie Belk** (Fishery Manager).
(T) 01302 883674
Profile: **FT:** Coarse; **WN:** Bull Hole; **WT:** Lake (Still). **Location:** **Nr. Rd:** Barnby Dun, take Arksey and Bentley road to River Don bridge, fishery on left; **Main Rd:** A19.
Ref: FH0725

BULLEY LANE FISHERY

Bulley Lane Fishery, Bulley Lane, Churcham, Ross-on-Wye, **HEREFORDSHIRE**, HR9, **England**.
Contact/s: **Mrs J Bennet** (Owner).
(T) 01452 750320
Profile: **FT:** Coarse; **WN:** Bulley Lane Fishery; **WT:** Lake (Still). **Location:** **Nr. Rd:** Bulley Lane.
Ref: FH0726

BULLFIELD LAKE

Bullfield Lake, Thrupp Lane, Home Farm, Abingdon, **OXFORDSHIRE**, OX1, **England**.
Contact/s: **Mr Roger Bateman** (Fishery Manager).
(T) 01865 391809
Profile: **FT:** Coarse; **WN:** Bullfield; **WT:** Gravel Pit (Still). **Location:** **Nr. Rd:** Thrupp Lane.
Ref: FH0727

BULLOCKS FARM FISHING LAKES

Bullocks Farm Fishing Lakes, Bullock Farm, Back Lane, Kingston Seymour, Clevedon, **SOMERSET**, BS21 6XA, **England**.
Contact/s: **Mr Philip Simmons** (Owner).
(T) 01934 835020 **(F)** 01934 835927
(E) bullockfarm@kingstonseymour.freeserve.co.uk
Profile: **FT:** Coarse; **WN:** Bullock's Farm; **WT:** Lake (Still); **F. Size:** 6 Acres; **W. Size:** 4 Acres. **Location:** **Nr. Rd:** Back Lane; **Main Rd:** B3133; **Rail:** Yatton.
Ref: FH0728

BULLS POOL

Bulls Pool, Hawthorn Lane, Sandbach Heath, Sandbach, **CHESHIRE**, **England**.
Contact/s: **Mr John Turner** (Hon Secretary), Prince Albert Angling Society, 15 Pexhill Drive, Macclesfield, Cheshire, SK10 3LP.
(T) 01625 422010
Profile: **FT:** Coarse; **WN:** Bulls Pool; **WT:**

Pool (Still); **F. Size:** 5 Acres; **W. Size:** 1 Acre. **Location:** **Nr. Rd:** Hawthorn Lane; **Main Rd:** A533; **Rail:** Sandbach.
Ref: FH0729

BULPHAN PARK FISHERIES

Bulphan Park Fisheries, Burrow Farm, Brentwood Rd, Bulphan, Upminster, **ESSEX**, RM14 3TL, **England**.
Contact/s: **Everett Wylde** (Manager). **(M)** 07967 850125
Mr Bill Blundell (Owner).
(T) 01375 892600 **(M)** 07770 677600
Profile: **FT:** Coarse; **WN:** Bulphan Park Fisheries; **WT:** Lake (Still) **W. Size:** 3 Acres. **Location:** **Main Rd:** A128, Brentwood.
Ref: FH0730

BULWORTHY FISHERY

Bulworthy Fishery, Bulworth Farm Cottage, The Barton, Instow, Bideford, **DEVON**, EX39 4LU, **England**.
Contact/s: **G J May**.
(T) 01271 860477
Profile: **FT:** Combination; **WN:** Bulworthy Fishery; **WT:** Lake (Still).
Ref: FH0731

BUNGAY (RIVER)

River Bungay, Bungay, **SUFFOLK**, NR35, **England**.
Contact/s: **Mr Ian Gosling** (Hon Secretary), Bungay Cherry Tree Angling Club, 37 St Marys Trce, Flixton Rd, Bungay, NR35 1DN.
(T) 01986 892982
Profile: **FT:** Coarse; **WN:** Bungay; **WT:** River (Moving) **W. Size:** 3200 Metres. **Location:** **Nr. Rd:** Earsham to Geldeston.
Ref: FH0732

BURBROOKS RESERVOIR

Burbrooks Reservoir, Bromham, Melksham, **WILTSHIRE**, SN12, **England**.
Contact/s: **Mr S Clunie** (Manager), Avon Angling and Sports Ctre, 13 Bath Rd, Melksham, Wiltshire, SN12 6LL.
(T) 01225 702219
Profile: **FT:** Coarse; **WN:** Burbrooks; **WT:** Reservoir (Still) **W. Size:** 1 Acre.
Ref: FH0733

BURE (RIVER)

River Bure, Great Yarmouth, **NORFOLK**, NR, **England**.
Contact/s: **Mr Dyble**, Scratby Rd, Scratby, Great Yarmouth, NR29 3PQ.
(T) 01493 731305
Profile: **FT:** Game; **WN:** Bure; **WT:** River (Moving).
Ref: FH0734

BURE (RIVER)

River Bure, Coltishall Common, Coltishall, Norwich, **NORFOLK**, NR12 7, **England**.
Contact/s: Manager, Wroxham Angling Ctre, Station Rd, Hoveton, Norwich, NR12 8UR.
(T) 01603 782453
Profile: **FT:** Coarse; **WN:** Bure; **WT:** River (Moving).
Ref: FH0735

BURE (RIVER)

River Bure, Norwich, **NORFOLK**, NR6, **England**.
Contact/s: **Mr R Westgate** (Club Secretary), Wroxham and District Angling Club, 31 The Paddocks, Old Catton, Norwich, NR6 7HF.
(T) 01603 401062 **(F)** 01603 897122 **(M)** 07885 244262
(E) wroxham.angling@virgin.net
Profile: **FT:** Coarse; **WN:** Bure; **WT:** River (Moving). **Location:** **Main Rd:** B1151.
Ref: FH0736

BURE VALLEY LAKES

Bure Valley Lakes, Oulton, Aylesham, **NORFOLK**, NR11 6NW, **England**.
Contact/s: **Mr Mike Smith** (Manager).
(T) 01263 587666
Profile: **FT:** Combination; **WN:** Bure Valley Lakes; **WT:** Gravel Pit (Still); **F. Size:** 22 Acres; **W. Size:** 10 Acres. **Location:** **Nr. Rd:** B1354; **Main Rd:** A140; **Rail:** Norwich.
Ref: FH0737

BURES LAKE

Bures Lake, Hoe St, Walthamstow, London, **LONDON (GREATER)**, E17, **England**.
Profile: **FT:** Coarse; **WN:** Bures; **WT:** Gravel Pit (Still).
Ref: FH0738

BURGHFIELD

Burghfield, Pinewood Rd, Burghfield, Reading, **BERKSHIRE**, RG, **England**.
(W) www.rmcangling.co.uk
Contact/s: **Mr Ian Welch** (Angling Manager), RMC Angling, The Square, Lightwater, Surrey, GU18 5SS.
(T) 01276 453300 **(F)** 01276 456611
(E) info@rmcangling.co.uk
Profile: **FT:** Coarse; **WN:** Kennet; **WT:** Combination (Still & Moving) **W. Size:** 94 Acres. **Location:** **Nr. Rd:** Pinewood Road or Cottage Lane; **Main Rd:** M4; **Rail:** Reading.
Ref: FH0739

BURGHFIELD BLUE POOL

Burghfield Blue Pool, Cottage Lane, Burghfield, Reading, **BERKSHIRE**, RG, **England**.
(W) www.rmcangling.co.uk
Contact/s: **Mr Ian Welch** (Angling Manager), RMC Angling, The Square, Lightwater, Surrey, GU18 5SS.
(T) 01276 453300 **(F)** 01276 456611
(E) info@rmcangling.co.uk
Profile: **FT:** Coarse; **WN:** Blue Pool; **WT:** Gravel Pit (Still) **W. Size:** 3 Acres. **Location:** **Nr. Rd:** Cottage Lane; **Main Rd:** A33, M4; **Rail:** Reading.
Ref: FH0740

BURGHFIELD CANAL

Burghfield Canal, Burghfield, Reading, **BERKSHIRE**, RG, **England**.
Contact/s: **Mr Dusty Millar** (Associate members secretary), 238 Elgar Road South, Reading, Berkshire, RG3 0BW.
(T) 0118 9874882
Mr Mick Cox (Chief Bailiff), Dorstans, Hatch Lane, Brimpton Village, Reading, RG7 4TR.
(T) 0118 9714917
Profile: **FT:** Coarse; **WN:** Burghfield; **WT:** Canal (Still). **Location:** **Nr. Rd:** Burghfield.
Ref: FH0741

BURGHFIELD MATCH LAKE

Burghfield Match Lake, Cottage Lane, Burghfield, Reading, **BERKSHIRE**, RG, **England**.
(W) www.rmcangling.co.uk
Contact/s: Manager, Reading Angling Ctre, 69 Northumberland Avenue, Reading, Berkshire, RG2 7PS.
(T) 0118 9872216
Mr Ian Welch (Angling Manager), RMC Angling, The Square, Lightwater, Surrey, GU18 5SS.
(T) 01276 453300 **(F)** 01276 456611
(E) info@rmcangling.co.uk
Profile: **FT:** Coarse; **WN:** Match Lake; **WT:** Lake (Still) **W. Size:** 2 Acres. **Location:** **Nr. Rd:** Cottage Lane; **Main Rd:** A4, M4; **Rail:** Reading.
Ref: FH0742

BURGHLEY PARK LAKE

Burghley Park Lake, Burghley Estate Office, St Martins, Stamford, **LINCOLNSHIRE**, PE9, **England**.
Contact/s: Manager.
(T) 01780 52075
Profile: **FT:** Coarse; **WN:** Burghley; **WT:** Lake (Still). **Location:** **Nr. Rd:** St Martins.
Ref: FH0743

BURLEY FIELDS LAKE

Burley Fields Lake, Crippetts Lane, Leckhampton, Cheltenham, **GLOUCESTERSHIRE**, GL, **England**.
Contact/s: Mr Steve Kingkart (Owner).
(T) 01242 862905
Profile: **FT:** Coarse; **WN:** Burley Fields; **WT:** Pond (Still). **Location:** **Nr. Rd:** Leckhampton Lane; **Main Rd:** A46.
Ref: FH0744

BURLINGTON POND

Burlington Pond, Dalton-In-Furness, **CUMBRIA**, LA15, **England**.
Contact/s: **Mr George Wadey** (Club Secretary).
(T) 01229 584118
Profile: **FT:** Coarse; **WN:** Burlington; **WT:** Pond (Still).
Ref: FH0745

BURN DENNET (RIVER)

River Burn Dennet, Strabane, **COUNTY TYRONE**, BT82, **Northern Ireland**.
Contact/s: **Mr Billy Diver**, Variety Shop, 5 Castle Prde, Strabane, County Tyrone, BT82.
(T) 028 71883021
Profile: **FT:** Game; **WN:** Burn Dennet; **WT:** River (Moving).
Ref: FH0746

BURN DENNETT (RIVER)

River Burn Dennett, Dunamanagh, Strabane, **COUNTY TYRONE**, BT82, **Northern Ireland**.
Contact/s: **Mr Roy McBrine**, 31 Lisnaragh Rd, Donemana, County Tyrone.
(T) 028 71398024
Mr William O'Neill (Manager), 22 Carrickatane Rd, Donemana, County Tyrone, BT82 0NG.
(T) 028 71398512
Profile: **FT:** Game; **WN:** Burn Dennett; **WT:** River (Moving) **W. Size:** 24000 Metres.
Ref: FH0747

BURNHAM RESERVOIR

Burnham Reservoir, Maidstone, **KENT**, ME1, **England**.
Contact/s: Manager, Maidstone and Victory Angling and, Medway Preservation Society, 33 Hackney Rd, Maidstone, Kent ME16 8LN.
(T) 01622 202686
Profile: **FT:** Coarse; **WN:** Burnham; **WT:** Reservoir (Still) **W. Size:** 12 Acres.
Ref: FH0748

BURNHOPE FISHERY

Burnhope Fishery, Darlington, **COUNTY DURHAM**, DL, **England**.
Contact/s: **Mr Giles Bilton** (Manager).
(T) 01423 523423
Profile: **FT:** Game; **WN:** Burnhope; **WT:** Reservoir (Still) **W. Size:** 105 Acres.
Ref: FH0749

BURNSIDE LAKE

Burnside Lake, Old Blue Circle Cement Works, Coldhams Lane, Cambridge, **CAMBRIDGESHIRE**, CB, **England**.
Contact/s: **Mr Hobson**, 25 Ivory Cl, Cherry Hinton, Cambridgeshire, CB1.
Profile: **FT:** Coarse; **WN:** Burnside; **WT:** Lake (Still) **W. Size:** 10 Acres. **Location:** **Nr. Rd:** Coldhams Lane.
Ref: FH0750

BURRATOR RESERVOIR

Burrator Reservoir, Burrator Inn, Dousland, Yelverton, Plymouth, **DEVON**, PL20 6PE, **England**.
Contact/s: , Burrator Inn, Dousland, Yelverton, Devon, PL20 6NP.
Mr Jeff Gale (Owner).
(T) 01837 871334
Profile: **FT:** Game; **WN:** Burrator; **WT:** Reservoir (Still).
Ref: FH0751

BURREN (RIVER)

River Burren, Carlow, **COUNTY CARLOW**, **Ireland**.
Contact/s: **Mrs Quinn** (Manager), The Locks, Milford, Carlow, County Carlow, Ireland.
(T) 050 346261

Profile: FT: Game; **WN:** Burren; **WT:** River (Moving).
Ref: FH0752

BURRISHOOLE FISHERY

Burrishoole Fishery, Newport, **COUNTY MAYO**, **Ireland**.
Contact/s: **Pat Hughes**.
(T) 098 41107 **(F)** 098 41107
Profile: FT: Game; **WN:** Furnace and Ballinlough; **WT:** Lough (Still).
Ref: FH0753

BURROWS FARM

Burrows Farm, Bulpham, Basildon, **ESSEX**, SS1, **England**.
Contact/s: Fishery Manager.
(T) 01375 891150
Profile: FT: Coarse; **WN:** Burrows Farm; **WT:** Lake (Still) **W. Size:** 5 Acres. **Location:** **Nr. Rd:** A127; **Main Rd:** M25.
Ref: FH0754

BURRS LODGE

Burrs Lodge, Bury, **MANCHESTER (GREATER)**, BL, **England**.
Contact/s: **Mr Metcalfe** (Secretary).
(T) 0161 7975597
Profile: FT: Coarse; **WN:** Burrs Lodge; **WT:** Reservoir (Still).
Ref: FH0755

BURSCOUGH BRICKWORKS LAKE

Burscough Brickworks Lake, Abbey Lane, Burscough, Ormskirk, **LANCASHIRE**, L40, **England**.
Profile: FT: Coarse; **WN:** Burscough Brickworks; **WT:** Lake (Still). **Location:** **Nr. Rd:** Abbey Lane.
Ref: FH0756

BURSHILL A POND

Burshill A Pond, Burshill, Brandesburton, Driffield, **HUMBERSIDE**, YO25, **England**.
Contact/s: **Mr Paul Caygill** (Secretary), Hull and District Angler's Association, PO Box 188, Hull, HU9 1AN.
(T) 01430 440624
Profile: FT: Coarse; **WN:** Burshill A; **WT:** Lake (Still) **W. Size:** 1 Acre. **Location:** **Nr. Rd:** Burshill; **Main Rd:** A165, A1035.
Ref: FH0757

BURSTWICK SKI LAKE

Burstwick Ski Lake, Burstwick, Hull, **HUMBERSIDE**, HU12, **England**.
Contact/s: **Mr Arnold Woodford** (Lake Warden).
(T) 01964 622777
Profile: FT: Coarse; **WN:** Burstwick Ski; **WT:** Gravel Pit (Still); **F. Size:** 8 Acres; **W. Size:** 5 Acres. **Location:** **Nr. Rd:** B1362; **Main Rd:** A165; **Rail:** Hull.
Ref: FH0758

BURTON CONSTABLE COUNTRY PARK

Burton Constable Country Park, Old Lodge, Spoatley, Hull, **HUMBERSIDE**, HU, **England**.
Contact/s: **Mr Paul Barrett** (Bailiff).
(T) 01964 563332 **(M)** 07801 633247
Profile: FT: Coarse; **WN:** Burton Constable Country Park; **WT:** Drain (Still) **W. Size:** 24 Acres. **Location:** **Nr. Rd:** B1240; **Main Rd:** M62; **Rail:** Hull.
Ref: FH0759

BURTON HILL LAKE

Burton Hill Lake, Malmesbury, **WILTSHIRE**, **England**.
Contact/s: .
(T) 01179 672977
Profile: FT: Coarse; **WN:** Burton Hill Lake; **WT:** Lake (Still).
Ref: FH0760

BURTON MERE FISHERIES

Burton Mere Carp Fisheries, Puddington Lane, Burton, Neston, **CHESHIRE**, CH64 5SF, **England**.
Contact/s: **Mr Terry Knight** (Owner).
(T) 0151 3530115
Profile: FT: Coarse; **WN:** Burton Mere; **WT:** Lake (Still) **W. Size:** 6 Acres. **Location:** **Nr. Rd:** A540; **Main Rd:** Chester to Heswell; **Rail:** Neston.
Ref: FH0761

BURTON MILL POND

Burton Mill Pond, Duncton Mill, Petworth, **SUSSEX (WEST)**, GU28 0LF, **England**.
Contact/s: **Mr David Hayler**, Tripp Hill Garage, Fittleworth, Pulborough, RH20 1ER.
(T) 01798 865267
Profile: FT: Coarse; **WN:** Arun; **WT:** Pond (Still).
Ref: FH0762

BURWELL LODE

Burwell Lode, Burwell, Cambridge, **CAMBRIDGESHIRE**, CB5, **England**.
Contact/s: **Mr Graham Tweed** (Secretary), Cambridge Fish Preservation Angling Society, 27a Villa Rd, Impington, Cambridge, CB4 9NZ.
(T) 01223 234616
Profile: FT: Coarse; **WN:** Burwell Lode; **WT:** Tributary (Moving).
Ref: FH0763

BURY HILL FISHERIES

Bury Hill Fisheries, Estate Office, Old Bury Hill, Westcott, Dorking, **SURREY**, RH4 3JU, **England**.
(W) www.bury-hill-fisheries.co.uk
Contact/s: **Mr A Clark**.
(T) 01306 877540or883621 **(F)** 01306 877545
Mr C Devere (Fisheries Manager).
(T) 01306 877540or883621 **(F)** 01306 877545
(E) bhfishery@aol.com
Mr David De Vere.
(T) 01306 877540or883621 **(F)** 01306 877545
Profile: FT: Coarse; **WN:** Old Bury Hill; **WT:** Lake (Still); **F. Size:** 30 Acres; **W. Size:** 18 Acres. **Location:** **Nr. Rd:** Westcott Road; **Main Rd:** A25; **Rail:** Dorking.
Ref: FH0764

BUSBRIDGE LAKE

Busbridge Lake, Tuesley Lane, Milford, **SURREY**, **England**.
Contact/s: .
(T) 01483 422791
Profile: FT: Coarse; **WN:** Busbridge; **WT:** Lake (Still); **F. Size:** 6 Acres; **W. Size:** 5 Acres. **Location:** **Nr. Rd:** Tuesley Lane; **Main Rd:** B2130; **Rail:** Godalming.
Ref: FH0765

BUSCOT LOCK

Buscot Lock, Buscot, Faringdon, **OXFORDSHIRE**, SN7, **England**.
Contact/s: Recreational Manager, The Environment Agency, Kings Meadow Rd, Reading, Berkshire, RG1 8DQ.
(T) 0118 9535000 **(F)** 0118 9500388
Mr Preedy (Water Bailiff).
(T) 01376 242411
Mr N Holder.
(T) 01793 820694
Profile: FT: Combination; **WN:** Thames; **WT:** Lock (Still). **Location:** **Nr. Rd:** Buscot; **Main Rd:** A417, Lechlade to Faringdon Road.
Ref: FH0766

BUSH (RIVER)

River Bush, Bushmills, **COUNTY ANTRIM**, BT57, **Northern Ireland**.
Contact/s: **Mr John Kane** (Manager), River Bush Salmon Station, Department of Arts, Culture and Leisure, 21 Church St, Bushmills, County Antrim, BT57 8QT.
(T) 028 20731435 **(F)** 028 20732130
Ms Hellen Louden.
(T) 028 20731435 **(F)** 028 20732130
Profile: FT: Game; **WN:** Bush; **WT:** River (Moving) **W. Size:** 33600 Metres. **Location:** **Main Rd:** B62; **Rail:** Coleraine.
Ref: FH0767

BUSH LAKES FARM

Bush Lakes Farm, Pellaton, Saltash, **CORNWALL**, PL12 6QY, **England**.
Contact/s: **Mr Jim Renfree** (Owner).
(T) 01752 842148
Profile: FT: Combination; **WN:** Bush; **WT:** Lake (Still). **Location:** **Nr. Rd:** Liskeard to Pillaton; **Main Rd:** A388.
Ref: FH0768

BUSHEY PARK

Bushey Park, Hampton Court Palace Gardens, East Molesey, **SURREY**, KT8 9AU, **England**.
Contact/s: **Mrs Jennifer Phillips**, Hampton Court Palace Gardens, Gardens Office, East Molesey, Surrey, KT8 9AU.
(T) 020 87819611
Ms Jacquie Cassidy (Co-Ordinator and Systems Manager), Hampton Court Palace Gardens, Barrack Block, East Molesey, Surrey, KT8 9AU.
(T) 020 87819676 **(F)** 020 87819669
Profile: FT: Coarse; **WN:** Bushey Park; **WT:** Pond (Still) **W. Size:** 2 Acres. **Location:** **Nr. Rd:** Bushey Park; **Main Rd:** A3; **Rail:** Hampton Court.
Ref: FH0769

BUSHYLEAZE TROUT FISHERY

Bushyleaze Trout Fishery, Lechlade Trout Farm, Burford Rd, Lechlade, **GLOUCESTERSHIRE**, GL7 3QQ, **England**.
(W) www.fishlink.com/lechlade
Contact/s: **Mr Tim Small** (Manager).
(T) 01367 253266 **(F)** 01367 252663
(E) tim@timtrout.co.uk
Profile: FT: Game; **WN:** Bushyleaze Trout Fishery; **WT:** Lake (Still); **F. Size:** 60 Acres; **W. Size:** 22 Acres. **Location:** **Nr. Rd:** A361; **Main Rd:** A361; **Rail:** Swindon.
Ref: FH0770

BUSS CREEK

Buss Creek, Southwold, **SUFFOLK**, IP18, **England**.
Contact/s: **Mr J Purdy** (Secretary), Purdy's Newsagent, High St, Southwold, Suffolk.
(T) 01502 724250
Profile: FT: Coarse; **WN:** Buss; **WT:** Stream (Moving).
Ref: FH0771

BUSSOW RESERVOIR

Bussow Reservoir, St Ives, **CORNWALL**, TR26, **England**.
Contact/s: **Mr Chris Bird** (Manager), Newtown Angling Ctre, Newtown, Germoe, Penzance, TR20 9AE.
(T) 01736 763721
Mr Reg England (Manager), Peninsula Coarse Fisheries, St Cleer Depot, Lewdown, Okehampton, Devon EX20 4QT.
(T) 01837 871565 **(F)** 01837 871534
Profile: FT: Coarse; **WN:** Bussow; **WT:** Reservoir (Still). **Location:** **Main Rd:** B3311.
Ref: FH0772

BUTE TOWN RESERVOIR

Bute Town Reservoir, Rhymney, Tredegar, **BLAENAU GWENT**, NP22, **Wales**.
Contact/s: Fishery Manager.
(T) 01495 717001
Mr Cal White (Hon Secretary), Rhymney Angling Club, 39 The Square, Pontlottyn, Glamorgan (Vale of), CF8 9PD.
(T) 01685 841245
Mr H Green (Manager), Green's Fishing Tackle, Bryn Rd, Pontllanfraith, Blackwood, NP12 2BU.
(T) 01495 221881
Profile: FT: Coarse; **WN:** Bute Town; **WT:** Pond (Still) **W. Size:** 1 Acre. **Location:** **Main Rd:** A465.
Ref: FH0773

BUTLEIGH ROAD PONDS

Butleigh Road Ponds, Butleigh Rd, Street, **SOMERSET**, BA16, **England**.
Contact/s: **Mr Nick Hughes** (Manager),

Street Angling Ctre, 160 High St, St, Somerset, BA16 0NH.
(T) 01458 447830 (F) 01458 447830
Profile: FT: Coarse; WN: Butleigh Road; WT: Pond (Still). Location: Nr. Rd: Butleigh Road.
Ref: FH0774

BUTLERS HILL FARM

Butlers Hill Farm, Great Rollright, Chipping Norton, **OXFORDSHIRE**, OX7 5SJ, **England**.
Contact/s: **Mr Ken Parker**.
(T) 01608 684319 (M) 07860 444313
Profile: FT: Coarse; WN: Butlers Hill Farm; WT: Lake (Still) W. Size: 1 Acre. Location: Nr. Rd: Rollright Crossroads; Main Rd: A3400.
Ref: FH0775

BUTTERLEY RESERVOIR

Butterley Reservoir, Ripley, **DERBYSHIRE**, DE5, **England**.
Contact/s: Secretary.
(T) 01773 746486
Mr Kev Davies, Rod and Line Tackle, 17 Nottingham Rd, Ripley, Derbyshire, DE5 3DJ.
(T) 01773 749545
Profile: FT: Coarse; WN: Butterley; WT: Reservoir (Still) W. Size: 75 Acres. Location: Nr. Rd: B6179; Main Rd: Alfreton to Ripley.
Ref: FH0776

BUTTERMERE LAKE

Buttermere Lake, Buttermere, Cockermouth, **CUMBRIA**, CA13, **England**.
Contact/s: **Mr Parker**, Dalegarth Guest House, Buttermere, Cockermouth, Cumbria, CA13 9XA.
(T) 01768 770233 (F) 01768 770233
Mr Mark Astley (Warden), National Trust, Beckfoot Office, Ennerdale, Cleator, Cumbria, CA23 3AU.
(T) 01946 861235 (F) 01946 861235
(E) rennpm@smtp.ntrust.org.uk
Profile: FT: Combination; WN: Buttermere; WT: Lake (Still) W. Size: 4800 Metres. Location: Nr. Rd: B5289; Main Rd: A66; Rail: Penrith.
Ref: FH0777

BUTTERSTONE LOCH

Butterstone Loch, Dunkeld, **PERTH AND KINROSS**, PH8, **Scotland**.
Contact/s: **Mr R Knight** (Manager).
(T) 01350 724238
Profile: FT: Game; WN: Butterstone; WT: Loch (Still).
Ref: FH0778

BUTTERWELL

Butterwell, Nanstallon, Bodmin, **CORNWALL**, PL30 5LQ, **England**.
(W) www.butterwell.u-net.com
Contact/s: **Mr Tyson Jackson** (Owner).
(T) 01208 831515 (F) 01208 831515
(E) tyson@butterwell.u-net.com
Mrs Janet Jackson (Owner).
(T) 01208 831515 (F) 01208 831515
(E) tyson@butterwell.u-net.com
Profile: FT: Game; WN: Camel; WT: River (Moving) W. Size: 2250 Metres. Location: Main Rd: A30; Rail: Bodmin.
Ref: FH0779

BUXTED OAST FISHERY

Oast Farm, Buxted Oast Farm, Lephams Bridge, Buxted, Uckfield, **SUSSEX (EAST)**, TN22 4AU, **England**.
Contact/s: **Mr Philip Greenland** (Manager).
(T) 01825 733446
(E) oast_farm@hotmail.com
Profile: FT: Coarse; WN: Oast Farm; WT: Dam (Still); F. Size: 1 Acre. Location: Nr. Rd: A272; Main Rd: A272; Rail: Buxted.
Ref: FH0780

BUXTED PARK FISHERY

Buxted Park Fishery, Buxted, Uckfield, **SUSSEX (EAST)**, TN22, **England**.
Contact/s: Manager.
(T) 01860 372625
Profile: FT: Coarse; WN: Buxted Park Fishery; WT: Lake (Still) W. Size: 4 Acres. Location: Main Rd: A272.
Ref: FH0781

BYERS GREEN

Byers Green, Spennymoor, **COUNTY DURHAM**, DL16, **England**.
Contact/s: **Mr Barry Hignett** (Secretary), Ferryhill and District Angling Club, 74 Grasmere Rd, Garden Farm Estate, Chester-le-Street, County Durham.
(T) 0191 3883557
Mr S Kent (Membership Secretary), 4 Belsay Cl, Ferryhill, County Durham, DL17 8SX.
Profile: FT: Combination; WN: Wear; WT: River (Moving) W. Size: 800 Metres. Location: Main Rd: A6074; Rail: Bishop Auckland.
Ref: FH0782

BYLEY FISHERIES

Byley Fisheries, Middlewich, **CHESHIRE**, CW10, **England**.
(W) www.baymalton-anglingclub.org
Contact/s: **Mr Stewart Godber** (Club Secretary), 38 Edenfield Rd, Mobberley, Knutsford, Cheshire, WA16 7HE.
(T) 01565 872582
Profile: FT: Coarse; WN: Byley; WT: Lake (Still); F. Size: 4 Acres; W. Size: 3 Acres. Location: Nr. Rd: Yatehouse Lane; Main Rd: B5309 from Middlewich.
Ref: FH0783

BYSINGWOOD

Bysingwood, Bysingwood Rd, Faversham, **KENT**, ME13, **England**.
Contact/s: **A O Baldock**, Faversham Angling Club, 5 Kennedy Cl, Faversham.
Profile: FT: Coarse; WN: Bysingwood; WT: Gravel Pit (Still) W. Size: 10 Acres. Location: Nr. Rd: A251, A2; Main Rd: M2; Rail: Faversham.
Ref: FH0784

BYWATER LAKE

Bywater Lake, Tyler Hill Coarse Fishery, Hackington Rd, Canterbury, **KENT**, CT1 2NG, **England**.
Contact/s: **Mr David Laugharne** (Manager), Tyler Hill Coarse Fishery, Canterbury, Kent.
(T) 01227 764048
Profile: FT: Coarse; WN: Bywater; WT: Lake (Still) W. Size: 4 Acres. Location: Nr. Rd: Hackington Road; Rail: Canterbury East.
Ref: FH0785

C J FISHERIES

C J Fisheries, Saddington Rd, Shearsby, Lutterworth, **LEICESTERSHIRE**, LE17 6NY, **England**.
Contact/s: **Mr John Tozer** (Owner), C J Fisheries, Saddington Rd, Shearsby, Lutterworth, Leicestershire, LE17 6NY.
(T) 0116 2478101
Profile: FT: Coarse; WN: Mallard Lake, Alder Lake & Willow Lake; WT: Lake (Still). Location: Nr. Rd: Saddington Road; Main Rd: A5199; Rail: Narborough.
Ref: FH0786

C.SCOTLAND TROUT FISHERY

Central Scotland Trout Fishery, Cumbernauld, Falkirk, FK2, **Scotland**.
Contact/s: **Mr Don O'Driscoll** (Manager).
(T) 01324 851672
Profile: FT: Game; WN: Central Scotland Trout Fishery; WT: Lake (Still) W. Size: 4 Acres.
Ref: FH0889

CACKLE HILL LAKES

Cackle Hill Lakes, Newcastle Farm, Headcorn Rd, Biddenden, Ashford, **KENT**, TN27 8JW, **England**.
Contact/s: **Mr Richard Brown**.
(T) 01622 890884
Mr Robert Brown (Owner).
Profile: FT: Coarse; WN: Cackle Hill; WT: Lake (Still) W. Size: 4 Acres. Location: Nr. Rd: Headcorn Road; Main Rd: A274, South of Maidstone; Rail: Headcorn.
Ref: FH0787

CADOVER BRIDGE PITS

Cadover Bridge Pits, St Germans, Cadover Bridge, Plymouth, **DEVON**, PL, **England**.
Contact/s: Manager, Clive's Tackle and Bait, 182 Exeter St, Plymouth, Devon, PL4 0NQ.
(T) 01752 228940 (F) 01752 603001
Mr Carl Bovey, 39 Hilton Avenue, Manadon, Plymouth, Devon, PI5 3HS.
(T) 01752 709339
Profile: FT: Coarse; WN: Cadover Bridge; WT: Gravel Pit (Still) W. Size: 2 Acres.
Ref: FH0788

CAER BERIS MANOR HOTEL

Caer Beris Manor Hotel, Builth Wells, **POWYS**, LD2 3NP, **Wales**.
(W) www.caerberis.co.uk
Contact/s: **Mr Peter Smith** (Manager), Caer Beris Manor, Builth Wells, Powys, LD2 3NP.
(T) 01982 552601 (F) 01982 552586
Profile: FT: Game; WN: Irfon; WT: River (Moving) W. Size: 1000 Metres. Location: Nr. Rd: A483; Rail: Climery. £Fr
Ref: FH0789

CAERPHILLY CASTLE LAKES

Caerphilly Castle Lakes, 14 Castle St, Caerphilly, CF83, **Wales**.
Contact/s: Fishery Manager.
(T) 029 20885409
Profile: FT: Coarse; WN: Caerphilly Castle; WT: Lake (Still).
Ref: FH0790

CAHA (RIVER)

Caha River, Dunmanway, **COUNTY CORK**, **Ireland**.
Profile: FT: Game; WN: Caha; WT: River (Moving).
Ref: FH0791

CALDER (RIVER)

Calder (River), Standen Estate, Great Mitton, Nr. Whalley, Blackburn, **LANCASHIRE**, **England**.
Contact/s: **Mr John Turner** (Hon Secretary), Prince Albert Angling Society, 15 Pexhill Drive, Macclesfield, Cheshire, SK10 3LP.
(T) 01625 422010
Profile: FT: Game; WN: Calder; WT: River (Moving) W. Size: 1000 Metres. Location: Main Rd: B6246; Rail: Billington.
Ref: FH0792

CALDER (RIVER)

Calder (River), Hole House Farm, Whalley, Burnley, **LANCASHIRE**, **England**.
Contact/s: **Mr John Turner** (Hon Secretary), Prince Albert Angling Society, 15 Pexhill Drive, Macclesfield, Cheshire, SK10 3LP.
(T) 01625 422010
Profile: FT: Game; WN: Calder (River); WT: River (Moving) W. Size: 1000 Metres. Location: Main Rd: B6246; Rail: Burnley.
Ref: FH0793

CALDER (RIVER)

River Calder, Todmorden, **YORKSHIRE (WEST)**, OL14, **England**.
Contact/s: **Mr Ray Barber** (Secretary), Todmorden Angling Society, 12 Grisedale Drive, Burnley, Lancashire, BB12 8AR.
(T) 01282 423780 (M) 07970 897849
Profile: FT: Combination; WN: Calder; WT: River (Moving) W. Size: 2000 Metres. Location: Nr. Rd: A646; Main Rd: A646.
Ref: FH0794

CALDER (RIVER)

River Calder, Huddersfield, **YORKSHIRE (WEST)**, HD, **England**.

Contact/s: Area Manager, Environment Agency, Ridings Area Office, Phoenix House, Global Avenue, Leeds, LS11 8PG.
(T) 0113 2440191or2314834 **(F)** 0113 2134609
Mr P Budd (Secretary), Holme Valley Piscatorial Association, 39 Derwent Rd, Honley, Huddersfield, HD7 2EL.
Profile: **FT:** Coarse; **WN:** Calder; **WT:** River (Moving). **Location:** **Nr. Rd:** Battyeford to Mirfield.
Ref: FH0795

CALDER (RIVER)

River Calder, Ganny Lock, Brighouse, Bradford, **YORKSHIRE (WEST)**, BD, **England**.
Contact/s: **Mr E K Mann** (Club Secretary), 19 Busfield St, Bradford, Yorkshire (West), BD4 7QX.
(T) 01274 720072
Profile: **FT:** Combination; **WN:** Calder (Ganny Lock to Sowerby Bridge); **WT:** River (Moving) **W. Size:** 800 Metres. **Location:** **Nr. Rd:** Elland Road.
Ref: FH0796

CALDER AND HEBBLE CANAL

Calder And Hebble Canal, Brighouse, **YORKSHIRE (WEST)**, HD6, **England**.
Contact/s: **Mr Chris Johnson** (Secretary).
(T) 01484 718598
Mr D Noble, Brighouse Angling Association, 1a Church Lane, Brighouse, Yorkshire (West), HD6 1AT.
(T) 01484 717034
Mr David Finnigan (Manager).
(T) 01422 373223or01442722310
Profile: **FT:** Coarse; **WN:** Calder and Hebble; **WT:** Canal (Still) **W. Size:** 1400 Metres.
Ref: FH0797

CALDER AND HEBBLE CANAL

Calder And Hebble Canal, Hebden Bridge, **YORKSHIRE (WEST)**, HX7, **England**.
Contact/s: **Mr Terry Hooson** (Fishery Manager).
(T) 01422 344223
Profile: **FT:** Coarse; **WN:** Calder and Hebble; **WT:** Canal (Still) **W. Size:** 5600 Metres. **Location:** **Nr. Rd:** Sowerby Bridge to Halifax; **Main Rd:** A646.
Ref: FH0798

CALDERSTONES PARK LAKE

Calderstones Park Lake, Woolton, Liverpool, **MERSEYSIDE**, **England**.
Contact/s: .
(T) 0151 2606015
Profile: **FT:** Coarse; **WN:** Calderstones Park Lake; **WT:** Lake (Still) **W. Size:** 3 Acres. **Location:** **Nr. Rd:** Yewtree Road; **Main Rd:** A562.
Ref: FH0799

CALDEW (RIVER)

River Caldew, Dalston, Carlisle, **CUMBRIA**, CA5, **England**.
Contact/s: Fishery Manager.
(T) 01228 71065
Profile: **FT:** Coarse; **WN:** Caldew; **WT:** River (Moving).
Ref: FH0800

CALIBER COARSE AND CARP LAKES

Caliber Coarse And Carp Lakes, Wingham, Canterbury, **KENT**, CT3, **England**.
Contact/s: Fishery Manager.
(T) 01303 813644
Profile: **FT:** Coarse; **WN:** Caliber Coarse And Carp Lakes; **WT:** Lake (Still).
Ref: FH0801

CALLAN (RIVER)

River Callan, Armagh, **COUNTY ARMAGH**, BT60, **Northern Ireland**.
Contact/s: **Dessie Cartmill** (Manager), Armagh Fisheries Ltd, G I Stores, 5 Dobbin St, Armagh, County Armagh.
(T) 028 37522335 **(F)** 028 37522335
Mr Peter McKinney (Project Manager), Armagh Fisheries Ltd, 50 Ballynahonemore Rd, Armagh, County Armagh, BT60 1HY.
(T) 028 37511738 **(M)** 07775 805670
Profile: **FT:** Game; **WN:** Callan; **WT:** River (Moving) **W. Size:** 14400 Metres.
Ref: FH0802

CALLOW LAKES

Callow Lakes, Foxford, **COUNTY MAYO**, **Ireland**.
Contact/s: Angling Officer, North Western Regional Fisheries Board, Ardnaree House, Abbey St, Ballina, County Mayo.
(T) 096 22623 **(F)** 096 70543
Profile: **FT:** Game; **WN:** Callows; **WT:** Lough (Still) **W. Size:** 1640 Acres. **Location:** **Nr. Rd:** Foxford to Swinford; **Main Rd:** N26.
Ref: FH0803

CALVES LANE LAKE

Calves Lane Lake, Love Hill Lane, Iver, **BUCKINGHAMSHIRE**, SL0, **England**.
Profile: **FT:** Coarse; **WN:** Calves Lane Lake; **WT:** Lake (Still) **W. Size:** 2 Acres. **Location:** **Nr. Rd:** Love Hill Lane off the B470.
Ref: FH0804

CAM (RIVER)

River Cam, Clayhithe Bridge, Cambridge, **CAMBRIDGESHIRE**, **England**.
(W) www.cambridgefpas.co.uk
Contact/s: **Mr Graham Tweed** (Secretary), Cambridge Fish Preservation Angling Society, 27a Villa Rd, Impington, Cambridge, CB4 9NZ.
(T) 01223 234616
Profile: **FT:** Coarse; **WN:** Cam; **WT:** River (Moving). **Location:** **Nr. Rd:** A10; **Main Rd:** A14.
Ref: FH0805

CAM (RIVER)

River Cam, Newnham, Ely, **CAMBRIDGESHIRE**, CB7, **England**.
Profile: **FT:** Coarse; **WN:** Cam; **WT:** River (Moving) **W. Size:** 1600 Metres. **Location:** **Main Rd:** A603. £Fr
Ref: FH0807

CAMEL (RIVER)

River Camel, Pencarrow, Wadebridge, **CORNWALL**, PL27, **England**.
Contact/s: **Mr Marcus Watts** (Manager), The Bait Bunker, 5 Polmorla Rd, Wadebridge, Cornwall, PL27 7NB.
(T) 01208 816403 **(F)** 01208 816403
Profile: **FT:** Game; **WN:** Camel; **WT:** River (Moving) **W. Size:** 9600 Metres. **Location:** **Nr. Rd:** Pencarrow and Wenford.
Ref: FH0808

CAMEL (RIVER)

River Camel, Gwendreath, Dunmere, Bodmin, **CORNWALL**, PL31 2RD, **England**.
Contact/s: **Mr Ray Burrows** (Hon Secretary), Bodmin Angling Association, 26 Meadow Pl, Bodmin, PL31 1JD.
(T) 01208 75513
Profile: **FT:** Game; **WN:** Camel; **WT:** River (Moving). **Location:** **Nr. Rd:** Gwendreath.
Ref: FH0809

CAMEL (RIVER)

River Camel, Bodmin, **DEVON**, PL3, **England**.
Contact/s: **Mr Ray Burrows** (Hon Secretary), Bodmin Angling Association, 26 Meadow Pl, Bodmin, PL31 1JD.
(T) 01208 75513
Profile: **FT:** Game; **WN:** Camel; **WT:** River (Moving). **Location:** **Nr. Rd:** A30; **Rail:** Bodmin Parkway.
Ref: FH0810

CAMEL (RIVER)

River Camel, Polbrock Bridge, Bodmin, **DEVON**, PL3, **England**.
Contact/s: **Mr Ray Burrows** (Hon Secretary), 26 Meadow Pl, Bodmin, PL31 1JD.
(T) 01208 75513
Profile: **FT:** Game; **WN:** Camel; **WT:** River (Moving) **W. Size:** 19200 Metres. **Location:** **Nr. Rd:** Polbrock Bridge and Upstream; **Main Rd:** A30; **Rail:** Bodmin Parkway.
Ref: FH0811

CAMELEY TROUT LAKES

Cameley Trout Lakes, Hillcrest Farm, Cameley, Temple Cloud, Bristol, **SOMERSET**, BS39 5AQ, **England**.
Contact/s: **Mr John Harris**.
(T) 01761 452423
Profile: **FT:** Game; **WN:** Cameley; **WT:** Combination (Still & Moving) **W. Size:** 4 Acres. **Location:** **Nr. Rd:** A37, Bristol to Wells Road; **Main Rd:** Bristol to Bath.
Ref: FH0812

CAMELOT LAKE

Camelot Lake, Wortwell, Harleston, **SUFFOLK**, IP20, **England**.
Contact/s: **Mr Phill Newcombe**.
(T) 01986 788208
Profile: **FT:** Coarse; **WN:** Camelot; **WT:** Lake (Still) **W. Size:** 3 Acres. **Location:** **Nr. Rd:** Bungy to Wortwell; **Main Rd:** A143.
Ref: FH0813

CAMERON RESERVOIR

Cameron Reservoir, St Andrews, **FIFE**, KY16, **Scotland**.
Contact/s: Fishery Manager.
(T) 01334 476347
Profile: **FT:** Game; **WN:** Cameron; **WT:** Reservoir (Still).
Ref: FH0814

CAMOWEN (RIVER)

River Camowen, Omagh, **COUNTY TYRONE**, BT78, **Northern Ireland**.
Contact/s: **Mr Ca Anderson** (Secretary), Omagh Angling Association, 64 Market St, Omagh, County Tyrone, BT78 1EN.
(E) andersonca@lineone.net
Mr Stephen Martin (License Distributor).
(T) 028 82242311 **(F)** 028 82249539 **(M)** 07776 343600
Profile: **FT:** Game; **WN:** Camowen; **WT:** River (Moving) **W. Size:** 6400 Metres. **Location:** **Nr. Rd:** A5; **Main Rd:** A5.
Ref: FH0815

CAMPHILL RESERVOIR

Camphill Reservoir, Kilbirnie, **AYRSHIRE (NORTH)**, KA25, **Scotland**.
Contact/s: Manager, R T Cycles, 73 Main St, Glengarnock, Beith, KA14 3AA.
(T) 01505 682191 **(F)** 01505 682191
Strathclyde Police Recreation Association Secretary.
(T) 0141 5326300
Mr David Campbell.
(T) 01505 684140
Profile: **FT:** Game; **WN:** Camphill; **WT:** Reservoir (Still); **F. Size:** 250 Acres; **W. Size:** 200 Acres. **Location:** **Nr. Rd:** A760 Langs to Kilbirnie; **Rail:** Kilbirnie.
Ref: FH0816

CAMPS RESERVOIR

Camps Reservoir, Glasgow, **GLASGOW (CITY OF)**, G, **Scotland**.
Profile: **FT:** Game; **WN:** Camps; **WT:** Reservoir (Still).
Ref: FH0817

CAMPSALL COUNTRY PARK

Campsall Country Park, Campsall, Askern, Doncaster, **YORKSHIRE (SOUTH)**, DN, **England**.
Contact/s: **Mr Martin Nowacki**.
(T) 01302 737409
Profile: **FT:** Coarse; **WN:** Campsall Clay; **WT:** Pond (Still). **Location:** **Main Rd:** A19.
Ref: FH0818

CANAL PIT

Canal Pit, Whatcroft, Northwich, **CHESHIRE**, CW, **England**.
Contact/s: **Mr J Clitheroe** (Secretary), Northwich Angling Association, PO Box 18, Northwich, Cheshire, CW9 5SE.
(T) 01606 75132

Profile: **FT:** Coarse; **WN:** Canal; **WT:** Gravel Pit (Still). **Location:** **Main Rd:** A530.
Ref: FH0819

CANAL RESERVOIRS

Canal Reservoirs, Muirhearlich, Fowlers Lane, Light Oaks, Stoke-on-Trent, **STAFFORDSHIRE**, ST2 7NB, **England**.
Contact/s: **Mr Albert Perkins** (Hon Secretary), 63 Fowlers Lane, Light Oaks, Stoke-on-Trent, Staffordshire, ST2 7NB.
Profile: **FT:** Coarse; **WN:** Canal; **WT:** Reservoir (Still).
Ref: FH0820

CANDOVER BROOK

Candover Brook, Alresford, **HAMPSHIRE**, SO24, **England**.
Profile: **FT:** Game; **WN:** Candover; **WT:** Brook (Moving).
Ref: FH0821

CANNOCK EXTENSION CANAL

Cannock Extension Canal, Wyrley Lane, Little Wyrley, Pelsall, **MIDLANDS (WEST)**, **England**.
Contact/s: .
(T) 01543 571482
Profile: **FT:** Coarse; **WN:** Cannock Extension; **WT:** Canal (Still) **W. Size:** 1609 Metres. **Location:** **Nr. Rd:** Wyrley Lane; **Main Rd:** B4154; **Rail:** Cheslyn Hay.
Ref: FH0822

CANNOP PONDS

Cannop Ponds, Forest Of Dean, **GLOUCESTERSHIRE**, **England**.
Contact/s: .
(T) 01594 833286
Profile: **FT:** Coarse; **WN:** Cannop Ponds; **WT:** Pond (Still).
Ref: FH0823

CANONS ASHBY LAKES

Canons Ashby Lakes, Canons Ashby, Daventry, **NORTHAMPTONSHIRE**, NN11, **England**.
Contact/s: **Mr Terry Rodhouse** (Secretary), Castle Angling Association, 12 Somerville Rd, Daventry, Northamptonshire, NN11 4RT.
(T) 01327 705692
Profile: **FT:** Coarse; **WN:** Canons Ashby; **WT:** Lake (Still) **W. Size:** 7 Acres. **Location:** **Nr. Rd:** B525; **Main Rd:** A5; **Rail:** Banbury.
Ref: FH0824

CANT CLOUGH RESERVOIR

Cant Clough Reservoir, Burnley, **LANCASHIRE**, BB9 6, **England**.
Contact/s: **Mr R Halstead** (Secretary), 32 Parrock Rd, Barrowford, Nelson, Lancashire, BB9 6QF.
Mr Roy Rhodes (Conservation, Access and Recreation Manager), Rivington Water Treatment Works, Bolton Rd, Horwich, Bolton, BL6 7RN.
(T) 01204 664300
Profile: **FT:** Game; **WN:** Cant Clough; **WT:** Reservoir (Still). **Location:** **Nr. Rd:** Cow Lane.
Ref: FH0825

CANTEF RESERVOIR

Cantef Reservoir, Brecon, **POWYS**, LD3, **Wales**.
Contact/s: Fishery Manager.
(T) 01443 450577
Profile: **FT:** Game; **WN:** Cantef; **WT:** Reservoir (Still).
Ref: FH0826

CANTLEY (RIVER)

River Cantley, Cantley, Norwich, **NORFOLK**, NR13, **England**.
Profile: **FT:** Coarse; **WN:** Cantley; **WT:** River (Moving).
Ref: FH0827

CANTLEY SUGAR FACTORY

Cantley Sugar Factory, Cantley, Norwich, **NORFOLK**, NR13, **England**.
Contact/s: Fishery Manager.
(T) 01493 700351
Profile: **FT:** Coarse; **WN:** Cantley Sugar Factory; **WT:** Lake (Still).
Ref: FH0828

CANTREF RESERVOIR

Cantref Reservoir, Hyder, Sluvad Treatment Works, Llandegfedd Reservoir, New Inn, Pontypool, **TORFAEN**, NP4 0TA, **Wales**.
Profile: **FT:** Game; **WN:** Cantref; **WT:** Reservoir (Still).
Ref: FH0829

CANTS MERE

Cants Mere, Hoe Mill, Hatfield Peverel, Witham, **ESSEX**, CM8, **England**.
Contact/s: **Ms Irene Lewis** (Secretary), 60 Delamere Rd, Chelmsford, CM1 2TG.
(T) 01245 264832
Profile: **FT:** Coarse; **WN:** Cants Mere; **WT:** Gravel Pit (Still) **W. Size:** 2 Acres. **Location:** **Main Rd:** A12, Chelmsford to Colchester.
Ref: FH0830

CAPESTHORNE HALL STOCK POND

Capesthorne Hall Stock Pond, Capesthorne Hall, Siddington, Macclesfield, **CHESHIRE**, SK11, **England**.
Contact/s: **Mr Keith Walley** (Water Bailiff).
(T) 01625 861584
Ms Liz Hayes (Manager).
(T) 01625 251262
Profile: **FT:** Coarse; **WN:** Capesthorne Hall Stock; **WT:** Pond (Still). **Location:** **Nr. Rd:** A34; **Main Rd:** A34; **Rail:** Alderley Edge.
Ref: FH0831

CAPESTHORNE MAIN POOL

Capesthorne Main Pool, Capesthorne Estate, Siddington, Macclesfield, **CHESHIRE**, SK11, **England**.
Contact/s: **Mr Albert Perkins** (Hon Secretary), Muirshearlich, 63 Fowlers Lane, Light Oaks, Stoke-on-Trent, Staffordshire ST2 7NB.
Ms Liz Hayes (Manager).
(T) 01625 251262
Profile: **FT:** Coarse; **WN:** Capesthorne Main; **WT:** Lake (Still) **W. Size:** 10 Acres. **Location:** **Nr. Rd:** A34; **Main Rd:** A34; **Rail:** Alderley Edge.
Ref: FH0832

CAPESTHORNE TOP POOL

Capesthorne Top Pool, Capesthorne Estate, Siddington, Macclesfield, **CHESHIRE**, SK11, **England**.
Contact/s: **Mr Albert Perkins** (Hon Secretary), 63 Fowlers Lane, Light Oaks, Stoke-on-Trent, Staffordshire, ST2 7NB.
Ms Liz Hayes (Manager).
(T) 01625 251262
Profile: **FT:** Coarse; **WN:** Capesthorne Top Pool; **WT:** Lake (Still); **F. Size:** 9 Acres; **W. Size:** 6 Acres. **Location:** **Nr. Rd:** A34; **Main Rd:** A34; **Rail:** Alderley Edge.
Ref: FH0833

CAPSTONE FARM COUNTRY PARK

Capstone Farm Country Park, Capstone Rd, Gillingham, **KENT**, ME7 3JG, **England**.
Contact/s: **Mr Hamish White** (Country Park Officer).
(T) 01634 812196
Profile: **FT:** Coarse; **WN:** Capstone Farm Country Park; **WT:** Lake (Still) **W. Size:** 3 Acres. **Location:** **Nr. Rd:** Capstone Road; **Main Rd:** A2; **Rail:** Gillingham.
Ref: FH0834

CAPTAINS POOL

Captains Pool, Spennells, Kidderminster, **WORCESTERSHIRE**, DY, **England**.
Contact/s: **Mr A Mobley** (Secretary), Phoenix Angling Club, 8 Pentaloe Cl, Mordiford, Herefordshire, HR1 4LS.
(T) 01432 870579
Profile: **FT:** Coarse; **WN:** Captains; **WT:** Pool (Still); **F. Size:** 8 Acres; **W. Size:** 5 Acres. **Location:** **Main Rd:** Comberton Road; **Rail:** Kidderminster.
Ref: FH0835

CARADOC FISHERY

Caradoc Fishery, Sellack, Ross-on-Wye, **HEREFORDSHIRE**, HR9, **England**.
Contact/s: **Mr Major Darling**, Caradoc Court, Sellack, Ross-on-Wye, Herefordshire.
Profile: **FT:** Game; **WN:** Wye; **WT:** River (Moving) **W. Size:** 1600 Metres. **Location:** **Nr. Rd:** Sellack to Hoarwithy; **Main Rd:** A40, then the A49.
Ref: FH0836

CARAGH FISHERY

Caragh Fishery, Glencar Hotel, Glencar, **COUNTY KERRY**, **Ireland**.
Contact/s: Fishery Manager.
(T) 066 60102
Profile: **FT:** Game; **WN:** Caragh; **WT:** Reservoir (Still).
Ref: FH0837

CARCUS WATERS

Carcus Waters, Kirklees St, Tottington, Bury, **MANCHESTER (GREATER)**, BL, **England**.
Contact/s: **Mr Bill Turner** (Secretary), 18 Hawthorn Avenue, Edenfield, Bury.
(T) 01706 823799
Profile: **FT:** Coarse; **WN:** Carcus; **WT:** Lake (Still). **Location:** **Nr. Rd:** Kirklees Street; **Main Rd:** B6213.
Ref: FH0838

CAREY (RIVER)

River Carey, Ballycastle, **COUNTY ANTRIM**, BT54, **Northern Ireland**.
Contact/s: **Mr Bill Williamson** (Hon Secretary), 26 Cushendall Rd, Ballycastle, County Antrim, BT54 6QR.
(T) 028 20762693
Profile: **FT:** Game; **WN:** Carey; **WT:** Tributary (Moving) **W. Size:** 4800 Metres.
Ref: FH0839

CAREYSVILLE

Careysville, Fermoy, **COUNTY CORK**, **Ireland**.
Contact/s: Manager, Brian Twomey Sports and Leisure, 18 McCurtain St, Fermoy, County Cork.
Mr Michael Penruddock (Agent To The Lismore Estates), Lismore Estate Office, Lismore Castle, Lismore, County Waterford, Ireland.
(T) 058 54424 **(F)** 058 54896
Profile: **FT:** Game; **WN:** Blackwater; **WT:** River (Moving) **W. Size:** 2650 Metres. **Location:** **Nr. Rd:** Fermoy to Fallow Road; **Main Rd:** N72; **Rail:** Mallow.
Ref: FH0840

CARGILL LAKE

Cargill Lake, Staines, London, **LONDON (GREATER)**, TW19, **England**.
Contact/s: **Mr Fred Lancaster** (Secretary), Blenheim Angling Society, Brairwood, Burtons Lane, Chalfont St Giles, Buckinghamshire, HP8 4BB.
(T) 01494 764977
(E) blenheim.angling@ntlworld.com
Mr John Gill (Assistant Fisheries Officer).
(T) 020 85612993
Profile: **FT:** Coarse; **WN:** Cargill; **WT:** Gravel Pit (Still) **W. Size:** 9 Acres. **Location:** **Nr. Rd:** B376; **Main Rd:** M25; **Rail:** Wraysbury.
Ref: FH0841

CARLETON HILL

Carleton Hill, Carlisle, **CUMBRIA**, CA, **England**.
Contact/s: **Mr Chris Wynne** (Manager).
(T) 01228 560793 **(M)** 07713 499296
Profile: **FT:** Coarse; **WN:** Carleton Mill; **WT:** Lake (Still). **Location:** **Main Rd:** A6.
Ref: FH0842

CARLTON LODGE LAKE

Carlton Lodge Lake, Carlton Miniott, Thirsk, **YORKSHIRE (NORTH)**, YO7, **England**.
Contact/s: Fishery Manager.

(T) 01845 522145
Profile: FT: Coarse; WN: Carlton; WT: Lake (Still).
Ref: FH0843

CARN LOCH

Carn Loch, Lochgilphead, **RENFREWSHIRE**, PA3, **Scotland**.
Contact/s: Mr Archie MacGilp (Secretary), Fyne Tackle, 22 Argyll St, Lochgilphead, Argyll and Bute, PA31 8NE.
(T) 01546 606878
Profile: FT: Game; WN: Carn; WT: Loch (Still); F. Size: 400 Acres; W. Size: 60 Acres. Location: Nr. Rd: Cairnbaan; Main Rd: B844; Rail: Oban.
Ref: FH0844

CARP FARM FRYERNING FISHERIES

Carp Farm Fryerning Fisheries (The), Handley Barn Farm, Little Hyde Lane, Ingatestone, **ESSEX**, CM4 0EA, **England**.
Contact/s: Mr C D Knowles (Owner).
(T) 01277 352245 or 821554 (F) 01227 821554
Mr James Clark (Manager). (M) 07711 664303
Profile: FT: Combination; WN: Carp Farm Fryerning Fisheries (The); WT: Lake (Still); F. Size: 200 Acres; W. Size: 20 Acres. Location: Nr. Rd: Little Hyde Lane; Main Rd: A12; Rail: Ingatestone.
Ref: FH0845

CARP VALE

Carp Vale, Church Lane, Moor Monkton, York, **YORKSHIRE (NORTH)**, YO26 8, **England**.
Contact/s: Mr Kevin Whincup (Fishery Manager), Southview House, Church Lane, Moor Monkton, York, YO26 8LA.
(T) 01904 738249 (F) 01904 738249 (M) 07774 704301
Profile: FT: Coarse; WN: Carp Vale; WT: Pool (Still) W. Size: 5 Acres. Location: Nr. Rd: Church Lane; Main Rd: A59; Rail: York.
Ref: FH0846

CARR LANE POOL

Carr Lane Pool, Carr Lane, Prescot, **MERSEYSIDE**, L34, **England**.
Contact/s: Manager, Ray's Tackle, 22 Childwall Lane, Bowring Park, Liverpool, L14 6TX.
(T) 0151 4896103 (F) 0151 4896103
Mr Wally Colsure (Secretary).
(T) 0151 4268405
Profile: FT: Coarse; WN: Carr Lane; WT: Pool (Still). Location: Nr. Rd: Carr Lane; Main Rd: M62, junction 7.
Ref: FH0847

CARR MILL DAM

Carr Mill Dam, Moss Bank, St Helens, **MERSEYSIDE**, WA11, **England**.
Contact/s: Mr Griffiths (Fishery Manager).
(T) 01606 723800
Mr Les Bromilow.
(T) 01744 601287
Profile: FT: Coarse; WN: Carr; WT: Mill Dam (Still) W. Size: 55 Acres. Location: Nr. Rd: A580 Manchester to Liverpool; Main Rd: A571.
Ref: FH0848

CARRICK LOUGH

Carrick Lough, Brantry, Greystone, Aughnacloy, **COUNTY TYRONE**, BT69, **Northern Ireland**.
Contact/s: Mrs Liz Salter (Manager), Aughnacloy Development Association, The McCreedy Mill Centre, Aughnacloy, County Tyrone, BT69 6AL.
(T) 028 85557002
Profile: FT: Coarse; WN: Carrick; WT: Lough (Still).
Ref: FH0849

CARRICKMANNON FISHERY

Carrickmannon Fishery, Station Rd, Saintfield, Ballynahinch, **COUNTY DOWN**, BT24 7EL, **Northern Ireland**.
Contact/s: Fishery Manager.
(T) 028 97510654
Profile: FT: Game; WN: Carrickmannon Fishery; WT: Loch (Still). Location: Nr. Rd: Station Road.
Ref: FH0850

CARRON (RIVER)

River Carron, Stonehaven, **ABERDEENSHIRE**, AB39, **Scotland**.
Contact/s: Mrs D Mcrae (manageress), D F S, 31 Market Sq, Stonehaven, Aberdeenshire, AB39 2BA.
(T) 01569 762239
Profile: FT: Game; WN: Carron; WT: River (Moving).
Ref: FH0851

CARRON ROW FARM PONDS

Carron Row Farm Ponds, Segensworth Rd, Titchfield, Fareham, **HAMPSHIRE**, PO14, **England**.
Contact/s: Mr Ian Hammond.
Profile: FT: Coarse; WN: Carron Row Farm; WT: Pond (Still). Location: Nr. Rd: Segensworth Road; Main Rd: M27, junction 9, A27 south to Titchfield.
Ref: FH0852

CARROWNISKY

Carrownisky, Louisberg, Louisburgh, **COUNTY MAYO**, **Ireland**.
Contact/s: Mr Charles Gaffney.
(T) 098 66150
Profile: FT: Game; WN: Carrownisky; WT: River (Moving).
Ref: FH0853

CARSINGTON WATER

Carsington Water, Fishery Office, Carsington Water, Ashbourne, **DERBYSHIRE**, DE6 1ST, **England**.
Contact/s: Manager.
(T) 01629 540478
Mr Lee Hollings (Fishery Manager).
(T) 01629 540769 (F) 01629 540558
Profile: FT: Game; WN: Carsington Water; WT: Reservoir (Still); F. Size: 1100 Acres; W. Size: 750 Acres. Location: Nr. Rd: B5035; Main Rd: A517; Rail: Cromford.
Ref: FH0854

CARTHAGENA FISHERY

Carthagena Fishery, Carthagena Lock, Carthagena Estate, Broxbourne, **HERTFORDSHIRE**, EN10 6TA, **England**.
Contact/s: Mr Peter Brill (Resident Manager).
(T) 01992 463656
Profile: FT: Coarse; WN: Carthagena Fishery; WT: Combination (Still & Moving) W. Size: 800 Metres. Location: Nr. Rd: B194 New Nazing Road; Main Rd: M25, junction 25; Rail: Broxbourne.
Ref: FH0855

CASTELL-PYR FISHERY

Castell-Pyr Fishery, Castell-Pyr, Llandysul, **CEREDIGION**, SA, **Wales**.
(W) www.fishing-in-wales.co.uk/llandysul-aa/beat8a
Contact/s: Mr Artie Jones (Hon Secretary), Llandysul Angling Association, Glas-y-Dorlan, Llyn-y-Fran Rd, Llandysul, SA44 4JW.
(T) 01559 362317
Profile: FT: Game; WN: Teifi; WT: River (Moving).
Ref: FH0856

CASTLE ASHBY LAKES

Castle Ashby Lakes, Castle Ashby, Gredon, Northampton, **NORTHAMPTONSHIRE**, NN7, **England**.
Contact/s: Mr M Hewlett, 176 Birchfield Road East, Abington, Northamptonshire, NN3 2HG.
(T) 01604 712346
Profile: FT: Coarse; WN: Castle Ashby; WT: Lake (Still).
Ref: FH0858

CASTLE BEAT

Castle Beat, Kenmore, Aberfeldy, **PERTH AND KINROSS**, PH15, **Scotland**.
(W) www.fishingnet.com/beats/castle.htm
Contact/s: Mr Paul Fishlock (Salmon Permit Contact), Taymouth Castle, 2 The Square, Kenmore, Perth and Kinross, PH15 2HH.
(T) 01887 830765 (F) 01887 830830
Mrs Heather Smith (Owner), The Kenmore Post Office, The Square, Kenmore, Aberfeldy, PH15 2HH.
(T) 01887 830200
Profile: FT: Game; WN: Castle, Ford, Battery, Pony Haugh and Tommy Price; WT: Pool (Still).
Ref: FH0859

CASTLE GREEN POOLS

Castle Green Farm, Leigh Sinton, Malvern, **WORCESTERSHIRE**, WR13 5, **England**.
Contact/s: Fishery Manager.
(T) 01886 832230
Profile: FT: Coarse; WN: Castle Green; WT: Pool (Still). Location: Nr. Rd: A4103 Worcester to Hereford; Main Rd: Leigh Sinton.
Ref: FH0860

CASTLE HOWARD GREAT LAKE

Castle Howard Great Lake, North Lodge, Castle Howard, Malton, York, **YORKSHIRE (NORTH)**, YO6 7DH, **England**.
Contact/s: Mr Richard Callan (Head Bailiff).
(T) 01653 684331
Profile: FT: Coarse; WN: Castle Howard; WT: Lake (Still) W. Size: 78 Acres.
Ref: FH0861

CASTLE LOCH

Castle Loch, Lochmaben, Lockerbie, **DUMFRIES AND GALLOWAY**, DG11, **Scotland**.
Contact/s: Fishery Manager.
(T) 01387 810832
Profile: FT: Coarse; WN: Castle; WT: Loch (Still).
Ref: FH0862

CASTLE MENZIES BEAT

Castle Menzies Beat, Kenmore, Aberfeldy, **PERTH AND KINROSS**, PH15, **Scotland**.
(W) www.fishingnet.com/beats/castlemenzies
Contact/s: Mr Freddie Dall (Secretary), Ironside and Co Solicitors, Struan House, The Square, Aberfeldy, PH15 2DD.
(T) 01887 820820
Profile: FT: Combination; WN: Home Farm and Twin Trees; WT: Pool (Still).
Ref: FH0863

CASTLE RISING STREAM

Castle Rising Stream, Babingley, King's Lynn, **NORFOLK**, PE31, **England**.
Profile: FT: Coarse; WN: Castle Rising; WT: Stream (Moving) W. Size: 14400 Metres. Location: Rail: North Wootton.
Ref: FH0864

CASTLE TROUT POND

Castle Trout Pond, Mill Rd, Arundel, **SUSSEX (WEST)**, BN18, **England**.
Contact/s: Mr Darren Smith (Manager).
(T) 01903 883742 (F) 01903 884482
Profile: FT: Game; WN: Castle; WT: Pond (Still). Location: Main Rd: Mill Road.
Ref: FH0865

CASTLEBAR LAKES

Castlebar Lakes (The), Castlebar, **COUNTY MAYO**, **Ireland**.
Contact/s: Mrs Kay McGrath, Windermere House, Bed and Breakfast, Islandeady, Castlebar, County Mayo.
(T) 094 23329
Profile: FT: Game; WN: Castlebar Lakes (The); WT: Lake (Still) W. Size: 8200 Acres. Location: Nr. Rd: Castlebar to Westport Road; Main Rd: N5.

Ref: FH0866

CASTLECONNELL SALMON FISHERY

Castleconnell Salmon Fishery, Castleconnell, **COUNTY LIMERICK**, **Ireland**.
Contact/s: Manager.
(T) 061 345589 (F) 061 344560
Mr Jim Robinson.
(T) 061 377666
Profile: **FT:** Game; **WN:** Shannon; **WT:** River (Moving). Location: **Nr. Rd:** N7; **Rail:** Castleconnell.
Ref: FH0867

CASTLEMORTON

Castlemorton, Ledbury, **HEREFORDSHIRE**, HR8, **England**.
Contact/s: **Mr I Rowat** (Director), Malvern Hills Conservators, Manor House, Grange Rd, Malvern, WR14 3EY.
(T) 01684 892002
Profile: **FT:** Coarse; **WN:** Catlemorton; **WT:** Lake (Still) **W. Size:** 2 Acres.
Ref: FH0868

CASTLEREAGH LOUGHS

Castlereagh Loughs, Claremorris, **COUNTY GALWAY**, **Ireland**.
Contact/s: **Mr Danny Goldrick** (Angling Officer), The Western Regional Fisheries Board, Weir Lodge, Earl's Island, Galway City, County Galway.
(T) 091 563118 (F) 091 566335
(E) wrfb@iol.ie
Profile: **FT:** Coarse; **WN:** Castlereagh; **WT:** Lough (Still).
Ref: FH0869

CASTLESHAW (LOWER) RESERVOIR

Castleshaw (Lower) Reservoir, Oldham, OL1, **England**.
Contact/s: **Mr J Lees** (Secretary), Oldham United Angling Club, 10 Packwood Chase, Chadderton, Oldham.
(T) 0161 6245176
Mr Roy Rhodes (Conservation, Access and Recreation Manager), Rivington Water Treatment Works, Bolton Rd, Horwich, Bolton, BL6 7RN.
(T) 01204 664300
Profile: **FT:** Coarse; **WN:** Castleshaw (lower); **WT:** Reservoir (Still).
Ref: FH0870

CASTLETON (RIVER)

River Castleton, Dundalk Harbour, Dundalk, **COUNTY LOUTH**, **Ireland**.
Contact/s: Secretary, Dundalk Brown Trout Angling Club, 3 Mill Rd, Forkhill, Newry, BT35 95J.
Mr John Clarke (Club Secretary).
(T) 028 3088 8378
Profile: **FT:** Game; **WN:** Castleton (Dundalk Harbour-Northern Island Border; **WT:** River (Moving) **W. Size:** 17600 Metres. Location: **Rail:** Dundalk.
Ref: FH0871

CATCH 22 FISHERY

Catch 22 Fishery, Easthaugh Rd, Lyng Easthaugh, Norwich, **NORFOLK**, NR9 5LN, **England**.
Contact/s: **Mr James Steggles** (Manager), Norfolk Koi (Import) Ltd, Walnut Tree Farm, Easthaugh Rd, Lyng, Norwich, NR9 5LN.
(T) 01603 872948 (F) 01603 620821
Profile: **FT:** Coarse; **WN:** Catch 22 Fishery; **WT:** Gravel Pit (Still); **F. Size:** 36 Acres; **W. Size:** 28 Acres. Location: **Nr. Rd:** Easthaugh Road; **Main Rd:** A1067; **Rail:** Norwich.
Ref: FH0872

CATCHPENNY POOL

Catchpenny Pool, Withington, Holmes Chapel, **CHESHIRE**, **England**.
Contact/s: **Mr John Turner** (Hon Secretary), Prince Albert Angling Society, 15 Pexhill Drive, Macclesfield, Cheshire, SK10 3LP.
(T) 01625 422010
Profile: **FT:** Game; **WN:** Catchpenny Pool; **WT:** Pit (Still); **F. Size:** 30 Acres; **W. Size:** 19 Acres. Location: **Nr. Rd:** Catchpenny Lane; **Main Rd:** A535; **Rail:** Holmes Chapel.
Ref: FH0873

CATTERICK LAKES

Catterick Lakes, Allotment Lane, Catterick, Richmond, **YORKSHIRE (NORTH)**, DL10, **England**.
Contact/s: **Mr Derek Taylor** (Secretary), Leeds ADASA, 75 Stoney Rock Lane, Beckett St, Leeds, LS29 7TB.
(T) 0113 2482373
Mr Gus Greaves (Fishery Manager).
(T) 01609 883773
Profile: **FT:** Coarse; **WN:** Catterick Lakes; **WT:** Lake (Still). Location: **Nr. Rd:** Allotment Lane; **Main Rd:** A1, South.
Ref: FH0874

CATTON PARK LAKE

Catton Park Lake, Catton Park Fisheries, Swadlincote, **DERBYSHIRE**, DE12, **England**.
Contact/s: **Mr Graham Davies**.
(T) 01283 716876 (M) 07889 918224
Profile: **FT:** Coarse; **WN:** Catton Park; **WT:** Combination (Still & Moving); **F. Size:** 20 Acres; **W. Size:** 10 Acres. Location: **Nr. Rd:** Catton Road; **Main Rd:** A38.
Ref: FH0875

CAUSEWAY LAKES

Causeway Lakes, Great Blackenham, Baylham, Ipswich, **SUFFOLK**, IP6, **England**.
Contact/s: **Mr George Alderson** (Secretary), Gipping APS, 19 Clover Cl, Needham Market, Ipswich, Suffolk IP2 0PW.
(T) 01473 602828
Profile: **FT:** Coarse; **WN:** Causeway; **WT:** Lake (Still) **W. Size:** 7 Acres. Location: **Nr. Rd:** Concrete Road; **Main Rd:** B1113 towards Needham Market.
Ref: FH0876

CAWOOD HOLIDAY PARK

Cawood Holiday Park, Ryther Rd, Cawood, Selby, **YORKSHIRE (NORTH)**, YO8 3TT, **England**.
Contact/s: **Mr Gerry Archer** (Fishery Manager).
(T) 01757 268450 (F) 01757 268537
Profile: **FT:** Coarse; **WN:** Cawood Holiday Park; **WT:** Lake (Still); **F. Size:** 8 Acres; **W. Size:** 2 Acres. Location: **Nr. Rd:** B1223; **Main Rd:** A1 to York; **Rail:** Selby.
Ref: FH0877

CEANN-AN-ORA FISHERY

Ceann-An-Ora Fishery, 'The Anchorage, Ardhasaig, Harris, **WESTERN ISLES**, HS3, **Scotland**.
Contact/s: **Sam Macleod**.
(T) 01859 502009
Profile: **FT:** Game; **WN:** Ceann-an-ora; **WT:** Combination (Still & Moving) **W. Size:** 1500 Metres. Location: **Nr. Rd:** A859.
Ref: FH0878

CEFN MABLEY

Cefn Mabley, Cardiff, CF24, **Wales**.
Contact/s: **Mr John Jones**.
(T) 01633 681101
Profile: **FT:** Combination; **WN:** Mabley; **WT:** Lake (Still) **W. Size:** 6 Acres.
Ref: FH0879

CEFN-BRYN FISHERY

Cefn-Bryn Fishery, Lampeter, **CEREDIGION**, SA48, **Wales**.
(W) www.fishing-in-wales.co.uk/llandysul-aa/beat5
Contact/s: **Mr Artie Jones** (Hon Secretary), Llandysul Angling Association, Glas-y-Dorlan, Llyn-y-Fran Rd, Llandysul, SA44 4JW.
(T) 01559 362317
Profile: **FT:** Game; **WN:** Teifi; **WT:** River (Moving). Location: **Nr. Rd:** A485 Cwmann to Llanybydder.
Ref: FH0880

CEFNI RESERVOIR

Cefni Reservoir, Llangefni, **ISLE OF ANGLESEY**, LL77, **Wales**.
Contact/s: **Mr D G Evans** (Hon Treasurer (Membership)), Wenllys, Capel Coch, Llangefni.
(T) 01248 470306
Mr G R Williams (Hon Secretary), Tyn Lon, Gaerwen, Pentre Berw, Isle of Anglesey.
(T) 01248 421238
(E) gwilym.williams@tynlon.freeserve.co.uk
Profile: **FT:** Game; **WN:** Cefni; **WT:** Reservoir (Still) **W. Size:** 172 Acres. Location: **Nr. Rd:** Llangefni to Bodffordd; **Main Rd:** B5109; **Rail:** Bangor.
Ref: FH0881

CEIRIOG (RIVER)

River Ceiriog, The West Arms Hotel, Llangollen, **DENBIGHSHIRE**, LL20, **Wales**.
Contact/s: **Mr Geoff Leigh-Ford** (Manager), Llanarmon Dyffryn Ceiriog, Llangollen, LL20 7LD.
(T) 01691 600665
Profile: **FT:** Game; **WN:** Ceiriog; **WT:** River (Moving). Location: **Main Rd:** A5.
Ref: FH0882

CEIRIOG (RIVER)

River Ceiriog, Chirk Castle Estate, Chirk, Wrexham, **DENBIGHSHIRE**, LL14, **Wales**.
Contact/s: **Mr A Hudson** (Hon Secretary), 96 Crogen, Longvale Park, Chirk, LL14 5BJ.
(T) 01691 773632
Profile: **FT:** Game; **WN:** Ceiriog; **WT:** River (Moving). Location: **Nr. Rd:** Pontfadog to Chirk.
Ref: FH0883

CEIRW STREAM

Ceirw Stream, Llais-Yr-Afon, Ruthin, **DENBIGHSHIRE**, LL15, **Wales**.
Mr Caerwyn Lewis (Secretary).
Mr Gordon Smith.
(T) 01824 7196091
Profile: **FT:** Game; **WN:** Ceirw; **WT:** Stream (Moving) **W. Size:** 3000 Metres. Location: **Nr. Rd:** A5; **Main Rd:** A5.
Ref: FH0884

CELLAN FISHERY

Cellan Fishery, Lampeter, **CEREDIGION**, SA48, **Wales**.
(W) www.fishing-in-wales.co.uk/llandysul-aa/beat2
Contact/s: **Mr Artie Jones** (Hon Secretary), Llandysul Angling Association, Glas-y-Dorlan, Llyn-y-Fran Rd, Llandysul, SA44 4JW.
(T) 01559 362317
Profile: **FT:** Game; **WN:** Teifi; **WT:** River (Moving) **W. Size:** 2400 Metres. Location: **Nr. Rd:** B4343 Cwmann to Llanfair Clydogau.
Ref: FH0885

CENTRAL PARK LAKE

Central Park Lake, Chelmsford, **ESSEX**, CM, **England**.
Contact/s: .
(T) 01245 257032
Profile: **FT:** Coarse; **WN:** Chelmsford Park; **WT:** Lake (Still). Location: **Main Rd:** A12 to Colchester.
Ref: FH0887

CENTRAL PARK LAKE

Central Park Lake, Wallasey, Wirral, **MERSEYSIDE**, CH44, **England**.
Contact/s: **Mr Billing**.
(T) 0151 3343174
Profile: **FT:** Coarse; **WN:** Central Park; **WT:** Lake (Still). Location: **Nr. Rd:** Wallasey.
Ref: FH0888

CHAD LAKES

Chad Lakes, Stow Rd, Bledington, Stow On The Wold, Chipping Norton, **OXFORDSHIRE**, OX7 6XL, **England**.
Contact/s: **Mr Dave Wren** (Proprietor).
(T) 01451 831470 (M) 07718 225135
Profile: **FT:** Coarse; **WN:** Chad; **WT:** Lake

(Still) **W. Size:** 4 Acres. **Location:** **Nr. Rd:** B4450; **Main Rd:** Fosse Way; **Rail:** Kingham. **Ref:** FH0890

CHALK SPRINGS TROUT FISHERY

Chalk Springs Trout Fishery, Park Bottom, Arundel, **SUSSEX (WEST)**, BN18 0AA, **England**.
(W) www.chalksprings.com
Contact/s: **Mr Darren Smith** (Manager).
(T) 01903 883742 (F) 01903 884482
Mr Jonathan Glover (Owner).
(T) 01903 883742 (F) 01903 883742
Profile: **FT:** Game; **WN:** Chalk Springs; **WT:** Lake (Still); **F. Size:** 7 Acres; **W. Size:** 5 Acres. **Location:** **Nr. Rd:** Arundel Roundabout; **Main Rd:** A27; **Rail:** Arundel.
Ref: FH0891

CHALYBEATE SPRINGS

Chalybeate Springs Trout Fishery, Eridge Green, Tunbridge Wells, **KENT**, TN3, **England**.
Contact/s: Manager, Sham Farm, Rotherfield Rd, Eridge Green, Kent, TN6 9JA.
(T) 01892 669119
Profile: **FT:** Game; **WN:** Chalybeate Springs Trout Fishery; **WT:** Lake (Still); **F. Size:** 2000 Acres; **W. Size:** 2 Acres. **Location:** **Nr. Rd:** A26.
Ref: FH0892

CHANNELL FISHERIES

Channell Fisheries, Brixham, **DEVON**, TQ5, **England**.
Contact/s: Manager, 13 Penpethy Rd, Brixham, Devon, TQ5 8NN.
(T) 01803 851210
Profile: **FT:** Coarse; **WN:** Channell Fisheries; **WT:** Lake (Still). **Location:** **Nr. Rd:** Penpethy Road.
Ref: FH0893

CHAPEL LAKE

Chapel Lake, Dunmanway, **COUNTY CORK**, **Ireland**.
Contact/s: **Mr P MacCarthy** (Secretary), Dunmanway Salmon and Trout Angling Association, Yew Tree Bar, Dunmanway, County Cork, Ireland.
Profile: **FT:** Game; **WN:** Chapel; **WT:** Lake (Still).
Ref: FH0894

CHAPEL ROAD LAKE

Chapel Road Lake, Roughton, Norwich, **NORFOLK**, NR11, **England**.
Contact/s: Fishery Manager.
(T) 01263 761369
Profile: **FT:** Coarse; **WN:** Chapel Road; **WT:** Lake (Still). **Location:** **Nr. Rd:** Chapel Road.
Ref: FH0895

CHAPEL WHEEL DAM

Chapel Wheel Dam, Chesterfield, **DERBYSHIRE**, S4, **England**.
Profile: **FT:** Coarse; **WN:** Chapel Wheel; **WT:** Mill Dam (Still) **W. Size:** 10 Acres.
Ref: FH0896

CHAPMANS POND

Chapmans Pond, Dringhouses, York, **YORKSHIRE (NORTH)**, YO, **England**.
Contact/s: Manager, Acomb Fishing Tackle, 227 Hamilton Drive West, York, Yorkshire (North), YO24 4PL.
(T) 01904 785237 (F) 01904 785237
Profile: **FT:** Coarse; **WN:** Chapmans; **WT:** Pond (Still). **Location:** **Nr. Rd:** Moor Lane; **Main Rd:** A1036. **£Fr**
Ref: FH0897

CHAR STREAM

Char Stream, Charmouth, Bridport, **DORSET**, DT6, **England**.
Profile: **FT:** Game; **WN:** Char; **WT:** Stream (Moving) **W. Size:** 11200 Metres.
Ref: FH0898

CHARD RESERVOIR

Chard Reservoir, Chard, **SOMERSET**, TA20, **England**.
Contact/s: **Mr Les Braunton**, Chard Angling Ctre, The Old Bakehouse, 2 Holyrood St, Chard, TA20 2AH.
(T) 01460 63771
Profile: **FT:** Coarse; **WN:** Chard; **WT:** Reservoir (Still) **W. Size:** 49 Acres. **Location:** **Main Rd:** A358.
Ref: FH0899

CHARITY FARM FISHERY

Charity Farm Fishery, Smith Brow, Heskin, Chorley, **LANCASHIRE**, PR7, **England**.
Contact/s: **Mr Waring**.
(T) 01257 451326
Profile: **FT:** Coarse; **WN:** Charity Farm Fishery; **WT:** Pool (Still). **Location:** **Nr. Rd:** Smith Brow; **Main Rd:** M6, junction 27, A5209, B5250, left onto Church Road.
Ref: FH0900

CHARITY LAKES

Charity Lakes, Great Witchingham, Norwich, **NORFOLK**, NR9, **England**.
Contact/s: Fishery Manager.
(T) 01603 872399
Mr Peter (Fishery Manager).
(T) 01362 691243
Profile: **FT:** Coarse; **WN:** Charity; **WT:** Lake (Still).
Ref: FH0901

CHARLECOMBE

Charlecombe, Lower Rocombe Farm, Rocombe, Maidencombe, Torquay, **DEVON**, TQ1, **England**.
Contact/s: **Dave** (Fishery Manager).
(T) 01626 364173
Profile: **FT:** Coarse; **WN:** Springs; **WT:** Pond (Still).
Ref: FH0902

CHARLES STREET POND

Charles Street Pond, Charles St, Louth, **LINCOLNSHIRE**, LN11, **England**.
Profile: **FT:** Coarse; **WN:** Charles Street; **WT:** Pond (Still). **Location:** **Nr. Rd:** Charles Street.
Ref: FH0903

CHARLTON PITS

Charlton Pits, Charlton, Andover, **HAMPSHIRE**, SP, **England**.
Contact/s: **R L Adcock** (Secretary), Andover Angling Club, Flat 2, Bridge House, 154 Junction Rd, Andover.
Profile: **FT:** Coarse; **WN:** Charlton; **WT:** Gravel Pit (Still) **W. Size:** 10 Acres. **Location:** **Nr. Rd:** A343; **Main Rd:** A303.
Ref: FH0904

CHARLTONS PONDS

Charltons Ponds, Billingham, Middlesbrough, **CLEVELAND**, TS, **England**.
Contact/s: **Mr Dave Munt**, Tackle Box, 46 Station Rd, Billingham, Cleveland.
(T) 01642 863598
Profile: **FT:** Coarse; **WN:** Charlton; **WT:** Pond (Still) **W. Size:** 8 Acres. **Location:** **Nr. Rd:** Hereford Terrace; **Main Rd:** A19, Billingham exit.
Ref: FH0905

CHARNWOOD WATER

Charnwood Water, Loughborough, Leicester, **LEICESTERSHIRE**, LE, **England**.
Contact/s: Area Manager, Charnwood Borough Council, Parks and Sports Grounds, Southfield Rd, Loughborough, LE11 2TT.
(T) 01509 634704
Profile: **FT:** Coarse; **WN:** Charnwood; **WT:** Lake (Still) **W. Size:** 27 Acres.
Ref: FH0906

CHASE FISHERY

Chase Fishery, Eastbrookend, Dagenham Rd, Dagenham, **ESSEX**, RM, **England**.
Contact/s: **Mr Jim Ryan** (Secretary), White Hart Angler's Club, 25 Dereham Rd, Barking, Essex.
(T) 01277 374072
(E) jim@jwryan.fsnet.co.uk
Profile: **FT:** Coarse; **WN:** Chase; **WT:** Gravel Pit (Still) **W. Size:** 8 Acres. **Location:** **Nr. Rd:** Dagenham Road; **Main Rd:** M25, A13 or A124; **Rail:** Dagenham East Underground.
Ref: FH0907

CHAWSTON LAKES

Chawston Lakes, St Neots And District Angling Society (Lakes), Skenbridge Cottage, Great Paxton, St Neots, Huntingdon, **CAMBRIDGESHIRE**, PE19 4RA, **England**.
Contact/s: **Mr Ian Benton** (Match Secretary).
(T) 01480 219706
Mr Ieuan Thomas (Bailiff).
(T) 01480 213115
Mrs Diane Linger (Secretary), Skenbridge Cottage, Great Paxton, St Neots, Cambridgeshire, PE19 4RA.
(T) 01480 216730
Profile: **FT:** Coarse; **WN:** Chawston; **WT:** Lake (Still) **W. Size:** 6 Acres. **Location:** **Nr. Rd:** A428; **Main Rd:** A428, A1.
Ref: FH0908

CHEDDAR RESERVOIR

Cheddar Reservoir, Cheddar Angling Club, Po Box 1183, Cheddar, **SOMERSET**, BS27 3LT, **England**.
Contact/s: **Mr Trevor Hardy** (Secretary / Treasurer).
(T) 01934 743959
Profile: **FT:** Coarse; **WN:** Cheddar; **WT:** Reservoir (Still); **F. Size:** 250 Acres; **W. Size:** 220 Acres. **Location:** **Nr. Rd:** A371; **Main Rd:** A371; **Rail:** Weston-super-Mare.
Ref: FH0909

CHELMER & BLACKWATER

Chelmer And Blackwater Navigation Canal, Rushes-Hoe Mill, Ulting, Maldon, **ESSEX**, CM9, **England**.
Contact/s: **Mr Frank Wright** (Membership Secretary), Chelmsford Angling Association, 61 Readers Court, Great Baddow, Chelmsford, CM2 8EX.
(T) 01245 474246or264832
(E) frank@chelmsfordaa.freeserve.co.uk
Profile: **FT:** Coarse; **WN:** Chelmer and Blackwater; **WT:** Canal (Still).
Ref: FH0912

CHELMER & BLACKWATER

Chelmer And Blackwater Navigation Canal, Heybridge Basin, Chelmsford, **ESSEX**, CM, **England**.
Contact/s: **Mr Frank Wright** (Membership Secretary), Chelmsford Angling Association, 61 Readers Court, Great Baddow, Chelmsford, CM2 8EX.
(T) 01245 474246or264832
(E) frank@chelmsfordaa.freeserve.co.uk
Mr T Lazell (Secretary), Maldon Angling Society, 14 Barn View Rd, Coggeshall, Essex CO6 1RF.
(T) 01621 892346
Ms Irene Lewis (Secretary), 60 Delamere Rd, Chelmsford, CM1 2TG.
(T) 01245 264832
Profile: **FT:** Coarse; **WN:** Chelmer & Blackwater; **WT:** Canal (Still). **Location:** **Nr. Rd:** A12 and A414; **Main Rd:** Chelmsford to Heybridge Basin; **Rail:** Chelmsford or Hatfield Peverel.
Ref: FH0913

CHELMER (RIVER)

River Chelmer, Chelmsford, **ESSEX**, CM, **England**.
(W) www.chelmsfordaa.freeserve.co.uk
Contact/s: **Mr Frank Wright** (Membership Secretary), Chelmsford Angling Association, 61 Readers Court, Great Baddow, Chelmsford, CM2 8EX.
(T) 01245 474246or264832
(E) frank@chelmsfordaa.freeserve.co.uk
Mr Len Stratton, 291 Dorset Avenue, Great Baddow, Chelmsford, CM2 8HB.
Profile: **FT:** Coarse; **WN:** Chelmer; **WT:**

River (Moving) **W. Size:** 22000 Metres. **Location:** **Rail:** Chelmsford.
Ref: FH0910

CHELMER (RIVER)

River Chelmer, Black Bridge, Boreham, Chelmsford, **ESSEX**, CM3, **England**.
Contact/s: **Mr Sid Hibbert** (Secretary), Basildon and District Angling Society, 15 Culverdown, Basildon, Essex, SS14 2AL.
(T) 01268 287798
Profile: **FT:** Coarse; **WN:** Chelmer; **WT:** River (Moving) **W. Size:** 2000 Metres. **Location:** **Nr. Rd:** Hammonds Road; **Main Rd:** A12; **Rail:** Chelmsford.
Ref: FH0911

CHEQUERTREE FISHERY

Chequertree Trout And Coarse Fishery, Standard Lane, Bethersden, Ashford, **KENT**, TN26 3JR, **England**.
(W) www.chequertree.co.uk
Contact/s: **Mr Chris Drew** (Owner).
(T) 01233 820078
Profile: **FT:** Combination; **WN:** Chequertree Trout And Coarse Fishery; **WT:** Lake (Still) **W. Size:** 8 Acres. **Location:** **Nr. Rd:** Ashford to Tenterden; **Main Rd:** A28; **Rail:** Ashford International.
Ref: FH0914

CHERTSEY

Chertsey, Thorpe Rd, Chertsey, **SURREY**, KT16, **England**.
(W) www.rmcangling.co.uk
Contact/s: **Mr Ian Welch** (Angling Manager), RMC Angling, The Square, Lightwater, Surrey, GU18 5SS.
(T) 01276 453300 **(F)** 01276 456611
(E) info@rmcangling.co.uk
Profile: **FT:** Coarse; **WN:** Bourne; **WT:** Combination (Still & Moving) **W. Size:** 4 Acres. **Location:** **Nr. Rd:** B388; **Main Rd:** A320; **Rail:** Chertsey.
Ref: FH0916

CHERWELL (RIVER)

River Cherwell, Hampton Poyle, Kidlington, **OXFORDSHIRE**, OX5 2QE, **England**.
(W) www.uxbridge-rovers.fsnet.co.uk
Contact/s: **Mr L Dalton** (Secretary), Uxbridge Rovers Angling and Conservation Society, PO Box 253, Harrow, Middlesex, HA3 8XN.
(T) 01814 281739
Profile: **FT:** Coarse; **WN:** Cherwell; **WT:** River (Moving) **W. Size:** 2400 Metres. **Location:** **Main Rd:** A43.
Ref: FH0917

CHERWELL (RIVER)

River Cherwell, Cherwell, Oxford, **OXFORDSHIRE**, OX, **England**.
Contact/s: **Mr Derek Button** (Secretary), Oxford and Abingdon Angling Preservation Soceity, 78 Appleford Drive, Abingdon, Oxfordshire, OX14 2BU.
(T) 01865 277950
Profile: **FT:** Coarse; **WN:** Cherwell; **WT:** River (Moving).
Ref: FH0918

CHERWELL (RIVER)

River Cherwell, Long Meadow, Woodstock, **OXFORDSHIRE**, OX20, **England**.
Contact/s: Manager, J and K Tackle, 8-10 Wesley Lane, Bicester, Oxfordshire, OX6 7JU.
(T) 01869 244143or242589 **(F)** 01869 320821
Profile: **FT:** Coarse; **WN:** Cherwell; **WT:** River (Moving). **Location:** **Nr. Rd:** Witney to Tackley; **Main Rd:** A4095.
Ref: FH0919

CHERWELL (RIVER)

River Cherwell, Marston, Oxford, **OXFORDSHIRE**, OX, **England**.
Contact/s: **Mr Andrew Crisp** (Secretary), North Oxford Angling Society, 4 Groves St, Summertown, Oxford, Oxfordshire OX3 7JT.
(T) 01865 553800
Profile: **FT:** Coarse; **WN:** Cherwell; **WT:** River (Moving).
Ref: FH0920

CHERWELL (RIVER)

River Cherwell, Somerton, Bicester, **OXFORDSHIRE**, OX6, **England**.
Contact/s: **Mr Geoff Bradbeer** (Secretary), Banbury and District Angling Association, 7 Bentley Cl, Banbury, Oxfordshire, OX16 7PB.
(T) 01295 268047
Profile: **FT:** Coarse; **WN:** Cherwell; **WT:** River (Moving) **W. Size:** 3200 Metres. **Location:** **Nr. Rd:** Bridge, park on verge nearby; **Main Rd:** B430.
Ref: FH0921

CHERWELL (RIVER)

River Cherwell, Upper Heyford, Bicester, **OXFORDSHIRE**, OX6, **England**.
Contact/s: **Mr Geoff Bradbeer** (Secretary), Banbury and District Angling Association, 7 Bentley Cl, Banbury, Oxfordshire, OX16 7PB.
(T) 01295 268047
Profile: **FT:** Coarse; **WN:** Cherwell; **WT:** River (Moving). **Location:** **Nr. Rd:** Lower Heyford to Upper Heyford; **Main Rd:** A4095.
Ref: FH0922

CHERWELL (RIVER)

River Cherwell, Shipton-on-Cherwell, Kidlington, **OXFORDSHIRE**, OX5, **England**.
Contact/s: , J and K Tackle, 8-10 Wesley Lane, Bicester, Oxfordshire, OX6 7JU.
(T) 01869 242589 **(F)** 01869 320821
Mr Geoff Bradbeer (Secretary), Banbury and District Angling Association, 7 Bentley Cl, Banbury, Oxfordshire, OX16 7PB.
(T) 01295 268047
Profile: **FT:** Coarse; **WN:** Cherwell; **WT:** River (Moving) **W. Size:** 1200 Metres. **Location:** **Main Rd:** A4260.
Ref: FH0923

CHERWELL (RIVER)

River Cherwell, Marston, Oxford, **OXFORDSHIRE**, OX, **England**.
Contact/s: **Mr N Brown** (Secretary), Marston Angling Club, 26 Kelburne Rd, Cowley, Oxford, Oxfordshire OX4 3SJ. **(M)** 07885 420717
Profile: **FT:** Coarse; **WN:** Cherwell; **WT:** River (Moving).
Ref: FH0924

CHESHIRE FISHING

Cheshire Fishing, Beehive Farm, Platts Lane, Tattenhall, Chester, **CHESHIRE**, CH3 9NT, **England**.
Contact/s: **Mr Ken Ellis** (Owner).
(T) 01829 770041
Mrs Ilene Ellis (Owner).
(T) 01829 770041
Profile: **FT:** Combination; **WN:** Cheshire Fishing; **WT:** Lake (Still) **W. Size:** 11 Acres. **Location:** **Nr. Rd:** Platts Lane; **Main Rd:** A41 Whitchurch Road.
Ref: FH0925

CHESHUNT SOUTH RESERVOIR

Cheshunt South Reservoir, Cheshunt, Waltham Cross, **HERTFORDSHIRE**, EN, **England**.
Profile: **FT:** Coarse; **WN:** Cheshunt South; **WT:** Reservoir (Still).
Ref: FH0926

CHESS (RIVER)

River Chess, Latimer Park Lakes, Latimer, Chesham, **BUCKINGHAMSHIRE**, HP5 1TT, **England**.
Contact/s: **Mr Chris W Cansdale**, Latimer Park Lakes, Chesham, Buckinghamshire, HP5 1TT.
(T) 01494 766333 **(F)** 01494 766555
Profile: **FT:** Game; **WN:** Chess; **WT:** River (Moving).
Ref: FH0927

CHESS (RIVER)

River Chess, Lahmer Bridge To Sarrat Bottom, Amersham, **BUCKINGHAMSHIRE**, HP7, **England**.
Contact/s: **Mr D Le Neve Foster** (Fishery Manager).
(T) 01494 766140
Profile: **FT:** Game; **WN:** Chess; **WT:** River (Moving).
Ref: FH0928

CHESTER FARM LAKE

Chester Farm Lake, Wellingborough, **NORTHAMPTONSHIRE**, NN8, **England**.
Contact/s: **Mr Mike Gibbs**.
Profile: **FT:** Coarse; **WN:** Chester Farm; **WT:** Lake (Still) **W. Size:** 40 Acres.
Ref: FH0929

CHESTERFIELD CANAL

Chesterfield Canal, Retford, **NOTTINGHAMSHIRE**, DN22, **England**.
Contact/s: **Mr R Whitehead** (Secretary), Worksop and District Angling Association, 72 Dryden Walk, Worksop, Nottinghamshire.
(T) 01909 486350
Profile: **FT:** Coarse; **WN:** Chesterfield; **WT:** Canal (Still) **W. Size:** 15000 Metres.
Ref: FH0930

CHESTERFIELD CANAL

Chesterfield Canal, Worksop, **YORKSHIRE (SOUTH)**, S8, **England**.
Contact/s: **Mr Glyn Williams** (Hon Secretary), 9 Edward St, Worksop, Nottinghamshire, S80 1QP.
(T) 01909 474940 **(F)** 01909 474940
(E) glyn@williamsok.freeserve.co.uk
Profile: **FT:** Coarse; **WN:** Chesterfield; **WT:** Canal (Still) **W. Size:** 7400 Metres. **Location:** **Nr. Rd:** Priors Well Road; **Main Rd:** Canal Road; **Rail:** Carlton Road.
Ref: FH0931

CHESTERFIELD CANAL

Chesterfield Canal, Sheffield, **YORKSHIRE (SOUTH)**, S, **England**.
Contact/s: **Mr G Woods** (Secretary), 1 Everingham Rd, Longley, Sheffield, S5 7LA.
Profile: **FT:** Game; **WN:** Chesterfield; **WT:** Canal (Still). **Location:** **Nr. Rd:** A631 to Trent junction; **Main Rd:** A631.
Ref: FH0932

CHESTERFORD FISHERIES

Chesterford Fisheries, Poslingford, Sudbury, **SUFFOLK**, CO10, **England**.
Contact/s: **Mr Paul Elsegood** (Manager), 2 Wentfords Cottages, Clare Rd, Poslingford, Sudbury, Suffolk.
(T) 01787 277468
Profile: **FT:** Combination; **WN:** Chesterford Fisheries; **WT:** Lake (Still) **W. Size:** 20 Acres. **Location:** **Main Rd:** M11, junction 9.
Ref: FH0933

CHESTERTON MILL

Chesterton Mill Pool Trout Fishery, Thaites Farms, Harbury Heath, Harbury, Leamington Spa, **WARWICKSHIRE**, CV33 9NL, **England**.
Contact/s: Fishery Manager.
(T) 024 76695671
Mr Brian Merriman.
(T) 01926 612508
Mr Ian Scandrett (Bailiff). **(M)** 07831 137277
Profile: **FT:** Game; **WN:** Chesterton Mill; **WT:** Pool (Still); **F. Size:** 10 Acres; **W. Size:** 4 Acres. **Location:** **Nr. Rd:** Harbury Lane; **Main Rd:** The Foss Way; **Rail:** Leamington Spa.
Ref: FH0934

CHEW (RIVER)

River Chew, Compton Dando, Keynsham, Bristol, BS31, **England**.
Contact/s: **Mr Dave Crookes** (Secretary), 25 Otago Trce, Larkhall, Bath, Somerset, BA1 6SX.
(T) 01225 427164

Profile: **FT:** Coarse; **WN:** Chew; **WT:** River (Moving) **W. Size:** 1600 Metres.
Ref: FH0935

CHEW VALLEY LAKE

Chew Valley Lake, Woodford Lodge, Chew, Stoke, Bristol, **SOMERSET**, BS40 8XH, **England**.
(W) www.bristolwater.co.uk
Contact/s: **Mr Bob Handford**, Bristol Water Plc, Woodford Lodge, Chew Stoke, Bristol, BS40 8XH.
(T) 01275 332339 (F) 01275 331377
(E) bob.handford@bristolwater.co.uk
S Taylor, Bristol Water Plc, Woodford Lodge, Chew Stoke, Bristol, BS40 8XH.
(T) 01275 332339 (F) 01275 331377
Profile: **FT:** Game; **WN:** Chew Valley; **WT:** Lake (Still) **W. Size:** 1200 Acres. **Location:** **Nr. Rd:** B3114, B3130; **Main Rd:** A38, A368, A370; **Rail:** Bristol.
Ref: FH0936

CHEYNEY MANOR FISHERY

Cheyney Manor Fishery, Manor House, Barford St Michael, Banbury, **OXFORDSHIRE**, OX15 0RJ, **England**.
Contact/s: **Mrs B Alt** (Manager).
(T) 01869 338207 (F) 01869 338207
Profile: **FT:** Coarse; **WN:** Cheyney Manor Fishery; **WT:** Combination (Still & Moving) **W. Size:** 2 Acres. **Location:** **Main Rd:** B4031.
Ref: FH0937

CHICESTER CANAL

Chicester Canal, Chichester, **SUSSEX (WEST)**, PO, **England**.
Contact/s: **Mr John Cooper**, Jaspers, Coney Rd, East Wittering, Chichester.
(T) 01243 671051
Profile: **FT:** Coarse; **WN:** Chicester; **WT:** Canal (Still).
Ref: FH0938

CHIDDINGSTONE CASTLE LAKE

Chiddingstone Castle Lake, Chiddingstone Castle, Edenbridge, **KENT**, TN8 7AD, **England**.
Contact/s: **Mr Vernon** (Estate Manager).
(T) 01892 870347
Profile: **FT:** Coarse; **WN:** Chiddingstone Castle; **WT:** Lake (Still) **W. Size:** 3 Acres. **Location:** **Nr. Rd:** B2027; **Main Rd:** A21, A22.
Ref: FH0939

CHIGBOROUGH

Chigborough, Scraley Rd, Heybridge, Maldon, **ESSEX**, CM9, **England**.
(W) www.rmcangling.co.uk
Contact/s: **Mr Ian Welch** (Angling Manager), RMC Angling, The Square, Lightwater, Surrey, GU18 5SS.
(T) 01276 453300 (F) 01276 456611
(E) info@rmcangling.co.uk
Profile: **FT:** Coarse; **WN:** Chigborough; **WT:** Lake (Still) **W. Size:** 2 Acres. **Location:** **Nr. Rd:** Scraley Road; **Main Rd:** A414.
Ref: FH0940

CHIGBOROUGH FISHERIES

Chigborough Fisheries, Chigborough Farm, Chigborough Rd, Heybridge, Maldon, **ESSEX**, CM9 7RE, **England**.
(W) www.freeserve.co.uk
Contact/s: **Mr David Western** (Owner).
(T) 01621 857368 (F) 01621 855563 (M) 07702 244440
(E) djw@chigboro.co.uk
Profile: **FT:** Combination; **WN:** Chigborough Fisheries; **WT:** Lake (Still) **W. Size:** 16 Acres. **Location:** **Nr. Rd:** B1026; **Main Rd:** A12; **Rail:** Witham.
Ref: FH0941

CHILHAM LAKE

Chilham Lake, Chilham, Canterbury, **KENT**, CT4, **England**.
Contact/s: **Mr Chris Logsdon** (Manager), Mid Kent Fisheries, Chilham Water Mill, Mill Lane, Chilham, CT4 8EE.
(T) 01227 730668
Profile: **FT:** Coarse; **WN:** Chilham Lake; **WT:** Lake (Still) **W. Size:** 26 Acres. **Location:** **Nr. Rd:** Mill Lane; **Main Rd:** A252.
Ref: FH0942

CHIPHALL LAKE TROUT FISHERY

Chiphall Lake Trout Fishery, Northfields Farm Lane, Wickham, Fareham, **HAMPSHIRE**, PO17 5AZ, **England**.
Contact/s: **Mr D J Paine** (Manager).
(T) 01329 833295 (F) 01329 841775
Profile: **FT:** Game; **WN:** Chiphall; **WT:** Lake (Still); **F. Size:** 5 Acres; **W. Size:** 5 Acres. **Location:** **Nr. Rd:** A32; **Main Rd:** A32; **Rail:** Fareham.
Ref: FH0943

CHIPSTEAD LAKES

Chipstead Lakes, Sevenoaks, **KENT**, TN, **England**.
Contact/s: **Mr S Banks**, 58 Chevening Rd, Chipstead, Sevenoaks, Kent.
(T) 01732 458216
Profile: **FT:** Coarse; **WN:** Chipstead; **WT:** Lake (Still) **W. Size:** 20 Acres. **Location:** **Nr. Rd:** A21; **Main Rd:** M25, M26.
Ref: FH0944

CHOONE FARM

Choone Farm, St Buryan, Penzance, **CORNWALL**, TR, **England**.
Contact/s: **Mr V B Care**.
(T) 01736 810220
Profile: **FT:** Coarse; **WN:** Choone Farm; **WT:** Lake (Still).
Ref: FH0945

CHORLTON WATER PARK

Chorlton Water Park, Maitland Avenue, Barlow More Rd, Chorlton-Cum-Hardy, Manchester, **MANCHESTER (GREATER)**, M21 7WH, **England**.
Contact/s: **Mr Dave Sykes** (Water Parks Manager), Charlton Water Park, Maitland Avenue, Manchester, Lancashire, M21 7WH.
(T) 0161 8815639 or 9051100
Profile: **FT:** Coarse; **WN:** Chorlton Water Park; **WT:** Lake (Still) **W. Size:** 19 Acres. **Location:** **Nr. Rd:** A5145; **Main Rd:** Darley Avenue.
Ref: FH0946

CHRISTCHURCH LAKE

Linch Hill, Linch Hill Leisure Park, Stanton Harcourt, Witney, **OXFORDSHIRE**, OX29 5BB, **England**.
(W) www.abcarrivals.co.uk/linchhill
Contact/s: **Mr Derek Reeves** (Owner).
(T) 01865 882215 (F) 01865 882870
Profile: **FT:** Coarse; **WN:** Christchurch, Stoneacre, & Willow Lakes; **WT:** Lake (Still); **F. Size:** 80 Acres. **Location:** **Nr. Rd:** Off Standlake Road; **Main Rd:** A415; **Rail:** Oxford.
Ref: FH0947

CHRISTCHURCH LOWER STOUR

Christchurch Lower Stour, Christchurch, **DORSET**, BH23, **England**.
Contact/s: **Mr R J Andrews** (Club Secretary), Christchurch Angling Club, 4 Marley Cl, New Milton, BH25 5LL.
(T) 01425 638502
Profile: **FT:** Combination; **WN:** Christchurch Lower Stour; **WT:** River (Moving) **W. Size:** 3000 Metres.
Ref: FH0948

CHURCH END TROUT FISHERY

Church End Trout Fishery, Church End, Twyning, Tewkesbury, **GLOUCESTERSHIRE**, GL20, **England**.
Contact/s: **Mr John Williams** (Secretary), Birmingham Anglers Association, 100 Icknield Port Rd, Rotton Park, Birmingham, B16 0AP.
(T) 0121 4549111
Profile: **FT:** Game; **WN:** Church End Trout Fishery; **WT:** River (Moving).
Ref: FH0949

CHURCH FARM

Church Farm, Sandhurst, **BERKSHIRE**, GU47, **England**.
Contact/s: Manager, R and R Tackle, 74 High St, Sandhurst, Berkshire, GU47 8ED.
(T) 01252 870007
Profile: **FT:** Coarse; **WN:** Church Farm; **WT:** Combination (Still & Moving) **W. Size:** 800 Metres. **Location:** **Nr. Rd:** Sandhurst Road; **Main Rd:** A321 from Woking.
Ref: FH0950

CHURCH FARM FISHERY

Church Farm Fishery, Llanfihangel-Ar-Arth, Pencader, **CARMARTHENSHIRE**, SA39, **Wales**.
(W) www.fishing-in-wales.co.uk/llandysul-aa/beat9
Contact/s: **Mr Artie Jones** (Hon Secretary), Llandysul Angling Association, Glas-y-Dorlan, Llyn-y-Fran Rd, Llandysul, SA44 4JW.
(T) 01559 362317
Profile: **FT:** Game; **WN:** Church Farm Fishery; **WT:** River (Moving) **W. Size:** 800 Metres.
Ref: FH0951

CHURCH GARDEN

Church Garden, Bradshaw, Chapel, Bolton, **LANCASHIRE**, BL2, **England**.
Contact/s: **Mr Eric Taylor** (Fishery Manager).
(T) 01706 630619
Profile: **FT:** Coarse; **WN:** Church Garden; **WT:** Pool (Still) **W. Size:** 2 Acres. **Location:** **Nr. Rd:** Bolton to Bury; **Main Rd:** Bolton Road.
Ref: FH0952

CHURCH HILL FISHERY

Church Hill Fishery, Swanbourne Rd, Mursley, Milton Keynes, **BUCKINGHAMSHIRE**, MK17 0JA, **England**.
Contact/s: **Mr Tim Daniels**.
(T) 01296 720524 (F) 01296 720524
Profile: **FT:** Game; **WN:** Duse; **WT:** Combination (Still & Moving); **F. Size:** 65 Acres; **W. Size:** 15 Acres. **Location:** **Nr. Rd:** B4032; **Main Rd:** A421; **Rail:** Bletchley.
Ref: FH0953

CHURCH LAKE

Church Lake, Childerditch, Little Warley, Brentwood, **ESSEX**, CM13, **England**.
Contact/s: Fishery Manager.
(T) 01708 451176
Profile: **FT:** Coarse; **WN:** Church; **WT:** Lake (Still).
Ref: FH0954

CHURCH POOL

Church Pool, Clehonger, Hereford, **HEREFORDSHIRE**, HR, **England**.
Profile: **FT:** Coarse; **WN:** Church Pool; **WT:** Pond (Still) **W. Size:** 1 Acre. **Location:** **Nr. Rd:** B4349; **Main Rd:** A465.
Ref: FH0955

CHURCH POOL

Church Pool, Lakeside Lodge Hotel, Pattingham, Wolverhampton, **MIDLANDS (WEST)**, WV6, **England**.
Contact/s: **Mr David Tooth** (Manager).
(T) 01902 700774
Profile: **FT:** Coarse; **WN:** Church; **WT:** Gravel Pit (Still). **Location:** **Nr. Rd:** Patshull Road; **Main Rd:** A454; **Rail:** Wolverhampton.
Ref: FH0956

CHURCHWOOD FISHERIES

Churchwood Fisheries, Doddington Pl, Blackmore Rd, Brentwood, **ESSEX**, CM15 0HX, **England**.
Contact/s: **Mr Derek Ritchie** (Carp Consultant), Brentwood Angling, 118 Warley Hill, Brentwood, Essex, CM14 5HB.
(T) 01277 200985 (F) 01277 219500
Profile: **FT:** Coarse; **WN:** Churchwood Fisheries; **WT:** Lake (Still). **Location:** **Nr.**

Rd: Blackmore Road; **Main Rd:** A128.
Ref: FH0957

CHURN CLOUGH RESERVOIR

Churn Clough Reservoir, North West Water Ltd, Pennine House, Stanley St, Preston, **LANCASHIRE**, PR1 4EA, **England**.
Contact/s: **Mr Roy Rhodes** (Conservation, Access and Recreation Manager), Rivington Water Treatment Works, Bolton Rd, Horwich, Bolton, BL6 7RN.
(T) 01204 664300
Profile: **FT:** Coarse; **WN:** Churn Clough; **WT:** Reservoir (Still).
Ref: FH0958

CHURN POOL TROUT FISHERY

Churn Pool Trout Fishery, Cotswold Water Park, South Cerney, Cirencester, **GLOUCESTERSHIRE**, GL7, **England**.
Contact/s: **Mr Martin Pollard**.
(T) 01285 861192
Profile: **FT:** Game; **WN:** Churn Pool Trout Fishery; **WT:** Pool (Still).
Ref: FH0959

CHURNET (RIVER)

River Churnet, Leek, **STAFFORDSHIRE**, ST13, **England**.
Contact/s: **Mr Roy Birch-Machin** (Secretary), 53 Novi Lane, Leek, Staffordshire, ST13 6NX.
Profile: **FT:** Game; **WN:** Churnet; **WT:** River (Moving).
Ref: FH0960

CHURNET (RIVER)

Churnet River, Farley Lane, Alton, **STAFFORDSHIRE**, **England**.
(W) www.fentondas.co.uk
Contact/s: **Mr C Yates** (Club Secretary), The Puzzles, 5 Gatley Gr, Meir Park, Stoke-on-Trent, Staffordshire ST3 7SH.
(T) 01782 396913
Profile: **FT:** Coarse; **WN:** Churnet; **WT:** River (Moving). **Location:** **Nr. Rd:** Farley Road; **Main Rd:** B5032; **Rail:** Uttoxeter.
Ref: FH0961

CHURNET (RIVER)

River Churnet, Uttoxeter, **STAFFORDSHIRE**, ST14, **England**.
Contact/s: Manager, Denston Hall Farm, Denston, Uttoxeter, Staffordshire, ST14 5HF.
(T) 01889 590253
Profile: **FT:** Game; **WN:** Churnet; **WT:** River (Moving) **W. Size:** 3000 Metres.
Ref: FH0962

CHURNET (RIVER)

Churnet (River), Brookhouse Farm, Cheddleton, Leek, **STAFFORDSHIRE**, ST13 7E, **England**.
Contact/s: **Mr John Turner** (Hon Secretary), Prince Albert Angling Society, 15 Pexhill Drive, Macclesfield, Cheshire, SK10 3LP.
(T) 01625 422010
Profile: **FT:** Coarse; **WN:** Churnet; **WT:** River (Moving) **W. Size:** 1000 Metres. **Location:** **Nr. Rd:** Cheadle Road (A520); **Main Rd:** A520; **Rail:** Stoke-On-Trent.
Ref: FH0963

CHYRAISE LODGE HOTEL

Chyraise Lodge Hotel, Millpool, Goldsithney, Penzance, **CORNWALL**, TR20 9JD, **England**.
Contact/s: Fishery Manager.
(T) 01736 763485
Profile: **FT:** Coarse; **WN:** Millpool; **WT:** Lake (Still). **Location:** **Nr. Rd:** A394.
Ref: FH0964

CICELY MILL POOL

Cicely Mill Pool, Knutsford, **CHESHIRE**, WA16, **England**.
Contact/s: **Mr Frank Lythgoe** (Secretary), Warrington Angling Association, 52 Parker St, Warrington, Lancashire.
(T) 01928 716238 **(F)** 01928 713898
(E) info@warrington-anglers.org.uk
Profile: **FT:** Coarse; **WN:** Cicely Mill; **WT:** Pool (Still) **W. Size:** 3 Acres.
Ref: FH0965

CISTERNS

Cisterns, Northwich, **CHESHIRE**, CW9, **England**.
Contact/s: Fishery Manager.
(T) 01606 782841
Profile: **FT:** Coarse; **WN:** Cisterns; **WT:** Drain (Still).
Ref: FH0966

CLACHAIG (LOCH)

Loch Clachaig, Lochgilphead, **RENFREWSHIRE**, PA3, **Scotland**.
Contact/s: **Mr Archie MacGilp** (Secretary), Fyne Tackle, 22 Argyll St, Lochgilphead, Argyll and Bute, PA31 8NE.
(T) 01546 606878
Profile: **FT:** Game; **WN:** Clachaig; **WT:** Loch (Still); **F. Size:** 400 Acres; **W. Size:** 35 Acres. **Location:** **Nr. Rd:** Cairnbaan; **Main Rd:** B844; **Rail:** Oban.
Ref: FH0967

CLADY (RIVER)

River Clady, Portglenone, Ballymena, **COUNTY ANTRIM**, BT44, **Northern Ireland**.
Contact/s: Manager, Maura's Shop, 60 Main St, Portglenone, Ballymena, BT44 8HR.
(T) 028 25822197
Ms Margaret Dillon (Manager), 33 Mayogall Rd, Magherafelt, County Londonderry.
(T) 028 79643331
Profile: **FT:** Game; **WN:** Clady; **WT:** River (Moving) **W. Size:** 40000 Metres.
Ref: FH0968

CLADY (RIVER)

River Clady, Ballymena, **COUNTY ANTRIM**, BT44, **Northern Ireland**.
Contact/s: Manager, Bannvalley Guns and Tackle, 18 Main St, Portglenone, Ballymena, BT44 8AB.
(T) 028 25821383
Profile: **FT:** Coarse; **WN:** Clady; **WT:** River (Moving).
Ref: FH0969

CLAERWEN RESERVOIR

Claerwen Reservoir, Elan Valley Ctre, Rhayader, **POWYS**, LD6, **Wales**.
Contact/s: **Mr C Easton** (Information Contact), Glanrhos, Llanwrthwl, Llandrindod Wells, Powys, LD1 6NT.
(T) 01597 810277or810898
Mr Noel Hughes (Secretary), Elan Valley Angling Club, 25 Brynheulog, Rhayader, Powys, LD6 5EF.
(T) 01597 811099
Profile: **FT:** Coarse; **WN:** Claerwen; **WT:** Reservoir (Still).
Ref: FH0970

CLANRYE (RIVER)

River Clanrye, Newry, **COUNTY DOWN**, BT34, **Northern Ireland**.
Contact/s: Manager, Vaughan Chambers, College Terrace View, Belfast Rd, Newry, County Down.
Mr Ronald McCamley (Hon Secretary), Newry and District Anglers Association, 28 High St, Newry, County Down, BT34 1HB.
(T) 028 30268768
Mrs E McAllinden, Lisgullion Drive, Armagh Rd, Newry, County Down.
Profile: **FT:** Combination; **WN:** Clanrye; **WT:** River (Moving) **W. Size:** 20600 Metres. **Location:** **Nr. Rd:** Maysbridge Road; **Main Rd:** A1; **Rail:** Bessbrook.
Ref: FH0972

CLAPHAM COMMON POND

Clapham Common Pond, Clapham Common, London, **LONDON (GREATER)**, SW4, **England**.
Contact/s: **Clive**, Gerry's of Wimbledon, 170 The Broadway, London, SW19 1RX.
(T) 020 85406773
Profile: **FT:** Coarse; **WN:** Clapham Common; **WT:** Pond (Still). **Location:** **Nr. Rd:** Windmill Drive; **Main Rd:** Balham High Road to Balham Hill. **£Fr**
Ref: FH0973

CLARE LOUGH

Clare Lough, Claremorris, **COUNTY GALWAY**, **Ireland**.
Contact/s: **Mr Danny Goldrick** (Angling Officer), The Western Regional Fisheries Board, Weir Lodge, Earl's Island, Galway City, County Galway.
(T) 091 563118 **(F)** 091 566335
(E) wrfb@iol.ie
Profile: **FT:** Coarse; **WN:** Clare; **WT:** Lough (Still). **Location:** **Rail:** Claremorris.
Ref: FH0974

CLARE PARK LAKE

Clare Park Lake, Cavendish, Sudbury, **SUFFOLK**, CO10, **England**.
Contact/s: **Mr Chris Wilson** (Manager).
(T) 01638 730078
Profile: **FT:** Coarse; **WN:** Clare Park; **WT:** Lake (Still). **Location:** **Nr. Rd:** A1092; **Main Rd:** A1017, Halsted to Cambridge.
Ref: FH0975

CLAREMONT LAKE

Claremont Lake, Claremont School, Battle, **SUSSEX (EAST)**, TN33, **England**.
Contact/s: **Mr M Beaumont** (Principal).
(T) 01424 751555
Profile: **FT:** Coarse; **WN:** Claremont; **WT:** Lake (Still); **F. Size:** 2 Acres. **Location:** **Nr. Rd:** A21; **Main Rd:** A21.
Ref: FH0976

CLARENCE RECREATION GROUND

Clarence Recreation Ground, Lido, Bury, **MANCHESTER (GREATER)**, BL, **England**.
Contact/s: **Mr Metcalfe** (Secretary).
(T) 0161 7975597
Profile: **FT:** Coarse; **WN:** Clarence Recreation Ground; **WT:** Lake (Still).
Ref: FH0977

CLATIO LOCH

Clatio Loch, Dundee, **ANGUS**, DD, **Scotland**.
Profile: **FT:** Coarse; **WN:** Clatio; **WT:** Loch (Still).
Ref: FH0978

CLATTERCOTE RESERVOIR

Clattercote Reservoir, Clattercote, Claydon, Banbury, **OXFORDSHIRE**, OX1, **England**.
Contact/s: **Mr Geoff Bradbeer** (Secretary), Banbury and District Angling Association, 7 Bentley Cl, Banbury, Oxfordshire, OX16 7PB.
(T) 01295 268047
Mr Ivor Campbell (Head Bailiff).
(T) 01295 270796 **(F)** 01442 234932
Mr John Ellis (Manager).
(T) 01923 208717 **(F)** 01923 208787
Profile: **FT:** Coarse; **WN:** Clattercote; **WT:** Reservoir (Still); **F. Size:** 22 Acres; **W. Size:** 20 Acres. **Location:** **Nr. Rd:** Claydon; **Main Rd:** A423; **Rail:** Banbury.
Ref: FH0979

CLATTERINGSHAWS LOCH

Clatteringshaws Loch, New Galloway Rd, Newton Stewart, **DUMFRIES AND GALLOWAY**, DG8 6DE, **Scotland**.
Contact/s: **Mr Tony Dickinson** (Manager), Galloway Guns and Tackle, 36a Arthur St, Newton Stewart, Dumfries and Galloway, DG8 6DE.
(T) 01671 403404 **(F)** 01671 403404
Profile: **FT:** Game; **WN:** Clateringshaws; **WT:** Loch (Still). **Location:** **Nr. Rd:** New Galloway to Newton Stewart; **Main Rd:** A712.
Ref: FH0980

CLATWORTHY RESERVOIR

Clatworthy Reservoir, Hollands Lane, Clatworthy, Taunton, **SOMERSET**, TA4, **England**.
Contact/s: Customer Services, Wessex

Water, Billing Ctre, Clevedon Walk, Nailsea, Bristol, BS48 1WW.
(T) 01179 290611 (F) 01275 810519
Mr Dave Pursey (Ranger).
(T) 01984 624658or623549
Mr Fred Yeandle (Club Secretary).
(T) 01823 283959
Profile: **FT:** Game; **WN:** Clatworthy; **WT:** Reservoir (Still) **W. Size:** 130 Acres.
Location: **Main Rd:** B3190 or the B3227.
Ref: FH0981

CLAVERHAMBURY LAKE

Claverhambury Lake, Claverhambury, Galley Hill Rd, Waltham Abbey, **ESSEX**, EN9 2BL, **England**.
Contact/s: **Mr Kevin Hall** (Manager), Hall's Tackle, 44 Highbridge St, Waltham Abbey, Essex, EN9 1BS.
(T) 01992 711932
Mr Peter Hall (Owner), Hall's Tackle, 44 Highbridge St, Waltham Abbey, Essex, EN9 1BS.
(T) 01992 711932
Profile: **FT:** Coarse; **WN:** Claverhambury; **WT:** Lake (Still); **F. Size:** 12 Acres; **W. Size:** 6 Acres. **Location:** **Nr. Rd:** Galley Hill Road; **Main Rd:** M25, junction 26, Upshire Road; **Rail:** Waltham Cross.
Ref: FH0982

CLAVERING TROUT LAKE

Clavering Trout Lake, Clavering Farm, Clavering, Saffron Walden, **ESSEX**, CB11 4RL, **England**.
Contact/s: **Mr P G Greenhall** (Manager).
(T) 01799 550261
Profile: **FT:** Game; **WN:** Clavering; **WT:** Lake (Still) **W. Size:** 7 Acres.
Ref: FH0983

CLAWDD OFFAS DYKE

Clawdd Offas Dyke Coarse Fishing, Ffordd Llanfynydd, Treuddyn, Mold, **FLINTSHIRE**, CH7 4LQ, **Wales**.
(W) www.matchfishing.org.uk/venues
Contact/s: **Mr Roger Roberts**.
(T) 01352 770296
Profile: **FT:** Coarse; **WN:** Clawdd Offas Dyke; **WT:** Lake (Still) **W. Size:** 1 Acre. **Location:** **Nr. Rd:** B5101; **Main Rd:** A5104, Chester to Corwen; **Rail:** Wrexham.
Ref: FH0984

CLAWFORD FISHERIES

Clawford Vineyard And Fisheries, Clawton, Holsworthy, **DEVON**, EX22 6PN, **England**.
Contact/s: **Mr John Ray** (Owner).
(T) 01409 254177 (F) 01409 254177
Profile: **FT:** Coarse; **WN:** Clawford Vineyard And Fisheries; **WT:** Lake (Still); **F. Size:** 78 Acres; **W. Size:** 18 Acres. **Location:** **Nr. Rd:** Clawton; **Main Rd:** A388; **Rail:** Exeter.
Ref: FH0985

CLAXTON BRICKWORKS

Claxton Brickworks, Claxton, York, **YORKSHIRE (NORTH)**, YO60, **England**.
Contact/s: **Mr Doug Dalton** (Fishery Manager).
(T) 01904 692046
Profile: **FT:** Coarse; **WN:** Claxton Brickworks; **WT:** Combination (Still).
Ref: FH0986

CLAY LANE FISHERY

Clay Lane Fishery, Mobberly, Knutsford, **CHESHIRE**, WA16, **England**.
Contact/s: **Mr Brian Cooper**.
(T) 01565 873337
Profile: **FT:** Game; **WN:** Clay Lane Fishery; **WT:** Lake (Still) **W. Size:** 2 Acres.
Ref: FH0987

CLAY PIT

Clay Pit, Elmfield House Hotel, Tank Rd, Arrathorne, Bedale, **YORKSHIRE (NORTH)**, DL8, **England**.
Contact/s: **Mr Angus Robertson** (Fishery Manager).
(T) 01967 421288
Mr Jim Lillie (owner).
(T) 01677 450558
Ms Edith Lillie (owner).
(T) 01677 450558
Profile: **FT:** Coarse; **WN:** Clay Pit; **WT:** Gravel Pit (Still). **Location:** **Nr. Rd:** Tank Road; **Main Rd:** A1, A684.
Ref: FH0988

CLAYBRIDGE TROUT LAKES

Claybridge Trout Lakes, Bullington, Wragby, Market Rasen, **LINCOLNSHIRE**, LN8 5NN, **England**.
Contact/s: **Mr Trevor Fenton**.
(T) 01673 857014
Profile: **FT:** Game; **WN:** Claybridge; **WT:** Lake (Still).
Ref: FH0989

CLAYDON LAKE

Claydon Lake, Middle Claydon, Winslow, Leighton Buzzard, **BEDFORDSHIRE**, LU7, **England**.
Contact/s: **Mr B Smalley** (Secretary), 3 Isis Walk, Leighton Buzzard, Bedfordshire.
(T) 01525 852227
Profile: **FT:** Coarse; **WN:** Claydon; **WT:** Lake (Still) **W. Size:** 3 Acres. **Location:** **Main Rd:** A413, Buckingham.
Ref: FH0990

CLAYDON LAKE

Claydon Lake, Claydon House, Steeple Claydon, Buckingham, **BUCKINGHAMSHIRE**, MK18, **England**.
Contact/s: **Mr John Weatherall** (Secretary).
(T) 01869 278155
Profile: **FT:** Coarse; **WN:** Claydon; **WT:** Lake (Still).
Ref: FH0991

CLAYDON PARK FISHERY

Claydon Park Fishery, Lechlade, Fairford, **GLOUCESTERSHIRE**, GL7, **England**.
Contact/s: **Mr B Sparkles** (Fishery Manager).
(T) 01367 252689
Profile: **FT:** Coarse; **WN:** Claydon Park Fishery; **WT:** Gravel Pit (Still) **W. Size:** 5 Acres. **Location:** **Nr. Rd:** A417 Lechlade to Fairford; **Main Rd:** A361.
Ref: FH0992

CLAYHIDON (RIVER)

River Clayhidon, Clayhidon, Cullompton, **DEVON**, EX15, **England**.
Profile: **FT:** Coarse; **WN:** Clayhidon; **WT:** River (Moving) **W. Size:** 6400 Metres.
Ref: FH0993

CLAYLANDS CARAVAN SITE

Claylands Caravan Site, Garstang, Preston, **LANCASHIRE**, PR3, **England**.
Contact/s: **Mr Robinson**.
(T) 01524 791242
Profile: **FT:** Coarse; **WN:** Claylands Caravan Site; **WT:** Pond (Still). **Location:** **Nr. Rd:** Lancaster Road; **Main Rd:** A6.
Ref: FH0994

CLAYTON WOOD PONDS

Clayton Wood Ponds, Horsforth, Leeds, **YORKSHIRE (WEST)**, LS, **England**.
Contact/s: Area Manager, Environment Agency, Ridings Area Office, Phoenix House, Global Avenue, Leeds, LS11 8PG.
(T) 0113 2440191or2314834 (F) 0113 2134609
Mr Chris Child.
(T) 0113 2676220
Profile: **FT:** Coarse; **WN:** Clayton Wood; **WT:** Pond (Still).
Ref: FH0995

CLEABARROW TARN

Cleabarrow Tarn, Windermere, **CUMBRIA**, LA23, **England**.
Contact/s: Fishery Manager.
(T) 01539 433203
Manager, Go Fishing, Robinson Pl, Bowness-on-Windermere, Cumbria, LA23 3DQ.
(T) 01539 447086
Mr Chris Sodo (Hon Treasurer), Windermere, Ambleside and District Angling Association, Ecclerigg Court, Ecclerigg, Windermere, LA23 1LQ.
(T) 01539 445083
Profile: **FT:** Coarse; **WN:** Cleabarrow; **WT:** Tarn (Still); **F. Size:** 2 Acres. **Location:** **Nr. Rd:** B5284 Bowness to Kendal road.
Ref: FH0996

CLEARWATER FISH FARM

Clearwater Fish Farm, Ludbridge Mill, East Hendred, Wantage, **OXFORDSHIRE**, OX12 8LN, **England**.
Contact/s: **Mr Peter Austin**.
Mr Tim Lobb (Manager).
(T) 01235 833732 (F) 01235 835586
Profile: **FT:** Game; **WN:** Clearwater Fish Farm; **WT:** Pond (Still); **F. Size:** 10 Acres. **Location:** **Nr. Rd:** A417; **Main Rd:** A417; **Rail:** Didcot.
Ref: FH0997

CLEARWATER LAKE

Clearwater Lake, Pye Nest, Halifax, **YORKSHIRE (WEST)**, HX, **England**.
Contact/s: Area Manager, Environment Agency, Ridings Area Office, Phoenix House, Global Avenue, Leeds, LS11 8PG.
(T) 0113 2440191or2314834 (F) 0113 2134609
Mr P Cororan.
(T) 01422 346895
Profile: **FT:** Coarse; **WN:** Clearwater; **WT:** Lake (Still). **Location:** **Nr. Rd:** Darnes Avenue.
Ref: FH0998

CLEARWATERS COARSE FISHERY

Clearwaters Coarse Fishery, Earith, Huntingdon, **CAMBRIDGESHIRE**, PE17, **England**.
Profile: **FT:** Coarse; **WN:** Clearwaters; **WT:** Lake (Still) **W. Size:** 13 Acres.
Ref: FH0999

CLEETHORPES COUNTRY PARK

Cleethorpes Country Park, Cleethorpes, **HUMBERSIDE**, DN35, **England**.
Contact/s: Fishery Manager.
(T) 01472 698828
Profile: **FT:** Coarse; **WN:** Cleethorpes Country Park; **WT:** Lake (Still).
Ref: FH1000

CLEGG HALL LAKES

Clegg Hall Lakes, Clegg Hall Rd, Littleborough, **MANCHESTER (GREATER)**, OL15, **England**.
Contact/s: **Mr Bill Alger**.
(T) 01706 659040
Profile: **FT:** Combination; **WN:** Clegg Hall; **WT:** Lake (Still) **W. Size:** 4 Acres. **Location:** **Nr. Rd:** Clegg Hall Road; **Main Rd:** A58.
Ref: FH1001

CLEGGAN (RIVER)

River Cleggan, Crossmaglen, Newry, **COUNTY DOWN**, BT35, **Northern Ireland**.
Contact/s: **Mr Eugene Murphy**.
(T) 028 30868607
Mr J Cunningham (Secretary), 21 Forkhill Rd, Mullach Ban, County Armagh, BT35 9XL.
(T) 028 30889187
Mr Phil Nolan.
(T) 028 30868074
Profile: **FT:** Game; **WN:** Cleggan; **WT:** River (Moving).
Ref: FH1002

CLERKLAND FLY FISHERY

Clerkland Fly Fishery, Clerklands Loch, Clerklands Farm, Melrose, **SCOTTISH BORDERS**, TD6 9JR, **Scotland**.
Contact/s: **Mr Colin Moody** (Manager).
(T) 01835 870757
Mr Kenneth Summersgill (Owner).
Profile: **FT:** Game; **WN:** Clerkland Fly Fishery; **WT:** Loch (Still) **W. Size:** 4 Acres.

Location: Main Rd: A7.
Ref: FH1003

CLEVELEY BRIDGE FISHERY

Cleveley Bridge Fishery, Scorton, Preston, **LANCASHIRE**, PR3, **England**.
Contact/s: **Mr Eric Fishwick**.
(T) 01524 791637
Profile: FT: Coarse; WN: Cleveley Bridge Fishery; WT: Lake (Still). Location: Main Rd: A6 South.
Ref: FH1004

CLICKETTS HILL AND PLANTATION

Clicketts Hill And Plantation, Nayland Rd, Bures, **SUFFOLK**, CO8, **England**.
Contact/s: **Mr Rob Hayward** (Manager), Sudbury Angling Ctre, 1 Acton Sq, Sudbury, Suffolk, CO10 1HG.
(T) 01787 312118
Mr Trevor Fairless (Secretary), Sudbury and District Angling Association, 39 Pot Kiln Rd, Sudbury, Suffolk, CO10 0DG.
(T) 01787 312536
Profile: FT: Coarse; WN: Stow (Suffolk); WT: River (Moving) W. Size: 375 Metres.
Location: Nr. Rd: Nayland Road; Main Rd: A604, A12; Rail: Bures.
Ref: FH1005

CLIFTON LAKES FISHERY

Clifton Lakes Fishery, Clifton-upon-Dunsmore, Rugby, **WARWICKSHIRE**, CV, **England**.
Contact/s: **Mr Andy Mason. (M)** 07956 634079
Profile: FT: Coarse; WN: Clifton; WT: Lake (Still). Location: Nr. Rd: A5 opposite the truck stop; Main Rd: M1, junction 18.
Ref: FH1006

CLIFTON LOCK

Clifton Lock, Clifton Hampden, Abingdon, **OXFORDSHIRE**, OX14 4NE, **England**.
Contact/s: Fishery Contact.
(T) 01865 407821
Recreational Manager, The Environment Agency, Kings Meadow Rd, Reading, Berkshire, RG1 8DQ.
(T) 0118 9535000 (F) 0118 9500388
Profile: FT: Combination; WN: Thames; WT: Lock (Still). Location: Nr. Rd: Clifton Hampden Bridge; Main Rd: A415.
Ref: FH1007

CLIFTON MARINA

Clifton Marina, Clifton House Rd, Salford, **MANCHESTER (GREATER)**, M6, **England**.
Contact/s: **Mr Albert Morris** (Owner).
(T) 0161 7922684
Mr Eddie Batersby (Manager), Swinton Angling Ctre, 57 Worsley Rd, Swinton, Manchester, M27 5NE.
(T) 0161 7942784
Profile: FT: Coarse; WN: Clifton Marina; WT: Gravel Pit (Still) W. Size: 14 Acres.
Location: Nr. Rd: Clifton House road; Main Rd: A666 Manchester to Bolton.
Ref: FH1008

CLIFTON MOOR LAKE

Clifton Moor Lake, Clifton, **YORKSHIRE (NORTH)**, **England**.
Contact/s: **Mr H. D. Doulton** (Club Treasurer).
(T) 01904 692046
Profile: FT: Coarse; WN: Clifton Moor Lake; WT: Lake (Still); F. Size: 12 Acres; W. Size: 7 Acres.
Ref: FH1009

CLIVE VALE RESERVOIRS

Clive Vale Reservoirs, Harold Rd, Clive Vale, Hastings, **SUSSEX (EAST)**, TN35, **England**.
Contact/s: **Mr Kevin Thorney** (Chairman).
(T) 01424 719703
Profile: FT: Coarse; WN: Clive Vale; WT: Reservoir (Still). Location: Main Rd: A21; Rail: Hastings. £Free
Ref: FH1010

CLIVEY PONDS

Clivey Ponds, Lakeside, Ditton Marsh, Westbury, **WILTSHIRE**, BA13 4BA, **England**.
Contact/s: **Mr Mike Mortimer** (Owner).
(T) 01373 858311
Profile: FT: Coarse; WN: Clivey; WT: Pond (Still) W. Size: 1 Acre.
Ref: FH1011

CLIVIGER FISH PONDS

Cliviger Fish Ponds, Burnley, **LANCASHIRE**, BB, **England**.
Contact/s: **Mr Andrew Crossley** (Membership Secretary), Todmorden Angling Society, 296 Bacup Rd, Cloughfoot, Todmorden, Lancashire.
(T) 01706 816319
Mr Ray Barber (Secretary), Todmorden Angling Society, 12 Grisedale Drive, Burnley, Lancashire, BB12 8AR.
(T) 01282 702344 (M) 07970 897849
Profile: FT: Coarse; WN: Clivger; WT: Lake (Still) W. Size: 2 Acres. Location: Nr. Rd: A646; Main Rd: A646; Rail: Burnley.
Ref: FH1012

CLOCHFOLDICH BEAT

Clochfoldich Beat, Aberfeldy, **PERTH AND KINROSS**, PH15, **Scotland**.
(W) www.fishingnet.com/beats/clochfoldich.htm
Contact/s: **Ms Em Honeyman** (Manager), Wade Newsagents, 31 Bank St, Aberfeldy, Perth and Kinross, PH15 2BB.
(T) 01887 820397
Profile: FT: Combination; WN: Lower/Craggan, Clochfoldich and The Pot; WT: Pool (Still).
Ref: FH1013

CLODIAGH (RIVER)

River Clodiagh, Kilsheelin, **COUNTY TIPPERARY**, **Ireland**.
Contact/s: **Mr J O'Keeffe** (Manager), OK Sports, New St, Carrick-on-Suir, County Tipperary, Ireland.
(T) 051 40626
Profile: FT: Game; WN: River Clodiagh; WT: River (Moving).
Ref: FH1014

CLODIAGH (RIVER)

Clodiagh (River), Thurles, **COUNTY TIPPERARY**, **Ireland**.
Contact/s: **J Grene** (Manager), Farm Guesthouse, Cappamurra House, Dundrum, County Tipperary, Ireland.
(T) 062 71127
Mr Jimmy Purcell (Secretary), Thurles, Hollycross and Ballycamas Angling Association, Rathcannon, Holycross, Thurles, County Tipperary, Ireland.
Profile: FT: Game; WN: Suir; WT: River (Moving).
Ref: FH1015

CLOGHAN LODGE ESTATE FISHERY

Cloghan Lodge Estate Fishery, Cloghan Lodge, Cloghan, **COUNTY DONEGAL**, **Ireland**.
Contact/s: **Mr David Wilde**.
(T) 074 33003 (F) 074 33003
Profile: FT: Game; WN: Cloghan Lodge Estate Fishery; WT: Combination (Still & Moving); F. Size: 11520 Acres; W. Size: 5760 Acres. Location: Nr. Rd: Creamery Brae; Main Rd: Ballybofey to Glenties; Rail: Londonderry.
Ref: FH1016

CLOGHWATER (RIVER)

River Cloghwater, Ballymena, **COUNTY ANTRIM**, BT43, **Northern Ireland**.
Contact/s: **Mr Robin Russel**, 2 Riverlea, Rathkenny, Ballymena, BT43 6QG.
(T) 028 2558496
Mr Stephen Coulter, 50 The Knockans, Broughshane, Ballymena, County Antrim, BT43 7LQ.
(T) 028 25861616
Profile: FT: Game; WN: Cloghwater; WT: River (Moving) W. Size: 7200 Metres.
Ref: FH1017

CLONANAU FLY FISHING CENTRE

Clonanau Fly Fishing Centre, Nire Valley, Ballymacarbry, Clonmel, **COUNTY TIPPERARY**, **Ireland**.
Contact/s: **Mr Andrew Ryan**.
Profile: FT: Game; WN: Suir, Nire & Tar; WT: Combination (Still & Moving). Location: Rail: Thurles.
Ref: FH1018

CLOONAMOYNE FISHERY

Cloonamoyne Fishery, Crossmolina, **COUNTY MAYO**, **Ireland**.
Contact/s: **Mr Barry Seagrave**.
(T) 096 31851 (F) 096 31773
Profile: FT: Game; WN: Cloonamoyne Fishery; WT: Lough (Still).
Ref: FH1019

CLOONDROON LAKE

Cloondroon Lake, Claremorris, **COUNTY GALWAY**, **Ireland**.
Contact/s: **Mr Danny Goldrick** (Angling Officer), The Western Regional Fisheries Board, Weir Lodge, Earl's Island, Galway City, County Galway.
(T) 091 563118 (F) 091 566335
(E) wrfb@iol.ie
Profile: FT: Coarse; WN: Cloondroon; WT: Lake (Still).
Ref: FH1020

CLOONGEE FISHERY

Cloongee Fishery, Cloongee, Foxford, **COUNTY MAYO**, **Ireland**.
Contact/s: **Mr John Ruane** (Fishery Manager).
(T) 094 56960 (F) 094 56960
(E) cloongeefishery@yahoo.com
Profile: FT: Game; WN: Cloongee; WT: Reservoir (Still) W. Size: 5500 Metres.
Location: Nr. Rd: Foxford to Castlebar; Rail: Foxford.
Ref: FH1021

CLOUGH (RIVER)

River Clough, Ballymena, **COUNTY ANTRIM**, BT42, **Northern Ireland**.
Contact/s: **M Weir**, 23 Beechwood Avenue, Ahoghill, County Antrim.
(T) 028 25871242
Mr S Tuff, 122 Toome Rd, Ballymena, County Antrim.
(T) 028 2545202after5pm
Profile: FT: Game; WN: Clough; WT: Tributary (Moving) W. Size: 4800 Metres.
Ref: FH1022

CLOUGH (RIVER)

River Clough, Garsdale Valley, Sedbergh, **CUMBRIA**, LA10, **England**.
Contact/s: **Mr C Richardson**, Three Peaks Ltd, 25 Main St, Sedbergh, Cumbria, LA10 5BW.
(T) 01539 620446
Mr D Eccles, Three Peaks Ltd, 25 Main St, Sedbergh, Cumbria, LA10 5BW.
(T) 01539 620446
Profile: FT: Game; WN: Clough; WT: River (Moving). Location: Main Rd: A684; Rail: Kendal.
Ref: FH1023

CLOVELLY LAKES

Clovelly Lakes, Clifford Farm, Clifford Cross, Woolsery, Clovelly, Bideford, **DEVON**, EX39, **England**.
Contact/s: Manager, Clifford Farm Holidays, Clifford Cross, Woolsery, Bideford, EX39 5RB.
(T) 01237 431219 (F) 01237 431075
Mr A Cartwright.
(T) 01237 431442
Profile: FT: Coarse; WN: Clovelly; WT: Lake (Still) W. Size: 3 Acres. Location: Nr. Rd: A39; Main Rd: Clovelly.
Ref: FH1024

CLOWBRIDGE RESERVOIR

Clowbridge Reservoir, Bolton, **LANCASHIRE**, BL, **England**.
Contact/s: **Mr Roy Rhodes** (Conservation, Access and Recreation Manager), Rivington Water Treatment Works, Bolton Rd, Horwich, Bolton, BL6 7RN.
(T) 01204 664300
Profile: **FT:** Coarse; **WN:** Clowbridge; **WT:** Reservoir (Still). **Location:** **Main Rd:** A682.
Ref: FH1025

CLOWES PARK LAKE

Clowes Park Lake, Salford, **MANCHESTER (GREATER)**, M6, **England**.
Contact/s: **Mr Albert Morris**.
(T) 0161 7922684
Profile: **FT:** Coarse; **WN:** Clowes Park; **WT:** Lake (Still).
Ref: FH1026

CLUB LAKE

Club Lake, Dorchester, **DORSET**, DT2, **England**.
(W) www.orchid-lakes.com
Contact/s: **Mr Marsh Pratley** (Manager).
(T) 01865 341810 **(M)** 07885 618190
(E) mpratley@aol.com
Profile: **FT:** Coarse; **WN:** Club; **WT:** Lake (Still) **W. Size:** 2 Acres. **Location:** **Nr. Rd:** Abingdon Road; **Main Rd:** A4074 south to Berinsfield.
Ref: FH1027

CLUB PIT

Club Pit, Ditchinsham, Norwich Rd, Ditchingham, Bungay, **SUFFOLK**, NR35, **England**.
Contact/s: **Mr Ian Gosling** (Hon Secretary), Bungay Cherry Tree Angling Club, 37 St Marys Trce, Flixton Rd, Bungay, NR35 1DN.
(T) 01986 892982
Profile: **FT:** Coarse; **WN:** Club; **WT:** Gravel Pit (Still) **W. Size:** 4 Acres. **Location:** **Nr. Rd:** Norwich Road; **Main Rd:** A143, B1332.
Ref: FH1028

CLUBBIEDEAN RESERVOIR

Clubbiedean Reservoir, Edinburgh, **EDINBURGH (CITY OF)**, EH, **Scotland**.
Contact/s: Area Manager, East of Scotland Water, 55 Buckstone Trce, Edinburgh, EH10 6XH.
(T) 0131 4456462
Profile: **FT:** Game; **WN:** Clubbiedean; **WT:** Reservoir (Still).
Ref: FH1029

CLUMBER LAKE

Clumber Lake, Clumber Park, Estate Office, Worksop, **NOTTINGHAMSHIRE**, S80 3AZ, **England**.
Contact/s: **Mr Trevor Pressley**, The National Trust, Clumber Park, Estate Office, Worksop.
(T) 01909 4765926
Profile: **FT:** Coarse; **WN:** Clumber; **WT:** Lake (Still); **F. Size:** 4000 Acres; **W. Size:** 90 Acres. **Location:** **Main Rd:** A614; **Rail:** Worksop.
Ref: FH1030

CLUTTO LOCH

Clutto Loch, St Andrews, **FIFE**, KY16, **Scotland**.
Profile: **FT:** Game; **WN:** Clutto; **WT:** Loch (Still).
Ref: FH1031

CLWYD (RIVER)

River Clwyd, Bodfari, Denbigh, **CONWY**, LL16, **Wales**.
Contact/s: **Mr Martin Fowell** (Secretary), Bon Amie, 28 Ffordd Tanrallt, Meliden, Prestatyn.
(T) 01745 854390
Profile: **FT:** Game; **WN:** Clwyd; **WT:** River (Moving). **Location:** **Nr. Rd:** Pontruffydd to Bach-y-Graig.
Ref: FH1032

CLWYD (RIVER)

River Clwyd, Ruthin, **DENBIGHSHIRE**, LL15, **Wales**.
Contact/s: **Mr C P Harness** (Membership Secretary), 8 Llwyn Menlli, Ruthin, Clwyd.
(T) 01824 705208
Profile: **FT:** Game; **WN:** Clwyd; **WT:** River (Moving) **W. Size:** 24000 Metres. **Location:** **Nr. Rd:** Ruthin Town Weir to Llannerch Park; **Main Rd:** A494.
Ref: FH1033

CLWYD (RIVER)

River Clwyd, St Asaph, **DENBIGHSHIRE**, LL17, **Wales**.
Contact/s: **Mr Arthur Foxon** (Manager), Foxon's Tackle, Penrhewl, St Asaph, Denbighshire, LL17 0ED.
(T) 01745 583583 **(F)** 01745 583175
Mr W J P Staines (Hon Secretary), Delamere, Coed Esgob Lane, St Asaph.
(T) 01745 583926
Profile: **FT:** Game; **WN:** Clwyd; **WT:** River (Moving) **W. Size:** 400 Metres. **Location:** **Nr. Rd:** Pont Dafydd; **Main Rd:** A55.
Ref: FH1034

CLWYD (RIVER)

River Clwyd, Nannerch, Mold, **FLINTSHIRE**, CH7, **Wales**.
Contact/s: **Mr W J P Staines** (Hon Secretary), Delamere, Coed Esgob Lane, St Asaph.
(T) 01745 583926
Profile: **FT:** Game; **WN:** Clwyd; **WT:** River (Moving) **W. Size:** 8000 Metres.
Ref: FH1035

CLWYD (RIVER)

River Clwyd, Llannerch, Pwllheli, **GWYNEDD**, LL53, **Wales**.
Contact/s: **Mr W J P Staines** (Hon Secretary), Delamere, Coed Esgob Lane, St Asaph.
(T) 01745 583926
Profile: **FT:** Game; **WN:** Clwyd; **WT:** River (Moving) **W. Size:** 800 Metres.
Ref: FH1036

CLYDE (RIVER)

River Clyde, Swanston St, Glasgow, **GLASGOW (CITY OF)**, G, **Scotland**.
Contact/s: **Mr Bruce Macmartin** (Manager), Tackle and Guns, 920 Pollokshaws Rd, Glasgow, Lanarkshire, G41 2ET.
(T) 0141 6322005 **(F)** 0141 6322005
Mr Ronnie Macleod (Manager), MacLeod's Fishing Tackle, 176 High St, Motherwell, Lanarkshire, ML1 5JQ.
(T) 01698 860530
Profile: **FT:** Game; **WN:** Clyde; **WT:** River (Moving).
Ref: FH1037

CLYDE (RIVER)

River Clyde, Pine Wood, Greenock, **INVERCLYDE**, PA, **Scotland**.
Contact/s: Fishery Manager.
(T) 01589 033403
Profile: **FT:** Game; **WN:** Clyde; **WT:** River (Moving).
Ref: FH1038

CLYDE (RIVER)

River Clyde, Wishaw, **LANARKSHIRE (NORTH)**, ML2, **Scotland**.
Contact/s: **Mr Joseph Quigley**, 39 Hillfoot Avenue, Branchalwood, Wishaw, ML2 8TR.
(T) 01698 382479
Mr Thomas McGregor (Public Relations Officer).
(T) 01501 740928
Profile: **FT:** Combination; **WN:** Clyde; **WT:** River (Moving).
Ref: FH1039

CLYDE ESTUARY

Clyde Estuary, Gairloch, Helensbourgh, **ARGYLL AND BUTE**, G84, **Scotland**.
Contact/s: **Mr Brady**, Loch Lomond Angling Association, PO Box 3559, Glasgow, G71 7SJ.
(T) 0141 7811545 **(F)** 0141 7811545
Profile: **FT:** Game; **WN:** Clyde; **WT:** Estuary (Moving).
Ref: FH1040

CLYNWEDOG RESERVOIR

Clynwedog Reservoir, Llanidloes, **POWYS**, SY18, **Wales**.
Contact/s: **Mr J Dallas Davies** (Owner), Llyn Glywedog, Dresden House, Great Oak St, Llanidloes, SY18 6BW.
(T) 01686 412644 **(F)** 01686 412644
Mrs Gough (Manager), Travellers Rest Restaurant, 9 Long Bridge St, Llanidloes, Powys, SY18 6EE.
(T) 01686 412329
Profile: **FT:** Game; **WN:** Clynwedog; **WT:** Reservoir (Still) **W. Size:** 600 Acres. **Location:** **Main Rd:** A470; **Rail:** Newtown.
Ref: FH1041

CLYWEDOG (RIVER)

River Clywedog, Rhewl, Ruthin, **DENBIGHSHIRE**, LL15, **Wales**.
Contact/s: **Mr C P Harness** (Membership Secretary), 8 Llwyn Menlli, Ruthin, Clwyd.
(T) 01824 705208
Profile: **FT:** Game; **WN:** Clywedog; **WT:** River (Moving) **W. Size:** 4800 Metres. **Location:** **Nr. Rd:** Clwyd-Clyweddog to Bachymbyd Bridge; **Main Rd:** A525.
Ref: FH1042

CLYWEDOG (RIVER)

River Clywedog, Llanidloes, **POWYS**, SY18, **Wales**.
Contact/s: **Mr J Dallas Davies**, Llyn Glywedog, Dresden House, Great Oak St, Llanidloes, SY18 6BW.
(T) 01686 412644 **(F)** 01686 412644
Mrs Gough (Manager), Travellers Rest Restaurant, 9 Long Bridge St, Llanidloes, Powys, SY18 6EE.
(T) 01686 412329
Profile: **FT:** Game; **WN:** Clywedog; **WT:** River (Moving) **W. Size:** 6400 Metres. **Location:** **Main Rd:** A470; **Rail:** Newtown.
Ref: FH1043

CLYWEDOG (RIVER)

Clywedog (River), Willow Farm, Bangor-on-Dee, **WREXHAM**, **England**.
Contact/s: **Mr John Turner** (Hon Secretary), Prince Albert Angling Society, 15 Pexhill Drive, Macclesfield, Cheshire, SK10 3LP.
(T) 01625 422010
Profile: **FT:** Coarse; **WN:** Clywedog; **WT:** River (Moving) **W. Size:** 300 Metres. **Location:** **Nr. Rd:** Sun Lane; **Main Rd:** B5130; **Rail:** Wrexham.
Ref: FH1044

CMPRAC (RIVER)

River Cmprac, Treorchy, **RHONDDA CYNON TAFF**, CF42, **Wales**.
Contact/s: **Mr John Evans** (General Secretary), 126 Ystrad Rd, Ystrad, Rhondda, Glamorgan.
(T) 01443 439961
Profile: **FT:** Game; **WN:** Cmprac; **WT:** River (Moving) **W. Size:** 16000 Metres. **Location:** **Nr. Rd:** Stag Bridge to Trehatd.
Ref: FH1045

COATE WATER COUNTRY PARK

Coate Water Country Park, Swindon, **WILTSHIRE**, SN, **England**.
Contact/s: Fishery Manager.
(T) 01793 721173
Mr D Hoar (Fishery Manager).
(T) 01793 433255
Profile: **FT:** Coarse; **WN:** Coate Water Country Park; **WT:** Reservoir (Still) **W. Size:** 65 Acres. **Location:** **Nr. Rd:** A4259; **Main Rd:** M4, junction 15 to A419.
Ref: FH1046

COBBLEACRES LAKES

Cobbleacres Lakes, Hevingham, Norwich, **NORFOLK**, NR10, **England**.
Contact/s: Fishery Manager.
(T) 01603 754305
Profile: **FT:** Coarse; **WN:** Cobbleacres; **WT:** Lake (Still).
Ref: FH1047

COBBLERS MEAD LAKE

Cobblers Mead Lake, Corringham, Standford-Le-Hope, **ESSEX**, SS17 9, **England**.
Mr Steve O'Rourke (Owner), Basildon Angling Ctre, 402 Whitmore Way, Basildon, Essex, SS14 2HB.
(T) 01268 520144
Profile: **FT:** Coarse; **WN:** Cobblers Mead; **WT:** Lake (Still). Location: **Nr. Rd:** Herd Land; **Main Rd:** A1014.
Ref: FH1048

COD BECK

Cod Beck, Thirsk, **YORKSHIRE (NORTH)**, YO7, **England**.
Contact/s: **Mr Colin Weaver** (Secretary), 2 Garden Cottage, South Cres, Sowerby, Thirsk YO7 1RA.
(T) 01845 524633
Mr Derek Stratton (Manager), Thirsk Angling Ctre, 7 Sowerby Rd, Thirsk, YO7 1HR, YO7 1HR.
(T) 01845 524684 (F) 01845 525549
Profile: **FT:** Coarse; **WN:** Cod Beck; **WT:** Stream (Moving) **W. Size:** 9000 Metres. Location: **Nr. Rd:** A61; **Main Rd:** A19; **Rail:** Thirsk.
Ref: FH1049

CODALE TARN

Codale Tarn, Grasmere, Ambleside, **CUMBRIA**, LA22, **England**.
Profile: **FT:** Game; **WN:** Codale Tarn; **WT:** River (Moving).
Ref: FH1050

CODNOR PARK RESERVOIR

Codnor Park Reservoir, Ambergate, Belper, **DERBYSHIRE**, DE56, **England**.
Contact/s: **Mr Kev Davies**, Rod and Line Tackle, 17 Nottingham Rd, Ripley, Derbyshire, DE5 3DJ.
(T) 01773 749545
Profile: **FT:** Coarse; **WN:** Codnor Park; **WT:** Reservoir (Still); **F. Size:** 40 Acres.
Ref: FH1051

COFTON PARK FARM

Cofton Park Farm, Starcross, Dawlish, **DEVON**, EX7, **England**.
Contact/s: **Mrs T Jeffery**.
(T) 01626 890358
Profile: **FT:** Coarse; **WN:** Cofton Park Farm; **WT:** Lake (Still).
Ref: FH1052

COGHURST HALL

Coghurst Hall, Ivyhouse Lane, Ore, Hastings, **SUSSEX (EAST)**, TN34, **England**.
Contact/s: **Ms Tracey Byrne** (Area Sales Controller).
(T) 01424 756814
Profile: **FT:** Coarse; **WN:** Coghurst Hall; **WT:** Lake (Still).
Ref: FH1053

COGRA MOSS

Cogra Moss, Cockermouth, **CUMBRIA**, CA13, **England**.
Contact/s: **Mr Ken Simpson**, Cockermouth Angling Association, 36 High Rigg, Brigham, Cockermouth, Cumbria.
Profile: **FT:** Game; **WN:** Cogra Moss; **WT:** Lake (Still) **W. Size:** 40 Acres.
Ref: FH1054

COILLE BHAR (LOCH)

Loch Coille Bhar, Lochgilphead, **RENFREWSHIRE**, PA3, **Scotland**.
Contact/s: **Mr Archie MacGilp** (Secretary), Fyne Tackle, 22 Argyll St, Lochgilphead, Argyll and Bute, PA31 8NE.
(T) 01546 606878
Profile: **FT:** Game; **WN:** Coille Bhar; **WT:** Loch (Still); **F. Size:** 400 Acres; **W. Size:** 100 Acres. Location: **Nr. Rd:** B8025; **Main Rd:** A83; **Rail:** Oban.
Ref: FH1055

COKES PIT

Cokes Pit, Keynes Country Park, Spratsgate Lane, Shorncote, Cirencester, **GLOUCESTERSHIRE**, GL7 6DF, **England**.
Contact/s: **Mr J Parker** (Secretary), Ashton Keynes Angling Club, 81 Dunnington Rd, Wootton Bassett, Swindon, SN4 7EL.
(T) 01793 852028
Profile: **FT:** Coarse; **WN:** Cokes; **WT:** Gravel Pit (Still) **W. Size:** 10 Acres. Location: **Nr. Rd:** B4696, Spratsgate Lane; **Main Rd:** A419, A429; **Rail:** Kemble.
Ref: FH1056

COLDINGHAM LOCH

Coldingham Loch, Coldingham, Eyemouth, **SCOTTISH BORDERS**, TD14, **Scotland**.
Contact/s: **Mrs Ej Wise** (Manager).
(T) 01890 771270
Profile: **FT:** Game; **WN:** Coldingham; **WT:** Loch (Still) **W. Size:** 22 Acres.
Ref: FH1057

COLDWELL (LOWER) RESERVOIR

Coldwell (Lower) Reservoir, Coldwell Inn Activity Ctre, Pendle, Burnley, **LANCASHIRE**, BB10 3RG, **England**.
Contact/s: **Mr H Hargreaves** (Secretary), 171 Reedley Rd, Briarfield, Nelson, Burnley.
(T) 01282 68965
Mr Roy Rhodes (Conservation, Access and Recreation Manager), Rivington Water Treatment Works, Bolton Rd, Horwich, Bolton, BL6 7RN.
(T) 01204 664300
Profile: **FT:** Game; **WN:** Coldwell; **WT:** Reservoir (Still).
Ref: FH1058

COLEBROOKE (RIVER)

River Colebrooke, Maguiresbridge, **COUNTY FERMANAGH**, BT94, **Northern Ireland**.
Contact/s: **Mr Patrick Trotter** (Secretary), 7 Tattinderry Estate, Maguiresbridge, County Fermanagh.
(T) 028 67721877
Profile: **FT:** Game; **WN:** Colebrooke; **WT:** River (Moving) **W. Size:** 7200 Metres.
Ref: FH1059

COLEBROOKE PARK

Colebrooke Park, Brookeborough, Enniskillen, **COUNTY FERMANAGH**, BT94, **Northern Ireland**.
(W) www.colebrookepark.com
Contact/s: **Mr Alan** (Fishery Manager).
(T) 028 66531402
(E) alan@colebrookepark.com
Profile: **FT:** Game; **WN:** Colebrooke Park; **WT:** Canal (Still & Moving) **W. Size:** 4800 Metres.
Ref: FH1060

COLEMERE COUNTRY PARK

Colemere Country Park, Welshampton, Ellesmere, **SHROPSHIRE**, SY12 0, **England**.
Contact/s: Manager, Shropshire County Council Countryside Service, Swan Hill, Ellesmere, SY12 0DQ.
(T) 01691 623461
Ms Liz Hayes (Manager).
(T) 01625 251262
Profile: **FT:** Coarse; **WN:** Colemere Country Park; **WT:** Lake (Still) **W. Size:** 70 Acres. Location: **Nr. Rd:** A495.
Ref: FH1061

COLIN GODMANS TROUTING

Colin Godmans Trouting, Furners Green, Isfield, Uckfield, **SUSSEX (EAST)**, TN22 3RR, **England**.
Contact/s: **Mr E B Worthington** (Manager).
(T) 01825 740322
Profile: **FT:** Game; **WN:** Colin Godmans Trouting; **WT:** Lake (Still) **W. Size:** 7 Acres.
Ref: FH1062

COLLEGE FARM FISHING

College Farm Fishing, Aynho Rd, Banbury, **OXFORDSHIRE**, OX17 3AB, **England**.
Contact/s: **Mr Nigel Oakey** (Fishery Manager).
(T) 01869 810258 (M) 07887 845836
Profile: **FT:** Coarse; **WN:** College Farm; **WT:** Lake (Still). Location: **Nr. Rd:** Aynho Road; **Main Rd:** B4031.
Ref: FH1063

COLLEGE RESERVOIR

College Reservoir, Falmouth, **CORNWALL**, TR11, **England**.
Contact/s: **Mr Chris Bird** (Manager), Newtown Angling Ctre, Newtown, Germoe, Penzance, TR20 9AE.
(T) 01736 763721 (F) 01736 763721
Mr Reg England (Manager), Peninsula Coarse Fisheries, St Cleer Depot, Lewdown, Okehampton, Devon EX20 4QT.
(T) 01837 871565 (F) 01837 871534
Profile: **FT:** Coarse; **WN:** College; **WT:** Reservoir (Still) **W. Size:** 38 Acres. Location: **Nr. Rd:** A38 to Penryn; **Main Rd:** B3291.
Ref: FH1064

COLLIFORD LAKE

Colliford Lake, Jamaica Inn, Bolventor, Liskeard, **CORNWALL**, PL14, **England**.
Contact/s: **Mr Chris Hall** (Manager).
(T) 01837 871565 (F) 01837 871534
Profile: **FT:** Game; **WN:** Colliford; **WT:** Lake (Still) **W. Size:** 900 Acres. Location: **Main Rd:** A30.
Ref: FH1065

COLN (RIVER)

River Coln, Fairford, **GLOUCESTERSHIRE**, GL7, **England**.
Contact/s: **Mark**.
(T) 01285 712535 (F) 01285 713782
Mr Dudley, The Market Place, Fairford, GL7 4AA.
Profile: **FT:** Game; **WN:** Coln; **WT:** River (Moving) **W. Size:** 1900 Metres. Location: **Nr. Rd:** A417; **Main Rd:** A417; **Rail:** Swindon.
Ref: FH1066

COLN (RIVER)

River Coln, Bilbury, Cirencester, **GLOUCESTERSHIRE**, GL7, **England**.
Contact/s: **Mr I Peters**.
(T) 01285 740215
Profile: **FT:** Game; **WN:** Coln; **WT:** River (Moving).
Ref: FH1067

COLNBROOK WEST

Colnbrook West, Lakeside Rd, Colnbrook, Slough, **BUCKINGHAMSHIRE**, SL3, **England**.
Contact/s: **Buzz** (Manager), Boyer Leisure Ltd, Heron's Point Tackle Shop, Farlow's Lake, Ford Lane, Iver SL0 9LL.
(T) 01753 630302or01895444707 (F) 01753 630302
(E) info@boyer.co.uk
Profile: **FT:** Coarse; **WN:** Clonbrook West; **WT:** Gravel Pit (Still) **W. Size:** 4 Acres. Location: **Nr. Rd:** Lakeside Road; **Main Rd:** A4 to Heathrow.
Ref: FH1068

COLNE (RIVER)

River Colne, Colchester, **ESSEX**, CO, **England**.
Profile: **FT:** Coarse; **WN:** Colne; **WT:** River (Moving).
Ref: FH1069

COLNE (RIVER)

River Colne, Aldham, Colchester, **ESSEX**, CO6, **England**.
Contact/s: **Mr P Emson** (Secretary), Emson and Son Tackle Shop, 88 High St, Earls

Colne, Colchester, CO6 2QX.
(T) 01787 223331
Profile: FT: Coarse; WN: Aldham and Colne; WT: Combination (Still & Moving).
Ref: FH1070

COLNE (RIVER)

River Colne, Rickmansworth, **HERTFORDSHIRE**, WD3, **England**.
Contact/s: Mr L Dalton (Secretary), Uxbridge Rovers Angling and Conservation Society, PO Box 253, Harrow, Middlesex, HA3 8XU.
(T) 01814 281739
Profile: FT: Coarse; WN: Colne; WT: River (Moving) W. Size: 1200 Metres.
Ref: FH1071

COLNE (RIVER)

River Colne, New Denham, Uxbridge, London, **LONDON (GREATER)**, UB9, **England**.
Contact/s: Buzz (Manager), Boyer Leisure Ltd, Heron's Point Tackle Shop, Farlow's Lake, Ford Lane, Iver SL0 9LL.
(T) 01753 630302or01895444707 (F) 01753 630302
(E) info@boyer.co.uk
Mr Tom Wilkinson (Secretary).
(T) 020 84210769
Profile: FT: Coarse; WN: Colne; WT: River (Moving). Location: Nr. Rd: A4020; Main Rd: M40, junction 1.
Ref: FH1072

COLNE (RIVER)

River Colne, New Denham, Uxbridge, London, **LONDON (GREATER)**, UB9, **England**.
Contact/s: Mr L Dalton (Secretary), Uxbridge Rovers Angling and Conservation Society, PO Box 253, Harrow, Middlesex, HA3 8XN.
(T) 01814 281739
Profile: FT: Coarse; WN: Colne; WT: River (Moving) W. Size: 2400 Metres. Location: Nr. Rd: Denham Court Drive; Main Rd: B416; Rail: Ruslip.
Ref: FH1073

COLNE (RIVER)

River Colne, Cellars Clough, Huddersfield, **YORKSHIRE (WEST)**, HD, **England**.
Contact/s: Mr J D Jones (Bailiff), 16 Malvern Rd, Nemsome, Huddesfield, Yorkshire (West).
(T) 01484 308948
Mr R Carter (Bailiff), 10 Varley Rd, Slaithwaite, Yorkshire (West).
(T) 01484 843163
Profile: FT: Game; WN: Colne (Marsden to Linthwaite); WT: River (Moving). Location: Nr. Rd: Cellars Clough; Main Rd: A62.
Ref: FH1074

COLNE WATER

Colne Water, Laneshaw Bridge, Colne, **LANCASHIRE**, BB8, **England**.
Contact/s: Mr Robin Varley (Secretary).
(T) 01535 634426
(E) robin.varley@btinternet.com
Profile: FT: Game; WN: Colne; WT: River (Moving). Location: Nr. Rd: Keighley Road to Lanshaw Bridge; Main Rd: B6250, A6068.
Ref: FH1075

COLNEBROOK (RIVER)

River Colnebrook, Colnebrook, Slough, **BUCKINGHAMSHIRE**, SL3 0, **England**.
(W) www.blenheim-angling.ic24.net
Contact/s: Mr Fred Lancaster (Secretary), Blenheim Angling Society, Brairwood, Burtons Lane, Chalfont St Giles, Buckinghamshire, HP8 4BB.
(T) 01494 764977
(E) blenheim.angling@ntlworld.com
Mr John Gill (Assistant Fisheries Officer).
(T) 020 85612993
Profile: FT: Coarse; WN: Colnebrook; WT: River (Moving) W. Size: 2300 Metres. Location: Nr. Rd: B376; Main Rd: M25; Rail: Wraysbury.
Ref: FH1076

COLNEY HEATH LAKE

Colney Heath Pits, Colney Heath, St Albans, **HERTFORDSHIRE**, AL4, **England**.
Contact/s: Mr Dave Eves (Secretary), De Havilland Angling Society, 74 Drovers Way, Hatfield, Hertfordshire, AL10 0PX.
(T) 01707 273435
Profile: FT: Coarse; WN: Colney Heath; WT: Lake (Still).
Ref: FH1077

COLTON LAKE

Colton Lake, Barford, Norwich, **NORFOLK**, **England**.
(W) www.fisheries.co.uk/barford/index.htm
Contact/s: Ms Sarah Thomson (Manager), Barford Lakes Fishery, Common Farm, Chapel St, Barford, NR9 4AB.
(T) 01603 759624 (F) 01603 758111
(E) barfordlakes@barfordlakes.force9.co.uk
Profile: FT: Coarse; WN: Colton; WT: Lake (Still); F. Size: 3 Acres; W. Size: 2 Acres.
Location: Main Rd: A47; Rail: Thorpe Station, Norwich.
Ref: FH1078

COLTSFORD MILL FISHERY

Coltsford Mill Fishery, Mill Lane, Hurst Green, Oxted, **SURREY**, RH8 9DG, **England**.
Contact/s: Mr Shaun Moore (Owner).
(T) 01883 715666
Profile: FT: Coarse; WN: Coltsford Mill Fishery; WT: Lake (Still).
Ref: FH1079

COLWICK COUNTRY PARK

Colwick Country Park, River Rd, Off Mile End Rd, Nottingham, **NOTTINGHAMSHIRE**, NG4 2DW, **England**.
(W) www.boat86.freeserve.co.uk
Contact/s: , Nottingham City Council, Woodthorpe Grange, Woodthorpe, Nottingham, NG5 4HA.
Mr Mick Weaver (Park Warden), Colwick Country Park, Colwick Hall, Colwick, Nottingham, NG4 2DW.
(T) 0115 9870785
(E) rainbow@boat86.freeserve.co.uk
Ms Vivienne Craig (Booking Secretary).
(T) 0115 9155555
Profile: FT: Combination; WN: Colwick Country Park; WT: Lake (Still); F. Size: 250 Acres; W. Size: 88 Acres. Location: Nr. Rd: Mile End Road; Main Rd: A612 Colwick to Southwell; Rail: Netherfield.
Ref: FH1080

COMBS RESERVOIR

Combs Reservoir, Manchester Rd, Chapel-En-Le-Frith, High Peak, **DERBYSHIRE**, SK23, **England**.
Contact/s: Mr H Ollerenshaw (Secretary), 133 Manchester Rd, Hyde, Cheshire.
(T) 0161 4940722or01613680263
Profile: FT: Coarse; WN: Combs; WT: Reservoir (Still) W. Size: 50 Acres.
Location: Nr. Rd: Manchester Road; Main Rd: B5470, A6.
Ref: FH1081

COMBWICH PONDS

Combwich Ponds, Hinkley Point Rd, Bridgwater, **SOMERSET**, TA, **England**.
Contact/s: Mr Mark Pople (Secretary), 14 Edward St, Bridgwater, Somerset.
(T) 01278 422397
Profile: FT: Coarse; WN: Combwich; WT: Pond (Still). Location: Nr. Rd: Hinkley Point Road; Main Rd: M5.
Ref: FH1082

COMMON POND

Common Pond, Common, Gerrards Cross, **BUCKINGHAMSHIRE**, SL9, **England**.
Profile: FT: Coarse; WN: Common; WT: Pond (Still) W. Size: 1 Acre. Location: Nr. Rd: Common. £Fr
Ref: FH1083

CONDER VALLEY FLY FISHERY

Conder Valley Fly Fishery, Forrest Hills, Hazel Rigg Lane, Ellel, Lancaster, **LANCASHIRE**, LA2 0PL, **England**.
Contact/s: Mr Colin Newsham.
(T) 01524 752566
Profile: FT: Game; WN: Conder Valley Fly Fishery; WT: Reservoir (Still).
Ref: FH1084

CONDOR PARK RESERVOIR

Condor Park Reservoir, Ripley, **DERBYSHIRE**, DE5, **England**.
Contact/s: Secretary.
(T) 01773 746486
Profile: FT: Coarse; WN: Condor; WT: Reservoir (Still).
Ref: FH1085

CONISTON WATER

Coniston Water, Coniston, **CUMBRIA**, LA21, **England**.
Contact/s: Fishery Manager.
(T) 01768 866666
Profile: FT: Game; WN: Coniston; WT: Lake (Still).
Ref: FH1086

CONNAUGHT WATER

Connaught Water, Epping Forest Ponds, The Warren, Loughton, **ESSEX**, IG10 4RW, **England**.
Contact/s: Ranger, Epping Forest Information Ctre, Nursery Rd, High Beech, Loughton, IG10 4AF.
(T) 020 85321010
A Clark (Manager), Corporation of London, The Warren, Loughton, Essex, IG10 4RW.
(T) 0208 5080028
Profile: FT: Coarse; WN: Connaught; WT: Lake (Still). Location: Nr. Rd: Rangers Road; Main Rd: A104; Rail: Chingford.
Ref: FH1087

CONNINGBROOK

Conningbrook, Ashford, **KENT**, **England**.
(W) www.midkentfish.demon.co.uk
Contact/s: Mr Chris Logsdon (Fisheries Manager), Mid Kent Fisheries, Chilham Water Mill, Mill Lane, Chilham, CT4 8EE.
(T) 01227 730668
(E) chilham@midkentfisheries.co.uk
Profile: FT: Coarse; WN: Conningbrook; WT: Lake (Still); F. Size: 40 Acres; W. Size: 23 Acres. Location: Nr. Rd: B2164; Main Rd: M20; Rail: Ashford.
Ref: FH1088

CONON (RIVER)

River Conon, Dingwall, **HIGHLAND**, IV7, **Scotland**.
Contact/s: Mr Matheson, Seaforth Highland Country Estate, Brahan, Dingwall, Highland, IV7 8EE.
(T) 01349 861150 (F) 01349 861745
(E) enquiry@seaestate.com
Profile: FT: Combination; WN: Conon; WT: River (Moving) W. Size: 3500 Metres.
Location: Nr. Rd: A835; Main Rd: A9; Rail: Dingwall.
Ref: FH1089

CONON (RIVER)

River Conon, Dingwall, **HIGHLAND**, IV7, **Scotland**.
Contact/s: Mr H C Furlong (Secretary), The Sports and Model Shop, 66 High St, Dingwall, Highland, IV15 9RY.
(T) 01349 862346
Profile: FT: Game; WN: Conon; WT: River (Moving).
Ref: FH1090

CONSALL NATURE PARK

Consall Nature Reserve, Consall Forge, Wetley Rocks, Stoke-on-Trent, **STAFFORDSHIRE**, **England**.
Contact/s: Park Ranger, Rangers Office, Consall Nature Reserve, Consall Forge, Wetley Rocks, Staffordshire.

(T) 01782 550939
Park Ranger, Rangers Office, Consall Nature Reserve, Consall Forge, Wetley Rocks, Staffordshire.
(T) 01782 550939
Profile: **FT:** Coarse; **WN:** Consall Nature ReserveWT: (Still); **F. Size:** 30 Acres; **W. Size:** 6 Acres. **Location:** **Nr. Rd:** Consall Road from Wetley Rocks; **Main Rd:** A522; **Rail:** Stoke-on-Trent.
Ref: FH1091

CONSTANTINE BROOK

Constantine Brook, Constantine, Falmouth, **CORNWALL**, TR11, **England**.
Profile: **FT:** Game; **WN:** Constantine; **WT:** Stream (Moving) **W. Size:** 9600 Metres.
Location: **Rail:** Penryn.
Ref: FH1092

CONWY (RIVER)

River Conwy, Dolgarrog, Conwy, LL32, **Wales**.
Contact/s: **Mr Peter Jones**, 12 Hillside Cottages, Dolgarrog, LL32.
Profile: **FT:** Combination; **WN:** Conwy; **WT:** River (Moving).
Ref: FH1093

CONWY (RIVER)

River Conwy, Betws-Y-Coed, **CONWY**, LL24, **Wales**.
Contact/s: **Mr G Parry** (Manager), Tan Lan Restaurant, Holyhead Rd, Betws-y-coed, Gwynedd, LL24 0AB.
(T) 01690 710232
Mr Melfyn Hughes (Secretary), Betws-y-Coed Angling Club, Cae Garw, Betws-y-Coed, Gwynedd, LL24 0BY.
(T) 01690 710618
Profile: **FT:** Combination; **WN:** Conwy; **WT:** River (Moving) **W. Size:** 7200 Metres.
Location: **Nr. Rd:** Waterloo Bridge.
Ref: FH1094

CONWY (RIVER)

River Conwy, Betws-Y-Coed, **CONWY**, LL24, **Wales**.
Contact/s: **Mr Melfyn Hughes** (Secretary), Betws-y-Coed Angling Club, Cae Garw, Betws-y-Coed, Gwynedd, LL24 0BY.
(T) 01690 710618
Profile: **FT:** Game; **WN:** Conwy; **WT:** River (Moving). **Location:** **Nr. Rd:** Waterloo Bridge to River Llugwy.
Ref: FH1095

CONWY (RIVER)

River Conwy, The Gwydir Hotel, Bangor Rd, Betws-Y-Coed, **CONWY**, LL24, **Wales**.
Contact/s: **Mr Owen Wainwright** (Manager).
(T) 01690 710777
Profile: **FT:** Game; **WN:** Conwy; **WT:** River (Moving). **Location:** **Nr. Rd:** Bangor Road; **Main Rd:** A5.
Ref: FH1096

CONWY (RIVER)

River Conwy, Llanrwst, **CONWY**, LL26, **Wales**.
Contact/s: , Library Tackle Shop, Bridge St, Llanrwst, Gwynedd.
(T) 01492 641477
Mr David Hughes (Hon Secretary), 36 Station Rd, Llanrwst, Gwynedd, LL26 09A.
Profile: **FT:** Game; **WN:** Conwy; **WT:** River (Moving) **W. Size:** 2000 Metres. **Location:** **Nr. Rd:** Old Bridge Road; **Main Rd:** A470.
Ref: FH1097

CONWY (RIVER)

Conway (River), Maenan Abbey, Llanrwst, **GWYNEDD**, **Wales**.
Contact/s: **Mr John Turner** (Hon Secretary), Prince Albert Angling Society, 15 Pexhill Drive, Macclesfield, Cheshire, SK10 3LP.
(T) 01625 422010
Profile: **FT:** Game; **WN:** Conwy; **WT:** River (Moving) **W. Size:** 420 Metres. **Location:** **Nr. Rd:** A470; **Rail:** Llanrwst.
Ref: FH1098

CONWY VALLEY FISHERIES

Conwy Aquatics And Water Garden Centre And Fishery, Glyn Isa, Rowen, Conwy, LL32 8PT, **Wales**.
Contact/s: **Mr Len Boud** (Owner).
(T) 01492 650063 (F) 01492 650063
Profile: **FT:** Coarse; **WN:** Conwy Aquatics And Water Garden Centre And Fishery; **WT:** Lake (Still); **F. Size:** 7 Acres; **W. Size:** 3 Acres. **Location:** **Nr. Rd:** B5106; **Main Rd:** A55; **Rail:** Conwy. £Fr
Ref: FH1099

COOKS POND

Cooks Pond, Chithurst Lane, Milland, Liphook, **HAMPSHIRE**, GU30, **England**.
Contact/s: **Mr C Boxall** (Treasurer), Rother Angling Club, Innisfree, Ashfield Rd, Midhurst, West Sussex, GU29 9JX.
(T) 01730 813885
Profile: **FT:** Coarse; **WN:** Cooks; **WT:** Pond (Still) **W. Size:** 3 Acres. **Location:** **Nr. Rd:** Chithurst Lane; **Main Rd:** A272.
Ref: FH1100

COOLMORE ESTATE FISHERY

Coolmore Estate Fishery, Coolmore Estate, Thomastown, **COUNTY KILKENNY**, **Ireland**.
Contact/s: Fishery Manager.
(T) 056 2414
Profile: **FT:** Game; **WN:** Coolmore Estate Fishery
Ref: FH1101

COOLNAMUCK FISHERIES

Coolnamuck Fisheries, Carrick-on-Suir, **COUNTY TIPPERARY**, **Ireland**.
Contact/s: **Mr J O'Keeffe**.
(T) 051 40626
Profile: **FT:** Game; **WN:** Suir; **WT:** River (Moving).
Ref: FH1102

COOLYERMER LOUGH FISHERY

Coolyermer Lough Fishery, Leambeg, Letterbreen, Enniskillen, **COUNTY FERMANAGH**, BT74 9ED, **Northern Ireland**.
(W) www.flyfishery.com
Contact/s: **Mr Rob Henshall** (Manager).
(T) 028 66341676 (F) 028 66341676 (M) 07771 728388
(E) robhenshall@lineone.com
Profile: **FT:** Game; **WN:** Coolyermer; **WT:** Lough (Still) **W. Size:** 45 Acres. **Location:** **Nr. Rd:** A4; **Main Rd:** A4.
Ref: FH1103

COOMBE ABBEY LAKE

Coombe Abbey Lake, Coombe Country Park, Brinklow Rd, Binley, Coventry, **MIDLANDS (WEST)**, CV3 2AB, **England**.
Contact/s: Area Manager, Coventry City Council, Coombe Country Park, Brinklow Rd, Binley, Coventry, CV3 2AB.
(T) 024 76453720
Profile: **FT:** Coarse; **WN:** Coombe Abbey; **WT:** Lake (Still) **W. Size:** 80 Acres.
Ref: FH1104

COOMBE FARM FISHPONDS

Coombe Farm Fishponds, Little Silver, Cadeleigh, Tiverton, **DEVON**, EX16, **England**.
Contact/s: **Mrs Curtis**.
(T) 01884 855337
Profile: **FT:** Coarse; **WN:** Coombe Farm Fishponds; **WT:** Pond (Still).
Ref: FH1105

COOMBE FISHERIES

Coombe Fisheries, Miltoncombe, Yelverton, Tavistock, **DEVON**, PL19 8RR, **England**.
Contact/s: **Mr Melvin Wood**.
(T) 01752 518167
Mr Steven Horn (Manager), New Venn Farm, Lamerton, Tavistock, Devon, PL19 8RR.
(T) 01822 616624 (F) 01822 616624 (M) 07899 958493
Profile: **FT:** Coarse; **WN:** Coombe Fisheries; **WT:** Lake (Still) **W. Size:** 2 Acres. **Location:** **Nr. Rd:** A386; **Main Rd:** A386; **Rail:** Plymouth.
Ref: FH1106

COOMBE LAKE

Coombe Lake, Langport, **SOMERSET**, TA10, **England**.
Contact/s: **Mr Colin Dyer**, Tackle Shack, North St, Langport, Somerset, TA10 9RQ.
(T) 01458 253665
Mr Den Barlow (Secretary), Langport and District Angling Association, Florissant, Northfield, Somerton, TA11 6SJ.
(T) 01458 272119
Profile: **FT:** Coarse; **WN:** Coombe; **WT:** Lake (Still) **W. Size:** 3 Acres. **Location:** **Nr. Rd:** Coombe; **Main Rd:** A372, Langport to Bridgewater.
Ref: FH1107

COOMBE MILL

Coombe Mill, St Breward, Bodmin, **CORNWALL**, PL30 4LZ, **England**.
Contact/s: Fishery Manager.
(T) 01208 850344
Profile: **FT:** Coarse; **WN:** Coombe; **WT:** Mill Dam (Still).
Ref: FH1108

COOMBE POOL

Coombe Pool, Coombe Country Park, Brinklow Rd, Binley, Coventry, **MIDLANDS (WEST)**, CV3 2AB, **England**.
Contact/s: Ranger Service.
(T) 024 76453720 (F) 024 76635350
Profile: **FT:** Coarse; **WN:** Coombe; **WT:** Pool (Still); **F. Size:** 500 Acres; **W. Size:** 85 Acres.
Ref: FH1109

COOMBE WATER FISHERY

Coombe Water Fishery, Coombe Farm, Coombe Lane, Kingsbridge, **DEVON**, TQ7 4AB, **England**.
Contact/s: **Mr Jonathan Robinson**.
(T) 01548 852038 (F) 01548 852038 (M) 07971 077980
Profile: **FT:** Coarse; **WN:** Coombe Water Fishery; **WT:** Lake (Still) **W. Size:** 3 Acres. **Location:** **Nr. Rd:** B1396 to Kingsbridge; **Main Rd:** A381; **Rail:** Totnes.
Ref: FH1110

COPPER MILLSTREAM

Copper Millstream, Tottenham, London, **LONDON (GREATER)**, N17, **England**.
Contact/s: **Mr Chris King**, Walthamstow Reservoir Group, Thames Water Gatehouse, 2 , Forest Rd, Tottenham, London, N17 9NH.
(T) 020 88081527
Profile: **FT:** Coarse; **WN:** Copper Mill; **WT:** Stream (Moving) **W. Size:** 1200 Metres. **Location:** **Nr. Rd:** Forest Road; **Main Rd:** A10, North London; **Rail:** Tottenham Hale Underground.
Ref: FH1111

COPPICE LAKE

Coppice Lake, Shipley, Heanor, **DERBYSHIRE**, DE75 7JH, **England**.
Contact/s: **Mr Robert Booth** (Fishing Officer), Counter Solutions, Lakeside Business Ctre, The Field, Shipley, Derbyshire, DE75 7JH.
(T) 01773 530303
Profile: **FT:** Coarse; **WN:** Coppice Water; **WT:** Lake (Still) **W. Size:** 6 Acres. **Location:** **Main Rd:** A6007, Ilkeston and Heanor.
Ref: FH1112

COPPICE POND

Coppice Pond, St Ive's, Harden, Bingley, **YORKSHIRE (WEST)**, BD16, **England**.
Contact/s: **Mr Ian Ward**.
(T) 01274 567422
Profile: **FT:** Coarse; **WN:** Coppice; **WT:** Lake (Still) **W. Size:** 2 Acres. **Location:** **Nr. Rd:** Bingley to Harden; **Main Rd:** B6429.
Ref: FH1113

COPPICE TROUT FISHERY

Coppice Trout Fishery, St Weonards, Hereford, **HEREFORDSHIRE**, HR2 8QH, **England**.
Contact/s: Mr Colin Evans.
(T) 01981 580267
Profile: **FT:** Game; **WN:** Coppice Trout Fishery; **WT:** Lake (Still) **W. Size:** 1 Acre.
Ref: FH1114

COPTHORNE COARSE FISHERIES

Copthorne Coarse Fisheries, Skitham Lane, Pilling, Preston, **LANCASHIRE**, PR3 6BD, **England**.
Contact/s: Mr Derek Halworth (Owner).
(T) 01995 601100
Profile: **FT:** Coarse; **WN:** Copthorne; **WT:** Lake (Still). **Location:** **Nr. Rd:** Skitham Lane; **Main Rd:** A6.
Ref: FH1115

COQUET (RIVER)

River Coquet, Gimmerknowle, Rothbury, Morpeth, **NORTHUMBERLAND**, NE65, **England**.
Contact/s: Mr Colin Bell (Treasurer), Rothbury and Thropton Angling Club, 1 Silverdale Cottage, Snitter, Rothbury, Morpeth, NE65 7EL.
(T) 01669 621083
Profile: **FT:** Game; **WN:** Coquet; **WT:** River (Moving) **W. Size:** 2000 Metres.
Ref: FH1116

COQUET (RIVER)

River Coquet, Thirston Mill, Felton, Morpeth, **NORTHUMBERLAND**, NE65, **England**.
Contact/s: Mr Alan Bagnall (Head Bailiff), Northumbrian Anglers Federation, Mill Thirston, Felton, Northumberland, NE65 9EH.
(T) 01670 787663
Profile: **FT:** Game; **WN:** Coquet; **WT:** River (Moving).
Ref: FH1117

CORBY BOATING LAKE

Corby Boating Lake, Cottinghan Rd, Corby, **NORTHAMPTONSHIRE**, NN17 1QG, **England**.
Contact/s: Fishery Manager.
(T) 01536 402551
Profile: **FT:** Coarse; **WN:** Corby; **WT:** Lake (Still).
Ref: FH1118

CORK LOUGH

Cork Lough, Cork, **COUNTY CORK**, **Ireland**.
Profile: **FT:** Coarse; **WN:** Cork Lough; **WT:** Lough (Still) **W. Size:** 10 Acres. **Location:** **Nr. Rd:** Western Road.
Ref: FH1119

CORNBURY PARK FISHERY

Cornbury Park Fishery, South Hill Lodge, Cornbury Park, Charlbury, Chipping Norton, **OXFORDSHIRE**, OX7 3EW, **England**.
Contact/s: Cornbury Park Estate.
(T) 01608 811276 (F) 01608 811252
Mr Brian D Morris.
(T) 01608 811509 (F) 01608 811509
Profile: **FT:** Game; **WN:** Cornbury Park Fishery; **WT:** Lake (Still); **F. Size:** 14 Acres. **Location:** **Nr. Rd:** B4022; **Main Rd:** A40 to A34; **Rail:** Charlbury.
Ref: FH1120

CORNHILL PONDS

Cornhill Ponds, East Cowton, Northallerton, **YORKSHIRE (NORTH)**, DL7, **England**.
Contact/s: Mr Bob Greaves.
(T) 01325 378175
Profile: **FT:** Coarse; **WN:** Cornhill; **WT:** Pond (Still). **Location:** **Nr. Rd:** B1263 to Richmond; **Main Rd:** A167 to Darlington.
£Fr
Ref: FH1121

COSGROVE LEISURE PARK

Cosgrove Leisure Park, Cosgrove, Milton Keynes, **BUCKINGHAMSHIRE**, MK19 7JP, **England**.
Contact/s: Manager.
(T) 01908 563360 (F) 01908 263615
Profile: **FT:** Coarse; **WN:** Cosgrove Leisure Park; **WT:** Combination (Still & Moving) **W. Size:** 25 Acres.
Ref: FH1122

COSHIEVILLE FARM

Coshieville Farm, Grandtully, Aberfeldy, **PERTH AND KINROSS**, PH15, **Scotland**.
(W) www.fishingnet.com/beats/coshiville.htm
Contact/s: Mr S Henderson, Coshieville Farm, Grandtully, Aberfeldy, Perth and Kinross, PH15 2.
(T) 01887 840449
Profile: **FT:** Combination; **WN:** Craggan and lower Craggan; **WT:** Pool (Still).
Ref: FH1123

COSTELLO AND FERMOYLE FISHERY

Costello And Fermoyle Fishery, Bridge Cottage, Costello, **COUNTY GALWAY**, **Ireland**.
Contact/s: Mr R Fitzjohn.
(T) 091 72196 (F) 091 72366
Profile: **FT:** Game; **WN:** Costello And Fermoyle Fishery; **WT:** Lough (Still).
Ref: FH1124

COSTESSEY PITS

Costessey Pits, Costessey, Norwich, **NORFOLK**, NR8, **England**.
Contact/s: Ms Jo Cottingham, Taverham Mills Fishing Lodge, Costessey Rd, Taverham, Norfolk, NR8 6TA.
(T) 01603 861014 (F) 01603 861014
Profile: **FT:** Coarse; **WN:** Costessey; **WT:** Combination (Still) **W. Size:** 12 Acres. **Location:** **Nr. Rd:** Drayton to Costessey; **Main Rd:** A1067.
Ref: FH1125

COTE LODGE RESERVOIR

Cote Lodge Reservoir, High Peak, **DERBYSHIRE**, SK23, **England**.
Contact/s: Mr Peter Sharples (Conservation, Access and Recreation Manager), North West Water Ltd, Woodhead Rd, Tintwhistle, Hadfiled via Hyde, SK14 7HR.
(T) 01457 864187
Mr R North (Secretary), 1 Morpeth Cl, Ashton-under-Lyne, Lancaster, OL7 9SH.
Profile: **FT:** Game; **WN:** Cote Lodge; **WT:** Reservoir (Still).
Ref: FH1126

COTHI (RIVER)

River Cothi, Llanfynydd Rd, Carmarthen, **CARMARTHENSHIRE**, SA32 7, **Wales**.
Contact/s: Ms Hazel Hudson (Manager), Pantglas Hall, 2 Llanfynydd Rd, Carmarthen, Carmarthenshire, SA32 7BY.
(T) 01558 668741 (F) 01558 668018
Profile: **FT:** Game; **WN:** Cothi; **WT:** River (Moving). **Location:** **Nr. Rd:** Llanfynydd Road.
Ref: FH1127

COTHI (RIVER)

River Cothi, Banc-Y-Daren, Ammanford, **CARMARTHENSHIRE**, SA18, **Wales**.
Contact/s: Mr Wyndham Gill (Hon Secretary), 6 Llwynant Drive, Cwmgors, Ammanford, Carmarthenshire, SA18 1RP.
(T) 01269 823648
Profile: **FT:** Game; **WN:** Cothi; **WT:** River (Moving) **W. Size:** 120 Metres.
Ref: FH1128

COTHI (RIVER)

River Cothi, Carmarthen, **CARMARTHENSHIRE**, SA, **Wales**.
Contact/s: Manager, The Fishfinder, 51 King St, Carmarthen, Carmarthenshire, SA31 1BH.
(T) 01267 220226
Profile: **FT:** Game; **WN:** Cothi; **WT:** River (Moving) **W. Size:** 12800 Metres.
Ref: FH1129

COTHI (RIVER)

Cothi (River), Cothi Vale Fishery, Llansawel, Llandovery, **CARMARTHENSHIRE**, **Wales**.
Contact/s: Mr John Turner (Hon Secretary), Prince Albert Angling Society, 15 Pexhill Drive, Macclesfield, Cheshire, SK10 3LP.
(T) 01625 422010
Profile: **FT:** Game; **WN:** Cothi; **WT:** River (Moving) **W. Size:** 525 Metres. **Location:** **Main Rd:** B4337; **Rail:** Llandovery.
Ref: FH1130

COTSWOLD HOBURNE

Cotswold Hoburne, Broadway Lane, South Cerney, Cirencester, **GLOUCESTERSHIRE**, GL7 5UK, **England**.
Contact/s: Manager.
(T) 01285 860216
Profile: **FT:** Coarse; **WN:** Cotswold Hoburne; **WT:** Gravel Pit (Still); **F. Size:** 70 Acres. **Location:** **Nr. Rd:** B4696; **Main Rd:** A419.
Ref: FH1131

COTSWOLD WATER PARK

Cotswold Water Park, Kemble, Cirencester, **GLOUCESTERSHIRE**, GL7, **England**.
Contact/s: Mr Anthony Edmondson (Fishery Manager).
(T) 01285 770226
Profile: **FT:** Coarse; **WN:** Cotswold Water Park; **WT:** Lake (Still).
Ref: FH1132

COTTAGE GREEN GARDEN CENTRE

Cottage Green Garden Centre, Brindle Rd, Chorley, **LANCASHIRE**, PR6, **England**.
Contact/s: Mr Derek Sunderland.
(T) 01772 323546
Profile: **FT:** Coarse; **WN:** Cottage Green Garden Centre; **WT:** Pool (Still) **W. Size:** 1 Acre. **Location:** **Nr. Rd:** Bamber Bridge to Higher Walton; **Main Rd:** B6258.
Ref: FH1133

COTTAGE LANE

Cottage Lane, Pingewood, Reading, **BERKSHIRE**, RG, **England**.
Mr Dusty Millar (Associate members secretary), 238 Elgar Road South, Reading, Berkshire, RG3 0BW.
(T) 0118 9874882
Mr Mick Cox (Chief Bailiff), Dorstans, Hatch Lane, Brimpton Village, Reading, RG7 4TR.
(T) 0118 9714917
Profile: **FT:** Coarse; **WN:** Cottage Lane; **WT:** Gravel Pit (Still) **W. Size:** 7 Acres. **Location:** **Nr. Rd:** Cottage Lane; **Main Rd:** Pingewood.
Ref: FH1134

COTTERELL FISHERY

Cotterell Fishery, Kilmacshane, Inistioge, **COUNTY KILKENNY**, **Ireland**.
Contact/s: Fishery Manager.
(T) 056 58403
Profile: **FT:** Game; **WN:** Cotterell Fishery
Ref: FH1135

COTTERSTOCK RIVER

River Cotterstock, Cotterstock, Peterborough, **CAMBRIDGESHIRE**, PE8, **England**.
Contact/s: Mr B Wing, Manor Farm Cottage, Cotterstock, Peterborough, Cambridgeshire, PE8.
(T) 01832 226340
Profile: **FT:** Coarse; **WN:** Cotterstock; **WT:** River (Moving) **W. Size:** 1600 Metres.
Ref: FH1136

COTTINGTON LAKES

Cottington Lakes Trout And Coarse Fishery, The Lodge, Cottington Lakes, Sholden, Deal, **KENT**, CT14 0AR, **England**.
Contact/s: Mr I G Steed (Owner).
(T) 01304 380691 (F) 01304 380691 (M) 07721 030371
Mr Jeff Watts (Manager).
(T) 01304 380691 (F) 01304 380691
Profile: **FT:** Combination; **WN:** Cottington Lakes; **WT:** Combination (Still & Moving); **F.**

Size: 30 Acres; **W. Size:** 12 Acres. **Location:** **Nr. Rd:** A248; **Main Rd:** A248; **Rail:** Deal.
Ref: FH1137

COTTON FARM FISHERY

Cotton Farm Fishery, Dartford, **KENT**, DA, **England**.
Contact/s: Manager, The Tackle Box, Watling St, Dartford, Kent, DA2 6EG.
(T) 01322 298240 **(F)** 01322 292411
Profile: **FT:** Coarse; **WN:** Cotton Farm Fishery; **WT:** Gravel Pit (Still) **W. Size:** 10 Acres. **Location:** **Nr. Rd:** Dartford Tunnel; **Main Rd:** M25.
Ref: FH1138

COUMSHINGAUN LOUGH

Coumshingaun Lough, Kilsheelin, **COUNTY TIPPERARY**, **Ireland**.
Contact/s: **Mr J O'Keeffe** (Manager), OK Sports, New St, Carrick-on-Suir, County Tipperary, Ireland.
(T) 051 40626
Profile: **FT:** Game; **WN:** Coumshingaun Lough; **WT:** Lough (Still).
Ref: FH1139

COUND TROUT FISHERY

Cound Trout Fishery, Cound, Cressage, Nr Crosshouses, Shrewsbury, **SHROPSHIRE**, SY5 6BA, **England**.
Contact/s: **Mr Brian Davies** (Owner).
(T) 01743 761114
Profile: **FT:** Game; **WN:** Cound Trout Fishery; **WT:** Lake (Still); **F. Size:** 79 Acres; **W. Size:** 25 Acres. **Location:** **Nr. Rd:** A458; **Main Rd:** A458; **Rail:** Sibury.
Ref: FH1140

COURT FARM

Court Farm, Aldermaston, Reading, **BERKSHIRE**, RG7 4NT, **England**.
Contact/s: **Mr Bissett** (Owner), Court Farm, Aldermaston, Reading, Berkshire, RG7 4NT..
(T) 0118 9713105
Profile: **FT:** Coarse; **WN:** Court Farm; **WT:** Lake (Still). **Location:** **Nr. Rd:** Raghill; **Main Rd:** A340; **Rail:** Aldermaston Wharf.
Ref: FH1141

COURT FARM

Court Farm, Lower Lemington, Moreton-In-Marsh, **GLOUCESTERSHIRE**, GL56 9NP, **England**.
Contact/s: **Mr Bill Gadsby** (Owner).
(T) 01608 650872
Profile: **FT:** Combination; **WN:** Court Farm; **WT:** Lake (Still) **W. Size:** 3 Acres. **Location:** **Nr. Rd:** Todenham Road; **Main Rd:** A44, A429.
Ref: FH1142

COURT FARM

Court Farm, Tillington, Hereford, **HEREFORDSHIRE**, HR4 8LG, **England**.
Contact/s: **Mr Tim Gilbert** (Manager).
(T) 01432 760271
Profile: **FT:** Coarse; **WN:** Court Farm; **WT:** Lake (Still) **W. Size:** 2 Acres. **Location:** **Main Rd:** A4110.
Ref: FH1143

COVENTRY CANAL

Coventry Canal, Tamworth, **STAFFORDSHIRE**, B77, **England**.
Contact/s: Secretary.
(T) 024 76347270
Profile: **FT:** Coarse; **WN:** Coventry; **WT:** Canal (Still) **W. Size:** 900 Metres.
Ref: FH1144

COVENTRY CANAL

Coventry Canal, Tamworth, **STAFFORDSHIRE**, B77, **England**.
Contact/s: Secretary.
(T) 024 76347270
Profile: **FT:** Coarse; **WN:** Coventry; **WT:** Canal (Still) **W. Size:** 900 Metres.
Ref: FH1145

COVENTRY CANAL

Coventry Canal, Nuneaton, **WARWICKSHIRE**, CV11, **England**.
Contact/s: Manager, Attleborough Sports Club, Marston Lane, Nuneaton, Warwickshire, CV11 4RD.
(T) 024 76349670or76371586
Profile: **FT:** Coarse; **WN:** Coventry; **WT:** Canal (Still) **W. Size:** 3200 Metres.
Ref: FH1146

COVERT SPRINGS FISHERIES

Covert Springs Fisheries, Epperstone By Passage, Woodborough, Nottingham, **NOTTINGHAMSHIRE**, NG14 6DH, **England**.
Contact/s: **Mr Dave Kemp** (Owner).
(T) 0115 9588719
Mr g Binant (Owner).
Profile: **FT:** Coarse; **WN:** Covert springs; **WT:** Lake (Still).
Ref: FH1147

COW GREEN FISHERY

Cow Green Wild Brown Trout Fishery, Langdon Beck, Forest In Teesdale, Barnard Castle, **COUNTY DURHAM**, DL12, **England**.
Contact/s: **Mr Paul Russell**, Northumbrian Water Ltd, Head Office, Recreation Department, Abbey Rd, Durham DH1 5FJ.
(T) 0191 3832222 **(F)** 0191 3841920
Profile: **FT:** Game; **WN:** Cow Green; **WT:** Reservoir (Still).
Ref: FH1148

COWANS FARM

Cowans Farm And Guest House, Kirkgunzeon, Dumfries, **DUMFRIES AND GALLOWAY**, DG2 8JY, **Scotland**.
Contact/s: **Mr Craig Denman** (Manager).
(T) 01387 760284
Profile: **FT:** Coarse; **WN:** Cowans Farm And Guest House; **WT:** Loch (Still). **Location:** **Main Rd:** A711 Dalbeattie Road.
Ref: FH1149

COWANS LAW TROUT FISHERY

Cowans Law Trout Fishery, Hemphill Rd, Moscow, Galston, **AYRSHIRE (EAST)**, KA4 8PP, **Scotland**.
Contact/s: **Mr Jay Steel** (Manager).
(T) 01560 700666
Profile: **FT:** Game; **WN:** Cowans Law; **WT:** Lake (Still).
Ref: FH1150

COWIN (RIVER)

River Cowin, St Clears Angling Association, Madras Cottage, Laugharne, Carmarthen, **CARMARTHENSHIRE**, SA33 4NU, **Wales**.
Contact/s: **Mr C J Jenkins** (President).
(T) 01994 230456
Mr David J Bryan (Hon Secretary), St Clears Angling Association, Madras Cottage, Laugharne, Carmarthen, SA33 4NU.
(T) 01994 427331
Profile: **FT:** Combination; **WN:** Cowin; **WT:** River (Moving) **W. Size:** 800 Metres. **Location:** **Nr. Rd:** A40; **Main Rd:** A4777; **Rail:** Carmarthen.
Ref: FH1151

COWLEY LAKE

Cowley Lake, Yiewsley, Uxbridge, London, **LONDON (GREATER)**, UB9, **England**.
Contact/s: **Mrs T Denslow** (Fishery Manager), Canal Bridge Yard, Packet Boat Lane, Cowley, Middlesex, UB8 2JR.
(T) 01895 847889
Profile: **FT:** Coarse; **WN:** Cowley; **WT:** Lake (Still). **Location:** **Nr. Rd:** Packet Boat Lane; **Main Rd:** M4, junction 4.
Ref: FH1152

COYLE WATER FISHERY

Coyle Water Fishery, Shieldmains Farm, Coalhall, Ayr, **AYRSHIRE (SOUTH)**, KA, **Scotland**.
Contact/s: **Mr Alex Stevenson**.
(T) 01292 570715
Profile: **FT:** Game; **WN:** Coyle Water Fishery; **WT:** River (Moving).
Ref: FH1153

CRABMILL FLASH

Crabmill Flash, Moston, Sandbach, **CHESHIRE**, CW11, **England**.
Contact/s: **Mr Doug Summers** (Secretary).
(T) 01270 762579
Profile: **FT:** Coarse; **WN:** Crabmill Flash; **WT:** Lake (Still) **W. Size:** 10 Acres.
Ref: FH1154

CRABTREE ANGLING LAKE

Crabtree Angling Lake, Gilling West, Scotch Corner, Richmond, **YORKSHIRE (NORTH)**, DL10 5JD, **England**.
Contact/s: **Mrs Barbara Willis** (Manager).
(T) 01748 850158
Profile: **FT:** Game; **WN:** Crabtree Angling; **WT:** Lake (Still); **F. Size:** 12 Acres; **W. Size:** 3 Acres. **Location:** **Main Rd:** A66 Scotch Corner.
Ref: FH1155

CRABTREE MOSS FARM POOL

Crabtree Moss Farm Pool, Marton, Congleton, **CHESHIRE**, **England**.
Contact/s: **Mr John Turner** (Hon Secretary), Prince Albert Angling Society, 15 Pexhill Drive, Macclesfield, Cheshire, SK10 3LP.
(T) 01625 422010
Profile: **FT:** Coarse; **WN:** Crabtree Moss; **WT:** Pool (Still); **F. Size:** 1 Acre; **W. Size:** 1 Acre. **Location:** **Nr. Rd:** School Lane; **Main Rd:** A34 at Marton; **Rail:** Congleton.
Ref: FH1156

CRAFTHOLE LAKE

Crafthole Lake, Torpoint, **CORNWALL**, PL, **England**.
Contact/s: **Mr Reg England** (Manager), Peninsula Coarse Fisheries, St Cleer Depot, Lewdown, Okehampton, Devon EX20 4QT.
(T) 01837 871565 **(F)** 01837 871534
Profile: **FT:** Coarse; **WN:** Crafthole; **WT:** Lake (Still); **F. Size:** 3 Acres; **W. Size:** 3 Acres. **Location:** **Main Rd:** A374.
Ref: FH1157

CRAI RESERVOIR

Crai Reservoir, Senny Bridge, Brecon, **POWYS**, LD3, **Wales**.
Contact/s: **Mrs R Chapel** (Managing Director).
(T) 01874 636207
Profile: **FT:** Game; **WN:** Crai; **WT:** Reservoir (Still). **Location:** **Nr. Rd:** Senny Bridge.
Ref: FH1158

CRAIGHLAW

Craighlaw Fisheries, Kirkcowan, Newton Stewart, **DUMFRIES AND GALLOWAY**, DG8, **Scotland**.
Contact/s: **Mr David Henderson** (Shop Manager), Palakona Bait Supplies, 30a Queen St, Newton Stewart, Dumfries and Galloway, DG8 9NR.
(E) palakona@supanet.com
Ms Clare McClymont (Manager), Palakona Bait Supplies, 30-32 Queen St, Newton Stewart, Dumfries and Galloway, DG8 9NR.
(T) 01671 402323
(E) palakona@supanet.com
Profile: **FT:** Coarse; **WN:** Craighlaw/Glendarroch; **WT:** Loch (Still) **W. Size:** 8 Acres. **Location:** **Main Rd:** A75; **Rail:** Stranraer.
Ref: FH1159

CRAIGLUSCAR RESERVOIR

Craigluscar Reservoir, Craigluscar Rd, Dunfermline, **FIFE**, KY, **Scotland**.
Contact/s: **Mr W B Stewart** (Secretary), 13 Foresters Lea Cres, Dunfermline, Fife, KY12 7TE.
(T) 01383 727920
Profile: **FT:** Game; **WN:** Craigluscar; **WT:** Reservoir (Still); **F. Size:** 26 Acres; **W. Size:** 26 Acres. **Location:** **Nr. Rd:** Craigluscar

Road; **Main Rd:** Oakley Road; **Rail:** Dunfermline.
Ref: FH1160

CRAIGNAVIE

Craignavie, Killin, **STIRLING**, FK21, **Scotland**.
(W) www.fishingnet.com/beats/dochart/craignavie.htm
Contact/s: **Mr Alec Stewart** (Membership Secretary), 2 Dochart Rd, Killin, Perth and Kinross, FK21 8SN.
(T) 01567 820224
Mr Dave Murray, J R News, Fishing Tackle Shop, Main St, Killin, FR21 8UJ.
(T) 01567 820362
Profile: **FT:** Combination; **WN:** Dochart; **WT:** River (Moving).
Ref: FH1161

CRAITH RESERVOIR

Craith Reservoir, Tarbolton Rd, Prestwick, **AYRSHIRE (SOUTH)**, KA9 1DW, **Scotland**.
Contact/s: **Mr J Murphy** (Secretary).
(T) 01292 671520
Profile: **FT:** Game; **WN:** Craith; **WT:** Reservoir (Still); **F. Size:** 25 Acres; **W. Size:** 20 Acres. **Location:** **Nr. Rd:** Tarbolton Road; **Main Rd:** Tarbolton Road; **Rail:** Prestwick.
Ref: FH1162

CRANBOURNE FRUIT FARM

Cranbourne Fruit Farm, Daggon's Rd, Alderholt, Wimborne, **DORSET**, BH21, **England**.
Contact/s: **Mr Alan Phillips**.
(T) 01425 672 451
Profile: **FT:** Coarse; **WN:** Cranbourne Fruit Farm; **WT:** Lake (Still). **Location:** **Nr. Rd:** Alderholt to Cranborne; **Main Rd:** B3078.
Ref: FH1163

CRANEBROOK TROUT FISHERY

Cranebrook Trout Fishery, Potterne Bridge, Manor Rd, Verwood, Wimborne, **DORSET**, BH21 6JD, **England**.
Contact/s: **Mr Dudley Barker** (Game Secretary).
(T) 01202 821997
Profile: **FT:** Game; **WN:** Cranebrook Trout Fishery; **WT:** Lake (Still). **Location:** **Nr. Rd:** Manor Road.
Ref: FH1164

CRANFLEET CANAL

Cranfleet Canal, Long Eaton, Nottingham, **NOTTINGHAMSHIRE**, NG10, **England**.
Contact/s: **Mr W Parker** (Secretary), Long Eaton and District Angling Federation, 75 College St, Long Eaton, Nottingham, NG9 1HR.
(T) 0115 9726170
Profile: **FT:** Coarse; **WN:** Cranfleet; **WT:** Canal (Still) **W. Size:** 350 Metres.
Ref: FH1165

CRANOGUE FISHERY

Cranogue Fishery, Lascolmen, Ballymoney, **COUNTY ANTRIM**, BT53, **Northern Ireland**.
Profile: **FT:** Game; **WN:** Cranogue Fishery
Ref: FH1166

CRANS LOUGH

Crans Lough, Aughnacloy, **COUNTY TYRONE**, BT69 6, **Northern Ireland**.
Contact/s: **Mrs Liz Salter** (Manager), Aughnacloy Development Association, The McCreedy Mill Centre, Aughnacloy, County Tyrone, BT69 6AL.
(T) 028 85557002
Profile: **FT:** Coarse; **WN:** Crans; **WT:** Lough (Still).
Ref: FH1167

CRANWELL LANE TROUT FISHERY

Cranwell Lane Trout Fishery, Newark, **NOTTINGHAMSHIRE**, NG, **England**.
Contact/s: Fishery Manager.
(T) 01636 822425
Profile: **FT:** Game; **WN:** Cranwell Lane Trout Fishery; **WT:** Reservoir (Still).
Ref: FH1168

CRAUFURDLAND FISHERY

Craufurdland Fishery, East Lodge, Craufurdland, Kilmarnock, **AYRSHIRE (SOUTH)**, KA3, **Scotland**.
Contact/s: **Mr Bill Jones**.
(T) 01560 600569
Profile: **FT:** Game; **WN:** Craufurdland Fishery; **WT:** River (Moving).
Ref: FH1169

CRAYFISH FARM

Crayfish Farm, Old Hollow, Pound Hill, Worth, Crawley, **CORNWALL**, RH10, **England**.
Profile: **FT:** Coarse; **WN:** Crayfish Farm; **WT:** Lake (Still).
Ref: FH1170

CRAYFISH POOL

Crayfish Pool, Park Lane, Horton, Slough, **BUCKINGHAMSHIRE**, SL3, **England**.
(W) www.rmcangling.co.uk
Contact/s: **Mr Ian Welch** (Angling Manager), RMC Angling, The Square, Lightwater, Surrey, GU18 5SS.
(T) 01276 453300 **(F)** 01276 456611
(E) info@rmcangling.co.uk
Profile: **FT:** Coarse; **WN:** Crayfish Pool; **WT:** Lake (Still) **W. Size:** 2 Acres. **Location:** **Nr. Rd:** Park Lane; **Main Rd:** M25, junction 14; **Rail:** Wraysbury.
Ref: FH1171

CRAYFORD (RIVER)

River Crayford, Darenth, Dartford, **KENT**, DA, **England**.
Contact/s: **Mr R Graham** (Secretary), Thameside Works Angling Society, 186 Waterdales, Northfleet, Crayford, DA11 8JW.
Profile: **FT:** Coarse; **WN:** Crayford; **WT:** River (Moving).
Ref: FH1172

CREE (RIVER)

River Cree, Girvan, Newton Stewart, **DUMFRIES AND GALLOWAY**, DG8, **Scotland**.
Contact/s: **Mr Tony Dickinson** (Shop Proprietor), Galloway Guns and Tackle, 36a Arthur St, Newton Stewart, Dumfries and Galloway, DG8 6DE.
(T) 01671 403404 **(F)** 01671 403404
Profile: **FT:** Game; **WN:** Cree; **WT:** River (Moving). **Location:** **Nr. Rd:** A714; **Main Rd:** A75; **Rail:** Barrhill.
Ref: FH1173

CREEDY (RIVER)

River Creedy, Cowley Bridge, Exeter, **DEVON**, EX, **England**.
Contact/s: **Mr Barry Lucas** (Hon Secretary), Mayfield, Gorwyn Lane, Cheriton Bishop, Exeter, EX6 6JL.
(T) 01647 24566
Profile: **FT:** Combination; **WN:** Creedy; **WT:** River (Moving). **Location:** **Main Rd:** A377 to Crediton.
Ref: FH1174

CREEDY (RIVER)

River Creedy, Crediton, **DEVON**, EX17, **England**.
Contact/s: **Mr Howard Thresher** (Treasurer), Crediton and Fly Fishing Club, 30 Tuckers Meadow, Crediton, Devon, EX17 3NX.
(T) 01363 774926
Mr Stewart Turner.
(T) 01363 772684
Profile: **FT:** Combination; **WN:** Creedy; **WT:** River (Moving) **W. Size:** 6400 Metres. **Location:** **Main Rd:** A377 to Exeter.
Ref: FH1175

CREEDY LAKES

Creedy Lakes, Long Barn Farm, Crediton, **DEVON**, EX17 4AB, **England**.
(W) www.creedylakes.com
Contact/s: **Mr Stewart Turner**.
(T) 01363 772684 **(F)** 01363 772684 **(M)** 07773 416987
(E) creedylakes@eclipse.co.uk
Mrs S Stuart (Owner).
Profile: **FT:** Coarse; **WN:** Creedy; **WT:** Lake (Still) **W. Size:** 5 Acres. **Location:** **Main Rd:** A3072; **Rail:** Crediton.
Ref: FH1176

CREGENNAN LAKES

Cregennan Lakes, Ffridd Boedel Farm, Arthog, Dolgellau, **GWYNEDD**, LL39 1LJ, **Wales**.
Contact/s: **Mr Emlyn Lloyd** (Manager).
(T) 01341 250468
Profile: **FT:** Game; **WN:** Cregennan; **WT:** Lake (Still) **W. Size:** 40 Acres. **Location:** **Nr. Rd:** Cader Idris Road; **Main Rd:** A493; **Rail:** Fairbourne.
Ref: FH1177

CREGGAN RESERVOIRS

Creggan Reservoirs, Glenown Fisheries, Westway, Creggan, Londonderry, **COUNTY LONDONDERRY**, BT48 9NX, **Northern Ireland**.
Contact/s: **Mr Gerry Quinn**.
(T) 028 71371544 **(F)** 028 71371544
Profile: **FT:** Game; **WN:** Creggan; **WT:** Reservoir (Still); **F. Size:** 100 Acres; **W. Size:** 20 Acres. **Location:** **Nr. Rd:** Westway; **Main Rd:** Westway; **Rail:** Waterside Derry.
Ref: FH1178

CRESCENT LAKE

Crescent Lake, Salthouse Rd, Brackmills, Northampton, **NORTHAMPTONSHIRE**, NN4, **England**.
Contact/s: **Mr Terry Rodhouse** (Secretary), Castle Angling Association, 12 Somerville Rd, Daventry, Northamptonshire, NN11 4RT.
(T) 01327 705692
Profile: **FT:** Coarse; **WN:** Crescent; **WT:** Lake (Still). **Location:** **Main Rd:** A45, A428, A43; **Rail:** Northampton.
Ref: FH1179

CRIME LAKE

Crime Lake, Daisy Nook Country Park, Ashton-under-Lyne, **MANCHESTER (GREATER)**, OL, **England**.
Contact/s: **Mr Tony Green** (Chairman).
(T) 0161 6651404
Profile: **FT:** Coarse; **WN:** Crime; **WT:** Lake (Still).
Ref: FH1180

CROCKERTON POND

Crockerton Pond, Shearwater, Crockerton, Warminster, **WILTSHIRE**, BA12, **England**.
Contact/s: **Mr Nick Robbins**.
(T) 01985 844496 **(F)** 01985 844885
Profile: **FT:** Coarse; **WN:** Crockerton; **WT:** Pond (Still).
Ref: FH1181

CROFT FISHERIES

Croft Fisheries, Huyton Rd, Adlington, Chorley, **LANCASHIRE**, PR7 4JG, **England**.
Contact/s: **Mr John King**.
(T) 01257 483147or0410659024
Profile: **FT:** Coarse; **WN:** Croft Fisheries; **WT:** Lake (Still) **W. Size:** 3 Acres. **Location:** **Nr. Rd:** Huyton Road; **Main Rd:** M61, junction 6; **Rail:** Adlington.
Ref: FH1182

CROFT HEAD FISHERY

Croft Head Fishery, Lower Town House, Littleborough, **MANCHESTER (GREATER)**, OL15, **England**.
Contact/s: **Mr Ray Barber** (Secretary), Todmorden Angling Society, 12 Grisedale Drive, Burnley, Lancashire, BB12 8AR.
(T) 01282 423780 **(M)** 07970 897849
Profile: **FT:** Coarse; **WN:** Croft Head; **WT:** Reservoir (Still); **F. Size:** 10 Acres; **W. Size:** 4 Acres. **Location:** **Nr. Rd:** Calderbrook; **Rail:** Littleborough.

Ref: FH1183

CROMBIE RESERVOIR

Crombie Reservoir, Carnoustie, **ANGUS**, DD7, **Scotland**.
Profile: **FT:** Game; **WN:** Crombie; **WT:** Reservoir (Still).
Ref: FH1184

CROMPTON LODGE

Crompton Lodge, Farnworth, Bolton, **LANCASHIRE**, BL4, **England**.
Contact/s: Park Ranger.
(T) 01204 571561
Profile: **FT:** Coarse; **WN:** Crompton Lodge; **WT:** Lake (Still).
Ref: FH1185

CROMPTONS WATER

Cromptons Water, Railway Trce, Bury, **MANCHESTER (GREATER)**, BL, **England**.
Contact/s: Secretary.
(T) 01204 886001
Profile: **FT:** Coarse; **WN:** Cromptons Water; **WT:** Lake (Still) **W. Size:** 3 Acres. Location: **Main Rd:** A56 North of Manchester, M66.
Ref: FH1186

CROMWELL LAKE TROUT FISHERY

Cromwell Lake Trout Fishery, Newark, **NOTTINGHAMSHIRE**, NG, **England**.
Contact/s: **Mr Victor Collins** (Manager).
(T) 0115 9790009
Profile: **FT:** Game; **WN:** Cromwell Lake Trout Fishery; **WT:** Lake (Still).
Ref: FH1187

CROOKED WILLOWS

Crooked Willows, Holt Rd, Mannington, Ringwood, **HAMPSHIRE**, BH24, **England**.
Contact/s: **Mr John Percy**.
(T) 01202 825628
Profile: **FT:** Coarse; **WN:** Crooked Willows; **WT:** Lake (Still) **W. Size:** 1 Acre. Location: **Nr. Rd:** Holt Road; **Main Rd:** A31, B3072.
Ref: FH1188

CROOKES VALLEY PARK LAKE

Crookes Valley Park Lake, Crookes Valley Rd, Sheffield, **YORKSHIRE (SOUTH)**, S, **England**.
Contact/s: **Mr Terry Fiddler**, Tight Lines Tackle, Glenshiel, Birley Moor Rd, Sheffield, S12 4WG.
(T) 0114 2658178
Profile: **FT:** Coarse; **WN:** Crookes Valley; **WT:** Lake (Still) **W. Size:** 3 Acres. Location: **Nr. Rd:** Crookes Valley Road; **Main Rd:** A57.
£Fr
Ref: FH1189

CROSEMERE

Crosemere, Ellesmere, **SHROPSHIRE**, SY12, **England**.
Profile: **FT:** Coarse; **WN:** Crosemere; **WT:** Lake (Still). Location: **Nr. Rd:** Shrewsbury Road.
Ref: FH1190

CROSS DROVE

Cross Drove, Hockwold, **SUFFOLK**, **England**.
Contact/s: .
(T) 01842 828102
Profile: **FT:** Coarse; **WN:** Cross Drove**WT:** (Still).
Ref: FH1191

CROSS GREEN FLY FISHERY

Cross Green Fly Fishery, Cross Green Farm, Cockfield, Bury St Edmunds, **SUFFOLK**, IP30 0LS, **England**.
Contact/s: **K B M Steward**.
(T) 01284 828820or828323
Profile: **FT:** Game; **WN:** Cross Green Fly Fishery; **WT:** Lake (Still); **F. Size:** 8 Acres; **W. Size:** 4 Acres. Location: **Nr. Rd:** A1141; **Main Rd:** A134, A1141.
Ref: FH1192

CROSSFIELD FISHERY

Crossfield Fishery, Kirkoswald, Penrith, **CUMBRIA**, CA, **England**.
Contact/s: Fishery Manager.
(T) 01768 898711
Mr R Lassingham, Crossfield Farm, Kirkoswald, Penrith, CA10.
(T) 01768 896275 (F) 01768 896275
Profile: **FT:** Game; **WN:** Crossfield; **WT:** Lake (Still) **W. Size:** 3 Acres. Location: **Nr. Rd:** Nunnery; **Main Rd:** B6413; **Rail:** Blazonry.
Ref: FH1193

CROSSWATER MILL FISHERY

Crosswater Mill Fishery, Crosswater Lane, Churt, Farnham, **SURREY**, GU, **England**.
Contact/s: **Mr Richard Twite** (Manager).
(T) 01252 794321 (F) 01252 792611
(E) countryleisure@msn.com
Profile: **FT:** Game; **WN:** Crosswater Mill Fishery; **WT:** Lake (Still) **W. Size:** 3 Acres. Location: **Nr. Rd:** A287; **Main Rd:** A3; **Rail:** Farnham.
Ref: FH1194

CROSSWOOD RESERVOIR

Crosswood Reservoir, Livingston, **LOTHIAN (WEST)**, EH54, **Scotland**.
Contact/s: Fisheries Manager, East of Scotland Water, Lothians Division, Lomond House, Beveridge Sq, Livingstone, Lothian Scotland.
(T) 01506 425709
Profile: **FT:** Game; **WN:** Crosswood; **WT:** Reservoir (Still).
Ref: FH1195

CROTTYS LOUGH

Crottys Lough, Kilsheelin, **COUNTY TIPPERARY**, **Ireland**.
Contact/s: **Mr J O'Keeffe** (Manager), OK Sports, New St, Carrick-on-Suir, County Tipperary, Ireland.
(T) 051 40626
Profile: **FT:** Game; **WN:** Crottys Lough; **WT:** Lough (Still).
Ref: FH1196

CROW GREEN FISHERY

Crow Green Fishery, Brentwood, **ESSEX**, CM1, **England**.
Contact/s: **Mr Derek Ritchie** (Manager), Brentwood Angling, 118 Warley Hill, Brentwood, Essex, CM14 5HB.
(T) 01277 200985 (F) 01277 219500
Mr Jason Jopson.
(T) 01277 375172 (M) 07976 904387
Profile: **FT:** Coarse; **WN:** Crow Green Fishery; **WT:** Lake (Still).
Ref: FH1197

CROW POOL

Crow Pool, Ibsley Pools, Christchurch, **DORSET**, BH23, **England**.
Contact/s: **Mr R J Andrews** (Club Secretary), Christchurch Angling Club, 4 Marley Cl, New Milton, BH25 5LL.
(T) 01425 638502
Profile: **FT:** Coarse; **WN:** Crow Pool; **WT:** Pond (Still). Location: **Main Rd:** A338.
Ref: FH1198

CROWDY RESERVOIR

Crowdy Reservoir, Camelford, **CORNWALL**, PL32, **England**.
Contact/s: Manager, Spar Shop, Camelford, PL32 9PA.
(T) 01840 212356
Profile: **FT:** Game; **WN:** Crowdy; **WT:** Reservoir (Still) **W. Size:** 115 Acres.
Ref: FH1199

CROWLAND ANGLING CLUB LAKES

Crowland Angling Club Lakes, Welland Bank, Crowland, Peterborough, **CAMBRIDGESHIRE**, PE6, **England**.
Contact/s: **Mrs Janet Jones** (Club Secretary), 3 Nelson Close, Off Postland Road, Crowland, Peterborough, PE6 0ET.
(T) 01733 210449
Profile: **FT:** Coarse; **WN:** Crowland Angling Club Lakes; **WT:** Lake (Still).
Ref: FH1200

CROWN NETHERHALL

Crown Netherhall (The), Dobb's Weir Rd, Nazeing, Waltham Abbey, **ESSEX**, EN9, **England**.
Contact/s: **Mr Anthony Johnson** (Secretary), Johnson Ross Tackle, Anwell St, Hoddesdon, Hertfordshire.
(T) 01992 462044
Mr Bill Hancock.
(T) 01992 642401
Profile: **FT:** Coarse; **WN:** Crown Netherhall (The); **WT:** Lake (Still); **F. Size:** 5 Acres; **W. Size:** 4 Acres. Location: **Nr. Rd:** Dobbs Weir Road; **Main Rd:** A10; **Rail:** Broxbourne.
Ref: FH1201

CROWN POOLS

Crown Pools, Bury, **MANCHESTER (GREATER)**, BL, **England**.
Contact/s: **Mr Metcalfe** (Secretary).
(T) 0161 7975597
Profile: **FT:** Coarse; **WN:** Crown; **WT:** Pool (Still).
Ref: FH1202

CROXLEY HALL TROUT FISHERY

Croxley Hall Trout Fishery, Croxley Hall Farm, Croxley Green, Rickmansworth, **HERTFORDSHIRE**, WD3 3BQ, **England**.
Contact/s: **Mr Paul Sansom-Timms**.
(T) 01923 778290
(E) paul@croxleyhall.co.uk
Profile: **FT:** Combination; **WN:** Croxley Hall; **WT:** Gravel Pit (Still); **F. Size:** 65 Acres; **W. Size:** 25 Acres. Location: **Nr. Rd:** A412; **Main Rd:** Ricky to Watford Road; **Rail:** Croxley Green.
Ref: FH1203

CRUMLIN (RIVER)

River Crumlin, Crumlin, **COUNTY ANTRIM**, BT29, **Northern Ireland**.
Contact/s: Manager, Fur, Feather and Fin, 1 West Trce, Mill Rd, Crumlin, BT29 4XY.
(T) 028 94453648
Profile: **FT:** Game; **WN:** Crumlin; **WT:** River (Moving) **W. Size:** 19200 Metres.
Ref: FH1204

CRUMLIN FISHERIES

Crumlin Fisheries, Inverin, Coonemara, **COUNTY GALWAY**, **Ireland**.
Contact/s: Fishery Manager.
(T) 091 593105
Profile: **FT:** Game; **WN:** Crumlin Fisheries; **WT:** Loch (Still).
Ref: FH1205

CRUMMOCK WATER LAKE

Crummock Water Lake, Cockermouth, **CUMBRIA**, CA13, **England**.
Contact/s: **Mr Mark Astley** (Warden), National Trust, Beckfoot Office, Ennerdale, Cleator, Cumbria, CA23 3AU.
(T) 01946 861235 (F) 01946 861235
(E) rennpm@smtp.ntrust.org.uk
Profile: **FT:** Combination; **WN:** Crummock; **WT:** Lake (Still). Location: **Nr. Rd:** B5289; **Main Rd:** A66; **Rail:** Penrith.
Ref: FH1206

CUCKFIELD FISHERY

Cuckfield Fishery, Cuckfield, Haywards Heath, **SUSSEX (WEST)**, RH17, **England**.
Contact/s: **Mr A J Ponsford** (Manager).
(T) 01444 459999
Profile: **FT:** Coarse; **WN:** Cuckfield Fishery; **WT:** Lake (Still).
Ref: FH1207

CUCKMERE (RIVER)

River Cuckmere, Horsebridge, Hailsham, **SUSSEX (EAST)**, BN27, **England**.
Contact/s: **Mr Geoff Begley** (Fishery Manager).
(T) 01323 832939
Profile: **FT:** Coarse; **WN:** Cuckmere; **WT:** River (Moving).
Ref: FH1208

CUCKMERE (RIVER)

River Cuckmere, Abbots Wood, Seaford, **SUSSEX (EAST)**, BN25, **England**.
Contact/s: Manager, Anglers Den, 6 North Rd, Pevensey Bay, Sussex (East), BN24 6AY.
(T) 01323 460441
Mr T Lelliott (Manager), Polegate Angling Ctre, 101 Station Rd, Polegate, Sussex (East), BN26 6EB.
(T) 01323 486379 **(F)** 01323 486379
Profile: FT: Coarse; **WN:** Cuckmere; **WT:** River (Moving). **Location: Nr. Rd:** Horsebridge to Alfriston.
Ref: FH1209

CUCKMERE (RIVER)

River Cuckmere, Alfriston, Polegate, **SUSSEX (EAST)**, BN26, **England**.
Contact/s: Manager, Tony's Tackle, 211 Seaside, Eastbourne, Sussex (East), BN22 7NP.
(T) 01323 731388 **(F)** 01323 647247
Profile: FT: Coarse; **WN:** Cuckmere; **WT:** River (Moving).
Ref: FH1210

CUCKOOS REST

Cuckoos Rest, Fairwood Rd, Westbury, **WILTSHIRE**, BA13, **England**.
Contact/s: Manager.
(T) 01373 826792
Profile: FT: Coarse; **WN:** Cuckoo's; **WT:** Lake (Still) **W. Size:** 4 Acres. **Location: Nr. Rd:** Fairwood Road; **Main Rd:** A36.
Ref: FH1211

CUERDEN VALLEY LAKE

Cuerden Valley Lake, Clayton Green, Preston, **LANCASHIRE**, PR, **England**.
Contact/s: Mr Longbottom.
(T) 01772 324129
Profile: FT: Coarse; **WN:** Cuerden Valley; **WT:** Lake (Still). **Location: Nr. Rd:** Berkley Drive; **Main Rd:** A6.
Ref: FH1212

CUILALUINN BEAT

Cuilaluinn Beat, Aberfeldy, **PERTH AND KINROSS**, PH15, **Scotland**.
(W) www.fishingnet.com/beats/cuilaluinn.htm
Contact/s: Mr Micheal Smith (Manager), Cuilaluinn, Aberfeldy, Perth and Kinross, PH15 2JW.
(T) 01887 802302 **(F)** 01887 829644
Profile: FT: Game; **WN:** Bridge and Whirley; **WT:** Pool (Still).
Ref: FH1213

CULCREUCH CASTLE POND

Culcreuch Castle Pond, Fintry, Glasgow, **GLASGOW (CITY OF)**, G66, **Scotland**.
Contact/s: Area Manager, Scottish Carp Group, 57 Iona Way, Kirkintilloch, Glasgow, Lanarkshire.
Manager.
(T) 01360 860555
Mr David Littlefair (Director), J B Angling Ctre, 37 Eastside, Kirkintilloch, Glasgow, G66 1QA.
(T) 0141 7750083
Profile: FT: Coarse; **WN:** Culcreuch Castle; **WT:** Lake (Still).
Ref: FH1214

CULFIN FISHERY

Culfin Fishery, The Coachouse, Salruck, Renvyle, **COUNTY GALWAY**, **Ireland**.
Contact/s: Fishery Manager.
(T) 095 43993
Profile: FT: Game; **WN:** Culfin Fishery
Ref: FH1215

CULLY (RIVER)

River Cully, Crossmaglen, Newry, **COUNTY DOWN**, BT35, **Northern Ireland**.
Contact/s: Mr Eugene Murphy.
(T) 028 30868607
Mr J Cunningham (Secretary), 21 Forkhill Rd, Mullach Ban, County Armagh, BT35 9XL.
(T) 028 30889187
Mr Phil Nolan.
(T) 028 30868074
Profile: FT: Game; **WN:** Cully; **WT:** River (Moving).
Ref: FH1216

CULM (RIVER)

River Culm, Stoke Canon, Exeter, **DEVON**, EX5, **England**.
Contact/s: Mr Barry Lucas (Hon Secretary), Mayfield, Gorwyn Lane, Cheriton Bishop, Exeter, EX6 6JL.
(T) 01647 24566
Mr Dave Stuart, Exeter Angling Ctre, Smythen St, Exeter, Devon, EX1 1BN.
(T) 01392 436404 **(F)** 01392 433855
Profile: FT: Combination; **WN:** Culm; **WT:** River (Moving) **W. Size:** 3200 Metres. **Location: Nr. Rd:** A377 Exeter to Crediton; **Main Rd:** A396.
Ref: FH1217

CULM (RIVER)

River Culm, Stoke Canon, Exeter, **DEVON**, EX, **England**.
Contact/s: Mr Barry Lucas (Hon Secretary), Mayfield, Gorwyn Lane, Cheriton Bishop, Exeter, EX6 6JL.
(T) 01647 24566
Mr Dave Stuart (Manager), Exeter Angling Ctre, Smythen St, Exeter, Devon, EX1 1BN.
(T) 01392 436404or435591 **(F)** 01392 433855
Profile: FT: Combination; **WN:** Culm; **WT:** River (Moving) **W. Size:** 4000 Metres. **Location: Nr. Rd:** Huxham; **Main Rd:** A377, A396 north to Stoke Canon.
Ref: FH1218

CULSCADDEN FARM POND

Culscadden Farm Pond, Craighlaw Fisheries, Newton Stewart, **DUMFRIES AND GALLOWAY**, DG8, **Scotland**.
Contact/s: Ms Clare McClymont (Manager), Palakona Bait Supplies, 30-32 Queen St, Newton Stewart, Dumfries and Galloway, DG8 9NR.
(T) 01671 402323
(E) palakonswscot@cs.com
Profile: FT: Coarse; **WN:** Culscadden; **WT:** Pond (Still).
Ref: FH1219

CULVERS FARM FISHERIES

Culvers Farm Fisheries, Gillingham, **DORSET**, SP8 5DS, **England**.
Contact/s: Mr V J Pitman.
(T) 01747 822466
Profile: FT: Coarse; **WN:** Culvers Farm Fisheries; **WT:** Lake (Still) **W. Size:** 4 Acres.
Ref: FH1220

CULVERTHORPE LAKES

Culverthorpe Lakes, Culverthorpe Hall, Grantham, **LINCOLNSHIRE**, NG32, **England**.
Profile: FT: Coarse; **WN:** Culverthorpe; **WT:** Lake (Still).
Ref: FH1221

CUMWELL LANE

Cumwell Lane, Rotherham, **YORKSHIRE (SOUTH)**, **England**.
Contact/s: .
(T) 0114 2442398
Profile: FT: Coarse; **WN:** Cumwell Lane**WT:** Lake.
Ref: FH1222

CUNDALL LODGE FISHERY

Cundall Lodge Fishery, Cundall, York, **YORKSHIRE (NORTH)**, YO61, **England**.
Contact/s: Mr D Barker.
(T) 01423 360203 **(F)** 01423 360805
Profile: FT: Coarse; **WN:** Swale; **WT:** Combination (Still & Moving) **W. Size:** 1600 Metres. **Location: Main Rd:** A168.
Ref: FH1223

CUR (RIVER)

River Cur, Dunoon, **ARGYLL AND BUTE**, PA23, **Scotland**.
Contact/s: Mr A H Young (Hon Secretary), 112 Argyll St, Dunoon, Argyll and Bute.
(T) 01369 705732or703232
(E) archie@telinco.co.uk
Profile: FT: Game; **WN:** Cur; **WT:** River (Moving) **W. Size:** 3200 Metres. **Location: Main Rd:** A815.
Ref: FH1224

CURRAGHALICKEY LAKE

Curraghalickey Lake, Dunmanway, **COUNTY CORK**, **Ireland**.
Contact/s: Mr P MacCarthy (Secretary), Dunmanway Salmon and Trout Angling Association, Yew Tree Bar, Dunmanway, County Cork, Ireland.
Profile: FT: Game; **WN:** Curraghalickey; **WT:** Lake (Still).
Ref: FH1225

CURTISS POOL

Curtiss Pool, Bewdley, **WORCESTERSHIRE**, DY12, **England**.
Contact/s: Mr Stuart Norgrove (Haye Farm Manager).
(T) 01299 403371
Profile: FT: Coarse; **WN:** Curtiss; **WT:** Pool (Still) **W. Size:** 1 Acre.
Ref: FH1226

CUSHINA (RIVER)

River Cushina, Portarlington, **COUNTY LAOIS**, **Ireland**.
Contact/s: Mr Kieran Cullen (Manager), Gun and Tackle, Monasterevin, County Laois, Ireland.
(T) 045 25902 **(F)** 045 25329
Profile: FT: Game; **WN:** Cushina; **WT:** River (Moving).
Ref: FH1227

CUSWORTH HALL LAKE

Cusworth Hall Lake, Cusworth Lane, Doncaster, **YORKSHIRE (SOUTH)**, DN5, **England**.
Contact/s: Mr Maurice Tate (Secretary), Doncaster and District Angling Association, 28 Holmescarr Rd, New Rossington, Doncaster, DN11 0QF.
(T) 01302 865482
Profile: FT: Coarse; **WN:** Cusworth Hall; **WT:** Lake (Still). **Location: Nr. Rd:** Cusworth Lane; **Main Rd:** A638, Doncaster north.
Ref: FH1228

CUT OFF CHANNEL

Cut Off Channel, King's Lynn, **NORFOLK**, PE, **England**.
Contact/s: K Allen (Chairman), Mole Cottage, 15 Ten Mile Bank, Littleport, CB6 1EE.
(T) 01383 860936
Mr G Baker (Owner), The Tackle Box, 38 Tower St, King's Lynn, Norfolk, PE30 1EJ.
(T) 01553 761293
Mr Mick Grief (Secretary), King's Lynn Angling Association, 67 Peckover Way, South Wootton, King's Lynn, PE30 3UE.
(T) 01553 671545
Profile: FT: Coarse; **WN:** Cut Off Channel; **WT:** River (Moving) **W. Size:** 17600 Metres.
Ref: FH1229

CUTT MILL

Cutt Mill, 70 Prince Charles Cres, Farnborough, **HAMPSHIRE**, GU14, **England**.
Profile: FT: Coarse; **WN:** Cutt Mill; **WT:** Lake (Still).
Ref: FH1230

CUTTING LAKE

Cutting Lake, Yiewsley, Uxbridge, London, **LONDON (GREATER)**, UB9, **England**.
Contact/s: Mrs T Denslow (Fishery Manager), Canal Bridge Yard, Packet Boat Lane, Cowley, Middlesex, UB8 2JR.
(T) 01895 847889
Profile: FT: Coarse; **WN:** Cutting Lake; **WT:** Lake (Still).
Ref: FH1231

CUTTLE MILL CARP FISHERY

Cuttle Mill Carp Fishery, Cuttle Mill Lane, Wishaw, Sutton Coldfield, **MIDLANDS (WEST)**, B76 9PU, **England**.
Contact/s: **Mr Tony Higgins** (Fishery Owner).
(T) 01827 872253
Profile: **FT:** Coarse; **WN:** Cuttle Mill; **WT:** Lake (Still); **F. Size:** 13 Acres; **W. Size:** 7 Acres. Location: **Nr. Rd:** A4091; **Main Rd:** A4091; **Rail:** Tamworth.
Ref: FH1232

CWM PRYSOR LAKE

Cwm Prysor Lake, Bala, **GWYNEDD**, LL23, **Wales**.
Contact/s: **Mr Dewi Evans** (Secretary), Bala and District Angling Club, 33 High St, Bala, Gwynedd, LL23 7AF.
(T) 01678 520370 (F) 01678 520370
Profile: **FT:** Game; **WN:** Cwm Prysor; **WT:** Lake (Still).
Ref: FH1233

CWM RHEIDOL FISHERY

Cwm Rheidol Fishery, Capel Bangor, Aberystwyth, **CEREDIGION**, SY23, **Wales**.
Contact/s: **Mr Peter Bevan** (Manager).
(T) 01970 880667
Profile: **FT:** Game; **WN:** Cwm Rheidol; **WT:** Dam (Still) **W. Size:** 20 Acres.
Ref: FH1234

CWM SILYN LAKE

Cwm Silyn Lake, Llanllyfni, Caernarfon, **GWYNEDD**, LL54, **Wales**.
Contact/s: **Mr Huw P Hughes** (Hon Secretary), Seiont, Gwyrfai and Llyfni Anglers Society, Llugwy, Ystad Eryri, Bethel, Caernarfon, LL55 1BX.
(T) 01248 670666
(E) huw.hughes@lineone.net
Profile: **FT:** Game; **WN:** Cwm Silyn; **WT:** Lake (Still) **W. Size:** 80 Acres. Location: **Main Rd:** A487; **Rail:** Bangor.
Ref: FH1235

CWMBRAN BOATING LAKE

Cwmbran Boating Lake, Llanfrechfa Way, Llanyravon, Cwmbran, **TORFAEN**, NP44, **Wales**.
Contact/s: Manager, Torfaen Leisure County Council, 46 Cocker Avenue, Cwmbran, Gwent, NP44 7JJ.
(T) 01495 762200
Mr Richard Ball (Manager).
(T) 01495 766788
Profile: **FT:** Coarse; **WN:** Cwmbran Boating; **WT:** Lake (Still) **W. Size:** 3 Acres. Location: **Nr. Rd:** A4042; **Main Rd:** M48 north; **Rail:** Cwmbran.
Ref: FH1236

CWMCELYN POND

Cwmcelyn Pond, Blaina, Abertillery, **MONMOUTHSHIRE**, NP13, **Wales**.
Contact/s: **Mr T Dee** (Secretary), 19 Waun Fawr, Winchestown, Brynmawr, Gwent, NP23 4BD.
(T) 01495 312289
Profile: **FT:** Coarse; **WN:** Cwmcelyn; **WT:** Pond (Still) **W. Size:** 2 Acres. Location: **Nr. Rd:** A467; **Main Rd:** A467.
Ref: FH1237

CWMMACKWITH FISHERY

Cwmmackwith Fishery, Llandysul, **CEREDIGION**, SA44, **Wales**.
(W) www.fishing-in-wales.co.uk/llandysul-aa/beat10
Contact/s: **Mr Artie Jones** (Hon Secretary), Llandysul Angling Association, Glas-y-Dorlan, Llyn-y-Fran Rd, Llandysul, SA44 4JW.
(T) 01559 362317
Profile: **FT:** Game; **WN:** Teifi; **WT:** River (Moving). Location: **Nr. Rd:** Llandysul to Llanfihangel-ar-arth; **Main Rd:** B4436.
Ref: FH1238

CWMTILLERY RESERVOIR

Cwmtillery Reservoir, Abertillery, **MONMOUTHSHIRE**, NP13, **Wales**.
Contact/s: **Mr A Griffin** (Secretary), Abertillery Angling Club, 41 Duke St, Abertillery, Gwent, NP3 1BE.
(T) 01495 320504
Profile: **FT:** Game; **WN:** Cwmtillery; **WT:** Reservoir (Still) **W. Size:** 14 Acres.
Ref: FH1239

CYCH (RIVER)

River Cych, Cardigan, **CEREDIGION**, SA43, **Wales**.
Contact/s: **Mr Brian Gore** (Hon Secretary), Cwm Broch, Bribwll, Cardigan, Carmarthenshire, SA43 3DG.
(T) 01239 841332
Profile: **FT:** Game; **WN:** Cych; **WT:** River (Moving).
Ref: FH1240

CYNIN (RIVER)

River Cynin, Carmarthen, **CARMARTHENSHIRE**, SA, **Wales**.
Contact/s: **Mr C J Jenkins** (President).
(T) 01994 230456
Mr David J Bryan (Hon Secretary), St Clears Angling Association, Madras Cottage, Laugharne, Carmarthen, SA33 4NU.
(T) 01994 427331
Profile: **FT:** Combination; **WN:** Cynin; **WT:** River (Moving) **W. Size:** 2400 Metres. Location: **Nr. Rd:** A40; **Main Rd:** A4777; **Rail:** Carmarthen.
Ref: FH1241

CYPRUS WOOD TROUT FISHERY

Cyprus Wood Trout Fishery, Tallanmoor Cottage, Howbourne Lane, Buxted, Uckfield, **SUSSEX (EAST)**, TN22 4QD, **England**.
Contact/s: **Mr Peter Cottenham**.
(T) 01825 733455
Profile: **FT:** Game; **WN:** Cyprus Wood Trout Fishery; **WT:** Lake (Still).
Ref: FH1242

DACRE BECK

Dacre Beck, Dacre, Penrith, **CUMBRIA**, CA11, **England**.
Contact/s: Fishery Manager.
(T) 01768 867441
Profile: **FT:** Coarse; **WN:** Dacre; **WT:** Stream (Moving).
Ref: FH1243

DACRE LAKESIDE PARK

Dacre Lakeside Park, Catwick Lane, Brandesburton, Driffield, **HUMBERSIDE**, YO25, **England**.
Contact/s: **Mrs Sandra Turner** (Co-Owner).
(T) 01964 543704or01482804783
Profile: **FT:** Coarse; **WN:** Dacre; **WT:** Lake (Still) **W. Size:** 10 Acres. Location: **Nr. Rd:** Catwick Lane; **Main Rd:** A165.
Ref: FH1244

DAER RESERVOIR

Daer Reservoir, Strathclyde, **GLASGOW (CITY OF)**, G71, **Scotland**.
Contact/s: **Mr J Miles**, 27a Blantyre Mill Rd, Bothwell, Strathclyde, G71 8ER.
(T) 01698 854648
Profile: **FT:** Game; **WN:** Daer; **WT:** Reservoir (Still).
Ref: FH1245

DAIRY FISHERY

Dairy Fishery, 179 Belfast Rd, Ballynahinch, **COUNTY DOWN**, BT24, **Northern Ireland**.
Profile: **FT:** Game; **WN:** Quoile; **WT:** River (Moving).
Ref: FH1246

DAIWA GULL POOL

Daiwa Gull Pool, Gainsborough, **LINCOLNSHIRE**, DN21, **England**.
Contact/s: **Mr Neville Fickling** (Manager), 27 Lodge Lane, Upton, Gainsborough, Lincolnshire, DN21 5NW.
(T) 01427 838731 (F) 01427 838532
Profile: **FT:** Coarse; **WN:** Gull Pool; **WT:** Pool (Still); **F. Size:** 45 Acres; **W. Size:** 44 Acres. Location: **Main Rd:** A15.
Ref: FH1247

DALBEATTIE RESERVOIR

Dalbeattie Reservoir, Dalbeattie, **DUMFRIES AND GALLOWAY**, DG5, **Scotland**.
Contact/s: **Mr M McCowan** (Manager).
(T) 01556 610270
Profile: **FT:** Game; **WN:** Dalbeattie; **WT:** Reservoir (Still).
Ref: FH1248

DALL (RIVER)

River Dall, Cushendun, Cushendall, **COUNTY ANTRIM**, BT44, **Northern Ireland**.
Contact/s: Manager, O'Neill's Country Sports, Sea and Game Tackle, 25 Mill St, Cushendall, County Antrim.
(T) 028 21772009
Mrs C McFetridge, 116 Tromara Rd, Cushendun, County Antrim, BT44 0ST.
(T) 028 21761251
Profile: **FT:** Game; **WN:** Dall; **WT:** Tributary (Moving).
Ref: FH1249

DALVENNAN FISHERY

Dalvennan Country Sports Fishery, Ayr, **AYRSHIRE (SOUTH)**, KA, **Scotland**.
Contact/s: **Mr Gerry Lapsley** (Owner).
(T) 01292 531134
Profile: **FT:** Game; **WN:** Dalvennan Country Sports Fishery; **WT:** River (Moving).
Ref: FH1250

DAM FLASK RESERVOIR

Dam Flask Reservoir, Low Bradfield, Sheffield, **YORKSHIRE (SOUTH)**, S, **England**.
Contact/s: Manager, Dawson's of Hillsborough, 70 Holme Lane, Sheffield, Yorkshire (South), S6 4JW.
(T) 0114 2812178
Mr Paul Yates (Bailiff). (M) 07973 442953
Profile: **FT:** Coarse; **WN:** Dam Flask; **WT:** Reservoir (Still) **W. Size:** 116 Acres. Location: **Nr. Rd:** B6077 Loxley Road; **Main Rd:** A6101.
Ref: FH1251

DANBURY COUNTRY PARK

Danbury Country Park, Danbury, Sandon, Chelmsford, **ESSEX**, CM2, **England**.
Contact/s: **Mr K Smith** (Fishery Contact), Essex County Council, Danbury Country Park, Danbury, Chelmsford, CM3 4AN.
(T) 01245 222350
Profile: **FT:** Coarse; **WN:** Danbury Country Park; **WT:** Lake (Still) **W. Size:** 2 Acres.
Ref: FH1252

DANBY (RIVER)

River Danby, Whitby, **YORKSHIRE (NORTH)**, YO2, **England**.
Contact/s: **Mr F Farrow** (Secretary), Danby Angling Club, 11 Dale End, Danby, Whitby, YO21 2JF.
Profile: **FT:** Game; **WN:** Danby; **WT:** River (Moving) **W. Size:** 12800 Metres.
Ref: FH1253

DANDYS & KNIGHTINGALE LAKES

Dandys Lake And Knightingale Lake, Wellow, Bath, **SOMERSET**, BA2, **England**.
Contact/s: **Mr Ron Hillier** (Secretary), 29 New Zealand Avenue, Salisbury, Wiltshire, SP2 7JX.
(T) 01722 321164
Profile: **FT:** Coarse; **WN:** Dandys Lake and Knightingale; **WT:** Lake (Still). Location: **Rail:** Salisbury.
Ref: FH1254

DANE (RIVER)

River Dane, Cotton Farm, Croxton, Middlewich, **CHESHIRE**, CW10, **England**.
(W) www.baymalton-anglingclub.org
Contact/s: **Mr Cliff Bratt**, Dave's of Middlewich, Lewin St, Middlewich, Cheshire,

CW10 9AX.
(T) 01606 832287
Mr Stewart Godber (Club Secretary), 38 Edenfield Rd, Mobberley, Cheshire, WA16 7HE.
(T) 01565 872582
Profile: FT: Coarse; **WN:** Dane; **WT:** River (Moving) **W. Size:** 3218 Metres. **Location: Nr. Rd:** Middlewich to Homles Chapel, Byley Bridge to King Street Bridge; **Main Rd:** B5081.
Ref: FH1255

DANE (RIVER)

Dane (River), Hermitage Farm, Holmes Chapel, **CHESHIRE**, **England**.
Contact/s: Mr John Turner (Hon Secretary), Prince Albert Angling Society, 15 Pexhill Drive, Macclesfield, Cheshire, SK10 3LP.
(T) 01625 422010
Profile: FT: Coarse; **WN:** Dane; **WT:** River (Moving) **W. Size:** 500 Metres. **Location: Main Rd:** A535; **Rail:** Holmes Chepel.
Ref: FH1256

DANE (RIVER)

Dane (River), Clough Brook, Allgreave Farm, Nr. Wildboarclough, Macclesfield, **CHESHIRE**, **England**.
Contact/s: Mr John Turner (Hon Secretary), Prince Albert Angling Society, 15 Pexhill Drive, Macclesfield, Cheshire, SK10 3LP.
(T) 01625 422010
Profile: FT: Game; **WN:** Dane or Clough Brook; **WT:** River (Moving) **W. Size:** 500 Metres. **Location: Nr. Rd:** A54 Bosley to Buxton; **Main Rd:** A54; **Rail:** Buxton.
Ref: FH1257

DANE (RIVER)

River Dane, Daisybank, Middlewich, **CHESHIRE**, CW10, **England**.
Contact/s: Mr Neil Jupp (Club Secretary), Lymm Angling Club, PO Box 350, Warrington, Cheshire, WA2 9FB.
(T) 01925 411744
Profile: FT: Coarse; **WN:** Dane; **WT:** River (Moving). **Location: Nr. Rd:** A54; **Main Rd:** M6, junction 18.
Ref: FH1258

DANE (RIVER)

Dane (River), Hall Farm, Swettenham Rd, Swettenham, Congleton, **CHESHIRE**, **England**.
Contact/s: Mr John Turner (Hon Secretary), Prince Albert Angling Society, 15 Pexhill Drive, Macclesfield, Cheshire, SK10 3LP.
(T) 01625 422010
Profile: FT: Coarse; **WN:** Dane; **WT:** River (Moving) **W. Size:** 700 Metres. **Location: Nr. Rd:** Swettenham Road; **Main Rd:** A54; **Rail:** Congleton.
Ref: FH1259

DANE (RIVER)

Dane (River), Radnor Bank Farm, Congleton, **CHESHIRE**, **England**.
Contact/s: Mr John Turner (Hon Secretary), Prince Albert Angling Society, 15 Pexhill Drive, Macclesfield, Cheshire, SK10 3LP.
(T) 01625 422010
Profile: FT: Coarse; **WN:** Dane; **WT:** River (Moving) **W. Size:** 1000 Metres. **Location: Main Rd:** A54; **Rail:** Congleton.
Ref: FH1260

DANE (RIVER)

River Dane, Macclesfield, **CHESHIRE**, SK11, **England**.
Contact/s: Mr John Turner (Hon Secretary), Prince Albert Angling Society, 15 Pexhill Drive, Macclesfield, Cheshire, SK10 3LP.
(T) 01625 422010
Profile: FT: Game; **WN:** Dane; **WT:** River (Moving).
Ref: FH1261

DANE (RIVER)

Dane (River), Clough Brook, Allmeadows Farm, Nr. Wincle, Macclesfield, **CHESHIRE**, **England**.
Contact/s: Mr John Turner (Hon Secretary), Prince Albert Angling Society, 15 Pexhill Drive, Macclesfield, Cheshire, SK10 3LP.
(T) 01625 422010
Profile: FT: Game; **WN:** Dane, or Clough Brook; **WT:** River (Moving). **Location: Nr. Rd:** A54; **Rail:** Buxton.
Ref: FH1262

DANE (RIVER)

River Dane, Byley, Middlewich, **CHESHIRE**, CW10, **England**.
Contact/s: Fishery Manager.
(T) 01606 834676
Profile: FT: Coarse; **WN:** Dane; **WT:** River (Moving).
Ref: FH1263

DANE (RIVER)

River Dane, Manor Farm, Middlewich, **CHESHIRE**, CW10, **England**.
Contact/s: Mr Neil Jupp (Club Secretary), Lymm Angling Club, PO Box 350, Warrington, Cheshire, WA2 9FB.
(T) 01925 411744
Profile: FT: Coarse; **WN:** Dane; **WT:** River (Moving). **Location: Nr. Rd:** A54; **Main Rd:** M6, junction 18.
Ref: FH1264

DANE (RIVER)

Dane (River), Colley Farm, North Rode, Congleton, **CHESHIRE**, **England**.
Contact/s: Mr John Turner (Hon Secretary), Prince Albert Angling Society, 15 Pexhill Drive, Macclesfield, Cheshire, SK10 3LP.
(T) 01625 422010
Profile: FT: Game; **WN:** Dane; **WT:** River (Moving) **W. Size:** 600 Metres. **Location: Nr. Rd:** A54; **Rail:** Congleton.
Ref: FH1265

DANE (RIVER)

Dane (River), Manor Farm, Byley, Middlewich, **CHESHIRE**, **England**.
Contact/s: Mr John Turner (Hon Secretary), Prince Albert Angling Society, 15 Pexhill Drive, Macclesfield, Cheshire, SK10 3LP.
(T) 01625 422010
Profile: FT: Coarse; **WN:** Dane; **WT:** River (Moving) **W. Size:** 600 Metres. **Location: Main Rd:** B5081; **Rail:** Middlewich.
Ref: FH1266

DANE RIVERSIDE FISHERY

Dane Riverside Fishery, Rear Of Bleak House, Shipbrook Rd, Rudheath, Northwich, **CHESHIRE**, CW9 7HF, **England**.
Contact/s: Manager.
(T) 01606 351566
Profile: FT: Coarse; **WN:** Dane Riverside Fishery; **WT:** Combination (Still) **W. Size:** 1200 Metres. **Location: Nr. Rd:** Shipbrook Road; **Main Rd:** M6, junction 19, A556.
Ref: FH1267

DANEBRIDGE FISHERIES

Danebridge Fisheries Ltd, Pingle Cottage, Danebridge, Wincle, Macclesfield, **CHESHIRE**, SK11 0QE, **England**.
Contact/s: Mr Doug Chadwick.
(T) 01260 227293 **(F)** 01260 227330
Mr S Peterson (Owner).
(T) 01260 227293 **(F)** 01260 227330
Profile: FT: Game; **WN:** Danebridge Fisheries Ltd; **WT:** Lake (Still); **F. Size:** 12 Acres; **W. Size:** 2 Acres. **Location: Main Rd:** A54, Congleton to Buxton; **Rail:** Macclesfield.
Ref: FH1268

DANESHILL LAKES

Daneshill Lakes, Retford, **NOTTINGHAMSHIRE**, DN22, **England**.
Contact/s: Fishery Manager.
(T) 01909 770917
Profile: FT: Coarse; **WN:** Daneshill Lakes; **WT:** Lake (Still) **W. Size:** 30 Acres.
Ref: FH1269

DANSON PARK LAKE

Danson Park Lake, Bexleyheath, **KENT**, DA, **England**.
Contact/s: Ms C Wells, Leisure Link, 45 Crook Log Bungalow, Bexleyheath, Kent, DA6 8EH.
(T) 020 82980266
Profile: FT: Coarse; **WN:** Danson Park; **WT:** Lake (Still) **W. Size:** 20 Acres. **Location: Nr. Rd:** Danson Road; **Main Rd:** A2.
Ref: FH1270

DARENT (RIVER)

River Darent, Crayford, Dartford, **KENT**, DA1, **England**.
Contact/s: Mr R Graham (Manager), Thameside Works Angling Society, 186 Waterdales, Northfleet, Crayford, DA11 8JW.
Profile: FT: Coarse; **WN:** Darent; **WT:** Tributary (Moving).
Ref: FH1271

DARENT (RIVER)

River Darent, Darent Valley Trout Fishers, 21 Ramus Wood Avenue, Farnborough, Orpington, **KENT**, BR6 7HF, **England**.
Contact/s: D J Rees.
Profile: FT: Game; **WN:** Darent; **WT:** River (Moving) **W. Size:** 3600 Metres. **Location: Nr. Rd:** Sevenoaks to Dartford; **Rail:** Eynsford.
Ref: FH1272

DARENTH FISHING COMPLEX

Darenth Fishing Complex, Darenth Hill, Darenth, Dartford, **KENT**, DA2 7QY, **England**.
Contact/s: Mr Mike Bevan (Owner).
(T) 01322 290150
Profile: FT: Coarse; **WN:** Darenth; **WT:** Gravel Pit (Still); **F. Size:** 76 Acres; **W. Size:** 36 Acres. **Location: Nr. Rd:** Darenth Hill; **Main Rd:** A225.
Ref: FH1273

DARK LANE PONDS

Dark Lane Ponds, Cadland Estate, Blackfield, Southampton, **HAMPSHIRE**, SO45 1YE, **England**.
(W) www.mfcfishery.f9.co.uk
Contact/s: Mr Brian Tillman (Manager), The Ruffs, Chapel Lane, Blackfield, Southampton, SO45 1YX.
(T) 023 80891617 **(F)** 023 80891616
(E) brian@mfcfishery.f9.co.uk
Profile: FT: Coarse; **WN:** Dark Lane; **WT:** Pond (Still) **W. Size:** 3 Acres. **Location: Nr. Rd:** Hampton Lane; **Main Rd:** M27, junction 2; **Rail:** Southampton.
Ref: FH1274

DARLOW LAKE

Darlow Lake, Freeland, Witney, **OXFORDSHIRE**, OX8, **England**.
Contact/s: Mr W Ward (Secretary), Farmoor Fly Fishing Club, 17 Perrot Cl, North Leigh, Oxfordshire, OX8 6RU.
(T) 01993 881503
Profile: FT: Game; **WN:** Darlow; **WT:** Gravel Pit (Still) **W. Size:** 26 Acres. **Location: Nr. Rd:** B4449; **Main Rd:** A415; **Rail:** Oxford.
Ref: FH1275

DARRACOTT RESERVOIR

Darracott Reservoir, Torrington, **DEVON**, EX38, **England**.
Contact/s: Mr Chris Hall (Manager).
(T) 01837 871565
Mr Reg England (Manager), South West Lake Fisheries, Higher Coombe Park, Lewdown, Okehampton, Devon EX20 4QT.
(T) 01837 871565 **(F)** 01837 871534

Profile: FT: Coarse; **WN:** Darracott; **WT:** Reservoir (Still) **W. Size:** 3 Acres. **Location:** **Main Rd:** A386, Okehampton to Bideford.
Ref: FH1276

DART (RIVER)

River Dart, Holn Chase Hotel, Ashburton, Buckfastleigh, **DEVON**, TQ13 7NS, **England**.
Contact/s: **Mr Sebastian Hughes** (Fishery Manager).
(T) 01364 631471
Profile: FT: Game; **WN:** Dart; **WT:** River (Moving).
Ref: FH1277

DARTMOUTH PARK

Dartmouth Park, West Bromwich, **MIDLANDS (WEST)**, B70, **England**.
Contact/s: Manager, Sandwell Valley Country Park, Salters Lane, West Bromwich, B71 4BG.
(T) 0121 5530220 (F) 0121 5259435
Profile: FT: Coarse; **WN:** Dartmouth; **WT:** Lake (Still) **W. Size:** 7 Acres.
Ref: FH1278

DARWELL WATER

Darwell Water, Mountfield, Robertsbridge, **SUSSEX (EAST)**, TN32 5DR, **England**.
Contact/s: **Commander Donald E Tack** (Company Secretary).
(T) 01580 880407
Profile: FT: Game; **WN:** Darwell; **WT:** Reservoir (Still); **F. Size:** 250 Acres; **W. Size:** 180 Acres. **Location:** **Nr. Rd:** A21; **Main Rd:** A21; **Rail:** Battle.
Ref: FH1279

DAVENPORT

Davenport, Stockport, **MANCHESTER (GREATER)**, SK, **England**.
Profile: FT: Coarse; **WN:** Davenport; **WT:** Lake (Still).
Ref: FH1280

DAVENTRY COUNTRY PARK

Daventry Country Park, Northern Way, Daventry, **NORTHAMPTONSHIRE**, NN11 5JB, **England**.
Contact/s: **Mr Dewi Morris** (Rangers Office).
(T) 01327 877193
Mr Tony Newby (Rangers Office).
(T) 01327 877193
Ms Claire Bird (Rangers Office).
(T) 01327 877193
Profile: FT: Coarse; **WN:** Daventry Country Park; **WT:** Reservoir (Still); **F. Size:** 107 Acres; **W. Size:** 80 Acres. **Location:** **Nr. Rd:** Northern Way; **Rail:** Long Buckby.
Ref: FH1281

DAYHOUSE FARM

Dayhouse Farm, Dayhouse Bank, Romsley, Halesowen, **MIDLANDS (WEST)**, B62 0EX, **England**.
Contact/s: **Mr L Stron** (Fishery Manager).
(T) 01562 710663
Profile: FT: Coarse; **WN:** Dayhouse Farm; **WT:** Pool (Still); **F. Size:** 2 Acres; **W. Size:** 1 Acre. **Location:** **Nr. Rd:** Dayhouse Bank; **Main Rd:** B4551.
Ref: FH1282

DAYLANDS FARM

Daylands Farm, Honeybridge Lane, Ashurst Wood, Ashurst, East Grinstead, **SUSSEX (WEST)**, RH19, **England**.
Contact/s: **Mr Derek Crush**.
(T) 01403 711057
Profile: FT: Coarse; **WN:** Daylands Farm; **WT:** Pond (Still). **Location:** **Nr. Rd:** Honeybridge Lane.
Ref: FH1283

DAYS LOCK

Days Lock, Little Wittenham, Abingdon, **OXFORDSHIRE**, OX14, **England**.
Contact/s: Fishery Contact.
(T) 01865 407768
Recreational Manager, The Environment Agency, Kings Meadow Rd, Reading, Berkshire, RG1 8DQ.
(T) 0118 9535000 (F) 0118 9500388
Profile: FT: Combination; **WN:** Thames; **WT:** Lock (Still).
Ref: FH1284

DEAN (RIVER)

River Dean, Dundee, **ANGUS**, DD2, **Scotland**.
Contact/s: **Mrs M C Milne** (Secretary), 1 West Park Gardens, Dundee, Angus, DD2 1NY.
Profile: FT: Combination; **WN:** Dean; **WT:** River (Moving).
Ref: FH1285

DEAN (RIVER)

Dean (River), Bar Green Farm, Woodford, Wilmslow, **CHESHIRE**, **England**.
Contact/s: **Mr John Turner** (Hon Secretary), Prince Albert Angling Society, 15 Pexhill Drive, Macclesfield, Cheshire, SK10 3LP.
(T) 01625 422010
Profile: FT: Coarse; **WN:** Dean; **WT:** River (Moving) **W. Size:** 500 Metres. **Location:** **Nr. Rd:** A5102; **Rail:** Wilmslow.
Ref: FH1286

DEAN CLOUGH RESERVOIR

Dean Clough Reservoir, Hyndburn, Accrington, **LANCASHIRE**, BB5, **England**.
Contact/s: **Mr J Winnard** (Secretary), Manor House, Grunsagill, Torside, Skipton, Yorkshire.
Mr Roy Rhodes (Conservation, Access and Recreation Manager), Rivington Water Treatment Works, Bolton Rd, Horwich, Bolton, BL6 7RN.
(T) 01204 664300
Profile: FT: Game; **WN:** Dean Clough; **WT:** Reservoir (Still).
Ref: FH1287

DEAN RESERVOIR

Dean Reservoir, 45 Holden Farm, Darwen, **LANCASHIRE**, BB3 3AU, **England**.
Contact/s: **Mr Fred Kendall** (Secretary), 45 Holden Fold, Darwen, Lancashire, BB3 3AH.
(T) 01254 775501
Profile: FT: Game; **WN:** Dean; **WT:** Reservoir (Still).
Ref: FH1288

DEARNE (RIVER)

River Dearne, Adwick Upon Dearne, Mexborough, **YORKSHIRE (SOUTH)**, S64, **England**.
Contact/s: Fisheries Contact, Environment Agency, Ridings Area Office, Phoenix House, Global Avenue, Leeds, LS11 8PG.
(T) 0113 2440191or2314834 (F) 0113 2134609
Manager, Paul's Fishing Tackle Ctre, Denaby Main, Doncaster, Yorkshire (South), DN12 4HU.
(T) 01709 862558
Profile: FT: Coarse; **WN:** Dearne; **WT:** River (Moving). **Location:** **Main Rd:** A6023.
Ref: FH1289

DEARNE VALLEY PARK LAKE

Dearne Valley Park Lake, Barnsley, **YORKSHIRE (SOUTH)**, S7, **England**.
Contact/s: Area Manager, Environment Agency, Ridings Area Office, Phoenix House, Global Avenue, Leeds, LS11 8PG.
(T) 0113 2440191or2314834 (F) 0113 2134609
Mr Brian Hearne.
(T) 01226 774529
Profile: FT: Coarse; **WN:** Dearne Valley Park; **WT:** Lake (Still).
Ref: FH1290

DEARNFORD HALL TROUT FISHERY

Dearnford Hall Trout Fishery, Dearnford Hall, Tilstock Rd, Whitchurch, **SHROPSHIRE**, SY13 3JJ, **England**.
Contact/s: **Mr Charles Bebbington** (Owner).
(T) 01948 665914 (F) 01948 666670
Mr Karl Humphries (Manager).
(T) 01948 665914 (F) 01948 666670 (M) 07710 837551
(E) dearnford_hall@yahoo.com
Profile: FT: Game; **WN:** Dearnford Hall Trout Fishery; **WT:** Lake (Still); **F. Size:** 25 Acres; **W. Size:** 16 Acres. **Location:** **Nr. Rd:** B5476; **Main Rd:** A41, A49; **Rail:** Whitchurch.
Ref: FH1291

DEBDALE RESERVOIRS

Debdale Reservoirs, Hyde Rd, Gorton, Manchester, **MANCHESTER (GREATER)**, M, **England**.
Contact/s: Area Manager, Manchester City Council, Town Hall, Albert Sq, Manchester, M60 2AF.
(T) 0161 2230816
Profile: FT: Coarse; **WN:** Debdale; **WT:** Reservoir (Still) **W. Size:** 50 Acres. **Location:** **Nr. Rd:** A57; **Main Rd:** M66, junction 11.
Ref: FH1292

DEBEN (RIVER)

River Deben, Woodbridge, **SUFFOLK**, IP, **England**.
Profile: FT: Coarse; **WN:** Deben; **WT:** River (Moving).
Ref: FH1293

DECOY FARM

Decoy Farm, Ormesby St Michael, Great Yarmouth, **NORFOLK**, NR29, **England**.
Contact/s: Fishery Manager.
(T) 01493 731294
Profile: FT: Coarse; **WN:** Decoy Farm; **WT:** Lake (Still).
Ref: FH1294

DECOY LAKE

Decoy Lake, Decoy Farm, Eastrea, Whittlesey, Peterborough, **CAMBRIDGESHIRE**, PE, **England**.
Contact/s: **Mr Peter Band**.
(T) 01733 202230
Profile: FT: Coarse; **WN:** Decoy Lake; **WT:** Gravel Pit (Still). **Location:** **Main Rd:** A605.
Ref: FH1295

DECOY LAKE

Decoy Lake, Halland, Lewes, **SUSSEX (EAST)**, BN, **England**.
Contact/s: Manager, East Hoathly Post Office, 2 High St, East Hoathly, Lewes, BN8 6EB.
(T) 01825 840321
Profile: FT: Coarse; **WN:** Decoy; **WT:** Lake (Still). **Location:** **Nr. Rd:** A22 to Eastbourne.
Ref: FH1296

DEDHAM MILL

Dedham Mill Mngmt Co Ltd, 34 Dedham Mill, Mill Lane, Dedham, Colchester, **ESSEX**, CO7 6DJ, **England**.
Contact/s: **Mr L M Ward**.
(T) 01206 322049
Profile: FT: Coarse; **WN:** Deham Mill; **WT:** Lock (Still).
Ref: FH1297

DEE (RIVER)

River Dee, Newbridge, Newport, NP11, **Wales**.
Contact/s: **Mr Kerry Clutton** (Hon Secretary), 28 Worsley Avenue, Johnstown, Wrexham.
(T) 01978 840377
Profile: FT: Game; **WN:** Dee; **WT:** River (Moving). **Location:** **Nr. Rd:** Wynnstay Waters; **Rail:** Ruabon.
Ref: FH1298

DEE (RIVER)

River Dee, Isycoed, Wrexham, LL13, **Wales**.
Contact/s: **Mr A Hogg** (Hon Secretary), 6 Llwynon Cl, Bryn y Baal, Mold, Clwyd, CH7 6TN.
(T) 01352 754745

Profile: **FT:** Game; **WN:** Dee; **WT:** River (Moving) **W. Size:** 1600 Metres.
Ref: FH1299

DEE (RIVER)

River Dee, Wrexham, LL!, **Wales**.
Contact/s: **Mr W D Barton**, Bangor-On-Dee Salmon Angling Association, 32 Laurels Avenue, Bangor-on-Dee, LL13 0BB.
Profile: **FT:** Combination; **WN:** Dee; **WT:** River (Moving).
Ref: FH1300

DEE (RIVER)

River Dee, Almere Farm, Rossett, Wrexham, LL12, **Wales**.
(W) www.warrington-anglers.org.uk
Contact/s: **Mr Frank Lythgoe** (Secretary), Warrington Angling Association, 52 Parker St, Warrington, Lancashire.
(T) 01928 716238 **(F)** 01928 713898
(E) info@warrington-anglers.org.uk
Profile: **FT:** Game; **WN:** Dee; **WT:** River (Moving) **W. Size:** 3200 Metres. **Location:** **Main Rd:** B5102.
Ref: FH1301

DEE (RIVER)

River Dee, Overton, Wrexham, LL13, **Wales**.
Contact/s: **Mrs Ann Phillips** (Hon Secretary), 2 Ruabon Rd, Wrexham, LL13 7PB.
(T) 01978 351815
Profile: **FT:** Game; **WN:** Dee; **WT:** River (Moving) **W. Size:** 92 Metres. **Location:** **Nr. Rd:** Overton Bridge; **Main Rd:** Clay's Fords to Bangor Bridge.
Ref: FH1302

DEE (RIVER)

River Dee, Erbistock, Wrexham, LL13, **Wales**.
Contact/s: **Mr Andrew Coke** (Landlord), The Boat Inn, Erbistock, Wrexham, LL13 0DL.
(T) 01978 780666 **(F)** 01978 780607
Profile: **FT:** Game; **WN:** Dee; **WT:** River (Moving).
Ref: FH1303

DEE (RIVER)

River Dee, Holt, Wrexham, LL13, **Wales**.
Contact/s: **Mr A Hogg** (Hon Secretary), 6 Llwynon Cl, Bryn y Baal, Mold, Clwyd, CH7 6TN.
(T) 01352 754745
Profile: **FT:** Game; **WN:** Dee; **WT:** River (Moving) **W. Size:** 24000 Metres. **Location:** **Nr. Rd:** New Road bridge, Dee Lane.
Ref: FH1304

DEE (RIVER)

River Dee, Dentdale Valley, Sedbergh, **CUMBRIA**, LA10, **England**.
Contact/s: **Mr C Richardson**, Three Peaks Ltd, 25 Main St, Sedbergh, Cumbria, LA10 5BW.
(T) 01539 620446
Mr D Eccles, Three Peaks Ltd, 25 Main St, Sedbergh, Cumbria, LA10 5BW.
(T) 01539 620446
Profile: **FT:** Game; **WN:** Dee; **WT:** River (Moving). **Location:** **Main Rd:** A684; **Rail:** Kendal.
Ref: FH1305

DEE (RIVER)

Dee (River), Catholes Farm, Sedbergh, **CUMBRIA**, **England**.
Contact/s: **Mr John Turner** (Hon Secretary), Prince Albert Angling Society, 15 Pexhill Drive, Macclesfield, Cheshire, SK10 3LP.
(T) 01625 422010
Profile: **FT:** Game; **WN:** Dee; **WT:** River (Moving) **W. Size:** 1000 Metres. **Location:** **Nr. Rd:** Abbot Holme Bridge; **Main Rd:** A684; **Rail:** Kendal.
Ref: FH1306

DEE (RIVER)

Dee (River), Dee Lodge, Newbridge, Llangollen, **DENBIGHSHIRE**, **Wales**.
Contact/s: **Mr John Turner** (Hon Secretary), Prince Albert Angling Society, 15 Pexhill Drive, Macclesfield, Cheshire, SK10 3LP.
(T) 01625 422010
Profile: **FT:** Game; **WN:** Dee; **WT:** River (Moving) **W. Size:** 650 Metres. **Location:** **Nr. Rd:** B5605; **Rail:** Pentre.
Ref: FH1307

DEE (RIVER)

River Dee, Llangollen, **DENBIGHSHIRE**, LL20, **Wales**.
Contact/s: **Ms Sara Hughes** (Manager), Hughes Newsagent, 12 Chapel St, Llangollen, Denbighshire, LL20 8NN.
(T) 01978 860155
Profile: **FT:** Game; **WN:** Dee; **WT:** River (Moving).
Ref: FH1308

DEE (RIVER)

River Dee, Wrexham, **DENBIGHSHIRE**, LL14, **Wales**.
Contact/s: **Mr Ken Bathers** (Chairman), Maelor Angling Association, Sunnyside, Hill St, Cefn Mawr, Wrexham, LL14 3AY.
(T) 01978 820608 **(M)** 07714 612651
(E) ken.bathers@1c24.net
Profile: **FT:** Game; **WN:** Dee; **WT:** River (Moving) **W. Size:** 3600 Metres. **Location:** **Nr. Rd:** Pontcysyllte to Sun Bank.
Ref: FH1309

DEE (RIVER)

River Dee, Llangollen, **DENBIGHSHIRE**, LL20, **Wales**.
Contact/s: **Mr Greer Williams** (General Manager), Hand Hotel, Bridge St, Llangollen, Denbighshire, LL20 8PL.
(T) 01978 860303 **(F)** 01978 861277
Profile: **FT:** Game; **WN:** Dee; **WT:** River (Moving). **Location:** **Nr. Rd:** Bridge Street; **Rail:** Ruabon. **£Fr**
Ref: FH1310

DEE (RIVER)

River Dee, Llais-Yr-Afon, Ruthin, **DENBIGHSHIRE**, LL15, **Wales**.
Contact/s: **Mr Caerwyn Lewis** (Secretary).
Mr Gordon Smith.
(T) 01824 7196091
Profile: **FT:** Game; **WN:** Dee; **WT:** River (Moving) **W. Size:** 20000 Metres. **Location:** **Nr. Rd:** A5; **Main Rd:** A5.
Ref: FH1311

DEE (RIVER)

River Dee, Farndon Bridge, Mold, **FLINTSHIRE**, CH7, **Wales**.
Contact/s: **Mr A Hogg** (Hon Secretary), 6 Llwynon Cl, Bryn y Baal, Mold, Clwyd, CH7 6TN.
(T) 01352 754745
Profile: **FT:** Game; **WN:** Dee; **WT:** River (Moving) **W. Size:** 2400 Metres.
Ref: FH1312

DEE (RIVER)

River Dee, Bala, **GWYNEDD**, LL23, **Wales**.
Contact/s: Manager, Pale Hall Country House Hotel, Llandderfel, Bala, Gwynedd, LL23 7PS.
(T) 01678 530285
Profile: **FT:** Game; **WN:** Dee; **WT:** River (Moving) **W. Size:** 9600 Metres.
Ref: FH1313

DEE (RIVER)

River Dee, Bala, **GWYNEDD**, LL23, **Wales**.
Contact/s: **Mr Dewi Evans** (Secretary), Bala and District Angling Club, 33 High St, Bala, Gwynedd, LL23 7AF.
(T) 01678 520370 **(F)** 01678 520370
Profile: **FT:** Combination; **WN:** Dee; **WT:** River (Moving); **F. Size:** 900 Acres; **W. Size:** 5200 Metres. **Location:** **Nr. Rd:** A494; **Rail:** Wrexham.
Ref: FH1314

DEE (RIVER)

Dee (River), Holt, **NORFOLK**, **Wales**.
Profile: **FT:** Combination; **WN:** Dee; **WT:** River (Moving) **W. Size:** 400 Metres. **Location:** **Nr. Rd:** A534; **Rail:** Wrexham.
Ref: FH1315

DEE (RIVER)

Dee (River), Cynwyd, Four Crosses, Llanymynech, **POWYS**, **Wales**.
Contact/s: **Mr John Turner** (Hon Secretary), Prince Albert Angling Society, 15 Pexhill Drive, Macclesfield, Cheshire, SK10 3LP.
(T) 01625 422010
Profile: **FT:** Game; **WN:** Dee; **WT:** River (Moving) **W. Size:** 800 Metres. **Location:** **Main Rd:** A494; **Rail:** Llangollen.
Ref: FH1316

DEE (RIVER)

River Dee, Sutton Green, Guildford, **SURREY**, GU4, **England**.
Contact/s: **Mr A Hogg** (Hon Secretary), 6 Llwynon Cl, Bryn y Baal, Mold, Clwyd, CH7 6TN.
(T) 01352 754745
Profile: **FT:** Game; **WN:** Dee; **WT:** River (Moving) **W. Size:** 1600 Metres.
Ref: FH1317

DEE (RIVER)

Dee (River), Dongray Hall, Bangor-on-Dee, **WREXHAM**, **Wales**.
Contact/s: **Mr John Turner** (Hon Secretary), Prince Albert Angling Society, 15 Pexhill Drive, Macclesfield, Cheshire, SK10 3LP.
(T) 01625 422010
Profile: **FT:** Combination; **WN:** Dee; **WT:** River (Moving) **W. Size:** 1700 Metres. **Location:** **Nr. Rd:** B5069; **Main Rd:** A525; **Rail:** Wrexham.
Ref: FH1318

DEE (RIVER)

Dee (River), Bangor-on-Dee, **WREXHAM**, **England**.
Contact/s: **Mr John Turner** (Hon Secretary), Prince Albert Angling Society, 15 Pexhill Drive, Macclesfield, Cheshire, SK10 3LP.
(T) 01625 422010
Profile: **FT:** Coarse; **WN:** Dee; **WT:** River (Moving) **W. Size:** 500 Metres. **Location:** **Nr. Rd:** A525; **Rail:** Wrexam.
Ref: FH1319

DEE (RIVER)

Dee (River), Brook Farm, Worthenbury, **WREXHAM**, **Wales**.
Contact/s: **Mr John Turner** (Hon Secretary), Prince Albert Angling Society, 15 Pexhill Drive, Macclesfield, Cheshire, SK10 3LP.
(T) 01625 422010
Profile: **FT:** Combination; **WN:** Dee; **WT:** River (Moving) **W. Size:** 900 Metres. **Location:** **Main Rd:** B5069; **Rail:** Wrexham.
Ref: FH1320

DEE ABBEY FISHERIES

Dee Abbey Fisheries, Overton, Wrexham, LL13, **Wales**.
Contact/s: **Mrs Ann Phillips** (Hon Secretary), 2 Ruabon Rd, Wrexham, LL13 7PB.
(T) 01978 351815
Profile: **FT:** Combination; **WN:** Dee; **WT:** River (Moving) **W. Size:** 11200 Metres. **Location:** **Nr. Rd:** Overton Bridge to Bangor-on-Dee.
Ref: FH1321

DEEP HAYES COUNTRY PARK

Deep Hayes Country Park, Sutherland Road, Longsdon, Leek, **STAFFORDSHIRE**, ST13, **England**.
Contact/s: Park Rangers Office, Deep Hayes Country Park, Sutherland Road, Longsdon, Leek, Staffordshire.

(T) 01538 387655
Profile: FT: Coarse; **WN:** Deep Hayes; **WT:** Lake (Still); **F. Size:** 20 Acres; **W. Size:** 5 Acres. **Location:** **Nr. Rd:** Sutherland Road; **Main Rd:** A53; **Rail:** Stoke-on-Trent.
Ref: FH1322

DEEP PIT

Deep Pit, Hindley, Wigan, **LANCASHIRE**, WN, **England**.
Contact/s: **Mr Gerry Wilson** (Hon Secretary), Wigan and District Angling Association, 11 Guildford Avenue, Chorley, Lancashire, PR6 8TG.
(T) 01257 265905
Profile: **FT:** Coarse; **WN:** Hindlley Deep; **WT:** Gravel Pit (Still) **W. Size:** 1 Acre. **Location:** **Nr. Rd:** A58; **Main Rd:** A577.
Ref: FH1323

DEER PARK COUNTRY HOTEL

Deer Park Country Hotel (The), Buckerell Village, Weston, Honiton, **DEVON**, EX14 3PG, **England**.
Contact/s: **Mr Stephen Noah** (Manager), The Deer Park Country Hotel, Weston, Honiton, Devon, EX14 3PG.
(T) 01404 41266 (F) 01404 46598
Profile: **FT:** Combination; **WN:** Deer Park Country Hotel (The); **WT:** Combination (Still & Moving) **W. Size:** 80 Acres. **Location:** **Main Rd:** A30; **Rail:** Honiton.
Ref: FH1324

DELBROOK VALLEY TROUT FISHERY

Delbrook Valley Trout Fishery, Oakford, Tiverton, **DEVON**, EX16, **England**.
Contact/s: **Mr Mike Pusey**.
(T) 01398 351292
Profile: **FT:** Game; **WN:** Delbrook Valley Trout Fishery; **WT:** Reservoir (Still).
Ref: FH1325

DELBURY HALL TROUT FISHERY

Delbury Hall Trout Fishery, Diddlebury, Craven Arms, **SHROPSHIRE**, SY7 9DH, **England**.
Contact/s: **Mr Patrick Wrigley** (Manager).
(T) 01584 841267 (F) 01584 841441
(E) wrigley@delbury.com
Profile: **FT:** Game; **WN:** Delbury Hall Trout Fishery; **WT:** Lake (Still); **F. Size:** 8 Acres; **W. Size:** 6 Acres. **Location:** **Nr. Rd:** B4368; **Main Rd:** A49; **Rail:** Craven Arms.
Ref: FH1326

DELEPRE PARK LAKE

Delepre Park Lake, Northampton, **NORTHAMPTONSHIRE**, NN, **England**.
Contact/s: Fishery Manager.
(T) 01604 757589
Profile: **FT:** Coarse; **WN:** Delepre; **WT:** Lake (Still).
Ref: FH1327

DELPHI FISHERY

Delphi Fishery, Delphi Lodge, Leenane, **COUNTY GALWAY**, **Ireland**.
Contact/s: **Mr Peter Mantle**.
(T) 095 42296
Profile: **FT:** Game; **WN:** Bundorragha; **WT:** River (Moving).
Ref: FH1328

DELVES FISH PONDS

Delves Fish Ponds, Doncaster, **YORKSHIRE (SOUTH)**, DN, **England**.
Contact/s: **Mr Derek Burke** (Secretary), Thorne and District Angling Association, Bali-Hai, North Eastern Rd, Thorne, DN8 4AS.
(T) 01937 585764or01405812088
Profile: **FT:** Coarse; **WN:** Delves; **WT:** Pond (Still).
Ref: FH1329

DELVES LAKES

Delves Lakes, Thorne, Doncaster, **YORKSHIRE (SOUTH)**, DN8, **England**.
Contact/s: **Mr Tony Green** (Manager), Peg Two Tackle, 27 King St, Thorne, Yorkshire (South), DN8 5AU.
(T) 01405 814417
Profile: **FT:** Coarse; **WN:** Delve's; **WT:** Lake (Still). **Location:** **Nr. Rd:** A614 Goole to Thorne; **Main Rd:** M18, junction 6.
Ref: FH1330

DENNIS RAINWATER LAKE

Dennis Rainwater Lake, Low Rd, Croft, Skegness, **LINCOLNSHIRE**, PE24, **England**.
Contact/s: **Mrs Marie Dennis** (Owner).
(T) 01754 765783
Profile: **FT:** Coarse; **WN:** Dennis Rainwater; **WT:** Lake (Still) **W. Size:** 2 Acres. **Location:** **Nr. Rd:** Low Road; **Main Rd:** A52 Boston to Skegness.
Ref: FH1331

DENTON RESERVOIR

Denton Reservoir, Denton, Grantham, **LINCOLNSHIRE**, NG32, **England**.
Contact/s: **Mr W Hutchins** (Hon Secretary).
(T) 01476 575628
Profile: **FT:** Coarse; **WN:** Denton; **WT:** Reservoir (Still).
Ref: FH1332

DENTS OF HILGAY

Dents Of Hilgay, Steels Gr, West Fen, Hilgay, Downham Market, **NORFOLK**, PE38 0QH, **England**.
Contact/s: **Mr Tom Dent**.
(T) 01366 385661
Profile: **FT:** Coarse; **WN:** Dents Of Hilgay; **WT:** Lake (Still); **F. Size:** 15 Acres; **W. Size:** 7 Acres. **Location:** **Nr. Rd:** A10 from Kings Lynn..
Ref: FH1333

DERBYSHIRE TROUT FISHERY

Derbyshire Trout Fishery, Alton Manor Farm, Idridgehay, Belper, **DERBYSHIRE**, DE56 2FH, **England**.
Contact/s: **Mr Stephen Jones** (Manager).
(T) 01629 822318
Profile: **FT:** Game; **WN:** Derbyshire Trout Fishery; **WT:** Lake (Still) **W. Size:** 4 Acres.
Ref: FH1334

DERCULICH BEAT

Derculich Beat, Aberfeldy, **PERTH AND KINROSS**, PH15, **Scotland**.
(W) www.fishingnet.com/beats/derculich.htm
Contact/s: **Ms Em Honeyman** (Manager), Wade Newsagents, 31 Bank St, Aberfeldy, Perth and Kinross, PH15 2BB.
(T) 01887 820397
Profile: **FT:** Combination; **WN:** Derculich and Green Bank; **WT:** Pool (Still).
Ref: FH1335

DERG (LOUGH)

Derg (Lough), Nenagh, **COUNTY TIPPERARY**, **Ireland**.
(W) www.shannon-dev.ie/loughderg
Contact/s: Manager, Shannon Development, Shannon Town Ctre, County Clare.
(T) 061 361555 (F) 061 363180
(E) info@shannon-dev.ie
Profile: **FT:** Combination; **WN:** Derg; **WT:** Lough (Still) **W. Size:** 32000 Acres.
Ref: FH1336

DERG (RIVER)

River Derg, Castlederg, **COUNTY TYRONE**, BT81, **Northern Ireland**.
Contact/s: **Mr Joseph Fleming**, Rockfield, Newtown St, Strabane, County Tyrone.
(T) 028 71882416after5.30pm
R Harron, Brookevale, Castledreg, County Tyrone.
(T) 028 81621256
Profile: **FT:** Game; **WN:** Derg; **WT:** River (Moving) **W. Size:** 32000 Metres.
Ref: FH1337

DERG (RIVER)

River Derg, Omagh, **COUNTY TYRONE**, BT78, **Northern Ireland**.
Contact/s: **Mr David Campbell** (Manager), Mourne Valley Tackle, 50 Main St, Newtownstewart, Omagh, County Tyrone, BT78 4AA.
(T) 028 81661543
Profile: **FT:** Game; **WN:** Derg; **WT:** River (Moving).
Ref: FH1338

DERG (RIVER)

River Derg, Ardstraw, Omagh, **COUNTY TYRONE**, BT78, **Northern Ireland**.
Contact/s: Manager, N M Tackle, 9 Alexandra Pl, Sion Mills, Strabane, BT82 9HR.
(T) 028 81659501
Mr David Campbell (Manager), Mourne Valley Tackle, 50 Main St, Newtownstewart, Omagh, County Tyrone, BT78 4AA.
(T) 028 81661543
Mr John Duncan, 22 Abbey Villas, Ardstraw, County Tyrone.
(T) 028 81661693
Profile: **FT:** Game; **WN:** Derg; **WT:** River (Moving) **W. Size:** 4800 Metres. **Location:** **Nr. Rd:** Ardstraw Bridge to Crewe Bridge.
Ref: FH1339

DERG (RIVER)

River Derg, Strabane, **COUNTY TYRONE**, BT82, **Northern Ireland**.
Contact/s: **Mr Billy Diver**, Variety Shop, 5 Castle Prde, Strabane, County Tyrone, BT82.
(T) 028 71883021
Mr David Campbell (Manager), Mourne Valley Tackle, 50 Main St, Newtownstewart, Omagh, County Tyrone, BT78 4AA.
(T) 028 81661543
Profile: **FT:** Game; **WN:** Derg; **WT:** River (Moving).
Ref: FH1340

DERRYVEGALL LAKE

Derryvegall Lake, Castletownbere, **COUNTY CORK**, **Ireland**.
(W) www.swrfb.ie
Contact/s: Area Manager, South West Regional Fisheries Board, 1 Nevilles Trce, Macroom, County Cork, Ireland.
(T) 026 41221
(E) swrfb@swrfb.ie
Profile: **FT:** Game; **WN:** Derryvegall; **WT:** Lake (Still) **W. Size:** 15 Acres.
Ref: FH1341

DERRYVEGALL LAKE

Derryvegall Lake, Castletownbere, **COUNTY CORK**, **Ireland**.
Contact/s: Area Manager, South West Fisheries Board, Castletownbere, County Cork, Ireland.
(T) 026 41221
(E) eileen@swrfb.ie
Mr Micheal Harrington.
(T) 027 70011
Profile: **FT:** Game; **WN:** Derryvegall; **WT:** Lake (Still) **W. Size:** 15 Acres. **Location:** **Nr. Rd:** Ardgroom to Castletownbere.
Ref: FH1342

DERWENT (RIVER)

River Derwent, Shotley Bridge, Consett, **COUNTY DURHAM**, DH8, **England**.
Contact/s: **Mr Jason Hughes** (Manager), The Royal Derwent Hotel, Hole Row, Allensford, Consett, DH8 9BB.
(T) 01207 592000 (F) 01207 502472
Profile: **FT:** Game; **WN:** Derwent; **WT:** River (Moving) **W. Size:** 22400 Metres.
Ref: FH1343

DERWENT (RIVER)

River Derwent, Cockermouth, **CUMBRIA**, CA13, **England**.
Contact/s: **Mr A Cumber** (Owner), Castle Fishery, The Castle, Cockermouth, Cumbria, CA13 9EU.
(T) 01900 826320 (0900 to 1100) or 01946 861556
Profile: **FT:** Game; **WN:** Derwent (Cockermouth to Workington); **WT:** River (Moving).
Ref: FH1344

DERWENT (RIVER)

River Derwent, Keswick, **CUMBRIA**, CA12, **England**.
Contact/s: Manager, Field and Stream, 79 Main St, Keswick, Cumbria, CA12 5DS.
(T) 01768 774396
Profile: FT: Game; WN: Derwent Water; WT: River (Moving).
Ref: FH1345

DERWENT (RIVER)

River Derwent, Whatstandwell, Matlock, **DERBYSHIRE**, DE4, **England**.
Contact/s: **Mr Andy Bunting** (Tennant), Derwent Hotel, Derby Rd, Whatstandwell, Matlock, DE4 5HG.
(T) 01773 856616
Profile: FT: Game; WN: Derwent; WT: River (Moving) W. Size: 400 Metres.
Ref: FH1346

DERWENT (RIVER)

River Derwent, Ambergate, Belper, **DERBYSHIRE**, DE56, **England**.
Contact/s: Secretary.
(T) 01773 826257
Profile: FT: Coarse; WN: Derwent (Amber Gate to Milford Weir); WT: River (Moving).
Ref: FH1347

DERWENT (RIVER)

River Derwent, Chatsworth Fishery, The Estate Office, Edensor, Bakewell, **DERBYSHIRE**, DE45 1PJ, **England**.
Contact/s: **Mr Ian Nott** (Agent), Chatsworth and Monsal Dale Fishery, The Estate Office, Edensor, Bakewell, Derbyshire DE45 1PJ.
(T) 01246 565300
Profile: FT: Game; WN: Derwent; WT: River (Moving). Location: Main Rd: A6.
Ref: FH1348

DERWENT (RIVER)

River Derwent, Borrowash, Derby, **DERBYSHIRE**, DE72, **England**.
Contact/s: Manager, Derwent Tackle, 2 Station Rd, Borrowash, Derby, DE72 3LG.
(T) 01332 662379
Profile: FT: Coarse; WN: Derwent; WT: River (Moving).
Ref: FH1349

DERWENT (RIVER)

River Derwent, Hull, **HUMBERSIDE**, HU1, **England**.
Contact/s: **Mr Bill Brame** (Secretary), Hull and District Angler's Association, PO Box 188, Hull, HU9 1AN.
Mr Paul Caygill (Secretary), Hull and District Anglers Association, 17 Linley Cl, Leven, Beverley, HU17 5NP.
(T) 01964 542677
Profile: FT: Coarse; WN: Derwent; WT: River (Moving) W. Size: 2400 Metres.
Ref: FH1350

DERWENT (RIVER)

River Derwent, Barmby Barrage, Barmby-on-the-Marsh, Goole, **HUMBERSIDE**, DN14 7H, **England**.
Profile: FT: Coarse; WN: Derwent (Barrage to Loftsome Bridge); WT: River (Moving).
Location: Main Rd: A63. £Fr
Ref: FH1351

DERWENT (RIVER)

River Derwent, Kirkham Abbey, Kirkham, Preston, **LANCASHIRE**, PR4, **England**.
Profile: FT: Coarse; WN: Derwent; WT: River (Moving). Location: Main Rd: A64.
Ref: FH1352

DERWENT (RIVER)

River Derwent, Rowlands Gill, **TYNE AND WEAR**, NE4, **England**.
Contact/s: Manager, Derwent Park Caravan and Camping Site, The Derwent Park Bungalow, Rowlands Gill, Tyne and Wear, NE39 1LG.
(T) 01207 543383 (F) 01207 549983
Profile: FT: Game; WN: Derwent; WT: River (Moving). Location: Nr. Rd: Derwent Haugh to Lintzford.
Ref: FH1353

DERWENT (RIVER)

River Derwent, York, **YORKSHIRE (NORTH)**, YO, **England**.
Contact/s: **Mr Les Rogers** (Secretary), Goole and District Angling Association, 39 Clifton Gardens, Goole, Humberside (North), DN14 6AR.
(T) 01405 769096
Profile: FT: Coarse; WN: Derwent; WT: River (Moving) W. Size: 400 Metres.
Ref: FH1354

DERWENT (RIVER)

River Derwent, Hackness, Scarborough, **YORKSHIRE (NORTH)**, YO13, **England**.
Contact/s: **Mr Paul Datham** (Manager), Hackness Grange Hotel, Country House Hotel, Hackness, Scarborough, YO13 0JW.
(T) 01723 882345
Profile: FT: Game; WN: Derwent; WT: River (Moving).
Ref: FH1355

DERWENT (RIVER)

River Derwent, Huttons Ambo, Firby, York, **YORKSHIRE (NORTH)**, YO60 7LH, **England**.
Contact/s: **Mr Paul Thompson**, Firby Hall, Firby, Yorkshire.
(T) 01653 618602
Profile: FT: Coarse; WN: Derwent; WT: River (Moving). Location: Nr. Rd: Malton to York; Main Rd: A64 to York.
Ref: FH1356

DERWENT (RIVER)

River Derwent, Ferry Boat Inn, Thorganby, York, **YORKSHIRE (NORTH)**, YO19, **England**.
Contact/s: Manager, Jefferson Arms, Main St, Thorganby, York, North Yorkshire YO19 6DB.
(T) 01904 448316
Profile: FT: Coarse; WN: Derwent; WT: River (Moving).
Ref: FH1357

DERWENT (RIVER)

River Derwent, East Cottingwith, York, **YORKSHIRE (NORTH)**, YO42, **England**.
Contact/s: **Mr S Skelton**.
(T) 01759 388138
Profile: FT: Coarse; WN: Derwent; WT: River (Moving). Location: Main Rd: B1228.
Ref: FH1358

DERWENT (RIVER)

River Derwent, Stamford Bridge, York, **YORKSHIRE (NORTH)**, YO41, **England**.
Profile: FT: Coarse; WN: Derwent; WT: River (Moving). Location: Main Rd: A166.
£Fr
Ref: FH1359

DERWENT RESERVOIR

Derwent Reservoir, Edmundbyers, Consett, **COUNTY DURHAM**, DH8, **England**.
Contact/s: **Customer Contact Department**, Environment Agency, Northumbria Area Office, Tyneside House, Skinnerburn Rd, Newcastle Business Park, Newcastle upon Tyne NE4 7AR.
(T) 0191 2034000 (F) 0191 2034004
Mr Don Coe (Manager).
(T) 01207 255250
Mr Paul Russell, Northumbrian Water Ltd, Head Office, Recreation Department, Abbey Rd, Durham DH1 5FJ.
(T) 0191 3832222 (F) 0191 3841920
Profile: FT: Coarse; WN: Derwent; WT: Reservoir (Still).
Ref: FH1360

DERWENT VALLEY FISHERY

Derwent Valley Fishery, Darley Abbey, Derby, **DERBYSHIRE**, DE, **England**.
Contact/s: , Derwent Valley Fisheries, 45 Holmes Rd, Breaston, Derby, DE72 3BT.
Profile: FT: Coarse; WN: Derwent Valley Fishery; WT: Lake (Still).
Ref: FH1361

DEVER SPRINGS TROUT FISHERY

Dever Springs Trout Fishery, Barton Stacey, Winchester, **HAMPSHIRE**, SO21 3NP, **England**.
Contact/s: **Mr Niall Staig**, Con Wilson Organisation Ltd, T/A Dever Springs Trout Fishery, Barton Stacey, Winchester, SO21 3NP.
(T) 01264 720592 (F) 01264 720738
Ms Philippa Bull (Manager), Con Wilson Organisation Ltd, T/A Dever Springs Trout Fishery, Barton Stacey, Winchester, SO21 3NP.
(T) 01264 720592 (F) 01264 720738
Profile: FT: Game; WN: Dever Springs Trout Fishery; WT: Combination (Still & Moving); F. Size: 8 Acres; W. Size: 6 Acres.
Location: Main Rd: A303; Rail: Winchester.
Ref: FH1362

DEVOKE WATER

Devoke Water, Ravenglass, **CUMBRIA**, CA18, **England**.
Profile: FT: Game; WN: Devoke Water; WT: River (Moving).
Ref: FH1363

DEXTER POOL

Dexter Pool, Bewdley, **WORCESTERSHIRE**, DY12, **England**.
Contact/s: **Mr Stuart Norgrove** (Haye Farm Manager).
(T) 01299 403371
Profile: FT: Coarse; WN: Dexter; WT: Pool (Still).
Ref: FH1364

DICKENS STREET LODGE

Dickens Street Lodge, Blackburn, **LANCASHIRE**, BB2, **England**.
Contact/s: **Mr Gerry Lee**.
(T) 01254 385290
Profile: FT: Coarse; WN: Dickens Street Lodge; WT: Lake (Still).
Ref: FH1365

DICKERSONS PIT

Dickersons Pit, Milton Pits, Cambridge, **CAMBRIDGESHIRE**, CB, **England**.
Contact/s: **Mr R Cooper** (Secretary), 236 Histon Rd, Cottenham, Cambridgeshire.
(T) 01223 420060or365987
Profile: FT: Coarse; WN: Dickersons; WT: Gravel Pit (Still) W. Size: 1 Acre. Location: Nr. Rd: Milton Road.
Ref: FH1366

DILHORNE HALL POOLS

Dilhorne Hall Pools, New Rd, Dilhorne, Stoke-on-Trent, **STAFFORDSHIRE**, **England**.
(W) www.fentondas.co.uk
Contact/s: **Mr C Yates** (Club Secretary), The Puzzles, 5 Gatley Gr, Meir Park, Stoke-on-Trent, Staffordshire ST3 7SH.
(T) 01782 396913
Profile: FT: Coarse; WN: Dilhorne Pools; WT: Lake (Still); F. Size: 5 Acres; W. Size: 3 Acres. Location: Nr. Rd: New Road; Main Rd: Cheadle Road; Rail: Blythe Bridge.
Ref: FH1367

DILWORTH (UPPER) RESERVOIR

Dilworth (Upper) Reservoir, Ribble Valley, Longridge, Preston, **LANCASHIRE**, PR3, **England**.
Contact/s: **Mr D Harwood** (Secretary), Ribblesdale House, Blackburn Rd, Preston, PR3 3ZQ.
Mr Roy Rhodes (Conservation, Access and Recreation Manager), Rivington Water Treatment Works, Bolton Rd, Horwich, Bolton, BL6 7RN.
(T) 01204 664300
Profile: FT: Game; WN: Upper Dilworth; WT: Reservoir (Still).
Ref: FH1368

DINA FISHERY

Dina Fishery, Rheidol Power Station, Cwmrheidol, Aberystwyth, **CEREDIGION**, SY23, **Wales**.
Contact/s: Mr Peter Bevan (Manager).
(T) 01970 890664
Profile: **FT:** Game; **WN:** Dinas, Nant-y-Moch; **WT:** Reservoir (Still).
Ref: FH1369

DINAS RESERVOIR

Dinas Reservoir, Erwyd Garage, Ponterwyd, Aberystwyth, **CEREDIGION**, SY23 3, **Wales**.
Contact/s: Mr Peter Bevan (Manager).
(T) 01970 890664
Profile: **FT:** Game; **WN:** Dinas; **WT:** Reservoir (Still).
Ref: FH1370

DINDINNIE RESERVOIR

Dindinnie Reservoir, Stranraer, **DUMFRIES AND GALLOWAY**, DG9, **Scotland**.
Contact/s: Mr Eric McLean (Manager), The Sports Shop, 86 George St, Stranraer, Dumfries and Galloway, DG9 7JS.
(T) 01776 702705
Profile: **FT:** Game; **WN:** Dindinnie; **WT:** Reservoir (Still). **Location:** **Main Rd:** A718.
Ref: FH1371

DINGLE LODGE

Dingle Lodge, Radcliffe, Manchester, **MANCHESTER (GREATER)**, M26, **England**.
Contact/s: Mr Terence A McKee (Secretary), Bolton and District Angling Association, 1 Lever Edge Lane, Bolton, Lancashire, BL3 3BU.
(T) 01204 393726
Profile: **FT:** Coarse; **WN:** Dingle Lodge; **WT:** Lake (Still) **W. Size:** 1 Acre. **Location:** **Nr. Rd:** A6053; **Main Rd:** A58 Bury to Bolton.
Ref: FH1372

DINGLE RESERVOIR

Dingle Reservoir, Horwich, Bolton, **LANCASHIRE**, BL6, **England**.
Contact/s: Mr Gordon Roscoe (Secretary), 8 Kiln Brow, Bromley Cross, Bolton.
(T) 01204 306875
Mr J Griffiths (Membership Secretary), 49 Kernmoor Avenue, Sharples, Bolton.
(T) 01204 308037
Mr Roy Rhodes (Conservation, Access and Recreation Manager), Rivington Water Treatment Works, Bolton Rd, Horwich, Bolton, BL6 7RN.
(T) 01204 664300
Profile: **FT:** Coarse; **WN:** Dingle; **WT:** Reservoir (Still). **Location:** **Main Rd:** A675.
Ref: FH1373

DININ (RIVER)

River Dinin, Kilkenny, **COUNTY KILKENNY**, **Ireland**.
Contact/s: Mr Edward Stack (Secretary), Kilkenny Angling Association, c/o Garda Station, Kilkenny, County Kilkenny, Ireland.
Profile: **FT:** Game; **WN:** Dinin; **WT:** River (Moving).
Ref: FH1374

DINTON PASTURES COUNTRY PARK

Dinton Pastures Country Park, Hurst, Reading, **BERKSHIRE**, RG10 0, **England**.
Contact/s: Mr Simon Bartlam (Manager).
(T) 0118 9342016
Profile: **FT:** Coarse; **WN:** White Swan; **WT:** Combination (Still & Moving) **W. Size:** 24 Acres. **Location:** **Nr. Rd:** B3030 Robin Hood Lane; **Main Rd:** A329.
Ref: FH1375

DISS MERE

Diss Mere (The), Diss, **NORFOLK**, IP22 3, **England**.
Contact/s: Fishery Contact, PM Pegg Angling Supplies, Victoria Rd, Diss, Norfolk, IP22 4.
(T) 01379 640430
Mr Phil Pegg (Owner), Unit 7 Wills Yard, Chapel St, Diss, Norfolk, IP22 4AN.
(T) 01379 652980
Profile: **FT:** Coarse; **WN:** Waveney; **WT:** Combination (Still & Moving) **W. Size:** 5 Acres. **Location:** **Nr. Rd:** A143; **Rail:** Diss.
Ref: FH1376

DISSINGTON POND

Dissington Pond, Limestone Lane, Ponteland, Newcastle Upon Tyne, **TYNE AND WEAR**, NE20, **England**.
Contact/s: Mr Dave Stafford.
(T) 0191 2424441
Mr Gary Rutherford (Secretary), 21 Blagdon Trce, Seaton Burn, Newcastle-upon-Tyne, NE13 6EY.
(T) 0191 2366703
Profile: **FT:** Coarse; **WN:** Dissington; **WT:** Pond (Still) **W. Size:** 1 Acre. **Location:** **Nr. Rd:** Limestone Lane; **Main Rd:** A696.
Ref: FH1377

DITCHFORD PITS

Ditchford Pits, Wellingborough, **NORTHAMPTONSHIRE**, NN, **England**.
Contact/s: Mr D Perkins (Secretary).
(T) 01933 651400
Profile: **FT:** Coarse; **WN:** Ditchford; **WT:** Gravel Pit (Still).
Ref: FH1378

DITCHINGHAM PIT

Ditchingham Pit, Ditchingham, Bungay, **SUFFOLK**, NR35 2, **England**.
Contact/s: Mr Ian Gosling (Hon Secretary), Bungay Cherry Tree Angling Club, 37 St Marys Trce, Flixton Rd, Bungay, NR35 1DN.
(T) 01986 892982
Profile: **FT:** Coarse; **WN:** Ditchingham; **WT:** Lake (Still). **Location:** **Main Rd:** B1332.
Ref: FH1379

DIXON GREEN RESERVOIR

Dixon Green Reservoir, Harrowby St, Farnworth, Bolton, **LANCASHIRE**, BL4, **England**.
Contact/s: Mr Bob Fearnhead (Secretary), Farnworth and District Angling Association, 3 Windmill Rd, Walkden, Manchester (Greater), M28 3RP.
(T) 0161 7994242
Profile: **FT:** Coarse; **WN:** Dixon Green; **WT:** Reservoir (Still) **W. Size:** 4 Acres. **Location:** **Nr. Rd:** Harrowby Street; **Main Rd:** M6, junction 4, Highfield Road; **Rail:** Farnworth.
Ref: FH1380

DOBBS WEIR FISHERY

Dobbs Weir Fishery, Dobb's Weir Rd, Hoddesdon, **HERTFORDSHIRE**, EN11, **England**.
Contact/s: Mr Gary Smith (Information Officer), Lee Valley Park Information Ctre, Abbey Gardens, Waltham Abbey, Essex, EN9 1XQ.
(T) 01992 702200
Mr Krizim Seltham (Angling Manager), Lee Valley Regional Park Authority, Myddleton House, Bulls Cross, Enfield, EN2 9HG.
(T) 01992 709832
(E) garysmith@leevalleypark.org.uk
Profile: **FT:** Coarse; **WN:** Lea Navigation; **WT:** Canal (Still) **W. Size:** 600 Metres. **Location:** **Nr. Rd:** Dobbs Weir Road; **Main Rd:** A10 to Hoddesdon; **Rail:** Rye.
Ref: FH1381

DOCHART (RIVER)

River Dochart, Killin, **STIRLING**, FK21, **Scotland**.
(W) www.fishingnet.com/clubs/killin.htm
Contact/s: Mr Alec Stewart (Membership Secretary), 2 Dochart Rd, Killin, Perth and Kinross, FK21 8SN.
(T) 01567 820224
Mrs Joanne Airey (Owner), J R News, Fishing Tackle Shop, Main St, Killin, FR21 8UJ.
(T) 01567 820362
Profile: **FT:** Game; **WN:** Dochart; **WT:** River (Moving) **W. Size:** 2500 Metres. **Location:** **Nr. Rd:** A827; **Main Rd:** A85; **Rail:** Crianlarich.
Ref: FH1382

DOCHART (RIVER)

River Dochart, Killin, **STIRLING**, FK21, **Scotland**.
(W) www.fishingnet.com/beats/dochart/clachaig_hotel.htm
Contact/s: Manager, Clachaig Hotel, Killin, Perth and Kinross, FK21 8SL.
(T) 01567 820270
Profile: **FT:** Combination; **WN:** Dochart; **WT:** River (Moving). **Location:** **Nr. Rd:** Dochart Bridge to Old Railway Viaduct. **£Free**
Ref: FH1383

DOCHART (RIVER)

River Dochart, Ledcharrie Farm, Killin, **STIRLING**, FK21 8RG, **Scotland**.
(W) www.fishingnet.com/beats/dochart/ledcharrie.htm
Contact/s: Mr Alec Stewart (Membership Secretary), 2 Dochart Rd, Killin, Perth and Kinross, FK21 8SN.
(T) 01567 820224
Mrs J Bowser (Gamekeeper/Bailiff), Auchlyne Keeper's Cottage, Auchlyne Estate, Glendochart, Killin, Perth and Kinross.
(T) 01567 820487
Profile: **FT:** Combination; **WN:** Dochart; **WT:** River (Moving). **Location:** **Nr. Rd:** Curling Pond to Altile Burn; **Main Rd:** A85; **Rail:** Crianlarich.
Ref: FH1384

DOCHART (RIVER)

River Dochart, Keepers Cottage, Auchlyne, Killin, **STIRLING**, FK21 8RG, **Scotland**.
Contact/s: Mr G D Coyne (Gamekeeper), Auchlyne Keeper's Cottage, Auchlyne Estate, Glendochart, Killin, Perth and Kinross.
(T) 01567 820487
Mrs J Bowse.
Profile: **FT:** Game; **WN:** Dochart; **WT:** River (Moving) **W. Size:** 10500 Metres. **Location:** **Nr. Rd:** A82; **Main Rd:** A82; **Rail:** Crianlarich.
Ref: FH1385

DOCKLOW POOLS

Docklow Pools, West End Farm, Docklow, Leominster, **HEREFORDSHIRE**, HR6 0RU, **England**.
(W) www.fisheries.co.uk/docklow
Contact/s: Mr Mike Bozward.
(T) 01568 760256 (F) 01568 760256
(E) mbozward@aol.com
Mr Simon Bozward (Tackle Shop (Summer) Manager).
(T) 01568 760544
Profile: **FT:** Combination; **WN:** Teme; **WT:** Combination (Still & Moving); **F. Size:** 100 Acres; **W. Size:** 18 Acres. **Location:** **Nr. Rd:** A44; **Main Rd:** A44; **Rail:** Leominster.
Ref: FH1386

DOCTOR DAM FISHERY

Doctor Dam Fishery, Greenbooth Rd, Rochdale, **MANCHESTER (GREATER)**, OL, **England**.
Contact/s: Mr John Jeffreys (Secretary), Heaton Park Angling Club, Hook and Line Fishing Tackle, 375 Victoria Avenue, Manchester, M9 8WQ.
(T) 0161 7206577 (F) 0161 7206577
Profile: **FT:** Coarse; **WN:** Doctor Dam Fishery; **WT:** Reservoir (Still). **Location:** **Nr. Rd:** Greenbooth Road; **Main Rd:** A680, Edenfield Road.
Ref: FH1387

DOCTORS LAKE

Doctors Lake, Horsham, **SUSSEX (WEST)**, RH12, **England**.
Contact/s: Fishery Manager.
(T) 01903 764818

Profile: FT: Coarse; WN: Doctors; WT: Lake (Still).
Ref: FH1388

DODDS FARM

Dodds Farm, Fryering Lane, Ingatestone, **ESSEX**, CM4, **England**.
Contact/s: Mr Sid Hibbert (Secretary), Basildon and District Angling Society, 15 Culverdown, Basildon, Essex, SS14 2AL.
(T) 01268 287798
Profile: FT: Coarse; WN: Dodds Farm; WT: Lake (Still). **Location:** Nr. Rd: Fryering Lane; Main Rd: A12, Mountnessing.
Ref: FH1389

DOE (RIVER)

River Doe, Ingleton, Carnforth, **CUMBRIA**, LA6, **England**.
Contact/s: Mr Ian Crack (Secretary), Ingleton Angling Association, Khardains, Ingleton Carnforth, Lancashire, LA6 3BS.
(T) 01524 241171
Profile: FT: Game; WN: Doe; WT: River (Moving) W. Size: 4000 Metres. **Location:** Nr. Rd: B6255; Main Rd: A65; Rail: High Bentham.
Ref: FH1390

DOE PARK RESERVOIR

Doe Park Reservoir, Bradford, **YORKSHIRE (WEST)**, BD, **England**.
Contact/s: Mr N Briggs, 4 Brown Hill Cl, Birkenshaw, Bradford, Yorkshire (West).
Profile: FT: Coarse; WN: Doe Park; WT: Reservoir (Still).
Ref: FH1391

DOFFCOCKER LODGE

Doffcocker Lodge, Chorley Old Rd, Doffcocker, Bolton, **LANCASHIRE**, BL1, **England**.
Contact/s: Mr Terence A McKee (Secretary), Bolton and District Angling Association, 1 Lever Edge Lane, Bolton, Lancashire, BL3 3BU.
(T) 01204 393726
Profile: FT: Coarse; WN: Doffcocker Lodge; WT: Lake (Still) W. Size: 4 Acres. **Location:** Nr. Rd: M61 junction 5; Main Rd: A58 Moss Bank Way.
Ref: FH1392

DOGGETTS FARM FISHERY

Doggetts Farm Fishery, Rochford, **ESSEX**, SS4, **England**.
Contact/s: Mr Cliff.
(T) 01702 714338 (M) 07958 204002
Profile: FT: Coarse; WN: Doggetts Farm Fishery; WT: Lake (Still).
Ref: FH1393

DOL LLYS FARM

Dol Llys Farm, Trefeglwys Road, Llanidloes, **POWYS**, SY18 6JA, **Wales**.
Contact/s: Mr O S Evans (Farmer).
(T) 01686 412694
Profile: FT: Game; WN: Severn; WT: River (Moving). **Location:** Rail: Caersws. £Fr
Ref: FH1394

DOL WATTS FISHERY

Dol Watts Fishery, Pentre Cwrt, Newcastle Emlyn, **CARMARTHENSHIRE**, SA38, **Wales**.
(W) www.fishing-in-wales.co.uk/llandysul-aa/beat14
Contact/s: Mr Artie Jones (Hon Secretary), Llandysul Angling Association, Glas-y-Dorlan, Llyn-y-Fran Rd, Llandysul, SA44 4JW.
(T) 01559 362317
Profile: FT: Game; WN: Teifi; WT: River (Moving) W. Size: 800 Metres.
Ref: FH1395

DOLAR POND

Dolar Pond, Gunthorpe, Nottingham, **NOTTINGHAMSHIRE**, NG, **England**.
Contact/s: Mr William Belshaw, 17 Spring Green, Clifton Estate, Nottingham, NG11 9EF.
(T) 0115 9216645
Profile: FT: Coarse; WN: Dolar Pond; WT: Gravel Pit (Still).
Ref: FH1396

DOLGWM MILL FISHERY

Dolgwm Mill Fishery, Llanybydder, **CARMARTHENSHIRE**, SA40, **Wales**.
(W) www.fishing-in-wales.co.uk/llandysul-aa/beat6
Contact/s: Mr Artie Jones (Hon Secretary), Llandysul Angling Association, Glas-y-Dorlan, Llyn-y-Fran Rd, Llandysul, SA44 4JW.
(T) 01559 362317
Profile: FT: Game; WN: Teifi; WT: River (Moving) W. Size: 2400 Metres. **Location:** Nr. Rd: A485.
Ref: FH1397

DOLWEN AND PLAS UCHAF

Dolwen And Plas Uchaf, St Asaph, **DENBIGHSHIRE**, LL17, **Wales**.
Contact/s: Manager, Spar, 5 Church View, Bodelwyddan, Rhyl, LL18 5TF.
(T) 01745 582100
Mr David Scutter (Area manager), Llyn Brenig Visitors Ctre, Cerrigdrudion, Corwen, Conwy, LL21 9TT.
(T) 01490 420463 (F) 01490 420694
(E) llyn.brenig@hyder.com
Profile: FT: Game; WN: Dolwen And Plas Uchaf; WT: Reservoir (Still) W. Size: 28 Acres.
Ref: FH1398

DON (RIVER)

River Don, Conisbrough, Doncaster, **YORKSHIRE (SOUTH)**, DN12, **England**.
Contact/s: Mr Mick Peverley.
(T) 01709 866333
Profile: FT: Coarse; WN: Don; WT: River (Moving).
Ref: FH1399

DON (RIVER)

River Don, Eden Gr, Hexthorpe, Doncaster, **YORKSHIRE (SOUTH)**, DN, **England**.
Contact/s: Mr Maurice Tate (Secretary), Doncaster and District Angling Association, 28 Holmescarr Rd, New Rossington, Doncaster, DN11 0QF.
(T) 01302 865482
Profile: FT: Coarse; WN: Don; WT: River (Moving) W. Size: 400 Metres.
Ref: FH1400

DON (RIVER)

River Don, Sprotborough, Doncaster, **YORKSHIRE (SOUTH)**, DN, **England**.
Contact/s: Mr Maurice Tate (Secretary), Doncaster and District Angling Association, 28 Holmescarr Rd, New Rossington, Doncaster, DN11 0QF.
(T) 01302 865482
Profile: FT: Coarse; WN: Don; WT: River (Moving) W. Size: 1600 Metres.
Ref: FH1401

DON (RIVER)

Don (River), Barnby Dun, **YORKSHIRE (SOUTH)**, **England**.
Contact/s: .
(T) 01302 881707
Profile: FT: Coarse; WN: Don; WT: River (Moving).
Ref: FH1402

DON (RIVER)

River Don, Sprotbrough, Doncaster, **YORKSHIRE (SOUTH)**, DN5, **England**.
Contact/s: Area Manager, Environment Agency, Ridings Area Office, Phoenix House, Global Avenue, Leeds, LS11 8PG.
(T) 0113 2440191or2314834 (F) 0113 2134609
Mr Maurice Tate (Secretary), Doncaster and District Angling Association, 28 Holmescarr Rd, New Rossington, Doncaster, DN11 0QF.
(T) 01302 865482
Profile: FT: Coarse; WN: Don; WT: River (Moving). **Location:** Nr. Rd: Sprotborough Weir to Newton; Main Rd: A1.
Ref: FH1403

DONKHILL FISHERIES

Donkhill Fisheries, Donkhill Farm, Catton, Swadlincote, **DERBYSHIRE**, DE12 8LW, **England**.
Contact/s: Manager, Donkhill Fisheries, Donkhill Farm, Catton, Swadlincote, DE12 8LW.
(T) 01827 383719
Mr Martin Hodson Walker (Farmer).
(T) 01827 383719or383296 (M) 07778 858867
Profile: FT: Game; WN: Donkhill Fisheries; WT: Lake (Still) W. Size: 2 Acres. **Location:** Nr. Rd: A38 Burton to Lichfield; Main Rd: A38; Rail: Lichfield.
Ref: FH1404

DONNINGTON TROUT FISHERY

Donnington Trout Fishery, Lower Swell, Stow On The Wold, Cheltenham, **GLOUCESTERSHIRE**, GL54 1EP, **England**.
Contact/s: Mr Gordon Bull (Owner).
(T) 01451 830873
Profile: FT: Game; WN: Donnington Trout Fishery; WT: Lake (Still) W. Size: 1 Acre. **Location:** Main Rd: A434.
Ref: FH1405

DONYLANDS LAKES

Snake Pit, Donylands, Old Heath, Colchester, **ESSEX**, CO, **England**.
Contact/s: Mr Rob Hayward (Manager), Sudbury Angling Ctre, 1 Acton Sq, Sudbury, Suffolk, CO10 1HG.
(T) 01787 312118
Mr Trevor Fairless (Secretary), Sudbury and District Angling Association, 39 Pot Kiln Rd, Sudbury, Suffolk, CO10 0DG.
(T) 01787 312536
Profile: FT: Coarse; WN: Snake; WT: Gravel Pit (Still); F. Size: 16 Acres; W. Size: 12 Acres. **Location:** Nr. Rd: Fingeringhoe Road; Main Rd: A12 or A120; Rail: Colchester.
Ref: FH1406

DOODLESPOOL FARM LAKE

Doodlespool Farm Lake, Betley, Crewe, **CHESHIRE**, CW, **England**.
Contact/s: Fishery Manager.
(T) 01270 820216
Profile: FT: Coarse; WN: Doodlespool Farm; WT: Lake (Still); F. Size: 1 Acre.
Ref: FH1407

DOOHULLA

Doohulla, Ballyconneely, **COUNTY GALWAY**, **Ireland**.
Contact/s: Mr Nicholas Tinne (Manager), Ballyconneely, Ireland.
(T) 095 23529
Profile: FT: Game; WN: Doohulla; WT: Combination (Still & Moving). **Location:** Nr. Rd: The Coast Road; Rail: Galway.
Ref: FH1408

DOOLIN POND

Doolin Pond, Gaybrook Cross, Mullingar, **COUNTY WESTMEATH**, **Ireland**.
Profile: FT: Coarse; WN: Doolin Pond; WT: Lake (Still). **Location:** Main Rd: R40 from Mullingar.
Ref: FH1409

DOON (RIVER)

River Doon, Dalrymple, Ayr, **AYRSHIRE (SOUTH)**, KA6 6, **Scotland**.
Contact/s: Mr George Campbell (Estate Manager), Skeldon House, Skeldon Estate Office, Dalrymple, Ayr, KA6 6AT.
(T) 01292 560656 (F) 01292 560732
Mr S E Brodie.
Profile: FT: Game; WN: Doon; WT: River (Moving) W. Size: 7200 Metres. **Location:** Nr. Rd: B7034; Main Rd: A713; Rail: Ayr.
Ref: FH1410

DORCHESTER LAGOON

Dorchester Lagoon, Abingdon Rd, Dorchester-on-Thames, Wallingford, **OXFORDSHIRE**, OX1 7LP, **England**.
Contact/s: **Mr Marsh Pratley**.
(T) 01865 341810 (M) 07885 618190
Profile: FT: Coarse; **WN:** Dorchester Lagoon; **WT:** Gravel Pit (Still).
Ref: FH1412

DORES POND - RACKERHAYES

Dores Pond - Rackerhayes, Newton Abbot, **DEVON**, TQ1, **England**.
Contact/s: Shop Manager, Drum Sports Limited, 47 Courtenay St, Newton Abbot, Devon, TQ12 2QN.
(T) 01626 205040
Profile: FT: Coarse; **WN:** Dores; **WT:** Pond (Still); **F. Size:** 10 Acres; **W. Size:** 9 Acres.
Ref: FH1413

DORKHAM STORMWATER

Dorkham Stormwater, Swindon, **WILTSHIRE**, SN4, **England**.
Contact/s: **Mr Campbell** (Secretary), 72 Rodbourne Rd, Swindon, Wiltshire, SN2 1DH.
(T) 01793 529909
Profile: FT: Coarse; **WN:** Dorkham Stormwater; **WT:** Lake (Still).
Ref: FH1414

DORMONT LAKE COARSE FISHERY

Dormont Lake Coarse Fishery, Dormont, Lockerbie, **DUMFRIES AND GALLOWAY**, DG11 1DJ, **Scotland**.
Contact/s: **Mr D McMinn** (Fishery Assistant).
(T) 01387 840363 (F) 01387 840222
Mr J A Carruthers.
(T) 01387 840222 (F) 01387 840363
(E) carruthers.dormont@btinternet.com
Profile: FT: Coarse; **WN:** Dormont; **WT:** Lake (Still) **W. Size:** 2 Acres. **Location:** **Rail:** Lockerbie.
Ref: FH1415

DORNOCH LOCHANS

Dornoch Lochans, Dornoch, **HIGHLAND**, IV25, **Scotland**.
Contact/s: **Mr Malcolm Magillwray**.
(T) 01862 810600
Profile: FT: Game; **WN:** Dornoch; **WT:** Loch (Still).
Ref: FH1416

DORSET FROME

Dorset Frome, Wool, Wareham, **DORSET**, BH20, **England**.
Contact/s: **Mr Bill Lucy** (Secretary), Dorchester and District Angling Society, 7 Celtic Cresent, Dorchester, Dorset, DT1 2QJ.
(T) 01305 264873
Mr John Parkes (Membership Secretary), Dorchester and District Angling Society, 5 Malta Cl, Dorchester, Dorset, DT1 2QA.
(T) 01305 262813
Profile: FT: Coarse; **WN:** Dorset Frome; **WT:** River (Moving) **W. Size:** 1200 Metres. **Location:** **Nr. Rd:** A352; **Main Rd:** A352; **Rail:** Wool.
Ref: FH1417

DOUBLEWOODS

Doublewoods, Altrincham, Manchester, **MANCHESTER (GREATER)**, M2, **England**.
Contact/s: Secretary, Altrincham Angling Society, 37 Crossgates Avenue, Sharston, Manchester.
(T) 0161 2863952
Profile: FT: Coarse; **WN:** Doublewoods; **WT:** Gravel Pit (Still). **Location:** **Nr. Rd:** Warrington to Knutsford; **Main Rd:** A50.
Ref: FH1418

DOUGLAS (RIVER)

River Douglas, Carlow, **COUNTY CARLOW**, **Ireland**.
Contact/s: **Mrs Quinn** (Manager), The Locks, Milford, Carlow, County Carlow, Ireland.
(T) 050 346261
Profile: FT: Game; **WN:** Douglas; **WT:** River (Moving).
Ref: FH1419

DOUGLAS (RIVER)

River Douglas, Wigan, **LANCASHIRE**, WN, **England**.
(W) www.wiganaa.f9.co.uk
Contact/s: **Mr Gerry Wilson** (Hon Secretary), Wigan and District Angling Association, 11 Guildford Avenue, Chorley, Lancashire, PR6 8TG.
(T) 01257 265905
(E) gerry@wiganna.freeserve.co.uk
Profile: FT: Coarse; **WN:** Douglas; **WT:** River (Moving) **W. Size:** 3200 Metres. **Location:** **Nr. Rd:** B5206.
Ref: FH1420

DOUNHURST FARM FISHERY

Dounhurst Farm Fishery, Billinghurst, **SUSSEX (WEST)**, RH14, **England**.
Contact/s: **Mr Gerald Cranford** (Secretary), Henfield and District Angling Society, 7 Wantley Hill Estate, Henfield, Sussex (West), BN5 9JR.
(T) 01273 493441
Profile: FT: Coarse; **WN:** Dounhurst Farm Fishery; **WT:** Pond (Still).
Ref: FH1421

DOVE (RIVER)

River Dove, Draycott Mill, Draycott In The Clay, Ashbourne, **DERBYSHIRE**, DE6, **England**.
(W) www.warrington-anglers.org.uk
Contact/s: **Mr Frank Lythgoe** (Secretary), Warrington Angling Association, 52 Parker St, Warrington, Lancashire.
(T) 01928 716238 (F) 01928 713898
(E) info@warrington-anglers.org.uk
Profile: FT: Coarse; **WN:** Dove; **WT:** River (Moving). **Location:** **Nr. Rd:** Draycott in the Clay to Sudbury; **Main Rd:** A515.
Ref: FH1422

DOVE (RIVER)

Dove (River), Long Doles Farm, Mayfield, Ashbourne, **DERBYSHIRE**, **England**.
Contact/s: **Mr John Turner** (Hon Secretary), Prince Albert Angling Society, 15 Pexhill Drive, Macclesfield, Cheshire, SK10 3LP.
(T) 01625 422010
Profile: FT: Game; **WN:** Dove; **WT:** River (Moving) **W. Size:** 500 Metres. **Location:** **Nr. Rd:** Watery Lane; **Main Rd:** A52; **Rail:** Ashbourne.
Ref: FH1423

DOVE (RIVER)

River Dove, Uttoxeter, **STAFFORDSHIRE**, ST14, **England**.
Contact/s: **Mr John Fearn** (Ticket Secretary), 70 Hawthornden Avenue, Uttoxeter, Staffordshire, ST14 7NZ.
(T) 01889 563070
Profile: FT: Game; **WN:** Dove; **WT:** River (Moving).
Ref: FH1424

DOVE (RIVER)

Dove (River), Stiff Close Farm, Longnor, **STAFFORDSHIRE**, **England**.
Contact/s: **Mr John Turner** (Hon Secretary), Prince Albert Angling Society, 15 Pexhill Drive, Macclesfield, Cheshire, SK10 3LP.
(T) 01625 422010
Profile: FT: Game; **WN:** Dove; **WT:** River (Moving) **W. Size:** 1000 Metres. **Location:** **Main Rd:** B5053; **Rail:** Buxton.
Ref: FH1425

DOVE (RIVER)

Dove (River), Oldhall Farm and Rednick Meadow, Doveridge, Uttoxeter, **STAFFORDSHIRE**, **England**.
Contact/s: **Mr John Turner** (Hon Secretary), Prince Albert Angling Society, 15 Pexhill Drive, Macclesfield, Cheshire, SK10 3LP.
(T) 01625 422010
Profile: FT: Coarse; **WN:** Dove; **WT:** River (Moving) **W. Size:** 3000 Metres. **Location:** **Nr. Rd:** Church Lane; **Main Rd:** A50; **Rail:** Uttoxeter.
Ref: FH1426

DOVE (RIVER)

River Dove, Fauld Cottage Farm, Fauld, Tutbury, Burton-on-Trent, **STAFFORDSHIRE**, DE, **England**.
Contact/s: **Mr Albert Perkins** (Hon Secretary), 63 Fowlers Lane, Light Oaks, Stoke-on-Trent, Staffordshire, ST2 7NB.
Ms Liz Hayes (Manager).
(T) 01625 251262
Profile: FT: Combination; **WN:** Dove; **WT:** River (Moving) **W. Size:** 1200 Metres. **Location:** **Nr. Rd:** Sudbury to Coton in the Clay; **Main Rd:** A50; **Rail:** Tutbury.
Ref: FH1427

DOVE (RIVER)

River Dove, Riverside Farm, Scropton, Burton-on-Trent, **STAFFORDSHIRE**, DE, **England**.
Contact/s: **Mr Albert Perkins** (Hon Secretary), 63 Fowlers Lane, Light Oaks, Stoke-on-Trent, Staffordshire, ST2 7NB.
Ms Liz Hayes (Manager).
(T) 01625 251262
Profile: FT: Combination; **WN:** Dove; **WT:** River (Moving) **W. Size:** 800 Metres. **Location:** **Nr. Rd:** Sudbury to Scropton; **Main Rd:** A515; **Rail:** Tutbury.
Ref: FH1428

DOVE BROOK

Dove Brook, Eye, **NORFOLK**, IP21, **England**.
Contact/s: **Mr Bowman**.
(T) 01379 852248
Profile: FT: Coarse; **WN:** Dove; **WT:** Stream (Moving).
Ref: FH1429

DOVECOTE LAKE FISHERY

Dovecote Lake Fishery, Dovecote Lake, Little Linford Lane, Milton Keynes, **BUCKINGHAMSHIRE**, MK19 7EB, **England**.
Contact/s: **A Wilcox**.
(T) 01908 271703 (F) 01525 261127
Mr Des Rambridge.
(T) 01908 211535
Profile: FT: Coarse; **WN:** Ouse; **WT:** Combination (Still & Moving); **F. Size:** 90 Acres; **W. Size:** 60 Acres. **Location:** **Main Rd:** M1; **Rail:** Milton Keynes.
Ref: FH1430

DOVEMERE, SANDMERE & WOODLANDS

Dovemere, Sandmere And Woodlands, Allostock, Knutsford, **CHESHIRE**, WA16, **England**.
Contact/s: **Mr John Turner** (Hon Secretary), Prince Albert Angling Society, 15 Pexhill Drive, Macclesfield, Cheshire, SK10 3LP.
(T) 01625 422010
Profile: FT: Coarse; **WN:** Woodlands, Sandmere, Dovemere; **WT:** Lake (Still). **Location:** **Main Rd:** M6.
Ref: FH1431

DOWLES BROOK

Dowles Brook, Upper Arley, Bewdley, **WORCESTERSHIRE**, DY12, **England**.
Contact/s: **Mr John Williams** (Secretary), Birmingham Anglers Association, 100 Icknield Port Rd, Rotton Park, Birmingham, B16 0AP.
(T) 0121 4549111
Profile: FT: Coarse; **WN:** Dowles; **WT:** Brook (Moving).
Ref: FH1432

DOWRY & NEW YEARS BRIDGE

Dowry And New Years Bridge Reservoir, Huddersfield Rd, Denshaw, Oldham, **MANCHESTER (GREATER)**, OL4, **England**.
Contact/s: **Mr Nigel Bunn**, Lees and Hey Angling Club, 4 Hey Cres, Lees, Oldham, OL4 3LJ.

(T) 0161 6269183 (M) 01949 549358
Profile: FT: Combination; WN: Dowry And New Years Bridge Reservoir; WT: Reservoir (Still) W. Size: 38 Acres. Location: Nr. Rd: A640; Rail: Greenfield.
Ref: FH1433

DRAGONFLY FISHERIES

Dragonfly Fisheries, Cerrig-Y-Drudion, Corwen, **DENBIGHSHIRE**, LL21 9SW, **Wales**.
Contact/s: Manager.
(T) 01490 420530 (M) 07713 232126
Profile: FT: Game; WN: Dragonfly; WT: Lake (Still) W. Size: 2 Acres. Location: Nr. Rd: A5.
Ref: FH1434

DRAKELANDS GAME FISHERY

Drakelands Game Fishery, Higher Drakelands, Hemerdon, Nr Plympton, Plymouth, **DEVON**, PL7 5BS, **England**.
Contact/s: Mr Henry Elford (Owner).
(T) 01752 344691
Profile: FT: Game; WN: Plym; WT: Lake (Still) W. Size: 2 Acres. Location: Main Rd: A38; Rail: Plymouth.
Ref: FH1435

DRAKESHEAD FLY FISHERY

Drakeshead Fly Fishery, Lodge Bank, Brinscall, Chorley, **LANCASHIRE**, PR6 8QU, **England**.
(W) www.chelmsfordaa.freeserve.co.uk
Contact/s: Mr Frank Wright (Membership Secretary), Chelmsford Angling Association, 61 Readers Court, Great Baddow, Chelmsford, CM2 8EX.
(T) 01245 474246or264832
(E) frank@chelmsfordaa.freeserve.co.uk
Profile: FT: Game; WN: Drakeshead Fly Fishery; WT: Lake (Still); F. Size: 7 Acres; W. Size: 4 Acres. Location: Nr. Rd: Lodge Bank; Rail: Chorley.
Ref: FH1436

DRAX LAKE

Drax Lake, 2 Oaklands, Camblesforth, Selby, **YORKSHIRE (NORTH)**, YO8, **England**.
Contact/s: Mr G Simms.
Profile: FT: Coarse; WN: Drax; WT: Lake (Still).
Ref: FH1437

DRAYCOTE WATER

Draycote Water, Kites Hardwick, Rugby, **WARWICKSHIRE**, CV23 8AB, **England**.
Contact/s: Manager, Severn Trent Water plc, 2297 Coventry Rd, Sheldon, Birmingham, B26 3PU.
(T) 01788 811107 (F) 01788 522936
Mr Kieth Corser (Fishery Manager), Fishing Lodge, Kiles Hardwick, Rubgy, Warwickshire, CV23 8AB.
(T) 01788 812018
Profile: FT: Game; WN: Draycote Water; WT: Reservoir (Still); F. Size: 800 Acres; W. Size: 600 Acres. Location: Nr. Rd: A426; Main Rd: M45 or A45; Rail: Rugby.
Ref: FH1438

DRAYTON BRIDGE

Drayton Bridge, Birmingham Fazeley Canal, Drayton Bassett, Tamworth, **STAFFORDSHIRE**, B78, **England**.
Contact/s: Mr John Williams (Secretary), Birmingham Anglers Association, 100 Icknield Port Rd, Rotton Park, Birmingham, B16 0AP.
(T) 0121 4549111
Profile: FT: Coarse; WN: Birmingham Fazeley; WT: Canal (Still) W. Size: 9600 Metres. Location: Nr. Rd: A446; Main Rd: M42, junction 9.
Ref: FH1439

DRAYTON GREEN (RIVER)

River Drayton Green, Drayton Green Lane, Drayton, Norwich, **NORFOLK**, NR8, **England**.
Profile: FT: Coarse; WN: Drayton Green; WT: River (Moving) W. Size: 800 Metres.
Ref: FH1440

DRAYTON RESERVOIR

Drayton Reservoir, 19 Collingwood Way, Daventry, **NORTHAMPTONSHIRE**, NN11 4JA, **England**.
Contact/s: Southern Region Manager, British Waterways, Hemel Hempstead.
(T) 01442 278717
Mr John Ellis. (M) 07889 532561
Mr Mick Carrick. (M) 05815 32561or07889532563
Profile: FT: Coarse; WN: Drayton; WT: Reservoir (Still); F. Size: 22 Acres; W. Size: 20 Acres. Location: Nr. Rd: A361; Main Rd: A361; Rail: Long Buckby.
Ref: FH1441

DRIFFIELD CANAL

Driffield Canal, Wansford, Driffield, Beverley, **HUMBERSIDE**, HU17, **England**.
Contact/s: Mr Simon Marsh. (M) 07889 348841
Profile: FT: Combination; WN: Driffield; WT: Combination (Still & Moving) W. Size: 4800 Metres. Location: Nr. Rd: Wansford Village; Main Rd: B1249.
Ref: FH1442

DRIFT RESERVOIR

Drift Reservoir, Driftways, Drift Dam, Penzance, **CORNWALL**, TR19 6AB, **England**.
Contact/s: Owner, Drift Reservoir Chyandour Estate, Chyandour Estate Office, Chyandour Sq, Penzance, Cornwall TR18 3LW.
(T) 01736 365306 (F) 01736 368142
Mr T B Shorland (Manager).
(T) 01736 363869
Profile: FT: Game; WN: Drift; WT: Reservoir (Still) W. Size: 65 Acres. Location: Nr. Rd: A30; Main Rd: A30; Rail: Penzance.
Ref: FH1443

DRIMINIDY LAKE

Driminidy Lake, Drimoleague, **COUNTY CORK**, **Ireland**.
(W) www.swrfb.ie
Contact/s: Area Manager, South West Regional Fisheries Board, 1 Nevilles Trce, Macroom, County Cork, Ireland.
(T) 026 41221
(E) swrfb@swrfb.ie
Mr Micheal Harrington.
(T) 027 70011
Profile: FT: Game; WN: Driminidy; WT: Lake (Still) W. Size: 5 Acres. Location: Main Rd: Drimoleague.
Ref: FH1444

DRISH (RIVER)

Drish (River), Thurles, **COUNTY TIPPERARY**, **Ireland**.
Contact/s: J Grene (Manager), Farm Guesthouse, Cappamurra House, Dundrum, County Tipperary, Ireland.
(T) 062 71127
Mr Jimmy Purcell (Secretary), Thurles, Hollycross and Ballycamas Angling Association, Rathcannon, Holycross, Thurles, County Tipperary, Ireland.
Profile: FT: Game; WN: Drish; WT: River (Moving).
Ref: FH1445

DROITWICH CANAL

Droitwich Canal, Droitwich, **WORCESTERSHIRE**, WR9, **England**.
Contact/s: Fishery Manager.
(T) 01299 403725
Profile: FT: Coarse; WN: Droitwich; WT: Canal (Still).
Ref: FH1446

DROMAHAIR LODGE FISHERY

Dromahair Lodge Fishery, Dromahair, **COUNTY LEITRIM**, **Ireland**.
Contact/s: Fishery Manager.
(T) 071 64103
Profile: FT: Game; WN: Dromahair Lodge Fishery; WT: Lough (Still).
Ref: FH1447

DROMANA LAKE

Dromana Lake, Cappoquin, **COUNTY CORK**, **Ireland**.
Contact/s: Mr Michael Penruddock (Manager), Lismore Estate Office, Lismore Castle, Lismore, County Waterford, Ireland.
(T) 058 54424
Profile: FT: Game; WN: Dromana; WT: Lake (Still).
Ref: FH1448

DROMORE AND BALLYLINE

Dromore And Ballyline, Corofin, **COUNTY CLARE**, **Ireland**.
Contact/s: Mr Micheal Cleary (Manager).
(T) 065 6837675
Profile: FT: Game; WN: Dromore and Ballyline; WT: Lake (Still) W. Size: 400 Acres.
Ref: FH1449

DRUMMOND DUB

Drummond Dub, Upton Bishop, Ross-on-Wye, **HEREFORDSHIRE**, HR9, **England**.
Contact/s: Mr Les Bullock (Manager), GB Sports, 10 Broad St, Ross-on-Wye, Herefordshire, HR9 7EA.
(T) 01989 563723
Profile: FT: Coarse; WN: Drummond Dub; WT: Lake (Still); F. Size: 20 Acres; W. Size: 16 Acres. Location: Main Rd: A40; Rail: Hereford.
Ref: FH1450

DRUMMOND FISHERIES

Drummond Fisheries, Comrie, Crieff, **PERTH AND KINROSS**, PH, **Scotland**.
Contact/s: Mr Simon Barnes (Fisheries Manager), Drummond Estate, Fish Farm Aberughill, Comrie, Crieff, Perth and Kinross PH6 2LD.
(T) 01764 670500 (F) 01764 679480
Profile: FT: Game; WN: Drummond Fisheries; WT: Loch (Still).
Ref: FH1451

DRUMMOND LOCH

Drummond Loch, Crieff, **PERTH AND KINROSS**, PH, **Scotland**.
Contact/s: Mr Percy Wilson (Secretary), Crieff Angling Club, Tulliallan, Duchlage Rd, Crieff, PH7 3BN.
(T) 01764 655723
Profile: FT: Game; WN: Drummond; WT: Loch (Still).
Ref: FH1452

DRUMRAGH (RIVER)

River Drumragh, Omagh, **COUNTY TYRONE**, BT78, **Northern Ireland**.
Contact/s: Mr Ca Anderson (Secretary), Omagh Angling Association, 64 Market St, Omagh, County Tyrone, BT78 1EN.
(E) andersonca@lineone.net
Mr Stephen Martin (License Distributor).
(T) 028 82242311 (F) 028 82249539 (M) 07776 343600
Profile: FT: Game; WN: Drumragh; WT: River (Moving) W. Size: 6400 Metres. Location: Nr. Rd: A5; Main Rd: A5.
Ref: FH1453

DRUNKEN DUCK TARN FISHERY

Drunken Duck Tarn Fishery, Duck Hill, Ambleside, **CUMBRIA**, LA22, **England**.
Contact/s: Mr Nick Munford, Drunken Duck Inn, Water Barnetts, Barngates, Ambleside, Cumbria LA22 0NG.
(T) 01539 436347
Profile: FT: Game; WN: Drunken Duck Tarns; WT: River (Moving). Location: Nr. Rd: B5285 to Hawkeshead.
Ref: FH1454

DUAD (RIVER)

River Duad, Conwil Elfed, Carmarthen, **CARMARTHENSHIRE**, SA3, **Wales**.
Contact/s: Mr Colin Evans, Avondale, Conwil Elfed, Carmarthen, Carmarthenshire.
(T) 01267 281410

Profile: FT: Game; WN: Duad; WT: River (Moving).
Ref: FH1455

DUAG ANNER STREAM

Duag Anner Stream, Clonmel, **COUNTY TIPPERARY**, **Ireland**.
Contact/s: **Mr Andrew Ryan** (Manager), Clonanav Angling Ctre, Ballymacabry, Clonmel, County Tipperary, Ireland.
(T) 052 36141
Profile: FT: Game; WN: Daug Anner; WT: Stream (Moving).
Ref: FH1456

DUBBS RESERVOIR

Dubbs Reservoir, South Lakeland, Bowness On Windermere, **CUMBRIA**, LA23, **England**.
Contact/s: **Mr J Newton** (Secretary), Windermere, Ambleside and District Angling Association, Brackenthwaite Lodge, Black Beck Wood, Bowness on Windermere, Cumbria, LA23 3LS.
Mr Roy Rhodes (Conservation, Access and Recreation Manager), Rivington Water Treatment Works, Bolton Rd, Horwich, Bolton, BL6 7RN.
(T) 01204 664300
Profile: FT: Coarse; WN: Dubbs; WT: Reservoir (Still).
Ref: FH1457

DUBBS TROUT FISHERY

Dubbs Trout Fishery, Dubbs Rd, Windermere, **CUMBRIA**, LA23, **England**.
Contact/s: **Mr Chris Sodo** (Hon Treasurer), Windermere, Ambleside and District Angling Association, Ecclerigg Court, Ecclerigg, Windermere, LA23 1LQ.
(T) 01539 445083
Profile: FT: Game; WN: Dubbs; WT: Reservoir (Still) **W. Size:** 7 Acres. **Location:** Nr. Rd: Dubbs Road; **Main Rd:** A591 to Windermere.
Ref: FH1458

DUDDINGSTON LOCH

Duddingston Loch, Edinburgh, **EDINBURGH (CITY OF)**, EH, **Scotland**.
Contact/s: Manager, Mikes Tackle Shop, 46 Portobello High St, Edinburgh, Lothian (Mid), EH15 1DA.
(T) 0131 6573258
Profile: FT: Coarse; WN: Duddingston; WT: Loch (Still) **W. Size:** 50 Acres. **Location:** Nr. Rd: City Centre. £Fr
Ref: FH1459

DUDDON (RIVER)

River Duddon, Broughton-In-Furness, **LANCASHIRE**, LA1, **England**.
Contact/s: **Mr D J Dixon** (Secretary), 1 Churchill Drive, Millom, Cumbria, LA18 5DD.
(T) 01229 774241
Profile: FT: Game; WN: Duddon; WT: River (Moving). **Location:** Nr. Rd: A595; **Main Rd:** A595.
Ref: FH1460

DUGOED (RIVER)

Dugoed (River), Collfryn, Nr. Nant-Y-Dugoed, Dolgellau, **GWYNEDD**, **Wales**.
Contact/s: **Mr John Turner** (Hon Secretary), Prince Albert Angling Society, 15 Pexhill Drive, Macclesfield, Cheshire, SK10 3LP.
(T) 01625 422010
Profile: FT: Game; WN: Afon Dugoed or Cleifion; WT: River (Moving) **W. Size:** 3000 Metres. **Location:** Nr. Rd: A458 Welshpool to Mallwyd; **Main Rd:** A458; **Rail:** Glantwymyn.
Ref: FH1462

DUKE OF RUTLAND ESTATE

Duke Of Rutland Estate, Raper Lodge, Bakewell, **DERBYSHIRE**, DE45 1WR, **England**.
Contact/s: Fishery Manager.
(T) 01629 636255 **(M)** 07801 457 225
Profile: FT: Coarse; WN: Duke Of Rutland Estate; WT: Lake (Still).
Ref: FH1463

DUKERIES LAKES

Dukeries Lakes, Welbeck Estate Fisheries, Worksop, **YORKSHIRE (SOUTH)**, S8, **England**.
Profile: FT: Coarse; WN: Dukeries; WT: Lake (Still).
Ref: FH1464

DUKES POOL

Dukes Pool, Holmes Chapel, Crewe, **CHESHIRE**, CW4, **England**.
Contact/s: **Mr Neil Jupp** (Club Secretary), Lymm Angling Club, PO Box 350, Warrington, Cheshire, WA2 9FB.
(T) 01925 411744
Profile: FT: Coarse; WN: Dukes; WT: Pool (Still). **Location:** Nr. Rd: B5022 to Holmes Chapel; **Main Rd:** M6, south to Birmingham, junction 17.
Ref: FH1465

DULAIS (RIVER)

River Dulais, Aberdulais Falls, Neath, **NEATH PORT TALBOT**, SA, **Wales**.
Contact/s: **Mr Garry Davis** (Membership Secretary), 6 Martins Avenue, Seven Sisters, Neath, Glamorgan (Vale of).
(T) 01639 701828
Mr Ivor Jones (Hon Secretary), 5 Bryndulais Row, Seven Sisters, Neath, Glamorgan (Vale of), SA10 9EB.
(T) 01639 701187
Profile: FT: Game; WN: Dulais; WT: River (Moving). **Location:** Nr. Rd: Crynant to Aberdulais.
Ref: FH1466

DULAS (RIVER)

Dulas (River), Glas-Dulas Mawr, Machynlleth, **POWYS**, **Wales**.
Contact/s: **Mr John Turner** (Hon Secretary), Prince Albert Angling Society, 15 Pexhill Drive, Macclesfield, Cheshire, SK10 3LP.
(T) 01625 422010
Profile: FT: Game; WN: Dulas; WT: River (Moving) **W. Size:** 1500 Metres. **Location:** Nr. Rd: A487; **Rail:** Machynlleth.
Ref: FH1467

DULAS (RIVER)

River Dulais, Llanidloes, **POWYS**, SY18, **Wales**.
Contact/s: **Mr J Dallas Davies**, Llyn Glywedog, Dresden House, Great Oak St, Llanidloes, SY18 6BW.
(T) 01686 412644 **(F)** 01686 412644
Mrs Gough (Manager), Travellers Rest Restaurant, 9 Long Bridge St, Llanidloes, Powys, SY18 6EE.
(T) 01686 412329
Profile: FT: Game; WN: Dulas; WT: River (Moving) **W. Size:** 4800 Metres. **Location:** Main Rd: A470; **Rail:** Newtown.
Ref: FH1468

DULAS (RIVER)

Dulas (River), Dolgau, Machynlleth, **POWYS**, **Wales**.
Contact/s: **Mr John Turner** (Hon Secretary), Prince Albert Angling Society, 15 Pexhill Drive, Macclesfield, Cheshire, SK10 3LP.
(T) 01625 422010
Profile: FT: Game; WN: Dulas; WT: River (Moving) **W. Size:** 1000 Metres. **Location:** Nr. Rd: A489; **Rail:** Machynlleth.
Ref: FH1469

DUN (RIVER)

River Dun, Cushendun, Cushendall, **COUNTY ANTRIM**, BT44, **Northern Ireland**.
Contact/s: Manager, O'Neill's Country Sports, Sea and Game Tackle, 25 Mill St, Cushendall, County Antrim.
(T) 028 21772009
Mrs C McFetridge, 116 Tromara Rd, Cushendun, County Antrim, BT44 0ST.
(T) 028 21761251
Profile: FT: Game; WN: Dun; WT: River (Moving) **W. Size:** 48000 Metres.
Ref: FH1470

DUNALASTAIR LOCH

Dunalastair Loch, Kinloch Rannoch, Pitlochry, **PERTH AND KINROSS**, PH16, **Scotland**.
Contact/s: **Mr Paul Edwards** (Manager), Dunalastair Hotel, Kinloch Rannoch, Pitlochry, Perth and Kinross, PH16 5PW.
(T) 01882 632323
Profile: FT: Game; WN: Dunalastair; WT: Loch (Still).
Ref: FH1471

DUNCANS POND

Duncans Pond, Pulborough, **SUSSEX (WEST)**, **England**.
Contact/s: **Mr Mick Booth** (Membership Secretary).
(T) 01798 831525
Profile: FT: Coarse; WN: Duncan's Pond; WT: Pond (Still); **F. Size:** 1 Acre; **W. Size:** 1 Acre. **Location:** Rail: Pulborough.
Ref: FH1472

DUNCTON MILL

Duncton Mill, Dye House Lane, Duncton, Petworth, **SUSSEX (WEST)**, GU28 0LF, **England**.
(W) www.ductonmill.com
Contact/s: **Mr Tom Bishop**.
(T) 01798 342048 **(F)** 01798 344122
(E) tom@ductonmill.com
Profile: FT: Game; WN: Duncton Mill; WT: Lake (Still); **F. Size:** 20 Acres; **W. Size:** 8 Acres. **Location:** Nr. Rd: A285; **Main Rd:** A285; **Rail:** Pulborough.
Ref: FH1473

DUNDALE LAKE

Dundale Lake, Bells Yew Green, Golden Green, Golden Green, Tunbridge Wells, **KENT**, TN3 9, **England**.
Contact/s: **Mr Ken Crow** (Fishery Manager), Honey Croft Lane, 3 Elm Lane, Golden Green, Tonbridge, TN11 0BS.
(T) 01732 851544 **(M)** 07710 626501
Profile: FT: Coarse; WN: Dundale; WT: Lake (Still).
Ref: FH1474

DUNGANNON PARK FISHERY

Dungannon Park Fishery, Moy Rd, Dungannon, **COUNTY TYRONE**, BT71 6BU, **Northern Ireland**.
Contact/s: **Mr Nigel Hill** (Manager), The Pavillion, Dungannon Park, Moy Rd, Dungannon, County Tyrone, BT71 6DY.
(T) 028 87727327
Profile: FT: Coarse; WN: Park; WT: Lake (Still) **W. Size:** 13 Acres. **Location:** Nr. Rd: Moy Road; **Rail:** Dungannon.
Ref: FH1475

DUNGENESS LONG PIT

Dungeness Long Pit, Dungeness, Romney Marsh, **KENT**, TN29, **England**.
Contact/s: Fishery Manager.
(T) 01303 262013
Profile: FT: Coarse; WN: Dungeness; WT: Gravel Pit (Still).
Ref: FH1476

DUNHAM CARP AND TENCH LAKES

Dunham Carp And Tench Lakes, Necton, Swaffham, **NORFOLK**, PE37, **England**.
Contact/s: **Mr David Harris** (Fishery Manager).
(T) 01760 725286
Profile: FT: Coarse; WN: Dunham Carp And Tench Lakes; WT: Lake (Still).
Ref: FH1477

DUNOON RESERVOIR

Dunoon Reservoir, Dunoon, **ARGYLL AND BUTE**, PA23, **Scotland**.
Contact/s: **Mr A H Young** (Hon Secretary), 112 Argyll St, Dunoon, Argyll and Bute.

(T) 01369 705732or703232
(E) archie@telinco.co.uk
Profile: **FT:** Game; **WN:** Dunoon; **WT:** Reservoir (Still) **W. Size:** 22 Acres.
Ref: FH1478

DUNSCAR SHORE LODGE

Dunscar Shore Lodge, Bolton, **LANCASHIRE**, BL, **England**.
Contact/s: **Mr Terence A McKee** (Secretary), Bolton and District Angling Association, 1 Lever Edge Lane, Bolton, Lancashire, BL3 3BU.
(T) 01204 393726
Profile: **FT:** Coarse; **WN:** Dunscar Shore Lodge; **WT:** Lake (Still). **Location:** **Nr. Rd:** Blackburn Road; **Main Rd:** A666.
Ref: FH1479

DUNSKEY LOCHS

Dunskey Lochs, Stranraer, **DUMFRIES AND GALLOWAY**, DG9, **Scotland**.
Contact/s: **Mr P C Hoyer** (Manager).
(T) 01776 810364
Profile: **FT:** Game; **WN:** Dunskey; **WT:** Loch (Still) **W. Size:** 14 Acres.
Ref: FH1480

DUNSLEY FARM

Dunsley Farm, West Anstey, South Molton, **DEVON**, EX36 3PF, **England**.
Contact/s: **Mrs M Robins** (Owner).
(T) 01398 341246
Profile: **FT:** Coarse; **WN:** Dunsley Farm; **WT:** Pond (Still). **Location:** **Nr. Rd:** Yeo Mill to East Anstey; **Main Rd:** South Molton.
Ref: FH1481

DUNWEAR LAKES

Dunwear Lakes, Westonzoyland Rd, Bridgwater, **SOMERSET**, TA, **England**.
Contact/s: **Mr Mark Pople** (Secretary), 14 Edward St, Bridgwater, Somerset.
(T) 01278 422397
Profile: **FT:** Coarse; **WN:** Dunwear; **WT:** Pond (Still). **Location:** **Nr. Rd:** Plum Lane; **Main Rd:** Westonzoyland Road, A372.
Ref: FH1482

DURHAM BECK

Durham Beck, Durham, **COUNTY DURHAM**, DH, **England**.
Contact/s: **Mr Barry Hignett** (Secretary), Ferryhill and District Angling Club, 74 Grasmere Rd, Garden Farm Estate, Chester-le-Street, County Durham.
(T) 0191 3883557
Profile: **FT:** Coarse; **WN:** Durham; **WT:** Stream (Moving).
Ref: FH1483

DURLEIGH RESERVOIR

Durleigh Reservoir, Durleigh Fishing Lodge, Bridgwater, **SOMERSET**, TA5 2AF, **England**.
Contact/s: Customer Services, Wessex Water, Billing Ctre, Clevedon Walk, Nailsea, Bristol, BS48 1WW.
(T) 01179 290611 (F) 01275 810519
Mr Paul Martin (Ranger).
(T) 01278 424786
Mr Steve Kedge (Manager), Somerset Angling, 74 Bath Rd, Bridgwater, Somerset, TA6 4PL.
(T) 01278 431777 or 786934
Profile: **FT:** Coarse; **WN:** Durleigh; **WT:** Reservoir (Still) **W. Size:** 80 Acres.
Location: **Nr. Rd:** Durleigh Hill; **Main Rd:** M25, junction 24.
Ref: FH1484

DURRANTS LAKE

Durrants Lake, Apsley End, Hitchin, **HERTFORDSHIRE**, SG, **England**.
Contact/s: Fishery Manager.
(T) 01442 395143
Profile: **FT:** Coarse; **WN:** Durrant's; **WT:** Lake (Still). **Location:** **Nr. Rd:** A4251 Kings Langley to Hemel Hempstead; **Main Rd:** Durrants Hill.
Ref: FH1485

DUSTON RESERVOIR

Duston Reservoir, Sixfields, Northampton, **NORTHAMPTONSHIRE**, NN, **England**.
Contact/s: **Mr Terry Rodhouse** (Secretary), Castle Angling Association, 12 Somerville Rd, Daventry, Northamptonshire, NN11 4RT.
(T) 01327 705692
Profile: **FT:** Coarse; **WN:** Duston; **WT:** Reservoir (Still) **W. Size:** 30 Acres.
Location: **Nr. Rd:** A45; **Main Rd:** A45; **Rail:** Northampton.
Ref: FH1486

DUTSON WATER

Dutson Water, Lower Dutson Farm, Launceston, **CORNWALL**, PL15 9SP, **England**.
Contact/s: **Mr F E Broad** (Farmer), Lower Dutson Farm, Launceston, Cornwall, PL15 9SP.
(T) 01566 776456 (F) 01566 776456
Profile: **FT:** Combination; **WN:** Duston; **WT:** Lake (Still) **W. Size:** 1 Acre. **Location:** **Nr. Rd:** Holsworthy; **Main Rd:** A388, North; **Rail:** Liskeard.
Ref: FH1487

DWYFACH (RIVER)

River Dwyfach, Criccieth, **GWYNEDD**, LL52, **Wales**.
Contact/s: Manager, R T Pritchard and Son, 41-43 High St, Criccieth, Gwynedd, LL52 0EY.
(T) 01766 523342or522116
Mr W E Hughes (Secretary), Llanystumdwy and District Angling Association, Kinlet, Penruat, Llanystumdwy, Criccieth LL52 0SR.
(T) 01766 523342
(E) elfyn@ndirect.co.uk
Profile: **FT:** Game; **WN:** Dwyfach; **WT:** River (Moving) **W. Size:** 3200 Metres. **Location:** **Nr. Rd:** Porthmadog to Pwllheli; **Main Rd:** A497; **Rail:** Criccieth.
Ref: FH1488

DWYFAWR (RIVER)

River Dwyfawr, Criccieth, **GWYNEDD**, LL52, **Wales**.
Contact/s: **Mr R T Pritchard**, Sheffield House, High St, Cricceth, Gwynedd, LL52 0EY.
(T) 01766 523342
Profile: **FT:** Game; **WN:** Dwyfawr; **WT:** River (Moving).
Ref: FH1489

DWYRYD (RIVER)

River Dwyryd, Maentwrog, Blaenau Ffestiniog, **GWYNEDD**, LL41, **Wales**.
Contact/s: **Mrs M Wilson** (Secretary), 1 Bryn Tirion, Glan y Pwll, Blaenau Ffestiniog, Gwynedd, LL41 3PW.
(T) 01766 831676
Profile: **FT:** Game; **WN:** Dwyryd; **WT:** River (Moving) **W. Size:** 1600 Metres. **Location:** **Nr. Rd:** Maentwrog Bridge; **Main Rd:** A496.
Ref: FH1490

DWYRYD (RIVER)

River Dwyryd, Ffestiniog, Blaenau Ffestiniog, **GWYNEDD**, LL41, **Wales**.
Contact/s: **Mr Gareth Price** (Tackle Shop Manager), Hafan, Fford Peniel, Ffestiniog, Gwynedd, Wales.
(T) 01766 762451
Profile: **FT:** Game; **WN:** Dwyryd; **WT:** River (Moving).
Ref: FH1491

DWYTHWCH LAKE

Cwm, Llanberis, Caernarfon, **GWYNEDD**, LL55, **Wales**.
Contact/s: **Mr Huw P Hughes** (Hon Secretary), Seiont, Gwyrfai and Llyfni Anglers Society, Llugwy, Ystad Eryri, Bethel, Caernarfon, LL55 1BX.
(T) 01248 670666
(E) huw.hughes@lineone.net
Profile: **FT:** Game; **WN:** Dwythwch; **WT:** Lake (Still) **W. Size:** 100 Acres. **Location:** **Main Rd:** A4086; **Rail:** Bangor.
Ref: FH1492

DYEHOUSE POND

Dyehouse Pond, Oakenshaw, Bradford, **YORKSHIRE (WEST)**, BD12, **England**.
Contact/s: **Mr E K Mann** (Club Secretary), 19 Busfield St, Bradford, Yorkshire (West), BD4 7QX.
(T) 01274 720072
Profile: **FT:** Coarse; **WN:** Dyehouse; **WT:** Pond (Still) **W. Size:** 2 Acres. **Location:** **Main Rd:** A641 South of Bradford.
Ref: FH1493

DYFI (RIVER)

River Dyfi, Machynlleth, **POWYS**, SY20, **Wales**.
Contact/s: **Mr Ian Rees** (Hon Secretary), Leeds House, 20 Maengwyn St, Machynlleth, Powys, SY20 8DT.
(T) 01654 702721 (F) 01654 702721
Profile: **FT:** Game; **WN:** Dyfi; **WT:** River (Moving) **W. Size:** 24000 Metres.
Ref: FH1494

DYKES COTTAGE LAKES

Dykes Cottage Lakes, Chapel Hill, Lincoln, **LINCOLNSHIRE**, LN4, **England**.
Contact/s: **Mr N Dolby** (Fishery Manager).
(T) 01526 343315
Profile: **FT:** Coarse; **WN:** Dykes Cottage; **WT:** Lake (Still).
Ref: FH1495

DYSYNNI (RIVER)

River Dysynni, Abergynolwyn, Tywyn, **GWYNEDD**, LL36, **Wales**.
Contact/s: **Mr J Baxter** (Hon Secretary), Estimaner Angling Association, 11 Tan y Fedw, Abergynolwyn, Gwynedd, LL36 9YU.
(T) 01654 782632
Mr Tom Rowlands (Hotel Manager), Tyn-y-Cornel Hotel, Talyllyn, Tywyn, Gwynedd, LL36 9AJ.
(T) 01654 782282 (F) 01654 782679
Profile: **FT:** Game; **WN:** Dysynni; **WT:** River (Moving) **W. Size:** 3000 Metres. **Location:** **Nr. Rd:** B4405; **Main Rd:** A487; **Rail:** Tywyn.
Ref: FH1496

DYSYNNI (RIVER)

River Dysynni, Tal Y Llyn, Tywyn, **GWYNEDD**, LL36, **Wales**.
Contact/s: **Mr T Rowlands** (Hotel Manager), Tyn-y-Cornel Hotel, Talyllyn, Tywyn, Gwynedd, LL36 9AJ.
(T) 01654 782282
Profile: **FT:** Game; **WN:** Dysynni; **WT:** River (Moving) **W. Size:** 5600 Metres.
Ref: FH1497

DYWARCHEN RESERVOIR

Dywarchen Reservoir, Dryscoed Uchaf, Rhyd-Ddu, Caernarfon, **GWYNEDD**, LL54, **Wales**.
Contact/s: **Mr Huw P Hughes** (Hon Secretary), Seiont, Gwyrfai and Llyfni Anglers Society, Llugwy, Ystad Eryri, Bethel, Caernarfon, LL55 1BX.
(T) 01248 670666
(E) huw.hughes@lineone.net
Profile: **FT:** Game; **WN:** Dywarchen; **WT:** Reservoir (Still) **W. Size:** 45 Acres.
Location: **Nr. Rd:** B4418; **Main Rd:** A4085; **Rail:** Bangor.
Ref: FH1498

EAGLEY WATERS

Eagley Waters, Bromley Cross, Bolton, **LANCASHIRE**, BL7, **England**.
Contact/s: Fishery Manager.
Profile: **FT:** Coarse; **WN:** Eagley Waters; **WT:** Lake (Still).
Ref: FH1499

EAMONT (RIVER)

River Eamont, Penrith, **CUMBRIA**, CA, **England**.
Contact/s: **Mr Charles Sykes**, Charles R Sykes (Gunsmiths), 4 Great Dockray, Penrith, Cumbria, CA11 7BL.
(T) 01768 862418 (F) 01768 862418

Profile: **FT:** Game; **WN:** Eamont; **WT:** River (Moving) **W. Size:** 1600 Metres.
Ref: FH1500

EARITH FISHERY

Earith Fishery, Holme Fen Drove, Earith, St Ives, Huntingdon, **CAMBRIDGESHIRE**, PE17 3RE, **England**.
Mr R Bermeister (Owner).
(T) 01487 740301 **(M)** 07946 74792
Profile: **FT:** Combination; **WN:** Earith; **WT:** Lake (Still) **W. Size:** 18 Acres. **Location:** **Main Rd:** A142.
Ref: FH1501

EARLSTOUN LOCH

Earlstoun Loch, Dalry, Castle Douglas, **DUMFRIES AND GALLOWAY**, DG7, **Scotland**.
Contact/s: **Mr M Newton** (Owner), 17 Main St, St Johns Town, Dalry, Castle Douglas, DG7 3UP.
(T) 01644 430225
(E) gmnewton@supanet.com
Profile: **FT:** Game; **WN:** Earlstoun; **WT:** Loch (Still). **Location:** **Nr. Rd:** A713; **Main Rd:** A713.
Ref: FH1502

EARLSWOOD LAKES

Earlswood Lakes, Solihull, **MIDLANDS (WEST)**, B91, **England**.
Contact/s: **Mr John Howse** (Bailiffs Department).
(T) 0121 7834233 **(M)** 07711 0175067
Profile: **FT:** Coarse; **WN:** Earlswood Lakes; **WT:** Lake (Still) **W. Size:** 58 Acres.
Location: **Main Rd:** M42 junction 4, A34.
Ref: FH1503

EARNSDALE RESERVOIR

Earnsdale Reservoir, Blackburn, **LANCASHIRE**, BB3, **England**.
Contact/s: **Mr Fred Kendall** (Secretary), 45 Holden Fold, Darwen, Lancashire, BB3 3AH.
(T) 01254 775501
Mr Roy Rhodes (Conservation, Access and Recreation Manager), Rivington Water Treatment Works, Bolton Rd, Horwich, Bolton, BL6 7RN.
(T) 01204 664300
Profile: **FT:** Game; **WN:** Earnsdale; **WT:** Reservoir (Still).
Ref: FH1504

EASEDALE TARN

Easedale Tarn, National Trust, The Hollens, Grasmere, Ambleside, **CUMBRIA**, LA22 9QZ, **England**.
Contact/s: Manager, The National Trust, North West Regional Office, The Hollens, Grasmere, Ambleside, LA22 9QZ.
(T) 01539 435599 **(F)** 01539 435353
Mr David Wilkinson.
(T) 01539 437663
Profile: **FT:** Combination; **WN:** Easedale Tarn; **WT:** River (Moving) **W. Size:** 4800 Metres.
Ref: FH1505

EAST COTTINGWITH WATERS

East Cottingwith Waters, East Cottingwith, York, **YORKSHIRE (NORTH)**, YO42, **England**.
Contact/s: **Mr John Lane** (Secretary), York and District Angling Association, 39 Lowfields Drive, Acomb, York, YO2 3DQ.
(T) 01904 783178
Profile: **FT:** Coarse; **WN:** East Cottingwith Waters; **WT:** River (Moving) **W. Size:** 3200 Metres. **Location:** **Rail:** High Field.
Ref: FH1506

EAST DELPH LAKES

East Delph Lakes, East Delph, Whittlesey, **CAMBRIDGESHIRE**, **England**.
Contact/s: .
(T) 01733 202140
Profile: **FT:** Coarse; **WN:** East Delph Lakes; **WT:** Lake (Still); **F. Size:** 15 Acres; **W. Size:** 12 Acres.
Ref: FH1507

EAST DOCK

East Dock, Cardiff, **Wales**.
Contact/s: **Mr M Roberts**.
Profile: **FT:** Coarse; **WT:** Lock (Still).
Ref: FH1508

EAST FARLEIGH

East Farleigh, Maidstone, **KENT**, ME1, **England**.
Profile: **FT:** Coarse; **WN:** East Farleigh; **WT:** Lake (Still).
Ref: FH1509

EAST HALTON FISHING LAKES

East Halton Fishing Lakes, East Halton, Immingham, **LINCOLNSHIRE**, DN40, **England**.
Contact/s: **Mr Winter**, Winter Brothers Pond, Marsh Lane, East Halton, Lincolnshire.
(T) 01469 540238
Profile: **FT:** Coarse; **WN:** East Halton; **WT:** Lake (Still).
Ref: FH1510

EAST MOORS LAKE

East Moors Lake, East Moors Farm, East Moors Lane, St Leonards, Ferndale, Ringwood, **HAMPSHIRE**, BH24 2SB, **England**.
(W) www.carplake.co.uk
Contact/s: **Mr N Hoare** (Owner).
(T) 01202 872302
Profile: **FT:** Coarse; **WN:** East Moors; **WT:** Lake (Still); **F. Size:** 75 Acres; **W. Size:** 2 Acres.
Ref: FH1511

EAST PARK LAKE

East Park Lake, Holderness Rd, Hull, **HUMBERSIDE**, HU, **England**.
Contact/s: Area Manager, Environment Agency, Ridings Area Office, Phoenix House, Global Avenue, Leeds, LS11 8PG.
(T) 0113 2440191or2314834 **(F)** 0113 2134609
Mr S Myers, Hull City Council, Temple St, Hull, Yorkshire (East), HU5 1AD.
(T) 01482 614964
Profile: **FT:** Coarse; **WN:** East Park; **WT:** Lake (Still).
Ref: FH1512

EAST ROSE FARM

East Rose Farm, St Breward, Bodmin, **CORNWALL**, PL30 4NL, **England**.
(W) www.eastrose.co.uk
Contact/s: **Mr John Stansfield** (Manager).
(T) 01208 850674
(E) eastrose@globalnet.co.uk
Profile: **FT:** Coarse; **WN:** East Rose; **WT:** Lake (Still) **W. Size:** 3 Acres. **Location:** **Nr. Rd:** A30; **Main Rd:** A30; **Rail:** Bodmin Parkway.
Ref: FH1513

EAST TOWNEY

East Towney, Kennet And Avon Canal, Ufton Nervett, Reading, **BERKSHIRE**, RG, **England**.
Contact/s: **Mr Mick Cox** (Secretary), Dorstans, Hatch Lane, Brimpton Village, Reading, RG7 4TR.
(T) 0118 9714917
Ms Dusty Millar (Ticket Administrator), 238 Elgar Road South, Reading, Berkshire, RG3 0BW.
(T) 0118 9874882
Profile: **FT:** Coarse; **WN:** Kennet and Avon; **WT:** Canal (Still) **W. Size:** 32000 Metres.
Location: **Nr. Rd:** Padworth to East Towney; **Main Rd:** A4 to Newbury.
Ref: FH1514

EAST VIEW FISHERY

East View Fishery, Broadfield, Southwaite, Carlisle, **CUMBRIA**, CA4 0PT, **England**.
Contact/s: **Mr Kevin Lancaster** (Farmer).
(T) 01697 473324
Profile: **FT:** Coarse; **WN:** East View Fishery; **WT:** Quarry (Still) **W. Size:** 1 Acre. **Location:** **Nr. Rd:** M6 junction 42; **Main Rd:** Penrith to Carlisle back road; **Rail:** Southwaite.
Ref: FH1515

EAST WARWICK

East Warwick, Ferry Lane, Tottenham, London, **LONDON (GREATER)**, N17, **England**.
Contact/s: **Mr Chris King**, Walthamstow Reservoir Group, Thames Water Gatehouse, 2 Forest Rd, Tottenham, London, N17 9NH.
(T) 020 88081527
Profile: **FT:** Coarse; **WN:** East Warwick; **WT:** Lake (Still) **W. Size:** 43 Acres. **Location:** **Nr. Rd:** Ferry Lane; **Main Rd:** A10, A503.
Ref: FH1516

EAST WHIPLEY RESERVOIR

East Whipley Reservoir, Cranleigh, **SURREY**, GU6, **England**.
Contact/s: **Mr Nick Bamford** (Publicity Officer), Cranleigh Angling Club, 20 High St, Cranleigh, Surrey, GU6 8AE.
(T) 01483 274566
Mrs Sue Buxton, 5 Ginger's Cl, Cranleigh, Surrey, GU6 7JL.
Profile: **FT:** Coarse; **WN:** East Whipley; **WT:** Reservoir (Still). **Location:** **Nr. Rd:** Guilford to Rushett Common; **Main Rd:** B2128.
Ref: FH1517

EASTCOTT FARM AND LODGES

Eastcott Farm And Lodges, North Tamerton, Holsworthy, **DEVON**, EX22 6SB, **England**.
Contact/s: **Mr David Whitmill** (Owner).
(T) 01409 271172
Profile: **FT:** Coarse; **WN:** Eastcott Farm And Lodges; **WT:** Lake (Still) **W. Size:** 1 Acre.
Ref: FH1518

EASTER BALADO (KINROSS)

Easter Balado Trout Fishery (Kinross), Frandy Farm, Glendevon, **CLACKMANNANSHIRE**, FK14 7JZ, **Scotland**.
Contact/s: **Ms Helen Philp** (Manager). **(F)** 01259 781306 **(M)** 07801 547869
Profile: **FT:** Game; **WN:** Easter Balado; **WT:** Lake (Still) **W. Size:** 7 Acres. **Location:** **Nr. Rd:** Glendevon; **Main Rd:** M90.
Ref: FH1519

EASTERN CLEDDAU (RIVER)

River Eastern Cleddau, Ian Heaps Premier Fisheries, Holgan Farm, Narberth, **PEMBROKESHIRE**, SA67 8DJ, **Wales**.
(W) www.fisheries.co.uk/ianheaps
Contact/s: **Mr Ian Heaps**.
(T) 01437 541285
Profile: **FT:** Game; **WN:** Eastern Cleddau; **WT:** River (Moving) **W. Size:** 1600 Metres.
Location: **Nr. Rd:** A40; **Main Rd:** A40; **Rail:** Narberth.
Ref: FH1520

EASTERN CLEDDAU (RIVER)

River Eastern Cleddau, Clynderwen, Llanycefn, **PEMBROKESHIRE**, SA66 7, **Wales**.
Contact/s: **Mr T Murphy** (Manager), Langwm Farm, Clynderwen, Llanycefn, Pembrokeshire, SA66 7LN.
(T) 01437 563604 **(F)** 01437 563604
Profile: **FT:** Game; **WN:** East Cleddau; **WT:** River (Moving) **W. Size:** 1500 Metres.
Location: **Nr. Rd:** Off road leadind to Llandissilio near to Ford at Vicar's Mill; **Main Rd:** Llandissilio; **Rail:** Clynderwen.
Ref: FH1521

EASTERN CLEDDAU (RIVER)

River Eastern Cleddau, Wiston, Haverfordwest, **PEMBROKESHIRE**, SA62, **Wales**.
Contact/s: **Mr Ian Richards** (Secretary), North Pines, Wiston, Haverfordwest, Pembrokeshire, SA62 4PS.
(T) 01437 731628
Profile: **FT:** Game; **WN:** Eastern Cleddau; **WT:** River (Moving) **W. Size:** 4800 Metres.
Location: **Nr. Rd:** Gelly Bridge to Holgan Farm, also on Penlan Farm to Llawhaden Bridge.
Ref: FH1522

EASTERN ROTHER (RIVER)

River Eastern Rother, Newenden, Cranbrook, **KENT**, TN18, **England**.
Contact/s: Fishery Manager.
(T) 01797 253291
Profile: **FT:** Coarse; **WN:** Rother; **WT:** River (Moving).
Ref: FH1523

EASTERTYRE BEAT

Eastertyre Beat, Pitlochry, **PERTH AND KINROSS**, PH, **Scotland**.
(W) www.fishingnet.com/beats/eastertyre.htm
Contact/s: **Mrs E J M MacPhail**, Eastertyre, Ballinluig, Pitochry, Perth and Kinross, PH9 0LN.
Profile: **FT:** Combination; **WN:** Eastertyre; **WT:** Pool (Still).
Ref: FH1524

EASTNOR CASTLE

Eastnor Castle, Eastnor, Ledbury, **HEREFORDSHIRE**, HR8, **England**.
Profile: **FT:** Coarse; **WN:** Eastnor Castle; **WT:** Lake (Still) **W. Size:** 5 Acres. Location: **Nr. Rd:** A438; **Main Rd:** A449.
Ref: FH1525

EATON SOCON LAKE

Eaton Socon Lake, Eaton Socon, St Neots, Huntingdon, **CAMBRIDGESHIRE**, PE1, **England**.
Contact/s: **Mr Lg Day** (Secretary), Hitchin and District Angling Club, 14 Thatchers End, Hitchin, Hertfordshire.
Profile: **FT:** Coarse; **WN:** Eaton Socon; **WT:** Lake (Still).
Ref: FH1527

EBBW (RIVER)

River Ebbw, Cwm Argoed, Blackwood, **CAERPHILLY**, NP12, **Wales**.
Contact/s: **Mr Alfred Stevenson** (Hon Secretary), 58 James St, Markham, Blackwood, Gwent, NP2 0QP.
(T) 01495 226331
Profile: **FT:** Game; **WN:** Ebbw; **WT:** River (Moving). Location: **Nr. Rd:** Cwm Argoed to Tredegar Road.
Ref: FH1528

ECCLESBOURNE RESERVOIR

Ecclesbourne Reservoir, Hastings, **SUSSEX (EAST)**, TN, **England**.
Contact/s: Fishery Manager.
(T) 01424 423031
Profile: **FT:** Coarse; **WN:** Ecclesbourne; **WT:** Reservoir (Still).
Ref: FH1529

ECCLESFIELD POND

Ecclesfield Pond, Sheffield, **YORKSHIRE (SOUTH)**, **England**.
Contact/s: Fishery Manager.
(T) 0114 2467627
Profile: **FT:** Coarse; **WN:** Ecclesfield; **WT:** Pond (Still).
Ref: FH1530

ECTON GRAVEL PITS

Ecton Gravel Pits, Billing, Ecton, Northampton, **NORTHAMPTONSHIRE**, NN, **England**.
Contact/s: Fishery Manager.
(T) 01604 757589
Profile: **FT:** Coarse; **WN:** Ecton; **WT:** Gravel Pit (Still).
Ref: FH1531

EDDISON POND

Eddison Pond, Kingsteighton, Newton Abbot, **DEVON**, TQ12, **England**.
Contact/s: **Mr David Horder** (Secretary), Mistlemead, Woodlands, Higher Sandygate, Newton Abbot, TQ12 3QN.
(T) 01626 364173
Profile: **FT:** Coarse; **WN:** Eddison; **WT:** Pond (Still). Location: **Nr. Rd:** Newton Abbot to Kingsteignton; **Main Rd:** B3195.
Ref: FH1532

EDEN (RIVER)

River Eden, Kirkby Stephen, **CUMBRIA**, CA17, **England**.
Contact/s: **Mr Andrew Murray** (Manager), Murrays Tackle Shop, 5-6 Lowther Arcade, Carlisle, Cumbria, CA3 8LX.
(T) 01228 523816
Profile: **FT:** Game; **WN:** Eden; **WT:** River (Moving) **W. Size:** 46900 Metres.
Ref: FH1533

EDEN (RIVER)

River Eden, Carlisle, **CUMBRIA**, CA, **England**.
Contact/s: Fishery Manager.
(T) 01228 401151
Profile: **FT:** Coarse; **WN:** Eden; **WT:** River (Moving).
Ref: FH1534

EDEN (RIVER)

River Eden, Appleby-In-Westmorland, **CUMBRIA**, CA16, **England**.
Contact/s: Manager, Tufton Arms Hotel, 10 Market Sq, Appleby-in-Westmorland, Cumbria, CA16 6XA.
(T) 01768 351593 **(F)** 01768 352764
Profile: **FT:** Game; **WN:** Eden; **WT:** River (Moving).
Ref: FH1535

EDEN (RIVER)

River Eden, Irthing, Brampton, Appleby-In-Westmorland, **CUMBRIA**, CA16, **England**.
Profile: **FT:** Combination; **WN:** Eden; **WT:** Tributary (Moving) **W. Size:** 3200 Metres.
Ref: FH1536

EDEN (RIVER)

River Eden, Warwick Bridge, Carlisle, **CUMBRIA**, CA4, **England**.
Contact/s: Fishery Manager.
(T) 01228 560545
Profile: **FT:** Coarse; **WN:** Eden; **WT:** River (Moving).
Ref: FH1537

EDEN (RIVER)

River Eden, Dolgellau, **GWYNEDD**, LL40, **Wales**.
Contact/s: **Mr Idwal Wyn Williams** (Secretary), 8 Pantycelyn, Trawsffynydd, Gwynedd, LL41 4UH.
(T) 01766 540435 **(F)** 01766 540435
(E) idwalwyn@idwal.freeserve.co.uk
Mr Mitch Atherton (Owner), Newsagent, Manchester House, Trawsfynydd, Gwynedd, LL41 4UB.
(T) 01766 540234
Mr S Davies (Secretary).
(T) 01766 770276
Profile: **FT:** Game; **WN:** Eden; **WT:** River (Moving).
Ref: FH1538

EDEN (RIVER)

River Eden, Penshurst, Tonbridge, **KENT**, TN11, **England**.
Contact/s: **Mr Adrian Bewley** (Manager), Ashvale Fisheries, 69 Fortescue Rd, Wimbledon, London, SW19 2EA.
Profile: **FT:** Coarse; **WN:** Medway; **WT:** Tributary (Moving) **W. Size:** 461 Metres. Location: **Nr. Rd:** Southborough to Chiddlingstone; **Main Rd:** Penshurst.
Ref: FH1539

EDEN (RIVER)

River Eden, Edenbridge, **KENT**, TN8, **England**.
Contact/s: **Mr Alex Heggie** (Membership Secretary), Little Lucy's Farmhouse, Lower St, Hildenborough, Tonbridge, TN11 8PT.
(T) 01732 832352 **(F)** 01732 832352
Profile: **FT:** Coarse; **WN:** Eden; **WT:** River (Moving).
Ref: FH1540

EDEN (RIVER)

River Eden, Mill Farm, Chiddingstone, Edenbridge, **KENT**, TN8, **England**.
(W) www.calpac.bizland.com
Contact/s: **Mr Colin Trafford** (General Secretary).
(T) 020 82242617
Mrs Diane Wheeler (Secretary), 314 Old Lodge Lane, Purley, Surrey, CR8 4AQ.
(T) 020 86602766
Profile: **FT:** Coarse; **WN:** Eden; **WT:** River (Moving) **W. Size:** 1600 Metres. Location: **Nr. Rd:** Bough Beech to Chiddingstone Road; **Main Rd:** B269.
Ref: FH1541

EDEN (RIVER)

River Eden, Beggars Barn, Leigh Rd, Penshurst, Tonbridge, **KENT**, TN11, **England**.
Contact/s: **Mr Alex Heggie** (Membership Secretary), Little Lucy's Farmhouse, Lower St, Hildenborough, Tonbridge, TN11 8PT.
(T) 01732 832352 **(F)** 01732 832352
Mr Tom Creasey (Hon Secretary), 3 Invicta Flats, Great Brooms Rd, Tunbridge Wells, Kent, TN4 9DD.
(T) 01892 520520
Profile: **FT:** Coarse; **WN:** Eden; **WT:** River (Moving) **W. Size:** 3200 Metres. Location: **Nr. Rd:** Leigh Road; **Rail:** Penshurst.
Ref: FH1542

EDEN VALLEY TROUT LAKE

Eden Valley Trout Lake, Bearsett, Kirkby Stephen, **CUMBRIA**, CA17 4SR, **England**.
Contact/s: **Mr Hughes**.
(T) 01768 371489
Mr J Norris (Manager), 21 Victoria Rd, Penrith, CA11 8HP.
(T) 01768 864211 **(F)** 01768 890476
Profile: **FT:** Game; **WN:** Eden Valley; **WT:** Lake (Still); **F. Size:** 5 Acres; **W. Size:** 1 Acre. Location: **Rail:** Kirby Stephen.
Ref: FH1543

EDENDERRY OFFALY EIRE

Edenderry Offaly Eire, 48 Murphy St, Edenderry, **COUNTY OFFALY**, **Ireland**.
Contact/s: **Mr Pauric Kelly**.
(T) 040 532021
Profile: **FT:** Coarse; **WN:** Grand; **WT:** Canal (Still) **W. Size:** 27000 Metres. Location: **Nr. Rd:** Edenderry to Dublin Road; **Rail:** Enfield.
Ref: FH1544

EDGBASTON RESERVOIR

Edgbaston Reservoir, Reservoir Rd, Edgbaston, Birmingham, **MIDLANDS (WEST)**, B16 9, **England**.
Contact/s: Rangers Office, Birmingham City Council, 115 Reservoir Rd, Edgbaston, Birmingham, B16 9EE.
(T) 0121 4541908
Profile: **FT:** Coarse; **WN:** Edgbaston; **WT:** Reservoir (Still). Location: **Nr. Rd:** Reservoir Road; **Main Rd:** A4540 to Laydwood.
Ref: FH1545

EDISFORD AND BRUNGERLEY PARK

Edisford And Brungerley Park, Clitheroe, **LANCASHIRE**, BB7, **England**.
Contact/s: **Mr David Jones** (Manager), Clitheroe Tourist Information Ctre, 12 - 14 Market Pl, Clitheroe, Lancashire BB7 2DA.
(T) 01200 425566
Profile: **FT:** Coarse; **WN:** Ribble; **WT:** River (Moving) **W. Size:** 600 Metres. Location: **Nr. Rd:** Edisford Road and Waddington Road; **Rail:** Clitheroe.
Ref: FH1546

EDMONDSLEY POND

Edmondsley Pond, Edmondsley, Chester-Le-Street, **COUNTY DURHAM**, DH, **England**.
Contact/s: **Mr Colin Donnelly** (Chairman), Langley Park Angling Club, 10 South View, Langley Park, Durham, DH7 9YQ.
(T) 0191 3736325
Profile: **FT:** Coarse; **WN:** Edmondsley; **WT:** Lake (Still). Location: **Nr. Rd:** B6313; **Main Rd:** A1, junction 64.
Ref: FH1547

EDNEYS FISHERIES

Edneys Fisheries, Mells, Frome, **SOMERSET**, BA11 3RE, **England**.
Contact/s: **Mr John Candy** (Fishery Manager).
(T) 01373 812294
Profile: **FT:** Coarse; **WN:** Edneys Fisheries; **WT:** Lake (Still). **Location:** **Main Rd:** Mells Road.
Ref: FH1548

EDWINSFORD FISHERY

Edwinsford Fishery, Edwinsford Farmhouse, Talley, Llandeilo, **CARMARTHENSHIRE**, SA19 7BX, **Wales**.
Contact/s: Fishery Manager.
(T) 01558 685848
(E) jheron@vinexports.co.uk
Profile: **FT:** Game; **WN:** Edwinsford Fishery; **WT:** Lake (Still).
Ref: FH1549

EGERTON LAKE

Egerton Lake, Egerton Hall, Shay Lane, Cholmondeley, Malpas, **CHESHIRE**, SY14 8AE, **England**.
Contact/s: **Mr James Mitchell**.
Profile: **FT:** Coarse; **WN:** Egerton; **WT:** Lake (Still); **F. Size:** 6 Acres; **W. Size:** 4 Acres. **Location:** **Nr. Rd:** Shay Lane; **Main Rd:** A41 and A49; **Rail:** Chester.
Ref: FH1550

EGGESFORD WATERS

Eggesford Country Hotel Waters, Eggesford, Chulmleigh, **DEVON**, EX18 7JZ, **England**.
Contact/s: **Mr John C Pitts** (Owner).
(T) 01769 580345 **(F)** 01769 580262
Profile: **FT:** Game; **WN:** Taw; **WT:** River (Moving) **W. Size:** 10500 Metres. **Location:** **Nr. Rd:** A377; **Main Rd:** A377; **Rail:** Eggesford.
Ref: FH1551

EGLINGTON LOCH

Eglington Loch, Irvine, **AYRSHIRE (NORTH)**, KA12, **Scotland**.
Contact/s: Fishery Manager.
(T) 01294 551776
Profile: **FT:** Coarse; **WN:** Eglington; **WT:** Loch (Still).
Ref: FH1552

EGLWYS NUNYDD RESERVOIR

Eglwys Nunydd Reservoir, Margam, Port Talbot, **NEATH PORT TALBOT**, SA13, **Wales**.
Contact/s: **Gwyn Evans**, 16 Kenilworth Court, Baglan, Port Talbot, Glamorgan, SA12 8NN.
(T) 01639 768567
Mr C Hatch (Area Manager), Hamdden Ltd, Sluvad Treatment Works, Llandegfedd Reservoir, New Inn, Pontypool, Gwent NP4 0TA.
(T) 01495 769281 **(F)** 01495 769283
Mrs S Murphy (Fisheries Contact), Sports Club, British Steel plc, Groes, Margam, Port Talbot SA13 2.
(T) 01639 871111Ext3368
Profile: **FT:** Game; **WN:** Eglwys Nunydd; **WT:** Reservoir (Still) **W. Size:** 250 Acres. **Location:** **Main Rd:** M4.
Ref: FH1553

EGTON BRIDGE (RIVER)

River Egton Bridge, Whitby, **YORKSHIRE (NORTH)**, YO2, **England**.
Contact/s: Manager, Egton Estate Offices, Egton Bridge, Whitby, Yorkshire (North), YO21 1UY.
(T) 01947 895466 **(F)** 01947 895505
Profile: **FT:** Game; **WN:** Egton Bridge; **WT:** River (Moving).
Ref: FH1554

EGTON ESTATE BEAT

Egton Estate Beat, The Egton Estate, Estate Office, Egton Bridge, Whitby, **YORKSHIRE (NORTH)**, YO21 1UY, **England**.
Contact/s: **Mr S Foster** (Owner/Agent), Egton Estate Offices, Egton Bridge, Whitby, Yorkshire (North), YO21 1UY.
(T) 01947 895466 **(F)** 01947 895505
Profile: **FT:** Game; **WN:** Esk; **WT:** River (Moving) **W. Size:** 1903 Metres.
Ref: FH1555

EHEN (RIVER)

River Ehen, Egremont, **CUMBRIA**, CA22, **England**.
Contact/s: **Mr W Holmes** (owner), Holmes Egremont, 45 Main St, Egremont, Cumbria, CA22 2AB.
(T) 01946 820368
Profile: **FT:** Game; **WN:** Ehen; **WT:** River (Moving).
Ref: FH1556

ELAN (RIVER)

River Elan, Rhayader, **POWYS**, LD6, **Wales**.
Contact/s: **Mr David Evans** (Secretary), Rhayader Angling Association, 72 Brynheulog, Rhayader, Powys, LD6 5EG.
(T) 01597 811404
Profile: **FT:** Game; **WN:** Elan; **WT:** River (Moving) **W. Size:** 4800 Metres.
Ref: FH1557

ELAN VALLEY RESERVOIR

Elan Valley Reservoir, Rhayader, **POWYS**, LD6, **Wales**.
Contact/s: **Mr Alan Lewis**, The Crown Inn, North St, Rhayader, Powys, LD6 5BT.
Mr Noel Hughes, Elan Valley Angling Club, 25 Brynheulog, Rhayader, Powys, LD6 5EF.
(T) 01597 811099
Profile: **FT:** Game; **WN:** Elan Valley; **WT:** Reservoir (Still).
Ref: FH1558

ELDERNELL LAKE

Eldernell Lake, Eldernell Rd, Coates, Peterborough, **CAMBRIDGESHIRE**, PE7, **England**.
Contact/s: **Mr Frank Vaira** (Owner).
(T) 01733 840077
Profile: **FT:** Coarse; **WN:** Eldernell; **WT:** Lake (Still) **W. Size:** 4 Acres. **Location:** **Nr. Rd:** Eldernell Road; **Main Rd:** A605 to Wibech.
Ref: FH1559

ELECTRICITY POOL

Electricity Pool, St Dennis, St Austell, **CORNWALL**, PL26, **England**.
Contact/s: **Mr Nigel Britton**, 2 The Willows, New St, Bugle, St Austell, PL26 8PG.
(T) 01726 851559
Profile: **FT:** Coarse; **WN:** Electricity; **WT:** Gravel Pit (Still) **W. Size:** 1 Acre. **Location:** **Nr. Rd:** B3279; **Main Rd:** Indian Queens to St. Dennis.
Ref: FH1560

ELINOR COARSE LAKE

Elinor Coarse Lake, Thrapston, Kettering, **NORTHAMPTONSHIRE**, NN14, **England**.
Contact/s: **Mr Harold Foster** (Manager).
(T) 01933 622960
Profile: **FT:** Coarse; **WN:** Elinor Coarse Lake; **WT:** Lake (Still).
Ref: FH1561

ELINOR TROUT FISHERY

Elinor Trout Fishery, Lowick Rd, Aldwincle, Kettering, **NORTHAMPTONSHIRE**, NN14 3EE, **England**.
Contact/s: **Mr Edward Foster**.
(T) 01832 720786or01933461958
Profile: **FT:** Combination; **WN:** Elinor Trout Fishery; **WT:** Combination (Still); **F. Size:** 80 Acres; **W. Size:** 54 Acres. **Location:** **Nr. Rd:** Lowick Road; **Main Rd:** A14; **Rail:** Kettering.
Ref: FH1562

ELLEN (RIVER)

River Ellen, Maryport, **CUMBRIA**, CA15 6NF, **England**.
Contact/s: **Mr D S Renac** (Secretary), Ellen Angling Association, 10 Selby Trce, Maryport, Cumbria, CA15 6NF.
(T) 01900 813595
Mr P Martin (Treasurer).
(T) 01900 819149
Profile: **FT:** Game; **WN:** Ellen; **WT:** River (Moving) **W. Size:** 11200 Metres. **Location:** **Nr. Rd:** A594; **Main Rd:** A596; **Rail:** Maryport.
Ref: FH1563

ELLENHALL NINE POOLS

Ellenhall Nine Pools, Ellenhall Park Farm, Ellenhall, Eccleshall, Stafford, **STAFFORDSHIRE**, ST21, **England**.
Contact/s: **Mr Albert Perkins** (Hon Secretary), 63 Fowlers Lane, Light Oaks, Stoke-on-Trent, Staffordshire, ST2 7NB.
Ms Liz Hayes (Manager).
(T) 01625 251262
Profile: **FT:** Coarse; **WN:** Ellenhall Nine; **WT:** Pond (Still) **W. Size:** 1 Acre. **Location:** **Nr. Rd:** A519; **Main Rd:** A519; **Rail:** Stafford.
Ref: FH1564

ELLERBECK FARM AND FISHERY

Ellerbeck Farm And Fishery, Brigham, Cockermouth, **CUMBRIA**, CA13 0SY, **England**.
Contact/s: **Mr Taylor Lawson**.
(T) 01900 825268 **(F)** 01900 825268
Profile: **FT:** Coarse; **WN:** Ellerbeck Farm And Fishery; **WT:** Pond (Still); **F. Size:** 5 Acres; **W. Size:** 1 Acre. **Location:** **Main Rd:** A66; **Rail:** Workington.
Ref: FH1565

ELLERDINE LAKES

Ellerdine Lakes, Hall Farm, Ellerdine, Telford, **SHROPSHIRE**, TF6 6QR, **England**.
Contact/s: **Mr Edward Upton** (Fishery Owner).
(T) 01952 771215 **(F)** 01952 771215 **(M)** 07860 299342
(E) ellerdinelakes@aol.com
Profile: **FT:** Combination; **WN:** Ellerdine; **WT:** Lake (Still) **W. Size:** 10 Acres. **Location:** **Nr. Rd:** A442; **Main Rd:** A442; **Rail:** Wellington.
Ref: FH1566

ELLERTON LANDING

Ellerton Landing, Ellerton, York, **YORKSHIRE (NORTH)**, YO42, **England**.
Contact/s: **Mr Mike Redman** (Manager), 2 Meadowfield, Breighton Rd, Bubwith, YO8 7DZ.
(T) 01757 288891
Profile: **FT:** Coarse; **WN:** Ellerton Landing; **WT:** Lake (Still).
Ref: FH1567

ELLERTON PARK

Ellerton Park, Ellerton-on-Swale, Scorton, Richmond, **YORKSHIRE (NORTH)**, DL10 6AP, **England**.
Contact/s: **Mr John Thompson** (Manager).
(T) 01748 811373 **(F)** 01748 811373
Profile: **FT:** Coarse; **WN:** Ellerton Park; **WT:** Gravel Pit (Still) **W. Size:** 54 Acres. **Location:** **Nr. Rd:** B6271; **Main Rd:** A1; **Rail:** Northallerton.
Ref: FH1568

ELMBRIDGE LAKES

Elmbridge Fishery, Addis Lane, Cutnall Green, Droitwich, **WORCESTERSHIRE**, WR9 0ND, **England**.
Contact/s: **Mr Nick Simons** (Owner).
(T) 01299 851321
Profile: **FT:** Coarse; **WN:** Elmbridge; **WT:** Lake (Still) **W. Size:** 5 Acres. **Location:** **Nr. Rd:** A442, Addis Lane; **Main Rd:** A38, A449.
Ref: FH1569

ELMFIELD FARM COARSE FISHERY

Elmfield Farm Coarse Fishery, Canworthy Water, Launceston, **CORNWALL**, PL15, **England**.
Contact/s: **Mr J Elmer**.
(T) 01566 781243
Profile: **FT:** Coarse; **WN:** Elmfield Farm Coarse Fishery; **WT:** Lake (Still) **W. Size:** 3

Acres. Location: Nr. Rd: Okehampton to Bodmin; Main Rd: A30 to B3254.
Ref: FH1570

ELSECAR CANAL

Elsecar Canal, Brampton, Barnsley, **YORKSHIRE (SOUTH)**, S7, **England**.
Contact/s: Area Manager, Environment Agency, Ridings Area Office, Phoenix House, Global Avenue, Leeds, LS11 8PG.
(T) 0113 2440191or2314834 (F) 0113 2134609
Mr Tony Eaton (Secretary), Barnsley and District Ammalgamated Angling Society, 60 Wolton St, Gawber, Barnsley, S75 2PD.
(T) 01226 203090
Profile: FT: Coarse; **WN:** Elsecar; **WT:** Canal (Still). **Location: Main Rd:** M1.
Ref: FH1571

ELSECAR RESERVOIR

Elsecar Reservoir, Elsecar Park, Holyland Nether, Barnsley, **YORKSHIRE (SOUTH)**, S7, **England**.
Contact/s: **Mr I Hodgson**.
(T) 01226 743933
Profile: FT: Coarse; **WN:** Elsecar; **WT:** Reservoir (Still) **W. Size:** 12 Acres.
Location: Main Rd: M1, junction 36.
Ref: FH1572

ELSTOW PITS

Elstow Pits, Elstow, **BEDFORDSHIRE**, **England**.
(W) www.linear-fisheries.co.uk
Contact/s: **Mr Len Gurd** (Fisheries Manager), The Secretary, Linear Fisheries Bedford, 10a Rackstraw Grove, Old Farm Park, Milton Keynes, MK7 8PZ.
(T) 01908 645135 (F) 01908 645115
(E) elstow@linear-fisheries.co.uk
Profile: FT: Coarse; **WN:** Pit 1, and Pit 2.; **WT:** Gravel Pit (Still); **F. Size:** 120 Acres.
Location: Nr. Rd: A6; **Rail:** Elstow.
Ref: FH1573

ELTON RESERVOIR

Elton Reservoir, Bury, **MANCHESTER (GREATER)**, BL, **England**.
Contact/s: Fishery Manager.
(T) 0161 7642858
Profile: FT: Coarse; **WN:** Elton; **WT:** Reservoir (Still). **Location: Nr. Rd:** B6222, A56; **Main Rd:** A58, M66.
Ref: FH1574

ELVINGTON LAKE

Elvington Lake, Wheldrake Lane, York, **YORKSHIRE (NORTH)**, YO41 4AZ, **England**.
Contact/s: **Mr Stanley Britton**.
(T) 01904 608255
Profile: FT: Coarse; **WN:** Elvington; **WT:** Gravel Pit (Still) **W. Size:** 3 Acres. **Location: Nr. Rd:** B1228; **Main Rd:** A1079; **Rail:** York.
Ref: FH1575

ELWY (RIVER)

River Elwy, Llanfairtalhaiarn, Abergele, **CONWY**, LL22, **Wales**.
Contact/s: **Mr W J P Staines** (Hon Secretary), Delamere, Coed Esgob Lane, St Asaph.
(T) 01745 583926
Profile: FT: Game; **WN:** Elwy; **WT:** River (Moving) **W. Size:** 1600 Metres. **Location: Nr. Rd:** A548.
Ref: FH1576

ELWY (RIVER)

River Elwy, Pont-Y-Ddol, Llannefydd, Denbigh, **CONWY**, LL16, **Wales**.
Contact/s: **Mr C P Harness** (Membership Secretary), 8 Llwyn Menlli, Ruthin, Clwyd.
(T) 01824 705208
Profile: FT: Game; **WN:** Elwy; **WT:** River (Moving) **W. Size:** 1200 Metres. **Location: Nr. Rd:** Pont-y-Ddol to Llannefydd.
Ref: FH1577

ELWY (RIVER)

River Elwy, St Asaph, **DENBIGHSHIRE**, LL17, **Wales**.
Contact/s: **Mr W J P Staines** (Hon Secretary), Delamere, Coed Esgob Lane, St Asaph.
(T) 01745 583926
Profile: FT: Game; **WN:** Elwy; **WT:** River (Moving) **W. Size:** 6400 Metres. **Location: Nr. Rd:** A55.
Ref: FH1578

ELY (RIVER)

River Ely, Miskin, Pontyclun, **RHONDDA CYNON TAFF**, CF72, **Wales**.
Contact/s: **Mr Bill Martin** (Hon Secretary), 12 Cowbridge Rd, Brynsaddler, Pontyclun, Glamorgan (Vale of).
(T) 01443 223677
Profile: FT: Game; **WN:** Ely; **WT:** River (Moving) **W. Size:** 16000 Metres.
Ref: FH1579

EMBER (RIVER)

River Ember, East Molesey, **FIFE**, KY8, **England**.
Contact/s: Manager, Fishing Unlimited, 2-3 Hampton Centre Prde, East Molesey, Surrey, KT8 9HB.
(T) 020 89416633
Profile: FT: Coarse; **WN:** Ember; **WT:** River (Moving).
Ref: FH1580

EMBOROUGH POND

Emborough Pond, Bath, **SOMERSET**, BA1 5LT, **England**.
Contact/s: **Mr I Crudgington**, 37 Broad St, Bath, Somerset, BA1 5LT.
(T) 01225 466325
Profile: FT: Coarse; **WN:** Emborough; **WT:** Pond (Still).
Ref: FH1581

EMBOROUGH POOL

Emborough Pool, Wells, **SOMERSET**, BA5, **England**.
Contact/s: **Mr Rodney** (Manager), Thatcher's Pet and Tackle, 18 Queen St, Wells, Somerset, BA5 2DP.
(T) 01749 673513
Profile: FT: Coarse; **WN:** Emborough; **WT:** Pool (Still) **W. Size:** 4 Acres. **Location: Nr. Rd:** Gurney Slade, 2nd right; **Main Rd:** B3139 to Emborough.
Ref: FH1582

EMBORUGH LAKE

Emborugh Lake, Emborugh Gr, Emborough, **SOMERSET**, **England**.
Contact/s: **Mr Rodney Miles** (Thatchers Tackle Shop), Thatchers Pet & Tackle Shop, 18 Queen St, Wells, Somerset, BA5 2DP.
(T) 01749 673513
Profile: FT: Coarse; **WN:** Emborugh Lake; **WT:** Lake (Still); **F. Size:** 5 Acres; **W. Size:** 4 Acres. **Location: Main Rd:** B3139; **Rail:** Bath.
Ref: FH1583

EMBSAY RESERVOIR

Embsay Reservoir, Embsay, Skipton, **YORKSHIRE (NORTH)**, BD23, **England**.
Contact/s: **Mr Ronnie Noble** (Secretary).
(T) 01756 795222
Profile: FT: Game; **WN:** Embsay; **WT:** Reservoir (Still).
Ref: FH1584

EMERALD POOL FISHERY

Emerald Pool Fishery, Puriton Rd, West Huntspill, Highbridge, **SOMERSET**, TA9 3NL, **England**.
Contact/s: **Mr Alan Wilkinson** (Manager).
(T) 01278 685304or794707
Profile: FT: Coarse; **WN:** Emerald; **WT:** Pond (Still); **F. Size:** 2 Acres; **W. Size:** 2 Acres.
Location: Nr. Rd: Puriton Road; **Main Rd:** A38 Bridgwater to Highbridge; **Rail:** Highbridge.
Ref: FH1585

EMFIELD COARSE FISHERY

Emfield Coarse Fishery, Egloskerry, Launceston, **CORNWALL**, **England**.
Profile: FT: Coarse; **WN:** Emfield; **WT:** Lake (Still); **F. Size:** 10 Acres; **W. Size:** 4 Acres.
Location: Main Rd: A30; **Rail:** Okehampton.
Ref: FH1586

EMMOTLAND PONDS

Emmotland Ponds, North Frodingham, Driffield, **HUMBERSIDE**, YO25 8JS, **England**.
Contact/s: **Ms Margaret Whitfield**.
(T) 01262 488226 (F) 01262 488226
Profile: FT: Coarse; **WN:** Emmotland; **WT:** Lake (Still) **W. Size:** 8 Acres. **Location: Nr. Rd:** B1249; **Main Rd:** A165; **Rail:** Driffield.
Ref: FH1587

EMRAL BROOK

Emral Brook, Halghton Mill, Worthenbury, **WREXHAM**, **England**.
Contact/s: **Mr John Turner** (Hon Secretary), Prince Albert Angling Society, 15 Pexhill Drive, Macclesfield, Cheshire, SK10 3LP.
(T) 01625 422010
Profile: FT: Coarse; **WN:** Emral; **WT:** Brook (Moving) **W. Size:** 1000 Metres. **Location: Nr. Rd:** B5069; **Rail:** Wrexham.
Ref: FH1588

EMY LAKE FISHERY

Emy Lake Fishery, Emyvale, Clones, **COUNTY MONAGHAN**, **Ireland**.
Profile: FT: Game; **WN:** Erne; **WT:** River (Moving).
Ref: FH1589

ENAGH TROUT FISHERY

Enagh Trout Fishery, 12 Judges Rd, Londonderry, **COUNTY LONDONDERRY**, BT47 1LN, **Northern Ireland**.
Profile: FT: Game; **WN:** Enagh Trout Fishery
Ref: FH1590

ENDCROFTS POND

Endcrofts Pond, Bury, **MANCHESTER (GREATER)**, BL, **England**.
Contact/s: **Mr Metcalfe** (Secretary).
(T) 0161 7975597
Profile: FT: Coarse; **WN:** Endcroft's; **WT:** Pond (Still).
Ref: FH1591

ENDRICK (RIVER)

River Endrick, Killearn, Glasgow, **STIRLING**, G63, **Scotland**.
Profile: FT: Game; **WN:** Endrick; **WT:** River (Moving) **W. Size:** 32000 Metres. **Location: Nr. Rd:** Killarn to Balfron.
Ref: FH1592

ENFIELD LOCK

Enfield Lock, Enfield, London, **LONDON (GREATER)**, EN2, **England**.
Contact/s: **Mr Terry Mansbridge** (Secretary), Lee Anglers Consortium, 7 Warren Rd, Chingford, London, E4 6QR.
(T) 020 75240869 (F) 020 75240869
Profile: FT: Game; **WN:** Enfield; **WT:** Lock (Still).
Ref: FH1593

ENGLEFIELD LAGOON

Englefield Lagoon, Searles Farm Lane, Pingewood, Reading, **BERKSHIRE**, RG, **England**.
Contact/s: **Mr Mick Cox** (Secretary), Dorstans, Hatch Lane, Brimpton Village, Reading, RG7 4TR.
(T) 0118 9714917
Ms Dusty Millar (Ticket Administrator), 238 Elgar Road South, Reading, Berkshire, RG3 0BW.
(T) 0118 9874882
Profile: FT: Coarse; **WN:** Englefield Lagoon; **WT:** Lake (Still) **W. Size:** 42 Acres.
Location: Nr. Rd: Berrys Lane; **Main Rd:** M4, junction 12.

Ref: FH1594

ENNERDALE LAKE FISHERY

Ennerdale Lake Fishery, Egremont, **CUMBRIA**, CA22, **England**.
Contact/s: **Mr D Crellin** (Secretary), 3 Parklands Drive, Egremont, Cumbria, CA22 2JL.
Mr E Brereton.
(T) 01946 814112
Mr Roy Rhodes (Conservation, Access and Recreation Manager), Rivington Water Treatment Works, Bolton Rd, Horwich, Bolton, BL6 7RN.
(T) 01204 664300
Profile: **FT:** Game; **WN:** Ennerdale; **WT:** Lake (Still). Location: **Rail:** Whitehaven.
Ref: FH1595

ENTON LAKES TROUT FISHERY

Enton Lakes Trout Fishery, Petworth Rd, Witley, Godalming, **SURREY**, GU8 5LZ, **England**.
Contact/s: **Mr Steve Hillbery**.
(T) 01428 682620 (F) 01428 682620
Profile: **FT:** Game; **WN:** Enton; **WT:** Lake (Still); **F. Size:** 40 Acres; **W. Size:** 16 Acres. Location: **Nr. Rd:** Petworth Road; **Main Rd:** A3; **Rail:** Milford.
Ref: FH1596

ENTWHISTLES RESERVOIR

Entwhistles Reservoir, Blackburn, **LANCASHIRE**, BL, **England**.
Contact/s: **Mr I Rigby** (Secretary), 10 Wayoh Croft, Edgworth, Bolton, BL7 0DF.
(T) 01204 852049
Mr Roy Rhodes (Conservation, Access and Recreation Manager), Rivington Water Treatment Works, Bolton Rd, Horwich, Bolton, BL6 7RN.
(T) 01204 664300
Profile: **FT:** Game; **WN:** Entwistles; **WT:** Lake (Still).
Ref: FH1597

EPSOM STEW POND

Epsom Stew Pond, Epsom, **SURREY**, KT17, **England**.
(W) www.calpac.bizland.com
Contact/s: **Mr Colin Trafford** (General Secretary).
(T) 020 82242617
Mrs Diane Wheeler (Secretary), 314 Old Lodge Lane, Purley, Surrey, CR8 4AQ.
(T) 020 86602766
Profile: **FT:** Coarse; **WN:** Stew; **WT:** Pond (Still) **W. Size:** 1 Acre. Location: **Nr. Rd:** Epsom to Malden Rushett; **Main Rd:** B280.
Ref: FH1604

ERCH (RIVER)

River Erch, Pwllheli, **GWYNEDD**, LL53, **Wales**.
Contact/s: **E W Evans** (Membership Secretary), 2 Fron - Oleu, Caernarfon Rd, Pwllheli, Gwynedd, LL53 5LN.
Mr Len Hicks (Secretary), Pwllheli and District Angling Association, 82 Abererch Rd, Pwllheli, Gwynedd, LL53 5LS.
(T) 01758 614885
Profile: **FT:** Game; **WN:** Erch; **WT:** River (Moving) **W. Size:** 11200 Metres. Location: **Nr. Rd:** A497; **Rail:** Pwllheli.
Ref: FH1605

ERCH (RIVER)

River Erch, Four Crosses, Llanymynech, **POWYS**, SY22, **Wales**.
Contact/s: **Mr G Pritchard** (Hon Secretary), 8 Dolwar, Four Crosses, Pwllheli.
(T) 01766 810548
Profile: **FT:** Game; **WN:** Erch; **WT:** River (Moving) **W. Size:** 12800 Metres. Location: **Nr. Rd:** Four Crosses to Pwllheli.
Ref: FH1606

EREWASH CANAL

Erewash Canal, Long Eaton, Nottingham, **NOTTINGHAMSHIRE**, NG10, **England**.
Contact/s: **Mr W Parker** (Secretary), Long Eaton and District Angling Federation, 75 College St, Long Eaton, Nottingham, NG9 1HR.
(T) 0115 9726170
Profile: **FT:** Coarse; **WN:** Erewash; **WT:** Canal (Still) **W. Size:** 2500 Metres.
Ref: FH1607

ERIC FISHWICK NATURE RESERVE

Eric Fishwick Nature Reserve, Cleveley Bridge, Cleveley Bank Lane, Scorton, Garstang, Preston, **LANCASHIRE**, PR3 1BY, **England**.
Contact/s: **Mr Eric Fishwick**.
(T) 01524 791637
Profile: **FT:** Combination; **WN:** Eric Fishwick Nature Reserve; **WT:** Combination (Still & Moving); **F. Size:** 20 Acres; **W. Size:** 8 Acres. Location: **Nr. Rd:** Cleveley Bridge Bank Lane; **Main Rd:** A1.
Ref: FH1608

ERICS POOL

Erics Pool, Shatterford Fishery, Kidderminster, **WORCESTERSHIRE**, DY, **England**.
Contact/s: **Mr Eric Lloyd** (Shatterford Fishery Manager).
(T) 01299 861597
Profile: **FT:** Coarse; **WN:** Erics; **WT:** Pool (Still) **W. Size:** 3 Acres. Location: **Nr. Rd:** A442.
Ref: FH1609

ERKINA (RIVER)

River Erkina, Kilkenny, **COUNTY KILKENNY**, **Ireland**.
Contact/s: **Ms Susan Lawlor** (Manager), Foodmarket, The Square, Durrow, County Kilkenny, Ireland.
(T) 050 236437
Profile: **FT:** Game; **WN:** Nore; **WT:** River (Moving).
Ref: FH1610

ERKINA (RIVER)

River Erkina, Rathdowney, **COUNTY LAOIS**, **Ireland**.
Contact/s: **Mr M White** (Secretary), Rathdowney Angling Club, Moorville, Rathdowney, County Laois, Ireland.
Profile: **FT:** Game; **WN:** Erkina; **WT:** River (Moving) **W. Size:** 6400 Metres.
Ref: FH1611

ERLESTOKE LAKE

Erlestoke Lake, Longwater, Erlestoke, Devizes, **WILTSHIRE**, SN10 5UE, **England**.
Contact/s: **D Hampton**.
Profile: **FT:** Coarse; **WN:** Erlestoke; **WT:** Lake (Still).
Ref: FH1612

ERNE (RIVER)

River Erne, Enniskillen, **COUNTY FERMANAGH**, BT93, **Northern Ireland**.
Contact/s: Manager, Erne Tackle, 118 Main St, Lisnaskea, Enniskillen, BT92 0JD.
(T) 028 67721969
Profile: **FT:** Game; **WN:** Erne; **WT:** River (Moving).
Ref: FH1613

ERNE (RIVER)

River Erne, Belleek, **COUNTY FERMANAGH**, BT93, **Northern Ireland**.
Contact/s: **Mr Michael McGrath**, Belleek Angling Ctre, The Thatch, Belleek, County Fermanagh, BT93 3FX.
(T) 028 68658181 (F) 028 68658181
Profile: **FT:** Combination; **WN:** Erne; **WT:** Combination (Still & Moving) **W. Size:** 3000 Metres. Location: **Nr. Rd:** Main Street; **Main Rd:** A46, A47, N3; **Rail:** Sligo.
Ref: FH1614

ERRIFF FISHERY

Erriff Fishery, Killary Harbour, Leenane, **COUNTY GALWAY**, **Ireland**.
Contact/s: Manager, Erriff Fishery Office, Aasleagh Lodge, Leenane.
(T) 095 42252
Profile: **FT:** Game; **WN:** Erriff Fishery; **WT:** Combination (Still & Moving) **W. Size:** 12800 Metres.
Ref: FH1615

ERRWOOD RESERVOIR

Errwood Reservoir, High Peak, **DERBYSHIRE**, SK17, **England**.
Contact/s: **Mr T Davis** (Chairman).
(T) 0161 4271180
Mr T Speake (Treasurer), 11 Cliffmere Cl, Cheadle Hulme, Cheshire.
(T) 0161 4397268
Profile: **FT:** Game; **WN:** Errwood; **WT:** Reservoir (Still) **W. Size:** 80 Acres. Location: **Nr. Rd:** Buxton; **Main Rd:** A5004.
Ref: FH1616

ESK (RIVER)

Esk (River), Forge Water & Gatehouse Water, Beckfoot, Ravenglass, **CUMBRIA**, **England**.
Contact/s: **Mr John Turner** (Hon Secretary), Prince Albert Angling Society, 15 Pexhill Drive, Macclesfield, Cheshire, SK10 3LP.
(T) 01625 422010
Profile: **FT:** Game; **WN:** Esk; **WT:** River (Moving) **W. Size:** 1000 Metres. Location: **Main Rd:** A595; **Rail:** Ravenglass.
Ref: FH1617

ESK (RIVER)

River Esk, Ravenglass, **CUMBRIA**, CA18, **England**.
Contact/s: **Mr D J Dixon** (Secretary), 1 Churchill Drive, Millom, Cumbria, LA18 5DD.
(T) 01229 774241
Profile: **FT:** Game; **WN:** Esk; **WT:** River (Moving). Location: **Nr. Rd:** Broad Muncaster Bridge; **Main Rd:** A595; **Rail:** Ravenglass.
Ref: FH1618

ESK (RIVER)

River Esk, Langholm, **DUMFRIES AND GALLOWAY**, DG13, **Scotland**.
Contact/s: **Mr Stephen Laverack** (Manager), Burnfoot House and Cottages, Burnfoot House, Langholm, Dumfries and Galloway, DG13 0NG.
(T) 01387 370611
Profile: **FT:** Game; **WN:** Esk; **WT:** River (Moving) **W. Size:** 1600 Metres. Location: **Main Rd:** M6.
Ref: FH1619

ESK (RIVER)

River Esk, Langholm, **DUMFRIES AND GALLOWAY**, DG13, **Scotland**.
Contact/s: **Mr George Graham** (Head River Watcher), Hagg Old School House, Canonbie, Dumfries and Galloway.
(T) 01387 71416
Profile: **FT:** Game; **WN:** Esk; **WT:** River (Moving). Location: **Main Rd:** A7.
Ref: FH1620

ESK (RIVER)

River Esk, Canonbie, **DUMFRIES AND GALLOWAY**, DG14, **Scotland**.
Contact/s: **Mr George Graham** (Head River Watcher), Hagg Old School House, Canonbie, Dumfries and Galloway.
(T) 01387 71416
Profile: **FT:** Game; **WN:** Esk; **WT:** River (Moving).
Ref: FH1621

ESK (RIVER)

River Esk, Limber Hill, Grimsby, **HUMBERSIDE**, DN37, **England**.
Profile: **FT:** Game; **WN:** Esk; **WT:** River (Moving). Location: **Nr. Rd:** Concrete Apron to Railway Bridge. **£Fr**
Ref: FH1622

ESK (RIVER)

River Esk, Lealholm, Whitby, **YORKSHIRE (NORTH)**, YO21, **England**.
Profile: **FT:** Game; **WN:** Esk; **WT:** River (Moving). Location: **Main Rd:** A171.
£Fr

Ref: FH1623

ESK (RIVER)

River Esk, Glaisdale, Whitby, **YORKSHIRE (NORTH)**, YO21, **England**.
Profile: **FT:** Game; **WN:** Esk; **WT:** River (Moving). **Location:** **Nr. Rd:** Ford; **Main Rd:** A171. £Fr
Ref: FH1624

ESK (RIVER)

River Esk, Danby, Whitby, **YORKSHIRE (NORTH)**, YO21, **England**.
Profile: **FT:** Game; **WN:** Esk; **WT:** River (Moving) **W. Size:** 12800 Metres.
Ref: FH1625

ESK (RIVER)

River Esk, Sleights, Whitby, **YORKSHIRE (NORTH)**, YO22, **England**.
Profile: **FT:** Game; **WN:** Esk; **WT:** River (Moving). **Location:** **Nr. Rd:** A169 road bridge. £Fr
Ref: FH1626

ESK (RIVER)

River Esk, Whitby, **YORKSHIRE (NORTH)**, YO2, **England**.
Contact/s: **Mr Eric Wilson** (Owner), Whitby Angling Supplies, 65 Haggersgate, Whitby, Yorkshire (North), YO21 3PP.
(T) 01947 603855 **(F)** 01947 603855
Profile: **FT:** Game; **WN:** Esk; **WT:** River (Moving) **W. Size:** 12800 Metres.
Ref: FH1627

ESK AND LIDDLE FISHERIES

Esk And Liddle Fisheries, Bailey Mill, Newcastleton, **SCOTTISH BORDERS**, TD9 0, **Scotland**.
(W) www.hoildaycottagescumbria.co.uk
Contact/s: **Mr George Graham** (Head River Watcher), Hagg Old School House, Canonbie, Dumfries and Galloway.
(T) 01387 71416
Mr Ian Bell (Manager), The Buccleuch Estate Limited, Ewesbank, Langholm, Dumfries and Galloway, DG13 0ND.
(T) 01387 380202
Mr T Ewart (Secretary), Esk and Liddle Fisheries Association, Drapers, Douglas Sq, Newcastleton, Scotland.
(T) 01387 375257
Mrs J Copeland (Accommodation Manager), Bailey Mill Farm Holidays and Trekking Ctre, Bailey Mill, Newcastleton, Scottish Borders, TD9 0TR.
(T) 01697 748617 **(F)** 01697 748074
Profile: **FT:** Game; **WN:** Esk And Liddle Fisheries; **WT:** River (Moving) **W. Size:** 11200 Metres. **Location:** **Nr. Rd:** B6318; **Main Rd:** A7; **Rail:** Carlisle.
Ref: FH1628

ESSEX CARP FISHERY

Essex Carp Fishery, Mollands Lane, South Ockendon, **ESSEX**, RM15, **England**.
Contact/s: Manager, Hornchurch Angling Ctre, 226 Hornchurch Rd, Hornchurch, Essex, RM11 1QJ.
(T) 01708 620608
Profile: **FT:** Coarse; **WN:** Essex Carp Fishery; **WT:** Lake (Still).
Ref: FH1629

ESTHWAITE WATER

Esthwaite Water, The Boathouse, Ridding Wood, Hawkshead, Ambleside, **CUMBRIA**, LA22 0QF, **England**.
(W) www.fishlink.com/hawkshead
Contact/s: **Mr David Coleman** (Fishery Manager).
(T) 01539 436541 **(F)** 01539 436541
(E) trout@hawkshead.demon.co.uk
Mr Nigel Woodhouse (Owner).
(T) 01539 436541 **(F)** 01539 436541
(E) trout@hawkshead.demon.co.uk
Profile: **FT:** Combination; **WN:** Esthwaite; **WT:** Lake (Still) **W. Size:** 280 Acres. **Location:** **Nr. Rd:** B5285 Hawkshead to Bowness; **Main Rd:** A590; **Rail:** Windermere.
Ref: FH1630

ETTERICK (RIVER)

River Etterick, Selkirk, **SCOTTISH BORDERS**, TD7, **Scotland**.
Contact/s: **Mr Ian Gibson** (owner), Gibson and Gibson, 9 High St, Selkirk, Selkirkshire, TD7 4BZ.
(T) 01750 21398
Profile: **FT:** Game; **WN:** Etterick; **WT:** River (Moving).
Ref: FH1631

ETTRICK AND YARROW (RIVER)

Rivers Ettrick And Yarrow, The Buccleuch Estates Limited, The Estate Office, Bowhill, Selkirk, **SCOTTISH BORDERS**, TD7 5ES, **Scotland**.
Contact/s: **Mrs J Crosbie** (Per The Factor Ghillie).
(T) 01750 20753or32334 **(F)** 01750 22172
(E) jcrosbie@buccleuch.com
Profile: **FT:** Game; **WN:** Ettrick and Yarrow; **WT:** River (Moving).
Ref: FH1632

EUREKA

Eureka Fisheries, Ashford, **KENT**, **England**.
Contact/s: **Hugh** (Owner).
(T) 07973 410973
Terry.
(T) 07931 211243
Profile: **FT:** Coarse; **WN:** Eureka FisheriesWT: Lake.
Ref: FH1633

EVE A LYN FARM

Eve-A-Lyn Farm, Tarran Way, Moreton, Wirral, **MERSEYSIDE**, CH46, **England**.
Contact/s: **Brain**.
(T) 0151 6051003
Profile: **FT:** Coarse; **WN:** Eve-a-Lyn; **WT:** Lake (Still). **Location:** **Nr. Rd:** Tarran Way; **Main Rd:** A551.
Ref: FH1634

EVESBATCH FISHERIES

Evesbatch Fisheries, Evesbatch, Worcester, **WORCESTERSHIRE**, WR, **England**.
Contact/s: **Mr Dave Beresford** (Manager), Allans Fishing Tackle, 26-30 Malvern Rd, Worcester, Worcestershire, WR2 4LG.
(T) 01905 422107 **(F)** 01905 422107
Profile: **FT:** Coarse; **WN:** Evesbatch Fisheries; **WT:** Lake (Still) **W. Size:** 3 Acres. **Location:** **Nr. Rd:** Worcester to Hereford; **Main Rd:** A4103.
Ref: FH1635

EVESBATCH TOP LAKE

Evesbatch Top Lake, Ledbury, **HEREFORDSHIRE**, HR8, **England**.
Contact/s: **Mr S A Sturge** (Manager), Ledbury Tackle Ctre, 3 The Southend, Ledbury, Herefordshire, HR8 2EY.
(T) 01531 632768 **(F)** 01531 632768
Profile: **FT:** Coarse; **WN:** Top; **WT:** Lake (Still) **W. Size:** 2 Acres.
Ref: FH1636

EWENNY (RIVER)

River Ewenny, Waterston, Milford Haven, **PEMBROKESHIRE**, SA73, **Wales**.
Contact/s: **Mr P Lawson** (Hon Secretary), 26 Meadow Rise, Brynna, Glamorgan (Vale of), CF72 9TB.
Profile: **FT:** Game; **WN:** Ewenny; **WT:** River (Moving) **W. Size:** 17600 Metres. **Location:** **Nr. Rd:** Waterston to Pencoed.
Ref: FH1637

EWSONS WATER

Ewsons Water, Kings Court Farm, Roxwell, Chelmsford, **ESSEX**, CM, **England**.
(W) www.bdac.co.uk
Contact/s: **Mr Derek Howard** (Hon Treasurer), Billericay and District Angling Club, 4 Long Meadow Drive, Wickford, Essex, SS11 8AX.
(T) 01268 734468
Profile: **FT:** Coarse; **WN:** Ewsons Water; **WT:** Lake (Still); **F. Size:** 6 Acres; **W. Size:** 5 Acres. **Location:** **Nr. Rd:** A414; **Main Rd:** A414; **Rail:** Chelmsford.
Ref: FH1638

EXE (RIVER)

River Exe, Cowley Bridge, Exeter, **DEVON**, EX, **England**.
Contact/s: **Mr Barry Lucas** (Hon Secretary), Mayfield, Gorwyn Lane, Cheriton Bishop, Exeter, EX6 6JL.
(T) 01647 24566
Profile: **FT:** Coarse; **WN:** Exe; **WT:** River (Moving) **W. Size:** 9600 Metres. **Location:** **Main Rd:** A380, South of Exeter.
Ref: FH1639

EXE (RIVER)

River Exe, Hatswell Beat, Hatswell, Lower Washfield, Tiverton, **DEVON**, EX16 9, **England**.
Contact/s: **Mr David Rice**, Hatswell Cottage, Lower Washfield, Tiverton, Devon, EX16 9PE. **(F)** 01884 243991 **(M)** 07976 354962
Profile: **FT:** Game; **WN:** Exe; **WT:** River (Moving) **W. Size:** 670 Metres. **Location:** **Nr. Rd:** A396; **Main Rd:** M5; **Rail:** Tiverton Parkway.
Ref: FH1640

EXE (RIVER)

River Exe, Killerton Estate, Killerton, Exeter, **DEVON**, EX5 3LE, **England**.
Profile: **FT:** Coarse; **WN:** Exe; **WT:** Tributary (Moving).
Ref: FH1641

EXE (RIVER)

River Exe, Stoke Canon, Exeter, **DEVON**, EX, **England**.
Contact/s: **Mr Roddy Rae**, Half Stone Sporting Agency, 6 Hescane Park, Cheriton Bishop, Exeter, EX6 6JP.
(T) 01647 24643 **(F)** 01647 24643
Profile: **FT:** Game; **WN:** Exe; **WT:** River (Moving) **W. Size:** 4000 Metres. **Location:** **Nr. Rd:** Stoke Canon and Crewe.
Ref: FH1642

EXE (RIVER)

Exe (River), Flood Relief & Trews Weir, Okehampton Rd, Exeter, **DEVON**, **England**.
Contact/s: **Exeter Angling**.
(T) 01392 436404
Profile: **FT:** Coarse; **WN:** Exe; **WT:** River (Moving). **Location:** **Nr. Rd:** Okehampton Street; **Main Rd:** A30; **Rail:** Exeter.
Ref: FH1643

EXE (RIVER)

River Exe, Dulverton, **SOMERSET**, TA22, **England**.
Contact/s: **Mr Lance Nicholson** (Manager), Lance Nicholson, 9 High St, Dulverton, Somerset, TA22 9HB.
(T) 01398 323409
Profile: **FT:** Game; **WN:** Exe; **WT:** River (Moving).
Ref: FH1644

EXE VALLEY FISHERY

Exe Valley Fishery, Exebridge, Dulverton, **SOMERSET**, TA22 9AY, **England**.
Contact/s: **Mr Hugh Maund** (Manager).
(T) 01398 323328 **(F)** 01398 324079
Profile: **FT:** Game; **WN:** Exe Valley Fishery; **WT:** Lake (Still). **Location:** **Nr. Rd:** B3222; **Main Rd:** A396; **Rail:** Tiverton Parkway.
Ref: FH1645

EXEMOOR FARM

Exemoor Farm, Week St. Mary, Bude, **DEVON**, EX22 6UX, **England**.
Contact/s: **Mr A R Mills**.
(T) 01566 781366
Profile: **FT:** Coarse; **WN:** Exemoor Farm; **WT:** Lake (Still) **W. Size:** 1 Acre. **Location:** **Nr. Rd:** Bude to Camelford Road; **Main Rd:** A39.

Ref: FH1646

EXETER CANAL

Exeter Canal, Haven Rd, Lime Kilns, Exeter, **DEVON**, EX, **England**.
Contact/s: **Mr Barry Lucas** (Hon Secretary), Mayfield, Gorwyn Lane, Cheriton Bishop, Exeter, EX6 6JL.
(T) 01647 24566
Profile: **FT:** Coarse; **WN:** Exeter; **WT:** Canal (Still) **W. Size:** 3600 Metres. **Location:** **Nr. Rd:** Haven Road; **Main Rd:** A379.
Ref: FH1647

EXETER SHIP CANAL

Exeter Ship Canal, Exeter, **DEVON**, EX, **England**.
Contact/s: **Mr Barry Lucas** (Hon Secretary), Mayfield, Gorwyn Lane, Cheriton Bishop, Exeter, EX6 6JL.
(T) 01647 24566
Profile: **FT:** Coarse; **WN:** Exeter Ship; **WT:** Canal (Still) **W. Size:** 9600 Metres. **Location:** **Nr. Rd:** Basin to Turflock.
Ref: FH1648

EYEBROOK TROUT FISHERY

Eyebrook Trout Fishery, Corus Tubes, Corby Water Company, Great Easton Rd, Market Harborough, **LEICESTERSHIRE**, LE16 8RP, **England**.
Contact/s: **Mr Roger Marshall** (Manager).
(T) 01536 770264or770256 **(F)** 01536 404699
(E) roger.marshall@tubes.britishsteel.co.uk
Profile: **FT:** Game; **WN:** Eyebrook; **WT:** Reservoir (Still); **F. Size:** 650 Acres; **W. Size:** 400 Acres. **Location:** **Nr. Rd:** Great Easton Road; **Main Rd:** A6003; **Rail:** Kettering to Oakham.
Ref: FH1649

EYNSHAM LOCK

Eynsham Lock, Eynsham, Witney, **OXFORDSHIRE**, OX8, **England**.
Contact/s: Fishery Contact.
(T) 01865 881324
Recreational Manager, The Environment Agency, Kings Meadow Rd, Reading, Berkshire, RG1 8DQ.
(T) 0118 9535000 **(F)** 0118 9500388
Profile: **FT:** Coarse; **WN:** Thames; **WT:** Lock (Still). **Location:** **Nr. Rd:** Swinford Toll Bridge; **Main Rd:** B4044.
Ref: FH1650

FACHWEN POOL

Fachwen Pool, Newtown, **POWYS**, SY16, **Wales**.
Contact/s: **Mr Brian Bancroft** (Club Secretary).
(T) 01686 624172
Mr Steve Potts (Secretary), Severnside and Newtown Angling Club, 902 Falcon Court, Newton, Powys, SY16 1LQ.
(T) 01686 624871
Profile: **FT:** Coarse; **WN:** Fachwen; **WT:** Pool (Still) **W. Size:** 12 Acres.
Ref: FH1651

FAIRLANDS VALLEY PARK

Fairlands Valley Park, Stevenage, **HERTFORDSHIRE**, SG2 0BL, **England**.
Contact/s: **Mr Gavin Davis** (Park Manager), Six Hills Way, Stevenage, Hertfordshire, SG2 0BL.
(T) 01438 353241
Profile: **FT:** Coarse; **WN:** Fairlands; **WT:** Lake (Still) **W. Size:** 10 Acres. **Location:** **Nr. Rd:** Signposted from the A1m junction 7; **Main Rd:** A1.
Ref: FH1652

FAIRLOP EAST LAKE

Fairlop East Lake, Hainault, Romford, **ESSEX**, RM, **England**.
Contact/s: Fishery Manager.
(T) 020 85009911
Profile: **FT:** Coarse; **WN:** Fairlop East; **WT:** Lake (Still) **W. Size:** 3 Acres. **Location:** **Nr. Rd:** Forest Road; **Main Rd:** Fulwell Cross roundabout to Romford Road,; **Rail:** Fairlop Underground.
Ref: FH1653

FAIRLOP WATERS

Fairlop Waters, Forest Rd, Fulwell Cross, Ilford, **ESSEX**, IG6 3HN, **England**.
Contact/s: **Mr Bob Able** (Head Grounds Man).
(T) 020 85009911 or 85041929
Profile: **FT:** Coarse; **WN:** Fairlop Waters; **WT:** Lake (Still) **W. Size:** 11 Acres. **Location:** **Nr. Rd:** A123 to Fulwell Cross.
Ref: FH1654

FAIROAK FISHERY

Fairoak Fishery, The Cot, St. Arvans, Chepstow, **MONMOUTHSHIRE**, NP16 6HQ, **Wales**.
Contact/s: **Mr Nick Brewin** (Proprietor).
(T) 01291 689711
Profile: **FT:** Game; **WN:** Fairoak Fishery; **WT:** Pond (Still); **F. Size:** 5 Acres; **W. Size:** 3 Acres. **Location:** **Main Rd:** A466; **Rail:** Chepstow.
Ref: FH1655

FAIRVIEW LAKE

Fairview Lake, Carwood Common, Thorpe Willoughby, Carwood, **YORKSHIRE (NORTH)**, **England**.
Contact/s: Fishery Manager.
(T) 01757 268566
Profile: **FT:** Coarse; **WN:** Fairview; **WT:** Lake (Still); **F. Size:** 4 Acres; **W. Size:** 2 Acres. **Location:** **Nr. Rd:** A63; **Rail:** Selby.
Ref: FH1656

FAIRY WATER

Fairy Water, Omagh, **COUNTY TYRONE**, BT78 5, **Northern Ireland**.
Profile: **FT:** Coarse; **WN:** Fairy Water; **WT:** River (Moving). **Location:** **Nr. Rd:** Beltany Road; **Main Rd:** A5.
Ref: FH1657

FALKENVIL FISHERY

Falkenvil Fishery, The Barn, Falkenvil, Downash, Hailsham, **SUSSEX (EAST)**, BN27 2RJ, **England**.
Contact/s: **Mr Roland Knight** (Partner).
(T) 01323 440700
Profile: **FT:** Coarse; **WN:** Falkenvil Fishery; **WT:** Lake (Still) **W. Size:** 4 Acres. **Location:** **Nr. Rd:** B2104; **Main Rd:** A22 to Eastbourne.
Ref: FH1658

FAN LODGE

Fan Lodge, Bickershaw, Wigan, **LANCASHIRE**, WN, **England**.
(W) www.wiganaa.f9.co.uk
Contact/s: **Mr Gerry Wilson** (Hon Secretary), Wigan and District Angling Association, 11 Guildford Avenue, Chorley, Lancashire, PR6 8TG.
(T) 01257 265905 **(M)** gerry
Profile: **FT:** Coarse; **WN:** Fan Lodge; **WT:** Lake (Still) **W. Size:** 2 Acres. **Location:** **Nr. Rd:** B5375; **Main Rd:** A573, A577, M6, junction 26.
Ref: FH1659

FANE (RIVER)

River Fane, Crossmaglen, Newry, **COUNTY DOWN**, BT35, **Northern Ireland**.
Contact/s: **Mr Eugene Murphy**.
(T) 028 30868607
Mr J Cunningham (Secretary), 21 Forkhill Rd, Mullach Ban, County Armagh, BT35 9XL.
(T) 028 30889187
Mr Phil Nolan.
(T) 028 30868074
Profile: **FT:** Game; **WN:** Fane; **WT:** River (Moving).
Ref: FH1660

FANE (RIVER)

River Fane, Knock Bridge, Dundalk, **COUNTY LOUTH**, **Ireland**.
Contact/s: Secretary, Dundalk Brown Trout Angling Club, 3 Mill Rd, Forkhill, Newry, BT35 95J.
Mr John Clarke (Club Secretary).
(T) 028 30888378
Profile: **FT:** Game; **WN:** Fane; **WT:** River (Moving) **W. Size:** 32000 Metres. **Location:** **Rail:** Dundalk.
Ref: FH1661

FANSHAWE LANE POOL

Fanshawe Lane Pool, Capesthorne Estate, Siddington, Macclesfield, **CHESHIRE**, SK11, **England**.
Contact/s: **Ms Liz Hayes** (Manager).
(T) 01625 251262
Profile: **FT:** Coarse; **WN:** Fanshawe Lane; **WT:** Pond (Still) **W. Size:** 2 Acres. **Location:** **Nr. Rd:** Famshawe Lane; **Main Rd:** A34; **Rail:** Alderley Edge.
Ref: FH1662

FAR GRANGE PARK

Far Grange Caravan And Country Park, Horsea Rd, Skipsea, Driffield, **HUMBERSIDE**, YO25 8SY, **England**.
(W) www.fargrangepark.co.uk
Contact/s: **Mr Mike McCann** (Owner).
(T) 01262 468293 **(F)** 01262 468648
(E) enquires@fargrangepark.co.uk
Profile: **FT:** Coarse; **WN:** Far Grange Caravan And Country Park; **WT:** Lake (Still); **F. Size:** 160 Acres; **W. Size:** 8 Acres. **Location:** **Nr. Rd:** B1242; **Main Rd:** A165; **Rail:** Bridlington.
Ref: FH1663

FARINGDON LAKE

Faringdon Lake, Faringdon, **OXFORDSHIRE**, SN7, **England**.
Contact/s: **Mr Peter Turner** (Fishery Manager).
(T) 01367 241044
Profile: **FT:** Coarse; **WN:** Faringdon; **WT:** Lake (Still).
Ref: FH1664

FARINGTON LODGES

Farington Lodges, Lodge Lane, Farington, Preston, **LANCASHIRE**, PR, **England**.
Contact/s: **Brian** (Manager), Lostock Tackle Box, 16 Watkin Lane, Lostock Hall, Preston, PR5 5RD.
(T) 01772 626585 **(F)** 01772 626584
Profile: **FT:** Coarse; **WN:** Farington Lodges; **WT:** Lake (Still). **Location:** **Nr. Rd:** Lodge Lane; **Main Rd:** A6 south.
Ref: FH1665

FARLEYER BEAT

Farleyer Beat, Kenmore, Aberfeldy, **PERTH AND KINROSS**, PH15, **Scotland**.
(W) www.fishingnet.com/beats/farleyer.htm
Contact/s: **Mr Micheal Smith** (Manager), Cuilaluinn, Aberfeldy, Perth and Kinross, PH15 2JW.
(T) 01887 820302 **(F)** 01887 829644
Profile: **FT:** Game; **WN:** See above; **WT:** Pool (Still).
Ref: FH1666

FARLEYMOOR LAKE

Farleymoor Lake, Nine Mile Ride, Bracknell, **BERKSHIRE**, RG12 2QW, **England**.
Mr Nigel Smith (Senior Ranger).
(T) 01344 354441
Profile: **FT:** Coarse; **WN:** Farleymoor; **WT:** Lake (Still) **W. Size:** 8 Acres. **Location:** **Main Rd:** A246.
Ref: FH1667

FARLOWS LAKE

Farlows Lake, Ford Lane, Iver, **BUCKINGHAMSHIRE**, SL0 9LL, **England**.
Contact/s: **Buzz** (Manager), Boyer Leisure Ltd, Heron's Point Tackle Shop, Farlow's Lake, Ford Lane, Iver SL0 9LL.
(T) 01753 630302or01895444707 **(F)** 01753 630302
(E) info@boyer.co.uk
Profile: **FT:** Coarse; **WN:** Farlows Lake; **WT:** Gravel Pit (Still) **W. Size:** 35 Acres. **Location:** **Main Rd:** M25, A4007, A412;

Rail: West Drayton.
Ref: FH1668

FARM LODGE

Farm Lodge, Far Hey Cl, Radcliffe, Manchester, **MANCHESTER (GREATER)**, M26, **England**.
Contact/s: **Mr Terence A McKee** (Secretary), Bolton and District Angling Association, 1 Lever Edge Lane, Bolton, Lancashire, BL3 3BU.
(T) 01204 393726
Profile: **FT:** Coarse; **WN:** Farm Lodge; **WT:** Lake (Still). **Location:** **Nr. Rd:** Far Hey Close; **Main Rd:** A6053 from Bolton to Little Lever.
Ref: FH1669

FARM PONDS

Farm Ponds, Burshill, Driffield, **HUMBERSIDE**, YO25, **England**.
Contact/s: Fishery Manager.
(T) 01964 542375
Profile: **FT:** Coarse; **WN:** Farm; **WT:** Gravel Pit (Still) **W. Size:** 2 Acres. **Location:** **Nr. Rd:** Brandesburton to Hempholme; **Main Rd:** A165.
Ref: FH1670

FARM POOL

Farm Pool, Antrobus, Northwich, **CHESHIRE**, CW9, **England**.
Contact/s: **Mr Neil Jupp** (Club Secretary), Lymm Angling Club, PO Box 350, Warrington, Cheshire, WA2 9FB.
(T) 01925 411774
Profile: **FT:** Coarse; **WN:** Farm; **WT:** Pool (Still). **Location:** **Nr. Rd:** Foggs Lane; **Main Rd:** A559 to Warrington.
Ref: FH1671

FARMHOUSE LAKE (THE)

Farmhouse Lake (The), Kemble, Cirencester, **GLOUCESTERSHIRE**, GL7, **England**.
Contact/s: **Mr Steve Rowley**, Golden Lands Cottage, 177 Collingbourne Rd, Burbage, Malborogh, Wiltshire, SN8 3RU.
(T) 01793 562163
Profile: **FT:** Coarse; **WN:** The Farmhouse Lake; **WT:** Lake (Still).
Ref: FH1672

FARMIRE

Farmire, North St, Ripon, **YORKSHIRE (NORTH)**, HG4, **England**.
Contact/s: **Mr Bernard Thain** (Manager), Ripon Angling Ctre, 58-59 North St, Ripon, Yorkshire (North), HG4 1EN.
(T) 01765 604666 **(F)** 01765 603933
Profile: **FT:** Coarse; **WN:** Farmire; **WT:** Lake (Still). **Location:** **Nr. Rd:** North Street.
Ref: FH1673

FARMIRE TROUT FISHERY

Farmire Trout Fishery, Farmire House, Stang Lane, Farnham, Knaresborough, **YORKSHIRE (NORTH)**, HG5 9JW, **England**.
Contact/s: **Mr Rob McDougall** (Owner).
(T) 01423 866417
Profile: **FT:** Game; **WN:** Farmire Trout Fishery; **WT:** Reservoir (Still).
Ref: FH1674

FARMOOR 1 RESERVOIR

Farmoor 1 Reservoir, Cumnor Rd, Witney, **OXFORDSHIRE**, OX8, **England**.
Contact/s: **Mr W Ward** (Hon Secretary), Farmoor Fly Fishing Club, 17 Perrot Cl, North Leigh, Oxfordshire, OX8 6RU.
(T) 01993 881503
Profile: **FT:** Game; **WN:** Farmoor 1; **WT:** Reservoir (Still). **Location:** **Nr. Rd:** B4017; **Main Rd:** B4044; **Rail:** Oxford.
Ref: FH1675

FARMOOR TROUT FISHERY

Farmoor Trout Fishery, Cumnor Rd, Farmoor, Oxford, **OXFORDSHIRE**, OX2 9NS, **England**.
Contact/s: **Mr Damien Wood**.
(T) 01865 863033
Mr Steven Symonds.
(T) 01865 863033
Profile: **FT:** Game; **WN:** Farmoor Trout Fishery; **WT:** Lake (Still); **F. Size:** 500 Acres; **W. Size:** 240 Acres. **Location:** **Nr. Rd:** B4017; **Main Rd:** A420; **Rail:** Oxford.
Ref: FH1676

FARNHAM FLINT

Farnham Flint, Cottage Lane, Reading, **BERKSHIRE**, RG, **England**.
Contact/s: **Mr Bill Brown-Lee** (Manager).
(T) 0118 9417368
Ms Dusty Millar (Ticket Administrator), 238 Elgar Road South, Reading, Berkshire, RG3 0BW.
(T) 0118 9874882
Profile: **FT:** Coarse; **WN:** Farnham Flint; **WT:** Lake (Still) **W. Size:** 27 Acres. **Location:** **Nr. Rd:** Cottage Lane; **Main Rd:** M4, junction 12.
Ref: FH1677

FAUGHAN (RIVER)

River Faughan, Claudy, Londonderry, **COUNTY LONDONDERRY**, BT47, **Northern Ireland**.
Contact/s: Manager, The Loughs Agency, 24 Victoria Rd, Londonderry, County Londonderry, BT47 2AB.
(T) 028 71342100
Ms Sharon Thompson (Office Manager), The River Faughan Anglers Limited, 26A Carlise Rd, Londonderry, County Londonderry, BT48 6JW.
(T) 028 71267781 **(F)** 028 71267781 **(M)** 07790 018956
Profile: **FT:** Game; **WN:** Faughan; **WT:** River (Moving) **W. Size:** 49600 Metres. **Location:** **Main Rd:** Belfast; **Rail:** Londonderry.
Ref: FH1678

FAUGHAN (RIVER)

River Faughan, Londonderry, **COUNTY LONDONDERRY**, BT47, **Northern Ireland**.
Contact/s: **Mr Lance Thompson** (Manager), 26a Carlisle Rd, Londonderry, County Londonderry, BT47 6JW.
(T) 028 71342383
Profile: **FT:** Game; **WN:** Faughan; **WT:** River (Moving) **W. Size:** 46500 Metres. **Location:** **Nr. Rd:** Belfast to Limarady; **Rail:** Londonderry.
Ref: FH1679

FEILDES WEIR

Feildes Weir, Old River Lea, Hoddesdon, **HERTFORDSHIRE**, EN11, **England**.
Contact/s: **Mr Terry Mansbridge** (Secretary), Lee Anglers Consortium, 7 Warren Rd, Chingford, London, E4 6QR.
(T) 020 75240869 **(F)** 020 75240869
Profile: **FT:** Coarse; **WN:** Feildes; **WT:** Weir (Moving). **Location:** **Nr. Rd:** Ratty's Lane; **Main Rd:** A1170.
Ref: FH1680

FELBRIGG HALL LAKE

Felbrigg Hall Lake, Felbrigg Hall, Hall Rd, Cromer, **NORFOLK**, NR27, **England**.
Contact/s: Fishery Manager.
(T) 01692 403162
Profile: **FT:** Coarse; **WN:** Felbrigg; **WT:** Lake (Still); **F. Size:** 5 Acres; **W. Size:** 3 Acres. **Location:** **Nr. Rd:** Hall Road; **Main Rd:** B1436; **Rail:** Cromer.
Ref: FH1681

FELGRIGG LAKE

Felgrigg Lake, Holt, **NORFOLK**, NR25, **England**.
Contact/s: Fishery Manager.
(T) 01263 712366
Profile: **FT:** Coarse; **WN:** Felgrigg; **WT:** Lake (Still).
Ref: FH1682

FELIN-Y-GORS FISHERIES

Felin-Y-Gors Fisheries, St Asaph Rd, Bodelwyddan, Rhyl, **DENBIGHSHIRE**, LL18 5UY, **Wales**.
Contact/s: **Mr Robert Monshin** (Manager).
(T) 01352 720965 daytime
Profile: **FT:** Game; **WN:** Felin-Y-Gors Fisheries; **WT:** Lake (Still) **W. Size:** 10 Acres. **Location:** **Nr. Rd:** St Asaph Road.
Ref: FH1683

FELIX FARM TROUT FISHERY

Felix Farm Trout Fishery, Howe Lane, Binfield, Bracknell, **BERKSHIRE**, RG42 5QL, **England**.
Contact/s: **Mr Martin J Suddards**.
(T) 0118 9345527or01734345527 **(F)** 0118 9345527
Mr P Penrhain (Owner).
(T) 01734 345527
Profile: **FT:** Game; **WN:** Felix Farm Trout Fishery; **WT:** Gravel Pit (Still); **F. Size:** 10 Acres; **W. Size:** 7 Acres. **Location:** **Nr. Rd:** Howe Lane; **Main Rd:** B3024 to Twyford; **Rail:** Bracknell.
Ref: FH1684

FELLGATE FISHERIES

Fellgate Fisheries, Lakeside Public House, Bolden, Jarrow, **TYNE AND WEAR**, NE32, **England**.
Contact/s: Warden, Tyne Anglers Alliance, PO Box 72, Heaton Rd, Newcastle upon Tyne.
(T) 0191 2681613
Warden.
(T) 0191 2742547or4286393
Profile: **FT:** Coarse; **WN:** Fellgate Fisheries; **WT:** Gravel Pit (Still).
Ref: FH1685

FELLGATE PONDS

Fellgate Ponds, Gateshead, **TYNE AND WEAR**, NE11, **England**.
Contact/s: **Mr George Atkin**, 82 Glebe Trce, Dunston, Gateshead, Tyne and Wear, NE11 9NQ.
(T) 0191 4600200
Profile: **FT:** Coarse; **WN:** Fellgate; **WT:** Pond (Still).
Ref: FH1686

FELMERSHAM (RIVER)

River Felmersham, Pavenham, Bedford, **BEDFORDSHIRE**, MK43, **England**.
Contact/s: **Mr R Ward** (Secretary), 15 Kingfisher Rd, Flitwick, Bedfordshire, MK45 1RA.
Profile: **FT:** Coarse; **WN:** Felmersham; **WT:** River (Moving).
Ref: FH1687

FELMERSHAM GRAVEL PITS

Felmersham Gravel Pits, Felmersham, Bedford, **BEDFORDSHIRE**, MK43, **England**.
Contact/s: **Mr G Buss** (Secretary), 1 Easthill Rd, Houghton Regis, Dunstable, Bedfordshire, LU5 5EQ.
(T) 01582 28114
Profile: **FT:** Coarse; **WN:** Felmersham Gravel Pits; **WT:** Gravel Pit (Still). **Location:** **Main Rd:** A6 to Bedford.
Ref: FH1688

FELMINGHAM MILL LAKES

Felmingham Mill Lakes, Aylsham, Norwich, **NORFOLK**, NR11, **England**.
Contact/s: Fishery Manager.
(T) 01263 735106
Profile: **FT:** Coarse; **WN:** Felmingham Mill; **WT:** Lake (Still).
Ref: FH1689

FELTHORPE LAKE

Felthorpe Lake, Brick Kiln Rd, Felthorpe, Norwich, **NORFOLK**, NR, **England**.
Contact/s: **Mr David Brandish** (Fishery Manager).
(T) 07754 277937 **(M)** 07769 704808
Profile: **FT:** Coarse; **WN:** Felthorpe; **WT:** Lake (Still). **Location:** **Nr. Rd:** Brick Kiln Road; **Main Rd:** B1149.
Ref: FH1690

FELTON FENCE FARM PONDS

Felton Fence Farm Ponds, Long Framlington, Morpeth, **NORTHUMBERLAND**, NE65,

England.
Contact/s: Mr A Robinson.
(T) 01665 570205
Profile: FT: Coarse; WN: Felton Fence; WT: Pond (Still). Location: Nr. Rd: B6345; Main Rd: A697.
Ref: FH1691

FEN DRAYTON COMPLEX

Fen Drayton Complex, Fen Drayton, Cambridge, **CAMBRIDGESHIRE**, CB4, **England**.
Contact/s: Manager, Emneth Angling Ctre, 21 Gaultree Sq, Emneth, Wisbech, Cambridgeshire, PE14 8DA.
(T) 01945 589920
Mr Neil Prior (Head Bailiff).
(T) 01954 303345evenings
Profile: FT: Combination; WN: Fen Drayton; WT: Lake (Still). Location: Nr. Rd: St Ives to Cambridge; Main Rd: A604.
Ref: FH1692

FEN DRAYTON LAKE

Fen Drayton Lake, Fen Drayton, Cambridge, **CAMBRIDGESHIRE**, CB4, **England**.
Profile: FT: Coarse; WN: Fen Drayton; WT: Gravel Pit (Still) W. Size: 30 Acres.
Ref: FH1693

FENDROD LAKE

Fendrod Lake, Llansamlet Enterprise Park, Valley Way, Llansanlet, Swansea, SA2 0RU, **Wales**.
Contact/s: Mr Alan Godrich (Head Bailiff).
(T) 01792 797868
Mr Davie Gough (Secretary), Brynmill and District Angling Club, 226 Mynydd Garnllwyd Rd, Morrington, Swansea.
(T) 01792 701191
Profile: FT: Coarse; WN: Fendrod; WT: Lake (Still); F. Size: 25 Acres; W. Size: 17 Acres.
Location: Nr. Rd: Llansanlet; Main Rd: M4; Rail: Swansea.
Ref: FH1694

FENECK POND

Feneck Pond, Cowley Bridge, Exeter, **DEVON**, EX, **England**.
Contact/s: Mr Barry Lucas (Hon Secretary), Mayfield, Gorwyn Lane, Cheriton Bishop, Exeter, EX6 6JL.
(T) 01647 24566
Profile: FT: Coarse; WN: Feneck; WT: Pond (Still).
Ref: FH1695

FENLAND FISHERIES

Fenland Fisheries, Fish Farm, Meadow Drove, Earith, Huntingdon, **CAMBRIDGESHIRE**, PE17 3QF, **England**.
Contact/s: Mr Mike Hawes (Manager).
(T) 01487 841858
Profile: FT: Combination; WN: Fenland Fisheries; WT: Lake (Still) W. Size: 9 Acres.
Location: Nr. Rd: A1123 to Earith; Main Rd: M11.
Ref: FH1696

FENNES FISHERIES

Fennes Fisheries, Fennes Rd, Bocking, Braintree, **ESSEX**, CM7 5LB, **England**.
(W) www.fisheries.co.uk
Contact/s: Mr Kevin Chapman (Manager).
(T) 01376 323285 (F) 01376 322591
Profile: FT: Coarse; WN: Fennes Fisheries; WT: Combination (Still & Moving) W. Size: 11 Acres. Location: Nr. Rd: Bocking Church Street; Main Rd: A120 or A131 North of Chelmsford; Rail: Braintree.
Ref: FH1697

FENWICK TROUT FISHERY

Fenwick Trout Fishery, Old Coach Rd, Dunmere, Bodmin, **CORNWALL**, PL31 2RD, **England**.
Contact/s: Mr David Thomas.
(T) 01208 78296
Profile: FT: Game; WN: Fenwick Trout Fishery; WT: Combination (Still & Moving) W. Size: 2 Acres. Location: Nr. Rd: Weybridge Road; Main Rd: A389.
Ref: FH1698

FERNDALE

Ferndale, Rockhead, Delabole, **CORNWALL**, PL33 9AA, **England**.
Contact/s: Mr Steve Davey.
(T) 01840 212091
Profile: FT: Coarse; WN: Ferndale; WT: Lake (Still) W. Size: 2 Acres. Location: Nr. Rd: B3314; Main Rd: A39, Camelford; Rail: Bodmin.
Ref: FH1699

FERNWORTHY RESERVOIR

Fernworthy Reservoir, South West Water Fishery, Chagford, Dartmoor, Newton Abbot, **DEVON**, TQ13, **England**.
Profile: FT: Game; WN: Fernworthy; WT: Reservoir (Still) W. Size: 76 Acres.
Ref: FH1700

FERRY MEADOWS

Ferry Meadows, Ham Lane, Orton Rd, Peterborough, **CAMBRIDGESHIRE**, PE, **England**.
Contact/s: Martin Parker (Webbs Tackle), Webbs Tackle, 196 Newark Avenue, Wansford, Peterborough, Cambridgeshire, PE1 4NP.
(T) 01733 566466
Mr Peter Garod, Peterborough and District Angling Association, 6 Stephenson Way, Bourne, Peterborough.
(T) 01733 571676
Profile: FT: Coarse; WN: Ferry Meadows; WT: Lake (Still). Location: Nr. Rd: A605; Main Rd: A1.
Ref: FH1701

FFESTINIOG FISHERY

Ffestiniog Fishery, Ffestiniog Power Station, Blaenau Ffestiniog, **GWYNEDD**, LL41 3TP, **Wales**.
Contact/s: G Price.
(T) 01766 830583 (F) 01766 830888
M J Hyde.
(T) 01766 830259home (F) 01766 830888
Profile: FT: Game; WN: Ffestiniog Fishery; WT: Reservoir (Still) W. Size: 95 Acres.
Location: Nr. Rd: A470; Main Rd: A470; Rail: Blaenau Ffestiniog.
Ref: FH1702

FIELD LODGE POND

Field Lodge Pond, Tottington, Bury, **MANCHESTER (GREATER)**, BL8, **England**.
Contact/s: Mr Bill Turner (Secretary), 18 Hawthorn Avenue, Edenfield, Bury.
(T) 01706 823799
Profile: FT: Coarse; WN: Field Lodge; WT: Pond (Still).
Ref: FH1703

FIELDS END WATER

Fields End Water, Benwick Rd, Doddington, March, **CAMBRIDGESHIRE**, PE15 0TY, **England**.
Contact/s: Mrs V Boughton (Owner).
(T) 01354 740373 (F) 01354 740125
Profile: FT: Coarse; WN: Fields End Water; WT: Lake (Still); F. Size: 3 Acres; W. Size: 3 Acres. Location: Rail: March. £Fr
Ref: FH1704

FIELDSONS POND

Fieldsons Pond, Shildon, Bishop Auckland, **COUNTY DURHAM**, DL14, **England**.
Contact/s: Mr Barry Hignett (Secretary), Ferryhill and District Angling Club, 74 Grasmere Rd, Garden Farm Estate, Chester-le-Street, County Durham.
(T) 0191 3883557
Mr W Curtis (Chairman), 14 Bakewell Pl, Newton Aycliffe, County Durham.
(T) 01325 320291
Profile: FT: Coarse; WN: Fieldsons; WT: Pond (Still) W. Size: 2 Acres. Location: Nr. Rd: Shildon to Redworth; Main Rd: A6072; Rail: Darlington.
Ref: FH1705

FIGHTING COCKS RESERVOIR

Fighting Cocks Reservoir, Middleton St George, Darlington, **COUNTY DURHAM**, DL, **England**.
Profile: FT: Coarse; WN: Fighting Cocks; WT: Reservoir (Still) W. Size: 10 Acres.
Location: Nr. Rd: A67; Main Rd: A66.
Ref: FH1706

FIGILE (RIVER)

River Figile, Portarlington, **COUNTY LAOIS**, **Ireland**.
Contact/s: Mr Pat Maher (Secretary), Portarlington Angling Club, Inchacooley, Monasterevin, County Laois, Ireland.
Profile: FT: Game; WN: Figile; WT: River (Moving) W. Size: 8000 Metres.
Ref: FH1707

FINA HAYFIELD LAKES

Fina Hayfield Lakes, Doncaster, **YORKSHIRE (SOUTH)**, DN, **England**.
Contact/s: Mr Robin Goforth (Manager), Hayfield Lodge, Hayfield Lane, Auckley, Doncaster, DN9 3NP.
(T) 01302 864555 (F) 01302 863419
Profile: FT: Coarse; WN: Lacy and Adam; WT: Lake (Still).
Ref: FH1708

FINCHALE ABBEY FARM

Finchale Abbey Farm, Durham, **COUNTY DURHAM**, DH1 5SH, **England**.
Contact/s: E Welsh.
(T) 0191 3866528
Profile: FT: Combination; WN: Wear; WT: River (Moving) W. Size: 3200 Metres.
Ref: FH1709

FINDYNATE BEAT

Findynate Beat, Aberfeldy, **PERTH AND KINROSS**, PH15, **Scotland**.
(W) www.fishingnet.com/beats/fyndynate.htm
Contact/s: Ms Em Honeyman (Manager), Wade Newsagents, 31 Bank St, Aberfeldy, Perth and Kinross, PH15 2BB.
(T) 01887 820397
Profile: FT: Game; WN: Big Stone, Split Oak and The Fiddle; WT: Pool (Still).
Ref: FH1710

FINGERPOST POOL

Fingerpost Pool, Knutsford, **CHESHIRE**, WA16, **England**.
Contact/s: Mr Neil Jupp (Club Secretary), Lymm Angling Club, PO Box 350, Warrington, Cheshire, WA2 9FB.
(T) 01925 411774
Profile: FT: Coarse; WN: Fingerpost; WT: Pool (Still). Location: Nr. Rd: A50 to Knutsford; Main Rd: M56.
Ref: FH1711

FINISK (RIVER)

River Finisk, Cappoquin, **COUNTY CORK**, **Ireland**.
Contact/s: Mr Michael Penruddock (Manager), Lismore Estate Office, Lismore Castle, Lismore, County Waterford, Ireland.
(T) 058 54424
Profile: FT: Game; WN: Finisk; WT: River (Moving).
Ref: FH1712

FINLAKE PONDS

Finlake Ponds, Chudleigh Knighton, Newton Abbot, **DEVON**, TQ1, **England**.
Contact/s: Mr Tony Irving.
(T) 01626 853833
Profile: FT: Coarse; WN: Finlake; WT: Pond (Still) W. Size: 2 Acres. Location: Nr. Rd: A38 Exeter to Plymouth; Main Rd: B3193.
Ref: FH1713

FINLARIG

Finlarig, Killin, **STIRLING**, FK21, **Scotland**.
(W) www.fishingnet.com/beats/lochay/finlarig.htm
Contact/s: Mr Alec Stewart (Membership Secretary), 2 Dochart Rd, Killin, Perth and Kinross, FK21 8SN.

(T) 01567 820224
Mr Dave Murray, J R News, Fishing Tackle Shop, Main St, Killin, FR21 8UJ.
(T) 01567 820362
Profile: **FT:** Combination; **WN:** Lochay; **WT:** River (Moving).
Ref: FH1714

FINN (RIVER)

River Finn, Cloghan, **COUNTY DONEGAL**, **Ireland**.
Contact/s: **Mr David Wilde**.
(T) 074 33003 (F) 074 33003
Profile: **FT:** Game; **WN:** Finn; **WT:** River (Moving); **F. Size:** 150 Acres; **W. Size:** 2500 Metres. **Location:** **Nr. Rd:** Creamery Brae; **Main Rd:** Ballybofey to Glenties; **Rail:** Londonderry.
Ref: FH1715

FINN (RIVER)

River Finn, Newtownstewart, Omagh, **COUNTY TYRONE**, BT78, **Northern Ireland**.
Contact/s: **Mr Jim Neeson** (Vice Chairman).
(T) 028 81659726
Mr William Cochrane (Secretary), Glebe Angling Club, 87 Mourne Park, Newtownstewart, County Tyrone, BT78 4BN.
(T) 028 81661469 (F) 028 81661469
(E) w.w.cochrane@talk21.com
Profile: **FT:** Game; **WN:** Finn; **WT:** River (Moving). **Location:** **Nr. Rd:** Donegal Road; **Main Rd:** Bally Bofey Road; **Rail:** Londonderry.
Ref: FH1716

FINN (RIVER)

River Finn, Strabane, **COUNTY TYRONE**, BT82, **Northern Ireland**.
Contact/s: **Mr Billy Diver**, Variety Shop, 5 Castle Prde, Strabane, County Tyrone, BT82.
(T) 028 71883021
Mr Charlie Hegarty, Foyle Fisheries Commission, 8 Victoria Rd, Londonderry, County Tyrone.
(T) 028 71342100 (F) 028 71342720
Profile: **FT:** Game; **WN:** Finn; **WT:** River (Moving) **W. Size:** 7200 Metres. **Location:** **Nr. Rd:** Flushtown Bridge to Castlefinn Bridge.
Ref: FH1717

FINNART (RIVER)

River Finnart, Ardentinny, Dunoon, **ARGYLL AND BUTE**, PA23, **Scotland**.
Contact/s: **Mr A H Young** (Hon Secretary), 112 Argyll St, Dunoon, Argyll and Bute.
(T) 01369 705732or703232
(E) archie@telinco.co.uk
Profile: **FT:** Game; **WN:** Finnart; **WT:** River (Moving) **W. Size:** 1600 Metres. **Location:** **Nr. Rd:** A880.
Ref: FH1718

FIR COUNTRY PARK

Fir Country Park, Barkers Lane, Bedford, **BEDFORDSHIRE**, MK41 9SH, **England**.
Contact/s: **Mr Roy Bates** (Fishery Warden), Bedford Borough Council, Town Hall, St Pauls Sq, Bedford, MK40 1SJ.
(T) 01234 211182
Profile: **FT:** Coarse; **WN:** Fir Country Park; **WT:** Lake (Still).
Ref: FH1719

FIR TREE FLASH

Fir Tree Flash, Edna Rd, Leigh, **MANCHESTER (GREATER)**, WN7, **England**.
Contact/s: Fishery Manager.
(T) 01942 511596
Profile: **FT:** Coarse; **WN:** Fir Tree Flash; **WT:** Lake (Still).
Ref: FH1720

FIR TREE LODGE

Fir Tree Lodge, The Nook, Appley Nridge, Wigan, **LANCASHIRE**, **England**.
Contact/s:
(T) 01257 252607
Profile: **FT:** Coarse; **WN:** Fir Tree Lodge; **WT:** Lake (Still).
Ref: FH1721

FIRGROVE LAKES

Firgrove Lakes, Yateley, **HAMPSHIRE**, GU46, **England**.
Contact/s: Manager, R and R Tackle, 74 High St, Sandhurst, Berkshire, GU47 8ED.
(T) 01252 870007
Society Information.
(T) 01252 679414
Profile: **FT:** Coarse; **WN:** Firgrove; **WT:** Lake (Still). **Location:** **Nr. Rd:** Firgrove Road; **Main Rd:** A30, A327, B3016.
Ref: FH1722

FIRS PARK LAKE

Firs Park Lake, Leigh, **MANCHESTER (GREATER)**, WN7, **England**.
Contact/s: Manager, Leigh Angling Ctre, 261 Twist Lane, Leigh, Lancashire, WN7 4EH.
(T) 01942 670890 (F) 01942 670890
Profile: **FT:** Coarse; **WN:** Firs Park; **WT:** Lake (Still).
Ref: FH1723

FIRWOOD LODGE AND THE BUNK

Firwood Lodge And The Bunk, Bolton, **LANCASHIRE**, BL, **England**.
Contact/s: **Mr Terence A McKee** (Secretary), Bolton and District Angling Association, 1 Lever Edge Lane, Bolton, Lancashire, BL3 3BU.
(T) 01204 393726
Profile: **FT:** Coarse; **WN:** Firwood Lodge And The Bunk; **WT:** Lake (Still).
Ref: FH1724

FISH POND FARM

Fish Pond Farm, Usselby, Market Rasen, **LINCOLNSHIRE**, LN8 3YU, **England**.
Contact/s: Manager, 374 Warrington Rd, Culceth, Cheshire.
(T) 01673 828219
Profile: **FT:** Coarse; **WN:** Fish; **WT:** Pond (Still). **Location:** **Main Rd:** Usselby.
Ref: FH1725

FISH TRADES POND

Fish Trades Pond, Newport, Brough, **HUMBERSIDE**, HU15, **England**.
Contact/s: **Mr J Holdenbury**, 1 Grebe Rd, Thimblehall Lane, Newport, HU15 2PJ.
Profile: **FT:** Combination; **WN:** Fish Trades; **WT:** Pond (Still) **W. Size:** 1 Acre. **Location:** **Nr. Rd:** B1239, Newport village.
Ref: FH1726

FISHER TARN

Fisher Tarn, 1 Rydal Mount, Kendal, **CUMBRIA**, LA9 4RS, **England**.
Contact/s: **Mr A Moore**, 65 Waterside, Kendal, Cumbria.
Mr D Bird, 1 Rydal Mount, Kendal, Cumbria.
Mr Roy Rhodes (Conservation, Access and Recreation Manager), Rivington Water Treatment Works, Bolton Rd, Horwich, Bolton, BL6 7RN.
(T) 01204 664300
Profile: **FT:** Game; **WN:** Fisher Tarn; **WT:** River (Moving). **Location:** **Rail:** Kendal.
Ref: FH1727

FISHERIES THE

Fisheries (The), The Drive, Cranleigh, **SURREY**, GU6, **England**.
Contact/s: **Mr Nick Bamford** (Publicity Officer), Cranleigh Angling Club, 20 High St, Cranleigh, Surrey, GU6 8AE.
(T) 01483 274566
Mrs Sue Buxton (membership secretary), 5 Gingers Cl, Cranleigh, Surrey, GU6 7JL.
(T) 01483 271240
Profile: **FT:** Coarse; **WN:** Fisheries (The); **WT:** Pond (Still) **W. Size:** 1 Acre.
Ref: FH1729

FISHERMANS RETREAT

Fishermans Retreat, Ridinghead Lane, Bye Rd, Shuttleworth, Ramsbottom, Bury, **MANCHESTER (GREATER)**, BL0 0HH, **England**.
Contact/s: **Mr Hervey Magnall** (Owner).
(T) 01706 825314 (F) 01706 825314
Profile: **FT:** Game; **WN:** Fishermans Retreat; **WT:** River (Still).
Ref: FH1730

FISHERS GREEN

Fishers Green, Stubbins Hall Lane, Waltham Abbey, **ESSEX**, EN9, **England**.
(W) www.rmcangling.co.uk
Contact/s: **Mr Ian Welch** (Angling Manager), RMC Angling, The Square, Lightwater, Surrey, GU18 5SS.
(T) 01276 453300 (F) 01276 456611
(E) info@rmcangling.co.uk
Profile: **FT:** Coarse; **WN:** Lee; **WT:** Combination (Still & Moving) **W. Size:** 133 Acres. **Location:** **Nr. Rd:** B194; **Main Rd:** Stubbins Hall Lane.
Ref: FH1731

FISHERWICK LAKES

Fisherwick Lakes, Midland Game Fisheries, Fisherwick Wood Lane, Whittington, Lichfield, **STAFFORDSHIRE**, WS13 8QF, **England**.
Contact/s: **Mr F R J Gray** (Owner).
(T) 01543 433606 (F) 01543 433390
Mr Peter Jackson (Manager).
(T) 01543 433606 (F) 01543 433390
Profile: **FT:** Combination; **WN:** Fisherwick Lakes; **WT:** Combination (Still); **F. Size:** 32 Acres; **W. Size:** 23 Acres. **Location:** **Nr. Rd:** Fisherwick Wood Lane; **Main Rd:** Whittington Hurst; **Rail:** Lichfield.
Ref: FH1732

FISHMOOR RESERVOIR

Fishmoor Reservoir, Haslingden, Rossendale, **LANCASHIRE**, BB4, **England**.
Contact/s: **Mr Roy Rhodes** (Conservation, Access and Recreation Manager), Rivington Water Treatment Works, Bolton Rd, Horwich, Bolton, BL6 7RN.
(T) 01204 664300
Profile: **FT:** Coarse; **WN:** Fishmoor; **WT:** Reservoir (Still). **Location:** **Main Rd:** B6232 to Haslingden.
Ref: FH1733

FISHPONDS FARM AND FISHERY

Fishponds Farm And Fishery, Woldgate, Bridlington, **HUMBERSIDE**, YO16, **England**.
Contact/s: **Mr John Nadin**.
(T) 01262 605873
Profile: **FT:** Coarse; **WN:** Fishponds Farm And Fishery; **WT:** Pool (Still). **Location:** **Nr. Rd:** B1253; **Main Rd:** Bridlington, A614
Ref: FH1734

FISHPONDS FARM AND FISHERY

Fishponds Farm And Fishery, Woldgate, Boynton, Bridlington, **HUMBERSIDE**, YO16 4XE, **England**.
Contact/s: **Mr John Nadin** (Owner).
(T) 01262 605873 (F) 01262 605873
Profile: **FT:** Coarse; **WN:** Fishponds Farm And Fishery; **WT:** Pond (Still); **F. Size:** 4 Acres; **W. Size:** 4 Acres. **Location:** **Nr. Rd:** A614; **Main Rd:** A614; **Rail:** Bridlington.
Ref: FH1735

FISHPONDS HOUSE

Fishponds House, Dunkeswell, Honiton, **DEVON**, EX14 4SH, **England**.
Contact/s: **Mrs Semmens** (Manager).
(T) 01404 891358 (F) 01404 891109
Profile: **FT:** Coarse; **WN:** Fishponds; **WT:** Pond (Still); **F. Size:** 45 Acres; **W. Size:** 3 Acres. **Location:** **Nr. Rd:** Dunkeswell to Luppit Common; **Main Rd:** A303; **Rail:** Honiton.
Ref: FH1736

FISHPONDS LIDO

Fishponds Lido, Alcove Rd, Bristol, BS, **England**.
Contact/s: **Mr Ken Davis** (Membership Secretary).
(T) 01179 654778
Profile: **FT:** Coarse; **WN:** Fish; **WT:** Pond

(Still) **W. Size:** 1 Acre. **Location:** **Nr. Rd:** Alcove Road.
Ref: FH1737

FITZWILLIAM CANAL

Fitzwilliam Canal, Pargate, Rotherham, **YORKSHIRE (SOUTH)**, S, **England**.
Contact/s: **Mr Alan Duncan** (Countryside Ranger), Thrybergh Country Park, Doncaster Rd, Thrybergh, Rotherham, S65 4NU.
(T) 01709 850353 **(F)** 01709 851532
(E) thrybergh32.freeserve.co.uk
Profile: **FT:** Coarse; **WN:** Fitzwilliam; **WT:** Canal (Still) **W. Size:** 800 Metres.
Ref: FH1738

FIVE OAKS TROUT LAKE

Five Oaks Trout Lake, Southampton, **HAMPSHIRE**, SO, **England**.
Contact/s: **Mr Jeff Purkiss**, 5 St Pauls Rd, Sarisbury Green, Southampton, Hampshire, SO31 7BB.
(T) 01489 575359
Profile: **FT:** Game; **WN:** Five Oaks; **WT:** Lake (Still); **F. Size:** 6 Acres; **W. Size:** 2 Acres. **Location:** **Main Rd:** A27.
Ref: FH1739

FIVE TREES

Five Trees, Trelleck, Monmouth, **MONMOUTHSHIRE**, NP25, **Wales**.
Contact/s: Fishery Manager.
(T) 01600 860411
Profile: **FT:** Coarse; **WN:** Five Trees; **WT:** Pond (Still).
Ref: FH1740

FLAKE STREAM

Flake Stream, Harefield, Uxbridge, London, **LONDON (GREATER)**, UB9 6, **England**.
Contact/s: **Mr I Flindall** (Secretary), Tumbling Bay Angling Club, The White Cottage, Canalside, Harefield, Middlesex, WD3 1LB. **(M)** 07836 605183
Profile: **FT:** Coarse; **WN:** Flake; **WT:** Stream (Moving).
Ref: FH1741

FLANSHAW DAM

Flanshaw Dam, Wakefield, **YORKSHIRE (WEST)**, WF, **England**.
Contact/s: Fishery Manager.
(T) 01924 369556
Profile: **FT:** Coarse; **WN:** Flanshaw; **WT:** Mill Dam (Still).
Ref: FH1742

FLASH

Flash (The), Gresford, Llay, Wrexham, LL, **Wales**.
Contact/s: **J Henshaw**, 2 Queens Trce, Mold Rd, Cefn-y-Bedd, Wrexham.
Profile: **FT:** Coarse; **WN:** Flash (The); **WT:** Lake (Still).
Ref: FH1743

FLECKNOE FARM FISHERIES

Flecknoe Farm Fisheries, Daventry, **NORTHAMPTONSHIRE**, NN11, **England**.
Contact/s: Flecknoe Farm Manager.
(T) 01788 890228
Profile: **FT:** Coarse; **WN:** Flecknoe Farm Fisheries; **WT:** Lake (Still) **W. Size:** 5 Acres.
Ref: FH1744

FLEET (RIVER)

River Fleet, Trent Lane, Collingham, Newark, **NOTTINGHAMSHIRE**, NG, **England**.
Contact/s: **Ms D Wilson** (Secretary), Collingham Angling Association Tidal Trent, 93 Braemar Rd, Collingham, Newark, NG23 7PN.
(T) 01636 892700
Ms M Nicholson (Chairperson).
(T) 01636 892280
Profile: **FT:** Coarse; **WN:** Fleet; **WT:** River (Moving) **W. Size:** 4500 Metres. **Location:** **Nr. Rd:** Trent Lane; **Main Rd:** A1133; **Rail:** Collingham.
Ref: FH1745

FLEETS DAM

Fleets Dam, Barnsley, **YORKSHIRE (SOUTH)**, S7, **England**.
Contact/s: **Mr Allan Hanson** (Manager).
(T) 01226 292579
Profile: **FT:** Coarse; **WN:** Fleets; **WT:** Mill Dam (Still).
Ref: FH1746

FLETCHERS POND

Fletchers Pond, Crockley Hill, Wheldrake, York, **YORKSHIRE (NORTH)**, YO19, **England**.
Contact/s: **Mr Ron Fletcher** (Manager).
(T) 01904 620304or637854
Profile: **FT:** Coarse; **WN:** Fletcher's; **WT:** Pond (Still). **Location:** **Nr. Rd:** B1228; **Main Rd:** A19.
Ref: FH1747

FLIXTON DECOY

Flixton Decoy, South Lodge, Flixton, Lowestoft, **SUFFOLK**, NR, **England**.
Contact/s: **Mr E Green**.
(T) 01502 730568
Profile: **FT:** Coarse; **WN:** Waveney; **WT:** Lake (Still). **Location:** **Nr. Rd:** Flixton.
Ref: FH1748

FLOOD PARK

Flood Park, Haverhill, **SUFFOLK**, CB9, **England**.
Ms Debbie Rowe (Manager), Haverhill Angling Centre, 2a Primrose Hill, Haverhill.
(T) 01440 705011
Profile: **FT:** Coarse; **WN:** Flood; **WT:** Lake (Still) **W. Size:** 2 Acres. **Location:** **Nr. Rd:** A604 to Linton; **Main Rd:** A1307.
Ref: FH1749

FLOWERS FARM TROUT LAKES

Flowers Farm Trout Lakes, Flowers Farm, Hilfield, Dorchester, **DORSET**, DT2 7BA, **England**.
Contact/s: **Mr Alan J Bastone** (Owner).
(T) 01300 341351 **(F)** 01300 341351
Profile: **FT:** Game; **WN:** Flowers Farm; **WT:** Lake (Still); **F. Size:** 10 Acres; **W. Size:** 4 Acres. **Location:** **Nr. Rd:** Batcombe to Mintern Magna; **Main Rd:** A37; **Rail:** Chetnole.
Ref: FH1750

FLUSHING MEADOWS FISHERY

Flushing Meadows Fishery, Acton Bridge, Northwich, **CHESHIRE**, CW8, **England**.
Contact/s: Fishery Manager.
(T) 01606 851036
Profile: **FT:** Coarse; **WN:** Flushing Meadows Fishery; **WT:** Lake (Still).
Ref: FH1751

FLYLANDS POND

Flylands Pond, Bishop Auckland, **COUNTY DURHAM**, **England**.
Contact/s: .
(T) 01388 832362
Profile: **FT:** Coarse; **WN:** Flylands Pond; **WT:** Pond (Still).
Ref: FH1752

FOGGLESKYTE WATERS

Foggleskyte Waters, Millington, York, **YORKSHIRE (NORTH)**, YO42, **England**.
Contact/s: Fishery Manager.
(T) 01759 306334
Profile: **FT:** Coarse; **WN:** Foggleskyte Waters; **WT:** Lake (Still). **Location:** **Main Rd:** B1246.
Ref: FH1753

FOLLY FARM POOL

Folly Farm Pool, Montford, Shrewsbury, **SHROPSHIRE**, **England**.
Contact/s: **Mr John Turner** (Hon Secretary), Prince Albert Angling Society, 15 Pexhill Drive, Macclesfield, Cheshire, SK10 3LP.
(T) 01625 422010
Profile: **FT:** Coarse; **WN:** Folly Pool; **WT:** Pool (Still); **F. Size:** 2 Acres; **W. Size:** 2 Acres. **Location:** **Nr. Rd:** Nesscliffe to Shrawardine; **Main Rd:** A5; **Rail:** Shrewsbury.
Ref: FH1754

FOLLY FOOT FARM

Folly Foot Farm, Taunton Rd, North Petherton, Bridgwater, **SOMERSET**, TA6 6NW, **England**.
Contact/s: **Mr Rupert Preston** (Owner), Folly Foot Farm, Taunton Rd, North Petherton, Somerset, TA6 6NW.
(T) 01278 662979
Profile: **FT:** Coarse; **WN:** Folly Foot Farm; **WT:** Lake (Still); **F. Size:** 4 Acres; **W. Size:** 3 Acres. **Location:** **Nr. Rd:** Taunton Road (A38); **Main Rd:** M5 (J24); **Rail:** Bridgwater.
Ref: FH1755

FOLLY POND

Folly Pond, Market Harborough, **LEICESTERSHIRE**, LE16, **England**.
Contact/s: Fishery Manager.
(T) 01858 433067
Profile: **FT:** Coarse; **WN:** Folly; **WT:** Pond (Still).
Ref: FH1756

FOLLYFOOT FARM

Follyfoot Farm, North Petherton, Bridgwater, **SOMERSET**, **England**.
Contact/s: Fisheries Manager.
(T) 01278 662979
Profile: **FT:** Coarse; **WN:** Follyfoot Farm; **WT:** River (Still); **F. Size:** 5 Acres; **W. Size:** 3 Acres. **Location:** **Main Rd:** A38.
Ref: FH1757

FONTBURN RESERVOIR

Fontburn Reservoir, Rothbury, Morpeth, **NORTHUMBERLAND**, NE65, **England**.
Contact/s: Fisheries Contact, Broken Scar Treatment Works, Coniscliffe Rd, Darlington, Northumberland, DL3 8TF.
(T) 01669 62368
Mr Ray Demesne (Office Manager), Kirkwhelpington, Northumberland, NE19 2RG.
(T) 01830 540341
Profile: **FT:** Game; **WN:** Fontburn; **WT:** Reservoir (Still). **Location:** **Nr. Rd:** B6342.
Ref: FH1758

FOOTBALL PIT

Football Pit, Ince Blundell, Liverpool, **MERSEYSIDE**, L38, **England**.
Contact/s: Fishery Manager.
(T) 0151 9292577
Profile: **FT:** Coarse; **WN:** Football; **WT:** Gravel Pit (Still).
Ref: FH1759

FORBURY FARM LAKES

Forbury Farm Lakes, Forbury, Kingsclere, Newbury, **BERKSHIRE**, RG20, **England**.
Contact/s: **Mr Paul F Oldring** (Fishery Manager).
(T) 01635 298436or01635297122 **(F)** 01635 298463
Profile: **FT:** Coarse; **WN:** Forbury; **WT:** Lake (Still).
Ref: FH1760

FORDA HOLIDAY LODGES

Forda Holiday Lodges, Kilkhampton, Bude, **CORNWALL**, EX23 9RZ, **England**.
Contact/s: **Mr Jim Chibbett** (Manager).
(T) 01288 321413
Profile: **FT:** Coarse; **WN:** Forda Holiday Lodges; **WT:** Pond (Still).
Ref: FH1761

FORDCOMBE

Fordcombe, Tunbridge Wells, **KENT**, TN, **England**.
Profile: **FT:** Coarse; **WN:** Fordcombe; **WT:** Lake (Still).
Ref: FH1762

FORDWICH LAKE

Fordwich Lake, Canterbury, **KENT**, CT2 0AF, **England**.
Contact/s: **Mr Barten** (Secretary), Canterbury and District Angling Association, Riversdale, 14 Mill Rd, Sturry, Canterbury, CT2 0AF.
(T) 01227 710830
Profile: **FT:** Coarse; **WN:** Fordwich; **WT:**

Gravel Pit (Still).
Ref: FH1763

FOREMARK TROUT FISHERY

Foremark Trout Fishery, Milton, Derby, **DERBYSHIRE**, DE65 6EG, **England**.
Contact/s: Manager, Foremark Reservoir Fishing Lodge, Milton, Derby, DE65 6EG.
(T) 01283 703202or701709 **(F)** 01283 703901
Mr Colin Lawrenson (Manager).
(T) 01283 701709 **(F)** 01283 703901
Profile: **FT:** Game; **WN:** Foremark; **WT:** Reservoir (Still); **F. Size:** 800 Acres; **W. Size:** 230 Acres. Location: **Nr. Rd:** Repton Road; **Main Rd:** A514; **Rail:** Willington.
Ref: FH1764

FOREST FARM

Forest Farm, Pinvin, Pershore, **WORCESTERSHIRE**, WR10, **England**.
Contact/s: Fishery Manager.
(T) 01386 552240
Profile: **FT:** Coarse; **WN:** Forest Farm; **WT:** Lake (Still) **W. Size:** 2 Acres. Location: **Nr. Rd:** A442 to B4084; **Main Rd:** A4538.
Ref: FH1765

FOREST HILL TROUT FARM

Forest Hill Trout Farm, Mostyn, Holywell, **FLINTSHIRE**, CH8 9EQ, **Wales**.
Contact/s: Manager.
(T) 01745 560151
Profile: **FT:** Game; **WN:** Forest Hill Trout Farm; **WT:** Lake (Still) **W. Size:** 1 Acre.
Ref: FH1766

FOREST LODGE HOME FARM

Forest Lodge Home Farm, Fawley Rd, Hythe, Southampton, **HAMPSHIRE**, SO45 3NJ, **England**.
Contact/s: **Mr John Penny** (Owner).
(T) 023 80843188
Profile: **FT:** Coarse; **WN:** Forest Lodge Home Farm; **WT:** Lake (Still) **W. Size:** 1 Acre.
Ref: FH1767

FORKHILL (RIVER)

River Forkhill, Crossmaglen, Newry, **COUNTY DOWN**, BT35, **Northern Ireland**.
Contact/s: **Mr Eugene Murphy**.
(T) 028 30868607
Mr J Cunningham (Secretary), 21 Forkhill Rd, Mullach Ban, County Armagh, BT35 9XL.
(T) 028 30889187
Mr Phil Nolan.
(T) 028 30868074
Profile: **FT:** Game; **WN:** Forkhill; **WT:** River (Moving).
Ref: FH1768

FORSINARD

Forsinard, 8 Sinclair St, Thurso, **HIGHLAND**, KW14, **Scotland**.
Contact/s: **Mr Bob Rogers** (Manager), Harpers Fly Fishing Services, 57 High St, Thurso, Caithness, KW14 8AZ.
(T) 01847 893179
Mrs J Atkinson (Factor).
(T) 01847 63291
Profile: **FT:** Game; **WN:** Forsinard; **WT:** River (Moving).
Ref: FH1769

FORSTERS LODGES

Forsters Lodges, Copperas Lane, Haigh, Wigan, **LANCASHIRE**, WN2, **England**.
Contact/s: Manager, North West Angling Ctre, 160 Market St, Hindley, Wigan, Lancashire, WN2 3AY.
(T) 01257 265905
Profile: **FT:** Coarse; **WN:** Forsters Lodges; **WT:** Pond (Still). Location: **Nr. Rd:** Copperas Lane; **Main Rd:** M61, junction 6, A6, B5239.
Ref: FH1770

FORT WILLIAM FISHERY

Fort William Fishery, Glencairn, Tallow, **COUNTY WATERFORD**, **Ireland**.
Contact/s: Fishery Manager.
(T) 058 30140
Profile: **FT:** Game; **WN:** Fort William Fishery; **WT:** Moat (Still).
Ref: FH1771

FORTH AND CLYDE CANAL

Forth And Clyde Canal, Kelvindale, Glasgow, **GLASGOW (CITY OF)**, G, **Scotland**.
Profile: **FT:** Coarse; **WN:** Forth and Clyde; **WT:** Canal (Still).
Ref: FH1772

FORTY HALL LAKE

Forty Hall Lake, Enfield, London, **LONDON (GREATER)**, EN2 9HT, **England**.
Contact/s: **Mr Simon Maddock** (Secretary), Palmers Green Angling Society, 32 Leaforis Rd, Chestnut, Hertfordshire, EN7 6ND.
(T) 01992 628992
Profile: **FT:** Coarse; **WN:** Forty Hall; **WT:** Lake (Still).
Ref: FH1773

FOSFELLE COUNTRY HOUSE HOTEL

Fosfelle Country House Hotel, Hartland, Bideford, **DEVON**, EX39 6EF, **England**.
Contact/s: **E D Underhill**.
(T) 01237 441273
Profile: **FT:** Combination; **WN:** Fosfelle Country House Hotel; **WT:** Stream (Moving); **F. Size:** 2 Acres. Location: **Nr. Rd:** B3248; **Main Rd:** A39; **Rail:** Barnstable.
Ref: FH1774

FOSS (RIVER)

River Foss, Tower St, York, **YORKSHIRE (NORTH)**, YO, **England**.
Contact/s: **Mr John Lane** (Secretary), York and District Angling Association, 39 Lowfields Drive, Acomb, York, YO2 3DQ.
(T) 01904 783178
Profile: **FT:** Coarse; **WN:** Foss; **WT:** River (Moving). Location: **Nr. Rd:** City Centre.
£Fr
Ref: FH1775

FOSSEHILL LAKES

Fossehill Lakes, Beverley, **HUMBERSIDE**, HU17, **England**.
Contact/s: Area Manager, Environment Agency, Ridings Area Office, Phoenix House, Global Avenue, Leeds, LS11 8PG.
(T) 0113 2440191or2314834 **(F)** 0113 2134609
Mr P Thornton.
(T) 01964 542080or544357
Profile: **FT:** Coarse; **WN:** Fossehill; **WT:** Lake (Still).
Ref: FH1776

FOSTERS END PIT

Fosters End Pit, Blackborough End, King's Lynn, **NORFOLK**, PE32, **England**.
Contact/s: **Mr Mick Grief** (Secretary), King's Lynn Angling Association, 67 Peckover Way, South Wootton, King's Lynn, PE30 3UE.
(T) 01553 671545
Profile: **FT:** Coarse; **WN:** Foster's End; **WT:** Gravel Pit (Still).
Ref: FH1777

FOULRIDGE RESERVOIR

Foulridge Reservoir, Foulridge, Colne, **LANCASHIRE**, BB8, **England**.
(W) www.pearce81.freeserve.co.uk
Contact/s: **Mr Bob Pearce**.
(T) 01282 863381
Mr Terry Hartley (Outdoor Recreation Officer), Pendle Leisure Services, Crown Way, Colne, Lancashire, BB8 8NP.
(T) 01282 661230 **(F)** 01282 661137 **(M)** 07718 601881
(E) plc@leisureinpendle.co.uk
Profile: **FT:** Coarse; **WN:** Foulridge; **WT:** Reservoir (Still) **W. Size:** 80 Acres. Location: **Nr. Rd:** Skipton Road; **Main Rd:** A56; **Rail:** Colne.
Ref: FH1778

FOUNDERS POOL

Founders Pool, Antrobus, Northwich, **CHESHIRE**, CW9, **England**.
Contact/s: **Mr Neil Jupp** (Club Secretary), Lymm Angling Club, PO Box 350, Warrington, Cheshire, WA2 9FB.
(T) 01925 411744
Profile: **FT:** Coarse; **WN:** Founders; **WT:** Pool (Still) **W. Size:** 1 Acre. Location: **Nr. Rd:** Foggs Lane; **Main Rd:** A559.
Ref: FH1779

FOUNDRY LODGE

Foundry Lodge, Town Lane, Whittle-Le-Woods, Chorley, **LANCASHIRE**, PR6, **England**.
Profile: **FT:** Coarse; **WN:** Foundry Lodge; **WT:** Lake (Still). Location: **Nr. Rd:** Town Lane; **Main Rd:** A6 north.
Ref: FH1780

FOUR PONDS

Four Ponds, Bowden Lane, Shillingford, Exeter, **DEVON**, EX2, **England**.
Contact/s: Fishery Manager.
(T) 01398 331169
Profile: **FT:** Coarse; **WN:** Four; **WT:** Pond (Still) **W. Size:** 2 Acres. Location: **Nr. Rd:** Bowden Lane; **Main Rd:** B3227, Bampton to Wiveliscombe.
Ref: FH1781

FOWEY (RIVER)

River Fowey, Lostwithiel, **CORNWALL**, PL22, **England**.
Contact/s: **F Cox**.
(T) 01208 872136
Mr J H Hooper (Secretary), Lostwithiel Fishing Association, Cott Rd, Lostwithiel, Cornwall, PL22 0HF.
(T) 01208 872937
Profile: **FT:** Game; **WN:** Fowey; **WT:** River (Moving) **W. Size:** 3500 Metres. Location: **Main Rd:** A390; **Rail:** Lostwithiel.
Ref: FH1782

FOWEY (RIVER)

River Fowey, Lanhydrock Park, Respryn Bridge, Lanhydrock Park, Bodmin, **CORNWALL**, PL30 4DE, **England**.
Profile: **FT:** Game; **WN:** Fowey; **WT:** River (Moving). Location: **Nr. Rd:** Respryn Bridge to Footbridge. **£Fr**
Ref: FH1783

FOWEY (RIVER)

River Fowey, Lostwithiel, **CORNWALL**, PL22, **England**.
Contact/s: **Roger Lashbrook** (Manager), Roger's Tackle Shop, Stanmays Store, Higher Bore St, Bodmin, PL31 1JB.
(T) 01208 78006
Profile: **FT:** Game; **WN:** Fowey; **WT:** River (Moving) **W. Size:** 5000 Metres. Location: **Nr. Rd:** A390; **Rail:** Bodmin Parkway.
Ref: FH1784

FOWEY (RIVER)

River Fowey, West Looe, Looe, **CORNWALL**, PL13, **England**.
Contact/s: **Mr Bill Eliot** (Secretary), Liskeard and District Angling Club, 64 Portbyhan Rd, West Looe, Cornwall, PL13 2QN.
(T) 01503 264173
Profile: **FT:** Game; **WN:** Fowey; **WT:** River (Moving) **W. Size:** 4000 Metres. Location: **Nr. Rd:** A38; **Main Rd:** A38; **Rail:** Liskeard.
Ref: FH1785

FOWEY (RIVER)

River Fowey, Lostwithiel, **CORNWALL**, PL22, **England**.
Mr Roger Lashbrook (Manager).
(T) 01208 872659
Profile: **FT:** Game; **WN:** Fowey; **WT:** River (Moving) **W. Size:** 4022 Metres. Location: **Main Rd:** A390; **Rail:** Bodmin Parkway.
Ref: FH1786

FOWEY (RIVER)

River Fowey, Draynes Valley, Liskeard, **CORNWALL**, PL14, **England**.
Contact/s: **Mr Bill Eliot** (Secretary), Liskeard and District Angling Club, 64 Portbyhan Rd, West Looe, Cornwall, PL13 2QN.
(T) 01503 264173
Profile: **FT:** Game; **WN:** Fowey; **WT:** River (Moving) **W. Size:** 12500 Metres. **Location:** **Nr. Rd:** A38; **Main Rd:** A38; **Rail:** Liskeard.
Ref: FH1787

FOWEY (RIVER)

River Fowey, Liskeard, **CORNWALL**, PL14, **England**.
Contact/s: **Trevor Sobey** (Manager), Trevartha Farm, Looe, Liskeard.
(T) 01566 781556
Profile: **FT:** Game; **WN:** Fowey; **WT:** River (Moving).
Ref: FH1788

FOXCOTTE LAKE

Foxcotte Lake, Charlton, Andover, **HAMPSHIRE**, SP, **England**.
Contact/s: Manager, Challis Tackle, 60 Mylen Rd, Andover, Hampshire, SP10 3HA.
(T) 01264 361103
Profile: **FT:** Coarse; **WN:** Foxcotte; **WT:** Gravel Pit (Still) **W. Size:** 3 Acres. **Location:** **Nr. Rd:** A343; **Main Rd:** A343, Charlton.
Ref: FH1789

FOXFORD FISHERY

Foxford Fishery, Foxford, **COUNTY MAYO**, **Ireland**.
Contact/s: **Mr Chris Downey**, 9 Moy View, Foxford, County Mayo, Ireland.
(T) 094 56824
Profile: **FT:** Game; **WT:** River (Moving).
Ref: FH1790

FOXHILLS FISHERY

Foxhills Fishery, Pinfold Lane, Barr Beacon, Adridge, Walsall, **MIDLANDS (WEST)**, WS9 0QP, **England**.
(W) www.foxhillsleisure.com
Contact/s: **Mr George Bull** (Owner).
(T) 0121 3609160 **(M)** 07966 456947
Profile: **FT:** Coarse; **WN:** Foxhills Fishery; **WT:** Pool (Still) **W. Size:** 3 Acres. **Location:** **Nr. Rd:** Birmingham Road; **Main Rd:** A34; **Rail:** Birmingham.
Ref: FH1791

FOXHOLES FISHERIES

Foxholes Fisheries, Foxholes Season Ticket Fishery, Crick, Northampton, **NORTHAMPTONSHIRE**, NN6 7US, **England**.
(W) www.foxholesfisheries.co.uk
Contact/s: **Mr Roger Chaplin**.
(T) 01788 823967
(E) chaplin@btconnect.com
Profile: **FT:** Coarse; **WN:** Foxholes Fisheries; **WT:** Clay Pit (Still) **W. Size:** 7 Acres. **Location:** **Nr. Rd:** A428; **Main Rd:** A428; **Rail:** Long Buckby.
Ref: FH1792

FOXTON DAM

Foxton Dam, Eckington, Sheffield, **DERBYSHIRE**, S21 4, **England**.
Profile: **FT:** Coarse; **WN:** Foxton Dam; **WT:** Lake (Still).
Ref: FH1793

FOYLE (RIVER)

River Foyle, Strabane, **COUNTY TYRONE**, BT82, **Northern Ireland**.
Contact/s: **Mr Billy Diver**, Variety Shop, 5 Castle Prde, Strabane, County Tyrone, BT82.
(T) 028 71883021
Mr Charlie Hegarty, Foyle Fisheries Commission, 8 Victoria Rd, Londonderry, County Tyrone.
(T) 028 71342100 **(F)** 028 71342720
Profile: **FT:** Game; **WN:** Foyle; **WT:** River (Moving) **W. Size:** 2400 Metres.
Ref: FH1794

FRADLEY CANAL

Fradley Canal, Burton-on-Trent, **STAFFORDSHIRE**, DE13, **England**.
Contact/s: **D J Clark**, 7 Denton Rise, Burton-on-Trent, Staffordshire DE13 0QB.
Profile: **FT:** Coarse; **WN:** Fradley; **WT:** Canal (Still).
Ref: FH1796

FRAMFIELD PARK FISHERIES

Framfield Park Fisheries, Brook House Rd, Framfield, Uckfield, **SUSSEX (EAST)**, TN22 5QJ, **England**.
Contact/s: **Mr Chris Sofianos** (Owner).
(T) 01825 890948 **(M)** 07798 751175
Profile: **FT:** Coarse; **WN:** Framfield Park Fisheries; **WT:** Combination (Still); **F. Size:** 14 Acres; **W. Size:** 8 Acres. **Location:** **Nr. Rd:** Brookhouse Road; **Main Rd:** A22; **Rail:** Uckfield.
Ref: FH1797

FRANT LAKES

Frant Lakes, Court Lodge Down Fishery, Hawkenbury, Bells Yew Green, Tunbridge Wells, **KENT**, TN3 9BJ, **England**.
Contact/s: **Mr P Bowmans** (Owner).
(T) 01892 616424 **(M)** 07802 429284
Profile: **FT:** Coarse; **WN:** Frant Lakes; **WT:** Lake (Still) **W. Size:** 30 Acres. **Location:** **Main Rd:** A21; **Rail:** Frant.
Ref: FH1798

FRENSHAM PONDS

Frensham Great And Little Ponds, Aldershot, **HAMPSHIRE**, GU11 1HT, **England**.
Contact/s: **Mr Mick Borra** (Secretary), Farnham Angling Society, The Creel, 36 Station Rd, Aldershot, GU11 1HT.
(T) 01252 320871
Profile: **FT:** Coarse; **WN:** Frensham; **WT:** Pond (Still).
Ref: FH1799

FRENSHAM TROUT FISHERY

Frensham Trout Fishery, Robinswood, Simmondstone Lane, Churt, Farnham, **SURREY**, GU10 2QQ, **England**.
Contact/s: **Mr Richard Twite** (Owner), Crosswater Mill, Crosswater Lane, Churt, Farnham, Surrey.
(T) 01252 794321 **(F)** 01252 792611
(E) countryleisure@msn.com
Mrs Jill Twite (Owner).
(T) 01252 794321 **(F)** 01252 794321
Profile: **FT:** Game; **WN:** Frensham Trout Fishery; **WT:** Lake (Still); **F. Size:** 20 Acres; **W. Size:** 6 Acres. **Location:** **Nr. Rd:** A287; **Main Rd:** A3; **Rail:** Farnham.
Ref: FH1800

FRIARS POOL

Friars Pool, Belmont Estate, Northwich, **CHESHIRE**, CW9, **England**.
Contact/s: **Mr Neil Jupp** (Club Secretary), Lymm Angling Club, PO Box 350, Warrington, Cheshire, WA2 9FB.
(T) 01925 411744
Profile: **FT:** Coarse; **WN:** Friars; **WT:** Pool (Still). **Location:** **Nr. Rd:** A559 to Northwich; **Main Rd:** M56 to Chester.
Ref: FH1801

FRIMLEY LAKES

Frimley Lakes, Ship Lane, Frimley, Farnborough, **HAMPSHIRE**, GU14, **England**.
(W) www.rmcangling.co.uk
Contact/s: **Mr Ian Welch** (Angling Manager), RMC Angling, The Square, Lightwater, Surrey, GU18 5SS.
(T) 01276 453300 **(F)** 01276 456611
(E) info@rmcangling.co.uk
Profile: **FT:** Combination; **WN:** Frimley; **WT:** Gravel Pit (Still) **W. Size:** 25 Acres. **Location:** **Nr. Rd:** Footbridge from Ship Lane; **Main Rd:** A331, M3; **Rail:** Farnborough North.
Ref: FH1802

FRISBY LAKES

Frisby Lakes, Leicester, **LEICESTERSHIRE**, LE, **England**.
Contact/s: **Mr A Smith** (Secretary), 10 Londs Avenue, Leicester, Leicestershire, LE4 2HY.
(T) 0116 2357210 **(M)** 07976 328836
Mr G Taylor (Membership Secretary), Broome Angling Society, 100 New Romney Cres, Leicester.
(T) 0116 2417018
Profile: **FT:** Coarse; **WN:** Frisby; **WT:** Lake (Still); **F. Size:** 20 Acres; **W. Size:** 8 Acres. **Location:** **Nr. Rd:** Leicester Road to Melton Road; **Main Rd:** M1; **Rail:** Leicester.
Ref: FH1803

FRITTON LAKE

Fritton Lake, Church Lane, Fritton, Great Yarmouth, **NORFOLK**, NR31 9HA, **England**.
(W) www.frittonlake.co.uk
Contact/s: **Lord Somerleyton** (Owner), Somerleyton Hall, Somerleyton, Lowestoft, Suffolk, NR32 5QQ.
(T) 01493 488288
Mr Edward Knowles (Manager).
(T) 01493 488288 **(F)** 01493 488355 **(M)** 07776 253062
(E) edwood@frittonlake.co.uk
Profile: **FT:** Coarse; **WN:** Fritton; **WT:** Lake (Still); **F. Size:** 250 Acres; **W. Size:** 150 Acres. **Location:** **Nr. Rd:** A143; **Main Rd:** A143; **Rail:** Haddiscoe.
Ref: FH1804

FROBURY FARM SPORTING CLUB

Frobury Farm Sporting Club, The Granary, Frobury Farm, Kingsclere, Newbury, **BERKSHIRE**, RG20 4QQ, **England**.
Contact/s: **Mr Paul F Oldring** (Fishery Manager).
(T) 01635 297122 **(F)** 01635 298463 **(M)** 07884 97393
(E) paul@frobury.co.uk
Profile: **FT:** Coarse; **WN:** Frobury Farm Sporting Club; **WT:** Clay Pit (Still); **F. Size:** 27 Acres; **W. Size:** 9 Acres. **Location:** **Nr. Rd:** A339; **Main Rd:** M4, M3; **Rail:** Basingstoke or Newbury.
Ref: FH1805

FROGMORE LAKE

Frogmore Lake, Forest Road Hall, Hervey Park Rd, Walthamstow, London, **LONDON (GREATER)**, E17 6LJ, **England**.
Contact/s: **Mr A E Hedges** (Secretary).
(T) 020 85207477
Profile: **FT:** Coarse; **WN:** Frogmore; **WT:** Lake (Still).
Ref: FH1806

FROME (RIVER)

River Frome, Bristol, BS, **England**.
Contact/s: **Mr I Moss**, 69 Long Rd, Mangutsfield, Bristol.
Mr S Coles (Secretary).
(T) 01454 778095
Profile: **FT:** Coarse; **WN:** Frome; **WT:** River (Moving) **W. Size:** 1600 Metres.
Ref: FH1807

FROME (RIVER)

River Frome, Tolpuddle, Dorchester, **DORSET**, DT2, **England**.
Contact/s: **Mr Richard Slocock** (Manager), Wessex Fly Fishing, Lawrences Farm, Tolpuddle, Dorset, DT2 7HF.
(T) 01305 848460 **(F)** 01305 849060
Profile: **FT:** Game; **WN:** Frome; **WT:** River (Moving).
Ref: FH1808

FROME (RIVER)

River Frome, Wareham, **DORSET**, BH20, **England**.
Contact/s: **Deano** (Manager), Purbeck Angling, 28 South St, Wareham, Dorset, BH20 4LU.
(T) 01929 550770
Mr Chris Burgess (Manager).

(T) 01929 550540
Profile: FT: Coarse; WN: Frome; WT: River (Moving) W. Size: 1200 Metres. **Location:** Nr. Rd: South Bridge to Redcliffe. £Fr
Ref: FH1809

FROME (RIVER)

River Frome, Frome, **SOMERSET**, BA11, **England**.
Contact/s: Mr Roger Lee, 51 Welshmill Lane, Frome, Somerset, BA11 3AP.
(T) 01373 461433
Profile: FT: Coarse; WN: Frome; WT: River (Moving) W. Size: 19200 Metres.
Ref: FH1810

FROME (RIVER)

River Frome, Langham Farm, Tellisford, Bath, **SOMERSET**, BA3, **England**.
Contact/s: Mr P O'Callaghan (Secretary), 4 Fitzmaurice Cl, Bradford-on-Avon, Wiltshire, BA15 1UE.
(T) 01225 863163
Profile: FT: Game; WN: Frome; WT: River (Moving) W. Size: 3200 Metres.
Ref: FH1811

FROME AND PIDDLE (RIVERS)

Rivers Frome And Piddle, Wimborne, **DORSET**, BH21, **England**.
Contact/s: Mr Bowerman (Manager), Morden Estate Office, Charbourgh Park, Wimborne, Dorset BH21.
Profile: FT: Combination; WN: Frome & Piddle; WT: River (Moving).
Ref: FH1812

FROME STREAM

Frome Stream, Stroud, **GLOUCESTERSHIRE**, GL, **England**.
Contact/s: Secretary, Stroud Angling Association, Batemans Sports, Kendrick, Stroud, Gloucestershire GL5 1AB.
(T) 01453 764320
Profile: FT: Combination; WN: Frome; WT: Stream (Moving) W. Size: 4800 Metres.
Ref: FH1813

FRON FARM FISHERY

Fron Farm Fishery, Fron Farm, Bontnewydd, Aberystwyth, **CEREDIGION**, SY23 4JG, **Wales**.
Contact/s: Mr Micheal Tovey.
(T) 01974 251392 (F) 01974 251392
(E) fron-farm-fishery@gofornet.co.uk
Profile: FT: Game; WN: Fron Farm Fishery; WT: Lake (Still) W. Size: 7 Acres. **Location:** Nr. Rd: Bronnant to Bontnewydd; Main Rd: A485; Rail: Aberystwyth.
Ref: FH1814

FROXFIELD A AND B

Froxfield A And B, Kennet And Avon Canal, Froxfield, Hungerford, **BERKSHIRE**, RG17, **England**.
Contact/s: Mr Dusty Millar (Ticket Administrator), 238 Elgar Road South, Reading, Berkshire, RG3 0BW.
(T) 0118 9874882
Mr Mick Cox (Secretary), Dorstans, Hatch Lane, Brimpton Village, Reading, RG7 4TR.
(T) 0118 9714917
Profile: FT: Coarse; WN: Kennet and Avon; WT: Canal (Still) W. Size: 28800 Metres. **Location:** Nr. Rd: Froxfield.
Ref: FH1815

FRUID RESERVOIR

Fruid Reservoir, Tweedsmuir, Biggar, **LANARKSHIRE (SOUTH)**, ML12, **Scotland**.
Contact/s: Mrs Bell (Manager), Crook Inn, Tweedsmuir, Biggar, Lanarkshire, ML12 6QN.
(T) 01899 888272 (F) 01899 880294
Profile: FT: Game; WN: Fruid; WT: Reservoir (Still) W. Size: 293 Acres. **Location:** Nr. Rd: Beattock to Tweedsmuir; Main Rd: A74 to A701.
Ref: FH1816

FRUIN (RIVER)

River Fruin, Helensbourgh, **ARGYLL AND BUTE**, G84, **Scotland**.
Contact/s: Mr Brady, Loch Lomond Angling Association, PO Box 3559, Glasgow, G71 7SJ.
(T) 0141 7811545 (F) 0141 7811545
Profile: FT: Game; WN: Fruin; WT: River (Moving) W. Size: 9600 Metres.
Ref: FH1817

FULL BAG FISHERY

Full Bag Fishery, Little Ellenglaze, Cubert, Newquay, **CORNWALL**, TR, **England**.
Contact/s: Mr Adam Coad.
(T) 01637 830839
Profile: FT: Game; WN: Full Bag Fishery; WT: Lake (Still).
Ref: FH1818

FUNTLEY POND

Funtley Pond, Fareham, **HAMPSHIRE**, PO14, **England**.
Contact/s: Mr Steve Jupp (Secretary), 172 Hawthorn Rd, Bognor Regis, Sussex (West), PO21 2UY.
(T) 01243 821950
Profile: FT: Coarse; WN: Funtley; WT: Pond (Still) W. Size: 2 Acres. **Location:** Main Rd: A27.
Ref: FH1819

FURNACE BROOK FISHERY

Furnace Brook Fishery, Cowbeach, Hailsham, **SUSSEX (EAST)**, BN27, **England**.
Contact/s: Fishery Manager.
(T) 01435 830882
Profile: FT: Coarse; WN: Furnace Brook; WT: Lake (Still) W. Size: 7 Acres. **Location:** Main Rd: A22, Eastbourne.
Ref: FH1820

FURNACE LAKES

Furnace Lakes, Furnace House, Guildford Rd, Slinfold, Horsham, **SUSSEX (WEST)**, RH13 7QZ, **England**.
Contact/s: Mr Derek Yeates.
(T) 01403 791163 (F) 01403 791804
Profile: FT: Coarse; WN: Furnace Lake, Furnace Pond, and Specimen Lake; WT: Lake (Still). **Location:** Nr. Rd: A281 Guildford, Horsham Road; Main Rd: A29; Rail: Horsham.
Ref: FH1821

FURNACE MILL FISHERY

Furnace Mill Fishery, Wyre Forest, Kidderminster, **WORCESTERSHIRE**, DY14 8NR, **England**.
Contact/s: Mr Edward Brown.
(T) 01746 862547 (F) 01299 266160 (M) 07860 570080
Profile: FT: Coarse; WN: Furnace Mill Fishery; WT: Lake (Still); F. Size: 27 Acres; W. Size: 3 Acres. **Location:** Nr. Rd: Meaton Lane; Main Rd: A4117; Rail: Kidderminster.
Ref: FH1822

FURNACE POND

Furnace Pond, South Norwood, London, **LONDON (GREATER)**, SE25, **England**.
Contact/s: Mrs A Yexley, 25 Oakley Rd, South Norwood, London.
Profile: FT: Combination; WN: Furnace; WT: Pond (Still).
Ref: FH1823

FURZE FARM

Furze Farm, Knowle Lane, Cranleigh, **SURREY**, GU6, **England**.
Contact/s: Mr Jerry (Manager).
(T) 01306 882708 (M) 07961 118558
Profile: FT: Coarse; WN: Furze; WT: Lake (Still) W. Size: 3 Acres. **Location:** Nr. Rd: Knowle Lane; Main Rd: A281.
Ref: FH1824

FURZTON LAKE

Furzton Lake, Chaffron Way, Furzton, Milton Keynes, **BUCKINGHAMSHIRE**, MK, **England**.
Contact/s: Mr Kv Osborne (Secretary), Milton Keynes Angling Association, 11 Gilpin Way, Olney, Buckinghamshire, MK46 4DN.
(T) 01234 713144
Profile: FT: Coarse; WN: Furzton Lake; WT: Lake (Still) W. Size: 40 Acres. **Location:** Nr. Rd: From junction 14 of M1, turn right off A509 at roundabout onto H5 Portway until watling street roundabout, take first left then right at second roundabout to Chaffron Way..
Ref: FH1825

FYNTALLOCH LOCH

Fyntalloch Loch, Newton Stewart, **DUMFRIES AND GALLOWAY**, DG8, **Scotland**.
Contact/s: Mr Tony Dickinson (Manager), Galloway Guns and Tackle, 36a Arthur St, Newton Stewart, Dumfries and Galloway, DG8 6DE.
(T) 01671 403404 (F) 01671 403404
Profile: FT: Game; WN: Fyntalloch; WT: Loch (Still).
Ref: FH1826

GADE (RIVER)

River Gade, Cassiobury Park, Watford, **HERTFORDSHIRE**, WD, **England**.
Profile: FT: Coarse; WN: Gade; WT: River (Moving). **Location:** Nr. Rd: A412; Main Rd: M1. £Fr
Ref: FH1827

GAILEY TROUT AND PIKE FISHERY

Gailey Trout And Pike Fishery, Gailey Lea Lane, Gailey, Stafford, **STAFFORDSHIRE**, ST19 5PT, **England**.
(W) www.ternfish.co.uk
Contact/s: Mr Allan.
(T) 01785 715848
(E) randle@ternfish.co.uk
Mr G R J Sparrow (Owner), Broomhill Grange, Market Drayton, Shropshire, TF9 2PA.
Profile: FT: Game; WN: Upper Gailey; WT: Reservoir (Still); F. Size: 40 Acres; W. Size: 38 Acres. **Location:** Nr. Rd: A5 or M6; Main Rd: A5; Rail: Cannock.
Ref: FH1828

GALLOWAY FOREST PARK

Galloway Forest Park, Newton Stewart, **DUMFRIES AND GALLOWAY**, DG8 6AJ, **Scotland**.
Contact/s: Ms Rena Tarwinska (District Forester), Forestry Commission Office, Forest Enterprise, Galloway Forest District, Creebridge, Newton Stewart, DG8 6AJ.
(T) 01671 402420 (F) 01671 403708
Profile: FT: Combination; WN: Galloway Forest Park; WT: Combination (Still & Moving) W. Size: 590 Acres. **Location:** Main Rd: A75.
Ref: FH1829

GALLOWS POOL

Gallows Pool, Grendon Underwood, Buckingham, **BUCKINGHAMSHIRE**, MK18, **England**.
Profile: FT: Coarse; WN: Gallows Pool; WT: Pool (Still) W. Size: 1 Acre.
Ref: FH1830

GALMOYLESTOWN LAKE

Galmoylestown Lake, Mullingar, **COUNTY WESTMEATH**, **Ireland**.
Profile: FT: Combination; WN: Galmoylestown; WT: Pond (Still). **Location:** Main Rd: R394.
Ref: FH1831

GALWAY FISHERY

Galway Fishery, Nun's Island, Galway, **COUNTY GALWAY**, **Ireland**.
Contact/s: Fishery Manager.
(T) 091 562388
Profile: FT: Game; WN: Corrib; WT: River (Moving).
Ref: FH1832

GAMMATON RESERVOIRS

Gammaton Reservoirs, Bideford, **DEVON**, EX39, **England**.
Contact/s: Mr William Akistar (Secretary).
(T) 01237 475906
Profile: FT: Game; WN: Gammaton; WT:

Reservoir (Still) **W. Size:** 4 Acres.
Ref: FH1833

GARDEN FARM FISHERIES

Garden Farm Fisheries, Garden Farm, Barlestone, Nuneaton, **WARWICKSHIRE**, CV13 ODG, **England**.
Contact/s: **Mr Baxter** (Owner).
(T) 01455 291193
Profile: **FT:** CoarseWT: (Still).
Ref: FH1834

GARDNERS POOL

Gardners Pool, Saul, Gloucester, **GLOUCESTERSHIRE**, GL, **England**.
Contact/s: **Mr J Gibby**, 70 Robert Raikes Avenue, Tuffley, Gloucestershire.
(T) 01452 413972
Mr Vic Roberts (Secretary).
(T) 01452 532799
Profile: **FT:** Coarse; **WN:** Gardners Pool; **WT:** Gravel Pit (Still) **W. Size:** 5 Acres. **Location:** **Nr. Rd:** B4071; **Main Rd:** A38.
Ref: FH1835

GARNFFRWD FISHERY

Garnffrwd Fishery, Mynydd Cerrig, Crosshands, Llanelli, **CARMARTHENSHIRE**, SA15 5BB, **Wales**.
Contact/s: **Mr Colin Miller** (Manager).
(T) 01269 870539
Profile: **FT:** Game; **WN:** Garnffrwd Fishery; **WT:** Lake (Still). **Location:** **Nr. Rd:** Mynydd Cerrig.
Ref: FH1836

GARNISH HALL

Garnish Hall, Coopersale Lane, Theydon, Garnon, **ESSEX**, **England**.
(W) www.becmain-as.dial.pipex.com
Contact/s: **Mr Leslie Ailey** (Club Secretary), 3 Meadow Rd, Rush Green, Romford, Essex, RM7 0LR.
(T) 01708 745985 **(M)** 07714 091884
(E) becmain-as@dial.pipex.com
Profile: **FT:** Coarse; **WN:** Garnish Hall; **WT:** Lake (Still); **F. Size:** 4 Acres; **W. Size:** 3 Acres. **Location:** **Nr. Rd:** Coopersale Lane; **Main Rd:** B172; **Rail:** Epping.
Ref: FH1837

GARRANES LAKE

Garranes Lake, Dunmanway, **COUNTY CORK**, **Ireland**.
(W) www.swrfb.ie
Contact/s: Area Manager, South West Regional Fisheries Board, 1 Nevilles Trce, Macroom, County Cork, Ireland.
(T) 026 41221
(E) swrfb@swrfb.ie
Manager, Garranes Filling Station, Garranas, Dunmanway, County Cork, Ireland.
(T) 028 31514
Profile: **FT:** Game; **WN:** Garranes; **WT:** Lake (Still) **W. Size:** 25 Acres. **Location:** **Nr. Rd:** Drimoleague to Dunmanway.
Ref: FH1838

GARRY UPPER (RIVER)

River Garry, Invergarry, **HIGHLAND**, PH35 4HS, **Scotland**.
Contact/s: **Mr Gordon Heath** (Manager), Tomdoun Hotel, Glengarry, Invergarry, Highland, PH35 4HS.
(T) 01809 511218 **(F)** 01809 511218
Profile: **FT:** Game; **WN:** Garry (Upper); **WT:** River (Moving) **W. Size:** 5600 Metres. **Location:** **Nr. Rd:** Tomdoun Road; **Main Rd:** A87; **Rail:** Fort William.
Ref: FH1839

GARTMORN DAM FISHERY

Gartmorn Dam Fishery, Speirs Ctre, 29 Primrose St, Alloa, **CLACKMANNANSHIRE**, FK10, **Scotland**.
Contact/s: Fishery Officer, Clackmannan District Council, 29 Primrose St, Alloa, Clackmannanshire, FK10 1JJ.
(T) 01259 213131
Profile: **FT:** Game; **WN:** Gartmorn Dam; **WT:** Lake (Still). **Location:** **Nr. Rd:** Gartmorn Road; **Main Rd:** A908 to Tillicoultry.
Ref: FH1840

GARW (RIVER)

River Garw, Garw Valley, Bridgend, CF32, **Wales**.
Contact/s: **Mr Ft Hughes** (Hon Secretary), 20 Heol Glannant, Bettws, Glamorgan (Vale of).
(T) 01656 722077
Profile: **FT:** Game; **WN:** Garw; **WT:** River (Moving) **W. Size:** 8000 Metres.
Ref: FH1841

GATTON MANOR LAKES

Gatton Manor Lakes, Wallis Wood, Dorking, **SURREY**, RH5, **England**.
Contact/s: **Mr Adrian Bewley** (Manager), Ashvale Fisheries, 69 Fortescue Rd, Wimbledon, London, SW19 2EA.
(T) 020 82873892
Profile: **FT:** Coarse; **WN:** Gatton Manor; **WT:** Lake (Still). **Location:** **Nr. Rd:** Forest Green to Walliswood; **Main Rd:** Walliswood to Billingshurst.
Ref: FH1842

GATTON WATER CARAVAN SITE

Gatton Water, Hillington, King's Lynn, **NORFOLK**, PE31 6BJ, **England**.
(W) www.adultstouring.co.uk
Contact/s: **Mr Mark Donaldson** (Director).
(T) 01485 600643
(E) gatton.waters@virgin.net
Profile: **FT:** Coarse; **WN:** Gatton Waters; **WT:** Gravel Pit (Still) **W. Size:** 8 Acres. **Location:** **Nr. Rd:** A148; **Main Rd:** A148; **Rail:** King's Lynn.
Ref: FH1843

GAUNTS LAKE

Gaunts Lake, Shimano Linear Fisheries (Oxford), Smiths Concrete Site, Hardwick Village, Witney, **OXFORDSHIRE**, OX8 7Q, **England**.
Contact/s: **Mr Len Gurd** (Owner), 10A Rackstraw Gr, Old Farm Park, Milton Keynes, Buckinghamshire, MK7 8PZ.
(T) 01908 645135 **(F)** 01908 645115
Profile: **FT:** Coarse; **WN:** Gaunts; **WT:** Lake (Still); **F. Size:** 25 Acres; **W. Size:** 20 Acres. **Location:** **Nr. Rd:** B4449; **Main Rd:** A40; **Rail:** Oxford.
Ref: FH1844

GAYWOODS

Gaywoods, Kings Langley, **HERTFORDSHIRE**, WD4, **England**.
Contact/s: **Ms Jane Grace** (Fishery Manager).
(T) 01923 269578 **(M)** 07778 030939
Profile: **FT:** Coarse; **WN:** Gaywoods; **WT:** Lake (Still).
Ref: FH1845

GEDGES LAKES

Gedges Lakes, Maidstone, **KENT**, ME1, **England**.
Contact/s: Secretary.
(T) 01892 832730
Profile: **FT:** Coarse; **WN:** Gedges; **WT:** Lake (Still).
Ref: FH1846

GEIGYS WATER

Geigys Water, Middleton, Manchester, **MANCHESTER (GREATER)**, M, **England**.
Contact/s: **Mr Gary Leigh** (Secretary), Middleton Angling Society, 151 Tennyson Rd, Boarshaw, Middleton, Manchester M24 2NS.
(T) 0161 6546253 **(M)** 07973 205280
Mr John Pole.
(T) 0161 2053887
Profile: **FT:** Coarse; **WN:** Geigy's; **WT:** Pond (Still) **W. Size:** 2 Acres. **Location:** **Nr. Rd:** A6045; **Main Rd:** M60.
Ref: FH1847

GEORGE BORROW HOTEL

George Borrow Hotel, Ponterwyd, Aberystwyth, **CEREDIGION**, SY23 3AD, **Wales**.
Contact/s: **Mr John Wall** (Manager).
(T) 01970 890230 **(F)** 01970 890587
Profile: **FT:** Game; **WN:** George Borrow Hotel; **WT:** Reservoir (Still & Moving).
Location: **Nr. Rd:** A44.
Ref: FH1848

GERARDS CARP LAKE

Gerards Carp Lake, Woodgate Lane, Maxey, Peterborough, **CAMBRIDGESHIRE**, PE, **England**.
Contact/s: **Mr I Bridgefoot** (Fishery Manager).
(T) 01945 780309
Profile: **FT:** Coarse; **WN:** Gerards; **WT:** Lake (Still) **W. Size:** 6 Acres. **Location:** **Nr. Rd:** Woodgate Lane.
Ref: FH1849

GHYLL HEAD

Ghyll Head (South Lakeland), South Lakeland, Bowness On Windermere, **CUMBRIA**, LA23, **England**.
Contact/s: **Mr Roy Rhodes** (Conservation, Access and Recreation Manager), Rivington Water Treatment Works, Bolton Rd, Horwich, Bolton, BL6 7RN.
(T) 01204 664300
Profile: **FT:** Coarse; **WN:** Ghyll Head; **WT:** Lake (Still).
Ref: FH1850

GHYLL HEAD TROUT FISHERY

Ghyll Head Trout Fishery, Beech Hill Hotel, Windermere, **CUMBRIA**, LA23, **England**.
Contact/s: **Mr Chris Sodo** (Hon Treasurer), Windermere, Ambleside and District Angling Association, Ecclerigg Court, Ecclerigg, Windermere, LA23 1LQ.
(T) 01539 445083
Profile: **FT:** Game; **WN:** Ghyll Head; **WT:** Reservoir (Still) **W. Size:** 11 Acres.
Location: **Nr. Rd:** A592 Bowness to Newby Bridge Road; **Main Rd:** A590 or A591.
Ref: FH1851

GIBBS HILL TROUT FISHERY

Gibbs Hill Trout Fishery, Once Brewed, Bardon Hall, Hexham, **NORTHUMBERLAND**, NE47, **England**.
Contact/s: Fishery Manager.
(T) 01434 344030
Profile: **FT:** Game; **WN:** Gibbs Hill Trout Fishery; **WT:** Lake (Still).
Ref: FH1852

GIFFORD HOPES RESERVOIR

Gifford Hopes Reservoir, Lothians Division, Alderston House, Haddington, **LOTHIAN (EAST)**, EH41, **Scotland**.
(W) www.esw.co.uk
Contact/s: **East Of Scotland Water**, East of Scotland Water, Lothians Division, Alderston House, Haddington, Lothian (East).
(T) 0131 445462
Mr Max Muir (Manager), Goblin Ha Hotel, Gifford, Scotland.
(T) 01620 810244
Profile: **FT:** Game; **WN:** Gifford Hopes; **WT:** Reservoir (Still).
Ref: FH1853

GILBRATAR LAKE

Gilbratar Lake, Ryding Court Farm, Langley, Slough, **BUCKINGHAMSHIRE**, SL3, **England**.
Contact/s: Manager, Hounslow Angling Ctre, 265 - 267 Bath Rd, Hounslow, Middlesex, TW3 3DA.
(T) 020 85706156 **(F)** 020 85708885
Profile: **FT:** Coarse; **WN:** Gilbrater; **WT:** Lake (Still) **W. Size:** 2 Acres. **Location:** **Nr. Rd:** Blenheim Road; **Main Rd:** M4.
Ref: FH1854

GILER ARMS LAKE

Giler Arms Lake, Rhydcydan, Betws-Y-Coed, **CONWY**, LL24 0LL, **Wales**.
(W) www.welcome.to/giler
Contact/s: **Mr Graham Gibson** (Owner),

The Giler Arms Hotel, Rhydcydan, Betws-y-Coed, Conwy, LL24 0LL.
(T) 01690 770612 (F) 01690 770347
(E) g.gibson@virgin.net
Profile: FT: Coarse; WN: Giler Lake; WT: Lake (Still); F. Size: 1 Acre; W. Size: 1 Acre. Location: Nr. Rd: A5; Rail: Betws-y-Coed.
Ref: FH1855

GILLEES POND

Gillees Pond, Stag Lane, Newport, **ISLE OF WIGHT**, PO30, **England**.
Contact/s: Mr Alan Bravery (Manager), Scotties Fishing Tackle, 11 Lugley St, Newport, Isle of Wight, PO30 5HD.
(T) 01983 522115 (F) 01983 522115
Mr Paul Jackson (Manager), Scotties Sandown, 22 Fitzroy St, Sandown, Isle of Wight, PO36 8HZ.
(T) 01983 404555
Profile: FT: Coarse; WN: Gillee's; WT: Pond (Still). Location: Nr. Rd: Stag Lane; Main Rd: A3020.
Ref: FH1856

GILSLAND LAKE

Gilsland Lake, Haltwhistle, **NORTHUMBERLAND**, NE49, **England**.
Profile: FT: Coarse; WN: Gilsland; WT: Lake (Still).
Ref: FH1857

GIMINGHAM LAKES

Gimingham Lakes, Gimingham, Norwich, **NORFOLK**, NR11, **England**.
Contact/s: Ms Brownie Gotts.
(T) 01263 720432
Profile: FT: Coarse; WN: Gimingham; WT: Lake (Still). Location: Nr. Rd: Trunch to Gimingham; Main Rd: B1145 north to Swaffield,.
Ref: FH1858

GINGERBREAD LAKE AND DRIFT

Gingerbread Lake And Drift, St Neots, Huntingdon, **CAMBRIDGESHIRE**, PE19, **England**.
Contact/s: Fishery Manager.
(T) 01767 314902
Profile: FT: Coarse; WN: Gingerbread; WT: Lake (Still).
Ref: FH1859

GIPPING (RIVER)

Gipping (River), Bramford Picnic Site, Bramford Rd, Ipswich, **SUFFOLK**, **England**.
(W) www.gippingaps.co.uk
Contact/s: Mr G Alderson (Club Secretary), 37 Heatherhayes, Ipswich, IP2 9SL.
(T) 01473 602828
Profile: FT: Coarse; WN: Gipping; WT: River (Moving). Location: Nr. Rd: Bramford Road (1067); Rail: Ipswich.
Ref: FH1860

GIPPING (RIVER)

Gipping (River), Barham Stretch, Ipswich, **SUFFOLK**, **England**.
(W) www.gippingaps.co.uk
Contact/s: Mr G Alderson (Club Secretary), 37 Heatherhayes, Ipswich, IP2 9SL.
(T) 01473 602828
Profile: FT: Coarse; WN: Gipping; WT: River (Moving). Location: Main Rd: A14; Rail: Claydon.
Ref: FH1861

GIPPING (RIVER)

Gipping (River), Sharmford Lock, Ipswich, **SUFFOLK**, **England**.
(W) www.gippingaps.co.uk
Contact/s: Mr G Alderson (Club Secretary), 37 Heatherhayes, Ipswich, IP2 9SL.
(T) 01473 602828
Profile: FT: Coarse; WN: Gipping; WT: River (Moving). Location: Main Rd: A14; Rail: Ipswich.
Ref: FH1862

GIPPING (RIVER)

Gipping (River), Upper Reach, Ipswich, **SUFFOLK**, **England**.
Contact/s: , Ipswich Council.
Profile: FT: Coarse; WN: Gipping; WT: River (Moving). Location: Nr. Rd: Yarmouth Road (B1067); Rail: Ipswich.
Ref: FH1863

GIPPING (RIVER)

Gipping (River), Sproughton Road Bridge, Ipswich, **SUFFOLK**, **England**.
(W) www.gippingaps.co.uk
Contact/s: Mr G Alderson (Club Secretary), 37 Heatherhayes, Ipswich, IP2 9SL.
(T) 01473 602828
Profile: FT: Coarse; WN: Gipping; WT: River (Moving). Location: Nr. Rd: Sproughton Road; Main Rd: Bamford Road (B1067); Rail: Ipswich.
Ref: FH1864

GIPPING (RIVER)

Gipping (River), Elton Water Bank, Yarmouth Rd, Ipswich, **SUFFOLK**, **England**.
(W) www.gippingaps.co.uk
Contact/s: Mr G Alderson (Club Secretary), 37 Heatherhayes, Ipswich, IP2 9SL.
(T) 01473 602828
Profile: FT: Coarse; WN: Gipping; WT: River (Moving). Location: Nr. Rd: Yarmouth Road (B1067); Rail: Ipswich.
Ref: FH1865

GLADHOUSE RESERVOIR

Gladhouse Reservoir, Penicuik, **LOTHIAN (MID)**, EH26, **Scotland**.
Contact/s: Mr Donald Newstead (Area Manager), East of Scotland Water, 55 Buckstone Trce, Edinburgh, EH10 6XH.
(T) 0131 4456462
Profile: FT: Game; WN: Gladhouse; WT: Reservoir (Still).
Ref: FH1866

GLAISDALE (RIVER)

River Glaisdale, Whitby, **YORKSHIRE (NORTH)**, YO2, **England**.
Contact/s: Mr D J Swales (Esk Fa Bailiff), Rosedene, Priory Park, Grosmont, Whitby, YO22 5QQ.
(T) 01947 895488
Profile: FT: Game; WN: Glaisdale; WT: River (Moving).
Ref: FH1867

GLAN MORFA MAWR FISHERY

Glan Morfa Mawr Fishery, Glan Morfa Mawr Farm, Morfa Bychan, Porthmadog, **GWYNEDD**, LL49 9YH, **Wales**.
Contact/s: Mr Justin Roberts.
(T) 01766 513333
Profile: FT: Game; WN: Glan Morfa Mawr Fishery; WT: Lake (Still); F. Size: 20 Acres; W. Size: 5 Acres. Location: Rail: Porthmadog.
Ref: FH1868

GLAS LLYN FISHERY

Glas-Llyn Fishery, Ffynnon- Las- Isaf, Blaenwaun, Llanboidy, **CARMARTHENSHIRE**, SA34, **Wales**.
Contact/s: Mr Owen Forbes.
(T) 01994 419466
Profile: FT: Game; WN: Glas-Llyn; WT: Lake (Still).
Ref: FH1869

GLAS-LLYN FISHERY

Glas-Llyn Fishery, Fynnon-Las-Isaf, Blaenwaun, Whitland, **CARMARTHENSHIRE**, SA34 0JH, **Wales**.
Contact/s: Mr Terry Forbes.
(T) 01994 419466
Profile: FT: Coarse; WN: Glas-Llyn Fishery; WT: Lake (Still) W. Size: 2 Acres.
Ref: FH1870

GLASLYN (RIVER)

River Glaslyn, Penrhyndeudraeth, **GWYNEDD**, LL48, **Wales**.
Contact/s: Mr A Edwards (Manager), Penrhyn Guns, 7 High St, Penrhyndeudraeth, Gwynedd.
(T) 01766 770339
Profile: FT: Game; WN: Glaslyn; WT: River (Moving).
Ref: FH1871

GLASS (RIVER)

River Glass, Evanton, Dingwall, **HIGHLAND**, IV16, **Scotland**.
Contact/s: A Alcock (Manager), Newsagent, 16 Balconie St, Evanton, Dingwall, IV16 9UN.
(T) 01349 830672 (F) 01349 830672
Profile: FT: Game; WN: Glass; WT: River (Moving).
Ref: FH1872

GLASS (RIVER)

River Glass, Cannich, Beauly, **HIGHLAND**, IV4 7NA, **Scotland**.
Contact/s: Mr Stephen Bassett.
(T) 01456 415243 (F) 01456 415425
Profile: FT: Game; WN: Glass; WT: River (Moving) W. Size: 4750 Metres. Location: Nr. Rd: Tomich; Main Rd: A831.
Ref: FH1873

GLASTONBURY

Glastonbury, Glastonbury, **SOMERSET**, BA6, **England**.
Profile: FT: Coarse; WN: Glastonbury; WT: River (Moving).
Ref: FH1874

GLEAN LOCH

Glean Loch, Lochgilphead, **RENFREWSHIRE**, PA3, **Scotland**.
Contact/s: Mr Archie MacGilp (Secretary), Fyne Tackle, 22 Argyll St, Lochgilphead, Argyll and Bute, PA31 8NE.
(T) 01546 606878
Profile: FT: Game; WN: Glean; WT: Loch (Still); F. Size: 400 Acres; W. Size: 30 Acres. Location: Nr. Rd: Cairnbaan; Main Rd: B844; Rail: Oban.
Ref: FH1875

GLEAVES RESERVOIR

Gleaves Reservoir, Dunscar, Bolton, **LANCASHIRE**, BL, **England**.
Contact/s: Mr Terence A McKee (Secretary), Bolton and District Angling Association, 1 Lever Edge Lane, Bolton, Lancashire, BL3 3BU.
(T) 01204 393726
Profile: FT: Combination; WN: Gleaves; WT: Reservoir (Still) W. Size: 2 Acres. Location: Nr. Rd: A666 South of Blackburn; Main Rd: Longworth Lane.
Ref: FH1876

GLEBE COURT LAKE

Glebe Court Lake, Stratton Audley, Bicester, **OXFORDSHIRE**, OX6, **England**.
Contact/s: Mr Robert Hearing (Fishery Manager).
(T) 01869 277410
Profile: FT: Coarse; WN: Glebe Court Lake; WT: Lake (Still).
Ref: FH1877

GLEBE LAKE

Glebe Lake, Earls Barton, Northampton, **NORTHAMPTONSHIRE**, NN6, **England**.
Contact/s: Fishery Manager.
(T) 01604 712591
Profile: FT: Coarse; WN: Glebe; WT: Lake (Still).
Ref: FH1878

GLEMELAG (RIVER)

River Glemelag, Omagh, **COUNTY TYRONE**, BT78, **Northern Ireland**.
Contact/s: Mr David Campbell (Manager), Mourne Valley Tackle, 50 Main St,

Newtownstewart, Omagh, County Tyrone, BT78 4AA.
(T) 028 81661543
Profile: FT: Game; WN: Glemelag; WT: River (Moving).
Ref: FH1879

GLEN ESK CARAVAN PARK

Glen Esk Caravan Park, Edzell, Brechin, **ANGUS**, DD9 7YP, **Scotland**.
Contact/s: Fishery Manager.
(T) 01356 644523or644565
Profile: FT: Coarse; WN: Glen Esk Caravan Park; WT: Lake (Still) W. Size: 1 Acre.
Location: Main Rd: B966.
Ref: FH1880

GLEN LATTERACH RESERVOIR

Glen Latterach Reservoir, High St, Elgin, **MORAY**, IV30, **Scotland**.
Contact/s: Fishery Manager.
(T) 01343 545121
Profile: FT: Game; WN: Glen Latterach; WT: Reservoir (Still).
Ref: FH1881

GLEN MERE

Glen Mere, Glen Farm House, Norwich, **NORFOLK**, NR11, **England**.
Contact/s: **Mr Stanley Barrett** (Fishery Manager).
(T) 01263 761303
Profile: FT: Coarse; WN: Glen Mere; WT: Lake (Still). Location: Main Rd: A410.
Ref: FH1882

GLEN OF ROTHES TROUT FISHERY

Glen Of Rothes Trout Fishery, Glen Of Rothes, Rothes, Aberlour, **MORAY**, AB38 7AG, **Scotland**.
(W) www.glen-of-rothes.co.uk
Contact/s: **Mr Mike Payne** (Proprietor), 13 Hermes Rd, Bishopmill, Elgin, Moray, IV30 4LH.
(T) 01340 831888 (F) 01340 831888 (M) 07899 803102
Profile: FT: Game; WN: Glen Of Rothes Trout Fishery; WT: Combination (Still & Moving) W. Size: 6 Acres. Location: Nr. Rd: A941 Elgin to Rothes Road; Main Rd: A941; Rail: Elgin.
Ref: FH1883

GLENARM (RIVER)

River Glenarm, Glenarm, Ballymena, **COUNTY ANTRIM**, BT44, **Northern Ireland**.
Contact/s: **Mr John Todd**, 7 Cooleen Park, Jordanstown, County Antrim.
(T) 028 90862419 (F) 028 90862419
(E) jtodd@gillaroo.force9.co.uk
Ms Cherry Robinson, Antrim Estates Office, 2 Castle Lane, Glenarm, Ballymena, BT44 0BQ.
(T) 028 28841203 (F) 028 28841305
Profile: FT: Game; WN: Glenarm; WT: River (Moving) W. Size: 7200 Metres.
Ref: FH1884

GLENARRIFF (RIVER)

River Glenarriff, Cushendun, Cushendall, **COUNTY ANTRIM**, BT44, **Northern Ireland**.
Contact/s: Manager, O'Neill's Country Sports, Sea and Game Tackle, 25 Mill St, Cushendall, County Antrim.
(T) 028 21772009
Mrs C McFetridge, 116 Tromara Rd, Cushendun, County Antrim, BT44 0ST.
(T) 028 21761251
Profile: FT: Game; WN: Glenarriff; WT: Tributary (Moving).
Ref: FH1885

GLENCOE LOCHAN

Glencoe Lochan, Glencoe Old Rd, Glencoe, Ballachulish, **HIGHLAND**, PA39 4HT, **Scotland**.
Contact/s: **Mr Andrew Shodon**, Forest Enterprise Limited, Millparil Rd, Oban, Argyll and Bute, PA34 4NH.
(T) 01631 566155
(E) john@scorrybrec.freeserve.co.uk
Profile: FT: Game; WN: Glencoe; WT: Lake (Still) W. Size: 3 Acres. Location: Nr. Rd: Glencoe Old Road; Main Rd: A82; Rail: Fort William.
Ref: FH1886

GLENDARROCH LOCH

Glendarroch Loch, Craighlaw Fisheries, Newton Stewart, **DUMFRIES AND GALLOWAY**, DG8, **Scotland**.
Contact/s: **Ms Clare McClymont** (Manager), Palakona Bait Supplies, 30-32 Queen St, Newton Stewart, Dumfries and Galloway, DG8 9NR.
(T) 01671 402323
(E) palakonswscot@cs.com
Profile: FT: Coarse; WN: Glandarroch; WT: Loch (Still).
Ref: FH1887

GLENELLY (RIVER)

River Glenelly, Gortin, Newtownstewart, **COUNTY TYRONE**, BT78, **Northern Ireland**.
Contact/s: Manager, Chism Fishing Tackle, 2 Bridge St, Omagh, County Tyrone, BT78 1BX.
(T) 028 82244932
Mr David Campbell (Manager), Mourne Valley Tackle, 50 Main St, Newtownstewart, Omagh, County Tyrone, BT78 4AA.
(T) 028 81661543
Profile: FT: Game; WN: Glenelly; WT: River (Moving).
Ref: FH1888

GLENFARG FISHERY

Glenfarg Fishery, Candy Farm, Glenfarg, Perth, **PERTH AND KINROSS**, PH2 9QL, **Scotland**.
Contact/s: **Mr Alex McAcney**.
(T) 01577 830822
Mr John Kenny.
(T) 01577 830727
Profile: FT: Game; WN: Glenfarg Fishery; WT: Combination (Still); F. Size: 7 Acres. Location: Nr. Rd: Path of Condie; Main Rd: M90.
Ref: FH1889

GLENGARIFF (RIVER)

River Glengariff, The Village, Glengariff, **COUNTY CORK**, **Ireland**.
Contact/s: Manager, The Maple Leaf Bar, Glengariff, County Cork.
Mr Bernard Harington.
(T) 027 63021
Mr Patrick Power.
(T) 027 63021
Profile: FT: Game; WN: Glengariff; WT: River (Moving) W. Size: 9000 Metres. Location: Nr. Rd: H71; Rail: Killarney.
Ref: FH1890

GLENKILN RESERVOIR

Glenkiln Reservoir, Dumfries, **DUMFRIES AND GALLOWAY**, DG2 9, **Scotland**.
Contact/s: , Dumfries and Galloway Regional Council, Department of Water and Sewerage, 70 Terregles St, Dumfries and Galloway, DG2 9B.
(T) 01387 263011
Profile: FT: Game; WN: Glenkiln; WT: Reservoir (Still).
Ref: FH1891

GLENLEIGH FARM FISHERY

Glenleigh Farm Fishery, Sticker, St Austell, **CORNWALL**, PL26 7JB, **England**.
Contact/s: **Mr Andrew Tregunna** (Owner).
(T) 01726 73154 (F) 01726 77465
Mrs Claire Tregunna (Owner).
(T) 01726 73154 (F) 01726 77465 (M) 07713 556356
Profile: FT: Coarse; WN: Glenleigh; WT: Lake (Still) W. Size: 1 Acre. Location: Nr. Rd: A390; Main Rd: A390; Rail: St Austell.
Ref: FH1892

GLENMORE FISHERY

Glenmore Fishery, Glenmore Estate, Ballybofey, **COUNTY DONEGAL**, **Ireland**.
Contact/s: **Mr Thomas McCreery**, Altnapaste, County Donegal.
(T) 073 32075
Profile: FT: Game; WN: Finn & Reelan; WT: River (Moving) W. Size: 18000 Metres.
Location: Nr. Rd: Ballybofey to Glenties; Rail: Derry.
Ref: FH1893

GLENSHERRUP FISHERIES

Glensherrup Fisheries, Glendevon, Frandy Farm, Glendevon, Dollar, **CLACKMANNANSHIRE**, FK14 7JY, **Scotland**.
Contact/s: **Mr Richard Philp**.
(T) 01592 614000
Profile: FT: Coarse; WN: Glensherrup; WT: Reservoir (Still).
Ref: FH1894

GLENSHESK (RIVER)

River Glenshesk, Ballycastle, **COUNTY ANTRIM**, BT54, **Northern Ireland**.
Contact/s: **Mr Bill Williamson** (Hon Secretary), 26 Cushendall Rd, Ballycastle, County Antrim, BT54 6QR.
(T) 028 20762693
Profile: FT: Game; WN: Glenshesk; WT: Tributary (Moving) W. Size: 4800 Metres.
Ref: FH1895

GLORE (RIVER)

River Glore, Kiltamagh, **COUNTY MAYO**, **Ireland**.
Contact/s: Angling Officer, North Western Regional Fisheries Board, Ardnaree House, Abbey St, Ballina, County Mayo.
(T) 096 22623 (F) 096 70543
Profile: FT: Game; WN: Glore; WT: River (Moving).
Ref: FH1896

GLOUCESTER & SHARPNESS

Gloucester And Sharpness Canal, Hardwicke, Gloucester, **GLOUCESTERSHIRE**, GL2, **England**.
Contact/s: **Mr Terry Girdlestone**.
(T) 01452 526850
Profile: FT: Coarse; WN: Gloucester and Sharpness; WT: Canal (Still). Location: Nr. Rd: Hardwicke; Main Rd: M5, junction 12.
Ref: FH1897

GLOUCESTER CANAL

Gloucester Canal, Sims Lane, Quedgeley, Gloucester, **GLOUCESTERSHIRE**, GL2 5, **England**.
Contact/s: Manager, Tredworth Fishing Tackle, 78 High St, Gloucester, Gloucestershire, GL1 4SR.
(T) 01452 523009
Manager, Gloucester Canal Angling, 24 Gambier Parry Gardens, Tewkesbury Rd, Gloucester, GL2 9RD.
(T) 01452 526850
Profile: FT: Coarse; WN: Gloucester; WT: Canal (Still). Location: Nr. Rd: Sims Lane; Main Rd: M5 junction 12, A38.
Ref: FH1898

GLOUCESTER CANAL

Gloucester Canal, Fretherne Bridge, Fretherne, Gloucester, **GLOUCESTERSHIRE**, GL2, **England**.
Contact/s: **Mr Terry Girdlestone**.
(T) 01452 526850
Profile: FT: Coarse; WN: Gloucester; WT: Canal (Still) W. Size: 2400 Metres.
Location: Nr. Rd: B4071; Main Rd: M5, junction 13.
Ref: FH1899

GLOUCESTER PARK LAKE

Gloucester Park Lake, Basildon, **ESSEX**, SS1, **England**.
Contact/s: **Mr Mick Toomer** (Manager), Tackle Shop, 10 Ravensdale, Kingswood, Basildon, Essex SS16 5HS.
(T) 01268 282317
Mr Stan Howard.
(T) 01268 530164
Profile: FT: Coarse; WN: Gloucester Park; WT: Lake (Still) W. Size: 7 Acres. Location: Nr. Rd: A1235; Main Rd: A176; Rail:

Basildon. £Fr
Ref: FH1900

GLUDY LAKE

Gludy Lake, Cradoc, Brecon, **POWYS**, LD3, **Wales**.
Contact/s: **Mr Paul Burgess** (Consultant).
(T) 01874 610093
Profile: **FT:** Game; **WN:** Gludy; **WT:** Lake (Still).
Ref: FH1901

GLWYDWERN TROUT FISHERY

Glwydwern Trout Fishery, Glwydwern, Llanwnnen, Lampeter, **CEREDIGION**, SA48 7LS, **Wales**.
Contact/s: **Mr T W Morgan** (Owner).
(T) 01570 434248
Mrs G Morgan (Owner).
(T) 01570 434248
Profile: **FT:** Game; **WN:** Rainbow; **WT:** Lake (Still). **Location:** **Nr. Rd:** B4337; **Main Rd:** A475 to Llanwnnen.
Ref: FH1902

GLYNCORRWG PONDS FISHERY

Glyncorrwg Ponds Fishery, Units 1-2 Ynyscorrwg Park, Glyncorrwg, Port Talbot, **NEATH PORT TALBOT**, SA13 3BD, **Wales**.
Contact/s: **Mr L Acteson**.
(T) 01639 851900
Profile: **FT:** Combination; **WN:** Rainbow; **WT:** Lake (Still). **Location:** **Nr. Rd:** A4107 to Cymmer; **Main Rd:** M4, junction 40.
Ref: FH1903

GLYNDWR FISHERY

Glyndwr Fishery, Crediton, **DEVON**, EX17 3, **England**.
Contact/s: **Mr Howard Thresher** (Treasurer), Crediton and Fly Fishing Club, 30 Tuckers Meadow, Crediton, Devon, EX17 3NX.
(T) 01363 774926
Profile: **FT:** Coarse; **WN:** Glyndwr Fishery; **WT:** Lake (Still).
Ref: FH1904

GODMANCHESTER (RIVER)

River Godmanchester, Godmanchester, Huntingdon, **CAMBRIDGESHIRE**, PE18, **England**.
Contact/s: **Mr Stan J Binge** (Manager), Stanjay Fishing Tackle and Trophies, 7 Old Court Wall, Godmanchester, Huntingdon, PE18 8HS.
(T) 01480 453303
Profile: **FT:** Coarse; **WN:** Godmanchester; **WT:** River (Moving) **W. Size:** 16000 Metres.
Ref: FH1905

GODNEY MOOR PONDS

Godney Moor Ponds, Glastonbury, **SOMERSET**, BA6, **England**.
Contact/s: **Mr Nick Hughes** (Manager), Street Angling Ctre, 160 High St, St, Somerset, BA16 0NH.
(T) 01458 447830 **(F)** 01458 447830
Profile: **FT:** Coarse; **WN:** Godney Moor; **WT:** Pond (Still) **W. Size:** 4 Acres. **Location:** **Nr. Rd:** Brabazon Drive; **Main Rd:** A39, Glastonbury to Godney.
Ref: FH1906

GODWINS POOL

Godwins Pool, Congleton, **CHESHIRE**, CW12, **England**.
Contact/s: **Mr Nigel Bours** (Hon Secretary), Congleton AS, 8 Norfolk Rd, Congleton, Cheshire, CW12 1NY.
(T) 01260 277284
Profile: **FT:** Coarse; **WN:** Godwins Pool; **WT:** Pond (Still).
Ref: FH1907

GOLD OAK FISH FARM

Gold Oak Fish Farm, Hare Lane, Cranbourne, Wimborne, **DORSET**, BH21 5QT, **England**.
Contact/s: **Mr John Butler**.
(T) 01725 517275
Profile: **FT:** Coarse; **WN:** Gold Oak Fish Farm; **WT:** Lake (Still). **Location:** **Nr. Rd:** B3078 Hare Lane; **Main Rd:** A31.
Ref: FH1908

GOLD VALLEY LAKES

Gold Valley Lakes, Gold Lane, Government Rd, Aldershot, **HAMPSHIRE**, GU11 2PT, **England**.
(W) www.goldvalleylakes.com
Contact/s: **Mr John Raison**.
(T) 01252 336333 **(F)** 01252 350257
Profile: **FT:** Coarse; **WN:** Gold Valley; **WT:** Lake (Still). **Location:** **Nr. Rd:** Goverment Road; **Main Rd:** A321 to Ash Vale.
Ref: FH1909

GOLDEN LOCH

Golden Loch, Goldenhill House, Berryhill, Newburgh, Cupar, **FIFE**, KY14, **Scotland**.
(W) www.goldenloch.co.uk
Contact/s: **Mr J D Nicol** (Owner).
(T) 01337 840412
Profile: **FT:** Game; **WN:** Golden; **WT:** Loch (Still).
Ref: FH1910

GOLDEN POND FISHERY

Golden Pond Fishery, Fullerton Rd, Fullerton, Andover, **HAMPSHIRE**, SP20 6AG, **England**.
Contact/s: **Mr Jeff Hounslow**.
(T) 01264 860627 **(F)** 01264 860813
Profile: **FT:** Coarse; **WN:** Golden; **WT:** Pond (Still); **F. Size:** 2 Acres; **W. Size:** 1 Acre. **Location:** **Nr. Rd:** Fullerton; **Main Rd:** A3057; **Rail:** Andover.
Ref: FH1912

GOLDEN SPRINGS LAKES

Golden Springs Lakes, Christchurch, **DORSET**, BH23, **England**.
Contact/s: **Mr R J Andrews** (Club Secretary), Christchurch Angling Club, 4 Marley Cl, New Milton, BH25 5LL.
(T) 01425 638502
Profile: **FT:** Combination; **WN:** Golden Springs; **WT:** Lake (Still). **Location:** **Nr. Rd:** A35, A337; **Main Rd:** A31.
Ref: FH1913

GOLDEN VALLEY

Golden Valley, Golden Valley Common, Castlemorton, Ledbury, **HEREFORDSHIRE**, HR8, **England**.
Contact/s: **Mr S A Sturge** (Manager), Ledbury Tackle Ctre, 3 The Southend, Ledbury, Herefordshire, HR8 2EY.
(T) 01531 632768 **(F)** 01531 632768
Profile: **FT:** Coarse; **WN:** Golden Valley Pool; **WT:** Lake (Still) **W. Size:** 2 Acres. **Location:** **Nr. Rd:** Golden Valley Road; **Main Rd:** A438. £Fr
Ref: FH1914

GOLDFISH BOWL (THE)

Goldfish Bowl (The), Boulderdyke Farm, Deddington, Oxford, **OXFORDSHIRE**, OX2, **England**.
Contact/s: **Mr Donald Wellford** (Fishery Manager).
(T) 01869 338539
Profile: **FT:** Coarse; **WN:** Goldfish Bowl (The); **WT:** Lake (Still).
Ref: FH1915

GOLDSWORTH WATER PARK

Goldsworth Water Park, Woking, **SURREY**, GU, **England**.
Contact/s: **Mr Brian Rich** (Head Bailiff).
(T) 01483 764836
Rick, Apollo Angling Ctre, 79 Brighton Rd, Addlestone, Surrey, KT15 1PT.
(T) 01932 848354
Profile: **FT:** Coarse; **WN:** Goldsworth Water Park; **WT:** Lake (Still) **W. Size:** 22 Acres. **Location:** **Nr. Rd:** A324; **Main Rd:** Working.
Ref: FH1916

GOLTHO LAKE

Goltho Lake, Shepherds Farm, Goltho, Wragby, Market Rasen, **LINCOLNSHIRE**, LN8 5JD, **England**.
Contact/s: **Mr David** (Helper).
(T) 01673 858907
Mr H Bruntlett, Shepards Farm, Goltho, Wragby, Market Rasen, Lincoln.
(T) 01673 858358
Profile: **FT:** Coarse; **WN:** Goltho; **WT:** Lake (Still) **W. Size:** 2 Acres. **Location:** **Nr. Rd:** Goltho Lane; **Main Rd:** A158.
Ref: FH1917

GOODENBURGH TARN

Goodenburgh Tarn, Burton-In-Lonsdale, Carnforth, **CUMBRIA**, LA6, **England**.
Profile: **FT:** Combination; **WN:** Goodenburgh; **WT:** Tarn (Still). **Location:** **Nr. Rd:** Raven Close Brow; **Main Rd:** A683 Lancashire, B6480, Wennington.
Ref: FH1918

GOODIFORD MILL TROUT FISHERY

Goodiford Mill Trout Fishery, Kentisbeare, Cullompton, **DEVON**, EX15 2AS, **England**.
Contact/s: **Mr David Wheeler**.
(T) 01884 266233
Profile: **FT:** Game; **WN:** Goodiford Mill Trout Fishery; **WT:** Lake (Still) **W. Size:** 4 Acres.
Ref: FH1919

GOONHAVERN LAKE

Goonhavern Coarse Fishing Lake, Oakridge Farm, Bodmin Rd, Goonhavern, Truro, **CORNWALL**, TR4 9QG, **England**.
Contact/s: **Mr Steven Arthur**.
(T) 01872 540590or572612 **(M)** 07773 075281
Profile: **FT:** Coarse; **WN:** Goonhavern; **WT:** Lake (Still) **W. Size:** 2 Acres. **Location:** **Nr. Rd:** B3285, Bodmin Road; **Main Rd:** A30, South of Redruth; **Rail:** Truro.
Ref: FH1920

GOOSELOAN POND

Gooseloan Pond, Kilwinning, **AYRSHIRE (NORTH)**, KA13, **Scotland**.
Profile: **FT:** Coarse; **WN:** Gooseloan; **WT:** Pond (Still) **W. Size:** 4 Acres.
Ref: FH1921

GORSE PIT RESERVOIR

Gorse Pit Reservoir, Whittle St, Walkden, Manchester, **MANCHESTER (GREATER)**, M28, **England**.
Contact/s: **Mr Bob Fearnhead** (Secretary), Farnworth and District Angling Association, 3 Windmill Rd, Walkden, Manchester (Greater), M28 3RP.
(T) 0161 7994242
Profile: **FT:** Coarse; **WN:** Gorse Pit; **WT:** Reservoir (Still); **F. Size:** 3 Acres; **W. Size:** 2 Acres. **Location:** **Nr. Rd:** Whittle Street; **Main Rd:** A6 Manchester Road.
Ref: FH1922

GORSTY HALL

Gorsty Hall, Balterley, Crewe, **CHESHIRE**, CW2, **England**.
Contact/s: **Mr Larry Panayi** (Manager).
(T) 01270 820252
Profile: **FT:** Coarse; **WN:** Gorsty Hall; **WT:** Lake (Still). **Location:** **Nr. Rd:** B5500; **Main Rd:** A531.
Ref: FH1923

GORTON (LOWER) RESERVOIR

Gorton (Lower) Reservoir, Alston Rd, Gorton, Manchester, **MANCHESTER (GREATER)**, M18 7, **England**.
Contact/s: Water Manager, Manchester City Council, Leisure Department, Debdale Ctre, Debdale Park, 1073 Hyde Road, Gorton, Manchester, M18 7LJ.
(T) 0161 2235182
Mr Malcolm Moore.
(T) 0161 2233682
Mr Roy Rhodes (Conservation, Access and Recreation Manager), Rivington Water Treatment Works, Bolton Rd, Horwich, Bolton, BL6 7RN.
(T) 01204 664300
Profile: **FT:** Coarse; **WN:** Gorton (Lower); **WT:** Reservoir (Still). **Location:** **Main Rd:** A57, M67.

Ref: FH1924

GORTON (UPPER) RESERVOIR

Gorton (Upper) Reservoir, Alston Rd, Gorton, Manchester, **MANCHESTER (GREATER)**, M18 7, **England**.
Contact/s: Water Manager, Manchester City Council, Leisure Department, Debdale Ctre, Debdale Park, 1073 Hyde Road, Gorton, Manchester, M18 7LJ.
(T) 0161 2235182
Mr Malcolm Moore.
(T) 0161 2233682
Mr Roy Rhodes (Conservation, Access and Recreation Manager), Rivington Water Treatment Works, Bolton Rd, Horwich, Bolton, BL6 7RN.
(T) 01204 664300
Profile: **FT:** Coarse; **WN:** Gorton (Upper); **WT:** Reservoir (Still). **Location:** **Main Rd:** A57, M67.
Ref: FH1925

GOSFIELD LAKE RESORT

Gosfield Lake Resort, Church Rd, Gosfield, Halstead, **ESSEX**, CO9 1UD, **England**.
Contact/s: **Mr Carl Turp**.
(T) 01787 475043 (F) 01787 478528
Profile: **FT:** Coarse; **WN:** Gosfield; **WT:** Lake (Still) **W. Size:** 36 Acres. **Location:** **Nr. Rd:** A1017; **Rail:** Braintree.
Ref: FH1926

GOSSA WATER

Gossa Water, Gairdie, Mid Yell, Shetland, **SHETLAND ISLANDS**, ZE2, **Scotland**.
Contact/s: **Mr Ian Nisbet** (Secretary).
(T) 01957 2204
Profile: **FT:** Game; **WN:** Gossa; **WT:** Lake (Still).
Ref: FH1927

GOWDALL LAKES

Gowdall Lakes, Gowdall, Goole, **HUMBERSIDE**, DN14, **England**.
Contact/s: **Mr Peter Berry**.
(T) 01405 860756
Profile: **FT:** Coarse; **WN:** Gowdall; **WT:** Pond (Still) **W. Size:** 4 Acres. **Location:** **Nr. Rd:** A645; **Main Rd:** M62.
Ref: FH1928

GOWERTON COARSE FISHERY

Gowerton Golf Range And Coarse Fishery, Victoria Rd, Gowerton, Swansea, SA4 3AB, **Wales**.
(W) www.gowertongolfrange.com
Contact/s: **Mr Steve Bromham** (Manager).
(T) 01792 875188 (F) 01792 874288 (M) 07885 789544
(E) stevenbromham@beeb.net
Profile: **FT:** Coarse; **WN:** Gowerton Golf Range And Coarse Fishery; **WT:** Pond (Still); **F. Size:** 3 Acres; **W. Size:** 2 Acres. **Location:** **Nr. Rd:** B4296; **Main Rd:** A484; **Rail:** Gowerton.
Ref: FH1929

GOWY (RIVER)

Gowy (River), Plemstall Church, Mickle Trafford, Chester, **CHESHIRE**, **England**.
(W) www.baymalton-anglingclub.org
Contact/s: **Mr Stewart Godber** (Club Secretary), 38 Edenfield Rd, Mobberley, Cheshire, WA16 7HE.
(T) 01565 872582
Profile: **FT:** Coarse; **WN:** Gowy; **WT:** River (Moving).
Ref: FH1930

GOWY (RIVER)

Gowy (River), Nags Head Stretch, Bridge Trafford, Chester, **CHESHIRE**, **England**.
(W) www.baymalton-anglingclub.org
Contact/s: **Mr Stewart Godber** (Club Secretary), 38 Edenfield Rd, Mobberley, Cheshire, WA16 7HE.
(T) 01565 872582
Profile: **FT:** Game; **WN:** Gowy; **WT:** River (Moving). **Location:** **Nr. Rd:** A56; **Rail:** Chester.
Ref: FH1931

GOWY FISHERY

Gowy Fishery, The Grange, Warrington Rd, Mickle Trafford, Chester, **CHESHIRE**, CH2 4EB, **England**.
Contact/s: **Mr Huw Rowlands** (Manager).
(T) 01244 300655 (F) 01244 300710 (M) 07941 169283
Profile: **FT:** Combination; **WN:** Gowy; **WT:** Combination (Moving) **W. Size:** 2000 Metres. **Location:** **Nr. Rd:** A56 Warrington Road; **Main Rd:** A56; **Rail:** Helsby. £Free
Ref: FH1932

GOYT (RIVER)

River Goyt, Whaley Bridge, High Peak, **DERBYSHIRE**, SK23, **England**.
Profile: **FT:** Game; **WN:** Goyt; **WT:** River (Moving).
Ref: FH1933

GRAFHAM WATER

Grafham Water, Grafham Water Fishing Lodge, West Perry, Huntingdon, **CAMBRIDGESHIRE**, PE18 0BX, **England**.
Contact/s: **Mr John Mees** (Senior Warden).
(T) 01480 810531 (F) 01480 812488
Profile: **FT:** Game; **WN:** Grafham Water; **WT:** Reservoir (Still). **Location:** **Main Rd:** A1.
Ref: FH1934

GRAFTON LOCK

Grafton Lock, Grafton, Clanfield, Bampton, **OXFORDSHIRE**, OX18 3RY, **England**.
Contact/s: Lock Keeper.
(T) 01367 810251
Recreational Manager, The Environment Agency, Kings Meadow Rd, Reading, Berkshire, RG1 8DQ.
(T) 0118 9535000 (F) 0118 9500388
Profile: **FT:** Combination; **WN:** Thames; **WT:** Lock (Still). **Location:** **Main Rd:** B4449 Lechlade to Clanfield Road.
Ref: FH1935

GRAFTON MERE

Grafton Mere, Prospect Farm, Marton Cum Grafton, Boroughbridge, York, **YORKSHIRE (NORTH)**, YO51, **England**.
Contact/s: **Mr Roger Naish** (Owner).
(T) 01423 322045
Profile: **FT:** Coarse; **WN:** Grafton Mere; **WT:** Lake (Still) **W. Size:** 3 Acres. **Location:** **Main Rd:** York to Ripon.
Ref: FH1936

GRAIGLWYD SPRINGS FISHERY

Graiglwyd Springs Fishery, Graiglwyd Spring, Graiglwyd Rd, Penmaenmawr, **CONWY**, LL34 6, **Wales**.
Contact/s: **Mr Huw Jones**.
(T) 01492 622338
Profile: **FT:** Game; **WN:** Graiglwyd Springs Fishery; **WT:** Reservoir (Still) **W. Size:** 2 Acres.
Ref: FH1937

GRAND CANAL

Grand Canal, Robertstown, **COUNTY KILDARE**, **Ireland**.
Contact/s: **Mr Jim Crean**, Milltown Cottage, Athy, County Kildare, Ireland.
(T) 050 225189 (F) 050 225652
Mr Pauric Kelly (Manager), Tackle Shop, 48 Murray St, Edenderry, County Offaly, Ireland.
(T) 040 532071
Profile: **FT:** Coarse; **WN:** Grand; **WT:** Canal (Still) **W. Size:** 32000 Metres.
Ref: FH1938

GRAND CANAL

Grand Canal, Prosperous, **COUNTY KILDARE**, **Ireland**.
Contact/s: **Mr Jim Crean**, Milltown Cottage, Athy, County Kildare, Ireland.
(T) 050 225189 (F) 050 225652
Mr Pauric Kelly (Manager), Tackle Shop, 48 Murray St, Edenderry, County Offaly, Ireland.
(T) 040 532071
Profile: **FT:** Coarse; **WN:** Grand; **WT:** Canal (Still) **W. Size:** 32000 Metres.
Ref: FH1939

GRAND CANAL

Grand Canal, Edenderry, **COUNTY OFFALY**, **Ireland**.
Contact/s: **Mr Jim Crean**, Milltown Cottage, Athy, County Kildare, Ireland.
(T) 050 225189 (F) 050 225652
Mr Pauric Kelly (Manager), Tackle Shop, 48 Murray St, Edenderry, County Offaly, Ireland.
(T) 040 532071 (M) 0872 458275
Profile: **FT:** Coarse; **WN:** Grand; **WT:** Canal (Still) **W. Size:** 28800 Metres.
Ref: FH1940

GRAND CANAL (BARROW BRANCH)

Grand Canal (Barrow Branch), Rathangon, **COUNTY KILDARE**, **Ireland**.
Contact/s: **Mr Mj Conway** (Manager), Caravan and Camping Site, Rathangon, County Kildare, Ireland.
(T) 045 524331
Profile: **FT:** Game; **WN:** Grand; **WT:** Canal (Still).
Ref: FH1941

GRAND CANAL (BARROW TRACK)

Grand Canal (Barrow Track), Athy, **COUNTY KILDARE**, **Ireland**.
Contact/s: Manager, Griffin Hawe Limited, 22 Duke St, Athy, County Kildare, Ireland.
(T) 050 731221 (F) 050 733885
(E) griffinhawe@tinet.ie
Profile: **FT:** Game; **WN:** Grand; **WT:** Canal (Still).
Ref: FH1942

GRAND UNION CANAL

Grand Union Canal, Milton Keynes, **BUCKINGHAMSHIRE**, MK, **England**.
Contact/s: Fishery Manager.
(T) 01908 502375
Profile: **FT:** Coarse; **WN:** Grand Union; **WT:** Canal (Still).
Ref: FH1943

GRAND UNION CANAL

Grand Union Canal, Aylesbury Arm, Tring, **HERTFORDSHIRE**, HP23, **England**.
(W) www.tringanglers.club24.co.uk
Contact/s: **Mr Stuart Riddle** (Secretary), The Tring Anglers, PO Box 1947, Tring, Hertfordshire, HP23 5LZ.
(T) 01442 826148
Profile: **FT:** Coarse; **WN:** Grand Union; **WT:** Canal (Still). **Location:** **Nr. Rd:** Aston Clinton to Harsworth; **Main Rd:** M1, A41.
Ref: FH1944

GRAND UNION CANAL

Grand Union Canal, Red Lion Section, St Albans, **HERTFORDSHIRE**, AL2, **England**.
Contact/s: **Mr Stuart Riddle** (Secretary), The Tring Anglers, PO Box 1947, Tring, Hertfordshire, HP23 5LZ.
(T) 01442 826148
Profile: **FT:** Coarse; **WN:** Grand Union; **WT:** Canal (Still).
Ref: FH1945

GRAND UNION CANAL

Grand Union Canal, Hunton Bridge, Watford, **HERTFORDSHIRE**, WD, **England**.
Contact/s: **Mr D McDonald** (Fishery Manager). (M) 07885 802216
Mr R Foulger (Secretary), Kings Langley Angling Society, 155-157 St Albans Rd, Watford, Hertfordshire, WD2 5BD.
(T) 01923 232393
Profile: **FT:** Coarse; **WN:** Grand Union; **WT:** Canal (Still).
Ref: FH1946

GRAND UNION CANAL

Grand Union Canal, Cooks Wharf, Tring, **HERTFORDSHIRE**, HP23, **England**.
(W) www.tringanglers.club24.co.uk
Contact/s: **Mr Stuart Riddle** (Secretary),

The Tring Anglers, PO Box 1947, Tring, Hertfordshire, HP23 5LZ.
(T) 01442 826148
Profile: FT: Coarse; WN: Grand Union; WT: Canal (Still) W. Size: 4000 Metres.
Location: Nr. Rd: Cooks Wharf, Bridge 126 to Ebridge 135; Rail: Tring.
Ref: FH1947

GRAND UNION CANAL

Grand Union Canal, Marsworth Basin, Tring, **HERTFORDSHIRE**, HP23, **England**.
(W) www.tringanglers.club24.co.uk
Contact/s: **Mr Martin Phipps**.
(T) 01442 891534
Mr Stuart Riddle (Secretary), The Tring Anglers, PO Box 1947, Tring, Hertfordshire, HP23 5LZ.
(T) 01442 826148
Profile: FT: Coarse; WN: Grand Union; WT: Canal (Still).
Ref: FH1948

GRAND UNION CANAL

Grand Union Canal, Berkhamsted, **HERTFORDSHIRE**, HP4, **England**.
Contact/s: **Mr Ae Hedges** (Secretary).
(T) 020 85207477
Profile: FT: Coarse; WN: Grand Union Canal; WT: Canal (Still).
Ref: FH1949

GRAND UNION CANAL

Grand Union Canal, Lady Chapels, Watford, **HERTFORDSHIRE**, WD, **England**.
Contact/s: **Mr R Foulger** (Secretary), Kings Langley Angling Society, 155-157 St Albans Rd, Watford, Hertfordshire, WD2 5BD.
(T) 01923 232393
Profile: FT: Coarse; WN: Grand Union; WT: Canal (Still).
Ref: FH1950

GRAND UNION CANAL

Grand Union Canal, White Lion Lock To Bulbourne, Tring, **HERTFORDSHIRE**, HP23, **England**.
Contact/s: **Mr Stuart Riddle** (Secretary), The Tring Anglers, PO Box 1947, Tring, Hertfordshire, HP23 5LZ.
(T) 01442 826148
Profile: FT: Coarse; WN: Grand Union; WT: Canal (Still).
Ref: FH1951

GRAND UNION CANAL

Grand Union Canal, Batchworth Lock To Denham Lock, Uxbridge, London, **LONDON (GREATER)**, UB9, **England**.
Contact/s: **Mr Fred Lancaster** (Secretary), Blenheim Angling Society, Brairwood, Burtons Lane, Chalfont St Giles, Buckinghamshire, HP8 4BB.
(T) 01494 764977
(E) blenheim.angling@ntlworld.com
Profile: FT: Coarse; WN: Grand Union; WT: Canal (Still).
Ref: FH1952

GRAND UNION CANAL

Grand Union Canal, Osterly, Brentford, London, **LONDON (GREATER)**, TW8, **England**.
(W) www.uxbridge-rovers.fsnet.co.uk
Contact/s: **Mr L Dalton** (Secretary), Uxbridge Rovers Angling and Conservation Society, PO Box 253, Harrow, Middlesex, HA3 8XN.
(T) 01814 281739
Profile: FT: Coarse; WN: Grand Union; WT: Canal (Still). Location: Nr. Rd: Transport Avenue; Main Rd: M4, junction 2, A4.
Ref: FH1953

GRAND UNION CANAL

Grand Union Canal, Denham Lock 87, Uxbridge, London, **LONDON (GREATER)**, UB9, **England**.
Contact/s: **Mr Ae Hedges** (Secretary).
(T) 020 85207477
Profile: FT: Coarse; WN: Grand Union; WT: Canal (Still) W. Size: 3200 Metres.
Location: Nr. Rd: A40; Main Rd: M40, junction 1 onto A40.
Ref: FH1954

GRAND UNION CANAL

Grand Union Canal, Denham, Uxbridge, London, **LONDON (GREATER)**, UB9, **England**.
Contact/s: **Mr Fred Lancaster** (Secretary), Blenheim Angling Society, Brairwood, Burtons Lane, Chalfont St Giles, Buckinghamshire, HP8 4BB.
(T) 01494 764977
(E) blenheim.angling@ntlworld.com
Profile: FT: Coarse; WN: Grand Union; WT: Canal (Still).
Ref: FH1955

GRAND UNION CANAL

Grand Union Canal, West Drayton, London, **LONDON (GREATER)**, UB7, **England**.
(W) www.calpac.bizland.com
Contact/s: **Mr Colin Trafford** (General Secretary).
(T) 020 82242617
Mrs Diane Wheeler, 314 Old Lodge Lane, Purley, Surrey, CR8 4AQ.
(T) 020 86602766
Profile: FT: Coarse; WN: Grand Union; WT: Canal (Still) W. Size: 4400 Metres.
Location: Main Rd: M4; Rail: West Drayton.
Ref: FH1956

GRAND UNION CANAL

Grand Union Canal, Knowle, Solihull, **MIDLANDS (WEST)**, B93, **England**.
Contact/s: **Mr John Powell** (Secretary).
(T) 0121 7062126
Profile: FT: Coarse; WN: Grand Union; WT: Canal (Still).
Ref: FH1957

GRAND UNION CANAL

Grand Union Canal, Section M, Bugbrooke, Northampton, **NORTHAMPTONSHIRE**, NN7, **England**.
Contact/s: Secretary, Northampton Nene Angling Club, 363 Kettering Rd, Northampton, NN3 6QT.
Profile: FT: Coarse; WN: Grand Union; WT: Canal (Still) W. Size: 1600 Metres.
Location: Nr. Rd: Pattishall; Main Rd: M1, junction 18.
Ref: FH1958

GRAND UNION CANAL

Grand Union Canal, Knightley Arms, High St, Yelvertoft, Northampton, **NORTHAMPTONSHIRE**, NN6 6LU, **England**.
Contact/s: **C Allen**.
(T) 01788 822401
Mr John Wale.
(T) 01788 822624
Profile: FT: Coarse; WN: Grand Union; WT: Canal (Still) W. Size: 4000 Metres.
Location: Main Rd: A428, M1 junction 18.
Ref: FH1959

GRAND UNION CANAL

Grand Union Canal, Bulbourne To Marshcroft, Bulbourne, **OXFORDSHIRE**, OX, **England**.
(W) www.tringanglers.club24.co.uk
Contact/s: **Mr Stuart Riddle** (Secretary), The Tring Anglers, PO Box 1947, Tring, Hertfordshire, HP23 5LZ.
(T) 01442 826148
Profile: FT: Coarse; WN: Grand Union; WT: Canal (Still).
Ref: FH1960

GRAND UNION CANAL

Grand Union Canal, Wendover Arm, Oxford, **OXFORDSHIRE**, OX, **England**.
(W) www.tringanglers.club24.co.uk
Contact/s: **Mr Stuart Riddle** (Secretary), The Tring Anglers, PO Box 1947, Tring, Hertfordshire, HP23 5LZ.
(T) 01442 826148
Profile: FT: Coarse; WN: Grand Union; WT: Canal (Still).
Ref: FH1961

GRAND UNION CANAL

Grand Union Canal, Warwick, **WARWICKSHIRE**, CV34, **England**.
Contact/s: Manager, Baileys of Warwick, 30 Emscote Rd, Warwick, Warwickshire, CV34 4PP.
(T) 01926 491984 (F) 01926 411264
Profile: FT: Coarse; WN: Grand Union; WT: Canal (Still) W. Size: 2400 Metres.
Ref: FH1962

GRAND UNION CANAL

Grand Union Canal, Warwick, **WARWICKSHIRE**, CV34, **England**.
Contact/s: Manager, Saltisford Canal Ctre, Birmingham Rd, Warwick, Warwickshire, CV34 5RJ.
(T) 01926 490006
Profile: FT: Coarse; WN: Grand Union; WT: Canal (Still).
Ref: FH1963

GRAND UNION CANAL

Grand Union Canal, Warwick, **WARWICKSHIRE**, CV34, **England**.
Contact/s: Manager, Baileys of Warwick, 30 Emscote Rd, Warwick, Warwickshire, CV34 4PP.
(T) 01926 491984 (F) 01926 411264
Mr Ken Waldenmar (Secretary), Stratford-upon-Avon Angling Club, Park Farm, Compton Verney, Combrook, Kineton, Warwickshire.
(T) 01789 720603
Profile: FT: Coarse; WN: Grand Union; WT: Canal (Still) W. Size: 4000 Metres.
Ref: FH1964

GRAND UNION CANAL

Grand Union Canal, Rowington, Leamington Spa, **WARWICKSHIRE**, CV31, **England**.
Contact/s: Manager, The Tackle Seller, 24 Russell Trce, Leamington Spa, Warwickshire, CV31 1EZ.
(T) 01926 888834
Mr A Bruce (Secretary), Oriental Angling Club, 42 Cherry Orchard, Stratford-upon-Avon, Warwickshire, CV37 9AP.
(T) 01789 205700
Profile: FT: Coarse; WN: Grand Union; WT: Canal (Still) W. Size: 3200 Metres.
Ref: FH1965

GRAND UNION CANAL

Grand Union Canal, Fosse Way Bridge, Leamington Spa, **WARWICKSHIRE**, CV, **England**.
Contact/s: **Mr Ernie Archer** (Secretary), Royal Lemington Spa Angling Association, 9 Southway, Leamington Spa, Warwickshire, CV31 2PG.
(T) 01926 334185
Profile: FT: Coarse; WN: Grand Union; WT: Canal (Still). Location: Nr. Rd: Southam to Lemington Spa; Main Rd: A425.
Ref: FH1966

GRAND WESTERN CANAL

Grand Western Canal, Halberton, Tiverton, **DEVON**, EX16, **England**.
Contact/s: , Exe Valley Angling, 19 West Exe South, Tiverton.
Secretary, Tiverton and District Angling Club, 21 Alstone Rd, Tiverton, Devon, EX16 4LH.
Mr John Smallwood (Owner).
(T) 01884 242275
Profile: FT: Coarse; WN: Grand Western; WT: Canal (Still) W. Size: 18400 Metres.
Location: Main Rd: North Devon Link Road; Rail: Tiverton Parkway.
Ref: FH1967

GRAND WESTERN CANAL

Grand Western Canal, Cullompton, **DEVON**, EX15, **England**.
Contact/s: **Mr Malcolm Trump** (Canal Liaison Officer), 5 Middle Lane, Cullompton, Devon, EX15.
(T) 01844 32059
Profile: FT: Coarse; WN: Grand Western;

WT: Canal (Still). **Location:** **Nr. Rd:** Tiverton Basin to Burlescombe.
Ref: FH1968

GRANGE FARM LEISURE

Grange Farm Leisure, Mablethorpe, **LINCOLNSHIRE**, LN12, **England**.
Contact/s: **Mr John Evans** (Manager), Grange Farm Leisure, 2 Grange Farm Cottage, Alford Rd, Mablethorpe, LN12 1NE.
(T) 01507 472814
Profile: **FT:** Combination; **WN:** Grange Farm Leisure; **WT:** Lake (Still) **W. Size:** 4 Acres. **Location:** **Nr. Rd:** A1104; **Main Rd:** A1031.
Ref: FH1969

GRANGE POOL

Grange Pool, Higham Wood, Tonbridge, **KENT**, TN1, **England**.
Contact/s: **Mr Adrian Bewley** (Manager), Ashvale Fisheries, 69 Fortescue Rd, Wimbledon, London, SW19 2EA.
(T) 020 82873892
Profile: **FT:** Coarse; **WN:** Grange; **WT:** Pool (Still) **W. Size:** 69 Metres. **Location:** **Nr. Rd:** A26 to Maidstone; **Main Rd:** Golf course.
Ref: FH1970

GRANGE WATER

Grange Water, South Ockendon, Thurrock, Grays, **ESSEX**, RM15, **England**.
Contact/s: Manager, Essex Angling, 5 Broadway Prde, Elm Park, Hornchurch, RM12 4RS.
(T) 01708 428220 (F) 01708 705800
Profile: **FT:** Coarse; **WN:** Grange Water; **WT:** Lake (Still) **W. Size:** 22 Acres. **Location:** **Nr. Rd:** B186; **Main Rd:** M25, 31 or 29.
Ref: FH1971

GRANSTOWN LAKE

Grandtown Lake, Grandtown, Ballacolla, Portlaoise, **COUNTY LAOIS**, **Ireland**.
Contact/s: **Mr Matt Doyle** (Manager).
(T) 050 234125
(E) mattdoyle@eircom.net
Profile: **FT:** Coarse; **WN:** Granstown; **WT:** Lough (Still) **W. Size:** 20 Acres. **Location:** **Nr. Rd:** R433; **Main Rd:** N8, Durrow; **Rail:** Ballybrophy. £Fr
Ref: FH1972

GRANTHAM CANAL

Grantham Canal, Cotgrave, Nottingham, **NOTTINGHAMSHIRE**, NG12 3, **England**.
Contact/s: **Mr I Foulds** (Secretary), Nottingham Angling Association, 95 Ilkeston Rd, Nottingham, Nottinghamshire, NG7 3HA.
(T) 0115 9033881or9708080
Profile: **FT:** Coarse; **WN:** Grantham; **WT:** Canal (Still) **W. Size:** 500 Metres.
Ref: FH1973

GRANTHAM CANAL

Grantham Canal, Owthorpe Lane, Kinoulton, Nottingham, **NOTTINGHAMSHIRE**, NG12, **England**.
Contact/s: **Mr Dave Fallows** (Secretary), British Waterways, 27 Woodstock Avenue, Radford, Nottingham, NG7 5QP.
(T) 0115 9787350
Profile: **FT:** Coarse; **WN:** Grantham; **WT:** Canal (Still) **W. Size:** 1145 Metres. **Location:** **Nr. Rd:** Owthorpe Lane; **Main Rd:** A46; **Rail:** Nottingham.
Ref: FH1974

GRANTHAM CANAL

Grantham Canal, Kinoulton, Nottingham, **NOTTINGHAMSHIRE**, NG2, **England**.
Contact/s: **Mr Dave Fallows** (Secretary), British Waterways, 27 Woodstock Avenue, Radford, Nottingham, NG7 5QP.
(T) 0115 9787350
Profile: **FT:** Coarse; **WN:** Grantham; **WT:** Canal (Still) **W. Size:** 1000 Metres. **Location:** **Main Rd:** A46; **Rail:** Nottingham Midland.
Ref: FH1975

GRASMERE COARSE FISHERY

Grasmere Coarse Fishery, Grasmere, Ambleside, **CUMBRIA**, LA22, **England**.
Contact/s: Manager, The National Trust, North West Regional Office, The Hollens, Grasmere, Ambleside, LA22 9QZ.
(T) 01539 435599 (F) 01539 435353
Mr Chris Sodo (Hon Treasurer), Windermere, Ambleside and District Angling Association, Ecclerigg Court, Ecclerigg, Windermere, LA23 1LQ.
(T) 01539 445083
Profile: **FT:** Combination; **WN:** Grasmere; **WT:** Lake (Still). **Location:** **Nr. Rd:** A591 to Keswick.
Ref: FH1976

GRASSHOLME RESERVOIR

Grassholme Reservoir, Mickleton, Barnard Castle, **COUNTY DURHAM**, DL12, **England**.
Contact/s: **Mr Paul Russell**, Northumbrian Water Ltd, Head Office, Recreation Department, Abbey Rd, Durham DH1 5FJ.
(T) 0191 3832222 (F) 0191 3841920
Profile: **FT:** Game; **WN:** Grassholme; **WT:** Reservoir (Still). **Location:** **Nr. Rd:** B6277; **Main Rd:** A66.
Ref: FH1977

GREASBROUGH DAMS

Greasbrough Dams, Greasbrough, Rotherham, **YORKSHIRE (SOUTH)**, S61, **England**.
Contact/s: Fishery Manager.
(T) 01226 742041
Profile: **FT:** Coarse; **WN:** Greasbrough; **WT:** Mill Dam (Still).
Ref: FH1978

GREAT BIRCH WOOD PONDS

Great Birch Wood Ponds, Warton, Preston, **LANCASHIRE**, PR4, **England**.
Contact/s: Fishery Manager.
(T) 01772 633162
Profile: **FT:** Coarse; **WN:** Great Birch Wood; **WT:** Pond (Still). **Location:** **Nr. Rd:** Lytham Road; **Main Rd:** A584.
Ref: FH1979

GREAT BUDWORTH MERE LAKE

Great Budworth Mere Lake, Northwich, **CHESHIRE**, CW, **England**.
Contact/s: **Mr J Clitheroe** (Secretary), Northwich Angling Association, PO Box 18, Northwich, Cheshire, CW9 5SE.
(T) 01606 75132
Profile: **FT:** Coarse; **WN:** Great Budworth Mere; **WT:** Lake (Still) **W. Size:** 50 Acres.
Ref: FH1980

GREAT BURROWS TROUT FISHERY

Great Burrows Trout Fishery, Orchard Mere, Pitt Court, North Nibley, Dursley, **GLOUCESTERSHIRE**, GL11, **England**.
Contact/s: **Mr V Baxter**.
(T) 01453 542343
Profile: **FT:** Game; **WN:** Great Burrows Trout Fishery; **WT:** Lake (Still) **W. Size:** 2 Acres. **Location:** **Nr. Rd:** A38; **Main Rd:** M5, junction 13 or 14.
Ref: FH1981

GREAT LINFORD LAKES

Great Linford Lakes, Wolverton Rd, Great Linford, **BUCKINGHAMSHIRE**, MK16, **England**.
Contact/s: **Mr Tim Hodges** (Fishery Manager).
(T) 01908 237233 (F) 01908 615776
Profile: **FT:** Coarse; **WN:** Great Linford; **WT:** Lake (Still). **Location:** **Nr. Rd:** Wolverton Road; **Main Rd:** A422; **Rail:** Wolverton.
Ref: FH1982

GREAT MELTON FISHERY

Great Melton Fishery, Great Melton, Norwich, **NORFOLK**, NR, **England**.
Contact/s: **Mr R Westgate** (Club Secretary), Wroxham and District Angling Club, 31 The Paddocks, Old Catton, Norwich, NR6 7HF.
(T) 01603 401062 (F) 01603 897122 (M) 07885 244262
(E) wroxham.angling@virgin.net
Profile: **FT:** Coarse; **WN:** Great Melton; **WT:** Lake (Still) **W. Size:** 6 Acres. **Location:** **Main Rd:** A47; **Rail:** Norwich.
Ref: FH1983

GREAT MYLES LAKE

Great Myles Lake, Chipping Ongar, Ongar, **ESSEX**, CM5, **England**.
Contact/s: Fishery Manager.
(T) 01277 362757
Profile: **FT:** Coarse; **WN:** Great Myles; **WT:** Lake (Still) **W. Size:** 4 Acres. **Location:** **Nr. Rd:** A128; **Main Rd:** Chipping Ongar to Brentwood.
Ref: FH1984

GREAT OUSE (RIVER)

River Great Ouse, Radwell, Bedford, **BEDFORDSHIRE**, MK43, **England**.
Contact/s: **Mr Dick Morris**.
(T) 01582 571738
Profile: **FT:** Coarse; **WN:** Great Ouse; **WT:** River (Moving).
Ref: FH1985

GREAT OUSE (RIVER)

River Great Ouse, Newton Blossomville, Bedford, **BEDFORDSHIRE**, MK43, **England**.
Contact/s: Fishery Manager.
(T) 01604 764847
Mrs P Walsh (Secretary), 363 Kettering Rd, Northampton, NN3 6QT.
Profile: **FT:** Coarse; **WN:** Newton Blossomville; **WT:** River (Moving).
Ref: FH1986

GREAT OUSE (RIVER)

River Great Ouse, Lavendon Mill, Olney, **BUCKINGHAMSHIRE**, MK46, **England**.
Profile: **FT:** Coarse; **WN:** Great Ouse; **WT:** River (Moving). **Location:** **Main Rd:** B565.
Ref: FH1987

GREAT OUSE (RIVER)

River Great Ouse, Ravenstone, Olney, **BUCKINGHAMSHIRE**, MK46 5, **England**.
Contact/s: **Mr Pemberton** (Secretary), Milton Keynes Angling Association, 45 Cranesbill Pl, Conniburrow, Milton Keynes, MK14 7BN.
(T) 01908 660579
Profile: **FT:** Coarse; **WN:** Great Ouse; **WT:** River (Moving). **Location:** **Main Rd:** B526.
Ref: FH1988

GREAT OUSE (RIVER)

River Great Ouse, Stone Park, Milton Keynes, **BUCKINGHAMSHIRE**, MK, **England**.
Contact/s: Fishery Manager.
(T) 01327 351156
Profile: **FT:** Coarse; **WN:** Ouse (Great); **WT:** River (Moving).
Ref: FH1989

GREAT OUSE (RIVER)

River Great Ouse, Hougton Meadows, St Ives, Huntingdon, **CAMBRIDGESHIRE**, PE17, **England**.
Contact/s: **Mr A Wilkinson** (Hon Secretary), 22 Erica Rd, St Ives, Cambridgeshire, PE17 6AE.
(T) 01480 381913
Profile: **FT:** Coarse; **WN:** Great Ouse; **WT:** River (Moving) **W. Size:** 12800 Metres. **Location:** **Main Rd:** A14; **Rail:** Huntington. £Fr
Ref: FH1990

GREAT OUSE (RIVER)

River Great Ouse, Willow Walk, Cresswells, Ely, **CAMBRIDGESHIRE**, CB, **England**.
(W) www.coopersanglingclub.org.uk
Contact/s: **Mr John Dickens** (Secretary), Coopers Angling Club, 2 Witchford Rd, Ely, Cambridgeshire, CB6 3DP.
(T) 01353 742103
Mr Rod Mayo (Bailiff).

(T) 01353 665492
Profile: FT: Coarse; WN: Great Ouse; WT: River (Moving) W. Size: 1000 Metres.
Location: Nr. Rd: A142; Main Rd: A10;
Rail: Ely.
Ref: FH1991

GREAT OUSE (RIVER)

River Great Ouse, Adelaide Bridge To Sandhills Bridge, Queen Adelaide, Ely, **CAMBRIDGESHIRE**, CB7 4, **England**.
Contact/s: Fishery Manager.
(T) 01353 662029
Profile: FT: Coarse; WN: Great Ouse; WT: River (Moving). Location: Nr. Rd: B1382; Main Rd: A10.
Ref: FH1992

GREAT OUSE (RIVER)

River Great Ouse, Sandhills Bridge, Littleport, Ely, **CAMBRIDGESHIRE**, CB, **England**.
Contact/s: Mr D Yardy (Secretary).
(T) 01353 669323
Mr John W Shelsher (Manager).
(T) 01353 860787
Profile: FT: Coarse; WN: Great Ouse; WT: River (Moving). Location: Nr. Rd: Littleport to Ely; Main Rd: A10.
Ref: FH1993

GREAT OUSE (RIVER)

River Great Ouse, Little Thetford, Ely, **CAMBRIDGESHIRE**, CB, **England**.
Contact/s: Mr N Roberts (Manager).
(T) 01223 836773
Profile: FT: Coarse; WN: Great Ouse; WT: River (Moving). Location: Main Rd: A10;
Rail: Ely.
Ref: FH1994

GREAT OUSE (RIVER)

River Great Ouse, Lttttle Paxton Paper Mill, St Neots, Huntingdon, **CAMBRIDGESHIRE**, PE1, **England**.
Contact/s: Mr Ian Benton (Match Secretary).
(T) 01480 219706
Mr Ieuan Thomas (Bailiff).
(T) 01480 213115
Mrs Diane Linger (Secretary), Skenbridge Cottage, Great Paxton, St Neots, Cambridgeshire, PE19 4RA.
(T) 01480 216730
Profile: FT: Coarse; WN: Great Ouse; WT: River (Moving) W. Size: 4000 Metres.
Location: Nr. Rd: A428; Main Rd: A428, A1.
Ref: FH1995

GREAT OUSE (RIVER)

River Great Ouse, Buckden, Offord Cluny, St Neots, Huntingdon, **CAMBRIDGESHIRE**, PE18, **England**.
Contact/s: Mr Dennis Burton (Chairman).
(T) 01480 810527
Mr Eric Blowfield (Bailiff), 4 Monks Cottages, Buckden, Huntingdon, Cambridgeshire, PE18 9ST.
(T) 01480 810166
Mr John Astell, Offord and Buckden Angling Society, 154 Eastree Rd, Whittlesey, Cambridgeshire, PE7 2AJ.
(T) 01733 755395
Mr Maurice Mobbs (Vice Chairman).
(T) 01480 830213
Profile: FT: Coarse; WN: Ouse; WT: River (Moving) W. Size: 4800 Metres. Location: Nr. Rd: Station Road or Mill Road; Main Rd: A1, B1043; Rail: St Neots.
Ref: FH1996

GREAT OUSE (RIVER)

River Great Ouse, Cut-Off Channel, Hilgay Bridge, Downham Market, **NORFOLK**, PE38, **England**.
Contact/s: Mr Mick Grief (Secretary), King's Lynn Angling Association, 67 Peckover Way, South Wootton, King's Lynn, PE30 3UE.
(T) 01553 671545
Profile: FT: Coarse; WN: Great Ouse; WT: River (Moving). Location: Nr. Rd: A10; Main Rd: A112.
Ref: FH1997

GREAT OUSE (RIVER)

River Great Ouse, Brandon Creek, Downham Market, **NORFOLK**, PE38, **England**.
Contact/s: Manager.
(T) 01233 234616
Profile: FT: Coarse; WN: Great Ouse; WT: River (Moving). Location: Nr. Rd: A10.
Ref: FH1998

GREAT OUSE RELIEF CHANNEL

Great Ouse Relief Channel, King's Lynn, **NORFOLK**, PE, **England**.
Contact/s: Manager, Algethi Guest House, 136 Lynn Rd, Wisbech, Cambridgeshire, PE13 3DP.
(T) 01945 582278
Profile: FT: Coarse; WN: Great Ouse Relief Channel; WT: River (Moving) W. Size: 15000 Metres. Location: Main Rd: A10 to Watlington.
Ref: FH1999

GREEN FARM LAKES

Green Farm Lakes, Wheedon Loit, Towcester, **NORTHAMPTONSHIRE**, NN12, **England**.
Contact/s: Mr Terry Rodhouse (Secretary), Castle Angling Association, 12 Somerville Rd, Daventry, Northamptonshire, NN11 4RT.
(T) 01327 705692
Profile: FT: Coarse; WN: Green Farm; WT: Lake (Still). Location: Main Rd: A5, A43;
Rail: Banbury.
Ref: FH2000

GREEN LAGOON

Green Lagoon, Arlesey, **BEDFORDSHIRE**, SG15, **England**.
Contact/s: Fishery Manager.
(T) 01438 355300
Profile: FT: Coarse; WN: Green; WT: Lake (Still).
Ref: FH2001

GREEN LANE PONDS

Green Lane Ponds, Ormskirk, **LANCASHIRE**, L40, **England**.
Profile: FT: Coarse; WN: Green Lane; WT: Pond (Still).
Ref: FH2002

GREEN OAKS TROUT FISHERY

Green Oaks Trout Fishery, Springfield Farm, Potash Rd, Billericay, **ESSEX**, CM11 1HH, **England**.
Contact/s: Fishery Manager.
(T) 01277 657357
Profile: FT: Game; WN: Green Oaks Trout Fishery; WT: Lake (Still) W. Size: 3 Acres.
Location: Nr. Rd: Billericay to Chelmsford Road; Main Rd: B1007.
Ref: FH2003

GREENACRE TROUT LAKES

Greenacre Trout Lakes, Half Moon Inn, Sheepwash, Beaworthy, **DEVON**, EX21 5NE, **England**.
Contact/s: Mr Charles Inniss (manager).
(T) 01409 231376
Profile: FT: Game; WN: Greenacre; WT: Lake (Still) W. Size: 6 Acres. Location: Nr. Rd: A3072.
Ref: FH2004

GREENBANK PARK LAKE

Greenbank Park Lake, Greenbank Lane, Liverpool, **MERSEYSIDE**, L, **England**.
Contact/s: Fishery Manager.
(T) 0151 2255910
Profile: FT: Coarse; WN: Greenbank; WT: Lake (Still) W. Size: 4 Acres. Location: Nr. Rd: Greenbank Lane; Main Rd: A562.
£Fr
Ref: FH2005

GREENCROFT POND

Greencroft Pond, Greencroft Industrial Estate, Annfield Plain, Stanley, **COUNTY DURHAM**, DH9, **England**.
Contact/s: Mr S Palmer.
(T) 01207 299094
Profile: FT: Coarse; WN: Greencroft; WT: Pond (Still) W. Size: 1 Acre. Location: Nr. Rd: B6168; Main Rd: A1, junction 63, A693 to Stanley.
Ref: FH2006

GREENHALGH LODGE FISHERY

Greenhalgh Lodge Fishery, Greenhalgh Lane, Kirkham, Preston, **LANCASHIRE**, PR4 3HL, **England**.
Contact/s: Manager.
(T) 01253 836348
Profile: FT: Coarse; WN: Greenhalgh Lodge Fishery; WT: Lake (Still) W. Size: 2 Acres.
Location: Nr. Rd: Kirkham to Fleetwood; Main Rd: A585.
Ref: FH2007

GREENHAMS

Greenhams, Hanworth, Feltham, London, **LONDON (GREATER)**, TW13, **England**.
Contact/s: Mr Peter Goole (Secretary), Chertsey Road Angling Club, 35 Fernside Avenue, Hamworth, Middlesex, TW13 7BJ.
(T) 020 8901688
Profile: FT: Coarse; WN: Greenhams; WT: Lake (Still).
Ref: FH2008

GREENRIDGE FARM LAKES

Greenridge Farm Lakes, Green Lane, Ampfield, Romsey, **HAMPSHIRE**, SO51 9BN, **England**.
Contact/s: J E Mazzoni.
Mr Jim Dalton (Lease Holder), 15 Nightingale Cl, Romsey, Hampshire, SO51 5AY.
(T) 01794 517322 (M) 07941 332102
Profile: FT: Coarse; WN: Greenridge Farm; WT: Lake (Still) W. Size: 3 Acres. Location: Nr. Rd: Green Lane by Stroud School; Main Rd: M27, junction 3; Rail: Romsey.
Ref: FH2009

GREESE (RIVER)

River Greese, Carlow, **COUNTY CARLOW**, **Ireland**.
Contact/s: Mrs Quinn (Manager), The Locks, Milford, Carlow, County Carlow, Ireland.
(T) 050 346261
Profile: FT: Game; WN: Greese; WT: River (Moving).
Ref: FH2010

GREESE (RIVER)

River Greese, Athy, **COUNTY KILDARE**, **Ireland**.
Contact/s: Manager, Griffin Hawe Limited, 22 Duke St, Athy, County Kildare, Ireland.
(T) 050 731221 (F) 050 733885
(E) griffinhawe@tinet.ie
Profile: FT: Game; WN: Greese; WT: River (Moving) W. Size: 12800 Metres.
Ref: FH2011

GREESE (RIVER)

River Greese, Ballytore, **COUNTY KILDARE**, **Ireland**.
Contact/s: Secretary, Greese Anglers, Woodhill, Narraghmore, Ballytore.
Mr Patrick Leigh (Secretary).
(T) 050 736611
Profile: FT: Game; WN: Greese; WT: River (Moving) W. Size: 10500 Metres. Location: Nr. Rd: N9 Dublin to Carlow; Main Rd: N9;
Rail: Athy.
Ref: FH2012

GREEVE LOUGH

Greeve Lough, Brantry, Aughnacloy, **COUNTY TYRONE**, BT69, **Northern Ireland**.
Contact/s: Mrs Liz Salter (Manager), Aughnacloy Development Association, The McCreedy Mill Centre, Aughnacloy, County Tyrone, BT69 6AL.
(T) 028 85557002

Profile: **FT:** Coarse; **WN:** Greeve; **WT:** Lough (Still). **Location:** **Nr. Rd:** Dungannon to Aughnacloy Road; **Main Rd:** B128.
Ref: FH2013

GREGANNAN LAKES

Gregannan Lakes, Arthog, Dolgellau, **GWYNEDD**, LL40, **Wales**.
Contact/s: **Mr Emlyn Lloyd** (Owner), Fridd Boedel Farm, Arthog, Gwynedd, LL39 1LJ.
(T) 01341 250426or01341250468
Profile: **FT:** Game; **WN:** Gregannan; **WT:** Lake (Still).
Ref: FH2014

GRENDON LAKES

Grendon Lakes, Northampton, **NORTHAMPTONSHIRE**, NN, **England**.
Contact/s: Fishery Manager.
(T) 01933 665335
Profile: **FT:** Coarse; **WN:** Grendon; **WT:** Lake (Still).
Ref: FH2015

GRETA (RIVER)

River Greta, Ingleton, Carnforth, **CUMBRIA**, LA6, **England**.
Contact/s: **Mr Ian Crack** (Secretary), Ingleton Angling Association, Khardains, Ingleton Carnforth, Lancashire, LA6 3BS.
(T) 01524 241171
Profile: **FT:** Game; **WN:** Greta; **WT:** River (Moving) **W. Size:** 4800 Metres. **Location:** **Nr. Rd:** Ingleton to Burton in Lonsdale; **Main Rd:** A65; **Rail:** High Bentham.
Ref: FH2016

GREY MILL FARM

Grey Mill Farm, Alcester Rd, Wootton Wawen, Solihull, **MIDLANDS (WEST)**, B95 6HL, **England**.
(W) www.fisheries.co.uk/greymill/index
Contact/s: **Mr Tony Ingram**.
(T) 01564 792582
Profile: **FT:** Coarse; **WN:** Alne; **WT:** River (Moving) **W. Size:** 800 Metres. **Location:** **Nr. Rd:** Birmingham to Stratford-upon-Avon; **Main Rd:** A3400. **£Fr**
Ref: FH2017

GREY MIST MERE

Grey Mist Mere, Woolston, Warrington, **CHESHIRE**, WA, **England**.
Contact/s: **Mr Frank Lythgoe** (Secretary), Warrington Angling Association, 52 Parker St, Warrington, Lancashire.
(T) 01928 716238 (F) 01928 713898
(E) info@warrington-anglers.org.uk
Profile: **FT:** Coarse; **WN:** Grey Mist Mere; **WT:** Lake (Still) **W. Size:** 10 Acres.
Ref: FH2018

GRIMERSTA LODGE

Grimersta Lodge, Grimersta Estate, Stornoway, **WESTERN ISLES**, HS2 9EJ, **Scotland**.
Contact/s: **Mr Simon Scott** (Manager).
(T) 01851 621358 (F) 01851 621389
Profile: **FT:** Game; **WN:** Grimersta Lodge; **WT:** Combination (Still & Moving).
Ref: FH2019

GRIMESDITCH MILL POOL

Grimesditch Mill Pool, Grimesditch Lane, Lower Whitley, Warrington, **CHESHIRE**, WA, **England**.
Contact/s: **Mr Neil Jupp** (Club Secretary), Lymm Angling Club, PO Box 350, Warrington, Cheshire, WA2 9FB.
(T) 01925 411774
Profile: **FT:** Coarse; **WN:** Grimesditch Mill; **WT:** Pond (Still) **W. Size:** 1 Acre. **Location:** **Nr. Rd:** Grimesditch Lane; **Main Rd:** M56, junction 10, then take A49.
Ref: FH2020

GRIMSARGH RESERVOIR

Grimsargh Reservoir, Ribbleton, Grimsargh, Preston, **LANCASHIRE**, PR, **England**.
Contact/s: **Mr N Watson** (Secretary), 14 Farrington Lane, Ribbleton, Preston.
Mr Roy Rhodes (Conservation, Access and Recreation Manager), Rivington Water Treatment Works, Bolton Rd, Horwich, Bolton, BL6 7RN.
(T) 01204 664300
Mrs D Dewhurst (Day Ticket Bookings), 14 Lonridge Rd, Ribbleton, Preston, PR2 6LX.
Profile: **FT:** Combination; **WN:** Grimsargh; **WT:** Reservoir (Still). **Location:** **Nr. Rd:** Ribbleton Lane; **Main Rd:** B6243 to Grimsargh.
Ref: FH2021

GRIMSBURY RESERVOIR

Grimsbury Reservoir, Banbury Angling Association, Banbury, **OXFORDSHIRE**, OX1, **England**.
Contact/s: **Mr Geoff Bradbeer** (Secretary), Banbury and District Angling Association, 7 Bentley Cl, Banbury, Oxfordshire, OX16 7PB.
(T) 01295 268047
Profile: **FT:** Coarse; **WN:** Grimsbury; **WT:** Reservoir (Still).
Ref: FH2022

GRIMSDITCH MILL POOL

Grimsditch Mill Pool, Grimsditch Lane, Whitley, Warrington, **CHESHIRE**, **England**.
Contact/s: **Mr Neil Jupp** (Secretary).
(T) 01925 411774
Profile: **FT:** Coarse; **WN:** Grimsditch; **WT:** Pool (Still); **F. Size:** 2 Acres; **W. Size:** 2 Acres. **Location:** **Nr. Rd:** Grimsditch lane; **Main Rd:** A49; **Rail:** Warrington.
Ref: FH2023

GRIMSTHORPE LAKE

Grimsthorpe Lake, Grimsthorpe Estate Office, Grimsthorpe Castle, Bourne, **LINCOLNSHIRE**, PE10 0NB, **England**.
Contact/s: Fishery Manager.
(T) 01778 32205
Profile: **FT:** Coarse; **WN:** Grimsthorpe; **WT:** Lake (Still) **W. Size:** 36 Acres. **Location:** **Main Rd:** A1, A151; **Rail:** Peterborough.
Ref: FH2024

GRIZEDALE BECK

Grizedale Beck, Hawkshead, Ambleside, **CUMBRIA**, LA22, **England**.
Contact/s: Area Land Agent, Forestry Commission, Grizedale, Ambleside, Cumbria, LA22 0QJ.
(T) 01229 860373
Profile: **FT:** Game; **WN:** Leven; **WT:** Stream (Moving).
Ref: FH2025

GRIZEDALE LEA RESERVOIR

Grizedale Lea Reservoir, Kirkham, Preston, **LANCASHIRE**, PR4, **England**.
Contact/s: **Mr A Helme**, The Old Police Station, Veterinary Surgery, 13-17 Freckllton St, Kirkham, Preston.
Mr D Wardman (Hon Secretary), 65 Longhouse Lane, Poulton-le-fylde, Lancashire, FY6 5DE.
(T) 01253 883993
Profile: **FT:** Game; **WN:** Grizedale Lea; **WT:** Reservoir (Still).
Ref: FH2026

GROBY FISHING LAKES

Groby Farm, Groby, Leicester, **LEICESTERSHIRE**, LE6 0FL, **England**.
Contact/s: Fishery Manager.
(T) 0116 2879372
Profile: **FT:** Coarse; **WN:** Groby Farm; **WT:** Lake (Still) **W. Size:** 4 Acres.
Ref: FH2027

GROOBYS PIT

Groobys Pit, Bridgefoot Farm, Thorpe Culvert, Wainfleet, Skegness, **LINCOLNSHIRE**, PE24, **England**.
Contact/s: **Mr Alec Grooby**.
(T) 01754 880216
Profile: **FT:** Coarse; **WN:** Groobys; **WT:** Gravel Pit (Still) **W. Size:** 2 Acres. **Location:** **Nr. Rd:** Thorpe Culvert; **Main Rd:** B1195.
Ref: FH2028

GROVE FARM

Grove Farm, Rushwick, Worcester, **WORCESTERSHIRE**, WR2, **England**.
Contact/s: **Ms Sue Cave**.
(T) 01886 832305 (F) 01886 833446
Profile: **FT:** Coarse; **WN:** Grove Farm; **WT:** Lake (Still).
Ref: FH2029

GROVE FARM FISHERY

Grove Farm Fishery, Llanfoist, Abergavenny, **MONMOUTHSHIRE**, NP7, **Wales**.
Contact/s: **Mr Ben Jones** (owner).
(T) 01873 852345
Profile: **FT:** Coarse; **WN:** Grove Farm Fishery; **WT:** Lake (Still).
Ref: FH2030

GROVE LODGE

Grove Lodge, Todmorden Rd, Littleborough, **MANCHESTER (GREATER)**, OL15, **England**.
Contact/s: **Mr Ray Barber** (Secretary), Todmorden Angling Society, 12 Grisedale Drive, Burnley, Lancashire, BB12 8AR.
(T) 01282 428780 (M) 07970 897849
Profile: **FT:** Coarse; **WN:** Grove Lodge; **WT:** Pond (Still).
Ref: FH2031

GRYFFE (RIVER)

River Gryffe, Kilmacolm, **INVERCLYDE**, PA13, **Scotland**.
Contact/s: **Mr K Wood** (Secretary), Strathgryffe Angling Association, Kingsley Wood and Co Solicitors, Burnside Chambers, The Cross, Kilmacolm, PA13 4ET.
(T) 01505 874114 (F) 01505 874009
Profile: **FT:** Game; **WN:** Gryffe; **WT:** River (Moving).
Ref: FH2032

GRYFFE (RIVER)

River Gryffe, Bridge Of Weir, **RENFREWSHIRE**, PA11, **Scotland**.
Contact/s: **Mr M Duncan** (Newsagents), Morrison Pl, Main St, Bridge of Weir PA11 3NU.
(T) 01505 612477
Profile: **FT:** Game; **WN:** Gryffe; **WT:** River (Moving).
Ref: FH2033

GUNSSONS LAKE

Gunssons Lake, White House Farm, Sibton, Saxmundham, **SUFFOLK**, IP17, **England**.
Contact/s: **Mr Kitson**.
Profile: **FT:** Coarse; **WN:** Gunssons; **WT:** Lake (Still).
Ref: FH2034

GUNTHORPE HALL LAKE

Gunthorpe Hall Lake, Melton Constable, **NORFOLK**, NR24, **England**.
Contact/s: Fishery Manager.
(T) 01263 861373
Profile: **FT:** Coarse; **WN:** Gunthorpe; **WT:** Lake (Still).
Ref: FH2035

GUNTON HALL LAKE

Gunton Hall Holiday Village, Gunton Avenue, Lowestoft, **SUFFOLK**, NR32 5DF, **England**.
Contact/s: **Mr Tony Cater** (Manager).
(T) 01502 730288
Profile: **FT:** Coarse; **WN:** Gunton Hall; **WT:** Lake (Still).
Ref: FH2036

GUNTON PARK LAKE

Gunton Park Lake, Roughton Village, Cromer, **NORFOLK**, NR27, **England**.
Contact/s: Fishery Manager.
(T) 01263 768284
Mr John Waite.
(T) 01263 376284
Profile: **FT:** Coarse; **WN:** Saw Mill; **WT:** Lake (Still) **W. Size:** 16 Acres. **Location:** **Nr. Rd:** Roughton Village, 2nd left; **Main Rd:** A140 from Cromer.
Ref: FH2037

KEY: **(w)**: Web address **(T)**: Telephone number **(F)**: Fax Number **(M)**: Mobile Number **(E)**: E-mail Address
F. Size: Fishery Size **FT:** Fisherytype **WN:** WaterName/s **WT:** WaterType **W. Size:** Water Size **£Fr**: Free Fishing

GUNVILLE LAKE

Gunville Lake, Carisbrooke, Newport, **ISLE OF WIGHT**, PO30, **England**.
(W) www.isleofwight.co.uk
Contact/s: **Mr Alan Bravery** (Manager), Scotties Tackle Shop, 11 Lugley St, Newport, Isle of Wight, PO30 5HD.
(T) 01983 522115 **(F)** 01983 522115
Mr Paul Johnson (Manager), Scotties Sandown, 22 Fitzroy St, Sandown, Isle of Wight, PO36 8HZ.
(T) 01983 404555
Mr R J Kirby (Hon Secretary), 125 Furrlongs, Pan Estate, Newport, Isle of Wight, PO30 2BN.
(T) 01983 529617
Profile: **FT:** Coarse; **WN:** Gunville; **WT:** Lake (Still) **W. Size:** 3 Acres. Location: **Nr. Rd:** B3401; **Main Rd:** B3401.
Ref: FH2038

GUNWADE LAKE

Gunwade Lake, Ferry Meadows Country Park, Peterborough, **CAMBRIDGESHIRE**, PE, **England**.
Contact/s: **Mr Kevin Crowther**.
(T) 01733 701982
Profile: **FT:** Coarse; **WN:** Gunwade; **WT:** Lake (Still).
Ref: FH2039

GWARNICK MILL TROUT FISHERY

Gwarnick Mill Trout Fishery, Gwarnick Mill, St Allen, Truro, **CORNWALL**, TR4 9QU, **England**.
Contact/s: **Ms Sue Dawkins** (Owner).
(T) 01872 540487
Profile: **FT:** Game; **WN:** Gwarnick Mill Trout Fishery; **WT:** Lake (Still); **F. Size:** 2 Acres; **W. Size:** 2 Acres. Location: **Nr. Rd:** Shortlanesend to Zelah; **Main Rd:** A30 and B3284; **Rail:** Truro. £Fr
Ref: FH2040

GWEESTION (RIVER)

River Gweestion, Bohola, **COUNTY MAYO**, **Ireland**.
Contact/s: Angling Officer, North Western Regional Fisheries Board, Ardnaree House, Abbey St, Ballina, County Mayo.
(T) 096 22623 **(F)** 096 70543
Profile: **FT:** Game; **WN:** Gweestion; **WT:** River (Moving).
Ref: FH2041

GWENDRAETH & MORIASIS

Gwendraeth And Moriasis Fishery, Llangennech, Llanelli, **CARMARTHENSHIRE**, SA14, **Wales**.
Contact/s: **Mr D A Owen** (Secretary), 99 Hendre Rd, Llangennech, Llanelli, Carmarthenshire, SA14 8TH.
(T) 01554 820948
Profile: **FT:** Game; **WN:** Gwendraeth And Moriasis Fishery; **WT:** Lake (Still).
Ref: FH2042

GWENDRAETH FACH (RIVER)

River Gwendraeth Fach, Llangennech, Llanelli, **CARMARTHENSHIRE**, SA14, **Wales**.
Contact/s: **Mr D A Owen** (Secretary), 99 Hendre Rd, Llangennech, Llanelli, Carmarthenshire, SA14 8TH.
(T) 01554 820948
Profile: **FT:** Game; **WN:** Gwendraeth Fach; **WT:** River (Moving) **W. Size:** 6400 Metres. Location: **Nr. Rd:** Llandyfaelog to Llangendeirne Bridge.
Ref: FH2043

GWENDRAETH FACH (RIVER)

River Gwendraeth Fach, Llandyfaelog, Kidwelly, **CARMARTHENSHIRE**, SA17, **Wales**.
Contact/s: **Mr D A Owen** (Secretary), 99 Hendre Rd, Llangennech, Llanelli, Carmarthenshire, SA14 8TH.
(T) 01554 820948
Profile: **FT:** Game; **WN:** Gwendraeth Fach; **WT:** River (Moving).
Ref: FH2044

GWENDRAETH FACH (RIVER)

River Gwendraeth Fach, Llandyfaelog, Kidwelly, **CARMARTHENSHIRE**, SA17, **Wales**.
Contact/s: **Mr Herbert Evans** (Hon Secretary), 25 Maple Cres, Carmarthen, Carmarthenshire.
(T) 01267 231945
Profile: **FT:** Game; **WN:** Gwendraeth Fach; **WT:** River (Moving). Location: **Nr. Rd:** Llandyfaelog to Kidwelly.
Ref: FH2045

GWERNAN LAKE FISHERY

Gwernan Lake Fishery, Cader Rd, Islawrdref, Dolgellau, **GWYNEDD**, LL40, **Wales**.
Contact/s: **Mr David Lathaen** (Owner).
(T) 01341 422488
Profile: **FT:** Game; **WN:** Gwernan; **WT:** Lake (Still). Location: **Nr. Rd:** Cader Road.
Ref: FH2046

GWERYD LAKES FISHING

Gweryd Lakes Fishing, Gweryd Lodge, Plas Lane, Llanarmon-Yn-Ial, Mold, **FLINTSHIRE**, CH7 4QJ, **Wales**.
Contact/s: Fishery Manager.
(T) 01824 708230 **(F)** 01824 780884
Profile: **FT:** Coarse; **WN:** Gweryd; **WT:** Lake (Still); **F. Size:** 150 Acres; **W. Size:** 14 Acres. Location: **Nr. Rd:** Plas Lane; **Main Rd:** B5430.
Ref: FH2047

GWILI (RIVER)

River Gwili, Bronwydd Arms, Carmarthen, **CARMARTHENSHIRE**, SA33, **Wales**.
Contact/s: **Mr Herbert Evans** (Hon Secretary), 25 Maple Cres, Carmarthen, Carmarthenshire.
(T) 01267 231945
Profile: **FT:** Game; **WN:** Gwili; **WT:** River (Moving) **W. Size:** 1200 Metres. Location: **Nr. Rd:** Bronwydd.
Ref: FH2048

GWINEAR POOLS COARSE FISHERY

Gwinear Pools Coarse Fishery, Gwinear Farm, Cubert, Newquay, **CORNWALL**, TR8 5JX, **England**.
Contact/s: **Mr Simon Waterhouse** (Owner).
(T) 01637 830165 **(F)** 01637 830165
Profile: **FT:** Coarse; **WN:** Gwinear; **WT:** Pool (Still); **F. Size:** 8 Acres; **W. Size:** 8 Acres. Location: **Nr. Rd:** A3075; **Main Rd:** A3075; **Rail:** Truro.
Ref: FH2049

GWINNEAR POOLS

Gwinear Pools, Newquay, **CORNWALL**, **England**.
Profile: **FT:** Coarse; **WN:** Gwinnear Pools; **WT:** Lake (Still); **F. Size:** 10 Acres; **W. Size:** 7 Acres. Location: **Nr. Rd:** A3075; **Rail:** Newquay.
Ref: FH2050

GWITHIAN BROOK

Gwithian Brook, Camborne, **CORNWALL**, TR14, **England**.
Contact/s: Manager, The County Angler, 39 Cross St, Camborne, TR14 8ES.
(T) 01209 718490
Profile: **FT:** Coarse; **WN:** Camborne; **WT:** Stream (Moving).
Ref: FH2051

GWYDDELWERN POOL

Gwyddelwern Pool, Corwen, **DENBIGHSHIRE**, LL21, **Wales**.
Contact/s: **Mr D Lewis**, Maes-y-Llyn, Gwyddelwern, Corwen, Conwy, LL21 9DU.
(T) 01490 412761
Profile: **FT:** Coarse; **WN:** Gwyddelwern; **WT:** Lake (Still).
Ref: FH2052

GWYDDIOR LAKE

Gwyddior Lake, Bryn-Llugwy, Llanbrynmair, **POWYS**, SY19, **Wales**.
Contact/s: **Mr E Lewis** (Chairman), Llanbrynmair Angling Club, Bryn-Llugwy, Llanbrynmair, Powys, SY19 7AA.
(T) 01650 521385
Mr H Hughes, Bodhyfryd, Llanbrynmair, Powys.
Profile: **FT:** Game; **WN:** Gwyddior; **WT:** Lake (Still) **W. Size:** 27 Acres. Location: **Main Rd:** A470.
Ref: FH2053

GWYNEDD (RIVER)

River Gwynedd, Criccieth, **GWYNEDD**, LL52, **Wales**.
Contact/s: Manager, R T Pritchard and Son, 41-43 High St, Criccieth, Gwynedd, LL52 0EY.
(T) 01766 522116
Mr Gordon Hamilton, Llanystumdwy and District Angling Association, Morawel, Llanystumdwy, Criccieth, LL52 0SF.
Profile: **FT:** Combination; **WN:** Gwyned; **WT:** Stream (Moving).
Ref: FH2054

GWYRFAI (RIVER)

River Gwyrfai, Caernarfon, **GWYNEDD**, LL55, **Wales**.
Contact/s: **Mr Huw P Hughes** (Hon Secretary), Seiont, Gwyrfai and Llyfni Anglers Society, Llugwy, Ystad Eryri, Bethel, Caernarfon, LL55 1BX.
(T) 01248 670666
(E) huw.hughes@lineone.net
Profile: **FT:** Game; **WN:** Gwyrfai; **WT:** River (Moving) **W. Size:** 16000 Metres. Location: **Nr. Rd:** B4418; **Main Rd:** A4085; **Rail:** Bangor.
Ref: FH2055

GYRN CASTLE FISHERY

Gyrn Castle Fishery, Llanasa, Holywell, **FLINTSHIRE**, CH8 9BG, **Wales**.
Contact/s: **Mr Steve Partington** (Fishery Manager).
(T) 01745 561672
Mrs Ellis, Gyrn Castle Estate, South Lodge, Glan-yr-Afon.
(T) 01745 561677
Profile: **FT:** Coarse; **WN:** Gyrn Castle Fishery; **WT:** Lake (Still). Location: **Main Rd:** A5151.
Ref: FH2056

HACK GREEN LAKE

Hack Green Lake, Hack Green, Nantwich, **CHESHIRE**, CW5, **England**.
Profile: **FT:** Coarse; **WN:** Hack Green; **WT:** Lake (Still) **W. Size:** 2 Acres.
Ref: FH2057

HADDISCOE PIT

Haddiscoe Pit, Haddiscoe, Norwich, **NORFOLK**, NR, **England**.
Contact/s: **Mr Arthur Crane** (Secretary), 27 Rigbourne Hill, Beccles, Suffolk, NR34 9JG.
(T) 01502 716716
Profile: **FT:** Coarse; **WN:** Haddiscoe; **WT:** Gravel Pit (Still) **W. Size:** 7 Acres. Location: **Nr. Rd:** Great Yarmouth to Haddiscoe Village; **Main Rd:** A143.
Ref: FH2058

HADDOE TROUT FISHERY

Haddoe Trout Fishery, Parlour Cottage, Higher Grants, Exebridge, Dulverton, **SOMERSET**, TA22, **England**.
Contact/s: **Mr John Sharpe**.
(T) 01398 23104
Profile: **FT:** Game; **WN:** Exe; **WT:** River (Moving).
Ref: FH2059

HADDON ESTATE FISHERIES

Haddon Estate Fisheries, Bakewell, **DERBYSHIRE**, DE45, **England**.
Contact/s: Manager, Haddon Hall Estate,

Bakewell, Derbyshire, DE45 1LA.
(T) 01629 812855
Profile: FT: Combination; WN: Haddon Estate Fisheries; WT: Lake (Still).
Ref: FH2060

HADRIAN LODGE

Hadrian Lodge, Hindfield Moss, North Rd, Haydon Bridge, Hexham, **NORTHUMBERLAND**, NE47 6NF, **England**.
Contact/s: **Mr Matthew Pandrick**.
(T) 01434 688688
Ms Lynn Murray (Manager).
(T) 01434 688688
Profile: FT: Game; WN: Hadrian Lodge; WT: Lake (Still).
Ref: FH2061

HAGGS RESERVOIR

Haggs Reservoir, Hyndburn Rd, Accrington, **LANCASHIRE**, BB5, **England**.
Profile: FT: Coarse; WN: Haggs; WT: Reservoir (Still).
Ref: FH2062

HAINAULT FOREST COUNTRY PARK

Hainault Forest Country Park, Fox Burrow Rd, Chigwell, **ESSEX**, IG7 4QN, **England**.
Contact/s: **Mr Terry Barton** (Manager).
(T) 020 85212884
Profile: FT: Coarse; WN: Hainault Country Park; WT: Lake (Still). Location: Nr. Rd: A1112 right opposite industrial estate; Main Rd: A12.
Ref: FH2063

HALE MANOR LAKES

Hale Manor Lakes, Hale Manor Common, Arreton, Newport, **ISLE OF WIGHT**, PO30 3AR, **England**.
Contact/s: **Mr David Brown**.
(T) 01983 865204
Profile: FT: Combination; WN: Hale Manor; WT: Lake (Still) W. Size: 1 Acre.
Ref: FH2064

HALF PIT

Half Pit, Ringwood, **HAMPSHIRE**, BH24, **England**.
Contact/s: **Mr Richard Middleton** (Manager), Ringwood Tackle, 5 The Bridges, Ringwood, Hampshire, BH24 1EA.
(T) 01425 475155
Profile: FT: Coarse; WN: Half; WT: Gravel Pit (Still).
Ref: FH2065

HALL FARM

Hall Farm, Frolesworth, Lutterworth, **LEICESTERSHIRE**, LE17, **England**.
Contact/s: **Mr A Smith** (Secretary), Broome Angling Society, 10 Lords Avenue, Leicester, Leicestershire, LE4 2HX.
(T) 0116 2357210 (M) 07976 328836
Mr G Taylor (Membership Secretary), Broome Angling Society, 100 New Romney Cres, Leicester.
(T) 0116 2417018
Profile: FT: Coarse; WN: Hall Farm; WT: Lake (Still) W. Size: 2 Acres. Location: Nr. Rd: Leicester to Sharnfold; Main Rd: M1; Rail: Leicester.
Ref: FH2066

HALL FARM FISHING

Hall Farm Fishing, Melton Mowbray, **LEICESTERSHIRE**, LE13, **England**.
Contact/s: Hall Farm Manager.
(T) 01427 668412
Profile: FT: Coarse; WN: Hall Farm Fishing; WT: Pool (Still) W. Size: 1 Acre.
Ref: FH2067

HALL FARM LAKES

Hall Farm Lakes, Burgh Castle, Mill Rd, Great Yarmouth, **NORFOLK**, NR, **England**.
Contact/s: **Mrs Riches**.
(T) 01493 781986
Profile: FT: Coarse; WN: Hall Farm; WT: Gravel Pit (Still) W. Size: 2 Acres. Location: Nr. Rd: Mill Road; Main Rd: A143 to Bradwell.
Ref: FH2068

HALLADALE SALMON FISHERY

Halladale Salmon Fishery, 106 Portskerra, Melvich, Thurso, **HIGHLAND**, KW14 7YL, **Scotland**.
Contact/s: Fishery Manager.
(T) 01641 531215 (F) 01641 531215
Profile: FT: Game; WN: Halladale Salmon Fishery; WT: River (Moving).
Ref: FH2069

HALLCROFT FISHERIES

Hallcroft Fisheries, Hallcroft Rd, Retford, **NOTTINGHAMSHIRE**, DN22 7RA, **England**.
Contact/s: **Mr Bryan Talbot** (Owner).
(T) 01777 710448 (F) 01777 710448
Profile: FT: Coarse; WN: Hallcroft Fisheries; WT: Combination (Still & Moving) W. Size: 13 Acres. Location: Nr. Rd: Hallcroft Road; Main Rd: A638; Rail: Retford.
Ref: FH2070

HALLIFORD MERE LAKES

Halliford Mere Lakes, Chertsey Rd, Shepperton, London, **LONDON (GREATER)**, TW17 9NU, **England**.
Contact/s: **Mr Bill Berwick** (Owner).
(T) 01932 248547 (F) 01932 253553
Mr Robin Berwick (Owner).
(T) 01932 248547 (F) 01932 253553
Profile: FT: Game; WN: Halliford Mere; WT: Lake (Still); F. Size: 87 Acres; W. Size: 42 Acres. Location: Nr. Rd: Chertsey Road; Main Rd: Chertsey Road; Rail: Shepperton.
Ref: FH2071

HALLINGTON RESERVOIRS

Hallington Reservoirs, Westwater Angling, The Club House, Corbridge, **NORTHUMBERLAND**, NE45, **England**.
Contact/s: **J J Todd**.
Profile: FT: Coarse; WN: Hallington; WT: Reservoir (Still).
Ref: FH2072

HALLMORE FISHERIES

Hallmore Fisheries, Carnforth, **CUMBRIA**, LA6, **England**.
Contact/s: Fishery Manager.
Profile: FT: Coarse; WN: Hallmore Fisheries; WT: Lake (Still).
Ref: FH2073

HALNEBY LAKE

Halneby Lake, Middleton Tyas, Darlington, **COUNTY DURHAM**, DL, **England**.
Profile: FT: Coarse; WN: Halneby; WT: Lake (Still) W. Size: 6 Acres. Location: Main Rd: A1 and A66.
Ref: FH2074

HALSHAM POND

Halsham Pond, Dalton Lane, Halsham, Hull, **HUMBERSIDE**, HU12 0DG, **England**.
Contact/s: **Mr Gallop**, Ash Gr, Dalton Lane, Halsham, Hull, HU12 0DG.
(T) 01964 670481
Profile: FT: Coarse; WN: Halsham; WT: Pond (Still). Location: Nr. Rd: B1362; Main Rd: A1033.
Ref: FH2075

HALTON FISHERY

Halton Fishery, Greenup Cottage, Hornby Rd, Caton, Lancaster, **LANCASHIRE**, LA2, **England**.
Contact/s: **Mr Price** (Secretary).
(T) 01524 770078
Profile: FT: Combination; WN: Halton Fishery; WT: River (Moving). Location: Nr. Rd: Hornby Road.
Ref: FH2076

HAM GREEN LAKE

Ham Green Lake, Bristol, BS, **England**.
Contact/s: **Mr Richard Barnes** (Syndicate Leader).
Profile: FT: Coarse; WN: Ham Green; WT: Lake (Still).
Ref: FH2077

HAM POOL

Ham Pool, South Cerney, Cirencester, **GLOUCESTERSHIRE**, GL7, **England**.
Contact/s: Fishery Manager.
(T) 01285 861618
Mr Dave Savage (Manager), D and J Sports Limited, 75 Cricklake St, Cirencester, Gloucestershire, GL7 1HY.
(T) 01285 652227 (F) 01285 641615
Profile: FT: Coarse; WN: Ham Pool; WT: Gravel Pit (Still) W. Size: 24 Acres. Location: Nr. Rd: Cirencester; Main Rd: A419, A417.
Ref: FH2078

HAMBRIDGE LANE

Hambridge Lane, Thatcham, Newbury, **BERKSHIRE**, RG, **England**.
Contact/s: **Mr Dusty Millar** (Associate members secretary), 238 Elgar Road South, Reading, Berkshire, RG3 0BW.
(T) 0118 9874882
Mr Mick Cox (Chief Bailiff), Dorstans, Hatch Lane, Brimpton Village, Reading, RG7 4TR.
(T) 0118 9714917
Profile: FT: Coarse; WN: Hambridge Lane; WT: Gravel Pit (Still) W. Size: 25 Acres. Location: Nr. Rd: Hambridge Lane; Main Rd: Thatcham.
Ref: FH2079

HAMBROOK TROUT FISHERY

Hambrook Trout Fishery, Leaze Lane, Ham Brook, Chichester, **SUSSEX (WEST)**, PO18 8RQ, **England**.
Contact/s: **Mr Peter Yates** (Manager).
(T) 01243 575076
Profile: FT: Game; WN: Hambrook; WT: Lake (Still) W. Size: 3 Acres. Location: Nr. Rd: Leaze Lane.
Ref: FH2080

HAMPS (RIVER)

Hamps (River), Longditch, Winkhill, Leek, **STAFFORDSHIRE**, ST13, **England**.
Contact/s: **Mr John Turner** (Hon Secretary), Prince Albert Angling Society, 15 Pexhill Drive, Macclesfield, Cheshire, SK10 3LP.
(T) 01625 422010
Profile: FT: Combination; WN: Hamps; WT: River (Moving) W. Size: 750 Metres. Location: Main Rd: A52; Rail: Ashbourne.
Ref: FH2081

HAMPSHIRE AVON

River Hampshire Avon, Lifelands, Ringwood, **HAMPSHIRE**, BH24, **England**.
Contact/s: **Mr R J Andrews** (Club Secretary), Christchurch Angling Club, 4 Marley Cl, New Milton, BH25 5LL.
(T) 01425 638502
Mr Richard Middleton (Manager), Ringwood Tackle, 5 The Bridges, Ringwood, Hampshire, BH24 1EA.
(T) 01425 475155
Mr Steve Richards.
(T) 01425 279710
Profile: FT: Coarse; WN: Hampshire Avon; WT: River (Moving) W. Size: 1600 Metres. Location: Nr. Rd: A338; Main Rd: A31; Rail: Christchurch.
Ref: FH2082

HAMPSHIRE AVON (RIVER)

River Hampshire Avon, New Queen Beat, Sopley, Christchurch, **DORSET**, BH23, **England**.
Contact/s: **Mr Graham Pepler** (Manager), Davis Tackle Shop, 75 Bargates, Christchurch, Dorset, BH23 1QE.
(T) 01202 485169or395532 (F) 01202 474261
Profile: FT: Coarse; WN: Hampshire; WT: River (Moving) W. Size: 4430 Metres. Location: Nr. Rd: B3347; Main Rd: B3347.
Ref: FH2083

HAMPSHIRE AVON (RIVER)

River Hampshire Avon, Avon Tyrrell, Sopley,

Christchurch, **DORSET**, BH23, **England**.
Contact/s: **Mr Pete Reading** (Secretary), 17 Mayford Rd, Poole, Dorset, BH12 1PT.
(T) 01202 733110
Profile: **FT:** Coarse; **WN:** Hampshire Avon; **WT:** River (Moving). **Location:** **Nr. Rd:** B3347 North; **Main Rd:** Avon Causeway.
Ref: FH2084

HAMPSHIRE AVON (RIVER)

River Hampshire Avon, Sopley Mill, Sopley, Christchurch, **DORSET**, BH23, **England**.
Contact/s: **Mr Pete Reading** (Secretary), 17 Mayford Rd, Poole, Dorset, BH12 1PT.
(T) 01202 733110
Profile: **FT:** Coarse; **WN:** Hampshire Avon; **WT:** Stream (Moving) **W. Size:** 1600 Metres. **Location:** **Main Rd:** B3347 to Christchurch.
Ref: FH2085

HAMPSHIRE AVON (RIVER)

River Hampshire Avon, Winkton Fishery, Christchurch, **DORSET**, BH23, **England**.
Contact/s: **Mr Graham Pepler** (Manager), Davis Tackle Shop, 75 Bargates, Christchurch, Dorset, BH23 1QE.
(T) 01202 485169or395532 **(F)** 01202 474261
Profile: **FT:** Coarse; **WN:** Hampshire Avon; **WT:** River (Moving) **W. Size:** 1600 Metres. **Location:** **Nr. Rd:** From Christchurch, A35 towards Southampton, B3347 or Ringwood; **Main Rd:** B3347.
Ref: FH2086

HAMPSHIRE AVON (RIVER)

River Hampshire Avon, Royalty Fishery, Christchurch, **DORSET**, BH23, **England**.
Contact/s: Fishery Manager.
(T) 01202 485262
Mr Andy Sloane (Head Bailiff). **(M)** 07802 761417
Profile: **FT:** Coarse; **WN:** Hampshire Avon; **WT:** River (Moving).
Ref: FH2087

HAMPSHIRE AVON (RIVER)

River Hampshire Avon, East Mills, Fordingbridge, **HAMPSHIRE**, SP6, **England**.
Contact/s: Manager, The Crown Inn, High St, Fordingbridge, Hampshire, SP6 1AX.
(T) 01425 652552
Mrs Dommett.
(T) 01425 653030
Profile: **FT:** Coarse; **WN:** Hampshire Avon; **WT:** River (Moving) **W. Size:** 2400 Metres. **Location:** **Nr. Rd:** B3078; **Main Rd:** M27, junction 1, B3078 to Fordingbridge.
Ref: FH2088

HAMPSHIRE AVON (RIVER)

River Hampshire Avon, Ibsley Bridge To Bickton, Ringwood, **HAMPSHIRE**, BH24, **England**.
Contact/s: **Mr Pete Reading** (Secretary), Christchurch Angling Club, 17 Mayford Rd, Poole, Dorset, BH12 1PT.
(T) 01202 733110
Profile: **FT:** Coarse; **WN:** Hampshire Avon; **WT:** River (Moving) **W. Size:** 3200 Metres. **Location:** **Nr. Rd:** A338; **Main Rd:** A31.
Ref: FH2089

HAMPSHIRE AVON (RIVER)

River Hampshire Avon, Severals Fishery, Ringwood, **HAMPSHIRE**, BH24, **England**.
Contact/s: **Mr Kevin Grozier** (Permit Secretary), 15 Greenfinch Walk, Hightown, Ringwood, Hampshire, BH24 3RJ.
(T) 01425 471466 **(F)** 01425 471466
Mr Richard Middleton (Manager), Ringwood Tackle, 5 The Bridges, Ringwood, Hampshire, BH24 1EA.
(T) 01425 475155
Profile: **FT:** Coarse; **WN:** Severals Fishery; **WT:** River (Moving) **W. Size:** 3200 Metres. **Location:** **Nr. Rd:** B3081.
Ref: FH2090

HAMPSHIRE AVON (RIVER)

River Hampshire Avon, Ellingham, Ringwood, **HAMPSHIRE**, BH24, **England**.
Contact/s: **Mr Pete Reading** (Secretary), 17 Mayford Rd, Poole, Dorset, BH12 1PT.
(T) 01202 733110
Profile: **FT:** Coarse; **WN:** Hampshire Avon; **WT:** River (Moving) **W. Size:** 2700 Metres. **Location:** **Nr. Rd:** Ellingham bridges; **Main Rd:** A338, Ringwood to Fordingbridge.
Ref: FH2091

HAMPSHIRE AVON (RIVER)

River (Hampshire) Avon, Breamore, Fordingbridge, **HAMPSHIRE**, SP6 2EA, **England**.
(W) www.thebatandball.com
Contact/s: **Mr Paul Harling** (Landlord), Bat and Ball Pub, Breamore, Hampshire, SP6 2EA.
(T) 01725 512252 **(F)** 01725 510980
(E) amanda@thebatandball.com
Profile: **FT:** Combination; **WN:** Avon; **WT:** River (Moving) **W. Size:** 700 Metres. **Location:** **Nr. Rd:** A338; **Main Rd:** A338; **Rail:** Salisbury. **£Fr**
Ref: FH2092

HAMPSHIRE AVON (RIVER)

River Hampshire Avon, Salisbury, **WILTSHIRE**, SP, **England**.
Contact/s: **Mr Ron Hillier** (Secretary), 29 New Zealand Avenue, Salisbury, Wiltshire, SP2 7JX.
(T) 01722 321164
Profile: **FT:** Coarse; **WN:** Avon; **WT:** River (Moving).
Ref: FH2093

HAMPSTEAD HEATH

Hampstead Heath, East Heath Rd, Hampstead Common, Hampstead, London, **LONDON (GREATER)**, NW3, **England**.
Contact/s: Ranger, Rangers Office, Parliament Hill Fields, High Gate Rd, Hampstead Heath.
(T) 020 74854491
Mr Bob Sharpe (Manager), Sharps Tackle, 162 Malden Rd, London, NW5 4BS.
(T) 020 74851759
Profile: **FT:** Coarse; **WN:** Hampstead Heath; **WT:** Combination (Still) **W. Size:** 22 Acres. **Location:** **Nr. Rd:** East Heath Road. **£Fr**
Ref: FH2094

HAMPTON LOCK

Hampton Lock, Old Forge House, Hampton Loade, Bridgnorth, **SHROPSHIRE**, WV16, **England**.
Contact/s: **Mr Bill Turner** (Secretary).
(T) 01902 457906
Profile: **FT:** Coarse; **WN:** Hampton; **WT:** Canal (Still) **W. Size:** 1875 Metres.
Ref: FH2095

HAMPTON SPRINGS

Hampton Springs, Cholmondeley, Malpas, **CHESHIRE**, SY14, **England**.
Contact/s: Fishery Manager.
(T) 01630 655037
Profile: **FT:** Coarse; **WN:** Hampton Springs; **WT:** Lake (Still).
Ref: FH2096

HAMSTALL FISHERY

Hamstall Fishery, Riverside Yoxall Rd, Hamstall Ridware, Rugeley, **STAFFORDSHIRE**, WS15 2VR, **England**.
Contact/s: **Mr Geoff Payne** (Owner). **(M)** 07775 518769
(E) geoff.payne@fishing.co.uk
Mr M Masters (Bailiff).
(T) 01889 504449
Profile: **FT:** Coarse; **WN:** Hamstall Fishery; **WT:** Combination (Still & Moving) **W. Size:** 15 Acres. **Location:** **Main Rd:** A515; **Rail:** Rugeley.
Ref: FH2097

HAMWORTHY LAKE

Hamworthy Lake, Napier Rd, Poole, **DORSET**, BH17, **England**.
Contact/s: **Mr Simon Barber**, Wessex Angling Ctre, 321 Wimborne Rd, Poole, Dorset, BH15 3DH.
(T) 01202 668244 **(F)** 01202 668244
Profile: **FT:** Coarse; **WN:** Hamworthy; **WT:** Lake (Still). **Location:** **Nr. Rd:** Napier Road; **Main Rd:** A350 to Upton. **£Fr**
Ref: FH2098

HANCHURCH FISHERIES

Hanchurch Fisheries, Model Farm, Hanchurch Lane, Hanchurch, Stoke-on-Trent, **STAFFORDSHIRE**, ST4 8SD, **England**.
Contact/s: **Mr Raymond Sant** (Manager).
(T) 01782 657434or642481 **(F)** 01782 657515
Profile: **FT:** Combination; **WN:** Hanchurch Fisheries; **WT:** Lake (Still); **F. Size:** 50 Acres; **W. Size:** 30 Acres. **Location:** **Nr. Rd:** Hanchurch Lane; **Main Rd:** A519; **Rail:** Stoke-on-Trent.
Ref: FH2099

HANDLE LAKE

Handle Lake, Howfield Lane, Chartham Hatch, Canterbury, **KENT**, **England**.
(W) www.midkentfish.demon.co.uk
Contact/s: **Mr Chris Logsdon** (Fisheries Manager), Mid Kent Fisheries, Chilham Water Mill, Mill Lane, Chilham, CT4 8EE.
(T) 01227 730668
(E) chilham@midkentfisheries.co.uk
Profile: **FT:** Coarse; **WN:** Handle; **WT:** Lake (Still); **F. Size:** 30 Acres; **W. Size:** 9 Acres. **Location:** **Nr. Rd:** Howfield Lane; **Main Rd:** A28; **Rail:** Canterbury.
Ref: FH2100

HANNINGFIELD TROUT FISHERY

Hanningfield Trout Fishery, Giffords Lane, South Hanningfield, Chelmsford, **ESSEX**, CM3 8HX, **England**.
Contact/s: **Mr Brian Joslin**.
(T) 01268 710101or01245212031 **(F)** 01268 711787
Ms Tracey MacLennan.
(T) 01268 710101or01245212031 **(F)** 01268 711787
Profile: **FT:** Game; **WN:** Hanningfield Trout Fishery; **WT:** Reservoir (Still); **F. Size:** 800 Acres; **W. Size:** 600 Acres. **Location:** **Nr. Rd:** South Hanningfield Road; **Main Rd:** A130; **Rail:** Wickford.
Ref: FH2101

HARDLEY MARSHES

Hardley Marshes, Loddon, Norwich, **NORFOLK**, NR14, **England**.
Contact/s: **Mr C Nichols**, 16 The Market Place, Loddon, Norwich, Norfolk, NR14 6E.
Profile: **FT:** Coarse; **WN:** Hardley Marshes; **WT:** Lake (Still) **W. Size:** 50 Acres.
Ref: FH2102

HARDWATER LAKE

Hardwater Lake, Earls Barton, Northampton, **NORTHAMPTONSHIRE**, NN6, **England**.
Contact/s: Fishery Manager.
(T) 01604 812059
Profile: **FT:** Coarse; **WN:** Hardwater; **WT:** Lake (Still).
Ref: FH2103

HARDWICK LAKE AND SMITHS POOL

Hardwick Lake & Smiths Pool, Shimano Linear Fisheries (Oxfordshire), Smiths Concrete Site, Hardwick Village, Witney, **OXFORDSHIRE**, OX8 7Q, **England**.
Contact/s: **Mr Len Gurd** (Owner), 10A Rackstraw Gr, Old Farm Park, Milton Keynes, Buckinghamshire, MK7 8PZ.
(T) 01908 645135 **(F)** 01908 645115
Profile: **FT:** Coarse; **WN:** Smiths & Hardwick; **WT:** Lake (Still); **F. Size:** 35 Acres; **W. Size:** 30 Acres. **Location:** **Nr. Rd:** B4449; **Main Rd:** A40; **Rail:** Oxford.
Ref: FH2104

HAREFIELD CARP LAKE

Harefield Carp Lake, Moorhall Rd, Harefield, Uxbridge, London, **LONDON (GREATER)**, UB9, **England**.
Contact/s: **Buzz** (Manager), Boyer Leisure

Ltd, Heron's Point Tackle Shop, Farlow's Lake, Ford Lane, Iver SL0 9LL.
(T) 01753 630302or01895444707 **(F)** 01753 630302
(E) info@boyer.co.uk
Profile: **FT:** Coarse; **WN:** Harefield Carp; **WT:** Gravel Pit (Still) **W. Size:** 47 Acres.
Location: **Nr. Rd:** A412; **Main Rd:** A413, M25; **Rail:** Denham.
Ref: FH2105

HARLAW RESERVOIR

Harlaw Reservoir, Balerno, **EDINBURGH (CITY OF)**, EH14, **Scotland**.
Contact/s: **Mr A Flemming** (owner), Flemmings Grocery Shop, 42 Main St, Balerno, Edinburgh, EH30 9TQ.
(T) 0131 4493833
Profile: **FT:** Game; **WN:** Harlaw; **WT:** Reservoir (Still).
Ref: FH2106

HARLESTHORPE DAM

Harlesthorpe Dam, Clowne, Chesterfield, **DERBYSHIRE**, S43 4PS, **England**.
Contact/s: **Ms Caroline Sibbring** (Owner).
(T) 01246 810231
Profile: **FT:** Coarse; **WN:** Harlesthorpe; **WT:** Dam (Still); **F. Size:** 11 Acres; **W. Size:** 11 Acres. **Location:** **Nr. Rd:** Rotherham Road; **Main Rd:** A618; **Rail:** Chesterfield.
Ref: FH2107

HARLOCK RESERVOIR

Harlock Reservoir, South Lakeland, Dalton-In-Furness, **CUMBRIA**, LA15, **England**.
Contact/s: **Mr J R Jones** (Hon Secretary), Barrow Angling Association, 69 Prince St, Dalton in Furness, Cumbria, LA15 8ET.
Mr Roy Rhodes (Conservation, Access and Recreation Manager), Rivington Water Treatment Works, Bolton Rd, Horwich, Bolton, BL6 7RN.
(T) 01204 664300
Profile: **FT:** Game; **WN:** Harlock; **WT:** Reservoir (Still).
Ref: FH2108

HAROLD FISHERY

Harold Fishery, Sharnbrook, Bedford, **BEDFORDSHIRE**, MK44, **England**.
Contact/s: **Mr Ian Welch** (Manager), RMC Angling, RMC House, High St, Feltham, Middlesex TW13 4HD.
(T) 020 88931168
Profile: **FT:** Coarse; **WN:** Harold; **WT:** Combination (Still & Moving).
Ref: FH2109

HARROLD ODELL COUNTRY PARK

Harrold-Odell Country Park, Bedford, **BUCKINGHAMSHIRE**, MK4, **England**.
Contact/s: Manager, Bedfordshire County Council, Leisure Services, Cauldwell St, Bedford, MK42 9AP.
(T) 01234 363222/0193355696
Mr Cliff Roberts (Secretary).
(T) 01933 55696
Profile: **FT:** Coarse; **WN:** Harrold- Odell Country Park; **WT:** Gravel Pit (Still) **W. Size:** 7 Acres. **Location:** **Main Rd:** A6.
Ref: FH2110

HARROW POND

Harrow Pond, Harrow Lodge, Holmesley, Christchurch, **DORSET**, BH23, **England**.
Contact/s: Manager.
(T) 01202 733110
Mr R J Andrews (Club Secretary), Christchurch Angling Club, 4 Marley Cl, New Milton, BH25 5LL.
(T) 01425 638502
Profile: **FT:** Coarse; **WN:** Harrow; **WT:** Pond (Still) **W. Size:** 2 Acres. **Location:** **Nr. Rd:** Lyndhurst Road; **Main Rd:** A35, Christchurch.
Ref: FH2111

HART RESERVOIR

Hart Reservoir, Hart, Hartlepool, **CLEVELAND**, TS27 3, **England**.
Contact/s: **Mr Alan Wilkinson** (Fishery Manager).
(T) 01429 866880
Mr Mark Arrow-Smith (Membership Secretary), Angler's Services, 27 Park Rd, Hartlepool, Cleveland, TS24 7PW.
(T) 01429 274844or266522
Profile: **FT:** Coarse; **WN:** Hart; **WT:** Reservoir (Still). **Location:** **Main Rd:** A179.
Ref: FH2112

HARTBURN BRICK PIT

Hartburn Brick Pit, Hartburn Lane, Stockton-on-Tees, **CLEVELAND**, TS, **England**.
Contact/s: Fishery Manager.
(T) 01642 588796or588789
Profile: **FT:** Coarse; **WN:** Brick Pit; **WT:** Gravel Pit (Still).
Ref: FH2113

HARTHILL

Harthill, Broxton, Nantwich, **CHESHIRE**, CW5, **England**.
Contact/s: **Ms Fiona Morris**.
(T) 01829 782475
Profile: **FT:** Coarse; **WN:** Harthill; **WT:** Pond (Still). **Location:** **Nr. Rd:** Boldsworth Hill Road; **Main Rd:** A41 South of Chester.
Ref: FH2114

HARTHILL RESERVIORS

Harthill Reserviors, Carver Way, Worksop, **YORKSHIRE (SOUTH)**, S8, **England**.
Contact/s: **Mr Martin Willyed**.
(T) 01909 770075 **(M)** 07966 501068
Mr Ray Panter.
(T) 01909 770075 **(M)** 07966 501068
Profile: **FT:** Coarse; **WN:** Harthill; **WT:** Reservoir (Still). **Location:** **Nr. Rd:** Carver Way; **Main Rd:** M1.
Ref: FH2115

HARTLAND FOREST FISHERY

Hartland Forest Fishery Golf Club, Wolsley, Bideford, **DEVON**, EX39 5RA, **England**.
Contact/s: **Mr A Cartwright**.
(T) 01237 431442
Profile: **FT:** Coarse; **WN:** Hartland Forest Fishery Golf Club; **WT:** Lake (Still). **Location:** **Main Rd:** A39.
Ref: FH2116

HARTLEPOOL RESERVOIR

Hartlepool Reservoir, Stockton-on-Tees, **CLEVELAND**, TS, **England**.
Contact/s: **Mr J Hartland** (Secretary), Hartlepool and District Angling Club, 7 Chillingham Cresent, Billingham, Stockton, Cleveland.
Profile: **FT:** Coarse; **WN:** Hartlepool; **WT:** Reservoir (Still).
Ref: FH2117

HARTLEY LANDS FARM

Hartley Lands Farm, Swattenden Lane, Hartley, Cranbrook, **KENT**, TN17, **England**.
(W) www.hartleylands.co.uk
Contact/s: **Mr Paul Ward** (Owner).
(T) 01580 720319 **(M)** 07710 538505
(E) paul@hartleylands.com
Profile: **FT:** Coarse; **WN:** Hartley Lands Farm; **WT:** Reservoir (Still); **F. Size:** 45 Acres.
Location: **Nr. Rd:** B2085; **Rail:** Staplehurst.
Ref: FH2118

HARTSHOLME PARK LAKE

Hartsholme Park Lake, Skellingthorpe Rd, Lincoln, **LINCOLNSHIRE**, LN6 0EY, **England**.
Contact/s: **Mr Colin Parker** (Secretary), Lincoln and District Angling Association, 4 Pottergate Cl, Waddington, Lincoln, LN5 9LY.
(T) 01522 720777
Mr Frank Butler (Chairman).
(T) 01522 534174
Profile: **FT:** Coarse; **WN:** Hartsholme Park; **WT:** Lake (Still); **F. Size:** 20 Acres; **W. Size:** 20 Acres. **Location:** **Nr. Rd:** B1378; **Main Rd:** A46; **Rail:** Lincoln.
Ref: FH2119

HARTSHORNE DAMS

Hartshorne Dams, Hartshorne, Burton-on-Trent, **STAFFORDSHIRE**, DE, **England**.
Contact/s: Manager, Rooney Inn, Hartshorne, Burton-upon-Trent, Staffordshire.
(T) 01283 536041
Profile: **FT:** Coarse; **WN:** Hartshorne; **WT:** Mill Dam (Still). **Location:** **Nr. Rd:** A50.
Ref: FH2120

HARTSMOOR FISHERIES

Hartsmoor Fisheries, Bolham Water, Clayhidon, Cullompton, **DEVON**, EX15 3QB, **England**.
Contact/s: **Mr John Griss** (Manager), Rose Cottage, Bolham, Clayhidon, Cullompton, EX15 3QB.
(T) 01823 680460
Profile: **FT:** Coarse; **WN:** Hartsmoor Fisheries; **WT:** Lake (Still); **F. Size:** 7 Acres; **W. Size:** 4 Acres. **Location:** **Main Rd:** B3391; **Rail:** Honiton.
Ref: FH2121

HARVEY POOL

Harvey Pool, Hucks Farm Fishery, Willow Rd, Martley, Worcester, **WORCESTERSHIRE**, WR6 6PS, **England**.
Contact/s: **Mr K Fidoe** (Manager).
(T) 01886 821374
Profile: **FT:** Coarse; **WN:** Harvey; **WT:** Pool (Still).
Ref: FH2122

HARVINGTON MANOR FISHERY

Harvington Manor Fishery, Harvington Manor Farm, Evesham, **WORCESTERSHIRE**, WR11, **England**.
Contact/s: Area Manager, Environment Agency, Sapphire East, 550 Streetsbrook Rd, Solihull, B91 1QT.
(T) 0121 7112324 **(F)** 0121 7115824
Mr David Byrd (Manager), Manor Farm Leisure, Herons Roost, Anchor Lane, Evesham, WR11 5NR.
(T) 01386 870039
Profile: **FT:** Coarse; **WN:** Avon; **WT:** River (Moving) **W. Size:** 1200 Metres.
Ref: FH2123

HARWICK HALL LAKES

Harwick Hall Lakes, Mansfield, **NOTTINGHAMSHIRE**, NG21, **England**.
Profile: **FT:** Coarse; **WN:** Harwick Hall; **WT:** Lake (Still). **Location:** **Main Rd:** Mansfield and Chesterfield.
Ref: FH2124

HARWOOD HALL LAKE

Parklands, Harwood Hall Lane, Upminster, **ESSEX**, **England**.
(W) www.becmain-as.dial.pipex.com
Contact/s: **Mr Ivor Setter**.
(T) 020 89957579
Mr Leslie Ailey (Club Secretary), 3 Meadow Rd, Rush Green, Romford, Essex, RM7 0LR.
(T) 01708 745985 **(M)** 07714 091884
(E) becmain-as@dial.pipex.com
Profile: **FT:** Coarse; **WN:** Harwood Hall; **WT:** Lake (Still); **F. Size:** 6 Acres; **W. Size:** 4 Acres. **Location:** **Nr. Rd:** Harwood Hall lane; **Main Rd:** B1421; **Rail:** Cranham.
Ref: FH2125

HASTINGS LAKE

Hastings Lake, Hastings, **SUSSEX (EAST)**, TN, **England**.
Contact/s: **Mr Peter Maclean** (Hon Secretary), 37 Collier Rd, Hastings, Sussex (East), TN34 3JR.
(T) 01424 715218
Profile: **FT:** Coarse; **WN:** Hastings; **WT:** Lake (Still).
Ref: FH2126

HATCHERY HOUSE TROUT LAKES

Hatchery House Trout Lakes, Hatchery House, Mill Lane, Bury St Edmunds, **SUFFOLK**, IP29 5BT, **England**.
Contact/s: **Mrs Chris Paine** (Manager),

MacRae Farms Limited, Hatchery House, Mill Lane, Barrow, Bury St Edmonds, IP29 5BT.
(T) 01284 810300 (F) 01284 810300
Profile: **FT:** Game; **WN:** Hatchery; **WT:** Lake (Still) **W. Size:** 2 Acres. **Location:** **Nr. Rd:** Barrow; **Main Rd:** Bury Road; **Rail:** Bury St Edmonds.
Ref: FH2127

HATCHET POND

Hatchet Pond, Beaulieu, Brockenhurst, **HAMPSHIRE**, SO42, **England**.
Contact/s: Manager, Recreation Section, Forestry Commission Office, The Queen's House, Lyndhurst, SO43 7NH.
(T) 023 80283141 (F) 023 80283929
Mr Jonathan Cook (New Forest Keeper), Stockely Cottage, Beaulieu Rd, Brockenhurst, Hampshire.
(T) 01590 623698
Profile: **FT:** Coarse; **WN:** Hatchet Pond; **WT:** Lake (Still) **W. Size:** 26 Acres. **Location:** **Nr. Rd:** B3055, Beaulieu to Brockenhurst; **Main Rd:** M27, junction 1; **Rail:** Brockenhurst.
Ref: FH2128

HATCHLAND TROUT FISHERY

Hatchland Trout Fishery, Greyshot Lane, Rattery, South Brent, **DEVON**, TQ10 9LL, **England**.
Contact/s: **Mr Malcolm Davies**.
(T) 01364 73500
Profile: **FT:** Combination; **WN:** Harbourne; **WT:** Combination (Still & Moving). **Location:** **Nr. Rd:** A385; **Main Rd:** A385; **Rail:** Totnes.
Ref: FH2129

HATFIELD BROADWATER

Hatfield Broadwater, Essendon, Hatfield, **HERTFORDSHIRE**, AL9, **England**.
Contact/s: E F Denchfield (Secretary), Hatfield and District AS, 44 Stockbreach Rd, Hatfield, Hertfordshire.
Profile: **FT:** Coarse; **WN:** Hatfield; **WT:** Lake (Still) **W. Size:** 7 Acres. **Location:** **Nr. Rd:** B158 River Lea; **Main Rd:** A414.
Ref: FH2130

HATFIELD FOREST LAKE

Hatfield Forest Lake, The Shell House, Takeley, Bishops Stortford, **HERTFORDSHIRE**, CM23, **England**.
Contact/s: Warden, The National Trust, Hatfield Estate Office, Takeley, Bishop's Stortford, CM22 6NE.
(T) 01279 870678 (F) 01279 871938
Profile: **FT:** Coarse; **WN:** Hatfield Forest; **WT:** Lake (Still). **Location:** **Nr. Rd:** A1250; **Main Rd:** M11.
Ref: FH2131

HATSWELL

Hatswell, Lower Washfield, Tiverton, **DEVON**, EX16 9PE, **England**.
Profile: **FT:** Game; **WN:** Exe; **WT:** River (Moving).
Ref: FH2132

HATTON PARK POND

Hatton Park Pond, Longstanton, Cambridge, **CAMBRIDGESHIRE**, CB, **England**.
Profile: **FT:** Coarse; **WN:** Hatton Park Pool; **WT:** Gravel Pit (Still) **W. Size:** 2 Acres. **Location:** Nr. Rd: Station Road. £Fr
Ref: FH2133

HATTON TROUT LAKE

Hatton Trout Lake, Hatton, Wragby, Market Rasen, **LINCOLNSHIRE**, LN8 5QE, **England**.
Contact/s: **Mr E Oxley** (Manager).
(T) 01673 858682
Profile: **FT:** Coarse; **WN:** Hatton Trout; **WT:** Lake (Still) **W. Size:** 2 Acres. **Location:** **Nr. Rd:** Lincoln to Skegness; **Main Rd:** A158.
Ref: FH2134

HAUGH OF GRANDTULLY BEAT

Haugh Of Grandtully Beat, Aberfeldy, **PERTH AND KINROSS**, PH15, **Scotland**.
(W) www.fishingnet.com/beats/haughgrandtully.htm
Ms Em Honeyman (Manager), Wade Newsagents, 31 Bank St, Aberfeldy, Perth and Kinross, PH15 2BB.
(T) 01887 820397
Profile: **FT:** Combination; **WN:** Tullpowrie, Hall, Church and above Falls; **WT:** Pool (Still).
Ref: FH2135

HAVEN

Haven, Stainforth, Doncaster, **YORKSHIRE (SOUTH)**, DN7 5, **England**.
Contact/s: Fishery Manager.
(T) 01032 842857
Manager.
(T) 01032 350403
Profile: **FT:** Coarse; **WN:** Haven; **WT:** Lake (Still).
Ref: FH2136

HAVERHOLME PARK

Haverholme Park, Manor St, Ruskington, Sleaford, **LINCOLNSHIRE**, NG34 9EN, **England**.
Contact/s: Fishery Manager.
(T) 01526 832125
Profile: **FT:** Coarse; **WN:** Haverholme Park; **WT:** Lake (Still). **Location:** **Nr. Rd:** Manor Street; **Main Rd:** A153; **Rail:** Ruskington.
Ref: FH2137

HAVERINGLAND HALL PARK

Haveringland Hall Park, Haveringland, Cawston, Norwich, **NORFOLK**, NR10 4PN, **England**.
(W) www.haveringlandhall.co.uk/
Contact/s: **Mr Michael Ward** (Fishery Manager).
(T) 01603 871302 (F) 01603 879223
(E) haveringland@claranet.com
Profile: **FT:** Coarse; **WN:** Haveringland; **WT:** Lake (Still); **F. Size:** 120 Acres; **W. Size:** 12 Acres. **Location:** **Nr. Rd:** B1149; **Main Rd:** B1145. £Fr
Ref: FH2138

HAWESWATER

Haweswater, Eden, Penrith, **CUMBRIA**, CA10, **England**.
Contact/s: **Mr John Newton** (Secretary).
(T) 01539 728341
Mr Roy Rhodes (Conservation, Access and Recreation Manager), Rivington Water Treatment Works, Bolton Rd, Horwich, Bolton, BL6 7RN.
(T) 01204 664300
Profile: **FT:** Combination; **WN:** Haweswater; **WT:** Combination (Still & Moving). **Location:** **Rail:** Shap. £Fr
Ref: FH2139

HAWESWATER RESERVOIR

Haweswater Reservoir, Hartsop, Ambleside, **CUMBRIA**, LA22, **England**.
Contact/s: **Mr Chris Sodo** (Hon Treasurer), Windermere, Ambleside and District Angling Association, Ecclerigg Court, Ecclerigg, Windermere, LA23 1LQ.
(T) 01539 445083
Profile: **FT:** Coarse; **WN:** Haweswater; **WT:** Reservoir (Still) **W. Size:** 34 Acres. **Location:** **Nr. Rd:** A592 Kirkstone Pass Road.
Ref: FH2140

HAWKESBURY FISHERY

Hawkesbury Fishery, Bedworth, **WARWICKSHIRE**, CV12, **England**.
Contact/s: **Mr Richard Grant**.
(T) 024 76491144
Profile: **FT:** Coarse; **WN:** Hawkesbury Fishery; **WT:** Lake (Still). **Location:** **Nr. Rd:** B4113 Coventry to Bedworth; **Main Rd:** M6, junction 3.
Ref: FH2141

HAWKHURST FISH FARM

Hawkhurst Fish Farm, Hastings Rd, Hawkhurst, Cranbrook, **KENT**, TN18 4RT, **England**.
Contact/s: **Mr Tony Wilkinson** (Owner).
(T) 01580 753813 (F) 01580 754182
Ms Arlene (Booking TR).
(T) 01580 753813 (F) 01580 754182
Profile: **FT:** Combination; **WN:** Hawkhurst Fish Farm; **WT:** Combination (Still); **F. Size:** 42 Acres; **W. Size:** 21 Acres. **Location:** **Nr. Rd:** B2244; **Main Rd:** A21; **Rail:** Etchingham.
Ref: FH2142

HAWKINS POND

Hawkins Pond, Horsham, **SURREY**, RH1, **England**.
Contact/s: **G Kempson**, 11 Clarence Rd, Horsham, Sussex (West).
Profile: **FT:** Coarse; **WN:** Hawkins; **WT:** Pond (Still).
Ref: FH2143

HAWKRIDGE RESERVOIR

Hawkridge Reservoir, Spaxton, Bridgwater, **SOMERSET**, TA, **England**.
Contact/s: Customer Services, Wessex Water, Billing Ctre, Clevedon Walk, Nailsea, Bristol, BS48 1WW. **(M)** 03453 00600
Mr Gary Howe (Ranger).
(T) 01278 671840 (F) 01278 671840
Mrs Sally Prizii (Club Membership Secretary).
(T) 01823 480710
Profile: **FT:** Game; **WN:** Hawkridge; **WT:** Reservoir (Still) **W. Size:** 32 Acres. **Location:** **Nr. Rd:** Spaxton; **Main Rd:** A38 south; **Rail:** Bridgwater.
Ref: FH2144

HAWKSHEAD TROUT FISHING

Hawkshead Trout Fishing, The Boat House, House Ridding Wood, Hawkshead, Ambleside, **CUMBRIA**, LA22 0QF, **England**.
Contact/s: **Mr David Coleman** (Fishery Manager).
(T) 01539 436541 (F) 01539 436541
(E) trout@hawkshead.demon.co.uk
Profile: **FT:** Game; **WN:** Hawkshead; **WT:** Lake (Still). **Location:** **Main Rd:** House Ridding Wood.
Ref: FH2145

HAWKSTONE PARK LAKE

Hawkstone Park Lake, Hawk Lake Trust, 4 Soulton Cres, Wem, Shrewsbury, **SHROPSHIRE**, SY4 5HY, **England**.
Contact/s: **Mr P Johnson**.
Profile: **FT:** Coarse; **WN:** Hawkstone Park; **WT:** Lake (Still).
Ref: FH2146

HAWLEY LAKE

Hawley Lake, Camberley, **HAMPSHIRE**, GU14 9, **England**.
Contact/s: Manager, Noel's Fishing Tackle, 314 Fernhill Rd, Farnborough, Hampshire, GU14 9EE.
(T) 01276 32488
Profile: **FT:** Coarse; **WN:** Hawley; **WT:** Gravel Pit (Still).
Ref: FH2147

HAY-A-PARK

Hay A Park, Knaresborough, **YORKSHIRE (NORTH)**, HG5, **England**.
Contact/s: **Mr M Johnson** (Owner), Johnson Fishing Tackle, 2 Briggate, Knaresborough, Yorkshire (North), HG5 8BH.
(T) 01423 863065
Profile: **FT:** Coarse; **WN:** Hay A Park; **WT:** Gravel Pit (Still).
Ref: FH2148

HAYCASTLE TROUT FISHERY

Haycastle Trout Fishery, Haycastle, Haverfordwest, **PEMBROKESHIRE**, SA62 5PU, **Wales**.
Contact/s: **Mr Robert Griffiths** (Owner).
(T) 01348 840393
Profile: **FT:** Game; **WN:** Haycastle; **WT:** Lake (Still) **W. Size:** 2 Acres.
Ref: FH2149

HAYCASTLE WATER

Haycastle Water, Hay-on-Wye, Hereford, **HEREFORDSHIRE**, HR3, **England**.
Contact/s: Mr Bryan Wigington (Local Agent), Hay-on-Wye Fishermens Association, Flat 2, Pembertons, 4 Hightown, Hay-on-Wye, Hereford, HR3 5AE.
(T) 01497 820545
Profile: FT: Combination; **WN:** Haycastle Water; **WT:** River (Moving) **W. Size:** 1600 Metres.
Ref: FH2150

HAYDAN FISHERY

Haydan Fishery, Norley Rd, Norley, Warrington, **CHESHIRE**, WA6 6LJ, **England**.
Contact/s: Mr John Farmer.
(T) 01928 788340
Profile: FT: Coarse; **WN:** Haydan Fishery; **WT:** Lake (Still) **W. Size:** 1 Acre.
Ref: FH2151

HAYE FARM FISHERY

Haye Farm Fishery, Bewdley, **WORCESTERSHIRE**, DY12, **England**.
Contact/s: Mr Stuart Norgrove (Haye Farm Manager).
(T) 01299 403371
Profile: FT: Coarse; **WN:** Haye Farm Fishery; **WT:** Pond (Still). **Location: Main Rd:** B4194; **Rail:** Bewdley.
Ref: FH2152

HAYES TROUT FISHERY

Hayes Trout Fishery, Hayes Street Farm, Hayes Lane, Bromley, **KENT**, BR2 7LB, **England**.
Contact/s: Mr George Hoeltschi, Hayes Trout Fishery, Hayes Lane, Bromley, BR2 7LB.
(T) 020 84621186
Profile: FT: Game; **WN:** Hayes; **WT:** Lake (Still); **F. Size:** 3 Acres; **W. Size:** 3 Acres. **Location: Nr. Rd:** Hayes Street; **Main Rd:** A21; **Rail:** Hayes Bromley.
Ref: FH2153

HAYESWATER RESERVOIR

Hayeswater Reservoir, Eden, Ambleside, **CUMBRIA**, LA22, **England**.
Contact/s: Mr Chris Sodo (Hon Treasurer), Windermere, Ambleside and District Angling Association, Ecclerigg Court, Ecclerigg, Windermere, LA23 1LQ.
(T) 01539 445083
Mr J Newton (Secretary), 3 Lumley Rd, Kendal, Cumbria.
Mr Roy Rhodes (Conservation, Access and Recreation Manager), Rivington Water Treatment Works, Bolton Rd, Horwich, Bolton, BL6 7RN.
(T) 01204 664300
Profile: FT: Game; **WN:** Hayeswater; **WT:** Reservoir (Still) **W. Size:** 34 Acres. **Location: Nr. Rd:** A592 Kirkstone Pass Road.
Ref: FH2154

HAYFIELD LAKES

Hayfield Lakes, Hayfield Lane, Auckley, Doncaster, **YORKSHIRE (SOUTH)**, DN9 3NP, **Scotland**.
Contact/s: Mr Robin Goforth (Manager).
(T) 01302 864555 **(F)** 01302 863419
Profile: FT: Coarse; **WN:** Hayfield and Adams; **WT:** Lake (Still) **W. Size:** 8 Acres. **Location: Nr. Rd:** Hayfield Lane; **Main Rd:** A638; **Rail:** Doncaster.
Ref: FH2155

HAYLE CAUSEWAY

Hayle Causeway, Hayle, **CORNWALL**, TR27, **England**.
Contact/s: Manager, The County Angler, 39 Cross St, Camborne, TR14 8ES.
(T) 01209 718490
Profile: FT: Coarse; **WN:** Hayle; **WT:** Stream (Moving).
Ref: FH2156

HAYLIE FISHERY

Haylie Fishery, Haylie Brae, Largs, **AYRSHIRE (NORTH)**, KA30 8JA, **Scotland**.
Contact/s: Mr John Weir (Owner).
(T) 01475 676005
Mr Ulus Kokbourne (Manager).
Profile: FT: Game; **WN:** Haylie Fishery; **WT:** Loch (Still).
Ref: FH2157

HAYRICK LAKES

Hayrick Lakes, Graig Rhymney Farm, Tir-Phil, Tredegar, **BLAENAU GWENT**, NP24 6LA, **Wales**.
Contact/s: Mr Jeff James (Fishery Manager).
(T) 01443 829262
Profile: FT: Game; **WN:** Hayrick; **WT:** Lake (Still). **Location: Main Rd:** A469.
Ref: FH2158

HAYSCASTLE TROUT FISHERY

Hayscastle Trout Fishery, Upper Hayscastle Farm, Hayscastle, Haverfordwest, **PEMBROKESHIRE**, SA62, **Wales**.
Contact/s: Mr Robert Griffiths (Owner).
(T) 01348 840393
Profile: FT: Game; **WN:** Hayscastle Trout Fishery; **WT:** Lake (Still) **W. Size:** 3 Acres.
Ref: FH2159

HAYSDEN COUNTRY PARK

Haysden Country Park, Lower Haysden Rd, Tonbridge, **KENT**, TN1, **England**.
Contact/s: Mr Alex Heggie (Membership Secretary), Little Lucy's Farmhouse, Lower St, Hildenborough, Tonbridge, TN11 8PT.
(T) 01732 832352 **(F)** 01732 832352
Mr Tom Creasey (Hon Secretary), 3 Invicta Flats, Great Brooms Rd, Tunbridge Wells, Kent, TN4 9DD.
(T) 01892 520520
Profile: FT: Coarse; **WN:** Haysden Country Park; **WT:** Combination (Still & Moving); **F. Size:** 160 Acres; **W. Size:** 75 Acres. **Location: Nr. Rd:** Lower Haysden Lane, under A21 flyover; **Main Rd:** Under A21 Flyover, off A26; **Rail:** Tonbridge.
Ref: FH2160

HAYWARDS HEATH RIVER

River Haywards Heath, Haywards Heath, **SUSSEX (WEST)**, RH17, **England**.
Contact/s: Mr J Kenward (Secretary), Haywards Heath and District Angling Society, 60 Franklyn Rd, Haywards Heath, Sussex (West), RH16 4DH.
(T) 01444 452572
Profile: FT: Game; **WN:** Haywards Heath; **WT:** River (Moving) **W. Size:** 18400 Metres. **Location: Nr. Rd:** Linfield to Newick.
Ref: FH2161

HAZEL HALL FARM FISHING

Hazel Hall Farm Fishing, Clapham, Northallerton, **YORKSHIRE (NORTH)**, DL7, **England**.
Profile: FT: Coarse; **WN:** Hazel Hall Farm Fishing; **WT:** Lake (Still).
Ref: FH2162

HAZELCOPSE LAKES

Hazelcopse Lakes, Knowle Lane, Rudgwick, Horsham, **SUSSEX (WEST)**, RH12 3AF, **England**.
Contact/s: Mr Ian Welch (Angling Manager).
(T) 01403 822878
Profile: FT: Game; **WN:** Hazelcopse; **WT:** Lake (Still). **Location: Nr. Rd:** Knowle Lane.
Ref: FH2163

HAZELCOURT PONDS

Hazelcourt Ponds, Llysworney, Kelbridge, Cowbridge, **GLAMORGAN (VALE OF)**, CF71, **Wales**.
Contact/s: Manager.
(T) 01443 229601
Profile: FT: Coarse; **WN:** Hazelcourt; **WT:** Pond (Still). **Location: Nr. Rd:** Pentre Meyrick Cross-Roads on B4268; **Main Rd:** A48.
Ref: FH2164

HAZELHEAD LAKE

Hazelhead Lake, Newgate Foot Farm, Saltersgate, Pickering, **YORKSHIRE (NORTH)**, YO18 7NR, **England**.
Contact/s: Mrs A M Johnson.
(T) 01751 460215 **(F)** 01751 460215
Profile: FT: Game; **WN:** Hazelhead; **WT:** Lake (Still) **W. Size:** 2 Acres. **Location: Main Rd:** A169; **Rail:** Malton.
Ref: FH2165

HEADSHAW FISHERY

Headshaw Fishery, Headshaw Farm, Ashkirk, Selkirk, **SCOTTISH BORDERS**, TD7, **Scotland**.
Contact/s: Ms Nancy Hunter.
(T) 01750 32233
Profile: FT: Game; **WN:** Headshaw; **WT:** Loch (Still) **W. Size:** 17 Acres.
Ref: FH2166

HEAPEY NO 1

Heapey No 1, Chorley, **LANCASHIRE**, PR, **England**.
(W) www.wiganaa.f9.co.uk
Contact/s: Mr Gerry Wilson (Hon Secretary), Wigan and District Angling Association, 11 Guildford Avenue, Chorley, Lancashire, PR6 8TG.
(T) 01257 265905
(E) gerry@wiganna.freeserve.co.uk
Profile: FT: Coarse; **WN:** Heapey No 1; **WT:** Lake (Still) **W. Size:** 7 Acres. **Location: Main Rd:** M61, junction 8.
Ref: FH2167

HEAPEY NO 2

Heapey No 2, Chorley, **LANCASHIRE**, PR, **England**.
(W) www.wiganaa.f9.co.uk
Contact/s: Mr Gerry Wilson (Hon Secretary), Wigan and District Angling Association, 11 Guildford Avenue, Chorley, Lancashire, PR6 8TG.
(T) 01257 265905
(E) gerry@wiganna.freeserve.co.uk
Profile: FT: Coarse; **WN:** Heapey No 2; **WT:** Lake (Still) **W. Size:** 9 Acres. **Location: Main Rd:** M61, junction 8.
Ref: FH2168

HEAPEY NO 3

Heapey No 3, Chorley, **LANCASHIRE**, PR, **England**.
(W) www.wiganaa.f9.co.uk
Contact/s: Mr Gerry Wilson (Hon Secretary), Wigan and District Angling Association, 11 Guildford Avenue, Chorley, Lancashire, PR6 8TG.
(T) 01257 265905
(E) gerry@wiganna.freeserve.co.uk
Profile: FT: Coarse; **WN:** Heapey No 3; **WT:** Lake (Still) **W. Size:** 5 Acres. **Location: Main Rd:** M61, junction 8.
Ref: FH2169

HEAPEY NO 6

Heapey No 6, Chorley, **LANCASHIRE**, PR, **England**.
(W) www.wiganaa.f9.co.uk
Contact/s: Mr Gerry Wilson (Hon Secretary), Wigan and District Angling Association, 11 Guildford Avenue, Chorley, Lancashire, PR6 8TG.
(T) 01257 265905
(E) gerry@wiganna.freeserve.co.uk
Profile: FT: Coarse; **WN:** Heapey No 6; **WT:** Lake (Still) **W. Size:** 1 Acre. **Location: Main Rd:** M61, junction 8.
Ref: FH2170

HEART OF ENGLAND FISHERY

Heart Of England Fishery, Thenford, Banbury, **OXFORDSHIRE**, OX17 2BX, **England**.
Contact/s: Mr Alec Bond (Manager).
(T) 01295 711587
Profile: FT: Game; **WN:** Heart Of England Fishery; **WT:** Lake (Still) **W. Size:** 4 Acres. **Location: Main Rd:** M40, junction 11.
Ref: FH2171

HEATH VALE POND
Heath Vale Pond, Hampstead Heath, Hampstead, London, **LONDON (GREATER)**, NW3, **England**.
Profile: FT: Coarse; WN: Heath Vale; WT: Pond (Still). Location: Nr. Rd: A502; Main Rd: A41, A1. £Fr
Ref: FH2172

HEATHCOTE LAKE
Heathcote Lake, Heathcote, Warwick, **WARWICKSHIRE**, CV34 6, **England**.
Contact/s: Mr George Moreton (Manager), Lower Heathcote Farm, Harbury Lane, Heathcote, Warwick, CV34 6SL.
(T) 01926 336814or426983
Profile: FT: Game; WN: Heathcote; WT: Reservoir (Still) W. Size: 3 Acres.
Ref: FH2173

HEATHERYFORD FISHERY
Heatheryford Fishery, Kinross, **PERTH AND KINROSS**, KY13 0NQ, **Scotland**.
Contact/s: Mr John Cairns.
(T) 01577 864212 (F) 01577 864920
Profile: FT: Game; WN: Heatheryford Fishery; WT: Gravel Pit (Still); F. Size: 40 Acres; W. Size: 10 Acres. Location: Nr. Rd: A977; Main Rd: M90, junction 6; Rail: Inverkeithing.
Ref: FH2174

HEATHFIELD POOL
Heathfield Pool, Heathfield Rd, Darlaston, Walsall, **MIDLANDS (WEST)**, **England**.
Contact/s: Mr Fred Crump (Owner), FC Services Retail, 159 Heath Lane, West Bromwich, Midlands (West), B71 2BL.
(T) 0121 5675100
Profile: FT: Coarse; WN: Heathfield; WT: Lake (Still); F. Size: 3 Acres; W. Size: 2 Acres. Location: Nr. Rd: Heathfield Road.
Ref: FH2175

HEATON PARK
Heaton Park, Sheepfoot Lane, Meade Hill, Prestwich, Manchester, **MANCHESTER (GREATER)**, M25, **England**.
Contact/s: Mr Frank Hamer.
(T) 0161 7952087
Mr John Jeffreys (Secretary), Heaton Park Angling Club, Hook and Line Fishing Tackle, 375 Victoria Avenue, Manchester, M9 8WQ.
(T) 0161 7206577 (F) 0161 7206577
Profile: FT: Coarse; WN: Heaton Park; WT: Lake (Still); F. Size: 600 Acres; W. Size: 9 Acres. Location: Nr. Rd: Sheepfoot Lane, Middleton Road, Bury Old Road; Main Rd: B1230.
Ref: FH2176

HEDNESFORD ROAD LAKE
Hednesford Road Lake, Rugeley, **STAFFORDSHIRE**, WS15, **England**.
Contact/s: Mr Terry Morgan.
(T) 01543 502995
Profile: FT: Coarse; WN: Hednesford Road; WT: Lake (Still) W. Size: 4 Acres. Location: Main Rd: A460 to Cannock.
Ref: FH2177

HELLMOOR LOCH
Hellmoor Loch, Hawick, **SCOTTISH BORDERS**, TD9, **Scotland**.
Contact/s: Mr Penman (Manager), Pet Store, 1 Union St, Hawick, Scottish Borders, TD9 9LF.
(T) 01450 373543 (F) 01450 373543
Mr Eric Stewart (Secretary/Treasurer), Hawick Angling Club, 5 Sandbed, Hawick, Scottish Borders, TD9 0HE.
(T) 01450 373771
Profile: FT: Game; WN: Hellmoor; WT: Loch (Still) W. Size: 14 Acres. Location: Nr. Rd: B711; Main Rd: A7; Rail: Carlisle.
Ref: FH2178

HEMLINGTON LAKE
Hemlington Lake, Hemlington, Middlesbrough, **CLEVELAND**, TS, **England**.
Contact/s: Mr John Ferry (Centre Manager), Hemlington and Lake Recreation Ctre, Cass House Rd, Hemlington, Middlesbrough, TS8 9QW.
(T) 01642 596546
Profile: FT: Coarse; WN: Hemlington; WT: Lake (Still) W. Size: 8 Acres.
Ref: FH2179

HENDRE LAKE
Hendre Lake, Cardiff, CF, **Wales**.
Contact/s: Manager, Garry Evans Fishing Tackle, 105-109 Whitchurch Rd, Cardiff, Glamorgan (Vale of), CF14 3JQ.
(T) 029 20619828or20692968
Profile: FT: Coarse; WN: Hendre; WT: Lake (Still).
Ref: FH2180

HENDY FISHERY
Hendy Fishery, Hendy, Llanybydder, **CARMARTHENSHIRE**, SA40, **Wales**.
(W) www.fishing-in-wales.co.uk/llandysul-aa/beat7
Contact/s: Mr Artie Jones (Hon Secretary), Llandysul Angling Association, Glas-y-Dorlan, Llyn-y-Fran Rd, Llandysul, SA44 4JW.
(T) 01559 362317
Profile: FT: Game; WN: Teifi; WT: River (Moving) W. Size: 2000 Metres.
Ref: FH2181

HENFOLD LAKES FISHERY
Henfold Lakes Fishery, Henfold Lane, Beare Green, Dorking, **SURREY**, RH5 4RW, **England**.
Contact/s: Mr James Atkinson (Owner).
(T) 01306 631164or885725 (F) 01306 631164
Ms Wendy Cox (Clubhouse Manager).
(T) 01306 885725 (F) 01306 631164
Profile: FT: Coarse; WN: Henfold Lakes Fishery; WT: Combination (Still & Moving); F. Size: 95 Acres; W. Size: 4 Acres. Location: Nr. Rd: Henfold Lane; Main Rd: A24; Rail: Beare Green.
Ref: FH2182

HENHAM DAIRY POND
Henham Dairy Pond, Henham, Beccles, **SUFFOLK**, NR34, **England**.
Contact/s: Fishery Manager.
(T) 01502 578762
Profile: FT: Coarse; WN: Henham; WT: Pond (Still).
Ref: FH2183

HENLEAZE LAKE
Henleaze Lake, 63 Hill View, Henleaze, Bristol, BS, **England**.
Contact/s: Fishery Manager.
(T) 01179 623748
Profile: FT: Coarse; WN: Avon; WT: Lake (Still) W. Size: 3 Acres.
Ref: FH2184

HENLOW GRANGE
Henlow Grange, Henlow, **BEDFORDSHIRE**, SG, **England**.
Profile: FT: Coarse; WN: Henlow Grange; WT: Combination (Still) W. Size: 17 Acres. Location: Nr. Rd: Arlesey to Henlow; Main Rd: A1, junction 10.
Ref: FH2185

HENMORE (RIVER)
Henmore (River), Long Doles Farm, Mayfield, Ashbourne, **DERBYSHIRE**, **England**.
Contact/s: Mr John Turner (Hon Secretary), Prince Albert Angling Society, 15 Pexhill Drive, Macclesfield, Cheshire, SK10 3LP.
(T) 01625 422010
Profile: FT: Game; WN: Henmore; WT: River (Moving) W. Size: 1000 Metres. Location: Nr. Rd: Watery Lane; Main Rd: A52; Rail: Ashbourne.
Ref: FH2186

HENRY STREETER LAKE
Henry Streeter Lake, Cranford, Hounslow, London, **LONDON (GREATER)**, TW5 9, **England**.
Contact/s: Mrs V Sivyer (Secretary), Feltham Piscatorial Society, 96 Raleigh Rd, Feltham, Middlesex, TW13 4LP.
(T) 020 8909005
Profile: FT: Coarse; WN: Henry Streeter Lake; WT: Lake (Still).
Ref: FH2187

HEPSTE (STREAM)
Hepste (Stream), Glynneath, Neath, **NEATH PORT TALBOT**, SA, **Wales**.
Contact/s: Mr Gareth Evans (Treasurer), 21 Godfrey Avenue, Glynneath, Neath, Glamorgan (Vale of), SA11 5HF.
(T) 01639 721301
Mr Tony May (Secretary).
(T) 01685 871337
Mrs R Jones (Chairperson).
(T) 01639 720927
Profile: FT: Game; WN: Hepste; WT: Stream (Moving) W. Size: 7500 Metres. Location: Main Rd: A465; Rail: Neath.
Ref: FH2188

HERMITAGE LAKES
Hermitage Lakes, Common Farm, Hermitage, Dorchester, **DORSET**, DT2 7BB, **England**.
Contact/s: Mr Nigel Richardson.
(T) 01963 210556
Profile: FT: Combination; WN: Hermiage; WT: Lake (Still) W. Size: 2 Acres. Location: Main Rd: A352; Rail: Sherborne.
Ref: FH2189

HERON BROOK FISHERY
Heron Brook Fishery, Tettenhall, Wolverhampton, **MIDLANDS (WEST)**, WV, **England**.
Contact/s: Mr Don Smallman.
(T) 01902 677402after6pm
Profile: FT: Coarse; WN: Heron Brook Fishery; WT: Lake (Still).
Ref: FH2190

HERONBROOK FISHERY
Heronbrook Fishery, Slindon, Eccleshall, Stafford, **STAFFORDSHIRE**, ST5 8HQ, **England**.
Contact/s: Mr Neil Dale (Owner), 7 Falmouth Avenue, Weeping Cross, Stafford, ST17 0JQ.
(T) 01785 613666
Profile: FT: Coarse; WN: Heronbrook Fishery; WT: Combination (Still). Location: Nr. Rd: A519; Main Rd: M6, junction 14 or 15; Rail: Stafford.
Ref: FH2191

HERONS MEAD
Herons Mead, Orby, Skegness, **LINCOLNSHIRE**, PE24, **England**.
Contact/s: Jane.
(T) 01754 873357
Profile: FT: Coarse; WN: Herons Mead; WT: Lake (Still).
Ref: FH2192

HERONSVIEW FISHERIES
Heronsview Fisheries, Chilham Castle Carp Syndicate, Drovers End, Pudding Lane, Ash, Canterbury, **KENT**, CT3 2EJ, **England**.
Contact/s: Mr Albert Brown (Owner).
(T) 01304 812651or01843296031
Profile: FT: Coarse; WN: Heronsview Fisheries; WT: Lake (Still) W. Size: 5 Acres. Location: Nr. Rd: A252.
Ref: FH2193

HERRIOTS POOL
Herriots Pool, Droitwich, Hereford, **HEREFORDSHIRE**, HR, **England**.
Contact/s: Fishery Manager.
(T) 01905 770848
Manager, Fishermans Friend, Woodland Veiw, Haye Lane, Ombersley, Droitwich, WR9 0EJ.
(T) 01905 621521

Profile: **FT:** Coarse; **WN:** Herriot's; **WT:** Pool (Still) **W. Size:** 1 Acre. **Location:** **Nr. Rd:** B4090; **Main Rd:** M5, junction 5. **£Fr**
Ref: FH2194

HESKIN OLD FARM FISHERY

Heskin Old Farm Fishery, Halfpenny Lane, Heskin, Chorley, **LANCASHIRE**, PR7, **England**.
Contact/s:
Profile: **FT:** Coarse; **WN:** Heskin Old Farm Fishery; **WT:** Lake (Still). **Location:** **Nr. Rd:** Halfpenny Lane; **Main Rd:** A681.
Ref: FH2195

HESSAY POND

Hessay Pond, Holly House Farm, Hessay, York, **YORKSHIRE (NORTH)**, YO26 8JN, **England**.
Contact/s: **Mr E Wilkin** (Manager).
(T) 01904 738204
Profile: **FT:** Coarse; **WN:** Hessay; **WT:** Pond (Still). **Location:** **Nr. Rd:** Long Marston to Hessay; **Main Rd:** A59 West of York.
Ref: FH2196

HEVINGHAM LAKES

Hevingham Lakes, The Heath, Hevingham, Norwich, **NORFOLK**, NR10 5QL, **England**.
Contact/s: **Mr Clive Mathewson** (Owner).
(T) 01603 754368
Profile: **FT:** Coarse; **WN:** Hevingham; **WT:** Lake (Still). **Location:** **Nr. Rd:** B1149; **Main Rd:** A140; **Rail:** Thorpe.
Ref: FH2197

HEXDEN CHANNEL

Hexden Channel, Potmans Heath, Wittersham, Tenterden, **KENT**, TN30, **England**.
Contact/s: **Mr Peter Maclean** (Hon Secretary), 37 Collier Rd, Hastings, Sussex (East), TN34 3JR.
(T) 01424 715218
Profile: **FT:** Coarse; **WN:** Hexden Channel; **WT:** River (Moving). **Location:** **Main Rd:** Moons Green.
Ref: FH2198

HEXHAM FISHERIES

Hexham Fisheries, Hexham, **NORTHUMBERLAND**, NE46 1UB, **England**.
Contact/s: Manager, M R Tackle, 14 Market St, Hexham, Northumberland, NE46 3NU.
(T) 01434 606988
Mr Clifford Watt (Fishery Manager).
(T) 01434 609725
Profile: **FT:** Game; **WN:** Hexham Fisheries; **WT:** Lake (Still).
Ref: FH2199

HEYFORD FISHERY

Heyford Fishery, Weedon Rd, Nether Heyford, Northampton, **NORTHAMPTONSHIRE**, NN7 3LG, **England**.
Contact/s: **Mr Ken Silverlock**.
(T) 01327 340002 **(F)** 01327 341697
Profile: **FT:** Coarse; **WN:** Snake, & Acorn Lake; **WT:** Lake (Still); **F. Size:** 40 Acres. **Location:** **Nr. Rd:** Weedon Road; **Main Rd:** A45, A5; **Rail:** Northampton.
Ref: FH2200

HEYFORD LAKES

Heyford Lakes, Standlake, Witney, **OXFORDSHIRE**, OX8, **England**.
Contact/s: **Mr Graham State** (Manager), States Fishing Tackle, 19 Fettiplace Rd, Witney, Oxfordshire, OX8 5AP.
(T) 01993 702587
Profile: **FT:** Coarse; **WN:** Specimen Lake, Bents Pool, and Surman Lake; **WT:** Gravel Pit (Still). **Location:** **Nr. Rd:** B4449.
Ref: FH2201

HICKLING BROAD

Hickling Broad, Hickling, Norwich, **NORFOLK**, NR12, **England**.
Contact/s: Fishery Manager.
(T) 01692 598314
Profile: **FT:** Coarse; **WN:** Hickling; **WT:** River (Moving).
Ref: FH2202

HIDDEN VALLEY

Hidden Valley, Tredidon, St Thomas, Launceston, **CORNWALL**, PL15 8SJ, **England**.
Contact/s: **Mr Peter Jones**.
(T) 01566 86463
Profile: **FT:** Coarse; **WN:** Hidden Valley; **WT:** Lake (Still) **W. Size:** 2 Acres. **Location:** **Nr. Rd:** A395; **Main Rd:** A30.
Ref: FH2203

HIGH ARNSIDE TARN

High Arnside Tarn, Hartsop, Ambleside, **CUMBRIA**, LA22, **England**.
Contact/s: Manager, The National Trust, North West Regional Office, The Hollens, Grasmere, Ambleside, LA22 9QZ.
(T) 01539 435599 **(F)** 01539 435353
Profile: **FT:** Game; **WN:** High Arnside; **WT:** Tarn (Still). **Location:** **Main Rd:** A592 Kirkstone Pass Road.
Ref: FH2204

HIGH CLAYS FARM

High Clays Farm, Southam, **WARWICKSHIRE**, CV47, **England**.
Contact/s: High Clays Farm Manager.
(T) 01926 814577
Profile: **FT:** Coarse; **WN:** High Clays Farm; **WT:** Lake (Still) **W. Size:** 4 Acres.
Ref: FH2205

HIGH FLYER LAKE

High Flyer Lake, Ely, **CAMBRIDGESHIRE**, CB, **England**.
Contact/s: **Mr Ken Gammon** (Fishery Manager).
(T) 01353 720141
Profile: **FT:** Coarse; **WN:** High Flyer; **WT:** Lake (Still). **Location:** **Nr. Rd:** A10.
Ref: FH2206

HIGH MAYNARD RESERVOIR

High Maynard Reservoir, Tottenham, London, **LONDON (GREATER)**, N17, **England**.
Contact/s: Amenity and Recreation Officer, Thames Water, Nugent House, Vasten Rd, Reading, Berkshire.
(T) 01734 593391
Mr Chris King, Walthamstow Reservoir Group, Thames Water Gatehouse, 2 Forest Rd, Tottenham, London, N17 9NH.
(T) 020 88081527
Profile: **FT:** Coarse; **WN:** High Maynard; **WT:** Reservoir (Still) **W. Size:** 45 Acres. **Location:** **Nr. Rd:** Forest Road; **Main Rd:** A10, North London; **Rail:** Tottenham Hale Underground.
Ref: FH2207

HIGH MOOR FARM PARK

High Moor Farm Park, Harrogate, **YORKSHIRE (NORTH)**, HG, **England**.
Contact/s: Fishery Manager.
(T) 01423 563637
Profile: **FT:** Coarse; **WN:** High Moor Farm Park; **WT:** Lake (Still). **Location:** **Nr. Rd:** A59 to Skipton; **Main Rd:** A59 Harrogate to Skipton.
Ref: FH2208

HIGH NEWTON RESERVOIR

High Newton Reservoir, South Lakeland, High Newton, Windermere, **CUMBRIA**, LA23, **England**.
Contact/s: **Mr Chris Sodo** (Hon Treasurer), Windermere, Ambleside and District Angling Association, Ecclerigg Court, Ecclerigg, Windermere, LA23 1LQ.
(T) 01539 445083
Mr Dave Helm (Manager).
(T) 01229 585342
Mr J Newton (Secretary), 3 Lumley Rd, Kendal, Cumbria.
Mr Roy Rhodes (Conservation, Access and Recreation Manager), Rivington Water Treatment Works, Bolton Rd, Horwich, Bolton, BL6 7RN.
(T) 01204 664300
Profile: **FT:** Game; **WN:** High Newton; **WT:** Reservoir (Still); **F. Size:** 11 Acres; **W. Size:** 11 Acres. **Location:** **Nr. Rd:** A590 near High Newton Village; **Main Rd:** M6.
Ref: FH2209

HIGH PENN

High Penn, Calne, **WILTSHIRE**, SN11, **England**.
Contact/s: **Mr Terry Strange**.
(T) 01793 851178
Profile: **FT:** Coarse; **WN:** High Penn; **WT:** Gravel Pit (Still) **W. Size:** 2 Acres. **Location:** **Main Rd:** A3102 to Lyneham.
Ref: FH2210

HIGHAM FARM COARSE FISHING

Higham Farm Coarse Fishing, The Cabin, Higham Farm Hotel, Higham, Alfreton, **DERBYSHIRE**, DE55 6EH, **England**.
Contact/s: **Mr Brian Varley** (Owner/Manager).
(T) 01773 602741 or 521102
Profile: **FT:** Coarse; **WN:** Higham Farm Coarse Fishing; **WT:** Lake (Still) **W. Size:** 12 Acres. **Location:** **Main Rd:** A61.
Ref: FH2211

HIGHAMPTON TROUT LAKES

Highampton Trout Lakes, Greenacres, Highampton, Beaworthy, **DEVON**, EX21, **England**.
Contact/s: **Mr Lee Adey** (Owner).
(T) 01409 231376
Profile: **FT:** Game; **WN:** Highampton; **WT:** Lake (Still). **Location:** **Nr. Rd:** Greenacres.
Ref: FH2212

HIGHAMS PARK LAKE

Highams Park Lake, Falmouth Avenue, Chingford, London, **LONDON (GREATER)**, E4, **England**.
Contact/s: **A Clark** (Manager), Corporation of London, Conservators of Epping Forest, The Warren, Loughton, Essex, IG10 4RW.
(T) 020 85082266
Mr Terry Barton (Chairman), Hollow Angling Society, 103 Beular Rd, Walthamstow, London, E17 9LD.
(T) 020 85212884
Profile: **FT:** Coarse; **WN:** Highams Park; **WT:** Lake (Still) **W. Size:** 7 Acres. **Location:** **Rail:** Higham Park.
Ref: FH2213

HIGHER COWNHAYNE LAKES

Higher Cownhayne Lakes, Cownhayne Lane, Colyton, **DEVON**, EX, **England**.
Contact/s: **Mrs E Pady**.
(T) 01279 552267
Profile: **FT:** Game; **WN:** Higher Cownhayne; **WT:** Lake (Still). **Location:** **Nr. Rd:** Cownhayne Lane.
Ref: FH2214

HIGHER HALL FLASH

Opencast, Smiths Lane, Leigh, Wigan, **LANCASHIRE**, **England**.
Contact/s: **Mr B Smith** (Owner).
(T) 01942 670890
Profile: **FT:** Coarse; **WN:** Opencast or Flash; **WT:** Lake (Still); **F. Size:** 40 Acres; **W. Size:** 30 Acres. **Location:** **Nr. Rd:** Smiths Lane (B5237); **Rail:** Daisy Hill Station.
Ref: FH2215

HIGHFIELD FISHERY

Highfield Fishery, Thorpe Abbots, Harleston, **SUFFOLK**, IP20, **England**.
Contact/s: Fishery Manager.
(T) 01986 874869
Manager, Waveney Angling, 5 London Rd, Harleston, Norfolk, IP20 9BH.
(T) 01379 854886or01986874869
Profile: **FT:** Coarse; **WN:** Highfield Fishery; **WT:** Lake (Still). **Location:** **Nr. Rd:** Thorpe Abbots to Diss; **Main Rd:** A143.
Ref: FH2216

HIGHGATE PONDS

Highgate Ponds, Parliament Hill Fields,

Parliament Hill, London, **LONDON (GREATER)**, NW5, **England**.
Contact/s: **Mr Bob Sharpe** (Manager), Sharps Tackle, 162 Malden Rd, London, NW5 4BS.
(T) 020 74851759
Profile: **FT:** Coarse; **WN:** Highgate; **WT:** Pond (Still). **Location:** **Nr. Rd:** Kentish Town to Highgate West Hill; **Main Rd:** Millfield Lane. **£Fr**
Ref: FH2217

HIGHLANDS DAIRY LAKE

Highlands Dairy Lake, Highlands Dairy Farm, Hewish, Crewkerne, **SOMERSET**, TA18, **England**.
Contact/s: **J Wyatt**.
(T) 01460 741180
Profile: **FT:** Coarse; **WN:** Highlands Dairy; **WT:** Lake (Still) **W. Size:** 1 Acre.
Ref: FH2218

HIGHNAM COURT LAKE

Highnam Court Lake, Ross-on-Wye Rd, Gloucester, **GLOUCESTERSHIRE**, GL, **England**.
Profile: **FT:** Coarse; **WN:** Highnam Court; **WT:** Lake (Still) **W. Size:** 3 Acres. **Location:** **Nr. Rd:** Ross-on-Wye Road; **Main Rd:** A40.
Ref: FH2219

HIGHTOWN LAKE

Hightown Lake, Ringwood, **HAMPSHIRE**, BH24, **England**.
Contact/s: **Mr Kevin Grozier** (Permit Secretary), 15 Greenfinch Walk, Hightown, Ringwood, Hampshire, BH24 3RJ.
(T) 01425 471466 **(F)** 01425 471466
Profile: **FT:** Coarse; **WN:** Hightown Lake; **WT:** Gravel Pit (Still) **W. Size:** 22 Acres. **Location:** **Nr. Rd:** Crow Lane; **Main Rd:** A31.
Ref: FH2220

HILGAY (RIVER)

River Hilgay, Hilgay, Downham Market, **NORFOLK**, PE38, **England**.
Profile: **FT:** Coarse; **WN:** Hilgay; **WT:** River (Moving) **W. Size:** 3200 Metres.
Ref: FH2221

HILL TOP RESERVOIR

Hill Top Reservoir, Slaithwaite, Huddersfield, **YORKSHIRE (WEST)**, HD7, **England**.
Contact/s: **Mr A J Abbott** (Bailiff), 24 Moorcroft Avenue, Golcar, Huddersfield, Yorkshire (West), HD7.
(T) 01484 646868
Mr D Rushforth (Membership Secretary), 122 Longwood Gate, Longwood, Huddersfield, Yorkshire (West), HD3 4US.
(T) 01484 651028
Mr R Carter (Bailiff), 10 Varley Rd, Slaithwaite, Yorkshire (West).
(T) 01484 843163
Profile: **FT:** Coarse; **WN:** Hill Top; **WT:** Reservoir (Still) **W. Size:** 11 Acres. **Location:** **Nr. Rd:** Bank Gate; **Main Rd:** A62 Manchester Road.
Ref: FH2222

HILL VIEW LAKES

Hill View Lakes, Cherry Orchard Lane, Twyning, Tewkesbury, **GLOUCESTERSHIRE**, GL20 6JH, **England**.
Contact/s: **Mr Keith Hill** (Manager).
(T) 01684 296719
Profile: **FT:** Coarse; **WN:** Hill view; **WT:** Lake (Still). **Location:** **Nr. Rd:** Cherry Orchard Lane.
Ref: FH2223

HILL VIEW LAKES

Hill View Lakes, Skegness Rd, Hogsthorpe, Skegness, **LINCOLNSHIRE**, PE24 5NR, **England**.
Contact/s: **Mr Kevin Palmer** (Director).
(T) 01754 872979 **(F)** 01754 872979
Profile: **FT:** Coarse; **WN:** Hill View; **WT:** Lake (Still) **W. Size:** 4 Acres. **Location:** **Nr. Rd:** A52; **Main Rd:** A52; **Rail:** Skegness.
Ref: FH2224

HILL WOOD POND

Hill Wood Pond, High Wycombe, **BUCKINGHAMSHIRE**, HP11, **England**.
Contact/s: **Mr J Woodhouse** (Secretary), Marlow Angling Club, Conifers, Ash Rd, High Wycombe, Buckinghamshire, HP12 4SW.
(T) 01494 523988
Profile: **FT:** Coarse; **WN:** Hill Wood; **WT:** Pond (Still).
Ref: FH2225

HILLEND LOCH

Hillend Loch, Airdrie, **LANARKSHIRE (NORTH)**, ML6, **Scotland**.
Contact/s: **Mr Jim Potter** (Manager), Airdrie and District Angling Club, 12 Sharp Avenue, Kirkwood, Coatbridge, ML5 5RP.
(T) 01236 425576
Profile: **FT:** Combination; **WN:** Hillend; **WT:** Loch (Still) **W. Size:** 375 Acres. **Location:** **Nr. Rd:** A89; **Main Rd:** A89; **Rail:** Clarkston.
Ref: FH2226

HILLVIEW FARM LAKE

Hillview Farm Lake, Holtwood, Horton, Wimborne, **DORSET**, BH21, **England**.
Contact/s: Fishery Manager.
(T) 01258 857238
Profile: **FT:** Coarse; **WN:** Hillview Farm; **WT:** Lake (Still) **W. Size:** 2 Acres.
Ref: FH2227

HILLVIEW FISHERY

Hillview Lakes, Hillview Nurseries, Cherry Orchard Lane, Twyning, Tewkesbury, **GLOUCESTERSHIRE**, GL20 6JH, **England**.
Contact/s: **Mr Keith Hill** (Manager).
(T) 01684 296719
Profile: **FT:** Coarse; **WN:** Hillview Lakes; **WT:** Pond (Still). **Location:** **Nr. Rd:** A38; **Main Rd:** M50, junction 1.
Ref: FH2228

HILSEA MOATS

Hilsea Moats, Peronne Rd, Portsmouth, **HAMPSHIRE**, PO, **England**.
Contact/s: **Mr Ash Girdler**, 3 Chase Plain Cottages, Portsmouth Rd, Hindhead, Surrey, GU26 6BZ.
(T) 01428 607768
Profile: **FT:** Coarse; **WN:** Hilsea; **WT:** Moat (Still). **Location:** **Nr. Rd:** Peronne Road; **Main Rd:** M27.
Ref: FH2229

HIMLEY HALL AND PARK LAKE

Himley Hall And Park Lake, Himley, Dudley, **STAFFORDSHIRE**, DY3 4DF, **England**.
Contact/s: **Mr Alan Peace** (Park Warden).
(T) 01902 324093or324093 **(F)** 01902 894163
Profile: **FT:** Coarse; **WN:** Himley; **WT:** Lake (Still); **F. Size:** 184 Acres; **W. Size:** 16 Acres. **Location:** **Nr. Rd:** B4176; **Main Rd:** A449; **Rail:** Wolverhampton.
Ref: FH2230

HIMLEY ISLAND POOL

Himley Island Pool, Beddows Tackle Shop, Wombourne, Wolverhampton, **MIDLANDS (WEST)**, WV5, **England**.
Profile: **FT:** Coarse; **WN:** Himley Island; **WT:** Pool (Still).
Ref: FH2231

HINCHINGBROOKE COUNTRY PARK

Hinchingbrooke Country Park, Huntingdon, **CAMBRIDGESHIRE**, PE1, **England**.
Contact/s: Bailiff.
(T) 01480 451568
Profile: **FT:** Coarse; **WN:** Hinchingbrooke Country Park; **WT:** Lake (Still); **F. Size:** 50 Acres; **W. Size:** 20 Acres. **Location:** **Main Rd:** A1.
Ref: FH2232

HINDERCLAY LAKES

Hinderclay Lakes, Hinderclay, Diss, **NORFOLK**, IP, **England**.
Contact/s: **Mr Stuart Platt**.
(T) 01508 532323or01379890110
Profile: **FT:** Coarse; **WN:** Hinderclay; **WT:** Lake (Still). **Location:** **Main Rd:** A143.
Ref: FH2233

HINGHAM FISHMERE

Fishmere Carp Lakes, Low Rd, Hingham, Nr Wymondham, Norwich, **NORFOLK**, **England**.
Contact/s: .
(T) 01953 850179
Profile: **FT:** Coarse; **WN:** Fishmere; **WT:** Lake (Still). **Location:** **Nr. Rd:** Low Road; **Main Rd:** B1108; **Rail:** Attleborough.
Ref: FH2234

HINKSHAY POOLS

Hinkshay Pools, Telford, **SHROPSHIRE**, TF, **England**.
Contact/s: Manager.
(T) 01952 503550
Profile: **FT:** Coarse; **WN:** Hinkshay; **WT:** Pool (Still).
Ref: FH2235

HMS DRYAD LAKE

Hms Dryad Lake, Portsmouth, **HAMPSHIRE**, PO, **England**.
Profile: **FT:** Coarse; **WN:** HMS Dryad; **WT:** Lake (Still) **W. Size:** 4 Acres. **Location:** **Main Rd:** M3 south, M27, A27.
Ref: FH2236

HOATHLEY FISHERY

Hoathley Fishery, Hoathley Farm, Clay Hill Rd, Lamberhurst, **KENT**, TN3 8LS, **England**.
Profile: **FT:** Combination; **WN:** Medway; **WT:** Tributary (Moving).
Ref: FH2237

HOBHOLE DRAIN

Hobhole Drain, Midville, Stickney, Boston, **LINCOLNSHIRE**, PE22, **England**.
Contact/s: **Mr Alan Greaves**.
(T) 01205 270484
Profile: **FT:** Coarse; **WN:** Hobhole; **WT:** Drain (Moving) **W. Size:** 3200 Metres. **Location:** **Nr. Rd:** Station Road; **Main Rd:** A16 to Boston. **£Fr**
Ref: FH2238

HOCKLEY LAKES

Hockley Lakes, Rayleigh, **ESSEX**, SS6, **England**.
Contact/s: **Robin**.
(T) 01268 781556
Profile: **FT:** Coarse; **WN:** Hockley; **WT:** Lake (Still). **Location:** **Nr. Rd:** A130.
Ref: FH2239

HODDER (RIVER)

River Hodder, Slaidburn, Clitheroe, **LANCASHIRE**, BB7, **England**.
Profile: **FT:** Game; **WN:** Hodder; **WT:** River (Moving).
Ref: FH2240

HODDER (RIVER)

Hodder (River), Standen Estate, Great Mitton, Nr. Whalley, Blackburn, **LANCASHIRE**, **England**.
Contact/s: **Mr John Turner** (Hon Secretary), Prince Albert Angling Society, 15 Pexhill Drive, Macclesfield, Cheshire, SK10 3LP.
(T) 01625 422010
Profile: **FT:** Game; **WN:** Hodder; **WT:** River (Moving) **W. Size:** 3000 Metres. **Location:** **Nr. Rd:** B6243; **Rail:** Billington.
Ref: FH2241

HODDLESDEN LAKE

Hoddlesden Lake, Blackburn, **LANCASHIRE**, BB3 2, **England**.
Contact/s: **Mr Roy Rhodes** (Conservation, Access and Recreation Manager), Rivington Water Treatment Works, Bolton Rd, Horwich, Bolton, BL6 7RN.
(T) 01204 664300
Mr T Berry (Secretary), 5 Springvale, Garden Village, Darwen, BB3 2HJ.

Profile: **FT:** Game; **WN:** Hoddlesden; **WT:** Lake (Still).
Ref: FH2242

HODDLESDEN RESERVOIR

Hoddlesden Reservoir, Marsh House Lane, Darwen, **LANCASHIRE**, BB3 3, **England**.
Contact/s: Manager, Angler's Den, 19 Blackburn Rd, Darwen, Lancashire, BB3 1EJ.
(T) 01254 706713
Profile: **FT:** Coarse; **WN:** Hoddlesden Reservoir; **WT:** Reservoir (Still). **Location:** **Nr. Rd:** Marsh House Lane; **Main Rd:** A666.
Ref: FH2243

HODDOM WATER

Hoddom Water, Hoddom, Lockerbie, **DUMFRIES AND GALLOWAY**, DG11, **Scotland**.
Contact/s: D Graham (Bailiff), Hoddom and Kinmount Estates, Hoddom Estate Office, Lockerbie, Dumfries and Galloway, DG11 1BE.
(T) 01576 300417 **(M)** 07711 681507
Profile: **FT:** Game; **WN:** Annan; **WT:** River (Moving) **W. Size:** 4450 Metres. **Location:** **Nr. Rd:** B725 or B723; **Main Rd:** M74; **Rail:** Lockerbie.
Ref: FH2244

HOE HILL POND

Hoe Hill Pond, Pasture Rd, Barton-upon-Humber, **LINCOLNSHIRE (NORTH)**, DN18, **England**.
Contact/s: , Barton Kingfishers Tackle Shop, Fleetgate, Barton, Lincolnshire.
Mr Andy Kirby (Match Secretary), 5 Queens Avenue, Barton-upon-Humber, Lincolnshire.
(T) 01652 636868day01652636243
Mr Jim Gowans (Secretary), 24 East Ackridge, Barton-upon-Humber, Lincolnshire (North).
(T) 01652 633274
Profile: **FT:** Coarse; **WN:** Hoe Hill; **WT:** Pond (Still) **W. Size:** 9 Acres. **Location:** **Nr. Rd:** Barrow Road; **Main Rd:** A1077; **Rail:** Waterside Road.
Ref: FH2245

HOGSBROOK LAKES

Hogsbrook Lakes, Greendale Barton, Woodbury Salterton, Exeter, **DEVON**, EX5 1EW, **England**.
Mr Desmond Pearson (Manager), F W S Carter and Sons Ltd, Greensdale Barton, Woodbury Salterton, Exeter, EX5 1EW.
(T) 01395 233340
Profile: **FT:** Coarse; **WN:** Hogsbrook; **WT:** Lake (Still) **W. Size:** 3 Acres. **Location:** **Main Rd:** A3052.
Ref: FH2246

HOLBURY LAKES

Holbury Lakes, Holbury Lane, Lockerley, Romsey, **HAMPSHIRE**, SO51 0JR, **England**.
(W) www.holburylakes.co.uk
Contact/s: **Mr Stewart Guest** (Manager).
(T) 01794 341619
Profile: **FT:** Game; **WN:** Dun; **WT:** Combination (Still & Moving); **F. Size:** 20 Acres; **W. Size:** 7 Acres. **Location:** **Nr. Rd:** East Dean Road; **Main Rd:** A30; **Rail:** Dunbridge.
Ref: FH2247

HOLBURY MANOR POND

Holbury Manor Pond, Blackfield, Southampton, **HAMPSHIRE**, SO45, **England**.
Contact/s: Manager, Gang Warily Recreation and Community Ctre, Newlands Rd, Fawley, SO45 1GA.
(T) 023 80893603
Profile: **FT:** Coarse; **WN:** Holbury Manor; **WT:** Pond (Still).
Ref: FH2248

HOLDEN LANE POOL

Holden Lane Pool, Sneyd Green, Stoke-on-Trent, **STAFFORDSHIRE**, ST4, **England**.
Contact/s: Ranger Service.
(T) 01782 536920
Mr Peter Johnsen (Secretary), Stoke City District Angling Society, 31 East Cres, Sneyd Green, Stoke-on-Trent, ST10 6ES.
(T) 01782 214840
Profile: **FT:** Coarse; **WN:** Holden Lane; **WT:** Pool (Still) **W. Size:** 2 Acres.
Ref: FH2249

HOLDEN WOOD RESERVOIR

Holden Wood Reservoir, Grane Rd, Haslingden, Rossendale, **LANCASHIRE**, BB4, **England**.
Contact/s: **Mr William Monk** (Membership Secretary), Haslingden and District Fly Fishing Club, 6 Ryde Cl, Haslingden, Rossendale, Lancashire BB4 6QR.
(T) 01706 211724
Profile: **FT:** Coarse; **WN:** Holden Wood; **WT:** Reservoir (Still) **W. Size:** 40 Acres.
Location: **Main Rd:** M65; **Rail:** Blackburn.
Ref: FH2250

HOLEHIRD TARN

Holehird Tarn, Holehird, Windermere, **CUMBRIA**, LA23, **England**.
Contact/s: Manager, Go Fishing, Robinson Pl, Bowness-on-Windermere, Cumbria, LA23 3DQ.
(T) 01539 447086
Mr Chris Sodo (Hon Treasurer), Windermere, Ambleside and District Angling Association, Ecclerigg Court, Ecclerigg, Windermere, LA23 1LQ.
(T) 01539 445083
Profile: **FT:** Coarse; **WN:** Holehird; **WT:** Lake (Still) **W. Size:** 3 Acres. **Location:** **Nr. Rd:** A592 Kirkstone Pass Road; **Main Rd:** A591.
Ref: FH2251

HOLGAN TROUT FARM FISHERY

Holgan Trout Farm Fishery, Holgan Farm, Llawhaden, Narberth, **PEMBROKESHIRE**, SA67 8DJ, **Wales**.
Contact/s: **Mr Ian Heaps**, Ian Heaps Premier Fisheries and School of Angling, Holgan Farm, Llawhaden, Narberth, Pembrokeshire SA67 8DJ.
(T) 01437 541285
Profile: **FT:** Combination; **WN:** Holgan Trout Farm Fishery; **WT:** Lake (Still). **Location:** **Nr. Rd:** A40; **Main Rd:** West to end of M4.
Ref: FH2252

HOLKHAM LAKE

Holkham Lake, Wells-Next-The-Sea, **NORFOLK**, NR23, **England**.
Contact/s: Fishery Manager.
(T) 01328 710227
Profile: **FT:** Coarse; **WN:** Holkham; **WT:** Lake (Still).
Ref: FH2253

HOLL RESERVOIR

Holl Reservoir, Fife Division, Flemington Rd, Glenrothes, **FIFE**, KY7, **Scotland**.
Contact/s: **Mr Richard Philp**.
(T) 01592 614000
Profile: **FT:** Game; **WN:** Holl; **WT:** Reservoir (Still). **Location:** **Nr. Rd:** Flemington Road.
Ref: FH2254

HOLLAND PARK

Holland Park, Wedland Lane, Thorpe St Peter, Skegness, **LINCOLNSHIRE**, PE24 4PW, **England**.
Contact/s: **Mrs J Newham** (Owner).
(T) 01754 880576
Profile: **FT:** Combination; **WN:** Holland Park; **WT:** Pond (Still); **F. Size:** 8 Acres; **W. Size:** 3 Acres. **Location:** **Nr. Rd:** Wedland Lane; **Rail:** Thorpe Culvert.
Ref: FH2255

HOLLIES TROUT FISHERY

Hollies Trout Farm And Fishery, Slade Lane, Sheldon, Honiton, **DEVON**, EX14 0QL, **England**.
Contact/s: **Mrs J Roles**, Hollies Trout Farm and Fishery, The Hollies, Sheldon, Honiton, EX14 4QS.
(T) 01404 841428
Profile: **FT:** Game; **WN:** Hollies Trout Farm And Fishery; **WT:** Lake (Still).
Ref: FH2256

HOLLINGWOOD FISHERY

Hollingwood Fishery, Roman Rd, Leeming, Northallerton, **YORKSHIRE (NORTH)**, DL7 9SB, **England**.
Contact/s: **Mr Clive Lambert**.
(T) 01677 424706 **(M)** 07712 737754
Profile: **FT:** Coarse; **WN:** Hollingwood Pool; **WT:** Lake (Still). **Location:** **Nr. Rd:** Garden centre; **Main Rd:** A1; **Rail:** Northallerton.
Ref: FH2257

HOLLINGWORTH LAKE

Hollingworth Lake Country Park, Country Park Visitor Ctre, Rakewood Rd, Littleborough, **MANCHESTER (GREATER)**, OL15 0AQ, **England**.
Contact/s: **Ms Anna Jordan** (Countryside Ranger).
(T) 01706 373421 **(F)** 01706 378753
Profile: **FT:** Coarse; **WN:** Hollingworth; **WT:** Lake (Still) **W. Size:** 212 Acres. **Location:** **Nr. Rd:** B6225; **Main Rd:** A58; **Rail:** Little Borough or Smithy Bridge.
Ref: FH2258

HOLLOW PONDS

Hollow Ponds, Whipps Cross Rd, Leytonstone, London, **LONDON (GREATER)**, E10, **England**.
Contact/s: Manager, Corporation of London, The Warren, Loughton, Essex, IG10 4RW.
Mr Terry Barton, Hollow Angling Society, 103 Beulah Rd, Walthamstow, London, E17 9LD.
(T) 020 75082266 **(F)** 020 75082176
Profile: **FT:** Coarse; **WN:** Hollow; **WT:** Lake (Still) **W. Size:** 16 Acres. **Location:** **Nr. Rd:** Whipps Road; **Rail:** Leystone Underground.
Ref: FH2259

HOLLOWELL RESERVOIR

Hollowell Reservoir, Pitsford Water, Holcot, Northampton, **NORTHAMPTONSHIRE**, NN6 9SJ, **England**.
Contact/s: **Mr Nathan Clayton** (Fishery Warden), Pitsford Fishing Lodge, Brixworth Rd, Holcot, NN6 9SJ.
(T) 01604 781350
Profile: **FT:** Coarse; **WN:** Hollowell; **WT:** Reservoir (Still).
Ref: FH2260

HOLLY FARM FISHERY

Hollybush Farm, Holly Farm, Willoughby Rd, Ashby Manga, Lutterworth, **LEICESTERSHIRE**, LE17 5NP, **England**.
Contact/s: **Ken Or Rita** (Owner), Holly Farm, Willoughby Rd, Ashby Manga, Nr Lutterworth, Leicestershire, LE17 5NP.
(T) 01455 202391
Profile: **FT:** Coarse; **WN:** Gills, Trotters, and Moby; **WT:** Lake (Still); **F. Size:** 5 Acres.
Location: **Nr. Rd:** Willoughby Road; **Main Rd:** A426; **Rail:** Narborough.
Ref: FH2261

HOLLYBUSH LANE LAKES

Hollybush Lane Lakes, North Camp, Farnborough, **HAMPSHIRE**, GU14, **England**.
Contact/s: Manager, Raison Bros Tackle Shop, 2 Park Rd, Farnborough, Hampshire, GU14 6JG.
(T) 01252 543470
Mr David Rance (Secretary), Farnborough and District Angling Society, Orchard Bungalow, Henley Park, Normandy, Guildford, GU3 2AB.
(T) 01483 234054
Profile: **FT:** Coarse; **WN:** Hollybush Lane; **WT:** Gravel Pit (Still); **F. Size:** 40 Acres; **W. Size:** 20 Acres. **Location:** **Nr. Rd:** A331; **Main Rd:** M3, junction 4; **Rail:** North Camp.
Ref: FH2262

HOLME (RIVER)

River Holme, Holmbridge, Holmfirth, Huddersfield, **YORKSHIRE (WEST)**, HD, **England**.
Contact/s: **Mr D Rushforth** (Secretary),

122 Longwood Gate, Longwood, Huddersfield, Yorkshire (West), HD3 4US.
(T) 01484 651028
Mr N Blacker (Bailiff), 49 Towenend Rd, Wooldale, Huddersfield.
(T) 01484 686894
Profile: **FT:** Game; **WN:** Holme (Holmebridge); **WT:** River (Moving). **Location:** **Nr. Rd:** A6024; **Main Rd:** A6024 Woodhead Road; **Rail:** Huddersfield.
Ref: FH2263

HOLME FEN FISHING

Holme Fen Fishing, Holme Fen Drove, Earith, Huntingdon, **CAMBRIDGESHIRE**, PE1, **England**.
Contact/s: **Mr Del Maginn**.
(T) 01354 695559
Profile: **FT:** Coarse; **WN:** Holme Fen Fishing; **WT:** Lake (Still). **Location:** **Main Rd:** B1050.
Ref: FH2264

HOLME GRANGE

Holme Grange, Crowthorne, **BERKSHIRE**, RG45, **England**.
Contact/s: **Mr John Baker**, Crowthorne Sports and Angling, 91-95 Church St, Crowthorne, Berkshire, RG45 7AW.
(T) 01344 777411
Profile: **FT:** Coarse; **WN:** Holme Grange; **WT:** Lake (Still).
Ref: FH2265

HOLME LAKE FISHERY

Holme Lake Fishery, Holme Lane, Messingham, Scunthorpe, **HUMBERSIDE**, DN, **England**.
Contact/s: **Mr Alan Barton**.
Profile: **FT:** Coarse; **WN:** Home; **WT:** Lake (Still) **W. Size:** 20 Acres. **Location:** **Nr. Rd:** A159; **Main Rd:** M18.
Ref: FH2266

HOLME MILL DAM (SQUARE DAM)

Holme Mill Dam (Square Dam), Manchester Rd, Marsden, Huddersfield, **YORKSHIRE (WEST)**, HD7 6LN, **England**.
Contact/s: **Mr D Rushforth** (Secretary), 122 Longwood Gate, Longwood, Huddersfield, Yorkshire (West), HD3 4US.
(T) 01484 651028
Mr R Carter (Bailiff), 10 Varley Rd, Slaithwaite, Yorkshire (West).
(T) 01484 843163
Profile: **FT:** Coarse; **WN:** Holme Mill Dam; **WT:** Pond (Still). **Location:** **Nr. Rd:** Manchester Road; **Main Rd:** A62; **Rail:** Marsden.
Ref: FH2267

HOLME PIERPOINT

Holme Pierpoint, The Viaducts, Nottingham, **NOTTINGHAMSHIRE**, NG, **England**.
Contact/s: **Mr William Belshaw**, 17 Spring Green, Clifton Estate, Nottingham, NG11 9EF.
(T) 0115 9216645
Profile: **FT:** Coarse; **WN:** Holme Pierpoint; **WT:** Gravel Pit (Still).
Ref: FH2268

HOLMER LAKE

Holmer Lake, Holmer Lane, Telford, **SHROPSHIRE**, TF, **England**.
Contact/s: **Mr Stan Harris** (Secretary), Telford Angling Association, 73 Burnside, Brookside, Telford, TF3 1DA.
(T) 01952 590605
Profile: **FT:** Coarse; **WN:** Holmer; **WT:** Lake (Still). **Location:** **Nr. Rd:** Holmer Lane; **Main Rd:** A442.
Ref: FH2269

HOLMSTON HALL FISHERY

Holmston Hall Fishery, Holmston Hall, Little Budworth, Tarporley, **CHESHIRE**, CW6 9AY, **England**.
Contact/s: **Mr Richard Hopkins** (Owner).
(T) 01829 760366 (F) 01829 760366
Profile: **FT:** Coarse; **WN:** Holmston Hall Fishery; **WT:** Lake (Still); **F. Size:** 4 Acres; **W. Size:** 2 Acres. **Location:** **Nr. Rd:** Hickhurst Lane; **Main Rd:** A49 Tarporley to Warrington; **Rail:** Crewe.
Ref: FH2270

HOLT FLEET POOL

Holt Fleet Pool, Worcester, **WORCESTERSHIRE**, WR, **England**.
Contact/s: Manager, The Wharf Inn, Holt Heath, Worcester, Worcestershire, WR6 6NN.
(T) 01905 620289 (F) 01905 620140
Profile: **FT:** Coarse; **WN:** Holt Fleet; **WT:** Pool (Still).
Ref: FH2271

HOLT WOOD PONDS

Holt Wood Ponds, Holtwood, Horton, Wimborne, **DORSET**, BH21, **England**.
Contact/s: **Mr C Harrison** (Hon Secretary), Old Mill House, Bickerley, Ringwood, Hamptonshire, BH24 1EQ.
(T) 01202 880684
Mr Pete Reading (Secretary), 17 Mayford Rd, Poole, Dorset, BH12 1PT.
(T) 01202 733110
Profile: **FT:** Coarse; **WN:** Holt Wood; **WT:** Pond (Still); **F. Size:** 5 Acres; **W. Size:** 1 Acre. **Location:** **Nr. Rd:** Holt Wood to Lower Row, turn off on Queens Copse; **Main Rd:** B3078.
Ref: FH2272

HOLTON PIT

Holton Pit, Halesworth, **SUFFOLK**, IP19, **England**.
Contact/s: Manager.
(T) 01394 382377
Mr Martin Reed (manager).
(T) 01473 271769
Profile: **FT:** Coarse; **WN:** Holton; **WT:** Gravel Pit (Still) **W. Size:** 5 Acres. **Location:** **Nr. Rd:** B1124; **Main Rd:** A144.
Ref: FH2273

HOLTS LAKES

Holts Lakes, Burnt Oak Rd, Crowborough, **SUSSEX (EAST)**, TN6, **England**.
Contact/s: **Sean** (Manager), Crowborough Tackle, Whitehill Rd, Crowborough, Sussex (East), TN6 1JU.
(T) 01892 661145
Profile: **FT:** Coarse; **WN:** Holt's; **WT:** Lake (Still); **F. Size:** 4 Acres; **W. Size:** 2 Acres. **Location:** **Nr. Rd:** Burnt Oak Road; **Main Rd:** A26; **Rail:** Jarvis Brook, Crowborough.
Ref: FH2274

HOLWELL HYDE LAKE

Holwell Hyde Lake, Holwell Hyde Lane, Cole Green, Welwyn Garden City, **HERTFORDSHIRE**, AL7, **England**.
Contact/s: **Mr Glen Bird** (Partner), The Aquatic Warehouse, Birchall Lane, Cole Green, Hertford, SG14 2NR.
(T) 01707 391196
Mr Keith Day (Bailiff).
(T) 01707 336526 (M) 07889 905603
Profile: **FT:** Coarse; **WN:** Holwell Hyde; **WT:** Lake (Still) **W. Size:** 2 Acres. **Location:** **Nr. Rd:** Holwell Hyde Lane; **Main Rd:** A414.
Ref: FH2275

HOLWELL WORKS RESERVOIR

Holwell Works Reservoir, The Limes, Ashford-By-Valley, Melton Mowbray, **LEICESTERSHIRE**, LE14, **England**.
Contact/s: **Mr E Edwards** (Bailiff).
Mr E Madden.
Profile: **FT:** Coarse; **WN:** Holwell Works; **WT:** Reservoir (Still).
Ref: FH2276

HOLYBROOK

Holybrook, Calcot Mill, Reading, **BERKSHIRE**, RG, **England**.
Contact/s: **Mr Mick Cox** (Secretary), Dorstans, Hatch Lane, Brimpton Village, Reading, RG7 4TR.
(T) 0118 9714917
Ms Dusty Millar (Ticket Administrator), 238 Elgar Road South, Reading, Berkshire, RG3 0BW.
(T) 0118 9874882
Profile: **FT:** Coarse; **WN:** Kennet; **WT:** River (Moving) **W. Size:** 1600 Metres. **Location:** **Nr. Rd:** Burghfield Road; **Main Rd:** M4, Junction 12.
Ref: FH2277

HOLYFIELD FISHERY

Holyfield Fishery, Fishers Green Lane, Crooked Mile, Waltham Abbey, **ESSEX**, EN9 2ED, **England**.
Contact/s: **Mr Don Spinks** (Owner).
(T) 01992 768012
Profile: **FT:** Coarse; **WN:** Holyfield Fishery; **WT:** Lake (Still); **F. Size:** 11 Acres; **W. Size:** 4 Acres. **Location:** **Nr. Rd:** Fishers Green Lane; **Main Rd:** M25 junction 26, A10; **Rail:** Waltham Cross.
Ref: FH2278

HOME FARM FISHERIES

Home Farm Fisheries, Sudbury, **SUFFOLK**, CO10, **England**.
Contact/s: **Mr Paul Elsegood** (Manager), 2 Wentfords Cottages, Clare Rd, Poslingford, Sudbury, Suffolk.
(T) 01787 277468
Profile: **FT:** Coarse; **WN:** Home Farm Fisheries; **WT:** Lake (Still).
Ref: FH2279

HOME FARM FISHERY

Home Farm Fishery, Manhead, Kenton, Exeter, **DEVON**, EX6 8HP, **England**.
Contact/s: **Mr F Williams** (Owner).
(T) 01626 866259
Profile: **FT:** Coarse; **WN:** Home Farm Fishery; **WT:** Lake (Still) **W. Size:** 1 Acre. **Location:** **Nr. Rd:** B3381 Dawlish Starcross; **Main Rd:** A38; **Rail:** Starcross.
Ref: FH2280

HOME FARM FISHERY

Home Farm Fishery, Petts Lane, Little Walden, Saffron Walden, **ESSEX**, CB10 1XE, **England**.
Contact/s: **Mr Paul Elsegood** (Manager), 2 Wentfords Cottages, Clare Rd, Poslingford, Sudbury, Suffolk.
(T) 01787 277468
Mr Paul Jenkins.
(T) 01799 524038
Profile: **FT:** Coarse; **WN:** Home Farm Fishery; **WT:** Lake (Still) **W. Size:** 2 Acres. **Location:** **Nr. Rd:** B1052 to Saffron Walden; **Main Rd:** M11.
Ref: FH2281

HOME PARK

Home Park, Hampton Court Palace Gardens, East Molesey, **SURREY**, KT8 9AU, **England**.
Contact/s: **Mrs Jennifer Phillips**, Hampton Court Palace Gardens, Gardens Office, East Molesey, Surrey, KT8 9AU.
(T) 020 87819611
Ms Jacquie Cassidy (Co-Ordinator and Systems Manager), Hampton Court Palace Gardens, Barrack Block, East Molesey, Surrey, KT8 9AU.
(T) 020 87819676 (F) 020 87819669
Profile: **FT:** Coarse; **WN:** Home Park; **WT:** Pond (Still) **W. Size:** 2 Acres. **Location:** **Nr. Rd:** Bushey Park; **Main Rd:** A3; **Rail:** Hampton Court.
Ref: FH2282

HOMERSFIELD (RIVER)

River Homersfield, Bungay, **SUFFOLK**, NR35, **England**.
Profile: **FT:** Coarse; **WN:** Homersfield; **WT:** River (Moving) **W. Size:** 270 Metres.
Ref: FH2283

HOMERSFIELD LAKE

Homersfield Lake, Church Lane, Wortwell, Harleston, **SUFFOLK**, **England**.
(W) www.tmikoi.com/about_tmi.htm
Contact/s: .
(T) 01438 718558 (F) 01438 840096

Profile: **FT:** Coarse; **WN:** Homersfield; **WT:** Lake (Still); **F. Size:** 50 Acres; **W. Size:** 35 Acres. **Location:** **Nr. Rd:** Church Lane; **Main Rd:** B1062; **Rail:** Diss.
Ref: FH2284

HOMESTEAD LAKE

Homestead Lake, Immingham, **LINCOLNSHIRE**, DN40, **England**.
Contact/s: Fishery Manager.
(T) 01469 574606
Profile: **FT:** Coarse; **WN:** Homestead; **WT:** Lake (Still).
Ref: FH2285

HONEYS GREEN COARSE FISHERY

Honeys Green Coarse Fishery, Lower Honeys Green Farm, Easons Green, Uckfield, **SUSSEX (EAST)**, TN22 5RE, **England**.
Contact/s: **Mr P C Harvey**.
(T) 01825 840334
Profile: **FT:** Coarse; **WN:** Honeys Green Coarse Fishery; **WT:** Lake (Still) **W. Size:** 2 Acres. **Location:** **Nr. Rd:** B2192; **Main Rd:** A22; **Rail:** Uckfield.
Ref: FH2286

HOO LAKES

Hoo Lakes, Rochester, **KENT**, **England**.
Contact/s: .
(T) 01474 334264
Profile: **FT:** Coarse; **WN:** Hoo Lakes; **WT:** Lake (Still).
Ref: FH2287

HOOK LAKE

Hook Lake, Hook Lane, Northaw, Potters Bar, **HERTFORDSHIRE**, SG14 2NZ, **England**.
(W) www.landing-net.com
Contact/s: **Mr Richard Stangroom** (Director), Northaw Fisheries Management, 126 Byng Drive, Potters Bar, Hertfordshire, EN6 1VJ.
(T) 01707 268613
Profile: **FT:** Coarse; **WN:** Hook Lake; **WT:** Lake (Still) **W. Size:** 2 Acres. **Location:** **Nr. Rd:** B156; **Main Rd:** M25, junction 4; **Rail:** Potters Bar.
Ref: FH2288

HOOKS MARSH

Hooks Marsh, Fishers Green Farm Rd, Waltham Abbey, **ESSEX**, EN9, **England**.
(W) www.rmcangling.co.uk
Contact/s: **Mr Ian Welch** (Angling Manager), RMC Angling, The Square, Lightwater, Surrey, GU18 5SS.
(T) 01276 453300 **(F)** 01276 456611
(E) info@rmcangling.co.uk
Profile: **FT:** Coarse; **WN:** Hook's Marsh; **WT:** Lake (Still) **W. Size:** 40 Acres. **Location:** **Nr. Rd:** Fishers Green Farm Road; **Main Rd:** B194.
Ref: FH2289

HOOKSTEAD LAKE

Hookstead Lake, Seeds Lane, Kingsnorth, Ashford, **KENT**, TN23, **England**.
Contact/s: **Mr Dave Rolfe** (Fishery Manager).
(T) 01233 66349
Profile: **FT:** Coarse; **WN:** Hookstead; **WT:** Lake (Still). **Location:** **Nr. Rd:** Seeds Lane; **Main Rd:** A2042.
Ref: FH2290

HOPETOUN FISHERY

Hopetoun Fishery, 1 Swineburn, Winchburgh, Broxburn, **LOTHIAN (WEST)**, EH52 6QJ, **Scotland**.
Contact/s: **Mrs T Hamblin** (Owner).
(T) 0131 3315312 **(M)** 07831 261237
Profile: **FT:** Combination; **WN:** Hopetoun Fishery; **WT:** Pond (Still); **F. Size:** 4 Acres; **W. Size:** 2 Acres. **Location:** **Rail:** Dalmeny.
Ref: FH2291

HOPSFORD HALL FISHERY

Hopsford Hall Fishery, Withybrook Lane, Shilton, Coventry, **MIDLANDS (WEST)**, CV7 9JJ, **England**.
Contact/s: **Mr Andrew Wright** (Owner).
(T) 01455 220974
Profile: **FT:** Coarse; **WN:** Hopsford Hall Fishery; **WT:** Lake (Still) **W. Size:** 3 Acres. **Location:** **Nr. Rd:** Withybrook Lane; **Main Rd:** M6, junction 2.
Ref: FH2292

HOPTON WATERS

Hopton Waters, Upper Hopton, Mirfield, **YORKSHIRE (WEST)**, WF14, **England**.
Contact/s: Area Manager, Environment Agency, Ridings Area Office, Phoenix House, Global Avenue, Leeds, LS11 8PG.
(T) 0113 2440191or2314834 **(F)** 0113 2134609
Mr T Heathcote-Walker.
(T) 01274 877498
Profile: **FT:** Coarse; **WN:** Hopton Waters; **WT:** Lake (Still).
Ref: FH2293

HORAM MANOR FISHERY

Horam Manor Fishery, Horam Manor, Horam, Heathfield, **SUSSEX (EAST)**, TN21 0JB, **England**.
Contact/s: **Mr Graham Axell** (Owner), 28 Falcon Way, Hailsham, Sussex (East), BN27 1HY.
(T) 01323 840889 **(M)** 07790 720582
(E) graham@axellg.freeserve.co.uk
Profile: **FT:** Combination; **WN:** Horam Manor Fishery; **WT:** Combination (Still & Moving); **F. Size:** 300 Acres; **W. Size:** 7 Acres. **Location:** **Nr. Rd:** A267; **Main Rd:** A22.
Ref: FH2294

HORBURY LAGOON

Horbury Lagoon, Wakefield, **YORKSHIRE (WEST)**, WF4, **England**.
Contact/s: **B D Harper**, 29 Victoria Cres, Horsforth, Leeds, Yorkshire (West).
Profile: **FT:** Coarse; **WN:** Horbury; **WT:** Quarry (Still).
Ref: FH2295

HORDLE LAKES

Hordle Lakes, Golden Hill, Ashley Lane, Hordle, New Milton, **HAMPSHIRE**, BH25, **England**.
Contact/s: **Mr Graham Pepler** (Manager), Davis Tackle Shop, 75 Bargates, Christchurch, Dorset, BH23 1QE.
(T) 01202 485169or395532 **(F)** 01202 474261
Mr Mike Smith (Fishery Manager).
(T) 01590 672300 **(M)** 07778 954799
Profile: **FT:** Coarse; **WN:** Hordle; **WT:** Lake (Still); **F. Size:** 11 Acres. **Location:** **Main Rd:** Ashley Lane.
Ref: FH2296

HORESHAY POOL

Horeshay Pool, Telford, **SHROPSHIRE**, TF, **England**.
Contact/s: **Mr Mick Tuff** (Secretary), Dawley Angling Society, 68 Coronation St, Madley, Telford, TF7 5EH.
(T) 01952 590348
Profile: **FT:** Coarse; **WN:** Horeshay; **WT:** Pool (Still).
Ref: FH2297

HORNER WATER

Horner Water, Selworthy, Minehead, **SOMERSET**, TA, **England**.
Contact/s: Manager, Horner Tea Garden, Holnicote Estate, Selworthy, Minehead, Somerset TA24 8TJ.
Profile: **FT:** Game; **WN:** Horner Water; **WT:** River (Moving) **W. Size:** 4000 Metres.
Ref: FH2298

HORNING (RIVER)

River Horning, Wroxham, Norwich, **NORFOLK**, NR12, **England**.
Profile: **FT:** Coarse; **WN:** Horning; **WT:** River (Moving). **Location:** **Rail:** Wroxham. **£Fr**
Ref: FH2299

HORNS

Horns (The), Rugeley, **STAFFORDSHIRE**, WS15, **England**.
Contact/s: **Mr Kevin Boan**.
(T) 01889 576697
Profile: **FT:** Coarse; **WN:** Horns (The); **WT:** Pond (Still) **W. Size:** 2 Acres. **Location:** **Nr. Rd:** A460; **Main Rd:** M6.
Ref: FH2300

HORNSEA MERE

Hornsea Mere, Hornsea, Huddersfield, **YORKSHIRE (WEST)**, HU18 1AX, **England**.
Contact/s: Area Manager, Environment Agency, Ridings Area Office, Phoenix House, Global Avenue, Leeds, LS11 8PG.
(T) 0113 2440191or2314834 **(F)** 0113 2134609
Mr G Hood.
(T) 01964 533277
Profile: **FT:** Coarse; **WN:** Hornsea Mere; **WT:** Lake (Still). **Location:** **Main Rd:** A165.
Ref: FH2301

HORROCKS FLASH

Horrocks Flash, Wigan, **LANCASHIRE**, WN, **England**.
(W) www.wiganaa.f9.co.uk
Contact/s: **Mr Gerry Wilson** (Hon Secretary), Wigan and District Angling Association, 11 Guildford Avenue, Chorley, Lancashire, PR6 8TG.
(T) 01257 265905
(E) gerry@wiganna.freeserve.co.uk
Profile: **FT:** Coarse; **WN:** Horracks Flash; **WT:** Canal (Still). **Location:** **Nr. Rd:** Canal Towpath; **Main Rd:** A575.
Ref: FH2302

HORSE AND GROOM INN

Horse And Groom Lakes, Milcombe, Banbury, **OXFORDSHIRE**, OX1, **England**.
Contact/s: **Mr Roger Nicholls** (Fishery Manager), Fern Hill Farm, Milcombe, Near Banbury, Oxfordshire, OX15 4RS.
(T) 01295 720471
Profile: **FT:** Coarse; **WN:** Horse And Groom Inn; **WT:** Lake (Still); **F. Size:** 10 Acres; **W. Size:** 4 Acres. **Location:** **Nr. Rd:** Bloxham Road; **Main Rd:** A361; **Rail:** Banbury.
Ref: FH2303

HORSEBRIDGE POOL

Horsebridge Pool, Longsoon, Leek, **STAFFORDSHIRE**, ST13, **England**.
Contact/s: **Mr Albert Perkins** (Hon Secretary), 63 Fowlers Lane, Light Oaks, Stoke-on-Trent, Staffordshire, ST2 7NB.
Ms Liz Hayes (Manager).
(T) 01625 251262
Profile: **FT:** Coarse; **WN:** Horsebridge; **WT:** Pond (Still) **W. Size:** 2 Acres. **Location:** **Nr. Rd:** Horesbridge Road; **Rail:** Stoke-on-Trent.
Ref: FH2304

HORSECOPPICE RESERVOIR

Horsecoppice Reservoir, Macclesfield, **CHESHIRE**, SK1, **England**.
Contact/s: **Mr G F Grime** (Hon Secretary), 4 Lostock Avenue, Hazel Gr, Stockport, Macclesfield, Cheshire.
Mr Peter Sharples (Conservation, Access and Recreation Manager), North West Water Ltd, Woodhead Rd, Tintwhistle, Hadfield via Hyde, SK14 7HR.
(T) 01457 864187
Profile: **FT:** Game; **WN:** Horsecoppice; **WT:** Reservoir (Still).
Ref: FH2305

HORSEMILL STREAM

Horsemill Stream, Waltons Walk Fishery, Enfield, London, **LONDON (GREATER)**, EN2, **England**.
Contact/s: **Mr Krizim Seltham** (Angling Manager), Lee Valley Regional Park Authority, Myddleton House, Bulls Cross, Enfield, EN2 9HG.
(T) 01992 709832
(E) garysmith@leevalleypark.org.uk

Profile: FT: Coarse; WN: Horsemill; WT: Stream (Moving).
Ref: FH2306

HORSESHOE LAKE

Horseshoe Lake, Burford Rd, Lechlade, **GLOUCESTERSHIRE**, GL7, **England**.
(W) www.carpsociety.com
Contact/s: Secretary, The Carp Society, Horseshoe Lake, Burford Rd, Lechlade, GL7 3QQ.
(T) 01367 253959
(E) info@carp-society.co.uk
Mr Clive Owden (Head Bailiff). **(M)** 07788 124671
(E) cliveo@carp-society.co.uk
Profile: FT: Coarse; WN: Horseshoe; WT: Lake (Still); F. Size: 83 Acres; W. Size: 69 Acres. **Location:** Nr. Rd: Burford Road; Main Rd: A361.
Ref: FH2307

HORSESHOE LAKE

Horseshoe Lake, Blakeway, West Hay Moor, Wedmore, **SOMERSET**, BS28, **England**.
Contact/s: **Mrs Sue Moore** (Owner), Broadway House Caravan Park, Axbridge Rd, Cheddar, Somerset, BS27 3DB.
(T) 01934 742610
Profile: FT: Coarse; WN: Horseshoe; WT: Lake (Still); F. Size: 3 Acres; W. Size: 2 Acres. **Location:** Nr. Rd: B3151; Main Rd: B3151; Rail: Weston-super-Mare.
Ref: FH2308

HORSESHOE LAKE TROUT FISHERY

Horseshoe Lake Trout Fishery, Sheffield, **YORKSHIRE (SOUTH)**, S26, **England**.
Contact/s: **Mr David Hull** (Manager).
(T) 01909 773826
Profile: FT: Game; WN: Horseshoe; WT: Lake (Still) W. Size: 2 Acres.
Ref: FH2309

HORTON BOAT POOL

Horton Boat Pool, Stanwell Rd, Horton, Slough, **BUCKINGHAMSHIRE**, SL3 9PE, **England**.
(W) www.rmcangling.co.uk
Contact/s: **Mr Ian Welch** (Angling Manager), RMC Angling, The Square, Lightwater, Surrey, GU18 5SS.
(T) 01276 453300 (F) 01276 456611
(E) info@rmcangling.co.uk
Profile: FT: Coarse; WN: Boat Pool; WT: Lake (Still) W. Size: 6 Acres. **Location:** Nr. Rd: Stanwell Road; Main Rd: M25, junction 14; Rail: Wraysbury.
Ref: FH2310

HORTON CHURCH LAKE

Horton Church Lake, Stanwell Rd, Horton, Slough, **BUCKINGHAMSHIRE**, SL3 9PE, **England**.
(W) www.rmcangling.co.uk
Contact/s: **Mr Ian Welch** (Angling Manager), RMC Angling, The Square, Lightwater, Surrey, GU18 5SS.
(T) 01276 453300 (F) 01276 456611
(E) info@rmcangling.co.uk
Profile: FT: Coarse; WN: Church; WT: Lake (Still) W. Size: 14 Acres. **Location:** Nr. Rd: Stanwell Road; Main Rd: M25, junction 14; Rail: Wraysbury.
Ref: FH2311

HORTON GRANGE LAKE

Horton Grange Lake, Horton Grange, Blyth, **NORTHUMBERLAND**, NE24, **England**.
Contact/s: **Mr Albert Robson** (Membership Secretary), Wansbeck and Cramlington Angling Club, 10 Second Avenue, Ashington, Northumberland, NE63 0BJ.
(T) 01670 819647
Mr Brendon Heslop.
(T) 0191 3887199
Profile: FT: Coarse; WN: Horton Grange; WT: Lake (Still) W. Size: 2 Acres. **Location:** Nr. Rd: Milkhope Centre; Main Rd: A1, Newcastle, A19; Rail: Newcastle.
Ref: FH2312

HORTON KIRBY

Horton Kirby, Dartford, **KENT**, DA, **England**.
Contact/s: **D E Reeve**, 29 Berkeley Cresent, Dartford, Kent.
Profile: FT: Coarse; WN: Horton Kirby; WT: Gravel Pit (Still).
Ref: FH2313

HOSPITAL LOCHAN

Hospital Lochan, Glencoe, Ballachulish, **HIGHLAND**, PA39, **Scotland**.
Contact/s: **Mr J Alabaster** (owner), Scorry Breac Guest House, Glencoe Village, Ballachulish, Highland, PA39 4HT.
(T) 01855 811354 (F) 01855 811354
Profile: FT: Game; WN: Hospital; WT: Loch (Still).
Ref: FH2314

HOUCHINS RESERVOIRS

Houchins Reservoirs, Houchins Lane, Coggeshall, Colchester, **ESSEX**, CO6, **England**.
(W) www.c-a-p-s.co.uk
Contact/s: **Mr Paul Masters** (Secretary), CAPS Membership, 17 Azalea Court, Sycamore Rd, Colchester Essex, CO4 3NU.
(T) 01376 512255
(E) secretary@c-a-p-s.co.uk
Profile: FT: Coarse; WN: Houchins; WT: Reservoir (Still); F. Size: 4 Acres; W. Size: 3 Acres. **Location:** Nr. Rd: Houchins lane; Main Rd: A12.
Ref: FH2315

HOUGHTON REGIS QUARRY

Houghton Regis Quarry, Houghton Rd, Dunstable, **BEDFORDSHIRE**, LU, **England**.
Contact/s: **Mr Peter Garner**.
(T) 01582 472067
Profile: FT: Coarse; WN: Houghton Regis; WT: Lake (Still) W. Size: 11 Acres. **Location:** Nr. Rd: Houghton Road.
Ref: FH2316

HOUGHTONS LODGE

Houghtons Lodge, Wigan, **LANCASHIRE**, WN, **England**.
(W) www.wiganaa.f9.co.uk
Contact/s: **Mr Gerry Wilson** (Hon Secretary), Wigan and District Angling Association, 11 Guildford Avenue, Chorley, Lancashire, PR6 8TG.
(T) 01257 265905
(E) gerry@wiganna.freeserve.co.uk
Profile: FT: Coarse; WN: Houghton's Lodge; WT: Lake (Still) W. Size: 1 Acre. **Location:** Nr. Rd: B5375; Main Rd: M6, junction 26, A49, A577.
Ref: FH2317

HOWBROOK RESERVOIR

Howbrook Dam, High Green, Chapeltown, Sheffield, **YORKSHIRE (SOUTH)**, S35, **England**.
Contact/s: **Mr Steve Hinson**, 22a Eilam Cl, Kimberworth, Rotherham, S61 3QE.
(T) 01709 555225
Profile: FT: Coarse; WN: Howbrook; WT: Reservoir (Still) W. Size: 4 Acres. **Location:** Main Rd: A61.
Ref: FH2318

HOWIETOUN FISHERY

Howietoun Fishery, Milnholm House, Stirling, FK7 9QN, **Scotland**.
Contact/s: **Mr Rob Murray** (General Manager).
(T) 01786 812473
Profile: FT: Coarse; WN: Howietoun Fishery; WT: River (Moving). **Location:** Nr. Rd: Milnholm House.
Ref: FH2319

HOWLEY STREET POND

Howley Street Pond, Chard, **SOMERSET**, TA20, **England**.
Contact/s: **Mr Les Braunton**, Chard Angling Ctre, The Old Bakehouse, 2 Holyrood St, Chard, TA20 2AH.
Profile: FT: Coarse; WN: Howley; WT: Pond (Still) W. Size: 1 Acre. **Location:** Main Rd: A30.
Ref: FH2320

HOWWOOD TROUT FISHERY

Howwood Trout Fishery, Bowfield Rd, Howwood, Johnstone, **RENFREWSHIRE**, PA9 1DG, **Scotland**.
(W) www.howwoodtroutfishery.co.uk
Contact/s: **Mr John Cassells** (Owner), 100 Abbotsford Cres, Paisley, PA2 0SE.
(T) 01505 702688 (F) 01505 813068 (M) 07050 174589
Profile: FT: Coarse; WN: Howwood Dam; WT: Dam (Still) W. Size: 8 Acres. **Location:** Nr. Rd: B776; Main Rd: A737; Rail: Howwood.
Ref: FH2321

HOXNE FARM PONDS

Hoxne Farm Ponds, Sheriff Hutton Rd, Stensall, York, **YORKSHIRE (NORTH)**, YO, **England**.
Contact/s: **Mr D Bassindale** (Fishery Manager).
(T) 01904 490726
Profile: FT: Coarse; WN: Hoxne Farm; WT: Pond (Still). **Location:** Nr. Rd: Sheriff Hutton Road; Main Rd: A64, A1237.
Ref: FH2322

HOYLE MILL DAM

Hoyle Mill Dam, Kinsley, Pontefract, **YORKSHIRE (WEST)**, WF, **England**.
Contact/s: **Mr Stan Pollington**, 2 Common Rd, Kinsley, Pontefract, Yorkshire (West).
(T) 01977 612556
Profile: FT: Coarse; WN: Hoyle Mill; WT: Mill Dam (Still).
Ref: FH2323

HUCKLESBROOK LAKE

Hucklesbrook Lake, Fordingbridge, **HAMPSHIRE**, SP6, **England**.
Contact/s: **Mr Pete Reading** (Secretary), 17 Mayford Rd, Poole, Dorset, BH12 1PT.
(T) 01202 733110
Profile: FT: Coarse; WN: Hucklesbrook; WT: Lake (Still). **Location:** Nr. Rd: A338.
Ref: FH2324

HUDDERSFIELD BROAD CANAL

Huddersfield Broad Canal, Huddersfield, **YORKSHIRE (WEST)**, HD, **England**.
Contact/s: **Mr Martyn Highe**.
(T) 01924 498121
Mr Tim Worsnop (Secretary).
(T) 01484 713397
Profile: FT: Coarse; WN: Huddersfield Broad; WT: Canal (Still) W. Size: 6400 Metres.
Ref: FH2325

HUDDERSFIELD NARROW CANAL

Huddersfield Narrow Canal, Greenfield, Stalybridge, **CHESHIRE**, SK15, **England**.
Contact/s: **Mr Ian Baxter** (Membership Secretary), 6 Bagnall Cl, Uppermill, Oldham, Lancashire, OL3 6DW.
(T) 01457 875818 (M) 07973 345128
Profile: FT: Coarse; WN: Huddersfield Narrow; WT: Canal (Still). **Location:** Nr. Rd: Royal George Mills; Main Rd: A635.
Ref: FH2326

HUDDERSFIELD NARROW CANAL

Huddersfield Narrow Canal, Saddleworth, Oldham, **MANCHESTER (GREATER)**, OL3, **England**.
Contact/s: Fishery Manager.
(T) 01457 875500
Profile: FT: Coarse; WN: Hudderfield Narrow; WT: Canal (Still).
Ref: FH2327

HUDDERSFIELD NARROW CANAL

Huddersfield Narrow Canal, Wool Rd, Diggle, Oldham, **MANCHESTER (GREATER)**,

OL, **England**.
Contact/s: **Mr Ian Baxter** (Membership Secretary), 6 Bagnall Cl, Uppermill, Oldham, Lancashire, OL3 6DW.
(T) 01457 875818 **(M)** 07973 345128
Mr S Griffiths (Fishery Manager).
(T) 01606 723800
Profile: **FT:** Coarse; **WN:** Huddersfield Narrow; **WT:** Canal (Still) **W. Size:** 19200 Metres. Location: **Nr. Rd:** Wool Road to Royal George Mills; **Main Rd:** Oldham; **Rail:** Greenfield.
Ref: FH2328

HUDSONS FARM

Hudsons Farm, Rawcliffe Rd, St Michaels-on-Wyre, Preston, **LANCASHIRE**, PR3 0UH, **England**.
Profile: **FT:** Coarse; **WN:** Hudsons Farm; **WT:** Combination (Still).
Ref: FH2329

HULL (RIVER)

River Hull, Tickton, Beverley, **HUMBERSIDE**, HU17, **England**.
Contact/s: **Mr Paul Caygill** (Secretary), Hull and District Anglers Association, 17 Linley Cl, Leven, Beverley, HU17 5NP.
(T) 01964 542677
Profile: **FT:** Coarse; **WN:** Hull; **WT:** River (Moving). Location: **Main Rd:** A1035. **£Fr**
Ref: FH2330

HULL (RIVER)

River Hull, Beverley, **HUMBERSIDE**, HU17, **England**.
Contact/s: Manager, Minster News and Tackle, 3 Flemingate, Beverley, Humberside (North), HU17 0NP.
(T) 01482 882653
Mr Paul Caygill (Secretary), Hull and District Anglers Association, 17 Linley Cl, Leven, Beverley, HU17 5NP.
(T) 01964 542677
Profile: **FT:** Coarse; **WN:** Hull; **WT:** River (Moving).
Ref: FH2331

HULL (RIVER)

River Hull, Beverley, **HUMBERSIDE**, HU17, **England**.
Contact/s: Manager. **(M)** 07976 779983
Profile: **FT:** Coarse; **WN:** Hull; **WT:** River (Moving) **W. Size:** 3200 Metres. Location: **Main Rd:** A1079, A1174. **£Fr**
Ref: FH2332

HULLDOWN TROUT FISHERY

Hulldown Trout Fishery, Colne, **LANCASHIRE**, BB8 1EQ, **England**.
Contact/s: Fishery Manager.
(T) 01282 869789
Profile: **FT:** Game; **WN:** Hulldown Trout Fishery; **WT:** Lake (Still).
Ref: FH2333

HULTON PARK LAKE

Hulton Park Lake, Garthmere Rd, Over Hutton, Bolton, **LANCASHIRE**, BL, **England**.
Contact/s: **Mr Terence A McKee** (Secretary), Bolton and District Angling Association, 1 Lever Edge Lane, Bolton, Lancashire, BL3 3BU.
(T) 01204 393726
Profile: **FT:** Coarse; **WN:** Hulton Park Lake; **WT:** Pond (Still) **W. Size:** 1 Acre. Location: **Nr. Rd:** A6; **Main Rd:** A58 South of Bolton.
Ref: FH2334

HUMBERSIDE FISHERIES

Humberside Fisheries, Cleaves Farm, Skerne, Driffield, **HUMBERSIDE**, YO25 9HU, **England**.
Contact/s: Fishery Manager.
(T) 01377 253613
Profile: **FT:** Coarse; **WN:** Humberside Fisheries; **WT:** Lake (Still). Location: **Nr. Rd:** Cleaves Farm.
Ref: FH2335

HUNDRED FOOT (RIVER)

River Hundred Foot, Earith Bridge, Earith, Huntingdon, **CAMBRIDGESHIRE**, PE1, **England**.
Contact/s: **Mr Graham Tweed** (Secretary), Cambridge Fish Preservation Angling Society, 27a Villa Rd, Impington, Cambridge, CB4 9NZ.
(T) 01223 234616
Profile: **FT:** Coarse; **WN:** Hundred Foot; **WT:** River (Moving) **W. Size:** 6400 Metres. Location: **Nr. Rd:** Earith Bridge to Sutton Gault.
Ref: FH2336

HUNDRED POOL

Hundred Pool, Great Witley, Hereford, **HEREFORDSHIRE**, HR, **England**.
Contact/s: **Mr Stan Lewis** (Manager), S Lewis Fishing Tackle, 2 Severnside South, Bewdley, Worcestershire, DY12 2DX.
(T) 01299 403358
Profile: **FT:** Coarse; **WN:** The Hundred; **WT:** Pool (Still) **W. Size:** 4 Acres. Location: **Nr. Rd:** Abberley to Stourport-on-Severn; **Main Rd:** Great Witley to Witley Court.
Ref: FH2337

HUNSTRETE LAKE COMPLEX

Hunstrete Lake Complex, Hunstrete, Nr Marksbury, Bath, **SOMERSET**, BS, **England**.
(W) www.homeusers.prestel.co.uk/rope/bathampton
Contact/s: **Mr Dave Crookes** (Secretary), 25 Otago Trce, Larkhall, Bath, Somerset, BA1 6SX.
(T) 01225 427164
Profile: **FT:** Coarse; **WN:** Main Lake, Bridge Pool, & Withy Pool; **WT:** Lake (Still); **F. Size:** 12 Acres. Location: **Nr. Rd:** Hunstrete; **Main Rd:** A368; **Rail:** Bath.
Ref: FH2338

HUNTERS MOON

Hunters Moon, Hunters Moon Lodge, Henford Marsh, Warminster, **WILTSHIRE**, BA12 9PA, **England**.
Contact/s: **Ron**.
(T) 01985 21997
Profile: **FT:** Combination; **WN:** Avon; **WT:** Combination (Still).
Ref: FH2339

HUNTINGDON (RIVER)

River Huntingdon, Huntingdon, **CAMBRIDGESHIRE**, PE1, **England**.
Contact/s: **Mrs A Wallis** (Secretary), Huntington A and FPS, 8 Clayton's Way, Huntingdon, Cambridgeshire, PE18 7UT.
Profile: **FT:** Coarse; **WN:** Huntingdon; **WT:** River (Moving). Location: **Nr. Rd:** Town Bridge to Hartford Church.
Ref: FH2340

HUNTLEY CARP POOLS

Huntley Carp Pools, Huntley, Gloucester, **GLOUCESTERSHIRE**, GL19, **England**.
Contact/s: **Mr J R Tipper**, South View, Green Lane, Hardwicke, Gloucestershire, GL4 7TH.
(T) 01452 883207
Profile: **FT:** Combination; **WN:** Huntley Carp Pools; **WT:** Lake (Still) **W. Size:** 8 Acres. Location: **Nr. Rd:** A40.
Ref: FH2341

HUNTS CORNER

Hunts Corner, Shimano Linear Fisheries (Oxford), Smiths Concrete Site, Hardwick Village, Witney, **OXFORDSHIRE**, OX8 7Q, **England**.
Contact/s: **Mr Len Gurd** (Owner), 10A Rackstraw Gr, Old Farm Park, Milton Keynes, Buckinghamshire, MK7 8PZ.
(T) 01908 645135 **(F)** 01908 645115
Profile: **FT:** Coarse; **WN:** Hunts; **WT:** Lake (Still); **F. Size:** 10 Acres; **W. Size:** 9 Acres. Location: **Nr. Rd:** B4449; **Main Rd:** A40; **Rail:** Oxford.
Ref: FH2342

HUNTSPILL (RIVER)

River Huntspill, Bridgwater, **SOMERSET**, TA, **England**.
Contact/s: Manager, Somerset Angling, 74 Bath Rd, Bridgwater, Somerset, TA6 4PL.
(T) 01278 431777or786934
Profile: **FT:** Coarse; **WN:** Huntspill; **WT:** River (Moving). Location: **Nr. Rd:** Sloway to Woolavington; **Main Rd:** M5, A38. **£Fr**
Ref: FH2343

HURCOTT POOL

Hurcott Pool, Kidderminster, **WORCESTERSHIRE**, DY, **England**.
Contact/s: Fishery Manager.
(T) 01562 861587
Mr Mal Storey, Mal Storey Angling Ctre, 129 Sutton Rd, Kidderminster, Worcestershire, DY11 6QR.
(T) 01562 745221 **(F)** 01562 745221
Profile: **FT:** Coarse; **WN:** Hurcott Pool; **WT:** Lake (Still) **W. Size:** 5 Acres.
Ref: FH2344

HURLEY LOCK

Hurley Lock, Hurley, Maidenhead, **BERKSHIRE**, SL6, **England**.
Contact/s: **Customer Service** (Recreational Manager), The Environment Agency, Kings Meadow Rd, Reading, Berkshire, RG1 8DQ.
(T) 0118 9535000 **(F)** 0118 9500388
Mr B Webb (The Lock Keeper).
(T) 01628 824334
Profile: **FT:** Combination; **WN:** Thames; **WT:** Lock (Still). Location: **Main Rd:** A423.
Ref: FH2345

HURST POND

Hurst Pond, Headland Business Park, Blashford, Ringwood, **HAMPSHIRE**, BH24, **England**.
Contact/s: **Mr Richard Middleton** (Manager), Ringwood Tackle, 5 The Bridges, Ringwood, Hampshire, BH24 1EA.
(T) 01425 475155
Profile: **FT:** Coarse; **WN:** Hurst; **WT:** Pond (Still) **W. Size:** 2 Acres. Location: **Nr. Rd:** Fordingbridge to Ringwood; **Main Rd:** A338.
Ref: FH2346

HURSTON LANE

Hurston Lane, Hurst Lane, Storrington, Pulborough, **SUSSEX (WEST)**, RH20, **England**.
Contact/s: **Mr Ash Girdler**, 3 Chase Plain Cottages, Portsmouth Rd, Hindhead, Surrey, GU26 6BZ.
(T) 01428 607768
Profile: **FT:** Coarse; **WN:** Hurston Lane; **WT:** Lake (Still) **W. Size:** 2 Acres. Location: **Nr. Rd:** Brighton to Petworth; **Main Rd:** A283, left into Hurst Lane.
Ref: FH2347

HURWORTH BURN RESERVOIR

Hurworth Burn Reservoir, Hurworth Burn, Darlington, **COUNTY DURHAM**, DL2, **England**.
Contact/s: Manager, Anglers Services Ltd, 45 Claypath, Durham, County Durham, DH1 1QS.
(T) 0191 3847584
Mr Mark Arrow-Smith (Membership Secretary), Angler's Services, 27 Park Rd, Hartlepool, Cleveland, TS24 7PW.
(T) 01429 274844or266522
Profile: **FT:** Combination; **WN:** Hurworth Burn; **WT:** Reservoir (Still) **W. Size:** 50 Acres. Location: **Nr. Rd:** Billingham to Trimdon; **Main Rd:** A19.
Ref: FH2348

HURY RESERVOIR

Hury Reservoir, Romaldkirk, Barnard Castle, **COUNTY DURHAM**, DL12, **England**.
Contact/s: **Mr Paul Russell**, Northumbrian Water Ltd, Head Office, Recreation Department, Abbey Rd, Durham DH1 5FJ.
(T) 0191 3832222 **(F)** 0191 3841920

Profile: FT: Game; WN: Hury; WT: Reservoir (Still). **Location:** Nr. Rd: Romaldkirk.
Ref: FH2349

HUTON POND

Huton Pond, Hutton Moor Rd, Weston-Super-Mare, **SOMERSET**, BS22, **England**.
Profile: FT: Coarse; WN: Huton Pond; WT: Gravel Pit (Still) W. Size: 2 Acres. **Location:** Nr. Rd: Hutton Moor Road; Main Rd: M5, Weston-Super-Mare.
Ref: FH2350

HUTTON RUDBY PONDS

Hutton Rudby Ponds, Campion Lane, Hutton Rudby, Yarm, **CLEVELAND**, TS1, **England**.
Contact/s: Mr Ron Thompson (Secretary), 25 Endsleigh Drive, Acklam, Middlesbrough, TS5 4RG.
(T) 01642 863067
Profile: FT: Coarse; WN: Hutton Rudby; WT: Pond (Still). **Location:** Nr. Rd: Campion Lane; Main Rd: Crathorne to Hutton Rudby. £Fr
Ref: FH2351

HUXLEYS HAMPTON FERRY FISHERY

Huxleys Hampton Ferry Fisheries, Hampton Ferry, Boat Lane, Evesham, **WORCESTERSHIRE**, WR11 4BP, **England**.
Contact/s: Mrs Diana Raphael (Manager).
(T) 01386 442458 (F) 01386 41270 (M) 07808 848970
(E) diana@raphael.wynel.com.uk
Profile: FT: Combination; WN: Warwickshire Avon; WT: River (Moving) W. Size: 1560 Metres. **Location:** Nr. Rd: Boat Lane; Main Rd: A46; Rail: Evesham. £Fr
Ref: FH2352

HYDE LAKE

Hyde Lake, Hyde, Wareham, **DORSET**, BH20, **England**.
Contact/s: Mr Jim Bagley (Secretary), Hyde Angling Club, Heather Lodge, Hyde, Wareham.
(T) 01929 471402or463127
Profile: FT: Coarse; WN: Hyde; WT: Lake (Still) W. Size: 2 Acres.
Ref: FH2353

HYDE LANE LAKES

Hyde Lane Lakes, Hyde Lane, Buckingham, **BUCKINGHAMSHIRE**, MK18, **England**.
Contact/s: Mrs J Begley (Secretary), Buckinghamshire District Angling Association, 20 Vicarage Rd, Steeple Claydon, Buckinghamshire, MK18 2PU.
(T) 01296 730577
Profile: FT: Coarse; WN: Hyde Lane; WT: Lake (Still) W. Size: 40 Acres. **Location:** Nr. Rd: Hyde Lane.
Ref: FH2354

HYKEHAM PIT

Hykeham Pit, North Hykeham, Lincoln, **LINCOLNSHIRE**, LN6, **England**.
Contact/s: Mr Peter Mason (Bailiff), 16 Phonthonock Drive, Saxby, Lincoln, LN1 2JE.
(T) 01522 809364
Profile: FT: Coarse; WN: Hyke Pit; WT: Lake (Still).
Ref: FH2355

IAN HEAPS PREMIER FISHERIES

Ian Heaps Premier Fisheries And School Of Angling, Holgan Farm, Llawhaden, Narberth, **PEMBROKESHIRE**, SA67 8DJ, **Wales**.
(W) www.fisheries.co.uk/ianheaps
Contact/s: Mr Ian Heaps.
(T) 01437 541285
Profile: FT: Coarse; WN: Ian Heaps Premier Fisheries And School Of Angling; WT: Lake (Still); F. Size: 12 Acres; W. Size: 8 Acres. **Location:** Nr. Rd: Robeston Wathen to Canaston Bridge; Main Rd: A40; Rail: Narberth.
Ref: FH2356

IBSLEY POOLS

Ibsley Pools, Ibsley, Ringwood, **HAMPSHIRE**, BH24, **England**.
Contact/s: Mr Andrews (Secretary), 4 Marley Cl, New Milton, Hamptonshire, BH25 5LL.
Mr Pete Reading (Secretary), 17 Mayford Rd, Poole, Dorset, BH12 1PT.
(T) 01202 733110
Profile: FT: Coarse; WN: Ibsley; WT: Pool (Still). **Location:** Nr. Rd: Ringwood to Fordingbridge; Main Rd: A338.
Ref: FH2357

IDEN WOOD FISHERY

Iden Wood Fishery, The Grayling, Main St, Peasmarsh, Rye, **SUSSEX (EAST)**, TN31 6YA, **England**.
Contact/s: Mr Andy Ashdown.
(T) 01797 230241 (F) 01797 230241 (M) 07803 790862
Profile: FT: Coarse; WN: Iden Wood Fishery; WT: Combination (Still); F. Size: 60 Acres. **Location:** Nr. Rd: Coldharbour Lane; Main Rd: A268; Rail: Rye.
Ref: FH2358

IDLE (RIVER)

River Idle, Bailey Bridge, Bawtry, Doncaster, **YORKSHIRE (SOUTH)**, DN10, **England**.
Contact/s: Mr Maurice Tate (Secretary), Doncaster and District Angling Association, 28 Holmescarr Rd, New Rossington, Doncaster, DN11 0QF.
(T) 01302 865482
Profile: FT: Coarse; WN: Idle; WT: River (Moving) W. Size: 3200 Metres. **Location:** Nr. Rd: Bailey Bridge; Main Rd: South Yorkshire.
Ref: FH2359

IDLE (RIVER)

River Idle, Bawtry, Doncaster, **YORKSHIRE (SOUTH)**, DN10, **England**.
Contact/s: Mr Maurice Tate (Secretary), Doncaster and District Angling Association, 28 Holmescarr Rd, New Rossington, Doncaster, DN11 0QF.
(T) 01302 865482
Mr Richard Britten (Manager), Environment Agency, Trentside Offices, Scarrington Rd, West Bridgford, Nottingham NG2 5FA.
(T) 0115 9455722 (F) 0115 9817743
Mr W Sams (Secretary), Doncaster and District Angling Association, 28 Pipering Lane, Scawthorpe, Doncaster.
(T) 01302 780271
Profile: FT: Coarse; WN: Idle; WT: River (Moving) W. Size: 3200 Metres.
Ref: FH2360

IDLE (RIVER)

River Idle, Bawtry, Doncaster, **YORKSHIRE (SOUTH)**, DN10, **England**.
Contact/s: Manager, Environment Agency, Trentside Offices, Scarrington Rd, West Bridgford, Nottingham NG2 5FA.
(T) 0115 9455722 (F) 0115 9817743
Profile: FT: Coarse; WN: Idle; WT: River (Moving) W. Size: 480 Metres.
Ref: FH2361

ILEN (RIVER)

River Ilen, Cois Abhann, Coolnagarrane, Skibbereen, **COUNTY CORK**, **Ireland**.
Contact/s: Area Manager, South Western Regional Fisheries Board, 1 Neville Trce, Macroom, County Cork, Ireland.
(T) 026 41221 (F) 026 41222
(E) swrfb@swrfb.ie
Manager, Fallons Sports Shop, North St, Skibbereen, County Cork.
Mr Arthur Taylor.
(T) 028 21472
Profile: FT: Game; WN: Ilen; WT: River (Moving) W. Size: 33600 Metres. **Location:** Nr. Rd: Drimoleague Road; Rail: Cork.
Ref: FH2362

INCE MOSS FISHERIES

Ince Moss Fisheries, Spring View, Wigan, **LANCASHIRE**, **England**.
Contact/s: Mr Phil Aspinall (Owner), Platt Bridge Angling Ctre, 68 Warrington Rd, Platt Bridge, Wigan, Lancashire, WN2 5JA.
(T) 01942 865540
Profile: FT: Coarse; WN: Ince Moss Fisheries; WT: Pit (Still).
Ref: FH2363

INCE PARK LAKE

Ince Park Lake, Wigan, **LANCASHIRE**, WN, **England**.
(W) www.wiganaa.f9.co.uk
Contact/s: Mr Gerry Wilson (Hon Secretary), Wigan and District Angling Association, 11 Guildford Avenue, Chorley, Lancashire, PR6 8TG.
(T) 01257 265905
(E) gerry@wiganna.freeserve.co.uk
Profile: FT: Coarse; WN: Ince Park; WT: Lake (Still) W. Size: 1 Acre. **Location:** Nr. Rd: A577; Main Rd: A49, A577, M6, junction 26.
Ref: FH2364

INDIO POND

Indio Pond, Newton Rd, Bovey Tracey, Newton Abbot, **DEVON**, TQ13 9DY, **England**.
(W) www.indiopond.com
Contact/s: Mr Marcel Charlier (Manager).
(T) 01626 832508 (F) 01626 835310
(E) holidays@indiopond.com
Profile: FT: Coarse; WN: Indio; WT: Pond (Still); F. Size: 10 Acres; W. Size: 3 Acres. **Location:** Nr. Rd: Newton Road; Main Rd: A38; Rail: Newton Abbot.
Ref: FH2365

INGESTONE FISHERY

Ingestone Fishery, Foy, Ross-on-Wye, **HEREFORDSHIRE**, HR9, **England**.
Contact/s: Ms Lyn Cobley (Information Contact), 8 Brick End, Foy, Ross-on-Wye.
(T) 01989 565943
Profile: FT: Game; WN: Wye; WT: River (Moving) W. Size: 3200 Metres.
Ref: FH2366

INGS FARM TROUT FISHERY

Ings Farm Trout Fishery, Ing Ends Farm, Barley, Nelson, **LANCASHIRE**, BB9 8AR, **England**.
Contact/s: Mr Ernest Bullough (Owner).
(T) 01282 613819
Profile: FT: Game; WN: Mirewater; WT: Lake (Still).
Ref: FH2367

INLER (RIVER)

River Inler, Comber, Newtownards, **COUNTY DOWN**, BT23, **Northern Ireland**.
Contact/s: Mr John Rowan, Comber Angling and Country Pursuits, 23 Bridge St, Comber, Newtownards, BT23 5AT.
(T) 028 91870777 (F) 028 91870777
Profile: FT: Game; WN: Inler; WT: River (Moving) W. Size: 3200 Metres.
Ref: FH2368

INNIS MOORE TROUT FISHERY

Innis Moore Trout Fishery, Stan Mays Garage, Higher Bore St, Bodmin, **DEVON**, PL3, **England**.
Contact/s: Mr Roger Lashbrook (Manager).
(T) 01208 72659
Profile: FT: Game; WN: Camel; WT: River (Moving). **Location:** Nr. Rd: Higher Bore Street.
Ref: FH2369

INNISCARRA LAKE

Inniscarra Lake, Inniscarra, **COUNTY CORK**, **Ireland**.
(W) www.swrfb.ie
Contact/s: Area Manager, South West Regional Fisheries Board, 1 Nevilles Trce, Macroom, County Cork, Ireland.
(T) 026 41221

(E) swrfb@swrfb.ie
Profile: **FT:** Coarse; **WN:** Inniscarra; **WT:** Lake (Still) **W. Size:** 1300 Acres.
Ref: FH2370

INNS LAKE

Inns Lake, Rickmansworth, **HERTFORDSHIRE**, WD3, **England**.
Contact/s: **Mr T Pritchard** (Secretary), Three Valleys Angling Club, London Rd, Rickmansworth, Hertfordshire, WD3 1LB. **(M)** 08457 823333
Profile: **FT:** Coarse; **WN:** Inns Lake; **WT:** Combination (Still & Moving).
Ref: FH2371

INNY (RIVER)

River Inny, Trecarrel Bridge, Liskeard, **CORNWALL**, PL14, **England**.
Contact/s: **Mr Bill Eliot** (Secretary), Liskeard and District Angling Club, 64 Portbyhan Rd, West Looe, Cornwall, PL13 2QN.
(T) 01503 264173
Profile: **FT:** Game; **WN:** Inny; **WT:** River (Moving) **W. Size:** 1000 Metres. **Location:** **Nr. Rd:** A38; **Main Rd:** A38; **Rail:** Liskeard.
Ref: FH2372

INVER (RIVER)

River Inver, Larne, **COUNTY ANTRIM**, BT40, **Northern Ireland**.
Contact/s: **Mr Frank Quigley**, 124 Low Rd, Islandmagee, Larne, County Antrim.
(T) 028 93382610
Profile: **FT:** Game; **WN:** Inver; **WT:** River (Moving) **W. Size:** 3200 Metres.
Ref: FH2373

INVERAWE FISHERIES

Inverawe Fisheries, Taynuilt, **ARGYLL AND BUTE**, PA35 1HU, **Scotland**.
Contact/s: **Mr Robert Campbell-Preston** (Owner).
(T) 01866 822446 **(F)** 01866 822274
Profile: **FT:** Game; **WN:** Inverawe Fisheries; **WT:** Combination (Still & Moving); **F. Size:** 10 Acres; **W. Size:** 7 Acres. **Location:** **Nr. Rd:** A82; **Main Rd:** A82; **Rail:** Taynuilt.
Ref: FH2374

IRFON (RIVER)

River Irfon, Llanwrtyd Wells, **POWYS**, LD5, **Wales**.
Contact/s: **Mr Nigel Roff** (Manager), Abernant Lake Hotel, Station Rd, Llanwrtyd Wells, Powys, LD5 4RR.
Profile: **FT:** Game; **WN:** Irfon; **WT:** River (Moving) **W. Size:** 1600 Metres.
Ref: FH2375

IRFON (RIVER)

River Irfon, Llangammarch Wells, **POWYS**, LD4, **Wales**.
Contact/s: **Mrs Jackie Smith** (Head Receptionist), The Lake Country House, Llangammarch Wells, Powys, LD4 4BS.
(T) 01591 620202 **(F)** 01591 620457
Profile: **FT:** Game; **WN:** Irfon; **WT:** River (Moving) **W. Size:** 5600 Metres.
Ref: FH2376

IRFON (RIVER)

River Irfon, Builth Wells, **POWYS**, LD2, **Wales**.
Contact/s: **Mr Charles Picton** (Manager), Hendre, Llanynis, Builth Wells, Powys, LD2 3HN.
(T) 01982 552237or551070 **(F)** 01982 553942
Profile: **FT:** Game; **WN:** Irfon; **WT:** River (Moving) **W. Size:** 4800 Metres.
Ref: FH2377

IRFON (RIVER)

River Irfon, Builth Wells, **POWYS**, LD2, **Wales**.
Contact/s: **Mr Lance Burton** (Secretary), Angler House, Pentrosfa, Cresent, Llandrindod Wells, Powys.
(T) 01597 823119
Profile: **FT:** Combination; **WN:** Irfon; **WT:** River (Moving) **W. Size:** 2400 Metres.
Location: **Main Rd:** At Builth Wells; **Rail:** Builth Road.
Ref: FH2378

IRONMONGERS POND

Ironmongers Pond, Wilford, Nottingham, **NOTTINGHAMSHIRE**, NG11 7, **England**.
Contact/s: **Mr I Foulds** (Secretary), Nottingham Angling Association, 95 Ilkeston Rd, Nottingham, Nottinghamshire, NG7 3HA.
(T) 0115 9033881or9708080
Profile: **FT:** Coarse; **WN:** Ironmongers; **WT:** Pond (Still) **W. Size:** 6 Acres.
Ref: FH2379

IRT (RIVER)

River Irt, Holmrook, **CUMBRIA**, CA19, **England**.
Contact/s: **Mr D J Dixon** (Secretary), 1 Churchill Drive, Millom, Cumbria, LA18 5DD.
(T) 01229 774241
Profile: **FT:** Game; **WN:** Irt; **WT:** River (Moving). **Location:** **Nr. Rd:** A595; **Rail:** Drigg.
Ref: FH2380

IRTHING (RIVER)

River Irthing, Haltwhistle, **NORTHUMBERLAND**, NE49, **England**.
Contact/s: **Mr Chris Wilson** (Secretary), Melkridge House, Melkridge, Haltwhistle, NE49 0LT.
(T) 01434 320942
Profile: **FT:** Game; **WN:** Irthing; **WT:** River (Moving) **W. Size:** 20000 Metres. **Location:** **Nr. Rd:** A69; **Main Rd:** A69; **Rail:** Haltwhistle.
Ref: FH2381

IRWELL (RIVER)

River Irwell, Clifton, Preston, **LANCASHIRE**, PR4, **England**.
Contact/s: Fishery Manager.
Profile: **FT:** Coarse; **WN:** Irwell; **WT:** River (Moving).
Ref: FH2382

IRWELL (RIVER)

River Irwell, Bury, **MANCHESTER (GREATER)**, BL8, **England**.
Contact/s: Fishery Manager.
(T) 0161 7642858
Profile: **FT:** Coarse; **WN:** Irwell; **WT:** River (Moving). **Location:** **Main Rd:** M63, junction 4.
Ref: FH2383

ISE (RIVER)

River Ise, Kettering, **NORTHAMPTONSHIRE**, NN14, **England**.
Contact/s: **Mr D Garrett**, Kettering and Thrapston Angling Association, 17 Browning Avenue, Kettering, Northamptonshire, NN16 8NP.
(T) 01536 515547
Mr Mick Cardy, 50 Warmton Lane, Kettering, Northamptonshire.
(T) 01536 518178
Profile: **FT:** Coarse; **WN:** Ise; **WT:** River (Moving) **W. Size:** 2400 Metres. **Location:** **Main Rd:** A6003.
Ref: FH2384

ISFIELD (RIVER)

River Isfield, Isfield, Uckfield, **SUSSEX (EAST)**, TN22, **England**.
Profile: **FT:** Coarse; **WN:** Isfield; **WT:** River (Moving). **Location:** **Nr. Rd:** Isfield to Uckfield.
Ref: FH2385

ISIS NO 1 LAKE 19

Isis No 1 Lake 19, The Cotswold Water Park, South Cerney, Cirencester, **GLOUCESTERSHIRE**, GL7, **England**.
Contact/s: **Mr Peter Gilbert** (Chairman), 31 Havelock St, Swindon, Wiltshire, SN1 1SD.
(T) 01793 353396 **(F)** 01793 353396
Profile: **FT:** Coarse; **WN:** Lake 19; **WT:** Gravel Pit (Still) **W. Size:** 8 Acres. **Location:** **Nr. Rd:** Broadway to South Cerney; **Main Rd:** A419, A429.
Ref: FH2386

ISLA (RIVER)

River Isla, Blairgowrie, **ANGUS**, DD2, **Scotland**.
Contact/s: **Mrs M C Milne** (Secretary), 1 West Park Gardens, Dundee, Angus, DD2 1NY.
Profile: **FT:** Combination; **WN:** Isla; **WT:** River (Moving).
Ref: FH2387

ISLAND AND CARTWHEEL LODGES

Island And Cartwheel Lodges, Bury, **MANCHESTER (GREATER)**, BL, **England**.
Profile: **FT:** Coarse; **WN:** Island And Cartwheel Lodges; **WT:** Lake (Still).
Ref: FH2388

ISLAND DAM

Island Dam, Billinge, Wigan, **LANCASHIRE**, WN5, **England**.
Contact/s: Fishery Manager.
(T) 01695 624119
Profile: **FT:** Coarse; **WN:** Island Dam; **WT:** Lake (Still). **Location:** **Main Rd:** A571 St Helens Road.
Ref: FH2389

ISLAND FISH FARM/MEADOW LAKES

Island Fish Farm And Meadow Lakes, Muggleton Lane, Limerstone, Brighstone, Newport, **ISLE OF WIGHT**, PO30 4PL, **England**.
(W) www.islandfishing.co.uk
Contact/s: **Mr Julian Bagnall**.
(T) 01983 740941
(E) julian.bagnall@lineone.net
Ms Stephanie Bagnall.
(T) 01983 740941
Profile: **FT:** Combination; **WN:** Island Fish Farm And Meadow Lakes; **WT:** Lake (Still); **F. Size:** 5 Acres; **W. Size:** 2 Acres. **Location:** **Nr. Rd:** Muggleton Lane; **Main Rd:** B3323; **Rail:** Shanklin.
Ref: FH2390

ISLAND POND - RACKERHAYES

Island Pond - Rackerhayes, Newton Abbot, **DEVON**, TQ1, **England**.
Contact/s: Shop Manager, Drum Sports Limited, 47 Courtenay St, Newton Abbot, Devon, TQ12 2QN.
(T) 01626 205040
Mr David Horder (Secretary), Mistlemead, Woodlands, Higher Sandygate, Newton Abbot, TQ12 3QN.
(T) 01626 364173
Profile: **FT:** Coarse; **WN:** Island Pool; **WT:** Gravel Pit (Still) **W. Size:** 5 Acres.
Ref: FH2391

ISLAND WATERS

Island Waters, Whinney Hill, Stockton-on-Tees, **CLEVELAND**, TS, **England**.
Contact/s: **Mr John Taylor**.
(T) 01642 589092
Profile: **FT:** Coarse; **WN:** Island Waters; **WT:** Lake (Still). **Location:** **Nr. Rd:** A66.
Ref: FH2392

ISLE (RIVER)

River Isle, Langport, **SOMERSET**, TA10, **England**.
Contact/s: **Mr R Payne** (Secretary), 194 Milton Rd, Weston-Super-Mare, Somerset, BS22 8AE.
(T) 01934 414445
Profile: **FT:** Coarse; **WN:** Isle; **WT:** River (Moving) **W. Size:** 800 Metres.
Ref: FH2393

ISLE (RIVER)

River Isle, Hambridge, Langport, **SOMERSET**, TA10, **England**.
Contact/s: **Mr David Horder** (Secretary), Mistlemead, Woodlands, Higher Sandygate, Newton Abbot, TQ12 3QN.
(T) 01626 364173

Profile: **FT:** Coarse; **WN:** Isle; **WT:** River (Moving).
Ref: FH2394

ISLE LAKE

Isle Lake, Isle Estate, Bicton Village, Shrewsbury, **SHROPSHIRE**, **England**.
Contact/s: **Mr John Turner** (Hon Secretary), Prince Albert Angling Society, 15 Pexhill Drive, Macclesfield, Cheshire, SK10 3LP.
(T) 01625 422010
Profile: **FT:** Coarse; **WN:** Isle; **WT:** Lake (Still); **F. Size:** 10 Acres; **W. Size:** 10 Acres. **Location:** **Main Rd:** B4380; **Rail:** Shrewsbury.
Ref: FH2395

ISLIP NATURE LAKE

Islip Nature Lake, Mill Lane, Islip, Thrapston, Kettering, **NORTHAMPTONSHIRE**, NN14, **England**.
Contact/s: **Mr D Garrett**, Kettering and Thrapston Angling Association, 17 Browning Avenue, Kettering, Northamptonshire, NN16 8NP.
(T) 01536 515547
Mr Mick Cardy, 50 Warmton Lane, Kettering, Northamptonshire.
(T) 01536 518178
Profile: **FT:** Coarse; **WN:** Islip Nature; **WT:** Lake (Still). **Location:** **Nr. Rd:** A604 to Islip; **Main Rd:** A14.
Ref: FH2396

ITCHEN (RIVER)

River Itchen, Winchester, **HAMPSHIRE**, SO21, **England**.
Contact/s: **Mr Simon Cooper**, Fishing Breaks Ltd, 23 Compton Trce, Romsey, London, N1 2UN.
(T) 020 73598818 **(F)** 020 73594540 **(M)** 07973 766639
(E) info@fishingbreaks.co.uk
Profile: **FT:** Game; **WN:** Itchen; **WT:** River (Moving) **W. Size:** 2500 Metres. **Location:** **Nr. Rd:** B3047; **Main Rd:** A272; **Rail:** Winchester.
Ref: FH2397

ITCHEN (RIVER)

River Itchen, Winchester, **HAMPSHIRE**, SO21, **England**.
Contact/s: **Mr Ian Hay** (Manager), The Rod Box, London Rd, King's Worthy, Winchester, SO23 7QN.
(T) 01962 883600
Profile: **FT:** Game; **WN:** Itchen; **WT:** River (Moving).
Ref: FH2398

ITCHEN NAVIGATION

Itchen Navigation, Itchen, Southampton, **HAMPSHIRE**, SO19, **England**.
Contact/s: Manager, The Rod Box, London Rd, King's Worthy, Winchester, SO23 7QN.
(T) 01962 883600
Mr F Hefford (Secretary), 20 Stoatley Rise, Haslemere, Surrey, GU27 1AF.
Profile: **FT:** Coarse; **WN:** Itchen Navigation; **WT:** Canal (Still).
Ref: FH2399

ITHON (RIVER)

River Ithon, Llandrindod Wells, **POWYS**, LD1, **Wales**.
Contact/s: Manager, Wayfarers Camping and Caravans, Ddole Rd, Llandrindod Wells, Powys.
(T) 01597 825100
Mr Bryan Price (Secretary), Llandrindod Wells Angling Association, The Cedars, Llanyre, Llandrindod Wells, LD1 6DY.
(T) 01597 823539 **(F)** 01597 823539
Profile: **FT:** Combination; **WN:** Ithon; **WT:** River (Moving) **W. Size:** 8000 Metres. **Location:** **Nr. Rd:** A4081, B4358; **Main Rd:** A483; **Rail:** Llandrindod Wells.
Ref: FH2400

IVEL (RIVER)

River Ivel, Twin Bridges, Henlow, **BEDFORDSHIRE**, SG16 6, **England**.
(W) www.badac.co.uk
Contact/s: **Mr D Porter** (Secretary), 72 Rivington Cres, Mill Hill, London, NW7 2LF.
(T) 020 84401303
Profile: **FT:** Coarse; **WN:** Ivel; **WT:** River (Moving) **W. Size:** 280 Metres. **Location:** **Nr. Rd:** A6001; **Main Rd:** A1.
Ref: FH2401

IVEL (RIVER)

River Ivel, Manor Farm, Lower Caldecote, Biggleswade, **BEDFORDSHIRE**, SG18 9BB, **England**.
(W) www.rmcangling.co.uk
Contact/s: **Mr Ian Welch** (Angling Manager), RMC Angling, The Square, Lightwater, Surrey, GU18 5SS.
(T) 01276 453300 **(F)** 01276 456611
(E) info@rmcangling.co.uk
Profile: **FT:** Coarse; **WN:** Ivel; **WT:** River (Moving) **W. Size:** 1200 Metres. **Location:** **Main Rd:** A1, London to Sandy.
Ref: FH2402

IVY HOUSE FARM

Ivy House Farm, Grittenham, Chippenham, **WILTSHIRE**, SN15 4JU, **England**.
Contact/s: **Mr Jo Warner** (Secretary).
(T) 01666 510368
Profile: **FT:** Coarse; **WN:** Ivy House; **WT:** Lake (Still) **W. Size:** 7 Acres. **Location:** **Main Rd:** M4.
Ref: FH2403

IZAAK WALTON FISHERY

Izaak Walton Fishery, Chebsey, Stafford, **STAFFORDSHIRE**, ST21 6JU, **England**.
Contact/s: **Mrs Brenda Jefferson**.
(T) 01785 761535 **(F)** 01785 761535
Profile: **FT:** Combination; **WN:** Izaak Walton Fishery; **WT:** Combination (Still); **F. Size:** 43 Acres; **W. Size:** 7 Acres. **Location:** **Nr. Rd:** Stafford to Eccleshall Road; **Main Rd:** A5013; **Rail:** Stafford.
Ref: FH2404

JACKLETTS FARM

Jackletts Farm, Bicknacre, Chelmsford, **ESSEX**, CM, **England**.
(W) www.bdac.co.uk
Contact/s: **Mr Derek Howard** (Hon Treasurer), Billericay and District Angling Club, 4 Long Meadow Drive, Wickford, Essex, SS11 8AX.
(T) 01268 734468
Profile: **FT:** Coarse; **WN:** Jackletts Farm; **WT:** Lake (Still); **F. Size:** 6 Acres; **W. Size:** 6 Acres. **Location:** **Nr. Rd:** B1418; **Main Rd:** A132; **Rail:** South Woodham Ferrers.
Ref: FH2405

JANESMOOR POND

Janesmoor Pond, Stoney Cross, Lyndhurst, **HAMPSHIRE**, SO43, **England**.
Contact/s: Manager, Recreation Section, Forestry Commission Office, The Queen's House, Lyndhurst, SO43 7NH.
(T) 023 80283141 **(F)** 023 80283929
Mr Jonathan Cook (New Forest Keeper), Stockely Cottage, Beaulieu Rd, Brockenhurst, Hampshire.
(T) 01590 623698
Mr Richard Middleton (Manager), Ringwood Tackle, 5 The Bridges, Ringwood, Hampshire, BH24 1EA.
(T) 01425 475155
Profile: **FT:** Coarse; **WN:** Janesmoor; **WT:** Lake (Still) **W. Size:** 1 Acre. **Location:** **Nr. Rd:** Fritham and Linwood; **Main Rd:** A31.
£Fr
Ref: FH2406

JARMAN FARM POOL

Jarman Farm Pool, Sutton, Macclesfield, **CHESHIRE**, **England**.
Contact/s: **Mr John Turner** (Hon Secretary), Prince Albert Angling Society, 15 Pexhill Drive, Macclesfield, Cheshire, SK10 3LP.
(T) 01625 422010
Profile: **FT:** Coarse; **WN:** Jarman Farm; **WT:** Pool (Still); **F. Size:** 1 Acre; **W. Size:** 1 Acre. **Location:** **Nr. Rd:** Byrons Lane; **Main Rd:** A52; **Rail:** Macclesfield.
Ref: FH2407

JED (RIVER)

River Jed, Jedburgh, **SCOTTISH BORDERS**, TD8, **Scotland**.
Contact/s: **Mr J Tait** (Secretary), 9 Boundaries, Jedburgh, Scottish Borders, TD8 6EX.
Profile: **FT:** Game; **WN:** Jed; **WT:** River (Moving).
Ref: FH2408

JENNETTS RESERVOIR

Jennetts Reservoir, South West Water Fishery, Bideford, **DEVON**, EX39, **England**.
Contact/s: **Mr Ashley Starr** (Ranger).
(T) 01288 321262
Mr Reg England (Manager), Peninsula Coarse Fisheries, St Cleer Depot, Lewdown, Okehampton, Devon EX20 4QT.
(T) 01837 871565 **(F)** 01837 871534
Profile: **FT:** Coarse; **WN:** Jennetts; **WT:** Reservoir (Still) **W. Size:** 8 Acres. **Location:** **Nr. Rd:** A386; **Main Rd:** Bideford.
Ref: FH2409

JERICHO LOCHS

Jericho Lochs, Dumfries, **DUMFRIES AND GALLOWAY**, DG1, **Scotland**.
Contact/s: **Mr Jimmy Younger** (Manager).
(T) 01387 750247
Mr M Pattie (Owner), Pattie's of Dumfries, 109 Queensberry St, Dumfries, Dumfries and Galloway, DG1 1BH.
(T) 01387 252891
Profile: **FT:** Game; **WN:** Jericho; **WT:** Lake (Still) **W. Size:** 12 Acres. **Location:** **Nr. Rd:** A701.
Ref: FH2410

JIMMYS LAKE

Jimmys Lake, Slinfold, Corringham, Standford-Le-Hope, **ESSEX**, SS17, **England**.
Mr Jim Housden (Manager), Rods N Reels, 17 Grover Walk, Corringham, Stanford-le-Hope, SS17 7LP.
(T) 01375 670742
Profile: **FT:** Coarse; **WN:** Jimmys; **WT:** Lake (Still). **Location:** **Nr. Rd:** B1420; **Main Rd:** A13.
Ref: FH2411

JINGLES FARM

Jingles Farm, Finchampstead, Wokingham, **BERKSHIRE**, RG40, **England**.
Contact/s: Fishery Manager.
(T) 0116 9732648
Profile: **FT:** Coarse; **WN:** Jingles Farm; **WT:** Lake (Still) **W. Size:** 1 Acre. **Location:** **Main Rd:** M3 and M4.
Ref: FH2412

JOHN OGAUNTS FISHERY

John Ogaunts Fishery, Kings Sombourne, Stockbridge, **HAMPSHIRE**, SO20, **England**.
Contact/s: **Mr Keith Purse** (Fishery Manager).
(T) 02380 252268
Profile: **FT:** Game; **WN:** John Ogaunts Fishery; **WT:** Lake (Still).
Ref: FH2413

JOHNS LAKE FISHERIES

Johns Lake Fisheries, Galley Hill, Aimes Green, Waltham Abbey, **ESSEX**, EN9, **England**.
Contact/s: **Karen Or Colin**.
(T) 01958 938153 **(M)** 07958 938152
Mr Colin Bartlett. **(M)** 07958 938153
Profile: **FT:** Coarse; **WT:** Lake (Still); **F. Size:** 15 Acres; **W. Size:** 7 Acres. **Location:** **Nr. Rd:** Galley Hill Road; **Main Rd:** Waltham Abbey to Upshire Road.
Ref: FH2414

JOHNSONS LAKE

Johnsons Lake, Water Lane, Enton Green, Milford, **SURREY**, **England**.
Contact/s: .
(T) 01483 422791
Profile: FT: Coarse; WN: Johnsons, formerly Enton Big Lake; WT: Lake (Still); F. Size: 30 Acres. Location: Nr. Rd: Water Lane; Main Rd: A286; Rail: Milford Station.
Ref: FH2415

JONES PIT

Jones Pit, Heath And Reach, Leighton Buzzard, **BEDFORDSHIRE**, LU7, **England**.
(W) www.rmcangling.co.uk
Contact/s: Mr Ian Welch (Angling Manager), RMC Angling, The Square, Lightwater, Surrey, GU18 5SS.
(T) 01276 453300 (F) 01276 456611
(E) info@rmcangling.co.uk
Profile: FT: Coarse; WN: Jones Pit; WT: Gravel Pit (Still) W. Size: 11 Acres.
Location: Nr. Rd: A5; Main Rd: A5.
Ref: FH2416

JUBILEE LAKES

Jubilee Lakes, Redworth, Darlington, **COUNTY DURHAM**, DL2 2UH, **England**.
Contact/s: Mr David Hayman (Owner).
(T) 01388 772611
Profile: FT: Game; WN: Jubilee; WT: Lake (Still); F. Size: 7 Acres; W. Size: 2 Acres.
Location: Main Rd: A68.
Ref: FH2417

JUMBLES RESERVOIR

Jumbles Reservoir, Bradshaw Rd, Bolton, **LANCASHIRE**, BL12 4JS, **England**.
Contact/s: Mr Glynn Haworth (North West Water Ranger), Jumbles Country Park, Bradshaw Rd, Bolton, Lancashire, BL12 4JS.
(T) 01204 853360
Mr Roy Rhodes (Conservation, Access and Recreation Manager), Rivington Water Treatment Works, Bolton Rd, Horwich, Bolton, BL6 7RN.
(T) 01204 664300
Profile: FT: Coarse; WN: Jumbles; WT: Reservoir (Still). Location: Nr. Rd: Bradshaw Road; Main Rd: A676. £Fr
Ref: FH2418

KAILZIE GARDENS FISHERY

Kailzie Gardens Fishery, Kailzie Gardens, Peebles, **SCOTTISH BORDERS**, EH45 9HT, **Scotland**.
Contact/s: Mr Guy Crowhurst.
(T) 01721 720099
Profile: FT: Game; WN: Kailzie Gardens Fishery; WT: Lake (Still) W. Size: 2 Acres.
Ref: FH2419

KAYS LAKES

Kays Lakes, Sessay, Thirsk, **YORKSHIRE (NORTH)**, YO7, **England**.
Contact/s: Mr David Kay (Fishery Manager).
(T) 01845 501321
Profile: FT: Coarse; WN: Kays; WT: Lake (Still).
Ref: FH2420

KAZAKO PONDS

Kazako Ponds, Macclesfield, **CHESHIRE**, **England**.
Profile: FT: Combination; WN: Kazako Ponds; WT: Gravel Pit (Still); F. Size: 132 Acres; W. Size: 1 Acre.
Ref: FH2421

KEAL COATES FISHERY

Keal Coates Lake, Fen Lane, East Keel, Spilsby, **LINCOLNSHIRE**, **England**.
Contact/s: Mark (Bailiff).
(T) 01790 763598
Profile: FT: Coarse; WN: Keal Coates Lake; WT: Lake (Still). Location: Nr. Rd: A16; Rail: Thorpe Culvert.
Ref: FH2422

KEARNS ALLEN LODGES

Kearns Allen Lodges, Accrington, **LANCASHIRE**, BB5, **England**.
Contact/s: Mr Gerry Lee.
(T) 01254 385290
Profile: FT: Coarse; WN: Kearns Allen Lodges; WT: Lake (Still).
Ref: FH2423

KEGWORTH DEEP LOCK

Kegworth Deep Lock, Kegworth, Derby, **DERBYSHIRE**, DE74, **England**.
Contact/s: Mr Stan Sharpe (Secretary).
(T) 0402 305132
Profile: FT: Coarse; WN: Soar (Devils Elbow to Kegworth Deep Lock); WT: River (Moving) W. Size: 2500 Metres.
Ref: FH2424

KELHEAD WATER

Kelhead Water, Annan, **DUMFRIES AND GALLOWAY**, DG12, **Scotland**.
Contact/s: Mr D Rothwell (Factor), Hoddom and Kinmount Estates, Hoddom Estate Office, Lockerbie, Dumfries and Galloway, DG11 1BE.
(T) 01576 300244 (F) 01576 300757
Ms Ross, Kinmount Bungalow, Kinmount, Annan.
(T) 01461 700344 (F) 01576 300757
Profile: FT: Coarse; WN: Kelhead Quarry; WT: Gravel Pit (Still); F. Size: 15 Acres; W. Size: 6 Acres. Location: Nr. Rd: A75; Main Rd: A75; Rail: Annan.
Ref: FH2425

KELLOW LAW POND

Kellow Law Pond, Deaf Hill, Ferryhill, **COUNTY DURHAM**, DL17, **England**.
Contact/s: Mr Barry Hignett (Secretary), Ferryhill and District Angling Club, 74 Grasmere Rd, Garden Farm Estate, Chester-le-Street, County Durham.
(T) 0191 3883557
Profile: FT: Coarse; WN: Kellow Law; WT: Pond (Still). Location: Nr. Rd: A167.
Ref: FH2426

KELLSWATER (RIVER)

River Kellswater, Ballymena, **COUNTY ANTRIM**, BT42, **Northern Ireland**.
Contact/s: Mr Phillip Mailey.
(T) 028 94473619after6pm
Mr Roy Fullerton.
(T) 028 25892455after6pm
Mr Trevor Duncan, Filling Station, Ferninsky Rd, Kells, Ballymena, County Antrim.
(T) 028 25891577
Profile: FT: Game; WN: Kellswater; WT: River (Moving) W. Size: 22400 Metres.
Ref: FH2427

KEMPSTONE HARDWICK

Kempstone Hardwick, Ampthill Rd, Kempstone Hardwick Village, Bedford, **BUCKINGHAMSHIRE**, MK4, **England**.
Profile: FT: Coarse; WN: Kempstone Hardwick; WT: Lake (Still) W. Size: 30 Acres.
Location: Nr. Rd: Ampthill Road.
Ref: FH2428

KEN (RIVER)

River Ken, Castle Douglas, **DUMFRIES AND GALLOWAY**, DG7, **Scotland**.
Contact/s: Mr Allan Cairnie (Secretary), New Galloway Angling Association, 4 Carsons Knowe, New Galloway, Castle Douglas, Dumfries and Galloway DG7 3RY. (M) 07747 178029
Mr James Hopkins (Treasurer), New Galloway Angling Association, 4 Carsons Knowe, New Galloway, Castle Douglas, Dumfries and Galloway DG7 3RY.
(T) 01644 420229
Profile: FT: Game; WN: Ken; WT: River (Moving). Location: Main Rd: A713; Rail: Dumfries.
Ref: FH2429

KENFIG LAKE

Kenfig Lake, Bridgend, CF31, **Wales**.
Contact/s: Mr S Evans, 110 Quarella Rd, Bridgend, Glamorgan (Vale of).
(T) 01656 785938
Profile: FT: Coarse; WN: Kenfig; WT: Lake (Still).
Ref: FH2430

KENMORE BEAT

Kenmore Beat, Taymouth Castle, Kenmore, Aberfeldy, **PERTH AND KINROSS**, PH15, **Scotland**.
(W) www.fishingnet.com/beats/kenmore.htm
Contact/s: Mr Paul Fishlock (Salmon Permit Contact), Taymouth Castle, 2 The Square, Kenmore, Perth and Kinross, PH15 2HH.
(T) 01887 830765 (F) 01887 830830
Profile: FT: Game; WN: Hotel, Ladies, Dairy and Chinese; WT: Pool (Still). Location: Nr. Rd: Kenmore Bridge to Chinese Bridge.
Ref: FH2431

KENN (RIVER)

River Kenn, Highbridge, **SOMERSET**, TA9, **England**.
Contact/s: Mr R L Purchase, 28 The Tynings, Clevedon, Somerset, BS21 7YP.
(T) 01275 878384
Profile: FT: Coarse; WN: Kenn; WT: River (Moving). Location: Nr. Rd: Highbridge and Burnham.
Ref: FH2432

KENN (RIVER)

River Kenn, Blind Yeo, Clevedon, **SOMERSET**, BS21, **England**.
Contact/s: Mr S Bonwick (Secretary), 13 Tennyson Avenue, Clevedon, Somerset, BS21 7QQ.
(T) 01275 791933
Profile: FT: Coarse; WN: Blind Yeo; WT: River (Moving) W. Size: 8000 Metres.
Location: Nr. Rd: Kenn Road; Main Rd: B3133 Southern Road.
Ref: FH2433

KENNEL LANE

Kennel Lane, Billericay, **ESSEX**, CM, **England**.
Contact/s: Mr Sid Hibbert (Secretary), Basildon and District Angling Society, 15 Culverdown, Basildon, Essex, SS14 2AL.
(T) 01268 287798
Profile: FT: Coarse; WN: Kennel; WT: Lake (Still); F. Size: 3 Acres; W. Size: 2 Acres.
Location: Main Rd: A176 Noak Hill; Rail: Billericay.
Ref: FH2434

KENNET (RIVER)

River Kennet, Beat 2, Southcote, Reading, **BERKSHIRE**, RG, **England**.
Contact/s: Mr Dusty Millar (Associate members secretary), 238 Elgar Road South, Reading, Berkshire, RG3 0BW.
(T) 0118 9874882
Mr Mick Cox (Chief Bailiff), Dorstans, Hatch Lane, Brimpton Village, Reading, RG7 4TR.
(T) 0118 9714917
Profile: FT: Coarse; WN: Kennet; WT: River (Moving).
Ref: FH2435

KENNET (RIVER)

River Kennet, Padworth Lane, Padworth, Reading, **BERKSHIRE**, RG7, **England**.
(W) www.calpac.bizland.com
Contact/s: Mr Colin Trafford (General Secretary).
(T) 020 82242617
Profile: FT: Coarse; WN: Kennet; WT: River (Moving) W. Size: 750 Metres. Location: Nr. Rd: Padworth Lane; Main Rd: A4.
Ref: FH2436

KENNET (RIVER)

River Kennet, Lower Benyons, Reading, **BERKSHIRE**, RG, **England**.

Contact/s: **Mr Bill Brown-Lee** (Secretary), Reading District Angling Association, 47 Calbourne Drive, The Orchard, Calcot, Reading, RG3 7DB.
(T) 0118 9417368
Ms Dusty Millar (Ticket Administrator), 238 Elgar Road South, Reading, Berkshire, RG3 0BW.
(T) 0118 9874882
Profile: **FT:** Coarse; **WN:** Kennet; **WT:** River (Moving) **W. Size:** 1600 Metres. **Location:** **Main Rd:** A4.
Ref: FH2437

KENNET (RIVER)

River Kennet, Old Mill, Aldermaston, Reading, **BERKSHIRE**, RG74 4LB, **England**.
Contact/s: **Mr Peter Arlott** (Bailiff).
(T) 0118 9712365
Profile: **FT:** Coarse; **WN:** Kennet; **WT:** River (Moving). **Location:** **Nr. Rd:** A340; **Main Rd:** A4, Newbury to Reading.
Ref: FH2438

KENNET (RIVER)

River Kennet, Barton Court Fishery, Kintbury, Newbury, **BERKSHIRE**, RG, **England**.
Contact/s: **Mr Bob Bailey**.
(T) 01488 658905 **(F)** 01488 658094
Profile: **FT:** Game; **WN:** Kennet; **WT:** River (Moving).
Ref: FH2439

KENNET (RIVER)

River Kennet, Beat 4, Reading, **BERKSHIRE**, RG, **England**.
Contact/s: **Mr Mick Cox** (Secretary), Dorstans, Hatch Lane, Brimpton Village, Reading, RG7 4TR.
(T) 0118 9714917
Ms Dusty Millar (Ticket Administrator), 238 Elgar Road South, Reading, Berkshire, RG3 0BW.
(T) 0118 9874882
Profile: **FT:** Combination; **WN:** Kennet; **WT:** River (Moving).
Ref: FH2440

KENNET (RIVER)

River Kennet, Calcot A And B, Calcot, Reading, **BERKSHIRE**, RG, **England**.
Contact/s: **Mr Dusty Millar** (Associate members secretary), 238 Elgar Road South, Reading, Berkshire, RG3 0BW.
(T) 0118 9874882
Mr Mick Cox (Chief Bailiff), Dorstans, Hatch Lane, Brimpton Village, Reading, RG7 4TR.
(T) 0118 9714917
Profile: **FT:** Coarse; **WN:** Kennet; **WT:** River (Moving). **Location:** **Nr. Rd:** Calcot.
Ref: FH2441

KENNET (RIVER)

River Kennet, Ufton, Reading, **BERKSHIRE**, RG, **England**.
Contact/s: **Mr Dusty Millar** (Associate members secretary), 238 Elgar Road South, Reading, Berkshire, RG3 0BW.
(T) 0118 9874882
Mr Mick Cox (Chief Bailiff), Dorstans, Hatch Lane, Brimpton Village, Reading, RG7 4TR.
(T) 0118 9714917
Profile: **FT:** Coarse; **WN:** Kennet; **WT:** River (Moving). **Location:** **Nr. Rd:** Ufton.
Ref: FH2442

KENNET (RIVER)

River Kennet, Burghfield, Reading, **BERKSHIRE**, RG, **England**.
Contact/s: **Mr Dusty Millar** (Associate members secretary), 238 Elgar Road South, Reading, Berkshire, RG3 0BW.
(T) 0118 9874882
Mr Mick Cox (Chief Bailiff), Dorstans, Hatch Lane, Brimpton Village, Reading, RG7 4TR.
(T) 0118 9714917
Profile: **FT:** Coarse; **WN:** Kennet; **WT:** River (Moving). **Location:** **Nr. Rd:** Burghfield.
Ref: FH2443

KENNET (RIVER)

River Kennet, Upper Benyons, Padworth, Reading, **BERKSHIRE**, RG, **England**.
Contact/s: **Mr Dusty Millar** (Associate members secretary), 238 Elgar Road South, Reading, Berkshire, RG3 0BW.
(T) 0118 9874882
Mr Mick Cox (Chief Bailiff), Dorstans, Hatch Lane, Brimpton Village, Reading, RG7 4TR.
(T) 0118 9714917
Profile: **FT:** Coarse; **WN:** Kennet; **WT:** River (Moving) **W. Size:** 1200 Metres. **Location:** **Nr. Rd:** M4 junction 12 to Newbury; **Main Rd:** Padworth Court Hotel.
Ref: FH2444

KENNET (RIVER)

River Kennet, Padworth Mill, Reading, **BERKSHIRE**, RG7, **England**.
Contact/s: Fishery Manager.
(T) 01734 417368
Mr Tony Jenkinson (Secretary).
(T) 01737 643821
Mrs D Wheeler (Secretary), CALPAC, 314 Old Lodge Lane, Purley, Surrey, CR8 4AQ.
Profile: **FT:** Coarse; **WN:** Kennet; **WT:** River (Moving) **W. Size:** 800 Metres. **Location:** **Nr. Rd:** Padworth Lane; **Main Rd:** M4, junction 12.
Ref: FH2445

KENNET (RIVER)

River Kennet, Theale, Reading, **BERKSHIRE**, RG, **England**.
Contact/s: **Mr Dusty Millar** (Associate members secretary), 238 Elgar Road South, Reading, Berkshire, RG3 0BW.
(T) 0118 9874882
Mr Mick Cox (Chief Bailiff), Dorstans, Hatch Lane, Brimpton Village, Reading, RG7 4TR.
(T) 0118 9714917
Profile: **FT:** Coarse; **WN:** Kennet; **WT:** River (Moving). **Location:** **Nr. Rd:** Theale.
Ref: FH2446

KENNET (RIVER)

River Kennet, Aldermaston Mill To Padworth Mill, Aldemaston, Reading, **BERKSHIRE**, RG7, **England**.
Contact/s: , Wasing Estate Farm Office, Woolhampton, Berkshire.
(T) 0118 9714140
Fishery Manager.
(T) 01734 712365
Mr Peter Arlott (Bailiff).
(T) 0118 9712365
Profile: **FT:** Coarse; **WN:** Kennet; **WT:** River (Moving). **Location:** **Main Rd:** A4.
Ref: FH2448

KENNET AND AVON CANAL

Kennet And Avon Canal, Padworth, Reading, **BERKSHIRE**, RG7, **England**.
Contact/s: **Mr Bill Brown-Lee** (Secretary), Reading District Angling Association, 47 Calbourne Drive, The Orchard, Calcot, Reading, RG3 7DB.
(T) 0118 9417368
Profile: **FT:** Coarse; **WN:** Kennet and Avon; **WT:** Canal (Still) **W. Size:** 2000 Metres. **Location:** **Main Rd:** M4, junction 12.
Ref: FH2449

KENNET AND AVON CANAL

Kennet And Avon Canal, Sulhamstead, Reading, **BERKSHIRE**, RG7, **England**.
(W) www.calpac.bizland.com
Contact/s: **Mr Colin Trafford** (General Secretary).
(T) 020 82242617
Mrs Diane Wheeler (Secretary), 314 Old Lodge Lane, Purley, Surrey, CR8 4AQ.
(T) 020 86602766
Profile: **FT:** Combination; **WN:** Kennet and Avon; **WT:** Canal (Still) **W. Size:** 1600 Metres. **Location:** **Main Rd:** A4 to Newbury.
Ref: FH2450

KENNET AND AVON CANAL

Kennet And Avon Canal, Beat 1, Southcote, Reading, **BERKSHIRE**, RG, **England**.
Contact/s: **Mr Dusty Millar** (Associate members secretary), 238 Elgar Road South, Reading, Berkshire, RG3 0BW.
(T) 0118 9874882
Mr Mick Cox (Chief Bailiff), Dorstans, Hatch Lane, Brimpton Village, Reading, RG7 4TR.
(T) 0118 9714917
Profile: **FT:** Coarse; **WN:** Kennet and Avon; **WT:** Canal (Still) **W. Size:** 18 Acres.
Ref: FH2451

KENNET AND AVON CANAL

Kennet And Avon Canal, Beat 3A, Southcote, Reading, **BERKSHIRE**, RG, **England**.
Contact/s: **Mr Dusty Millar** (Associate members secretary), 238 Elgar Road South, Reading, Berkshire, RG3 0BW.
(T) 0118 9874882
Mr Mick Cox (Chief Bailiff), Dorstans, Hatch Lane, Brimpton Village, Reading, RG7 4TR.
(T) 0118 9714917
Profile: **FT:** Coarse; **WN:** Kennet and Avon; **WT:** Canal (Still).
Ref: FH2452

KENNET AND AVON CANAL

Kennet And Avon Canal, Midgham, Reading, **BERKSHIRE**, RG, **England**.
Contact/s: **Mr Dusty Millar** (Associate members secretary), 238 Elgar Road South, Reading, Berkshire, RG3 0BW.
(T) 0118 9874882
Mr Mick Cox (Chief Bailiff), Dorstans, Hatch Lane, Brimpton Village, Reading, RG7 4TR.
(T) 0118 9714917
Profile: **FT:** Coarse; **WN:** Midgham; **WT:** Canal (Still) **W. Size:** 12800 Metres. **Location:** **Nr. Rd:** Midgham.
Ref: FH2454

KENNET AND AVON CANAL

Kennet And Avon Canal, Salmon Cut A And B, Aldermaston, Reading, **BERKSHIRE**, RG, **England**.
Contact/s: **Mr Dusty Millar** (Associate members secretary), 238 Elgar Road South, Reading, Berkshire, RG3 0BW.
(T) 0118 9874882
Mr Mick Cox (Chief Bailiff), Dorstans, Hatch Lane, Brimpton Village, Reading, RG7 4TR.
(T) 0118 9714917
Profile: **FT:** Coarse; **WN:** Salmon cut A and B; **WT:** Canal (Still) **W. Size:** 32000 Metres. **Location:** **Nr. Rd:** Aldermaston.
Ref: FH2455

KENNET AND AVON CANAL

Kennet And Avon Canal, Limpley Stoke, Bath, **SOMERSET**, BA3, **England**.
Contact/s: **Mr Dave Crookes** (Secretary), 25 Otago Trce, Larkhall, Bath, Somerset, BA1 6SX.
(T) 01225 427164
Profile: **FT:** Coarse; **WN:** Kennet and Avon; **WT:** Canal (Still).
Ref: FH2456

KENNET AND AVON CANAL

Kennet And Avon Canal, Dundas, Millbrook, Limpley Stoke, Bath, **SOMERSET**, BA3, **England**.
Contact/s: **Mr Dave Crookes** (Secretary), 25 Otago Trce, Larkhall, Bath, Somerset, BA1 6SX.
(T) 01225 427164
Profile: **FT:** Coarse; **WN:** Kennet and Avon; **WT:** Canal (Still) **W. Size:** 1200 Metres. **Location:** **Nr. Rd:** Bath to Limpley Stoke; **Main Rd:** A36.
Ref: FH2457

KENNET AND AVON CANAL

Kennet And Avon Canal, Hunstrete, Newton Park, Bristol, **SOMERSET**, BS39, **England**.
Contact/s: **Mr K Rippin**, Bathampton Angling Association, The Grove, Langridge, Bath.
Profile: **FT:** Coarse; **WN:** Kennet and Avon; **WT:** Canal (Still). **Location:** **Nr. Rd:** Hunstrete.

Ref: FH2458

KENNET AND AVON CANAL

Kennet And Avon Canal, Stanton St Bernard, Marlborough, **WILTSHIRE**, SN8, **England**.
Contact/s: Mr T W Fell (Secretary), Devizes Angling Association, 21 Cornwall Cres, Devizes, Wiltshire, SN10 5HG.
(T) 01380 725189or01380722350
Profile: **FT:** Coarse; **WN:** Kennet and Avon (Devizes to Pewsey); **WT:** Canal (Still) **W. Size:** 1600 Metres. **Location:** **Main Rd:** Stanton St Bernard.
Ref: FH2459

KENNET AND AVON CANAL

Kennet And Avon Canal, Bradford-on-Avon, **WILTSHIRE**, BA15, **England**.
Contact/s: Mr P O'Callaghan (Secretary), 4 Fitzmaurice Cl, Bradford-on-Avon, Wiltshire, BA15 1UE.
(T) 01225 863163
Profile: **FT:** Coarse; **WN:** Kennet and Avon; **WT:** Canal (Still) **W. Size:** 8000 Metres.
Ref: FH2460

KENNET AND AVON CANAL

Kennet And Avon Canal, Pewsey, **WILTSHIRE**, SN9, **England**.
Contact/s: Mr Don Underwood, 51 Swan Meadow, Pewsey, Wiltshire, SN9 5HP.
(T) 01672 562541
Profile: **FT:** Coarse; **WN:** Kennet and Avon; **WT:** Canal (Still) **W. Size:** 6400 Metres.
Ref: FH2461

KENNET AND AVON CANAL

Kennet And Avon Canal, Avoncliffe, Trowbridge, **WILTSHIRE**, BA14, **England**.
Contact/s: Manager, Whitshire Angling, 5 Trimbrell St, Trowbridge, Wiltshire, BA14 8PP.
(T) 01225 763835
Mr Tim Baker (Secretary).
(T) 01225 761797
Profile: **FT:** Coarse; **WN:** Kennet and Avon; **WT:** Canal (Still) **W. Size:** 2000 Metres. **Location:** **Nr. Rd:** Avoncliffe to Beehive.
Ref: FH2462

KENNET AND AVON CANAL

Kennet And Avon Canal, Pewsey, **WILTSHIRE**, SN9, **England**.
Contact/s: **Mr Steve Trevitt**.
(T) 01722 412568
Profile: **FT:** Coarse; **WN:** Kennet and Avon; **WT:** Canal (Still).
Ref: FH2463

KENNET AND AVON CANAL

Kennet And Avon Canal, Froxfield, Marlborough, **WILTSHIRE**, SN8, **England**.
Contact/s: **Mr Bill Brown-Lee** (Secretary), Reading District Angling Association, 47 Calbourne Drive, The Orchard, Calcot, Reading, RG3 7DB.
(T) 0118 9417368
Profile: **FT:** Coarse; **WN:** Kennet and Avon; **WT:** Canal (Still).
Ref: FH2464

KENNET AND AVON CANAL

Kennet And Avon Canal, Semington, Devizes, **WILTSHIRE**, SN10, **England**.
Contact/s: A Brown.
(T) 01793 497285
Mr T W Fell (Secretary), Devizes Angling Association, 21 Cornwall Cres, Devizes, Wiltshire, SN10 5HG.
(T) 01380 725189or01380722350
Profile: **FT:** Coarse; **WN:** Kennet and Avon (Semington to Pewsey); **WT:** Canal (Still). **Location:** **Main Rd:** A361 to A365; **Rail:** Chippenham.
Ref: FH2465

KENNET AND AVON CANAL

Kennet And Avon Canal, Melksham, **WILTSHIRE**, SN12, **England**.
Contact/s: **Mr R Edwards** (Secretary), Avon Angling Club, 56 Addison Rd, Melksham, Wiltshire, SN12 8DR.
(T) 01225 763835
Profile: **FT:** Coarse; **WN:** Kennet and Avon; **WT:** Canal (Still) **W. Size:** 1600 Metres.
Ref: FH2466

KENNET AND AVON CANAL

Kennet And Avon Canal, Marlborough, **WILTSHIRE**, SN8, **England**.
Contact/s: **Mr M Ellis**, Failte, Elcot Cl, Marlborough, SN8 2BB.
(T) 01672 512922
Profile: **FT:** Coarse; **WN:** Kennet and Avon; **WT:** Canal (Still) **W. Size:** 19200 Metres. **Location:** **Main Rd:** A346, South of Swindon.
Ref: FH2467

KENNET AND ENTORNE (RIVERS)

Rivers Kennet And Entorne, Wasing Kennet Syndicate, Wasing Estate, Reading, **BERKSHIRE**, RG7 4NG, **England**.
Contact/s: **Mr Kevin Rolls** (Fishery Manager), Estate Office, Wasing Estate, Aldermaston, Reading, RG7 4NG.
(T) 0118 9714281
Mr Patrick Todd (Estate Manager), Wasing Estate Farm Office, Wasing Park, Aldermaston, Reading, RG7 4NG.
(T) 0118 9714140 **(F)** 0118 9713251
Profile: **FT:** Coarse; **WN:** Kennet and Entorne; **WT:** River (Moving) **W. Size:** 11200 Metres. **Location:** **Main Rd:** A4; **Rail:** Midgham.
Ref: FH2468

KENNICK RESERVOIR

Kennick Reservoir, South West Water Fishery, Kennick, Christow, Exeter, **DEVON**, EX6, **England**.
Contact/s: **Mr Mike Boston** (Secretary), Kennick Fly Fishers Association, 5 Shirburn Rd, Torquay, Devon, TQ1 3JL.
(T) 01803 325722
Profile: **FT:** Game; **WN:** Kennick; **WT:** Reservoir (Still) **W. Size:** 45 Acres.
Ref: FH2469

KENT (RIVER)

River Kent, Kendal, **CUMBRIA**, LA, **England**.
Contact/s: **Mr A Atkinson** (Manager), Kendal Sports, 28-30 Stramondgate, Kendal, Cumbria, LA9 4BN.
(T) 01539 721554 **(F)** 01539 721554
Mrs A Parsons (Leaseholder), Olde Peat Coates, Sampool Lane, Levens.
(T) 01539 560096
Profile: **FT:** Game; **WN:** Kent; **WT:** River (Moving).
Ref: FH2470

KENT (RIVER)

River Kent, Kendal, **CUMBRIA**, LA9 6, **England**.
Contact/s: **Mr Chris Green** (Secretary), Burneside Angling Association, Millside, Hall Rd, Burneside, LA9 6QE. **(F)** 01539 818486 **(M)** 07788 854539
Profile: **FT:** Combination; **WN:** Kent; **WT:** River (Moving). **Location:** **Rail:** Burneside Station. £Free
Ref: FH2471

KENT (RIVER)

Lower Levens Beat, Olde Peat Cotes, Sampool Lane, Levens, Kendal, **CUMBRIA**, LA8 8EH, **England**.
Contact/s: **Mrs A Parsons**, Olde Peat Coates, Sampool Lane, Levens.
(T) 01539 560096
Profile: **FT:** Game; **WN:** Kent; **WT:** River (Moving) **W. Size:** 2000 Metres. **Location:** **Nr. Rd:** Sampool Lane; **Main Rd:** A590; **Rail:** Kendal.
Ref: FH2472

KENTMERE FISHERY

Kentmere Fishery, Penrith, **CUMBRIA**, CA10, **England**.
Contact/s: **Mr Harrison**, The Birches, Staveley, Penrith, Cumbria, CA10 2DU.
(T) 01768 882263
Profile: **FT:** Game; **WN:** Kentmere; **WT:** Lake (Still) **W. Size:** 24 Acres.
Ref: FH2473

KERRYFISHERIES

Kerryfisheries, Waterville, **COUNTY KERRY**, **Ireland**.
(W) www.kerryfisheries.com
Contact/s: **Mr Charlie Butler** (Manager), The Butler Arms Hotel, Waterville, County Kerry, Ireland.
(T) 087 2260083
Profile: **FT:** Game; **WN:** Lower Caragh; **WT:** Combination (Still & Moving) **W. Size:** 1200 Acres.
Ref: FH2474

KEYNES COUNTRY PARK

Keynes Country Park, Spratsgate Lane, Shorncote, Cirencester, **GLOUCESTERSHIRE**, GL7 6DF, **England**.
Contact/s: On Duty Ranger, Cotswold Water Park Society, Keynes Country Park, Spratsgate Lane, Shorncote, Cirencester, Gloucestershire.
(T) 01285 861459 **(F)** 01285 860186
Mr J Parker (Secretary), Ashton Keynes Angling Club, 81 Dunnington Rd, Wootton Bassett, Swindon, SN4 7EL.
(T) 01793 852028
Profile: **FT:** Coarse; **WN:** Keynes Country Park; **WT:** Gravel Pit (Still) **W. Size:** 135 Acres. **Location:** **Nr. Rd:** B4696, Spratsgate Lane; **Main Rd:** A419; **Rail:** Swindon.
Ref: FH2475

KEYNES PARK TOP LAKE

Keynes Park Top Lake, Keynes Country Park, Spratsgate Lane, Shorncote, Cirencester, **GLOUCESTERSHIRE**, GL7 6DF, **England**.
Contact/s: Manager, Cotswold Water Park Society, Keynes Country Park, Spratsgate Lane, Shorncote, Cirencester, Gloucestershire.
(T) 01285 861459 **(F)** 01285 860186
Mr J Parker (Secretary), Ashton Keynes Angling Club, 81 Dunnington Rd, Wootton Bassett, Swindon, SN4 7EL.
(T) 01793 852028
Profile: **FT:** Coarse; **WN:** Top Lake; **WT:** Gravel Pit (Still) **W. Size:** 35 Acres. **Location:** **Nr. Rd:** B4696, Spratsgate Lane; **Main Rd:** A419; **Rail:** Kemble.
Ref: FH2476

KIELDER WATER

Kielder Water, Bellingham, Hexham, **NORTHUMBERLAND**, NE48, **England**.
Contact/s: **Mr Paul Russell**, Northumbrian Water Ltd, Head Office, Recreation Department, Abbey Rd, Durham DH1 5FJ.
(T) 0191 3832222 **(F)** 0191 3841920
Ms Tanya Reeve (Fishery Manager).
(T) 01434 240398
Profile: **FT:** Game; **WN:** Kielder Water; **WT:** Reservoir (Still) **W. Size:** 2700 Acres. **Location:** **Main Rd:** A68.
Ref: FH2477

KILBARRY FISHERY

Kilbarry Fishery, The Nursery, Llyons Cross, Upper Ballyduff, **COUNTY WATERFORD**, **Ireland**.
Contact/s: Manager.
(T) 058 60146
Profile: **FT:** Game; **WN:** Kilbarry Fishery
Ref: FH2478

KILBURN POND

Kilburn Pond, Kilburn, York, **YORKSHIRE (NORTH)**, YO61, **England**.
Contact/s: **Mr Norman Twidle** (Secretary).
(T) 01642 276452
Profile: **FT:** Coarse; **WN:** Kilburn; **WT:** Pool (Still) **W. Size:** 1 Acre. **Location:** **Nr. Rd:** Thirsk to Coxwold; **Main Rd:** A170, Thirsk.
Ref: FH2479

KILCOLEMAN FISHERY

Kilcoleman Fishery, Enniskeane, **COUNTY CORK**, **Ireland**.
Contact/s: Manager.
(T) 023 47279 **(F)** 023 47408
Profile: **FT:** Game; **WN:** Bandon; **WT:** River

(Moving).
Ref: FH2480

KILKEEL (RIVER)

River Kilkeel, Kilkeel, Newry, **COUNTY DOWN**, BT34, **Northern Ireland**.
Contact/s: Manager, Kilkeel Sub Post Office, 4 The Square, Kilkeel, County Down, BT34 4AA.
(T) 028 41762225
Profile: **FT:** Game; **WN:** Kilkeel; **WT:** River (Moving) **W. Size:** 6400 Metres.
Ref: FH2481

KILLEARN HOUSE FISHERY

Killearn House Fishery, Killearn Home Farm, Killearn, Glasgow, **STIRLING**, G63 9QH, **Scotland**.
Contact/s: **Mr David Young** (Owner).
(T) 01360 550994 **(F)** 01360 550994
Profile: **FT:** Game; **WN:** Killearn House Fishery; **WT:** Lake (Still); **F. Size:** 10 Acres; **W. Size:** 2 Acres. Location: **Nr. Rd:** B834; **Main Rd:** A81 and A809.
Ref: FH2482

KILLIN BREADALBANE AC WATERS

Killin Breadalbane Angling Club Waters, "clan Alpine", Main St, Strathyre, Callander, **STIRLING**, FK18 8NA, **Scotland**.
(W) www.fishingnet.com/clubs/killin.htm
Contact/s: **Mr Alec Stewart** (Membership Secretary), 2 Dochart Rd, Killin, Perth and Kinross, FK21 8SN.
(T) 01567 820224
Ms Joanne Airy (Owner), News First, Fishing Tackle Shop, Main St, Killin, FR21 8UJ.
(T) 01567 820362
Profile: **FT:** Combination; **WN:** Loch Tay, River Lochay, River Dochart; **WT:** Combination (Still & Moving). Location: **Nr. Rd:** A827; **Main Rd:** A85; **Rail:** Crianlarich.
Ref: FH2483

KILLINEER RESERVOIR

Killineer Reservoir, Drogheda, **COUNTY LOUTH**, **Ireland**.
Contact/s: **Mr John Murphy** (Secretary).
(T) 077 1034078
Profile: **FT:** Game; **WN:** Killineer; **WT:** Reservoir (Still).
Ref: FH2484

KILLINGTON RESERVOIR

Killington Reservoir, Oxenholme, Kendal, **CUMBRIA**, LA9, **England**.
Contact/s: **Mr J Atkinson** (Secretary), Town End, Natland, Cumbria, LA9 7QL.
Mrs Vera Carlson (Owner), Carlsons Fishing Tackle, 64/66 Kirkland, Kendal, Cumbria, Kendal.
(T) 01539 724867
Profile: **FT:** Combination; **WN:** Killington; **WT:** Reservoir (Still). Location: **Nr. Rd:** B6254; **Main Rd:** M6, junction 37.
Ref: FH2485

KILLINGWORTH LAKE

Killingworth Lake, Killingworth, Newcastle Upon Tyne, **TYNE AND WEAR**, NE12, **England**.
Contact/s: Warden, Tyne Anglers Alliance, PO Box 72, Heaton Rd, Newcastle upon Tyne.
(T) 0191 2681613
Profile: **FT:** Coarse; **WN:** Killingworth; **WT:** Lake (Still) **W. Size:** 4 Acres. Location: **Nr. Rd:** A1056.
Ref: FH2486

KILNSEY PARK AND TROUT FARM

Kilnsey Park And Trout Farm, Kilnsey Park, Kilnsey, Skipton, **YORKSHIRE (NORTH)**, BD23 5PS, **England**.
Contact/s: **Mr Anthony Roberts** (Manager).
(T) 01756 752150 **(F)** 01756 752224
(E) kilnseypark@hotmail.com
Profile: **FT:** Game; **WN:** Kilnsey Park And Trout Farm; **WT:** Lake (Still) **W. Size:** 27 Acres. Location: **Nr. Rd:** B6160; **Rail:** Skipton.
Ref: FH2487

KIMBRIDGE

Kimbridge, Orvis, Vermont House, Unit 30A, North Way, Andover, **HAMPSHIRE**, SP10 5RW, **England**.
Contact/s: **Ms Judith Thornton**.
(T) 01264 349519 **(F)** 01264 349505
Profile: **FT:** Game; **WN:** Test; **WT:** River (Moving). Location: **Main Rd:** A3057.
Ref: FH2488

KING GEORGE V POOL

King George V Pool, Altrincham, Manchester, **MANCHESTER (GREATER)**, M, **England**.
Contact/s: **Mr Jimmy Botherton**.
(T) 0161 9122976
Mr Steve Thomas.
(T) 0161 9122976
Profile: **FT:** Coarse; **WN:** King George; **WT:** Pool (Still) **W. Size:** 2 Acres. Location: **Nr. Rd:** Urban Road; **Main Rd:** A538; **Rail:** Altrincham.
Ref: FH2489

KING SEDGEMOOR DRAIN

King Sedgemoor Drain, Greylake Bridge, Othery, Bridgwater, **SOMERSET**, TA7, **England**.
Contact/s: Manager, Somerset Angling, 74 Bath Rd, Bridgwater, Somerset, TA6 4PL.
(T) 01278 431777or786934
Mr Mark Pople (Secretary), 14 Edward St, Bridgwater, Somerset.
(T) 01278 422397
Mrs Carol Howe, 3 Cedar Cl, Bridgwater, Somerset, TA6 5DP.
Profile: **FT:** Coarse; **WN:** King Sedgemoor Drain; **WT:** Combination (Still & Moving) **W. Size:** 12800 Metres. Location: **Nr. Rd:** A361.
Ref: FH2490

KING WILLIAM IV RESERVOIR

King William Iv Reservoir, Blackley New Rd, Manchester, **MANCHESTER (GREATER)**, M2, **England**.
Profile: **FT:** Coarse; **WN:** King William IV; **WT:** Reservoir (Still) **W. Size:** 4 Acres. Location: **Nr. Rd:** Blackley New Road.
Ref: FH2491

KINGCOMBE COARSE FARM

Higher Kingcombe Farm, Higher Kingcombe, Toller Porcoum, Dorchester, **DORSET**, DT2 0EH, **England**.
Contact/s: **Mr Paul Crocker** (Owner).
(T) 01300 320537 **(M)** 07974 937972
Ms Andrea Crocker.
(T) 01300 320537
Profile: **FT:** Coarse; **WN:** Higher Kingcombe Farm; **WT:** Lake (Still); **F. Size:** 6 Acres; **W. Size:** 4 Acres. Location: **Nr. Rd:** Kingcombe Road; **Main Rd:** A356; **Rail:** Maiden Newton.
Ref: FH2492

KINGCOMBE LAKE

Kingcombe Lake, Kingcombe, Maiden Newton, Dorchester, **DORSET**, DT2, **England**.
Contact/s: **Mr Bill Lucy** (Secretary), Dorchester and District Angling Society, 7 Celtic Cresent, Dorcester, Dorset, DT1 2QJ.
(T) 01305 264873
Mr John Parkes (Membership Secretary), Dorchester and District Angling Society, 5 Malta Cl, Dorcester, Dorset, DT1 2QA.
(T) 01305 262813
Profile: **FT:** Coarse; **WN:** Kingcombe; **WT:** Lake (Still) **W. Size:** 2 Acres. Location: **Nr. Rd:** A356; **Main Rd:** A356; **Rail:** Maiden Newton.
Ref: FH2493

KINGENNIE FISHINGS

Kingennie Fishings (The), Kingennie, Broughty Ferry, Dundee, **ANGUS**, DD5 3RD, **Scotland**.
Contact/s: **Mr Neil Anderson** (Manager).
(T) 01382 350777 **(F)** 01382 350400 **(M)** 07759 022503
(E) kingennie@easynet.co.uk
Profile: **FT:** Game; **WN:** Kingennie Fishings (The); **WT:** Pond (Still); **F. Size:** 20 Acres; **W. Size:** 12 Acres. Location: **Nr. Rd:** Arbroath Road; **Main Rd:** A92; **Rail:** Dundee.
Ref: FH2494

KINGFISHER FISHERY

Kingfisher Fishery, Sandy Lane, Hammer Vale, Haslemere, **SURREY**, GU27 1QE, **England**.
Contact/s: **Mr Peter Sherrington** (Manager).
(T) 01428 604928
Profile: **FT:** Combination; **WN:** Kingfisher Fishery; **WT:** Pond (Still); **F. Size:** 33 Acres; **W. Size:** 2 Acres. Location: **Nr. Rd:** Sandy Lane; **Main Rd:** A3; **Rail:** Haslemere Liphook.
Ref: FH2495

KINGFISHER GOLF CLUB

Kingfisher Golf Club, Deanshanger, Stony Stratford, Milton Keynes, **BUCKINGHAMSHIRE**, MK19 6DG, **England**.
Contact/s: Manager, Golf Lodge, Kingfisher Golf Club, Deanshanger, Stony Stratford, Buckinghamshire, MK19 6DG.
(T) 01908 560354
Profile: **FT:** Game; **WN:** Kingfisher Golf Club; **WT:** Lake (Still) **W. Size:** 1 Acre. Location: **Nr. Rd:** A422.
Ref: FH2496

KINGFISHER LAKE

Kingfisher Lake, Tansor, Oundle, Peterborough, **CAMBRIDGESHIRE**, PE8 5HN, **England**.
Contact/s: **Mr Tony Bridgefoot** (Owner).
(T) 01832 226042
Profile: **FT:** Coarse; **WN:** Kingfisher; **WT:** Lake (Still); **F. Size:** 108 Acres; **W. Size:** 7 Acres. Location: **Nr. Rd:** Tansor to Fotheringhay; **Main Rd:** A605; **Rail:** Peterborough.
Ref: FH2497

KINGFISHER LAKE

Kingfisher Lake, Denham, Uxbridge, Uxbridge, London, **LONDON (GREATER)**, UB9, **England**.
Contact/s: **Mr M Francis** (Principal Land Agent), Hillingdon Borough Council, Civic Ctre, Uxbridge, UB8 1UW.
(T) 01895 250111
Profile: **FT:** Coarse; **WN:** Kingfisher Lake; **WT:** Gravel Pit (Still) **W. Size:** 19 Acres. Location: **Nr. Rd:** A412; **Main Rd:** A413, M40.
Ref: FH2498

KINGFISHER LAKE (A)

Kingfisher Lake (A), Teswood Lane, Southampton, **HAMPSHIRE**, SO, **England**.
Contact/s: **Mr Hoskins**, 40 Aldermoor Aven, Aldermoor, Southampton.
(T) 023 80780105
Profile: **FT:** Coarse; **WN:** Kingfisher Lake (A); **WT:** Gravel Pit (Still) **W. Size:** 3 Acres. Location: **Nr. Rd:** A36; **Main Rd:** A35.
Ref: FH2499

KINGFISHER LAKES

Kingfisher Lakes, Quarry Lane, Lyng, Norwich, **NORFOLK**, NR9 5RS, **England**.
Contact/s: **Mr C Rodgers** (Owner), Kingfisher Lakes, Quarry Lane, Lyng, Norwich, NR9 5RS.
(T) 01603 870400
Profile: **FT:** Coarse; **WN:** Kingfisher, Wensum, Club, and Lobster Pot Lake.; **WT:** Lake (Still); **F. Size:** 35 Acres. Location: **Nr. Rd:** Quarry Lane; **Main Rd:** A1067; **Rail:** Norwich.
Ref: FH2500

KINGFISHER LODGE

Kingfisher Lodge, Cross Carr Lane, Hibaldstow, Brigg, **LINCOLNSHIRE (NORTH)**, DN20 9PL, **England**.
Contact/s: **Mr Nigel Coulson**.

The Derriboot Range — Designed to Give Total Protection

Boots you can safely walk in — Featuring Derri's unique non slip safety sole.

No more cold feet — Super warm, comfortable, detachable, machine washable thermal lining.

Stylish Fit — Tailored for right and left feet, individually sized, 5-12 for a perfect fit.

They also come with a **No Quibble Guarantee** against splitting and leaking.

Made in the UK without compromise — Who else can offer you the same?

See the list below of some of the leading angler's who choose to wear the quality of Derri.

Bob Nudd · Des Taylor · Julian Cundiff · Terry Hearn · Alan Yates · Mick Brown · Keith Arthur · Graham Marsden · Jan Porter · Max Cottis · Chris Ball · Tim Paisley · Dickie Carr · Mark Addy · Dave Vincent · Jim Whippy · Dave Barham · Liam Dale

Available from all good tackle shops, telephone for your local stockist.

Freephone: 0800 9179598

(Trade enquires welcome) Lines open 7 days a week, 7am - 9pm

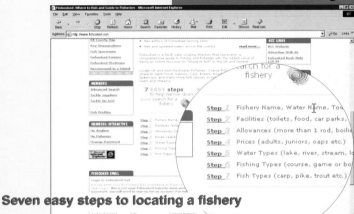

(T) 01652 652210
Profile: **FT:** Coarse; **WN:** Kingfisher Lodge; **WT:** Pond (Still) **W. Size:** 3 Acres. **Location:** **Nr. Rd:** B1206; **Main Rd:** A15; **Rail:** Scunthorpe.
Ref: FH2501

KINGFISHER TROUT LAKE

Kingfisher Trout Lake, Home Farm, Green Lane, Bromyard, **HEREFORDSHIRE**, HR7 4SZ, **England**.
(W) www.fisheries.co.uk/kingfisher
Contact/s: **Mr Dennis Wall** (Owner).
(T) 01885 488464 (F) 01885 488464
Ms Kath Hill (Assistant).
(T) 01885 488464 (F) 01885 488464
Profile: **FT:** Game; **WN:** Kingfisher; **WT:** Lake (Still) **W. Size:** 4 Acres. **Location:** **Nr. Rd:** Green Lane; **Main Rd:** A44; **Rail:** Hereford or Ledbury.
Ref: FH2502

KINGHORN LOCH

Kinghorn Loch, Kinghorn, Burntisland, **FIFE**, KY3, **Scotland**.
Contact/s: **Mr Eric Dey**.
(T) 01383 413183
Profile: **FT:** Coarse; **WN:** Kinghorn; **WT:** Loch (Still) **W. Size:** 18 Acres. **Location:** **Nr. Rd:** Kilcaldy to Burntisland; **Main Rd:** B923. £Fr
Ref: FH2503

KINGLAKE FISHERY

Kinglake Fishery, Chilla, Beaworthy, **DEVON**, EX21, **England**.
Contact/s: **Mr Gordon King** (owner).
(T) 01409 231401
Profile: **FT:** Game; **WN:** King; **WT:** Lake (Still).
Ref: FH2504

KINGS (RIVER)

River Kings, Kilkenny, **COUNTY KILKENNY**, **Ireland**.
Contact/s: **Mr Matt Doyle**, Grandtown, Ballacolla, Portlaoise, County Laois, Ireland.
Profile: **FT:** Game; **WN:** Kings; **WT:** River (Moving).
Ref: FH2505

KINGS (RIVER)

River Kings, Kilkenny, **COUNTY KILKENNY**, **Ireland**.
Contact/s: **Mr Chris Vaughan** (Secretary), Callan and District Angling Association, Green St, Callan, County Kilkenny, Ireland.
Profile: **FT:** Game; **WN:** Kings; **WT:** River (Moving) **W. Size:** 8000 Metres.
Ref: FH2506

KINGS MILL RESERVOIR

Kings Mill Reservoir, Mansfield, Sutton-In-Ashfield, **NOTTINGHAMSHIRE**, NG17, **England**.
Contact/s: **Mr I Foulds** (Secretary), Nottingham Angling Association, 95 Ilkeston Rd, Nottingham, Nottinghamshire, NG7 3HA.
(T) 0115 9033881or9708080
Profile: **FT:** Coarse; **WN:** Kings Mill; **WT:** Reservoir (Still) **W. Size:** 15 Acres.
Ref: FH2507

KINGS STANDING LAKES

Kings Standing Lakes, Duddleswell, Crowborough, **SUSSEX (EAST)**, TN6, **England**.
Contact/s: Fishery Manager.
(T) 01825 712854or712108
Sean (Manager), Crowborough Tackle, Whitehill Rd, Crowborough, Sussex (East), TN6 1JU.
(T) 01892 661145
Profile: **FT:** Game; **WN:** Kings Standing; **WT:** Lake (Still).
Ref: FH2508

KINGS WEIR FISHERY

Kings Weir Fishery, King's Weir House, Wharfe Rd, Wormley, Broxbourne, **HERTFORDSHIRE**, EN10, **England**.
Contact/s: **Ms Barbara Newton** (Owner).
(T) 01992 468394
Profile: **FT:** Coarse; **WN:** Kings Weir Fishery; **WT:** Combination (Still & Moving) **W. Size:** 1600 Metres. **Location:** **Nr. Rd:** Wharfe Road; **Main Rd:** A10, A1170 to Broxbourne.
Ref: FH2509

KINGSBURY WATER PARK

Kingsbury Water Park, Visitors Ctre, Bodymoor Heath Lane, Bodymoor Heath, Sutton Coldfield, **MIDLANDS (WEST)**, B76 0DY, **England**.
(W) www.fisheries.co.uk/kingsbury
Contact/s: **Mr Fred Hopkins** (Senior Park Ranger), Kingsbury Water Park, Bodymoor Heath Lane, Bodymoor Heath, Sutton Coldfield, B76 0DY.
(T) 01327 372660
(E) parks@warwickshire.gov.uk
Profile: **FT:** Coarse; **WN:** Kingsbury; **WT:** Lake (Still); **F. Size:** 620 Acres; **W. Size:** 50 Acres. **Location:** **Nr. Rd:** M42 junction 9; **Main Rd:** Bodymoor Heath Lane. £Fr
Ref: FH2510

KINGSHURST LAKE

Kingshurst Lake, Chelmsley Wood, Solihull, **MIDLANDS (WEST)**, B92, **England**.
Contact/s: **Mr David Chipping** (Secretary), Solihull MBC, Environment Services, Environmental Maintenance GrpCentral Depot, Moat Lane, Solihull, B91 2LW.
(T) 0121 7046577
Profile: **FT:** Coarse; **WN:** Kingshurst; **WT:** Lake (Still) **W. Size:** 14 Acres.
Ref: FH2511

KINGSLAND RESERVOIRS

Kingsland Reservoirs, March Rd, Coates, Whittlesey, Peterborough, **CAMBRIDGESHIRE**, PE7, **England**.
Contact/s: **Mr Richard Stevenson**.
(T) 01733 840312
Profile: **FT:** Coarse; **WN:** Kingsland; **WT:** Reservoir (Still); **F. Size:** 5 Acres; **W. Size:** 3 Acres. **Location:** **Nr. Rd:** March Road; **Main Rd:** Turves just south of A605.
Ref: FH2512

KINGSLEY CARP LAKE

Kingsley Carp Lake, Bogs Lane, Harrogate, **YORKSHIRE (NORTH)**, HG, **England**.
Contact/s: , Harrogate Angling Supplies, 61 High St, Starbeck, Harrogate, HG2 7LQ.
(T) 01423 883270 (F) 01423 883270
Mr Stuart Blake (Manager), 49 St Johns Cres, Bilton, Harrogate, Yorkshire (North), HG1 3AD.
(T) 01423 509074 (M) 07944 419519
Profile: **FT:** Coarse; **WN:** Kingsley; **WT:** Lake (Still) **W. Size:** 2 Acres. **Location:** **Nr. Rd:** A59 to Knaresborough Road; **Main Rd:** Knaresborough Road; **Rail:** Starbeck.
Ref: FH2513

KINGSMEAD 1

Kingsmead 1, Stanwell Rd, Horton, Slough, **BUCKINGHAMSHIRE**, SL3 9PE, **England**.
(W) www.rmcangling.co.uk
Contact/s: **Mr Ian Welch** (Angling Manager), RMC Angling, The Square, Lightwater, Surrey, GU18 5SS.
(T) 01276 453300 (F) 01276 456611
(E) info@rmcangling.co.uk
Profile: **FT:** Coarse; **WN:** Kingsmead; **WT:** Gravel Pit (Still) **W. Size:** 30 Acres. **Location:** **Nr. Rd:** Stanwell Road; **Main Rd:** M4, M25, junction 14; **Rail:** Wraysbury.
Ref: FH2514

KINGSMEAD CENTRE

Kingsmead Fishing And Field Centre, Clayhidon, Cullompton, **DEVON**, EX15 3TR, **England**.
(W) www.kingsmeadcentre.com
Contact/s: .
(T) 01823 421630
Profile: **FT:** Coarse; **WN:** Valley Lake, and Woodland Lake; **WT:** Lake (Still); **F. Size:** 8 Acres. **Location:** **Main Rd:** B3391; **Rail:** Taunton.
Ref: FH2515

KINGSMEAD ISLAND LAKE

Kingsmead Island Lake, Stanwell Rd, Horton, Slough, **BUCKINGHAMSHIRE**, SL3 9PE, **England**.
(W) www.rmcangling.co.uk
Contact/s: **Mr Ian Welch** (Angling Manager), RMC Angling, The Square, Lightwater, Surrey, GU18 5SS.
(T) 01276 453300 (F) 01276 456611
(E) info@rmcangling.co.uk
Profile: **FT:** Coarse; **WN:** Island; **WT:** Gravel Pit (Still) **W. Size:** 50 Acres. **Location:** **Nr. Rd:** Stanwell Road; **Main Rd:** M25, junction 14; **Rail:** Wraysbury.
Ref: FH2516

KINGSNORDLEY

Kingsnordley, Quatt, Bridgnorth, **MIDLANDS (WEST)**, WV1, **England**.
Contact/s: Fishery Manager.
(T) 01746 780247
Mrs Pat Rochdale.
(T) 01746 781215
Profile: **FT:** Coarse; **WN:** kingsnordley; **WT:** Pool (Still). **Location:** **Nr. Rd:** Alveley; **Main Rd:** A442.
Ref: FH2517

KINGSTON POOLS

Kingston Pools, Kingston Grange, Banbury Rd, Lighthorne, Warwick, **WARWICKSHIRE**, CV35 0AE, **England**.
(W) www.fisheries.co.uk/kingston
Contact/s: **Mr Rob White**, Kingston Grange Farm, Banbury Rd, Lighthorne, Warwickshire, CV35 0AE.
(T) 01926 640479
(E) rob.white@lineone.net
Profile: **FT:** Coarse; **WN:** Kingston; **WT:** Pool (Still); **F. Size:** 360 Acres. **Location:** **Nr. Rd:** Warwick to Banbury; **Main Rd:** M40, junction 12, B4100; **Rail:** Warwick.
Ref: FH2518

KINLIN HALL TROUT FARM

Kinlin Hall Trout Farm, Ripon, **YORKSHIRE (NORTH)**, HG4 5LW, **England**.
Contact/s: **Mr Brian Moorland** (Manager).
(T) 01677 470716
Profile: **FT:** Game; **WN:** Kinlin Hall Trout Farm; **WT:** Lake (Still).
Ref: FH2519

KINMOUNT LAKE

Kinmount Lake, Annan, **DUMFRIES AND GALLOWAY**, DG12, **Scotland**.
Contact/s: Manager, Hoddom and Kinmount Estates, Hoddom Estate Office, Lockerbie, Dumfries and Galloway, DG11 1BE.
(T) 01576 300244 (F) 01567 300757
Mr George Birkbeck.
(T) 01461 700461
Profile: **FT:** Coarse; **WN:** Kinmount; **WT:** Lake (Still) **W. Size:** 12 Acres. **Location:** **Nr. Rd:** A75; **Main Rd:** A75.
Ref: FH2520

KINNEL

Kinnel, Killin, **STIRLING**, FK21, **Scotland**.
(W) www.fishingnet.com/beats/dochart/kinnel.htm
Contact/s: Manager, Kinnel Estate Office, Kinnel House, Kinnel Estate, Killin, Perth and Kinross FK21 8SR.
(T) 01567 820590
Profile: **FT:** Game; **WN:** Kinnel; **WT:** River (Moving).
Ref: FH2521

KINPTON RESERVOIR

Kinpton Reservoir, Grantham, **LINCOLNSHIRE**, NG32 1PD, **England**.
Contact/s: **Mr Don Wells** (Manager), Belvoir Estate, Estate Office, Belvoir Castle, Belvoir, Grantham, NG32 1PD.
(T) 01476 870262 (F) 01476 870443
Profile: **FT:** Coarse; **WN:** Knipton; **WT:**

Reservoir (Still) **W. Size:** 35 Acres.
Ref: FH2522

KIPLIN TROUT FISHERY

Kiplin Trout Fishery, Kiplin Hall, Great Langton, Northallerton, **YORKSHIRE (NORTH)**, DL, **England**.
Contact/s: **Mr Brian Moorland** (Manager).
(T) 01677 470716
Profile: **FT:** Game; **WN:** Kiplin Trout Fishery; **WT:** Lake (Still) **W. Size:** 20 Acres.
Location: **Nr. Rd:** Kiplin Hall.
Ref: FH2523

KIPPAX POND

Kippax Pond, Kippax, Leeds, **YORKSHIRE (WEST)**, LS25, **England**.
Contact/s: Fishery Manager.
(T) 0113 2482373
Profile: **FT:** Coarse; **WN:** Kippax; **WT:** Pond (Still).
Ref: FH2524

KIRKBY THORE (RIVER)

River Kirkby Thore, Kirkby Thore, Penrith, **CUMBRIA**, CA10, **England**.
Profile: **FT:** Coarse; **WN:** Kirkby; **WT:** River (Moving).
Ref: FH2525

KIRKCHRIST

Kirkchrist, Newton Stewart, **DUMFRIES AND GALLOWAY**, DG8, **Scotland**.
Contact/s: **Mr R P Scott** (Manager).
(T) 01671 830336
Profile: **FT:** Game; **WN:** Kirkchrist; **WT:** Lake (Still) **W. Size:** 4 Acres.
Ref: FH2526

KIRKWOOD WATER

Kirkwood Water, Dalton, Lockerbie, **DUMFRIES AND GALLOWAY**, DG11 1DH, **Scotland**.
Contact/s: **Mr A Steel**.
(T) 01576 510200 (F) 01576 510363
Profile: **FT:** Game; **WN:** Annan; **WT:** River (Moving); **F. Size:** 500 Acres; **W. Size:** 2000 Metres. **Location:** **Main Rd:** A74.
Ref: FH2527

KIRRIEREOCH LOCH

Kirriereoch Loch, Straiton, Newton Stewart, **DUMFRIES AND GALLOWAY**, DG8, **Scotland**.
Contact/s: **Mr Tony Dickinson** (Shop Proprietor), Galloway Guns and Tackle, 36a Arthur St, Newton Stewart, Dumfries and Galloway, DG8 6DE.
(T) 01671 403404 (F) 01671 403404
Profile: **FT:** Coarse; **WN:** Kirriereoch; **WT:** Loch (Still). **Location:** **Nr. Rd:** Straiton; **Main Rd:** A714; **Rail:** Barrhill.
Ref: FH2528

KIRTLE WATER STREAM

Kirtle Water Stream, Rigg And Kirtleside Farm, Rigg, Gretna, **DUMFRIES AND GALLOWAY**, DG16, **Scotland**.
Profile: **FT:** Game; **WN:** Esk (Kirtle Water Stream); **WT:** Stream (Moving).
Ref: FH2529

KITCLIFFE RESERVOIR

Kitcliffe Reservoir, Oldham, **MANCHESTER (GREATER)**, OL, **England**.
Contact/s: Manager, Oldham Angling Ctre, 159 Oldham Rd, Springhead, Oldham, OL4 4QJ.
(T) 0161 6247711
Mr J Lees (Secretary), Oldham United Angling Club, 10 Packwood Chase, Chadderton, Oldham.
(T) 0161 6245176
Mr Roy Rhodes (Conservation, Access and Recreation Manager), Rivington Water Treatment Works, Bolton Rd, Horwich, Bolton, BL6 7RN.
(T) 01204 664300
Profile: **FT:** Game; **WN:** Kitcliffe; **WT:** Reservoir (Still).
Ref: FH2530

KIVETON HALL

Kiveton Hall, Kiveton Hall Farm, Kiveton Park, Sheffield, **YORKSHIRE (SOUTH)**, S26, **England**.
Contact/s: **Mr John Hague** (Manager).
(T) 0114 2864179or0378178710
Profile: **FT:** Coarse; **WN:** Match, Carp and Strip; **WT:** Lake (Still). **Location:** **Nr. Rd:** B6059; **Main Rd:** M1, junction 31, A57 to Worksop.
Ref: FH2531

KJS FISHERIES

Kjs Fisheries, Station Rd, Killamarsh, Sheffield, **YORKSHIRE (SOUTH)**, S21 1EN, **England**.
Contact/s: **Mr Ken Swain** (Owner).
(T) 0114 2470876
Profile: **FT:** Coarse; **WN:** Kjs Fisheries; **WT:** Lake (Still). **Location:** **Nr. Rd:** B6058; **Main Rd:** M1, junction 31.
Ref: FH2532

KNAPP HILL FARM LAKES

Knapp Hill Farm Lakes, Buckland Newton, **DORSET**, DT2, **England**.
Contact/s: **Mr Tony Cairns** (Match Secretary).
(T) 01963 363688
Profile: **FT:** Coarse; **WN:** Knapp Hill Farm; **WT:** Lake (Still). **Location:** **Nr. Rd:** B3143; **Main Rd:** Sturminster to Dorchester.
Ref: FH2533

KNIGHT BOTTOMS LAKE

Knight Bottoms Lake, Samlesbury Bottoms, Green Lane, Preston, **LANCASHIRE**, PR5 0RJ, **England**.
Contact/s: **Mr Barry Green**.
(T) 01254 852206
Profile: **FT:** Coarse; **WN:** Knight Bottoms; **WT:** Lake (Still). **Location:** **Nr. Rd:** Green Lane; **Main Rd:** M6, junction 31.
Ref: FH2534

KNIGHTS PIT

Knights Pit, Nazeing, Waltham Abbey, **ESSEX**, EN9, **England**.
Contact/s: **Mr Krizim Seltham** (Angling Manager), Lee Valley Regional Park Authority, Myddleton House, Bulls Cross, Enfield, EN2 9HG.
(T) 01992 709832
(E) garysmith@leevalleypark.org.uk
Profile: **FT:** Coarse; **WN:** Knights Pit; **WT:** Lake (Still) **W. Size:** 6 Acres. **Location:** **Main Rd:** M25, junction 25.
Ref: FH2535

KNIGHTS POOL

Knights Pool, Bank St, Macclesfield, **CHESHIRE**, SK1, **England**.
Contact/s: **Mr John Turner** (Hon Secretary), Prince Albert Angling Society, 15 Pexhill Drive, Macclesfield, Cheshire, SK10 3LP.
(T) 01625 422010
Profile: **FT:** Coarse; **WN:** Knights; **WT:** Pool (Still). **Location:** **Nr. Rd:** Bank Street; **Main Rd:** A537 Buxton Road; **Rail:** Macclesfield.
Ref: FH2536

KNIGHTSCOTE PONDS

Knightscote Ponds, Harefield, Uxbridge, London, **LONDON (GREATER)**, UB9, **England**.
(W) www.uxbridge-rovers.fsnet.co.uk
Contact/s: **Mr L Dalton** (Secretary), Uxbridge Rovers Angling and Conservation Society, PO Box 253, Harrow, Middlesex, HA3 8XN.
(T) 01814 281739
Profile: **FT:** Coarse; **WN:** Knightscote Ponds; **WT:** Pond (Still). **Location:** **Nr. Rd:** Breakspear Road; **Main Rd:** M25, A412; **Rail:** Denham.
Ref: FH2537

KNITSLEY MILL TROUT FISHERIES

Knitsley Mill Trout Fisheries And Stud Farm, The Lodge, Knitsley Mill Farm, Consett, **COUNTY DURHAM**, DH8 9EL, **England**.
Contact/s: **Mr Jeff Watson** (Manager).
(T) 01207 581642
Profile: **FT:** Game; **WN:** Knitsley Mill Trout Fisheries And Stud Farm; **WT:** Lake (Still).
Ref: FH2538

KNOCKBRACKEN TROUT LAKES

Knockbracken Trout Lakes, Trillick Rd, Ballinamallard, **COUNTY FERMANAGH**, BT94 2, **Northern Ireland**.
Contact/s: **Mr Tom Keys** (Manager), Knockbracken Trout Lakes, 56 Trellick Rd, Ballinamallard, County Fermanagh, BT94 2RF.
(T) 028 66389990
Profile: **FT:** Game; **WN:** Knockbracken; **WT:** Lake (Still) **W. Size:** 4 Acres. **Location:** **Nr. Rd:** Trillick Road.
Ref: FH2539

KNOCKDERRY

Knockderry, Waterford, **COUNTY WATERFORD**, **Ireland**.
Contact/s: Booking Secretary.
(T) 051 84107
Manager, Shannon Regional Fisheries Board, Thomond Weir, Limerick, County Limerick, Ireland.
(T) 061 455171
Profile: **FT:** Game; **WN:** Knockderry; **WT:** Reservoir (Still) **W. Size:** 70 Acres.
Ref: FH2540

KNOCKQUASSEN RESERVOIR

Knockquassen Reservoir, Stranraer, **DUMFRIES AND GALLOWAY**, DG9, **Scotland**.
Contact/s: **Mr Eric McLean** (Proprietor of Sports Shop), The Sports Shop, 86 George St, Stranraer, Dumfries and Galloway, DG9 7JS.
(T) 01776 702705
Profile: **FT:** Game; **WN:** Knockquassen; **WT:** Reservoir (Still). **Location:** **Main Rd:** A77.
Ref: FH2541

KNOTFORD LAGOON

Knotford Lagoon, Angling And Country Sports, Pool Rd, Otley, **YORKSHIRE (WEST)**, LS21, **England**.
Contact/s: Secretary, Bradford No1 Angling Association, 60 Brow Lane, Shibden, Halifax, HX3 7UT.
Mr John Sparks, 12 Fairway Walk, Wibsey, Bradford, BD7 4JW.
Profile: **FT:** Coarse; **WN:** Knotford; **WT:** Lake (Still). **Location:** **Nr. Rd:** Otley to Pool; **Main Rd:** A659.
Ref: FH2542

KNOTT END TARN

Knott End Tarn, Birkby, Maryport, **CUMBRIA**, CA15 6, **England**.
Contact/s: **Mr W Arnold**.
(T) 01229 717255
Profile: **FT:** Game; **WN:** Knott End; **WT:** Tarn (Still).
Ref: FH2543

KNYPERSLEY RESERVOIR

Knypersley Reservoir, Knypersley Country Park, Greenway Bank, Stoke-on-Trent, **STAFFORDSHIRE**, ST8, **England**.
Contact/s: **Mr C Yates** (Club Secretary Fenton & District As), The Puzzles, 5 Gatley Gr, Meir Park, Stoke-on-Trent, Staffordshire ST3 7SH.
(T) 01782 396913
Ms Liz Hayes (Manager).
(T) 01625 251262
Profile: **FT:** Coarse; **WN:** Knypersley; **WT:** Reservoir (Still) **W. Size:** 20 Acres.
Location: **Nr. Rd:** Greenway Bank; **Main Rd:** A527; **Rail:** Kidsgrove.
Ref: FH2544

KORDA LAKE

Korda Lake, Colne Valley, Harefield, Uxbridge, Uxbridge, London, **LONDON (GREATER)**, UB9, **England**.
Profile: **FT:** Coarse; **WN:** Korda Lake; **WT:** Gravel Pit (Still) **W. Size:** 15 Acres.

Location: **Nr. Rd:** A412; **Main Rd:** A413, A30.
Ref: FH2545

KYLEMORE HOUSE FISHERY

Kylemore House Fishery And Accomodation, Kylemore House Fishery, Kylemore, Connemara, **COUNTY GALWAY**, **Ireland**.
Contact/s: **Ms Nancy Noughton**.
(T) 095 41143 **(F)** 095 41143
Profile: **FT:** Game; **WN:** Kylemore House Fishery And Accomodation; **WT:** Lake (Still).
Location: **Nr. Rd:** N59 West Port Road; **Main Rd:** N59; **Rail:** Galway.
Ref: FH2546

LABRAX FISHING

Labrax Fishing, Stranraer, **DUMFRIES AND GALLOWAY**, DG9, **Scotland**.
Contact/s: **Mr Logie** (Manager).
(T) 01581 400285
Profile: **FT:** Game; **WN:** Labrax; **WT:** Reservoir (Still).
Ref: FH2547

LACASDALE LOCHS

Lacasdale Lochs, The Old Schoolhouse, Bunavonadder, Harris, **WESTERN ISLES**, HS3 3AL, **Scotland**.
Contact/s: **Elsa**.
(T) 01859 502180or01417793718
Profile: **FT:** Game; **WN:** Lacasdale; **WT:** Loch (Still) **W. Size:** 1600 Metres. **Location:** **Nr. Rd:** Bunavonadder.
Ref: FH2548

LADYBOWER RESERVOIR

Ladybower Reservoir, Ashopton Rd, Bamford, Hope Valley, **DERBYSHIRE**, S33 0AZ, **England**.
(W) www.peakland.com
Contact/s: Manager, Peak Tourist Office, 8 Eccles House Telebusiness Ctre, Eccles Lane, Hope, S33 6RW.
(T) 01433 623333or623330 **(F)** 01433 623334
(E) peakland@peakland.com
Mr Allan Purnell (Manager).
(T) 01433 651254 **(F)** 01433 651254
Profile: **FT:** Game; **WN:** Ladybower; **WT:** Reservoir (Still) **W. Size:** 504 Acres.
Location: **Nr. Rd:** Ashopton Road; **Main Rd:** A6013; **Rail:** Bamford.
Ref: FH2549

LAGAN (RIVER)

River Lagan, Belfast, **COUNTY ANTRIM**, BT, **Northern Ireland**.
Contact/s: Manager, Tourist Information Ctre, St Annes Court, 59 North St, Belfast, BT1 1NB.
(T) 028 902246609
Profile: **FT:** Coarse; **WN:** Lagan; **WT:** River (Moving).
Ref: FH2550

LAGAN (RIVER)

River Lagan, Donacloney, Craigavon, **COUNTY ARMAGH**, BT66, **Northern Ireland**.
Contact/s: Manager, Premier Angling Ctre, 17 Queen St, Lurgan, Craigavon, BT66 8BQ.
(T) 028 38325204
Manager, F C Computers and Tackle, 28 High St, Lurgan, Craigavon, BT66 8AW.
(T) 028 38328543
Profile: **FT:** Game; **WN:** Lagan; **WT:** River (Moving) **W. Size:** 22400 Metres.
Ref: FH2551

LAGAN (RIVER)

River Lagan, Dromore, **COUNTY DOWN**, BT25, **Northern Ireland**.
Contact/s: **Mr Donald McClurnan**.
(T) 028 92692820
Ms Jackie McCracken, Gallow St, Dromore, County Down.
(T) 028 92693247
Profile: **FT:** Game; **WN:** Lagan; **WT:** River (Moving) **W. Size:** 14400 Metres.
Ref: FH2552

LAIRDMANNOCH LOCH

Lairdmannoch Loch, Castle Douglas, **DUMFRIES AND GALLOWAY**, DG7, **Scotland**.
Contact/s: Manager, G M Thomson and Co, 27 King St, Castle Douglas, Dumfries and Galloway, DG7 1AB.
(T) 01556 502701
Profile: **FT:** Game; **WN:** Lairdmannoch; **WT:** Loch (Still).
Ref: FH2553

LAKE BLAENMELINDWR

Lake Blaenmelindwr, Aberystwyth, **CEREDIGION**, SY23, **Wales**.
Contact/s: **Mr Peredur Eklund** (Hon Secretary), 42 Erwgoch, Waunfawr, Aberystwyth, Carmarthenshire, SY23 3AZ.
(T) 01970 623021
Profile: **FT:** Game; **WN:** Blaenmelindwr; **WT:** Lake (Still).
Ref: FH2554

LAKE CRAIGYPISTYLL

Lake Craigypistyll, Aberystwyth, **CEREDIGION**, SY23, **Wales**.
Contact/s: **Mr Peredur Eklund** (Hon Secretary), 42 Erwgoch, Waunfawr, Aberystwyth, Carmarthenshire, SY23 3AZ.
(T) 01970 623021
Profile: **FT:** Game; **WN:** Craigypistyll; **WT:** Lake (Still).
Ref: FH2555

LAKE FARM

Lake Farm, Bull Hill, Sandleheath, Fordingbridge, **HAMPSHIRE**, SP6 3EF, **England**.
Contact/s: **Mr P S Birch** (Manager), 18 Elmwood Avenue, Fordingbridge, Hampshire.
(T) 01425 653383 **(F)** 01425 653383 **(M)** 07974 804250
(E) phil@birch50.fsnet.co.uk
Profile: **FT:** Coarse; **WN:** Farm; **WT:** Lake (Still) **W. Size:** 4 Acres. **Location:** **Nr. Rd:** Lower Daggons; **Main Rd:** A354; **Rail:** Salisbury.
Ref: FH2556

LAKE FRONGOCH

Lake Frongoch, Aberystwyth, **CEREDIGION**, SY23, **Wales**.
Contact/s: **Mr Peredur Eklund** (Hon Secretary), 42 Erwgoch, Waunfawr, Aberystwyth, Carmarthenshire, SY23 3AZ.
(T) 01970 623021
Profile: **FT:** Game; **WN:** Frongoch; **WT:** Lake (Still).
Ref: FH2557

LAKE HELEN

Lake Helen, Mill Lane, Sutterton, Boston, **LINCOLNSHIRE**, PE20 2EN, **England**.
Contact/s: **Mr Hadyn Greeves** (Manager).
(T) 01205 460681
Profile: **FT:** Coarse; **WN:** Helen; **WT:** Lake (Still) **W. Size:** 3 Acres. **Location:** **Nr. Rd:** Mill Lane; **Main Rd:** B1397 to A17; **Rail:** Boston.
Ref: FH2558

LAKE HOUSE HOLIDAYS

Lake House Holidays, Benllech, **ISLE OF ANGLESEY**, **Wales**.
Contact/s: **Mr K Twist** (Manager), Tyddyn Sargent, Tynygongl, Benllech, Isle of Anglesey, Wales.
(T) 01248 853024
(E) k.twist@ukonline.co.uk
Profile: **FT:** Game; **WN:** Lake House Holidays; **WT:** Lake (Still).
Ref: FH2559

LAKE HOUSE HOTEL

Lake House Hotel, Cloonee Lakes, Kenmare, **COUNTY KERRY**, **Ireland**.
Contact/s: **Ms Mary O'Shea** (Manager).
(T) 064 84205
Profile: **FT:** Game; **WN:** Lake House Hotel; **WT:** Lake (Still).
Ref: FH2560

LAKE LLYGAD

Lake Llygad, Aberystwyth, **CEREDIGION**, SY23, **Wales**.
Contact/s: **Mr Peredur Eklund** (Hon Secretary), 42 Erwgoch, Waunfawr, Aberystwyth, Carmarthenshire, SY23 3AZ.
(T) 01970 623021
Profile: **FT:** Game; **WN:** Llygad; **WT:** Lake (Still).
Ref: FH2561

LAKE MEADOWS

Lake Meadows, Radford Cres, Billericay, **ESSEX**, CM1, **England**.
Contact/s: **Mr Mick Toomer** (Manager), Tackle Shop, 10 Ravensdale, Kingswood, Basildon, Essex SS16 5HS.
(T) 01268 282317
Profile: **FT:** Coarse; **WN:** Meadows; **WT:** Lake (Still) **W. Size:** 5 Acres. **Location:** **Nr. Rd:** Radford Crescent; **Rail:** Billericay.
Ref: FH2562

LAKE MOCHDRE

Lake Mochdre, Newtown, **POWYS**, SY16 4JN, **Wales**.
Contact/s: Fishery Manager.
(T) 01686 623888
Profile: **FT:** Game; **WN:** Mochdre; **WT:** Reservoir (Still) **W. Size:** 2 Acres.
Ref: FH2563

LAKE NA LEIBE

Lake Na Leibe, Castlebaldwin, **COUNTY SLIGO**, **Ireland**.
Contact/s: J Hargadon, Lough Arrow Fish Preservation Association, Annaghloy, Riverstown, County Sligo.
(T) 079 66666or65065
Profile: **FT:** Game; **WN:** Na Leibe; **WT:** Lake (Still). **Location:** **Rail:** Boyle.
Ref: FH2564

LAKE NUMBER ONE (LAKE19)

Lake Number One (Lake19), Cotswold Water Park, South Cerney, Cirencester, **GLOUCESTERSHIRE**, GL7, **England**.
Contact/s: Manager, The Cotswold Water Park Society, 44 Black Jack St, Cirencester, Gloucestershire, GL7 2AA.
(T) 01285 642694
Mr Peter Gilbert (Chairman), 31 Havelock St, Swindon, Wiltshire, SN1 1SD.
(T) 01793 535396
Profile: **FT:** Coarse; **WN:** Lake Number One (Lake 19); **WT:** Gravel Pit (Still); **F. Size:** 7 Acres; **W. Size:** 6 Acres. **Location:** **Nr. Rd:** Broadway to South Cerney; **Main Rd:** A419, A429.
Ref: FH2565

LAKE OF MENTEITH FISHERIES

Lake Of Menteith Fisheries, 'Ryeyards', Port Of Menteith, Stirling, FK8 3RA, **Scotland**.
Contact/s: **Mr Quint Glen** (Manager).
(T) 01877 385664 **(F)** 01877 385648
Mrs Nesbit (Booking Secretary).
(T) 01877 385664 **(F)** 01877 385648
Profile: **FT:** Game; **WN:** Menteith; **WT:** Lake (Still) **W. Size:** 700 Acres. **Location:** **Nr. Rd:** B8034; **Main Rd:** A81; **Rail:** Stirling.
Ref: FH2566

LAKE PENDHAM

Lake Pendham, Aberystwyth, **CEREDIGION**, SY23, **Wales**.
Contact/s: **Mr Peredur Eklund** (Hon Secretary), 42 Erwgoch, Waunfawr, Aberystwyth, Carmarthenshire, SY23 3AZ.
(T) 01970 623021
Profile: **FT:** Game; **WN:** Pendham; **WT:** Lake (Still).
Ref: FH2567

LAKE PENRYN

Lake Penryn, Argal, Penryn, **CORNWALL**, TR10, **England**.
Contact/s: Ranger, Watersports Ctre, Siblyback, Common Moor, Liskeard, PL14 6.
(T) 01579 342366

Profile: **FT:** Game; **WN:** Penryn; **WT:** Lake (Still) **W. Size:** 65 Acres. **Location:** **Nr. Rd:** Argal.
Ref: FH2568

LAKE RHEIDOL

Lake Rheidol, Aberystwyth, **CEREDIGION**, SY23, **Wales**.
Contact/s: **Mr Peredur Eklund** (Hon Secretary), 42 Erwgoch, Waunfawr, Aberystwyth, Carmarthenshire, SY23 3AZ.
(T) 01970 623021
Profile: **FT:** Game; **WN:** Rheidol; **WT:** Lake (Still).
Ref: FH2569

LAKE RHOSGOCH

Lake Rhosgoch, Aberystwyth, **CEREDIGION**, SY23, **Wales**.
Contact/s: **Mr Peredur Eklund** (Hon Secretary), 42 Erwgoch, Waunfawr, Aberystwyth, Carmarthenshire, SY23 3AZ.
(T) 01970 623021
Profile: **FT:** Game; **WN:** Rhosgoch; **WT:** Lake (Still).
Ref: FH2570

LAKE RHOSRHYDD

Lake Rhosrhydd, Aberystwyth, **CEREDIGION**, SY23, **Wales**.
Contact/s: **Mr Peredur Eklund** (Hon Secretary), 42 Erwgoch, Waunfawr, Aberystwyth, Carmarthenshire, SY23 3AZ.
(T) 01970 623021
Profile: **FT:** Game; **WN:** Rhosrhydd; **WT:** Lake (Still).
Ref: FH2571

LAKE ROSS FISHERY

Lake Ross Caravan Park And Fishery, Dozews Bank, West Pinchbeck, Spalding, **LINCOLNSHIRE**, PE11 3NA, **England**.
Contact/s: **Mr Martyn Frey** (Owner).
(T) 01775 761690
Profile: **FT:** Coarse; **WN:** Ross; **WT:** Lake (Still); **F. Size:** 2 Acres; **W. Size:** 1 Acre. **Location:** **Nr. Rd:** A151; **Main Rd:** A16 or A151; **Rail:** Spalding.
Ref: FH2572

LAKE VYRNWY

Lake Vyrnwy, Lake Vyrnwy Hotel, Llanwddyn, Oswestry, **SHROPSHIRE**, SY10 0LY, **England**.
Contact/s: **Mr Jim Talbot** (Manager).
(T) 01691 870692
Profile: **FT:** Game; **WN:** Vyrnwy; **WT:** Lake (Still) **W. Size:** 1100 Acres.
Ref: FH2573

LAKE WINDERMERE

Lake Windermere, Windermere, **CUMBRIA**, LA23, **England**.
Contact/s: **Mr Chris Sodo** (Hon Treasurer), Windermere, Ambleside and District Angling Association, Ecclerigg Court, Ecclerigg, Windermere, LA23 1LQ.
(T) 01539 445083
Profile: **FT:** Combination; **WN:** Windermere; **WT:** Lake (Still). **Location:** **Nr. Rd:** A591; **Main Rd:** M6, junctions 36 or 37 to Kendal.
Ref: FH2574

LAKEDOWN TROUT FISHERY

Lakedown Trout Fishery, Swife Lane, Broad Oak, Burwash Common, Etchingham, **SUSSEX (EAST)**, TN21 8UX, **England**.
Contact/s: **Mr Alan Bristow** (Manager).
(T) 01435 883449
Mr Ashley McLenahan.
(T) 01435 883449
Profile: **FT:** Game; **WN:** Lakedown; **WT:** Lake (Still) **W. Size:** 5 Acres. **Location:** **Nr. Rd:** Swife Lane.
Ref: FH2575

LAKEHOUSE LAKE

Lakehouse Lake, Kelfield, York, **YORKSHIRE (NORTH)**, YO19 6, **England**.
Contact/s: **Mrs K Hargreaves** (Fishery Manager), Lake House, Riccall Lane, Kelfield, Yorkshire (North), YO19 6RE.
(T) 01757 248627 **(F)** 01757 249446
Profile: **FT:** Coarse; **WN:** Lakehouse; **WT:** Clay Pit (Still) **W. Size:** 3 Acres. **Location:** **Nr. Rd:** Riccall Lane; **Main Rd:** A19.
Ref: FH2576

LAKEMINSTER PARK

Lakeminster Park, Beverley, **HUMBERSIDE**, HU17, **England**.
Contact/s: **Mr Brian Rushworth** (Secretary).
(T) 01482 882655
Profile: **FT:** Coarse; **WN:** Lakeminster; **WT:** Lake (Still). **Location:** **Nr. Rd:** A1174.
Ref: FH2577

LAKEMORE COUNTRY PARK

Lakemore Country Park, Lane Ends Farm, Clay Lane, Haslington, Crewe, **CHESHIRE**, CW11 3GF, **England**.
Contact/s: **Mr Mark Ashmore** (Manager).
(M) 07771 848801
Ms Liz Hayes (Manager).
(T) 01625 251262
Profile: **FT:** Coarse; **WN:** Lakemore; **WT:** Lake (Still) **W. Size:** 4 Acres. **Location:** **Nr. Rd:** Clay Lane; **Main Rd:** A534; **Rail:** Crewe.
Ref: FH2578

LAKES OF KILLARNEY

Lakes Of Killarney, Ross Castle, Killarney, **COUNTY KERRY**, **Ireland**.
Contact/s: **Mr Harry Clifton**.
(T) 064 32252
Profile: **FT:** Combination; **WN:** Killarney; **WT:** Lake (Still); **F. Size:** 26000 Acres; **W. Size:** 5000 Acres. **Location:** **Nr. Rd:** Ross Road; **Rail:** Killarney.
Ref: FH2579

LAKESIDE

Lakeside Trout And Coarse Fishery, Wine Rd, Cublington, Leighton Buzzard, **BEDFORDSHIRE**, LU7 0LF, **England**.
Contact/s: **Ms Sarah Ellis** (Manager).
(T) 01296 682201 **(F)** 01296 682215
Profile: **FT:** Combination; **WN:** Lakeside Trout And Coarse Fishery; **WT:** Lake (Still). **Location:** **Nr. Rd:** Aylesbury to Leighton Buzzard.
Ref: FH2597

LAKESIDE

Lakeside, Eastleigh Angling Ctre, Eastleigh, Southampton, **HAMPSHIRE**, SO, **England**.
Contact/s: **Mr Dave Banks** (Fishery Manager).
(T) 023 80619491
Mr J Remington (Secretary), Eastleigh and District Angling Club, 121 Desborough Rd, Eastleigh, Hampshire, SO50 5NP.
(T) 023 80635540
Profile: **FT:** Coarse; **WN:** Lakeside; **WT:** Lake (Still) **W. Size:** 7 Acres. **Location:** **Nr. Rd:** A335; **Main Rd:** M27, junction 5.
Ref: FH2580

LAKESIDE

Lakeside, Lakeside Rd, Ash, Aldershot, **HAMPSHIRE**, GU12, **England**.
Contact/s: Manager, R and R Tackle, 74 High St, Sandhurst, Berkshire, GU47 8ED.
(T) 01252 870007
Secretary.
(T) 01252 679414
Profile: **FT:** Coarse; **WN:** Lakeside; **WT:** Lake (Still). **Location:** **Nr. Rd:** Lakeside Road; **Main Rd:** A323, B3411.
Ref: FH2581

LAKESIDE

Lakeside, Barlings Lane, Langworth, Lincoln, **LINCOLNSHIRE**, LN3 5DF, **England**.
Contact/s: **Val Wilkinson**.
(T) 01522 595933
Profile: **FT:** Coarse; **WN:** Kingfisher, Match, Childrens Pool; **WT:** Lake (Still). **Location:** **Nr. Rd:** A158 Lincoln to Langworth; **Main Rd:** Barlings Lane.
Ref: FH2582

LAKESIDE

Lakeside, Biggs Rd, Walsoken, King's Lynn, **NORFOLK**, PE, **England**.
Contact/s: **Mr M R Stratton** (Fishery Manager).
(T) 01945 584435
Profile: **FT:** Coarse; **WN:** Lakeside; **WT:** Lake (Still). **Location:** **Nr. Rd:** Biggs Road.
Ref: FH2583

LAKESIDE

Lakeside, Exebridge, Dulverton, **SOMERSET**, TA22 9BE, **England**.
Contact/s: **Mr John Smallwood**, Exe Valley Angling, 19 West Exe South, Tiverton.
(T) 01884 242275
Profile: **FT:** Coarse; **WN:** Lakeside; **WT:** Pool (Still) **W. Size:** 1 Acre. **Location:** **Nr. Rd:** B3222; **Main Rd:** A396.
Ref: FH2584

LAKESIDE

Lakeside, Onehouse, Stowmarket, **SUFFOLK**, IP14, **England**.
Contact/s: Fishery Manager.
(T) 01449 613770
Profile: **FT:** Coarse; **WN:** Lakeside; **WT:** Lake (Still).
Ref: FH2585

LAKESIDE

Lakeside, Heath End, **SURREY**, **England**.
Contact/s: .
(T) 07774 816583
Profile: **FT:** Coarse; **WN:** Lakeside; **WT:** Lake (Still).
Ref: FH2586

LAKESIDE CARAVAN PARK

Lakeside Caravan Park, Denver, Downham Market, **NORFOLK**, PE38, **England**.
Contact/s: **Mr Bob Riches**.
(T) 01366 383291or01366387074
Profile: **FT:** Coarse; **WN:** Lakeside Caravan Park; **WT:** Lake (Still) **W. Size:** 2 Acres. **Location:** **Nr. Rd:** Denver Sluice road; **Main Rd:** A10 through Downham Market to Denver.
Ref: FH2587

LAKESIDE COUNTRY CLUB

Lakeside Country Club, Rushden, **NORTHAMPTONSHIRE**, NN10, **England**.
Contact/s: Fishery Manager.
(T) 01933 53808
Profile: **FT:** Coarse; **WN:** Lakeside Country Club; **WT:** Lake (Still).
Ref: FH2588

LAKESIDE COUNTRY PARK

Lakeside Country Park, Park Office, Eastleigh, **HAMPSHIRE**, SO50 5PD, **England**.
Contact/s: **Mr Jim Cook** (Secretary).
(T) 023 80422098
Mr Mike Anderson (Country Park Officer).
(T) 023 80617882
Profile: **FT:** Coarse; **WN:** Lakeside Country Park; **WT:** Gravel Pit (Still) **W. Size:** 5 Acres. **Location:** **Main Rd:** A335.
Ref: FH2589

LAKESIDE FARM

Lakeside Farm, Caythorpe, Frieston, Grantham, **NOTTINGHAMSHIRE**, NG32 3BW, **England**.
Contact/s: **Mrs J Ullyatt**.
(T) 01400 272758
Profile: **FT:** Game; **WN:** Lakeside; **WT:** Lake (Still) **W. Size:** 3 Acres. **Location:** **Nr. Rd:** Caythorpe.
Ref: FH2590

LAKESIDE FISHERIES

Lakeside Fisheries, Lakeside Cottage, Brompton-on-Swale, Richmond, **YORKSHIRE (NORTH)**, DL10 7HA, **England**.
Contact/s: **Ms Irene Bake** (owner).
(T) 01748 812405
Profile: **FT:** Game; **WN:** Lakeside Fisheries; **WT:** Lake (Still). **Location:** **Nr. Rd:** A1.

Ref: FH2591

LAKESIDE FISHERY

Lakeside Fishery, Access Rd, Ranskill, Retford, **NOTTINGHAMSHIRE**, DN22 8LW, **England**.
Contact/s: **Mr Nigel Hawke** (Director).
(T) 01777 818524 **(F)** 01777 818524
Mrs Lynda Hawke.
(T) 01777 818524 **(F)** 01777 818524
Profile: **FT:** Combination; **WN:** Lakeside Fishery; **WT:** Lake (Still); **F. Size:** 24 Acres; **W. Size:** 10 Acres. Location: **Nr. Rd:** Access Road; **Main Rd:** A1M; **Rail:** Retford.
Ref: FH2592

LAKESIDE FISHING

Lakeside Fishing, Leicester Grange, Wolvey, Hinckley, **LEICESTERSHIRE**, LE10 3JB, **England**.
Contact/s: **Mr Noel Gibbons** (Fishery Manager).
(T) 01455 633016
Profile: **FT:** Coarse; **WN:** Lakeside; **WT:** Lake (Still); **F. Size:** 100 Acres; **W. Size:** 8 Acres. Location: **Main Rd:** M69 then B4109 to Wolvey.
Ref: FH2593

LAKESIDE LEISURE PARK

Lakeside Leisure Park, Trunch Lane, Chapel St Leonards, Skegness, **LINCOLNSHIRE**, PE24 5TU, **England**.
Contact/s: **Mr John Cook** (Owner).
(T) 01754 872631 **(F)** 01754 872631ringtoswitchover
Profile: **FT:** Combination; **WN:** Lakeside Leisure Park; **WT:** Combination (Still); **F. Size:** 10 Acres; **W. Size:** 7 Acres. Location: **Nr. Rd:** Just off Trunch Lane; **Main Rd:** A52; **Rail:** Skegness.
Ref: FH2594

LAKESIDE LODGES

Lakeside Lodges, Moor Lane, York, **YORKSHIRE (NORTH)**, YO24 2QU, **England**.
(W) www.yorklakesidelodges.co.uk
Contact/s: **Mr Neil Manasir**.
(T) 01904 702346 **(F)** 01904 701631 **(M)** 07831 885824
(E) neil@yorklakesidelodges.co.uk
Profile: **FT:** Coarse; **WN:** Lakeside Lodges; **WT:** Lake (Still) **W. Size:** 10 Acres. Location: **Nr. Rd:** Moor Lane; **Main Rd:** A1036; **Rail:** York.
Ref: FH2595

LAKESIDE SPORTING

Lakeside Sporting, Wide Lane, Wymeswold, Loughborough, Leicester, **LEICESTERSHIRE**, LF12 6SE, **England**.
Contact/s: **Mr Dave White** (Manager).
(T) 01509 881714
Profile: **FT:** Game; **WN:** Lakeside Sporting; **WT:** Lake (Still).
Ref: FH2596

LAKEVIEW COUNTRY CLUB

Lakeview Country Club, Old Coach Rd, Lanivet, Bodmin, **CORNWALL**, PL30 5JJ, **England**.
Contact/s: **Mr David Daw** (Manager).
(T) 01208 831079
Mr Don Bassett (Proprietor).
(T) 01208 831808 **(M)** 07733 345456
Profile: **FT:** Coarse; **WN:** Lakeview Country Club; **WT:** Lake (Still) **W. Size:** 4 Acres. Location: **Nr. Rd:** Old Coach Road; **Main Rd:** A30, Bodmin by-pass.
Ref: FH2598

LAMALOAD RESERVOIR

Lamaload Reservoir, Macclesfield, **CHESHIRE**, SK1, **England**.
Mr John Turner (Hon Secretary), Prince Albert Angling Society, 15 Pexhill Drive, Macclesfield, Cheshire, SK10 3LP.
(T) 01625 422010
Profile: **FT:** Game; **WN:** Lamaload; **WT:** Reservoir (Still). Location: **Nr. Rd:** Hooleyhey Lane; **Main Rd:** A537 Macclesfield to Buxton; **Rail:** Macclesfield.
Ref: FH2599

LAMBWATH LAKES

Lambwath Lakes, Aldbrough, Hull, **HUMBERSIDE**, HU11, **England**.
Contact/s: **Mr Adrian Heslop**.
(T) 01482 7996627
Mr Dave Heslop (Manager).
(T) 01482 796627
Profile: **FT:** Coarse; **WN:** Lambwath; **WT:** Lake (Still).
Ref: FH2600

LAMPETER FISHERY

Lampeter Fishery, Lampeter, **CEREDIGION**, SA48, **Wales**.
(W) www.fishing-in-wales.co.uk/llandysul-aa/beat4
Contact/s: **Mr Artie Jones** (Hon Secretary), Llandysul Angling Association, Glas-y-Dorlan, Llyn-y-Fran Rd, Llandysul, SA44 4JW.
(T) 01559 362317
Profile: **FT:** Game; **WN:** Teifi; **WT:** River (Moving) **W. Size:** 6400 Metres.
Ref: FH2601

LANARK LOCH

Lanark Loch, Lanark Loch Country Park, Lanark, **LANARKSHIRE (SOUTH)**, ML11, **Scotland**.
Contact/s: **Mr Malcolm Mackay** (Bailiff).
(T) 0131 4771804
Profile: **FT:** Coarse; **WN:** Lanark; **WT:** Loch (Still) **W. Size:** 18 Acres. Location: **Nr. Rd:** Hyndford Road; **Main Rd:** A72.
Ref: FH2602

LANCASTER CANAL

Lancaster Canal, Preston, **LANCASHIRE**, PR, **England**.
Profile: **FT:** Coarse; **WN:** Lancaster; **WT:** Canal (Still).
Ref: FH2603

LANCASTER CANAL

Lancaster Canal, Lancaster, **LANCASHIRE**, LA1, **England**.
Profile: **FT:** Coarse; **WN:** Lancaster; **WT:** Canal (Still).
Ref: FH2604

LANCASTER HOUSE

Lancaster House, Charnock Richard, Chorley, **LANCASHIRE**, PR7, **England**.
Contact/s: **Mr Harold Heaton** (Manager).
(T) 01257 791312
Profile: **FT:** Coarse; **WN:** Lancaster House; **WT:** Lake (Still). Location: **Nr. Rd:** Charnock Richard; **Main Rd:** A681.
Ref: FH2605

LANCASTER HOUSE FARM FISHERY

Lancaster House Farm Fishery, Langwood Farm Lodge, Haslingden, Rossendale, **LANCASHIRE**, BB4, **England**.
Contact/s: Fishery Manager.
(T) 01706 218300
Profile: **FT:** Coarse; **WN:** Lancaster House Farm Fishery; **WT:** Lake (Still). Location: **Nr. Rd:** A681, Haslingden Road; **Main Rd:** A680, Manchester Road.
Ref: FH2606

LANDS END FARM

Lands End Farm, Heath House, Wedmore, **SOMERSET**, BS28 4UQ, **England**.
Contact/s: **Mr Martin Duckett** (Partner).
(M) 07977 545882
Profile: **FT:** Coarse; **WN:** Lands End Farm; **WT:** Lake (Still) **W. Size:** 3 Acres. Location: **Main Rd:** B3199.
Ref: FH2607

LANDS END FISHERIES

Lands end Fisheries, Heath House, Wedmore, **SOMERSET**, BS28 4UQ, **England**.
Contact/s: **Mr Michael Duckett** (Owner), Heathmore House, Wedmore, Somerset. BS28 4UQ..
(T) 07977 545882
Profile: **FT:** Coarse; **WN:** Landsend Fisheries; **WT:** Lake (Still); **F. Size:** 10 Acres; **W. Size:** 4 Acres.
Ref: FH2608

LANESHAW RESERVOIR

Laneshaw Reservoir, Pendle, Burnley, **LANCASHIRE**, BB10, **England**.
Contact/s: **Mr Robin Varley** (Hon Secretary).
(T) 01535 634426
Mr Roy Rhodes (Conservation, Access and Recreation Manager), Rivington Water Treatment Works, Bolton Rd, Horwich, Bolton, BL6 7RN.
(T) 01204 664300
Profile: **FT:** Combination; **WN:** Laneshaw; **WT:** Reservoir (Still) **W. Size:** 16 Acres. Location: **Nr. Rd:** Laneshaw Bridge; **Main Rd:** B6250, A6068, Keighley Road.
Ref: FH2609

LANGARTH POOLS

Threemilestone Lake, Threemilestone, Truro, **CORNWALL**, TR, **England**.
Contact/s: **Mr Ken Hart** (Chairman), Threemilestone Angling Club, 75 Polstain Rd, Truro, Cornwall, TR3 6DH.
(T) 01872 272021
(E) khaux@aol.com
Profile: **FT:** Coarse; **WN:** Langarth; **WT:** Pond (Still) **W. Size:** 2 Acres. Location: **Nr. Rd:** Truro to St Agnes; **Main Rd:** A390; **Rail:** Truro.
Ref: FH2610

LANGFORD FISHERIES

Langford Fisheries, Duck St, Steeple Langford, Salisbury, **WILTSHIRE**, SP3 4NH, **England**.
Contact/s: **Mr Paul Knight**.
(T) 01722 790770 **(F)** 01722 790016
Profile: **FT:** Game; **WN:** Langford Fisheries; **WT:** Combination (Still & Moving) **W. Size:** 17 Acres. Location: **Nr. Rd:** Duck Street; **Main Rd:** A36; **Rail:** Salisbury.
Ref: FH2611

LANGFORD LAKES

Langford Lakes, Middle Hill Farm, Langford Budville, Wellington, **SOMERSET**, TA21 0RS, **England**.
Contact/s: **Mr Reg Hendy** (Owner).
(T) 01823 400476 **(F)** 01823 400476
Profile: **FT:** Coarse; **WN:** Langford; **WT:** Lake (Still); **F. Size:** 5 Acres; **W. Size:** 3 Acres. Location: **Nr. Rd:** Middle Hill Farm; **Main Rd:** B3187; **Rail:** Taunton.
Ref: FH2612

LANGFORD MILL

Langford Mill, Langford, Biggleswade, **BEDFORDSHIRE**, SG18, **England**.
Contact/s: **Mr P N Jones** (Secretary), 79 Howard Drive, Letchworth, Hertfordshire, S96 2BO.
Profile: **FT:** Coarse; **WN:** Langford; **WT:** Mill Dam (Still).
Ref: FH2613

LANGHOLME FISHERIES

Langholme Fisheries, Emmotland, Driffield, **HUMBERSIDE**, YO25 8JS, **England**.
Contact/s: **Ms M Whitfield**.
(T) 01262 488226
Profile: **FT:** Combination; **WN:** Langholme Fisheries; **WT:** Pond (Still) **W. Size:** 3 Acres. Location: **Nr. Rd:** B1249; **Main Rd:** Church End opposite the church.
Ref: FH2614

LANGLEY DAM FISHERIES

Langley Dam Fisheries, Langley, Hexham, **NORTHUMBERLAND**, NE, **England**.
Contact/s: **Mrs Margaret Hope**, Beech House, Langley on Tyne, Hexham, NE47 5LD.
(T) 01434 688846
Profile: **FT:** Game; **WN:** Langley Dam; **WT:** Lake (Still). Location: **Main Rd:** A69.
Ref: FH2615

LANGOLD LAKES

Langold Lakes, Eastgate, Worksop, **NOTTINGHAMSHIRE**, S81, **England**.
Contact/s: **Mr Darryl Layden** (Senior Park Ranger).
(T) 01909 730189
Mr Tony Lewis (Manager), Bassetlaw Leisure Ctre, Eastgate, Worksop, Nottinghamshire, S80 1QS.
(T) 01909 480164
Profile: FT: Coarse; **WN:** Langold; **WT:** Lake (Still) **W. Size:** 20 Acres. **Location: Nr. Rd:** A60; **Main Rd:** Doncaster Road; **Rail:** Worksop.
Ref: FH2616

LANGSDALE LAKE

Langsdale Lake, Melsonby, Darlington, **COUNTY DURHAM**, DL, **England**.
Contact/s: **Mr Clive Simpson**.
(T) 01748 825647 **(F)** 01748 850619
Mr Peter Breathm (Manager). **(F)** 01748 850619 **(M)** 07711 277248
Profile: FT: Coarse; **WN:** Langdale; **WT:** Lake (Still). **Location: Nr. Rd:** Melsonby; **Main Rd:** B6275 to Piercebridge.
Ref: FH2617

LANGTON POND

Langton Pond, Great Langton, Northallerton, **YORKSHIRE (NORTH)**, DL7, **England**.
Contact/s: **Mr Peter Bennet**.
(T) 01748 824894
Profile: FT: Coarse; **WN:** Langton; **WT:** Gravel Pit (Still). **Location: Nr. Rd:** B6271 to Catterick; **Main Rd:** A1.
Ref: FH2618

LANKYS MILL POND

Lankys Mill Pond, Blackley, Manchester, **MANCHESTER (GREATER)**, M2, **England**.
Profile: FT: Coarse; **WN:** Lankys Mill; **WT:** Pond (Still) **W. Size:** 2 Acres. **Location: Nr. Rd:** A664; **Main Rd:** A6104, Junction 19 M62. **£Fr**
Ref: FH2619

LANNYS LAGOON

Lannys Lagoon, Stretton-under-Fosse, Rugby, **WARWICKSHIRE**, CV23, **England**.
Contact/s: Lanny. **(M)** 07970 907995
Profile: FT: Coarse; **WN:** Main, Middle, Fry; **WT:** Pool (Still). **Location: Nr. Rd:** Stretton Wharfroad junction; **Main Rd:** Brinklow to High Cross, B4455.
Ref: FH2620

LAPSLEYS FISHERY

Lapsleys Fishery, Allens Farm, Bickton, Fordingbridge, **HAMPSHIRE**, SP6, **England**.
Contact/s: Manager, Bickton Mill Farm Shop, Bickton, Fordingbridge, Hampshire, SP6 2HA.
(T) 01425 652412
Profile: FT: Coarse; **WN:** Avon; **WT:** Lake (Still).
Ref: FH2621

LARK (RIVER)

River Lark, Pickwillow, Ely, **CAMBRIDGESHIRE**, CB7 4, **England**.
(W) www.cambridge-fpas.co.uk
Contact/s: **Mr Graham Tweed** (Secretary), Cambridge Fish Preservation Angling Society, 27a Villa Rd, Impington, Cambridge, CB4 9NZ.
(T) 01223 234616
Profile: FT: Coarse; **WN:** Lark; **WT:** River (Moving). **Location: Main Rd:** B1382.
Ref: FH2622

LARK (RIVER)

River Lark, Mildenhall, Bury St Edmunds, **SUFFOLK**, IP28, **England**.
Contact/s: **Mr M Hampshire** (Secretary), Mildenhall Angling Club, 63 Downing Cl, Mildenhall, Bury St Edmunds, IP28 7PB.
(T) 01638 718205
Profile: FT: Combination; **WN:** Lark; **WT:** River (Moving).
Ref: FH2623

LARK (RIVER)

River Lark, Brandon, **SUFFOLK**, IP27, **England**.
Contact/s: **Mr E T West**, 8 Arrowhead Drive, Lakenheath, Brandon, IP27 9JN.
(T) 01842 861369
Profile: FT: Combination; **WN:** Lark; **WT:** River (Moving) **W. Size:** 20000 Metres. **Location: Main Rd:** A11; **Rail:** Newmarket.
Ref: FH2624

LARKFIELD LAKES

Larkfield Lakes, Brook St, Snodland, Maidstone, **KENT**, ME1, **England**.
(W) www.rmcangling.co.uk
Contact/s: **Mr Chris Logsdon** (Manager).
(T) 01227 730668 **(F)** 01227 738894
Profile: FT: Coarse; **WN:** Larkfield; **WT:** Lake (Still) **W. Size:** 93 Acres. **Location: Nr. Rd:** Brook Street; **Main Rd:** A228, Snodland by-pass, M20.
Ref: FH2625

LARKWOOD TROUT FISHERY

Larkwood Trout Fishery, Icklingham Rd, West Stow, Bury St Edmunds, **SUFFOLK**, IP28 6EY, **England**.
Contact/s: **Mr Ian McGregor** (Partner And Manager).
(T) 01284 728612
Profile: FT: Game; **WN:** West Stow; **WT:** Lake (Still); **F. Size:** 11 Acres; **W. Size:** 6 Acres. **Location: Nr. Rd:** Icklingham Road; **Main Rd:** A1101; **Rail:** Bury St Edmunds.
Ref: FH2626

LATHOM FISHERIES

Lathom Fisheries, Burscough, **LANCASHIRE**, **England**.
Contact/s: .
(T) 01704 893914
Profile: FT: Coarse; **WN:** Lathom Fisheries; **WT:** Lake (Still).
Ref: FH2627

LATIMER PARK FLY FISHERY

Latimer Park Fly Fishery, Latimer, Chesham, **BUCKINGHAMSHIRE**, HP5 1TT, **England**.
Contact/s: **Mr Chris W Cansdale**, Latimer Park Lakes, Chesham, Buckinghamshire, HP5 1TT.
(T) 01494 766444 **(F)** 01494 766555
Profile: FT: Game; **WN:** Latimer Park Fly Fishery; **WT:** Combination (Still & Moving) **W. Size:** 12 Acres. **Location: Nr. Rd:** Chesham to Chorleywood.
Ref: FH2628

LAUNDE ABBEY LAKES

Launde Abbey Lakes, Launde, Leicester, **LEICESTERSHIRE**, LE7 9XB, **England**.
Contact/s: Fishery Manager.
(T) 01572 717254
Profile: FT: Coarse; **WN:** Launde Abbey; **WT:** Lake (Still).
Ref: FH2629

LAUNDRY LAKE

Laundry Lake, Laundry Lane, Little Easton, Dunmow, **ESSEX**, CM6 2JW, **England**.
Contact/s: Fishery Manager.
(T) 01260 873468
Profile: FT: Coarse; **WN:** Laundry; **WT:** Lake (Still). **Location: Nr. Rd:** B184 Great Dunmow to Thaxted; **Main Rd:** Little Easton.
Ref: FH2630

LAVENDER FARM

Lavender Farm, Faversham, **KENT**, ME13, **England**.
Contact/s: **Mr David Figgis** (Manager).
(T) 01227 751149
Mr John Larraman (Manager).
(T) 01634 301537 **(M)** 07957 663204
Profile: FT: Coarse; **WN:** Lavender Farm; **WT:** Lake (Still); **F. Size:** 6 Acres; **W. Size:** 4 Acres. **Location: Nr. Rd:** A299; **Main Rd:** A299 Ramsgate to London; **Rail:** Faversham.
Ref: FH2631

LAVENDER HALL

Lavender Hall, Lavender Hall Lane, Berkswell, Coventry, **MIDLANDS (WEST)**, CV7 7BN, **England**.
Contact/s: **Mrs Louise Weaver** (Owner).
(T) 01676 530299or01676534814
Profile: FT: Coarse; **WN:** Lavender Hall; **WT:** Lake (Still). **Location: Nr. Rd:** Lavender Hall Lane; **Main Rd:** A452; **Rail:** Berkswell Station.
Ref: FH2632

LAVER (RIVER)

River Laver, Ripon, **YORKSHIRE (NORTH)**, HG4, **England**.
Contact/s: **Mr Bernard Thain** (Manager), Ripon Angling Ctre, 58-59 North St, Ripon, Yorkshire (North), HG4 1EN.
(T) 01765 604666 **(F)** 01765 603933
Profile: FT: Game; **WN:** Laver; **WT:** River (Moving). **Location: Nr. Rd:** Winksley to Bishopton Bridge; **Main Rd:** A1.
Ref: FH2633

LAWFIELD TROUT FISHERY

Lawfield Trout Fishery, Houston Rd, Kilmacolm, **INVERCLYDE**, PA13 4NY, **Scotland**.
Contact/s: **Mr Billy McFern** (Manager).
(T) 01505 874182
Profile: FT: Game; **WN:** Lawfield Trout Fishery; **WT:** Reservoir (Still). **Location: Nr. Rd:** Houston Road.
Ref: FH2634

LAWNS (THE)

Lawns (The), Swindon, **WILTSHIRE**, SN4, **England**.
Contact/s: **Mr Campbell** (Secretary), 72 Rodbourne Rd, Swindon, Wiltshire, SN2 1DH.
(T) 01793 529909
Profile: FT: Coarse; **WN:** Lawns (The); **WT:** Lake (Still).
Ref: FH2635

LAWRENCES FARM

Lawrences Farm, Southover, Tolpuddle, Dorchester, **DORSET**, DT2 7HF, **England**.
Contact/s: **Mr Richard Slocock** (Manager), Wessex Fly Fishing, Lawrences Farm, Tolpuddle, Dorset, DT2 7HF.
(T) 01305 848460 **(F)** 01305 849060
Profile: FT: Game; **WN:** Lawrences Farm; **WT:** Lake (Still).
Ref: FH2636

LAWTON HALL POOL

Lawton Hall Pool, Nicks Tackle Supplies, Kidsgrove, Newcastle-under-Lyme, **STAFFORDSHIRE**, ST5, **England**.
Contact/s: Fishery Manager.
(T) 01782 775871
Profile: FT: Coarse; **WN:** Lawton Hall; **WT:** Lake (Still).
Ref: FH2637

LAYBROOK LAKES

Laybrook Lakes, Ashington, Pulborough, **SUSSEX (WEST)**, RH20, **England**.
Contact/s: Fishery Manager.
(T) 01903 764818
Manager, Arun Angling Ctre, Roundstone Garden Ctre, Angmenring, Littlehampton, BN16 4BD.
(T) 01903 859315
Oliver Beamish (Assistant Manager), Alldays Stores Ltd, London Rd, Ashington, Pulborough, RH20 3JT.
(T) 01903 893879
Profile: FT: Coarse; **WN:** Shelly, Milton, Byron; **WT:** Lake (Still).
Ref: FH2638

LAYER PIT

Layer Pit, Layer Rd, Colchester, **ESSEX**, CO, **England**.
(W) www.c-a-p-s.co.uk
Contact/s: **Mr Paul Masters** (Secretary), CAPS Membership, 17 Azalea Court, Sycamore Rd, Colchester Essex, CO4 3NU.

(T) 01376 512255
(E) secretary@c-a-p-s.co.uk
Profile: **FT:** Coarse; **WN:** Layer; **WT:** Gravel Pit (Still); **F. Size:** 20 Acres; **W. Size:** 15 Acres. **Location:** **Nr. Rd:** Layer Road; **Main Rd:** A12 or A120.
Ref: FH2639

LAYZELLS FARM

Layzells Farm, Sudbury Rd, Great Cornard, Sudbury, **SUFFOLK**, CO10, **England**.
Contact/s: **Mr Rob Hayward** (Manager), Sudbury Angling Ctre, 1 Acton Sq, Sudbury, Suffolk, CO10 1HG.
(T) 01787 312118
Mr Trevor Fairless (Secretary), Sudbury and District Angling Association, 39 Pot Kiln Rd, Sudbury, Suffolk, CO10 0DG.
(T) 01787 312536
Profile: **FT:** Coarse; **WN:** Stow (Suffolk); **WT:** River (Moving) **W. Size:** 2500 Metres. **Location:** **Nr. Rd:** Sudbury to Bures Road; **Main Rd:** A134; **Rail:** Sudbury.
Ref: FH2640

LAZY (RIVER)

River Lazy, Haverigg Village, Millom, **CUMBRIA**, LA, **England**.
Contact/s: **Mr D J Dixon** (Secretary), 1 Churchill Drive, Millom, Cumbria, LA18 5DD.
(T) 01229 774241
Profile: **FT:** Game; **WN:** Lazy; **WT:** River (Moving). **Location:** **Nr. Rd:** A5093; **Main Rd:** A5093.
Ref: FH2641

LEA (RIVER)

River Lea, Waltham Abbey, **ESSEX**, EN, **England**.
Contact/s: **Mr Ian Welch** (Angling Manager), RMC Angling, The Square, Lightwater, Surrey, GU18 5SS.
(T) 01276 453300 (F) 01276 456611
(E) info@rmcangling.co.uk
Profile: **FT:** Coarse; **WN:** Lea; **WT:** River (Moving).
Ref: FH2642

LEA (RIVER)

River Lea, Rye House Bridge, Rye House, Hoddesdon, **HERTFORDSHIRE**, EN11, **England**.
Contact/s: Manager, Rye House, Rye Rd, Hoddesdon, Hertfordshire, EN11 0EH.
Profile: **FT:** Coarse; **WN:** Lea; **WT:** River (Moving). **Location:** **Nr. Rd:** Rye House Bridge to October Hole.
Ref: FH2643

LEA (RIVER)

Lea (River), Stanborough, Welwyn Garden City, **HERTFORDSHIRE**, **England**.
Contact/s:
(T) 01707 334462
Profile: **FT:** Coarse; **WN:** Lea; **WT:** River (Moving).
Ref: FH2644

LEA (RIVER)

Lea (River), Dobbs Weir, Hoddesdon, **HERTFORDSHIRE**, **England**.
Contact/s: .
(T) 01992 709962
Profile: **FT:** Coarse; **WN:** Lea; **WT:** River (Moving).
Ref: FH2645

LEA (RIVER)

River Lea, King's Weir, Wormley, **HERTFORDSHIRE**, EN10, **England**.
Contact/s: Ms Barbara.
(T) 01992 468394
Profile: **FT:** Coarse; **WN:** Lea; **WT:** River (Moving).
Ref: FH2646

LEA NAVIGATION

Lea Navigation, Wormley, Broxbourne, **HERTFORDSHIRE**, EN10, **England**.
Contact/s: **Mr Dave Coster**, Tottenham Angling Ctre, 80a White Hart Lane, Tottenham, London, N17 8HP.
(T) 020 88010062 (F) 020 88010062
Mr Terry Mansbridge (Secretary), Lee Anglers Consortium, 7 Warren Rd, Chingford, London, E4 6QR.
(T) 020 75240869 (F) 020 75240869
Profile: **FT:** Coarse; **WN:** Lea Navigation; **WT:** River (Moving).
Ref: FH2647

LEA NAVIGATION

Lea Navigation, Ponder's End, Mollison Avenue, Enfield, London, **LONDON (GREATER)**, EN2, **England**.
Contact/s: **Mr Peter Green** (Secretary), Lea Anglers Consortium, PO Box 19426, London, E4 8UZ.
(T) 01279 654434
Mr Terry Mansbridge (Secretary), Lee Anglers Consortium, 7 Warren Rd, Chingford, London, E4 6QR.
(T) 020 75240869 (F) 020 75240869
Profile: **FT:** Coarse; **WN:** Lea Navigation; **WT:** Canal (Still) **W. Size:** 3200 Metres. **Location:** **Nr. Rd:** A1055 Mollison Avenue; **Main Rd:** M25, junction 25.
Ref: FH2648

LEA NAVIGATION

Lea Navigation, Stonebridge Lock To Tottenham Hale, Tottenham, London, **LONDON (GREATER)**, N17, **England**.
Contact/s: **Mr Peter Green** (Secretary), Lee Anglers Consortium, PO Box 19426, London, E4 8UZ.
(T) 01279 654434
Profile: **FT:** Coarse; **WN:** Lea Navigation; **WT:** River (Moving). **Location:** **Main Rd:** A503.
Ref: FH2649

LEABRIDGE FARM

Leabridge Farm, Hellingly, Hailsham, **SUSSEX (EAST)**, BN27 4, **England**.
Contact/s: **Mr Don Ralph** (Manager).
(T) 01323 844481
Profile: **FT:** Coarse; **WN:** Leabridge Farm; **WT:** Lake (Still). **Location:** **Nr. Rd:** A267; **Main Rd:** A22.
Ref: FH2650

LEADBEATERS RESERVOIR

Leadbeaters Reservoir, Macclesfield, **CHESHIRE**, SK10 5, **England**.
Contact/s: **Mr Peter Sharples** (Conservation, Access and Recreation Manager), North West Water Ltd, Woodhead Rd, Tintwhistle, Hadfield via Hyde, SK14 7HR.
(T) 01457 864187
Mr Tony Wolley (Secretary), 51 Palmerston St, Bollington, Macclesfield, SK10 5PW.
Profile: **FT:** Coarse; **WN:** Leadbeaters; **WT:** Reservoir (Still).
Ref: FH2651

LEADER (RIVER)

River Leader, Earlston, **SCOTTISH BORDERS**, TD4, **Scotland**.
Contact/s: **Mr W Lothian**, Westfield St, Earlston, Scottish Borders, Scotland.
Profile: **FT:** Game; **WN:** Leader; **WT:** River (Moving).
Ref: FH2652

LEAM (RIVER)

River Leam, Leamington Mill Gardens, Leamington Spa, **WARWICKSHIRE**, CV32 4, **England**.
Contact/s: Fisheries Manager, Warwick District Council, Town Hall, The Parade, Lemington Spa, CV32 4AT.
(T) 01926 450000
Profile: **FT:** Coarse; **WN:** Leam; **WT:** River (Moving) **W. Size:** 350 Metres.
Ref: FH2653

LEAM (RIVER)

River Leam, Pump Room Gardens, Leamington Spa, **WARWICKSHIRE**, CV, **England**.
Contact/s: **Mr Alan Churchward** (Fisheries Manager), Warwick District Council, Town Hall, The Parade, Lemington Spa, CV32 4AT.
(T) 01684 850951
Profile: **FT:** Coarse; **WN:** Leam; **WT:** River (Moving) **W. Size:** 750 Metres.
Ref: FH2654

LEAZES PARK LAKE

Leazes Park Lake, Newcastle Upon Tyne, **TYNE AND WEAR**, NE1, **England**.
Contact/s: Secretary, Leazes Park Angling Association, PO Box 57, Gosforth, Newcastle upon Tyne, NE3 4AF.
Mr Eddie Prady (Club Chairman), 46 Camberley Avenue, Hadrian Park, Tyne and Wear, NE28 9QF.
(T) 0191 2629951
Profile: **FT:** Coarse; **WN:** Leazes Park; **WT:** Lake (Still) **W. Size:** 4 Acres. **Location:** **Nr. Rd:** Richardson Road.
Ref: FH2655

LECHLADE TROUT FISHERY

Lechlade Trout Fishery, Lechlade, **GLOUCESTERSHIRE**, GL7 3QQ, **England**.
(W) www.fishlink.com/lechlade
Contact/s: **Mr Tim Small** (Manager).
(T) 01367 253266 (F) 01367 252663
(E) tim@timtrout.co.uk
Profile: **FT:** Game; **WN:** Lechlade Trout Fishery; **WT:** Lake (Still); **F. Size:** 20 Acres; **W. Size:** 9 Acres. **Location:** **Nr. Rd:** A361; **Main Rd:** A361; **Rail:** Swindon.
Ref: FH2656

LECKEE FISHERY

Leckee Fishery, Post Office, Foxford, **COUNTY MAYO**, **Ireland**.
Profile: **FT:** Game; **WT:** River (Moving).
Ref: FH2657

LECONFIELD ESTATE

Leconfield Estate, Smiths Gore, Estate Office, Petworth, **SUSSEX (WEST)**, GU28, **England**.
Profile: **FT:** Game; **WN:** Western Rother; **WT:** River (Moving).
Ref: FH2658

LEDBURN ROAD

Ledbury Road, Mentmore Rd, Leighton Buzzard, **BEDFORDSHIRE**, LU7, **England**.
(W) www.rmcangling.co.uk
Contact/s: **Mr Ian Welch** (Angling Manager), RMC Angling, The Square, Lightwater, Surrey, GU18 5SS.
(T) 01276 453300 (F) 01276 456611
(E) info@rmcangling.co.uk
Profile: **FT:** Coarse; **WN:** Ledburn; **WT:** Lake (Still) **W. Size:** 5 Acres. **Location:** **Nr. Rd:** Mentmore Road; **Main Rd:** Leighton Buzzard By-Pass.
Ref: FH2659

LEDWYCHE BROOK

Ledwyche Brook, Tenbury Wells, **WORCESTERSHIRE**, WR15, **England**.
Contact/s: **Mr Bill Drew** (Hon Secretary), Oak Tree Cottage, Berrington Rd, Tenbury Wells, WR15 8BB.
Profile: **FT:** Combination; **WN:** Teme; **WT:** River (Moving) **W. Size:** 4 Metres.
Ref: FH2660

LEE FLOOD RELIEF CHANNEL

Lee Flood Relief Channel, Fishers Green Lane, Waltham Abbey, **ESSEX**, EN9 2ED, **England**.
Contact/s: **Mr Krizim Seltham** (Angling Manager), Lee Valley Regional Park Authority, Myddleton House, Bulls Cross, Enfield, EN2 9HG.
(T) 01992 709832
(E) garysmith@leevalleypark.org.uk
Profile: **FT:** Coarse; **WN:** Lee Relief Channel; **WT:** River (Moving) **W. Size:** 2400 Metres. **Location:** **Nr. Rd:** Hooks Marsh and Highbridge Street; **Main Rd:** A121; **Rail:** Cheshunt or Waltham Cross.
Ref: FH2661

LEE NAVIGATION

Lee Navigation, Hertford, **HERTFORDSHIRE**, SG12, **England**.
Contact/s: **Mr Peter Green** (Secretary), Lee Anglers Consortium, PO Box 19426, London, E4 8UZ.
(T) 01279 654434
Mr Terry Mansbridge (Secretary), Lee Anglers Consortium, 7 Warren Rd, Chingford, London, E4 6QR.
(T) 020 75240869 **(F)** 020 75240869
Profile: **FT:** Coarse; **WN:** Lee Navigation; **WT:** River (Moving) **W. Size:** 34500 Metres.
Location: **Nr. Rd:** East London to Hertford.
Ref: FH2662

LEE NAVIGATION

Lee Navigation, Wormley, Broxbourne, **HERTFORDSHIRE**, EN10, **England**.
Contact/s: **Mr Peter Green** (Secretary), Lee Anglers Consortium, PO Box 19426, London, E4 8UZ.
(T) 01279 654434
Profile: **FT:** Coarse; **WN:** Lee Navigation; **WT:** River (Moving).
Ref: FH2663

LEE NAVIGATION

Lee Navigation, Old Ford Lock To Bow Lock, Bishops Stortford, **HERTFORDSHIRE**, CM23, **England**.
Contact/s: **Mr Peter Green** (Secretary), Lee Anglers Consortium, PO Box 19426, London, E4 8UZ.
(T) 01279 654434
Profile: **FT:** Coarse; **WN:** Lee Navigation; **WT:** River (Moving).
Ref: FH2664

LEE NAVIGATION

Lee Navigation, Ware, **HERTFORDSHIRE**, SG12, **England**.
Contact/s: **Mr Peter Green** (Secretary), Lee Anglers Consortium, PO Box 19426, London, E4 8UZ.
(T) 01279 654434
Profile: **FT:** Coarse; **WN:** Lee Navigation; **WT:** River (Moving).
Ref: FH2665

LEE NAVIGATION

Lee Navigation, Fieldes Weir Pool, Bishops Stortford, **HERTFORDSHIRE**, CM23, **England**.
Contact/s: **Mr Peter Green** (Secretary), Lee Anglers Consortium, PO Box 19426, London, E4 8UZ.
(T) 01279 654434
Profile: **FT:** Combination; **WN:** Lee Navigation; **WT:** River (Moving).
Ref: FH2666

LEE NAVIGATION

Lee Navigation, Lee Bridge Road To Old Ford Lock, Bishops Stortford, **HERTFORDSHIRE**, CM23, **England**.
Contact/s: **Mr Peter Green** (Secretary), Lee Anglers Consortium, PO Box 19426, London, E4 8UZ.
(T) 01279 654434
Profile: **FT:** Coarse; **WN:** Lee Navigation; **WT:** River (Moving).
Ref: FH2667

LEE NAVIGATION

Lee Navigation, Waltham Common To Rammey Marsh, Waltham Cross, **HERTFORDSHIRE**, EN8, **England**.
Contact/s: **Mr Peter Green** (Secretary), Lee Anglers Consortium, PO Box 19426, London, E4 8UZ.
(T) 01279 654434
Profile: **FT:** Coarse; **WN:** Lee Navigation; **WT:** River (Moving).
Ref: FH2668

LEE NAVIGATION

Lee Navigation, Rammey Marsh To Ponders End Lock, Bishops Stortford, **HERTFORDSHIRE**, CM23, **England**.
Contact/s: **Mr Peter Green** (Secretary), Lee Anglers Consortium, PO Box 19426, London, E4 8UZ.
(T) 01279 654434
Profile: **FT:** Coarse; **WN:** Lee Navigation; **WT:** River (Moving).
Ref: FH2669

LEE NAVIGATION

Lee Navigation, Lee Park Way, Edmonton, London, **LONDON (GREATER)**, N18 3, **England**.
Contact/s: **Mr Derek Green** (Fishery Manager).
(T) 020 84498706
Profile: **FT:** Coarse; **WN:** Lee Navigation; **WT:** River (Moving).
Ref: FH2670

LEEDS AND LIVERPOOL CANAL

Leeds To Liverpool, Shipley, **YORKSHIRE (WEST)**, BD, **England**.
Contact/s: **Mr W M Troman** (Ticket Secretary), Saltaire Angling Association, 7 Hall Royd, Shipley, Yorkshire (West), BD18 3ED.
(T) 01274 583088
Profile: **FT:** Coarse; **WN:** Leeds and Liverpool**WT:** Canal **W. Size:** 4800 Metres.
Location: **Nr. Rd:** A650; **Main Rd:** A650; **Rail:** Saltaire.
Ref: FH2671

LEEDS TO LIVERPOOL

Leeds To Liverpool, Green Lane, Liverpool, **MERSEYSIDE**, L, **England**.
Contact/s: **Mr Jim Brown** (Secretary), Liverpool DAS, 33 Eleanor Rd, Bootle, Merseyside, L20 6BP.
(T) 0151 2863270
Profile: **FT:** Coarse; **WN:** Leeds to Liverpool; **WT:** Canal (Still). Location: **Nr. Rd:** Green Lane.
Ref: FH2672

LEEDS TO LIVERPOOL CANAL

Leeds To Liverpool Canal, Rufford Arms, Plox Brow, Tarleton, Preston, **LANCASHIRE**, PR4, **England**.
Contact/s: Fishery Manager.
(T) 01772 613606
Profile: **FT:** Coarse; **WN:** Leeds to Liverpool; **WT:** Canal (Still). Location: **Nr. Rd:** Coe Lane; **Main Rd:** A59 Preston to Tarleton.
Ref: FH2673

LEEDS TO LIVERPOOL CANAL

Leeds To Liverpool Canal, Chorley, **LANCASHIRE**, PR, **England**.
(W) www.wiganaa.f9.co.uk
Contact/s: **Mr Gerry Wilson** (Hon Secretary), Wigan and District Angling Association, 11 Guildford Avenue, Chorley, Lancashire, PR6 8TG.
(T) 01257 265905
(E) gerry@wiganna.freeserve.co.uk
Profile: **FT:** Coarse; **WN:** Leeds to Liverpool; **WT:** Canal (Still) **W. Size:** 4500 Metres.
Location: **Nr. Rd:** A581; **Main Rd:** A6, M6, M61.
Ref: FH2674

LEEDS TO LIVERPOOL CANAL

Leeds To Liverpool Canal, Rufford, Ormskirk, **LANCASHIRE**, L40, **England**.
Contact/s: Fishery Manager.
(T) 01942 206807
Profile: **FT:** Coarse; **WN:** Leeds to Liverpool; **WT:** Canal (Still).
Ref: FH2675

LEEDS TO LIVERPOOL CANAL

Leeds To Liverpool Canal, Burnley, **LANCASHIRE**, BB1, **England**.
Profile: **FT:** Coarse; **WN:** Leeds to Liverpool; **WT:** Canal (Still).
Ref: FH2676

LEEDS TO LIVERPOOL CANAL

Leeds To Liverpool Canal, Leigh, **MANCHESTER (GREATER)**, WN7, **England**.
Contact/s: Fishery Manager.
(T) 01942 604388
Profile: **FT:** Coarse; **WN:** Leeds to Liverpool; **WT:** Canal (Still).
Ref: FH2677

LEEDS TO LIVERPOOL CANAL

Leeds To Liverpool Canal, Lydiate, Maghull, Liverpool, **MERSEYSIDE**, L31, **England**.
Contact/s: **Mr Jim Brown** (Secretary), Liverpool DAS, 33 Eleanor Rd, Bootle, Merseyside, L20 6BP.
(T) 0151 2863270
Profile: **FT:** Coarse; **WN:** Leeds to Liverpool; **WT:** Canal (Still). Location: **Nr. Rd:** Hall Road; **Main Rd:** A5147.
Ref: FH2678

LEEDS TO LIVERPOOL CANAL

Leeds To Liverpool Canal, Bells Lane, Maghull, Liverpool, **MERSEYSIDE**, L31, **England**.
Contact/s: **Mr Jim Brown** (Secretary), Liverpool DAS, 33 Eleanor Rd, Bootle, Merseyside, L20 6BP.
(T) 0151 2863270
Profile: **FT:** Coarse; **WN:** Leeds to Liverpool; **WT:** Canal (Still) **W. Size:** 2400 Metres.
Location: **Nr. Rd:** Bells Lane; **Main Rd:** A5147.
Ref: FH2679

LEEDS TO LIVERPOOL CANAL

Leeds To Liverpool Canal, Liverpool City Ctre, Liverpool, **MERSEYSIDE**, **England**.
Contact/s: **Mr Jim Brown** (Secretary), Liverpool DAS, 33 Eleanor Rd, Bootle, Merseyside, L20 6BP.
(T) 0151 2863270
Profile: **FT:** Coarse; **WN:** Leeds to Liverpool; **WT:** Canal (Still). Location: **Main Rd:** A59.
Ref: FH2680

LEEDS TO LIVERPOOL CANAL

Leeds To Liverpool Canal, Rodley, Leeds, **YORKSHIRE (WEST)**, LS, **England**.
Contact/s: Area Manager, Environment Agency, Ridings Area Office, Phoenix House, Global Avenue, Leeds, LS11 8PG.
(T) 0113 2440191or2314834 **(F)** 0113 2134609
Mr E Harrison (Secretary).
(T) 01274 503141
Profile: **FT:** Coarse; **WN:** Leeds to Liverpool; **WT:** Canal (Still) **W. Size:** 1200 Metres.
Location: **Nr. Rd:** Rodley.
Ref: FH2681

LEEDS TO LIVERPOOL CANAL

Leeds To Liverpool Canal, Stansford Swing Bridge, Esholt, Shipley, **YORKSHIRE (WEST)**, BD17, **England**.
Contact/s: **Mr E K Mann** (Club Secretary), 19 Busfield St, Bradford, Yorkshire (West), BD4 7QX.
(T) 01274 720072
Profile: **FT:** Coarse; **WN:** Leeds to Liverpool; **WT:** Canal (Still). Location: **Main Rd:** A6038.
Ref: FH2682

LEEKES WATER

Leekes Water, Walmersley, Manchester, **MANCHESTER (GREATER)**, M2, **England**.
Contact/s: **Mr Bill Turner** (Secretary), 18 Hawthorn Avenue, Edenfield, Bury.
(T) 01706 823799
Profile: **FT:** Coarse; **WN:** Leekes; **WT:** Lake (Still). Location: **Main Rd:** A56.
Ref: FH2683

LEEMING (RIVER)

River Leeming, Northallerton, **YORKSHIRE (NORTH)**, DL, **England**.
Contact/s: **Mr R M Wright**, 5 Lascelles Lane, Northallerton, Yorkshire (North), DL7.
Profile: **FT:** Combination; **WN:** Leeming; **WT:** River (Moving). Location: **Nr. Rd:** Leeming Bridge; **Main Rd:** A1.
Ref: FH2684

LEES BROOK

Lees Brook, Berry Lane, Godmanchester, Huntingdon, **CAMBRIDGESHIRE**, PE29 2LA, **England**.
Contact/s: **Mr Stan J Binge** (Manager), Stanjay Fishing Tackle and Trophies, 7 Old Court Wall, Godmanchester, Huntingdon, PE18 8HS.
(T) 01480 453303
Profile: **FT:** Coarse; **WN:** Lees Brook; **WT:** Tributary (Moving). **Location:** **Nr. Rd:** Berry Lane.
Ref: FH2685

LEET (RIVER)

River Leet, Market Sq, Coldstream, **NORTHUMBERLAND**, TD12, **England**.
Contact/s: **Mr H F Bell** (Secretary), 12 Priory Hill, Coldstream, Scottish Borders.
Profile: **FT:** Game; **WN:** Leet; **WT:** River (Moving).
Ref: FH2686

LEG OMUTTON DAM

Leg Omutton Dam, St Helens, **MERSEYSIDE**, WA11, **England**.
Contact/s: **Mr D Fishwick** (Secretary), 4 Sherwell Gr, Sutton Leach, St Helens, Merseyside.
(T) 01744 819518
Mr Roy Rhodes (Conservation, Access and Recreation Manager), Rivington Water Treatment Works, Bolton Rd, Horwich, Bolton, BL6 7RN.
(T) 01204 664300
Profile: **FT:** Coarse; **WN:** Leg O' Mutton; **WT:** Dam (Still).
Ref: FH2687

LEGGE FARM COARSE FISHERY

Legge Farm Coarse Fishery, Church Rd, Highampton, Beaworthy, **DEVON**, EX21 5LF, **England**.
Contact/s: **Mr Graham Hall** (Owner).
(T) 01409 231464
Profile: **FT:** Coarse; **WN:** Legge Farm Coarse Fishery; **WT:** Lake (Still); **F. Size:** 30 Acres; **W. Size:** 4 Acres. **Location:** **Nr. Rd:** Church Road; **Main Rd:** A386, Okehampton to Bideford.
Ref: FH2688

LEICESTER CANAL

Leicester Canal, Wreake Junction, Cossington Mill, Leicester, **LEICESTERSHIRE**, LE7 4UZ, **England**.
Contact/s: **Mr R Fossey** (Secretary), Leicester and District Amalgamated Society of Anglers, 431 Gleneagles Avenue, Rushley Mead, Leicester, LE67.
(T) 0116 2666911
Profile: **FT:** Coarse; **WN:** Leicester; **WT:** Canal (Still).
Ref: FH2689

LEICESTER GRAND UNION CANAL

Leicester Grand Union Canal, Leicester, **LEICESTERSHIRE**, LE1, **England**.
Contact/s: **Mr R Fossey** (Secretary), Leicester and District Amalgamated Society of Anglers, 431 Gleneagles Avenue, Rushley Mead, Leicester, LE67.
(T) 0116 2666911
Profile: **FT:** Coarse; **WN:** Leicester Grand Union; **WT:** Canal (Still) **W. Size:** 2250 Metres.
Ref: FH2690

LEIGH BRANCH CANAL

Leigh Branch Canal, Leigh, **MANCHESTER (GREATER)**, WN7, **England**.
Contact/s: Fishery Manager.
(T) 01942 604388
Profile: **FT:** Coarse; **WN:** Leigh Branch; **WT:** Canal (Still).
Ref: FH2691

LEIGH SINTON FISHING LAKES

Leigh Sinton Fishing Lakes, Leigh Sinton Farm & Nurseries Ltd, Lower Interfield, Malvern, **WORCESTERSHIRE**, WR14 1UU, **England**.
Contact/s: **Mr Nick Beard**. **(F)** 01886 833446 **(M)** 07798 533896
(E) leigh.sinton@virgin.net
Ms Sue Cave.
(T) 01886 832305 **(F)** 01886 833446
Profile: **FT:** Coarse; **WN:** Leigh Sinton; **WT:** Lake (Still); **F. Size:** 260 Acres; **W. Size:** 2 Acres. **Location:** **Nr. Rd:** B4503; **Main Rd:** A4103, Worcester to Hereford; **Rail:** Great Malvern or Malvern Link.
Ref: FH2692

LEIGHTON RESERVOIR

Leighton Reservoir, Healey, Masham, Ripon, **YORKSHIRE (NORTH)**, HG4 4JR, **England**.
Contact/s: Estate Office Manager.
(T) 01765 689224
Mr Mike Driver (Manager).
(T) 01765 689359
Profile: **FT:** Game; **WN:** Leighton; **WT:** Reservoir (Still); **F. Size:** 105 Acres; **W. Size:** 105 Acres. **Location:** **Main Rd:** A1.
Ref: FH2693

LEIPEIG (LOCH)

Loch Leipeig, Lochgilphead, **RENFREWSHIRE**, PA3, **Scotland**.
Contact/s: **Mr Archie MacGilp** (Secretary), Fyne Tackle, 22 Argyll St, Lochgilphead, Argyll and Bute, PA31 8NE.
(T) 01546 606878
Profile: **FT:** Game; **WN:** Leipeig; **WT:** Loch (Still); **F. Size:** 400 Acres; **W. Size:** 5 Acres. **Location:** **Nr. Rd:** Cairnbaan; **Main Rd:** B844; **Rail:** Oban.
Ref: FH2694

LEISURE LAKES

Leisure Lakes, Mere Brow, Preston, **LANCASHIRE**, PR4, **England**.
Contact/s: Fishery Manager.
(T) 01772 611380
Fishery Manager.
(T) 01772 813446
Profile: **FT:** Coarse; **WN:** Leisure; **WT:** Lake (Still); **F. Size:** 300 Acres. **Location:** **Nr. Rd:** B5246; **Main Rd:** A59 south to Tarleton.
Ref: FH2695

LEMINGTON LAKES

Lemington Lakes, Todenham Rd, Moreton-In-Marsh, **GLOUCESTERSHIRE**, GL56 9NP, **England**.
Contact/s: **Mr Bill Gadsby**.
(T) 01608 650872
Mrs Ann Gadsby.
(T) 01608 650872
Profile: **FT:** Coarse; **WN:** Lemington; **WT:** Lake (Still) **W. Size:** 11 Acres. **Location:** **Nr. Rd:** Todenham Road; **Main Rd:** A429, Stratford-upon-Avon to Moreton-in-Marsh.
Ref: FH2696

LENCHES LAKES

Lenches Lakes, Hill Barn Orchard, Evesham Rd, Church Lench, Evesham, **WORCESTERSHIRE**, WR11 4UB, **England**.
Contact/s: Fishery Manager.
(T) 01386 871306
Mr Philip Badger (Owner).
(T) 01386 871035 **(F)** 01386 871035
Mrs Marlene Badger (Owner).
(T) 01386 871035 **(F)** 01386 871035
Profile: **FT:** Game; **WN:** The Lenches; **WT:** Lake (Still); **F. Size:** 26 Acres; **W. Size:** 4 Acres. **Location:** **Nr. Rd:** Evesham Road; **Main Rd:** A46; **Rail:** Evesham.
Ref: FH2697

LENCHFORD

Lenchford, Shrawley, Holt Fleet, Worcester, **WORCESTERSHIRE**, WR6, **England**.
Contact/s: **Mr J A Mobley** (Secretary), Phoenix Angling Club, 8 Pentaloe Cl, Mordiford, Herefordshire, HR1 4LS.
(T) 01432 870579
Profile: **FT:** Combination; **WN:** Severn; **WT:** River (Moving) **W. Size:** 1800 Metres. **Location:** **Nr. Rd:** B4196; **Main Rd:** A443; **Rail:** Worcester.
Ref: FH2698

LENNOX WOOD LAKE

Lennox Wood Lake, Southwater, Horsham, **SUSSEX (WEST)**, RH13, **England**.
Contact/s: Fishery Manager.
(T) 01403 731218
Profile: **FT:** Coarse; **WN:** Lennox Wood; **WT:** Lake (Still).
Ref: FH2699

LENWADE COMMON LAKES

Lenwade Common Lakes, Common Lane, Lenwade, Norwich, **NORFOLK**, NR9 5SD, **England**.
Mr J Roberts (Bailiff), Rose Cottage, Common Lane, Lenwade, Norwich, NR9 5QH.
(T) 01603 872978
Mrs B Wright (Bailiff), 12 Common Lane, Lenwade, Norwich, Norfolk.
(T) 01603 872286
Profile: **FT:** Coarse; **WN:** Wensum; **WT:** Combination (Still & Moving); **F. Size:** 25 Acres; **W. Size:** 5 Acres. **Location:** **Nr. Rd:** A1067; **Main Rd:** Norwich to Fakenham; **Rail:** Norwich.
Ref: FH2700

LENWADE TROUT FISHERY

Lenwade Trout Fishery, Great Witchingham, Norwich, **NORFOLK**, NR, **England**.
Contact/s: **Mr Mark Taylor** (Manager).
(T) 01603 787163
Profile: **FT:** Game; **WN:** Lenwade Trout Fishery; **WT:** Lake (Still).
Ref: FH2701

LEOMINSTEAD MILL POND

Leominstead Mill Pond, Minstead, Lyndhurst, **HAMPSHIRE**, SO43, **England**.
Contact/s: **Mr Neil Branscombe** (Manager), Leominstead Trout Fishery, Emerydown, Linhurst, Hampshire, SO43 7GA.
(T) 023 80282610 **(M)** 07071 200809
Profile: **FT:** Coarse; **WN:** Leominstead Mill; **WT:** Pond (Still) **W. Size:** 5 Acres. **Location:** **Nr. Rd:** Cadnam to Lynstead; **Main Rd:** A337.
Ref: FH2702

LEOMINSTEAD TROUT FISHERY

Leominstead Trout Fishery, Emery Down, Lyndhurst, **HAMPSHIRE**, SO43 7GA, **England**.
Contact/s: **Mr Neil Branscombe**.
(T) 023 80282610 **(M)** 07720 612982
(E) leominstead@aol.com
Profile: **FT:** Game; **WN:** Leominstead; **WT:** Lake (Still) **W. Size:** 4 Acres. **Location:** **Nr. Rd:** Emery Down; **Main Rd:** A31 to A35.
Ref: FH2703

LERI (RIVER)

River Leri, Talybont, **GWYNEDD**, LL43, **Wales**.
Contact/s: **Mr Ithel Jones** (Hon Secretary), Wern, Talybont, Carmarthenshire, SY24 5ER.
(T) 01970 832363
Mr Rod Bird, Gwynfryn Lodge, Taliesin, Machynlleth, Powys, SY20 8PU.
(T) 01970 832586
Profile: **FT:** Game; **WN:** Leri; **WT:** River (Moving) **W. Size:** 1600 Metres.
Ref: FH2704

LERR (RIVER)

River Lerr, Carlow, **COUNTY CARLOW**, **Ireland**.
Contact/s: **Mrs Quinn** (Manager), The Locks, Milford, Carlow, County Carlow, Ireland.
(T) 050 346261
Profile: **FT:** Game; **WN:** Lerr; **WT:** River (Moving).
Ref: FH2705

LESKINE

Leskine, Glendochart, Killin, **STIRLING**, FK21, **Scotland**.
(W) www.fishingnet.com/beats/dochart/leskine.htm
Contact/s: Manager, Leskine Farm,

Glenochart, Killin, Perth and Kinross.
(T) 01567 820536
Profile: FT: Game; WN: Leskine; WT: Pool (Still). Location: Nr. Rd: Auchlyne Bridge to Bovin Farm House.
Ref: FH2706

LETHERINGSETT FISHERY

Letheringsett Fishery, Holt, **NORFOLK**, NR25, **England**.
Contact/s: Sue (Fishery Manager).
(T) 01263 588323
Profile: FT: Coarse; WN: Letheringsett Fishery; WT: Lake (Still).
Ref: FH2707

LEVEN (RIVER)

River Leven, Low Leven, Yarm, **TYNE AND WEAR**, TS15 9JN, **England**.
Contact/s: Manager, The Cross Keys Inn, Low Leven, Yarm, Cleveland, TS15 9JN.
Profile: FT: Coarse; WN: Leven; WT: River (Moving).
Ref: FH2708

LEVEN CANAL

Leven Canal, Carr Lane, Leven, Hull, **HUMBERSIDE**, HU, **England**.
Contact/s: Mr Dave Heslop (Manager).
(T) 01482 796627
Profile: FT: Coarse; WN: Leven; WT: Canal (Still). Location: Nr. Rd: Carr Lane; Main Rd: A165.
Ref: FH2709

LEVEN CANAL

Leven Canal, Hull Angling Association, Trailer And Marina Ltd, Beverley, **HUMBERSIDE**, HU17, **England**.
Contact/s: Mr Dave Heslop (Fishery Manager).
(T) 01482 896879
Profile: FT: Coarse; WN: Leven; WT: Canal (Still).
Ref: FH2710

LEVEN PARK LAKE

Leven Park Lake, Leven, Beverley, **HUMBERSIDE**, HU17, **England**.
Contact/s: Fishery Manager.
(T) 01482 872516
Mr Graham Skinner.
(T) 01964 544510
Profile: FT: Coarse; WN: Leven; WT: Lake (Still).
Ref: FH2711

LEWORTHY FARM

Leworthy Farm, Holsworthy, Bude, **DEVON**, EX22 6SJ, **England**.
Contact/s: Manager.
(T) 01409 253485
Profile: FT: Coarse; WN: Leworthy Farm; WT: Lake (Still). Location: Nr. Rd: A3072.
Ref: FH2712

LICKEEN LAKE

Lickeen Lake, Kilfenara, **COUNTY CLARE**, **Ireland**.
Contact/s: Mr John Vaughen (Manager).
(T) 065 7071069
Profile: FT: Game; WN: Lickeen; WT: Lake (Still) W. Size: 200 Acres.
Ref: FH2713

LICKLE (RIVER)

River Lickle, Broughton-In-Furness, **CUMBRIA**, LA20, **England**.
Contact/s: Mr D J Dixon (Secretary), 1 Churchill Drive, Millom, Cumbria, LA18 5DD.
(T) 01229 774241
Profile: FT: Game; WN: Lickle; WT: River (Moving). Location: Nr. Rd: A595; Main Rd: A595.
Ref: FH2714

LIDDEL WATER

Liddel Water, Penton Bridge, Carlisle, **CUMBRIA**, CA6 5QN, **England**.
Contact/s: Mr Denis (Manager).
(T) 01697 772793
Profile: FT: Game; WN: Liddel; WT: River (Moving) W. Size: 800 Metres.
Ref: FH2715

LIDDLE (RIVER)

River Liddle, Newcastleton, **SCOTTISH BORDERS**, TD9, **Scotland**.
Contact/s: Mr George Graham (Head River Watcher), Hagg Old School House, Canonbie, Dumfries and Galloway.
(T) 01387 71416
Mr Tj Ewart (Secretary), Esk and Liddle Fisheries Association, Drapers, Douglas Sq, Newcastleton, Dumfries and Galloway.
(T) 01387 375257
Profile: FT: Game; WN: Liddle; WT: River (Moving). Location: Nr. Rd: B6357.
Ref: FH2716

LIDEN LAGOON

Liden Lagoon, Swindon, **WILTSHIRE**, SN4, **England**.
Contact/s: Mr Dave Cleaver (Manager), Swindon Angling Ctre, 5 Sheppard St, Swindon, Wiltshire, SN1 5DB.
(T) 01793 619909
Profile: FT: Coarse; WN: Liden Lagoon; WT: Lake (Still).
Ref: FH2717

LIFELANDS FISHERY

Lifelands Fishery, Martins Farm Carp Lake, Woodlands, Christchurch, **DORSET**, BH23, **England**.
Contact/s: Mr Ball (Manager).
(T) 01202 822335
Profile: FT: Coarse; WN: Avon; WT: River (Moving). Location: Nr. Rd: Woodlands.
Ref: FH2718

LIGHTMOOR POOL

Lightmoor Pool, Cinderford, **GLOUCESTERSHIRE**, GL14, **England**.
Contact/s: Mr Dennis Sherwood.
(T) 01594 543796
Mr Paul Reed (Secretary), Royal Forest of Dean Angling Club, 20 Abbey St, Cinderford, Gloucestershire, GR14 2NW.
(T) 01594 824413
Profile: FT: Coarse; WN: Lightmoor; WT: Pool (Still) W. Size: 1 Acre. Location: Nr. Rd: Cinderford to Speech House Road; Main Rd: B4226.
Ref: FH2719

LILLIES LOCH

Lillies Loch, Newton Stewart, **DUMFRIES AND GALLOWAY**, DG8, **Scotland**.
Contact/s: Mr Sandy White (Recreational Forester), Forestry Commission Office, Forest Enterprise, Galloway Forest District, Creebridge, Newton Stewart, DG8 6AJ.
(T) 01671 402420 (F) 01671 403708
Profile: FT: Game; WN: Lillies; WT: Loch (Still).
Ref: FH2720

LILY AND WILLOW POOLS

Lily And Willow Pools, Ledbury, **HEREFORDSHIRE**, HR8, **England**.
Contact/s: Mr Brian Powell (Red Banks Pools Manager), Three Counties Fisheries, Field Cottage, Ryton, Dymock, Gloucestershire, GL18 2DH.
(T) 01531 890455
Profile: FT: Coarse; WN: Lily and Willow; WT: Pool (Still).
Ref: FH2721

LILY LOCH

Lily Loch, 16 Luing, Airdrie, **LANARKSHIRE (NORTH)**, ML6 8EB, **Scotland**.
Contact/s: Mr Sam Armstrong.
(T) 01236 769221
Profile: FT: Game; WN: Lily; WT: Loch (Still); F. Size: 52 Acres; W. Size: 50 Acres. Location: Nr. Rd: A89; Main Rd: A89; Rail: Drumgellock.
Ref: FH2722

LILY PARK LAKES

Lily Park Lakes, Earith, Huntingdon, **CAMBRIDGESHIRE**, PE17, **England**.
Contact/s: Fishery Manager.
(T) 01223 461361
Profile: FT: Coarse; WN: Lily Park; WT: Lake (Still). Location: Nr. Rd: A142.
Ref: FH2723

LINACRE RESERVOIRS

Linacre Reservoirs, Netherthorpe, Staveley, Chesterfield, **DERBYSHIRE**, S4, **England**.
Contact/s: G Nixon.
Profile: FT: Coarse; WN: Linacre; WT: Reservoir (Still).
Ref: FH2724

LINCH HILL FISHERY

Linch Hill Fishery, Linch Hill Leisure Park, Stanton Harcourt, Witney, **OXFORDSHIRE**, OX8 1BB, **England**.
Contact/s: Mr Derek Reeves (Owner).
(T) 01865 882215 (F) 01865 882870
Profile: FT: Coarse; WN: Linch Hill Fishery; WT: Gravel Pit (Still); F. Size: 87 Acres; W. Size: 61 Acres. Location: Nr. Rd: Stanton Harcourt and Standlake Village; Rail: Oxford.
Ref: FH2725

LINCOMB LOCK

Lincomb Lock, Courtnay House, Feiashill Rd, Trysull, Wolverhampton, **MIDLANDS (WEST)**, WV5 7HT, **England**.
Contact/s: Mr Peter Henry Gough.
(T) 01902 324337
Profile: FT: Coarse; WN: Lincomb; WT: Lock (Still).
Ref: FH2726

LINDEAN RESERVOIR

Lindean Reservoir, Selkirk, **SCOTTISH BORDERS**, TD7, **Scotland**.
Contact/s: Mr B Rogerson (Owner), Rogersons, 6 High St, Selkirk, Scottish Borders, TD7 4DD.
(T) 01750 20749
Profile: FT: Game; WN: Lindean; WT: Reservoir (Still). Location: Nr. Rd: Selkirk to Kelso; Main Rd: A699 east.
Ref: FH2727

LINDEN WALK POND

Linden Walk Pond, Louth, **LINCOLNSHIRE**, LN11, **England**.
Contact/s: Fishery Manager.
(T) 01507 603908
Profile: FT: Coarse; WN: Linden Walk; WT: Pond (Still).
Ref: FH2728

LINDHOLME FISHERIES (1)

Lindholme Leisure Lakes Fisheries (1), Don Farm, West Carr, Epworth, Doncaster, **YORKSHIRE (SOUTH)**, DN9 1LF, **Scotland**.
(W) www.lindholmelakefisheries.co.uk
Contact/s: Mr Alan Temperton (Manager).
(T) 01427 872905 (F) 01427 872281
Profile: FT: Coarse; WN: Pond (Still); F. Size: 25 Acres; W. Size: 2 Acres. Location: Nr. Rd: C2002; Main Rd: A18; Rail: Crowle.
Ref: FH2729

LINDHOLME FISHERIES (2)

Lindholme Leisure Lakes Fisheries (2), Don Farm, Sandtoft, Epworth, Doncaster, **YORKSHIRE (SOUTH)**, DN9 1LF, **Scotland**.
(W) www.lindholmelakefisheries.co.uk
Contact/s: Mr Alan Temperton (Manager).
(T) 01427 872905 (F) 01427 872281
Profile: FT: Coarse; WN: Willows; WT: Pool (Still); F. Size: 25 Acres; W. Size: 4 Acres. Location: Nr. Rd: C2002; Main Rd: A18; Rail: Crowle.
Ref: FH2730

LINDHOLME FISHERIES (3)

Lindholme Leisure Lakes Fisheries (3), Don

Farm, Sandtoft, Epworth, Doncaster, **YORKSHIRE (SOUTH)**, DN9 1LF, **Scotland**.
(W) www.lindholmelakefisheries.co.uk
Contact/s: Manager.
(T) 01427 872015
Mr Alan Temperton (Manager).
(T) 01427 872905 **(F)** 01427 872281
Profile: FT: Game; **WN:** Trout; **WT:** Pool (Still); **F. Size:** 25 Acres; **W. Size:** 4 Acres. **Location: Nr. Rd:** C2002; **Main Rd:** A18; **Rail:** Crowle.
Ref: FH2731

LINDHOLME FISHERIES 4)

Lindholme Leisure Lakes Fisheries (4), Don Farm, Sandtoft, Epworth, Doncaster, **YORKSHIRE (SOUTH)**, DN9 1LF, **Scotland**.
(W) www.lindholmelakefisheries.co.uk
Contact/s: Mr Alan Temperton (Manager).
(T) 01427 872905 **(F)** 01427 872281
Profile: FT: Coarse; **WN:** Big Lake; **WT:** Lake (Still); **F. Size:** 25 Acres; **W. Size:** 11 Acres. **Location: Nr. Rd:** C2002; **Main Rd:** A18; **Rail:** Crowle.
Ref: FH2732

LINDORES LOCH

Lindores Loch, Cupar, **FIFE**, KY15, **Scotland**.
Contact/s: A Mitchell, 28 Main St, Springfield, Cupar, Fife, Scotland.
(T) 01334 654107
Profile: FT: Game; **WN:** Lindores; **WT:** Loch (Still).
Ref: FH2733

LINGAUN (RIVER)

River Lingaun, Carrick-on-Suir, **COUNTY TIPPERARY**, **Ireland**.
Contact/s: Mr J O'Keeffe (Manager), OK Sports, New St, Carrick-on-Suir, County Tipperary, Ireland.
(T) 051 40626
Profile: FT: Game; **WN:** Lingaun; **WT:** River (Moving).
Ref: FH2734

LINGCROFT FARM POND

Lingcroft Farm Pond, York, **YORKSHIRE (NORTH)**, YO6 4, **England**.
Contact/s: Mr Rounthwaite (Fishery Manager).
(T) 01904 633146
Profile: FT: Coarse; **WN:** Lingcroft Farm Pond; **WT:** Pond (Still). **Location: Nr. Rd:** A19; **Main Rd:** A64.
Ref: FH2735

LINLITHGOW LOCH

Linlithgow Loch, The Forth Area Federation Of Anglers, 212A High Streeet, Linlithgow, **LOTHIAN (WEST)**, EH49 7ES, **Scotland**.
Contact/s: Fafa Loch Manager, FAFA, PO Box 7, Linlithgow, EH49 7LA.
(T) 01506 844170
Mr C McGrath (Fafa Treasurer), 31 Dovecot Park, Linlithgow, Lothian (West), EH49 7LH.
(T) 01506 847266
Ms Lorraine (Booking Secretary).
(T) 07860 299342 **(M)** 07831 288921
Profile: FT: Game; **WN:** Linlithgow; **WT:** Loch (Still); **F. Size:** 120 Acres; **W. Size:** 110 Acres. **Location: Nr. Rd:** High Street; **Main Rd:** High Street; **Rail:** Linlithgow.
Ref: FH2736

LINNEL WOOD LAKE

Linnel Wood Lake, Slaley, Hexham, **NORTHUMBERLAND**, NE, **England**.
Contact/s: Mr Cliff Waitt.
(T) 01434 609725
Profile: FT: Game; **WN:** Linnel Wood; **WT:** Lake (Still). **Location: Nr. Rd:** B6306; **Main Rd:** A69; **Rail:** Hexham.
Ref: FH2737

LISVANE RESERVOIR

Lisvane Reservoir, Hamdden Limited, Sluvad, New Inn, Pontypool, **TORFAEN**, NP4 0TA, **Wales**.
Contact/s: Mr C Hatch (Area Manager), Hamdden Ltd, Sluvad Treatment Works, Llandegfedd Reservoir, New Inn, Pontypool, Gwent NP4 0TA.
(T) 01495 769281 **(F)** 01495 769283
Profile: FT: Game; **WN:** Lisane; **WT:** Reservoir (Still) **W. Size:** 19 Acres.
Ref: FH2738

LITTLE ALLERS COARSE FISHERY

Little Allers Coarse Fishery, Little Allers Farm, Avonlick, South Brent, **DEVON**, TQ10 9HA, **England**.
Contact/s: Mr Mike Wakeham (Owner).
(T) 01364 72563 **(M)** 07855 427510
Mrs Jenny Wakeham (Owner).
(T) 01364 72563
Profile: FT: Coarse; **WN:** Little Allers Coarse Fishery; **WT:** Lake (Still) **W. Size:** 2 Acres. **Location: Nr. Rd:** South Brent to Plymouth; **Main Rd:** A38, A3121.
Ref: FH2739

LITTLE BEVILLS ESTATE

Little Bevills Estate, Sudbury Rd, Bures, **SUFFOLK**, CO8 5JN, **England**.
Contact/s: Mr Trevor Fairless (Secretary), Sudbury and District Angling Association, 39 Pot Kiln Rd, Sudbury, Suffolk, CO10 0DG.
(T) 01787 312536
Profile: FT: Coarse; **WN:** Stow (Suffolk); **WT:** River (Moving) **W. Size:** 800 Metres. **Location: Nr. Rd:** Sudbury Road; **Main Rd:** B1508; **Rail:** Bures.
Ref: FH2740

LITTLE BIG WATER

Little Big Water, Wideopen, Newcastle Upon Tyne, **TYNE AND WEAR**, NE13, **England**.
Contact/s: Mr Gary Rutherford (Secretary), 21 Blagdon Trce, Seaton Burn, Newcastle-upon-Tyne, NE13 6EY.
(T) 0191 2366703
Profile: FT: Coarse; **WN:** Little Big Water; **WT:** Lake (Still).
Ref: FH2741

LITTLE BRAXTED FARM ESTATE

Little Braxted Farm Estate, Braxted Rd, Braxted, Witham, **ESSEX**, CM8 3DJ, **England**.
(W) www.chelmsfordaa.freeserve.co.uk
Contact/s: Mr Frank Wright (Membership Secretary), Chelmsford Angling Association, 61 Readers Court, Great Baddow, Chelmsford, CM2 8EX.
(T) 01245 474246or264832
(E) frank@chelmsfordaa.freeserve.co.uk
Ms Irene Lewis (Secretary), 60 Delamere Rd, Chelmsford, CM1 2TG.
(T) 01245 264832
Profile: FT: Coarse; **WN:** Blackwater; **WT:** Combination (Still & Moving) **W. Size:** 8 Acres. **Location: Main Rd:** A12; **Rail:** Witham.
Ref: FH2742

LITTLE BRITAIN LAKE

Little Britain Lake, Packet Boat Lane, Uxbridge, London, **LONDON (GREATER)**, UB9, **England**.
Contact/s: Mr John Batton.
(T) 020 85733196 **(M)** 07710 518545
Profile: FT: Coarse; **WN:** Little Britain; **WT:** Lake (Still) **W. Size:** 7 Acres. **Location: Nr. Rd:** B483, A4007; **Main Rd:** A412, M25; **Rail:** West Drayton.
Ref: FH2743

LITTLE BUDWORTH

Little Budworth, Little Budworth, Tarporley, **CHESHIRE**, CW6, **England**.
Contact/s: Mr M J Clays (Secretary), 58 Churchhill Drive, Tarporley, Cheshire, CW6 0BZ.
Profile: FT: Coarse; **WN:** Little Budworth; **WT:** Lake (Still) **W. Size:** 5 Acres.
Ref: FH2744

LITTLE CANSIRON FISHING LAKES

Little Cansiron Fishing Lakes, Cansiron Lane, Holtye, Edenbridge, **KENT**, TN8 7EE, **England**.
Contact/s: Mr Johnathan Latham (Fishery Manager).
(T) 01342 850739 **(M)** 07836 564778
Profile: FT: Coarse; **WN:** Little Cansiron; **WT:** Lake (Still) **W. Size:** 2 Acres. **Location: Nr. Rd:** A264; **Main Rd:** A264; **Rail:** East Grinstead.
Ref: FH2745

LITTLE COMFORT FARM

Little Comfort Farm, West Down, Braunton, **DEVON**, EX33 2NJ, **England**.
Contact/s: Mr R P Milsom (Owner).
(T) 01271 812414
Profile: FT: Coarse; **WN:** Little Comfort Farm; **WT:** Pond (Still) **W. Size:** 1 Acre. **Location: Main Rd:** A361 from Barnstaple.
Ref: FH2746

LITTLE DALE HALL

Little Dale Hall Coarse Fishery, Morecambe, **LANCASHIRE**, LA4 5PB, **England**.
Contact/s: Mr Howard Parker, Morecambe Angling Ctre, Thornton Rd, Morecambe, Lancashire, LA4 5PB.
(T) 01524 832332
Profile: FT: Coarse; **WN:** Little Dale; **WT:** Lake (Still); **F. Size:** 2 Acres; **W. Size:** 2 Acres. **Location: Main Rd:** A683; **Rail:** Lancaster.
Ref: FH2747

LITTLE DAWLEY POOLS

Little Dawley Pools, Ironbridge, Telford, **SHROPSHIRE**, TF8, **England**.
Contact/s: Mr Stan Harris (Secretary), Telford Angling Association, 73 Burnside, Brookside, Telford, TF3 1DA.
(T) 01952 590605
Profile: FT: Coarse; **WN:** Little Dawley; **WT:** Pool (Still).
Ref: FH2748

LITTLE DUNHAM CARP LAKES

Little Dunham Carp Lakes, Lakeside, Little Dunham, King's Lynn, **NORFOLK**, PE32 2LQ, **England**.
Contact/s: Mr David Harris (Fishery Manager).
(T) 01760 725286
Profile: FT: Coarse; **WN:** Little Dunham; **WT:** Lake (Still) **W. Size:** 1600 Metres. **Location: Nr. Rd:** Necton to Great Dunham; **Main Rd:** A47.
Ref: FH2749

LITTLE EASTON FISHERIES

Little Easton Fisheries, Little Easton, Dunmow, **ESSEX**, CM6, **England**.
(W) www.bdac.co.uk
Contact/s: Mr Derek Howard (Hon Treasurer), Billericay and District Angling Club, 4 Long Meadow Drive, Wickford, Essex, SS11 8AX.
(T) 01268 734468
Profile: FT: Coarse; **WN:** Rectory Ponds and Laundry Lake; **WT:** Lake (Still); **F. Size:** 10 Acres; **W. Size:** 7 Acres. **Location: Nr. Rd:** Laundry Lane; **Main Rd:** B184; **Rail:** Bishops Stortford.
Ref: FH2750

LITTLE EASTON MANOR

Little Easton Manor, Little Easton Manor, Park Rd, Little Easton, Dunmow, **ESSEX**, CM6, **England**.
Contact/s: Mr Tony King (Bailiff).
(T) 01371 876651
Mrs Vera Pedley (Owner).
(T) 01371 872857 **(F)** 01371 878479
(E) verapedley@compuserve.com
Profile: FT: Coarse; **WN:** Little Easton Manor; **WT:** Pond (Still) **W. Size:** 4 Acres. **Location: Nr. Rd:** Park Road, B184; **Main Rd:** A120; **Rail:** Stansted.
Ref: FH2751

LITTLE EXE

Little Exe, Dulverton, **SOMERSET**, TA22, **England**.
Contact/s: Mr P Veale.
(T) 0131 9323409

Profile: FT: Game; WN: Little Exe; WT: River (Moving).
Ref: FH2752

LITTLE HEATH FARM

Little Heath Farm Trout Fishery, Little Heath Farm, Gamlingay, Sandy, **BEDFORDSHIRE**, SG19 3LL, **England**.
Contact/s: **Mr Alan Garghwaite** (Owner), Little Heath Farm, Gamlingay, Sandy, Bedfordshire.
(T) 01767 650301
Profile: FT: Game; WN: Little Heath Farm Trout Fishery; WT: Lake (Still). **Location:** Main Rd: A1.
Ref: FH2753

LITTLE IRCHESTER COMPLEX

Little Irchester Complex, Newport Pagnell Rd, Little Irchester, Wellingborough, **NORTHAMPTONSHIRE**, NN, **England**.
Contact/s: **Mr Terry Rodhouse** (Secretary), Castle Angling Association, 12 Somerville Rd, Daventry, Northamptonshire, NN11 4RT.
(T) 01327 705692
Profile: FT: Coarse; WN: Little Irchester Complex; WT: Combination (Still & Moving); F. Size: 30 Acres; W. Size: 16 Acres.
Location: Nr. Rd: A509; Main Rd: A509; Rail: Wellingborough.
Ref: FH2754

LITTLE MILL

Little Mill, Tarporley, **CHESHIRE**, CW6, **England**.
Contact/s: **Mr M J Clays** (Secretary), 58 Churchhill Drive, Tarporley, Cheshire, CW6 0BZ.
Profile: FT: Coarse; WN: Little Mill; WT: Lake (Still) W. Size: 3 Acres.
Ref: FH2755

LITTLE MUSGRAVE

Little Musgrave, Rowgate, Kirkby Stephen, **CUMBRIA**, CA17, **England**.
Contact/s: **Mr Norman Huges**, The Three Greyhounds Inn, Great Asby, Appleby-in-Westmorland, Cumbria, CA16 6EX.
(T) 01768 351428
Profile: FT: Coarse; WN: Little Musgrave; WT: Lake (Still).
Ref: FH2756

LITTLE OUSE (RIVER)

River Little Ouse, Little Ouse, King's Lynn, **NORFOLK**, PE, **England**.
Contact/s: **K Allen** (Chairman), Mole Cottage, 15 Ten Mile Bank, Littleport, CB6 1EE.
(T) 01383 860936
Mr Mick Grief (Secretary), King's Lynn Angling Association, 67 Peckover Way, South Wootton, King's Lynn, PE30 3UE.
(T) 01553 671545
Profile: FT: Coarse; WN: Little Ouse; WT: River (Moving) W. Size: 3200 Metres.
Location: Nr. Rd: White House Road; Main Rd: A1101.
Ref: FH2757

LITTLE OUSE (RIVER)

River Little Ouse, Brandon, Thetford, **SUFFOLK**, IP2, **England**.
Contact/s: Manager, Brandon Parish Council, Old School House, Market Hill, Brandon, IP27 0AA.
(T) 01842 811844
B Carter.
(T) 01842 828448
Mr Peter Cooper, 16 High St, Feltwell, Thetford, Norfolk, IP26 4AF.
(T) 01842 828448
Profile: FT: Coarse; WN: Little Ouse; WT: River (Moving) W. Size: 2000 Metres.
Location: Main Rd: A11, B134; Rail: Brandon.
Ref: FH2758

LITTLE PAXTON FISHERY

Little Paxton Fishery, 5 Hayling Avenue, Little Paxton, St Neots, Huntingdon, **CAMBRIDGESHIRE**, PE19 6GH, **England**.
Contact/s: **Mr Laurie Bowden** (Manager).
(T) 01480 496088
Mrs M R May (Manager), 5 Hayling Avenue, Little Paxton, Huntingdon.
(T) 01480 212059
Profile: FT: Coarse; WN: Little Paxton; WT: Gravel Pit (Still) W. Size: 30 Acres.
Location: Nr. Rd: Hayling Avenue.
Ref: FH2759

LITTLE REEDS MERE

Little Reeds Mere, Peover, Chelford, Knutsford, **CHESHIRE**, **England**.
(W) www.baymalton-anglingclub.org
Contact/s: **Mr Stewart Godber** (Club Secretary), 38 Edenfield Rd, Mobberley, Cheshire, WA16 7HE.
(T) 01565 872582
Profile: FT: Coarse; WN: Reeds Mere; WT: Pool (Still); F. Size: 3 Acres; W. Size: 2 Acres. **Location:** Main Rd: A537; Rail: Chelford.
Ref: FH2760

LITTLE SEA RESERVOIR

Little Sea Reservoir, Oldham, **MANCHESTER (GREATER)**, OL, **England**.
Contact/s: **Mr Brian Bough** (Secretary), 369 Shaw Rd, Royton, Oldham, Lancashire, OL2 6NZ.
(T) 0161 6200883
Mr Roy Rhodes (Conservation, Access and Recreation Manager), Rivington Water Treatment Works, Bolton Rd, Horwich, Bolton, BL6 7RN.
(T) 01204 664300
Profile: FT: Coarse; WN: Little Sea; WT: Reservoir (Still).
Ref: FH2761

LITTLE WARHAM FISHERY

Little Warham Fishery, Warham House, Beaford, Winkleigh, **DEVON**, EX19 8AB, **England**.
Contact/s: **Mr Norton Smith** (Team Captain).
(T) 01805 603317
Profile: FT: Game; WN: Torridge; WT: River (Moving).
Ref: FH2762

LITTLE WEACH

Little Weach, Westleigh, Bideford, **DEVON**, **England**.
Contact/s: .
(T) 01237 479303
Profile: FT: Coarse; WN: Little Weach; WT: Lake (Still).
Ref: FH2763

LITTLETONS AND MIDDLE POOL

Littletons And Middle Pool, Rugeley, **STAFFORDSHIRE**, WS15, **England**.
Contact/s: Manager, Chase Matchmen, 9 Station Rd, Cannock, Staffordshire, WS12 4DH.
(T) 01543 877478
Profile: FT: Coarse; WN: Littleton's and Middle; WT: Pool (Still). **Location:** Nr. Rd: Rugeley to Cannock; Main Rd: A460.
Ref: FH2764

LITTON RESERVOIR

Litton Reservoir, Coley, East Harptree, Bristol, **SOMERSET**, BS40, **England**.
(W) www.bristolwater.co.uk
Contact/s: **Mr Bob Handford** (Manager), Bristol Water Plc, Woodford Lodge, Chew Stoke, Bristol, BS40 8XH.
(T) 01275 332339 **(F)** 01275 331377
(E) bob.handford@bristolwater.co.uk
S Taylor, Bristol Water Plc, Woodford Lodge, Chew Stoke, Bristol, BS40 8XH.
(T) 01275 332339 **(F)** 01275 331377
Profile: FT: Game; WN: Litton; WT: Reservoir (Still) W. Size: 12 Acres.
Location: Main Rd: A368; Rail: Bristol.
Ref: FH2765

LIZARD LAKES

Lizard Lakes, Trout Rd, West Drayton, London, **LONDON (GREATER)**, UB7, **England**.
Contact/s: **Mr Ben Tucker** (Fishery Manager), 10-11 Pleasant Pl, West Hyde, Rickmansworth, Hertfordshire, WD3 2XZ.
(T) 01895 824455 **(M)** 07973 453711
Mr Dave Brett (Bailiff). **(M)** 07931 255897
Mr Steve Brett (Fishery Manager). **(M)** 07931 255907
Profile: FT: Coarse; WN: Lizard; WT: Lake (Still); F. Size: 5 Acres; W. Size: 4 Acres.
Location: Nr. Rd: Trout Road; Main Rd: Cowley Road; Rail: West Drayton.
Ref: FH2766

L-LAKE FISHERY

L-Lake Fishery, Lake Farm Rd, Rainworth, Mansfield, **NOTTINGHAMSHIRE**, NG21 0ED, **England**.
Contact/s: Fishery Manager.
(T) 01623 490731
Mr Jack Singleton.
(T) 01623 796536
Profile: FT: Coarse; WN: L-Lake Fishery; WT: Lake (Still) W. Size: 4 Acres. **Location:** Nr. Rd: Mansfield to Newark-on-Trent; Main Rd: A617.
Ref: FH2767

LLANARTH FISHERY

Llanarth Fishery, Ty'r Lon, Llanarth, **CEREDIGION**, SA47 0NT, **Wales**.
Contact/s: **Mr Nigel Pheysey**.
(T) 01545 580598 **(M)** 07855 993241
Profile: FT: Coarse; WN: Llanarth Fishery; WT: Lake (Still) W. Size: 2 Acres. **Location:** Nr. Rd: A487; Main Rd: A487; Rail: Aberystwyth.
Ref: FH2768

LLANDEGFEDD RESERVOIR

Llandegfedd Reservoir, Pontypool, **TORFAEN**, NP4, **Wales**.
Contact/s: **Mr Chris Hatch** (Manager), Sluvad Rd, New Inn, Pontypool, Gwent, NP4 0TA.
(T) 01291 673722
Profile: FT: Game; WN: Llandegfedd; WT: Reservoir (Still).
Ref: FH2769

LLANDEGLA TROUT FISHERY

Llandegla Trout Fishery, Ruthin Rd, Llandegla, Wrexham, LL11 3AA, **Wales**.
(W) www.llandeglatroutfishery.co.uk
Contact/s: **Mr Colin McNae** (Owner).
(T) 01978 755851 **(F)** 01978 755851
(E) colin@llandeglatroutfishery.co.uk
Ms Sue McNae (Owner).
(T) 01978 755851 **(F)** 01978 755851
Profile: FT: Game; WN: Llandegla Trout Fishery; WT: Pool (Still); F. Size: 6 Acres; W. Size: 6 Acres. **Location:** Nr. Rd: Ruthin Road; Main Rd: A525; Rail: Wrexham.
Ref: FH2770

LLANDRINIO WEST LAKE

Llandrinio West Lake, Domgay Rd, Four Crosses, Llanymynech, **POWYS**, SY22, **Wales**.
Contact/s: **Mr Mel Jarvill**, West Lake Café, Domgay Rd, Four Crosses, Llandrinio, Llanymynech, SY22 6SL.
(T) 01691 831475 **(F)** 01691 831475
(E) meljarvill@ic24.net
Profile: FT: Combination; WN: Llandrinio West; WT: Lake (Still) W. Size: 3 Acres.
Ref: FH2771

LLANGOLLEN CANAL

Llangollen Canal, Hurleston, Nantwich, **CHESHIRE**, CW5, **England**.
Contact/s: Fishery Manager.
(T) 01829 732748
Profile: FT: Coarse; WN: Llangollen; WT: Canal (Still).
Ref: FH2772

LLANGORSE LAKE

Llangorse Lake, Lakeside Caravan Park, Llangorse, Brecon, **POWYS**, LD3 7TR, **Wales**.
Contact/s: Mr Ray Davies.
(T) 01874 658226 **(F)** 01874 658430
Profile: FT: Coarse; **WN:** Llangorse; **WT:** Lake (Still) **W. Size:** 350 Acres. **Location:** **Main Rd:** A40; **Rail:** Abergavenny. £Fr
Ref: FH2773

LLANISHEN RESERVOIR

Llanishen Reservoir, Hamdden Limited, Sluvad, New Inn, Pontypool, **TORFAEN**, NP4 0TA, **Wales**.
Contact/s: Mr C Hatch (Area Manager), Hamdden Ltd, Sluvad Treatment Works, Llandegfedd Reservoir, New Inn, Pontypool, Gwent NP4 0TA.
(T) 01495 769281 **(F)** 01495 769283
Profile: FT: Game; **WN:** Llanishen; **WT:** Reservoir (Still) **W. Size:** 59 Acres.
Ref: FH2774

LLANLLAWDDOG FISHERY

Llanllawddog Fishery, Home Farm, Llanllawddog, Carmarthen, **CARMARTHENSHIRE**, SA32 7JE, **Wales**.
Contact/s: Mr S Prescott.
(T) 01267 253436
Profile: FT: Game; **WN:** Llanllawddog; **WT:** Lake (Still). **Location: Main Rd:** A485.
Ref: FH2775

LLAY RESERVOIR

Llay Reservoir, Llay, Wrexham, LL, **Wales**.
Contact/s: Manager, 20 Mold Road Estate, Cworsyllt, Wrexham, Clwyd.
J Henshaw.
Mr John Preston.
Profile: FT: Coarse; **WN:** Llay; **WT:** Reservoir (Still).
Ref: FH2776

LLEDR (RIVER)

River Lledr, Dolwyddelan, **CONWY**, LL25, **Wales**.
Contact/s: Manager, Post Office, Dolwyddelan, Gwynedd, LL25 0NJ.
(T) 01690 750201
Profile: FT: Game; **WN:** Lledr; **WT:** River (Moving).
Ref: FH2777

LLEIDI RESERVIORS

Lleidi Reserviors, Swiss Valley, Upper Leidi, Llanelli, **CARMARTHENSHIRE**, SA15, **Wales**.
Contact/s: Mr David Watkins (Hon Secretary), Llaneli Angling Association, Thomas Bros, 10 Thomas St, Llanelli, SA15 3JA.
(T) 01554 774849
Profile: FT: Game; **WN:** Lleidi Reserviors; **WT:** Reservoir (Still).
Ref: FH2778

LLETYTWPA FISHERY

Lletytwpa Fishery, Lampeter, **CEREDIGION**, SA48, **Wales**.
(W) www.fishing-in-wales.co.uk/llandysul-aa/beat3
Contact/s: Mr Artie Jones (Hon Secretary), Llandysul Angling Association, Glas-y-Dorlan, Llyn-y-Fran Rd, Llandysul, SA44 4JW.
(T) 01559 362317
Profile: FT: Game; **WN:** Teifi; **WT:** River (Moving). **Location: Nr. Rd:** Lampeter to Llanfair Clydogau.
Ref: FH2779

LLISWERRY POND

Lliswerry Pond, Newport, NP, **Wales**.
Profile: FT: Coarse; **WN:** Lliswerry Pond; **WT:** Lake (Still) **W. Size:** 2 Acres. **Location: Nr. Rd:** A4042.
Ref: FH2780

LLIW (RIVER)

River Lliw, Craig-Y-Tan, **GWYNEDD**, LL, **Wales**.
Contact/s: Mr Gumbley (Hon Secretary), Mawnog, Fach, Bala, Gwynedd.
(T) 01678 520816
Profile: FT: Game; **WN:** Lliw; **WT:** River (Moving) **W. Size:** 3200 Metres.
Ref: FH2781

LLNGWYN FISHERY

Llngwyn Fishery, Nant Y Mynach Farm, Nantmel, Rhayader, **POWYS**, LD6, **Wales**.
Contact/s: Mr J Price (Manager), Nant Y Mynach Farm, Nantmel, Powys, Wales.
(T) 01597 810491
Profile: FT: Coarse; **WN:** Wye; **WT:** River (Moving).
Ref: FH2782

LLORAN GANOL FARM

Lloran Ganol Farm, Llansilin, Oswestry, **SHROPSHIRE**, SY10, **England**.
Contact/s: Fishery Manager.
(T) 01691 70286or70287
Profile: FT: Coarse; **WN:** Lloran Ganol Farm; **WT:** Lake (Still).
Ref: FH2783

LLOYDS MEADOW FISHERIES

Lloyds Meadow Fisheries, Delamere Rd, Mouldsworth, Chester, **CHESHIRE**, CH3 8BD, **England**.
Contact/s: Mr Glen Fellows (Manager).
(T) 01928 740710
Mr Kevin Underhill.
(T) 01928 740710
Profile: FT: Coarse; **WN:** Top Lake and Bottom Lake; **WT:** Lake (Still) **W. Size:** 2 Acres. **Location: Nr. Rd:** Delamere Road; **Main Rd:** B5393; **Rail:** Wolworth.
Ref: FH2784

LLWCHWR (RIVER)

River Llwchwr, Ammanford, **CARMARTHENSHIRE**, SA18, **Wales**.
Contact/s: Mr Bill Price (Manager), Tightlines Direct, 72 Wind St, Ammanford, Carmarthenshire, SA18 3DR.
(T) 0870 8000123
Profile: FT: Game; **WN:** Llwchwr; **WT:** River (Moving).
Ref: FH2785

LLWYN ON RESERVOIR

Llwyn On Reservoir, Hyder, Sluvad Treatment Works, Llandegfedd Reservoir, New Inn, Pontypool, **TORFAEN**, NP4 0TA, **Wales**.
Contact/s: Mr C Hatch (Area Manager), Hamdden Ltd, Sluvad Treatment Works, Llandegfedd Reservoir, New Inn, Pontypool, Gwent NP4 0TA.
(T) 01495 769281 **(F)** 01495 769283
Profile: FT: Game; **WN:** Llwyn On; **WT:** Reservoir (Still).
Ref: FH2786

LLWYNDURIS MANSION FISHERY

Llwynduris Mansion Fishery, Llechryd, Cardigan, **CEREDIGION**, SA43, **Wales**.
Contact/s: Mrs Nica Prichard (Hon Secretary), Spring Gardens, Parrog Rd, Newport, Pembrokeshire, SA42 0RJ.
(T) 01239 820671
Profile: FT: Game; **WN:** Teifi; **WT:** River (Moving) **W. Size:** 1200 Metres. **Location: Nr. Rd:** Llechryd to Cenarth.
Ref: FH2787

LLYN ALAN

Llyn Alan, Llantrisant, Holyhead, **ISLE OF ANGLESEY**, LL65, **Wales**.
Contact/s: Mr Jim Clark (Manager), Llyn Alaw Visitor Ctre, Llantrisant, Holyhead, Isle of Anglesey, LL65 4TW.
(T) 01407 730762 **(F)** 01407 730037
Profile: FT: Game; **WN:** Alan; **WT:** Reservoir (Still) **W. Size:** 770 Acres.
Ref: FH2788

LLYN ALARCH

Llyn Alarch, Builth Wells, **POWYS**, LD2, **Wales**.
Contact/s: Mr M Morgan (Secretary), Groe Park and Irfon Angling Club, 23 Garth Rd, Builth Wells, Powys, LD2 3AR.
(T) 01982 552759
Profile: FT: Game; **WN:** Alarch; **WT:** Lake (Still); **F. Size:** 3 Acres; **W. Size:** 2 Acres. **Location: Main Rd:** A483; **Rail:** Builth Road.
Ref: FH2789

LLYN ALAW

Llyn Alaw, Llantrisant, Pontyclun, **RHONDDA CYNON TAFF**, CF72, **Wales**.
Contact/s: Mr Jim Clark (Head Ranger), Llyn Alaw Visitor Ctre, Llantrisant, Holyhead, Isle of Anglesey, LL65 4TW.
(T) 01407 730762 **(F)** 01407 730037
Profile: FT: Game; **WN:** Llyn Alaw; **WT:** Reservoir (Still); **F. Size:** 777 Acres; **W. Size:** 777 Acres. **Location: Nr. Rd:** Sign posted from A5; **Main Rd:** A5, A5025; **Rail:** Valley. £Fr
Ref: FH2790

LLYN ALED

Llyn Aled, Denbigh, **CONWY**, LL16, **Wales**.
Contact/s: Mr David Scutter (Manager), Llyn Brenig Visitors Ctre, Cerrigdrudion, Corwen, Conwy, LL21 9TT.
(T) 01490 420463 **(F)** 01490 420694
(E) llyn.brenig@hyder.com
Profile: FT: Combination; **WN:** Aled; **WT:** Reservoir (Still) **W. Size:** 110 Acres. **Location: Main Rd:** A543.
Ref: FH2791

LLYN ALWEN

Llyn Alwen, Llais-Yr-Afon, Ruthin, **DENBIGHSHIRE**, LL15 2BE, **Wales**.
Contact/s: Mr Gordon Smith.
(T) 01824 7196091
Profile: FT: Game; **WN:** Alwen; **WT:** Lake (Still) **W. Size:** 2 Acres. **Location: Nr. Rd:** A5; **Main Rd:** A5.
Ref: FH2792

LLYN BERWEN

Llyn Berwen, Tregaron A A, Swyn Teifi, Pontrhydfendigaid, Ystrad Meurig, **CEREDIGION**, SY25 6LF, **Wales**.
Contact/s: Mr M J Morgan Obe (Hon Secretary), Ivegoran Angling Association, Swyn Teifi, Pontrhydfendigaid, Ystrad Meurig, Carmarthenshire, SY25 6EF.
(T) 01974 831316 **(F)** 01974 831316
Profile: FT: Coarse; **WN:** Berwen; **WT:** Lake (Still).
Ref: FH2793

LLYN BERWYN

Llyn Berwyn, Tregaron, **CEREDIGION**, SY25, **Wales**.
Contact/s: Mr M J Morgan Obe (Hon Secretary), Ivegoran Angling Association, Swyn Teifi, Pontrhydfendigaid, Ystrad Meurig, Carmarthenshire, SY25 6EF.
(T) 01974 831316 **(F)** 01974 831316
Profile: FT: Game; **WN:** Berwyn; **WT:** Lake (Still). **Location: Nr. Rd:** Mountain Road; **Rail:** Aberystwyth.
Ref: FH2794

LLYN BRENIG

Llyn Brenig, Cerrig-y-drudion, Corwen, **DENBIGHSHIRE**, LL21 9, **Wales**.
Contact/s: Mr Dwr Cymrn (Manager), Llyn Brenig Visitors Ctre, Cerrigdrudion, Corwen, Conwy, LL21 9TT.
(T) 01490 420463 **(F)** 01490 420694
(E) llynbrenig@hyder.com
Profile: FT: Game; **WN:** Llyn Brenig; **WT:** Lake (Still); **F. Size:** 1600 Acres; **W. Size:** 920 Acres. **Location: Nr. Rd:** B4501; **Main Rd:** A5.
Ref: FH2795

LLYN BRYNTIRION

Llyn Bryntirion, Dwyran, Llanfair Pwllgwyngyll, **ISLE OF ANGLESEY**, LL61, **Wales**.
Contact/s: Fishery Manager.
(T) 01248 430237
Mr J Naylor (Owner), Bryntirion Working Farm, Dwyran, Isle of Anglesey, LL61 6BY.

(T) 01248 430232
Profile: **FT:** Coarse; **WN:** Bryntirion; **WT:** Lake (Still).
Ref: FH2796

LLYN BUGEILYN

Llyn Bugeilyn, Tal Y Llyn, Tywyn, **GWYNEDD**, LL36, **Wales**.
Contact/s: **Mr T Rowlands** (Hotel Manager), Tyn-y-Cornel Hotel, Talyllyn, Tywyn, Gwynedd, LL36 9AJ.
(T) 01654 782282
Profile: **FT:** Game; **WN:** Llyn Bugeilyn; **WT:** Lake (Still) **W. Size:** 45 Acres.
Ref: FH2797

LLYN CARFAN

Llyn Carfan, Carfan-Y-Ddol, Tavernspite, Whitland, **CARMARTHENSHIRE**, SA34 0NP, **Wales**.
Contact/s: **Mr Huw John** (Manager).
(T) 01994 240819 (M) 07779 459414
(E) hjohn70435@aol.com
Profile: **FT:** Combination; **WN:** Carfan; **WT:** Lake (Still) **W. Size:** 2 Acres. **Location:** **Main Rd:** A40; **Rail:** Whitland.
Ref: FH2798

LLYN CELYN FISHERY

Llyn Celyn Fishery, Bala, **GWYNEDD**, LL23, **Wales**.
Contact/s: **Mr Dewi Evans** (Secretary), Bala and District Angling Club, 33 High St, Bala, Gwynedd, LL23 7AF.
(T) 01678 520370 (F) 01678 520370
Profile: **FT:** Game; **WN:** Celyn; **WT:** Lake (Still).
Ref: FH2799

LLYN CLYWEDOG

Llyn Clywedog, Llanidloes, **POWYS**, SY18, **Wales**.
Contact/s: **Mrs Gough** (Manager), Travellers Rest Restaurant, 9 Long Bridge St, Llanidloes, Powys, SY18 6EE.
(T) 01686 412329
Ms Dallas Davies.
(T) 01686 412644after7pm
Profile: **FT:** Game; **WN:** Llyn Clywedog; **WT:** Lake (Still) **W. Size:** 600 Acres.
Ref: FH2800

LLYN CORON

Llyn Coron, Bodorgan Estate, Aberfraw, Llangefni, **ISLE OF ANGLESEY**, LL77, **Wales**.
Contact/s: **Mr Cliff Girling** (Bailiff).
(T) 01407 810801
Profile: **FT:** Game; **WN:** Coron; **WT:** Lake (Still).
Ref: FH2801

LLYN COWLYD AND HILL LAKES

Llyn Cowlyd And Hill Lakes, Rhyl, **DENBIGHSHIRE**, LL18, **Wales**.
Contact/s: Fisheries Manager, Welsh Water plc, Conwy Unit Office, Cefndy Rd, Rhyl, Gwynedd LL18 2HG.
(T) 01244 550015
Profile: **FT:** Game; **WN:** Cowlyd; **WT:** Lake (Still).
Ref: FH2802

LLYN CRAFNANT FISHERIES

Llyn Crafnant Fisheries, Lakeside Café, Llyn Crafnant Rd, Trefriw, **CONWY**, LL27 0JZ, **Wales**.
Contact/s: **Ms J A Collins** (Owner).
(T) 01492 640818
Profile: **FT:** Game; **WN:** Llyn Crafnant; **WT:** Lake (Still) **W. Size:** 63 Acres. **Location:** **Nr. Rd:** B5106.
Ref: FH2803

LLYN CWELLYN RESERVOIR

Llyn Cwellyn Reservoir, Rhyd-Ddu, Caernarfon, **GWYNEDD**, LL54, **Wales**.
Contact/s: **Mr Huw P Hughes** (Hon Secretary), Seiont, Gwyrfai and Llyfni Anglers Society, Llugwy, Ystad Eryri, Bethel, Caernarfon, LL55 1BX.
(T) 01248 670666
(E) huw.hughes@lineone.net
Profile: **FT:** Game; **WN:** Cwellyn; **WT:** Reservoir (Still); **F. Size:** 500 Acres; **W. Size:** 500 Acres. **Location:** **Main Rd:** A4085; **Rail:** Bangor.
Ref: FH2804

LLYN CWMYSTRADLLYN

Llyn Cwmystradllyn, Caernarfon Rd, Porthmadog, **GWYNEDD**, LL49, **Wales**.
Contact/s: **Mr Aled Roberts** (Owner), Central Buildings, High St, Porthmadog, Gwynedd, LL49 9LR.
(T) 01766 512464or523287
Mr Len Hicks (Secretary), Pwllheli and District Angling Association, 82 Abererch Rd, Pwllheli, Gwynedd, LL53 5LS.
(T) 01758 614885
Profile: **FT:** Game; **WN:** Cwmystradllyn; **WT:** Lake (Still) **W. Size:** 99 Acres. **Location:** **Nr. Rd:** A487; **Main Rd:** A5 to A55; **Rail:** Porthmadog.
Ref: FH2805

LLYN CYFYNWY

Llyn Cyfynwy Sport Trout Fishery, The Lodge, Llandegla, Wrexham, LL11 3BS, **Wales**.
Contact/s: **Mr Dave Penman**.
(T) 01978 790430
Profile: **FT:** Game; **WN:** Llyn Cyfynwy Sport Trout Fishery; **WT:** Lake (Still).
Ref: FH2806

LLYN CYNWCH LAKE

Llyn Cynwch Lake, 'Maescaled', Dolgellau, **GWYNEDD**, LL40 1UF, **Wales**.
Contact/s: **Mr E M Davies** (Secretary).
(T) 01341 422706
Profile: **FT:** Game; **WN:** Cynwch; **WT:** Reservoir (Still) **W. Size:** 22 Acres. **Location:** **Rail:** Barmouth.
Ref: FH2807

LLYN DDU (BLACK LAKE)

Llyn Ddu (Black Lake), Prenteg, Porthmadog, **GWYNEDD**, **Wales**.
Contact/s: **Mr John Turner** (Hon Secretary), Prince Albert Angling Society, 15 Pexhill Drive, Macclesfield, Cheshire, SK10 3LP.
(T) 01625 422010
Profile: **FT:** Game; **WN:** Llyn Ddu; **WT:** Lake (Still) **W. Size:** 5 Acres. **Location:** **Nr. Rd:** Prerteg to Golan Road; **Main Rd:** A498.
Ref: FH2808

LLYN DEWI

Llyn Dewi, Llanbabo, Anglesey, **ISLE OF ANGLESEY**, **Wales**.
Contact/s: **Mr Ray Swales** (Club Secretary), 36 Trem-y-mor, Rhosneiger, Isle of Anglesey, LL64 5QR.
(T) 01407 810136
(E) swales24@hotmail.com
Profile: **FT:** Coarse; **WN:** Dewi; **WT:** Pool (Still); **F. Size:** 2 Acres; **W. Size:** 1 Acre. **Location:** **Main Rd:** A5025; **Rail:** Holyhead.
Ref: FH2809

LLYN DINAS

Llyn Dinas, Beddgelert, Caernarfon, **GWYNEDD**, LL55, **Wales**.
Contact/s: **Mr J Daniel Hughes** (Secretary), Berthlwyd, Penrhyndeudraeth, Gwynedd, LL48 6RL.
Mrs Alison Pass (Manager), Beddgelert Post Office, Caernarfon Rd, Beddgelert, Gwynedd, LL55 4UY.
(T) 01766 890201
Profile: **FT:** Game; **WN:** Llyn Dinas; **WT:** Lake (Still).
Ref: FH2810

LLYN FAWR FISHERY

Llyn Fawr Fishery, Rhondda, Treorchy, **RHONDDA CYNON TAFF**, CF42, **Wales**.
Contact/s: **Mr C P Jeremiah** (owner), 10 Coldra Rd, Tynewydd Treorchy, Rhondda, Glamorgan, CF42 5ST.
(T) 01443 771698
Profile: **FT:** Game; **WN:** Fawr; **WT:** Lake (Still).
Ref: FH2811

LLYN GADAIR

Llyn Gadair, Caernarfon, **GWYNEDD**, LL, **Wales**.
Contact/s: **Mr Huw P Hughes** (Hon Secretary), Llugwy, Ystad Eryri, Bethel, Caernarfon, LL55 1BX.
(T) 01248 670666
Profile: **FT:** Game; **WN:** Gadair; **WT:** Lake (Still) **W. Size:** 24000 Metres. **Location:** **Nr. Rd:** A55; **Main Rd:** A5 to Bangor.
Ref: FH2812

LLYN GLAN MOFA MAWR

Llyn Glan Mofa Mawr, Morfa Bychan, Porthmadog, **GWYNEDD**, LL49, **Wales**.
Contact/s: Manager, Central Buildings, High St, Porthmadog, Gwynedd, LL49 9LR.
(T) 01766 512464or523287
Profile: **FT:** Game; **WN:** Llyn Glan Mofa Mawr; **WT:** Lake (Still) **W. Size:** 8 Acres. **Location:** **Nr. Rd:** Morfa Bychan.
Ref: FH2813

LLYN JANE FISHERY

Llyn Jane Fishery, Menai Bridge, **ISLE OF ANGLESEY**, LL59, **Wales**.
Contact/s: **Mr D W Owen** (Owner), Llynjane, Llandgfan, Isle of Anglesey, Gwynedd, LL59 5PN.
(T) 01248 713250
Profile: **FT:** Game; **WN:** Jane; **WT:** Lake (Still); **F. Size:** 6 Acres.
Ref: FH2814

LLYN LLWYDIARTH FAWR

Llyn Llwydiarth Fawr, Llanerchymedd, **ISLE OF ANGLESEY**, LL71 8DF, **Wales**.
Contact/s: Fishery Manager.
(T) 01248 470540
M L Hughes.
(T) 01248 470321
Mr R Hughes (Owner).
(T) 01248 470321
Profile: **FT:** Combination; **WN:** Llwydiarth Fawr; **WT:** Lake (Still).
Ref: FH2815

LLYN MAENOG TROUT FISHERY

Llyn Maenog Trout Fishery, Blaenmaenog, Velindre, Llandysul, **CEREDIGION**, SA44 5JA, **Wales**.
Contact/s: **Mrs Judith Davies**.
(T) 01559 370239
Profile: **FT:** Game; **WN:** Llyn Maenog Trout Fishery; **WT:** Reservoir (Still).
Ref: FH2816

LLYN NANT ANOG

Llyn Nant Anog, Nant Anog, Nr Carmel, Anglesey, **ISLE OF ANGLESEY**, **Wales**.
Contact/s: **Ray Swales** (Club Secretary), 36 Trem-y-mor, Rhosneiger, Isle of Anglesey, LL64 5QR.
(T) 01407 810136
(E) swales24@hotmail.com
Profile: **FT:** Coarse; **WN:** Nant Anog; **WT:** Lake (Still); **F. Size:** 6 Acres; **W. Size:** 5 Acres. **Location:** **Main Rd:** B5112; **Rail:** Holyhead.
Ref: FH2817

LLYN NANTLLE

Llyn Nantlle, Caernarfon, **GWYNEDD**, LL, **Wales**.
Contact/s: **Mr Huw P Hughes** (Hon Secretary), Llugwy, Ystad Eryri, Bethel, Caernarfon, LL55 1BX.
(T) 01248 670666
Profile: **FT:** Game; **WN:** Nantlle; **WT:** Lake (Still) **W. Size:** 24000 Metres. **Location:** **Nr. Rd:** A55; **Main Rd:** A5 to Bangor.
Ref: FH2818

LLYN NANT-Y-CERRIG

Llyn Nant-Y-Cerrig, Conwy, LL, **Wales**.
Contact/s: **Mr N Roberts** (Manager), Goleugell, Eglwysbach, Colwyn Bay, Clwyd,

LL28 5UH.
(T) 01492 650314
Profile: FT: Coarse; WN: Nant-y-Cerrig; WT: Lake (Still). **Location:** Nr. Rd: Bryn-y-maen; Main Rd: B5113.
Ref: FH2819

LLYN ON RESERVOIR

Llyn On Reservoir, Pontypool, **TORFAEN**, NP4 0, **Wales**.
Contact/s: **Mr C Hatch** (Area Manager), Hamdden Ltd, Sluvad Treatment Works, Llandegfedd Reservoir, New Inn, Pontypool, Gwent NP4 0TA.
(T) 01495 769281 (F) 01495 769283
Profile: FT: Game; WN: Llyn On; WT: Reservoir (Still) W. Size: 150 Acres.
Ref: FH2820

LLYN PADARN

Llyn Padarn, Lakeside Railway, Llanberis, Caernarfon, **GWYNEDD**, LL55, **Wales**.
Contact/s: **Mr Huw P Hughes** (Hon Secretary), Seiont, Gwyrfai and Llyfni Anglers Society, Llugwy, Ystad Eryri, Bethel, Caernarfon, LL55 1BX.
(T) 01248 670666
(E) huw.hughes@lineone.net
Profile: FT: Game; WN: Padarn; WT: Lake (Still) W. Size: 550 Acres. **Location:** Main Rd: A4086; Rail: Bangor.
Ref: FH2821

LLYN TACAN

Llyn Tacan, Llanfairyneubwll, Caergeiliog, Anglesey, **ISLE OF ANGLESEY**, **Wales**.
Contact/s: **Ray Swales** (Club Secretary), 36 Trem-y-mor, Rhosneiger, Isle of Anglesey, LL64 5QR.
(T) 01407 810136
(E) swales24@hotmail.com
Profile: FT: Coarse; WN: Tacan; WT: Lake (Still); F. Size: 4 Acres; W. Size: 3 Acres. **Location:** Main Rd: A5; Rail: Valley.
Ref: FH2822

LLYN TEGID (BALA LAKE)

Llyn Tegid (Bala Lake), The Warden Centre, Boat House, Pensarn Rd, Bala, **GWYNEDD**, LL23, **Wales**.
Contact/s: **Mr A Morris**, Warden's Office, 24 Ffordd Pensarn, Bala.
(T) 01678 520626
Profile: FT: Coarse; WN: Llyn Tegid; WT: Lake (Still) W. Size: 1100 Acres.
Ref: FH2823

LLYN Y GORS

Llyn Y Gors, Llandegfan, Menai Bridge, **ISLE OF ANGLESEY**, LL59 5PN, **Wales**.
(W) www.llynygors.co.uk
Contact/s: **Mr Roger Thompson**.
(T) 01248 713410 (F) 01248 716324
(E) llynygors@aol.com
Profile: FT: Coarse; WN: Llyn y gors; WT: Lake (Still); F. Size: 20 Acres. **Location:** Nr. Rd: Llandegfan; Main Rd: A5; Rail: Bangor.
Ref: FH2824

LLYN-COCH HWYAD

Llyn-Coch Hwyad, Llanbrynmair, **POWYS**, SY19, **Wales**.
Contact/s: **Mr E Lewis** (chairman), Bryn-Llugwy, Llanbrynmair, Powys, SY19 7AA.
(T) 01650 521385 (F) 01650 521385
Mr H Hughes, Bodhyfryd, Llanbrynmair, Powys.
Profile: FT: Game; WN: Coch Hwyad; WT: Lake (Still) W. Size: 25 Acres. **Location:** Main Rd: A470.
Ref: FH2825

LLYNFI (RIVER)

River Llynfi, Maesteg, **BRIDGEND**, CF34, **Wales**.
Contact/s: **Mr G Thomas** (Hon Secretary), 39 Darren View, Llangynwyd, Maesteg, Glamorgan (Vale of).
Profile: FT: Game; WN: Llynfi; WT: River (Moving) W. Size: 12800 Metres. **Location:** Nr. Rd: Maesteg to Tondu.
Ref: FH2826

LLYNFI (RIVER)

River Llynfi, Glasbury, Hereford, **HEREFORDSHIRE**, HR3, **England**.
Contact/s: **Mr A Lloyd** (Information Contact), Bridgend Cottage, Glasbury on Wye, Hereford, Herefordshire, HR3 5NP.
(T) 01497 847227
Profile: FT: Game; WN: Llynfi; WT: River (Moving) W. Size: 1600 Metres.
Ref: FH2827

LLYNGWYN LAKE

Llyngwyn Lake, Rhayader, **POWYS**, LD6 5, **Wales**.
Contact/s: **Mr David Evans** (Secretary), Rhayader Angling Association, 72 Brynheulog, Rhayader, Powys, LD6 5EG.
(T) 01597 811404
Profile: FT: Game; WN: Llyngwyn; WT: Lake (Still) W. Size: 16 Acres.
Ref: FH2828

LLYS Y FRAN RESERVOIR

Llys Y Fran Reservoir And Country Park, Clarbeston Rd, Haverfordwest, **PEMBROKESHIRE**, SA63 4RR, **Wales**.
Contact/s: **Mr John Waddington** (Head Ranger), Visitors Ctre, Llys-y-Fran Reservoir, Clarbeston Rd, Haverfordwest, SA63 4RR.
(T) 01437 532732 (F) 01437 532732 (M) 07771 916732
Profile: FT: Game; WN: Llys Y Fran; WT: Reservoir (Still) W. Size: 212 Acres. **Location:** Nr. Rd: B4313; Main Rd: A40; Rail: Haverfordwest.
Ref: FH2829

LLYSWEN CARP POOLS

Llyswen Carp Pools, The Dderw, Llyswen, Builth Wells, **POWYS**, LD2, **Wales**.
Contact/s: **Mr O Eckley** (Owner).
(T) 01874 754224
Profile: FT: Coarse; WN: Llyswen; WT: Pool (Still).
Ref: FH2830

LLYWD (RIVER)

River Llywd, Blaenavon, Pontypool, **TORFAEN**, NP4, **Wales**.
Contact/s: **Mr B J Jones** (Hon Secretary), 79 Robertson Way, Woodlands, Malpas, Newport, NP9 6QQ.
(T) 01633 853735
Profile: FT: Game; WN: Llywd; WT: River (Moving) W. Size: 20800 Metres. **Location:** Nr. Rd: Blaenavon to Croesyceiliog.
Ref: FH2831

LLYWN-ON RESERVOIR

Llywn-On Reservoir, Pentwyn Rd, Nelson, Treharris, **GLAMORGAN (VALE OF)**, CF46, **Wales**.
Contact/s: Fishery Manager.
(T) 01685 370771
Profile: FT: Game; WN: Llywn-on; WT: Reservoir (Still). **Location:** Nr. Rd: Pentwyn Road.
Ref: FH2832

LOAM POND

Loam Pond, Sutton, Woodbridge, **SUFFOLK**, IP12, **England**.
Contact/s: Manager, The Rod and Gun Shop, 18 Church St, Woodbridge, Suffolk, IP12.
Profile: FT: Coarse; WN: Loam; WT: Pond (Still); F. Size: 6 Acres; W. Size: 4 Acres. **Location:** Main Rd: B1083; Rail: Woodbridge.
Ref: FH2833

LOBBY FIELD PONDS

Lobby Field Ponds, Binbrook, Market Rasen, **LINCOLNSHIRE**, LN8, **England**.
Contact/s: **Mr D Price**, The Lobby Field Sports Centre, Orford Rd, Binbrook, Market Rasen, LN8.
(T) 01472 398782
Mr M W Pearce, Beauvale, Kirmond Rd, Binbrook, Market Rasen, LN8 6HY.
(T) 01472 398277
Profile: FT: Coarse; WN: Lobby Field; WT: Pond (Still) W. Size: 1 Acre. **Location:** Nr. Rd: Orford Road, on left after school; Main Rd: B1203 Kirmond Road; Rail: Market Rasen.
Ref: FH2834

LOCH ACHANALT

Loch Achanalt, Dingwall, **HIGHLAND**, IV7, **Scotland**.
Contact/s: **Mr H C Furlong**, The Sports and Model Shop, 66 High St, Dingwall, Highland, IV15 9RY.
(T) 01349 862346
Profile: FT: Game; WN: Achanalt; WT: Loch (Still).
Ref: FH2835

LOCH ACHILITY

Loch Achility, Strathpeffer, **HIGHLAND**, IV14, **Scotland**.
Contact/s: **Mr Mark Butcher**, Eilean View, Contin, Strathpeffer, Highland, Scotland.
(T) 01997 421245
Profile: FT: Game; WN: Loch Achility; WT: Loch (Still).
Ref: FH2836

LOCH ACHONACHIE

Loch Achonachie, Maryburgh, Dingwall, **HIGHLAND**, IV7, **Scotland**.
Contact/s: **Mr G Cameron** (Secretary), 33 Wrightfield Park, Maryburgh, Highland, Scotland.
(T) 01349 862455
Profile: FT: Game; WN: Achonachie; WT: Loch (Still).
Ref: FH2837

LOCH ACHRAY

Loch Achray, Aberfoyle, Stirling, FK8, **Scotland**.
Contact/s: **Mr David Marshall**.
(T) 01877 382229
Profile: FT: Game; WN: Achray; WT: Loch (Still).
Ref: FH2838

LOCH AFFRIC

Loch Affric, Inverness, **HIGHLAND**, IV, **Scotland**.
Contact/s: **Ms Louise Hodgson** (Manager), Glen Affric Hotel, Cannich, Beauly, Highland, IV4 7LW.
(T) 01456 415214 (F) 01456 415254
Profile: FT: Game; WN: Affric; WT: Loch (Still).
Ref: FH2839

LOCH AKRAN

Loch Akran, Melvich, Thurso, **HIGHLAND**, KW14, **Scotland**.
Contact/s: **Mr Peter Martin** (Owner), Melvich Hotel, Melvich, Thurso, Scotland, KW14 7YJ.
(T) 01641 531206 (F) 01641 531347
Profile: FT: Game; WN: Akran; WT: Loch (Still).
Ref: FH2840

LOCH ALVIE

Loch Alvie, Alvie Estate Office, Kincraig, Kingussie, **HIGHLAND**, PH21 1NE, **Scotland**.
Contact/s: **Mr David Kinnear** (Assistant Factor).
(T) 01479 810330
Profile: FT: Game; WN: Alvie; WT: Loch (Still).
Ref: FH2841

LOCH ARD

Loch Ard, Aberfoyle, Stirling, FK8 3TL, **Scotland**.
Contact/s: **Mr Alan Reigh** (Manager), Forest Hills Hotel, Kinlochard, Stirling, Stirling, FK8 3TL.
(T) 01877 387277
Profile: FT: Game; WN: Ard; WT: Loch (Still). **Location:** Nr. Rd: B829; Main Rd:

A873.
Ref: FH2842

LOCH ARKAIG

Loch Arkaig, Fort William, **HIGHLAND**, PH33, **Scotland**.
Contact/s: **Mr Richard Sidgewick** (Manager), West Highland Estate Offices, 33 High St, Fort William, Highland, PH33 6DH.
(T) 01397 702433
Profile: **FT:** Game; **WN:** Arkaig; **WT:** Loch (Still).
Ref: FH2843

LOCH ARKLET

Loch Arklet, Estate Office, Stronachlachar, Stirling, FK, **Scotland**.
Contact/s: **Mr Morris Meikle** (Owner), Strathclyde Water Services, Stronachlachar, Stirling.
(T) 01877 386256
Profile: **FT:** Game; **WN:** Arklet; **WT:** Loch (Still).
Ref: FH2844

LOCH ARKLET

Loch Arklet, Glasgow, **GLASGOW (CITY OF)**, G, **Scotland**.
Contact/s: Fisheries Officer, Strathclyde Reginal Council, 419 Balmore Rd, Glasgow.
(T) 0141 3365333
Profile: **FT:** Game; **WN:** Arklet; **WT:** Loch (Still). **Location:** **Nr. Rd:** B829; **Main Rd:** A84.
Ref: FH2845

LOCH ASSYNT

Loch Assynt, Inchnadamph, Lochinver, Lairg, **HIGHLAND**, IV27, **Scotland**.
Contact/s: Manager, Inchnadamph Hotel, Elphin, Lairg, Sutherland, IV27 4HN.
(T) 01571 822202 **(F)** 01571 822203
Profile: **FT:** Game; **WN:** Assynt; **WT:** Loch (Still).
Ref: FH2846

LOCH AVICH

Loch Avich, Oban, **ARGYLL AND BUTE**, PA34, **Scotland**.
Contact/s: **Mr T C MacNair** (Secretary), Loch Awe Improvement Association, Boswell House, Argyll Sq, Oban, PA34 4BD.
(T) 01631 562215 **(F)** 01631 565490
Profile: **FT:** Game; **WN:** Avich; **WT:** Loch (Still) **W. Size:** 4800 Metres. **Location:** **Nr. Rd:** B840; **Main Rd:** A85; **Rail:** Dalmally.
Ref: FH2847

LOCH AWE

Loch Awe, Oban, **ARGYLL AND BUTE**, PA34, **Scotland**.
Contact/s: **Mr Kenneth Baird** (Manager), Lochawe Stores, Lochawe, Dalmally, PA33 1AQ.
(T) 01838 200200 **(F)** 01838 200200
Mr T C MacNair (Secretary), Loch Awe Improvement Association, Boswell House, Argyll Sq, Oban, PA34 4BD.
(T) 01631 562215 **(F)** 01631 565490
Ms Mary McFee (Manager), Cruachan Filling Station, Lochawe, Dalmally, PA33 1AW.
(T) 01838 200345
Profile: **FT:** Combination; **WN:** Awe; **WT:** Loch (Still) **W. Size:** 43200 Metres. **Location:** **Nr. Rd:** B840; **Main Rd:** A85; **Rail:** Dalmally.
Ref: FH2848

LOCH BAD A CROTHA

Loch Bad A Crotha, Gairloch, **HIGHLAND**, IV21, **Scotland**.
Contact/s: **Mrs J Lagerman** (Manager), Shieldaig Lodge Hotel, Badachro, Gairloch, Highland, IV21 2AW.
(T) 01445 741250
Profile: **FT:** Game; **WN:** Loch Bad A Crotha; **WT:** Loch (Still).
Ref: FH2849

LOCH BADANLOCH

Loch Badanloch, Kinbrace, **HIGHLAND**, KW11, **Scotland**.
Contact/s: **Mr P Mackenzie**.
(T) 01431 831232
Profile: **FT:** Game; **WN:** Badanloch; **WT:** Loch (Still).
Ref: FH2850

LOCH BARAVAIG

Loch Baravaig, Isle Ornsay, **HIGHLAND**, IV43, **Scotland**.
Contact/s: **Mrs Morag Mcdonald** (Manager), Eilean Iarmain Hotel, Isle Ornsay, Isle of Skye, IV43 8QR.
(T) 01471 833332 **(F)** 01471 833275
Profile: **FT:** Game; **WN:** Baravaig; **WT:** Loch (Still).
Ref: FH2851

LOCH BARNBARROCH

Loch Barnbarroch, Craighlaw Fisheries, Newton Stewart, **DUMFRIES AND GALLOWAY**, DG8, **Scotland**.
Contact/s: **Ms Clare McClymont** (Manager), Palakona Bait Supplies, 30-32 Queen St, Newton Stewart, Dumfries and Galloway, DG8 9NR.
(T) 01671 402323
(E) palakonswscot@cs.com
Profile: **FT:** Coarse; **WN:** Barnbarroch; **WT:** Loch (Still).
Ref: FH2852

LOCH BARNLUASGAN

Loch Barnluasgan, Lochgilphead, **RENFREWSHIRE**, PA3, **Scotland**.
Contact/s: **Mr Archie MacGilp** (Secretary), Fyne Tackle, 22 Argyll St, Lochgilphead, Argyll and Bute, PA31 8NE.
(T) 01546 606878
Profile: **FT:** Game; **WN:** Barnluasgan; **WT:** Loch (Still); **F. Size:** 400 Acres; **W. Size:** 15 Acres. **Location:** **Nr. Rd:** B8025; **Main Rd:** A83; **Rail:** Oban.
Ref: FH2853

LOCH BEANNACH

Loch Beannach, Lairg, **HIGHLAND**, IV27, **Scotland**.
Contact/s: **Mr Alistair Ross** (Manager), Ross Hardware, Main St, Lairg, Highland, IV27 4DB.
(T) 01549 402239
Profile: **FT:** Game; **WN:** Beannach; **WT:** Loch (Still).
Ref: FH2854

LOCH BEANNACHAIRAN

Loch Beannachairan, Strathconon, Muir Of Ord, **HIGHLAND**, IV6, **Scotland**.
Contact/s: **Mr C.D Rumble** (Manager), East Lodge Hotel, Strathconon, Muir of Ord, Highland, IV6 7QQ.
(T) 01997 477222
Profile: **FT:** Game; **WN:** Beannachairan; **WT:** Loch (Still).
Ref: FH2855

LOCH BENEVEAN

Loch Benevean, Inverness, **HIGHLAND**, IV, **Scotland**.
Contact/s: , Glen Affric Hotel, Cannich, Beauly, Highland, IV4 7LW.
(T) 01456 415214 **(F)** 01456 415254
Profile: **FT:** Game; **WN:** Benevean; **WT:** Loch (Still).
Ref: FH2856

LOCH BHAC

Loch Bhac, Pitlochry, **PERTH AND KINROSS**, PH, **Scotland**.
Contact/s: **Mr Ross Gardiner** (Secretary).
(T) 01796 472157
Profile: **FT:** Game; **WN:** Bhac; **WT:** Loch (Still).
Ref: FH2857

LOCH BORRALAN

Loch Borralan, The Alt Motel, Altnacealgach, Lairg, **HIGHLAND**, IV27 4HF, **Scotland**.
Contact/s: **Mr B Ward**.
(T) 01854 666220 **(F)** 01854 666220
Profile: **FT:** Game; **WN:** Borralan; **WT:** Loch (Still); **F. Size:** 250 Acres. **Location:** **Nr. Rd:** A837; **Rail:** Lairg.
Ref: FH2858

LOCH BORRALIE

Loch Borralie, Keoldale, Lairg, **HIGHLAND**, IV27, **Scotland**.
Contact/s: Manager, Cape Wrath Hotel, Durness, Lairg, Highland, IV27 4SW.
(T) 01971 511212 **(F)** 01971 511313
Profile: **FT:** Game; **WN:** Borralie; **WT:** Loch (Still).
Ref: FH2859

LOCH BRADAN

Loch Bradan, Newton Stewart, **DUMFRIES AND GALLOWAY**, DG8, **Scotland**.
Contact/s: **Mr Sandy White** (Recreational Forester), Forestry Commission Office, Forest Enterprise, Galloway Forest District, Creebridge, Newton Stewart, DG8 6AJ.
(T) 01671 402420 **(F)** 01671 403708
Profile: **FT:** Game; **WN:** Bradan; **WT:** Loch (Still).
Ref: FH2860

LOCH BRECKBOWIE

Loch Breckbowie, Newton Stewart, **DUMFRIES AND GALLOWAY**, DG8, **Scotland**.
Contact/s: **Mr Sandy White** (Recreational Forester), Forestry Commission Office, Forest Enterprise, Galloway Forest District, Creebridge, Newton Stewart, DG8 6AJ.
(T) 01671 402420 **(F)** 01671 403708
Profile: **FT:** Game; **WN:** Breckbowie; **WT:** Loch (Still).
Ref: FH2861

LOCH BRORA

Loch Brora, Brora, **HIGHLAND**, KW9, **Scotland**.
Contact/s: **Mr Rob Wilsons** (Manager), Rob Wilson Tackle Shop, Rosslyn St, Brora, Highland, KW9 6NY.
(T) 01408 621373 **(F)** 01408 621373
Profile: **FT:** Game; **WN:** Brora; **WT:** Loch (Still).
Ref: FH2862

LOCH CHUILIN

Loch Chuilin, Dingwall, **HIGHLAND**, IV7, **Scotland**.
Contact/s: **Mr H C Furlong**, The Sports and Model Shop, 66 High St, Dingwall, Highland, IV15 9RY.
(T) 01349 862346
Profile: **FT:** Game; **WN:** Chuilin; **WT:** Loch (Still).
Ref: FH2863

LOCH CONNAN

Loch Connan, Struan, Portree, **HIGHLAND**, IV51, **Scotland**.
Contact/s: **Mr J.W. Mulford** (Manager), Ullinish Lodge Hotel, Ullinish, Struan, Isle of Skye, IV56 8FD.
(T) 01470 572214
Profile: **FT:** Game; **WN:** Connan; **WT:** Loch (Still).
Ref: FH2864

LOCH CRAGGIE

Loch Craggie, Tongue, Lairg, **HIGHLAND**, IV27, **Scotland**.
Contact/s: **Mr Paul Lewis** (Owner), Ben Loyal Hotel, Tongue, Lairg, Highland, IV27 4XE.
(T) 01847 611216 **(F)** 01847 611212
Mrs Elaine Lewis (Owner).
(T) 01847 611216
Profile: **FT:** Game; **WN:** Craggie; **WT:** Loch (Still).
Ref: FH2865

LOCH CULAG

Loch Culag, Lochinver, Lairg, **HIGHLAND**, IV27, **Scotland**.
Contact/s: Manager, Culag Hotel, Culag, Lochinver, Lairg, Highland IV27 4LQ.

(T) 01571 844720 (F) 01571 844483
Profile: FT: Game; WN: Culag; WT: Loch (Still).
Ref: FH2866

LOCH DALLAS
Loch Dallas, Forres, **MORAY**, IV36, **Scotland**.
Contact/s: **Mr McKenzie**, 79 High St, Forres, Moray, Scotland.
Profile: FT: Game; WN: Dallas; WT: Loch (Still).
Ref: FH2867

LOCH DAMH
Loch Damh, Torridon, Achnasheen, **HIGHLAND**, IV22, **Scotland**.
Contact/s: **Mr I Fraser** (Manager), Loch Torridon Hotel, Torridon, Achnasheen, Highland, IV22 2EY.
(T) 01445 791242 (F) 01445 791296
Profile: FT: Game; WN: Damh; WT: Loch (Still).
Ref: FH2868

LOCH DEE
Loch Dee, Newton Stewart, **DUMFRIES AND GALLOWAY**, DG8, **Scotland**.
Contact/s: **Mr Sandy White** (Recreational Forester), Forestry Commission Office, Forest Enterprise, Galloway Forest District, Creebridge, Newton Stewart, DG8 6AJ.
(T) 01671 402420 (F) 01671 403708
Profile: FT: Game; WN: Dee; WT: Loch (Still).
Ref: FH2869

LOCH DHU
Loch Dhu, Lochgilphead, **RENFREWSHIRE**, PA3, **Scotland**.
Contact/s: **Mr Archie MacGilp** (Secretary), Fyne Tackle, 22 Argyll St, Lochgilphead, Argyll and Bute, PA31 8NE.
(T) 01546 606878
Profile: FT: Game; WN: Dhu; WT: Loch (Still); F. Size: 400 Acres; W. Size: 8 Acres. Location: Nr. Rd: Cairnbaan; Main Rd: B844; Rail: Oban.
Ref: FH2870

LOCH DOLA
Loch Dola, Lairg, **HIGHLAND**, IV27, **Scotland**.
Contact/s: Manager, Ross Hardware, Main St, Lairg, Highland, IV27 4DB.
(T) 01549 402239
Profile: FT: Game; WN: Dola; WT: Loch (Still).
Ref: FH2871

LOCH DORNAL
Loch Dornal, Drumlamford Estate, Barrhill, Girvan, **AYRSHIRE (SOUTH)**, KA26 0RB, **Scotland**.
Contact/s: **Mr Tony Dickinson** (Shop Proprietor), Galloway Guns and Tackle, 36a Arthur St, Newton Stewart, Dumfries and Galloway, DG8 6DE.
(T) 01671 403404 (F) 01671 403404
Profile: FT: Game; WN: Dornal; WT: Loch (Still). Location: Main Rd: A714; Rail: Barrhill.
Ref: FH2872

LOCH DRUNKIE
Loch Drunkie, Aberfoyle, Stirling, FK8, **Scotland**.
Contact/s: Manager, Queen Elizabeth Forest Park Visitors Ctre, Trossachs Rd, Aberfoyle, Stirling, FK8 3SX.
(T) 01877 382258 (F) 01877 382120
Profile: FT: Game; WN: Drunkie; WT: Loch (Still).
Ref: FH2873

LOCH DUAGRAICH
Loch Duagraich, Struan, Portree, **HIGHLAND**, IV51, **Scotland**.
Contact/s: **Mr J.W. Mulford** (Manager), Ullinish Lodge Hotel, Ullinish, Struan, Isle of Skye, IV56 8FD.
(T) 01470 572214
Profile: FT: Game; WN: Duagraich; WT: Loch (Still).
Ref: FH2874

LOCH EARN
Loch Earn, Falkirk, FK2, **Scotland**.
Contact/s: **Mr Alex Murray** (Manager).
(T) 01567 830400
Profile: FT: Game; WN: Earn; WT: Loch (Still).
Ref: FH2875

LOCH EIGHEACH
Loch Eigheach, Kinloch Rannoch, Pitlochry, **PERTH AND KINROSS**, PH16 5PN, **Scotland**.
Contact/s: **Mr John Brown** (Secretary), The Square, Kinloch Rannoch, Pitlochry, Perth and Kinross, PH16 5PN.
(T) 01882 632268
Profile: FT: Combination; WN: Eigheach; WT: Loch (Still). Location: Nr. Rd: Kinloch Rannoch to Rannoch Station; Rail: Rannoch.
£Fr
Ref: FH2876

LOCH ELDRIG
Loch Eldrig, Galloway Wildlife Museum, Newton Stewart, **DUMFRIES AND GALLOWAY**, DG8, **Scotland**.
Profile: FT: Coarse; WN: Eldrig, Garwachie and Spectacle; WT: Loch (Still).
Ref: FH2877

LOCH ERICHT
Loch Ericht, Dalwhinnie, **HIGHLAND**, PH19, **Scotland**.
Contact/s: **Mr Stewart Hutton** (Manager), Loch Ericht Hotel, Dalwhinnie, Highland, PH19 1AG.
(T) 01528 522257 (F) 01528 522270
Profile: FT: Game; WN: Ericht; WT: Loch (Still).
Ref: FH2878

LOCH FAD
Loch Fad, Isle Of Bute Trout Co Ltd, Ardmaleish, Rothesay, **ARGYLL AND BUTE**, PA20 0QJ, **Scotland**.
(W) www.lochfad.com
Contact/s: **Mr James Poole** (Fishery Manager), Loch Fad Fisheries Limited, Loch Fad, Isle of Bute.
(T) 01700 504871 (F) 01700 504871 (M) 07712 534511
Profile: FT: Game; WN: Fad; WT: Loch (Still) W. Size: 175 Acres. Location: Rail: Wemyss Bay.
Ref: FH2879

LOCH FANNICH
Loch Fannich, Strathpeffer, **HIGHLAND**, IV14, **Scotland**.
Contact/s: **Mrs J Dickinson** (Manager), Garve Country Hotel, Garve, Highland, IV23 2PR.
(T) 01997 414205
Profile: FT: Game; WN: Fannich; WT: Loch (Still).
Ref: FH2880

LOCH FASKALLY
Loch Faskally, Boating Station, Clunie Bridge Rd, Pitlochry, **PERTH AND KINROSS**, PH, **Scotland**.
Contact/s: **Mr Dougie McLaren** (owner).
(T) 01796 472919
Profile: FT: Game; WN: Faskally; WT: Loch (Still). Location: Nr. Rd: Clunie Bidge Road.
Ref: FH2881

LOCH FINLAS
Loch Finlas, Callander, **FALKIRK**, FK1, **Scotland**.
Contact/s: **Mr William Meikle** (Manager).
(T) 01786 841692
Profile: FT: Game; WN: Finlas; WT: Loch (Still) W. Size: 800 Metres.
Ref: FH2882

LOCH FITTY TROUT FISHERY
Loch Fitty Trout Fishery, Lochfitty, Lassodie, Dunfermline, **FIFE**, KY12 0SP, **Scotland**.
Contact/s: **Mr Gerald Mackenzie** (Manager), Loch Fitty Tackle Shop, Lassodie, Dunfermline, Fife, KY12 0SP.
(T) 01383 620666 (F) 01383 620666
Profile: FT: Game; WN: Fitty; WT: Loch (Still) W. Size: 217 Acres. Location: Main Rd: M90; Rail: Dunfermline, Saint Margaret.
Ref: FH2883

LOCH FREUCHIE
Loch Freuchie, Amulree, Dunkeld, **PERTH AND KINROSS**, PH8, **Scotland**.
(W) www.fishingnet.com/beats/braan/freuchie
Contact/s: **Mr Graham Stewart** (Manager), Amulree Hotel, Amulree, Dunkeld, Perth and Kinross, PH8 0EF.
(T) 01350 725218
Profile: FT: Combination; WN: Freuchie; WT: Loch (Still).
Ref: FH2884

LOCH GARRY
Loch Garry, Invergarry, **HIGHLAND**, PH35 4HS, **Scotland**.
Contact/s: **Mr Gordon Aorth** (Manager), Tomdoun Hotel, Glengarry, Invergarry, Highland, PH35 4HS.
(T) 01809 511218or511244 (F) 01809 511218
Profile: FT: Game; WN: Garry; WT: Loch (Still) W. Size: 1500 Acres. Location: Nr. Rd: Tomdoun Road; Main Rd: A87; Rail: Fort William.
Ref: FH2885

LOCH GARVE
Loch Garve, Strathpeffer, **HIGHLAND**, IV14, **Scotland**.
Contact/s: **Mrs J Dickinson** (Manager), Garve Country Hotel, Garve, Highland, IV23 2PR.
(T) 01997 414205
Profile: FT: Game; WN: Garve; WT: Loch (Still).
Ref: FH2886

LOCH GLASCARNOCH
Loch Glascarnoch, Aultguish, Garve, **HIGHLAND**, IV23, **Scotland**.
Contact/s: Manager, Aultguish Inn By Garve, Garve, Highland, IV23 2PQ.
(T) 01997 455214or455254
Profile: FT: Game; WN: Glascarnoch; WT: Loch (Still).
Ref: FH2887

LOCH GLASHAN
Loch Glashan, Minard, Inveraray, **ARGYLL AND BUTE**, PA32, **Scotland**.
Contact/s: **Mr R Hardie**.
(T) 01546 886630
Profile: FT: Game; WN: Glashan; WT: Loch (Still).
Ref: FH2888

LOCH GLENFINGLAS
Loch Glenfinglas, Estate Office, Stronachlachar, Stirling, FK, **Scotland**.
Contact/s: Area Manager, Strathclyde Water Services, Stronachlachar, Stirling.
(T) 01877 386256
Profile: FT: Game; WN: Glenfinglas; WT: Loch (Still).
Ref: FH2889

LOCH HERON
Loch Heron, Galloway Country Sports., Newton Stewart, **DUMFRIES AND GALLOWAY**, DG8, **Scotland**.
Contact/s: **Ms Clare McClymont** (Manager), Palakona Bait Supplies, 30-32 Queen St, Newton Stewart, Dumfries and Galloway, DG8 9NR.
(T) 01671 402323
(E) palakonswscot@cs.com
Profile: FT: Coarse; WN: Heron; WT: Loch (Still).
Ref: FH2890

LOCH HOPE

Loch Hope, Altnaharra, Lairg, **HIGHLAND**, IV27, **Scotland**.
Contact/s: Manager, Altnaharra Hotel, Altnaharra, Lairg, Highland, IV27 4UE.
(T) 01549 411222 **(F)** 01549 411222
Profile: **FT:** Game; **WN:** Hope; **WT:** Loch (Still).
Ref: FH2891

LOCH HORN

Loch Horn, Golspie, **HIGHLAND**, KW10, **Scotland**.
Contact/s: **Mr M Baddon** (Manager), Lindsay and Co, Main St, Golspie, Highland, KW10 6RA.
(T) 01408 633212 **(F)** 01408 634374
Profile: **FT:** Game; **WN:** Horn; **WT:** Loch (Still).
Ref: FH2892

LOCH INCH LAGGAN

Loch Inch Laggan, Invergarry, **HIGHLAND**, PH35 4HS, **Scotland**.
Contact/s: **Mr Gordon Heath** (Manager), Tomdoun Hotel, Glengarry, Invergarry, Highland, PH35 4HS.
(T) 01809 511218 **(F)** 01809 511218
Profile: **FT:** Game; **WN:** Inch Laggan; **WT:** Loch (Still) **W. Size:** 220 Acres. **Location:** **Nr. Rd:** Tomdoun Road; **Main Rd:** A87; **Rail:** Fort William.
Ref: FH2893

LOCH INSCH FISHERY

Loch Insch Fishery, Old Inn Farm Of Williamston, Colpy, Insch, **ABERDEENSHIRE**, AB52 6TS, **Scotland**.
(W) www.lochinschfishery.clara.net
Contact/s: **Ms Yvonne Mair** (Manager).
(T) 01464 841301 **(F)** 01464 841301 **(M)** 07899 943029
(E) lochinschfishery@bigfoot.com
Profile: **FT:** Game; **WN:** Insch; **WT:** Loch (Still); **F. Size:** 20 Acres; **W. Size:** 10 Acres. **Location:** **Nr. Rd:** A96; **Main Rd:** A96; **Rail:** Insch.
Ref: FH2894

LOCH INSH

Loch Insh, Kingussie, **HIGHLAND**, PH21 1, **Scotland**.
Contact/s: **Mr Clive Freshwater** (Managing Director), Loch Insh Watersports Ctre, Insh Hall, Kincraig, Highland, PH21 1NU.
(T) 01540 651272 **(F)** 01540 651280
Profile: **FT:** Combination; **WN:** Insh; **WT:** Loch (Still) **W. Size:** 700 Acres. **Location:** **Nr. Rd:** B970; **Main Rd:** A9; **Rail:** Aviemore.
Ref: FH2895

LOCH KATRINE

Loch Katrine, Estate Office, Stronachlachar, Stirling, FK, **Scotland**.
Contact/s: Area Manager, Strathclyde Water Services, Stronachlachar, Stirling.
(T) 01877 386256
Profile: **FT:** Game; **WN:** Katrine; **WT:** Loch (Still).
Ref: FH2896

LOCH KATRINE

Loch Katrine, Doune, **STIRLING**, FK16, **Scotland**.
Contact/s: **Mr Morris Meikle** (fisheries manager), 41 Buchanty, Doune, Stirling, Scotland.
(T) 01786 841692
Profile: **FT:** Game; **WN:** Katrine; **WT:** Loch (Still). **Location:** **Nr. Rd:** A821; **Main Rd:** A84.
Ref: FH2897

LOCH KEN

Loch Ken, New Galloway, Dumfries, **DUMFRIES AND GALLOWAY**, DG7 3, **Scotland**.
Contact/s: Fishery Manager.
(T) 01387 252075
Profile: **FT:** Coarse; **WN:** Ken; **WT:** Loch (Still).
Ref: FH2898

LOCH KENNY

Loch Kenny, Kennys Farm, Station Town, Wingate, Hartlepool, **CLEVELAND**, TS, **England**.
Contact/s: **Mr Mark Arrow-Smith** (Membership Secretary), Angler's Services, 27 Park Rd, Hartlepool, Cleveland, TS24 7PW.
(T) 01429 274844or266522
Profile: **FT:** Coarse; **WN:** Kenny; **WT:** Lake (Still) **W. Size:** 2 Acres. **Location:** **Nr. Rd:** B1280; **Main Rd:** A19 onto B1280.
Ref: FH2899

LOCH KNOCKIE

Loch Knockie, Gorthleck, Inverness, **HIGHLAND**, IV2, **Scotland**.
Contact/s: **Mr D Campbell** (Manager), Whitebridge Hotel, Whitebridge, Inverness, Highland, IV2 6UN.
(T) 01456 486226 **(F)** 01456 486413
Profile: **FT:** Game; **WN:** Knockie; **WT:** Loch (Still).
Ref: FH2900

LOCH LAGGAN

Loch Laggan, Dalwhinnie, **HIGHLAND**, PH19, **Scotland**.
Mr Sandy Bennet (Water Bailiff).
(T) 01540 661645
Profile: **FT:** Game; **WN:** Laggan; **WT:** Loch (Still).
Ref: FH2901

LOCH LEVEN FISHERIES

Loch Leven Fisheries, The Pier, Kinross, **PERTH AND KINROSS**, KY13 7AS, **Scotland**.
Contact/s: **Mr Chris Browne**.
(T) 01577 865407 **(F)** 01577 863180
Sir David Montgomerey.
(T) 01577 865386
W Wilson (Manager).
(T) 01577 865386 **(F)** 01577 863180
Profile: **FT:** Game; **WN:** Leven; **WT:** Loch (Still); **F. Size:** 3500 Acres; **W. Size:** 3500 Acres. **Location:** **Nr. Rd:** M90 junction 6; **Main Rd:** M90; **Rail:** Perth. £Fr
Ref: FH2902

LOCH LOCHY

Loch Lochy, Fort William, **HIGHLAND**, PH33, **Scotland**.
Contact/s: **Mrs Helen Whiley** (Manager), West Highland Estate Offices, 33 High St, Fort William, Highland, PH33 6DH.
(T) 01397 702433
Profile: **FT:** Game; **WN:** Lochy; **WT:** Loch (Still).
Ref: FH2903

LOCH LOMOND

Loch Lomond, Balmaha, Drymen, Glasgow, **STIRLING**, G63, **Scotland**.
Contact/s: **Mr Brady**, Loch Lomond Angling Association, PO Box 3559, Glasgow, G71 7SJ.
(T) 0141 7811545 **(F)** 0141 7811545
Profile: **FT:** Combination; **WN:** Lomond; **WT:** Loch (Still). **Location:** **Main Rd:** A82 from Dunbarton.
Ref: FH2904

LOCH LOSKIN (THE LOCHAN)

Loch Loskin (The Lochan), Dunoon, **ARGYLL AND BUTE**, PA23, **Scotland**.
Contact/s: **Mr A H Young** (Hon Secretary), 112 Argyll St, Dunoon, Argyll and Bute.
(T) 01369 705732or703232
(E) archie@telinco.co.uk
Profile: **FT:** Game; **WN:** Loskin; **WT:** Loch (Still) **W. Size:** 15 Acres. **Location:** **Nr. Rd:** A885 Sandbank Road.
Ref: FH2905

LOCH LOYAL

Loch Loyal, Tongue, Lairg, **HIGHLAND**, IV27, **Scotland**.
Contact/s: Manager, Ben Loyal Hotel, Tongue, Lairg, Highland, IV27 4XE.
(T) 01847 611216 **(F)** 01847 611212
Profile: **FT:** Game; **WN:** Loyal; **WT:** Loch (Still).
Ref: FH2906

LOCH LOYNE

Loch Loyne, Glenmoriston, Inverness, **HIGHLAND**, IV63, **Scotland**.
Contact/s: **Mr G Allen** (Manager), Cluanie Inn Hotel, Glenmoriston, Inverness, Highland, IV63 7YW.
(T) 01320 340238
Profile: **FT:** Game; **WN:** Loyne; **WT:** Loch (Still).
Ref: FH2907

LOCH LUBNAIG

Loch Lubnaig, Callander, **STIRLING**, FK17, **Scotland**.
Contact/s: **Mr Dougie Allen**, J Bayne Tackle Shop, Main St, Callander, Stirling, Scotland.
(T) 01786 841692
Profile: **FT:** Game; **WN:** Lubnaig; **WT:** Loch (Still).
Ref: FH2908

LOCH LUNDIE

Loch Lundie, Golspie, **HIGHLAND**, KW10, **Scotland**.
Contact/s: **Mr M Baddon** (Manager), Lindsay and Co, Main St, Golspie, Highland, KW10 6RA.
(T) 01408 633212 **(F)** 01408 634374
Profile: **FT:** Game; **WN:** Lundie; **WT:** Loch (Still).
Ref: FH2909

LOCH MAREE

Loch Maree, Achnasheen, **HIGHLAND**, IV22 2HL, **Scotland**.
Contact/s: **Mr Mark Vincent** (Manager), Loch Maree Hotel, Lochmaree, Achnasheen, Highland, IV22 2HL.
(T) 01445 760288 **(F)** 01445 760241
Profile: **FT:** Game; **WN:** Maree; **WT:** Loch (Still).
Ref: FH2910

LOCH MAYBERRY

Loch Mayberry, Drumlamford Estate, Barrhill, Girvan, **AYRSHIRE (SOUTH)**, KA26 0RB, **Scotland**.
Contact/s: **Mr Tony Dickinson** (Shop Proprietor), Galloway Guns and Tackle, 36a Arthur St, Newton Stewart, Dumfries and Galloway, DG8 6DE.
(T) 01671 403404 **(F)** 01671 403404
Profile: **FT:** Coarse; **WN:** Mayberry; **WT:** Loch (Still). **Location:** **Main Rd:** A714; **Rail:** Barrhill.
Ref: FH2911

LOCH MEADIE

Loch Meadie, Bettyhill, Thurso, **HIGHLAND**, KW14, **Scotland**.
Contact/s: **Mr J Mcloud** (owner), Farr Bay Inn, Clachan, Bettyhill, Highland, KW14 7SZ.
(T) 01641 521230 **(F)** 01641 521230
Profile: **FT:** Game; **WN:** Meadie; **WT:** Loch (Still).
Ref: FH2912

LOCH MEIG

Loch Meig, Strathpeffer, **HIGHLAND**, IV14, **Scotland**.
Contact/s: **Mr G Cameron** (Secretary), 33 Wrightfield Park, Maryburgh, Highland, Scotland.
(T) 01349 862455
Profile: **FT:** Game; **WN:** Meig; **WT:** Loch (Still).
Ref: FH2913

LOCH MERKLAND

Loch Merkland, Overscaig, Lairg, **HIGHLAND**, IV27, **Scotland**.
Contact/s: Manager, Overscaig Lochside Hotel, Lochside, Lairg, Highland, IV27 4NY.
(T) 01549 431203
Profile: **FT:** Game; **WN:** Merkland; **WT:** Loch

(Still).
Ref: FH2914

LOCH MONREITH

Loch Monreith, Newton Stewart, **DUMFRIES AND GALLOWAY**, DG8, **Scotland**.
Contact/s: **Ms Clare McClymont** (Manager), Palakona Bait Supplies, 30-32 Queen St, Newton Stewart, Dumfries and Galloway, DG8 9NR.
(T) 01671 402323
(E) palakonswscot@cs.com
Profile: **FT:** Coarse; **WN:** Monreith; **WT:** Loch (Still).
Ref: FH2915

LOCH MORAR

Loch Morar, Mallaig, **HIGHLAND**, PH41, **Scotland**.
Contact/s: **Mr Colin Macdonald** (Manager), Morar Motors Limited, Morar, Mallaig, Highland, PH40 4PA.
(T) 01687 462118
Profile: **FT:** Game; **WN:** Morar; **WT:** Loch (Still).
Ref: FH2916

LOCH MORLICH

Loch Morlich, Aviemore, **HIGHLAND**, PH22, **Scotland**.
Contact/s: **Mr Tim Walker** (Principal), Glenmore Lodge, Aviemore, Highland, PH22 1QU.
(T) 01479 861256 **(F)** 01479 861212
Profile: **FT:** Game; **WN:** Morlich; **WT:** Loch (Still).
Ref: FH2917

LOCH MULLARDOCH

Loch Mullardoch, Inverness, **HIGHLAND**, IV, **Scotland**.
Contact/s: **Ms Louise Hodgson** (Manager), Glen Affric Hotel, Cannich, Beauly, Highland, IV4 7LW.
(T) 01456 415214 **(F)** 01456 415254
Profile: **FT:** Game; **WN:** Mullardoch; **WT:** Loch (Still).
Ref: FH2918

LOCH NA BO

Loch Na Bo, Elgin, **MORAY**, IV30, **Scotland**.
Contact/s: , Keepers Cottage, Lhanbryde, Elgin, Moray, Scotland.
(T) 01343 842214
Profile: **FT:** Game; **WN:** Na Bo; **WT:** Loch (Still).
Ref: FH2919

LOCH NANT

Loch Nant, Oban, **ARGYLL AND BUTE**, PA34, **Scotland**.
Contact/s: **Mr Ross Binnie** (Manager), The Anglers Corner, John St, Oban, Argyll and Bute, PA34 5NS.
(T) 01631 566374
Profile: **FT:** Game; **WN:** Nant; **WT:** Loch (Still).
Ref: FH2920

LOCH NAVER

Loch Naver, Altnaharra, Lairg, **HIGHLAND**, IV27, **Scotland**.
Contact/s: Manager, Altnaharra Hotel, Altnaharra, Lairg, Highland, IV27 4UE.
(T) 01549 411222 **(F)** 01549 411222
Profile: **FT:** Game; **WN:** Naver; **WT:** Loch (Still).
Ref: FH2921

LOCH NEATON

Loch Neaton, Watton Sports Ctre, Watton, **NORFOLK**, **England**.
Contact/s: **Mr N Dumble**.
(T) 01953 883459
Profile: **FT:** Coarse; **WN:** Loch Neaton; **WT:** Lake (Still). **Location:** **Nr. Rd:** Dereham Road (A1075).
Ref: FH2922

LOCH NESS

Loch Ness, Fort Augustus, **HIGHLAND**, PH32, **Scotland**.
Contact/s: **Mr Guy Coombes** (Manager), Inchnacardoch Lodge Hotel, Fort Augustus, Highland, PH32 4BL.
(T) 01320 366258
Profile: **FT:** Game; **WN:** Ness; **WT:** Loch (Still).
Ref: FH2923

LOCH OF BLAIRS

Loch Of Blairs, Forres, **MORAY**, IV36, **Scotland**.
Contact/s: , Environment Department, The Moray Council, High Street, Elgin, Moray, IV30 1BX.
(T) 01353 543451
Warden.
(T) 01343 860234
Profile: **FT:** Game; **WN:** Blairs; **WT:** Loch (Still).
Ref: FH2924

LOCH OF BROUGH

Loch Of Brough, Gairdie, Mid Yell, Shetland, **SHETLAND ISLANDS**, ZE2, **Scotland**.
Contact/s: **Mr Ian Nisbet** (Secretary).
(T) 01957 2204
Profile: **FT:** Game; **WN:** Brough; **WT:** Loch (Still).
Ref: FH2925

LOCH OF COLVISTER

Loch Of Colvister, Gairdie, Mid Yell, Shetland, **SHETLAND ISLANDS**, ZE2, **Scotland**.
Contact/s: **Mr Ian Nisbet** (Secretary).
(T) 01957 2204
Profile: **FT:** Game; **WN:** Colvister; **WT:** Loch (Still).
Ref: FH2926

LOCH OF CULLIVOE

Loch Of Cullivoe, Gairdie, Mid Yell, Shetland, **SHETLAND ISLANDS**, ZE2, **Scotland**.
Contact/s: **Mr Ian Nisbet** (Secretary).
(T) 01957 2204
Profile: **FT:** Game; **WN:** Cullivoe; **WT:** Loch (Still).
Ref: FH2927

LOCH OF GUTCHER

Loch Of Gutcher, Gairdie, Mid Yell, Shetland, **SHETLAND ISLANDS**, ZE2, **Scotland**.
Contact/s: **Mr Ian Nisbet** (Secretary).
(T) 01957 2204
Profile: **FT:** Game; **WN:** Gutcher; **WT:** Loch (Still).
Ref: FH2928

LOCH OF LINTRATHEN

Loch Of Lintrathen, Kirriemuir, **ANGUS**, DD8, **Scotland**.
Contact/s: Secretary.
(T) 01575 560327or573816
Profile: **FT:** Game; **WN:** Lintrathen; **WT:** Loch (Still).
Ref: FH2929

LOCH OF LUMBISTER

Loch Of Lumbister, Gairdie, Mid Yell, Shetland, **SHETLAND ISLANDS**, ZE2, **Scotland**.
Contact/s: **Mr Ian Nisbet** (Secretary).
(T) 01957 2204
Profile: **FT:** Game; **WN:** Lumbister; **WT:** Loch (Still).
Ref: FH2930

LOCH OF PAPIL

Loch Of Papil, Gairdie, Mid Yell, Shetland, **SHETLAND ISLANDS**, ZE2, **Scotland**.
Contact/s: **Mr Ian Nisbet** (Secretary).
(T) 01957 2204
Profile: **FT:** Game; **WN:** Papil; **WT:** Loch (Still).
Ref: FH2931

LOCH OF VOLLISTER

Loch Of Vollister, Gairdie, Mid Yell, Shetland, **SHETLAND ISLANDS**, ZE2, **Scotland**.
Contact/s: **Mr Ian Nisbet** (Secretary).
(T) 01957 2204
Profile: **FT:** Game; **WN:** Vollister; **WT:** Loch (Still).
Ref: FH2932

LOCH OICH

Loch Oich, Invergarry, **HIGHLAND**, PH35, **Scotland**.
Contact/s: **Mr Donald Maccalum** (Manager), Glengarry Castle Hotel, Invergarry, Highland, PH35 4HW.
(T) 01809 501254 **(F)** 01809 501207
Profile: **FT:** Game; **WN:** Oich; **WT:** Loch (Still).
Ref: FH2933

LOCH ORE

Loch Ore, Lochgelly, **FIFE**, KY5 8BA, **Scotland**.
Contact/s: **Mr Davy Glencross**.
(T) 01592 860086
Mr Mike Gregge (Facilities Manager), Lochore Meadows Country Park, Main Ctre, Crosshill, Fife, KY5 8BA.
(T) 01592 414300
Profile: **FT:** Game; **WN:** Ore; **WT:** Loch (Still).
Ref: FH2934

LOCH POULARY

Loch Poulary, Invergarry, **HIGHLAND**, PH35 4HS, **Scotland**.
Contact/s: **Mr Gordon Heath** (Manager), Tomdoun Hotel, Glengarry, Invergarry, Highland, PH35 4HS.
(T) 01809 511218 **(F)** 01809 511218
Profile: **FT:** Game; **WN:** Poulary; **WT:** Loch (Still) **W. Size:** 100 Acres. **Location:** **Nr. Rd:** Tomdoun Road; **Main Rd:** A87; **Rail:** Fort William.
Ref: FH2935

LOCH QUIEN

Loch Quien, Rothesay, **ARGYLL AND BUTE**, PA20 9PA, **Scotland**.
(W) www.lochfad.com
Contact/s: **Mr James Poole** (Fishery Manager), Loch Fad Fisheries Limited, Loch Fad, Isle of Bute.
(T) 01700 504871 **(F)** 01700 504871 **(M)** 07712 534511
Profile: **FT:** Game; **WN:** Quein; **WT:** Loch (Still) **W. Size:** 90 Acres. **Location:** **Main Rd:** Barone Road; **Rail:** Wemyss Bay.
Ref: FH2936

LOCH QUOICH

Loch Quoich, Invergarry, **HIGHLAND**, PH35 4HS, **Scotland**.
Contact/s: **Mr Gordon Heath** (Manager), Tomdoun Hotel, Glengarry, Invergarry, Highland, PH35 4HS.
(T) 01809 511218 **(F)** 01809 511218
Profile: **FT:** Game; **WN:** Quoich; **WT:** Loch (Still). **Location:** **Nr. Rd:** Tomdoun Road; **Main Rd:** A87; **Rail:** Fort William.
Ref: FH2937

LOCH RANNOCH

Loch Rannoch, Kinloch Rannoch, Pitlochry, **PERTH AND KINROSS**, PH16, **Scotland**.
Contact/s: **Mr E M Beattie**, Loch Rannoch Conservation Association, 2 Schiehallion Pl, Kinloch Rannoch.
Profile: **FT:** Combination; **WN:** Rannoch; **WT:** Loch (Still).
Ref: FH2938

LOCH ROAN

Loch Roan, Crossmicheal, Castle Douglas, **DUMFRIES AND GALLOWAY**, DG7, **Scotland**.
Contact/s: **Mr Stanley Kaye** (Owner), 2 Cairnsmore Rd, Castle Douglas, Dumfries and Galloway, DG7 1BN.
(T) 01556 502695
Mrs Barbara Kirkpatrick (Manageress), Castle Douglas Angling Association, Tommys Sports, King St, Castle Douglas, Dumfries and Galloway.
(T) 01556 502851
Profile: **FT:** Combination; **WN:** Roan; **WT:** Loch (Still) **W. Size:** 50 Acres. **Location:** **Nr. Rd:** A713; **Main Rd:** A713; **Rail:** Dumfries.
Ref: FH2939

LOCH RONALD

Loch Ronald, Newton Stewart, **DUMFRIES AND GALLOWAY**, DG8, **Scotland**.
Contact/s: Fishery Manager.
(T) 01671 830202
Ms Clare McClymont (Manager), Palakona Bait Supplies, 30-32 Queen St, Newton Stewart, Dumfries and Galloway, DG8 9NR.
(T) 01671 402323
(E) palakonswscot@cs.com
Profile: **FT:** Coarse; **WN:** Ronald; **WT:** Loch (Still) **W. Size:** 100 Acres.
Ref: FH2940

LOCH RUITH A PHUILL

Loch Ruith A Phuill, Strathpeffer, **HIGHLAND**, IV14, **Scotland**.
Contact/s: Mr G Breau (Manager).
(T) 01997 421250 (F) 01997 421250
Profile: **FT:** Game; **WN:** Ruith a Phuill; **WT:** Loch (Still) **W. Size:** 13 Acres. **Location:** **Main Rd:** A835; **Rail:** Garve.
Ref: FH2941

LOCH RUTHVEN

Loch Ruthven, Inverness, **HIGHLAND**, IV, **Scotland**.
Contact/s: **Mr J Graham** (owner), J Graham and Co, 37 Castle St, Inverness, Highland, IV2 3DU.
(T) 01463 233178
Profile: **FT:** Game; **WN:** Ruthven; **WT:** Loch (Still).
Ref: FH2942

LOCH SAUGH

Loch Saugh, Fettercairn, Laurencekirk, **ABERDEENSHIRE**, AB30, **Scotland**.
Contact/s: **Mrs Irene Buxton** (Manager), Ramsay Arms Hotel, Fettercairn, Laurencekirk, Aberdeenshire, AB30 1XX.
(T) 01561 340334
Profile: **FT:** Game; **WN:** Saugh; **WT:** Loch (Still).
Ref: FH2943

LOCH SHIEL

Loch Shiel, Acharacrel, Fort William, **HIGHLAND**, PH33, **Scotland**.
Contact/s: **Ms Liz Duncan** (owner), Loch Sheil Hotel, Acharacle, Argyll and Bute, PH36 4JL.
(T) 01967 431224 (F) 01967 431200
Profile: **FT:** Game; **WN:** Shiel; **WT:** Loch (Still) **W. Size:** 32000 Metres.
Ref: FH2944

LOCH SHIN

Loch Shin, Lairg, **HIGHLAND**, IV27, **Scotland**.
Contact/s: Secretary, Lairg Angling Club, Church Hill Rd, Lairg, Highland, Scotland.
(T) 01549 402010
Profile: **FT:** Game; **WN:** Shin; **WT:** Loch (Still) **W. Size:** 25600 Metres.
Ref: FH2945

LOCH SIONASCAIG

Loch Sionascaig, Ullapool, **HIGHLAND**, IV26, **Scotland**.
Profile: **FT:** Game; **WN:** Sionascaig; **WT:** Loch (Still).
Ref: FH2946

LOCH SKERROW

Loch Skerrow, Castle Douglas, **DUMFRIES AND GALLOWAY**, DG7, **Scotland**.
Contact/s: **Mr G M Thomson** (owner), G M Thomson and Co, 27 King St, Castle Douglas, Dumfries and Galloway, DG7 1AB.
(T) 01556 504030 (F) 01556 503277
Profile: **FT:** Game; **WN:** Skerrow; **WT:** Loch (Still).
Ref: FH2947

LOCH TARSAN

Loch Tarsan, Dunoon, **ARGYLL AND BUTE**, PA23, **Scotland**.
Contact/s: **Mr A H Young** (Hon Secretary), 112 Argyll St, Dunoon, Argyll and Bute.
(T) 01369 705732or703232
(E) archie@telinco.co.uk
Profile: **FT:** Game; **WN:** Tarsan; **WT:** Loch (Still); **F. Size:** 273 Acres; **W. Size:** 273 Acres. **Location:** **Nr. Rd:** B838.
Ref: FH2948

LOCH TARVIE

Loch Tarvie, Strathpeffer, **HIGHLAND**, IV14 9EY, **Scotland**.
Contact/s: Mr G Breau (Manager), Coul House Hotel, Contin, Highland, IV14 9EY.
(T) 01997 421487
Profile: **FT:** Game; **WN:** Tarvie; **WT:** Loch (Still) **W. Size:** 42 Acres. **Location:** **Main Rd:** A835; **Rail:** Garve.
Ref: FH2949

LOCH TAY

Loch Tay, Kenmore, Aberfeldy, **PERTH AND KINROSS**, PH15, **Scotland**.
(W) www.lochtaylodges.co.uk
Contact/s: **Mr J Duncan Millar** (Manager), A and J Duncan Millar, Remony, Aberfeldy, Perth and Kinross, PH15 2HR.
(T) 01887 830209 (F) 01887 830802
(E) remony@btinternet.com
Mr John Heroz (owner), Kenmore Hotel, The Square, Kenmore, Aberfeldy, PH15 2NU.
(T) 01887 830205
Profile: **FT:** Game; **WN:** Tay; **WT:** Loch (Still). **Location:** **Nr. Rd:** A827; **Main Rd:** A827; **Rail:** Pitlochry.
Ref: FH2950

LOCH TAY HIGHLAND LODGES

Loch Tay Highland Lodges, Milton Morenish Estate, Killin, **STIRLING**, FK21 8TY, **Scotland**.
(W) www.lochtay-vacations.co.uk
Contact/s: **Mr Alec Stewart** (Membership Secretary), 2 Dochart Rd, Killin, Perth and Kinross, FK21 8SN.
(T) 01567 820224
Mr Clive Booth, Loch Tay Highland Lodges Ltd, Milton Morenish Estate, Killin, Perth and Kinross, FK21 8TY.
(T) 01567 820323 (F) 01567 820581
(E) info@lochtay-vacations.co.uk
Profile: **FT:** Combination; **WN:** Tay; **WT:** Loch (Still); **F. Size:** 160 Acres. **Location:** **Nr. Rd:** A827; **Main Rd:** A827; **Rail:** Crianlarich. £Fr
Ref: FH2951

LOCH THOM

Loch Thom, Greenock, **INVERCLYDE**, PA, **Scotland**.
Contact/s: **Mr Brian Peterson** (Manager), The Fishing Shop, 24 Union St, Greenock, Strathclyde, PA16 8DD.
(T) 01475 888085
Profile: **FT:** Game; **WN:** Thom; **WT:** Loch (Still) **W. Size:** 470 Acres. **Location:** **Nr. Rd:** Loch Thom Road; **Main Rd:** A78.
Ref: FH2952

LOCH TOFTINGALL

Loch Toftingall, Mybster, Wick, **HIGHLAND**, KW1 4BP, **Scotland**.
Contact/s: **Mr Hugo Ross** (Fishing Tackle Specialist), 56 High St, Wick, Caithness, KW1 4BP.
(T) 01955 604200 (F) 01955 604200
Profile: **FT:** Game; **WN:** Toftingall; **WT:** Loch (Still); **F. Size:** 130 Acres; **W. Size:** 130 Acres. **Location:** **Main Rd:** A9; **Rail:** Wick.
Ref: FH2953

LOCH USSIE

Loch Ussie, Dingwall, **HIGHLAND**, IV7 8, **Scotland**.
Contact/s: **Mr Andrew Matheson**, Brahan Estate, Dingwall, Highland, IV7 8EE.
(T) 01349 861150 (F) 01349 861745
(E) enquiry@seaestate.com
Profile: **FT:** Coarse; **WN:** Ussie; **WT:** Loch (Still); **F. Size:** 200 Acres; **W. Size:** 200 Acres. **Location:** **Nr. Rd:** A835; **Main Rd:** A9; **Rail:** Dingwall.
Ref: FH2954

LOCH VENACHAR

Loch Venachar, Callander, **FALKIRK**, FK1, **Scotland**.
Contact/s: **Mr William Meikle** (Manager).
(T) 01786 841692
Profile: **FT:** Game; **WN:** Venachar; **WT:** Loch (Still) **W. Size:** 1600 Metres.
Ref: FH2955

LOCH VOIL

Loch Voil, Lochearnhead, **STIRLING**, FK19 8, **Scotland**.
Contact/s: **Mrs Cartiona Oldham** (Owner), Muirlaggan, Balquhidder, Lochearnhead, Perth and Kinross, FK19 8PB.
(T) 01877 384219
Profile: **FT:** Game; **WN:** Voil; **WT:** Loch (Still) **W. Size:** 8000 Metres. **Location:** **Nr. Rd:** Sout Shore Loch Voil; **Main Rd:** A84; **Rail:** Stirling. £Fr
Ref: FH2956

LOCH WATTEN

Loch Watten, Watten, Wick, **HIGHLAND**, KW1, **Scotland**.
Contact/s: **Mr Hugo Ross** (Fishing Tackle Specialist), 56 High St, Wick, Caithness, KW1 4BP.
(T) 01955 604200 (F) 01955 604200
Profile: **FT:** Game; **WN:** Loch Watten; **WT:** Loch (Still); **F. Size:** 940 Acres; **W. Size:** 940 Acres. **Location:** **Nr. Rd:** Wick to Thurso; **Main Rd:** B847; **Rail:** Wick.
Ref: FH2957

LOCH WHINYEON

Loch Whinyeon, Gatehouse Of Fleet, Castle Douglas, **DUMFRIES AND GALLOWAY**, DG7, **Scotland**.
Contact/s: **Mr McKinnel**, McKinnel Ironmongers, 15 St Cuthbert St, Kirkcudbright, Dumfries and Galloway, DG6 4DJ.
(T) 01557 330693
Mr Charlie Jeffrey (Secretary).
(T) 01557 330693
Profile: **FT:** Game; **WN:** Whinyeon; **WT:** Loch (Still) **W. Size:** 110 Acres. **Location:** **Nr. Rd:** Laurieston Road; **Main Rd:** A75; **Rail:** Dumfries.
Ref: FH2958

LOCH WHITEFIELD

Loch Whitefield, Newton Stewart, **DUMFRIES AND GALLOWAY**, DG8, **Scotland**.
Contact/s: **Ms Clare McClymont** (Manager), Palakona Bait Supplies, 30-32 Queen St, Newton Stewart, Dumfries and Galloway, DG8 9NR.
(T) 01671 402323
(E) palakonswscot@cs.com
Profile: **FT:** Coarse; **WN:** Whitefield; **WT:** Loch (Still).
Ref: FH2959

LOCHAN NA LARAIG

Lochan Na Laraig, Killin, **STIRLING**, FK21, **Scotland**.
(W) www.fishingnet.com/clubs/killin.htm
Contact/s: **Mr Alec Stewart** (Membership Secretary), 2 Dochart Rd, Killin, Perth and Kinross, FK21 8SN.
(T) 01567 820224
Mrs Joanne Airey (Owner), J R News, Fishing Tackle Shop, Main St, Killin, FR21 8UJ.
(T) 01567 820362
Profile: **FT:** Game; **WN:** Lochan Na Laraig; **WT:** Loch (Still). **Location:** **Nr. Rd:** A827; **Main Rd:** A85; **Rail:** Crianlarich.
Ref: FH2960

LOCH-AN-ADD

Loch-An-Add, Lochgilphead, **RENFREWSHIRE**, PA3, **Scotland**.
Contact/s: **Mr Archie MacGilp** (Secretary), Fyne Tackle, 22 Argyll St, Lochgilphead, Argyll and Bute, PA31 8NE.
(T) 01546 606878
Profile: **FT:** Game; **WN:** Loch-An-Add; **WT:** Loch (Still); **F. Size:** 400 Acres; **W. Size:**

50 Acres. Location: Nr. Rd: Cairnbaan; Main Rd: B844; Rail: Oban.
Ref: FH2961

LOCHAY (RIVER)

River Lochay, Coach House Hotel, Lochay Rd, Killin, **STIRLING**, FK21 8TN, **Scotland**.
(W) www.fishingnet.com/beats/lochay/coach_house_hotel.htm
Contact/s: **Mr Keith Wheeler** (Manager).
(T) 01567 820349
Profile: FT: Combination; WN: Lochay; WT: River (Moving). Location: Nr. Rd: Lochay Road. £Fr
Ref: FH2962

LOCHAY (RIVER)

River Lochay, Killin, **STIRLING**, FK21, **Scotland**.
Contact/s: **Mr Alec Stewart** (Membership Secretary), 2 Dochart Rd, Killin, Perth and Kinross, FK21 8SN.
(T) 01567 820224

Joanne Airey (Owner), J R News, Fishing Tackle Shop, Main St, Killin, FR21 8UJ.
(T) 01567 820362
Profile: FT: Combination; WN: Lochay; WT: River (Moving) W. Size: 9000 Metres.
Location: Nr. Rd: A827; Main Rd: A85; Rail: Crianlarich.
Ref: FH2963

LOCHENBRECK LOCH

Lochenbreck Loch, Gatehouse Of Fleet, Castle Douglas, **DUMFRIES AND GALLOWAY**, DG7, **Scotland**.
Contact/s: **Mr McKinnel** (owner), McKinnel Ironmongers, 15 St Cuthbert St, Kirkcudbright, Dumfries and Galloway, DG6 4DJ.
(T) 01557 330693
Mr Charlie Jeffrey (Secretary).
(T) 01557 330693
Profile: FT: Game; WN: Lochenbreck; WT: Loch (Still) W. Size: 40 Acres. Location: Nr. Rd: Laurieston Road; Main Rd: A75; Rail: Dumfries.
Ref: FH2964

LOCHINVAR LOCH

Lochinvar Loch, Dalry, Castle Douglas, **DUMFRIES AND GALLOWAY**, DG7, **Scotland**.
Contact/s: **Mrs I Pennington** (owner), Lochnivar Hotel, 3 Main St, Dalry, Castle Douglas, Dumfries and Galloway DG7 3UP.
(T) 01644 430210 (F) 01644 430321
Profile: FT: Game; WN: Lochinvar; WT: Loch (Still).
Ref: FH2965

LOCHMORE MEADOWS

Lochmore Meadows, Crosshill, Lochgelly, **FIFE**, KY5, **Scotland**.
Contact/s: **Mr Mike Gregge** (Facilities Manager), Lochore Meadows Country Park, Main Ctre, Crosshill, Fife, KY5 8BA.
(T) 01592 414300
Profile: FT: Game; WN: Lochmore Meadows; WT: Lake (Still).
Ref: FH2966

LOCH-NA-BRIC

Loch-Na-Bric, Lochgilphead, **RENFREWSHIRE**, PA3, **Scotland**.
Contact/s: **Mr Archie MacGilp** (Secretary), Fyne Tackle, 22 Argyll St, Lochgilphead, Argyll and Bute, PA31 8NE.
(T) 01546 606878
Profile: FT: Game; WN: Na-Bric; WT: Loch (Still); F. Size: 400 Acres; W. Size: 10 Acres. Location: Nr. Rd: Cairnbaan; Main Rd: B844; Rail: Oban.
Ref: FH2967

LOCH-NA-FAOILINN

Loch-Na-Faoilinn, Lochgilphead, **RENFREWSHIRE**, PA3, **Scotland**.
Contact/s: **Mr Archie MacGilp** (Secretary), Fyne Tackle, 22 Argyll St, Lochgilphead, Argyll and Bute, PA31 8NE.
(T) 01546 606878
Profile: FT: Game; WN: Na-Faoilinn; WT: Loch (Still); F. Size: 400 Acres; W. Size: 30 Acres. Location: Nr. Rd: Cairnbaan; Main Rd: B844; Rail: Oban.
Ref: FH2968

LOCHNAW

Lochnaw, Stranraer, **DUMFRIES AND GALLOWAY**, DG9, **Scotland**.
Contact/s: .
(T) 01776 870227
Profile: FT: Game; WN: Lochnaw; WT: Lake (Still).
Ref: FH2969

LOCHO PARK LAKE

Locho Park Lake, Locho Rd, Spondon, Derby, **DERBYSHIRE**, DE, **England**.
Contact/s: **Mr K Glynn**.
(T) 01332 751938
Profile: FT: Coarse; WN: Locho; WT: Lake (Still) W. Size: 15 Acres. Location: Nr. Rd: Locho Road.
Ref: FH2970

LOCKE PARK

Locke Park, Redcar, Middlesbrough, **CLEVELAND**, TS, **England**.
Contact/s: **Mr Gordon Sanderson**.
(T) 01642 477832
Mr John McVey.
(T) 01642 863067
Profile: FT: Coarse; WN: Locke Park; WT: Lake (Still) W. Size: 4 Acres. Location: Nr. Rd: Middlesborough to Redcar; Main Rd: A1085.
Ref: FH2971

LOCKINGE TROUT FISHERY

Lockinge Trout Fishery, Orpwood, Ardington, Wantage, **OXFORDSHIRE**, OX12 8PN, **England**.
Contact/s: **Mr John Haigh**.
(T) 01235 821116 (F) 01235 820950
Profile: FT: Game; WN: Betterton Brook; WT: Combination (Still & Moving); F. Size: 12 Acres; W. Size: 4 Acres. Location: Nr. Rd: A417; Main Rd: A417; Rail: Didcot.
Ref: FH2972

LOCKWOOD BECK RESERVOIR

Lockwood Beck Reservoir, Guisborough, **CLEVELAND**, TS14, **England**.
Contact/s: **Mr Byers**.
(T) 01207 501237
Profile: FT: Game; WN: Lockwood; WT: Reservoir (Still) W. Size: 60 Acres.
Location: Nr. Rd: Guisborough to Whitby Road; Main Rd: A171.
Ref: FH2973

LOCKWOOD RESERVOIR

Lockwood Reservoir, Tottenham, London, **LONDON (GREATER)**, N17, **England**.
Contact/s: **Mr Chris King**, Walthamstow Reservoir Group, Thames Water Gatehouse, 2 Forest Rd, Tottenham, London, N17 9NH.
(T) 020 88081527
Profile: FT: Coarse; WN: Lockwood; WT: Reservoir (Still) W. Size: 74 Acres.
Location: Nr. Rd: Forest Road; Main Rd: A10, North London; Rail: Tottenham Hale Underground.
Ref: FH2974

LODDEN (RIVER)

River Loddon, Sindlesham Mill, Sindlesham, Wokingham, **BERKSHIRE**, RG41, **England**.
Contact/s: **Mr John Baker**, Crowthorne Sports and Angling, 91-95 Church St, Crowthorne, Berkshire, RG45 7AW.
(T) 01344 777411
Profile: FT: Coarse; WN: Loddon; WT: River (Moving).
Ref: FH2976

LODDISWELL STREAM

Loddiswell Stream, Kingsbridge, **DEVON**, TQ7, **England**.
Contact/s: **Mr J E Coombes** (Secretary), 19 Stella Rd, Preston, Paignton, South Devon, TQ3 1BH.
Profile: FT: Game; WN: Loddiswell; WT: Stream (Moving) W. Size: 23200 Metres.
Ref: FH2975

LODDON (RIVER)

River Loddon, Dinton Pastures, Hurst, Reading, **BERKSHIRE**, RG10, **England**.
Contact/s: **Simon** (Secretary).
(T) 0118 9342016
Profile: FT: Coarse; WN: Loddon; WT: River (Moving) W. Size: 15000 Metres.
Ref: FH2977

LODGE LAKES

Lodge Lakes, Dansteed Way, Great Holm, Milton Keynes, **BUCKINGHAMSHIRE**, MK, **England**.
Contact/s: **Mr Kv Osborne** (Secretary), Milton Keynes Angling Association, 11 Gilpin Way, Olney, Buckinghamshire, MK46 4DN.
(T) 01234 713144
Profile: FT: Coarse; WN: Lodge; WT: Lake (Still) W. Size: 8 Acres. Location: Nr. Rd: Bradwell Road; Main Rd: A509.
Ref: FH2978

LODGE PARK LAKE

Lodge Park Lake, Chaddesley Cl, Redditch, **WORCESTERSHIRE**, B98 7ND, **England**.
Contact/s: **Mr R Myall**, 19 Chaddesley Cl, Lodge Park, Redditch.
Profile: FT: Coarse; WN: Lodge Park; WT: Lake (Still). Location: Nr. Rd: A4023, A441; Main Rd: A448.
Ref: FH2979

LOGANLEA TROUT FISHERY

Loganlea Trout Fishery, Milton Bridge, Penicuik, **LOTHIAN (MID)**, EH26 0NY, **Scotland**.
Contact/s: **Mr Ronnie Gatti**.
(T) 01968 676329or01314402097
Profile: FT: Game; WN: Loganlea Trout Fishery; WT: Lake (Still); F. Size: 30 Acres; W. Size: 22 Acres. Location: Nr. Rd: Milton Bridge; Main Rd: A702; Rail: Waverly.
Ref: FH2980

LOGIERAIT BEAT

Logierait Beat, Pitlochry, **PERTH AND KINROSS**, PH, **Scotland**.
(W) www.fishingnet.com/beats/logierait.htm
Contact/s: **Mr E Brodie**, Logierait Pine Lodges, Logierait, Pitlochry, Perth and Kinross, PH9 0LH.
(T) 01796 482331
Profile: FT: Combination; WN: Sandbank; WT: Pool (Still).
Ref: FH2981

LONG COPSE PONDS

Long Copse Ponds, Great Brookham, Leatherhead, **SURREY**, KT23 4, **England**.
Contact/s: **Mr Ross Nursey**.
(T) 020 8397279
Profile: FT: Coarse; WN: Long Copse; WT: Pond (Still). Location: Main Rd: A246.
Ref: FH2982

LONG POND

Long Pond, Barnby Dun, Doncaster, **YORKSHIRE (SOUTH)**, DN3, **England**.
Contact/s: **Mr Tony Green** (Manager), Peg Two Tackle, 27 King St, Thorne, Yorkshire (South), DN8 5AU.
(T) 01405 814417
Mr Vinnie Belk (Fishery Manager).
(T) 01302 883674
Profile: FT: Coarse; WN: Long; WT: Pond (Still).
Ref: FH2983

LONG REACH

Long Reach, St Ives, Huntingdon, **CAMBRIDGESHIRE**, PE1, **England**.
Profile: FT: Coarse; WN: Long Reach; WT: Gravel Pit (Still) W. Size: 20 Acres.

Location: Nr. Rd: B1040; Main Rd: A604.
Ref: FH2984

LONGBARN POOL

Longbarn Pool, Fearnhead, Warrington, **CHESHIRE**, WA2, **England**.
Contact/s: **Mr Neil Jupp** (Club Secretary), Lymm Angling Club, PO Box 350, Warrington, Cheshire, WA2 9FB.
(T) 01925 411774
Profile: **FT:** Coarse; **WN:** Longbarn; **WT:** Pool (Still) **W. Size:** 1 Acre. **Location:** **Nr. Rd:** Meadow Lane; **Main Rd:** M6 to Preston, junction 21, B5210, A574.
Ref: FH2985

LONGBOTTOMS DAM

Longbottoms Dam, Bradford Rd, Birstall, Batley, **YORKSHIRE (WEST)**, WF17, **England**.
Contact/s: Area Manager, Environment Agency, Ridings Area Office, Phoenix House, Global Avenue, Leeds, LS11 8PG.
(T) 0113 2440191or2314834 **(F)** 0113 2134609
Mr W Lock.
(T) 01274 869917
Profile: **FT:** Coarse; **WN:** Longbottom's; **WT:** Mill Dam (Still). **Location:** **Nr. Rd:** Bradford Road.
Ref: FH2986

LONGBRIDGE LAKES

Longbridge Lakes, Broadlands Estate, Romsey, **HAMPSHIRE**, SO51 9ZE, **England**.
Contact/s: **Mr John Dennis** (Owner).
(T) 023 80739438 **(M)** 07973 523358
Profile: **FT:** Coarse; **WN:** Longbridge; **WT:** Lake (Still). **Location:** **Nr. Rd:** B3084; **Main Rd:** A27, A31.
Ref: FH2987

LONGFIELD LAKE

Longfield Lake, Haysden Country Park, Lower Haysden Rd, Tonbridge, **KENT**, TN1, **England**.
Contact/s: **Mr Alex Heggie** (Membership Secretary), Little Lucy's Farmhouse, Lower St, Hildenborough, Tonbridge, TN11 8PT.
(T) 01732 832352 **(F)** 01732 832352
Mr Tom Creasey (Hon Secretary), 3 Invicta Flats, Great Brooms Rd, Tunbridge Wells, Kent, TN4 9DD.
(T) 01892 520520
Profile: **FT:** Coarse; **WN:** Longfield; **WT:** Lake (Still) **W. Size:** 12 Acres. **Location:** **Nr. Rd:** Haysden Road; **Rail:** Tonbridge.
Ref: FH2988

LONGFORD LAKE

Longford Lake, Sevenoaks, **KENT**, TN, **England**.
Contact/s: Manager, Manklow Tackle Shop, 44 Seal Rd, Sevenoaks, Kent, TN14 5AR.
(T) 01732 454952
Secretary, Holmesdale CAS, Po Box 248, Orpington, Kent, BR6 6ZJ.
Colin, 4 Shoreham Lane, Riverhead, Chipstead, Sevenoaks, Kent.
(T) 01698 54067
Profile: **FT:** Coarse; **WN:** Longford; **WT:** Gravel Pit (Still) **W. Size:** 70 Acres.
Location: **Nr. Rd:** A21 junction 5; **Main Rd:** M25.
Ref: FH2989

LONGHOUSE LAKES

Tinker, The Longhouse, Teffont, Salisbury, **WILTSHIRE**, SP3 5RS, **England**.
Contact/s: **Mr Jon Burch** (Owner).
(T) 07790 694757
Profile: **FT:** Coarse; **WN:** Tinker**WT:** Lake.
Ref: FH2990

LONGLANDS FARM

Longlands Farm, Coombe Martin, Ilfracombe, **DEVON**, EX34 0PD, **England**.
Contact/s: **Ms Mary Peacock** (Owner).
(T) 01271 883522
Profile: **FT:** Coarse; **WN:** Longlands Farm; **WT:** Pond (Still). **Location:** **Nr. Rd:** Coombe Martin; **Main Rd:** A399, Ilfracombe to Lynmouth Road.
Ref: FH2991

LONGLEAT LAKES

Longleat Lakes, Longleat Estate, Horningsham, Warminster, **WILTSHIRE**, BA12 7NW, **England**.
Contact/s: **Mr Nick Robbins** (Owner).
(T) 01985 844496 **(F)** 01985 844885
Profile: **FT:** Coarse; **WN:** Longleat; **WT:** Lake (Still) **W. Size:** 22 Acres. **Location:** **Nr. Rd:** A361; **Main Rd:** A36; **Rail:** Frome.
Ref: FH2992

LONGMOOR FARM FISHING LAKE

Longmoor Farm Fishing Lake, Longmoor Farm, Park Lane, Finchampstead, **BERKSHIRE**, RG40 4PT, **England**.
Contact/s: **Mr Peter Wilkins** (Owner), Longmoor Farm, Park Lane, Finchampstead, Berkshire, RG40 4PT.
(T) 0118 9760296 **(F)** 0118 9760296 **(M)** 07903 113795
Profile: **FT:** Coarse; **WN:** Longmoor Farm Fishing Lake; **WT:** Lake (Still); **F. Size:** 3 Acres; **W. Size:** 2 Acres. **Location:** **Nr. Rd:** Park Lane; **Main Rd:** A327; **Rail:** Wokingham.
Ref: FH2993

LONGMOOR LAKE

Longmoor Lake, California Country Park, Nine Mile Ride, Finchampstead, Wokingham, **BERKSHIRE**, RG40, **England**.
Contact/s: **Mr Simon Bartcam**.
Profile: **FT:** Coarse; **WN:** Longmoor; **WT:** Lake (Still). **Location:** **Nr. Rd:** Nine Mile Ride.
Ref: FH2994

LONGSHAW FARM FISHING LAKES

Longshaw Lakes, Longshaw Farm, Calcott Hill, Sturry, Canterbury, **KENT**, CT3 4ND, **England**.
Contact/s: **Mr Ken Goldsmith** (Manager).
(T) 01227 710263
Profile: **FT:** Coarse; **WN:** Longshaw; **WT:** Lake (Still) **W. Size:** 4 Acres. **Location:** **Nr. Rd:** Calcott Hill.
Ref: FH2995

LONGTON BRICKCROFT

Longton Brickcroft, Longton, Preston, **LANCASHIRE**, PR, **England**.
Contact/s: Secretary.
(T) 01772 760918
Profile: **FT:** Coarse; **WN:** Longton Brickcroft; **WT:** Pond (Still). **Location:** **Main Rd:** A59, Preston to Liverpool.
Ref: FH2996

LONSDALE COUNTRY PARK

Lonsdale Country Park, Cotehill, Carlisle, **CUMBRIA**, CA6 4ND, **England**.
Contact/s: **Mr Paul Drinkall**.
(T) 01228 573375 **(M)** 07770 825896
Profile: **FT:** Coarse; **WN:** Lonsdale Country Park; **WT:** Lake (Still); **F. Size:** 30 Acres; **W. Size:** 10 Acres. **Location:** **Nr. Rd:** B6263 to Cotehill; **Main Rd:** M6, junction 42 to Cumwhinton village; **Rail:** Carlisle. £Fr
Ref: FH2997

LOUGH ACEELAGH

Lough Aceelagh, Moycullen, **COUNTY GALWAY**, **Ireland**.
Contact/s: **Mr Danny Goldrick** (Angling Officer), The Western Regional Fisheries Board, Weir Lodge, Earl's Island, Galway City, County Galway.
(T) 091 563118 **(F)** 091 566335
(E) wrfb@iol.ie
Profile: **FT:** Coarse; **WN:** Aceelagh; **WT:** Lough (Still) **W. Size:** 8 Acres.
Ref: FH2998

LOUGH ADERRA

Lough Aderra, Midleton, **COUNTY CORK**, **Ireland**.
(W) www.swrfb.ie
Contact/s: Area Manager, South West Regional Fisheries Board, 1 Nevilles Trce, Macroom, County Cork, Ireland.
(T) 026 41221
(E) swrfb@swrfb.ie
Profile: **FT:** Game; **WN:** Aderra; **WT:** Lough (Still) **W. Size:** 30 Acres. **Location:** **Nr. Rd:** Cork to Youghal Road.
Ref: FH2999

LOUGH ADERRY

Lough Aderry, Lough Aderry Fishery, Castlemartyr, Youghal, **COUNTY CORK**, **Ireland**.
Contact/s: , South West Regional Fisheries Board, Anglesea St, Clonmel, County Tipperary.
(T) 026 41222or5223971 **(F)** 052 23971
Profile: **FT:** Game; **WN:** Lough Aderry; **WT:** Lough (Still) **W. Size:** 30 Acres.
Ref: FH3000

LOUGH ALLEN

Lough Allen, Drumshanbo, **COUNTY LEITRIM**, **Ireland**.
(W) www.dbo.ie
Contact/s: **Mr Brian McGourty** (Fishing Expert), Lough Allen Conservation Assocaiation, Drumshanbo, County Leitrim, Ireland.
(T) 078 41648 **(F)** 078 41577
(E) dec@iol.ie
Mr Sean Wynne (Secretary), Lough Allen Conservation Assocaiation, Drumshanbo, County Leitrim, Ireland.
(T) 078 41564
Profile: **FT:** Game; **WN:** Allen; **WT:** Lough (Still) **W. Size:** 12800 Metres. **Location:** **Nr. Rd:** N4 from Dublin (110 miles); **Main Rd:** N4.
Ref: FH3001

LOUGH ARORAM

Lough Aroram, Moycullen, **COUNTY GALWAY**, **Ireland**.
Contact/s: **Mr Danny Goldrick** (Angling Officer), The Western Regional Fisheries Board, Weir Lodge, Earl's Island, Galway City, County Galway.
(T) 091 563118 **(F)** 091 566335
(E) wrfb@iol.ie
Profile: **FT:** Coarse; **WN:** Aroram; **WT:** Lough (Still) **W. Size:** 20 Acres.
Ref: FH3002

LOUGH ARROW

Lough Arrow, Ballydoon, Riverstown, Boyle, **COUNTY ROSCOMMON**, **Ireland**.
Contact/s: **J Hargadon**, Lough Arrow Fish Preservation Association, Annaghloy, Riverstown, County Sligo.
(T) 079 66666or65065
Mr Finian Dodd (Manager Dodds Boats).
(T) 071 65065 **(F)** 071 65065
Profile: **FT:** Game; **WN:** Arrow; **WT:** Lough (Still); **F. Size:** 3123 Acres; **W. Size:** 3123 Acres. **Location:** **Main Rd:** N4 Dublin to Sligo; **Rail:** Boyle.
Ref: FH3003

LOUGH ATARRIFF

Lough Atarriff, Dunmanway, **COUNTY CORK**, **Ireland**.
Contact/s: **Mr P MacCarthy** (Secretary), Dunmanway Salmon and Trout Angling Association, Yew Tree Bar, Dunmanway, County Cork, Ireland.
Profile: **FT:** Game; **WN:** Atarriff; **WT:** Lough (Still).
Ref: FH3004

LOUGH AUGH

Lough Augh, Castlebaldwin, **COUNTY SLIGO**, **Ireland**.
Contact/s: **J Hargadon**, Lough Arrow Fish Preservation Association, Annaghloy, Riverstown, County Sligo.
(T) 079 66666or65065
Mr Finian Dodd (Manager Dodds Boats).
(T) 071 65065 **(F)** 071 65065
Profile: **FT:** Game; **WN:** Augh; **WT:** Lough (Still). **Location:** **Rail:** Boyle.

Ref: FH3005

LOUGH AVAUL (LOWER)

Lower Lough Avaul, Glengariff, **COUNTY CORK**, **Ireland**.
(W) www.swrfb.ie
Contact/s: Area Manager, South West Regional Fisheries Board, 1 Nevilles Trce, Macroom, County Cork, Ireland.
(T) 026 41221
(E) swrfb@swrfb.ie
Mr Bernard Harrington (Manager).
(T) 027 63021
Profile: **FT:** Game; **WN:** Avaul (Lower); **WT:** Lough (Still) **W. Size:** 18 Acres. Location: **Nr. Rd:** Castletownberehaven Road.
Ref: FH3006

LOUGH AVAUL (UPPER)

Upper Lough Avaul, Glengariff, **COUNTY CORK**, **Ireland**.
(W) www.swrfb.ie
Contact/s: Area Manager, South West Regional Fisheries Board, 1 Nevilles Trce, Macroom, County Cork, Ireland.
(T) 026 41221
(E) swrfb@swrfb.ie
Mr Bernard Harrington (Manager).
(T) 027 63021
Profile: **FT:** Game; **WN:** Avaul (Upper); **WT:** Lough (Still) **W. Size:** 18 Acres. Location: **Nr. Rd:** Castletownberehaven Road.
Ref: FH3007

LOUGH BALLYLUIRKE

Lough Ballyluirke, Moycullen, **COUNTY GALWAY**, **Ireland**.
Contact/s: **Mr Danny Goldrick** (Angling Officer), The Western Regional Fisheries Board, Weir Lodge, Earl's Island, Galway City, County Galway.
(T) 091 563118 (F) 091 566335
(E) wrfb@iol.ie
Profile: **FT:** Coarse; **WN:** Ballyluirke; **WT:** Lough (Still) **W. Size:** 200 Acres.
Ref: FH3008

LOUGH BALLYNACARRIGA

Lough Ballynacarriga, Dunmanway, **COUNTY CORK**, **Ireland**.
Contact/s: **Mr P MacCarthy** (Secretary), Dunmanway Salmon and Trout Angling Association, Yew Tree Bar, Dunmanway, County Cork, Ireland.
Profile: **FT:** Game; **WN:** Ballynacarriga; **WT:** Lough (Still).
Ref: FH3009

LOUGH BARFINNIHY

Lough Barfinnihy, Kenmare, **COUNTY KERRY**, **Ireland**.
(W) www.swrfb.ie
Contact/s: Area Manager, South West Regional Fisheries Board, 1 Nevilles Trce, Macroom, County Cork, Ireland.
(T) 026 41221
(E) swrfb@swrfb.ie
Profile: **FT:** Game; **WN:** Barfinnihy; **WT:** Lough (Still) **W. Size:** 35 Acres. Location: **Nr. Rd:** Molls Gap; **Main Rd:** Kenmare to Killarney.
Ref: FH3010

LOUGH BEAGH

Lough Beagh, Beagh, **COUNTY DONEGAL**, **Ireland**.
Contact/s: **Mr James McGinley** (Manager).
(T) 074 37090
Profile: **FT:** Game; **WN:** Beagh; **WT:** Lough (Still) **W. Size:** 6400 Metres.
Ref: FH3011

LOUGH BO

Lough Bo, Castlebaldwin, **COUNTY SLIGO**, **Ireland**.
Contact/s: J Hargadon, Lough Arrow Fish Preservation Association, Annaghloy, Riverstown, County Sligo.
(T) 079 66666or65065
Profile: **FT:** Game; **WN:** Bo; **WT:** Lough (Still). Location: **Rail:** Boyle.
Ref: FH3012

LOUGH BOFINNE

Lough Bofinne, Bantry, **COUNTY CORK**, **Ireland**.
(W) www.swrfb.ie
Contact/s: Area Manager, South West Regional Fisheries Board, 1 Nevilles Trce, Macroom, County Cork, Ireland.
(T) 026 41221
(E) swrfb@swrfb.ie
Mr Jack Knight (Manager).
(T) 027 50614
Mrs J Spillane.
(T) 027 51866
Profile: **FT:** Game; **WN:** Bofinne; **WT:** Lough (Still) **W. Size:** 25 Acres. Location: **Nr. Rd:** Bantry to skibbereen.
Ref: FH3013

LOUGH CARRA

Lough Carra, Pawtry, Westport, **COUNTY MAYO**, **Ireland**.
(W) www.wrfb.ie
Contact/s: **Mr Danny Goldrick** (Angling Officer), The Western Regional Fisheries Board, Weir Lodge, Earl's Island, Galway City, County Galway.
(T) 091 563118 (F) 091 566335
(E) info@wrfb.ie
Profile: **FT:** Game; **WN:** Carra; **WT:** Lough (Still) **W. Size:** 4000 Acres. Location: **Nr. Rd:** N84; **Rail:** Castlebar.
Ref: FH3014

LOUGH CASHEL

Lough Cashel, Crossmaglen, Newry, **COUNTY DOWN**, BT35, **Northern Ireland**.
Contact/s: **Mr Eugene Murphy**.
(T) 028 30868607
Mr J Cunningham (Secretary), 21 Forkhill Rd, Mullach Ban, County Armagh, BT35 9XL.
(T) 028 30889187
Mr Phil Nolan.
(T) 028 30868074
Profile: **FT:** Game; **WN:** Cashel; **WT:** Lake (Still).
Ref: FH3015

LOUGH CAUM

Lough Caum, Castlegregory, **COUNTY KERRY**, **Ireland**.
(W) www.swrfb.ie
Contact/s: Area Manager, South West Regional Fisheries Board, 1 Nevilles Trce, Macroom, County Cork, Ireland.
(T) 026 41221
(E) swrfb@swrfb.ie
Profile: **FT:** Game; **WN:** Caum; **WT:** Lough (Still) **W. Size:** 20 Acres. Location: **Nr. Rd:** Tralee to Conor Pass Road; **Main Rd:** Aughacasla.
Ref: FH3016

LOUGH CLOONACOLLY

Lough Cloonacolly, Ballaghaderren, **COUNTY ROSCOMMON**, **Ireland**.
Contact/s: Manager, Boyle Tourist Office, King House, Boyle, County Roscommon, Ireland.
(T) 079 62145
Mr Jas Cogan (Secretary), Kilcolman Rd, Ballaghaderren, County Roscommon, Ireland.
(T) 090 760077
Profile: **FT:** Game; **WN:** Cloonacolly; **WT:** Lough (Still).
Ref: FH3017

LOUGH CLOONAGH

Lough Cloonagh, Ballaghaderren, **COUNTY ROSCOMMON**, **Ireland**.
Contact/s: Manager, Boyle Tourist Office, King House, Boyle, County Roscommon, Ireland.
(T) 079 62145
Mr Jas Cogan (Secretary), Kilcolman Rd, Ballaghaderren, County Roscommon, Ireland.
(T) 090 760077
Profile: **FT:** Game; **WN:** Cloonagh; **WT:** Lough (Still).
Ref: FH3018

LOUGH COOLIN

Lough Coolin, Fairhill House, Clonbur, **COUNTY GALWAY**, **Ireland**.
Contact/s: **Mr Edward Lynch**.
(T) 092 46176
Profile: **FT:** Combination; **WN:** Coolin; **WT:** Lough (Still). Location: **Rail:** Galway.
Ref: FH3019

LOUGH COOLKEELURE

Lough Coolkeelure, Dunmanway, **COUNTY CORK**, **Ireland**.
Contact/s: **Mr P MacCarthy** (Secretary), Dunmanway Salmon and Trout Angling Association, Yew Tree Bar, Dunmanway, County Cork, Ireland.
Profile: **FT:** Game; **WN:** Coolkeelure; **WT:** Lough (Still).
Ref: FH3020

LOUGH CORRIB

Lough Corrib, Portarra Lodge, Tullykyne, Moycullen, **COUNTY GALWAY**, **Ireland**.
Contact/s: **Mr Michael Canney**.
(T) 091 55051 (F) 091 55052
(E) portarralodge@eircom.net
Profile: **FT:** Combination; **WN:** Lough Corrib; **WT:** Lough (Still) **W. Size:** 44000 Acres. Location: **Main Rd:** N59 to Moycullen village; **Rail:** Salway. £Fr
Ref: FH3021

LOUGH CORRIB (UPPER)

Upper Lough Corrib, Derry Quay, Cross, Cong, **COUNTY MAYO**, **Ireland**.
Contact/s: **Mr Mike Holian**, Bayview Angling Ctre, Derry Quay, Cross, Cong, County Mayo.
(T) 092 46385 (F) 092 46385
Profile: **FT:** Combination; **WN:** Lough Corrib; **WT:** Lough (Still). Location: **Nr. Rd:** R334 Headford to Cross; **Rail:** Galway.
Ref: FH3022

LOUGH COWEY FISHERY

Lough Cowey Fishery, Lough Cowey Rd, Portaferry, Newtownards, **COUNTY DOWN**, BT22 1PJ, **Northern Ireland**.
Contact/s: **Mr Jim Crowthers** (Owner).
(T) 028 42728946
Ms Jenny Crossey (Manager).
Profile: **FT:** Game; **WN:** Cowey; **WT:** Lough (Still). Location: **Nr. Rd:** Lough Cowey Road.
Ref: FH3023

LOUGH CULLENAGH

Lough Cullenagh, Dunmanway, **COUNTY CORK**, **Ireland**.
Contact/s: **Mr P MacCarthy** (Secretary), Dunmanway Salmon and Trout Angling Association, Yew Tree Bar, Dunmanway, County Cork, Ireland.
Profile: **FT:** Game; **WN:** Cullenagh; **WT:** Lough (Still).
Ref: FH3024

LOUGH DOWN

Lough Down, Moycullen, **COUNTY GALWAY**, **Ireland**.
Contact/s: **Mr Danny Goldrick** (Angling Officer), The Western Regional Fisheries Board, Weir Lodge, Earl's Island, Galway City, County Galway.
(T) 091 563118 (F) 091 566335
(E) wrfb@iol.ie
Profile: **FT:** Coarse; **WN:** Down; **WT:** Lough (Still) **W. Size:** 20 Acres.
Ref: FH3025

LOUGH DOWNBEG

Lough Downbeg, Moycullen, **COUNTY GALWAY**, **Ireland**.
Contact/s: **Mr Danny Goldrick** (Angling Officer), The Western Regional Fisheries Board, Weir Lodge, Earl's Island, Galway City, County Galway.
(T) 091 563118 (F) 091 566335
(E) wrfb@iol.ie
Profile: **FT:** Coarse; **WN:** Downbeg; **WT:**

Lough (Still) **W. Size:** 5 Acres.
Ref: FH3026

LOUGH ENAGH

Lough Enagh, Dungannon, **COUNTY TYRONE**, BT71, **Northern Ireland**.
Contact/s: Manager, Cahoon Joe, 2 Irish St, Dungannon, County Tyrone, BT70 1DB.
(T) 028 87722754
Profile: **FT:** Game; **WN:** Lough Enagh; **WT:** Lough (Still).
Ref: FH3027

LOUGH ENNEL FISHERY

Lough Ennel Fishery, Mullingar, **COUNTY WESTMEATH**, **Ireland**.
Contact/s: **Mr Patrick Keenrghan**.
(T) 044 40563
Profile: **FT:** Game; **WN:** Lough Ennel Fishery; **WT:** Lough (Still) **W. Size:** 3500 Acres.
Ref: FH3028

LOUGH ERNE

Lough Erne, Enniskillen, **COUNTY FERMANAGH**, BT92 0J, **Northern Ireland**.
Contact/s: , Fermanagh Tourist Information Ctre, Wellington Rd, Enniskillen, County Fermanagh.
(T) 028 66323110
Manager, Erne Tackle, 118 Main St, Lisnaskea, Enniskillen, BT92 0JD.
(T) 028 67721969
Profile: **FT:** Game; **WN:** Erne; **WT:** Lake (Still).
Ref: FH3029

LOUGH FADDA

Lough Fadda, Sneem, **COUNTY KERRY**, **Ireland**.
(W) www.swrfb.ie
Contact/s: Area Manager, South West Regional Fisheries Board, 1 Nevilles Trce, Macroom, County Cork, Ireland.
(T) 026 41221
(E) swrfb@swrfb.ie
Profile: **FT:** Game; **WN:** Fadda; **WT:** Lough (Still) **W. Size:** 14 Acres. **Location:** **Nr. Rd:** Sneem to Kenmare road.
Ref: FH3030

LOUGH FEA

Lough Fea, Lough Fea Bar, Lough Fea Rd, Coagh, Cookstown, **COUNTY TYRONE**, BT80 9ST, **Northern Ireland**.
Contact/s: **Mr Danny Bonner** (Secretary).
(T) 028 86765920
Mr V Donaghy (Manager), The Lough Fea Bar, 140 Loughfea Rd, Cookstown, County Tyrone, BT80 9ST.
(T) 028 86763517
Profile: **FT:** Game; **WN:** Fea; **WT:** Lough (Still) **W. Size:** 365 Acres. **Location:** **Nr. Rd:** Logh Fea Road.
Ref: FH3031

LOUGH GARA

Lough Gara, Boyle, **COUNTY ROSCOMMON**, **Ireland**.
Contact/s: Manager, Boyle Tourist Office, King House, Boyle, County Roscommon, Ireland.
(T) 079 62145
Mr Jimmy Cogan (Water Keeper), Lung Valley, Kilcolman Rd, Ballaghaderren, County Roscommon, Ireland.
(T) 090 760077or761544
Profile: **FT:** Combination; **WN:** Gara; **WT:** Lough (Still); **F. Size:** 2000 Acres.
Location: **Main Rd:** N5; **Rail:** Castlerea.
Ref: FH3032

LOUGH GLASSDRUMMAN

Lough Glassdrumman, Crossmaglen, Newry, **COUNTY DOWN**, BT35, **Northern Ireland**.
Contact/s: **Mr Eugene Murphy**.
(T) 028 30868607
Mr J Cunningham (Secretary), 21 Forkhill Rd, Mullach Ban, County Armagh, BT35 9XL.
(T) 028 30889187
Mr Phil Nolan.
(T) 028 30868074
Profile: **FT:** Game; **WN:** Glassdrumman; **WT:** Lake (Still).
Ref: FH3033

LOUGH HEMUSHMACONRY

Lough Hemushmaconry, Moycullen, **COUNTY GALWAY**, **Ireland**.
Contact/s: **Mr Danny Goldrick** (Angling Officer), The Western Regional Fisheries Board, Weir Lodge, Earl's Island, Galway City, County Galway.
(T) 091 563118 (F) 091 566335
(E) wrfb@iol.ie
Profile: **FT:** Coarse; **WN:** Hemushmaconry; **WT:** Lough (Still) **W. Size:** 30 Acres.
Ref: FH3034

LOUGH INAGH FISHERY

Lough Inagh Fishery, Ballynahinch, **COUNTY DOWN**, BT24, **Northern Ireland**.
Contact/s: **Mrs Della MacAuley**.
(T) 095 34608
Profile: **FT:** Game; **WN:** Ballynahinch; **WT:** River (Moving).
Ref: FH3035

LOUGH KEENAGHAN

Lough Keenaghan, Belleek, **COUNTY FERMANAGH**, BT93 3, **Northern Ireland**.
Contact/s: **Mr Michael McGrath** (Owner), Belleek Angling Ctre, The Thatch, Belleek, County Fermanagh, BT93 3FX.
(T) 028 68658181 (F) 028 68658181
Profile: **FT:** Game; **WN:** Erne; **WT:** River (Moving).
Ref: FH3036

LOUGH KEY

Lough Key, Boyle, **COUNTY ROSCOMMON**, **Ireland**.
Contact/s: Manager, Boyle Tourist Office, King House, Boyle, County Roscommon, Ireland.
(T) 079 62145
Mr Jas Cogan (Secretary), Kilcolman Rd, Ballaghaderren, County Roscommon, Ireland.
(T) 090 760077
Profile: **FT:** Combination; **WN:** Key; **WT:** Lough (Still).
Ref: FH3037

LOUGH KEY

Lough Key, Castlebaldwin, **COUNTY SLIGO**, **Ireland**.
Contact/s: **J Hargadon**, Lough Arrow Fish Preservation Association, Annaghloy, Riverstown, County Sligo.
(T) 079 66666or65065
Profile: **FT:** Combination; **WN:** Key; **WT:** Lough (Still). **Location:** **Rail:** Boyle.
Ref: FH3038

LOUGH KILTYBAINE

Lough Kiltybaine, Crossmaglen, Newry, **COUNTY DOWN**, BT35, **Northern Ireland**.
Contact/s: **Mr Eugene Murphy**.
(T) 028 30868607
Mr J Cunningham (Secretary), 21 Forkhill Rd, Mullach Ban, County Armagh, BT35 9XL.
(T) 028 30889187
Mr Phil Nolan.
(T) 028 30868074
Profile: **FT:** Game; **WN:** Kiltybaine; **WT:** Lake (Still).
Ref: FH3039

LOUGH MACRONAN

Lough Macronan, Benburb, Dungannon, **COUNTY TYRONE**, BT71 7, **Northern Ireland**.
Contact/s: **Mrs Liz Salter** (Manager), Aughnacloy Development Association, The McCreedy Mill Centre, Aughnacloy, County Tyrone, BT69 6AL.
(T) 028 85557002
Profile: **FT:** Coarse; **WN:** Macronan; **WT:** Lough (Still).
Ref: FH3040

LOUGH MASK

Lough Mask, Fairhill House, Clonbur, **COUNTY GALWAY**, **Ireland**.
Contact/s: **Mr Edward Lynch**.
(T) 092 46176
Profile: **FT:** Combination; **WN:** Mask; **WT:** Lough (Still). **Location:** **Rail:** Galway.
Ref: FH3041

LOUGH MELVIN

Lough Melvin, Garrison, **COUNTY FERMANAGH**, BT93 4ER, **Northern Ireland**.
Contact/s: **Mr Sean Maguire** (Ghillie), Melvin Tackle, Main St, Garrison, Enniskillen, County Fermanagh.
(T) 028 68658194 (F) 028 68658194
Mrs Kare McGovern (Secretary), Garrison and Melvin Angling Club, Cornacully, Belcoo, County Fermanagh.
(T) 028 66386415
Profile: **FT:** Game; **WN:** Melvin; **WT:** Lough (Still) **W. Size:** 13000 Acres.
Ref: FH3042

LOUGH MELVIN

Lough Melvin, The Rossinver Fishery, Rossinver, **COUNTY LEITRIM**, **Ireland**.
Contact/s: **Mr Peter Bradley** (Secretary).
Profile: **FT:** Game; **WN:** Melvin; **WT:** Lough (Still) **W. Size:** 8000 Metres.
Ref: FH3043

LOUGH MULLAGHABAN

Lough Mullaghaban, Crossmaglen, Newry, **COUNTY DOWN**, BT35, **Northern Ireland**.
Contact/s: **Mr Eugene Murphy**.
(T) 028 30868607
Mr J Cunningham (Secretary), 21 Forkhill Rd, Mullach Ban, County Armagh, BT35 9XL.
(T) 028 30889187
Mr Phil Nolan.
(T) 028 30868074
Profile: **FT:** Game; **WN:** Mullaghaban; **WT:** Lake (Still).
Ref: FH3044

LOUGH NAKIRKA

Lough Nakirka, Killorglin, **COUNTY KERRY**, **Ireland**.
(W) www.swrfb.ie
Contact/s: Area Manager, South West Regional Fisheries Board, 1 Nevilles Trce, Macroom, County Cork, Ireland.
(T) 026 41221
(E) swrfb@swrfb.ie
Profile: **FT:** Game; **WN:** Nakirka; **WT:** Lough (Still) **W. Size:** 20 Acres. **Location:** **Nr. Rd:** Killorglin to Sneem road.
Ref: FH3045

LOUGH NAMUCKA

Lough Namucka, Louisburgh, **COUNTY MAYO**, **Ireland**.
Contact/s: **Mr Charles Gaffney**.
(T) 098 66150
Profile: **FT:** Game; **WN:** Carrownisky; **WT:** Lough (Moving).
Ref: FH3046

LOUGH NASOOL

Lough Nasool, Ballaghaderren, **COUNTY ROSCOMMON**, **Ireland**.
Contact/s: Manager, Boyle Tourist Office, King House, Boyle, County Roscommon, Ireland.
(T) 079 62145
Ms Eileen McDonagh.
(T) 071 65325
Profile: **FT:** Game; **WN:** Nasool; **WT:** Lough (Still).
Ref: FH3047

LOUGH NAVIGATION

Lough Navigation, Tetney Lock, Grimsby, **HUMBERSIDE**, DN36, **England**.
Contact/s: Fishery Manager.
(T) 01472 343536
Profile: **FT:** Coarse; **WN:** Lough Navigation; **WT:** Lock (Still).
Ref: FH3048

LOUGH NEAGH

Lough Neagh, Kinnego Marina Office, Oxford Island, Lurgan, Craigavon, **COUNTY ARMAGH**, BT66, **Northern Ireland**.
Contact/s: Fishery Manager.
(T) 028 38327573
Profile: FT: Game; WN: Neagh; WT: Lough (Still).
Ref: FH3049

LOUGH NEASKIN

Lough Neaskin, Dunmanway, **COUNTY CORK**, **Ireland**.
Contact/s: Manager, Jeffersports, Main St, Bandon, County Cork, Ireland.
(T) 023 41133 (F) 023 41133
Profile: FT: Game; WN: Neaskin; WT: Lough (Still).
Ref: FH3050

LOUGH PARKYFLAHERTY

Lough Parkyflaherty, Moycullen, **COUNTY GALWAY**, **Ireland**.
Contact/s: Mr Danny Goldrick (Angling Officer), The Western Regional Fisheries Board, Weir Lodge, Earl's Island, Galway City, County Galway.
(T) 091 563118 (F) 091 566335
(E) wrfb@iol.ie
Profile: FT: Coarse; WN: Parkyflaherty; WT: Lough (Still) W. Size: 20 Acres.
Ref: FH3051

LOUGH POLLALHY

Lough Pollalhy, Moycullen, **COUNTY GALWAY**, **Ireland**.
Contact/s: Mr Danny Goldrick (Angling Officer), The Western Regional Fisheries Board, Weir Lodge, Earl's Island, Galway City, County Galway.
(T) 091 563118 (F) 091 566335
(E) wrfb@iol.ie
Profile: FT: Coarse; WN: Pollalhy; WT: Lough (Still) W. Size: 20 Acres.
Ref: FH3052

LOUGH RAMOR

Lough Ramor, Virginia, **COUNTY CAVAN**, **Ireland**.
Contact/s: Mr Ned Tobin.
(T) 049 8547934
Mr Norman Andrews.
(T) 049 8547770
Mr Pat McCabe (Secretary), Virginia Coarse Angling Club, Rahardrum, Virginia, County Cavan, Ireland.
(T) 042 9694352or498547649 (F) 042 9666318
Profile: FT: Combination; WN: Ramor; WT: Lough (Still & Moving). Location: Nr. Rd: N3; Main Rd: Donegal to Dublin.
Ref: FH3053

LOUGH URLAUR

Lough Urlaur, Ballaghaderren, **COUNTY ROSCOMMON**, **Ireland**.
Contact/s: Manager, Boyle Tourist Office, King House, Boyle, County Roscommon, Ireland.
(T) 079 62145
Mr Jas Cogan (Secretary), Kilcolman Rd, Ballaghaderren, County Roscommon, Ireland.
(T) 090 760077
Profile: FT: Game; WN: Urlaur; WT: Lough (Still).
Ref: FH3054

LOUGHBOROUGH SOAR CANAL

Loughborough Soar Canal, Loughborough, **LEICESTERSHIRE**, LE11, **England**.
Contact/s: Manager, Soar Valley Tackle, 7 Woodbrook Rd, Loughborough, Leicestershire, LE11 3QB.
(T) 01509 231817
Secretary.
(T) 01509 813384
Profile: FT: Coarse; WN: Loughborough Soar; WT: Canal (Still) W. Size: 2400 Metres.
Ref: FH3055

LOUGHGALL COARSE FISHERY

Loughgall Coarse Fishery, Loughgall Country Park, Loughgall Rd, Loughgall, Armagh, **COUNTY ARMAGH**, BT60 8HZ, **Northern Ireland**.
Contact/s: Mr Greg Ferson (Country Park Manager).
(T) 028 38892900 (F) 028 38892902 (M) 07713 083022
(E) greg.ferson@ukgateway.net
Profile: FT: Coarse; WN: Gall; WT: Lough (Still) W. Size: 37 Acres. Location: Nr. Rd: Main Road; Main Rd: M1; Rail: Portadown.
Ref: FH3056

LOUGHMORE

Loughmore, Aughncloy, Augher, **COUNTY TYRONE**, BT77, **Northern Ireland**.
Contact/s: Mrs Liz Salter (Manager), Aughnacloy Development Association, The McCreedy Mill Centre, Aughnacloy, County Tyrone, BT69 6AL.
(T) 028 85557002
Profile: FT: Game; WN: More; WT: Lough (Still). Location: Nr. Rd: A28.
Ref: FH3057

LOUGHOR (RIVER)

River Loughor, Ammanford, **CARMARTHENSHIRE**, SA18, **Wales**.
Contact/s: Mr Ron Woodlands (Hon Secretary), Pontardulais Rd, Llangennech, Carmarthenshire.
Profile: FT: Game; WN: Loughor; WT: River (Moving) W. Size: 9600 Metres.
Ref: FH3058

LOUGHOR VALLEY FISHERY

Loughor Valley Fishery, Ammanford, **CARMARTHENSHIRE**, SA18, **Wales**.
Contact/s: Mr Gareth Blyth (Manager).
(T) 01269 593868
Profile: FT: Game; WN: Loughor; WT: Lake (Still) W. Size: 2 Acres.
Ref: FH3059

LOUGHRIGG TARN

Loughrigg Tarn, Tarn Foot Farm, Loughrigg, Ambleside, **CUMBRIA**, LA22 9HF, **England**.
Contact/s: Manager, The National Trust, North West Regional Office, The Hollens, Grasmere, Ambleside, LA22 9QZ.
(T) 01539 435599 (F) 01539 435353
Mr M A Murphy.
(T) 01539 432596
Profile: FT: Combination; WN: Loughrigg; WT: Tarn (Still). Location: Main Rd: A593 Coniston Road from Ambleside.
Ref: FH3060

LOUGHS COY CULLIN

Loughs Coy Cullin, Tiernan Brothers, North Mayo Angling Advice Ctre, Upper Main St, Foxford, **COUNTY MAYO**, **Ireland**.
Contact/s: Mr P J Tiernan (Partner).
(T) 094 56731 (F) 094 56731
Profile: FT: Game; WN: Lough Coy Cullin; WT: Lake (Still) W. Size: 14000 Acres. Location: Rail: Foxford.
Ref: FH3061

LOUGHSIDE FISHERY

Loughside Fishery, Thurstonfield, Carlisle, **CUMBRIA**, CA5 6HB, **England**.
Contact/s: Mr Richard Wise (Manager).
(T) 01228 576552
Profile: FT: Game; WN: Loughside; WT: Lake (Still). Location: Nr. Rd: B5307; Main Rd: M6, junction 43, A595.
Ref: FH3062

LOUGHTON LODGE LAKE

Loughton Lodge Lake, National Badminton Ctre, Bradwell Rd, Milton Keynes, **BUCKINGHAMSHIRE**, MK8 9LA, **England**.
Contact/s: Secretary, Milton Keynes Angling Association, 11 Gilpin Way, Olney, Buckinghamshire.
(T) 01908 374400
Profile: FT: Coarse; WN: Loughton Lodge; WT: Lake (Still) W. Size: 20 Acres. Location: Nr. Rd: Bradwell Road; Main Rd: A509.
Ref: FH3063

LOUND WINDSURF LAKE

Lound Windsurf Lake, East Midlands Windsurf Ctre, Lound, Retford, **NOTTINGHAMSHIRE**, DN22, **England**.
Profile: FT: Coarse; WN: Lound Windsurf; WT: Lake (Still).
Ref: FH3064

LOVECLOUGH TROUT FISHERY

Loveclough Trout Fishery, Commercial St, Loveclough, Rossendale, **LANCASHIRE**, BB4 8RG, **England**.
Contact/s: Mrs Gwendolin Bumbill (Owner).
(T) 01706 212541
Profile: FT: Game; WN: Loveclough Trout; WT: Lake (Still) W. Size: 3 Acres. Location: Nr. Rd: A682; Main Rd: M66; Rail: Burnley.
Ref: FH3065

LOW GILL

Low Gill, Firbank, Sedbergh, **CUMBRIA**, LA10, **England**.
Contact/s: Mr A Barnes, Nettlepot, Firbank, Cumbria, LA10 5EG.
(T) 01539 620204
Profile: FT: Game; WN: Low Gill; WT: Reservoir (Still).
Ref: FH3066

LOW MAYNARD RESERVOIR

Low Maynard Reservoir, Tottenham, London, **LONDON (GREATER)**, N17, **England**.
Contact/s: Mr Chris King, Walthamstow Reservoir Group, Thames Water Gatehouse, 2 Forest Rd, Tottenham, London, N17 9NH.
(T) 020 88081527
Profile: FT: Coarse; WN: Low Maynard; WT: Reservoir (Still) W. Size: 30 Acres. Location: Nr. Rd: Forest Road; Main Rd: A10, North London; Rail: Tottenham Hale Underground.
Ref: FH3067

LOW OSGOODBY LAKE

Low Osgoodby Lake, Alma House, Low Osgoodby, Thirsk, **YORKSHIRE (NORTH)**, YO7 2AL, **England**.
Contact/s: Mr Alan Fawcett.
(T) 01845 597601
Profile: FT: Game; WN: Low Osgoodby; WT: Lake (Still) W. Size: 2 Acres. Location: Nr. Rd: Low Osgoodby; Main Rd: A19, A170; Rail: Thirsk. £Fr
Ref: FH3068

LOWBELL LANE

Lowbell Lane, London Colney, St Albans, **HERTFORDSHIRE**, AL2, **England**.
(W) www.badac.co.uk
Contact/s: Mr D Porter (Secretary), 72 Rivington Cres, Mill Hill, London, NW7 2LF.
(T) 020 84401303
Profile: FT: Coarse; WN: Lowbell Lane; WT: Lake (Still). Location: Nr. Rd: Lowbell Lane.
Ref: FH3069

LOWER ABERUTHVEN FISHINGS

Lower Aberuthven Fishings, Haugh Of Aberuthven, Auchterarder, **PERTH AND KINROSS**, PH3 1HL, **Scotland**.
Contact/s: Mr James Haggart (Director).
(T) 01738 730206 (F) 01738 730206 (M) 07971 432766
(E) jhaggart@lineone.net
Profile: FT: Combination; WN: Earn; WT: River (Moving) W. Size: 1100 Metres. Location: Nr. Rd: Perth to Stirling; Main Rd: A9; Rail: Gleneagles.
Ref: FH3070

LOWER BANN (RIVER)

River Lower Bann, Toome, Ballymena, **COUNTY ANTRIM**, BT44, **Northern Ireland**.
Contact/s: Manager, Kingfisher Angling Ctre, 24 Hiltonstown Rd, Portglenone, BT44 8EG.

(T) 028 25821301
Manager, Bannvalley Guns and Tackle, 18 Main St, Portglenone, Ballymena, BT44 8AB.
(T) 028 25821383
Profile: **FT:** Coarse; **WN:** Bann; **WT:** River (Moving).
Ref: FH3071

LOWER BANN (RIVER)

River Lower Bann, Magherafelt, **COUNTY LONDONDERRY**, BT45 8NA, **Northern Ireland**.
Contact/s: Manager, Bann System Limited, 56 Castlroe Rd, Coleraine, County Londonderry, BT81 3RL.
(T) 028 70444769
Mr Richard Mulholland, Lough Beg Coach Houses, Ballyscullion Park, Magherafelt, County Londonderry, BT45 8NA.
(T) 028 79386235
Profile: **FT:** Coarse; **WN:** Lower Bann; **WT:** River (Moving) **W. Size:** 22400 Metres.
Ref: FH3072

LOWER BENYONS

Lower Benyons, River Kennet, Sulhamstead, Reading, **BERKSHIRE**, RG, **England**.
Contact/s: **Mr Dusty Millar** (Associate members secretary), 238 Elgar Road South, Reading, Berkshire, RG3 0BW.
(T) 0118 9874882
Mr Mick Cox (Chief Bailiff), Dorstans, Hatch Lane, Brimpton Village, Reading, RG7 4TR.
(T) 0118 9714917
Profile: **FT:** Coarse; **WN:** Kennet; **WT:** River (Moving). **Location:** **Nr. Rd:** Sulhampstead.
Ref: FH3073

LOWER BROADHEATH POOLS

Lower Broadheath Pools, Processing Factory, Lower Broadheath, Worcester, **WORCESTERSHIRE**, WR, **England**.
Contact/s: **Mr John Jordan** (Bailiff).
(T) 01905 421357
Profile: **FT:** Coarse; **WN:** Lower Broadheath; **WT:** Pool (Still) **W. Size:** 5 Acres. **Location:** **Nr. Rd:** B4204; **Main Rd:** A443, A44.
Ref: FH3074

LOWER CASTLESHAW RESERVOIR

Lower Castleshaw Reservoir, Oldham, **MANCHESTER (GREATER)**, OL, **England**.
Contact/s: Manager, Oldham Angling Ctre, 159 Oldham Rd, Springhead, Oldham, OL4 4QJ.
(T) 0161 6247711
Mr J K Lees, 10 Packwood Chase, Oldham, Lancashire.
Profile: **FT:** Game; **WN:** Lower Castleshaw; **WT:** Reservoir (Still).
Ref: FH3075

LOWER COLDWELL RESERVOIR

Lower Coldwell Reservoir, Pendle, Burnley, **LANCASHIRE**, BB10, **England**.
Contact/s: **Mr Roy Rhodes** (Conservation, Access and Recreation Manager), Rivington Water Treatment Works, Bolton Rd, Horwich, Bolton, BL6 7RN.
(T) 01204 664300
Profile: **FT:** Game; **WN:** Lower Coldwell; **WT:** Reservoir (Still).
Ref: FH3076

LOWER DUNSFORTH (RIVER)

River Lower Dunsforth, Lower Dunsforth, York, **YORKSHIRE (NORTH)**, YO26, **England**.
Contact/s: **Mr Derek Taylor** (Secretary), Leeds ADASA, 75 Stoney Rock Lane, Beckett St, Leeds, LS29 7TB.
(T) 0113 2482373
Profile: **FT:** Coarse; **WN:** Low Dunsforth; **WT:** River (Moving) **W. Size:** 6400 Metres. **Location:** **Nr. Rd:** Low Dunsforth to Aldwark Bridge.
Ref: FH3077

LOWER FARLEYER BEAT

Lower Farleyer Beat, Kenmore, Aberfeldy, **PERTH AND KINROSS**, PH15, **Scotland**.
(W) www.fishingnet.com/beats/lowerfarleyer.htm
Contact/s: **Mr Freddie Dall** (Secretary), Ironside and Co Solicitors, Struan House, The Square, Aberfeldy, PH15 2DD.
(T) 01887 820820
Profile: **FT:** Combination; **WN:** Lower Farleyer; **WT:** Pool (Still).
Ref: FH3078

LOWER FRANDY

Lower Frandy, Kinross, **PERTH AND KINROSS**, KY13, **Scotland**.
Contact/s: **Mr Richard Philp** (owner).
(T) 01259 781448
Profile: **FT:** Game; **WN:** Lower Frandy; **WT:** Loch (Still).
Ref: FH3079

LOWER HALLACOMBE FISHERY

Lower Hallacombe Fishery, Lower Hallacombe, Crediton, **DEVON**, EX17 5BW, **England**.
Contact/s: **Mr David Blanchford**.
(T) 01363 84331
Profile: **FT:** Coarse; **WN:** Lower Hallacombe Fishery; **WT:** Lake (Still) **W. Size:** 1 Acre. **Location:** **Main Rd:** A377, west towards Copplestone.
Ref: FH3080

LOWER HILL FARM

Lower Hill Farm Pools & Caravan Park, Lower Hill Farm, Hughley, Much Welock, **SHROPSHIRE**, **England**.
Contact/s: **Mr Fred Crump** (Owner), FC Services Retail, 159 Heath Lane, West Bromwich, Midlands (West), B71 2BL.
(T) 0121 5675100
Profile: **FT:** Coarse; **WN:** Farm House Pool & Wood Pool; **WT:** Lake (Still); **F. Size:** 5 Acres; **W. Size:** 3 Acres. **Location:** **Nr. Rd:** Minor road just off the B4371; **Main Rd:** B4371 at Presthope.
Ref: FH3081

LOWER HONEYS GREEN FARM

Lower Honeys Green Farm, Framfield, Uckfield, **SUSSEX (EAST)**, TN22, **England**.
Contact/s: **Mr P C Harvey**.
(T) 01825 840334
Profile: **FT:** Coarse; **WN:** Lower Honeys Green Farm; **WT:** Pond (Still).
Ref: FH3082

LOWER HOUSE LODGE

Lower House Lodge, Knotts Lane, Burnley, **LANCASHIRE**, BB12 6NF, **England**.
Contact/s: **Mr Mike Cookson** (Secretary).
(T) 01282 412437
Profile: **FT:** Coarse; **WN:** Lower House Lodge; **WT:** Lake (Still). **Location:** **Nr. Rd:** Knotts Lane; **Main Rd:** A671.
Ref: FH3083

LOWER ITCHEN FISHERY

Lower Itchen Fishery, Embley Ridge, Gardeners Lane, Romsey, **HAMPSHIRE**, SO51 6AD, **England**.
Contact/s: **Ms Lyndsey Farmiloe** (Director).
(T) 023 80814389or023808472672 **(F)** 023 80814389 **(M)** 07885 175540or
Profile: **FT:** Combination; **WN:** Itchen; **WT:** River (Moving) **W. Size:** 5600 Metres. **Location:** **Nr. Rd:** A27 Mansbridge Road, opposite kennels; **Main Rd:** M27, junction 5; **Rail:** Southampton Parkway.
Ref: FH3084

LOWER LAKE

Lower Lake, Birkenhead Park, Ashville Road Or Park Prde, Birkenhead, **MERSEYSIDE**, CH, **England**.
Contact/s: **Mr Billing**.
(T) 0151 3343174
Profile: **FT:** Coarse; **WN:** Lower; **WT:** Lake (Still). **Location:** **Nr. Rd:** Ashville Road or Park Parade.
Ref: FH3085

LOWER LIDDLE (RIVER)

River Lower Liddle, Canonbie, **DUMFRIES AND GALLOWAY**, DG14, **Scotland**.
Contact/s: **Mr George Graham** (Head River Watcher), Hagg Old School House, Canonbie, Dumfries and Galloway.
(T) 01387 71416
Mr Tj Ewart (Secretary), Esk and Liddle Fisheries Association, Drapers, Douglas Sq, Newcastleton, Dumfries and Galloway.
(T) 01387 375257
Profile: **FT:** Game; **WN:** Liddle; **WT:** River (Moving).
Ref: FH3086

LOWER LLIW

Lower Lliw, Felindre, Swansea, SA, **Wales**.
Contact/s: **Mr Jock Milne** (Fishery Manager).
(T) 01792 799479
Profile: **FT:** Game; **WN:** Lower Lliw; **WT:** Reservoir (Still).
Ref: FH3087

LOWER LOUGH ERNE

Lower Lough Erne, Belleek, Enniskillen, **COUNTY FERMANAGH**, BT93 3, **Northern Ireland**.
Contact/s: Manager, Erne Tackle, 118 Main St, Lisnaskea, Enniskillen, BT92 0JD.
(T) 028 67721969
Mr Michael McGrath (Manager), Belleek Angling Ctre, The Thatch, Belleek, County Fermanagh, BT93 3FX.
(T) 028 68658181 **(F)** 028 68658181
Profile: **FT:** Game; **WN:** Lower Erne; **WT:** Lough (Still) **W. Size:** 37800 Acres.
Ref: FH3088

LOWER LOVELYNCH FISHERIES

Lower Lovelynch Fisheries, Lower Lovelynch Farm, Milverton, Taunton, **SOMERSET**, TA4 1NR, **England**.
Contact/s: **Mrs Wendy Loram**.
(T) 01823 451178
Profile: **FT:** Coarse; **WN:** Lower Lovelynch Fisheries; **WT:** Lake (Still) **W. Size:** 3 Acres. **Location:** **Nr. Rd:** Wellington to Milverton; **Main Rd:** B3187.
Ref: FH3089

LOWER MOOR FISHERY

Lower Moor Fishery, Oaksey, Malmesbury, **WILTSHIRE**, SN16 9TW, **England**.
Contact/s: **Mrs Anne Raines** (Owner).
(T) 01666 860232
Profile: **FT:** Combination; **WN:** Lower Moor Fishery; **WT:** Gravel Pit (Still); **F. Size:** 50 Acres; **W. Size:** 40 Acres. **Location:** **Nr. Rd:** Oaksey to Somerford; **Main Rd:** A419; **Rail:** Kemble.
Ref: FH3090

LOWER RIVINGTON RESERVOIR

Lower Rivington Reservoir, Ardwick Green, Chorley, **LANCASHIRE**, M12, **England**.
Contact/s: Manager, First Organisation, St Thomas Ctre, Ardwick Green, Lancashire, M12 6F2.
(T) 01257 483304
Mr Roy Rhodes (Conservation, Access and Recreation Manager), Rivington Water Treatment Works, Bolton Rd, Horwich, Bolton, BL6 7RN.
(T) 01204 664300
Profile: **FT:** Coarse; **WN:** Lower Rivington; **WT:** Reservoir (Still). **Location:** **Nr. Rd:** Rivington Lane; **Main Rd:** A673; **Rail:** Blackrod.
Ref: FH3091

LOWER RODDLESWORTH RESERVOIR

Lower Roddlesworth Reservoir, Chorley, **LANCASHIRE**, PR, **England**.
Contact/s: **Mr Bernard Wren** (Secretary), 1 Belmont Cl, Brinscall, Chorley, Lancashire, PR6 8SX.
(T) 01254 830935
Mr Roy Rhodes (Conservation, Access and Recreation Manager), Rivington Water

Treatment Works, Bolton Rd, Horwich, Bolton, BL6 7RN.
(T) 01204 664300
Profile: FT: Coarse; WN: Lower Roddlesworth; WT: Reservoir (Still).
Ref: FH3092

LOWER SCONE BEAT

Lower Scone Beat, Perth, **PERTH AND KINROSS**, PH, **Scotland**.
(W) www.fishingnet.com/beats/lowerscone.htm
Contact/s: **Mrs S Woods** (Secretary), Mansfield Estates, Scone Palace, Scone, Perth and Kinross, PH2 6BD.
(T) 01738 522308
Profile: FT: Combination; WN: See above; WT: Pool (Still).
Ref: FH3093

LOWER SLADE RESERVOIR

Lower Slade Reservoir, Lee Rd, Ilfracombe, **DEVON**, EX34, **England**.
Contact/s: Manager, Variety Sports, 23 Broad St, Ilfracombe, Devon, EX34 9EE.
(T) 01271 862039
Ranger, South West Water, Leisure Services, Highercoombe Park, Lewdown, Okehampton EX20 4QT.
(T) 01288 321262
Profile: FT: Coarse; WN: Lower Slade; WT: Reservoir (Still) W. Size: 6 Acres. Location: Nr. Rd: Lee Road; Main Rd: B323.
Ref: FH3094

LOWER TOWN HOUSE FISHERY

Lower Town House Fishery, Littleborough, **MANCHESTER (GREATER)**, OL15, **England**.
Contact/s: **Mr Ray Barber** (Secretary), Todmorden Angling Society, 12 Grisedale Drive, Burnley, Lancashire, BB12 8AR.
(T) 01282 423780 (M) 07970 897849
Profile: FT: Coarse; WN: Croft Head; WT: Reservoir (Still); F. Size: 10 Acres; W. Size: 4 Acres. Location: Nr. Rd: Calderbrook; Rail: Littleborough.
Ref: FH3095

LOWESWATER LAKE

Loweswater Lake, Water End Farm, Loweswater, Cockermouth, **CUMBRIA**, CA13 0SU, **England**.
Contact/s: Manager, The National Trust, North West Regional Office, The Hollens, Grasmere, Ambleside, LA22 9QZ.
(T) 01539 435599 (F) 01539 435353
Mr Mark Astley (Warden), National Trust, Beckfoot Office, Ennerdale, Cleator, Cumbria, CA23 3AU.
(T) 01946 861235 (F) 01946 861235
(E) rennpm@smtp.ntrust.org.uk
Profile: FT: Combination; WN: Loweswater; WT: Lake (Still). Location: Main Rd: A5086; Rail: Workington.
Ref: FH3096

LOWRYS LAKE

Lowrys Lake, Armagh Fisheries Limited, Armagh, **COUNTY ARMAGH**, BT60, **Northern Ireland**.
Contact/s: **Mr Cathal Doyle** (Secretary), Armagh Fisheries Ltd, 6 Knockamell Park, Armagh, County Armagh, BT61 7HJ.
(T) 028 37522068after6pm
Mr Dessie Cartmill (Manager), Armagh Fisheries Ltd, G I Stores, 5 Dobbin St, Armagh, County Armagh.
(T) 028 37522335 (F) 028 37522335
Profile: FT: Game; WN: Lowry's; WT: Lake (Still) W. Size: 34 Acres. Location: Nr. Rd: A51 to Tandragee; Main Rd: A51.
Ref: FH3097

LOWTHER (RIVER)

River Lowther, Crown And Mitre Hotel, Bampton Grange, Penrith, **CUMBRIA**, CA10, **England**.
Contact/s: **Mr Charles Sykes**, Charles R Sykes (Gunsmiths), 4 Great Dockray, Penrith, Cumbria, CA11 7BL.
(T) 01768 862418 (F) 01768 862418
Profile: FT: Game; WN: Lowther; WT: River (Moving) W. Size: 4800 Metres.
Ref: FH3098

LOWTHER LAKE

Lowther Lake, Ninevah Lane, Allerton Bywater, Castleford, **YORKSHIRE (WEST)**, WF10 2EW, **England**.
Contact/s: **Mr Barry Wright** (Match Secretary).
(T) 01977 559022
Profile: FT: Coarse; WN: Lowther Lake; WT: Lake (Still); F. Size: 30 Acres; W. Size: 23 Acres. Location: Nr. Rd: Ninevah Lane; Main Rd: A656; Rail: Castleford.
Ref: FH3099

LOYNTON TROUT FISHERIES

Loynton Trout Fisheries, Loynton, Woodseaves, Stafford, **STAFFORDSHIRE**, ST20 0QA, **England**.
Mr Steve Masters (Owner).
(T) 01785 284261 (F) 01785 284616
Profile: FT: Game; WN: Loynton Trout Fisheries; WT: Lake (Still); F. Size: 60 Acres; W. Size: 12 Acres. Location: Nr. Rd: Newport to Eccleshall; Main Rd: A519; Rail: Telford.
Ref: FH3100

LUCCOMBES PONDS

Luccombes Ponds, Luccombes Coarse Fishery, Luccombes Barn, Towsington Lane, Exminster, Exeter, **DEVON**, EX6 8AY, **England**.
Contact/s: **Mr Julian Harrod** (Owner).
(T) 01392 832858 (M) 07970 717225
Profile: FT: Coarse; WN: Luccombes Ponds; WT: Lake (Still) W. Size: 1 Acre. Location: Nr. Rd: Towsington Lane; Main Rd: A38, A30, M5; Rail: Exeter. £Fr
Ref: FH3101

LUCKFIELD LAKE FISHERY

Luckfield Lake Fishery, Water Gate Lane, Broadmayne, Dorchester, **DORSET**, DT2, **England**.
Contact/s: **Mr John Alpin**, Specialist Angling Supplies, 1 Athelstan Rd, Dorchester, DT1 1NR.
(T) 01305 266500 (M) 07889 680464
Profile: FT: Coarse; WN: Luckfield; WT: Gravel Pit (Still) W. Size: 2 Acres. Location: Nr. Rd: Water Gate Lane; Main Rd: A352.
Ref: FH3102

LUDCHURCH LAKE

Ludchurch Lake, Ludchurch Farm, Ludchurch, Narberth, **PEMBROKESHIRE**, SA67 8JE, **Wales**.
Contact/s: **Mr Govan Davies** (Manager).
(T) 01834 831255
Profile: FT: Coarse; WN: Ludchurch; WT: Lake (Still) W. Size: 3 Acres. Location: Nr. Rd: Narberth to Amroth; Main Rd: A477, St Clears to Tenby; Rail: Narberth.
Ref: FH3103

LUDWORTH RESERVOIR

Ludworth Reservoir, Stockport, **MANCHESTER (GREATER)**, SK, **England**.
Contact/s: **Mr L Donaldson**, 57 The Ridgeway, Romiley, Stockport, SK6 3HA.
Profile: FT: Coarse; WN: Ludworth; WT: Reservoir (Still).
Ref: FH3104

LUGG (RIVER)

River Lugg, Hereford, **HEREFORDSHIRE**, HR, **England**.
Contact/s: **Mr J H Andrews** (Secretary), Meadow View, Dinedor, Hereford.
(T) 01432 870301
Profile: FT: Game; WN: Lugg; WT: River (Moving) W. Size: 20800 Metres.
Ref: FH3105

LUGG (RIVER)

River Lugg, Mordiford, Hereford, **HEREFORDSHIRE**, HR1, **England**.
Contact/s: Fishery Manager.
(T) 01568 611593
Profile: FT: Coarse; WN: Lugg; WT: River (Moving).
Ref: FH3106

LUNE (RIVER)

River Lune, Tebay, Penrith, **CUMBRIA**, CA10, **England**.
Contact/s: **Mr Harold Riley** (Secretary), Tebay Anglers, White Cross House, Tebay, Penrith, Cumbria.
(T) 01539 624376
Profile: FT: Game; WN: Lune; WT: River (Moving) W. Size: 27200 Metres. Location: Nr. Rd: M6; Main Rd: A598; Rail: Penrith.
Ref: FH3107

LUNE (RIVER)

River Lune, Howgills Valley, Sedbergh, **CUMBRIA**, LA10, **England**.
Contact/s: **Mr D Eccles** (Director), Three Peaks Ltd, 25 Main St, Sedbergh, Cumbria, LA10 5BW.
(T) 01539 620446
Profile: FT: Game; WN: Lune; WT: River (Moving). Location: Main Rd: A684; Rail: Kendal.
Ref: FH3108

LUNE (RIVER)

Lune (River), Drybeck, Nr Killington, Sedburgh, **CUMBRIA**, **England**.
Contact/s: **Mr John Turner** (Hon Secretary), Prince Albert Angling Society, 15 Pexhill Drive, Macclesfield, Cheshire, SK10 3LP.
(T) 01625 422010
Profile: FT: Game; WN: Lune; WT: River (Moving) W. Size: 1200 Metres. Location: Nr. Rd: A683; Rail: Kendal.
Ref: FH3109

LUNE (RIVER)

River Lune, Penrith, **CUMBRIA**, CA10 3, **England**.
Contact/s: Secretary, Tebay and District Angling Association, Cross Keys Inn, Tebay, Penrith, Cumbria, CA10 3UY.
Profile: FT: Game; WN: Lune; WT: River (Moving).
Ref: FH3110

LUNE (RIVER)

River Lune, Halton, Lancaster, **LANCASHIRE**, LA2, **England**.
Contact/s: **Mr Stephen Fawcetts** (Manager), Guns and Tackle, 7 Great John St, Lancaster, Lancashire, LA1 1NQ.
(T) 01524 32033
Profile: FT: Game; WN: Lune; WT: River (Moving).
Ref: FH3111

LUNE (RIVER)

River Lune (The), Bentham, Lancaster, **LANCASHIRE**, LA2, **England**.
Contact/s: **Mr Mick Ramsey** (Treasurer), 10 Mount Pleasant Trce, Bentham, Lancaster, Lancashire, LA2 7LB.
(T) 01524 262041
Profile: FT: Game; WN: Lune; WT: Tributary (Moving) W. Size: 6437 Metres. Location: Main Rd: A65; Rail: Bentham.
Ref: FH3112

LUNG RIVER

Lung River, Ballaghaderren, **COUNTY ROSCOMMON**, **Ireland**.
Contact/s: **Mr Jimmy Cogan** (Water Keeper), Lung Valley, Kilcolman Rd, Ballaghaderren, County Roscommon, Ireland.
(T) 090 760077or761544
Profile: FT: Game; WN: Lung; WT: River (Moving) W. Size: 35200 Metres. Location: Main Rd: N5; Rail: Castlerea.
Ref: FH3113

LYDNEY BOATING LAKE

Lydney Boating Lake, Chepstow, Lydney, **GLOUCESTERSHIRE**, GL15, **England**.
Contact/s: **Mr K Jones**, Lydney Angling Club, 45 Hughes Cres, Garden City, Chepstow, Gloucestershire.

Profile: **FT:** Coarse; **WN:** Lydney; **WT:** Lake (Still) **W. Size:** 5 Acres. **Location:** **Nr. Rd:** A48 Chepstow to Gloucester.
Ref: FH3114

LYMM DAM

Lymm Dam, Lymm, Warrington, **CHESHIRE**, WA, **England**.
Contact/s: **Mr Neil Jupp** (Club Secretary), Lymm Angling Club, PO Box 350, Warrington, Cheshire, WA2 9FB.
(T) 01925 411774
Profile: **FT:** Coarse; **WN:** Lymm Dam; **WT:** Lake (Still) **W. Size:** 15 Acres. **Location:** **Nr. Rd:** A56; **Main Rd:** M6, M56, or A50.
Ref: FH3115

LYMM VALE

Lymm Vale, Winsford, **CHESHIRE**, CW7, **England**.
Contact/s: **Mr Neil Jupp** (Club Secretary), Lymm Angling Club, PO Box 350, Warrington, Cheshire, WA2 9FB.
(T) 01925 411774
Profile: **FT:** Coarse; **WN:** Lymm Vale; **WT:** Quarry (Still) **W. Size:** 4 Acres. **Location:** **Nr. Rd:** Daleford's Lane; **Main Rd:** A49.
Ref: FH3116

LYMOOR POOL 1 AND 2

Lymoor Pool 1 And 2, Powys Estate, Newtown, Ebbw Vale, **BLAENAU GWENT**, NP23 5, **Wales**.
Contact/s: **Mr Steve Potts** (Secretary), Severnside and Newtown Angling Club, 902 Falcon Court, Newton, Powys, SY16 1LQ.
(T) 01686 624871
Profile: **FT:** Coarse; **WN:** Lymoor Pool 1 And 2; **WT:** Pool (Still) **W. Size:** 16 Acres.
Ref: FH3117

LYN (RIVER)

River Lyn, Lynton, Lynmouth, **DEVON**, EX35 6, **England**.
Contact/s: Fisheries Contact.
(T) 01398 371119
Manager, Lynton Toruist Office, Townhall, Lynton, Devon.
(T) 01598 752225
Profile: **FT:** Game; **WN:** Lyn; **WT:** River (Moving).
Ref: FH3118

LYNCHGATE LANE FISHERY

Lynchgate Lane Fishery, Lynchgate Farm, Lynchgate Lane, Burbage, Hinckley, **LEICESTERSHIRE**, LE10 2DS, **England**.
Contact/s: **Mr Tony Saunders** (Owner), Lynchgate Farm, Lynchgate Lane, Burbage, Hinkley, Leicestershire, LE10 2DS.
(T) 01455 631470
Profile: **FT:** Coarse; **WN:** Lynchgate Lane Fishery; **WT:** Lake (Still); **F. Size:** 5 Acres; **W. Size:** 2 Acres. **Location:** **Nr. Rd:** Lynchgate Lane; **Main Rd:** B578; **Rail:** Hinkley.
Ref: FH3119

LYNDHURST FARM LAKE

Lyndhurst Farm Lake, Halfpenny Lane, Longridge, Preston, **LANCASHIRE**, PR, **England**.
Contact/s: Fishery Manager.
(T) 01772 786420
Profile: **FT:** Coarse; **WN:** Lyndhurst; **WT:** Lake (Still) **W. Size:** 2 Acres. **Location:** **Nr. Rd:** Halfpenny Lane; **Main Rd:** B6243.
Ref: FH3120

LYNDHURST LAKE

Lyndhurst Lake, Parkhill Hotel, Beaulieu Rd, Lyndhurst, **HAMPSHIRE**, SO45 4PT, **England**.
Contact/s: Manager.
(T) 023 80619491
Mr J Remington (Secretary), Eastleigh and District Angling Club, 121 Desborough Rd, Eastleigh, Hampshire, SO50 5NP.
(T) 023 80635540
Profile: **FT:** Coarse; **WN:** Lyndhurst; **WT:** Lake (Still). **Location:** **Nr. Rd:** B3056, Beaulieu Road; **Main Rd:** M27, junction 1, A337, A35.
Ref: FH3121

LYNE (RIVER)

River Lyne, Market Sq, Coldstream, **NORTHUMBERLAND**, TD12, **England**.
Contact/s: **Mr H F Bell** (Secretary), 12 Priory Hill, Coldstream, Scottish Borders.
Profile: **FT:** Game; **WN:** Lyne; **WT:** River (Moving).
Ref: FH3122

LYNG PIT

Lyng Pit, Lyng, Norwich, **NORFOLK**, NR9, **England**.
Contact/s: Fishery Manager.
Profile: **FT:** Coarse; **WN:** Lyng; **WT:** Gravel Pit (Still).
Ref: FH3123

LYNHER (RIVER)

River Lynher, Lynher Farm, Liskeard, **CORNWALL**, PL14, **England**.
Contact/s: **Mr Bill Eliot** (Secretary), Liskeard and District Angling Club, 64 Portbyhan Rd, West Looe, Cornwall, PL13 2QN.
(T) 01503 264173
Profile: **FT:** Game; **WN:** Lynher; **WT:** River (Moving) **W. Size:** 15000 Metres. **Location:** **Nr. Rd:** A38; **Main Rd:** A38; **Rail:** Liskeard.
Ref: FH3124

LYNN POOL FISHERY

Lynn Pool, Corby, **NORTHAMPTONSHIRE**, **England**.
Contact/s: **Mr Mark Goodsir** (Owner), 196 Studfall Avenue, Corby, Northamptonshire, NN17 1LJ.
(T) 01536 203035
Profile: **FT:** Coarse; **WN:** Lynn Pool; **WT:** Pool (Still); **F. Size:** 3 Acres; **W. Size:** 2 Acres. **Location:** **Nr. Rd:** A43; **Rail:** Corby.
Ref: FH3125

LYONS GATE CARAVAN PARK

Lyons Gate Caravan Park, Lyons Gate, Cerne Abbas, Dorchester, **DORSET**, DT2 7, **England**.
Contact/s: **Mr Derek Powell**.
(T) 01300 345260
Profile: **FT:** Coarse; **WN:** Lyon's Gate Caravan Park; **WT:** Lake (Still). **Location:** **Nr. Rd:** A352.
Ref: FH3126

MACBIEHILL ESTATE

Macbiehill Estate, Macbiehill, West Linton, **SCOTTISH BORDERS**, EH46 7AZ, **Scotland**.
(W) www.fishingscotland.net
Contact/s: **Ms Marian Black** (Proprietor).
(T) 01968 660879 **(M)** 07768 042456
(E) enquires@fishingscotland.net
Profile: **FT:** Game; **WN:** Macbiehill; **WT:** Loch (Still) **W. Size:** 4 Acres. **Location:** **Nr. Rd:** A701; **Main Rd:** A701.
Ref: FH3127

MACCLESFIELD CANAL

Macclesfield Canal, Buxton Rd, Macclesfield, **CHESHIRE**, **England**.
Contact/s: **Mr John Turner** (Hon Secretary), Prince Albert Angling Society, 15 Pexhill Drive, Macclesfield, Cheshire, SK10 3LP.
(T) 01625 422010
Profile: **FT:** Coarse; **WN:** Macclesfield Canal; **WT:** Canal (Still). **Location:** **Nr. Rd:** A523; **Rail:** Macclesfield.
Ref: FH3128

MACCLESFIELD CANAL

Macclesfield Canal, Congleton, **CHESHIRE**, CW12, **England**.
Contact/s: Fishery Manager.
(T) 01782 514960
Profile: **FT:** Coarse; **WN:** Macclesfield; **WT:** Canal (Still).
Ref: FH3129

MACCLESFIELD CANAL

Macclesfield Canal, Marple, Stockport, **MANCHESTER (GREATER)**, SK6, **England**.
Contact/s: **Mr Griffiths** (Fishery Manager).
(T) 01606 723800
Profile: **FT:** Coarse; **WN:** Macclesfield; **WT:** Canal (Still).
Ref: FH3130

MACCLESFIELD CANAL

Macclesfield Canal, Kidsgrove, Stoke-on-Trent, **STAFFORDSHIRE**, ST7, **England**.
Contact/s: Fishery Manager.
(T) 01782 815523
Profile: **FT:** Coarse; **WN:** Macclesfield; **WT:** Canal (Still).
Ref: FH3131

MACHINE POND

Machine Pond, Warwick Rd, Brynmawr, Ebbw Vale, **BLAENAU GWENT**, NP23 4AR, **Wales**.
Contact/s: **Mr R Satterley** (Secretary), 8 Pen-y-lan, Ebbw Vale, Gwent, NP3 5LS.
Profile: **FT:** Coarse; **WN:** Machine; **WT:** Pond (Still). **Location:** **Nr. Rd:** A465; **Main Rd:** A467.
Ref: FH3132

MACOSQUIN (RIVER)

River Macosquin, Coleraine, **COUNTY LONDONDERRY**, BT51, **Northern Ireland**.
Contact/s: Manager, The Great Outdoors, 21 Society St, Colerine, County Londonderry, BT52 1LA.
(T) 028 70320701
Manager, Smyth's Country Sports, 1 Park St, Colerine, County Londonderry, BT52 1BD.
(T) 028 70343970 **(F)** 028 70343970
Af White (Manager), Rite Price Carpets, Cloyfin Rd, Colerine, County Londonderry, BT52 2N.
(T) 028 70344482
Profile: **FT:** Game; **WN:** Macosquin; **WT:** Tributary (Moving) **W. Size:** 12800 Metres.
Ref: FH3133

MADELEY POOL

Madeley Pool, Moss Lane, Newcastle-under-Lyme, **STAFFORDSHIRE**, ST5, **England**.
Contact/s: **Mr S D Long** (Area Supervisor), Newcastle-under-Lyme Borough Council, Civic Offices, Merrial St, Newcastle, Staffordshire, ST5 2AG.
(T) 01782 717717ext2633 **(F)** 01782 711032
Profile: **FT:** Coarse; **WN:** Madeley; **WT:** Pool (Still); **F. Size:** 1 Acre. **Location:** **Nr. Rd:** Moss Lane.
Ref: FH3134

MAERDY BROOK

Maerdy Brook, Llandrinio, Llanymynech, **POWYS**, SY22, **Wales**.
Contact/s: **Mr Terry Pain** (Secretary), 16 Highfield, Ferndale, Rhondda, Glamorgan (Vale of), CF43 4TA.
Profile: **FT:** Combination; **WN:** Maerdy; **WT:** Brook (Moving).
Ref: FH3135

MAES GWYN FISHERY

Maes Gwyn Fishery, Ammanford Rd, Craig Cefn Parc, Swansea, SA6 5RT, **Wales**.
Contact/s: **Mr Paul Coleman** (Proprietor).
(T) 01792 846488 **(F)** 01792 846488
(E) paulcoleman@btinternet.com
Profile: **FT:** Combination; **WN:** Maes Gwyn Fishery; **WT:** Pond (Still) **W. Size:** 5 Acres. **Location:** **Nr. Rd:** Ammanford Road; **Main Rd:** M4, junction 46; **Rail:** Swansea.
Ref: FH3136

MAES-ISAF FISHERY

Maes-Isaf Fishery, Llanybydder, **CARMARTHENSHIRE**, SA40, **Wales**.
(W) www.fishing-in-wales.co.uk/llandysul-aa/beat7
Contact/s: **Mr Artie Jones** (Hon Secretary), Llandysul Angling Association, Glas-y-Dorlan, Llyn-y-Fran Rd, Llandysul,

SA44 4JW.
(T) 01559 362317
Profile: **FT:** Game; **WN:** Teifi; **WT:** River (Moving) **W. Size:** 1600 Metres. **Location:** **Nr. Rd:** A485.
Ref: FH3137

MAGIC LAKE

Magic Lake, Waltham Abbey, **ESSEX**, EN9, **England**.
Contact/s: **Mr Derek Wooldridge** (Fishery Manager).
(T) 01992 767772
Profile: **FT:** Coarse; **WN:** Magic; **WT:** Lake (Still). **Location:** **Nr. Rd:** Parklands to Pickhill road; **Main Rd:** M25, junction 26 to A112.
Ref: FH3138

MAGPIE LAKE

Magpie Lake, Landbeach, Cambridge, **CAMBRIDGESHIRE**, CB4 8EA, **England**.
Contact/s: Manager, Farrington, 2-4 Ferry Lane, Cambridge, Cambridgeshire, CB4 1NT.
(T) 01223 461361
Manager.
(T) 01223 862951
Profile: **FT:** Coarse; **WN:** Magpie; **WT:** Lake (Still). **Location:** **Nr. Rd:** Waterbeach Road; **Main Rd:** A10.
Ref: FH3139

MAICH WATERS

Maich Waters, Maich Fishery, Wadlin, Ladyland Moor, Lochwinnoch, **RENFREWSHIRE**, PA12 4BN, **Scotland**.
Contact/s: **Mr Jim Morton** (Manager).
(T) 01505 842341
Profile: **FT:** Game; **WN:** Maich Waters; **WT:** Dam (Still) **W. Size:** 1 Acre. **Location:** **Main Rd:** A760; **Rail:** Lochwinnoch.
Ref: FH3140

MAIN TYNE

Main Tyne, Heddon Haugh, Heddon-on-the-Wall, Newcastle Upon Tyne, **TYNE AND WEAR**, NE15, **England**.
Contact/s: **Mr Barry Hignett** (Secretary), Ferryhill and District Angling Club, 74 Grasmere Rd, Garden Farm Estate, Chester-le-Street, County Durham.
(T) 0191 3883557
Mr W Curtis (Chairman), 14 Bakewell Pl, Newton Aycliffe, County Durham.
(T) 01325 320291
Profile: **FT:** Combination; **WN:** Main Tyne; **WT:** River (Moving) **W. Size:** 1600 Metres.
Ref: FH3141

MAINE (RIVER)

River Maine, Randalstown, **COUNTY ANTRIM**, BT41, **Northern Ireland**.
Contact/s: **Mr Shane O'Neill** (Agent), The Estate Office, Shanes Castle, Antrim, BT41 4NE.
(T) 028 94428216 **(F)** 028 94468457
Profile: **FT:** Game; **WN:** Maine; **WT:** River (Moving) **W. Size:** 4000 Metres.
Ref: FH3142

MAINE (RIVER)

River Maine, Shanes Castle, The Estate Office, Antrim, **COUNTY ANTRIM**, BT41 4NE, **Northern Ireland**.
Contact/s: Manager, Simpson's Newsagent, 52 Main St, Cullybackley, Ballymena, BT42 1BW.
(T) 028 25880264
Mr Shane O'Neill (Agent), The Estate Office, Shanes Castle, Antrim, BT41 4NE.
(T) 028 94428216 **(F)** 028 94468457
Profile: **FT:** Game; **WN:** Maine; **WT:** River (Moving).
Ref: FH3143

MAINE (RIVER)

River Maine, Cullybackey, Ballymena, **COUNTY ANTRIM**, BT43, **Northern Ireland**.
Contact/s: **Mr E Kennedy**, 8 Dromona Rd, Cullybackey, Ballymena, County Antrim, BT42 1NT.
(T) 028 25880752
Profile: **FT:** Game; **WN:** Maine; **WT:** River (Moving) **W. Size:** 5600 Metres.
Ref: FH3144

MAINE (RIVER)

River Maine, Ballymena, **COUNTY ANTRIM**, BT42, **Northern Ireland**.
Contact/s: **M Weir**, 23 Beechwood Avenue, Ahoghill, County Antrim.
(T) 028 25871242
Mr S Tuff, 122 Toome Rd, Ballymena, County Antrim.
(T) 028 2545202after5pm
Profile: **FT:** Game; **WN:** Maine; **WT:** River (Moving) **W. Size:** 6400 Metres.
Ref: FH3145

MAINE (RIVER)

River Maine, Randalstown, **COUNTY ANTRIM**, BT41, **Northern Ireland**.
Contact/s: **Mr Billy Mawhinney**, Whinney Hill, Randalstown, Ballymena, County Antrim.
(T) 028 94472409
Mr John Ellis, 92 Ahoghill Rd, Randalstown, BT41 3DG.
(T) 028 94479475
Profile: **FT:** Game; **WN:** Maine; **WT:** River (Moving) **W. Size:** 8000 Metres.
Ref: FH3146

MAINS OF MURTHLY

Mains Of Murthly, Aberfeldy, **PERTH AND KINROSS**, PH15, **Scotland**.
(W) www.fishingnet.com/beats/grandtullycastle.htm
Contact/s: **Mr Messrs McDiarmid**, Mains of Murthly, Aberfeldy, Perth and Kinross, PH15 2EA.
(T) 01887 820427
Profile: **FT:** Combination; **WN:** See above; **WT:** Pool (Still).
Ref: FH3147

MAINS OF PENNINGHAM FISHERY

Mains Of Penningham Fishery, 9 Dunkkitterick Drive, Newton Stewart, **DUMFRIES AND GALLOWAY**, DG8 6PB, **Scotland**.
Contact/s: **Jack** (Manager).
(T) 01671 403787
Profile: **FT:** Game; **WN:** Mains Of Penningham Fishery; **WT:** Loch (Still).
Ref: FH3148

MAINSFORTH POND

Mainsforth Pond, Ferryhill Station, Ferryhill, **COUNTY DURHAM**, DL17, **England**.
Contact/s: **Mr Barry Hignett** (Secretary), Ferryhill and District Angling Club, 74 Grasmere Rd, Garden Farm Estate, Chester-le-Street, County Durham.
(T) 0191 3883557
Mr W Curtis (Chairman), 14 Bakewell Pl, Newton Aycliffe, County Durham.
(T) 01325 320291
Profile: **FT:** Coarse; **WN:** Mainsforth; **WT:** Pond (Still). **Location:** **Nr. Rd:** Ferryhill Station; **Main Rd:** A1(M); **Rail:** Ferryhill.
Ref: FH3149

MAKIN FISHERIES

Makin Fisheries, Preston Innovations Makin Fisheries, The Roost, Wolvey Rd, Bulkington, Bedworth, **WARWICKSHIRE**, CV12 9JX, **England**.
Contact/s: **Mr William Makin**.
(T) 01455 220502
Ms Jan Porter.
(T) 0115 9664785
Profile: **FT:** Combination; **WN:** Makin; **WT:** Pool (Still). **Location:** **Nr. Rd:** Bulkington to Bramcote; **Main Rd:** M69, B4065; **Rail:** Nuneaton.
Ref: FH3150

MALEY GRAVEL PITS

Maley Gravel Pits, Maxey, Peterborough, **CAMBRIDGESHIRE**, PE6, **England**.
Contact/s: **Mr D Bailey** (Secretary).
(T) 01778 346355
Profile: **FT:** Coarse; **WN:** Maley; **WT:** Gravel Pit (Still).
Ref: FH3151

MALLORY PARK FISHERIES

Mallory Park Fisheries, Kirkby Mallory, Leicester, **LEICESTERSHIRE**, LE, **England**.
Contact/s: Manager, Sportsman Lodge, 39 Tudor Rd, Leicester, Leicestershire, LE3 5JF.
(T) 0116 2537714
Mr Roy Marlow, Mallory Fisheries, PO Box 5041, Leicester, LE8 6WR.
(T) 0116 2774131
Profile: **FT:** Coarse; **WN:** Mallory Park Fisheries; **WT:** Lake (Still) **W. Size:** 22 Acres. **Location:** **Nr. Rd:** Peckelton Common Road; **Main Rd:** A4.
Ref: FH3152

MALTINGS FISHERY

Maltings Fishery, Dunbar Trout Farm, West Barn, Dunbar, Haddington, **LOTHIAN (EAST)**, EH41, **Scotland**.
Contact/s: Fishery Manager.
(T) 01368 863244
Profile: **FT:** Coarse; **WN:** Maltings Fishery; **WT:** Lake (Still).
Ref: FH3153

MANCH HOUSE FISHERY

Manch House Fishery, Manch House, Ballineen, **COUNTY CORK**, **Ireland**.
(W) www.manchhouse.com
Contact/s: **Mr C H Conner** (Fishery Manager).
(T) 023 47256 **(F)** 023 47276
(E) conner@manchhouse.com
Profile: **FT:** Game; **WN:** Bandon; **WT:** River (Moving) **W. Size:** 3000 Metres. **Location:** **Main Rd:** R586; **Rail:** Cork.
Ref: FH3154

MANCHESTER CANAL

Manchester Canal, Hall Lane, Manchester, **MANCHESTER (GREATER)**, M, **England**.
Contact/s: **Mr Terence A McKee** (Secretary), Bolton and District Angling Association, 1 Lever Edge Lane, Bolton, Lancashire, BL3 3BU.
(T) 01204 393726
Profile: **FT:** Coarse; **WN:** Manchester; **WT:** Canal (Still). **Location:** **Nr. Rd:** Hall Lane to Blue Wall.
Ref: FH3155

MANCHESTER/BOLTON/BURY CANAL

Manchester, Bolton And Bury Canal, Tonge, Bolton, **LANCASHIRE**, BL2, **England**.
Contact/s: Fishery Manager.
(T) 01204 593640
Profile: **FT:** Coarse; **WN:** Manchester, Bolton and Bury; **WT:** Canal (Still).
Ref: FH3156

MANCHESTER/BOLTON/BURY CANAL

Manchester, Bolton And Bury Canal, Radcliffe, Manchester, **MANCHESTER (GREATER)**, M26, **England**.
Contact/s: **Mr Terence A McKee** (Secretary), Bolton and District Angling Association, 1 Lever Edge Lane, Bolton, Lancashire, BL3 3BU.
(T) 01204 393726
Profile: **FT:** Coarse; **WN:** Manchester, Bolton and Bury; **WT:** Canal (Still).
Ref: FH3157

MANCHESTER/BOLTON/BURY CANAL

Manchester, Bolton And Bury Canal, Bury, **MANCHESTER (GREATER)**, BL, **England**.
Contact/s: Fishery Manager.
(T) 01829 732748
Profile: **FT:** Coarse; **WN:** Manchester, Bolton And Bury Canal; **WT:** Canal (Still).
Ref: FH3158

MANNINGTREE RIVER POOLS

Manningtree River Pools, Manningtree, Colchester, **ESSEX**, CO, **England**.
Profile: **FT:** Coarse; **WN:** Manningtree River; **WT:** Pool (Still). **Location:** **Nr. Rd:** A137;

Main Rd: A12332 or A12.
Ref: FH3159

MANOR BROOK LAKE

Manor Brook Lake, The Leigh, Ashton Keynes, Swindon, **WILTSHIRE**, SN6, **England**.
Contact/s: Manager, Cotswold Aquarius, The Old Brickyard, Northend, Ashton Keynes, Swindon, SN6 6QR.
(T) 01285 650169
Mr Harry Harman (Fishery Manager).
(T) 01452 306050
Profile: **FT:** Combination; **WN:** Manor Brook; **WT:** Gravel Pit (Still) **W. Size:** 45 Acres. **Location:** **Nr. Rd:** A149.
Ref: FH3160

MANOR FARM

Manor Farm, Frolesworth, Lutterworth, **LEICESTERSHIRE**, LE17, **England**.
Contact/s: **Mr A Smith** (Secretary), 10 Londs Avenue, Leicester, Leicestershire, LE4 2HY.
(T) 0116 2357210
Mr G Taylor (Membership Secretary), Broome Angling Society, 100 New Romney Cres, Leicester.
(T) 0116 2417018
Profile: **FT:** Coarse; **WN:** Manor Farm; **WT:** Lake (Still) **W. Size:** 25 Acres. **Location:** **Main Rd:** M1; **Rail:** Leicester.
Ref: FH3161

MANOR FARM LAKE

Manor Farm Lake, Shimano Linear Fisheries (Oxford), Smiths Concrete Site, Hardwick Village, Witney, **OXFORDSHIRE**, OX8 7Q, **England**.
Contact/s: **Mr Len Gurd** (Owner), 10A Rackstraw Gr, Old Farm Park, Milton Keynes, Buckinghamshire, MK7 8PZ.
(T) 01908 645135 **(F)** 01908 645115
Profile: **FT:** Coarse; **WN:** Manor; **WT:** Lake (Still); **F. Size:** 20 Acres; **W. Size:** 15 Acres. **Location:** **Nr. Rd:** B4449; **Main Rd:** A40; **Rail:** Oxford.
Ref: FH3162

MANOR FARM LEISURE

Manor Farm Leisure, Manor Farm, Lower Caldecote, Biggleswade, **BEDFORDSHIRE**, SG18 9BB, **England**.
(W) www.manorfarmfishings.co.uk
Contact/s: **Mr Andrew Worboys** (Owner).
(T) 01767 313802 **(F)** 01767 313835
Mrs Sue Worboys (Owner).
(T) 01767 313802 **(F)** 01767 313802
(E) sueworboys@manorfarmleisure.fsnet.co.uk
Profile: **FT:** Combination; **WN:** Ivel; **WT:** Combination (Still); **F. Size:** 86 Acres; **W. Size:** 15 Acres. **Location:** **Nr. Rd:** A1; **Main Rd:** A1; **Rail:** Biggleswade. £Fr
Ref: FH3163

MANOR FARM POND

Manor Farm Pond, Malton, **YORKSHIRE (NORTH)**, YO17 6PY, **England**.
Contact/s: Fishery Manager.
(T) 01653 668458
Profile: **FT:** Coarse; **WN:** Manor; **WT:** Pond (Still).
Ref: FH3164

MANOR FARM POOLS

Manor Farm Pools, Manor Farm, Main Rd, Upton, Hinckley, **LEICESTERSHIRE**, CV13 6JX, **England**.
Contact/s: **Mr Chris White** (Manager), Manor Farm, Main Rd, Upton, Nr Hinkley, Leicester.
(T) 01455 212374
Profile: **FT:** Coarse; **WN:** Manor Farm; **WT:** Pool (Still) **W. Size:** 1 Acre. **Location:** **Nr. Rd:** Main Road; **Main Rd:** A444; **Rail:** Atherstone.
Ref: FH3165

MANOR HOUSE

Manor House, Deddington, Oxford, **OXFORDSHIRE**, OX2, **England**.
Contact/s: **Mrs B Alt** (Manager).
(T) 01869 338207 **(F)** 01869 338207
Profile: **FT:** Coarse; **WN:** Manor House; **WT:** Lake (Still).
Ref: FH3166

MANOR HOUSE FISHERY

Manor House Fishery, Nateby, Garstang, Preston, **LANCASHIRE**, PR3, **England**.
Contact/s: Fishery Manager.
(T) 01995 602203
Profile: **FT:** Coarse; **WN:** Manor House Fishery; **WT:** Pond (Still). **Location:** **Nr. Rd:** End of Hoole Lane; **Main Rd:** A6, Longmoor Lane, through Nateby.
Ref: FH3167

MANOR LAKE

Manor Lake, Rockland Manor, Scoulton Rd, Rocklands, Attleborough, **NORFOLK**, **England**.
Contact/s: **Mr Stephen Burroughes**.
(T) 01953 483226
Profile: **FT:** Coarse; **WN:** Manor Lake; **WT:** Lake (Still); **F. Size:** 4 Acres; **W. Size:** 3 Acres. **Location:** **Nr. Rd:** Scoulton Road; **Main Rd:** B1077.
Ref: FH3168

MANOR LAKE

Manor Lake, Weston-on-the-Green, Kirtlington, Bicester, **OXFORDSHIRE**, OX6, **England**.
Contact/s: **Mr Trevor Fairless** (Secretary), Sudbury and District Angling Association, 39 Pot Kiln Rd, Sudbury, Suffolk, CO10 0DG.
(T) 01787 312536
Profile: **FT:** Coarse; **WN:** Manor; **WT:** Lake (Still) **W. Size:** 9 Acres. **Location:** **Nr. Rd:** Weston on the Green; **Main Rd:** M40, junction 9.
Ref: FH3169

MANOR POND

Manor Pond, Convent Lane, Cobham, **SURREY**, KT11, **England**.
Contact/s: **Mr Colin Trafford** (General Secretary).
(T) 020 82242617
Mrs Diane Wheeler (Secretary), 314 Old Lodge Lane, Purley, Surrey, CR8 4AQ.
(T) 020 86602766
Profile: **FT:** Coarse; **WN:** Manor; **WT:** Pond (Still) **W. Size:** 4 Acres. **Location:** **Nr. Rd:** Convent Lane; **Main Rd:** A425.
Ref: FH3170

MANOR POOL

Manor Pool, Knutsford, **CHESHIRE**, **England**.
(W) www.baymalton-anglingclub.org
Contact/s: **Mr Stewart Godber** (Club Secretary), 38 Edenfield Rd, Mobberley, Cheshire, WA16 7HE.
(T) 01565 872582
Profile: **FT:** Coarse; **WN:** Manor; **WT:** Pool (Still); **F. Size:** 1 Acre; **W. Size:** 1 Acre. **Location:** **Rail:** Knutsford.
Ref: FH3171

MAPLEDURHAM A AND B

Mapledurham A And B, River Thames, Mapledurham, Reading, **BERKSHIRE**, RG, **England**.
Contact/s: **Mr Dusty Millar** (Associate members secretary), 238 Elgar Road South, Reading, Berkshire, RG3 0BW.
(T) 0118 9874882
Mr Mick Cox (Chief Bailiff), Dorstans, Hatch Lane, Brimpton Village, Reading, RG7 4TR.
(T) 0118 9714917
Profile: **FT:** Coarse; **WN:** Thames; **WT:** River (Moving). **Location:** **Nr. Rd:** Mapledurham.
Ref: FH3172

MAPPERLEY RESERVOIR

Mapperley Reservoir, Ilkeston, **DERBYSHIRE**, DE7, **England**.
Contact/s: Area Manager, Derbyshire County Council, Main Rd, Morlsy, Ilkeston, Derbyshire DE7 6DF.
(T) 01332 831295
Profile: **FT:** Coarse; **WN:** Mapperley; **WT:** Reservoir (Still). **Location:** **Main Rd:** A609.
Ref: FH3173

MAPPOWDER COURT

Mappowder Court, Mappowder, Sturminster Newton, **DORSET**, DT10, **England**.
Contact/s: **Mr Simon Hebditch** (Hon Secretary), 5 Ham Court, Shaftsbury Rd, Gillingham, Dorset, SP8 4LU.
(T) 01747 824817
Profile: **FT:** Coarse; **WN:** Mappowder Court; **WT:** Lake (Still). **Location:** **Main Rd:** B3143.
Ref: FH3174

MARBURY MERE

Marbury Mere, Marbury, Whitchurch, **CHESHIRE**, CW9, **England**.
Contact/s: **Mr John Turner** (Hon Secretary), Prince Albert Angling Society, 15 Pexhill Drive, Macclesfield, Cheshire, SK10 3LP.
(T) 01625 422010
Profile: **FT:** Coarse; **WN:** Marbury; **WT:** Lake (Still) **W. Size:** 30 Acres. **Location:** **Main Rd:** A49; **Rail:** Whitchurch.
Ref: FH3175

MARCOA LAKE

Marcoa Lake, Kenton, Harrow, London, **LONDON (GREATER)**, HA3, **England**.
Contact/s: **Mrs V Sivyer** (Secretary), Feltham Piscatorial Society, 96 Raleigh Rd, Feltham, Middlesex, TW13 4LP.
(T) 020 8909005
Profile: **FT:** Coarse; **WN:** Marcoa; **WT:** Lake (Still).
Ref: FH3176

MARCONIS PIT

Marconis Pit, Boreham, Chelmsford, **ESSEX**, CM, **England**.
Contact/s: **Mr Derek Ritchie** (Manager), Brentwood Angling, 118 Warley Hill, Bretwood, Essex, CM14 5HB.
(T) 01245 357689 **(F)** 01245 357689
Profile: **FT:** Coarse; **WN:** Marconi's; **WT:** Gravel Pit (Still) **W. Size:** 4 Acres. **Location:** **Nr. Rd:** B1137; **Main Rd:** A12.
Ref: FH3177

MARDEN QUARRY

Marden Quarry, Tynemouth, Newcastle Upon Tyne, **TYNE AND WEAR**, NE, **England**.
Contact/s: **Mr Gary Rutherford** (Secretary), 21 Blagdon Trce, Seaton Burn, Newcastle-upon-Tyne, NE13 6EY.
(T) 0191 2366703
Profile: **FT:** Coarse; **WN:** Marden Quarry; **WT:** Gravel Pit (Still) **W. Size:** 5 Acres.
Ref: FH3178

MARGEY (RIVER)

River Margey, Ballycastle, **COUNTY ANTRIM**, BT54, **Northern Ireland**.
Contact/s: **Mr Bill Williamson** (Hon Secretary), 26 Cushendall Rd, Ballycastle, County Antrim, BT54 6QR.
(T) 028 20762693
Profile: **FT:** Game; **WN:** Margey; **WT:** River (Moving) **W. Size:** 4800 Metres.
Ref: FH3179

MARGRAM PARK FISHERY

Margram Park Fishery, Port Talbot, **NEATH PORT TALBOT**, SA13 2TS, **Wales**.
Contact/s: **Mr Roger Derrick** (Manager).
(T) 01639 881635
Profile: **FT:** Game; **WN:** Margram Park Fishery; **WT:** Lake (Still); **F. Size:** 850 Acres; **W. Size:** 4 Acres.
Ref: FH3180

MARIONS POOL

Marions Pool, Five Acres, Coleford, **GLOUCESTERSHIRE**, GL16, **England**.
Contact/s: **Mr Dennis Sherwood** (Fishery Management Officer).

(T) 01594 543796
Mr Paul Reed (Secretary), Royal Forest of Dean Angling Club, 20 Abbey St, Cinderford, Gloucestershire, GR14 2NW.
(T) 01594 824413
Profile: FT: Coarse; WN: Marions; WT: Pool (Still). Location: Nr. Rd: A4136; Main Rd: A4136.
Ref: FH3181

MARK (RIVER)

River Mark, Brue, Basonbridge, Highbridge, **SOMERSET**, TA9, **England**.
Profile: FT: Coarse; WN: Mark; WT: River (Moving) W. Size: 4000 Metres.
Ref: FH3182

MARKEATON LAKE

Markeaton Lake, Markeaton Park, Markeaton Lane, Markeaton, Derby, **DERBYSHIRE**, DE1, **England**.
Contact/s: **Mr Allan Martin** (Head Ranger).
(T) 01332 367800
Profile: FT: Coarse; WN: Markeaton; WT: Lake (Still) W. Size: 7 Acres. Location: Nr. Rd: Markeaton Lane; Main Rd: A52; Rail: Derby.
Ref: FH3183

MARKET WEIGHTON CANAL

Market Weighton Canal, Newport, Goole, **HUMBERSIDE**, DN14, **England**.
Contact/s: **Mr Bill Brame** (Secretary), Hull and District Angler's Association, PO Box 188, Hull, HU9 1AN.
Mr Les Rogers (Secretary), Goole and District Angling Association, 39 Clifton Gardens, Goole, Humberside (North), DN14 6AR.
(T) 01405 769096
Mr Martin England (Manager), 4 Park Cl, Airman, Goole, DN14 8LX.
(T) 01405 765559
Profile: FT: Coarse; WN: Market Weighton; WT: Canal (Still) W. Size: 4800 Metres.
Ref: FH3184

MARKET WEIGHTON CANAL

Market Weighton Canal, Weighton Lock To Newport, Market Weighton, York, **YORKSHIRE (NORTH)**, YO43, **England**.
Contact/s: Area Manager, Environment Agency, Ridings Area Office, Phoenix House, Global Avenue, Leeds, LS11 8PG.
(T) 0113 2440191or2314834 (F) 0113 2134609
Fishery Manager.
(T) 0113 2312100
Profile: FT: Coarse; WN: Market Weighton (Weighton Lock to Newport); WT: Canal (Still).
Location: Main Rd: A614.
Ref: FH3185

MARKLE FISHERIES

Markle Fisheries, Markle, East Linton, **LOTHIAN (EAST)**, EH40 3EB, **Scotland**.
Contact/s: **Mr Jonathan Swift**.
(T) 01620 861213 (F) 01368 865252 (M) 07770 604182
Profile: FT: Combination; WN: Markle Fisheries; WT: Loch (Still); F. Size: 15 Acres; W. Size: 10 Acres. Location: Nr. Rd: A1; Main Rd: A1; Rail: Dunbar.
Ref: FH3186

MARL LAKE

Marl Lake, Dundrum, **COUNTY TIPPERARY**, **Ireland**.
Contact/s: **Mr Sean Breen** (Secretary), Dundrum and District Anglers, Garryduff West, Dundrum, County Tipperary, Ireland.
Profile: FT: Game; WN: Marl; WT: Lake (Still).
Ref: FH3187

MARLBOROUGH POOL

Marlborough Pool, Abingdon, **OXFORDSHIRE**, OX1, **England**.
Contact/s: **Mr R Bateman**, 16 The Gap, Marcham, Abingdon, Oxfordshire.
(T) 01865 391908
Profile: FT: Coarse; WN: Marlborough; WT: Gravel Pit (Still). Location: Nr. Rd: The Gap; Main Rd: Marcham.
Ref: FH3188

MARLIAS (RIVER)

River Marlias, Marlas, Hereford, **HEREFORDSHIRE**, HR2, **England**.
Contact/s: **Mr Pat Kiernan** (Hon Secretary), 48 Waterloo Rd, Penygroes, Llanelli, Carmarthenshire.
(T) 01269 842083
Profile: FT: Game; WN: Marlias; WT: River (Moving) W. Size: 5600 Metres. Location: Nr. Rd: Lower Marlias to junction.
Ref: FH3189

MARRIS LAKES

Marris Lakes, Langworth, Lincoln, **LINCOLNSHIRE**, LN3, **England**.
Contact/s: Fishery Manager.
(T) 01522 754327
Profile: FT: Coarse; WN: Marris; WT: Lake (Still) W. Size: 1 Acre. Location: Nr. Rd: Lincoln to Wragby road; Main Rd: A158.
Ref: FH3190

MARSH FARM LAKES

Marsh Farm Lakes, Red Lane, Sternfield, Saxmundham, **SUFFOLK**, IP17 1HW, **England**.
Contact/s: **Mr D B Bloomfield** (Manager).
(T) 01728 602168
Profile: FT: Coarse; WN: Marsh Farm; WT: Lake (Still); F. Size: 6 Acres; W. Size: 4 Acres. Location: Nr. Rd: Red Lane; Main Rd: A12, A1094; Rail: Saxmundham.
Ref: FH3191

MARSH HOUSE FARM

Marsh House Farm, Wellington, Hereford, **HEREFORDSHIRE**, HR4 8DT, **England**.
Contact/s: **Mr J Dykes** (Owner).
(T) 01432 830787 (F) 01432 830056
Profile: FT: Coarse; WN: Marsh House Farm; WT: Pond (Still) W. Size: 1 Acre. Location: Nr. Rd: A49; Main Rd: A49 North of Hereford; Rail: Hereford.
Ref: FH3192

MARSH LOCK

Marsh Lock, Mill Lane, Henley-on-Thames, **OXFORDSHIRE**, RG9, **England**.
Contact/s: Fishery Contact.
(T) 01491 572992
Recreational Manager, The Environment Agency, Kings Meadow Rd, Reading, Berkshire, RG1 8DQ.
(T) 0118 9535000 (F) 0118 9500388
Profile: FT: Combination; WN: Thames; WT: Lock (Still). Location: Nr. Rd: Mill Lane; Main Rd: A4155.
Ref: FH3193

MARSHLANDS

Marshlands, Barton-upon-Humber, **LINCOLNSHIRE (NORTH)**, DN18, **England**.
Contact/s: **Ivan** (Fishery Manager).
(T) 01652 635096
Profile: FT: Coarse; WN: Marshlands; WT: Lake (Still).
Ref: FH3194

MARSTON LAKE

Marston Lake, Frome, **SOMERSET**, BA11, **England**.
Contact/s: **Mr Roger Lee** (Secretary), 51 Welshmill Lane, Frome, Somerset, BA11 3AP.
(T) 01373 461433
Profile: FT: Coarse; WN: Marston; WT: Lake (Still) W. Size: 25 Acres. Location: Main Rd: B3092 to Maiden Bradley.
Ref: FH3195

MARSTON PITS

Marston Pits, Marston Moretaine, Kempston, Bedford, **BEDFORDSHIRE**, MK42, **England**.
Contact/s: **Mr R Ward** (Secretary), 15 Kingfisher Rd, Flitwick, Bedfordshire, MK45 1RA.
Mr Steve Barnett (Secretary).
(T) 01525 876993
Profile: FT: Coarse; WN: Marston; WT: Gravel Pit (Still) W. Size: 40 Acres.
Ref: FH3196

MARSTON WYSE TROUT FARM

Marston Wyse Trout Farm, Maran Lakes, Wetherby Rd, Marston, York, **YORKSHIRE (NORTH)**, YO26 7NH, **England**.
Contact/s: **Mr Martin Rhodes** (Owner).
(T) 01904 738383 (F) 0800 137660
Profile: FT: Game; WN: Marston Wyse; WT: Lake (Still); F. Size: 22 Acres; W. Size: 5 Acres. Location: Nr. Rd: Wetherby Road; Main Rd: B1224; Rail: York.
Ref: FH3197

MARSWORTH RESERVOIR

Marsworth Reservoir, Tring, **HERTFORDSHIRE**, HP23, **England**.
Contact/s: **Mr Bernard Double** (Bailiff).
(T) 01442 822379
Profile: FT: Coarse; WN: Marsworth; WT: Reservoir (Still).
Ref: FH3198

MARTHAM PITS

Martham Pits, Staithe Rd, Martham, Great Yarmouth, **NORFOLK**, NR29, **England**.
Contact/s: Manager, Molly's Sweet Shop, 15 Repps Rd, Marson, Great Yarmouth, NR29 4TJ.
(T) 01493 740366
Mr Ian Bradford.
(T) 01493 748358
Profile: FT: Coarse; WN: Martham; WT: Gravel Pit (Still) W. Size: 4 Acres. Location: Nr. Rd: B1152 to Martham; Main Rd: Staithe Road.
Ref: FH3199

MARTIN HALL FARM

Martin Hall Farm, Much Hoole, Preston, **LANCASHIRE**, PR4, **England**.
Contact/s: Manager.
(T) 01772 459049
Manager.
(T) 01772 615832
Profile: FT: Coarse; WN: Martin Hall Farm; WT: Lake (Still). Location: Nr. Rd: Moss House Lane; Main Rd: A59.
Ref: FH3200

MARTINS FARM

Martins Farm, Woodlands, Wimborne, **DORSET**, BH21 8LY, **England**.
Contact/s: **Mr Ball** (Manager).
(T) 01202 822335
Profile: FT: Coarse; WN: Martins Farm; WT: Lake (Still) W. Size: 2 Acres. Location: Nr. Rd: B3081; Main Rd: A31.
Ref: FH3201

MARTON HEATH COARSE POOL

Marton Heath Coarse Pool, Pikelow Farm, School Lane, Marton, Macclesfield, **CHESHIRE**, SK11 9HD, **England**.
Contact/s: **Mr David Taylor**.
(T) 01260 224231 (F) 01260 224231
Profile: FT: Coarse; WN: Marton Heath; WT: Pool (Still); F. Size: 2 Acres; W. Size: 1 Acre. Location: Nr. Rd: School Lane; Main Rd: A34; Rail: Chelford.
Ref: FH3202

MARTON HEATH TROUT POOLS

Marton Heath Trout Pools, Pikelow Farm, School Lane, Marton, Macclesfield, **CHESHIRE**, SK11 9HD, **England**.
Contact/s: **Mr David Taylor** (Owner).
(T) 01260 224231 (F) 01260 224231
Profile: FT: Game; WN: Marton Heath Trout Pools; WT: Pool (Still) W. Size: 8 Acres.
Location: Nr. Rd: School Lane; Main Rd: A34; Rail: Chelford.
Ref: FH3203

MARY ANN POND

Mary Ann Pond, Cromwell Avenue, Warrington, **CHESHIRE**, **England**.
(W) www.pohas.moonfruit.com
Contact/s: **Mr Joe Worsley** (Club

Secretary), 54, Shackleton Close, Old Hall, Warrington, WA5 9QE.
(T) 01925 413750
(E) joseph.worsley@btinternet.com
Profile: FT: Coarse; WN: Mary Ann Pond; WT: Pond (Still); F. Size: 1 Acre; W. Size: 1 Acre. Location: Nr. Rd: Cromwell Avenue; Main Rd: A57; Rail: Warrington.
Ref: FH3204

MASSAN (RIVER)

River Massan, Dunoon, **ARGYLL AND BUTE**, PA23, **Scotland**.
Contact/s: Mr A H Young (Hon Secretary), 112 Argyll St, Dunoon, Argyll and Bute.
(T) 01369 705732or703232
(E) archie@telinco.co.uk
Profile: FT: Game; WN: Massan; WT: River (Moving) W. Size: 4800 Metres. Location: Main Rd: A885.
Ref: FH3205

MASTERS (THE)

Masters (The), Kidderminster, **WORCESTERSHIRE**, DY10, **England**.
Contact/s: Mr Eric Lloyd (Shatterford Fishery Manager).
(T) 01299 861597
Profile: FT: Game; WN: Masters (The); WT: Lake (Still) W. Size: 2 Acres.
Ref: FH3206

MATCH AND BLUE POOLS

Match And Blue Pools, Berrys Lane, Burghfield, Reading, **BERKSHIRE**, RG7, **England**.
Contact/s: Mr Ian Welch (Manager), RMC Angling, RMC House, High St, Feltham, Middlesex TW13 4HD.
(T) 020 88931168
Profile: FT: Coarse; WN: Match and Blue; WT: Pool (Still) W. Size: 3 Acres. Location: Nr. Rd: Berrys Lane; Main Rd: M4, junction 12.
Ref: FH3207

MATCH LAKE

Match Lake, Bobbin Lodge Hill, Chilham, **KENT**, **England**.
(W) www.midkentfish.co.uk
Contact/s: Mr Chris Logsdon (Fisheries Manager), Mid Kent Fisheries, Chilham Water Mill, Mill Lane, Chilham, CT4 8EE.
(T) 01227 730668
(E) chilham@midkentfisheries.co.uk
Profile: FT: Coarse; WN: Match; WT: Lake (Still); F. Size: 5 Acres; W. Size: 3 Acres. Location: Main Rd: A28; Rail: Chartham.
Ref: FH3208

MAUN (RIVER)

River Maun, Edwinstowe, Mansfield, **NOTTINGHAMSHIRE**, NG21, **England**.
Contact/s: Mr Mick Langton, 173 Sherwood St, Warsop, Mansfield, Nottinghamshire, NG20 0HG.
(T) 01623 842617 (F) 01623 842617 (M) 07721 316334
(E) mickyfish@totalise.co.uk
Profile: FT: Coarse; WN: Maun; WT: River (Moving) W. Size: 1500 Metres. Location: Nr. Rd: A6075; Main Rd: M1; Rail: Mansfield Woodhouse.
Ref: FH3209

MAVER LARFORD

Maver Larford, Marver Lake And River Severn Complex, Larford Lane, Larford, Stourport-on-Severn, **WORCESTERSHIRE**, DY13 0SQ, **England**.
Contact/s: Mr Field (Manager).
(T) 01299 829373 (M) 07774 703067
Profile: FT: Coarse; WN: Maver Larford and Severn; WT: Combination (Still & Moving) W. Size: 28 Acres. Location: Nr. Rd: B4196.
Ref: FH3210

MAWDDACH (RIVER)

River Mawddach, Ganllwyd, Dolgellau, **GWYNEDD**, LL40, **Wales**.
Contact/s: Mr J Barkwith (Angling Manager), Dolmelynllyn Hall Hotel, Ganllwyd, Dolgellau, Gwynedd, LL40 2HP.
(T) 01341 440273
Profile: FT: Game; WN: Mawddach; WT: River (Moving) W. Size: 16000 Metres.
Ref: FH3211

MAWDDACH (RIVER)

River Mawddach, George III Hotel, Penmaenpool Rd, Dolgellau, **GWYNEDD**, LL40 1YD, **Wales**.
Contact/s: Mr J Cartwright (Manager), George III Hotel, Penmaenpool, Dolgellau, Gwynedd, LL40 1YD.
(T) 01341 422525
Profile: FT: Game; WN: Mawddach; WT: River (Moving) W. Size: 20800 Metres. Location: Nr. Rd: Penmaenpool Road; Main Rd: A470; Rail: Barmouth. £Fr
Ref: FH3212

MAWDDACH AND WNION (RIVERS)

Rivers Mawddach And Wnion, 'Maescaled', Dolgellau, **GWYNEDD**, LL40 1UF, **Wales**.
Contact/s: Mr E M Davies (Secretary).
(T) 01341 422706
Profile: FT: Game; WN: Mawddach & Wnion; WT: River (Moving) W. Size: 20000 Metres. Location: Rail: Barmouth.
Ref: FH3213

MAYBRAND FISHERY

Maybrand Fishery, Bournebridge Lane, Stapleford Abbotts, Romford, **ESSEX**, RM, **England**.
Contact/s: Mr Nick Devlin (Owner).
(T) 01708 688279
Profile: FT: Coarse; WN: New, Front, Middle, & Back Lake; WT: Lake (Still). Location: Nr. Rd: B175, Bournebridge Lane; Main Rd: A113 to Passingford Bridge.
Ref: FH3214

MAYFIELD LAKE

Mayfield Lake, Claremorris, **COUNTY GALWAY**, **Ireland**.
Contact/s: Mr Danny Goldrick (Angling Officer), The Western Regional Fisheries Board, Weir Lodge, Earl's Island, Galway City, County Galway.
(T) 091 563118 (F) 091 566335
(E) wrfb@iol.ie
Profile: FT: Coarse; WN: Mayfield; WT: Lake (Still). Location: Rail: Claremorris.
Ref: FH3215

MAYFIELDS LAKE

Mayfields Lake, Thorney Mill Rd, Langley, Slough, **BUCKINGHAMSHIRE**, SL3, **England**.
Contact/s: Buzz (Manager), Boyer Leisure Ltd, Heron's Point Tackle Shop, Farlow's Lake, Ford Lane, Iver SL0 9LL.
(T) 01753 630302or01895444707 (F) 01753 630302
(E) info@boyer.co.uk
Profile: FT: Coarse; WN: Mayfield's; WT: Gravel Pit (Still) W. Size: 4 Acres. Location: Nr. Rd: Thorney Mill Road; Main Rd: B470; Rail: West Drayton.
Ref: FH3216

MAYSBROOK LAKES

Maysbrook Lakes, Lodge Avenue, Barking, **ESSEX**, IG11, **England**.
Contact/s: Fishery Contact.
(T) 020 85920348
Profile: FT: Coarse; WN: Mayesbrook; WT: Lake (Still). Location: Nr. Rd: Lodge Avenue; Main Rd: A1153.
Ref: FH3217

MBK LEISURE BARRONS POND

Mbk Leisure Barrons Pond, St. Patrick's Lane, Liss, **HAMPSHIRE**, GU33, **England**.
Contact/s: Mr Peter Archer, Petersfield Angling Ctre, 34 Dragon St, Petersfield, Hampshire, GU31 4JJ.
(T) 01730 266999 (F) 01730 266999
Profile: FT: Coarse; WN: MBK Barron's; WT: Pond (Still). Location: Nr. Rd: St Patrick's Lane.
Ref: FH3218

MCCAMMANS LAKE

Mccammans Lake, Larne, **COUNTY ANTRIM**, BT40, **Northern Ireland**.
Contact/s: Mr Frank Quigley, 124 Low Rd, Islandmagee, Larne, County Antrim.
(T) 028 93382610
Profile: FT: Game; WN: McCammans; WT: Lake (Still) W. Size: 7 Acres.
Ref: FH3219

MCCOURTS LAKE

Mccourts Lake, Poyntspass, **COUNTY DOWN**, BT34, **Northern Ireland**.
Contact/s: Mr Ronald McCamley (Secretary), Newry and District Andling Association, 28 High St, Newry, County Down, BT34 1HB.
(T) 028 30268768
Mrs E McAllinden, Lisgullion Drive, Armagh Rd, Newry, County Down.
Profile: FT: Coarse; WN: McCourts; WT: Lake (Still) W. Size: 50 Acres. Location: Main Rd: A21; Rail: Bessbrook.
Ref: FH3220

MEADLEY RESERVOIR

Meadley Reservoir, Cleator Moor, **CUMBRIA**, CA25, **England**.
Contact/s: , North West Water Ltd, Pennine House, Stanley St, Preston, PR1 4EA.
Profile: FT: Game; WN: Meadley; WT: Reservoir (Still).
Ref: FH3221

MEADOW FISHERY

Meadow Fishery, Warrington Rd, Mickle Trafford, Chester, **CHESHIRE**, CH2 4EB, **England**.
Contact/s: Mr John Percival (Owner).
(T) 01244 300236 (F) 01244 300236
Profile: FT: Game; WN: Meadow Fishery; WT: Lake (Still); F. Size: 20 Acres; W. Size: 10 Acres. Location: Nr. Rd: A56 Warrington Road; Main Rd: A56; Rail: Chester.
Ref: FH3222

MEADOW LAKE

Meadow Lake, Old Rd, Narborough, King's Lynn, **NORFOLK**, PE32, **England**.
Contact/s: Grant.
(T) 01760 338005
Profile: FT: Coarse; WN: Meadow; WT: Lake (Still) W. Size: 1 Acre. Location: Nr. Rd: Old Road; Main Rd: A47.
Ref: FH3223

MEADOW POND

Meadow Pond, Norton, Gloucester, **GLOUCESTERSHIRE**, GL, **England**.
Contact/s: Mr J G Mitchell (Landlord), Red Lion Inn, Wainlode Hill, Norton, Gloucester, GL2 9LW.
(T) 01452 730251
Profile: FT: Coarse; WN: Meadow; WT: Pond (Still). Location: Nr. Rd: A38 to Twigworth; Main Rd: A48, M5.
Ref: FH3224

MEADOW VIEW FISHERY

Meadow View Fishery, Whitbarrow Rd, Statham, Lymm, Warrington, **CHESHIRE**, WA, **England**.
Contact/s: Mr David Berry.
(T) 01925 637397 (M) 07775 585727
Mr Paul Tinkley (Fishery Manager). (M) 07775 585727
Profile: FT: Coarse; WN: Meadow View Fishery; WT: Pond (Still); F. Size: 8 Acres; W. Size: 4 Acres. Location: Nr. Rd: Whitbarrow Road; Main Rd: Stockport Road; Rail: Bank Quay.
Ref: FH3225

MEADOWCLIFFE POOL

Meadowcliffe Pool, Northern United Industrial Estate, Brickworks Rd, Brierley, Gloucester, **GLOUCESTERSHIRE**, GL,

England.
Contact/s: Mr Dennis Sherwood (Fishery Management Officer).
(T) 01594 543796
Mr Paul Reed (Secretary), Royal Forest of Dean Angling Club, 20 Abbey St, Cinderford, Gloucestershire, GR14 2NW.
(T) 01594 824413
Profile: FT: Coarse; WN: Meadowcliffe; WT: Pond (Still) W. Size: 1 Acre. Location: Nr. Rd: Brickworks Road; Main Rd: A4136.
Ref: FH3226

MEADOWLANDS

Meadowlands, Oxford Rd, Ryton-upon-Dunsmore, Coventry, MIDLANDS (WEST), CV, England.
Contact/s: Fishery Manager.
(T) 024 76550638 (M) 07767 455211
Mr John Bloor.
(T) 024 76550638
Profile: FT: Coarse; WN: Meadowlands; WT: Gravel Pit (Still) W. Size: 18 Acres.
Location: Nr. Rd: Ryton-upon-Dunsmore to Southam; Main Rd: A423.
Ref: FH3227

MEADOWSIDE COARSE FISHERY

Meadowside Coarse Fishery, Winnard's Perch, Retallack Park, St Columb, CORNWALL, TR9 6DH, England.
Contact/s: Mr Terry Price (Fishing Manager).
(T) 01637 880544
Mrs M Price (Owner).
(T) 01637 880544
Profile: FT: Coarse; WN: Meadowside; WT: Lake (Still) W. Size: 5 Acres. Location: Nr. Rd: Winnards Perch; Main Rd: A39; Rail: Newquay.
Ref: FH3228

MEDKLIN TARN FISHERY

Medklin Tarn Fishery, Bridge End Farm, Santon Bridge, Holmrook, CUMBRIA, CA19, England.
Contact/s: Fishery Manager.
(T) 01946 726256
Profile: FT: Game; WN: Medklin; WT: Tarn (Still).
Ref: FH3229

MEDWAY (RIVER)

River Medway, Maidstone Court House, Maidstone, KENT, ME1, England.
Contact/s: Mr Rob Earl (Manager), Maidstone Angling Ctre, 15 Perryfield St, Maidstone, Kent, ME14 2SY.
(T) 01622 677326 (F) 01622 752021
Profile: FT: Coarse; WN: Medway; WT: River (Moving) W. Size: 3000 Metres. Location: Main Rd: A299; Rail: Maidstone. £Fr
Ref: FH3230

MEDWAY (RIVER)

River Medway, Lower Haysden Lane, Tonbridge, KENT, TN1, England.
Contact/s: Mr Alex Heggie (Membership Secretary), Little Lucy's Farmhouse, Lower St, Hildenborough, Tonbridge, TN11 8PT.
(T) 01732 832352 (F) 01732 832352
Profile: FT: Coarse; WN: Medway; WT: River (Moving) W. Size: 800 Metres. Location: Nr. Rd: Lower Haysden Lane, under A21 flyover; Main Rd: Under A21 Flyover, off A26; Rail: Tonbridge.
Ref: FH3231

MEDWAY (RIVER)

River Medway, Allington Lock, Maidstone, KENT, ME1, England.
Contact/s: Manager, Nicks Tackle Exchange, 10 Knightrider St, Maidstone, Kent, ME15 6LP.
(T) 01622 673899 (F) 01622 673899
Mr Rob Earl (Manager), Maidstone Angling Ctre, 15 Perryfield St, Maidstone, Kent, ME14 2SY.
(T) 01622 677326 (F) 01622 752021
Profile: FT: Coarse; WN: Medway; WT: River (Moving).
Ref: FH3232

MEDWAY (RIVER)

Medway (River), East Peckham, KENT, England.
(W) www.midkentfish.co.uk
Contact/s: Mr Chris Logsdon (Fisheries Manager), Mid Kent Fisheries, Chilham Water Mill, Mill Lane, Chilham, CT4 8EE.
(T) 01227 730668
(E) chilham@midkentfisheries.co.uk
Profile: FT: Coarse; WN: Medway; WT: River (Moving). Location: Main Rd: A228; Rail: Tonbridge.
Ref: FH3233

MEDWAY (RIVER)

River Medway, Fordcombe, Tunbridge Wells, KENT, TN, England.
Contact/s: Fishery Manager.
(T) 01342 826204
Profile: FT: Coarse; WN: Medway; WT: River (Moving) W. Size: 2400 Metres. Location: Nr. Rd: Tunbridge Wells to East Grinstead; Main Rd: A264 to Fordcombe.
Ref: FH3234

MEDWAY (RIVER)

River Medway, Yalding Number One, Maidstone, KENT, ME18, England.
(W) www.calpac.bizland.com
Contact/s: Mr Colin Trafford (General Secretary).
(T) 020 82242617
Profile: FT: Coarse; WN: Medway; WT: River (Moving) W. Size: 1200 Metres. Location: Main Rd: A2162; Rail: Yalding.
Ref: FH3235

MEDWAY (RIVER)

River Medway, Hartlake Bridge, Hartlake Rd, Golden Green, Tonbridge, KENT, TN1, England.
Contact/s: Mr Alex Heggie (Membership Secretary), Little Lucy's Farmhouse, Lower St, Hildenborough, Tonbridge, TN11 8PT.
(T) 01732 832352 (F) 01732 832352
Mr Tom Creasey (Hon Secretary), 3 Invicta Flats, Great Brooms Rd, Tunbridge Wells, Kent, TN4 9DD.
(T) 01892 520520
Profile: FT: Coarse; WN: Medway; WT: River (Moving) W. Size: 9600 Metres. Location: Nr. Rd: Hartlake Road; Main Rd: A26, Hadlow Road; Rail: Tonbridge.
Ref: FH3236

MEDWAY (RIVER)

River Medway, Yalding Number Two, Maidstone, KENT, ME18, England.
(W) www.calpac.bizland.com
Contact/s: Mr Colin Trafford (General Secretary).
(T) 020 82242617
Profile: FT: Coarse; WN: Medway; WT: River (Moving) W. Size: 200 Metres. Location: Main Rd: A2162; Rail: Yalding.
Ref: FH3237

MEDWAY (RIVER)

River Medway, Cannon Bridge, Cannon Lane, Tonbridge, KENT, TN1, England.
Contact/s: Mr Alex Heggie (Membership Secretary), Little Lucy's Farmhouse, Lower St, Hildenborough, Tonbridge, TN11 8PT.
(T) 01732 832352 (F) 01732 832352
Mr Tom Creasey (Hon Secretary), 3 Invicta Flats, Great Brooms Rd, Tunbridge Wells, Kent, TN4 9DD.
(T) 01892 520520
Profile: FT: Coarse; WN: Medway; WT: River (Moving) W. Size: 3000 Metres. Location: Nr. Rd: Cannon Lane; Main Rd: Hadlow Road; Rail: Tonbridge.
Ref: FH3238

MEDWAY (RIVER)

River Medway, Tonbridge Sports Ground, Avebury Avenue, Tonbridge, KENT, TN1, England.
Contact/s: Mr Alex Heggie (Membership Secretary), Little Lucy's Farmhouse, Lower St, Hildenborough, Tonbridge, TN11 8PT.
(T) 01732 832352 (F) 01732 832352
Mr Tom Creasey (Hon Secretary), 3 Invicta Flats, Great Brooms Rd, Tunbridge Wells, Kent, TN4 9DD.
(T) 01892 520520
Profile: FT: Coarse; WN: Medway; WT: River (Moving) W. Size: 2000 Metres. Location: Nr. Rd: Avebury Avenue; Main Rd: A21; Rail: Tonbridge.
Ref: FH3239

MEESE (RIVER)

River Meese, Aqualate Estate, Newport, SHROPSHIRE, TF10, England.
Contact/s: Mr Albert Perkins (Hon Secretary), 63 Fowlers Lane, Light Oaks, Stoke-on-Trent, Staffordshire, ST2 7NB.
Ms Liz Hayes (Manager).
(T) 01625 251262
Profile: FT: Coarse; WN: Meese; WT: River (Moving) W. Size: 1100 Metres. Location: Main Rd: A519.
Ref: FH3240

MEGGET RESERVOIR

Megget Reservoir, St Mary's Loch, Selkirk, SCOTTISH BORDERS, TD7, Scotland.
Contact/s: Mrs Jill Brown (Manager), The Tibby Shiels Inn, Selkirk, Scottish Borders, TD7 5LH.
(T) 01750 42231
Profile: FT: Game; WN: Megget; WT: Reservoir (Still). Location: Nr. Rd: Tweedsmuir Road; Main Rd: A708.
Ref: FH3241

MELANHYL LAKE

Melanhyl Lake, The Merrymoor Inn, Mawgan Porth, Newquay, CORNWALL, TR, England.
Contact/s: Mr T J Trevenna (Secretary), Lanvean House, St Mawgan, Newquay, Cornwall, TR8 4EY.
Profile: FT: Game; WN: Melanhyl; WT: Lake (Still).
Ref: FH3242

MELBOURNE POOL

Melbourne Pool, Melbourne Estate, Melbourne, Derby, DERBYSHIRE, DE73, England.
Contact/s: Mr A Williams, Melbourne Tackle and Gun, 64 Church St, Melbourne, Derbyshire, DE73 1EJ.
(T) 01332 862091
Profile: FT: Coarse; WN: Staunton Harold; WT: Pool (Still) W. Size: 20 Acres.
Location: Nr. Rd: Melbourne to Wilson; Main Rd: Church Street.
Ref: FH3243

MELBURY RESERVOIR

Melbury Reservoir, Parkham, Bideford, DEVON, EX39, England.
Contact/s: Mr Nick Laws (Manager), Summerlands Tackle, 3 Golf Links Rd, 16-20 Nelson Rd, Westward Ho!, Devon EX39 1LH.
(T) 01237 471291
Mr Reg England (Manager), Peninsula Coarse Fisheries, St Cleer Depot, Lewdown, Okehampton, Devon EX20 4QT.
(T) 01837 871565 (F) 01837 871534
Profile: FT: Coarse; WN: Melbury; WT: Reservoir (Still); F. Size: 12 Acres; W. Size: 7 Acres. Location: Nr. Rd: A39; Main Rd: Bideford to Bude.
Ref: FH3244

MELCHES POND

Melches Pond, Greater Manchester Transport A C, Farnworth, Bolton, LANCASHIRE, BL, England.
Profile: FT: Coarse; WN: Melches; WT: Pond (Still). Location: Nr. Rd: A666; Main Rd: Bolton.
Ref: FH3245

MELDON RESERVOIR

Meldon Reservoir, Meldon, Okehampton, DEVON, EX20, England.
Profile: FT: Game; WN: Meldon; WT:

Reservoir (Still) **W. Size:** 54 Acres.
Ref: FH3246

MELDUM WASHLANDS (FLOODPARK)

Meldum Washlands (Floodpark), Withersfield Rd, Haverhill, **SUFFOLK**, CB9, **England**.
Contact/s: **Mr D Tuffin** (Secretary), Haverhill Angling, 2a Primrose Hill, Haverhill, Suffolk, CB9 9LS.
(T) 01440 707061
Profile: **FT:** Coarse; **WN:** Meldum Washlands; **WT:** Lake (Still) **W. Size:** 2 Acres. **Location:** **Nr. Rd:** A1037.
Ref: FH3247

MELLINGS NO 1

Mellings No 1, Wigan, **LANCASHIRE**, WN, **England**.
(W) www.wiganaa.f9.co.uk
Contact/s: **Mr Gerry Wilson** (Hon Secretary), Wigan and District Angling Association, 11 Guildford Avenue, Chorley, Lancashire, PR6 8TG.
(T) 01257 265905
(E) gerry@wiganna.freeserve.co.uk
Profile: **FT:** Coarse; **WN:** Mellings No 1; **WT:** Lake (Still). **Location:** **Nr. Rd:** B5375; **Main Rd:** A49, A577, M6, junction 26.
Ref: FH3248

MELLONWATTS MILL

Mellonwatts Mill, Pensagillas Farm, Grampound, Truro, **CORNWALL**, TR, **England**.
Contact/s: **Mr David Kemp** (Fishery Manager).
(T) 01872 530232
Profile: **FT:** Coarse; **WN:** Mellonwatts Mill; **WT:** Pond (Still) **W. Size:** 2 Acres. **Location:** **Nr. Rd:** Grampound to Mevagissey.
Ref: FH3249

MELLS PIT

Mells Pit, Mells, Frome, **SOMERSET**, BA11, **England**.
Contact/s: **Mr M Coles**, Lyndhurst, Station Rd, Mells, Frome, Somerset.
(T) 01373 812094
Profile: **FT:** Coarse; **WN:** Mells Pit; **WT:** Pond (Still) **W. Size:** 1 Acre. **Location:** **Nr. Rd:** Station Road.
Ref: FH3250

MELLTE (STREAM)

Mellte (Stream), Glynneath, Neath, **GLAMORGAN (VALE OF)**, SA11, **Wales**.
Contact/s: **Mr Gareth Evans** (Treasurer), 21 Godfrey Avenue, Glynneath, Neath, Glamorgan (Vale of), SA11 5HF.
(T) 01639 721301
Mr Tony May (Secretary).
(T) 01685 871337
Mrs R Jones (Chairperson).
(T) 01639 720927
Profile: **FT:** Game; **WN:** Mellte; **WT:** Stream (Moving) **W. Size:** 7500 Metres. **Location:** **Main Rd:** A465; **Rail:** Neath.
Ref: FH3251

MELTON LAKE

Melton Lake, Melton, Woodbridge, **SUFFOLK**, IP12, **England**.
Contact/s: Manager.
(T) 01394 382377
Profile: **FT:** Coarse; **WN:** Melton; **WT:** Lake (Still).
Ref: FH3252

MENAGERIE POND

Menagerie Pond, Estate Office, Castle Ashby, Northampton, **NORTHAMPTONSHIRE**, NN7 1LJ, **England**.
Contact/s: **Mrs J L King** (Manager).
(T) 01604 696232 **(F)** 01604 696556
Profile: **FT:** Coarse; **WN:** Menagerie; **WT:** Pond (Still). **Location:** **Main Rd:** A45; **Rail:** Wellingborough.
Ref: FH3253

MENARDS LAKE

Menards Lake, Hammer Pond Rd, Horsham, **SUSSEX (WEST)**, RH12, **England**.
Contact/s: **Mr Paul De Luzy** (Fishery Manager).
(T) 01403 243213 **(M)** 07801 474488
Profile: **FT:** Coarse; **WN:** Menards; **WT:** Lake (Still) **W. Size:** 4 Acres. **Location:** **Nr. Rd:** Hammer Pond Road; **Main Rd:** A23.
Ref: FH3254

MEON SPRINGS FLY FISHERY

Meon Springs Fly Fishery, Whitewool Farm, East Meon, Petersfield, **HAMPSHIRE**, GU32 1HW, **England**.
Contact/s: **Mr s Feall** (Fishery Bailiff).
(T) 01730 823249 **(F)** 01730 823411 **(M)** 077907 951 163
Profile: **FT:** Game; **WN:** Meon; **WT:** Combination (Still & Moving); **F. Size:** 4 Acres; **W. Size:** 2 Acres.
Ref: FH3255

MEPAL PIT

Mepal Pit, Chattfris Rd, Mepal, Ely, **CAMBRIDGESHIRE**, CB6, **England**.
Contact/s: **Mr N Roberts** (Manager).
(T) 01223 836773
Profile: **FT:** Coarse; **WN:** Mepal; **WT:** Lake (Still) **W. Size:** 4 Acres. **Location:** **Nr. Rd:** A142; **Main Rd:** A142; **Rail:** Ely.
Ref: FH3256

MERCHANT TAYLORS SCL LAKES

Merchant Taylors Scl Lakes, Kings Langley, **HERTFORDSHIRE**, WD4, **England**.
Contact/s: **Mr C Wood** (Secretary), Carpenters Park Angling Club, 2 Long Pightie, Chandlers Cross, Rickmansworth, Hertfordshire, W3D3 4NE.
(T) 01923 268618
Profile: **FT:** Coarse; **WN:** Merchant Taylors Scl Lakes; **WT:** Lake (Still).
Ref: FH3257

MERSTONE FISHERIES

Merstone Fisheries, East Lane, Merstone, Newport, **ISLE OF WIGHT**, PO30, **England**.
(W) www.isleofwight.co.uk
Contact/s: **Mr Alan Bravery** (Manager), Scotties Tackle Shop, 11 Lugley St, Newport, Isle of Wight, PO30 5HD.
(T) 01983 522115 **(F)** 01983 522115
Mr Derek Holmes (Secretary).
(T) 01983 523230
(E) dkhiow@madasafish.com
Mr Paul Johnson (Manager), Scotties Sandown, 22 Fitzroy St, Sandown, Isle of Wight, PO36 8HZ.
(T) 01983 404555
Mr R J Kirby (Hon Secretary), 125 Furrlongs, Pan Estate, Newport, Isle of Wight, PO30 2BN.
(T) 01983 529617
Profile: **FT:** Coarse; **WN:** Merstone Fisheries; **WT:** Lake (Still) **W. Size:** 3 Acres. **Location:** **Nr. Rd:** East Lane; **Main Rd:** Newport to Sandown.
Ref: FH3258

MEXBOROUGH CANAL

Mexborough Canal, Mexborough, **YORKSHIRE (SOUTH)**, S64 0, **England**.
Contact/s: Manager, Ferryboat Inn, Church St, Mexborough, Yorkshire (South), S64 0ER.
(T) 01709 862558
Profile: **FT:** Coarse; **WN:** Mexborough; **WT:** Canal (Still).
Ref: FH3259

MICHELHAM PRIORY MOAT

Michelham Priory Moat, Upper Dicker, Hailsham, Eastbourne, **SUSSEX (EAST)**, BN22 3QS, **England**.
Contact/s: **Mr Chris Tuckett** (Fishery Manager).
(T) 01323 844224 **(M)** 07654 575181
Profile: **FT:** Coarse; **WN:** Michelham Priory; **WT:** Moat (Still). **Location:** **Main Rd:** A22; **Rail:** Berwick.
Ref: FH3260

MICKS LAKE

Micks Lake, Warrington, **CHESHIRE**, WA, **England**.
Contact/s: Fishery Manager.
(T) 01925 656441
Profile: **FT:** Coarse; **WN:** Mick's; **WT:** Lake (Still).
Ref: FH3261

MICKS PLACE

Micks Place, Woodhouse Grange, Hatfield Woodhouse, Thorne, Doncaster, **YORKSHIRE (SOUTH)**, DN8, **England**.
Contact/s: **Mr Tony Green** (Manager), Peg Two Tackle, 27 King St, Thorne, Yorkshire (South), DN8 5AU.
(T) 01405 814417
Mr Tony Sprott (Manager). **(M)** 07802 518612or07702189657
Profile: **FT:** Coarse; **WN:** Micks Place; **WT:** Lake (Still). **Location:** **Nr. Rd:** A614.
Ref: FH3262

MID KENT FISHERIES

Mid Kent Fisheries, Chilham Water Mill, Mill Lane, Ashford Rd, Canterbury, **KENT**, CT4 8EE, **England**.
Contact/s: **Mr Chris Logsdon** (Manager).
(T) 01227 730668 **(F)** 01227 738894
Profile: **FT:** Combination; **WN:** Stour and Medway; **WT:** Combination (Still & Moving); **F. Size:** 1000 Acres; **W. Size:** 165 Acres. **Location:** **Nr. Rd:** Mill Lane; **Main Rd:** A128; **Rail:** Chilham.
Ref: FH3263

MIDDLE BOSWIN FARM

Middle Boswin Farm, Nine Maidens Rd, Porkellis, Helston, **CORNWALL**, TR13 0HR, **England**.
Mr Martin Johnson (Owner).
(T) 01209 860420
Profile: **FT:** Coarse; **WN:** Boswin; **WT:** Lake (Still); **F. Size:** 2 Acres; **W. Size:** 1 Acre. **Location:** **Nr. Rd:** Nine Maidens Road; **Main Rd:** B3297; **Rail:** Redruth.
Ref: FH3264

MIDDLE HARLING LAKE

Middle Harling Lake, West Harling Rd, Middle Harling, Thetford, **NORFOLK**, **England**.
Contact/s: **Mr David Holden**.
(T) 01953 718205
Profile: **FT:** Coarse; **WN:** Middle Harling Lake; **WT:** Lake (Still). **Location:** **Nr. Rd:** West Harling Road; **Main Rd:** B1111; **Rail:** Roudham.
Ref: FH3265

MIDDLE LEVEL DRAIN

Middle Level Drain, Outwell, Wisbech, **CAMBRIDGESHIRE**, PE14 8, **England**.
Contact/s: **Mr Mick Grief** (Secretary), King's Lynn Angling Association, 67 Peckover Way, South Wootton, King's Lynn, PE30 3UE.
(T) 01553 671545
Profile: **FT:** Coarse; **WN:** Middle Level Drain; **WT:** Drain (Moving). **Location:** **Main Rd:** A1122.
Ref: FH3266

MIDDLE POOL

Middle Pool, Sommerfield Rd, Oakengates, Telford, **SHROPSHIRE**, TF2 6, **England**.
Contact/s: **Mr Stan Harris** (Secretary), Telford Angling Association, 73 Burnside, Brookside, Telford, TF3 1DA.
(T) 01952 590605
Profile: **FT:** Coarse; **WN:** Middle; **WT:** Pool (Still). **Location:** **Nr. Rd:** Sommerfield Road; **Main Rd:** A442.
Ref: FH3267

MIDDLETON FISHERY

Middleton Fishery, Brisbane Glen Rd, Largs, **AYRSHIRE (NORTH)**, KA30 8SL, **Scotland**.
Contact/s: **Mr John Dixon** (Owner).
(T) 01475 672095
Profile: **FT:** Game; **WN:** Middleton Fishery;

WT: Lake (Still); F. Size: 7 Acres; W. Size: 5 Acres.
Ref: FH3268

MIDDLETON WATER PARK

Middleton Water Park, Middleton St George, Darlington, **COUNTY DURHAM**, DL, **England**.
Contact/s: Manager, W P Adams Fishing Tackle, 42 Duke St, Darlington, County Durham, DL3 7AJ.
(T) 01325 468069
Parish Clerk, 8 Grendon Gardens, Middleton St George, Darlington, County Durham.
(T) 01325 332894
Profile: FT: Coarse; WN: Middleton Water Park; WT: Reservoir (Still). Location: Nr. Rd: A67; Main Rd: A66.
Ref: FH3269

MIDDLEWICH BRANCH CANAL

Middlewich Branch Canal, Church Minshull, Nantwich, **CHESHIRE**, CW5, **England**.
Contact/s: Fishery Manager.
(T) 0151 4246583
Profile: FT: Coarse; WN: Middlewich Branch; WT: Canal (Still).
Ref: FH3270

MIDDLEWICH BRANCH CANAL

Middlewich Branch Canal, Barbridge, Nantwich, **CHESHIRE**, CW5, **England**.
Contact/s: Fishery Manager.
(T) 01829 732748
Profile: FT: Coarse; WN: Middlewich Branch; WT: Canal (Still).
Ref: FH3271

MIDLAND GAME FISHERIES

Midland Game Fisheries, Fisherwick Lakes, Whittington, Lichfield, **STAFFORDSHIRE**, WS13 8QF, **England**.
Contact/s: Mr Peter Jackson.
(T) 01543 433606 (F) 01543 433390
Profile: FT: Combination; WN: Midland Game Fisheries; WT: Lake (Still) W. Size: 8 Acres.
Ref: FH3272

MILBY CUT

Milby Cut, Road Bridge, Boroughbridge, York, **YORKSHIRE (NORTH)**, YO51, **England**.
Contact/s: Mr E K Mann (Club Secretary), 19 Busfield St, Bradford, Yorkshire (West), BD4 7QX.
(T) 01274 720072
Profile: FT: Coarse; WN: Ure (Road Bridge to Clapper Gate); WT: River (Moving) W. Size: 369 Metres.
Ref: FH3273

MILEMEAD FISHERIES

Milemead Fisheries, Mill Hill, Tavistock, **DEVON**, PL19 8NP, **England**.
Contact/s: Mr Andrew Evenden (Owner).
(T) 01822 610888
Mr Harry Dickens (Fishery Manager), Milemead Fisheries, Mill Hill, Tavistock, Devon, PL19 8NP.
(T) 01822 610888
Mr Paul Evendoen (Owner).
(T) 01822 610888
Profile: FT: Coarse; WN: Milemead Fisheries; WT: Lake (Still); F. Size: 21 Acres; W. Size: 6 Acres. Location: Nr. Rd: B3362; Main Rd: B3362; Rail: Gunnislake.
Ref: FH3274

MILESTONE FISHERY

Milestone Fishery, London Rd, Fairford, **GLOUCESTERSHIRE**, GL7 4DS, **England**.
Mr Andy King (Manager).
(T) 01285 713908 (F) 01285 711113
Mr Bob Fletcher (Owner).
(T) 01285 713908
Profile: FT: Combination; WN: Milestone; WT: Lake (Still) W. Size: 60 Acres.
Location: Nr. Rd: Lechlade to Fairford Road; Main Rd: A417.
Ref: FH3275

MILKHOPE POND

Milkhope Pond, Milkhope Ctre, Ponteland, Newcastle Upon Tyne, **TYNE AND WEAR**, NE20, **England**.
Contact/s: Mr Albert Robson (Membership Secretary), Wansbeck and Cramlington Angling Club, 10 Second Avenue, Ashington, Northumberland, NE63 0BJ.
(T) 01670 819647
Profile: FT: Coarse; WN: Milkhope; WT: Lake (Still). Location: Nr. Rd: Milkhope Centre; Main Rd: A19, A1; Rail: Newcastle.
Ref: FH3276

MILL

Mill (The), Avonwick, South Brent, **DEVON**, TQ10, **England**.
Contact/s: Manager, Clive's Tackle and Bait, 182 Exeter St, Plymouth, Devon, PL4 0NQ.
(T) 01752 228940 (F) 01752 603001
Profile: FT: Coarse; WN: Mill (The); WT: Lake (Still).
Ref: FH3277

MILL AVON

Mill Avon, Lower Lodge Lane, Gloucester Rd, Tewkesbury, **GLOUCESTERSHIRE**, GL20, **England**.
Contact/s: Manager, Tewkesbury Fishing Tackle, 3 Barton St, Tewkesbury, Shropshire, GL20 1PR.
(T) 01684 293234
Profile: FT: Coarse; WN: Avon; WT: River (Moving) W. Size: 1200 Metres. Location: Nr. Rd: A38; Main Rd: M50, M5.
Ref: FH3278

MILL BARN FISHERY

Mill Barn Fishery, Great Wakering, Southend-on-Sea, **ESSEX**, SS3 0AG, **England**.
Contact/s: Mr Graham Jenner (Fishery Manager).
(T) 01702 216170 (M) 07721 053728
Profile: FT: Coarse; WN: Mill Barn; WT: Lake (Still) W. Size: 12 Acres. Location: Nr. Rd: Common Road; Main Rd: A127; Rail: Southend-on-Sea.
Ref: FH3279

MILL FARM FISHERY

Mill Farm Fishery, Peatling Rd, Gilmorton, Lutterworth, **LEICESTERSHIRE**, LE17 5NR, **England**.
(W) www.fisheries.co.uk/millfarm
Contact/s: Mr Tom Baker (Owner).
(T) 01455 552392 (F) 01455 552392
Profile: FT: Coarse; WN: Mill Farm Fishery; WT: Combination (Still); F. Size: 10 Acres; W. Size: 5 Acres. Location: Nr. Rd: Peatling Road; Main Rd: A426.
Ref: FH3280

MILL FARM FISHERY

Mill Farm Fishery, Great Ellingham, Attleborough, **NORFOLK**, NR17, **England**.
Contact/s: Mr Derek Beales.
(T) 01953 452769
Profile: FT: Coarse; WN: Mill Farm Fishery; WT: Lake (Still). Location: Nr. Rd: Attleborough to Great Ellingham; Main Rd: B1077.
Ref: FH3281

MILL FARM FISHERY

Mill Farm Fishery, Tasburgh, Norwich, **NORFOLK**, NR, **England**.
Contact/s: Mr R Westgate (Club Secretary), Wroxham and District Angling Club, 31 The Paddocks, Old Catton, Norwich, NR6 7HF.
(T) 01603 401062 (F) 01603 897122 (M) 07885 244262
(E) wroxham.angling@virgin.net
Profile: FT: Coarse; WN: Mill Farm; WT: Lake (Still) W. Size: 5 Acres. Location: Rail: Norwich.
Ref: FH3282

MILL FARM FISHERY

Mill Farm Fishery, Bury, Pulborough, **SUSSEX (WEST)**, RH20, **England**.
Contact/s: Mr Adrian Brown (Bailiff).
(T) 01798 874853
Profile: FT: Coarse; WN: Mill Pond & Specimen; WT: Lake (Still); F. Size: 20 Acres; W. Size: 15 Acres. Location: Nr. Rd: A29.
Ref: FH3283

MILL FARM TROUT LAKES

Mill Farm Trout Lakes, Worton, Devizes, **WILTSHIRE**, SN10 5UW, **England**.
Contact/s: Mr Bill Coleman (Owner).
(T) 01380 813138
Profile: FT: Game; WN: Avon; WT: Lake (Still).
Ref: FH3284

MILL HILL LAKES

Mill Hill Lakes, Bratoft, Skegness, **LINCOLNSHIRE**, PE24, **England**.
Contact/s: Andrew (Fishery Manager).
(T) 01754 810243 (F) 01754 810555 (M) 07836 596277
Profile: FT: Coarse; WN: Mill Hill; WT: Lake (Still).
Ref: FH3285

MILL HOUSE FISHERIES

Mill House Fisheries, Tighnabruaich, **ARGYLL AND BUTE**, PA21, **Scotland**.
Contact/s: Mr Allen Richardson.
(T) 01700 811486
Mr Baron Ronald Reisinger, Forest Enterprise, Allt Beag, Tighnabruaich, Argyll & Bute PA21 2BE.
(T) 01700 811486
Profile: FT: Game; WN: Mill House Fisheries; WT: Combination (Still); F. Size: 80 Acres; W. Size: 78 Acres. Location: Nr. Rd: B8000.
Ref: FH3286

MILL HOUSE FISHERY

Mill House Fishery, Mescar Lake, Greens Lane, Lydiate, Liverpool, **MERSEYSIDE**, L31, **England**.
Contact/s: Mr Andrew Molyneux (Manager).
(T) 07808 764374 (M) 07808 764374
Profile: FT: Coarse; WN: Mescar; WT: Lake (Still) W. Size: 4 Acres. Location: Nr. Rd: Greens Lane; Main Rd: A59, A5147.
Ref: FH3287

MILL HOUSE LAKES

Mill House Lakes, Mill House, Rosehill, Market Drayton, **SHROPSHIRE**, TF9 2JF, **England**.
Contact/s: Mr Chris Bates.
Profile: FT: Coarse; WN: Mill House; WT: Lake (Still).
Ref: FH3288

MILL LAKE (NO 44)

Mill Lake (No 44), Cotswold Water Park, Cirencester, **GLOUCESTERSHIRE**, GL7, **England**.
Contact/s: Mr Steve Rowley, Golden Lands Cottage, 177 Collingbourne Rd, Burbage, Malborogh, Wiltshire, SN8 3RU.
(T) 01793 562163
Profile: FT: Coarse; WN: Mill; WT: Gravel Pit (Still) W. Size: 21 Acres. Location: Nr. Rd: Mill Lane; Main Rd: A419.
Ref: FH3289

MILL LANE

Mill Lane, Sandhurst, **BERKSHIRE**, GU47, **England**.
Contact/s: Manager, The Creel, 36 Station Rd, Aldershot, Hampshire, GU11 1HT.
(T) 01252 320871
Profile: FT: Coarse; WN: Mill Lane; WT: Gravel Pit (Still) W. Size: 8 Acres. Location: Nr. Rd: Mill Lane; Main Rd: M3 junction 3, B3272.
Ref: FH3290

MILL LEAT TROUT FISHERY

Mill Leat Trout Fishery, Mill Leat, Thornbury,

Holsworthy, **DEVON**, EX22 7AY, **England**.
Contact/s: Mr R Birkett.
(T) 01409 261426
Profile: **FT:** Game; **WN:** Walden; **WT:** Combination (Still & Moving); **F. Size:** 14 Acres; **W. Size:** 3 Acres. **Location:** **Nr. Rd:** Thornbury to Sherbear; **Main Rd:** A388; **Rail:** Barnstaple.
Ref: FH3291

MILL LODGE

Mill Lodge, Bollington, Macclesfield, **CHESHIRE**, SK10, **England**.
Contact/s: **Mr John Turner** (Hon Secretary), Prince Albert Angling Society, 15 Pexhill Drive, Macclesfield, Cheshire, SK10 3LP.
(T) 01625 422010
Profile: **FT:** Coarse; **WN:** Oakbank Pool; **WT:** Mill Dam (Still). **Location:** **Nr. Rd:** Shrigley Road; **Main Rd:** B5090; **Rail:** Macclesfield.
Ref: FH3292

MILL LODGE FISHERY

Mill Lodge Fishery, Lurgan Rd, Dromore, **COUNTY DOWN**, **Northern Ireland**.
(W) www.ni-carp.co.uk
Contact/s: **Mr Gary Webb** (Society Chairman), 2 Balmoral Dale, Bangor, County Down, Northern Ireland, BT19 7XJ.
(T) 028 91275648
(E) chairman@ni-carp.co.uk
Profile: **FT:** Coarse; **WN:** Top, Middle, Bottom, & Match Lake; **WT:** Lake (Still); **F. Size:** 7 Acres. **Location:** **Nr. Rd:** Lurgan Road; **Main Rd:** M1.
Ref: FH3293

MILL LOUGH BELLANALECK

Mill Lough Bellanaleck, Bellanaleck, Enniskillen, **COUNTY FERMANAGH**, BT92 2BA, **Northern Ireland**.
Contact/s: Manager, Erne Tackle, 118 Main St, Lisnaskea, Enniskillen, BT92 0JD.
(T) 028 67721969
Mr Jim Foster (Manager).
(T) 028 66348313
Profile: **FT:** Game; **WN:** Mill; **WT:** Lough (Still) **W. Size:** 100 Acres.
Ref: FH3294

MILL OF CRIGGIE TROUT FISHERY

Mill Of Criggie Trout Fishery, St Cyrus, Montrose, **ANGUS**, DD10 0DR, **Scotland**.
Contact/s: **Mr Kevin Ramshaw**.
(T) 01674 850868 **(F)** 01674 850868
Ms Helen Ramshaw.
(T) 01674 850868 **(F)** 01674 850868
Profile: **FT:** Game; **WN:** Mill Of Criggie Trout Fishery; **WT:** Lake (Still); **F. Size:** 20 Acres; **W. Size:** 5 Acres. **Location:** **Nr. Rd:** St Cyrus to Laurencekirk; **Main Rd:** A92; **Rail:** Montrose.
Ref: FH3295

MILL OF ELRICK FISHERY

Mill Of Elrick Fishery, Auchnagatt, Ellon, **ABERDEENSHIRE**, AB41 8US, **Scotland**.
Contact/s: **Ms Donna Basford** (Part Owner).
(T) 01358 701628 **(F)** 01358 701628
(E) d.basford@talk21.com
Profile: **FT:** Game; **WN:** Mill Of Elrick Fishery; **WT:** Loch (Still) **W. Size:** 3 Acres. **Location:** **Nr. Rd:** A948; **Main Rd:** A948; **Rail:** Aberdeen.
Ref: FH3296

MILL PARK COARSE FISHING LAKE

Mill Park Coarse Fishing Lake, Mill Park, Berrynarbor, Ilfracombe, **DEVON**, EX34 9SH, **England**.
Contact/s: **Mr Brian Malin** (Manager), Mill Park Coarse Fishing Lake, Berrynarbor, Ilfracombe, Devon, EX34 9SH.
(T) 01271 882647 **(F)** 01271 882667
Profile: **FT:** Coarse; **WN:** Mill Park; **WT:** Lake (Still) **W. Size:** 1 Acre. **Location:** **Nr. Rd:** Mill Lane; **Main Rd:** A399; **Rail:** Barnstaple.
Ref: FH3297

MILL POND

Mill Pond, Mill Park, Mill Wildridings, Bracknell, **BERKSHIRE**, RG42 1, **England**.
Contact/s: **Mr Kevin Hiscock** (Match Secretary), Bracknell Angling Ctre, 2a Fowlers Lane, Bracknell, Berkshire, RG42 1XP.
(T) 01344 425130
Profile: **FT:** Coarse; **WN:** Mill Pond; **WT:** Lake (Still) **W. Size:** 6 Acres. **Location:** **Nr. Rd:** Wildridings Road; **Main Rd:** A329.
Ref: FH3298

MILL POND

Mill Pond, Dorking, **SURREY**, RH4, **England**.
Contact/s: **Mr S C Fuller** (Manager), Fuller's Tackle Shop, 28 South St, Dorking, Surrey, RH4 2HQ.
(T) 01306 882407
Profile: **FT:** Coarse; **WN:** Mill; **WT:** Pond (Still) **W. Size:** 2 Acres. **Location:** **Nr. Rd:** Reigate to Guildford; **Main Rd:** A25.
Ref: FH3299

MILL POND LAKE

Mill Pond Lake, Leominstead Trout Fishery, Emery Down, Lyndhurst, **HAMPSHIRE**, SO43 7GA, **England**.
Contact/s: **Mr David Hoskins** (Bailiff).
(M) 07714 114038
Mr Neil Branscombe.
(T) 023 80282610 **(M)** 07071 200809
Profile: **FT:** Coarse; **WN:** Mill Pond; **WT:** Lake (Still). **Location:** **Nr. Rd:** B3056; **Main Rd:** A337, Lyndhurst to Cadnam.
Ref: FH3300

MILL POOL

Mill Pool, Faversham, **KENT**, **England**.
(W) www.midkentfish.demon.co.uk
Contact/s: **Mr Chris Logsdon** (Fisheries Manager), Mid Kent Fisheries, Chilham Water Mill, Mill Lane, Chilham, CT4 8EE.
(T) 01227 730668
(E) chilham@midkentfisheries.co.uk
Profile: **FT:** Coarse; **WN:** Mill Pool; **WT:** Gravel Pit (Still); **F. Size:** 25 Acres; **W. Size:** 10 Acres. **Location:** **Main Rd:** A2; **Rail:** Faversham.
Ref: FH3301

MILL POOL

Mill Pool, Barby, Rugby, **WARWICKSHIRE**, CV23, **England**.
Contact/s: **Mr Richard Bubb** (Manager).
(T) 01788 890830or579521 **(M)** 07973 654336
Profile: **FT:** Coarse; **WN:** Mill Pool; **WT:** Lake (Still). **Location:** **Nr. Rd:** A361; **Main Rd:** A428.
Ref: FH3302

MILL POOL

Mill Pool, Bewdley, **WORCESTERSHIRE**, DY12, **England**.
Contact/s: Manager, Furnace Mill Fishery, Kidderminster.
(T) 01299 266160
Profile: **FT:** Coarse; **WN:** Mill; **WT:** Pool (Still) **W. Size:** 1 Acre.
Ref: FH3303

MILL ROAD LAKES

Mill Road Lakes, Brogden Farm, Mill Rd, Addlethorpe, Skegness, **LINCOLNSHIRE**, PE24 4TE, **England**.
Contact/s: **Mr Graham Wynn**.
(T) 01754 767586
Mr P Cumberworth.
(T) 01754 767586
Profile: **FT:** Coarse; **WN:** Mill Road; **WT:** Lake (Still); **F. Size:** 6 Acres; **W. Size:** 3 Acres. **Location:** **Nr. Rd:** Mill Road; **Main Rd:** A52.
Ref: FH3304

MILLBROOK COARSE FISHERY

Millbrook Coarse Fishery, Tregonhawke Cottage, Millbrook, Torpoint, **CORNWALL**, PL10 1JH, **England**.
Contact/s: **Mr Mark Blake** (Owner).
(T) 01752 823210
Ms Rebecca Blake (Owner).
(T) 01752 823210
(E) rebecca_l_blake@hotmail.com
Profile: **FT:** Coarse; **WN:** Millbrook; **WT:** Reservoir (Still); **F. Size:** 2 Acres; **W. Size:** 1 Acre. **Location:** **Nr. Rd:** Millbrook; **Main Rd:** B3247; **Rail:** Plymouth. **£Fr**
Ref: FH3305

MILLBROOK FISHERY

Millbrook Fishery, Manorowen, Fishguard, **PEMBROKESHIRE**, SA65 9PT, **Wales**.
Contact/s: **Mr Len Williams**.
(T) 01348 873385
(E) millbrook@tinyonline.co.uk
Profile: **FT:** Game; **WN:** Millbrook Fishery; **WT:** Lake (Still).
Ref: FH3306

MILLBROOK TROUT FARM

Millbrook Trout Farm, Cress Barn, Mill Lane, Fovant, Salisbury, **WILTSHIRE**, SP3 5JP, **England**.
Contact/s: Fishery Manager.
(T) 01722 714233
Profile: **FT:** Game; **WN:** Nadder; **WT:** River (Moving).
Ref: FH3307

MILLBUIES LOCH

Millbuies Loch, Elgin, **MORAY**, IV30, **Scotland**.
Contact/s: Fishery Manager.
(T) 01343 545121
Profile: **FT:** Game; **WN:** Millbuies; **WT:** Loch (Still).
Ref: FH3308

MILLENNIUM LAKES

Millennium Lakes, Thoby Lane, Ingatestone, **ESSEX**, CM4, **England**.
Contact/s: **John** (Manager).
(T) 020 7250059 **(M)** 07956 245484
Profile: **FT:** Coarse; **WN:** Millennium; **WT:** Lake (Still) **W. Size:** 3 Acres. **Location:** **Nr. Rd:** Thoby Lane; **Main Rd:** M25, junction 28.
Ref: FH3309

MILLERS LAKE

Millers Lake, Clare, **SUFFOLK**, **England**.
Contact/s: **Mr Len Miller** (Owner).
(T) 01440 708408
Profile: **FT:** Coarse; **WN:** Miller's Lake**WT:** Lake.
Ref: FH3310

MILLETS FARM TROUT FISHERY

Millets Farm Trout Fishery, Kingston Rd, Frilford, Abingdon, **OXFORDSHIRE**, OX13 5HB, **England**.
Contact/s: **Mr Peter Copsey**.
(T) 01865 391394
Profile: **FT:** Game; **WN:** Millets Farm; **WT:** Lake (Still) **W. Size:** 7 Acres. **Location:** **Nr. Rd:** Kingston Road.
Ref: FH3311

MILLHALL RESERVOIR

Millhall Reservoir, Polmont, Falkirk, FK2 0YA, **Scotland**.
Contact/s: **Mr Andrew Kirkham** (Fishery Manager).
(T) 01324 714190
Profile: **FT:** Coarse; **WN:** Millhall; **WT:** Reservoir (Still).
Ref: FH3312

MILLHAYES

Millhayes, Kentisbeare, Cullompton, **DEVON**, EX15 2AF, **England**.
Contact/s: **Mr Tony Howe**.
(T) 01884 266412
Profile: **FT:** Coarse; **WN:** Millhayes; **WT:** Lake (Still) **W. Size:** 4 Acres. **Location:** **Nr. Rd:** A373, Honiton to Cullompton; **Main Rd:** M5; **Rail:** Tiverton Parkway.
Ref: FH3313

MILLPOND

Millpond, Little Tarrington, Tarrington,

Hereford, **HEREFORDSHIRE**, HR1 4JA, **England**.
(W) www.millpond.co.uk
Contact/s: **Mr Phillip Stock** (Owner).
(T) 01432 890243 (F) 01432 890243
Ms Angela Stock (Owner).
(T) 01432 890243 (F) 01432 890243
(E) enquires@millpond.co.uk
Profile: **FT:** Coarse; **WN:** Mill; **WT:** Pond (Still) **W. Size:** 3 Acres. Location: **Nr. Rd:** A438, Ledbury to Hereford; **Main Rd:** A438; **Rail:** Ledbury.
Ref: FH3314

MILLPOOL FISHERIES

Millpool Fisheries, Millpool, Goldsithney, Penzance, **CORNWALL**, TR20, **England**.
Contact/s: , Chyraise Lodge Hotel, Millpool, Goldsithney, Penzance, Cornwall TR20 9JD.
Profile: **FT:** Coarse; **WN:** Millpool Fisheries; **WT:** Lake (Still). Location: **Nr. Rd:** Millpool; **Main Rd:** A394 between Helston and Marazion.
Ref: FH3315

MILLRACE

Millrace, Ligett Lane, Garforth, Leeds, **YORKSHIRE (WEST)**, LS25, **England**.
Contact/s: **Olga**.
(T) 0113 2862530
Profile: **FT:** Coarse; **WN:** Millrace; **WT:** Lake (Still). Location: **Nr. Rd:** Ligett Lane; **Main Rd:** A63.
Ref: FH3316

MILLRIDE FISHERY

Millride Fishery, Millride Ctre, Hill Farm, Bognop Rd, Essington, Wolverhampton, **SHROPSHIRE**, WV11 2AZ, **England**.
Contact/s: Manager, Millride Country Sports, Hill Farm, Bogner Rd, Essington, WV11 2AZ.
(T) 01902 725165
Ms Heather Mabbs.
(T) 01922 725165
Profile: **FT:** Combination; **WN:** Millride Fishery; **WT:** Pool (Still) **W. Size:** 3 Acres. Location: **Nr. Rd:** A460, Bognop Road; **Main Rd:** M54, junction 1, to Essington.
Ref: FH3317

MILTON COUNTRY PARK

Milton Country Park, Cambridge Rd, Milton, Cambridge, **CAMBRIDGESHIRE**, CB4 6AZ, **England**.
Contact/s: Manager, South Cambridgeshire District Council, 9-11 Hills Rd, Cambridge, CB2 1PB.
Mr Malcolm Busby (Ranger).
(T) 01223 420060 (F) 01223 420801
Mr R Cooper (Secretary), Histon and District Angling Club, 236 Histon Rd, Cottenham, Cambridgeshire, CB4 8UG.
(T) 01223 420060or365987
Profile: **FT:** Coarse; **WN:** Milton Country Park; **WT:** Gravel Pit (Still) **W. Size:** 11 Acres. Location: **Nr. Rd:** A10; **Main Rd:** A14; **Rail:** Cambridge.
Ref: FH3318

MILTON FARM PONDS

Milton Farm Ponds, Payhembury, Honiton, **DEVON**, EX14 0HE, **England**.
Contact/s: **Mr Brian Cook**.
(T) 01404 850236
Profile: **FT:** Coarse; **WN:** Milton Farm; **WT:** Pond (Still) **W. Size:** 2 Acres. Location: **Nr. Rd:** Payhembury to Feniton Road; **Main Rd:** A373.
Ref: FH3319

MILTON GREEN

Milton Green, Tattenhall, Chester, **CHESHIRE**, CH3, **England**.
Contact/s: Fishery Manager.
(T) 01829 771102
Profile: **FT:** Coarse; **WN:** Milton; **WT:** Lake (Still). Location: **Nr. Rd:** Chapel Lane; **Main Rd:** A41.
Ref: FH3320

MILTON KEYNES LAKES

Milton Keynes Lakes, Bedford, **BUCKINGHAMSHIRE**, MK4, **England**.
Contact/s: **Mr G Buss** (Secretary), 1 Easthill Rd, Houghton Regis, Dunstable, Bedfordshire, LU5 5EQ.
(T) 01582 28114
Profile: **FT:** Coarse; **WN:** Milton Keynes; **WT:** Lake (Still).
Ref: FH3321

MILTON MOUNT LAKE

Milton Mount Lake, Pound Hill, Crawley, **CORNWALL**, RH10, **England**.
Contact/s: , 24 Rillside, Furnace Green, Crawley, Sussex (West).
(T) 01342 842174/07703595439
Profile: **FT:** Coarse; **WN:** Milton Mount; **WT:** Lake (Still); **F. Size:** 2 Acres; **W. Size:** 2 Acres. Location: **Nr. Rd:** Grattons Drive; **Main Rd:** A2011; **Rail:** Crawley.
Ref: FH3322

MILTON PAN LAKE

Milton Pan Lake, Milton Complex, Canterbury, **KENT**, CT1, **England**.
Contact/s: **Mr Chris Logsdon** (Manager), Mid Kent Fisheries, Chilham Water Mill, Mill Lane, Chilham, CT4 8EE.
(T) 01227 730668 (F) 01277 38894
Profile: **FT:** Coarse; **WN:** Milton; **WT:** Gravel Pit (Still) **W. Size:** 15 Acres.
Ref: FH3323

MILTON PITS

Milton Pits, Old School Lane, Milton, Cambridge, **CAMBRIDGESHIRE**, CB, **England**.
Profile: **FT:** Coarse; **WN:** Milton; **WT:** Gravel Pit (Still). Location: **Nr. Rd:** Old School Lane; **Main Rd:** A45.
Ref: FH3324

MILTON PONDS

Milton Ponds, Milton Rd, Hoyland, Barnsley, **YORKSHIRE (SOUTH)**, S7, **England**.
Contact/s: Area Manager, Environment Agency, Ridings Area Office, Phoenix House, Global Avenue, Leeds, LS11 8PG.
(T) 0113 2440191or2314834 (F) 0113 2134609
Mr B Wilson (Fishery Manager).
(T) 01226 746041
Profile: **FT:** Coarse; **WN:** Milton; **WT:** Pond (Still). Location: **Nr. Rd:** Milton Road; **Main Rd:** A6135.
Ref: FH3325

MILTON POOLS FARM

Milton Pools Farm, Great Milton, Oxford, **OXFORDSHIRE**, OX44 7JE, **England**.
Contact/s: **Mr John Rust** (Fishery Manager).
(T) 01844 278150
Profile: **FT:** Coarse; **WN:** Milton; **WT:** Pool (Still). Location: **Nr. Rd:** A329; **Main Rd:** M40, junction 7.
Ref: FH3326

MINERS PONDS

Miners Ponds, Coleford, Somerton, **SOMERSET**, TA11, **England**.
Profile: **FT:** Game; **WN:** Miners; **WT:** Pond (Still).
Ref: FH3327

MISSION LINEBANK PONDS

Mission Linebank Ponds, Bawtry, Doncaster, **YORKSHIRE (SOUTH)**, DN10 6, **England**.
Contact/s: **Mr Maurice Tate** (Secretary), Doncaster and District Angling Association, 28 Holmescarr Rd, New Rossington, Doncaster, DN11 0QF.
(T) 01302 865482
Profile: **FT:** Coarse; **WN:** Mission Linebank Ponds; **WT:** Pond (Still) **W. Size:** 6 Acres.
Ref: FH3328

MITCHELLS HOUSE RESERVOIR

Mitchells House Reservoir, Higher Baxenden, Accrington, **LANCASHIRE**, BB5, **England**.
Contact/s: **Mr A Balderstone** (Secretary), 42 Townley Avenue, Huncoat, Lancashire, BB5 6LP.
(T) 01254 233517
Mr Roy Rhodes (Conservation, Access and Recreation Manager), Rivington Water Treatment Works, Bolton Rd, Horwich, Bolton, BL6 7RN.
(T) 01204 664300
Profile: **FT:** Game; **WN:** Mitchells House; **WT:** Reservoir (Still) **W. Size:** 20 Acres. Location: **Nr. Rd:** Higher Baxenden.
Ref: FH3329

MOATHOUSE LAKE

Moathouse Lake, Whitmore Way, Basildon, **ESSEX**, SS14 2AL, **England**.
Contact/s: **Mr Sid Hibbert** (Secretary), Basildon and District Angling Society, 15 Culverdown, Basildon, Essex, SS14 2AL.
(T) 01268 287798
Profile: **FT:** Coarse; **WN:** Moathouse; **WT:** Lake (Still); **F. Size:** 3 Acres; **W. Size:** 2 Acres. Location: **Nr. Rd:** Whitmore Way; **Main Rd:** A176 to Basildon; **Rail:** Basildon.
Ref: FH3330

MOATLANDS POOL

Moatlands Pool, Mill Rd, Reading, **BERKSHIRE**, RG, **England**.
Contact/s: **Mr Bill Brown-Lee** (Manager).
(T) 0118 9417368
Ms Dusty Millar (Ticket Administrator), 238 Elgar Road South, Reading, Berkshire, RG3 0BW.
(T) 0118 9874882
Profile: **FT:** Coarse; **WN:** Moatlands Pool; **WT:** Lake (Still); **F. Size:** 30 Acres; **W. Size:** 4 Acres. Location: **Nr. Rd:** Mill Road; **Main Rd:** M4, junction 12.
Ref: FH3331

MOBBERLEY POOL

Mobberley Pool, Small Lane, Mobberley, Altrincham, **CHESHIRE**, WA, **England**.
Contact/s: Secretary, Altrincham Angling Society, 37 Crossgates Avenue, Sharston, Manchester.
(T) 0161 2863952
Profile: **FT:** Coarse; **WN:** Mobberley Pool; **WT:** Lake (Still) **W. Size:** 1 Acre. Location: **Nr. Rd:** B5085.
Ref: FH3332

MOCCAS FISHERY

Moccas Fishery, The Red Lion Hotel, Bredwardine, Hereford, **HEREFORDSHIRE**, HR3 6BU, **England**.
Contact/s: **Mr Mike Taylor** (Secretary).
(T) 01981 500303
Profile: **FT:** Coarse; **WN:** Wye; **WT:** Combination (Still & Moving) **W. Size:** 6400 Metres. Location: **Nr. Rd:** B4352; **Main Rd:** A438; **Rail:** Hereford.
Ref: FH3333

MOCKERKIN TARN

Mockerkin Tarn, Loweswater, Cockermouth, **CUMBRIA**, CA13, **England**.
Contact/s: **Mr C D Knowles** (Manager).
(T) 01277 352245or821554 (F) 01227 821554
Profile: **FT:** Coarse; **WN:** Mockerkin; **WT:** Tarn (Still). Location: **Nr. Rd:** Cockermouth Road; **Main Rd:** A6086.
Ref: FH3334

MOCOLLOP FISHERY

Mocollop Fishery, Station Rd, Upper Ballyduff, Waterford, **COUNTY WATERFORD**, **Ireland**.
Contact/s: Fishery Manager.
(T) 058 60146
Profile: **FT:** Game; **WN:** Mocollop Fishery
Ref: FH3335

MOFFAT FISHERIES

Moffat Fisheries, Hammerlands, Moffat, **DUMFRIES AND GALLOWAY**, DG10 9QL, **Scotland**.

Contact/s: Mr Sean Ottewell.
(T) 01683 221068
Profile: FT: Game; WN: Moffat Fisheries; WT: Lake (Still).
Ref: FH3336

MOLE (RIVER)

River Mole, Kings Nympton, Umberleigh, **DEVON**, EX37, **England**.
Contact/s: Mr Roddy Rae, Half Stone Sporting Agency, 6 Hescane Park, Cheriton Bishop, Exeter, EX6 6JP.
(T) 01647 24643 (F) 01647 24643
Profile: FT: Game; WN: Mole; WT: River (Moving) W. Size: 1200 Metres. **Location:** Nr. Rd: B3226; Main Rd: A377 to Barnstaple.
Ref: FH3337

MOLE (RIVER)

River Mole, Southwood Manor Farm, Hersham, Walton-on-Thames, **SURREY**, KT12, **England**.
(W) www.calpac.bizland.com
Contact/s: Mr Colin Trafford (General Secretary).
(T) 020 82242617
Mrs Diane Wheeler (Secretary), 314 Old Lodge Lane, Purley, Surrey, CR8 4AQ.
(T) 020 86602766
Profile: FT: Coarse; WN: Mole; WT: River (Moving) W. Size: 2400 Metres. **Location:** Nr. Rd: Esher to Weybridge; Main Rd: A244.
Ref: FH3338

MOLE (RIVER)

River Mole, Dorking, **SURREY**, RH4, **England**.
Contact/s: Mr S C Fuller (Manager), Fuller's Tackle Shop, 28 South St, Dorking, Surrey, RH4 2HQ.
(T) 01306 882407
Profile: FT: Coarse; WN: Mole; WT: River (Moving). **Location:** Nr. Rd: Brockham to Leatherhead.
Ref: FH3339

MOLESEY LOCK

Molesey Lock, Hurst Rd, East Molesey, **SURREY**, KT8 9AW, **England**.
Contact/s: Fishery Contact.
(T) 020 89794482
Recreational Manager, The Environment Agency, Kings Meadow Rd, Reading, Berkshire, RG1 8DQ.
(T) 0118 9535000 (F) 0118 9500388
Profile: FT: Combination; WN: Thames; WT: Lock (Still). **Location:** Nr. Rd: Hurst Road or River Bank Road; Main Rd: A3050.
Ref: FH3340

MONEYCARRAGH (RIVER)

River Moneycarragh, Dundrum, Newcastle, **COUNTY DOWN**, BT33, **Northern Ireland**.
Contact/s: Mr John Milburne, 1 Beedham's Lane, Ballynahinch, County Down, BT24 8XA.
(T) 028 97563319
Profile: FT: Game; WN: Moneycarragh; WT: River (Moving) W. Size: 4000 Metres.
Ref: FH3341

MONK LAKE FISHERIES

Monk Lake Fisheries, Riverfield Carp Farm, Maidstone Rd, Marden, Tonbridge, **KENT**, TN12 9BU, **England**.
(W) www.monklake.co.uk
Contact/s: Mr Chris Davis (Fishery Manager).
(T) 01580 890120 (F) 01580 890120
Ned (Bailiff).
(T) 01580 890120 (F) 01580 890120
Profile: FT: Coarse; WN: Monk; WT: Lake (Still); F. Size: 50 Acres; W. Size: 8 Acres. **Location:** Nr. Rd: A229; Main Rd: A229; Rail: Staplehurst.
Ref: FH3342

MONKHALL FISHERIES

Monkhall Fisheries Limited, Lower Monkhall Farm, Monkhopton, Bridgnorth, **SHROPSHIRE**, WV16 6XF, **England**.
Contact/s: Mr Allan Parsonage (Manager).
(T) 01746 785281
Ms Nicola Cairns (Owner).
(T) 01746 785281
Profile: FT: Coarse; WN: Monkhall Fisheries Limited; WT: Lake (Still). **Location:** Nr. Rd: B4368; Main Rd: A458, A442.
Ref: FH3343

MONKLAND CANAL

Monkland Canal, Blair Rd, Coatbridge, **LANARKSHIRE (NORTH)**, ML5, **Scotland**.
Contact/s: Mr John McShane (Secretary), Monklands District Coarse Angling Club, 5 Crinan Cres, Townhead, Coatbridge, ML5 2LG.
Mr Ronnie Macleod (Manager), MacLeod's Fishing Tackle, 176 High St, Motherwell, Lanarkshire, ML1 5JQ.
(T) 01698 860530
Profile: FT: Coarse; WN: Monkland; WT: Canal (Still) W. Size: 2 Acres. **Location:** Nr. Rd: Blair Road; Main Rd: M8; Rail: Blairhill.
Ref: FH3344

MONKS MOAT

Monks Moat, Belmont Estate, Northwich, **CHESHIRE**, CW9, **England**.
Contact/s: Mr Neil Jupp (Club Secretary), Lymm Angling Club, PO Box 350, Warrington, Cheshire, WA2 9FB.
(T) 01925 411744
Profile: FT: Coarse; WN: Monks; WT: Moat (Still). **Location:** Nr. Rd: A559 to Northwich; Main Rd: M56 to Chester.
Ref: FH3345

MONKS POOL

Monks Pool, Ruabon, Wrexham, **DENBIGHSHIRE**, LL14 6, **Wales**.
Contact/s: Mr Tony Borelli (Manager), 16 Wynne Avenue, Rhosddu, Wrexham.
(T) 01978 366037
Profile: FT: Coarse; WN: Monk's Pool; WT: Gravel Pit (Still) W. Size: 7 Acres. **Location:** Nr. Rd: B5426; Main Rd: A483.
Ref: FH3346

MONKS POOL

Monks Pool, Weston Lane, Bulkington, Bedworth, **WARWICKSHIRE**, CV12, **England**.
Contact/s: Mr David Gibbs.
(T) 024 76316892
Profile: FT: Coarse; WN: Monks; WT: Pool (Still) W. Size: 2 Acres. **Location:** Nr. Rd: Weston Lane; Main Rd: B4029 to Bulkington.
Ref: FH3347

MONMOUTHSHIRE & BRECON CANAL

Monmouthshire And Brecon Canal, Newport, NP, **Wales**.
Profile: FT: Coarse; WN: Monmouthshire and Brecon Canal; WT: Canal (Still).
Location: Nr. Rd: A4042.
Ref: FH3348

MONNOW (RIVER)

River Monnow, Kentchurch, Hereford, **HEREFORDSHIRE**, HR2, **England**.
Contact/s: Mr G Kitchen (Manager), Bridge Inn, Kentchurch, Herford, Herefordshire, HR2 0BY.
(T) 01981 240408
Profile: FT: Game; WN: Monnow; WT: River (Moving).
Ref: FH3349

MONNOW (RIVER)

River Monnow, Osbaston, Leicester, **LEICESTERSHIRE**, LE, **England**.
Contact/s: Mr Mike Gulliford (Information Contact), 305 Llantarnam Rd, Cwmbran, Gwent.
(T) 01633 874472
Profile: FT: Game; WN: Monnow; WT: River (Moving) W. Size: 3200 Metres.
Ref: FH3350

MONNOW (RIVER)

River Monnow, Monmouth, Skenfrith, Abergavenny, **MONMOUTHSHIRE**, NP7, **Wales**.
Contact/s: Mr Bob Forrest-Webb (Hon Secretary), 1 Trelasdee Cottages, St Weonards, Herefordshire, HR2 8PU.
(T) 01981 580497 (F) 01981 580497
(E) forrest-webb@cwcom.net
Profile: FT: Combination; WN: Monnow; WT: River (Moving) W. Size: 1440 Metres. **Location:** Nr. Rd: Skenfrith to Gwent; Main Rd: A49.
Ref: FH3351

MONSAL DALE FISHERY

Monsal Dale Fishery, Monsal Dale, Bakewell, **DERBYSHIRE**, SK17 8SZ, **England**.
Contact/s: Mr Ian Knott (Assistant Agent), Chatsworth and Monsal Dale Fishery, The Estate Office, Edensor, Bakewell, Derbyshire DE45 1PJ.
(T) 01246 565300
Mr Stephen Moores (River Keeper), Rose Cottage, Upper Dale, Monsal Dale, Bakewell, SK17 8SZ.
(T) 01629 640159
Profile: FT: Game; WN: Wye; WT: River (Moving) W. Size: 1200 Metres. **Location:** Nr. Rd: B6465; Main Rd: A6; Rail: Chesterfield.
Ref: FH3352

MONTAGUE RESERVOIR

Montague Reservoir, Montague Fisheries, Mill Of Montague, Balbeggie, Perth, **PERTH AND KINROSS**, PH2 7PR, **Scotland**.
Contact/s: Mr J Watson (owner).
(T) 01821 640271 (F) 01821 640271
Profile: FT: Game; WN: Montague; WT: Reservoir (Still) W. Size: 4 Acres. **Location:** Rail: Perth.
Ref: FH3353

MONTE BISHOP

Holm Lacy Fishries, 12 Old Eign Hill, Hereford, **HEREFORDSHIRE**, HR1 1TU, **England**.
Contact/s: Mr Monte Bishop (Owner).
(T) 01432 342665
Profile: FT: Coarse; WN: Wye; WT: River (Moving).
Ref: FH3354

MONTGOMERY CANAL

Montgomery Canal, Abermule, Montgomery, **POWYS**, SY15 6, **Wales**.
Contact/s: Mr Steve Potts (Secretary), Severnside and Newtown Angling Club, 902 Falcon Court, Newton, Powys, SY16 1LQ.
(T) 01686 624871
Profile: FT: Coarse; WN: Montgomery; WT: Canal (Still) W. Size: 750 Metres.
Ref: FH3355

MOON LAKE

Moon Lake, Bank Farm, Marsh Lane, Tattershall, **LINCOLNSHIRE**, LN4 4JR, **England**.
Contact/s: Mrs Shirley Morrell (Owner), Bank Farm, Marsh Lane, Tattershall, Linconshire, LN4 4JR.
(T) 01526 342208
Profile: FT: Coarse; WN: Moon; WT: Lake (Still); F. Size: 2 Acres; W. Size: 1 Acre. **Location:** Nr. Rd: Marsh Lane; Main Rd: A153; Rail: Sleaford.
Ref: FH3356

MOOR HALL POOL

Moor Hall Pool, Moor Hall Farm, Ninfield, Battle, **SUSSEX (EAST)**, TN33, **England**.
Contact/s: Mr George Allen, Rowallen Fisheries, 26 Eastwood Rd, Bexhill on Sea, Sussex (East), TN39 3PS.
(T) 01424 217239
Profile: FT: Coarse; WN: Moor Hall; WT: Pool (Still) W. Size: 2 Acres. **Location:** Nr. Rd: A271.
Ref: FH3357

MOOR POOL

Moor Pool, Lymm, **CHESHIRE**, **England**.
(W) www.baymalton-anglingclub.org
Contact/s: **Mr Stewart Godber** (Club Secretary), 38 Edenfield Rd, Mobberley, Cheshire, WA16 7HE.
(T) 01565 872582
Profile: **FT:** Coarse; **WN:** Moor Pool; **WT:** Clay Pit (Still); **F. Size:** 1 Acre; **W. Size:** 1 Acre.
Ref: FH3358

MOORBROOK LODGE

Moorbrook Lodge, 46 Glebe Rd, Castlerock, Coleraine, **COUNTY LONDONDERRY**, BT51 4SW, **Northern Ireland**.
(W) www.moorbrooklodge.freeserve.co.uk
Contact/s: **Ms Stephanie Holmes** (Manager).
(T) 028 70849408 (F) 028 70849408
(E) stephanie@moorbrooklodge.freeserve.co.uk
Profile: **FT:** Game; **WN:** Moorbrook; **WT:** Lake (Still) **W. Size:** 3 Acres. **Location: Nr. Rd:** Glebe Road; **Main Rd:** A2; **Rail:** Castlerock.
Ref: FH3359

MOORE QUARRY

Moore Quarry, Moore, Warrington, **CHESHIRE**, WA4, **England**.
Contact/s: **Mr Frank Lythgoe** (Secretary), Warrington Angling Association, 52 Parker St, Warrington, Lancashire.
(T) 01928 716238 (F) 01928 713898
(E) info@warrington-anglers.org.uk
Profile: **FT:** Coarse; **WN:** Moore; **WT:** Quarry (Still). **Location: Main Rd:** A56.
Ref: FH3360

MOORHEN FARM TROUT LAKE

Moorhen Farm Trout Lake, Moorhen Farm, Warnford, Southampton, **HAMPSHIRE**, SO32 3LB, **England**.
Contact/s: **Mr Humphries** (Fishery Manager).
(T) 01730 829460 office hours please
Profile: **FT:** Game; **WN:** Moorhen Farm; **WT:** Lake (Still); **F. Size:** 5 Acres; **W. Size:** 5 Acres. **Location: Nr. Rd:** A32; **Main Rd:** A32; **Rail:** Petersfield.
Ref: FH3361

MOORHOUSE TARN

Moorhouse Tarn, Wigton, **CUMBRIA**, CA7, **England**.
Contact/s: **Mr Saunderson** (Manager), Saunderson Ironmongers Ltd, 11-13 King St, Wigton, Cumbria, CA7 9EB.
(T) 01697 342611 (F) 01697 342611
Profile: **FT:** Coarse; **WN:** Moorhouse Tarn; **WT:** Lake (Still) **W. Size:** 3200 Metres.
Ref: FH3362

MOORLANDS FARM

Moorlands Farm, Hartlebury, Kidderminster, **WORCESTERSHIRE**, DY11, **England**.
Contact/s: **Mr John Talbot** (Owner).
(T) 01299 250427
Profile: **FT:** Coarse; **WN:** Meadow, Bank, Middle, Moors, Island, Silver Fish,; **WT:** Pool (Still). **Location: Rail:** Hartlebury.
Ref: FH3363

MOORLANDS FARM PONDS

Moorlands Farm Ponds, Wiggington, York, **YORKSHIRE (NORTH)**, **England**.
Contact/s: .
(T) 01904 692046
Profile: **FT:** Coarse; **WN:** Moorlands Farm Ponds; **WT:** Lake (Still).
Ref: FH3364

MOORS POOL

Moors Pool, Hartlebury, Kidderminster, **WORCESTERSHIRE**, DY, **England**.
Profile: **FT:** Coarse; **WN:** Moors Pool; **WT:** Pond (Still). **Location: Main Rd:** A449 Kidderminster to Worcester.
Ref: FH3365

MOORS VALLEY COUNTRY PARK

Moors Valley Country Park, Horton Rd, Ashley Heath, Ringwood, **HAMPSHIRE**, BH24 2ET, **England**.
Contact/s: Information Officer.
(T) 01425 470721 (F) 01425 471656
Profile: **FT:** Coarse; **WN:** Moors Valley Country Park; **WT:** Lake (Still); **F. Size:** 1500 Acres; **W. Size:** 9 Acres. **Location: Nr. Rd:** Horton Road; **Main Rd:** A31.
Ref: FH3366

MOPLEY POND

Mopley Pond, Cadland Estate, Mopley Rd, Langley, Blackfield, Southampton, **HAMPSHIRE**, SO45 1YH, **England**.
(W) www.mfcfishery.f9.co.uk
Contact/s: **Mr Brian Tillman** (Manager), Mopley Farm Cadland Fishery, c/o The Ruffs, Chapel Lane, Blackfield, SO45 1YX.
(T) 023 80891617 (F) 023 80891616 (M) 07768 725621
(E) brian@mfcfishery.f9.co.uk
Profile: **FT:** Coarse; **WN:** Mopley; **WT:** Pond (Still) **W. Size:** 3 Acres. **Location: Nr. Rd:** Hampton Lane; **Main Rd:** M27, junction 2, A326; **Rail:** Southampton.
Ref: FH3367

MORE HALL RESERVOIR

More Hall Reservoir, Bolsterstone, Stocksbridge, Sheffield, **YORKSHIRE (SOUTH)**, S36, **England**.
Contact/s: Area Manager, Environment Agency, Ridings Area Office, Phoenix House, Global Avenue, Leeds, LS11 8PG.
(T) 0113 2440191or2314834 (F) 0113 2134609
Conservation and Recreation Officer.
Profile: **FT:** Game; **WN:** More hall; **WT:** Reservoir (Still).
Ref: FH3368

MORETON MERE

Moreton Mere, Tarran Way, Moreton, Wirral, **MERSEYSIDE**, CH46, **England**.
Contact/s: **Mr Norman Smith**.
(T) 0151 6457211
Profile: **FT:** Coarse; **WN:** Moreton Mere; **WT:** Pool (Still) **W. Size:** 4 Acres. **Location: Nr. Rd:** Tarran Way; **Main Rd:** Birkenhead to Pasture Road.
Ref: FH3369

MORETON MERE FISHERY

Moreton Mere Fishery, Whitethorn Farm, New Rd, Astbury, Congleton, **CHESHIRE**, CW12 4RY, **England**.
Contact/s: **Mr Malcolm Talbot** (Manager).
(T) 01260 272839 (M) 07974 846776
Profile: **FT:** Coarse; **WT:** Pool (Still); **F. Size:** 7 Acres. **Location: Nr. Rd:** New Road; **Main Rd:** A34; **Rail:** Congleton.
Ref: FH3370

MORETON PITS

Moreton Pits, Pickier Cl, Little Rissington, Bourton-on-the-Water, Cheltenham, **GLOUCESTERSHIRE**, GL54, **England**.
Contact/s: **Mr Bill McKenzie** (Secretary).
(T) 01451 821719
Profile: **FT:** Coarse; **WN:** Moreton; **WT:** Gravel Pit (Still) **W. Size:** 14 Acres. **Location: Nr. Rd:** Little Rissington; **Main Rd:** A429.
Ref: FH3371

MORGANS POND

Morgans Pond, Cwmbran, **TORFAEN**, NP44, **Wales**.
Contact/s: **L Clarke** (Secretary).
(T) 01633 664231
Profile: **FT:** Coarse; **WN:** Morgans Pond; **WT:** Lake (Still) **W. Size:** 4 Acres. **Location: Main Rd:** M5, junction 26.
Ref: FH3372

MORTON FARM

Morton Farm, Morton Old Rd, Brading, Sandown, **ISLE OF WIGHT**, PO36 0EN, **England**.
Contact/s: **Mr Graham Redfern** (Owner).
(T) 01983 406132 (F) 01983 408923
Profile: **FT:** Coarse; **WN:** Morton Farm; **WT:** Combination (Still & Moving) **W. Size:** 2 Acres. **Location: Nr. Rd:** Sandown Road; **Main Rd:** A3054; **Rail:** Brading.
Ref: FH3373

MORTON FISHERIES

Morton Fishery, Keepers Cottage, Mid Calder, Livingston, **LOTHIAN (WEST)**, EH53 0JT, **Scotland**.
Contact/s: **Ms Julie Hewat** (Owner).
(T) 01506 882293
Profile: **FT:** Coarse; **WN:** Morton Fisheries; **WT:** Combination (Still & Moving).
Ref: FH3374

MORTON LOCH

Morton Loch, Buccleuch Estates Ltd, Drumlanrig Mains, Thornhill, **DUMFRIES AND GALLOWAY**, DG3 4AG, **Scotland**.
Contact/s: **Mr N A G Waugh**.
(T) 01848 600283 (F) 01848 600244
Profile: **FT:** Game; **WN:** Morton; **WT:** Loch (Still) **W. Size:** 2 Acres. **Location: Nr. Rd:** A702; **Main Rd:** A76; **Rail:** Sanquhar.
Ref: FH3375

MORTON POND

Morton Pond, Buccleuch Estates Ltd, Drumlanrig Mains, Thornhill, **DUMFRIES AND GALLOWAY**, DG3 4AG, **Scotland**.
Contact/s: **Mr N A G Waugh**.
(T) 01848 600283 (F) 01848 600244
Profile: **FT:** Coarse; **WN:** Morton; **WT:** Pond (Still) **W. Size:** 2 Acres. **Location: Main Rd:** A702; **Rail:** Sanquhar.
Ref: FH3376

MOSS BROOK

Moss Brook, Church Field, Eckington, Staveley, Chesterfield, **DERBYSHIRE**, S43, **England**.
Contact/s: **Mr Derrick Morton**.
Profile: **FT:** Game; **WN:** Rother; **WT:** River (Moving). **Location: Main Rd:** M1.
Ref: FH3377

MOSS ECCLES TARN

Moss Eccles Tarn, Far Sawrey, Hawkshead, Ambleside, **CUMBRIA**, LA22, **England**.
Profile: **FT:** Game; **WN:** Moss Eccles; **WT:** Tarn (Still) **W. Size:** 5 Acres. **Location: Nr. Rd:** Tower Bank Arms, 20 minute walk from; **Main Rd:** B5285 from Hawkshead.
Ref: FH3378

MOSS POOLS

Moss Pool, Lymm, **CHESHIRE**, WA13, **England**.
Contact/s: **Mr Neil Jupp** (Club Secretary), Lymm Angling Club, PO Box 350, Warrington, Cheshire, WA2 9FB.
(T) 01925 411744
Profile: **FT:** Coarse; **WN:** Moss; **WT:** Pool (Still). **Location: Nr. Rd:** Seven Sisters Lane; **Main Rd:** A50 to Holmes Chapel.
Ref: FH3379

MOSSBANK POOL

Mossbank Pool, Lymm, **CHESHIRE**, WA13, **England**.
Contact/s: **Mr Neil Jupp** (Club Secretary), Lymm Angling Club, PO Box 350, Warrington, Cheshire, WA2 9FB.
(T) 01925 411744
Profile: **FT:** Coarse; **WN:** Mossbank; **WT:** Pool (Still). **Location: Nr. Rd:** Seven Sisters Lane; **Main Rd:** A50 to Holmes Chapel.
Ref: FH3380

MOTE PARK FISHERY

Mote Park Fishery, Mote Park, Maidstone, **KENT**, ME15 6LP, **England**.
Contact/s: Secretary, Medway Preservation Society, 33 Hackney Rd, Maidstone, Kent, ME16 8LN.
Mr Nick Puncher (Manager), Nicks Tackle Exchange, 10 Knightrider St, Maidstone, Kent,

ME15 6LP.
(T) 01622 673899 (F) 01622 673899
Profile: FT: Coarse; WN: Mote Park; WT: Lake (Still) W. Size: 26 Acres.
Ref: FH3381

MOTORWAY POND

Motorway Pond, Thimble Hall Lane, Newport, Brough, **HUMBERSIDE**, HU15, **England**.
Contact/s: Mr Bill Brame (Secretary), Hull and District Angler's Association, PO Box 188, Hull, HU9 1AN.
Mr Dave Harold (Fisheries Information Officer), 33 Jipdane Orchard Park, Hull, Yorkshire (East), HU6 9EE.
(T) 01482 809832
Profile: FT: Coarse; WN: Motorway; WT: Clay Pit (Still); F. Size: 25 Acres; W. Size: 18 Acres. Location: Nr. Rd: Thimbieham Lane or Canalside West; Main Rd: B1230; Rail: Broomfleet.
Ref: FH3382

MOULDSWORTH MERE

Mouldsworth Mere, Mouldsworth, Chester, **CHESHIRE**, CH3 8, **England**.
Contact/s: Mr Bill Bristow (Manager).
(T) 0151 2011894
Profile: FT: Coarse; WN: Mouldsworth; WT: Mere (Still) W. Size: 2 Acres. Location: Nr. Rd: Stable Lane; Main Rd: B5393.
Ref: FH3383

MOULTON LANE POND

Moulton Lane Pond, North Cowton, Thirsk, **YORKSHIRE (NORTH)**, DL7 0JR, **England**.
Contact/s: Mr Clarke (Manager), 8 Moulton Lane, North Cowton, Thirsk, Yorkshire (North), DL7 0JR.
(T) 01325 378345
Profile: FT: Coarse; WN: Moulton Lane; WT: Pond (Still) W. Size: 1 Acre. Location: Nr. Rd: Darlington to Northallerton.
Ref: FH3384

MOUNT FALCON SALMON FISHERY

Mount Falcon Salmon Fishery, Mount Falcon Castle, Foxford Rd, Ballina, **COUNTY MAYO**, **Ireland**.
Contact/s: Mr Steven Hannick.
(T) 096 21172
Profile: FT: Game; WT: River (Moving) W. Size: 5000 Metres. Location: Nr. Rd: Foxford Road; Rail: Ballina.
Ref: FH3385

MOUNT JULIET FISHERY

Mount Juliet Fishery, Mount Juliet House, Thomastown, **COUNTY KILKENNY**, **Ireland**.
Contact/s: Fishery Manager.
(T) 056 24455
Profile: FT: Game; WN: Mount Juliet Fishery; WT: River (Moving).
Ref: FH3386

MOUNT PLEASANT LAKE

Mount Pleasant Lake, Washington, **TYNE AND WEAR**, NE38, **England**.
Contact/s: Mr Dave Hancock.
(T) 0191 3857488
Profile: FT: Coarse; WN: Mount Pleasant; WT: Lake (Still) W. Size: 2 Acres. Location: Nr. Rd: Beatrice Terrace; Main Rd: A182, junction 13 Washington Highway.
Ref: FH3387

MOURNE (RIVER)

River Mourne, Newtownstewart, **COUNTY TYRONE**, BT78, **Northern Ireland**.
Contact/s: Manager, Baronscourt Estates, Baronscourt Rd, Newtownstewart, Omagh, BT78 4EZ.
(T) 028 81661683 (F) 028 81662059
Mr David Campbell (Manager), Mourne Valley Tackle, 50 Main St, Newtownstewart, Omagh, County Tyrone, BT78 4AA.
(T) 028 81661543
Profile: FT: Game; WN: Mourne; WT: River (Moving) W. Size: 4000 Metres.
Ref: FH3388

MOURNE (RIVER)

River Mourne, Victoria Bridge, Sion Mills, Strabane, **COUNTY TYRONE**, BT82, **Northern Ireland**.
Contact/s: Manager, Sion Mills Angling Club, Melmount Rd, Sion Mills, Strabane, BT82 9EX.
(T) 028 81658027
Profile: FT: Game; WN: Mourne; WT: River (Moving) W. Size: 12800 Metres.
Ref: FH3389

MOURNE (RIVER)

River Mourne, Strabane, **COUNTY TYRONE**, BT82, **Northern Ireland**.
Contact/s: Mr Billy Diver, Variety Shop, 5 Castle Prde, Strabane, County Tyrone, BT82.
(T) 028 71883021
Profile: FT: Game; WN: Mourne; WT: River (Moving).
Ref: FH3390

MOURNE (RIVER)

River Mourne, Omagh, **COUNTY TYRONE**, BT78, **Northern Ireland**.
Contact/s: Mr David Campbell (Manager), Mourne Valley Tackle, 50 Main St, Newtownstewart, Omagh, County Tyrone, BT78 4AA.
(T) 028 81661543
Profile: FT: Game; WN: Mourne; WT: River (Moving).
Ref: FH3391

MOUSEHOLE LAKE

Mousehole Lake, Nettleshead Green, Tonbridge, **KENT**, TN1, **England**.
Profile: FT: Game; WN: Mousehole; WT: Lake (Still) W. Size: 3 Acres. Location: Main Rd: B2015.
Ref: FH3392

MOY (RIVER)

River Moy, Tiernan Brothers, North Mayo Angling Advice Ctre, Upper Main St, Foxford, **COUNTY MAYO**, **Ireland**.
Contact/s: Mr P J Tiernan (Partner).
(T) 094 56731 (F) 094 56731
Profile: FT: Game; WN: Moy; WT: River (Moving). Location: Rail: Foxford.
Ref: FH3393

MOY FISHERY

Moy Fishery, Ardnaree House, Abbey St, Ballina, **COUNTY MAYO**, **Ireland**.
Contact/s: Mr Declan Cooke (Manager).
(T) 096 21332
(E) nwrfb@iol.ie
Profile: FT: Game; WN: Moy; WT: River (Moving). Location: Nr. Rd: N5; Main Rd: N26; Rail: Ballina.
Ref: FH3394

MOYOLA (RIVER)

River Moyola, Draperstown, Maghera, **COUNTY LONDONDERRY**, BT45, **Northern Ireland**.
(W) www.fishingholidaysireland.com
Contact/s: Mr Tom Maguire (Angling Development Officer), Moyola Angling Association, 3 Craigmore Rd, Maghera, County Londonderry, BT46 5AL.
(T) 028 79642793 (F) 028 79642793 (M) 07703 804040
(E) tom.maguire@lineone.net
Profile: FT: Game; WN: Erch; WT: River (Moving) W. Size: 43200 Metres. Location: Nr. Rd: A6.
Ref: FH3395

MUCK (LOUGH)

Lough Muck, Foxford, **COUNTY MAYO**, **Ireland**.
Contact/s: Angling Officer, North Western Regional Fisheries Board, Ardnaree House, Abbey St, Ballina, County Mayo.
(T) 096 22623 (F) 096 70543
Profile: FT: Game; WN: Muck; WT: Lough (Still). Location: Main Rd: N57.
Ref: FH3396

MUDEFORD WOOD LAKE

Mudeford Wood Lake, Christchurch, **DORSET**, BH23, **England**.
Contact/s: Mr Graham Pepler (Manager), Davis Tackle Shop, 75 Bargates, Christchurch, Dorset, BH23 1QE.
(T) 01202 485169or395532 (F) 01202 474261
Mr Peter Kidby.
(T) 01202 475976
Profile: FT: Coarse; WN: Mudeford Wood; WT: Lake (Still). Location: Main Rd: A35 then the A337.
Ref: FH3397

MULE (RIVER)

River Mule, Kerry, Newtown, **POWYS**, SY16 4LX, **Wales**.
Contact/s: Mr Ja Griffiths, Lower Penygelly Farm, Kerry, Newtown, Powys, SY16 4LX.
(T) 01686 670610
Profile: FT: Game; WN: Mule; WT: River (Moving) W. Size: 3000 Metres.
Ref: FH3398

MULGROVE POND

Mulgrove Pond, Rectory Pl, Woolwich, London, **LONDON (GREATER)**, SE18, **England**.
Contact/s: John (Bailiff).
(T) 020 83176807
Profile: FT: Coarse; WN: Brigadier's; WT: Lake (Still). Location: Nr. Rd: Rectory Place.
Ref: FH3399

MULLAGHANOE (RIVER)

River Mullaghanoe, Charlestown, **COUNTY MAYO**, **Ireland**.
Contact/s: Angling Officer, North Western Regional Fisheries Board, Ardnaree House, Abbey St, Ballina, County Mayo.
(T) 096 22623 (F) 096 70543
Profile: FT: Game; WN: Mullaghanoe; WT: River (Moving).
Ref: FH3400

MUNBY POND

Munby Pond, Barlow, Selby, **YORKSHIRE (NORTH)**, YO8, **England**.
Contact/s: Mr Ralph Tanner (Secretary), 2 Park Rd, Barlow, Selby, Yorkshire (North), YO8 8EN.
(T) 01757 617232
Profile: FT: Coarse; WN: Munby; WT: Pond (Still) W. Size: 1 Acre. Location: Nr. Rd: Brown Cow Road; Main Rd: A1041; Rail: Selby.
Ref: FH3401

MUNDERFIELD HAROLD

Munderfield Harold, Bromyard, **HEREFORDSHIRE**, HR7 4SZ, **England**.
Contact/s: Ms Christine Morgan.
(T) 01885 483231
Profile: FT: Coarse; WN: Munderfield Harold; WT: Combination (Still & Moving). Location: Nr. Rd: B4214; Main Rd: A44; Rail: Leominister.
Ref: FH3402

MUNSTER BLACKWATER (RIVER)

River Munster Blackwater (Ghillie Cottage), Fermoy, **COUNTY CORK**, **Ireland**.
(W) www.flyfish-ireland.com
Contact/s: Mr Doug Lock (Spey Casting Instructor), Ghillie Cottage, Fermoy, County Cork, Ireland.
(T) 025 32720 (F) 025 33000
Mrs Joy Lock (Manager), Ghillie Cottage, Fermoy, County Cork, Ireland.
(T) 025 32720 (F) 025 33000
Profile: FT: Game; WN: Munster Blackwater; WT: River (Moving).
Ref: FH3403

MUSKRA LOCH

Muskra Loch, Mid Yell, Shetland, **SHETLAND ISLANDS**, ZE2, **Scotland**.
Contact/s: Mr Ian Nisbet (Secretary).

(T) 01957 2204
Profile: FT: Game; WN: Muskra; WT: Loch (Still).
Ref: FH3404

MYLOR ANGLING LAKES

Mylor Angling Lakes, Comfort Rd, Mylor Bridge, Falmouth, **CORNWALL**, TR11, **England**.
Contact/s: Manager, 14 Willow Cl, Mylor Bridge, Falmouth, Cornwall, TR11 5SG.
Mr Rowland Palmer.
(T) 01326 373975
Profile: FT: Coarse; WN: Mylor Angling Lakes; WT: Lake (Still). Location: Nr. Rd: Comfort Road.
Ref: FH3405

MYRTLE ROAD LODGES

Myrtle Road Lodges, Myrtle Rd, Middleton, Manchester, **MANCHESTER (GREATER)**, M24, **England**.
Contact/s: **Mr Gary Leigh** (Secretary), Middleton Angling Society, 151 Tennyson Rd, Boarshaw, Middleton, Manchester M24 2NS.
(T) 0161 6546253
Profile: FT: Coarse; WN: Myrtle Road; WT: Reservoir (Still). Location: Nr. Rd: A669 Oldham Road.
Ref: FH3406

MYTHE POOL

Mythe Pool, Tewkesbury, **GLOUCESTERSHIRE**, GL20, **England**.
Contact/s: **Mr Dave Beresford** (Manager), Allans Fishing Tackle, 26-30 Malvern Rd, Worcester, Worcestershire, WR2 4LG.
(T) 01905 422107 (F) 01905 422107
Mr John Williams (Secretary), Birmingham Anglers Association, 100 Icknield Port Rd, Rotton Park, Birmingham, B16 0AP.
(T) 0121 4549111
Profile: FT: Coarse; WN: Mythe; WT: Lake (Still) W. Size: 10 Acres. Location: Main Rd: A38.
Ref: FH3407

NACCOLT LAKE

Naccolt Lake, Wye, Ashford, **KENT**, **England**.
(W) www.midkentfish.demon.co.uk
Contact/s: **Mr Chris Logsdon** (Fisheries Manager), Mid Kent Fisheries, Chilham Water Mill, Mill Lane, Chilham, CT4 8EE.
(T) 01227 730668
(E) chilham@midkentfisheries.co.uk
Profile: FT: Coarse; WN: Naccolt; WT: Clay Pit (Still); F. Size: 15 Acres; W. Size: 12 Acres.
Ref: FH3408

NADDER (RIVER)

River Nadder, Salisbury, **WILTSHIRE**, SP, **England**.
Contact/s: **Mr Ron Hillier** (Secretary), Salisbury and District Angling Club, 29 New Zealand Avenue, Salisbury, Wiltshire, SP2 7JX.
(T) 01722 321164
Profile: FT: Coarse; WN: Nadder; WT: River (Moving). Location: Rail: Salisbury.
Ref: FH3409

NADDER (RIVER)

River Nadder, Knapp Cottage, Fovant, Salisbury, **WILTSHIRE**, SP3 5JW, **England**.
Contact/s: **Mr E J Stevens**.
(T) 01722 714245
Profile: FT: Combination; WN: Nadder; WT: River (Moving) W. Size: 4800 Metres.
Ref: FH3410

NAHINE LOCH

Nahine Loch, Newton Stewart, **DUMFRIES AND GALLOWAY**, DG8, **Scotland**.
Contact/s: **Mr Tony Dickinson** (Manager), Galloway Guns and Tackle, 36a Arthur St, Newton Stewart, Dumfries and Galloway, DG8 6DE.
(T) 01671 403404 (F) 01671 403404
Profile: FT: Game; WN: Nahine; WT: Loch (Still).
Ref: FH3411

NAIRN (RIVER)

River Nairn, Nairn, **HIGHLAND**, IV12, **Scotland**.
Contact/s: **Mr Pat Fraser** (Manager), Nairn Angling Association, 41 High St, Nairn, Morayshire IV12 4AG.
(T) 01667 453038
(E) lauriefraser@freelall.co.uk
Profile: FT: Combination; WN: Nairn; WT: River (Moving) W. Size: 11200 Metres.
Location: Nr. Rd: Aberdeen to Inverness; Main Rd: A96; Rail: Nairn.
Ref: FH3412

NANANNAGH (LOUGH)

Nanannagh (Lough), Claremorris, **COUNTY GALWAY**, **Ireland**.
Contact/s: **Mr Danny Goldrick** (Angling Officer), The Western Regional Fisheries Board, Weir Lodge, Earl's Island, Galway City, County Galway.
(T) 091 563118 (F) 091 566335
(E) wrfb@iol.ie
Profile: FT: Coarse; WN: Nanannagh; WT: Lough (Still). Location: Nr. Rd: N83; Rail: Claremorris.
Ref: FH3413

NANCE LAKES

Nance Lakes, Trevarrack, Lelant, St Ives, **CORNWALL**, TR26 3EZ, **England**.
Contact/s: **Mrs Ellis**.
(T) 01736 740348
Profile: FT: Coarse; WN: Nance; WT: Lake (Still). Location: Main Rd: A30; Rail: St. Ives.
Ref: FH3414

NANCY POND

Nancy Pond, High Green, Sheffield, **YORKSHIRE (SOUTH)**, S, **England**.
Contact/s: Area Manager, Environment Agency, Ridings Area Office, Phoenix House, Global Avenue, Leeds, LS11 8PG.
(T) 0113 2440191or2314834 (F) 0113 2134609
Mr Jim Rowlinson (Secretary), Chapeltown and District Angling Association, 8 Brook Rd, High Green, Sheffield, S30 4GG.
(T) 0114 2844553
Profile: FT: Coarse; WN: Nancy; WT: Pond (Still).
Ref: FH3415

NANEVIN (LOUGH)

Lough Nanevin, Moycullen, **COUNTY GALWAY**, **Ireland**.
Contact/s: **Mr Danny Goldrick** (Angling Officer), The Western Regional Fisheries Board, Weir Lodge, Earl's Island, Galway City, County Galway.
(T) 091 563118 (F) 091 566335
(E) wrfb@iol.ie
Profile: FT: Coarse; WN: Nanevin; WT: Lough (Still) W. Size: 25 Acres.
Ref: FH3416

NANPANTAN RESERVOIR

Nanpantan Reservoir, Woodhouse Lane, Nanpantan, Loughborough, Leicester, **LEICESTERSHIRE**, LE11, **England**.
Contact/s: **Mr D Witts** (Bailiff), Home Farm, Woodhouse Lane, Nanpantan, Loughborough, LE11 3YG.
(T) 01509 550436
Profile: FT: Coarse; WN: Woodbrook; WT: Combination (Still & Moving); F. Size: 12 Acres; W. Size: 8 Acres. Location: Nr. Rd: Woodhouse Lane; Main Rd: A512; Rail: Loughborough.
Ref: FH3417

NANT Y MOCH RESERVOIR

Nant Y Moch Reservoir, Rheidol Power Station, Cwmrheidol, Aberystwyth, **CEREDIGION**, SY23 3NF, **Wales**.
Contact/s: **Mr Peter Bevan** (Manager).
(T) 01970 880667
Profile: FT: Game; WN: Nant Y Moch; WT: Reservoir (Still) W. Size: 600 Acres.
Ref: FH3418

NANTLLE LAKE

Nantlle Lake, Nantlle, Caernarfon, **GWYNEDD**, LL54, **Wales**.
Contact/s: **Mr Huw P Hughes** (Hon Secretary), Seiont, Gwyrfai and Llyfni Anglers Society, Llugwy, Ystad Eryri, Bethel, Caernarfon, LL55 1BX.
(T) 01248 670666
(E) huw.hughes@lineone.net
Profile: FT: Game; WN: Nantlle; WT: Lake (Still) W. Size: 80 Acres. Location: Nr. Rd: B4418; Main Rd: A4085; Rail: Bangor.
Ref: FH3419

NANT-Y-GAIN FISHERY

Nant-Y-Gain Fishery, Cilcain, Mold, **FLINTSHIRE**, CH7 5PE, **Wales**.
Contact/s: **Mr Glyn Jones** (Manager).
(T) 01352 740936
Profile: FT: Game; WN: Nant-Y-Gain Fishery; WT: Pool (Still).
Ref: FH3420

NAPTON RESERVOIR

Napton Reservoir, Napton On The Hill, Stockton, Southam, **WARWICKSHIRE**, CV47, **England**.
Contact/s: **Mr John Hyde** (Fishery Manager).
(T) 024 76418893
Profile: FT: Coarse; WN: Napton; WT: Reservoir (Still) W. Size: 17 Acres.
Location: Nr. Rd: Stockton Road; Main Rd: A425.
Ref: FH3421

NAR (RIVER)

River Nar, Apple Tree Lodge, Squires Hill, Upper Marham, King's Lynn, **NORFOLK**, PE33 9PJ, **England**.
Contact/s: **Mr David Burrows** (Manager), Apple Tree Lodge, Squires Hill, Marham, PE33 9PJ.
(T) 01760 337222
Profile: FT: Game; WN: Nar; WT: River (Moving).
Ref: FH3422

NAR STREAM

Nar Stream, Narborough Mill, King's Lynn, **NORFOLK**, PE, **England**.
Contact/s: **Mr David Burrows** (Manager), Apple Tree Lodge, Squires Hill, Marham, PE33 9PJ.
(T) 01760 337222
Profile: FT: Game; WN: Nar; WT: Stream (Moving) W. Size: 1600 Metres.
Ref: FH3423

NARBOROUGH TROUT FARM

Narborough Trout Farm, Main Rd, Narborough, King's Lynn, **NORFOLK**, PE32 1TE, **England**.
Mr Raymond Pritchard (Owner).
(T) 01760 338005
Profile: FT: Combination; WN: Narborough Trout Farm; WT: Combination (Still & Moving); F. Size: 28 Acres; W. Size: 8 Acres.
Location: Nr. Rd: A47, Old Road; Main Rd: A47; Rail: King's Lynn.
Ref: FH3424

NARROW CANAL

Narrow Canal (West Slaithwaite), Slaithwaite, Huddersfield, **YORKSHIRE (WEST)**, HD7, **England**.
Contact/s: **Mr D Rushforth** (Secretary), 122 Longwood Gate, Longwood, Huddersfield, Yorkshire (West), HD3 4US.
(T) 01484 651028
Profile: FT: Coarse; WN: Narrow; WT: Canal (Still). Location: Nr. Rd: West Slaithwaite Road to Marsden; Main Rd: A62 Manchester Road; Rail: Slaithwaite.
Ref: FH3425

NARROW CANAL

Narrow Canal (Bargate To Milnsbridge), Bargate, Low Westwood Lane, Linthwaite,

Huddersfield, **YORKSHIRE (WEST)**, HD, **England**.
Contact/s: **Mr D Rushforth** (Secretary), 122 Longwood Gate, Longwood, Huddersfield, Yorkshire (West), HD3 4US.
(T) 01484 651028
Mr J Booth (Secretary), 11 Kipling Cl, Crosland Moor, Huddersfield, HD4 5HA.
(T) 01484 644473
Profile: **FT:** Coarse; **WN:** Narrow; **WT:** Canal (Still). Location: **Nr. Rd:** Low Westwood Lane; **Main Rd:** A62; **Rail:** Slaithwaite.
Ref: FH3426

NARROW CANAL

Narrow Canal (Slaithwaite To Bargate), Carr Lane, Bridge St, Slaithwaite, Huddersfield, **YORKSHIRE (WEST)**, HD7, **England**.
Contact/s: **Mr A J Abbott** (Bailiff), 24 Moorcroft Avenue, Golcar, Huddersfield, Yorkshire (West), HD7.
(T) 01484 646868
Mr J Booth (Secretary), 11 Kipling Cl, Crosland Moor, Huddersfield, HD4 5HA.
(T) 01484 644473
Profile: **FT:** Coarse; **WN:** Narrow; **WT:** Canal (Still). Location: **Nr. Rd:** Carr Lane; **Main Rd:** A62.
Ref: FH3427

NASEBY RESERVOIR

Naseby Reservoir, Naseby, Northampton, **NORTHAMPTONSHIRE**, NN6, **England**.
Contact/s: **Mr I A McNeil** (Secretary), Bufton, Walcote, Leicester, LE17 4JS.
Profile: **FT:** Coarse; **WN:** Naseby; **WT:** Reservoir (Still) **W. Size:** 85 Acres.
Ref: FH3428

NATURES HAVEN LAKES

Natures Haven Lakes, Clay Lane, Swannington, **NORFOLK**, **England**.
Contact/s: **Mr Steve Barnes** (Fishery Manager), Penyghent, Post Office Corner, Stutton, Ipswich, IP9 2TJ.
(T) 01603 260303 **(M)** 07930 403296
(E) natures.haven@farmline.com
Mrs Penny Joseph (Head Bailiff).
(T) 01603 260303 **(M)** 07979 646374
(E) natures.haven@farmline.com
Profile: **FT:** Coarse; **WN:** Natures Haven Lakes; **WT:** Lake (Still); **F. Size:** 5 Acres; **W. Size:** 3 Acres. Location: **Nr. Rd:** Clay Lane; **Main Rd:** A1067; **Rail:** Norwich.
Ref: FH3429

NAVIES HOLE

Navies Hole, Ridgebridge Hill, Cranleigh, **SURREY**, GU6, **England**.
Contact/s: **Mr Adrian Bewley** (Manager), Ashvale Fisheries, 69 Fortescue Rd, Wimbledon, London, SW19 2EA.
(T) 020 82873892
Profile: **FT:** Coarse; **WN:** Navies Hole; **WT:** Lake (Still). Location: **Nr. Rd:** A281 or B2128; **Main Rd:** Guilford to Horsham.
Ref: FH3430

NAZEING MEADS

Nazeing Meads, Meadgate Lane, Nazeing, Waltham Abbey, **ESSEX**, EN9, **England**.
Contact/s: Information Officer, Lee Valley Park Information Ctre, Abbey Gardens, Waltham Abbey, Essex, EN9 1XQ.
(T) 01992 702200
Mr Gary Smith (Fisheries Manager), Lee Valley Regional Park Authority, Myddleton House, Bulls Cross, Enfield, EN2 9HG.
(T) 01992 709962
(E) garysmith@leevalleypark.org.uk
Profile: **FT:** Coarse; **WN:** Nazeing Meads; **WT:** Gravel Pit (Still) **W. Size:** 125 Acres. Location: **Nr. Rd:** Mead gate Road; **Main Rd:** M25, A10; **Rail:** Broxbourne.
Ref: FH3431

NEATH (RIVER)

River Neath, Neath, **NEATH PORT TALBOT**, SA, **Wales**.
Contact/s: **Mr Garry Davis** (Membership Secretary), 6 Martins Avenue, Seven Sisters, Neath, Glamorgan (Vale of).
(T) 01639 701828
Mr Ivor Jones (Hon Secretary), 5 Bryndulais Row, Seven Sisters, Neath, Glamorgan (Vale of), SA10 9EB.
(T) 01639 701187
Profile: **FT:** Game; **WN:** Neath; **WT:** River (Moving) **W. Size:** 5600 Metres. Location: **Nr. Rd:** Aberdulais Weir to Rheola Estate.
Ref: FH3432

NEATH (RIVER)

River Neath, Rehola, Neath, **NEATH PORT TALBOT**, SA, **Wales**.
Contact/s: **Mr Ivor Jones** (Hon Secretary), 5 Bryndulais Row, Seven Sisters, Neath, Glamorgan (Vale of), SA10 9EB.
(T) 01639 701187
Profile: **FT:** Game; **WN:** Neath; **WT:** River (Moving). Location: **Main Rd:** A465.
Ref: FH3433

NEATH (RIVER)

River Neath, Neath, **NEATH PORT TALBOT**, SA, **Wales**.
Contact/s: **Mr Gareth Evans**, 21 Godfrey Avenue, Glynneath, Neath, Glamorgan (Vale of), SA11 5HF.
(T) 01639 721301
Mr Ray Jones.
(T) 01639 720927
Mr Tony May.
(T) 01685 871337
Profile: **FT:** Game; **WN:** Neath; **WT:** River (Moving) **W. Size:** 7500 Metres. Location: **Main Rd:** A465; **Rail:** Neath.
Ref: FH3434

NEEDHAM LAKE

Needham Lake, Needham Market, Ipswich, **SUFFOLK**, IP6, **England**.
Contact/s: Manager, Bosmere Tackle, 59 High St, Needham Market, Ipswich, IP6 8AL.
(T) 01449 721808
Mr Ian Wood (Chairman).
(T) 01473 403098
Profile: **FT:** Coarse; **WN:** Gipping; **WT:** Combination (Still & Moving) **W. Size:** 4 Acres. Location: **Nr. Rd:** B1078; **Main Rd:** A14; **Rail:** Needham Market.
Ref: FH3435

NEETS VALLEY PARK

Neets Valley Park, Bude, **CORNWALL**, EX23, **England**.
Contact/s: **Mr Russell Barker**.
(T) 01283 588395
Profile: **FT:** Coarse; **WN:** Neets Valley; **WT:** Lake (Still).
Ref: FH3436

NEIGH BRIDGE LAKE

Neigh Bridge Lake, Somerford Keynes, Cirencester, **GLOUCESTERSHIRE**, GL7, **England**.
Contact/s: On Duty Ranger, Cotswold Water Park Society, Keynes Country Park, Spratsgate Lane, Shorncote, Cirencester, Gloucestershire.
(T) 01285 861459 **(F)** 01285 860186
Mr J Parker (Secretary), Ashton Keynes Angling Club, 81 Dunnington Rd, Wootton Bassett, Swindon, SN4 7EL.
(T) 01793 852028
Profile: **FT:** Coarse; **WN:** Neigh Bridge; **WT:** Gravel Pit (Still) **W. Size:** 12 Acres. Location: **Nr. Rd:** B4696; **Main Rd:** A419; **Rail:** Kemble.
Ref: FH3437

NEILSTON TROUT FISHERY

Neilston Trout Fishery, Snypes Rd, Neilston, Glasgow, **GLASGOW (CITY OF)**, G78 1GW, **Scotland**.
Contact/s: **Mr Donald MacDonald**.
(T) 0141 8807883
Profile: **FT:** Game; **WN:** Neilston Trout Fishery; **WT:** Combination (Still) **W. Size:** 14 Acres. Location: **Nr. Rd:** Snypes Road; **Main Rd:** Kirkton Road; **Rail:** Neilston.
Ref: FH3438

NELL BRIDGE FISHERY

Nell Bridge Fishery, Nell Bridge Farm, Aynho Rd, Banbury, **OXFORDSHIRE**, OX17 3NY, **England**.
Contact/s: **Mrs Sheila Belcher** (Manager).
(T) 01295 811227
Profile: **FT:** Coarse; **WN:** Nell Bridge Fishery; **WT:** Lake (Still) **W. Size:** 6 Acres. Location: **Nr. Rd:** Adderbury to Aynho, B4100; **Main Rd:** M40; **Rail:** Banbury.
Ref: FH3439

NENE (RIVER)

River Nene, Stibbington, Peterborough, **CAMBRIDGESHIRE**, PE8, **England**.
Contact/s: **Mr Pete Garrod** (Booking Secretary), 72 Pittneys, Paston, Peterborough, Cambridgeshire, PE4 7BB.
(T) 01733 571676
Profile: **FT:** Coarse; **WN:** Nene; **WT:** River (Moving). Location: **Nr. Rd:** A47 Leicester to Peterborough; **Main Rd:** A1; **Rail:** Wansford Station.
Ref: FH3440

NENE (RIVER)

River Nene, Oundle, Peterborough, **CAMBRIDGESHIRE**, PE8, **England**.
Contact/s: **D Laxton** (Secretary), 31 St Peters Rd, Oundle, Peterborough, PE8 4NU.
(T) 01832 272289
Profile: **FT:** Coarse; **WN:** Nene; **WT:** River (Moving) **W. Size:** 7500 Metres.
Ref: FH3441

NENE (RIVER)

River Nene, Oundle, Peterborough, **CAMBRIDGESHIRE**, PE8, **England**.
Contact/s: Area Manager, Environment Agency, Sapphire East, 550 Streetsbrook Rd, Solihull, B91 1QT.
(T) 0121 7112324 **(F)** 0121 7115824
Mr John Hyde (Secretary), Coventry and District Angling Club, 111 Lord Litton Avenue, Stoke, Coventry, CV2 5JT.
(T) 024 76418893
Profile: **FT:** Coarse; **WN:** Nene; **WT:** River (Moving).
Ref: FH3442

NENE (RIVER)

River Nene, Cotterstock, Peterborough, **CAMBRIDGESHIRE**, PE8, **England**.
Contact/s: **Mr B Wing**, Manor Farm Cottage, Cotterstock, Peterborough, Cambridgeshire, PE8.
(T) 01832 226340
Profile: **FT:** Coarse; **WN:** Nene; **WT:** River (Moving) **W. Size:** 1600 Metres.
Ref: FH3443

NENE (RIVER)

River Nene, Fotheringhay, Oundle, Peterborough, **CAMBRIDGESHIRE**, PE8, **England**.
Contact/s: Area Manager, Environment Agency, Sapphire East, 550 Streetsbrook Rd, Solihull, B91 1QT.
(T) 0121 7112324 **(F)** 0121 7115824
Mr John Hyde (Secretary), Coventry and District Angling Club, 111 Lord Litton Avenue, Stoke, Coventry, CV2 5JT.
(T) 024 76418893
Profile: **FT:** Coarse; **WN:** Nene; **WT:** River (Moving).
Ref: FH3444

NENE (RIVER)

River Nene, Peterborough, **CAMBRIDGESHIRE**, PE, **England**.
Contact/s: **Mr Pete Garrod** (Booking Secretary), 72 Pittneys, Paston, Peterborough, Cambridgeshire, PE4 7BB.
(T) 01733 571676
Profile: **FT:** Coarse; **WN:** Nene (Peterborough to Whittlesea); **WT:** River (Moving).
Ref: FH3445

NENE (RIVER)

River Nene, Tansor, Oundle, Peterborough, **CAMBRIDGESHIRE**, PE8 5HN, **England**.
Contact/s: **Mr Tony Bridgefoot** (Owner).
(T) 01832 226042 **(M)** 07702 641926
Profile: **FT:** Coarse; **WN:** Nene; **WT:** River (Moving); **F. Size:** 108 Acres; **W. Size:** 1800 Metres. **Location:** **Nr. Rd:** Tansor to Fotheringhay; **Main Rd:** A605; **Rail:** Peterborough.
Ref: FH3446

NENE (RIVER)

River Nene, Woodford, Thrapston, Kettering, **NORTHAMPTONSHIRE**, NN14, **England**.
Contact/s: **Mr D Garrett** (Treasurer), Kettering and Thrapston Angling Association, 17 Browning Avenue, Kettering, Northamptonshire, NN16 8NP.
(T) 01536 515547
Mr Mick Cardy, 50 Warmton Lane, Kettering, Northamptonshire.
(T) 01536 518178
Profile: **FT:** Coarse; **WN:** Nene; **WT:** River (Moving) **W. Size:** 14000 Metres. **Location:** **Nr. Rd:** A605; **Main Rd:** A14; **Rail:** Kettering.
Ref: FH3447

NENE (RIVER)

River Nene, Duston Mill, Northampton, **NORTHAMPTONSHIRE**, NN, **England**.
Contact/s: **Mr Terry Rodhouse** (Secretary), Castle Angling Association, 12 Somerville Rd, Daventry, Northamptonshire, NN11 4RT.
(T) 01327 705692
Profile: **FT:** Coarse; **WN:** Nene; **WT:** River (Moving) **W. Size:** 3500 Metres. **Location:** **Nr. Rd:** Duston Mill to Bedford Road; **Main Rd:** A45, A428; **Rail:** Northampton.
Ref: FH3448

NENE NORTH BANK (RIVER)

River Nene North Bank, North Bank, Peterborough, **CAMBRIDGESHIRE**, PE, **England**.
Contact/s: **Mr Ken Wade**.
Mr Pete Garad.
Profile: **FT:** Coarse; **WN:** Nene; **WT:** River (Moving). **Location:** **Main Rd:** A605; **Rail:** Whittlesey.
Ref: FH3449

NESS (RIVER)

River Ness, Inverness, **HIGHLAND**, IV, **Scotland**.
Contact/s: **Ms Kerry MacDonald** (Secretary), Inverness Angling Club, 30 Swanston Avenue, Inverness, IV3 8QW.
(T) 01463 240095 **(F)** 01463 240095
Profile: **FT:** Game; **WN:** Ness; **WT:** River (Moving) **W. Size:** 4500 Metres. **Location:** **Main Rd:** Junction of A9, A82, A96.
Ref: FH3450

NEST

Nest (The), Wintringham, Scunthorpe, **HUMBERSIDE**, DN, **England**.
Contact/s: Fishery Manager.
(T) 01724 732465
Profile: **FT:** Coarse; **WN:** Nest (The); **WT:** Lake (Still) **W. Size:** 1 Acre. **Location:** **Nr. Rd:** Western Green; **Main Rd:** A1077.
Ref: FH3451

NETHER WALLOP

Nether Wallop Fly Fishing School, Nether Wallop Mill, Heathman St, Nether Wallop, Stockbridge, **HAMPSHIRE**, SO20, **England**.
(W) www.fishingbreaks.co.uk
Contact/s: **Mr Simon Cooper**, Fishing Breaks Ltd, 23 Compton Trce, Romsey, London, N1 2UN.
(T) 020 73598818 **(F)** 020 73594540 **(M)** 07973 766639
(E) info@fishingbreaks.co.uk
Profile: **FT:** Game; **WN:** Wallop Brook; **WT:** Combination (Still & Moving); **F. Size:** 5 Acres; **W. Size:** 400 Metres. **Location:** **Nr. Rd:** B3084; **Main Rd:** A30; **Rail:** Andover.
Ref: FH3452

NETHERBY ESTATE

Netherby Estate, Carlisle, **CUMBRIA**, DG, **England**.
Contact/s: Manager, Edwin Thompson and Co, Bute House, Montgomery Way, Rosehill Industrial Estate, Carlise, CA1 2RW.
(T) 01228 548385 **(F)** 01228 511042
Profile: **FT:** Game; **WN:** Esk; **WT:** River (Moving).
Ref: FH3453

NETHERMOOR LAKE

Nethermoor Lake, Killamarsh, Sheffield, **DERBYSHIRE**, S21, **England**.
Contact/s: Fishery Manager.
(T) 0114 2471452
Profile: **FT:** Coarse; **WN:** Nethermoor; **WT:** Lake (Still).
Ref: FH3454

NETHERWOOD COUNTRY PARK

Netherwood Country Park, Wombwell, Barnsley, **YORKSHIRE (SOUTH)**, S7, **England**.
Contact/s: Area Manager, Environment Agency, Ridings Area Office, Phoenix House, Global Avenue, Leeds, LS11 8PG.
(T) 0113 2440191or2314834 **(F)** 0113 2134609
Mr Tom Askin.
(T) 01226 211209
Profile: **FT:** Coarse; **WN:** Plumton; **WT:** Pond (Still). **Location:** **Nr. Rd:** Wombwell.
Ref: FH3455

NETHERWOOD LAKE

Netherwood Lake, South Cerney, Cirencester, **GLOUCESTERSHIRE**, GL7, **England**.
Contact/s: **Mr Ray Daffon** (Secretary), South Cerney Angling Club, Broadway Lane, South Cerney, Cirencester, GL7 5UH.
(T) 01285 861876 **(M)** 07775 970643
Profile: **FT:** Coarse; **WN:** Netherwood; **WT:** Lake (Still).
Ref: FH3456

NETTLECOMBE FARMS

Nettlecombe Farms, Jolliffes And Nettlecombe Farms, Nettlecombe Lane, Whitwell, Ventnor, **ISLE OF WIGHT**, PO38, **England**.
Contact/s: **Mrs J Morris**.
(T) 01983 730783
Profile: **FT:** Coarse; **WN:** Nettlecombe Farms; **WT:** Lake (Still) **W. Size:** 2 Acres. **Location:** **Nr. Rd:** Nettlecombe Lane.
Ref: FH3457

NEUADDLAS COUNTRY GUEST HOUSE

Neuaddlas Country Guest House, Neuaddlas, Tregaron, **CEREDIGION**, SY25 6LG, **Wales**.
Contact/s: **Mr Will Davis** (Manager).
(T) 01974 298905 **(F)** 01974 298905
Profile: **FT:** Game; **WN:** Neuaddlas Country Guest House; **WT:** Lake (Still).
Ref: FH3458

NEVERN (RIVER)

River Nevern, Nevern, Newport, SA42, **Wales**.
Contact/s: **Mrs Nica Prichard** (Hon Secretary), Spring Gardens, Parrog Rd, Newport, Pembrokeshire, SA42 0RJ.
(T) 01239 820671
Profile: **FT:** Game; **WN:** Nevern; **WT:** River (Moving).
Ref: FH3459

NEW ABBEY DOW

New Abbey Dow, Dumfries, **DUMFRIES AND GALLOWAY**, DG2 8, **Scotland**.
Contact/s: Manager, Criffel Inn, 2 The Square, New Abbey, Dumfries, DG2 8BX.
(T) 01387 850244 **(F)** 01387 850305
Manager, Abbey Arms Hotel, 1 The Square, New Abbey, Dumfries, DG2 8BX.
(T) 01387 850489
Mr Ian Cooper (Secretary), New Abbey Fishing Association, West Shaunbellie, New Abbey, Dumfries, DG2 8HG.
(T) 01387 850280 **(M)** 07720 377958
Mr M J Carberry (Owner).
(T) 01387 850203
Profile: **FT:** Game; **WN:** New Abbey Dow; **WT:** River (Moving) **W. Size:** 4000 Metres. **Location:** **Nr. Rd:** A710; **Main Rd:** A75 then A710; **Rail:** Dumfries.
Ref: FH3460

NEW BARN ANGLING CENTRE

New Barn Farm, Totnes Rd, Collaton St. Mary, Paignton, **DEVON**, TQ4 7PT, **England**.
Contact/s: **Mr Andrew Buchanan** (Owner), New Barn Farm Cottages & Angling Ctre, Totnes Rd, Collaton St. Mary, Paignton, Devon TQ4 7PT.
(T) 01803 553602
Profile: **FT:** Coarse; **WN:** Mirror, Island, Rosie, Lulu, Willow, & Lily; **WT:** Lake (Still); **F. Size:** 40 Acres. **Location:** **Nr. Rd:** Totnes Road; **Main Rd:** A385; **Rail:** Paignton.
Ref: FH3461

NEW BRIDGE POOL

New Bridge Pool, Meadow Bank, Winsford, **CHESHIRE**, CW7, **England**.
Profile: **FT:** Coarse; **WN:** New Bridge; **WT:** Pool (Still). **Location:** **Nr. Rd:** Meadow Bank.
Ref: FH3462

NEW CUT

New Cut, Ferry Lane, Tottenham, London, **LONDON (GREATER)**, N17, **England**.
Contact/s: **Mr Chris King**, Walthamstow Reservoir Group, Thames Water Gatehouse, 2 Forest Rd, Tottenham, London, N17 9NH.
(T) 020 88081527
Profile: **FT:** Coarse; **WN:** Cut; **WT:** River (Moving) **W. Size:** 1050 Metres. **Location:** **Main Rd:** A10; **Rail:** Tottenham Hale Underground.
Ref: FH3463

NEW FOREST WATER PARK

New Forest Water Park, Ringwood Rd, Fordingbridge, **HAMPSHIRE**, SP6 2EY, **England**.
(W) www.newforestwaterpark.co.uk
Contact/s: **Mr Mark Jury** (Proprietor), New Forest, Ringwood Rd, Fordingbridge, Hampshire, SP6 2EY.
(T) 01425 656868 **(F)** 01425 650011
(E) info@newforestwaterpark.co.uk
Profile: **FT:** Coarse; **WN:** New Forest Water Park; **WT:** Lake (Still); **F. Size:** 55 Acres; **W. Size:** 30 Acres. **Location:** **Nr. Rd:** A338; **Main Rd:** A338; **Rail:** Salisbury.
Ref: FH3464

NEW HILLS TROUT FARM FISHERY

New Hills Trout Farm Fishery, Brampton, **CUMBRIA**, CA8 2QS, **England**.
Contact/s: **Mr Bill Gray** (Manager).
(T) 01697 772384
Profile: **FT:** Game; **WN:** New Hills Trout Farm Fishery; **WT:** Lake (Still) **W. Size:** 9 Acres. **Location:** **Nr. Rd:** A69; **Main Rd:** M6, junctions 43 or 44.
Ref: FH3465

NEW HOUSE FARM POOL

New House Farm Pool, Bramhall, Stockport, **MANCHESTER (GREATER)**, SK7, **England**.
Profile: **FT:** Coarse; **WN:** New House Farm; **WT:** Pool (Still). **Location:** **Nr. Rd:** Chudleigh Drive.
Ref: FH3466

NEW INN

New Inn, Llanbadarn Fynydd, Llandrindod Wells, **POWYS**, LD1, **Wales**.
Contact/s: **Mr S Armstorn** (Owner).
(T) 01597 840378
Profile: **FT:** Game; **WN:** Upper Ithon; **WT:** River (Moving).
Ref: FH3467

NEW JUNCTION CANAL

New Junction Canal, Tanker Bay, Barnby Dun,

Doncaster, **YORKSHIRE (SOUTH)**, DN, **England**.
Contact/s: **Mr Franco Pezzulo** (Manager), Franco's Angling Supplies, 148 High St, Bentley, Doncaster, DN5 0AT.
(T) 01302 874888
Profile: FT: Coarse; **WN:** New Junction; **WT:** Canal (Still). **Location: Main Rd:** Doncaster to Stainforth.
Ref: FH3468

NEW JUNCTION CANAL

New Junction Canal, Doncaster, **YORKSHIRE (SOUTH)**, DN3, **England**.
Contact/s: **Mr Roger Baker**.
(T) 01302 881707
Profile: FT: Coarse; **WN:** New Junction; **WT:** Canal (Still).
Ref: FH3469

NEW JUNCTION CANAL

New Junction Canal, Doncaster, **YORKSHIRE (SOUTH)**, DN, **England**.
Contact/s: **Mr Maurice Tate** (Secretary), Doncaster and District Angling Association, 28 Holmescarr Rd, New Rossington, Doncaster, DN11 0QF.
(T) 01302 865482
W Sams (Secretary), Doncaster and District Angling Association, 28 Pipering Lane, Scawthorpe, Doncaster.
(T) 01302 780271
Profile: FT: Coarse; **WN:** New Junction; **WT:** Canal (Still) **W. Size:** 8800 Metres.
Ref: FH3470

NEW LOCH

New Loch, Lochgilphead, **RENFREWSHIRE**, PA3, **Scotland**.
Contact/s: **Mr Archie MacGilp** (Secretary), Fyne Tackle, 22 Argyll St, Lochgilphead, Argyll and Bute, PA31 8NE.
(T) 01546 606878
Profile: FT: Game; **WN:** New; **WT:** Loch (Still); **F. Size:** 400 Acres; **W. Size:** 25 Acres. **Location: Nr. Rd:** Cairnbaan; **Main Rd:** B844; **Rail:** Oban.
Ref: FH3471

NEW MARSKE RESERVOIR

New Marske Reservoir, New Marske, Redcar, **CLEVELAND**, TS11, **England**.
Contact/s: **Mr Ron Thompson** (Secretary), 25 Endsleigh Drive, Acklam, Middlesbrough, TS5 4RG.
(T) 01642 863067
Profile: FT: Coarse; **WN:** Marske; **WT:** Reservoir (Still) **W. Size:** 4 Acres. **Location: Nr. Rd:** B1269; **Main Rd:** A174.
Ref: FH3472

NEW MEADOWS LAKE

New Meadows Lake, Christchurch, **DORSET**, BH23, **England**.
Contact/s: **Mr Pete Reading** (Secretary), 17 Mayford Rd, Poole, Dorset, BH12 1PT.
(T) 01202 733110
Profile: FT: Coarse; **WN:** New Meadows; **WT:** Lake (Still). **Location: Main Rd:** A35, then the A337. £Fr
Ref: FH3473

NEW MILL DAM

New Mill Dam, Woodhouse Rd, Todmorden, **YORKSHIRE (WEST)**, OL16, **England**.
(W) www.todmorden-angling.fsnet.co.uk
Contact/s: **Mr Andrew Crossley** (Membership Secretary), 296 Bacup Rd, Cloughfoot, Todmorden, Lancashire.
(T) 01706 816319
Mr Ray Barber (Secretary), Todmorden Angling Society, 12 Grisedale Drive, Burnley, Lancashire, BB12 8AR.
(T) 01282 702344 (M) 07970 897849
Profile: FT: Combination; **WN:** New Mill Dam; **WT:** Pond (Still); **F. Size:** 2 Acres; **W. Size:** 2 Acres. **Location: Nr. Rd:** Woodhouse Road; **Main Rd:** A646; **Rail:** Todmorden.
Ref: FH3474

NEW POND

New Pond, Pitsham Lane, Midhurst, **SUSSEX (WEST)**, GU29, **England**.
Contact/s: **Mr C Boxall** (Treasurer), Rother Angling Club, Innisfree, Ashfield Rd, Midhurst, West Sussex, GU29 9JX.
(T) 01730 813885
Profile: FT: Coarse; **WN:** New; **WT:** Pond (Still) **W. Size:** 2 Acres. **Location: Nr. Rd:** Bepton Road; **Main Rd:** A286; **Rail:** Haslemere.
Ref: FH3475

NEW POOL

New Pool, Antrobus, Northwich, **CHESHIRE**, CW9, **England**.
Contact/s: **Mr Neil Jupp** (Club Secretary), Lymm Angling Club, PO Box 350, Warrington, Cheshire, WA2 9FB.
(T) 01925 411774
Profile: FT: Coarse; **WN:** New; **WT:** Pool (Still). **Location: Nr. Rd:** Lake Lane; **Main Rd:** A559.
Ref: FH3476

NEW RIVER

New River, Ware, **HERTFORDSHIRE**, SG12, **England**.
Contact/s: **Mr Simon Maddock** (Secretary), Palmers Green Angling Society, 32 Leaforis Rd, Chestnut, Hertfordshire, EN7 6ND.
(T) 01992 628992
Profile: FT: Combination; **WN:** New; **WT:** River (Moving) **W. Size:** 2400 Metres. **Location: Nr. Rd:** A1170; **Main Rd:** A10, southbound to London.
Ref: FH3477

NEWBIGGIN POND

Newbiggin Pond, High Green, Rotherham, **YORKSHIRE (SOUTH)**, S7, **England**.
Contact/s: Area Manager, Environment Agency, Ridings Area Office, Phoenix House, Global Avenue, Leeds, LS11 8PG.
(T) 0113 2440191or2314834 (F) 0113 2134609
Mr Steve Hinson, 22a Eilam Cl, Rotherham, Yorkshire (South), S61 3QE.
(T) 01709 555225
Profile: FT: Coarse; **WN:** Newbiggin; **WT:** Pond (Still). **Location: Nr. Rd:** A616.
Ref: FH3478

NEWBOLD QUARRY

Newbold Quarry, Newbold on Avon, Rugby, **WARWICKSHIRE**, CV, **England**.
Contact/s: **G Lawerence**, 53 Manor Rd, Rugby, Warwickshire, CV21 2TG.
Profile: FT: Coarse; **WN:** Newbold Quarry; **WT:** Quarry (Still).
Ref: FH3479

NEWBURY TROUT LAKES

Newbury Trout Lakes, Lower Farm, Hambridge Lane, Newbury, **BERKSHIRE**, RG, **England**.
Contact/s: **Mr Fraser Reilly**.
(T) 01635 38280 (F) 01635 38280
Profile: FT: Game; **WN:** Newbury; **WT:** Lake (Still); **F. Size:** 23 Acres; **W. Size:** 14 Acres. **Location: Nr. Rd:** Hambridge Lane; **Main Rd:** London Road; **Rail:** Newbury.
Ref: FH3480

NEWBY HALL FISHERIES

Newby Hall Fisheries, Newby Hall, Ripon, **YORKSHIRE (NORTH)**, HG4, **England**.
Contact/s: Manager, Newby Hall Estates, Estate Office, Ripon, Yorkshire (North), HG4 5AE.
(T) 01423 322583
Profile: FT: Combination; **WN:** Ure; **WT:** River (Moving). **Location: Nr. Rd:** B6265; **Rail:** Harrogate.
Ref: FH3481

NEWCOURT PONDS

Newcourt Ponds, Langford, Cullompton, **DEVON**, EX15 1SE, **England**.
Contact/s: **Mr Andy Hitt**.
(T) 01884 277326
Profile: FT: Coarse; **WN:** Newcourt; **WT:** Pond (Still) **W. Size:** 2 Acres. **Location: Nr. Rd:** B3181; **Main Rd:** M5, junction 28.
Ref: FH3482

NEWELLS FISHERIES

Newells Specimen Carp And Coarse Fisheries, Newells Pond House, Newells Lane, Lower Beeding, Horsham, **SUSSEX (WEST)**, RH13 6LN, **England**.
Contact/s: **Mr Tim Cotton**.
(T) 01403 891424
(E) tnt@t.cotton.freeserve.co..uk
Profile: FT: Coarse; **WN:** Newells; **WT:** Lake (Still); **F. Size:** 12 Acres; **W. Size:** 8 Acres. **Location: Nr. Rd:** Newells Lane, A281; **Main Rd:** A23, M23; **Rail:** Horsham.
Ref: FH3483

NEWHAY DAY TICKET LAKE

Newhay Day Ticket Lake, Newhay Lodge, Newhay, Selby, **YORKSHIRE (NORTH)**, YO8 6PL, **England**.
Contact/s: **Mr Colin Forsyth**.
(T) 01757 638383 (F) 01757 638383
Mrs Sandra Forsyth.
(T) 01757 638383 (F) 01757 638383
Profile: FT: Coarse; **WN:** Newhay day; **WT:** Lake (Still); **F. Size:** 10 Acres; **W. Size:** 2 Acres. **Location: Nr. Rd:** Unclassified; **Main Rd:** A63; **Rail:** Selby.
Ref: FH3484

NEWHAY SPECIMEN LAKE

Newhay Specimen Lake, Newhay Lodge, Newhay, Selby, **YORKSHIRE (NORTH)**, YO8 6PL, **England**.
Contact/s: **Mr Colin Forsyth**.
(T) 01757 638383 (F) 01757 638383
Mrs Sandra Forsyth.
(T) 01757 638383 (F) 01757 638383
Profile: FT: Coarse; **WN:** Newhay Specimen; **WT:** Lake (Still); **F. Size:** 10 Acres; **W. Size:** 2 Acres. **Location: Nr. Rd:** Unclassified; **Main Rd:** A63; **Rail:** Selby.
Ref: FH3485

NEWHOUSE FISHERY

Newhouse Fishery, Newhouse Farm, Moreleigh, Totnes, **DEVON**, TQ9 7JS, **England**.
Contact/s: **Mr Adrian Cook**.
(T) 01548 821426 (F) 01548 821426
Mr Paul Cook (Manager).
(T) 01548 821426 (F) 01548 821426
Profile: FT: Game; **WN:** Newhouse Fishery; **WT:** Combination (Still & Moving); **F. Size:** 60 Acres; **W. Size:** 4 Acres. **Location: Nr. Rd:** B3207; **Main Rd:** A381; **Rail:** Totnes.
Ref: FH3486

NEWLAND HALL CARP FISHERY

Newland Hall Carp Fishery, Newland Hall, Roxwell, Chelmsford, **ESSEX**, CM1 4LH, **England**.
Contact/s: Reception.
(T) 01245 231010
Mr Simon Burton.
(T) 01245 231463 (F) 01245 231463
Ms Tracy Hunt.
(T) 01245 231463 (F) 01245 231463
Profile: FT: Coarse; **WN:** Newland Hall Carp Fishery; **WT:** Lake (Still); **F. Size:** 100 Acres; **W. Size:** 10 Acres. **Location: Nr. Rd:** A1060; **Main Rd:** A1060; **Rail:** Chelmsford.
Ref: FH3487

NEWMILL TROUT AND DEER FARM

Newmill Trout And Deer Farm, Newmills, Gleghorn, Lanark, **LANARKSHIRE (SOUTH)**, ML11 7SL, **Scotland**.
Contact/s: **Mr Dave Buchanan** (Owner).
(T) 01555 870730
Profile: FT: Game; **WN:** Newmill Trout And Deer Farm; **WT:** Lake (Still).
Ref: FH3488

NEWPORT CANAL

Newport Canal, Newport, Telford,

SHROPSHIRE, TF4, England.
Contact/s: Mr Stan Harris (Secretary), Telford Angling Association, 73 Burnside, Brookside, Telford, TF3 1DA.
(T) 01952 590605
Profile: FT: Coarse; WN: Newport; WT: Canal (Still) W. Size: 135 Metres.
Ref: FH3489

NEWPORT PAGNELL GRAVEL PITS

Newport Pagnell Gravel Pits, Bedford Rd, Newport Pagnell, BUCKINGHAMSHIRE, MK16, England.
Contact/s: Mr R Dorrill (Secretary), 7 Bury St, Newport Pagnell.
(T) 01909 610639
Profile: FT: Coarse; WN: Newport Pagnell; WT: Gravel Pit (Still). Location: Main Rd: Bedford Road.
Ref: FH3490

NEWRY CANAL

Newry Canal, Newry, COUNTY DOWN, BT34, Northern Ireland.
Contact/s: Fishery Manager.
(T) 028 3067322
Profile: FT: Coarse; WN: Newry Canal; WT: Canal (Still).
Ref: FH3491

NEWSHAM PARK

Newsham Park, Tuebrook, Liverpool, MERSEYSIDE, England.
Contact/s: Mr Steve Vose (Park Ranger).
(T) 0151 2333000
Profile: FT: CoarseWT: (Still).
Ref: FH3492

NEWTON ABBOT SPRING PONDS

Newton Abbot Spring Ponds, Rocombe, Newton Abbot, DEVON, TQ12, England.
Contact/s: Manager, Tackle Traders, 2 Wharf Rd, Newton Abbot, Devon, TQ12 2DA.
(T) 01626 331613
Mr David Horder (Secretary), Mistlemead, Woodlands, Higher Sandygate, Newton Abbot, TQ12 3QN.
(T) 01626 364173
Profile: FT: Coarse; WN: Newton Abbot Spring Ponds; WT: Pond (Still).
Ref: FH3493

NEWTON FARM FISHERY

Newton Farm Fishery, Newton Farm, Newport-on-Tay, FIFE, DD6 8RL, Scotland.
Contact/s: Mr Gordon Crawford (Owner).
(T) 01382 542513 (F) 01382 542513
Ms Katherine Crawford (Owner).
(T) 01382 542513 (F) 01382 542513
Profile: FT: Game; WN: Newton Farm Fishery; WT: Lake (Still); F. Size: 5 Acres; W. Size: 4 Acres. Location: Nr. Rd: B946; Main Rd: A92; Rail: Leuchars.
Ref: FH3494

NEWTON LOCHAN

Newton Lochan, Newton Farm House, Gatehouse Of Fleet, Castle Douglas, DUMFRIES AND GALLOWAY, DG7 2ER, Scotland.
Contact/s: Mrs E Hamilton (Owner).
(T) 01557 840234
Profile: FT: Coarse; WN: Newton Lochon; WT: Loch (Still) W. Size: 2 Acres. Location: Main Rd: A75.
Ref: FH3495

NEWTON OF LOGIERAIT BEAT

Newton Of Logierait Beat, Perth, PERTH AND KINROSS, PH, Scotland.
(W) www.fishingnet.com/beats/newton.htm
Contact/s: Mr P D Malloch (Manager), Fishing Tackle Shop, 259 Old High St, Perth, Perth and Kinross, PH1 5QN.
(T) 01738 632316
Profile: FT: Combination; WN: Neck of Newton and Newton; WT: Pool (Still).
Ref: FH3496

NEWTON PARK

Newton Park, Bath, SOMERSET, BA, England.
Contact/s: Fishery Manager.
(T) 01179 715003
Mr Dave Crookes (Secretary), Bathampton Angling Association, 25 Otago Trce, Larkhall, Bath, BA1 6SX.
(T) 01225 427164
Profile: FT: Coarse; WN: Newton Park; WT: Lake (Still) W. Size: 29 Acres. Location: Nr. Rd: Bath to Bristol; Main Rd: A4, A39 to Marksbury.
Ref: FH3497

NEWTON RIVER

River Newton, Newton, Bedale, YORKSHIRE (NORTH), DL8, England.
Contact/s: Mr John Lane (Secretary), York and District Angling Association, 39 Lowfields Drive, Acomb, York, YO2 3DQ.
(T) 01904 783178
Profile: FT: Coarse; WN: Newton; WT: River (Moving).
Ref: FH3498

NEWTOWN LAKE

Newtown Lake, Moorland Rd, Highbridge, SOMERSET, TA9, England.
Contact/s: Mr S Bonwick (Secretary), 13 Tennyson Avenue, Clevedon, Somerset, BS21 7QQ.
(T) 01275 791933
Profile: FT: Coarse; WN: Newtown; WT: Lake (Still) W. Size: 4 Acres. Location: Nr. Rd: Moorland Road; Main Rd: M5, junction 22.
Ref: FH3499

NIDD (RIVER)

River Nidd, Pateley Bridge, Harrogate, YORKSHIRE (NORTH), HG3 5XB, England.
Contact/s: Mr T Harpham, PO Box 7, Pateley Bridge, Harrogate, Yorkshire (North), HG3 5XB.
(T) 01423 711960
Profile: FT: Game; WN: Nidd; WT: River (Moving). Location: Main Rd: B6265.
Ref: FH3500

NIDD (RIVER)

River Nidd, Ness Lane, Tockwith, York, YORKSHIRE (NORTH), YO26, England.
Contact/s: Manager, Mitre Pets Fishing Tackle and Aquarium, 212-214 Shipton Rd, York, Yorkshire (North), YO30 5RZ.
(T) 01904 654841
Profile: FT: Coarse; WN: Nidd; WT: River (Moving) W. Size: 1600 Metres. Location: Nr. Rd: Ness Lane; Main Rd: A59.
Ref: FH3501

NIDD (RIVER)

River Nidd, Green Hammerton, York, YORKSHIRE (NORTH), YO26, England.
Contact/s: Mr Derek Taylor (Secretary), Leeds ADASA, 75 Stoney Rock Lane, Beckett St, Leeds, LS29 7TB.
(T) 0113 2482373
Profile: FT: Coarse; WN: Nidd; WT: River (Moving). Location: Main Rd: A59 between Harrogate and York.
Ref: FH3502

NIDD (RIVER)

River Nidd, Little Ribston, Knaresborough, YORKSHIRE (NORTH), HG5, England.
Contact/s: Mr B Thackrey (Secretary).
(T) 01423 866695
Mr G Hinds (Chairman).
(T) 01423 869647
Mr Norman Edward (Vice Chairman), 125 The Avenue, Starbeck, Harrogate, HG1 4QG.
(T) 01423 885399
Profile: FT: Combination; WN: Nidd (Guys Cragg to Little Ribston); WT: River (Moving) W. Size: 19200 Metres. Location: Nr. Rd: B6164; Main Rd: A1.
Ref: FH3503

NIDD (RIVER)

River Nidd, Moor Monkton, York, YORKSHIRE (NORTH), YO26, England.
Contact/s: Mr Park.
(T) 01904 738358
Profile: FT: Coarse; WN: Nidd; WT: River (Moving) W. Size: 1200 Metres. Location: Nr. Rd: Knaresborough to York; Main Rd: A59.
Ref: FH3504

NIDD (RIVER)

River Nidd, Blind Rd, Tockwith, York, YORKSHIRE (NORTH), YO26 7, England.
Contact/s: Manager.
(T) 01423 863065
Profile: FT: Coarse; WN: Nidd; WT: River (Moving). Location: Nr. Rd: Blind Road; Main Rd: A1, A59.
Ref: FH3505

NIDD (RIVER)

River Nidd, Nidd Estate, Knaresborough, YORKSHIRE (NORTH), HG5, England.
Contact/s: Mr B Thackrey (Secretary).
(T) 01423 866695
Mr G Hinds (Chairman).
(T) 01423 869647
Mr Norman Edward (Vice Chairman), 125 The Avenue, Starbeck, Harrogate, HG1 4QG.
(T) 01423 885399
Profile: FT: Combination; WN: Nidd; WT: River (Moving) W. Size: 19200 Metres. Location: Nr. Rd: Knaresborough to Harrogate Road; Main Rd: Knaresborough.
Ref: FH3506

NIDD (RIVER)

River Nidd, Goldborough Mill, Harrogate, YORKSHIRE (NORTH), HG, England.
Contact/s: Mr B Thackrey (Secretary).
(T) 01423 866695
Mr G Hinds (Chairman).
(T) 01423 869647
Mr Norman Edward (Vice Chairman), 125 The Avenue, Starbeck, Harrogate, HG1 4QG.
(T) 01423 885399
Profile: FT: Coarse; WN: Nidd; WT: River (Moving) W. Size: 19200 Metres. Location: Nr. Rd: Knaresborough to Wetherby; Main Rd: B1646.
Ref: FH3507

NIDD BRIDGE

Nidd Bridge, Ripley, Harrogate, YORKSHIRE (NORTH), HG3, England.
Contact/s: Mr M G Cooke (Secretary), 1 Kirkham Rd, Bilton, Harrogate, Yorkshire, HG1 4EL.
Profile: FT: Combination; WN: Nidd Bridge; WT: River (Moving) W. Size: 4000 Metres. Location: Nr. Rd: Harrogate to Ripon Road Bridge to Killinghall.
Ref: FH3508

NINE OAKS

Nine Oaks, Craigfryn, Oakford, Llanarth, CEREDIGION, SA47 0RW, Wales.
Contact/s: Mr John Steels.
(T) 01545 580482
Profile: FT: Coarse; WN: Nine Oaks; WT: Lake (Still) W. Size: 1 Acre. Location: Main Rd: A487.
Ref: FH3509

NIRE (RIVER)

River Nire, Clonmel, COUNTY TIPPERARY, Ireland.
Contact/s: Mrs Wall, Hanoras Cottage, Ballymacabry, Clonmel, County Tipperary, Ireland.
Profile: FT: Game; WN: Nire; WT: River (Moving) W. Size: 9600 Metres.
Ref: FH3510

NIRE STREAM

Nire Stream, Clonmel, COUNTY TIPPERARY, Ireland.
Contact/s: Mr Andrew Ryan (Manager), Clonanav Angling Ctre, Ballymacabry, Clonmel, County Tipperary, Ireland.
(T) 052 36141
Profile: FT: Game; WN: Nire; WT: Stream (Moving).
Ref: FH3511

NITH (RIVER)

River Nith, Buccleuch Estates Ltd, Drumlanrig Mains, Thornhill, **DUMFRIES AND GALLOWAY**, DG3 4AG, **Scotland**.
Contact/s: **Mr N A G Waugh**.
(T) 01848 600283 **(F)** 01848 600244
Profile: **FT:** Game; **WN:** Nith; **WT:** River (Moving) **W. Size:** 12000 Metres. **Location:** **Nr. Rd:** A76; **Main Rd:** A76; **Rail:** Sanquhar.
Ref: FH3512

NODDLE HILL LAKE

Noddle Hill Lake, Bransholme Rd, Noddle Hill Way, Bransholme, Hull, **HUMBERSIDE**, HU7, **England**.
Contact/s: Urban Park Ranger, Noddle Hill Playing Fields, Bransholme, Hull.
(T) 01482 374288 **(F)** 01482 374288 **(M)** 07775 678489
Profile: **FT:** Coarse; **WN:** Noddle Hill; **WT:** Lake (Still) **W. Size:** 10 Acres. **Location:** **Nr. Rd:** Noddle Hill Way; **Main Rd:** M62; **Rail:** Hull Paragon.
Ref: FH3513

NOOK & CRANNY LAKE

Nook & Cranny Lake, Shalmsford St, Canterbury, **KENT**, **England**.
(W) www.midkentfish.demon.co.uk
Contact/s: **Mr Chris Logsdon** (Fisheries Manager), Mid Kent Fisheries, Chilham Water Mill, Mill Lane, Chilham, CT4 8EE.
(T) 01227 730668
(E) chilham@midkentfisheries.co.uk
Profile: **FT:** Coarse; **WN:** Nook & Cranny; **WT:** Lake (Still); **F. Size:** 15 Acres; **W. Size:** 12 Acres. **Location:** **Main Rd:** A28; **Rail:** Chartham.
Ref: FH3514

NORBURY POOL

Norbury Pool, Lymm, **CHESHIRE**, WA13, **England**.
Contact/s: **Mr Neil Jupp** (Club Secretary), Lymm Angling Club, PO Box 350, Warrington, Cheshire, WA2 9FB.
(T) 01925 411744
Profile: **FT:** Coarse; **WN:** Norbury; **WT:** Pool (Still). **Location:** **Nr. Rd:** Seven Sisters Lane; **Main Rd:** A50 to Holmes Chapel.
Ref: FH3515

NORDLEY POOLS

Nordley Pools, Bridgnorth, **MIDLANDS (WEST)**, WV1, **England**.
Contact/s: **Mr John Williams** (Secretary), Birmingham Anglers Association, 100 Icknield Port Rd, Rotton Park, Birmingham, B16 0AP.
(T) 0121 4549111
Profile: **FT:** Coarse; **WN:** Nordley; **WT:** Pool (Still).
Ref: FH3516

NORE (RIVER)

River Nore, Kilkenny, **COUNTY KILKENNY**, **Ireland**.
Contact/s: **Mr Edward Stack** (Secretary), Kilkenny Angling Association, c/o Garda Station, Kilkenny, County Kilkenny, Ireland.
Profile: **FT:** Game; **WN:** Nore; **WT:** River (Moving) **W. Size:** 1600 Metres.
Ref: FH3517

NORE (RIVER)

River Nore, Inistoge Anglers Waters, Stony Batter, High St, Inistioge, **COUNTY KILKENNY**, **Ireland**.
Contact/s: **Mr Bill Doherty** (Secretary).
(T) 056 58571
Mr John O Donnell (Treasurer), Inistioge Angling Club, Castle Inn, Inistioge, County Kilkenny.
(T) 056 58483
Profile: **FT:** Combination; **WN:** Nore; **WT:** River (Moving) **W. Size:** 9000 Metres. **Location:** **Nr. Rd:** In village; **Rail:** Thomastown.
Ref: FH3518

NORE (RIVER)

River Nore, Kilkenny, **COUNTY KILKENNY**, **Ireland**.
Contact/s: **Ms Susan Lawlor** (Manager), Foodmarket, The Square, Durrow, County Kilkenny, Ireland.
(T) 050 236437
Profile: **FT:** Game; **WN:** Nore; **WT:** River (Moving).
Ref: FH3519

NORE (RIVER)

River Nore, Kilkenny, **COUNTY KILKENNY**, **Ireland**.
Contact/s: **Mr Edward Stack** (Secretary), Kilkenny Angling Association, c/o Garda Station, Kilkenny, County Kilkenny, Ireland.
Profile: **FT:** Game; **WN:** Nore; **WT:** River (Moving).
Ref: FH3520

NORE (RIVER)

Nore (River), Thomastown, **COUNTY KILKENNY**, **Ireland**.
Contact/s: **Mr P Heafey** (Secretary), Thomastown Angling Association, Castle Avenue, Thomastown, County Kilkenny, Ireland.
Profile: **FT:** Game; **WN:** Nore; **WT:** River (Moving).
Ref: FH3521

NORE (RIVER)

River Nore, Abbeyleix, **COUNTY LAOIS**, **Ireland**.
Contact/s: **Mr V Bowell** (Secretary), Abbeyleix District Angling Clubs, Sandymount, Abbeyleix, County Laois, Ireland.
Profile: **FT:** Game; **WN:** Nore; **WT:** River (Moving).
Ref: FH3522

NORE (RIVER)

River Nore, Mountrath, **COUNTY TIPPERARY**, **Ireland**.
Contact/s: **Mr Tommy Watkins** (Hon Secretary), 9 St Fiach's Trce, Mountrath, County Laois, Ireland.
(T) 050 232540
Profile: **FT:** Combination; **WN:** Nore; **WT:** Combination (Moving). **Location:** **Main Rd:** Dublin to Limerick Road; **Rail:** Clonmel.
Ref: FH3523

NORFOLK & SUFFOLK FLY FISHERY

Norfolk And Suffolk Fly Fisheries Lake, Dereham, **NORFOLK**, NR20, **England**.
Contact/s: **Mr D Armes** (Manager), 100 Cozens Hardy Rd, Sprowston, Norwich, NR7 8QQ.
(T) 01603 423169or01508520863
Profile: **FT:** Game; **WN:** Norfolk And Suffolk Fly Fisheries Lake; **WT:** Lake (Still) **W. Size:** 6 Acres.
Ref: FH3524

NORMANTON FISHING LODGE

Normanton Fishing Lodge, Rutland Water South Shore, Edith Weston, Oakham, **RUTLAND**, LE15 8HD, **England**.
Contact/s: Fishery Manager.
(T) 01572 653026
Profile: **FT:** Combination; **WN:** Normanton Fishing Lodge; **WT:** Lake (Still).
Ref: FH3525

NORTH BANK TROUT FISHERY

North Bank Trout Fishery, Northbank, Thorney, Peterborough, **CAMBRIDGESHIRE**, PE6 0RP, **England**.
Contact/s: **Mr John Cutteridge**.
(T) 01733 203998 **(F)** 01733 223658
Profile: **FT:** Game; **WN:** North Bank Trout Fishery; **WT:** Gravel Pit (Still) **W. Size:** 16 Acres. **Location:** **Nr. Rd:** B1040; **Main Rd:** A47; **Rail:** Peterborough.
Ref: FH3526

NORTH FARM FISHERY

North Farm Fishery, Priors Marston, Southam, **WARWICKSHIRE**, CV47, **England**.
Contact/s: Manager.
(T) 01327 260617
Profile: **FT:** Coarse; **WN:** North Farm Fishery; **WT:** Lake (Still) **W. Size:** 3 Acres.
Ref: FH3527

NORTH FIELD POOL

North Field Pool, Congleton, **CHESHIRE**, CW12, **England**.
Profile: **FT:** Coarse; **WN:** North Field; **WT:** Pool (Still). **Location:** **Nr. Rd:** Banks Lane; **Main Rd:** A536, Macclesfield Road.
Ref: FH3528

NORTH HOUSE LAKE

North House Lake, The North House, Great North Rd, Wyboston, St Neots, Huntingdon, **CAMBRIDGESHIRE**, PE1, **England**.
Contact/s: **Mr D Bacon** (Secretary), 18 The Hedgerows, Parkside, Furzton, Milton Keynes, MK4 1BP.
Mr David Edwards (Membership Secretary).
(T) 01582 728114
Mr Ken Scott (Fishing Officer).
(T) 01582 619757
Profile: **FT:** Coarse; **WN:** North House; **WT:** Gravel Pit (Still) **W. Size:** 5 Acres. **Location:** **Main Rd:** A1.
Ref: FH3529

NORTH KELSEY PARK

North Kelsey Park, North Kelsey, Market Rasen, **LINCOLNSHIRE**, LN7 6QH, **England**.
Contact/s: Manager, North Kelsey Park, North Kelsey, Lincolnshire, LN7 6QH.
(T) 01831 123819
Profile: **FT:** Coarse; **WN:** North Kelsey Park; **WT:** Lake (Still).
Ref: FH3530

NORTH MEADOWS

North Meadows, The Common Lands, Sudbury, **SUFFOLK**, CO10, **England**.
Contact/s: **Mr Rob Hayward** (Manager), Sudbury Angling Ctre, 1 Acton Sq, Sudbury, Suffolk, CO10 1HG.
(T) 01787 312118
Mr Trevor Fairless (Secretary), Sudbury and District Angling Association, 39 Pot Kiln Rd, Sudbury, Suffolk, CO10 0DG.
(T) 01787 312536
Profile: **FT:** Coarse; **WN:** Stow (Suffolk); **WT:** River (Moving) **W. Size:** 375 Metres. **Location:** **Nr. Rd:** Bury St Edmunds Road; **Main Rd:** A134; **Rail:** Sudbury.
Ref: FH3531

NORTH MET PIT

North Met Pit, Cheshunt Wash, Waltham Cross, **HERTFORDSHIRE**, EN8, **England**.
Contact/s: Information Officer, Lee Valley Park Information Ctre, Abbey Gardens, Waltham Abbey, Essex, EN9 1XQ.
(T) 01992 702200
Mr Krizim Seltham (Angling Manager), Lee Valley Regional Park Authority, Myddleton House, Bulls Cross, Enfield, EN2 9HG.
(T) 01992 709832
(E) garysmith@leevalleypark.org.uk
Profile: **FT:** Coarse; **WN:** North Met; **WT:** Gravel Pit (Still) **W. Size:** 58 Acres. **Location:** **Nr. Rd:** Cheshunt Wash; **Main Rd:** A10, North of the M25; **Rail:** Cheshunt.
Ref: FH3532

NORTH OXFORD CANAL

North Oxford Canal, Hillmorton To Barby Lane, Rugby, **WARWICKSHIRE**, CV, **England**.
Contact/s: Manager, Banks and Burr Tackle Shop, 27 Claremont Rd, Rugby, Warwickshire, CV21 3NA.
(T) 01788 576782
Mr Pete Felton.
(T) 01788 577329
Profile: **FT:** Coarse; **WN:** North Oxford; **WT:** Canal (Still) **W. Size:** 4800 Metres. **Location:** **Nr. Rd:** Rugby to Crick; **Main Rd:** A428, M1 junction 18.
Ref: FH3533

NORTH THIRD TROUT FISHERY

North Third Trout Fishery, Greathill House, Stirling, FK7 9QS, **Scotland**.
Contact/s: Mr George Holdsworth.
(T) 01786 471967 **(F)** 01786 447388
Profile: **FT:** Game; **WN:** North Third Trout Fishery; **WT:** Reservoir (Still); **F. Size:** 140 Acres; **W. Size:** 140 Acres. **Location:** **Rail:** Stirling.
Ref: FH3534

NORTH THORESBY FISHERIES

North Thoresby Fisheries, Fen Lane, North Thoresby, Grimsby, **HUMBERSIDE**, DN36, **England**.
Contact/s: J Casswell.
(T) 01472 812518
Profile: **FT:** Combination; **WN:** North Thoresby Fisheries; **WT:** Lake (Still).
Ref: FH3535

NORTH TROY LAKE & COLNE

North Troy Lake And River Colne, Coppermill Lane, Harefield, Uxbridge, London, **LONDON (GREATER)**, UB9, **England**.
Contact/s: Mr Terry Gray, 1 Orchard Way, Uxbridge, Middlesex.
Mr Tim Spencer.
(T) 01895 847967
Profile: **FT:** Coarse; **WN:** North Troy Lake And River Colne; **WT:** Combination (Still & Moving) **W. Size:** 800 Metres. **Location:** **Nr. Rd:** Harefield to West Hyde; **Main Rd:** Coppermill Lane; **Rail:** Uxbridge.
Ref: FH3536

NORTH TYNE (RIVER)

River North Tyne, Chesters, Bellingham, Hexham, **NORTHUMBERLAND**, NE48 2, **England**.
Contact/s: Mr Gaisford.
(T) 01434 602301
Profile: **FT:** Game; **WN:** North Tyne; **WT:** River (Moving) **W. Size:** 2400 Metres.
Ref: FH3537

NORTH TYNE (RIVER)

River North Tyne, Bellingham, Hexham, **NORTHUMBERLAND**, NE48, **England**.
Contact/s: Mr Barry Hignett (Secretary), Ferryhill and District Angling Club, 74 Grasmere Rd, Garden Farm Estate, Chester-le-Street, County Durham.
(T) 0191 3883557
Mr W Curtis (Chairman), 14 Bakewell Pl, Newton Aycliffe, County Durham.
(T) 01325 320291
Profile: **FT:** Combination; **WN:** North Tyne; **WT:** River (Moving) **W. Size:** 800 Metres. **Location:** **Nr. Rd:** B6320; **Main Rd:** A68.
Ref: FH3538

NORTH TYNE (RIVER)

River North Tyne, Chollerford, Hexham, **NORTHUMBERLAND**, NE46, **England**.
Contact/s: Manager, The George Hotel, Chollerford, Hexham, Northumberland, NE46 4EW.
(T) 01434 681611 **(F)** 01434 681727
Profile: **FT:** Combination; **WN:** North Tyne; **WT:** River (Moving) **W. Size:** 1200 Metres.
Ref: FH3539

NORTH TYNE (RIVER)

River North Tyne, Snabdough Farm, Hesleyside, Bellingham, Hexham, **NORTHUMBERLAND**, NE48, **England**.
Contact/s: Mr Gaisford.
(T) 01434 602301
Mr C Allgood.
(T) 01434 240239
Profile: **FT:** Game; **WN:** North Tyne; **WT:** River (Moving) **W. Size:** 800 Metres.
Ref: FH3540

NORTH TYNE (RIVER)

River North Tyne, Falstone, Hexham, **NORTHUMBERLAND**, NE48, **England**.
Contact/s: Mr Peter Laws (Owner).
(T) 01434 240200
Profile: **FT:** Game; **WN:** North Tyne; **WT:** River (Moving).
Ref: FH3541

NORTHAMPTON JUNCTION CANAL

Northampton Junction Canal, Northampton, **NORTHAMPTONSHIRE**, NN, **England**.
Contact/s: Mr Terry Rodhouse (Secretary), Castle Angling Association, 12 Somerville Rd, Daventry, Northamptonshire, NN11 4RT.
(T) 01327 705692
Profile: **FT:** Coarse; **WN:** Junction; **WT:** Canal (Still). **Location:** **Nr. Rd:** Milton Malsor to Northampton; **Main Rd:** A45, A43.
Ref: FH3542

NORTHEY PARK FISHERY

Northey Park Fishery, Whittlesey, Peterborough, **CAMBRIDGESHIRE**, PE7, **England**.
Contact/s: Mr Elliott Symak.
(T) 01733 558329 **(M)** 07889 711555
Profile: **FT:** Coarse; **WN:** Northey Park Fishery; **WT:** Lake (Still) **W. Size:** 25 Acres.
Ref: FH3543

NORTHFIELD LAKES

Northfield Lakes, Ringwood, **HAMPSHIRE**, BH24, **England**.
Contact/s: Mr Kevin Grozier (Permit Secretary), 15 Greenfinch Walk, Hightown, Ringwood, Hampshire, BH24 3RJ.
(T) 01425 471466 **(F)** 01425 471466
Mr Richard Middleton (Manager), Ringwood Tackle, 5 The Bridges, Ringwood, Hampshire, BH24 1EA.
(T) 01425 475155
Profile: **FT:** Coarse; **WN:** Northfield Lakes; **WT:** Gravel Pit (Still) **W. Size:** 20 Acres. **Location:** **Nr. Rd:** Fordingbridge Road; **Main Rd:** A31.
Ref: FH3544

NORTHINGALES FISHERY

Northingales Fishery, Rythergate Cottage, Cawood, York, **YORKSHIRE (NORTH)**, YO, **England**.
Contact/s: Mr Binks.
(T) 01757 268414
Profile: **FT:** Coarse; **WN:** Northingales Fishery; **WT:** Pond (Still) **W. Size:** 13 Acres. **Location:** **Main Rd:** A19, B1222.
Ref: FH3545

NORTHLANDS PARK

Northlands Park, Felmores, Basildon, **ESSEX**, SS1, **England**.
Contact/s: Mr Mick Toomer (Manager), Tackle Shop, 10 Ravensdale, Kingswood, Basildon, Essex SS16 5HS.
(T) 01268 282317
Profile: **FT:** Coarse; **WN:** Northlands Park; **WT:** Lake (Still) **W. Size:** 4 Acres. **Location:** **Nr. Rd:** A127; **Main Rd:** M25, junction 29; **Rail:** Pitsea.
Ref: FH3546

NORTON FISHERY

Norton Fishery, Epping Lane, Stapleford Tawney, Romford, **ESSEX**, RM4 1ST, **England**.
Contact/s: Mr Norton (Manager).
(T) 01708 688445 **(M)** 07973 506257
Profile: **FT:** Game; **WN:** Norton Fishery; **WT:** Gravel Pit (Still) **W. Size:** 5 Acres. **Location:** **Nr. Rd:** Epping Lane.
Ref: FH3547

NORTON FRUIT FARM

Norton Fruit Farm, Tewkesbury Rd, Norton, Gloucester, **GLOUCESTERSHIRE**, GL2 9LH, **England**.
Contact/s: Mrs E Morley.
(T) 01452 731203
Profile: **FT:** Combination; **WN:** Norton Fruit Farm; **WT:** Lake (Still) **W. Size:** 2 Acres. **Location:** **Nr. Rd:** A38 Tewkesbury Road; **Main Rd:** M5, M50.
Ref: FH3548

NORWOOD FISHERIES

Norwood Fisheries Ltd, The Mill, Killamarsh, Sheffield, **YORKSHIRE (SOUTH)**, S31 8DS, **England**.
Contact/s: Fishery Manager.
(T) 01909 515183
Profile: **FT:** Coarse; **WN:** Norwood; **WT:** Lake (Still).
Ref: FH3549

NORWOOD LAKE

Norwood Lake, Woodvale Avenue, Norwood Hill, London, **LONDON (GREATER)**, SE25, **England**.
Profile: **FT:** Coarse; **WN:** Norwood; **WT:** Lake (Still) **W. Size:** 3 Acres. **Location:** **Nr. Rd:** Woodvale Avenue; **Main Rd:** A215.
Ref: FH3550

NOSTELL PRIORY LAKE

Nostell Priory Lake, Fishery Office, Foulby Lodge, Doncaster, Foulby, Wakefield, **YORKSHIRE (WEST)**, WF4 1PY, **England**.
Contact/s: Mr John Austerfield (Manager).
(T) 01924 863562 **(F)** 01924 863562
Profile: **FT:** Coarse; **WN:** Nostell Priory; **WT:** Lake (Still); **F. Size:** 200 Acres. **Location:** **Nr. Rd:** A638; **Main Rd:** Wakefield to Doncaster Road; **Rail:** Fitzwilliam.
Ref: FH3551

NOTTINGHAM CANAL

Nottingham Canal, Nottingham, **NOTTINGHAMSHIRE**, NG1, **England**.
Contact/s: Mr I Foulds (Secretary), Nottingham Angling Association, 95 Ilkeston Rd, Nottingham, Nottinghamshire, NG7 3HA.
(T) 0115 9033881or9708080
Profile: **FT:** Coarse; **WN:** Nottingham; **WT:** Canal (Still) **W. Size:** 3000 Metres.
Ref: FH3552

NOTTINGHAM CASTLE MARINA

Nottingham Castle Marina, Castle Marina Rd, Castle Boulavard, Nottingham, **NOTTINGHAMSHIRE**, N67, **England**.
Contact/s: Mr Dave Fallows (Secretary), Parkside Fishing Club, 27 Woodstock Avenue, Radford, Nottingham, N67 5QP.
(T) 0115 9787350
Profile: **FT:** Coarse; **WN:** Nottingham Castle Marina; **WT:** Canal (Still). **Location:** **Nr. Rd:** A6005; **Main Rd:** A6005; **Rail:** Nottingham.
Ref: FH3553

NUN MONKTON (RIVER)

River Nun Monkton, Nun Monkton, York, **YORKSHIRE (NORTH)**, YO26, **England**.
Contact/s: Mr Howard Foster (Secretary), 6 Moorclose Lane, Queensbury, Bradford, Yorkshire (West), BD13 2BP.
(T) 01274 881851
Profile: **FT:** Coarse; **WN:** Nun Monkton; **WT:** River (Moving) **W. Size:** 1600 Metres.
Ref: FH3554

NUPERS FARM

Nupers Farm, Nupers Hatch, Stapleford Abbotts, Romford, **ESSEX**, RM4, **England**.
Contact/s: Mr Keith Rainbird (Fishery Manager).
(T) 01708 386480
Profile: **FT:** Coarse; **WN:** Nupers Farm; **WT:** Lake (Still) **W. Size:** 2 Acres. **Location:** **Nr. Rd:** Nupers Hatch; **Main Rd:** B175 to Romford.
Ref: FH3555

NUTRABAITS YATELEY COMPLEX

Nutrabaits Yateley Complex, Sandhurst Rd, Yateley, **HAMPSHIRE**, GU46, **England**.
(W) www.rmcangling.co.uk
Contact/s: Mr Ian Welch (Angling Manager), RMC Angling, The Square, Lightwater, Surrey, GU18 5SS.
(T) 01276 453300 **(F)** 01276 456611
(E) info@rmcangling.co.uk
Profile: **FT:** Coarse; **WN:** Nutrabaits Yateley Complex; **WT:** Combination (Still & Moving)

W. Size: 1500 Metres. **Location:** **Nr. Rd:** Sandhurst Road or Derby Green Lane; **Main Rd:** B3272 Reading to Camberley.
Ref: FH3556

NUTRABAITS YATELEY SOUTH LAKE

Nutrabaits Yateley South Lake, Sandhurst Rd, Yateley, **HAMPSHIRE**, GU46, **England**.
Contact/s: Manager, Yateley Angling Ctre, 16a Reading Rd, Yateley, Hampshire, GU46 7UN.
(T) 01252 861955
Mr Ian Welch (Angling Manager), RMC Angling, The Square, Lightwater, Surrey, GU18 5SS.
(T) 01276 453300 (F) 01276 456611
(E) info@rmcangling.co.uk
Profile: **FT:** Coarse; **WN:** Yateley South; **WT:** Lake (Still) **W. Size:** 8 Acres. **Location:** **Nr. Rd:** Sandhurst Road; **Main Rd:** B3272.
Ref: FH3557

OAK MERE FISHERY

Oak Mere Fishery, Hill Farm, Skipwith, Selby, York, **YORKSHIRE (NORTH)**, YO, **England**.
Contact/s: **Mr A W Patrick** (Owner).
(T) 01757 288910
Profile: **FT:** Coarse; **WN:** Oak Mere Fishery; **WT:** Pond (Still). **Location:** **Nr. Rd:** York to Market Weighton; **Main Rd:** A19, A163.
Ref: FH3558

OAK POOL

Oak Pool, Northwich, **CHESHIRE**, CW9, **England**.
Contact/s: **Mr Neil Jupp** (Club Secretary), Lymm Angling Club, PO Box 350, Warrington, Cheshire, WA2 9FB.
(T) 01925 411774
Profile: **FT:** Coarse; **WN:** Oak; **WT:** Pool (Still). **Location:** **Nr. Rd:** Pole Lane; **Main Rd:** A559.
Ref: FH3559

OAKBANK LAKES

Oakbank Lakes, Longtown, Carlisle, **CUMBRIA**, CA6 5NA, **England**.
Contact/s: **Ms Margaret Boulter** (Manager).
(T) 01228 791108 (F) 01228 791108
(E) oakbank@nlaq.globalnet.co.uk
Profile: **FT:** Game; **WN:** Oakbank; **WT:** Gravel Pit (Still) **W. Size:** 24 Acres. **Location:** **Nr. Rd:** A7; **Main Rd:** M6, junction 44; **Rail:** Carlisle.
Ref: FH3560

OAKFIELD FISHERY

Oakfield Fishery, Kingswood Lane, Kingswood, Aylesbury, **HERTFORDSHIRE**, HP1, **England**.
Contact/s: **Mr Craig Alland**, 25 Gisburne Way, Watford, Herefordshire, WD2 5BA.
(T) 01296 770492or01923248168 **(M)** 07778 414646
Profile: **FT:** Coarse; **WN:** Oakfield Fishery; **WT:** Lake (Still); **F. Size:** 8 Acres; **W. Size:** 2 Acres. **Location:** **Nr. Rd:** Kingswood Lane; **Main Rd:** A41; **Rail:** Aylesbury.
Ref: FH3561

OAKHAM FARM POOLS

Oakham Farm Pools, Loxley, Warwick, **WARWICKSHIRE**, CV35 9HY, **England**.
Contact/s: **Mr John Hutsby**.
(T) 01789 740627
Profile: **FT:** Coarse; **WN:** Oakham Farm; **WT:** Pool (Still). **Location:** **Nr. Rd:** Wellesbourne to Ettington; **Main Rd:** A429.
Ref: FH3562

OAKHILL LEISURE

Oakhill, Swinderby Rd, Swinderby, Lincoln, **LINCOLNSHIRE**, LN6 9QG, **England**.
Contact/s: **Mr Ron De Raad** (Fishery Manager). **(M)** 07773 814057
Profile: **FT:** Coarse; **WN:** Oakhill; **WT:** Lake (Still); **F. Size:** 70 Acres; **W. Size:** 4 Acres. **Location:** **Nr. Rd:** Swinderby Road; **Main Rd:** A46; **Rail:** Lincoln.
Ref: FH3563

OAKLANDS WATER

Oaklands Water, Gowdall Rd, Goole, **HUMBERSIDE**, DN14 0AP, **England**.
Contact/s: **Mr Peter Berry** (Owner).
(T) 01405 860756
Profile: **FT:** Coarse; **WN:** Oakland Waters; **WT:** Lake (Still). **Location:** **Nr. Rd:** Cowdall Road; **Main Rd:** Hensall.
Ref: FH3564

OAKS FISHERY

Oaks Fishery (The), Low Lane, Sessay, Thirsk, **YORKSHIRE (NORTH)**, YO7 3BG, **England**.
Contact/s: **Mr David Kay** (Fishery Manager), The Oaks Fishery, Low Lane, Sessay, Thirsk, North Yorkshire, YO7 3BG.
(T) 01845 501321or07715601320
Profile: **FT:** Coarse; **WN:** Alders, Willows, Oaks, Firs, Poplars, Maple; **WT:** Lake (Still); **F. Size:** 21 Acres. **Location:** **Nr. Rd:** Low Lane; **Main Rd:** A19; **Rail:** Thirsk.
Ref: FH3565

OAKS SCAR RESERVOIR

Oaks Scar Reservoir, Lamb Hall Rd, Longwood, Huddersfield, **YORKSHIRE (WEST)**, HD3 3TJ, **England**.
Contact/s: **Mr D Rushforth** (Secretary), 122 Longwood Gate, Longwood, Huddersfield, Yorkshire (West), HD3 4US.
(T) 01484 651028
Mr J Booth (Secretary), 11 Kipling Cl, Crosland Moor, Huddersfield, HD4 5HA.
(T) 01484 644473
Profile: **FT:** Coarse; **WN:** Oak Scar; **WT:** Reservoir (Still). **Location:** **Nr. Rd:** Lamb Hall Road; **Main Rd:** A640 New Hey; **Rail:** Huddersfield.
Ref: FH3566

OAKSIDE FISHERY

Oakside Fishery, Somercourt, Newquay, **CORNWALL**, TR, **England**.
Contact/s: **Mr Brian Hiscock**.
(T) 01637 871275
Profile: **FT:** Coarse; **WN:** Oakside Fishery; **WT:** Lake (Still) **W. Size:** 4 Acres. **Location:** **Nr. Rd:** Newquay to White Cross Road; **Main Rd:** A392.
Ref: FH3567

OAKTREE FISHERY

Oaktree Fishery, Yeo Mill, West Anstey, South Molton, **DEVON**, EX36 3PU, **England**.
Contact/s: **Mr George Andrews**.
(T) 01398 341568 (F) 01398 341511
Mrs Annette Andrews.
(T) 01398 341568 (F) 01398 341511
Profile: **FT:** Coarse; **WN:** Oaktree Fishery; **WT:** Lake (Still); **F. Size:** 19 Acres; **W. Size:** 6 Acres. **Location:** **Nr. Rd:** Yeo Mill; **Main Rd:** B3227; **Rail:** Tiverton Parkway.
Ref: FH3568

OAKTREE LEISURE

Oaktree Leisure, Huby, York, **YORKSHIRE (NORTH)**, YO61, **England**.
Contact/s: **Mr Tony Bowes**.
(T) 01347 810686
Profile: **FT:** Coarse; **WN:** Oaktree Leisure; **WT:** Lake (Still). **Location:** **Nr. Rd:** Thirsk to York; **Main Rd:** A19.
Ref: FH3569

OASIS LAKES

Oasis Lakes, Warren Rd, North Somercotes, Louth, **LINCOLNSHIRE**, LN11 7QX, **England**.
Contact/s: **Mr Colin Beckenham**.
(T) 01507 358488 **(M)** 07712 509519
Profile: **FT:** Coarse; **WN:** Oasis Lakes; **WT:** Gravel Pit (Still) **W. Size:** 6 Acres. **Location:** **Nr. Rd:** Warren Road; **Main Rd:** A1031; **Rail:** Grimsby.
Ref: FH3570

OBBE FISHINGS

Obbe Fishings, South Harris Fishery Ltd, 3 Lever Trce, Leverburgh, **WESTERN ISLES**, HS5 3TU, **Scotland**.
Contact/s: **Mr David Rankin**.
(T) 01859 520466 (F) 01859 520466
Profile: **FT:** Game; **WN:** Obbe Fishings; **WT:** Lake (Still); **F. Size:** 3000 Acres; **W. Size:** 1000 Acres. **Location:** **Nr. Rd:** A859; **Main Rd:** A859.
Ref: FH3571

OCEAN POOL

Ocean Pool, Winsford, **CHESHIRE**, CW7, **England**.
Contact/s: **J Stewart Bailey**.
Profile: **FT:** Coarse; **WN:** Ocean Pool; **WT:** Lake (Still). **Location:** **Nr. Rd:** A54.
Ref: FH3572

OCHILTREE LOCH

Ochiltree Loch, Newton Stewart, **DUMFRIES AND GALLOWAY**, DG8, **Scotland**.
Contact/s: **Mr Tony Dickinson** (Manager), Galloway Guns and Tackle, 36a Arthur St, Newton Stewart, Dumfries and Galloway, DG8 6DE.
(T) 01671 403404 (F) 01671 403404
Profile: **FT:** Game; **WN:** Ochiltree; **WT:** Loch (Still) **W. Size:** 150 Acres.
Ref: FH3573

OFFORD CLUNY

Offord Cluny, St Neots, Huntingdon, **CAMBRIDGESHIRE**, PE18, **England**.
Contact/s: **Mr Eric Blowfield** (Bailiff), 4 Monks Cottages, Buckden, Huntingdon, Cambridgeshire, PE18 9ST.
(T) 01480 810166
Profile: **FT:** Coarse; **WN:** Offord; **WT:** Canal (Still) **W. Size:** 5600 Metres. **Location:** **Nr. Rd:** St Neots to Huntingdon.
Ref: FH3574

OFFORD WEIRPOOL

Offord Weirpool, Offord, Huntingdon, **CAMBRIDGESHIRE**, PE1, **England**.
Contact/s: Secretary, Offord and Buckden Angling Club, The Boat House, Carters Boatyard, Mill Road, Buckden.
Profile: **FT:** Coarse; **WN:** Offord Weirpool; **WT:** Pond (Still). **Location:** **Main Rd:** A1.
Ref: FH3575

OGDEN LOWER RESERVOIR

Ogden Lower Reservoir, Milnrow, Rochdale, **MANCHESTER (GREATER)**, OL16, **England**.
Contact/s: Fishery Manager.
(T) 0161 6260160
Profile: **FT:** Coarse; **WN:** Ogden Lower; **WT:** Reservoir (Still).
Ref: FH3576

OGDEN RESERVOIR

Ogden Reservoir, Grane, Haslingden, Rossendale, **LANCASHIRE**, BB4, **England**.
Contact/s: **Mr Peter Wilson** (Secretary), 6 Holcombe Rd, Helmshore, Rossendale, Lancashire.
Mr Roy Rhodes (Conservation, Access and Recreation Manager), Rivington Water Treatment Works, Bolton Rd, Horwich, Bolton, BL6 7RN.
(T) 01204 664300
Mr William Monk (Membership Secretary), Haslingden and District Fly Fishing Club, 6 Ryde Cl, Haslingden, Rossendale, Lancashire BB4 6QR.
(T) 01706 211724
Profile: **FT:** Game; **WN:** Ogden; **WT:** Reservoir (Still); **F. Size:** 56 Acres; **W. Size:** 54 Acres. **Location:** **Nr. Rd:** Grane Road; **Main Rd:** M65; **Rail:** Blackburn.
Ref: FH3577

OGILVIE LAKE

Ogilvie Lake, Cwm Deri Park, Bargoed, **CAERPHILLY**, CF81, **Wales**.
Contact/s: Manager, Cefn Coed Tackle Shop, 185 High St, Merthyr Tydfil, Caerphilly, CF48 2PG.
(T) 01685 379809
Profile: **FT:** Coarse; **WN:** Ogilvie; **WT:** Lake (Still) **W. Size:** 7 Acres. **Location:** **Nr. Rd:** A469; **Main Rd:** A469 north.

Ref: FH3578

OGMORE (RIVER)

River Ogmore, Bridgend, CF31, **Wales**.
Contact/s: **Mr C Hatch** (Area Manager), Hamdden Ltd, Sluvad Treatment Works, Llandegfedd Reservoir, New Inn, Pontypool, Gwent NP4 0TA.
(T) 01495 769281 **(F)** 01495 769283
Mr G Keen (Manager), Marine and Angling Superstore, 117-119 Bridgend Rd, Aberkenfig, Bridgend, CF32 9AP.
(T) 01656 722448
Mr W A Protheroe (Secretary), Henllan, Coychurch Rd, Pencoed, Bridgend, CF35 5LY.
(T) 01656 861139
Profile: **FT:** Game; **WN:** Ogmore; **WT:** River (Moving) **W. Size:** 24000 Metres.
Ref: FH3579

OGMORE (RIVER)

River Ogmore, Brynmenyn, Bridgend, CF32, **Wales**.
Contact/s: **Mr Ft Hughes** (Hon Secretary), 20 Heol Glannant, Bettws, Glamorgan (Vale of).
(T) 01656 722077
Profile: **FT:** Game; **WN:** Ogmore; **WT:** River (Moving) **W. Size:** 1600 Metres.
Ref: FH3580

OGSTON RESERVOIR

Ogston Reservoir, Chesterfield, **DERBYSHIRE**, S4, **England**.
Contact/s: Manager, Severn Trent Water plc, 2297 Coventry Rd, Sheldon, Birmingham, B26 3PU.
(T) 01788 811107 **(F)** 01788 522936
Profile: **FT:** Game; **WN:** Ogston; **WT:** Reservoir (Still); **F. Size:** 200 Acres.
Ref: FH3581

OGWEN (RIVER)

River Ogwen, Bethesda, Bangor, **GWYNEDD**, LL57, **Wales**.
Contact/s: **Mr Bryn Evans** (Hon Secretary), 31 Erw Las, Bethesda, Gwynedd.
(T) 01248 602309
Mr J Holmes (Owner), Bangor Angling Supplies, 21 High St, Bangor, Gwynedd, LL57 1NP.
(T) 01248 355518
Profile: **FT:** Game; **WN:** Ogwen; **WT:** River (Moving) **W. Size:** 8000 Metres. **Location:** **Main Rd:** A5.
Ref: FH3582

OHAM LAKES

Oham Lakes, Main Rd, Maltby-Le-Marsh, Alford, **LINCOLNSHIRE**, LN13 0JP, **England**.
Contact/s: **Mr Colin Beckenham**.
(T) 01507 450623 **(F)** 01507 450110
Ms Steph Green (Manager).
(T) 01507 450623 **(F)** 01507 450110 **(M)** 07712 509519
Profile: **FT:** Coarse; **WN:** Oham Lakes; **WT:** Lake (Still); **F. Size:** 5 Acres; **W. Size:** 3 Acres. **Location:** **Nr. Rd:** A1104; **Main Rd:** Main Road; **Rail:** Skegness.
Ref: FH3583

OLD ANCHOLME (RIVER)

River (Old) Ancholme, Cadney Rd, Brigg, **LINCOLNSHIRE (NORTH)**, DN20, **England**.
Contact/s: **Mr Mike Sturey**.
(T) 01652 655849
Profile: **FT:** Coarse; **WN:** Old River Ancholme; **WT:** River (Moving) **W. Size:** 7200 Metres. **Location:** **Nr. Rd:** Cadney Road; **Main Rd:** A18, Scunthorpe to Brigg; **Rail:** Brigg Station.
Ref: FH3584

OLD DEARNE (RIVER)

River (Old) Dearne, Mexborough, **YORKSHIRE (SOUTH)**, S64, **England**.
Contact/s: Fishery Manager.
(T) 01709 893489
Profile: **FT:** Coarse; **WN:** Old Dearne; **WT:** River (Moving).
Ref: FH3585

OLD HALL FARM TROUT FISHERY

Old Hall Farm Trout Fishery, Old Hall Farm, Colchester Rd, Wakes Colne, Colchester, **ESSEX**, CO6 2DA, **England**.
Contact/s: Fishery Manager.
(T) 01787 222512
Profile: **FT:** Game; **WN:** Old Hall Farm Trout Fishery; **WT:** Lake (Still).
Ref: FH3586

OLD IRON (RIVER)

River Old Iron, Barcombe Mills, Barcombe, Lewes, **SUSSEX (EAST)**, BN8, **England**.
Contact/s: **Mr Jim Smith** (Bailiff), Ouse APS, 15 Northfields, Isfield, Uckfield, East Sussex TN22 5XN.
(T) 01825 750366
Profile: **FT:** Coarse; **WN:** Old Iron; **WT:** River (Moving) **W. Size:** 800 Metres.
Ref: FH3587

OLD IRWELL

Old Irwell, Irlam, Manchester, **MANCHESTER (GREATER)**, M44, **England**.
Contact/s: Fishery Manager.
(T) 0161 7750987
Profile: **FT:** Coarse; **WN:** Irwell (Old); **WT:** River (Moving).
Ref: FH3588

OLD LEE (RIVER)

River (Old) Lee, King's Weir, Wormley, **HERTFORDSHIRE**, EN10, **England**.
Contact/s: **Mr Simon Maddock** (Secretary), Palmers Green Angling Society, 32 Leaforis Rd, Chestnut, Hertfordshire, EN7 6ND.
(T) 01992 628992
Profile: **FT:** Combination; **WN:** River (Old) Lee; **WT:** River (Moving).
Ref: FH3589

OLD LEE (RIVER)

River (Old) Lee, Waltham Cross, **HERTFORDSHIRE**, EN8, **England**.
Contact/s: **Mr Simon Maddock** (Secretary), Palmers Green Angling Society, 32 Leaforis Rd, Chestnut, Hertfordshire, EN7 6ND.
(T) 01992 628992
Profile: **FT:** Combination; **WN:** Lee; **WT:** River (Moving).
Ref: FH3590

OLD LEE (RIVER)

River (Old) Lee, Ordnance Rd, Enfield, London, **LONDON (GREATER)**, EN2, **England**.
Contact/s: **Mr Terry Mansbridge** (Secretary), Lee Anglers Consortium, 7 Warren Rd, Chingford, London, E4 6QR.
Profile: **FT:** Coarse; **WN:** Lee; **WT:** River (Moving) **W. Size:** 400 Metres. **Location:** **Nr. Rd:** A1055 Ordnance Road; **Main Rd:** Mollison Avenue.
Ref: FH3591

OLD MILL

Old Mill (The), Aldermaston, Reading, **BERKSHIRE**, RG7, **England**.
Contact/s: **Mr R Arlott**.
(T) 01734 712365
Profile: **FT:** Coarse; **WN:** Old Mill (The); **WT:** Combination (Still & Moving).
Ref: FH3592

OLD MILL

Old Mill, Barcombe Mills, Barcombe, Lewes, **SUSSEX (EAST)**, BN8 5BS, **England**.
Contact/s: J A Brown, Old Mill Cottage, Barcombe Mills, Lewes, BN8 5BS.
(T) 01273 400442
Profile: **FT:** Combination; **WN:** Ouse; **WT:** River (Moving) **W. Size:** 1600 Metres. **Location:** **Nr. Rd:** Barcombe Lane; **Main Rd:** A26; **Rail:** Lewes.
Ref: FH3593

OLD MILL AND MEADOWS

Old Mill And Meadows, Mill Lane, Broxbourne, **HERTFORDSHIRE**, EN10, **England**.
Contact/s: **Mr Gary Smith** (Fishing Manager), Lee Valley Park Information Ctre, Abbey Gardens, Waltham Abbey, Essex, EN9 1XQ.
(T) 01992 702200
Ms Krizim Seltham (Angling Manager), Lee Valley Regional Park Authority, Myddleton House, Bulls Cross, Enfield, EN2 9HG.
(T) 01992 709832
(E) garysmith@leevalleypark.org.uk
Profile: **FT:** Coarse; **WN:** Old Mill And Meadows; **WT:** Combination (Still & Moving) **W. Size:** 1200 Metres. **Location:** **Nr. Rd:** A10; **Main Rd:** A10; **Rail:** Broxbourne.
Ref: FH3594

OLD MILL FISHERY

Old Mill Fishery (The), Tucking Mill Farm, Stoford, Yeovil, **SOMERSET**, BA22 9TX, **England**.
Contact/s: **Mr Michael Maxwell**.
(T) 01935 414771 **(F)** 01935 414771
Profile: **FT:** Coarse; **WN:** Old Mill Fishery (The); **WT:** Combination (Still & Moving); **F. Size:** 12 Acres. **Location:** **Nr. Rd:** Newton Road; **Main Rd:** A37; **Rail:** Yeovil Junction.
Ref: FH3595

OLD MILL RESERVOIR

Old Mill Reservoir, Old Mill Creek, Dartmouth, **DEVON**, TQ6, **England**.
Contact/s: **Mr Reg England** (Manager), Peninsula Coarse Fisheries, St Cleer Depot, Lewdown, Okehampton, Devon EX20 4QT.
(T) 01837 871565 **(F)** 01837 871534
Profile: **FT:** Coarse; **WN:** Old Mill; **WT:** Reservoir (Still) **W. Size:** 5 Acres. **Location:** **Nr. Rd:** B3207.
Ref: FH3596

OLD NENE (RIVER)

River (Old) Nene, Exhibition Bridge, Ramsey, St Mary's, Huntingdon, **CAMBRIDGESHIRE**, PE17, **England**.
Contact/s: Manager, H R Wade and Sons, 74-78 Great Whyte, Ramsey, Huntingdon, PE17 1HU.
(T) 01487 813537 **(F)** 01487 710639
Profile: **FT:** Coarse; **WN:** Nene; **WT:** River (Moving). **Location:** **Nr. Rd:** Exhibition Bridge.
Ref: FH3597

OLD QUAY CANAL

Old Quay Canal, Warrington, **CHESHIRE**, WA, **England**.
Contact/s: **Mr Neil Jupp** (Club Secretary), Lymm Angling Club, PO Box 350, Warrington, Cheshire, WA2 9FB.
(T) 01925 411774
Profile: **FT:** Coarse; **WN:** Old Quay; **WT:** Canal (Still). **Location:** **Nr. Rd:** Eastford Road; **Main Rd:** A56 to Chester.
Ref: FH3598

OLD SLADE LANE LAKE

Old Slade Lane Lake, Richins Park, Iver, **BUCKINGHAMSHIRE**, SL0, **England**.
Contact/s: **Buzz** (Manager), Boyer Leisure Ltd, Heron's Point Tackle Shop, Farlow's Lake, Ford Lane, Iver SL0 9LL.
(T) 01753 630302or01895444707 **(F)** 01753 630302
(E) info@boyer.co.uk
Profile: **FT:** Coarse; **WN:** Old Slade Lane Lake; **WT:** Combination (Still & Moving); **F. Size:** 50 Acres. **Location:** **Nr. Rd:** Old Slade Lane; **Main Rd:** B470.
Ref: FH3599

OLD WARDOUR

Old Wardour, Tisbury, Wilton, Salisbury, **WILTSHIRE**, SP2, **England**.
Profile: **FT:** Coarse; **WN:** Old Wardour; **WT:** Lake (Still).
Ref: FH3600

OLD WEST (RIVER)

River Old West, Cambridge, **CAMBRIDGESHIRE**, CB4 5, **England**.
Contact/s: **Mr Colin Dodd** (Bailiff), Queen

Holme Farm, Willingham Fen, Willingham, Cambridge, CB4 5JN.
(T) 01223 365987
Profile: FT: Coarse; WN: Old West; WT: River (Moving). Location: Nr. Rd: Sponge Drove; Main Rd: B1050.
Ref: FH3601

OLD WEST (RIVER)

River Old West, Little Thetford, Ely, **CAMBRIDGESHIRE**, CB, **England**.
Contact/s: Mr N Roberts (Manager).
(T) 01223 836773
Profile: FT: Coarse; WN: Old West; WT: River (Moving). Location: Main Rd: A10; Rail: Ely.
Ref: FH3602

OLD WEST (RIVER)

River Old West, Earith Bridge, Earith, Huntingdon, **CAMBRIDGESHIRE**, PE17, **England**.
Contact/s: Mr R Gentle (Secretary), Cambridge Albion Angling Society, 34 Ramsden Sq, Cambridge, Cambridgeshire, CB4 2BL.
Profile: FT: Coarse; WN: Old West (Earith Bridge to Pope's Corner); WT: River (Moving).
Ref: FH3603

OLDBOROUGH FISHING RETREAT

Oldborough Fishing Retreat, Aboveway Rd, Morchard Bishop, Crediton, **DEVON**, EX17 6SQ, **England**.
Contact/s: Mr Brian Wilshaw.
(T) 01363 877437
Mrs Wendy Wilshaw (Proprietor).
(T) 01363 877437
(E) fishingretreat@eclipse.co.uk
Profile: FT: Coarse; WN: Oldborough Fishing Retreat; WT: Quarry (Still); F. Size: 12 Acres; W. Size: 2 Acres. Location: Nr. Rd: Newbuildings Road; Main Rd: A377; Rail: Morchard Road.
Ref: FH3604

OLDFIELD

Oldfield, Arlesey, **HERTFORDSHIRE**, SG1, **England**.
Profile: FT: Coarse; WN: Oldfield; WT: Gravel Pit (Still) W. Size: 6 Acres. Location: Nr. Rd: Alongside A507 near Hitchen.
Ref: FH3605

OLDHAM FLY FISHING

Oldham Fly Fishing, Oldham, **MANCHESTER (GREATER)**, OL2, **England**.
Contact/s: Manager, Oldham Fly Fishing Club, 4 The Pastures, Sherwood Way, Shaw, Oldham, Lancashire OL2 7LX.
Profile: FT: Game; WN: Oldham Fly Fishing; WT: River (Moving).
Ref: FH3606

OLDHAMS WATER

Oldhams Water, Hyde, **CHESHIRE**, SK14, **England**.
Profile: FT: Coarse; WN: Oldham's water; WT: Canal (Still). Location: Nr. Rd: Dunkirk Lane; Main Rd: A627, Dukinfield Road north.
Ref: FH3607

OLIVERS LAKE

Olivers Lake, Witham, Colchester, **ESSEX**, CO, **England**.
(W) www.c-a-p-s.co.uk
Contact/s: Mr Paul Masters (Secretary), CAPS Membership, 17 Azalea Court, Sycamore Rd, Colchester Essex, CO4 3NU.
(T) 01376 512255
(E) secretary@c-a-p-s.co.uk
Profile: FT: Coarse; WN: Oliver's; WT: Lake (Still) W. Size: 4 Acres. Location: Nr. Rd: B1080 to Maldon; Main Rd: A12.
Ref: FH3608

OLIVES FARM FISHERY

Olives Farm Fishery, Hooe, Battle, **SUSSEX (EAST)**, TN33, **England**.
Contact/s: Mr Chas Rowland, Rowallen Fisheries, 26 Eastwood Rd, Bexhill on Sea, Sussex (East), TN39 3PS.
(T) 01424 223354
Mr George Allen, Rowallen Fisheries, 26 Eastwood Rd, Bexhill on Sea, Sussex (East), TN39 3PS.
(T) 01424 217239
Profile: FT: Coarse; WN: Olives Farm Fishery; WT: Combination (Still & Moving) W. Size: 2 Acres. Location: Nr. Rd: B2095; Main Rd: A259; Rail: Bexhill.
Ref: FH3609

OLSTEN FISHERY

Olsten Fishery, Mill Lane, Legbourne, Louth, **LINCOLNSHIRE**, LN11 8LT, **England**.
Contact/s: Mr R Oliver (Owner), Mill Lane, Legbourne, Louth, Lincolnshire.
(T) 01507 607432
Profile: FT: Combination; WN: Olsten Fishery; WT: Combination (Still & Moving). Location: Nr. Rd: Mill Lane.
Ref: FH3610

OLWAY BROOK

Olway Brook, Usk, **MONMOUTHSHIRE**, NP15, **Wales**.
Contact/s: Mr B J Jones (Hon Secretary), 79 Robertson Way, Woodlands, Malpas, Newport, NP9 6QQ.
(T) 01633 853735
Profile: FT: Game; WN: Olway; WT: Brook (Moving) W. Size: 4800 Metres.
Ref: FH3611

ONE ISLAND POND

One Island Pond, Mitcham Common, Mitcham, **SURREY**, CR4, **England**.
Contact/s: Mr Martin Boyle (Warden).
(T) 020 82880453
Profile: FT: Coarse; WN: One Island; WT: Pond (Still) W. Size: 1 Acre. Location: Nr. Rd: A236; Main Rd: A217. £Fr
Ref: FH3612

ONNY (RIVER)

River Onny, Ludlow, **SHROPSHIRE**, SY8, **England**.
Contact/s: Mr Sean Finnegan (Secretary), The Old School, Brimfield, Ludlow, Shropshire, SY8 4NZ.
(T) 01584 711202
Profile: FT: Game; WN: Onny; WT: River (Moving) W. Size: 7500 Metres. Location: Nr. Rd: A489; Main Rd: A49; Rail: Craven Arms.
Ref: FH3613

OONA RIVER

Oona River, Greystone, Benburb, Dungannon, **COUNTY TYRONE**, BT71 7, **Northern Ireland**.
Contact/s: Mrs Liz Salter (Manager), Aughnacloy Development Association, The McCreedy Mill Centre, Aughnacloy, County Tyrone, BT69 6AL.
(T) 028 85557002
Profile: FT: Game; WN: Oona; WT: River (Moving).
Ref: FH3614

ORCHARD FARM PONDS

Orchard Farm Ponds, Stillingfleet, York, **YORKSHIRE (NORTH)**, YO19, **England**.
Contact/s: Mr Tony Nightingale.
(T) 01904 728918
Profile: FT: Coarse; WN: Orchard Farm; WT: Pond (Still). Location: Nr. Rd: B1222; Main Rd: A19, South from York.
Ref: FH3615

ORCHARD LAKES

Orchard Lakes, New Lane, Bashley, New Milton, **HAMPSHIRE**, BH25 5TD, **England**.
Contact/s: Mr Richard Southcombe (Owner).
(T) 01425 612404
Profile: FT: Coarse; WN: Orchard; WT: Lake (Still); F. Size: 10 Acres. Location: Nr. Rd: New Lane; Main Rd: A35; Rail: New Milton.
Ref: FH3616

ORCHARD POND

Orchard Pond, Winteringham, Scunthorpe, **LINCOLNSHIRE (NORTH)**, DN15, **England**.
Contact/s: Mr A Smith, 7 Sliver St, Winteringham, Humberside.
(T) 01724 732498
Profile: FT: Coarse; WN: Orchard; WT: Pool (Still) W. Size: 1 Acre. Location: Nr. Rd: Scunthorpe to Winterton; Main Rd: A1077.
Ref: FH3617

ORCHID LAKES

Orchid Lakes, Abingdon Rd, Dorchester-on-Thames, Wallingford, **OXFORDSHIRE**, OX1 7LP, **England**.
(W) www.orchid-lakes.com
Contact/s: Mr Marsh Pratley (Owner).
(T) 01865 341810 (F) 01865 341810 (M) 07885 618190
(E) mpratley@aol.com
Profile: FT: Coarse; WN: Orchid Lake, Dorchester Lagoon, & Club Lake; WT: Lake (Still). Location: Nr. Rd: Abingdon Road; Main Rd: A4074 south to Berinsfield; Rail: Didcot.
Ref: FH3618

ORCHILL LOCH TROUT FISHERY

Orchill Loch Trout Fishery, South Lodge, Braco, Dunblane, **PERTH AND KINROSS**, FK15 9LF, **Scotland**.
Contact/s: Ms Elizabeth Jackson.
(T) 01764 682287
Profile: FT: Game; WN: Orchill; WT: Loch (Still); F. Size: 16 Acres; W. Size: 4 Acres. Location: Main Rd: A822 or A823; Rail: Gleneagles.
Ref: FH3619

ORCHY (RIVER)

River Orchy, Bridge Of Orchy, **ARGYLL AND BUTE**, PA36, **Scotland**.
Contact/s: Manager, Loch Awe Improvement Association, Lochawe Stores, Lochawe, Dalmally, Argyll PA33 1AQ.
(T) 01838 200200 (F) 01838 200200
Mrs Anne Marshall (owner), Inveroran Hotel, Bridge of Orchy, Argyll and Bute, PA36 4AQ.
(T) 01838 400220 (F) 01838 400399
Profile: FT: Game; WN: Orchy; WT: River (Moving).
Ref: FH3620

ORFORD PARK POND

Orford Park Pond, Orford, Warrington, **CHESHIRE**, WA2, **England**.
Contact/s: Fishery Manager.
(T) 01925 442712
Profile: FT: Coarse; WN: Orford Park; WT: Pond (Still).
Ref: FH3621

ORLITTS LAKES

Orlitts Lakes, Lakeside Rd, Colnbrook, Slough, **BUCKINGHAMSHIRE**, SL3, **England**.
Contact/s: Buzz (Manager), Boyer Leisure Ltd, Heron's Point Tackle Shop, Farlow's Lake, Ford Lane, Iver SLO 9LL.
(T) 01753 630302or01895444707 (F) 01753 630302
(E) info@boyer.co.uk
Profile: FT: Coarse; WN: Orlitts; WT: Lake (Still) W. Size: 19 Acres. Location: Nr. Rd: Lakeside Road; Main Rd: M25, M4; Rail: Slough.
Ref: FH3622

ORMESBY ROLLESBY

Ormesby Rollesby, Ormesby, Great Yarmouth, **NORFOLK**, NR29, **England**.
Contact/s: Fishery Manager.
(T) 01493 731441
Profile: FT: Coarse; WN: Ormesby Rollesby; WT: Stream (Moving).
Ref: FH3623

ORMSGILL LOWER RESERVOIR

Ormsgill Lower Reservoir, Furness Fishing Association, Hannays, 50 Crellin St, Barrow-

In-Furness, **CUMBRIA**, LA, **England**.
Contact/s: Manager, Robin Hood Inn, Crellin St, Barrow-in-Furness, Lancashire, LA14 1DU.
(T) 01229 825271
Profile: **FT:** Coarse; **WN:** Ormsgill Lower; **WT:** Reservoir (Still).
Ref: FH3624

ORRELL WATER PARK

Orrell Water Park, Lodge Rd, Orrell, Wigan, **LANCASHIRE**, WN5 7AT, **England**.
Contact/s: , Wigan Council, The Robin Park Indoors Sports Complex, Loire Drive, Robin Park, WN5 0UL.
Ms Pauline Greenhalgh (Ranger).
(T) 01695 625338or01942606576 **(F)** 01695 627357
Profile: **FT:** Coarse; **WN:** Orrell Water Park; **WT:** Lake (Still) **W. Size:** 8 Acres. **Location:** **Nr. Rd:** Logde Road, B5206; **Main Rd:** A577; **Rail:** Orrell Station.
Ref: FH3625

ORVIS INNIS FLY FISHERY

Orvis Innis Country Club And Fly Fishery, Innis Moor, Penwithick, St Austell, **CORNWALL**, PL26 8YH, **England**.
Contact/s: **Mr Dave Johns** (Owner).
(T) 01726 851162
Mrs Pamela Winch (Owner).
(T) 01726 851162
Profile: **FT:** Game; **WN:** Orvis Innis Country Club And Fly Fishery; **WT:** Lake (Still); **F. Size:** 20 Acres; **W. Size:** 15 Acres. **Location:** **Nr. Rd:** A391; **Main Rd:** M5 to Exeter; **Rail:** St Austell.
Ref: FH3626

OSMINGTON MILLS

Osmington Mills, Weymouth, **DORSET**, DT, **England**.
Contact/s: **Ms Louise Goucher** (Fishery Manager), The Ranch House, Osmington Mills, Weymouth, Dorset, DT3 6HB.
(T) 01305 832311
Profile: **FT:** Coarse; **WN:** Osmington Mills; **WT:** Lake (Still).
Ref: FH3627

OSS MERE

Oss Mere, Nr. Marbury, Whitchurch, **SHROPSHIRE**, **England**.
Contact/s: **Mr John Turner** (Hon Secretary), Prince Albert Angling Society, 15 Pexhill Drive, Macclesfield, Cheshire, SK10 3LP.
(T) 01625 422010
Profile: **FT:** Coarse; **WN:** Oss Mere; **WT:** Mere (Still); **F. Size:** 50 Acres; **W. Size:** 25 Acres. **Location:** **Main Rd:** A49; **Rail:** Whitchurch.
Ref: FH3628

OSTERLEY PARK MIDDLE LAKE

Osterley Park Middle Lake, The National Trust, Jersey Rd, Isleworth, London, **LONDON (GREATER)**, TW7 4RB, **England**.
Contact/s: Head Gardener.
(T) 020 85605421
Profile: **FT:** Coarse; **WN:** Osterley Park Middle; **WT:** Lake (Still); **F. Size:** 140 Acres; **W. Size:** 11 Acres. **Location:** **Nr. Rd:** Jersey Road; **Main Rd:** Great West Road; **Rail:** Syon.
Ref: FH3629

OTTER (RIVER)

River Otter, Deer Park Hotel, Buckerell, Honiton, **DEVON**, EX14 0PG, **England**.
Contact/s: **Mr Stephen Noah** (Owner), The Deer Park Country Hotel, Weston, Honiton, Devon, EX14 0PG.
(T) 01404 41266 **(F)** 01404 46598
Profile: **FT:** Combination; **WN:** Otter; **WT:** River (Moving) **W. Size:** 9656 Metres. **Location:** **Main Rd:** A30; **Rail:** Honiton.
Ref: FH3630

OTTER FALLS FISHERY

Otter Falls Fishery, Old Spurtham Farm, Upottery, Honiton, **DEVON**, EX14 9QD, **England**.
Contact/s: **Mr David Courtney** (Manager).
(T) 01404 861634or861706 **(F)** 01404 861634
Profile: **FT:** Combination; **WN:** Otter; **WT:** Combination (Still & Moving) **W. Size:** 4 Acres. **Location:** **Nr. Rd:** Upottery; **Main Rd:** A30; **Rail:** Honiton.
Ref: FH3631

OTTERHEAD LAKES

Otterhead Lakes, Churchingford, Taunton, **SOMERSET**, TA, **England**.
Contact/s: Customer Services, Wessex Water, Billing Ctre, Clevedon Walk, Nailsea, Bristol, BS48 1WW. **(M)** 03453 00600 Manager, Topp Tackle, 63 Station Rd, Taunton, Somerset, TA1 1PA.
(T) 01823 282518
Mr Bob Kemble (Club Secretary).
(T) 01823 271988
Profile: **FT:** Game; **WN:** Otterhead; **WT:** Lake (Still) **W. Size:** 3 Acres. **Location:** **Main Rd:** B3170; **Rail:** Taunton.
Ref: FH3632

OUGHTON (RIVER)

River Oughton, Ouse, Hitchin, **HERTFORDSHIRE**, SG4, **England**.
Contact/s: **Mr Peter Currell** (Secretary), Biggleswade, Hitchin and District Angling Association, 1 Woolfield, Sandy, Bedfordshire, SG19 1AR.
(E) peter.currell@rkharrison.co.uk
Profile: **FT:** Combination; **WN:** Oughton; **WT:** River (Moving).
Ref: FH3633

OULTON BROAD

Oulton Broad, Oulton, Lowestoft, **SUFFOLK**, NR, **England**.
Contact/s: Manager.
(T) 01502 572599or566559
Mr Peter Buttifant.
(T) 01502 586147
Profile: **FT:** Coarse; **WN:** Oulton; **WT:** Lake (Still) **W. Size:** 100 Acres. **Location:** **Nr. Rd:** Beccles to Great Yarmouth; **Main Rd:** A146, Lowestoft. **£Fr**
Ref: FH3634

OULTON DYKE

Oulton Dyke, Oulton, Lowestoft, **SUFFOLK**, NR32, **England**.
Profile: **FT:** Coarse; **WN:** Oulton; **WT:** Dyke (Still).
Ref: FH3635

OULTON MILL POOL

Oulton Mill Pool, Tarporley, **CHESHIRE**, CW6, **England**.
Contact/s: **Mr M J Clays** (Secretary), 58 Churchhill Drive, Tarporley, Cheshire, CW6 0BZ.
Profile: **FT:** Coarse; **WN:** Oulton Mill; **WT:** Pool (Still). **Location:** **Nr. Rd:** Beech Lane; **Main Rd:** A49.
Ref: FH3636

OUNDLE (RIVER)

River Oundle, Oundle, Peterborough, **CAMBRIDGESHIRE**, PE8, **England**.
Profile: **FT:** Coarse; **WN:** Oundle; **WT:** River (Moving).
Ref: FH3637

OUSE (RIVER)

River Ouse, Blunham, Bedford, **BEDFORDSHIRE**, MK44, **England**.
(W) www.badac.co.uk
Contact/s: **Mr D Porter** (Secretary), 72 Rivington Cres, Mill Hill, London, NW7 2LF.
(T) 020 84401303
Profile: **FT:** Coarse; **WN:** Ouse; **WT:** River (Moving) **W. Size:** 600 Metres. **Location:** **Main Rd:** A1.
Ref: FH3638

OUSE (RIVER)

River Ouse, Harrold Lodge Farm, Carlton Rd, Harrold, Bedford, **BEDFORDSHIRE**, MK43, **England**.
(W) www.rmcangling.co.uk
Contact/s: **Mr Ian Welch** (Angling Manager), RMC Angling, The Square, Lightwater, Surrey, GU18 5SS.
(T) 01276 453300 **(F)** 01276 456611
(E) info@rmcangling.co.uk
Profile: **FT:** Coarse; **WN:** Ouse; **WT:** River (Moving) **W. Size:** 1500 Metres. **Location:** **Nr. Rd:** Carlton Road; **Main Rd:** A6, A428.
Ref: FH3639

OUSE (RIVER)

River Ouse, Olney, **BUCKINGHAMSHIRE**, MK46, **England**.
Contact/s: **Mr K Osborne** (Secretary), Milton Keynes Angling Association, 11 Gilpin Way, Olney, Buckinghamshire, MK46 4DN.
(T) 01234 713144
Profile: **FT:** Coarse; **WN:** Ouse; **WT:** River (Moving). **Location:** **Main Rd:** A509.
Ref: FH3640

OUSE (RIVER)

River Ouse, Milton Keynes, **BUCKINGHAMSHIRE**, MK, **England**.
Contact/s: **Mr Michael Buchwalder** (Manager), Sportsmans Lodge, 26 Church St, Milton Keynes, Buckinghamshire, MK12 5JN.
(T) 01908 313158 **(F)** 01908 313189
Profile: **FT:** Coarse; **WN:** Ouse; **WT:** River (Moving). **Location:** **Nr. Rd:** Bradwell; **Rail:** Wolverton.
Ref: FH3642

OUSE (RIVER)

River Ouse, Rawcliffe, Goole, **HUMBERSIDE**, DN14, **England**.
Contact/s: **Mr Doug Dalton** (Fishery Manager).
(T) 01904 692046
Profile: **FT:** Coarse; **WN:** Ouse; **WT:** River (Moving).
Ref: FH3643

OUSE (RIVER)

River Ouse, Goldbridge, Newick, Lewes, **SUSSEX (EAST)**, BN8, **England**.
Contact/s: **Mr J Kenward** (Secretary), Haywards Heath and District Angling Society, 60 Franklyn Rd, Haywards Heath, Sussex (West), RH16 4DH.
(T) 01444 452572
Profile: **FT:** Coarse; **WN:** Ouse; **WT:** River (Moving) **W. Size:** 17600 Metres. **Location:** **Nr. Rd:** Lindfield to Goldbridge.
Ref: FH3644

OUSE (RIVER)

River Ouse, Barcombe Mills, Barcombe, Lewes, **SUSSEX (EAST)**, BN8, **England**.
Contact/s: **Mr John Goodrick** (Hon Secretary), Ouse Angling Preservation Society, 'Applegarth', School Lane, Barcombe, BN8 5DT.
(T) 01273 400380
Profile: **FT:** Combination; **WN:** Ouse; **WT:** River (Moving) **W. Size:** 8250 Metres. **Location:** **Rail:** Lewes.
Ref: FH3645

OUSE (RIVER)

River Ouse, Peak Lane, East Preston, Littlehampton, **SUSSEX (WEST)**, BN16, **England**.
Contact/s: **Mr Jim Smith** (Bailiff), Ouse APS, 15 Northfields, Isfield, Uckfield, East Sussex TN22 5XN.
(T) 01825 750366
Profile: **FT:** Game; **WN:** Ouse; **WT:** River (Moving). **Location:** **Nr. Rd:** Peak Lane.
Ref: FH3646

OUSE (RIVER)

River Ouse, Grassington, Skipton, **YORKSHIRE (NORTH)**, BD23, **England**.
Contact/s: Manager, Grassington Post Office, 15 Main St, Grassington, Skipton, BD23 5AD.
(T) 01756 752226
Profile: **FT:** Game; **WN:** Ouse; **WT:** Tributary (Moving) **W. Size:** 4000 Metres.
Ref: FH3647

OUSE (RIVER)

River Ouse, Malton, **YORKSHIRE (NORTH)**, YO17, **England**.
Contact/s: **Mr C Swift** (Secretary), 25 Castlegate, Malton, Yorkshire (North), YO17 7DP.
(T) 01653 694580
Profile: **FT:** Coarse; **WN:** Ouse; **WT:** Tributary (Moving) **W. Size:** 1600 Metres.
Location: **Nr. Rd:** Huttons Ambo.
Ref: FH3648

OUSE (RIVER)

River Ouse, Fulford, York, **YORKSHIRE (NORTH)**, YO10, **England**.
Contact/s: **Mr Doug Dalton** (Fishery Manager).
(T) 01904 692046
Profile: **FT:** Coarse; **WN:** Ouse; **WT:** River (Moving).
Ref: FH3649

OUSE (RIVER)

River Ouse, Nun Monkton, York, **YORKSHIRE (NORTH)**, YO26, **England**.
Contact/s: Fishery Manager.
(T) 0113 2645500
Profile: **FT:** Coarse; **WN:** Ouse; **WT:** River (Moving).
Ref: FH3650

OUSE (RIVER)

River Ouse, York, **YORKSHIRE (NORTH)**, YO, **England**.
Contact/s: **Mr B Thackrey** (Secretary).
(T) 01423 866695
Mr G Hinds (Chairman).
(T) 01423 869647
Mr Norman Edward (Vice Chairman), 125 The Avenue, Starbeck, Harrogate, HG1 4QG.
(T) 01423 885399
Profile: **FT:** Coarse; **WN:** Ouse; **WT:** River (Moving).
Ref: FH3651

OUSE (RIVER)

River Ouse, Cherryfields, Newton-on-Ouse, York, **YORKSHIRE (NORTH)**, YO30, **England**.
Contact/s: Manager, Mitre Pets Fishing Tackle and Aquarium, 212-214 Shipton Rd, York, Yorkshire (North), YO30 5RZ.
(T) 01904 654841
Mr Martin Dukes.
(T) 01347 848392
Profile: **FT:** Coarse; **WN:** Ouse; **WT:** River (Moving) **W. Size:** 1600 Metres.
Ref: FH3652

OUSE (RIVER)

River Ouse, Naburn Lock Caravan Park, Naburn Lock, York, **YORKSHIRE (NORTH)**, YO, **England**.
Contact/s: Manager, Naburn Lock Caravan Park, Naburn, York, Yorkshire (North), YO19 4RU.
(T) 01904 728697 (F) 01904 728697
Profile: **FT:** Coarse; **WN:** Ouse; **WT:** River (Moving) **W. Size:** 462 Metres. Location: **Nr. Rd:** B1222; **Main Rd:** A64.
Ref: FH3653

OUSE (RIVER)

River Ouse, York, **YORKSHIRE (NORTH)**, YO, **England**.
Profile: **FT:** Coarse; **WN:** Ouse; **WT:** River (Moving). Location: **Nr. Rd:** City Centre; **Main Rd:** A64 or A19. £Fr
Ref: FH3654

OUSE (RIVER)

River Ouse, Linton-on-Ouse Caravan Park, Linton-on-Ouse, York, **YORKSHIRE (NORTH)**, YO30, **England**.
Contact/s: Manager, Linton Lock Leisureways, Linton Lock House, Linton-on-Ouse, York, YO30 2AZ.
(T) 01347 848486
Profile: **FT:** Coarse; **WN:** Ouse; **WT:** River (Moving).
Ref: FH3655

OUSE (RIVER)

River Ouse, Fawdington, Helperby, **YORKSHIRE (NORTH)**, YO61, **England**.
Contact/s: **Mr F Marrison** (Hon Secretary), Helperby and Brafferton Angling Club, Gardeners Cottage, York Rd, Helperby, YO61 2PQ.
(T) 01423 360632
Mr H Plowman, C W Plowman-Render and Son, Main St, Helperby, York, YO61 2NT.
(T) 01423 360685
Profile: **FT:** Coarse; **WN:** Ouse; **WT:** River (Moving) **W. Size:** 2400 Metres. Location: **Nr. Rd:** Sessay Beck to Fawdington Wood.
Ref: FH3656

OUSE (RIVER)

River Ouse, Boston Spa, Wetherby, **YORKSHIRE (WEST)**, LS23, **England**.
Profile: **FT:** Combination; **WN:** Ouse; **WT:** Tributary (Moving).
Ref: FH3657

OUSE (RIVER) KEMPSTON MILL

River Ouse, Kempston Mill, Bedford, **BUCKINGHAMSHIRE**, MK4, **England**.
Contact/s: **Mr Ken Green** (Secretary), 24 The Elms, Kempston, Bedfordshire, MK42 7JW.
(T) 01234 854165
Profile: **FT:** Coarse; **WN:** Ouse; **WT:** River (Moving). Location: **Nr. Rd:** Riverview Road; **Main Rd:** Bedford Road; **Rail:** Bedford.
Ref: FH3641

OUZEL (RIVER)

River Ouzel, Milton Keynes, **BUCKINGHAMSHIRE**, MK, **England**.
Profile: **FT:** Coarse; **WN:** Ouzel; **WT:** River (Moving).
Ref: FH3658

OVER MAIN DRAIN

Over Main Drain, Earith, Huntingdon, **CAMBRIDGESHIRE**, PE17, **England**.
Contact/s: Manager, Webbs Tackle, 88 High St, Huntingdon, Cambridgeshire, PE18 6DP.
(T) 01480 386355
Profile: **FT:** Coarse; **WN:** Over Main; **WT:** Drain (Still). Location: **Main Rd:** B1050, left at Hermitage Lock.
Ref: FH3659

OWDY LANE TROUT FISHERY

Owdy Lane Trout Fishery, 1 Worksop Rd, Woodsetts, Worksop, **NOTTINGHAMSHIRE**, S81 8AW, **England**.
Contact/s: **Mr Neil Squires**.
(T) 01909 500186 (F) 01909 500186
Profile: **FT:** Game; **WN:** Owdy Lane; **WT:** Lake (Still) **W. Size:** 2 Acres. Location: **Nr. Rd:** Woodsetts; **Main Rd:** A57; **Rail:** Worksop.
Ref: FH3660

OWENGARVE (RIVER)

River Owengarve, Charlestown, **COUNTY MAYO**, **Ireland**.
Contact/s: Angling Officer, North Western Regional Fisheries Board, Ardnaree House, Abbey St, Ballina, County Mayo.
(T) 096 22623 (F) 096 70543
Profile: **FT:** Game; **WN:** Owengarve; **WT:** River (Moving) **W. Size:** 480 Metres.
Location: **Main Rd:** N17.
Ref: FH3661

OWENKILLEW (RIVER)

River Owenkillew, Omagh, **COUNTY TYRONE**, BT78, **Northern Ireland**.
Contact/s: **Mr Ca Anderson** (Secretary), Omagh Angling Association, 64 Market St, Omagh, County Tyrone, BT78 1EN.
(E) andersonca@lineone.net
Mr Stephen Martin (License Distributor).
(T) 028 82242311 (F) 028 82249539 (M) 07776 343600
Profile: **FT:** Game; **WN:** Camowen; **WT:** River (Moving) **W. Size:** 4800 Metres.
Location: **Nr. Rd:** A5; **Main Rd:** A5.
Ref: FH3662

OWENKILLEW (RIVER)

River Owenkillew, Gorton, Newtownstewart, **COUNTY TYRONE**, BT78, **Northern Ireland**.
Contact/s: Manager, G A and L E Martin, The Hardware House, 64 Market St, Omagh, BT78 1EN.
(T) 028 82242311
Ms Gabriel Trenor, Main St, Gorton, Newtownstewart, County Tyrone.
(T) 028 81648543
Profile: **FT:** Game; **WN:** Glenelly Owenkillew; **WT:** River (Moving).
Ref: FH3663

OWENREAGH (RIVER)

River Owenreagh, Dromore, **COUNTY DOWN**, BT25, **Northern Ireland**.
Contact/s: **Mr David Campbell** (Manager), Tackle Shop, 28 Main St, Newtownstewart.
(T) 028 79261543
Profile: **FT:** Game; **WN:** Owenreagh; **WT:** River (Moving).
Ref: FH3664

OWENSHED (RIVER)

River Owenshed, Cappoquin, **COUNTY CORK**, **Ireland**.
Contact/s: **Mr Michael Penruddock** (Manager), Lismore Estate Office, Lismore Castle, Lismore, County Waterford, Ireland.
(T) 058 54424
Profile: **FT:** Game; **WN:** Owenshed; **WT:** River (Moving).
Ref: FH3665

OXENLEAZE FARM FISHERY

Oxenleaze Farm Caravans And Coarse Fishery, Oxenleaze Farm, Chipstable, Wiveliscombe, Taunton, **SOMERSET**, TA4 2QH, **England**.
Contact/s: **Mr R Rottenbury**.
(T) 01984 623427 (F) 01984 623427
Profile: **FT:** Coarse; **WN:** Oxenleaze Farm Caravans And Coarse Fishery; **WT:** Lake (Still) **W. Size:** 2 Acres.
Ref: FH3666

OXFORD CANAL

Oxford Canal, Flecknoe, Daventry, **NORTHAMPTONSHIRE**, NN11, **England**.
Contact/s: **Mr Terry Rodhouse** (Secretary), Castle Angling Association, 12 Somerville Rd, Daventry, Northamptonshire, NN11 4RT.
(T) 01327 705692
Profile: **FT:** Coarse; **WN:** Oxford; **WT:** Canal (Still). Location: **Main Rd:** A45; **Rail:** Leamington Spa.
Ref: FH3667

OXFORD CANAL

Oxford Canal, Heyford Station, Lower Heyford, Bicester, **OXFORDSHIRE**, OX6, **England**.
Contact/s: **Mr Martin Room** (Secretary), Oxford and District Angling Association, 136 Oxford Rd, Cowley, Oxfordshire, OX4 2DU.
(T) 01865 711410
Profile: **FT:** Coarse; **WN:** Oxford; **WT:** Canal (Still). Location: **Main Rd:** B4030.
Ref: FH3668

OXFORD CANAL

Oxford Canal, Wolvercote, Oxford, **OXFORDSHIRE**, OX2, **England**.
Contact/s: Manager, North Oxford Tackle, 95 Islip Rd, Oxford, Oxfordshire, OX2 7SP.
(T) 01865 556955
Mr Andrew Crisp (Secretary), North Oxford Angling Society, 4 Grove St, Summertown, Oxford, Oxfordshire OX3 7JT.
(T) 01865 553800
Profile: **FT:** Coarse; **WN:** Oxford; **WT:** Canal (Still). Location: **Nr. Rd:** A44; **Main Rd:** A34.
Ref: FH3669

OXFORD CANAL

Oxford Canal, Hardwick Lock, Banbury, **OXFORDSHIRE**, OX1, **England**.
Contact/s: Mr John Hyde (Secretary), Coventry and District Angling Club, 111 Lord Litton Avenue, Stoke, Coventry, CV2 5JT.
(T) 024 76418893
Profile: FT: Coarse; **WN:** Oxford; **WT:** Canal (Still) **W. Size:** 1600 Metres. **Location: Nr. Rd:** Banbury to Farnborough; **Main Rd:** A423.
Ref: FH3670

OXFORD CANAL

Oxford Canal, Pigeon Lock, Enslow Bridge, Kidlington, **OXFORDSHIRE**, OX5, **England**.
Profile: FT: Coarse; **WN:** Oxford; **WT:** Canal (Still) **W. Size:** 3200 Metres. **Location: Nr. Rd:** A4095 to Bicester; **Main Rd:** A4260.
Ref: FH3671

OXFORD CANAL

Oxford Canal, Kensington To Enslow, Oxford, **OXFORDSHIRE**, OX, **England**.
(W) www.tringanglers.club24.co.uk
Contact/s: Mr Stuart Riddle (Secretary), The Tring Anglers, PO Box 1947, Tring, Hertfordshire, HP23 5LZ.
(T) 01442 826148
Profile: FT: Coarse; **WN:** Oxford Canal; **WT:** Canal (Still).
Ref: FH3672

OXFORD CANAL

Oxford Canal, Dukes Lock, Oxford, **OXFORDSHIRE**, OX, **England**.
Contact/s: Fishery Manager.
(T) 01865 770634
Profile: FT: Coarse; **WN:** Oxford (Dukes Lock to Wolvercote Green); **WT:** Canal (Still).
Ref: FH3673

OXFORD CANAL

Oxford Canal, Kidlington Down To Oxford, Oxford, **OXFORDSHIRE**, OX, **England**.
Contact/s: Mr Andrew Crisp (Secretary), North Oxford Angling Society, 4 Grove St, Summertown, Oxford, Oxfordshire OX3 7JT.
(T) 01865 553800
Profile: FT: Coarse; **WN:** Oxford; **WT:** Canal (Still).
Ref: FH3674

OXFORD CANAL

Oxford Canal, Wormleighton, Leamington Spa, **WARWICKSHIRE**, CV33, **England**.
Contact/s: Mr Terry Rodhouse (Secretary), Castle Angling Association, 12 Somerville Rd, Daventry, Northamptonshire, NN11 4RT.
(T) 01327 705692
Profile: FT: Coarse; **WN:** Oxford; **WT:** Canal (Still).
Ref: FH3675

OXFORD CANAL

Oxford Canal, Barby Lane, Rugby, **WARWICKSHIRE**, CV, **England**.
Contact/s: Manager, Banks and Burr Tackle Shop, 27 Claremont Rd, Rugby, Warwickshire, CV21 3NA.
(T) 01788 576782
Edgar.
(T) 01788 579838
Mr Dave Marshall.
(T) 01788 331535
Profile: FT: Coarse; **WN:** Oxford; **WT:** Canal (Still). **Location: Nr. Rd:** Onley Lane; **Main Rd:** A45 to Daventry.
Ref: FH3676

OXFORD CANAL

Oxford Canal, Hillmorton, Rugby, **WARWICKSHIRE**, CV23, **England**.
Contact/s: Mr Peter Felton (Chairman), Banks and Burr Tackle Shop, 27 Claremont Rd, Rugby, Warwickshire, CV21 3NA.
(T) 01788 576782
Profile: FT: Coarse; **WN:** Oxford; **WT:** Canal (Still) **W. Size:** 11200 Metres. **Location: Main Rd:** Hillmorton; **Rail:** Rugby.
Ref: FH3677

OXLEASE LAKE

Oxlease Lake, Shimano Linear Fisheries (Oxford), Smiths Concrete Site, Hardwick Village, Witney, **OXFORDSHIRE**, OX8 7Q, **England**.
Contact/s: Mr Len Gurd (Owner), 10A Rackstraw Gr, Old Farm Park, Milton Keynes, Buckinghamshire, MK7 8PZ.
(T) 01908 645135 **(F)** 01908 645115
Profile: FT: Coarse; **WN:** Oxlease; **WT:** Lake (Still); **F. Size:** 30 Acres; **W. Size:** 25 Acres. **Location: Nr. Rd:** B4449; **Main Rd:** A40; **Rail:** Oxford.
Ref: FH3678

PACKINGTON SOMERS FISHERY

Packington Somers Fishery, Somers Road, Meriden, Coventry, **MIDLANDS (WEST)**, CV7 7PL, **England**.
Contact/s: Mr John Burchell (Manager), Packington Fisheries, Maxstoke Lane, Meriden, Coventry, CV7 7HR.
(T) 01676 523833or522754 **(F)** 01676 522754
Profile: FT: Coarse; **WN:** Packington Somers Fishery; **WT:** Gravel Pit (Still); **F. Size:** 80 Acres; **W. Size:** 20 Acres. **Location: Nr. Rd:** Hampton Lane; **Main Rd:** A45; **Rail:** Birmingham International.
Ref: FH3679

PACKINGTON TROUT FISHERY

Packington Trout Fishery, Broadwater, Maxstoke Lane, Meriden, Coventry, **MIDLANDS (WEST)**, CV7 7HR, **England**.
Contact/s: Mr John Burchell (Manager), Packington Fisheries, Broadwater, Maxstoke Lane, Meriden, CV7 7HR.
(T) 01676 522754 **(F)** 01676 522754
Profile: FT: Game; **WN:** Packington Trout Fishery; **WT:** Lake (Still); **F. Size:** 150 Acres; **W. Size:** 90 Acres. **Location: Nr. Rd:** Maxstoke Lane; **Main Rd:** A45; **Rail:** Hampton-in-Arden.
Ref: FH3680

PADBROOK PARK

Padbrook Park, Cullompton, **DEVON**, EX15 1RU, **England**.
Contact/s: Fishery Manager.
(T) 01926 843939
Mr Richard Chard.
(T) 01884 38286
Profile: FT: Coarse; **WN:** Padbrook Park; **WT:** Lake (Still) **W. Size:** 3 Acres. **Location: Main Rd:** M5; **Rail:** Tiverton Parkway.
Ref: FH3681

PADDOCK DAM

Paddock Dam, St Helens, **MERSEYSIDE**, WA11, **England**.
Contact/s: Mr Alec Twiss (Secretary), 47 Exeter St, St Helens, WA10 4HS.
(T) 01744 611074
Mr Roy Rhodes (Conservation, Access and Recreation Manager), Rivington Water Treatment Works, Bolton Rd, Horwich, Bolton, BL6 7RN.
(T) 01204 664300
Profile: FT: Coarse; **WN:** Paddock; **WT:** Dam (Still).
Ref: FH3682

PADDY MCNAMARAS LAKE

Paddy Mcnamaras Lake, O'briens Bridge, Killaloo, Londonderry, **COUNTY LONDONDERRY**, BT47, **Northern Ireland**.
Profile: FT: Coarse; **WN:** Paddy McNamaras; **WT:** Lake (Still) **W. Size:** 10 Acres. **Location: Nr. Rd:** R463 Limerick to Killaloe, R466.
Ref: FH3683

PADESWOOD POOL

Padeswood Pool, Padeswood Lake Rd, Mold, **FLINTSHIRE**, CH7 2HZ, **Wales**.
Contact/s: Mr D W Sragg.
(T) 01244 545941
Mr P Ryan (Secretary), 5 New Brighton Rd, Sychdyn.
Profile: FT: Coarse; **WN:** Padeswood; **WT:** Pool (Still) **W. Size:** 2 Acres. **Location: Nr. Rd:** Padeswood Lake Road; **Main Rd:** A5118, Buckley to Mold; **Rail:** Penyffordd.
Ref: FH3684

PADWORTH MILL

Kennet (River), Padworth, Reading, **BERKSHIRE**, RG, **England**.
Contact/s: Mr Dusty Millar (Associate members secretary), 238 Elgar Road South, Reading, Berkshire, RG3 0BW.
(T) 0118 9874882
Mr Mick Cox (Chief Bailiff), Dorstans, Hatch Lane, Brimpton Village, Reading, RG7 4TR.
(T) 0118 9714917
Profile: FT: Coarse; **WN:** Kennet; **WT:** River (Moving). **Location: Nr. Rd:** Padworth.
Ref: FH2447

PADWORTH ROTA

Kennet And Avon Canal, Padworth Rota, Reading, **BERKSHIRE**, RG, **England**.
Contact/s: Mr Dusty Millar (Associate members secretary), 238 Elgar Road South, Reading, Berkshire, RG3 0BW.
(T) 0118 9874882
Mr Mick Cox (Chief Bailiff), Dorstans, Hatch Lane, Brimpton Village, Reading, RG7 4TR.
(T) 0118 9714917
Profile: FT: Coarse; **WN:** Padworth Rota; **WT:** Canal (Still) **W. Size:** 32000 Metres. **Location: Nr. Rd:** Padworth.
Ref: FH2453

PAINSHILL PARK LAKE

Painshill Park Lake, Cobham Rd, Cobham, **SURREY**, KT11, **England**.
Contact/s: Mr Reg Perry (Membership Secretary), Walton-on-Thames Angling Society, 9 Upper Cl, Forest Row, Sussex (East), RH18 5DS.
(T) 020 89419016
Profile: FT: Coarse; **WN:** Painshill Park; **WT:** Combination (Still) **W. Size:** 12 Acres. **Location: Nr. Rd:** A245; **Main Rd:** A245; **Rail:** Stoke Dabernon. **£Fr**
Ref: FH3685

PAINSWICK PARK LAKE

Painswick Park Lake, Portway, Wythenshawe, Manchester, **MANCHESTER (GREATER)**, M22, **England**.
Contact/s: Mr Paul Owen (President Of Woodhouse Park Anglers), Pauls Tackle Shop, 335 Portway, Wythenshawe, Manchester, M22 0EJ.
(T) 0161 4377215
Profile: FT: Coarse; **WN:** Painswick Park; **WT:** Lake (Still) **W. Size:** 2 Acres. **Location: Nr. Rd:** B5166.
Ref: FH3686

PALLINGTON LAKES

Pallington Lakes, Pallington, Dorchester, **DORSET**, DT2 8QU, **England**.
(W) www.pallington.freeuk.com
Contact/s: Mr Simon Pomeroy (Manager).
(T) 01305 848141 **(F)** 01305 849153 **(M)** 07887 840507
Mrs Carol Pomeroy (Administrator).
(T) 01305 848895 **(F)** 01305 849153
(E) cpomeroy@aol.com
Profile: FT: Combination; **WN:** Pallington Lakes; **WT:** Lake (Still); **F. Size:** 23 Acres; **W. Size:** 14 Acres. **Location: Nr. Rd:** B3329; **Main Rd:** A35; **Rail:** Moreton. **£Fr**
Ref: FH3687

PANG VALLEY TROUT LAKE

Pang Valley Trout Lake, Bradfield, Reading, **BERKSHIRE**, RG, **England**.
Contact/s: Mr Chris Ryan (Manager), Sportfish Limited, 21 Whitley St, Reading, Berkshire, RG2 0EG.
(T) 01189303860
Mr Michael Stratton (Fishery Manager).
(T) 0118 9323422

Profile: **FT:** Game; **WN:** Pang Valley; **WT:** Lake (Still).
Ref: FH3688

PANT (RIVER)

River Pant, Codham Mill, Shalford, Braintree, **ESSEX**, CM7, **England**.
Contact/s: **Mr Derek Howard** (Hon Treasurer), Billericay and District Angling Club, 4 Long Meadow Drive, Wickford, Essex, SS11 8AX.
(T) 01268 734468
Profile: **FT:** Combination; **WN:** Pant; **WT:** River (Moving) **W. Size:** 3000 Metres. **Location:** **Nr. Rd:** B1053; **Main Rd:** A131, B1053; **Rail:** Braintree.
Ref: FH3689

PANT (RIVER)

River Pant, Dukes Meadow, Deanery Hill, Bocking, Braintree, **ESSEX**, CM7, **England**.
(W) www.bdac.co.uk
Contact/s: **Mr Derek Howard** (Hon Treasurer), Billericay and District Angling Club, 4 Long Meadow Drive, Wickford, Essex, SS11 8AX.
(T) 01268 734468
Profile: **FT:** Coarse; **WN:** Pant; **WT:** River (Moving) **W. Size:** 700 Metres. **Location:** **Nr. Rd:** Deanery Hill; **Main Rd:** A131 to Braintree; **Rail:** Braintree.
Ref: FH3690

PANT GLAS RESERVOIR

Pant Glas Reservoir, Ruabon Mountain, Wrexham, **DENBIGHSHIRE**, LL14, **Wales**.
Contact/s: **Ms Sandra Wild** (Manager).
(T) 01928 723017
Profile: **FT:** Game; **WN:** Pant Glas; **WT:** Reservoir (Still) **W. Size:** 2 Acres.
Ref: FH3691

PANT TROUT POOL

Pant Trout Pool, Llandewi Brefi, Tregaron, **CEREDIGION**, SY25 6UQ, **Wales**.
Contact/s: Fishery Manager.
(T) 01974 298753
Profile: **FT:** Game; **WN:** Pant; **WT:** Pool (Still).
Ref: FH3692

PANT Y BEDW FISHING LAKES

Pant Y Bedw Fishing Lakes, Pant Y Bedw Farm, Nantgaredig, Carmarthen, **CARMARTHENSHIRE**, SA32 7LH, **Wales**.
Contact/s: **Mr Ian Williams** (Owner).
(T) 01267 290315
Ms Sue Williams (Owner).
(T) 01267 290315
Profile: **FT:** Game; **WN:** Pant Y Bedw; **WT:** Lake (Still); **F. Size:** 80 Acres; **W. Size:** 9 Acres. **Location:** **Nr. Rd:** B4300; **Main Rd:** A48T and A40; **Rail:** Carmarthen.
Ref: FH3693

PAPERCOURT FISHERY

Papercourt Fishery, Polesden Lane, Sendmarsh, Ripley, Woking, **SURREY**, GU23, **England**.
(W) www.rmcangling.co.uk
Contact/s: **Mr Ian Welch** (Angling Manager), RMC Angling, The Square, Lightwater, Surrey, GU18 5SS.
(T) 01276 453300 **(F)** 01276 456611
(E) info@rmcangling.co.uk
Profile: **FT:** Coarse; **WN:** Papercourt Fishery; **WT:** Lake (Still) **W. Size:** 32 Acres. **Location:** **Nr. Rd:** Polesden Lane; **Main Rd:** B367 Pyrford to Ripley road.
Ref: FH3694

PAR

Par, West Horndon, **ESSEX**, CM13, **England**.
Contact/s: **Mr Derek Ritchie** (Carp Consultant), Brentwood Angling, 118 Warley Hill, Brentwood, Essex, CM14 5HB.
(T) 01277 200985 **(F)** 01277 219500
Profile: **FT:** Coarse; **WN:** Par; **WT:** Lake (Still).
Ref: FH3695

PARC NEWYDD TROUT FISHERY

Parc Newydd Trout Fishery, Llyn Edna, Llanerchymedd, **ISLE OF ANGLESEY**, LL71 7BT, **Wales**.
Contact/s: **Mr Andrew Gannon** (Manager).
(T) 01248 470700
Profile: **FT:** Game; **WN:** Llyn Edna; **WT:** Lake (Still) **W. Size:** 5 Acres.
Ref: FH3696

PARK FARM

Park Farm, Compton Verney, Combrook, Kineton, Warwick, **WARWICKSHIRE**, CV35, **England**.
(W) www.fisheries.co.uk/parkfarm/index
Contact/s: **Mr Colin Barrett** (Bailiff).
(T) 01789 841712
Mr Ken Waldenmar (Secretary), Stratford-upon-Avon Angling Club, Park Farm, Compton Verney, Combrook, Kineton, Warwickshire.
(T) 01789 720603
Profile: **FT:** Coarse; **WN:** Park Farm; **WT:** Lake (Still) **W. Size:** 20 Acres. **Location:** **Nr. Rd:** Over crossroads; **Main Rd:** B4086 Wellesbourne to Kineton.
Ref: FH3697

PARK HALL FARM

Park Hall Farm, Park Hall Rd, West Coyney, Stoke-on-Trent, **STAFFORDSHIRE**, ST, **England**.
Contact/s: Manager, Stoke on Trent City Council, Environment Facilities Unit, Park Hall Country Park, Hulme, ST3 5BH.
Mr J Thomas (Owner), Trentside Angling Ctre, 1245 Leek Rd, Stoke-on-Trent, ST2 8BP.
(T) 01782 545493
Profile: **FT:** Coarse; **WN:** Park Hall Farm; **WT:** Lake (Still).
Ref: FH3698

PARK LAKE TROUT FISHERY

Park Lake Trout Fishery, Moy Rd, Dungannon, **COUNTY TYRONE**, BT71, **Northern Ireland**.
Contact/s: **Mr Nigel Hill** (Manager), The Pavillion, Dungannon Park, Moy Rd, Dungannon, County Tyrone, BT71 6DY.
(T) 028 87727327
Profile: **FT:** Game; **WN:** Park Lake Trout Fishery; **WT:** Lake (Still) **W. Size:** 13 Acres. **Location:** **Nr. Rd:** Moy Road; **Main Rd:** A29.
Ref: FH3699

PARK LIME PIT

Park Lime Pit, Local Nature Reserve, Park Rd, Rushall, Norwich, **NORFOLK**, NR9, **England**.
Contact/s: **Ms Diana Miles** (Senior Countryside Ranger).
(T) 01922 459813 **(F)** 01922 451830
Profile: **FT:** Coarse; **WN:** Park Lime Pit; **WT:** Pool (Still); **F. Size:** 1 Acre; **W. Size:** 1 Acre. **Location:** **Nr. Rd:** Dawend Lane; **Main Rd:** B4154; **Rail:** Walsall.
Ref: FH3700

PARK POOL

Park Pool, Gawsworth, Macclesfield, **CHESHIRE**, SK11, **England**.
Contact/s: **Mr John Birch**.
(T) 01260 223442
Profile: **FT:** Coarse; **WN:** Park; **WT:** Pool (Still). **Location:** **Nr. Rd:** Church Lane; **Main Rd:** A536, Congleton Road.
Ref: FH3701

PARKES HALL

Parkes Hall, Coseley, Dudley, **STAFFORDSHIRE**, DY3, **England**.
Contact/s: Secretary, Dudley Angling Society, 182 Gayfield Avenue, Wythmore Village, Brierley Hill, DY5 2BP.
(T) 01384 831924
Profile: **FT:** Coarse; **WN:** Parkes Hall; **WT:** Pool (Still) **W. Size:** 2 Acres.
Ref: FH3702

PARKLANDS

Parklands, Yafforth Rd, Northallerton, **YORKSHIRE (NORTH)**, DL7, **England**.
Contact/s: **Mr Andy Skaife** (Proprietor), Northallerton Angling Ctre, 3 East Rd, Northallerton, Yorkshire (North), DL6 1ND.
(T) 01609 779140 **(F)** 01609 779140
Profile: **FT:** Coarse; **WN:** Parklands; **WT:** Lake (Still) **W. Size:** 3 Acres. **Location:** **Nr. Rd:** Yafforth Road; **Main Rd:** B6271; **Rail:** Northallerton.
Ref: FH3703

PARKLANDS FISHERY

Parklands Fishery, Hinckley, **LEICESTERSHIRE**, LE10, **England**.
Contact/s: Manager.
(T) 01455 636219
Profile: **FT:** Coarse; **WN:** Parklands Fishery; **WT:** Lake (Still) **W. Size:** 3 Acres.
Ref: FH3704

PARKLEY FISHERY

Parkley Fishery, Edinburgh Rd, Linlithgow, **LOTHIAN (WEST)**, EH49 6QU, **Scotland**.
Contact/s: **Mr Jim Shanks** (Owner).
(T) 01506 842027 **(M)** 07836 348037
Profile: **FT:** Game; **WN:** Parkley Fishery; **WT:** Pond (Still); **F. Size:** 6 Acres; **W. Size:** 4 Acres. **Location:** **Nr. Rd:** B9080; **Main Rd:** Edinburgh Road; **Rail:** Linlithgow.
Ref: FH3705

PARRET (RIVER)

River Parret, Crewkerne, **SOMERSET**, TA18, **England**.
Profile: **FT:** Game; **WN:** Parret; **WT:** River (Moving). **Location:** **Nr. Rd:** Bow Mills to Creedy Bridge.
Ref: FH3706

PARRETT (RIVER)

River Parrett, Weston-Super-Mare, **SOMERSET**, BS22, **England**.
Contact/s: **Mr R Payne** (Secretary), 194 Milton Rd, Weston-Super-Mare, Somerset, BS22 8AE.
(T) 01934 414445
Profile: **FT:** Coarse; **WN:** Parrett; **WT:** River (Moving) **W. Size:** 3200 Metres.
Ref: FH3707

PARRETT (RIVER)

River Parrett, Langport, **SOMERSET**, TA10, **England**.
Contact/s: **Mr Den Barlow** (Secretary), Langport and District Angling Association, Florissant, Northfield, Somerton, TA11 6SJ.
(T) 01458 272119
Profile: **FT:** Coarse; **WN:** Parrett; **WT:** River (Moving) **W. Size:** 8000 Metres. **Location:** **Nr. Rd:** A372; **Main Rd:** A372.
Ref: FH3708

PARRETT (RIVER)

River Parrett, Stoke-Sub-Hamdon, **SOMERSET**, TA14, **England**.
Contact/s: **Mr Derek Goad** (Secretary), 2 Windsor Lane, Stoke-sub-Hamdon, Somerset.
Profile: **FT:** Coarse; **WN:** Parrett; **WT:** River (Moving).
Ref: FH3709

PARRETT (RIVER)

River Parrett, Oathe, Bridgwater, **SOMERSET**, TA7 0, **England**.
Contact/s: **Mr Colin Dyer**, Tackle Shack, North St, Langport, Somerset, TA10 9RQ.
(T) 01458 253665
Profile: **FT:** Coarse; **WN:** River Parrett; **WT:** River (Moving). **Location:** **Nr. Rd:** A378.
Ref: FH3710

PARSONAGE (RIVER) TEST

Parsonage River Test (The), Romsey, **HAMPSHIRE**, SO51, **England**.
(W) www.fishingbreaks.co.uk
Contact/s: **Mr Simon Cooper**, Fishing Breaks Ltd, 23 Compton Trce, Romsey, London, N1 2UN.

(T) 020 73598818 (F) 020 73594540 (M) 07973 766639
(E) info@fishingbreaks.co.uk
Profile: FT: Game; WN: Test; WT: River (Moving); F. Size: 80 Acres; W. Size: 100 Metres. Location: Nr. Rd: A3057; Main Rd: M27; Rail: Romsey.
Ref: FH3711

PARSONAGE FARM

Parsonage Farm Reservoir, High Easter, Chelmsford, **ESSEX**, CM, **England**.
(W) www.bdac.co.uk
Contact/s: **Mr Derek Howard** (Hon Treasurer), Billericay and District Angling Club, 4 Long Meadow Drive, Wickford, Essex, SS11 8AX.
(T) 01268 734468or01268734478
Profile: FT: Coarse; WN: Parsonage Farm Reservoir; WT: Lake (Still); F. Size: 4 Acres; W. Size: 3 Acres. Location: Nr. Rd: Minor Road; Main Rd: A1060; Rail: Chelmsford.
Ref: FH3712

PARSONAGE RESERVOIR

Parsonage Reservoir, Hyndburn Rd, Accrington, **LANCASHIRE**, BB5 1, **England**.
Contact/s: **Mr B Hoggart** (Secretary), 1 Moorfield Rd, Leyland, Preston, Lancashire, PR5 3AR.
(T) 01772 424018
Mr Roy Rhodes (Conservation, Access and Recreation Manager), Rivington Water Treatment Works, Bolton Rd, Horwich, Bolton, BL6 7RN.
(T) 01204 664300
Profile: FT: Coarse; WN: Parsonage; WT: Reservoir (Still).
Ref: FH3713

PARTRIDGE LAKES

Partridge Lakes, Glazier Lane, Culcheth, Warrington, **CHESHIRE**, WA3, **England**.
Contact/s: **Phil** (Fishery Manager).
(T) 01925 767505 (M) 07901 732063
Profile: FT: Coarse; WN: Partridge; WT: Lake (Still); F. Size: 9 Acres; W. Size: 7 Acres. Location: Nr. Rd: Glazier Lane; Main Rd: Culcheth to Warrington, right to Glazier Lane; Rail: Birchwood.
Ref: FH3714

PASSIES PONDS

Passies Ponds, Church Farm, Coombes, Lancing, **SUSSEX (WEST)**, BN15 0RS, **England**.
(W) www.coombes.co.uk
Contact/s: **Mr Trevor Passmore**.
(T) 01273 465257 (M) 07710 765257
(E) www.passie@farmline.co.uk
Profile: FT: Coarse; WN: Passies; WT: Pond (Still); F. Size: 10 Acres; W. Size: 10 Acres. Location: Nr. Rd: Coombes Road; Main Rd: A27; Rail: Shoreham-by-Sea.
Ref: FH3715

PASTURE HOUSE FISHERY

Pasture House Fishery, Pasture Road North, Barton-upon-Humber, **LINCOLNSHIRE (NORTH)**, DN18, **England**.
Contact/s: Fishery Manager.
(T) 01652 635119
Profile: FT: Coarse; WN: Pasture House Fishery; WT: Lake (Still). Location: Nr. Rd: Pasture Road North; Main Rd: A15 (T); Rail: Brocklesby Station.
Ref: FH3716

PATSHULL PARK

Patshull Park, Patshull Park Hotel, Patshull Rd, Pattingham, Wolverhampton, **MIDLANDS (WEST)**, WV6 7HY, **England**.
Contact/s: **Mr Colin Cooper** (Manager).
(T) 01902 700774
Mr Roland Dudley.
(T) 01902 700774
Profile: FT: Combination; WN: Church Pool & Lady Barbara Pool; WT: Lake (Still); F. Size: 260 Acres; W. Size: 100 Acres. Location: Nr. Rd: Patshull Road; Main Rd: A454; Rail: Wolverhampton. £Fr
Ref: FH3717

PAULTON LAKES

Paulton Lakes, Paulton, Bristol, **SOMERSET**, BS39 7SY, **England**.
Contact/s: **Mr Paul Rogers** (Manager), A M Hobbs, The Island, Midsomer Norton, Bath, BA3 2HQ.
(T) 01761 413961 (F) 01761 413961
Profile: FT: Coarse; WN: Paulton; WT: Lake (Still) W. Size: 2 Acres.
Ref: FH3718

PAWLETT PONDS

Pawlett Ponds, River Rd, Pawlett, Bridgwater, **SOMERSET**, TA, **England**.
Contact/s: **Mr Jeff Parker** (Secretary), Bristol, Bath and Wilts Amalgamation, 16 Lansdown View, Kingswood, Bristol, BS15 4AW.
(T) 01179 672977
Profile: FT: Coarse; WN: Pawlett; WT: Pond (Still) W. Size: 8 Acres. Location: Nr. Rd: River Road; Main Rd: A38; Rail: Bridgwater.
Ref: FH3719

PAXTON LAKE

Paxton Lake, Great Paxton, St Neots, Huntingdon, **CAMBRIDGESHIRE**, PE1, **England**.
Profile: FT: Coarse; WN: Paxton; WT: Lake (Still).
Ref: FH3720

PAYNES LANE PIT

Paynes Lane Pit, Paynes Lane, Waltham Cross, **HERTFORDSHIRE**, EN7, **England**.
Contact/s: **Mr Simon Maddock** (Secretary), Palmers Green Angling Society, 32 Leaforis Rd, Chestnut, Hertfordshire, EN7 6ND.
(T) 01992 628992
Profile: FT: Coarse; WN: Paynes Lane; WT: Pit (Still).
Ref: FH3721

PEA LANE FISHERY

Pea Lane Fishery, Dennises Lane, Upminster, **ESSEX**, **England**.
(W) www.becmain-as.dial.pipex.com
Contact/s: **Mr Leslie Ailey** (Club Secretary), 3 Meadow Rd, Rush Green, Romford, Essex, RM7 0LR.
(T) 01708 745985 (M) 07714 091884
(E) becmain-as@dial.pipex.com
Profile: FT: Coarse; WN: Pea Lane; WT: Gravel Pit (Still); F. Size: 10 Acres; W. Size: 8 Acres. Location: Nr. Rd: Dennises Lane; Main Rd: B1421; Rail: South Okendon.
Ref: FH3722

PEACOCK LAKE

Peacock Lake, Timberland, Timberland Fen, Woodhall Spa, **LINCOLNSHIRE**, **England**.
Contact/s: **Mr Barry Hill** (Owner).
(T) 01526 378721
Profile: FT: Coarse; WN: Peacock; WT: Lake (Still); F. Size: 5 Acres; W. Size: 3 Acres. Location: Main Rd: B1189; Rail: Metheringham.
Ref: FH3723

PEAK FOREST CANAL

Peak Forest Canal, Dukinfield, **CHESHIRE**, SK16, **England**.
Contact/s: Fishery Manager.
(T) 0161 3667253
Profile: FT: Coarse; WN: Peak Forest; WT: Canal (Still).
Ref: FH3724

PEAK FOREST CANAL

Peak Forest Canal, Marple Locks, Stockport, **MANCHESTER (GREATER)**, SK6, **England**.
Contact/s: Fishery Manager.
(T) 0161 4945422
Profile: FT: Coarse; WN: Peak Forest; WT: Canal (Still).
Ref: FH3725

PEARMOOR LAKE

Pearmoor Lake, Swindon, **WILTSHIRE**, SN, **England**.
Contact/s: Manager, House of Angling, 59-60 Commercial Rd, Swindon, Wiltshire, SN1 5NX.
(T) 01793 693460
Profile: FT: Coarse; WN: Pearmoor; WT: Lake (Still).
Ref: FH3726

PEATLING POOLS (1-6)

Peatling Pools (1-6), Lutterworth, **LEICESTERSHIRE**, LE17, **England**.
Contact/s: Manager, Lake Farm, Peatling Parva, Lutterworth, Leicestershire.
(T) 0116 2478222
Profile: FT: Coarse; WN: Peatling Pools 1-6; WT: Pool (Still) W. Size: 15 Acres.
Ref: FH3727

PEATMOOR LAGOON

Peatmoor Lagoon, Swindon, **WILTSHIRE**, SN4, **England**.
Contact/s: **Mr Bryan Jackson** (Secretary).
(T) 01249 817954
Mr Pete Sarahs, 3 Holly Cl, Swindon, Wiltshire, SN2 1HX.
(T) 01793 551320
Profile: FT: Coarse; WN: Peatmoor Lagoon; WT: Lake (Still).
Ref: FH3728

PEBLEY RESERVOIR

Pebley Reservoir, Clowne, Sheffield, **YORKSHIRE (SOUTH)**, S, **England**.
Contact/s: **Mr Dave Downes**.
(T) 0114 2474378
Profile: FT: Coarse; WN: Pebley; WT: Reservoir (Still) W. Size: 26 Acres. Location: Nr. Rd: A618; Main Rd: A619, Chesterfield and Worksop.
Ref: FH3729

PECK MEADOW POND

Peck Meadow Pond, Rockland Manor, Scoulton Rd, Rocklands, Attleborough, **NORFOLK**, **England**.
Contact/s: **Mr Stephen Burroughes**.
(T) 01953 483226
Profile: FT: Coarse; WN: Peck Meadow Pond; WT: Lake (Still); F. Size: 5 Acres; W. Size: 4 Acres. Location: Nr. Rd: Scoulton Road; Main Rd: B1077.
Ref: FH3730

PECK POOL

Peck Pool, Astbury, Congleton, **CHESHIRE**, CW12, **England**.
Profile: FT: Coarse; WN: Peck; WT: Pool (Still). Location: Nr. Rd: New Road; Main Rd: A34, South of Congleton.
Ref: FH3731

PELICAN POND

Pelican Pond, North Lincolnshire Sailing Club, Pasture Rd, Barton-upon-Humber, **LINCOLNSHIRE (NORTH)**, DN18, **England**.
Contact/s: **Mr Bontoft** (Bailiff), 2 Crakedale Rd, Winterton, Scunthorpe, Humberside (South), DN15 9UT.
(T) 01724 732858
Profile: FT: Coarse; WN: Pelican; WT: Pond (Still) W. Size: 80 Acres.
Ref: FH3732

PEMBROKE POND

Pembroke Pond, Swindon, **WILTSHIRE**, SN4, **England**.
Contact/s: **Mr Tony Aisbitt** (Fishery Manager).
(T) 01793 541740
Profile: FT: Coarse; WN: Pembroke; WT: Pond (Still).
Ref: FH3733

PENBEILI FISHERY

Penbeili Fishery, Llandyfriog, Newcastle Emlyn, **CARMARTHENSHIRE**, SA38, **Wales**.
(W) www.fishing-in-wales.co.uk/llandysul-aa/beat15
Contact/s: **Mr Artie Jones** (Hon Secretary), Llandysul Angling Association, Glas-y-Dorlan,

Llyn-y-Fran Rd, Llandysul, SA44 4JW.
(T) 01559 362317
Profile: **FT:** Game; **WN:** Teifi; **WT:** River (Moving). **Location:** **Nr. Rd:** Newcastle Emlyn to Lampeter Road; **Main Rd:** A475.
Ref: FH3734

PENDLE WATER

Pendle Water, Barden Rd, Nelson, **LANCASHIRE**, BB9, **England**.
Contact/s: **Mr Jeff Hartley**.
(T) 01282 603362
Mr Peter Brown.
(T) 01535 605387
Profile: **FT:** Combination; **WN:** Pendle Water; **WT:** River (Moving). **Location:** **Nr. Rd:** Barden Road to New-in-Pendle Bridge; **Main Rd:** A682 north.
Ref: FH3735

PENHOYLE FISHING PARK

Penhoyle Fishing Park, Trefloyne Lane, Penally, Tenby, **PEMBROKESHIRE**, SA70, **Wales**.
Contact/s: **Mr Martin Joel** (Fishery Manager).
(T) 01834 842255
Profile: **FT:** Game; **WN:** Penhoyle Fishing Park; **WT:** Lake (Still).
Ref: FH3736

PENNINE TROUT FISHERY

Pennine Trout Fishery, Calderbrook Rd, Littleborough, Rochdale, **MANCHESTER (GREATER)**, OL15 9HL, **England**.
Contact/s: **Mr Lee Moran**.
(T) 01706 378325
Profile: **FT:** Game; **WN:** Pennine Trout Fishery; **WT:** Lake (Still); **F. Size:** 16 Acres; **W. Size:** 5 Acres. **Location:** **Nr. Rd:** Calderbrook Road; **Rail:** Littleborough.
Ref: FH3737

PENNINGTON FLASH

Pennington Flash, Twist Lane, Leigh, **MANCHESTER (GREATER)**, WN7, **England**.
Contact/s: Leigh Angling Centre.
(T) 01942 670890
Profile: **FT:** Coarse; **WN:** Pennington Flash; **WT:** Lake (Still); **F. Size:** 1 Acre; **W. Size:** 1 Acre. **Location:** **Nr. Rd:** Twist Lane; **Main Rd:** A578; **Rail:** Daisy Hill Station.
Ref: FH3738

PENNINIGTON RESERVOIR

Penninigton Reservoir, South Lakeland, Dalton-In-Furness, **CUMBRIA**, LA15, **England**.
Contact/s: **Mr J R Jones** (Secretary), 69 Prince St, Dalton-in-Furness, Cumbria, LA15 8ET.
Mr Roy Rhodes (Conservation, Access and Recreation Manager), Rivington Water Treatment Works, Bolton Rd, Horwich, Bolton, BL6 7RN.
(T) 01204 664300
Profile: **FT:** Game; **WN:** Pennington; **WT:** Reservoir (Still).
Ref: FH3739

PENNS HALL LAKE

Penns Hall Lake, Sutton Coldfield, **MIDLANDS (WEST)**, B76, **England**.
Contact/s: **Mr Richard Foster** (Manager), Fosters of Birmingham.
(T) 0121 3443333
Profile: **FT:** Coarse; **WN:** Penns Hall; **WT:** Lake (Still); **F. Size:** 10 Acres; **W. Size:** 7 Acres.
Ref: FH3740

PENNY BRIDGE

Penny Bridge, Dovedale Farm, London Rd, Crowborough, **SUSSEX (EAST)**, TN6 1JU, **England**.
Contact/s: **Sean**, Crowborough Tackle, Whitehill Rd, Crowborough, Sussex (East), TN6 1JU.
(T) 01892 661145
Sean (Manager), Crowborough Tackle, Whitehill Rd, Crowborough, Sussex (East), TN6 1JU.
(T) 01892 661145
Profile: **FT:** Coarse; **WN:** Penny Bridge; **WT:** Pond (Still); **F. Size:** 1 Acre. **Location:** **Nr. Rd:** London Road; **Main Rd:** A26; **Rail:** Jarvis Brook, Crowborough.
Ref: FH3741

PENTNEY LAKES

Pentney Lakes, Common, Pentney, King's Lynn, **NORFOLK**, PE32, **England**.
Contact/s: **Mr Ashley Brown** (Bailiff).
(T) 01553 765496
Profile: **FT:** Coarse; **WN:** Pentney; **WT:** Gravel Pit (Still) **W. Size:** 150 Acres. **Location:** **Nr. Rd:** King's Lynn to Swaffham; **Main Rd:** A47, at East Winch turn right.
Ref: FH3742

PENTON HOOK LOCK

Penton Hook Lock, Thameside, Staines, London, **LONDON (GREATER)**, TW18 2JA, **England**.
Contact/s: Fishery Contact.
(T) 01784 452657
Recreational Manager, The Environment Agency, Kings Meadow Rd, Reading, Berkshire, RG1 8DQ.
(T) 0118 9535000 **(F)** 0118 9500388
Profile: **FT:** Combination; **WN:** Thames; **WT:** Lock (Still). **Location:** **Nr. Rd:** Thameside; **Main Rd:** B376 Laleham to Shepperton.
Ref: FH3743

PENTRE FARM FISHERY

Pentre Farm Fishery, Maesycrugiau, Lampeter, **CEREDIGION**, SA48, **Wales**.
(W) www.fishing-in-wales.co.uk/llandysul-aa/beat7a
Contact/s: **Mr Artie Jones** (Hon Secretary), Llandysul Angling Association, Glas-y-Dorlan, Llyn-y-Fran Rd, Llandysul, SA44 4JW.
(T) 01559 362317
Profile: **FT:** Game; **WN:** Teifi; **WT:** River (Moving). **Location:** **Nr. Rd:** Llanybydder to Maesycrugiau.
Ref: FH3744

PENTWYN RESERVOIR

Pentwyn Reservoir, Brecon National Park, Merthyr Tydfil, **GLAMORGAN (VALE OF)**, CF48, **Wales**.
Contact/s: Fishery Manager.
(T) 01685 379809
Profile: **FT:** Coarse; **WN:** Pentwyn; **WT:** Reservoir (Still) **W. Size:** 250 Acres. **Location:** **Nr. Rd:** Ponysticill and Merthyr Tydfil; **Main Rd:** A465.
Ref: FH3745

PENVOSE FARM

Penvose Farm, St Mowgan, Newquay, **CORNWALL**, TR8 4AE, **England**.
Contact/s: **Mr John** (Owner).
(T) 01637 860277
Profile: **FT:** Coarse; **WN:** Penvose Farm; **WT:** Lake (Still).
Ref: FH3746

PENWHIRN RESERVOIR

Penwhirn Reservoir, Stranraer, **DUMFRIES AND GALLOWAY**, DG9, **Scotland**.
Contact/s: **Mr Eric McLean** (Manager), The Sports Shop, 88 George St, Stranraer, Dumfries and Galloway, DG9 7JS.
(T) 01776 702705
Profile: **FT:** Game; **WN:** Penwhirn; **WT:** Reservoir (Still).
Ref: FH3747

PENYCAE LOWER RESERVOIR

Penycae Lower Reservoir, Gresford, Wrexham, LL12, **Wales**.
Contact/s: **Mr Tony Jackson** (Fisheries Manager), Dee Valley Service plc, Packsaddle, Wrexham Rd, Rhostyllen, Wrexham LL14 4DS.
(T) 01978 846946
Profile: **FT:** Game; **WN:** Penycae Lower; **WT:** Reservoir (Still) **W. Size:** 5 Acres.
Ref: FH3748

PENYCAE UPPER RESERVOIR

Penycae Upper Reservoir, Gresford, Wrexham, LL12, **Wales**.
Contact/s: **Mr Tony Jackson** (Fisheries Manager), Dee Valley Service plc, Packsaddle, Wrexham Rd, Rhostyllen, Wrexham LL14 4DS.
(T) 01978 846946
Profile: **FT:** Game; **WN:** Penycae Upper; **WT:** Reservoir (Still) **W. Size:** 7 Acres.
Ref: FH3749

PENYWERN PONDS

Penywern Ponds, Merthyr Tydfil, **GLAMORGAN (VALE OF)**, CF48, **Wales**.
Contact/s: **Mr Nigel Morgan** (Manager), 20 James St, Merthyr, Glamorgan (Vale of).
(T) 01685 377848
Profile: **FT:** Coarse; **WN:** Penywern; **WT:** Pond (Still). **Location:** **Nr. Rd:** A465 to Merthyr Tydfil.
Ref: FH3750

PERCH POND

Perch Pond, Wanstead Park Angling, 103 Empress Avenue, Manor Park, London, **LONDON (GREATER)**, E12 5SA, **England**.
Contact/s: **Mr Alan Gray**.
(T) 020 85305394
Mr Keith Prigmore.
(T) 020 85012256
Profile: **FT:** Coarse; **WN:** Perch; **WT:** Lake (Still) **W. Size:** 3 Acres. **Location:** **Nr. Rd:** Northumberland Avenue; **Main Rd:** Aldersbrook Road; **Rail:** Wanstead.
Ref: FH3751

PERIL LAKE

Peril Lake, Charlton Rd, Charlton, Andover, **HAMPSHIRE**, SP, **England**.
Contact/s: Fishery Manager.
(T) 01264 323610
Profile: **FT:** Coarse; **WN:** Peril Lake; **WT:** Lake (Still) **W. Size:** 2 Acres. **Location:** **Nr. Rd:** A303 to Andover; **Main Rd:** Goch Way.
Ref: FH3752

PERIO MILL

Perio Mill, Oundle, Peterborough, **CAMBRIDGESHIRE**, PE8, **England**.
Profile: **FT:** Game; **WN:** Perio Mill; **WT:** Stream (Moving) **W. Size:** 1000 Metres.
Ref: FH3753

PERRY (RIVER)

Perry (River), Adcote Mill, Baschurch, **SHROPSHIRE**, **England**.
Contact/s: **Mr John Turner** (Hon Secretary), Prince Albert Angling Society, 15 Pexhill Drive, Macclesfield, Cheshire, SK10 3LP.
(T) 01625 422010
Profile: **FT:** Coarse; **WN:** Perry; **WT:** River (Moving) **W. Size:** 2000 Metres. **Location:** **Nr. Rd:** Milford Road; **Main Rd:** B5067; **Rail:** Shrewsbury.
Ref: FH3754

PERRY (RIVER)

River Perry, Ruyton Xi Towns, Oswestry, **SHROPSHIRE**, SY10, **England**.
(W) www.warrington-anglers.org.uk
Contact/s: **Mr Frank Lythgoe** (Secretary), Warrington Angling Association, 52 Parker St, Warrington, Lancashire.
(T) 01928 716238 **(F)** 01928 713898
(E) info@warrington-anglers.org.uk
Profile: **FT:** Coarse; **WN:** Perry; **WT:** River (Moving) **W. Size:** 300 Metres. **Location:** **Nr. Rd:** Oswestry to Baschurch; **Main Rd:** B4397.
Ref: FH3755

PETERS FINGER LAKES

Peters Finger Lakes, Salisbury, **WILTSHIRE**, SP, **England**.
Contact/s: **Mr Ron Hillier** (Secretary), 29 New Zealand Avenue, Salisbury, Wiltshire, SP2 7JX.
(T) 01722 321164
Profile: **FT:** Coarse; **WN:** Peters Finger; **WT:**

Lake (Still). **Location:** **Nr. Rd:** A36; **Rail:** Salisbury.
Ref: FH3756

PETERSFIELD HEATH LAKE

Petersfield Heath Lake, Petersfield, **HAMPSHIRE**, GU, **England**.
Contact/s: **Mr Ash Girdler**, 3 Chase Plain Cottages, Portsmouth Rd, Hindhead, Surrey, GU26 6BZ.
(T) 01428 607768
Mr Steve Jupp (Secretary), 172 Hawthorn Rd, Bognor Regis, Sussex (West), PO21 2UY.
(T) 01243 821950
Profile: **FT:** Coarse; **WN:** Petersfield Heath; **WT:** Lake (Still) **W. Size:** 22 Acres.
Location: **Nr. Rd:** B2146; **Main Rd:** A3.
Ref: FH3757

PETERSTONE TROUT LAKE

Peterstone Trout Lake, Walnut Tree Farm, St Brides, Newport, NP10 8SQ, **Wales**.
Contact/s: Fishery Manager.
(T) 01633 680905
Profile: **FT:** Combination; **WN:** Peterstone; **WT:** Lake (Still).
Ref: FH3758

PETT POOLS

Pett Pools, Pett, Hastings, **SUSSEX (EAST)**, TN35, **England**.
Contact/s: Manager, T G King, Market Stores, Pett Level, Hastings, TN35 4EH.
(T) 01424 8152678
Mr Kevin Thornely (Chairman).
(T) 01424 719703
Profile: **FT:** Coarse; **WN:** Pett; **WT:** Pool (Still). **Location:** **Main Rd:** A21.
Ref: FH3759

PETTISTREE LAKES

Pettistree Lakes, Wickham Market, Woodbridge, **SUFFOLK**, IP13, **England**.
Contact/s: Manager, Saxmundham Angling Ctre, Rear of Market Pl, Saxmundham, Suffolk, IP17 1AH.
(T) 01728 603443
Profile: **FT:** Coarse; **WN:** Pettistree; **WT:** Lake (Still).
Ref: FH3760

PETTY POOL

Petty Pool, South Park Drive, Sandiway, Northwich, **CHESHIRE**, CW8, **England**.
Contact/s: **Mr J Clitheroe** (Secretary), Northwich Angling Association, PO Box 18, Northwich, Cheshire, CW9 5SE.
(T) 01606 75132
Profile: **FT:** Coarse; **WN:** Petty; **WT:** Pool (Still). **Location:** **Nr. Rd:** South Park Drive; **Main Rd:** A556.
Ref: FH3761

PEVENSEY HAVEN

Pevensey Haven, Hailsham, **SUSSEX (EAST)**, BN27, **England**.
Contact/s: **Mr Geoff Begley** (Fishery Manager).
(T) 01323 832939
Mr T Lelliott (Secretary), Polegate Angling Ctre, 101 Station Rd, Polegate, Sussex (East), BN26 6EB.
(T) 01323 486379 **(F)** 01323 486379
Profile: **FT:** Coarse; **WN:** Pevensey Haven; **WT:** Lake (Still).
Ref: FH3762

PEWI FACH (RIVER)

River Pewi Fach, Carmarthen, **CARMARTHENSHIRE**, SA, **Wales**.
Contact/s: **Mr C J Jenkins** (President).
(T) 01994 230456
Mr David J Bryan (Hon Secretary), St Clears Angling Association, Madras Cottage, Laugharne, Carmarthen, SA33 4NU.
(T) 01994 427331
Profile: **FT:** Combination; **WN:** Pewi Fach; **WT:** River (Moving) **W. Size:** 1600 Metres.
Location: **Nr. Rd:** A40; **Main Rd:** A4777; **Rail:** Carmarthen.
Ref: FH3763

PICFRESH

Picfresh, Exeter, **DEVON**, EX3, **England**.
Contact/s: **Mr Michael Dart** (Fishery Manager).
(T) 01392 875587
Profile: **FT:** Coarse; **WN:** Picfresh; **WT:** Lake (Still) **W. Size:** 2 Acres. **Location:** **Main Rd:** A376.
Ref: FH3765

PICKERING PARK FISHING LAKE

Pickering Park Fishing Lake, Pickering Rd, Pickering, **YORKSHIRE (NORTH)**, YO18 8JJ, **England**.
Contact/s: Manager, Cardy's Pag, 813 Hessle High Rd, Hull, Yorkshire (East), H14 6QF.
(T) 01482 572664
Mr Loz (Park Ranger), Everett's Tackle, 601 Holderness Rd, Hull, HU8 9AN.
(T) 01482 374201
Mr Loz Gill (Park Development Officer), William Parker House, Walton St, Hull, Humberside (North), HU3 6JU.
(T) 01482 614970 **(F)** 01482 342720 **(M)** 07775 678482
Mr P Sammon.
(T) 01482 614966
Mr S Myers, Hull City Council, Temple St, Hull, Yorkshire (East), HU5 1AD.
(T) 01482 614964
Profile: **FT:** Coarse; **WN:** Pickering Park Lake; **WT:** Lake (Still) **W. Size:** 15 Acres.
Location: **Nr. Rd:** Pickering Road; **Main Rd:** A63; **Rail:** Paragon Station, Hull.
Ref: FH3766

PICKERING TROUT LAKE

Pickering Trout Lake, Newbridge Rd, Pickering, **YORKSHIRE (NORTH)**, YO18 8JJ, **England**.
Contact/s: Fishery Manager.
(T) 01751 474219
Mr Peter Sisk (Manager).
(T) 020 75474219
Profile: **FT:** Game; **WN:** Pickering; **WT:** Lake (Still). **Location:** **Nr. Rd:** Newbridge Road.
Ref: FH3767

PICKS COTTAGE CARP LAKES

Picks Cottage Carp Lakes, Sewardstone, Waltham Abbey, **ESSEX**, EN9, **England**.
Contact/s: **Andrew** (Fishery Manager).
(T) 020 85293922
Profile: **FT:** Coarse; **WN:** Picks Cottage; **WT:** Lake (Still) **W. Size:** 3 Acres. **Location:** **Nr. Rd:** A112 to Chinford; **Main Rd:** M11 or M25.
Ref: FH3768

PIDDLE (RIVER)

River Piddle, Dorchester, **DORSET**, DT2, **England**.
Contact/s: **Mr Richard Slocock** (Manager), Wessex Fly Fishing, Lawrences Farm, Tolpuddle, Dorset, DT2 7HF.
(T) 01305 848460 **(F)** 01305 849060
Profile: **FT:** Game; **WN:** Piddle; **WT:** River (Moving) **W. Size:** 1400 Metres. **Location:** **Nr. Rd:** A35; **Main Rd:** A35; **Rail:** Moreton.
Ref: FH3769

PIDDLE (RIVER)

River Piddle, Wareham, **DORSET**, BH20, **England**.
Contact/s: **Mr Chris Burgess** (Manager).
(T) 01929 550540
Profile: **FT:** Coarse; **WN:** Piddle; **WT:** River (Moving). **Location:** **Main Rd:** A351.
Ref: FH3770

PIETHORNE RESERVOIR

Piethorne Reservoir, Waterworks Rd, Newhey, Milnrow, Rochdale, **MANCHESTER (GREATER)**, OL, **England**.
Contact/s: **Mr Alan Hill** (Hon Secretary), 111 Delph Lane, Delph, Oldham, Lancashire.
(T) 01457 875899
Mr Barrie Powell (Membership Secretary), 290 Middleton Rd, Heywood, Lancashire, OL10 2LG.
(T) 01706 369153
Profile: **FT:** Game; **WN:** Piethorne; **WT:** Reservoir (Still); **F. Size:** 70 Acres; **W. Size:** 40 Acres. **Location:** **Nr. Rd:** Waterworks Road; **Main Rd:** A640; **Rail:** Newhey.
Ref: FH3771

PILLATON POOLS

Pillaton Pools, Pillaton Hall Farm, Cannock Rd, Penkridge, **STAFFORDSHIRE**, ST19 5RZ, **England**.
(W) www.pillatonpools.co.uk
Contact/s: **Mr David Pearce** (Owner), Pillaton Hall Farm, Cannock Road, Penkridge, Stafford, ST19 5RZ.
(T) 01785 715177 **(F)** 01785 716564 **(M)** 07887 997092
(E) davek/pearce@aol.com
Profile: **FT:** Coarse; **WN:** Pillaton Pools; **WT:** Pool (Still); **F. Size:** 10 Acres; **W. Size:** 6 Acres. **Location:** **Nr. Rd:** Cannock Road; **Main Rd:** A449; **Rail:** Penkridge.
Ref: FH3772

PILSWORTH FISHERY COMPLEX

Pilsworth Fishery Complex, Heywood, **MANCHESTER (GREATER)**, OL10, **England**.
Contact/s: **Mr Eric Taylor** (Fishery Manager).
(T) 01706 630619
Profile: **FT:** Coarse; **WN:** Carp, Main; **WT:** Lake (Still). **Location:** **Nr. Rd:** Moss Hall Road; **Main Rd:** M66, junction 3.
Ref: FH3773

PILTDOWN POND

Piltdown Pond, Piltdown Common, Newick, Haywards Heath, **SUSSEX (WEST)**, RH17, **England**.
Profile: **FT:** Coarse; **WN:** Piltdown; **WT:** Pond (Still). **Location:** **Main Rd:** A272 to Newick.
£Fr
Ref: FH3774

PIMLICO FARM LAKES

Pimlico Farm Lakes, Tusmore, Bicester, **OXFORDSHIRE**, OX6 9SL, **England**.
Contact/s: **Mr John Harper** (Fishery Manager).
(T) 01869 810306 **(M)** 07788 711841
Profile: **FT:** Coarse; **WN:** Pimlico; **WT:** Lake (Still).
Ref: FH3775

PINDERS PONDS

Pinders Ponds, West Bridgeford, Holme Rd, Nottingham, **NOTTINGHAMSHIRE**, NG, **England**.
Contact/s: **Mr Dave Fallows** (Secretary), 27 Woodstock Avenue, Radford, Nottingham.
(T) 0115 9787350
Profile: **FT:** Coarse; **WN:** Pinders; **WT:** Pond (Still). **Location:** **Nr. Rd:** Holme Road; **Main Rd:** A52; **Rail:** Nottingham.
Ref: FH3776

PINE LODGE FISHERIES

Pine Lodge Fisheries, Clitheroe-By-Pass, Barrow, Clitheroe, **LANCASHIRE**, BB7 9DH, **England**.
Contact/s: **Geoff** (Manager).
(T) 01254 822211
Profile: **FT:** Coarse; **WN:** Pine Lodge Fisheries; **WT:** Lake (Still) **W. Size:** 12 Acres.
Location: **Nr. Rd:** A671; **Main Rd:** A59.
Ref: FH3777

PINE POOL

Pine Pool, Kingsbury, Tamworth, **STAFFORDSHIRE**, B78, **England**.
Contact/s: **Mr Fred Hopkins** (Park Ranger), Kingsbury Water Park, Bodymoor Heath Lane, Bodymoor Heath, Sutton Coldfield, B76 0DY.
(T) 01827 872660 **(F)** 01827 875161
(E) parks@warwickshire.gov.uk
Profile: **FT:** Coarse; **WN:** Pine; **WT:** Pool (Still). **Location:** **Nr. Rd:** A4097; **Main Rd:** M42.
Ref: FH3778

PINE TREES LAKES

Pine Trees Lakes, Wellingborough, **NORTHAMPTONSHIRE**, NN, **England**.
Contact/s: Fishery Manager.
(T) 01933 651508
Profile: FT: Coarse; WN: Pine Trees; WT: Lake (Still).
Ref: FH3779

PINEWOOD TROUT FISHERY

Pinewood Trout Fishery, Duchal Estate, Kilmacolm, **INVERCLYDE**, PA13 4RS, **Scotland**.
Contact/s: Mr Martin O'Pray (Owner).
(T) 01505 874479
Profile: FT: Game; WN: Pinewood Trout Fishery; WT: Pond (Still) W. Size: 2 Acres.
Location: Nr. Rd: B788; Main Rd: A726.
Ref: FH3780

PINFOLD DAMS

Pinfold Dams, Park Road West, Milnsbridge, Huddersfield, **YORKSHIRE (WEST)**, HD3, **England**.
Contact/s: Mr J D Jones (Bailiff), 16 Malvern Rd, Nemsome, Huddesfield, Yorkshire (West).
(T) 01484 308948
Mr K C Robertshaw (Bailiff).
(T) 024 84658692
Profile: FT: Coarse; WN: Pinfold Dams; WT: Lake (Still). Location: Nr. Rd: Park Road; Main Rd: A62 Linthwaite to Huddersfield.
Ref: FH3781

PINFOLD LAKE

Pinfold Lake, Riasbeck, Orton, Penrith, **CUMBRIA**, CA10, **England**.
Contact/s: Mr J Pape (Manager), Longcast Cottage, 12a High Wiend, Appleby, Cumbria, CA16 6RD.
(T) 01768 352148
Profile: FT: Game; WN: Pinfold; WT: Lake (Still).
Ref: FH3782

PINGEWOOD LAGOON

Pingewood Lagoon, Pingewood, Reading, **BERKSHIRE**, RG, **England**.
Contact/s: Mr Dusty Millar (Associate members secretary), 238 Elgar Road South, Reading, Berkshire, RG3 0BW.
(T) 0118 9874882
Mr Mick Cox (Chief Bailiff), Dorstans, Hatch Lane, Brimpton Village, Reading, RG7 4TR.
(T) 0118 9714917
Profile: FT: Coarse; WN: Pingewood Lagoon; WT: Gravel Pit (Still) W. Size: 38 Acres.
Location: Nr. Rd: Pingewood.
Ref: FH3783

PIPERDAM

Piperdam Golf And Country Park, Fowlis, Dundee, **ANGUS**, DD2 5LP, **Scotland**.
Contact/s: Mr Derek McFarlane.
(T) 01382 581374 (F) 01382 581102
Profile: FT: Game; WN: Piperdam Golf And Country Park; WT: Combination (Still); F. Size: 300 Acres; W. Size: 45 Acres.
Location: Nr. Rd: Dundee to Coupar Angus; Main Rd: A923; Rail: Dundee.
Ref: FH3784

PIPERDAM HOLDINGS

Piperdam Golf Country Park Limited, Fowlis, Dundee, **ANGUS**, DD2 5LP, **Scotland**.
Contact/s: Mr Murdie Smith (Fishery Manager).
(T) 01382 581374
Profile: FT: Game; WN: Piper; WT: Mill Dam (Still). Location: Nr. Rd: Broughty Ferry Road.
Ref: FH3785

PIPPINGFORD PARK ESTATE LAKES

Pippingford Park Estate Lakes, Pippingford Corner, Nutley, Uckfield, **SUSSEX (EAST)**, TN22 3NW, **England**.
Contact/s: Mr Richard Morris, Home Farm, Pippingford Park, Nutley, Sussex (East), TN22 3NW.
(T) 01825 712966 (F) 01825 713638
Profile: FT: Coarse; WN: Pippingford; WT: Lake (Still). Location: Nr. Rd: A22 to Eastbourne; Main Rd: A22; Rail: East Grinstead.
Ref: FH3786

PIPPINS FARM LAKE

Pippins Farm Lake, Stone Court Lane, Tonbridge, **KENT**, TN1, **England**.
Contact/s: Mr Alex Heggie (Membership Secretary), Little Lucy's Farmhouse, Lower St, Hildenborough, Tonbridge, TN11 8PT.
(T) 01732 832352 (F) 01732 832352
Mr Terry Dwyer (Chairman).
Profile: FT: Coarse; WN: Pippins Farm; WT: Lake (Still) W. Size: 1 Acre. Location: Nr. Rd: Stone Court Lane.
Ref: FH3787

PIPPS HILL FISHERIES

Pipps Hill Fisheries, Pipps Hill Country Club, Cranes Farm Rd, Basildon, **ESSEX**, SS1, **England**.
Profile: FT: Coarse; WN: Pipps Hill Fisheries; WT: Lake (Still) W. Size: 25 Acres.
Location: Main Rd: A13 or A127.
Ref: FH3788

PISCES FISHERY

Pisces Caravan Park And Fishery, Bedford Bank, Welney, Wisbech, **CAMBRIDGESHIRE**, PE14 9TB, **England**.
Contact/s: Mr Richard Shelton (Manager).
(T) 01354 610257
Profile: FT: Coarse; WN: Pisces Caravan Park And Fishery; WT: Combination (Still & Moving) W. Size: 6 Acres. Location: Main Rd: A1101. £Fr
Ref: FH3789

PITCASTLE BEAT

Pitcastle Beat, Aberfeldy, **PERTH AND KINROSS**, PH15, **Scotland**.
(W) www.fishingnet.com/beats/pitcastle.htm
Contact/s: Ms Em Honeyman (Manager), Wade Newsagents, 31 Bank St, Aberfeldy, Perth and Kinross, PH15 2BB.
(T) 01887 820397
Profile: FT: Game; WN: Pitcastle Beat; WT: Pool (Still).
Ref: FH3790

PITFOUR LAKE

Pitfour Lake, Cedar Lodge, Pitfour Estate, Old Deer, Peterhead, **ABERDEENSHIRE**, AB42, **Scotland**.
Contact/s: Mr W Adam.
(T) 01771 624448
Profile: FT: Game; WN: Pitfour; WT: Gravel Pit (Still).
Ref: FH3791

PITLOCHRY BOATING STATION

Pitlochry Boating Station And Lochside Café, Loch Faskally, Clunie Bridge Rd, Pitlochry, **PERTH AND KINROSS**, PH16 5JX, **Scotland**.
Contact/s: Mr Dougie McLaren (Owner).
(T) 01796 472919
Profile: FT: Combination; WN: Garry; WT: Combination (Still & Moving) W. Size: 800 Metres. Location: Nr. Rd: Clunie Bridge; Main Rd: A9; Rail: Pitlochry.
Ref: FH3792

PITNACREE BEAT

Pitnacree Beat, Aberfeldy, **PERTH AND KINROSS**, PH15, **Scotland**.
(W) www.fishingnet.com/beats/pitnacree.htm
Ms Em Honeyman (Manager), Wade Newsagents, 31 Bank St, Aberfeldy, Perth and Kinross, PH15 2BB.
(T) 01887 820397
Profile: FT: Combination; WN: Pitnacree, Pitnacree Island and Jubilee; WT: Pool (Still).
Ref: FH3793

PITSFORD RESERVOIR

Pitsford Reservoir, Pitsford Lodge, Brixworth Rd, Holcot, Northampton, **NORTHAMPTONSHIRE**, NN6 9SJ, **England**.
Contact/s: Mr John Marshall (Head Office).
(T) 01572 653017
Profile: FT: Game; WN: Pitsford; WT: Reservoir (Still). Location: Nr. Rd: Brixworth Road.
Ref: FH3794

PITTLANDS LAKES

Pittlands Lakes, Pittlands Farm, Church Lane, Horsmonden, Tonbridge, **KENT**, TN12 8HL, **England**.
Contact/s: Mr T Johnson (Owner).
(T) 01892 723838or3142
Profile: FT: Coarse; WN: Pittlands; WT: Lake (Still).
Ref: FH3795

PIXIES MERE

Pixies Mere, Bourne End, Hemel Hempstead, **HERTFORDSHIRE**, HP1, **England**.
Contact/s: Mr Dave Coster, Tottenham Angling Ctre, 80a White Hart Lane, Tottenham, London, N17 8HP.
(T) 020 88010062 (F) 020 88010062
Mr Peter Lawlor (Owner), 26 Lascotts Rd, Wood Green, London, N22 8JN.
(T) 020 88892726 (M) 07941 190337
Profile: FT: Coarse; WN: Pixies Mere; WT: Lake (Still) W. Size: 4 Acres. Location: Nr. Rd: Pix Farm Lane; Main Rd: A41; Rail: Hemel.
Ref: FH3796

PIXLEY POOL

Pixley Pool, Pixley, Ledbury, **HEREFORDSHIRE**, HR8, **England**.
Contact/s: Mr Brian Powell (Red Banks Pools Manager), Three Counties Fisheries, Field Cottage, Ryton, Dymock, Gloucestershire, GL18 2DH.
(T) 01531 890455
Profile: FT: Coarse; WN: Pixley; WT: Pool (Still) W. Size: 2 Acres. Location: Nr. Rd: A4172; Main Rd: A438, West of Hereford; Rail: Ledbury.
Ref: FH3797

PLANTATIONS LAKES

Plantations Lakes, Middle Lane Farm, Middle Lane, Kingston Seymour, Clevedon, **SOMERSET**, BS21 6XW, **England**.
Contact/s: Mr W Travis.
(T) 01934 832325
Profile: FT: Coarse; WN: Plantations; WT: Lake (Still) W. Size: 3 Acres.
Ref: FH3798

PLAS-Y-NANT TROUT FISHERY

Plas-Y-Nant Trout Fishery, Mynydd Mechell, Cemaes Bay, Anglesey, Amlwch, **ISLE OF ANGLESEY**, LL68 0TH, **Wales**.
Contact/s: Manager, Plas-y-Nant Trout Fishery, Mynydd Mechell, Amlwch, Isle of Anglesey, LL68 0TH.
(T) 01407 711206
Profile: FT: Game; WN: Plas-Y-Nant Trout Fishery; WT: Lake (Still) W. Size: 2 Acres.
Location: Nr. Rd: A5025 to Llanfechell; Main Rd: A5.
Ref: FH3799

PLATT FIELDS

Platt Fields, Platt Fields Park, Wilmslow Rd, Fallowfield, Manchester, **MANCHESTER (GREATER)**, M2, **England**.
Contact/s: Mr Les Aubert (Bailiff).
(T) 0161 4945350
Mr Malcolm Moore.
(T) 0161 2233682
Profile: FT: Coarse; WN: Platt Fields; WT: Lake (Still) W. Size: 3 Acres. Location: Nr. Rd: A46, B5167; Main Rd: M63.
Ref: FH3800

PLATTS LANE LAKE

Platts Lane Lake, Parbold Rd, Burscough, Ormskirk, **LANCASHIRE**, L40, **England**.
<u>Contact/s:</u> Mr Wright.
(T) 01704 894761
<u>Profile:</u> **FT:** Coarse; **WN:** Platts Lane; **WT:** Lake (Still). <u>Location:</u> **Nr. Rd:** Parbold Road; **Main Rd:** A59 Preston to Burscough.
Ref: FH3801

PLAUMS PIT

Plaums Pit, Cheney Manor Rd, Swindon, **WILTSHIRE**, SN, **England**.
<u>Contact/s:</u> **Mr Craig Dus**.
(T) 01793 541740
Mr Tony Aisbitt (Secretary), 8 St Mary's Gr, Swindon, Wiltshire, SN2 1RQ.
(T) 01793 541740
<u>Profile:</u> **FT:** Coarse; **WN:** Plaum's Pit; **WT:** Lake (Still); **F. Size:** 5 Acres; **W. Size:** 2 Acres. <u>Location:</u> **Nr. Rd:** Cheney Manor Road; **Rail:** Swindon.
Ref: FH3802

PLESSEY WOODS

Plessey Woods, Stannington, Morpeth, **NORTHUMBERLAND**, NE61, **England**.
<u>Contact/s:</u> **Mr S Symons** (Secretary).
(T) 01670 822011
<u>Profile:</u> **FT:** Combination; **WN:** Blyth; **WT:** River (Moving).
Ref: FH3803

PLEX FLASH

Plex Flash, Oakwood Lane, Moston, Sandbach, **CHESHIRE**, CW11, **England**.
<u>Contact/s:</u> Manager, J and A Tackle, 87 Victoria St, Crewe, Cheshire, CW1 2JH.
(T) 01270 253891
Mr Doug Summers (Secretary), Scotia, Muston Rd, Sandbach, Cheshire, CW11 3GL.
<u>Profile:</u> **FT:** Coarse; **WN:** Plex Flash; **WT:** Lake (Still). <u>Location:</u> **Nr. Rd:** Oakwood Lane.
Ref: FH3804

PLUCK MILL FISH FARM

Pluck Mill Fish Farm, 39 Cadian Rd, Dungannon, **COUNTY TYRONE**, BT70 1LY, **Northern Ireland**.
<u>Contact/s:</u> **Mr Cahill Quinn** (Manager).
(T) 028 37548351
<u>Profile:</u> **FT:** Game; **WN:** Pluck Mill Fish Farm; **WT:** Lake (Still).
Ref: FH3805

PLUMP HILL POOL

Plump Hill Pool, Wilderness, Plump Hill, Mitcheldean, **GLOUCESTERSHIRE**, GL17, **England**.
<u>Contact/s:</u> **Mr Dennis Sherwood** (Fishery Management Officer).
(T) 01594 543796
Mr Paul Reed (Secretary), Royal Forest of Dean Angling Club, 20 Abbey St, Cinderford, Gloucestershire, GR14 2NW.
(T) 01594 824413
<u>Profile:</u> **FT:** Coarse; **WN:** Plump Hill; **WT:** Pond (Still). <u>Location:</u> **Nr. Rd:** A4136; **Main Rd:** A4136.
Ref: FH3806

PLYM (RIVER)

River Plym, Plymouth, **DEVON**, PL, **England**.
<u>Contact/s:</u> **Mr D L Owen** (Secretary), Plymouth and District Freshwater Angling Association, 39 Burnett Rd, Crownhill, Plymouth, PL6 5BH.
(T) 01752 705033
Mr W Kingdom (Manager), D K Sports, 88 Vauxhall St, Plymouth, Devon, PL4 0EX.
(T) 01752 223141 (F) 01752 223141
<u>Profile:</u> **FT:** Game; **WN:** Plym; **WT:** River (Moving).
Ref: FH3807

POAKA BECK

Poaka Beck, South Lakeland, Barrow-In-Furness, **CUMBRIA**, LA, **England**.
<u>Contact/s:</u> **Mr J R Jones** (Hon Secretary), 69 Prince St, Dalton in Furness, Cumbria, LA15 8ET.
Mr Roy Rhodes (Conservation, Access and Recreation Manager), Rivington Water Treatment Works, Bolton Rd, Horwich, Bolton, BL6 7RN.
(T) 01204 664300
<u>Profile:</u> **FT:** Coarse; **WN:** Poaka; **WT:** Stream (Moving).
Ref: FH3808

POCKLINGTON CANAL

Pocklington Canal, Pocklington, York, **YORKSHIRE (NORTH)**, YO42, **England**.
<u>Contact/s:</u> **Mr John Lane** (Secretary), York and District Angling Association, 39 Lowfields Drive, Acomb, York, YO2 3DQ.
(T) 01904 783178
<u>Profile:</u> **FT:** Coarse; **WN:** Pocklington; **WT:** Canal (Still) **W. Size:** 16000 Metres.
Ref: FH3809

POLCOVERACK FARM

Polcoverack Farm, Coverack, Helston, **CORNWALL**, **England**.
<u>Profile:</u> **FT:** Coarse; **WN:** Polcoverack; **WT:** Lake (Still). <u>Location:</u> **Nr. Rd:** B3294; **Rail:** Falmouth.
Ref: FH3810

POLLAGH (RIVER)

River Pollagh, Kiltamagh, **COUNTY MAYO**, **Ireland**.
<u>Contact/s:</u> Angling Officer, North Western Regional Fisheries Board, Ardnaree House, Abbey St, Ballina, County Mayo.
(T) 096 22623 (F) 096 70543
<u>Profile:</u> **FT:** Game; **WN:** Pollagh; **WT:** River (Moving).
Ref: FH3811

POLLYS FLASH

Pollys Flash, Kingsdown Rd, Platt Bridge, Wigan, **LANCASHIRE**, WN2, **England**.
<u>Contact/s:</u> **Mr Adrian Bate** (Bailiff), Abram Angling Club, 189 Simpkin St, Abram, Witham, WN2 5PS.
(T) 01942 742603
<u>Profile:</u> **FT:** Coarse; **WN:** Pollys Flash; **WT:** Lake (Still) **W. Size:** 5 Acres. <u>Location:</u> **Nr. Rd:** A573; **Main Rd:** M6.
Ref: FH3812

PONDERS END

Ponders End, Tottenham, London, **LONDON (GREATER)**, N17, **England**.
<u>Contact/s:</u> Manager, Don's of Edmonton, 239 Fore St, London, N18 2TZ.
(T) 020 88075219 (F) 020 88075396
<u>Profile:</u> **FT:** Coarse; **WN:** Ponders End; **WT:** River (Moving).
Ref: FH3813

PONDWOOD CARP LAKES

Pondwood Carp Lakes, Pondwood Farm, Pondwood Lane, White Waltham, Maidenhead, **BERKSHIRE**, SL6 3SS, **England**.
<u>Contact/s:</u> **Mr Michael Holdaway** (Owner).
(T) 0118 9345299 (F) 0118 9340012
<u>Profile:</u> **FT:** Coarse; **WN:** Pondwood Carp Lakes; **WT:** Combination (Still & Moving) **W. Size:** 2 Acres. <u>Location:</u> **Nr. Rd:** Pondwood Lane; **Main Rd:** Waltham Road; **Rail:** Maidenhead.
Ref: FH3814

PONKY POOL

Ponky Pool, Johnstown, Wrexham, LL1, **Wales**.
<u>Profile:</u> **FT:** Coarse; **WN:** Ponky; **WT:** Pool (Still) **W. Size:** 2 Acres.
Ref: FH3815

PONTEFRACT PARK LAKE

Pontefract Park Lake, Pontefract Racecourse, Pontefract, **YORKSHIRE (WEST)**, WF2 7, **England**.
<u>Contact/s:</u> Area Manager, Environment Agency, Ridings Area Office, Phoenix House, Global Avenue, Leeds, LS11 8PG.
(T) 0113 2440191or2314834 (F) 0113 2134609
Mr Dave Millman, Pugneys Country Park, Asdale Rd, Off Denbydale Rd, Wakefield, WF2 7EQ.
(T) 01924 302360
<u>Profile:</u> **FT:** Coarse; **WN:** Pontefract Park; **WT:** Lake (Still) **W. Size:** 4 Acres. <u>Location:</u> **Nr. Rd:** Pontefract Racecourse.
Ref: FH3816

PONTSTICILL RESERVOIR

Pontsticill Reservoir, Merthyr Tydfil, **GLAMORGAN (VALE OF)**, CF48, **Wales**.
<u>Contact/s:</u> **Mr Bob Morgan**.
(T) 01865 379809
<u>Profile:</u> **FT:** Combination; **WN:** Pontsticill; **WT:** Reservoir (Still). <u>Location:</u> **Nr. Rd:** A465 to Pontsticill village.
Ref: FH3817

POOL BRIDGE FARM LAKES

Pool Bridge Farm Lakes, Crockley Hill, York, **YORKSHIRE (NORTH)**, YO, **England**.
<u>Contact/s:</u> **Mr Ron Fletcher** (Manager).
(T) 01904 637854or620304
<u>Profile:</u> **FT:** Coarse; **WN:** Pool Bridge; **WT:** Lake (Still).
Ref: FH3818

POOL HALL

Pool Hall, Alveley, Bridgnorth, **MIDLANDS (WEST)**, WV1, **England**.
<u>Contact/s:</u> **Mr Sid Mathews** (Manager), The Lodge, Poole Hall Fishery, Alverley, Shropshire.
(T) 01299 861458
<u>Profile:</u> **FT:** Combination; **WN:** Heron, Kingfisher, Moorhen and Moat; **WT:** Pool (Still). <u>Location:</u> **Main Rd:** A442.
Ref: FH3819

POOL HOUSE FARM

Pool House Farm, Brick Kiln Lane, Hunts Green, Middleton, Tamworth, **STAFFORDSHIRE**, B78 2BA, **England**.
<u>Contact/s:</u> **Mr Cedric Heys** (Fishery Manager).
(T) 01827 874856 (F) 01827 874856
(E) badges@cheys.fsnet.co.uk
<u>Profile:</u> **FT:** Coarse; **WN:** House Farm; **WT:** Pool (Still) **W. Size:** 1 Acre. <u>Location:</u> **Nr. Rd:** A4091; **Main Rd:** M42, junction 9; **Rail:** Tamworth.
Ref: FH3820

POOLE HALL FARM

Poole Hall Farm, Wolverhampton, **MIDLANDS (WEST)**, WV, **England**.
<u>Contact/s:</u> **Mr John Thacker**. **(M)** 07703 125829
<u>Profile:</u> **FT:** Coarse; **WN:** Pool Hall; **WT:** Lake (Still) **W. Size:** 12 Acres. <u>Location:</u> **Nr. Rd:** Trescott Garage; **Main Rd:** A454 Wolverhampton to Bridgnorth.
Ref: FH3821

POOLE HALL FISHERY

Poole Hall Fishery, Kidderminster, **WORCESTERSHIRE**, DY11, **England**.
<u>Contact/s:</u> **Mr Sid Mathews** (Manager), The Lodge, Poole Hall Fishery, Alverley, Shropshire.
(T) 01299 861458
<u>Profile:</u> **FT:** Combination; **WN:** Poole Hall Fishery; **WT:** Pool (Still) **W. Size:** 13 Acres.
Ref: FH3822

POPPLETON (RIVER)

River Poppleton, Poppleton, York, **YORKSHIRE (NORTH)**, YO26, **England**.
<u>Contact/s:</u> **Mr John Lane** (Secretary), York and District Angling Association, 39 Lowfields Drive, Acomb, York, YO2 3DQ.
(T) 01904 783178
<u>Profile:</u> **FT:** Coarse; **WN:** Poppleton; **WT:** River (Moving).
Ref: FH3823

PORT ELLIOT LAKE

Port Elliot Lake, St Germans, Saltash,

CORNWALL, PL12, **England**.
Contact/s: Secretary.
(T) 01752 783724
Profile: FT: Coarse; WN: Port Elliot; WT: Lake (Still) W. Size: 2 Acres. Location: Nr. Rd: B3249; Main Rd: A38.
Ref: FH3824

PORTH RESERVOIR

Porth Reservoir, Porth, Newquay, **CORNWALL**, TR7, **England**.
Contact/s: Fishery Manager, South West Lake Limited, Menherion, Redruth, Cornwall, TR16 6NW.
(T) 01209 860301
Mr Chris Bird (Manager), Newtown Angling Ctre, Newtown, Germoe, Penzance, TR20 9AE.
(T) 01736 763721
Mr Reg England (Manager), Peninsula Coarse Fisheries, St Cleer Depot, Lewdown, Okehampton, Devon EX20 4QT.
(T) 01837 871565 (F) 01837 871534
Profile: FT: Coarse; WN: Porth; WT: Reservoir (Still) W. Size: 80 Acres.
Location: Nr. Rd: A39 to Wadebridge; Main Rd: A392.
Ref: FH3825

PORTH WATERS FISHERY

Porth Waters Fishery, Fron Goch, Bala, **GWYNEDD**, LL23, **Wales**.
(W) www.fishing-in-wales.co.uk/llandysul-aa/beat11
Contact/s: **Mr Artie Jones** (Hon Secretary), Llandysul Angling Association, Glas-y-Dorlan, Llyn-y-Fran Rd, Llandysul, SA44 4JW.
(T) 01559 362317
Profile: FT: Game; WN: Teifi; WT: River (Moving) W. Size: 3200 Metres. Location: Nr. Rd: B4476.
Ref: FH3826

PORTLING FISHERIES

Portling Fisheries, Henderson Ac, Portling, Dalbeattie, **DUMFRIES AND GALLOWAY**, DG5 4PZ, **Scotland**.
Contact/s: Fishery Manager.
(T) 01556 630231
Profile: FT: Coarse; WN: Portling Fisheries; WT: Lake (Still).
Ref: FH3827

PORTMORE LOCH

Portmore Loch, Penicuik, **LOTHIAN (MID)**, EH26, **Scotland**.
Contact/s: **Mr W McGeachie** (Manager), 101 John St, Penicuik, Mid Lothian, Scotland.
(T) 01968 74345
Profile: FT: Game; WN: Portmore; WT: Loch (Still). Location: Main Rd: A703.
Ref: FH3828

PORT-NA-LOCHAN

Port-Na-Lochan, Kilpatrick, Blackwaterfoot, Brodick, **AYRSHIRE (NORTH)**, KA27 8, **Scotland**.
Contact/s: **Mr George Bannatyne**, Lochside Guest House, Blackwaterfoot, Brodick, Isle of Arran, KA27 8EY.
(T) 01770 860276
(E) bannatyne@lineone.net
Profile: FT: Game; WN: Port-Na-Lochan; WT: Loch (Still); F. Size: 5 Acres; W. Size: 3 Acres. Location: Nr. Rd: Main ring road; Main Rd: A841; Rail: Ardrossan (Ferry Terminal).
Ref: FH3829

PORTNELLAN

Portnellan, Crianlarich, **STIRLING**, FK20 8QS, **Scotland**.
(W) www.fishingnet.com/beat/dochart/portnellan
Contact/s: **Mr Trevor Taylor**.
(T) 01838 300284 (F) 01838 300332
(E) lodges@portnellan.demon.co.uk
Profile: FT: Game; WN: Portnellan; WT: Combination (Still & Moving); F. Size: 300 Acres; W. Size: 150 Acres. Location: Main Rd: A85; Rail: Crianlarich.
Ref: FH3830

PORTSMOUTH RESERVIOR

Portsmouth Reservoir, Burnley, **LANCASHIRE**, BB, **England**.
(W) www.todmorden-angling.fsnet.co.uk
Contact/s: **Mr Ray Barber** (Secretary), Todmorden Angling Society, 12 Grisedale Drive, Burnley, Lancashire, BB12 8AR.
(T) 01282 428780 (M) 07970 897849
Profile: FT: Coarse; WN: Portsmouth; WT: Reservoir (Still); F. Size: 2 Acres; W. Size: 2 Acres. Location: Main Rd: A646.
Ref: FH3831

POSSY LODGE PONDS

Possy Lodge Ponds, Ashbourne Rd, Cowers Lane, Belper, **DERBYSHIRE**, DE56, **England**.
Contact/s: **Mr Andy Henderson**, Hendersons Tackle, 37 Bridge St, Belper, Derbyshire, DE56 1AY.
(T) 0115 9723547
Profile: FT: Coarse; WN: Possy Lodge; WT: Pond (Still); F. Size: 3 Acres; W. Size: 1 Acre. Location: Nr. Rd: A517; Main Rd: A517; Rail: Belper.
Ref: FH3832

POTOMAC POND

Potomac Pond, Gunnersbury Park, Lionel Rd, Brentford, London, **LONDON (GREATER)**, TW8, **England**.
Contact/s: Fishery Manager.
(T) 020 88927660
Profile: FT: Coarse; WN: Potomac; WT: Pond (Still). Location: Nr. Rd: Lionel Road; Main Rd: A30, M4.
Ref: FH3833

POTTERY LAKE

Pottery Lake, Pottery Lane, Stensall, York, **YORKSHIRE (NORTH)**, YO32 5TJ, **England**.
Contact/s: **Mr Cedric Taylor**.
(T) 01347 810617
(E) olivia@stonecote.freeserve.co.uk
Profile: FT: Coarse; WN: Potteries; WT: Lake (Still). Location: Nr. Rd: Pottery Lane; Main Rd: 1237T; Rail: York.
Ref: FH3834

POULTON RECREATION FIELD POOL

Poulton Recreation Field Pool, Bebington, Wirral, **MERSEYSIDE**, CH63, **England**.
Contact/s: **Mr Billing**.
(T) 0151 3343174
Profile: FT: Coarse; WN: Poulton; WT: Pool (Still).
Ref: FH3835

POUND POND FARM

Pound Pond Farm, Butterley, Tiverton, **DEVON**, EX16, **England**.
Contact/s: **Mr A R Davey**.
(T) 01884 855208
Profile: FT: Coarse; WN: Pound Farm; WT: Pond (Still).
Ref: FH3836

POWDER MILLS FISHERY

Powder Mills Fishery, Blacksmiths Lane, Chilworth, Guildford, **SURREY**, GU4, **England**.
Contact/s: **Mr Tony Hern** (Manager), Albury Estate Fisheries, The Estate Office, Weston Yard, Guildford, GU5 9AF. (M) 07976 810737
Profile: FT: Game; WN: Powder Mills Fishery; WT: Lake (Still); F. Size: 4 Acres; W. Size: 4 Acres.
Ref: FH3837

POWDERMILL

Powdermill (Great Sanders) Water, Powdermill Lane, Sedlescombe, Battle, **SUSSEX (EAST)**, TN33 0PL, **England**.
Contact/s: **Captain Donald E Tack** (Secretary), The Hastings Fly Fishers Club Ltd, Ogwen, 23 Wealden Way, Bexhill-on-Sea, TN39 4NZ.
(T) 01424 870498or843957or720452 (F) 01424 420857 (M) 07773 926511
(E) cfg@povilian.co.uk
Profile: FT: Game; WN: Powdermill; WT: Lake (Still); F. Size: 65 Acres; W. Size: 54 Acres. Location: Nr. Rd: Powdermill Lane; Rail: Battle.
Ref: FH3838

POYNTON POOL

Poynton Pool, South Park Drive, Poynton, Stockport, **MANCHESTER (GREATER)**, SK12, **England**.
Contact/s: Secretary, Stockport DAF, 133 Manchester Rd, Hyde, Cheshire, SK14 2BK.
(T) 0161 4774536
Profile: FT: Coarse; WN: Poynton Pool; WT: Lake (Still) W. Size: 4 Acres. Location: Nr. Rd: South Park Drive.
Ref: FH3839

PRESS MANOR

Press Manor, Wingerworth, Chesterfield, **DERBYSHIRE**, S42 6, **England**.
Contact/s: **Mr Bernie Maher** (Manager).
(T) 01629 760996 (M) 07976 306073
Profile: FT: Combination; WN: Press Manor; WT: Pool (Still) W. Size: 6 Acres. Location: Nr. Rd: Press Lane; Main Rd: A362.
Ref: FH3840

PRESTON INNOVATIONS (SILVER)

Preston Innovations Silver Fishery, Hatfield Water Park, Old Thorne Rd, Doncaster, **YORKSHIRE (SOUTH)**, DN, **England**.
Contact/s: **Mr Robin Goforth** (Manager), Hayfield Lodge, Hayfield Lane, Auckley, Doncaster, DN9 3NP.
(T) 01302 864555 (F) 01302 863419
Profile: FT: Coarse; WN: Preston Innovations Silver Fishery; WT: Lake (Still) W. Size: 20 Acres. Location: Nr. Rd: Old Thorne Road; Main Rd: A18.
Ref: FH3841

PRESTONS LAKE

Prestons Lake, Pebmarsh, Colchester, **ESSEX**, CO, **England**.
(W) www.c-a-p-s.co.uk
Contact/s: **Mr Paul Masters** (Secretary), CAPS Membership, 17 Azalea Court, Sycamore Rd, Colchester Essex, CO4 3NU.
(T) 01376 512255
(E) secretary@c-a-p-s.co.uk
Profile: FT: Coarse; WN: Preston's; WT: Lake (Still) W. Size: 19 Acres. Location: Nr. Rd: A604; Main Rd: B1024 to Earls Colne.
Ref: FH3842

PRETTY PIGS FISHERY

Pretty Pigs Fishery, Shuttington Village, Tamworth, **STAFFORDSHIRE**, B7, **England**.
Contact/s: **Mr Peter Mason**.
(T) 01827 59783
Profile: FT: Coarse; WN: Pretty Pigs; WT: Lake (Still).
Ref: FH3843

PRIDEWOOD LAKE

Pridewood Lake, Pridewood, Ashperton, Ledbury, **HEREFORDSHIRE**, HR8 2SF, **England**.
Contact/s: **Ms Julia Powell-Tuck**.
(T) 01531 670416
Profile: FT: Coarse; WN: Pridewood; WT: Lake (Still). Location: Nr. Rd: A417; Main Rd: A438, Ledbury to Hereford; Rail: Ledbury.
Ref: FH3844

PRINCE PARK

Prince Park, Prince Park Farm, St Wenn, Bodmin, **CORNWALL**, PL30 5PD, **England**.
Contact/s: **Mr John Brown**.
(T) 01726 890095
Profile: FT: Coarse; WN: Prince Park; WT: Lake (Still). Location: Main Rd: A30.
Ref: FH3845

PRINCES PARK LAKE

Princes Park Lake, Prince's Avenue, Liverpool, **MERSEYSIDE**, L8 3SS, **England**.
Contact/s: Fishery Manager.
(T) 0151 7341943

Manager, Anfield Tackle, 119 Oakfield Rd, Walton, Liverpool, L4 0UE.
(T) 0151 2608223
Profile: FT: Coarse; WN: Princes Park; WT: Lake (Still). Location: Nr. Rd: Ullet Road; Main Rd: A561. £Fr
Ref: FH3846

PRIORY COTTAGE LAKE

Priory Cottage Lake, Guisborough, **CLEVELAND**, TS14, **England**.
Contact/s: **Mr Clive Bradley**.
(T) 01287 638816
Profile: FT: Coarse; WN: Priory Cottage; WT: Lake (Still) W. Size: 2 Acres. Location: Nr. Rd: Whitby Road; Main Rd: A171.
Ref: FH3847

PRIORY COUNTRY PARK

Priory Country Park, Barkers Lane, Bedford, **BEDFORDSHIRE**, MK41 9SH, **England**.
Contact/s: **Mr Roy Bates** (Fishery Warden), Bedford Borough Council, Town Hall, St Pauls Sq, Bedford, MK40 1SJ.
(T) 01234 211182 (M) 07780 954283
Profile: FT: Coarse; WN: Priory Lake, Fingers Lake, Riverside Pond, Ouse; WT: Lake (Still & Moving); F. Size: 150 Acres. Location: Nr. Rd: Barkers Lane; Main Rd: A6 or A428; Rail: Bedford.
Ref: FH3848

PRIORY PARK LAKES

Priory Park Lakes, Priory Park, Southend-on-Sea, **ESSEX**, SS, **England**.
Profile: FT: Coarse; WN: Priory Park; WT: Lake (Still). Location: Main Rd: A127 or A13.
Ref: FH3849

PRIORY WATER

Priory Water, Windsor, **BERKSHIRE**, SL4, **England**.
Contact/s: **Mr Peter Howes**.
(T) 01256 466343
Profile: FT: Coarse; WN: Priory Water; WT: Gravel Pit (Still). Location: Main Rd: M25, Wrasbury junction.
Ref: FH3850

PROCTORS PLEASURE PARK

Proctors Pleasure Park, Proctor Park Rd, Barrow-on-Soar, Loughborough, Leicester, **LEICESTERSHIRE**, LE12 8QF, **England**.
Contact/s: **Mr Richard Proctor** (Bailiff).
(M) 07976 284919
Profile: FT: Combination; WN: Proctors Pleasure Park; WT: Combination (Still & Moving) W. Size: 20 Acres. Location: Nr. Rd: Bridge Street; Main Rd: A6; Rail: Loughborough.
Ref: FH3851

PROSPECT FARM POND

Prospect Farm Pond, Prospect Farm, Haverah Park, Harrogate, **YORKSHIRE (NORTH)**, HG3 1SQ, **England**.
Contact/s: Fishery Manager.
(T) 01423 504166
Fishery Manager.
(T) 01423 507870
Profile: FT: Coarse; WN: Prospect Farm; WT: Pond (Still). Location: Nr. Rd: B6161 Penny Pot Lane; Main Rd: B6162; Rail: Harrogate.
Ref: FH3852

PRYHEAD FISHERY

Pryhead Fishery, Garrigill, Alston, **CUMBRIA**, CA9, **England**.
Contact/s: Fishery Manager.
(T) 01434 381976
Profile: FT: Game; WN: Pryhead Fishery; WT: Lake (Still) W. Size: 1 Acre. Location: Main Rd: A689.
Ref: FH3853

PUDDENHOLE POND

Puddenhole Pond, Dorking, **SURREY**, **England**.
Contact/s: .
(T) 01306 882177
Profile: FT: Coarse; WN: Puddenhole Pond; WT: Pond (Still).
Ref: FH3854

PUGNEYS COUNTRY PARK

Pugneys Country Park, Asdale Rd, Off Denbydale Rd, Wakefield, **YORKSHIRE (WEST)**, WF2 7EQ, **England**.
Contact/s: Area Manager, Environment Agency, Ridings Area Office, Phoenix House, Global Avenue, Leeds, LS11 8PG.
(T) 0113 2440191or2314834 (F) 0113 2134609
Mr Dave Millman, Pugneys Country Park, Asdale Rd, Off Denbydale Rd, Wakefield, WF2 7EQ.
(T) 01924 302360
Profile: FT: Coarse; WN: Pugneys Country Park; WT: Lake (Still) W. Size: 70 Acres. Location: Nr. Rd: Asdale Road; Main Rd: Denby Dale Road; Rail: Wakefield Westgate.
Ref: FH3855

PULBOROUGH LAKE

Pulborough Lake, Horsham, **SURREY**, RH1, **England**.
Contact/s: Fishery Manager.
(T) 01903 764818
Profile: FT: Coarse; WN: Pulborough; WT: Lake (Still).
Ref: FH3856

PURDOMSTONE RESERVOIR

Purdomstone Reservoir, Middlebie, Ecclefechan, Lockerbie, **DUMFRIES AND GALLOWAY**, DG11, **Scotland**.
Contact/s: Manager, Hoddom and Kinmount Estates, Hoddom Estate Office, Lockerbie, Dumfries and Galloway, DG11 1BE.
(T) 01576 300244 (F) 01567 300757
Secretary, Annan and District Anglers Club, 61-63 High St, Annan, Dumfries and Galloway, DG12 6AD.
(T) 01461 202616 (F) 01461 206456
D Graham (Bailiff), Hoddom and Kinmount Estates, Hoddom Estate Office, Lockerbie, Dumfries and Galloway, DG11 1BE.
(T) 01576 300417 (M) 07711 681507
Profile: FT: Game; WN: Purdomstone; WT: Reservoir (Still); F. Size: 8 Acres; W. Size: 5 Acres. Location: Main Rd: A74; Rail: Lockerbie.
Ref: FH3857

PURLEY

Purley, River Thames, Purley-on-Thames, Reading, **BERKSHIRE**, RG, **England**.
Contact/s: **Mr Dusty Millar** (Associate members secretary), 238 Elgar Road South, Reading, Berkshire, RG3 0BW.
(T) 0118 9874882
Mr Mick Cox (Chief Bailiff), Dorstans, Hatch Lane, Brimpton Village, Reading, RG7 4TR.
(T) 0118 9714917
Profile: FT: Coarse; WN: Thames; WT: River (Moving). Location: Nr. Rd: Purley-on-Thames.
Ref: FH3858

PURTON LAKE

Purton Lake, Blunsdon, Swindon, **WILTSHIRE**, SN4, **England**.
Contact/s: **Mr D Barker** (Owner).
(T) 01793 770219
Profile: FT: Coarse; WN: Purton; WT: Lake (Still).
Ref: FH3859

PUSH DAM

Push Dam, Cliffe Rd, Shepley, Huddersfield, **YORKSHIRE (WEST)**, HD8 8AG, **England**.
Contact/s: **Mr D Barrans** (Bailiff), 36a Marsh Lane, Shepley, Huddersfield.
(T) 01484 603348
Mr D Rushforth (Secretary), 122 Longwood Gate, Longwood, Huddersfield, Yorkshire (West), HD3 4US.
(T) 01484 651028
Profile: FT: Coarse; WN: Push Dam; WT: Lake (Still). Location: Nr. Rd: Cliffe Road; Main Rd: A629; Rail: Shipley.
Ref: FH3860

PYEWELL FARM

Pyewell Farm, Holmacott, Instow, Bideford, **DEVON**, EX39 4LR, **England**.
Contact/s: **Mrs Jane Steer**.
(T) 01271 860357
Profile: FT: Coarse; WN: Pyewell Farm; WT: Pond (Still).
Ref: FH3861

QUANTOCK FISHERIES

Quantock Fisheries, Stream Farm, Broomfield, Bridgwater, **SOMERSET**, TA5 2EN, **England**.
Contact/s: **Mr Neil Bruce - Miller** (Owner).
(T) 01823 451367 (F) 01823 451367
(E) brucemiller@onetel.net.uk
Mrs Sue Bruce - Miller (Owner).
(T) 01823 451367 (F) 01823 451367
Profile: FT: Game; WN: Quantock Fisheries; WT: Lake (Still) W. Size: 2 Acres. Location: Main Rd: M5; Rail: Taunton.
Ref: FH3862

QUARTER FISHERY

Quarter Fishery, Hamilton, **LANARKSHIRE (SOUTH)**, ML3, **Scotland**.
Contact/s: **Mr J Crooks** (owner).
(T) 01698 284309
Profile: FT: Game; WN: Quarter Fishery; WT: Lake (Still).
Ref: FH3863

QUEEN ELIZABETH II COUNTRY PK

Queen Elizabeth Ii Country Park, Woodhorn, Ashington, **NORTHUMBERLAND**, NE63, **England**.
Contact/s: **Mr Ed Armstrong**, Wansbeck District Council, Contracts and Leisure Department, East View, Stakeford, Choppington, Northumberland, NE62 5TR.
(T) 01670 819802
Profile: FT: Coarse; WN: Queen Elizabeth Ii Country Park; WT: Lake (Still) W. Size: 40 Acres.
Ref: FH3864

QUEEN MARYS POND

Queen Marys Pond, Park Lane, Ripon, **YORKSHIRE (NORTH)**, HG4, **England**.
Contact/s: **Mr Howard Foster** (Secretary), 6 Moorclose Lane, Queensbury, Bradford, Yorkshire (West), BD13 2BP.
(T) 01274 881851
Mr John Sparks, 12 Fairway Walk, Wibsey, Bradford, BD7 4JW.
Profile: FT: Coarse; WN: Queen Marys; WT: Pond (Still). Location: Nr. Rd: Park Lane.
Ref: FH3865

QUEENS PARK LAKE

Queens Park Lake, Heywood, **LANCASHIRE**, OL10, **England**.
Contact/s: Fishery Manager.
(T) 0161 6553402
Profile: FT: Coarse; WN: Queen's Park; WT: Lake (Still).
Ref: FH3866

QUEENS ROAD POND

Queens Road Pond, The Inn On The Sea, Queen's Rd, Lee-on-The-Solent, **HAMPSHIRE**, PO13, **England**.
Contact/s: **Mr Mike Sweeney**.
(T) 023 92550209
Profile: FT: Coarse; WN: Queens Road; WT: Pond (Still). Location: Nr. Rd: Queen's Road; Main Rd: B3333.
Ref: FH3867

QUIET WATERS

Quiet Waters, Coalisland, Dungannon, **COUNTY TYRONE**, BT71 4, **Northern Ireland**.
Contact/s: **Mrs Liz Salter** (Manager), Aughnacloy Development Association, The McCreedy Mill Centre, Aughnacloy, County Tyrone, BT69 6AL.
(T) 028 85557002

KEY: (w): Web address (T): Telephone number (F): Fax Number (M): Mobile Number (E): E-mail Address
F. Size: Fishery Size FT: Fisherytype WN: WaterName/s WT: WaterType W. Size: Water Size £Fr: Free Fishing

Profile: **FT:** Coarse; **WN:** Quiet Waters; **WT:** Lake (Still). **Location:** **Nr. Rd:** A5 to Coalisland; **Main Rd:** A5.
Ref: FH3868

QUOILE (RIVER)

River Quoile, 5 Quay Rd, Downpatrick, **COUNTY DOWN**, BT30, **Northern Ireland**.
Contact/s: Fishery Manager.
(T) 028 44615520
Profile: **FT:** Game; **WN:** Quoile; **WT:** River (Moving). **Location:** **Nr. Rd:** Quay Road.
Ref: FH3869

RABY ESTATES WATER

Raby Estates Water, Estate Office, Staindrop, Darlington, **COUNTY DURHAM**, DL2 3NF, **England**.
Contact/s: **Mrs Anna Parkinson** (Office Assistant).
(T) 01952 740223
Profile: **FT:** Combination; **WN:** Tees; **WT:** River (Moving) **W. Size:** 9000 Metres.
Ref: FH3870

RACECOURSE LAKE

Racecourse Lake, Ripon, **YORKSHIRE (NORTH)**, HG4, **England**.
Contact/s: **Mr Bernard Thain** (Manager), Ripon Angling Ctre, 58-59 North St, Ripon, Yorkshire (North), HG4 1EN.
(T) 01765 604666 **(F)** 01765 603933
Profile: **FT:** Coarse; **WN:** Racecourse; **WT:** Lake (Still) **W. Size:** 20 Acres. **Location:** **Nr. Rd:** North Street; **Main Rd:** A61.
Ref: FH3871

RACKHEATH SPRINGS

Rackheath Springs, Rackheath, Norwich, **NORFOLK**, NR, **England**.
Contact/s: **Mr R Westgate** (Club Secretary), Wroxham and District Angling Club, 31 The Paddocks, Old Catton, Norwich, NR6 7HF.
(T) 01603 401062 **(F)** 01603 897122 **(M)** 07885 244262
(E) robert.westgate@virgin.net
Profile: **FT:** Coarse; **WN:** Rackheath Springs; **WT:** Lake (Still) **W. Size:** 2 Acres. **Location:** **Nr. Rd:** Wroxham Road; **Main Rd:** A47; **Rail:** Wroxham.
Ref: FH3872

RACKLEY HILLS PIT

Rackley Hills Pit, Grovebury Rd, Leighton Buzzard, **BEDFORDSHIRE**, LU7, **England**.
Contact/s: **Mr B Smalley** (Secretary), 3 Isis Walk, Leighton Buzzard, Bedfordshire.
(T) 01525 852227
Profile: **FT:** Coarse; **WN:** Rackley Hill; **WT:** Gravel Pit (Still) **W. Size:** 8 Acres. **Location:** **Nr. Rd:** Grovebury Road.
Ref: FH3873

RADCOT LOCK

Radcot Lock, Radcot Bridge, Faringdon, **OXFORDSHIRE**, SN7 8JT, **England**.
Contact/s: Fishery Contact.
(T) 01367 240676
Recreational Manager, The Environment Agency, Kings Meadow Rd, Reading, Berkshire, RG1 8DQ.
(T) 0118 9535000 **(F)** 0118 9500388
Profile: **FT:** Combination; **WN:** Thames; **WT:** River (Moving). **Location:** **Main Rd:** A4095.
Ref: FH3874

RADIPOLE LAKE

Radipole Lake, Weymouth, **DORSET**, DT, **England**.
Contact/s: Manager, Weymouth Angling Ctre, 24 Trinity Rd, Weymouth, Dorset, DT4 8TJ.
(T) 01305 777771 **(F)** 01305 788881
Mr Dennings.
(T) 01305 783145
Mr Ian Harrington, Angler's Tackle Stores, 64 Park St, Weymouth, Dorset, DT4 7DE.
(T) 01305 782624
Profile: **FT:** Coarse; **WN:** Radipole; **WT:** Lake (Still) **W. Size:** 70 Acres. **Location:** **Nr. Rd:** Weymouth centre, 5 minutes walk from station; **Rail:** Weymouth.
Ref: FH3875

RADWELL COMPLEX

Radwell Complex, Milton Ernest, Bedford, **BEDFORDSHIRE**, MK44, **England**.
Contact/s: **Peter**, Leslies of Luton, 89-93 Park St, Luton, Bedfordshire, LU1 3HG.
(T) 01582 453542
Profile: **FT:** Coarse; **WN:** Radwell Complex; **WT:** Lake (Still). **Location:** **Main Rd:** A6, Bedford to Rushden.
Ref: FH3876

RAILWAY LAKE

Railway Lake, Worthing Rd, North Elmham, Dereham, **NORFOLK**, NR, **England**.
Contact/s: **Mr Dave Playford** (Manager), Dave's Tackle Shop, 8 Millers Walk, Fakenham, Norfolk, NR21 9AP.
(T) 01328 862543
Mr G Twite (Secretary), Fakenham Angling Club, 16 Back St, Hempton, Fakenham, NR21 7LR.
(T) 01328 863054
Profile: **FT:** Coarse; **WN:** Railway; **WT:** Lake (Still); **F. Size:** 2 Acres; **W. Size:** 1 Acre. **Location:** **Nr. Rd:** Worthing Road; **Main Rd:** Baldswell Road or North Elmham; **Rail:** Norwich.
Ref: FH3877

RAILWAY LAKE

Railway Lake, Thuxton, **NORFOLK**, **England**.
(W) www.fisheries.co.uk/barford/index.htm
Contact/s: **Ms Sarah Thomson** (Manager), Barford Lakes Fishery, Common Farm, Chapel St, Barford, NR9 4AB.
(T) 01603 759624 **(F)** 01603 758111
(E) barfordlakes@barfordlakes.force9.co.uk
Profile: **FT:** Coarse; **WN:** Railway Lake; **WT:** Lake (Still); **F. Size:** 6 Acres; **W. Size:** 5 Acres. **Location:** **Main Rd:** B1135; **Rail:** East Dereham.
Ref: FH3878

RAILWAY LAKES

Railway Lakes, Whittlesey, Peterborough, **CAMBRIDGESHIRE**, PE7, **England**.
Contact/s: Fishery Manager.
(T) 01733 202428
Profile: **FT:** Coarse; **WN:** Railway; **WT:** Lake (Still).
Ref: FH3879

RAILWAY POND

Railway Pond, Stockbridge Lane, Arksey, Doncaster, **YORKSHIRE (SOUTH)**, DN5, **England**.
Contact/s: **Mr Cliff Bunney**, 254 Ascott Rd, Bentley, Doncaster, DN5 0EU.
(T) 01302 820251
Profile: **FT:** Coarse; **WN:** Railway; **WT:** Lake (Still) **W. Size:** 2 Acres. **Location:** **Nr. Rd:** Stockbridge Lane; **Main Rd:** A19 to Bentley.
Ref: FH3880

RAINBOW LAKES

Rainbow Lakes, Wildmoorhay Lane, South Cerney, Cirencester, **GLOUCESTERSHIRE**, GL7, **England**.
Contact/s: **Mr Dave McPherson**.
(T) 01285 861133
Profile: **FT:** Game; **WN:** Rainbow; **WT:** Lake (Still). **Location:** **Nr. Rd:** Wildmoorhay Lane.
Ref: FH3881

RAITH LAKE FISHERY

Raith Lake Fishery, Boglily Rd, Kirkcaldy, **FIFE**, KY2 6, **Scotland**.
Contact/s: **Mr Rob Duffy** (Proprietor), 32 Lomond Gardens, Kirkcaldy, Fife, KY2 6AE.
(T) 01592 646466 **(M)** 07939 473940
Profile: **FT:** Game; **WN:** Raith Lake Fishery; **WT:** River (Moving); **F. Size:** 20 Acres; **W. Size:** 40 Metres. **Location:** **Nr. Rd:** B925; **Main Rd:** B925; **Rail:** Kirkcaldy.
Ref: FH3882

RAKE BROOK RESERVOIR

Rake Brook Reservoir, Abbey Village, Chorley, **LANCASHIRE**, PR6, **England**.
Contact/s: **Mr Bernard Wren** (Secretary), 1 Belmont Cl, Brinscall, Chorley, Lancashire, PR6 8SX.
(T) 01254 830935
Mr Roy Rhodes (Conservation, Access and Recreation Manager), Rivington Water Treatment Works, Bolton Rd, Horwich, Bolton, BL6 7RN.
(T) 01204 664300
Profile: **FT:** Combination; **WN:** Rake Brook; **WT:** Reservoir (Still). **Location:** **Nr. Rd:** A575 to Abbey Village; **Main Rd:** A674, Chorley to Blackburn Road.
Ref: FH3883

RAKER LAKES

Raker Lakes, Greengales Lane, Wheldrake, York, **YORKSHIRE (NORTH)**, YO19 6BW, **England**.
(W) www.rakerlakes.co.uk
Contact/s: **Mr Steven Thompson** (Manager).
(T) 01904 448793 **(F)** 01904 448793
Profile: **FT:** Combination; **WN:** Raker; **WT:** Lake (Still) **W. Size:** 14 Acres. **Location:** **Nr. Rd:** Elvington to Wheldrake; **Main Rd:** A19; **Rail:** York.
Ref: FH3884

RALLT FISHERY

Rallt Fishery, Cellan, Lampeter, **CEREDIGION**, SA48 8, **Wales**.
(W) www.fishing-in-wales.co.uk/llandysul-aa/beat1a
Contact/s: **Mr Artie Jones** (Hon Secretary), Llandysul Angling Association, Glas-y-Dorlan, Llyn-y-Fran Rd, Llandysul, SA44 4JW.
(T) 01559 362317
Profile: **FT:** Game; **WN:** Teifi; **WT:** River (Moving). **Location:** **Nr. Rd:** B4343 Cwmann to Llanfair Clydogau.
Ref: FH3885

RALOO TROUT FISHERIES

Raloo Trout Fisheries, 17- 19 Ballyrickyard Rd, Larne, Ballymena, **COUNTY ANTRIM**, BT43 EQ, **Northern Ireland**.
Contact/s: **Mr Andy McCowan** (Manager).
(T) 028 28272171
Profile: **FT:** Game; **WN:** Raloo Trout Fisheries; **WT:** Lough (Still). **Location:** **Nr. Rd:** Ballyrickyard Road.
Ref: FH3886

RANDALLS LAKE

Randalls Lake, Barway, Ely, **CAMBRIDGESHIRE**, CB7, **England**.
Profile: **FT:** Coarse; **WN:** Randalls; **WT:** Lake (Still). **Location:** **Main Rd:** A142 to Barway.
Ref: FH3887

RAPHAELS PARK

Raphaels Park, Romford Market, Romford, **ESSEX**, RM, **England**.
Contact/s: Fishery Manager.
(T) 020 85903521
Manager, B and T Angling, 3 Grange Rd, Romford, Essex, RM3 7DU.
(T) 01708 370033
Mr Doug Law (Secretary).
(T) 01708 521721 **(M)** 07990 440309
Profile: **FT:** Coarse; **WN:** Raphael's Park; **WT:** Lake (Still) **W. Size:** 7 Acres. **Location:** **Nr. Rd:** A118 Main Road; **Main Rd:** Romford Market to Gallows Corner.
Ref: FH3888

RASKELF LAKE

Raskelf Lake, Raskelf, York, **YORKSHIRE (NORTH)**, YO16, **England**.
Contact/s: **Mr Howard Foster** (Secretary), 6 Moorclose Lane, Queensbury, Bradford, Yorkshire (West), BD13 2BP.
(T) 01274 881851
Mr John Sparks, 12 Fairway Walk, Wibsey,

Bradford, BD7 4JW.
Profile: **FT:** Coarse; **WN:** Raskelf; **WT:** Lake (Still) **W. Size:** 3 Acres. **Location:** **Nr. Rd:** A19; **Main Rd:** York to Thirsk.
Ref: FH3889

RATHBEGGAN LAKES

Rathbeggan Lakes, Dunshaughlin, **COUNTY MEATH**, **Ireland**.
Contact/s: **Mr Dave Robinson** (Manager). **(T)** 01 8240197 **(F)** 001 8240196
Profile: **FT:** Game; **WN:** Rathbeggan; **WT:** Lake (Still) **W. Size:** 4 Acres.
Ref: FH3890

RATHER HEATH TARN

Rather Heath Tarn, Ratherheath Lane, Burnside, Kendal, **CUMBRIA**, LA, **England**.
Contact/s: **Mr Chris Sodo** (Hon Treasurer), Windermere, Ambleside and District Angling Association, Ecclerigg Court, Ecclerigg, Windermere, LA23 1LQ.
(T) 01539 445083
Profile: **FT:** Coarse; **WN:** Ratherheath; **WT:** Tarn (Still) **W. Size:** 5 Acres. **Location:** **Nr. Rd:** A591 North of Kendal; **Main Rd:** A5284.
Ref: FH3891

RATTLE (RIVER)

River Rattle, Stowmarket, **SUFFOLK**, IP14, **England**.
Contact/s: **Chris** (Manager), Bosmere Tackle, 59 High St, Needham Market, Ipswich, IP6 8AL.
(T) 01449 721808
Profile: **FT:** Coarse; **WN:** Rattle; **WT:** River (Moving).
Ref: FH3892

RAVELEY DRAIN

Raveley Drain, Upwood, Ramsey, **CAMBRIDGESHIRE**, PE, **England**.
Contact/s: **Mr Paul Marriet** (Secretary), Yaxley Farcet, Holme & District AC, 72 Portchester Cl, Park Farm, Peterborough, PE2 8UP. **(M)** 07885 439184
Profile: **FT:** Coarse; **WN:** Raveley; **WT:** Drain (Still) **W. Size:** 500 Metres. **Location:** **Nr. Rd:** Whittlsey to Ramsey; **Main Rd:** B1040.
Ref: FH3893

RAVENSNEST FISHERY

Ravensnest Fishery, Raglan Rd, Tintern, Chepstow, **MONMOUTHSHIRE**, NP16 6TP, **Wales**.
Contact/s: **Mr C.J Griffiths** (owner).
(T) 01291 689564
Profile: **FT:** Game; **WN:** Ravensnest; **WT:** Pond (Still). **Location:** **Main Rd:** A466, Chepstow to Monmouth.
Ref: FH3894

RAVENSTHORPE TROUT FISHERY

Ravensthorpe Trout Fishery, Fishing Lodge, Teeton Rd, Ravensthorpe, Northampton, **NORTHAMPTONSHIRE**, NN6 8EJ, **England**.
Contact/s: **Mr Nathan Clayton** (Fishery Warden), Pitsford Fishing Lodge, Brixworth Rd, Holcot, NN6 9SJ.
(T) 01604 781350
Profile: **FT:** Game; **WN:** Ravensthorpe Trout Fishery; **WT:** Lake (Still) **W. Size:** 100 Acres.
Ref: FH3895

RAWLSBURY WATERS

Rawlsbury Waters, Kingcombe Ponds, Kingcombe, Dorchester, **DORSET**, DT2, **England**.
Contact/s: **Mr Jack Langham** (Fishery Manager).
(T) 01258 817446
Profile: **FT:** Game; **WN:** Kingcombe; **WT:** Pond (Still).
Ref: FH3896

RAWTHEY (RIVER)

Rawthey (River), Abbotholme Farm, Sedburgh, **CUMBRIA**, **England**.
Contact/s: **Mr John Turner** (Hon Secretary), Prince Albert Angling Society, 15 Pexhill Drive, Macclesfield, Cheshire, SK10 3LP.
(T) 01625 422010
Profile: **FT:** Game; **WN:** Rawthey; **WT:** River (Moving) **W. Size:** 1200 Metres. **Location:** **Nr. Rd:** Abbot Holme Bridge; **Main Rd:** A684; **Rail:** Kendal.
Ref: FH3897

RAWTHEY (RIVER)

River Rawthey, Lune, Sedbergh, **CUMBRIA**, LA10 5, **England**.
Contact/s: **Mr G Bainbridge** (Secretary), Sedbergh and District Angling Association, El Kantara, Frostrow, Sedbergh, LA10 5JL.
(T) 01539 620044
Profile: **FT:** Game; **WN:** Rawthey; **WT:** River (Moving). **Location:** **Nr. Rd:** Fell End to Lune.
Ref: FH3898

RAWTHEY (RIVER)

River Rawthey, Valley Of Cautley, Sedbergh, **CUMBRIA**, LA10, **England**.
Contact/s: **Mr C Richardson**, Three Peaks Ltd, 25 Main St, Sedbergh, Cumbria, LA10 5BW.
(T) 01539 620446
Mr D Eccles, Three Peaks Ltd, 25 Main St, Sedbergh, Cumbria, LA10 5BW.
(T) 01539 620446
Profile: **FT:** Game; **WN:** Rawthey; **WT:** River (Moving). **Location:** **Nr. Rd:** A684; **Rail:** Kendal.
Ref: FH3899

RAY (RIVER)

River Ray, Seven Bridges, Swindon, **WILTSHIRE**, SN2, **England**.
Contact/s: **Mr Ray Daffon** (Secretary), South Cerney Angling Club, Broadway Lane, South Cerney, Cirencester, GL7 5UH.
(T) 01285 861876 **(M)** 07775 970643
Profile: **FT:** Coarse; **WN:** Ray; **WT:** River (Moving). **Location:** **Main Rd:** A419.
Ref: FH3900

RAYDON PONDS

Raydon Ponds, Southwold, **SUFFOLK**, IP18, **England**.
Contact/s: **Mr J Purdy** (Secretary), Purdy's Newsagent, High St, Southwold, Suffolk.
(T) 01502 724250
Profile: **FT:** Coarse; **WN:** Raydon; **WT:** Pond (Still).
Ref: FH3901

RAYGILL FISHERY

Raygill Fishery, Lothersdale, Keighley, **YORKSHIRE (WEST)**, BD20 8, **England**.
Contact/s: **Mr Bernard Clemments** (Manager), 1 Raygill Cottage, Lothersdale, Keighley, Yorkshire (West), BD20 8HH.
(T) 01535 632500 **(F)** 01535 632141
(E) raygillfisheries@hotmail.com
Profile: **FT:** Combination; **WN:** Raygill; **WT:** Lake (Still) **W. Size:** 24 Acres. **Location:** **Nr. Rd:** A629; **Main Rd:** A59; **Rail:** Skipton.
Ref: FH3902

RAYNE LODGE FARM

Rayne Lodge Farm, Rayne Rd, Braintree, **ESSEX**, CM7 2QT, **England**.
Contact/s: **Mr Tony Pearson** (Owner).
(T) 01376 345719 **(M)** 07710 483850
Profile: **FT:** Coarse; **WN:** Rayne Lodge Farm; **WT:** Pool (Still) **W. Size:** 2 Acres. **Location:** **Nr. Rd:** Rayne Road, 1 mile; **Main Rd:** A120 or A131.
Ref: FH3903

REASEHEATH COLLEGE LAKE

Reaseheath College Lake, Reaseheath College, Reaseheath, Nantwich, **CHESHIRE**, CW5 6DF, **England**.
Contact/s: **Mr Albert Perkins** (Hon Secretary), 63 Fowlers Lane, Light Oaks, Stoke-on-Trent, Staffordshire, ST2 7NB.
Ms Liz Hayes (Manager).
(T) 01625 251262
Profile: **FT:** Coarse; **WN:** Reaseheath College; **WT:** Lake (Still) **W. Size:** 2 Acres. **Location:** **Nr. Rd:** A51; **Main Rd:** A51; **Rail:** Nantwich.
Ref: FH3904

RECTORY FARM FISHERY

Rectory Farm Fishery, Hingham, Norwich, **NORFOLK**, NR9, **England**.
Contact/s: Fishery Manager.
(T) 01953 851509
Profile: **FT:** Coarse; **WN:** Rectory Farm Fishery; **WT:** Lake (Still).
Ref: FH3905

RECTORY FARM POND

Rectory Farm Pond, Rectory Farm, Bradwell, Braintree, **ESSEX**, CM7, **England**.
(W) www.bdac.co.uk
Contact/s: **Mr Derek Howard** (Hon Treasurer), Billericay and District Angling Club, 4 Long Meadow Drive, Wickford, Essex, SS11 8AX.
(T) 01268 734468
Profile: **FT:** Coarse; **WN:** Rectory Farm; **WT:** Lake (Still); **F. Size:** 5 Acres; **W. Size:** 4 Acres. **Location:** **Nr. Rd:** A120; **Main Rd:** A131 to Braintree; **Rail:** Braintree.
Ref: FH3906

RED BANK POOLS

Red Bank Pools, Ledbury, **HEREFORDSHIRE**, HR8, **England**.
Contact/s: **Mr Brian Powell** (Red Banks Pools Manager), Three Counties Fisheries, Field Cottage, Ryton, Dymock, Gloucestershire, GL18 2DH.
(T) 01531 890455
Profile: **FT:** Coarse; **WN:** Red Bank Pools; **WT:** Pond (Still) **W. Size:** 1 Acre. **Location:** **Main Rd:** B4216, A449.
Ref: FH3907

RED BARNS POND

Red Barns Pond, Mill Lane, Hebburn, Newcastle Upon Tyne, **TYNE AND WEAR**, NE18, **England**.
Contact/s: **Mr Micky Kincaird** (Fishery Manager).
(T) 0191 5366991
Profile: **FT:** Coarse; **WN:** Red Barns; **WT:** Pond (Still). **Location:** **Nr. Rd:** Mill Lane; **Main Rd:** A194.
Ref: FH3908

RED BECK LAKE

Red Beck Lake, Evesham, **WORCESTERSHIRE**, WR11, **England**.
Contact/s: **Mr Peter Mohan** (Fishery Controller), 149 Harrowden Rd, Bedford, Gloucester, MK42 0RU.
(T) 01264 212066 **(M)** 07884 332523
Profile: **FT:** Game; **WN:** Red Beck; **WT:** Lake (Still) **W. Size:** 4 Acres. **Location:** **Nr. Rd:** A4184, A44.
Ref: FH3909

RED LION FISHERY

Red Lion Fishery, Red Lion Inn, Wainlode Hill, Norton, Gloucester, **GLOUCESTERSHIRE**, GL2 9LW, **England**.
Contact/s: **Mr J G Mitchell** (Landlord), Red Lion Inn, Wainlode Hill, Norton, Gloucester, GL2 9LW.
(T) 01452 730251
Profile: **FT:** Coarse; **WN:** Severn; **WT:** Combination (Still & Moving); **F. Size:** 12 Acres; **W. Size:** 900 Metres. **Location:** **Nr. Rd:** Country Lane; **Main Rd:** A38; **Rail:** Gloucester.
Ref: FH3910

RED ROCKS FISHERY

Red Rocks Fishery, Potter Lane, Higher Walton, Preston, **LANCASHIRE**, PR, **England**.
Contact/s: **Mr Bill Cooper**.
(T) 01772 877277
Profile: **FT:** Coarse; **WN:** Red Rocks; **WT:** Lake (Still) **W. Size:** 2 Acres. **Location:** **Nr. Rd:** Potter Lane; **Main Rd:** A59 to Blackburn.
Ref: FH3911

REDBROOK RESERVOIR

Redbrook Reservoir, Saddleworth, Oldham, **MANCHESTER (GREATER)**, OL3, **England**.
Contact/s: Fishery Manager.
(T) 01457 875993
Profile: **FT:** Coarse; **WN:** Redbrook; **WT:** Reservoir (Still).
Ref: FH3912

REDDISH VALE MILL PONDS

Reddish Vale Mill Ponds, Mill Lane, Reddish, Stockport, **MANCHESTER (GREATER)**, SK5 7HE, **England**.
Contact/s: **Mr David Armes**.
(T) 0161 4775637 **(F)** 0161 4779296
Profile: **FT:** Coarse; **WN:** Reddish Vale Mill; **WT:** Pond (Still). **Location:** **Nr. Rd:** Mill Lane; **Main Rd:** B6167 Manchester to Stockport Road; **Rail:** South Reddish.
Ref: FH3913

REDE (RIVER)

River Rede, West Woodburn, Hexham, **NORTHUMBERLAND**, NE48, **England**.
Contact/s: **Mr John Armstrong**, 55 Calder Walk, Sunneyside, Whickham, Newcastle upon Tyne.
(T) 0191 4886496
Profile: **FT:** Game; **WN:** Rede; **WT:** River (Moving).
Ref: FH3914

REDE (RIVER)

River Rede, Otterburn Tower Hotel, Otterburn, Newcastle Upon Tyne, **TYNE AND WEAR**, NE19, **England**.
Contact/s: **Mr J Goodfellow** (Manager), The Towers Hotel, Otterburn, Newcastle-upon-Tyne, Tyne and Wear, NE19 1NS.
(T) 01830 520620
Profile: **FT:** Game; **WN:** Rede; **WT:** River (Moving) **W. Size:** 5600 Metres. **Location:** **Nr. Rd:** Mill Bridge.
Ref: FH3915

REDESMERE

Redesmere, Capesthorne Estate, Siddington, Macclesfield, **CHESHIRE**, SK11, **England**.
Contact/s: **Mr Albert Perkins** (Hon Secretary), 63 Fowlers Lane, Light Oaks, Stoke-on-Trent, Staffordshire, ST2 7NB.
Ms Liz Hayes (Manager).
(T) 01625 251262
Profile: **FT:** Coarse; **WN:** Redesmere; **WT:** Lake (Still); **F. Size:** 55 Acres; **W. Size:** 40 Acres. **Location:** **Nr. Rd:** Farnshawe Lane; **Main Rd:** A34, Alderley Edge to Congleton Road; **Rail:** Alderley Edge.
Ref: FH3916

REDFERNS POND

Redferns Pond, 20 Canal Side East, Newport, Brough, **HUMBERSIDE**, HU15, **England**.
Contact/s: **Ms Sandra Taylor**.
(T) 01430 441896
Profile: **FT:** Coarse; **WN:** Redfern's; **WT:** Pond (Still). **Location:** **Nr. Rd:** Canal Side East; **Main Rd:** M62, junction 38.
Ref: FH3917

REDHOUSE LAGOON

Redhouse Lagoon, Clifton, York, **YORKSHIRE (NORTH)**, YO, **England**.
Contact/s: **Mr Bob Hutchinson** (Central Secretary), 57 Water Lane, Clifton, York, Yorkshire (North).
(T) 01904 651346
Profile: **FT:** Coarse; **WN:** Redhouse Lagoon; **WT:** Lake (Still).
Ref: FH3918

REDLANDS LAKE

Redlands Lake, Reading, **BERKSHIRE**, RG, **England**.
Contact/s: **Mr Williams**, 24 Duncan Rd, Woodley, Reading, Berkshire.
Profile: **FT:** Combination; **WN:** Redlands; **WT:** Lake (Still).
Ref: FH3919

REDLANDS PITS

Redlands Pits, West Deeping, Peterborough, **CAMBRIDGESHIRE**, PE6, **England**.
Contact/s: **Mr D Bailey** (Secretary).
(T) 01778 346355
Profile: **FT:** Coarse; **WN:** Redlands Pit; **WT:** Lake (Still). **Location:** **Rail:** Lolham level crossing.
Ref: FH3920

REDMIRE POOL

Redmire Pool, Ross-on-Wye, **HEREFORDSHIRE**, HR9, **England**.
(W) www.carpsociety.com
Contact/s: Secretary, The Carp Society, Horseshoe Lake, Burford Rd, Lechlade, GL7 3QQ.
(T) 01367 253959
Mr Les Bamford (Booking Manager).
(T) 01923 896994
Profile: **FT:** Coarse; **WN:** Redmire; **WT:** Pond (Still); **F. Size:** 4 Acres; **W. Size:** 3 Acres.
Ref: FH3921

REDWELL FISHERIES

Redwell Fisheries, Arkholme, Over Kellet, Carnforth, **CUMBRIA**, LA6 1BQ, **England**.
Contact/s: Fishery Manager.
(T) 01542 221979
Profile: **FT:** Coarse; **WN:** Redwell Fisheries; **WT:** Lake (Still).
Ref: FH3922

REED LAKE

Reed Lake, Bobbin Lodge Hill, Chartham, Canterbury, **KENT**, **England**.
(W) www.midkentfish.demon.co.uk
Contact/s: **Mr Chris Logsdon** (Fisheries Manager), Mid Kent Fisheries, Chilham Water Mill, Mill Lane, Chilham, CT4 8EE.
(T) 01227 730668
(E) chilham@midkentfisheries.co.uk
Profile: **FT:** Coarse; **WN:** Reed Lake; **WT:** Lake (Still); **F. Size:** 30 Acres; **W. Size:** 2 Acres. **Location:** **Main Rd:** A28; **Rail:** Chartham.
Ref: FH3923

REEPHAM FISHERY

Reepham Fishery, Reepham Beck Farm, Norwich Rd, Reepham, Norwich, **NORFOLK**, NR10 4NR, **England**.
Mrs C Neal (Owner).
(T) 01603 870829
Profile: **FT:** Coarse; **WN:** Reepham; **WT:** Lake (Still) **W. Size:** 4 Acres. **Location:** **Nr. Rd:** Norwich Road; **Rail:** Aylsham.
Ref: FH3924

REGENTS CANAL

Regents Canal, Camden Lock, Camden, London, **LONDON (GREATER)**, NW1, **England**.
Contact/s: **Mr Mac McEndoo**, Acton Angling Ctre, 185 Old Oak Rd, London, W3 7HH.
(T) 020 87433381 **(F)** 020 87434482
Mr Rick Dennis (Manager).
(T) 020 85876656
Profile: **FT:** Coarse; **WN:** Regent's; **WT:** Canal (Still). **Location:** **Nr. Rd:** Camden Road; **Rail:** Kings Cross Underground.
Ref: FH3925

REGENTS CANAL

Regents Canal, Camley St, St Pancras Way, St Pancras, London, **LONDON (GREATER)**, NW1, **England**.
Contact/s: **Mr Rick Dennis** (Manager).
(T) 020 85876656
Profile: **FT:** Coarse; **WN:** Regents; **WT:** Canal (Still). **Location:** **Nr. Rd:** Camden Lock to York Way; **Main Rd:** B525.
Ref: FH3926

REGENTS CANAL

Regents Canal, Kings Cross, London, **LONDON (GREATER)**, WC1X, **England**.
Contact/s: **Mr Rick Dennis** (Manager).
(T) 020 85876656
Profile: **FT:** Coarse; **WN:** Regents; **WT:** Canal (Still). **Location:** **Nr. Rd:** Islington Tunnel to York Way; **Rail:** Kings Cross.
Ref: FH3927

REGENTS CANAL

Regents Canal, Mile End Lock, London, **LONDON (GREATER)**, E14, **England**.
Contact/s: **Mr T E Taylor**, Brunswick Brothers Angling Society, 40 St Andrews Rd, Cranbrook, Ilford, IG1 3PF.
(T) 020 85544600 **(F)** 020 73576065
Profile: **FT:** Coarse; **WN:** Regents; **WT:** Canal (Still) **W. Size:** 1600 Metres. **Location:** **Nr. Rd:** Mile End Lock to Commercial Road Lock.
Ref: FH3928

RELIEF CHANNEL

Relief Channel, Wiggenhall St Mary Magdalen To Stowbridge, King's Lynn, **NORFOLK**, PE34, **England**.
Contact/s: **Mr Mick Grief** (Secretary), King's Lynn Angling Association, 67 Peckover Way, South Wootton, King's Lynn, PE30 3UE.
(T) 01553 671545
Profile: **FT:** Coarse; **WN:** Relief Channel; **WT:** River (Moving). **Location:** **Main Rd:** A10.
Ref: FH3929

RESCOBIE LOCH

Rescobie Loch, The Lodge, Burnside, Dundee, **ANGUS**, DD8, **Scotland**.
Contact/s: **Mr Jack Yule**.
(T) 01307 830367
Profile: **FT:** Game; **WN:** Rescobie; **WT:** Loch (Still).
Ref: FH3930

RETALLACK WATERS

Retallack Waters, Spirit Of The West American Theme Park, Retallack Park, Winnard's Perch, St Columb, **CORNWALL**, TR9 6DE, **England**.
(W) www.chycor.co.uk
Contact/s: **Mr Barrance Browning** (Manager).
(T) 01637 881160 **(F)** 01637 881104 **(M)** 07971 795907
Profile: **FT:** Coarse; **WN:** Retallack Waters; **WT:** Lake (Still); **F. Size:** 100 Acres; **W. Size:** 10 Acres. **Location:** **Nr. Rd:** A39; **Main Rd:** A30; **Rail:** Newquay.
Ref: FH3931

REVEL'S FISHERY

Revels Fishery, Revells Farm, Sherborne Rd, Cosmore, Dorchester, **DORSET**, DT2 7TW, **England**.
Contact/s: **Mr Jason Fricher** (Fishery Manager).
(T) 01300 345301
Profile: **FT:** Coarse; **WN:** Revels Fishery; **WT:** Lake (Still). **Location:** **Nr. Rd:** Sherborne Road.
Ref: FH3932

REVESBY RESERVOIR

Revesby Reservoir, Horncastle, **LINCOLNSHIRE**, LN9, **England**.
Contact/s: **Mr Wiggins Davis** (Owner), Revesby Estate Office, Revesby, Boston.
(T) 01507 568395
Profile: **FT:** Coarse; **WN:** Revesby; **WT:** Reservoir (Still).
Ref: FH3933

REYDON LAKES

Reydon Lakes, Lakeside Park Rd, Reydon, Southwold, **SUFFOLK**, IP18, **England**.
Contact/s: **Mr J Purdy** (Secretary), Purdy's Newsagent, High St, Southwold, Suffolk.
(T) 01502 724250
Profile: **FT:** Coarse; **WN:** Reydon; **WT:** Lake (Still). **Location:** **Nr. Rd:** Lakeside Park Road.
Ref: FH3934

RHEIDOL (RIVER)

River Rheidol, Aberystwyth, **CEREDIGION**,

SY23, **Wales**.
Contact/s: **Mr Peredur Eklund** (Hon Secretary), 42 Erwgoch, Waunfawr, Aberystwyth, Carmarthenshire, SY23 3AZ.
(T) 01970 623021
Profile: **FT:** Game; **WN:** Rheidol; **WT:** River (Moving) **W. Size:** 19200 Metres. **Location:** **Nr. Rd:** A44 and A4120. **£Fr**
Ref: FH3935

RHODES LODGE

Rhodes Lodge, Old Rd, Middleton, Manchester, **MANCHESTER (GREATER)**, M, **England**.
Contact/s: **Mr Doug Summers** (Secretary).
(T) 01270 762579
Mr Gary Leigh (Club Secretary), Middleton Angling Society, 151 Tennyson Rd, Boarshaw, Middleton, Manchester M24 2NS.
(T) 0161 6546253 **(M)** 07973 205280
Profile: **FT:** Coarse; **WN:** Rhodes Lodge; **WT:** Pond (Still) **W. Size:** 18 Acres. **Location:** **Nr. Rd:** Old Road; **Main Rd:** A576.
Ref: FH3936

RHONDDA (RIVER)

River Rhondda, Treorchy, **RHONDDA CYNON TAFF**, CF42, **Wales**.
Contact/s: **Mr John Evans** (General Secretary), 126 Ystrad Rd, Ystrad, Rhondda, Glamorgan.
(T) 01443 439961
Profile: **FT:** Game; **WN:** Rhondda; **WT:** River (Moving) **W. Size:** 4800 Metres. **Location:** **Nr. Rd:** Treorchy to Trehadfod.
Ref: FH3937

RHYDFACH FISHERY

Rhydfach Fishery (The), Pentrecagal, Newcastle Emlyn, **CARMARTHENSHIRE**, SA38, **Wales**.
Contact/s: **Mr Peter Jones**, Oldfield Lodge, Oldfield Rd, Bickley, Kent, BR1 2LE.
(T) 020 72609315or84674106evening
Profile: **FT:** Game; **WN:** Teifi; **WT:** River (Moving) **W. Size:** 800 Metres. **Location:** **Nr. Rd:** Pentrecagal to Pentre Cwrt.
Ref: FH3938

RHYDHIR (RIVER)

River Rhydhir, Pwllheli, **GWYNEDD**, LL53, **Wales**.
Contact/s: **E W Evans** (Membership Secretary), 2 Fron - Oleu, Caernarfon Rd, Pwllheli, Gwynedd, LL53 5LN.
Mr Len Hicks (Secretary), Pwllheli and District Angling Association, 82 Abererch Rd, Pwllheli, Gwynedd, LL53 5LS.
(T) 01758 614885
Profile: **FT:** Game; **WN:** Rhydhir; **WT:** River (Moving) **W. Size:** 12800 Metres. **Location:** **Nr. Rd:** A497; **Rail:** Pwllheli.
Ref: FH3939

RHYDLEWIS TROUT FISHERY

Rhydlewis Trout Fishery, Rhydlewis, Llandysul, **CEREDIGION**, SA44 5QS, **Wales**.
Contact/s: Fishery Manager.
(T) 01239 851224
Profile: **FT:** Game; **WN:** Rhydlewis Trout Fishery; **WT:** Lake (Still).
Ref: FH3940

RHYDYGALFE FISHERY

Rhydygalfe Fishery, Rhydygalfe, Llandysul, **CEREDIGION**, SA, **Wales**.
(W) www.fishing-in-wales.co.uk/llandysul-aa/beat13
Contact/s: **Mr Artie Jones** (Hon Secretary), Llandysul Angling Association, Glas-y-Dorlan, Llyn-y-Fran Rd, Llandysul, SA44 4JW.
(T) 01559 362317
Profile: **FT:** Game; **WN:** Teifi; **WT:** River (Moving).
Ref: FH3941

RIB VALLEY FISHING LAKE

Rib Valley Fishing Lake, West Mill Rd, Ware, **HERTFORDSHIRE**, SG12 0ES, **England**.
(W) www.ribvalleyfishinglakes.com
Contact/s: **Mr Richard Vigus** (Bailiff), Revels Croft Farm, Wadesmill Rd, Bengo, Hertford, SG14 8HJ.
(T) 01920 484913
Profile: **FT:** Game; **WN:** Rib Valley; **WT:** Lake (Still) **W. Size:** 18 Acres. **Location:** **Nr. Rd:** West Mill Road.
Ref: FH3942

RIBBLE (RIVER)

Ribble (River), Standen Estate, Great Mitton, Nr. Whalley, Blackburn, **LANCASHIRE**, **England**.
Contact/s: **Mr John Turner** (Hon Secretary), Prince Albert Angling Society, 15 Pexhill Drive, Macclesfield, Cheshire, SK10 3LP.
(T) 01625 422010
Profile: **FT:** Game; **WN:** Ribble; **WT:** River (Moving) **W. Size:** 1000 Metres. **Location:** **Nr. Rd:** B6246; **Rail:** Billington.
Ref: FH3943

RIBBLE (RIVER)

River Ribble, Elston, Preston, **LANCASHIRE**, PR, **England**.
(W) www.wiganaa.f9.co.uk
Contact/s: **Mr Gerry Wilson** (Hon Secretary), Wigan and District Angling Association, 11 Guildford Avenue, Chorley, Lancashire, PR6 8TG.
(T) 01257 265905
(E) gerry@wiganna.freeserve.co.uk
Profile: **FT:** Coarse; **WN:** Ribble; **WT:** River (Moving) **W. Size:** 1600 Metres. **Location:** **Main Rd:** M6, B6243.
Ref: FH3944

RIBBLE (RIVER)

River Ribble, Mitton, Whalley, Clitheroe, **LANCASHIRE**, BB7, **England**.
Contact/s: **Mrs Haynes**, Mitton Hall Farm, Mitton Rd, Mitton, Whalley, Clitheroe, BB7 9PQ.
(T) 01254 826002
Profile: **FT:** Combination; **WN:** Ribble; **WT:** River (Moving) **W. Size:** 3200 Metres. **Location:** **Rail:** Whalley.
Ref: FH3945

RIBBLE (RIVER)

River Ribble, Ribchester, Preston, **LANCASHIRE**, PR3, **England**.
Contact/s: **Brian** (Manager), Lostock Tackle Box, 16 Watkin Lane, Lostock Hall, Preston, PR5 5RD.
(T) 01772 626585 **(F)** 01772 626585
Profile: **FT:** Combination; **WN:** Ribble; **WT:** River (Moving).
Ref: FH3946

RICCAL (RIVER)

River Riccal, Nunnington, Malton, **YORKSHIRE (NORTH)**, YO17, **England**.
Contact/s: **Mr K Metcalf**.
(T) 01723 378824
Profile: **FT:** Game; **WN:** Riccal; **WT:** River (Moving). **Location:** **Main Rd:** A64.
Ref: FH3947

RICHMOND LAKES

Richmond Lakes, Lincoln, **LINCOLNSHIRE**, LN, **England**.
Contact/s: **Mr Len Kirk**.
(T) 01522 681329
Profile: **FT:** Coarse; **WN:** Richmond; **WT:** Lake (Still).
Ref: FH3948

RIDDINGS FISHERY

Riddings Fishery (The), Watling St, Grendon, Atherstone, **WARWICKSHIRE**, CV9 2PE, **England**.
(W) www.fisheries.co.uk/riddings
Contact/s: **Mr Tom Everitt** (Manager).
(T) 01827 713244or01827718754 **(F)** 01827 713244
Profile: **FT:** Coarse; **WN:** Riddings Fishery (The); **WT:** Pool (Still) **W. Size:** 15 Acres. **Location:** **Nr. Rd:** Slacks Lane off A5; **Main Rd:** A5 at Grendon; **Rail:** Atherstone.
Ref: FH3949

RIDGEGATE RESERVOIR

Ridgegate Reservoir, Langley, Macclesfield, **CHESHIRE**, SK11, **England**.
Contact/s: **Mr Peter Sharples** (Conservation, Access and Recreation Manager), North West Water Ltd, Woodhead Rd, Tintwhistle, Hadfiled via Hyde, SK14 7HR.
(T) 01457 864187
Mr W Williams (Secretary), 1 Westwood Drive, Brooklands, Sale, M33 3QZ.
(T) 0161 9621233
Mrs S Stones (Day Ticket Bookings), Plough House, Gurnett, Sutton, Macclesfield, SK11 0HG.
Profile: **FT:** Game; **WN:** Ridgegate; **WT:** Reservoir (Still).
Ref: FH3950

RINGDUFFERIN ESTUARY

Ringdufferin Estuary, 34 Ringdufferin Rd, Toye, Downpatrick, **COUNTY DOWN**, BT30 9PH, **Northern Ireland**.
Contact/s: **Mr Frank Gibson** (Manager).
(T) 028 44828321 **(F)** 028 44821769 **(M)** 07799 887571
(E) frankgibson@tinyworld.co.uk
Profile: **FT:** Game; **WN:** Ringdufferin; **WT:** Lake (Still) **W. Size:** 1 Acre. **Location:** **Nr. Rd:** Ringdufferin Road; **Main Rd:** Killyleagh.
Ref: FH3951

RINGLAND LAKES

Ringland Lakes, Norwich, **NORFOLK**, NR, **England**.
Contact/s: **Mr Russell Francis** (Head Bailiff).
(T) 01603 870885
Profile: **FT:** Coarse; **WN:** Ringland; **WT:** Lake (Still).
Ref: FH3952

RINGLAND PITS

Ringland Pits, Old Costessey, Norwich, **NORFOLK**, NR, **England**.
(W) www.rmcangling.co.uk
Contact/s: **Mr Ian Welch** (Angling Manager), RMC Angling, The Square, Lightwater, Surrey, GU18 5SS.
(T) 01276 453300 **(F)** 01276 456611
(E) info@rmcangling.co.uk
Profile: **FT:** Coarse; **WT:** Combination (Still & Moving) **W. Size:** 500 Metres. **Location:** **Nr. Rd:** Ringland Road; **Main Rd:** A47.
Ref: FH3953

RINGSTEAD GRANGE

Ringstead Grange Trout Fishery, Ringstead, Kettering, **NORTHAMPTONSHIRE**, NN14 4DT, **England**.
Contact/s: **Mr Harold Foster** (Manager).
(T) 01933 622960
Profile: **FT:** Game; **WN:** Ringstead Grange; **WT:** Gravel Pit (Still) **W. Size:** 36 Acres. **Location:** **Nr. Rd:** A45; **Main Rd:** A14; **Rail:** Kettering.
Ref: FH3954

RINGSTEAD ISLAND

Ringstead Island, Thrapston, Kettering, **NORTHAMPTONSHIRE**, NN14, **England**.
Contact/s: Fishery Manager.
(T) 01933 53636
Profile: **FT:** Coarse; **WN:** Ringstead Island; **WT:** Lake (Still).
Ref: FH3955

RINGWOOD LAKE

Ringwood Park Lake, Brimington, Chesterfield, **DERBYSHIRE**, S4, **England**.
Contact/s: .
(T) 01246 345666
Profile: **FT:** Coarse; **WN:** Ringwood; **WT:** Lake (Still) **W. Size:** 4 Acres. **Location:** **Nr. Rd:** A619; **Rail:** Chesterfield.
Ref: FH3956

RIPLEY CASTLE

Ripley Castle, Ripley, Harrogate, **YORKSHIRE (NORTH)**, HG3, **England**.

Contact/s: Manager, Ripley Castle, Estate Office, Ripley, Harrogate, HG3 3AY.
(T) 01423 770152 (F) 01423 771745
Profile: FT: Coarse; WN: Ripley Castle; WT: Lake (Still). Location: Main Rd: A61.
Ref: FH3957

RIPON CANAL

Ripon Canal, Ripon, **YORKSHIRE (NORTH)**, HG4, **England**.
Contact/s: **Mr Bernard Thain** (Manager), Ripon Angling Ctre, 58-59 North St, Ripon, Yorkshire (North), HG4 1EN.
(T) 01765 604666 (F) 01765 603933
Profile: FT: Coarse; WN: Ripon; WT: Canal (Still). Location: Main Rd: A61.
Ref: FH3958

RIPON RACECOURSE LAKE

Ripon Racecourse Lake, Ripon, **YORKSHIRE (NORTH)**, HG4, **England**.
Contact/s: **Mr Bernard Thain** (Manager), Ripon Angling Ctre, 58-59 North St, Ripon, Yorkshire (North), HG4 1EN.
(T) 01765 604666 (F) 01765 603933
Profile: FT: Coarse; WN: Ripon Racecourse; WT: Lake (Still) W. Size: 20 Acres.
Location: Nr. Rd: A61, Hewick Bridge to Ripon; Main Rd: B6265.
Ref: FH3959

RISHTON RESERVOIR

Rishton Reservoir, Cut Lane, Rishton, Blackburn, **LANCASHIRE**, BB1, **England**.
Contact/s: **Mr Clarke**.
(T) 01200 425336
Mr Gerry Lee.
(T) 01254 385290
Profile: FT: Coarse; WN: Rishton; WT: Reservoir (Still). Location: Nr. Rd: Cut Lane; Main Rd: A678, Rishton to Blackburn.
Ref: FH3960

RISING TROUT FISHERY

Rising Trout Fishery, Blakeley Lane, Whiston, Cheadle, Stoke-on-Trent, **STAFFORDSHIRE**, ST, **England**.
Contact/s: Fishery Manager.
(T) 01889 507496
Profile: FT: Game; WN: Rising Trout Fishery; WT: Lake (Still).
Ref: FH3961

RISLIP LAKE

Rislip Lake, Tring, **HERTFORDSHIRE**, HP23, **England**.
Contact/s: **Mr Stuart Riddle** (Secretary), The Tring Anglers, PO Box 1947, Tring, Hertfordshire, HP23 5LZ.
(T) 01442 826148
Profile: FT: Coarse; WN: Rislip; WT: Lake (Still). Location: Nr. Rd: Rislip.
Ref: FH3962

RIVER (TERN)

River (Tern), Rea Farm, Upton Manga, Shrewsbury, **SHROPSHIRE**, **England**.
Contact/s: **Mr John Turner** (Hon Secretary), Prince Albert Angling Society, 15 Pexhill Drive, Macclesfield, Cheshire, SK10 3LP.
(T) 01625 422010
Profile: FT: Combination; WN: Tern; WT: River (Moving) W. Size: 500 Metres.
Location: Main Rd: A49; Rail: Shrewsbury.
Ref: FH3963

RIVER FARM

River Farm, Fontley Rd, Fareham, Fareham, **HAMPSHIRE**, PO15 6QZ, **England**.
Contact/s: **Mr F P Reid** (Manager), River Farm, Fontley Rd, Titchfield, Winchester, PO15 6QZ.
(T) 01329 841215
Profile: FT: Game; WN: River Farm; WT: Lake (Still); F. Size: 14 Acres; W. Size: 2 Acres. Location: Nr. Rd: Fontley Road; Main Rd: A27; Rail: Fareham.
Ref: FH3964

RIVER GWENLLIAN FISHERY

River Gwenllian Fishery, New Cydweli Camus, Nynydd-Y-Garreg, Kidwelly, **CARMARTHENSHIRE**, SA17, **Wales**.
Contact/s: Fishery Manager.
(T) 01554 890232
Profile: FT: Game; WN: Gwenllian; WT: River (Moving).
Ref: FH3965

RIVER VIEW COTTAGE

River View Cottage, Church St, Topcliffe, Thirsk, **YORKSHIRE (NORTH)**, YO7 3PA, **England**.
Contact/s: **Mr Roger Coaten** (Manager).
(T) 0113 2610052
Profile: FT: Game; WN: Swale; WT: Combination (Still & Moving).
Ref: FH3966

RIVERFIELD CARP FARM

Riverfield Carp Farm, Monk Lake, Marden, Maidstone, **KENT**, ME1, **England**.
Contact/s: **Mr Chris Davis** (Fishery Manager).
(T) 01580 890120
Profile: FT: Coarse; WN: Riverfield Carp Farm; WT: Lake (Still).
Ref: FH3967

RIVERSIDE CARAVAN PARK

Riverside Caravan Park, Llangammarch Wells, **POWYS**, LD4 4BY, **Wales**.
Contact/s: **Mr Edward Pryce - Lewis** (Owner).
(T) 01591 620465
Profile: FT: Combination; WN: Wye; WT: River (Moving) W. Size: 1200 Metres.
Ref: FH3968

RIVERSIDE TROUT FISHERY

Riverside Trout Fishery, Ffrwd Farm, Maesycwmmer, Hengoed, **CAERPHILLY**, CF82 7SN, **Wales**.
Contact/s: **Mr Victor Baker** (Manager).
(T) 029 20867513
Profile: FT: Combination; WN: Riverside Trout Fishery; WT: Lake (Still) W. Size: 10 Acres. Location: Main Rd: A469.
Ref: FH3969

RIVERTON HOUSE AND LAKES

Riverton House And Lakes, Swimbridge, Barnstaple, **DEVON**, EX32 0QX, **England**.
Mr Dave Shepherd (Fishery Manager).
(T) 01271 830009 (F) 01271 830009
(E) fishing@riverton.fsnet.co.uk
Mr Paul Oliver (Fishery Owner).
(T) 01271 830009 (F) 01271 830009
(E) fishing@riverton.fsnet.co.uk
Ms Sue Bryant.
(T) 01271 830009 (F) 01271 830009
(E) fishing@riverton.fsnet.co.uk
Profile: FT: Coarse; WN: Riverton House And Lakes; WT: Pool (Still); F. Size: 12 Acres; W. Size: 4 Acres. Location: Nr. Rd: Langdkey June or Westbuckland; Main Rd: A361; Rail: Barnstaple.
Ref: FH3970

ROACH BRIDGE FISHERY

Roach Bridge Fishery, Preston, **LANCASHIRE**, PR, **England**.
Contact/s: **Mr Bernard Wren** (Secretary), 1 Belmont Cl, Brinscall, Chorley, Lancashire, PR6 8SX.
(T) 01254 830935
Profile: FT: Coarse; WN: Roach Bridge Fishery; WT: Lake (Still).
Ref: FH3971

ROACH FARM PARK

Roach Farm Park, Skegness, **LINCOLNSHIRE**, **England**.
Contact/s: .
(T) 01754 898049
Profile: FT: Coarse; WN: Roach Farm Park; WT: Lake (Still).
Ref: FH3972

ROADFORD RESERVOIR

Roadford Reservoir, South West Water Fishery, Angling And Watersports Ctre, Lower Goodacre, Roadford, Okehampton, **DEVON**, EX20, **England**.
Contact/s: Manager.
(T) 01409 211507
Profile: FT: Game; WN: Roadford; WT: Reservoir (Still); F. Size: 900 Acres; W. Size: 830 Acres.
Ref: FH3973

ROADSIDE FARM

Roadside Farm, Templeton, Narberth, **PEMBROKESHIRE**, SA67 8DA, **Wales**.
Contact/s: **Mr Dave Crowley**.
(T) 01834 891283
Profile: FT: Coarse; WN: Roadside Farm; WT: Reservoir (Still). Location: Nr. Rd: A4115; Main Rd: A40 to Haverfordwest; Rail: Narberth.
Ref: FH3974

ROANHEAD FISHERIES

Roanhead Fisheries, Barrow-In-Furness, **CUMBRIA**, LA, **England**.
Contact/s: Secretary, Hannay, 50 Crellin St, Barrow, Lancashire.
(T) 01229 832129
Profile: FT: Coarse; WN: Roanhead Fisheries; WT: Gravel Pit (Still) W. Size: 10 Acres.
Ref: FH3975

ROBERTS POND

Roberts Pond, Keighley, **YORKSHIRE (WEST)**, BD2, **England**.
Contact/s: **Mr Dennis Freeman** (Secretary), Keighley Angling Club, 62 Eelholme View St, Beechcliffe, Keighley, West Yorkshire, BD20 6AY.
(T) 01535 663695
Mr Nigel Bower, K and L Tackle, 131 Mornington St, Keighley, Yorkshire (West), BD21 2EB.
(T) 01535 667574 (F) 01535 661805
Profile: FT: Coarse; WN: Robert's; WT: Pond (Still). Location: Nr. Rd: Royd Lane; Main Rd: A629 North of Keighley.
Ref: FH3976

ROCHDALE CANAL

Rochdale Canal, Rochdale, **MANCHESTER (GREATER)**, OL, **England**.
Contact/s: Area Manager, Environment Agency, Ridings Area Office, Phoenix House, Global Avenue, Leeds, LS11 8PG.
(T) 0113 2440191or2314834 (F) 0113 2134609
Profile: FT: Coarse; WN: Rochdale; WT: Canal (Still).
Ref: FH3977

ROCHDALE CANAL

Rochdale Canal, Sowerby Bridge To Halifax, Halifax, **YORKSHIRE (WEST)**, HX3, **England**.
Contact/s: **Mr Terry Hooson** (Fishery Manager).
(T) 01422 344223
Profile: FT: Coarse; WN: Rochdale; WT: Canal (Still).
Ref: FH3978

ROCHDALE CANAL

Rochdale Canal, Todmorden, **YORKSHIRE (WEST)**, OL14, **England**.
Contact/s: **Mr Ray Barber** (Secretary), Todmorden Angling Society, 12 Grisedale Drive, Burnley, Lancashire, BB12 8AR.
(T) 01282 428780 (M) 07970 897849
Profile: FT: Coarse; WN: Rochdale; WT: Canal (Still) W. Size: 21600 Metres.
Location: Nr. Rd: A646; Main Rd: A646.
Ref: FH3979

ROCHDALE CANAL

Rochdale Canal, Luddenden Foot, Hebden Bridge, **YORKSHIRE (WEST)**, HX7, **England**.
Contact/s: **Mr Steve Greenwood**.
(T) 01706 812968

Profile: FT: Coarse; WN: Rochdale; WT: Canal (Still) W. Size: 11200 Metres. **Location:** Nr. Rd: Sowerby Bridge to Hebden Bridge; Main Rd: A646.
Ref: FH3980

ROCHFORD RESERVOIR

Rochford Reservoir, Rochford, **ESSEX**, SS4, **England**.
Contact/s: Mr L Dorey (Secretary), Rochford Angling Club, 231 Kents Hill Rd, Benfleet, Essex, SS7 5PF.
(T) 01702 547010
Profile: FT: Coarse; WN: Rochford; WT: Reservoir (Still) W. Size: 2 Acres. **Location:** Nr. Rd: Railway station; Main Rd: A127,B1013.
Ref: FH3981

ROCKBOURNE TROUT FISHERY

Rockbourne Trout Fishery, Rockbourne Rd, Sandleheath, Fordingbridge, **HAMPSHIRE**, SP6 1QG, **England**.
Mr Geoff Wood (Owner).
(T) 01725 518603 (F) 01725 518228
Profile: FT: Game; WN: Sweatford Water; WT: Combination (Still & Moving); F. Size: 30 Acres; W. Size: 6 Acres. **Location:** Nr. Rd: Rockbourne Road; Main Rd: B3078; Rail: Salisbury.
Ref: FH3982

ROCKELLS FARM

Rockells Farm, Duddenhoe End, Saffron Walden, **ESSEX**, CB11 4UY, **England**.
Contact/s: Mr E Westerhuis (Owner).
(T) 01763 838053 (F) 01763 837001
Profile: FT: Coarse; WN: Rockells Farm; WT: Lake (Still); F. Size: 3 Acres; W. Size: 3 Acres. **Location:** Nr. Rd: B1039 to Royston; Main Rd: M11; Rail: Audley End.
Ref: FH3983

ROCKFORD LAKE

Rockford Lake, Ringwood, **HAMPSHIRE**, BH24, **England**.
Contact/s: Mr Pete Reading (Secretary), 17 Mayford Rd, Poole, Dorset, BH12 1PT.
(T) 01202 733110
Profile: FT: Coarse; WN: Rockford; WT: Lake (Still) W. Size: 40 Acres. **Location:** Nr. Rd: Rockford; Main Rd: A338.
Ref: FH3984

ROCKLAND BROAD

Rockland Broad, Rockland St Mary, Norwich, **NORFOLK**, NR14, **England**.
Contact/s: Fishery Manager.
(T) 01508 825655
Profile: FT: Coarse; WN: Rockland; WT: River (Moving).
Ref: FH3985

ROCOMBE PONDS

Rocombe Ponds, Combeinteignhead, Newton Abbot, **DEVON**, TQ12, **England**.
Contact/s: Mr Mike Harper.
(T) 01803 328652
Profile: FT: Coarse; WN: Rocombe; WT: Pond (Still) W. Size: 1 Acre. **Location:** Nr. Rd: Combeinteignhead to Middle Rocombe; Main Rd: B3195.
Ref: FH3986

ROD AND LINE CARAVAN PARK

Rod And Line Caravan Park, Wainfleet, Skegness, **LINCOLNSHIRE**, PE24, **England**.
Contact/s: Fishery Manager.
(T) 01754 880494
Profile: FT: Coarse; WN: Rod And Line Caravan Park; WT: Lake (Still).
Ref: FH3987

RODBOURNE LAGOON

Rodbourne Lagoon, Swindon, **WILTSHIRE**, SN4, **England**.
Contact/s: Mr M Bowsher (Secretary), 5 Nevis Cl, Sparcells, Swindon, Wiltshire, SN5 9FP.
(T) 01793 876865
Profile: FT: Coarse; WN: Rodbourne Lagoon; WT: Lake (Still).
Ref: FH3988

RODE POOL

Rode Pool, Townsend Lane, Rode Heath, Sandbach, **CHESHIRE**, CW11, **England**.
Contact/s: Fishery Manager.
(T) 01270 873237
Profile: FT: Coarse; WN: Rode Pool; WT: Lake (Still). **Location:** Nr. Rd: Scoller Green to Rode Heath; Main Rd: A50 to A34.
Ref: FH3989

RODING (RIVER)

River Roding, Passingford Bridge, Abridge, Romford, **ESSEX**, RM4, **England**.
Profile: FT: Coarse; WN: Roding; WT: River (Moving). **Location:** Nr. Rd: A13; Main Rd: M11 to M25.
Ref: FH3990

RODING (RIVER)

River Roding, Fyfield, Ongar, **ESSEX**, CM5, **England**.
Contact/s: Mr Derek Howard (Hon Treasurer), Billericay and District Angling Club, 4 Long Meadow Drive, Wickford, Essex, SS11 8AX.
(T) 01268 734468
Profile: FT: Coarse; WN: Roding; WT: River (Moving) W. Size: 3000 Metres. **Location:** Nr. Rd: B184; Rail: Epping.
Ref: FH3991

RODING (RIVER)

River Roding, Stanford Rivers, Ongar, **ESSEX**, CM5, **England**.
Contact/s: Mr Derek Howard (Hon Treasurer), Billericay and District Angling Club, 4 Long Meadow Drive, Wickford, Essex, SS11 8AX.
(T) 01268 734468
Profile: FT: Coarse; WN: Roding; WT: River (Moving) W. Size: 800 Metres. **Location:** Nr. Rd: A113; Rail: Romford.
Ref: FH3992

RODING (RIVER)

River Roding, Patch Park, Abridge, Romford, **ESSEX**, RM4, **England**.
Contact/s: Mr Derek Howard (Hon Treasurer), Billericay and District Angling Club, 4 Long Meadow Drive, Wickford, Essex, SS11 8AX.
(T) 01268 734468
Profile: FT: Coarse; WN: Roding; WT: River (Moving) W. Size: 1000 Metres. **Location:** Nr. Rd: A113.
Ref: FH3993

RODING VALLEY LAKE

Roding Valley Lake, Buckhurst Hill, Chigwell, **ESSEX**, IG7, **England**.
Profile: FT: Coarse; WN: Roding Valley; WT: Lake (Still). **Location:** Main Rd: A1168.
Ref: FH3994

RODNEY MEADOW

Rodney Meadow, West Drayton, London, **LONDON (GREATER)**, UB7, **England**.
Contact/s: Mr Richard Myers (Manager), Boyer Leisure Ltd, Heron's Point Tackle Shop, Farlow's Lake, Ford Lane, Iver SL0 9LL.
(T) 01753 630302or01895444707 (F) 01753 630302
(E) info@boyer.co.uk
Profile: FT: Coarse; WN: Rodney Meadow; WT: Lake (Still) W. Size: 12 Acres. **Location:** Main Rd: M4, junction 5.
Ref: FH3995

ROE (RIVER)

River Roe, Limavady, **COUNTY LONDONDERRY**, BT49, **Northern Ireland**.
Contact/s: Manager, Douglas' Fishing and Shooting Supplies, Irish Green St, Limavady, County Londonderry.
(T) 028 71763244
Mr Te Mullan (Manager), 184 Drumrane Rd, Limavady, County Londonderry, BT49 9LJ.
(T) 028 71765821
Profile: FT: Game; WN: Roe; WT: River (Moving) W. Size: 40000 Metres.
Ref: FH3996

ROGERS POND

Rogers Pond, Ripon, **YORKSHIRE (NORTH)**, HG4, **England**.
Contact/s: Mr Bernard Thain (Manager), Ripon Angling Ctre, 58-59 North St, Ripon, Yorkshire (North), HG4 1EN.
(T) 01765 604666 (F) 01765 603933
Profile: FT: Coarse; WN: Roger's Pond; WT: Gravel Pit (Still) W. Size: 3 Acres. **Location:** Main Rd: B6265.
Ref: FH3997

ROLFS LAKE

Rolf's Lake, Oxford, **OXFORDSHIRE**, OX33 1, **England**.
Contact/s: Mr Martin Room (Manager), Oxford and District Angling Association, 136 Oxford Rd, Cowley, Oxfordshire, OX4 2DU.
(T) 01865 711410
Mr Rolf Wobbeking. (M) 07802 708937
Profile: FT: Coarse; WN: Rolf's; WT: Lake (Still). **Location:** Nr. Rd: A40 to Wheatley, Waterperry; Main Rd: M40, junction 8.
Ref: FH3998

ROLIETH FISHERY

Rolieth Fishery, Station Farm, Station Rd, South Otterington, Northallerton, **YORKSHIRE (NORTH)**, DL7 9JB, **England**.
Contact/s: K Bowe.
(T) 01609 780263
Profile: FT: Coarse; WN: Rolieth Fishery; WT: Lake (Still). **Location:** Nr. Rd: A167; Main Rd: A168.
Ref: FH3999

ROMAN LAKE LEISURE PARK

Roman Lake Leisure Park, Marple, Stockport, **MANCHESTER (GREATER)**, SK6 7HB, **England**.
Contact/s: Mr B Sewart.
(T) 0161 4272039
Profile: FT: Coarse; WN: Roman; WT: Lake (Still) W. Size: 10 Acres.
Ref: FH4000

ROMNEY ISLAND AND MEADOW

Romney Island And Meadow, Romney Lock Lane, Windsor, **BERKSHIRE**, SL4, **England**.
Contact/s: Mr Alan Beaven (Secretary), Old Windsor Angling Club, 88 St Andrew's Way, Slough, Berkshire, SL1 5LJ.
(T) 01628 602537
Profile: FT: Combination; WN: Thames; WT: River (Moving); F. Size: 47 Acres. **Location:** Nr. Rd: B470; Main Rd: A308; Rail: Windsor.
Ref: FH4001

ROOD ASHTON LAKE

Rood Ashton Lake, Home Farm, Rood Ashton, Trowbridge, **WILTSHIRE**, BA14 6BG, **England**.
Contact/s: Ms M A Pike.
(T) 01380 870272
Profile: FT: Coarse; WN: Rood Ashton; WT: Lake (Still); F. Size: 15 Acres; W. Size: 8 Acres. **Location:** Nr. Rd: Sandpits Road; Main Rd: A350; Rail: Trowbridge.
Ref: FH4002

ROODEE MERE

Roodee Mere, Royden Park, Wirral, **MERSEYSIDE**, CH48 1NP, **England**.
Contact/s: Mr Billing.
(T) 0151 3343174
Profile: FT: Coarse; WN: Roodee Mere; WT: Lake (Still). **Location:** Nr. Rd: Royden Park.
Ref: FH4003

ROOKERY LAKE

Rookery Lake, Rookery Lane, Bromley, **KENT**, **England**.
Contact/s: .
(T) 020 83673003
Profile: FT: Coarse; WN: Rookery; WT: Lake (Still); F. Size: 5 Acres; W. Size: 3 Acres.

Location: **Nr. Rd:** Rookery Lane; **Main Rd:** A21; **Rail:** Bromley.
Ref: FH4004

ROOKERY POOL

Rookery Pool, Whitegate, Northwich, **CHESHIRE**, CW8, **England**.
Profile: **FT:** Coarse; **WN:** Rockery; **WT:** Pool (Still).
Ref: FH4005

ROOKLEY COUNTRY PARK

Rookley Country Park, Main Rd, Rookley, Ventnor, **ISLE OF WIGHT**, PO38 3LU, **England**.
Contact/s: **Mr Tim Oatley** (Manager).
(T) 07798 918717
Profile: **FT:** Coarse; **WN:** Rookley Country Park; **WT:** Lake (Still) **W. Size:** 2 Acres.
Location: **Nr. Rd:** Main Road.
Ref: FH4006

ROOKSBURY MILL

Rooksbury Mill Trout Fisheries, Rooksbury Road, Andover, **HAMPSHIRE**, SP10 2LR, **England**.
Contact/s: Secretary, Rooksbury Mill Fishing Association Ltd, Rooksbury Rd, Andover, Hampshire, SP10 2LP.
(T) 01264 352912
Profile: **FT:** Game; **WT:** Combination (Still & Moving); **F. Size:** 17 Acres; **W. Size:** 9 Acres. **Location:** **Nr. Rd:** Rooksbury Road; **Main Rd:** A303; **Rail:** Andover.
Ref: FH4007

ROOSTHOLE

Roosthole, Horsham, **SURREY**, RH1, **England**.
Contact/s: **G Kempson**, 11 Clarence Rd, Horsham, Sussex (West).
Profile: **FT:** Coarse; **WN:** Roosthole; **WT:** Lake (Still).
Ref: FH4008

ROOSTING HILLS

Roosting Hills, Two Oaks, Fakenham Rd, Beetley, Dereham, **NORFOLK**, NR20, **England**.
Contact/s: **Mr P Green**, Beetley Garage, Fakenham Rd, Beetley, Dereham, NR20 4BT.
(T) 01362 860219
Profile: **FT:** Coarse; **WN:** Roosting Hills; **WT:** Lake (Still) **W. Size:** 6 Acres.
Ref: FH4009

ROSE (RIVER)

River Rose, Limavady, Londonderry, **COUNTY LONDONDERRY**, BT47, **Northern Ireland**.
Contact/s: Manager, SJ Mithcell and Co, Central Car Park, 29 Main St, Limavady, BT49 0ER.
(T) 028 71722128
Profile: **FT:** Game; **WN:** Rose; **WT:** River (Moving).
Ref: FH4010

ROSE PARK FISHERY

Rose Park Fishery, Trezibbett, Altarnun, Launceston, **CORNWALL**, PL15 7RF, **England**.
Contact/s: **Mr Roy Burford** (Owner).
(T) 01566 86278
Ms Anne Burford (Owner).
(T) 01566 86278
Profile: **FT:** Game; **WN:** Rose Park Fishery; **WT:** Lake (Still); **F. Size:** 5 Acres; **W. Size:** 2 Acres. **Location:** **Main Rd:** A30; **Rail:** Bodmin.
Ref: FH4011

ROSEBANK FARM FISHERY

Rosebank Farm Fishery, Gun Hill, Horam, Heathfield, **SUSSEX (EAST)**, TN21, **England**.
Contact/s: **Mr Graham Axell**, 28 Falcon Way, Hailsham, Sussex (East), BN27 1HY.
(T) 01323 840889
Profile: **FT:** Coarse; **WN:** Rosebank Farm Fishery; **WT:** Combination (Still); **F. Size:** 50 Acres; **W. Size:** 5 Acres. **Location:** **Nr. Rd:** Chiddingly Road; **Main Rd:** A267, A22; **Rail:** Uckfield.
Ref: FH4012

ROSEBUSH RESERVOIR

Rosebush Reservoir, Prescelly Hills, Haverfordwest, **PEMBROKESHIRE**, SA, **Wales**.
Contact/s: **Mr John Waddington** (Head Ranger), Visitors Ctre, Llys-y-Fran Reservoir, Clarbeston Rd, Haverfordwest, SA63 4RR.
(T) 01437 532732 **(F)** 01437 532694 **(M)** 07771 916732
Profile: **FT:** Game; **WN:** Rosebush; **WT:** Reservoir (Still) **W. Size:** 33 Acres.
Location: **Nr. Rd:** Prescelly Hills; **Main Rd:** B4329; **Rail:** Haverfordwest.
Ref: FH4013

ROSEWATER LAKE

Rosewater Lake, Rose, Truro, **CORNWALL**, TR4 9PL, **England**.
Contact/s: **Mr Mike Waters**.
(T) 01872 573040 **(M)** 07977 666025
Profile: **FT:** Coarse; **WN:** Rosewater; **WT:** Lake (Still); **F. Size:** 5 Acres; **W. Size:** 2 Acres. **Location:** **Nr. Rd:** Newquay to Redruth; **Main Rd:** B3285; **Rail:** Newquay.
Ref: FH4014

ROSLYNLEE FISHERY

Roslynlee Fishery, Newbigginhill, Penicuik, **LOTHIAN (MID)**, EH26, **Scotland**.
Contact/s: **Gibby Scott**.
(T) 01968 679606
Profile: **FT:** Game; **WN:** Roslynlee Fishery; **WT:** Reservoir (Still).
Ref: FH4015

ROSS LAKE

Ross Lake, Moycullen, **COUNTY GALWAY**, **Ireland**.
Contact/s: **Mr Danny Goldrick** (Angling Officer), The Western Regional Fisheries Board, Weir Lodge, Earl's Island, Galway City, County Galway.
(T) 091 563118 **(F)** 091 566335
(E) wrfb@iol.ie
Profile: **FT:** Coarse; **WN:** Ross; **WT:** Lake (Still) **W. Size:** 400 Acres.
Ref: FH4016

ROSSES FISHERY

Rosses Fishery, Keadue, Burtonport, **COUNTY DONEGAL**, **Ireland**.
Contact/s: **Mr Frankie Byrne** (Chairman).
(T) 075 42124 **(F)** 075 42252 **(M)** 080 860 0739
(E) netman007@eircom.net
Profile: **FT:** Game; **WN:** Rosses Fishery; **WT:** Combination (Moving) **W. Size:** 12800 Metres. **Location:** **Rail:** Derry.
Ref: FH4017

ROSSINGTON BRICK POND

Rossington Brick Pond, Rossington, Doncaster, **YORKSHIRE (SOUTH)**, DN, **England**.
Contact/s: Area Manager, Environment Agency, Ridings Area Office, Phoenix House, Global Avenue, Leeds, LS11 8PG.
(T) 0113 2440191or2314834 **(F)** 0113 2134609
Mr Martin Nowacki.
(T) 01302 737409
Profile: **FT:** Coarse; **WN:** Rossington Brick; **WT:** Pond (Still). **Location:** **Main Rd:** M18.
Ref: FH4018

ROSSMERE

Rossmere, Newgate, Wilmslow, **CHESHIRE**, SK9, **England**.
Contact/s: **Mr John Turner** (Hon Secretary), Prince Albert Angling Society, 15 Pexhill Drive, Macclesfield, Cheshire, SK10 3LP.
(T) 01625 422010
Profile: **FT:** Coarse; **WN:** Rossmere; **WT:** Lake (Still) **W. Size:** 6 Acres. **Location:** **Nr. Rd:** Newgate Lane; **Main Rd:** A538 Wilmslow to Altringham; **Rail:** Wilmslow.
Ref: FH4019

ROSSMERE PARK LAKE

Rossmere Park Lake, Rossmere Way, Hartlepool, **CLEVELAND**, TS, **England**.
Contact/s: **Mr Mark Arrow-Smith** (Membership Secretary), Angler's Services, 27 Park Rd, Hartlepool, Cleveland, TS24 7PW.
(T) 01429 274844or266522
Profile: **FT:** Coarse; **WN:** Rossmere Park; **WT:** Lake (Still) **W. Size:** 2 Acres.
Ref: FH4020

ROSSWAYS WATER

Rossways Water, Wyberton, Boston, **LINCOLNSHIRE**, PE21 7HG, **England**.
Contact/s: **Mr Steve Farrands**, Rossways Water, 189 London Rd, Wyberton, PE21 7HG.
(T) 01205 361643
Profile: **FT:** Coarse; **WN:** Rossways Water; **WT:** Lake (Still). **Location:** **Nr. Rd:** London Road; **Main Rd:** B1397; **Rail:** Boston.
Ref: FH4021

ROSWELL PITS

Roswell Pits, Ely, **CAMBRIDGESHIRE**, CB7, **England**.
Contact/s: Bailiff. **(M)** 07710 859133
Mr Paul Vernon (Fishery Manager).
(T) 01353 667132
Profile: **FT:** Coarse; **WN:** Roswell; **WT:** Pit (Still). **Location:** **Main Rd:** B1382.
Ref: FH4022

ROTHAY (RIVER)

River Rothay, Ambleside, **CUMBRIA**, LA22, **England**.
Contact/s: Fisheries Contact, Tourist Information Ctre, Central Buildings, Market Cross, Ambleside, Cumbria LA22 9BS.
(T) 01539 432582
Fishery Manager.
(T) 01539 433203
Profile: **FT:** Game; **WN:** Rothay; **WT:** River (Moving).
Ref: FH4023

ROTHER (RIVER)

River Rother, Tenterden, **KENT**, TN30, **England**.
Contact/s: Manager, Tackle and Gun, 3 East Well, High St, Tenterden, TN30 6AH.
(T) 01580 764851
Profile: **FT:** Game; **WN:** Rother; **WT:** River (Moving).
Ref: FH4024

ROTHER (RIVER)

River Rother, Potmans Heath, Wittersham, Tenterden, **KENT**, TN30, **England**.
Contact/s: **Mr Peter Maclean** (Hon Secretary), 37 Collier Rd, Hastings, Sussex (East), TN34 3JR.
(T) 01424 715218
Profile: **FT:** Coarse; **WN:** Rother; **WT:** River (Moving). **Location:** **Main Rd:** Moons Green.
Ref: FH4025

ROTHER (RIVER)

River Rother, Wittersham, Tenterden, **KENT**, TN30, **England**.
Contact/s: **Mr A J Baker**, 4 Greyfriars Pl, Sea Rd, Winchelsea Beach, Sussex (East).
(T) 01797 226016
Mr J Greenhalf.
(T) 01424 420370
Profile: **FT:** Coarse; **WN:** Rother; **WT:** River (Moving).
Ref: FH4026

ROTHER (RIVER)

River Rother, Juction Rd, Bodiam, Robertsbridge, **SUSSEX (EAST)**, TN32, **England**.
Contact/s: **Mr Peter Maclean** (Hon Secretary), 37 Collier Rd, Hastings, Sussex (East), TN34 3JR.
(T) 01424 715218
Profile: **FT:** Game; **WN:** Rother; **WT:** River (Moving) **W. Size:** 462 Metres. **Location:** **Nr. Rd:** Cripps Corner to Hawkhurst; **Main**

Rd: A229.
Ref: FH4027

ROTHER (RIVER)

River Rother, North Mill, Midhurst, **SUSSEX (WEST)**, GU29, **England**.
Contact/s: **Mr C Boxall** (Treasurer), Rother Angling Club, Innisfree, Ashfield Rd, Midhurst, West Sussex, GU29 9JX.
(T) 01730 813885
Profile: **FT:** Coarse; **WN:** Western Rother; **WT:** River (Moving) **W. Size:** 1500 Metres. Location: **Nr. Rd:** A286 at North Mill; **Main Rd:** A272; **Rail:** Haslemere.
Ref: FH4028

ROTHER (RIVER)

River Rother, Woolbeding, Midhurst, **SUSSEX (WEST)**, GU29, **England**.
Contact/s: **Mr C Boxall** (Treasurer), Rother Angling Club, Innisfree, Ashfield Rd, Midhurst, West Sussex, GU29 9JX.
(T) 01730 813885
Profile: **FT:** Coarse; **WN:** Rother; **WT:** River (Moving) **W. Size:** 2400 Metres. Location: **Nr. Rd:** A286; **Main Rd:** A272; **Rail:** Haslemere.
Ref: FH4029

ROTHERFIELD POND

Rotherfield Pond, Dodsley Lane, Easebourne, Midhurst, **SUSSEX (WEST)**, GU29, **England**.
Contact/s: **Mr C Boxall** (Treasurer), Rother Angling Club, Innisfree, Ashfield Rd, Midhurst, West Sussex, GU29 9JX.
(T) 01730 813885
Profile: **FT:** Coarse; **WN:** Rotherfield; **WT:** Pond (Still); **F. Size:** 2 Acres; **W. Size:** 2 Acres. Location: **Nr. Rd:** A286; **Main Rd:** A286; **Rail:** Haslemere.
Ref: FH4030

ROTHERWAS LONG POOL

Rotherwas Long Pool, Industrial Estate, Hereford, **HEREFORDSHIRE**, HR, **England**.
Profile: **FT:** Coarse; **WN:** Rotherwas Long Pool; **WT:** Pool (Still) **W. Size:** 1 Acre. Location: **Nr. Rd:** Rotherwas Chapel; **Main Rd:** B4299.
Ref: FH4031

ROTHERWICK & NIGHTINGALE

Rotherwick And Nightingale Lakes, Rotherwick, Hook, **HAMPSHIRE**, RG27 2BZ, **England**.
Contact/s: **Mr G A Patch**.
Profile: **FT:** Coarse; **WN:** Rotherwick and Nightingale Lakes; **WT:** Pond (Still) **W. Size:** 2 Acres. Location: **Nr. Rd:** A30; **Main Rd:** M3, junction 5.
Ref: FH4032

ROUGHAN LOUGH

Roughan Lough, Newmills, Dungannon, **COUNTY TYRONE**, BT71 4, **Northern Ireland**.
Contact/s: **Mrs Liz Salter** (Manager), Aughnacloy Development Association, The McCreedy Mill Centre, Aughnacloy, County Tyrone, BT69 6AL.
(T) 028 85557002
Profile: **FT:** Coarse; **WN:** Roughan; **WT:** Lough (Still).
Ref: FH4033

ROUGHLEE TROUT FISHERY

Roughlee Trout Fishery, Pasture Lane, Roughlee, Barrow Ford, Nelson, **LANCASHIRE**, BB9 6NR, **England**.
Contact/s: **Mrs Tricia Strickland** (Owner).
(T) 01282 613416
Steve Strickland (Owner), Anglers All, The Old Forge, 6 Raglan St, Colne, BB8 0ET.
(T) 01282 860515 **(F)** 01282 860515
Profile: **FT:** Game; **WN:** Roughlee Trout Fishery; **WT:** Lake (Still); **F. Size:** 4 Acres; **W. Size:** 2 Acres. Location: **Nr. Rd:** Pasture Lane; **Main Rd:** M65; **Rail:** Nelson.
Ref: FH4034

ROUKES DRIFT FARM

Roukes Drift Farm, Finglesham, Deal, **KENT**, CT14, **England**.
Contact/s: Mr Frend.
Mr Pete Young.
Profile: **FT:** Coarse; **WN:** Roukes Drift Farm; **WT:** Pond (Still); **F. Size:** 7 Acres; **W. Size:** 4 Acres. Location: **Nr. Rd:** A258; **Main Rd:** A258; **Rail:** Deal.
Ref: FH4035

ROUND LAKE

Round Lake, Fivemiletown, **COUNTY TYRONE**, BT75 0, **Northern Ireland**.
Contact/s: **Mrs Liz Salter** (Manager), Aughnacloy Development Association, The McCreedy Mill Centre, Aughnacloy, County Tyrone, BT69 6AL.
(T) 028 85557002
Profile: **FT:** Coarse; **WN:** Round; **WT:** Lake (Still). Location: **Nr. Rd:** B122 to Fintona; **Main Rd:** A4.
Ref: FH4036

ROUNDHAY PARK LAKES

Roundhay Park Lakes, Roundhay, Leeds, **YORKSHIRE (WEST)**, LS, **England**.
Contact/s: Area Manager, Environment Agency, Ridings Area Office, Phoenix House, Global Avenue, Leeds, LS11 8PG.
(T) 0113 2440191or2314834 **(F)** 0113 2134609
Manager, Headingley Angling Ctre, 58 North Lane, Headingley, Leeds, LS6 3HU.
(T) 0113 2784445
Profile: **FT:** Coarse; **WN:** Roundhay Park; **WT:** Lake (Still).
Ref: FH4037

ROUNDWOOD POND

Roundwood Pond, Bristol, BS, **England**.
Contact/s: Manager, BR Staff Association, 8 Upper Belmont Rd, St Andrews, Bristol, Somerset BS7.
Profile: **FT:** Coarse; **WN:** Roundwood; **WT:** Pond (Still).
Ref: FH4038

ROWFANT HOUSE FISHERY

Rowfant House Fishery, Turners Hill, Crawley, **CORNWALL**, RH10 4, **England**.
Contact/s: Manager, Sporting Chance, Unit 2 Sheffield House, 29 Boltro Rd, Haywards Heath, RH16 1BP.
(T) 01444 454095
Profile: **FT:** Coarse; **WN:** Rowfant House Fishery; **WT:** Lake (Still) **W. Size:** 3 Acres. Location: **Rail:** Crawley.
Ref: FH4039

ROWLEY DAM

Rowley Dam, Lepton, Huddersfield, **YORKSHIRE (WEST)**, HD, **England**.
Contact/s: **Mr D Rushforth** (Secretary), 122 Longwood Gate, Longwood, Huddersfield, Yorkshire (West), HD3 4US.
(T) 01484 651028
Profile: **FT:** Coarse; **WN:** Rowley Dam; **WT:** Lake (Still). Location: **Nr. Rd:** Penistone Road; **Main Rd:** A629, Penistone; **Rail:** Sheply.
Ref: FH4040

ROWLEY PARK LAKE

Rowley Park Lake, Burnley, **LANCASHIRE**, BB, **England**.
Contact/s: **Mr Mike Cookson** (Secretary).
(T) 01282 412437
Profile: **FT:** Coarse; **WN:** Rowley Park; **WT:** Lake (Still). Location: **Nr. Rd:** Brunshaw Road; **Main Rd:** A682.
Ref: FH4041

ROYAL BERKSHIRE FISHERY

Royal Berkshire Fishery, North St, Winkfield, Windsor, **BERKSHIRE**, SL4 4TE, **England**.
Contact/s: **Mr Brian Hunter** (Fishery Manager/Owner).
(T) 01344 891101
Mrs Heather Hunter (Business Partner).
(T) 01344 891101
Profile: **FT:** Coarse; **WN:** Royal Berkshire; **WT:** Lake (Still); **F. Size:** 6 Acres; **W. Size:** 4 Acres. Location: **Nr. Rd:** North Street; **Main Rd:** B383; **Rail:** Bracknall.
Ref: FH4042

ROYAL BRITISH LEGION POOLS

Royal British Legion Pools, Ryton On Dunsmore, Coventry, **MIDLANDS (WEST)**, CV8, **England**.
Contact/s: Secretary, Ryton British Legion Angling Club, Leamington Rd, Ryton on Dunsmore, Coventry, CV8 3FL.
(T) 01203 301479
Profile: **FT:** Coarse; **WN:** Royal British Legion; **WT:** Pool (Still) **W. Size:** 2 Acres. Location: **Nr. Rd:** A45, Leamington Road.
Ref: FH4043

ROYAL GEORGE MILL COMPLEX

Royal George Mill Complex, Friezland, Greenfield, Oldham, **MANCHESTER (GREATER)**, OL, **England**.
Contact/s: **Mr Ian Baxter** (Membership Secretary), 6 Bagnall Cl, Uppermill, Oldham, Lancashire, OL3 6DW.
(T) 01457 875818 **(M)** 07973 345128
Profile: **FT:** Coarse; **WN:** Royal George Mill Complex; **WT:** Lake (Still) **W. Size:** 4 Acres. Location: **Nr. Rd:** Hole Road; **Main Rd:** A635 Ashton under Lyne to Holmfirth; **Rail:** Greenfield.
Ref: FH4044

ROYAL MILITARY CANAL

Royal Military Canal, Romney Marsh, **KENT**, TN29, **England**.
Contact/s: Fishery Manager.
(T) 01303 262013
Mr Steve Crowley (Hon Secretary), 9 Haydens Cl, Orpington, Kent, BR5 4JE.
Profile: **FT:** Coarse; **WN:** Rother; **WT:** River (Moving).
Ref: FH4045

ROYAL MILITARY CANAL

Royal Military Canal, Appledore, Kennardington, **KENT**, **England**.
(W) www.midkentfish.co.uk
Contact/s: **Mr Chris Logsdon** (Fisheries Manager), Mid Kent Fisheries, Chilham Water Mill, Mill Lane, Chilham, CT4 8EE.
(T) 01227 730668
(E) chilham@midkentfisheries.co.uk
Profile: **FT:** Coarse; **WN:** Royal Military; **WT:** Canal (Still). Location: **Main Rd:** B2080; **Rail:** Appledore.
Ref: FH4046

ROYAL OAK POOL

Royal Oak Pool, Portway, Hereford, **HEREFORDSHIRE**, HR, **England**.
Profile: **FT:** Coarse; **WN:** Royal Oak Pool; **WT:** Pond (Still) **W. Size:** 1 Acre. Location: **Nr. Rd:** A4110 to Portway village.
Ref: FH4047

ROYAL PIONEER CORPS AA WATER

Royal Pioneer Corps Angling Association Water, Bicester, **OXFORDSHIRE**, OX6, **England**.
Contact/s: **Mr Tony Hoodles** (Secretary).
(T) 01869 601872
Profile: **FT:** Coarse; **WN:** Royal Pioneer Corps Angling Association Water; **WT:** Lake (Still).
Ref: FH4048

ROYALTY FISHERY

Royalty Fishery, Avon Buildings, Christchurch, **DORSET**, BH23, **England**.
Contact/s: **Mr Graham Pepler** (Manager), Davis Tackle Shop, 75 Bargates, Christchurch, Dorset, BH23 1QE.
(T) 01202 485169or395532 **(F)** 01202 474261
Mr Steve Richards (Secretary), Christchurch Angling Club, 4 Marley Cl, New Milton, Hampshire, BH25 5LL.
(T) 01425 279710

Profile: FT: Combination; **WN:** Avon (Hampshire); **WT:** River (Moving) **W. Size:** 2250 Metres. **Location:** Nr. Rd: Barrack Road to Bournemouth; **Main Rd:** Bargates; **Rail:** Christchurch.
Ref: FH4049

ROYDS HALL DAM

Royds Hall Dam, Bradford, **YORKSHIRE (WEST)**, BD6, **England**.
Contact/s: Manager, Wibsey Angling Ctre, 208 High St, Wibsey, Bradford, BD6 1QP.
(T) 01274 604542
Profile: FT: Coarse; **WN:** Royds Hall; **WT:** Reservoir (Still) **W. Size:** 6 Acres. **Location:** Nr. Rd: Lindale Road; **Main Rd:** M606 from M62.
Ref: FH4050

RUB - A - DUB POND

Rub - A - Dub Pond, Exeter Rd, Kingsteignton, Newton Abbot, **DEVON**, TQ1, **England**.
Contact/s: Mr David Horder (Secretary), Newton Abbot Fishing Association, 22 Mount Pleasant Rd, Newton Abbot, Devon, TQ1.
(T) 01626 364173
Profile: FT: Coarse; **WN:** Rub - a - Dub; **WT:** Pond (Still) **W. Size:** 1 Acre.
Ref: FH4051

RUDYARD LAKE

Rudyard Lake, Lake House, Rudyard, Leek, **STAFFORDSHIRE**, ST13, **England**.
Contact/s: Mr John Davey (Bailiff), Hotel Rudyard, Lake Rd, Rudyard, Leek, ST13 8RN.
(T) 01538 306280 (F) 01538 306280
Profile: FT: Coarse; **WN:** Rudyard; **WT:** Lake (Still) **W. Size:** 180 Acres. **Location:** Nr. Rd: Rudyard Road; **Main Rd:** B5331; **Rail:** Macclesfield.
Ref: FH4052

RUEL (RIVER)

River Ruel, Glendaruel, Dunoon, **ARGYLL AND BUTE**, PA23, **Scotland**.
Contact/s: Mr A H Young (Hon Secretary), 112 Argyll St, Dunoon, Argyll and Bute.
(T) 01369 705732or703232
(E) archie@telinco.co.uk
Profile: FT: Game; **WN:** Ruel; **WT:** River (Moving) **W. Size:** 1600 Metres. **Location:** Nr. Rd: A888.
Ref: FH4053

RUFFORD CANAL

Rufford Canal, Burscough, Ormskirk, **LANCASHIRE**, L40, **England**.
(W) www.wiganaa.f9.co.uk
Contact/s: Mr Gerry Wilson (Hon Secretary), Wigan and District Angling Association, 11 Guildford Avenue, Chorley, Lancashire, PR6 8TG.
(T) 01257 265905
(E) gerry@wiganna.freeserve.co.uk
Profile: FT: Coarse; **WN:** Rufford; **WT:** Canal (Still). **Location:** Nr. Rd: A5209, A59; **Main Rd:** M6, M58.
Ref: FH4054

RUMBLING BRIDGE

Rumbling Bridge, Dunkeld, **PERTH AND KINROSS**, PH8, **Scotland**.
(W) www.fishingnet.com/beats/braan/rumblingbridge83a.htm
Contact/s: Mrs Diana MacDonald (Permit Contact).
Mrs Vicky Hammer (Owner), Kettles of Dunkeld, 15-17 Atholl St, Dunkeld, Perth and Kinross, PH8 0AR.
(T) 01350 727556
Profile: FT: Game; **WN:** Rumbling Bridge; **WT:** Pool (Still). **Location:** Nr. Rd: Allt Coire a' Mhor-fhir to Forestry Commission March.
Ref: FH4055

RUMWORTH LODGE RESERVOIR

Rumworth Lodge Reservoir, Rumworth, Bolton, **LANCASHIRE**, BL, **England**.
Contact/s: Mr Dt Dobson (Secretary).
(T) 01942 817969
Mr Roy Rhodes (Conservation, Access and Recreation Manager), Rivington Water Treatment Works, Bolton Rd, Horwich, Bolton, BL6 7RN.
(T) 01204 664300
Profile: FT: Coarse; **WN:** Rumworth; **WT:** Reservoir (Still). **Location:** Nr. Rd: Junction Road West; **Main Rd:** Deane Road A676.
Ref: FH4056

RUNCORN PARK LAKE

Runcorn Park Lake, Norton Priory Recreation Ctre, Runcorn, **CHESHIRE**, WA7, **England**.
Contact/s: Fishery Manager.
(T) 01928 576796
Profile: FT: Coarse; **WN:** Runcorn Park; **WT:** Lake (Still).
Ref: FH4057

RUSH LYVARS LAKE

Rush Lyvars Lake, Hedon, Hull, **HUMBERSIDE**, HU, **England**.
Contact/s: Mr Peter Everingham (Bailiff).
(T) 01482 898970
Profile: FT: Coarse; **WN:** Rush Lyvars; **WT:** Lake (Still) **W. Size:** 14 Acres.
Ref: FH4058

RUSHALL CANAL

Rushall Canal, Longwood, Aldright, Rushall, Walsall, **MIDLANDS (WEST)**, WS4, **England**.
Contact/s: Fishery Manager.
(T) 0121 5688227
Profile: FT: Coarse; **WN:** Rushall; **WT:** Canal (Still).
Ref: FH4059

RUSHALL CANAL

Rushall Canal, Winterley Lane, Walsall, **MIDLANDS (WEST)**, WS, **England**.
Contact/s: Fishery Manager.
(T) 01543 452145
Profile: FT: Coarse; **WN:** Rushall; **WT:** Canal (Still). **Location:** Nr. Rd: Winterley Lane or Park Road; **Main Rd:** B4154.
Ref: FH4060

RUSHEY LOCK

Rushey Lock, Tadpole Bridge, Buckland, Faringdon, **OXFORDSHIRE**, SN7 8RF, **England**.
Contact/s: Fishery Contact.
(T) 01367 870218
Recreational Manager, The Environment Agency, Kings Meadow Rd, Reading, Berkshire, RG1 8DQ.
(T) 0118 9535000 (F) 0118 9500388
Profile: FT: Combination; **WN:** Thames; **WT:** River (Moving). **Location:** Nr. Rd: Tadpole Bridge; **Main Rd:** A420 or the A4095.
Ref: FH4061

RUSHEY WEIR

Rushey Weir, Bampton, **OXFORDSHIRE**, OX18, **England**.
Contact/s: Mr Tom Gerring (Bailiff).
(T) 01993 850594
Profile: FT: Coarse; **WN:** Thames; **WT:** River (Moving) **W. Size:** 1200 Metres. **Location:** Nr. Rd: Tadpole Bridge; **Main Rd:** Bampton to Buckland.
Ref: FH4062

RUSHMOOR LAKES

Rushmoor Lakes, Tilford Rd, Rushmoor, Farnham, **SURREY**, GU, **England**.
Contact/s: Mr Dennis Smale (Boss), 'Silva', Wellesley Rd, Rushmoor, Farnham, GU10 2EH.
(T) 01252 793968
Profile: FT: Coarse; **WN:** Rushmoor; **WT:** Lake (Still) **W. Size:** 3 Acres. **Location:** Nr. Rd: Tilford Road; **Main Rd:** Tilfield to Hindhead Road; **Rail:** Farnham.
Ref: FH4063

RUSHYVARS LAKES

Rushyvars Lakes, Preston, **LANCASHIRE**, PR, **England**.
Contact/s: Mr Peter Everingham (Bailiff).
(T) 01482 898970
Profile: FT: Combination; **WN:** Rushyvars; **WT:** Lake (Still). **Location:** Nr. Rd: A1033.
Ref: FH4064

RUSSELLS END RESERVOIR

Russells End Reservoir, Playley Green, Ledbury, **HEREFORDSHIRE**, HR8, **England**.
Contact/s: Mr Brian Powell (Red Banks Pools Manager), Three Counties Fisheries, Field Cottage, Ryton, Dymock, Gloucestershire, GL18 2DH.
(T) 01531 890455
Profile: FT: Coarse; **WN:** Russells End; **WT:** Reservoir (Still) **W. Size:** 4 Acres. **Location:** Nr. Rd: Playley Green; **Main Rd:** M50, junction 2, A417 to Gloucester.
Ref: FH4065

RUSTON REACHES

Ruston Reaches, Chapel Rd, East Ruston, Norwich, **NORFOLK**, NR12 9AA, **England**.
Contact/s: Mr Peter Mantell-Sayer (Owner).
(T) 01692 583311 (F) 01692 583311
(E) peter@mantell-sayer.freeserve.co.uk
Profile: FT: Coarse; **WN:** Ruston Reaches; **WT:** Lake (Still). **Location:** Nr. Rd: Chapel Road; **Main Rd:** A149; **Rail:** North Walsham.
£Fr
Ref: FH4066

RUSWARP (RIVER)

River Ruswarp, Ruswarp Pleasure Boats, Millbeck The Carrs, Ruswarp, Whitby, **YORKSHIRE (NORTH)**, YO22, **England**.
Contact/s: Mr P Sims, Ruswarp Boat Landing, Whitby, Yorkshire.
(T) 01947 604658
Profile: FT: Game; **WN:** Esk; **WT:** River (Moving) **W. Size:** 2000 Metres. **Location:** Main Rd: A169, Pickering; **Rail:** Ruswarp.
Ref: FH4067

RUTLAND WATER

Rutland Water, Oakham, Rutland, **LEICESTERSHIRE**, LE15, **England**.
Contact/s: Fisheries Manager, Anglian Water Services Ltd, Normanton Fishing Lodge, Rutland Water South Shore, Edith Weston, Oakham LE15 8HD.
(T) 01780 86770
Profile: FT: Combination; **WN:** Rutland Water; **WT:** Combination (Still & Moving) **W. Size:** 3100 Acres. **Location:** Nr. Rd: Stamford; **Main Rd:** A1.
Ref: FH4068

RUXLEY PITS

Ruxley Pits, Orpington, **KENT**, BR5, **England**.
Contact/s: Manager, A and I Fishing Tackle, 33 High St, Green Street Green, Orpington, BR6 6BG.
(T) 01689 862302 (F) 01689 856294
Secretary, Orpington Angling Association, PO Box 7, Orpington, Kent, BR6 7LW.
Profile: FT: Coarse; **WN:** Ruxley; **WT:** Gravel Pit (Still) **W. Size:** 40 Acres.
Ref: FH4069

RYDAL WATER

Rydal Water, Ambleside, **CUMBRIA**, LA22, **England**.
Contact/s: Mrs Vera Carlson (Fishery Manager), Carlsons Fishing Tackle, 64/66 Kirkland, Kendal, Cumbria, LA9 5AP.
(T) 01539 724867
Profile: FT: Coarse; **WN:** Tydal Water; **WT:** Lake (Still).
Ref: FH4070

RYDAL WATER

Rydal Water, Rydal, Ambleside, **CUMBRIA**, LA22, **England**.
Contact/s: Manager, Barney's News Box, Broadgate, Grasmere, Cumbria, LA22 9TA.
(T) 01539 435627
Profile: FT: Combination; **WN:** Rydal Water; **WT:** Lake (Still). **Location:** Nr. Rd: A591 Windermere to Keswick.
Ref: FH4071

RYE (RIVER)

River Rye, York, **YORKSHIRE (NORTH)**, YO, **England**.
Contact/s: Manager, The Hawnby Hotel, Hawnby, York, Yorkshire (North), YO62 5QS.
(T) 01439 798202 **(F)** 01439 798344
Profile: FT: Game; **WN:** Rye; **WT:** River (Moving).
Ref: FH4072

RYE (RIVER)

River Rye, Newsham, Malton, **YORKSHIRE (NORTH)**, YO17, **England**.
Contact/s: **Mr Howard Foster** (Secretary), 6 Moorclose Lane, Queensbury, Bradford, Yorkshire (West), BD13 2BP.
(T) 01274 881851
Mr John Sparks, 12 Fairway Walk, Wibsey, Bradford, BD7 4JW.
Profile: FT: Combination; **WN:** Rye; **WT:** River (Moving) **W. Size:** 4800 Metres.
Location: Nr. Rd: Newsham Bridge; **Main Rd:** B1257 west to Amotherby.
Ref: FH4073

RYE AND SEVEN (RIVERS)

Rivers Rye And Seven, Manor Farm, Brawby, Malton, **YORKSHIRE (NORTH)**, YO17, **England**.
Contact/s: Fishery Manager.
(T) 01653 668458
Profile: FT: Combination; **WN:** Rye and Seven; **WT:** River (Moving) **W. Size:** 1600 Metres. **Location: Nr. Rd:** Malton to Amotherby; **Main Rd:** B1257.
Ref: FH4074

RYE NOOK FISHERY

Rye Nook Fishery, Rye Harbour Rd, Rye, Hastings, **SUSSEX (EAST)**, **England**.
(W) www.rye-nook-fishery.co.uk
Contact/s: **Mr Peter Gould**, 16 Edmund Road, Hastings, East Sussex. TN35 5JZ..
(T) 01424 434464 **(F)** 01424 434464 **(M)** 07961 433701
(E) fish@ryenookfishery.co.uk
Profile: FT: Coarse; **WN:** Nook, Little Nook, Moorhen, and Ocean.; **WT:** Gravel Pit (Still); **F. Size:** 150 Acres. **Location: Nr. Rd:** Rye Harbour Road; **Main Rd:** A259; **Rail:** Rye.
Ref: FH4075

RYEMEADS

Ryemeads, Toll Rd, Rye House, Royston, **HERTFORDSHIRE**, SG8, **England**.
(W) www.rmcangling.co.uk
Contact/s: **Mr Ian Welch** (Angling Manager), RMC Angling, The Square, Lightwater, Surrey, GU18 5SS.
(T) 01276 453300 **(F)** 01276 456611
(E) info@rmcangling.co.uk
Profile: FT: Coarse; **WN:** Ryemeads; **WT:** Combination (Still & Moving) **W. Size:** 16 Acres. **Location: Nr. Rd:** Toll Road; **Main Rd:** B181, A414.
Ref: FH4076

RYTON POOLS COUNTRY PARK

Ryton Pools Country Park, Ryton Rd, Bubbenhall, Coventry, **MIDLANDS (WEST)**, CV8 3BH, **England**.
Contact/s: Fisheries Manager, Warwickshire County Council, Montague Rd, Warwick, Warwickshire, CV34 5LW.
(T) 024 76305592
Profile: FT: Coarse; **WN:** Ryton; **WT:** Pool (Still); **F. Size:** 100 Acres; **W. Size:** 7 Acres.
Ref: FH4077

S YORKS NAVIGATION CANAL

South Yorkshire Navigation Canal, Gas House Bight, Doncaster, **YORKSHIRE (SOUTH)**, DN, **England**.
Contact/s: **Mr Maurice Tate** (Secretary), Doncaster and District Angling Association, 28 Holmescarr Rd, New Rossington, Doncaster, DN11 0QF.
(T) 01302 865482
Profile: FT: Coarse; **WN:** South Yorkshire Navigation; **WT:** Canal (Still).
Ref: FH4346

S YORKS NAVIGATION CANAL

South Yorkshire Navigation Canal, Long Sandall Lock, Long Sandall, Doncaster, **YORKSHIRE (SOUTH)**, DN, **England**.
Contact/s: **Mr Maurice Tate** (Secretary), Doncaster and District Angling Association, 28 Holmescarr Rd, New Rossington, Doncaster, DN11 0QF.
(T) 01302 865482
W Sams (Secretary), Doncaster and District Angling Association, 28 Pipering Lane, Scawthorpe, Doncaster.
(T) 01302 780271
Profile: FT: Coarse; **WN:** South Yorkshire Navigation; **WT:** Canal (Still) **W. Size:** 400 Metres.
Ref: FH4347

S YORKS NAVIGATION CANAL

South Yorkshire Navigation Canal, Barnby Dun, Doncaster, **YORKSHIRE (SOUTH)**, DN, **England**.
Contact/s: Fishery Manager.
(T) 01302 886024
Mr Franco Pezzulo (Manager), Franco's Angling Supplies, 148 High St, Bentley, Doncaster, DN5 0AT.
(T) 01302 874888
Profile: FT: Coarse; **WN:** South Yorkshire Navigation; **WT:** Canal (Still). **Location: Nr. Rd:** Barnby Dun to Kirk Sandall.
Ref: FH4348

SABDEN RESERVOIR

Sabden Reservoir, Accrington And District Fishing Club, Whalley Rd, Sabden, Clitheroe, **LANCASHIRE**, BB7, **England**.
Contact/s: **Mr A Balderstone** (Secretary), 42 Townley Avenue, Huncoat, Lancashire, BB5 6LP.
(T) 01254 233517
Profile: FT: Game; **WN:** Sabden; **WT:** Reservoir (Still).
Ref: FH4078

SABRE AND SWORDS LAKES

Sabre And Swords Lakes, Calne, **WILTSHIRE**, SN11, **England**.
Contact/s: **Mr Tony Knowler** (Manager), T and K Tackle, 123A London Rd, Calne, Wiltshire.
(T) 01249 812003
Profile: FT: Coarse; **WN:** Sabre and Swords; **WT:** Lake (Still). **Location: Nr. Rd:** Calne to Marlborough; **Main Rd:** A4 to Marlborough.
Ref: FH4079

SABRE TOOTH

Sabre Tooth, Upper Thurston Farmhouse, Thurston Lane, Sardis, Milford Haven, **PEMBROKESHIRE**, SA73, **Wales**.
Contact/s: Fishery Manager.
(T) 01646 690027 **(M)** 07768 632251
Profile: FT: Game; **WN:** Sabre Tooth; **WT:** River (Moving).
Ref: FH4080

SALE WATER PARK

Sale Water Park, Rifle Rd, Sale, **CHESHIRE**, M33 2LX, **England**.
Contact/s: **Mr Mark Brazil** (Manager), Trafford Water Sports Ctre, Rifle Rd, Sale, Manchester, M33 2LX.
(T) 0161 9123410
Profile: FT: Coarse; **WN:** Sale Water Park; **WT:** Lake (Still) **W. Size:** 55 Acres.
Location: Nr. Rd: M60 junction 6.
Ref: FH4081

SALFORD QUAYS

Salford Quays, Salford, **MANCHESTER (GREATER)**, M6, **England**.
Contact/s: Fishery Manager.
(T) 0161 8777252
Mr Eddie Batersby (Manager), Swinton Angling Ctre, 57 Worsley Rd, Swinton, Manchester, M27 5NE.
(T) 0161 7942784
Mr Stan Yates.
(T) 0161 8488242
Profile: FT: Coarse; **WN:** Salford; **WT:** Quay (Still). **Location: Nr. Rd:** Manchester to Old Trafford; **Main Rd:** M602 junction 3.
Ref: FH4082

SALFORD TROUT LAKES

Salford Trout Lakes, Rectory Farm, Salford, Chipping Norton, **OXFORDSHIRE**, OX7 5YZ, **England**.
Contact/s: **Mr N G Colston** (Owner).
(T) 01608 643209 **(F)** 01608 643209
Mrs E A Colston (Owner).
(T) 01608 643209 **(F)** 01608 643209
Profile: FT: Game; **WN:** Salford; **WT:** Lake (Still); **F. Size:** 25 Acres; **W. Size:** 9 Acres.
Location: Main Rd: A44; **Rail:** Moreton in Marsh.
Ref: FH4083

SALLY WALSHES DAM

Sally Walshes Dam, Hemsworth, Barnsley, **YORKSHIRE (SOUTH)**, S7, **England**.
Contact/s: **Mr Geoff Brown**.
(T) 01226 297169
Mr Tony Eaton (Club Secretary), 60 Walton St, Gawber, Barnsley, S75 2PD.
(T) 01226 203090 **(M)** 07979 970201
Profile: FT: Coarse; **WN:** Sally Walshs; **WT:** Mill Dam (Still); **F. Size:** 15 Acres.
Location: Main Rd: A628; **Rail:** Kinsley.
Ref: FH4084

SALMON & TROUT ASSOC LAKES

Salmon And Trout Association Lakes, Roosting Hills, Dereham, **NORFOLK**, NR, **England**.
Contact/s: **Mr R Bunning**, GT Bunning and Sons Limited, Gressenhall, Dereham, Norfolk, NR20 4DT.
(T) 01362 860352
Profile: FT: Game; **WN:** Salmon And Trout Association Lakes; **WT:** Lake (Still).
Ref: FH4085

SALMON FISHING STATION

Salmon Fishing Station, Tr Paterson And Sons, Strathy Point, Strathy, Thurso, **HIGHLAND**, KW14 7RY, **Scotland**.
Contact/s: Fishery Manager.
(T) 01641 541246
Profile: FT: Game; **WN:** Salmon Fishing Station; **WT:** River (Moving).
Ref: FH4086

SALMONHUTCH COARSE FISHERY

Salmonhutch Coarse Fishery, Uton, Crediton, **DEVON**, EX17 3QJ, **England**.
Contact/s: **Mr John Mortimer** (Owner).
(T) 01363 772749 **(F)** 01647 24035
Profile: FT: Coarse; **WN:** Salmonhutch Coarse Fishery; **WT:** Lake (Still); **F. Size:** 4 Acres; **W. Size:** 3 Acres. **Location: Main Rd:** A377 to Crediton; **Rail:** Crediton.
Ref: FH4087

SALTHOUSE BROAD

Salthouse Broad, Salthouse, Holt, **NORFOLK**, NR25, **England**.
Profile: FT: Coarse; **WN:** Salthouse Broad; **WT:** Canal (Still).
Ref: FH4088

SALWARPE (RIVER)

River Salwarpe, Mildenham Fishery, Kidderminster, **WORCESTERSHIRE**, DY, **England**.
Contact/s: Fishery Manager.
(T) 01299 250021
Profile: FT: Coarse; **WN:** Salwarpe; **WT:** River (Moving). **Location: Nr. Rd:** Ladywood, towards; **Main Rd:** A449.
Ref: FH4089

SAMPFORD PEVERAL PONDS

Sampford Peveral Ponds, Tinerton Park Railway Station, Tiverton, **DEVON**, EX16, **England**.
Contact/s: **Mr Barry Lucas** (Hon Secretary), Mayfield, Gorwyn Lane, Cheriton Bishop, Exeter, EX6 6JL.

(T) 01647 24566
Profile: FT: Coarse; WN: Sampford Peveral; WT: Pond (Still).
Ref: FH4090

SAND MARTIN LAKE

Sand Martin Lake, Tansor, Oundle, Peterborough, **CAMBRIDGESHIRE**, PE8 5HN, **England**.
Contact/s: Mr Tony Bridgefoot (Owner).
(T) 01832 226042
Profile: FT: Coarse; WN: Sand Martin; WT: Lake (Still); F. Size: 108 Acres; W. Size: 10 Acres. Location: Nr. Rd: Tansor to Fotheringhay; Main Rd: A605; Rail: Peterborough.
Ref: FH4091

SAND MERE LAKE

Sand Mere Lake, Allostock, Knutsford, **CHESHIRE**, WA16, **England**.
Contact/s: Mr John Turner (Hon Secretary), Prince Albert Angling Society, 15 Pexhill Drive, Macclesfield, Cheshire, SK10 3LP.
(T) 01625 422010
Profile: FT: Coarse; WN: Sand Mere; WT: Lake (Still).
Ref: FH4092

SANDERSONS POND

Sandersons Pond, Wheatley, Doncaster, **YORKSHIRE (SOUTH)**, DN, **England**.
Contact/s: Area Manager, Environment Agency, Ridings Area Office, Phoenix House, Global Avenue, Leeds, LS11 8PG.
(T) 0113 2440191or2314834 (F) 0113 2134609
Mr Martin Nowacki.
(T) 01302 737409
Profile: FT: Coarse; WN: Sandersons; WT: Pond (Still).
Ref: FH4093

SANDFORD ARMS

Sandford Arms, Sandford, Appleby-In-Westmorland, **CUMBRIA**, CA16 6NR, **England**.
Contact/s: Manager, Sandford Arms, Sandford, Appleby-in-Westmorland, Cumbria, CA16 6NR.
(T) 01768 351121 (F) 01768 353200
Profile: FT: Game; WN: Sandford Arms; WT: River (Moving) W. Size: 8000 Metres.
Ref: FH4094

SANDFORD LOCK

Sandford Lock, Church Lane, Sandford-on-Thames, Oxford, **OXFORDSHIRE**, OX4, **England**.
Contact/s: Fishery Contact.
(T) 01865 775889
Recreational Manager, The Environment Agency, Kings Meadow Rd, Reading, Berkshire, RG1 8DQ.
(T) 0118 9535000 (F) 0118 9500388
Profile: FT: Combination; WN: Thames; WT: River (Moving). Location: Nr. Rd: Church Lane; Main Rd: A423.
Ref: FH4095

SANDHILL LAKE

Sandhill Lake, Worksop, **NOTTINGHAMSHIRE**, S80, **England**.
Contact/s: Mr R Whitehead (Secretary), Worksop and District Angling Association, 72 Dryden Walk, Worksop, Nottinghamshire.
(T) 01909 486350
Profile: FT: Coarse; WN: Sandhill; WT: Lake (Still).
Ref: FH4096

SANDY BEACH

Sandy Beach, Middleton, Manchester, **MANCHESTER (GREATER)**, M24, **England**.
Contact/s: Mr Gary Lee (Secretary). (M) 07973 205280
Profile: FT: Coarse; WN: Sandy Beach; WT: Lake (Still).
Ref: FH4097

SANDYBANK POOL

Sandybank Pool, Sandbach, **CHESHIRE**, CW11, **England**.
Contact/s: Mr Neil Jupp (Club Secretary), Lymm Angling Club, PO Box 350, Warrington, Cheshire, WA2 9FB.
(T) 01925 411744
Profile: FT: Coarse; WN: Sandybank; WT: Pool (Still). Location: Nr. Rd: Old Sanbach Road; Main Rd: M6, junction 17, A534 to Crewe.
Ref: FH4098

SANDYKNOWES FISHING

Sandyknowes Fishing, Rhynd Rd, Bridge Of Earn, Perth, **PERTH AND KINROSS**, PH2 8PT, **Scotland**.
Contact/s: Mr D M Brien (Owner), Bridge of Earn, Tayside, Scotland.
(T) 01738 813033
Mr Eoin C Christie (Manager).
(T) 01738 813033
Profile: FT: Game; WN: Earn and Burn; WT: Combination (Still & Moving); F. Size: 10 Acres; W. Size: 8 Acres. Location: Nr. Rd: A912; Rail: Perth.
Ref: FH4099

SANKEY ST HELENS CANAL

Sankey St Helens Canal, Halton, Runcorn, **CHESHIRE**, WA7, **England**.
Contact/s: Mr Neil Jupp (Club Secretary), Lymm Angling Club, PO Box 350, Warrington, Cheshire, WA2 9FB.
(T) 01925 411774
Profile: FT: Coarse; WN: Sankey St Helens; WT: Canal (Still) W. Size: 2400 Metres. Location: Nr. Rd: Tanhouse Lane; Main Rd: A50 to Warrington; Rail: Bank Quay.
Ref: FH4100

SANKEY ST HELENS CANAL

Sankey St Helens Canal, Carterhouse, Bewsey, Widnes, **CHESHIRE**, WA8, **England**.
Contact/s: Fishery Manager.
(T) 0151 4245185
Mr Neil Jupp (Club Secretary), Lymm Angling Club, PO Box 350, Warrington, Cheshire, WA2 9FB.
(T) 01925 411774
Profile: FT: Coarse; WN: Sankey St Helens; WT: Canal (Still). Location: Main Rd: A562.
Ref: FH4101

SANKEY ST HELENS CANAL (LAC)

Sankey St Helens Canal (Lac), Widnes, **CHESHIRE**, WA8, **England**.
Contact/s: Mr Neil Jupp (Club Secretary), Lymm Angling Club, PO Box 350, Warrington, Cheshire, WA2 9FB.
(T) 01925 411774
Profile: FT: Coarse; WN: Sankey St Helens; WT: Canal (Still). Location: Main Rd: A562 to Warrington.
Ref: FH4102

SANTHILL FISHERY

Santhill Fishery, Rissington Rd, Bourton-on-the-Water, Cheltenham, **GLOUCESTERSHIRE**, GL54 2DZ, **England**.
Contact/s: Mr Stuart Rob (Fishery Manager).
(T) 01454 810291 (M) 07958 203864
Profile: FT: Game; WN: Santhill Fishery; WT: Gravel Pit (Still); F. Size: 42 Acres; W. Size: 1 Acre. Location: Nr. Rd: Rissington Road.
Ref: FH4103

SAPPHIRE LAKES

Sapphire Lakes, Norwell Lane, Cromwell, Newark, **NOTTINGHAMSHIRE**, NG23 6JQ, **England**.
(W) www.sapphirelakes.co.uk
Mr Ken Barker.
(T) 01636 821131
Mrs Eunice Barker.
(T) 01636 821131
Profile: FT: Coarse; WN: Sapphire; WT: Gravel Pit (Still) W. Size: 12 Acres. Location: Nr. Rd: Norwell Lane; Main Rd: A1; Rail: Newark.
Ref: FH4104

SARK STREAM

Sark Stream, Gretna, **DUMFRIES AND GALLOWAY**, DG16, **Scotland**.
Profile: FT: Game; WN: Sark; WT: Stream (Moving) W. Size: 16000 Metres.
Ref: FH4105

SARN MILL FISHERIES

Sarn Mill Fisheries, Sarn Mill Cottage, Denbigh Rd, Nannerton, Mold, **FLINTSHIRE**, CH7 5RH, **Wales**.
Contact/s: Mr R McGuire.
(T) 01352 720854
Profile: FT: Combination; WN: Sarn Mill Fisheries; WT: Pond (Still) W. Size: 2 Acres. Location: Nr. Rd: A451; Main Rd: A451 at Nannerton; Rail: Flint.
Ref: FH4106

SAVAY LAKE

Savay Lake, Moorhall Rd, Harefield, Denham, London, **LONDON (GREATER)**, UB9, **England**.
Contact/s: Mr Peter Broxup (Manager), 309 Shirland Rd, London, W9.
(T) 020 89696980
Profile: FT: Coarse; WN: Savay Lake; WT: Gravel Pit (Still) W. Size: 60 Acres. Location: Nr. Rd: Moorhall Road; Main Rd: A412, M40; Rail: Denham.
Ref: FH4107

SAVERNAKE POND

Savernake Pond, Forest Park, Bracknell, **BERKSHIRE**, RG, **England**.
Contact/s: Mr Nigel Smith (Senior Ranger).
(T) 01344 354441
Profile: FT: Coarse; WN: Savernake; WT: Pond (Still) W. Size: 2 Acres. Location: Main Rd: B3430.
Ref: FH4108

SAWMILLS LAKE

Sawmills Lake, Kingsteignton, Newton Abbot, **DEVON**, TQ1, **England**.
Contact/s: Mr Mike Harper.
(T) 01803 328652
Profile: FT: Coarse; WN: Sawmills; WT: Lake (Still) W. Size: 2 Acres. Location: Nr. Rd: B3193; Main Rd: B3195.
Ref: FH4109

SCALAND WOOD

Scaland Wood, Hadlow Down Rd, Crowborough, **SUSSEX (EAST)**, TN6, **England**.
Contact/s: Sean, Crowborough Tackle, Whitehill Rd, Crowborough, Sussex (East), TN6 1JU.
(T) 01892 661145
Profile: FT: Coarse; WN: Scaland Wood; WT: Pond (Still); F. Size: 1 Acre; W. Size: 1 Acre. Location: Nr. Rd: Hadlow Down Road; Main Rd: A26; Rail: Jarvis Brook, Crowborough.
Ref: FH4110

SCALING DAM

Scaling Dam, Guisborough, **CLEVELAND**, TS14, **England**.
Contact/s: Mr Paul Russell, Northumbrian Water Ltd, Head Office, Recreation Department, Abbey Rd, Durham DH1 5FJ.
(T) 0191 3832222 (F) 0191 3841920
Profile: FT: Game; WN: Scaling; WT: Mill Dam (Still) W. Size: 105 Acres.
Ref: FH4111

SCAR HOUSE RESERVOIR

Scar House Reservoir, Upper Nidderdale, Ripon, **YORKSHIRE (NORTH)**, HG4, **England**.
Contact/s: Ms Barbara Breckon.
(T) 01423 711633
Profile: FT: Game; WN: Scar House; WT: Reservoir (Still).
Ref: FH4112

SCARBOROUGH MERE

Scarborough Mere, Seamer Rd, Scarborough, **YORKSHIRE (NORTH)**, YO, **England**.
Contact/s: Mr D Pratt.
(T) 01723 585155
Mr Jim Taylor (Fishery Manager).
(T) 01723 353114
Profile: FT: Coarse; **WN:** Scarborough Mere; **WT:** Lake (Still) **W. Size:** 18 Acres.
Location: Nr. Rd: Seamer Road.
Ref: FH4113

SCARLETTS LAKE

Scarletts Lake, Furnace Lane, Cowden, Edenbridge, **KENT**, TN8 7JJ, **England**.
Contact/s: Mr Jackson (Manager).
(T) 01342 850414
Profile: FT: Coarse; **WN:** Scarletts; **WT:** Lake (Still) **W. Size:** 3 Acres. **Location: Main Rd:** A264 to Tunbridge Wells.
Ref: FH4114

SCHOOL KNOTT TARN

School Knott Tarn, School Knott Fell, Windermere, **CUMBRIA**, LA23, **England**.
Contact/s: Mr Chris Sodo (Hon Treasurer), Windermere, Ambleside and District Angling Association, Ecclerigg Court, Ecclerigg, Windermere, LA23 1LQ.
(T) 01539 445083
Profile: FT: Game; **WN:** School Knott Tarn; **WT:** Tarn (Still) **W. Size:** 1 Acre. **Location: Nr. Rd:** School Knott Stores; **Main Rd:** A591.
Ref: FH4115

SCHOOL POOL

School Pool, Oare, Faversham, **KENT**, ME13, **England**.
Contact/s: Mr Kennett, 14 Millfield Rd, Faversham, Kent.
(T) 01795 534516
Profile: FT: Coarse; **WN:** School Pool; **WT:** Lake (Still) **W. Size:** 11 Acres.
Ref: FH4116

SCHULL RESERVOIR

Schull Reservoir, Schull, **COUNTY CORK**, **Ireland**.
(W) www.swrfb.ie
Contact/s: Area Manager, South West Regional Fisheries Board, 1 Nevilles Trce, Macroom, County Cork, Ireland.
(T) 026 41221
(E) swrfb@swrfb.ie
Ms Kitty Newman (Manager).
(T) 028 28223
Profile: FT: Game; **WN:** Schull; **WT:** Reservoir (Still) **W. Size:** 5 Acres. **Location: Nr. Rd:** Schull to Skibbereen road.
Ref: FH4117

SCOT LANE PONDS

Scot Lane Ponds, Wigan, **LANCASHIRE**, WN, **England**.
(W) www.wiganaa.f9.co.uk
Contact/s: Mr Gerry Wilson (Hon Secretary), Wigan and Distirct Angling Association, 11 Guildford Avenue, Chorley, Lancashire, PR6 8TG.
(T) 01257 265905
(E) gerry@wiganna.freeserve.co.uk
Profile: FT: Coarse; **WN:** Scot Lane; **WT:** Pond (Still) **W. Size:** 1 Acre. **Location: Nr. Rd:** B5375; **Main Rd:** A49, A577, M6, junction 26.
Ref: FH4118

SCOULTON MERE

Scoulton Mere, Scoulton, Norwich, **NORFOLK**, NR9, **England**.
Contact/s: John Baker (Fishery Manager).
(T) 01603 811003
Profile: FT: Coarse; **WN:** Scoulton; **WT:** Mere (Still); **F. Size:** 20 Acres; **W. Size:** 6 Acres. **Location: Nr. Rd:** Mere Road; **Main Rd:** Norwich Road (B1108); **Rail:** Attleborough.
Ref: FH4119

SCOURIE HOTEL

Scourie Hotel, Scourie, Lairg, **HIGHLAND**, IV27 4SX, **Scotland**.
(W) www.scourie-hotel.co.uk
Contact/s: Mr Patrick Price.
(T) 01971 502396 (F) 01971 502423
Profile: FT: Game; **WN:** Scourie Hotel; **WT:** Loch (Still) **W. Size:** 400 Acres. **Location: Nr. Rd:** A894; **Main Rd:** A894; **Rail:** Lairg.
£Fr
Ref: FH4120

SCOUT DYKE RESERVOIR

Scout Dyke Reservoir, Penistone Rd, Penistone, Sheffield, **YORKSHIRE (SOUTH)**, S, **England**.
Contact/s: Mr A Haynes, 3 Albert Rd, Clayton West, Huddersfield, Yorkshire (West), HD8 9NL.
(T) 01484 863642
Profile: FT: Game; **WN:** Scout Dyke; **WT:** Reservoir (Still) **W. Size:** 2 Acres. **Location: Nr. Rd:** Penistone Road; **Rail:** Penistone.
Ref: FH4121

SCREEBE FISHERY

Screebe Fishery, Screebe House, Camus, Connemara, **COUNTY GALWAY**, **Ireland**.
Contact/s: Fishery Manager.
(T) 091 574110
Profile: FT: Game; **WN:** Screebe Fishery; **WT:** Lake (Still).
Ref: FH4122

SCREECH OWL PONDS

Screech Owl Ponds, Taunton Rd, Huntworth, Bridgwater, **SOMERSET**, TA7, **England**.
Contact/s: Mr Mark Pople (Secretary), 14 Edward St, Bridgwater, Somerset.
(T) 01278 422397
Profile: FT: Coarse; **WN:** Screech Owl; **WT:** Pond (Still). **Location: Nr. Rd:** Taunton Road; **Main Rd:** M5.
Ref: FH4123

SEACOURT (STREAM)

Seacourt Stream, Thames To Botley Rd, Reading, **BERKSHIRE**, RG7, **England**.
Contact/s: Mr Andrew Crisp (Secretary), North Oxford Angling Society, 4 Grove St, Summertown, Oxford, Oxfordshire OX3 7JT.
(T) 01865 553800
Profile: FT: Coarse; **WN:** Seacourt; **WT:** Stream (Moving).
Ref: FH4124

SEAGAHAN RESERVOIR DAM

Seagahan Reservoir Dam, Armagh, **COUNTY ARMAGH**, BT61, **Northern Ireland**.
Contact/s: Cathal Doyle (Secretary), Armagh Fisheries Ltd, 6 Knockamell Park, Armagh, County Armagh, BT61 7HJ.
(T) 028 37522068after6pm
Mr Dessie Cartmill (Sub Treasurer), Armagh Fisheries Ltd, G I Stores, 5 Dubbin St, Armagh, County Armagh.
(T) 028 37522335 (F) 028 37522335
Profile: FT: Game; **WN:** Seagahan Dam; **WT:** Reservoir (Still). **Location: Nr. Rd:** B31 Armagh to Newtown Hamilton; **Main Rd:** B31.
Ref: FH4125

SEAMAW LOCH

Seamaw Loch, Montague Fisheries, Mill Of Montague, Balbeggie, Perth, **PERTH AND KINROSS**, PH2 7PR, **Scotland**.
Contact/s: Mr J Watson.
(T) 01821 640271 (F) 01821 640271
Profile: FT: Game; **WN:** Seamaw; **WT:** Loch (Still) **W. Size:** 3 Acres. **Location: Rail:** Perth.
Ref: FH4126

SEATON (RIVER)

River Seaton, Hessenford, Liskeard, **CORNWALL**, PL14, **England**.
Contact/s: Mr Bill Eliot (Secretary), Liskeard and District Angling Club, 64 Portbyhan Rd, West Looe, Cornwall, PL13 2QN.
(T) 01503 264173
Profile: FT: Game; **WN:** Seaton; **WT:** River (Moving) **W. Size:** 2000 Metres. **Location: Nr. Rd:** A38; **Main Rd:** A38; **Rail:** Liskeard.
Ref: FH4127

SEDGES

Sedges (The), River Lane, Dunwear, Bridgwater, **SOMERSET**, TA7 0AA, **England**.
Contact/s: Mr Mike Whale (Bailiff).
(T) 01278 445221
Profile: FT: Coarse; **WN:** Sedges; **WT:** Lake (Still) **W. Size:** 4 Acres. **Location: Nr. Rd:** Dunwear Lane; **Main Rd:** M5.
Ref: FH4128

SELBY 3 LAKES

Bawtry Road, Selby, **YORKSHIRE (NORTH)**, **England**.
(W) www.selby3lakes.co.uk
Contact/s: Mr Gordon Fowler (Fishery Manager), 14 The Cause Way, Thorpewilloughby, Selby, N Yorks, YO9 9PE.
(M) 07818 092420
Profile: FT: Coarse; **WN:** Selby 3 lakes; **WT:** Lake (Still); **F. Size:** 8 Acres. **Location: Main Rd:** A1047; **Rail:** Selby.
Ref: FH4129

SELBY CANAL

Selby Canal, Paper House Farm, Selby Canal, West Haddlesey, Selby, **YORKSHIRE (NORTH)**, YO8, **England**.
Contact/s: Mr Harry Park (Club Treasurer), 18 Court Gardens, Snaith, Goole, Yorkshire (East), DN14 9JP.
(T) 01405 860791
Profile: FT: Coarse; **WN:** Selby; **WT:** Canal (Still) **W. Size:** 1200 Metres. **Location: Nr. Rd:** Paper House Farm to Tankard Bridge; **Main Rd:** M62, junction 34.
Ref: FH4130

SELBY CANAL

Selby Canal, Selby To Haddlesey, Selby, **YORKSHIRE (NORTH)**, YO8, **England**.
Contact/s: Manager, Selby Angling Ctre, 69 Brook St, Selby, Yorkshire (North), YO8 4AL.
(T) 01757 703471 (F) 01757 703471
Mr Kelvin Wethererell (Secretary), Selby District Angling Association, 2 Poplars, Brayton, Selby, YO8 9HF.
(T) 01757 704667
Profile: FT: Coarse; **WN:** Selby; **WT:** Canal (Still).
Ref: FH4131

SELBY CANAL

Selby Canal, Brayton Bridge, Selby, **YORKSHIRE (NORTH)**, YO8, **England**.
Contact/s: Mr Les Rogers (Secretary), Goole and District Angling Association, 39 Clifton Gardens, Goole, Humberside (North), DN14 6AR.
(T) 01405 769096
Mr Robert Howgate (Secretary), Wheatsheaf Angling Club, 4 Sprigfield Rd, Sherburn in Elmet, Leeds, LS25 6BD.
(T) 01977 684772
Profile: FT: Coarse; **WN:** Selby; **WT:** Canal (Still) **W. Size:** 1600 Metres. **Location: Nr. Rd:** Brayton Bridge; **Main Rd:** A63, A19.
Ref: FH4132

SELBY CANAL

Selby Canal, Burn Bridge, Paperhouse Bridge, Selby, **YORKSHIRE (NORTH)**, YO8, **England**.
Contact/s: Mr Les Rogers (Secretary), Goole and District Angling Association, 39 Clifton Gardens, Goole, Humberside (North), DN14 6AR.
(T) 01405 769096
Profile: FT: Coarse; **WN:** Selby; **WT:** Canal (Still) **W. Size:** 4800 Metres. **Location: Nr. Rd:** A19; **Main Rd:** A19; **Rail:** Selby.
Ref: FH4133

SELLEY BRIDGE LAKE

Selley Bridge Lake, Low Marshes, Malton, **YORKSHIRE (NORTH)**, YO17 ORJ, **England**.
Contact/s: Mr Colin Newlove (Fishery

Manager).
(T) 01751 474280
Profile: FT: Coarse; WN: Selley Bridge; WT: Lake (Still). Location: Main Rd: A169.
Ref: FH4134

SELM MUIR FISHERY

Selm Muir Fishery, Mid Calder, Livingston, **LOTHIAN (WEST)**, EH53 0JT, **Scotland**.
Contact/s: Mr G Gowland.
(T) 01506 884550
Profile: FT: Game; WN: Selmmuir Fishery; WT: Pond (Still); F. Size: 6 Acres; W. Size: 3 Acres. Location: Nr. Rd: Morton Road; Main Rd: A71; Rail: Murieston.
Ref: FH4135

SELSET RESERVOIR

Selset Reservoir, Middleton-In-Teesdale, Barnard Castle, **COUNTY DURHAM**, DL12, **England**.
Contact/s: Mr Paul Russell, Northumbrian Water Ltd, Head Office, Recreation Department, Abbey Rd, Durham DH1 5FJ.
(T) 0191 3832222 (F) 0191 3841920
Profile: FT: Game; WN: Selset; WT: Reservoir (Still).
Ref: FH4136

SEMERWATER

Semerwater, Countersett, Bainbridge, Hawes, **YORKSHIRE (NORTH)**, DL8, **England**.
Contact/s: Mr Metcalfe.
(T) 01969 650436
Profile: FT: Combination; WN: Semerwater; WT: Lake (Still) W. Size: 65 Acres.
Ref: FH4137

SEND

Send Pit, Maymont, Guildford Rd, Knaphill, Woking, **SURREY**, GU21, **England**.
Contact/s: D Powell.
Profile: FT: Coarse; WN: Send Pit; WT: Gravel Pit (Still).
Ref: FH4138

SEPHAM TROUT FISHERY

Sepham Trout Fishery, Sepham Farm, Filstone Lane, Shoreham, Sevenoaks, **KENT**, TN14 5JT, **England**.
Contact/s: Fishery Manager.
(T) 01732 454952
Profile: FT: Game; WN: Darent; WT: Lake (Still).
Ref: FH4139

SEVEN ISLANDS

Seven Islands, Mitcham Common, Mitcham, **SURREY**, CR4, **England**.
Contact/s: Mr Martin Boyle (Warden).
(T) 020 82880453
Profile: FT: Coarse; WN: Seven Islands; WT: Pond (Still) W. Size: 1 Acre. Location: Nr. Rd: A236; Main Rd: A237. £Fr
Ref: FH4140

SEVEN OAKS FISHERY

Seven Oaks Fishery, Cowbridge Rd, Talygarn, Pontyclun, **RHONDDA CYNON TAFF**, CF72 9JU, **Wales**.
Contact/s: Mr Terry Rosier.
(T) 01446 775474 (F) 01446 775474
(E) junerosier@hotmail.com
Mrs June Rosier (Proprietor).
(T) 01446 775474 (F) 01446 775474
(E) junerosier@hotmail.com
Profile: FT: Combination; WN: Seven Oaks Fishery; WT: Combination (Still); F. Size: 10 Acres; W. Size: 4 Acres. Location: Nr. Rd: A4222; Main Rd: M4; Rail: Pontyclun.
Ref: FH4141

SEVEN OAKS LOG CABIN PARK

Seven Oaks Log Cabin Park, Crewe Green, Codeway, Shrewsbury, **SHROPSHIRE**, SY, **England**.
Contact/s: Fishery Manager.
(T) 01743 884271
Profile: FT: Coarse; WN: Seven Oaks Log Cabin Park; WT: Pond (Still) W. Size: 350 Metres.
Ref: FH4142

SEVEN SPRINGS FISHERIES

Seven Springs Trout Farm And Fisheries, Caerwys, Mold, **FLINTSHIRE**, CH7 5BZ, **Wales**.
Contact/s: Mr W R Forkings (Owner).
(T) 01352 720511
Mrs Jane E Forkings - Russell (Owner).
(T) 01352 720511
Profile: FT: Game; WN: Seven Springs Trout Farm And Fisheries; WT: Pond (Still); F. Size: 6 Acres; W. Size: 4 Acres. Location: Nr. Rd: B5122; Main Rd: A55; Rail: Flint.
Ref: FH4143

SEVERALLS FARM A AND B

Severalls Farm A And B, River Thames, Willingford, Oxford, **OXFORDSHIRE**, OX1, **England**.
Contact/s: Mr Dusty Millar (Associate members secretary), 238 Elgar Road South, Reading, Berkshire, RG3 0BW.
(T) 0118 9874882
Mr Mick Cox (Chief Bailiff), Dorstans, Hatch Lane, Brimpton Village, Reading, RG7 4TR.
(T) 0118 9714917
Profile: FT: Coarse; WN: Thames; WT: River (Moving).
Ref: FH4144

SEVERN (RIVER)

River Severn, Ryton, Dymock, **GLOUCESTERSHIRE**, GL18, **England**.
Contact/s: Manager, Field Cottage, Ryton, Dymock, Gloucestershire, GL18 2DH. (M) 05318 90455
Profile: FT: Combination; WN: Severn; WT: Tributary (Moving).
Ref: FH4145

SEVERN (RIVER)

River Severn, Uckinghall, Tewkesbury, **GLOUCESTERSHIRE**, GL20, **England**.
Contact/s: Mr John Williams (Secretary), Birmingham Anglers Association, 100 Icknield Port Rd, Rotton Park, Birmingham, B16 0AP.
(T) 0121 4549111
Profile: FT: Coarse; WN: Severn; WT: River (Moving). Location: Main Rd: M50, junction 1.
Ref: FH4146

SEVERN (RIVER)

River Severn, Wainlodes, Norton, Gloucester, **GLOUCESTERSHIRE**, GL2, **England**.
Contact/s: Mr J G Mitchell (Landlord), Red Lion Inn, Wainlode Hill, Norton, Gloucester, GL2 9LW.
(T) 01452 730251
Profile: FT: Coarse; WN: Severn; WT: River (Moving) W. Size: 800 Metres. Location: Nr. Rd: A38 Gloucester to Worcester; Main Rd: A38.
Ref: FH4147

SEVERN (RIVER)

River Severn, Ship Inn Site, Bridgnorth, **MIDLANDS (WEST)**, WV1, **England**.
Contact/s: Mr J Good (Manager).
(T) 01746 861219
Profile: FT: Coarse; WN: Severn; WT: River (Moving) W. Size: 270 Metres.
Ref: FH4148

SEVERN (RIVER)

River Severn, Old Town Bridge, Bridgnorth, **MIDLANDS (WEST)**, WV1, **England**.
Contact/s: Ms Rosa Bailey (Manager), 58 Mill St, Bridgnorth, Shropshire, WV15 5AG.
(T) 01746 767286
Profile: FT: Coarse; WN: Severn; WT: River (Moving).
Ref: FH4149

SEVERN (RIVER)

River Severn, Hampton Loade, Bridgnorth, **MIDLANDS (WEST)**, WV1, **England**.
Contact/s: Fishery Manager.
(T) 01384 77204
Profile: FT: Coarse; WN: Severn; WT: River (Moving) W. Size: 350 Metres.
Ref: FH4150

SEVERN (RIVER)

River Severn, Llandrinio, Llanymynech, **POWYS**, SY22, **Wales**.
Contact/s: Mr Neil Jupp (Club Secretary), Lymm Angling Club, PO Box 350, Warrington, Cheshire, WA2 9FB.
(T) 01925 411744
Profile: FT: Combination; WN: Severn; WT: River (Moving). Location: Nr. Rd: B4393; Main Rd: M53 to Wrexham, A483.
Ref: FH4151

SEVERN (RIVER)

River Severn, Halfpenny Bridge, Newtown, **POWYS**, SY16, **Wales**.
Contact/s: Mr P Hulme.
Profile: FT: Combination; WN: Severn; WT: River (Moving). Location: Main Rd: A483.
Ref: FH4152

SEVERN (RIVER)

River Severn, Llanidloes, **POWYS**, SY18, **Wales**.
Contact/s: Mr J Dallas Davies, Llyn Glywedog, Dresden House, Great Oak St, Llanidloes, SY18 6BW.
(T) 01686 412644 (F) 01686 412644
Mrs Gough (Manager), Travellers Rest Restaurant, 9 Long Bridge St, Llanidloes, Powys, SY18 6EE.
(T) 01686 412329
Profile: FT: Game; WN: Severn; WT: River (Moving) W. Size: 3200 Metres. Location: Main Rd: A470; Rail: Newtown.
Ref: FH4153

SEVERN (RIVER)

Severn (River), Lower Thehelig Farm, Welshpool, **POWYS**, **Wales**.
Contact/s: Mr John Turner (Hon Secretary), Prince Albert Angling Society, 15 Pexhill Drive, Macclesfield, Cheshire, SK10 3LP.
(T) 01625 422010
Profile: FT: Combination; WN: Severn; WT: River (Moving) W. Size: 2000 Metres. Location: Nr. Rd: A483; Rail: Welshpool.
Ref: FH4154

SEVERN (RIVER)

Severn (River), Manor House Farm, Pool Quay, Welshpool, **POWYS**, **Wales**.
Contact/s: Mr John Turner (Hon Secretary), Prince Albert Angling Society, 15 Pexhill Drive, Macclesfield, Cheshire, SK10 3LP.
(T) 01625 422010
Profile: FT: Combination; WN: Severn; WT: River (Moving) W. Size: 2000 Metres. Location: Nr. Rd: A483; Rail: Welshpool.
Ref: FH4155

SEVERN (RIVER)

River Severn, Caersws, Newtown, **POWYS**, SY17, **Wales**.
Contact/s: Mr Trevor Farrington (Manager), The Bucks Hotel, Main St, Caersws, Powys, SY17 5EL.
(T) 01686 688267
Profile: FT: Coarse; WN: Severn; WT: River (Moving) W. Size: 7500 Metres.
Ref: FH4156

SEVERN (RIVER)

River Severn, Upper Penrhyddlan, Llanidloes, **POWYS**, SY18, **Wales**.
Contact/s: Mr Price, Upper Penrhyddlan, Llandinam, Powys.
(T) 01686 412548
Profile: FT: Game; WN: Severn; WT: River (Moving) W. Size: 1125 Metres.
Ref: FH4157

SEVERN (RIVER)

Severn (River), Lower Farm, Criggion, Welshpool, **POWYS**, **Wales**.
Contact/s: Mr John Turner (Hon Secretary), Prince Albert Angling Society, 15

Pexhill Drive, Macclesfield, Cheshire, SK10 3LP.
(T) 01625 422010
Profile: **FT:** Combination; **WN:** Severn; **WT:** River (Moving) **W. Size:** 3500 Metres.
Location: **Nr. Rd:** Back Lane; **Main Rd:** B4393; **Rail:** Welshpool.
Ref: FH4158

SEVERN (RIVER)

River Severn, Abermule, Glan Hafron, Newtown, **POWYS**, SY16, **Wales**.
Contact/s: **Mr Neil Jupp** (Club Secretary), Lymm Angling Club, PO Box 350, Warrington, Cheshire, WA2 9FB.
(T) 01925 411744
Profile: **FT:** Combination; **WN:** Severn; **WT:** River (Moving) **W. Size:** 910 Metres.
Location: **Nr. Rd:** Welshpool to Newtown; **Main Rd:** M53 to Chester.
Ref: FH4159

SEVERN (RIVER)

River Severn, Dolerw, Newtown, **POWYS**, SY16, **Wales**.
Contact/s: **Mr Steve Potts** (Secretary), Severnside and Newtown Angling Club, 902 Falcon Court, Newton, Powys, SY16 1LQ.
(T) 01686 624871
Profile: **FT:** Game; **WN:** Severn; **WT:** River (Moving) **W. Size:** 1500 Metres.
Ref: FH4160

SEVERN (RIVER)

River Severn, Mochdre, Newtown, **POWYS**, SY16, **Wales**.
Mr Steve Potts (Secretary), Severnside and Newtown Angling Club, 902 Falcon Court, Newton, Powys, SY16 1LQ.
(T) 01686 624871
Profile: **FT:** Coarse; **WN:** Severn; **WT:** River (Moving) **W. Size:** 1500 Metres.
Ref: FH4161

SEVERN (RIVER)

Wingfield Arms (The), Montford Bridge, Shrewsbury, **SHROPSHIRE**, SY4 1EB, **England**.
Contact/s: **Mr Bert Waters**.
(T) 01743 850750 **(F)** 01743 850750
Profile: **FT:** Combination; **WN:** Severn; **WT:** River (Moving); **F. Size:** 10 Acres; **W. Size:** 1500 Metres. **Location:** **Rail:** Shrewsbury.
Ref: FH4162

SEVERN (RIVER)

River Severn, Moors Tile Museum, Coalport, Telford, **SHROPSHIRE**, TF8, **England**.
Contact/s: Area Manager, Environment Agency, Sapphire East, 550 Streetsbrook Rd, Solihull, B91 1QT.
(T) 0121 7112324 **(F)** 0121 7115824
Mr Stan Harris (Secretary), Telford Angling Association, 73 Burnside, Brookside, Telford, TF3 1DA.
(T) 01952 590605
Profile: **FT:** Coarse; **WN:** Severn; **WT:** River (Moving). **Location:** **Main Rd:** A442, B4373 North of Bridgnorth.
Ref: FH4163

SEVERN (RIVER)

River Severn, Montford Bridge, Shrewsbury, **SHROPSHIRE**, SY, **England**.
Contact/s: **Mr Bill Turner** (Secretary).
(T) 01902 457906
Profile: **FT:** Coarse; **WN:** Severn; **WT:** River (Moving) **W. Size:** 1125 Metres. **Location:** **Nr. Rd:** Montford Bridge.
Ref: FH4164

SEVERN (RIVER)

River Severn, Castlemeadows, Shrewsbury, **SHROPSHIRE**, SY, **England**.
Contact/s: **J H Owens** (Secretary), Ditherington Angling Club, Monhafen Rd, Copethorn, Shrewsbury, SY3 8NG.
(T) 01743 369007
Mr Alan Churchward (Area Manager), Environment Agency, Sapphire East, 550 Streetsbrook Rd, Solihull, B91 1QT.
(T) 0121 7112324 **(F)** 0121 7115824
Profile: **FT:** Coarse; **WN:** Severn; **WT:** River (Moving).
Ref: FH4165

SEVERN (RIVER)

River Severn, Ironbridge, Telford, **SHROPSHIRE**, TF8, **England**.
Contact/s: **Mr Mick Tuff** (Secretary), Dawley Angling Society, 68 Coronation St, Madley, Telford, TF7 5EH.
(T) 01952 590348
Profile: **FT:** Coarse; **WN:** Severn; **WT:** River (Moving) **W. Size:** 1600 Metres. **Location:** **Nr. Rd:** Bridgnorth Road; **Main Rd:** B4373 from Bridgnorth to Ladywood Bank.
Ref: FH4166

SEVERN (RIVER)

River Severn, Monkmoor Rd, Shrewsbury, **SHROPSHIRE**, SY, **England**.
Contact/s: Fishery Manager.
(T) 01743 365063
Manager, Kingfisher Angling Ctre, 9 New St, Shrewsbury, Shropshire, SY3 8JN.
(T) 01743 240602 **(F)** 01743 240602
Manager, Sundorne Fishng Tackle, 1 Sundorne Avenue, Shrewsbury, Shropshire, SY1 4JW.
(T) 01743 361804
Profile: **FT:** Combination; **WN:** Severn; **WT:** River (Moving) **W. Size:** 4000 Metres.
Location: **Nr. Rd:** Telford Way; **Main Rd:** A5112.
Ref: FH4167

SEVERN (RIVER)

River Severn, Emstrey, Shrewsbury, **SHROPSHIRE**, SY, **England**.
Contact/s: Manager, Sundorne Fishng Tackle, 1 Sundorne Avenue, Shrewsbury, Shropshire, SY1 4JW.
(T) 01743 361804
Mr Cyril Bruce (Secretary).
(T) 01743 873305
Profile: **FT:** Coarse; **WN:** Severn; **WT:** River (Moving).
Ref: FH4168

SEVERN (RIVER)

River Severn, Atcham, Shrewsbury, **SHROPSHIRE**, SY5, **England**.
Contact/s: **Dr John Wooland** (Fisheries Manager), Environment Agency, Upper Severn Area Office, Hafren House, Welshpool Rd, Shelton SY3 8BB.
(T) 01743 272828 **(F)** 01743 272138
Profile: **FT:** Coarse; **WN:** Severn; **WT:** River (Moving) **W. Size:** 2895 Metres.
Ref: FH4169

SEVERN (RIVER)

River Severn, Ironbridge, Telford, **SHROPSHIRE**, TF8, **England**.
Contact/s: Manager, Environment Agency, Upper Severn Area Office, Hafren House, Welshpool Rd, Shelton SY3 8BB.
(T) 01743 272828 **(F)** 01743 272138
Profile: **FT:** Coarse; **WN:** Severn; **WT:** River (Moving) **W. Size:** 549 Metres. **Location:** **Nr. Rd:** B4377. **£Fr**
Ref: FH4170

SEVERN (RIVER)

River Severn, Rossall, West Felton, Oswestry, **SHROPSHIRE**, SY11 4, **England**.
Contact/s: **Mr Neil Jupp** (Club Secretary), Lymm Angling Club, PO Box 350, Warrington, Cheshire, WA2 9FB.
(T) 01925 411744
Profile: **FT:** Coarse; **WN:** Severn; **WT:** River (Moving). **Location:** **Nr. Rd:** A5, Isle Lane; **Main Rd:** A483 to Wrexham.
Ref: FH4171

SEVERN (RIVER)

Severn (River), Isle Estate, Bicton Village, Shrewsbury, **SHROPSHIRE**, **England**.
Contact/s: **Mr John Turner** (Hon Secretary), Prince Albert Angling Society, 15 Pexhill Drive, Macclesfield, Cheshire, SK10 3LP.
(T) 01625 422010
Profile: **FT:** Combination; **WN:** Severn; **WT:** River (Moving) **W. Size:** 7000 Metres.
Location: **Main Rd:** B4380; **Rail:** Shrewsbury.
Ref: FH4172

SEVERN (RIVER)

River Severn, Sydney Avenue, Shrewsbury, **SHROPSHIRE**, SY, **England**.
Contact/s: Manager, Shrewsbury Bait Ctre, Unit 1, 198 Whitchurch Rd, Shrewsbury, Shropshire, SY1 4EY.
(T) 01743 446759 **(F)** 01743 446759
Profile: **FT:** Coarse; **WN:** Severn; **WT:** River (Moving). **Location:** **Nr. Rd:** Sydney Avenue; **Main Rd:** Shrewsbury Centre.
Ref: FH4173

SEVERN (RIVER)

Severn (River), Longner Hall, Nr Atcham, Shrewsbury, **SHROPSHIRE**, **England**.
Contact/s: **Mr John Turner** (Hon Secretary), Prince Albert Angling Society, 15 Pexhill Drive, Macclesfield, Cheshire, SK10 3LP.
(T) 01625 422010
Profile: **FT:** Combination; **WN:** Severn; **WT:** River (Moving) **W. Size:** 2000 Metres.
Location: **Main Rd:** A5; **Rail:** Shrewsbury.
Ref: FH4174

SEVERN (RIVER)

Severn (River), Uffington, Shrewsbury, **SHROPSHIRE**, **England**.
Contact/s: **Mr John Turner** (Hon Secretary), Prince Albert Angling Society, 15 Pexhill Drive, Macclesfield, Cheshire, SK10 3LP.
(T) 01625 422010
Profile: **FT:** Coarse; **WN:** Severn; **WT:** River (Moving) **W. Size:** 300 Metres. **Location:** **Main Rd:** B5062; **Rail:** Shrewsbury.
Ref: FH4175

SEVERN (RIVER)

Severn (River), White Abbey, Alberbury, Shrewsbury, **SHROPSHIRE**, **England**.
Contact/s: **Mr John Turner** (Hon Secretary), Prince Albert Angling Society, 15 Pexhill Drive, Macclesfield, Cheshire, SK10 3LP.
(T) 01625 422010
Profile: **FT:** Coarse; **WN:** Severn; **WT:** River (Moving) **W. Size:** 2000 Metres. **Location:** **Nr. Rd:** Abbey Lane; **Main Rd:** B4393; **Rail:** Shrewsbury.
Ref: FH4176

SEVERN (RIVER)

Severn (River), Royal Hill, Pentre, Shrewsbury, **SHROPSHIRE**, **England**.
Profile: **FT:** Combination; **WN:** Severn; **WT:** River (Moving) **W. Size:** 500 Metres.
Location: **Main Rd:** A5; **Rail:** Shrewsbury.
Ref: FH4177

SEVERN (RIVER)

Severn (River), Cound, Nr Cressage, Shrewsbury, **SHROPSHIRE**, **England**.
Contact/s: **Mr John Turner** (Hon Secretary), Prince Albert Angling Society, 15 Pexhill Drive, Macclesfield, Cheshire, SK10 3LP.
(T) 01625 422010
Profile: **FT:** Coarse; **WN:** Severn; **WT:** River (Moving) **W. Size:** 1000 Metres. **Location:** **Nr. Rd:** A458; **Main Rd:** A458; **Rail:** Shrewsbury.
Ref: FH4178

SEVERN (RIVER)

Severn (River), Church Farm, Cressage, Much Wenlock, **SHROPSHIRE**, **England**.
Contact/s: **Mr John Turner** (Hon Secretary), Prince Albert Angling Society, 15 Pexhill Drive, Macclesfield, Cheshire, SK10 3LP.
(T) 01625 422010
Profile: **FT:** Combination; **WN:** Severn; **WT:** River (Moving) **W. Size:** 1000 Metres.

Location: Nr. Rd: B4380; **Rail:** Telford.
Ref: FH4179

SEVERN (RIVER)

River Severn, Atcham, Shrewsbury, **SHROPSHIRE**, SY5, **England**.
Contact/s: Manager, Environment Agency, Upper Severn Area Office, Hafren House, Welshpool Rd, Shelton SY3 8BB.
(T) 01743 272828 **(F)** 01743 272138
Profile: **FT:** Coarse; **WN:** Severn; **WT:** River (Moving) **W. Size:** 600 Metres. **Location:** **Nr. Rd:** B4380; **Main Rd:** A458 to Cross Houses, turn left to Atcham.
Ref: FH4180

SEVERN (RIVER)

River Severn, Stanley Meadow, Highley, Bridgnorth, **SHROPSHIRE**, WV16, **England**.
Contact/s: **Mr John Williams** (Secretary), Birmingham Anglers Association, 100 Icknield Port Rd, Rotton Park, Birmingham, B16 0AP.
(T) 0121 4549111
Profile: **FT:** Coarse; **WN:** Severn; **WT:** River (Moving). **Location:** **Nr. Rd:** Signposted; **Main Rd:** B4555 South from Bridgnorth.
Ref: FH4181

SEVERN (RIVER)

River Severn, Sundorne Estate, Uffington, Shrewsbury, **SHROPSHIRE**, SY, **England**.
Contact/s: **Mr Albert Perkins** (Hon Secretary), 63 Fowlers Lane, Light Oaks, Stoke-on-Trent, Staffordshire, ST2 7NB.
Ms Liz Hayes (Manager).
(T) 01625 251262
Profile: **FT:** Coarse; **WN:** Severn; **WT:** River (Moving) **W. Size:** 1600 Metres. **Location:** **Nr. Rd:** B5062; **Main Rd:** A49; **Rail:** Shrewsbury.
Ref: FH4182

SEVERN (RIVER)

River Severn, Hampstall Hotel, Stourport-on-Severn, **WORCESTERSHIRE**, DY13, **England**.
Contact/s: Manager, Hampstall Hotel, Astley Burf, Stourport-on-Severn, Worcestershire, DY13 0RY.
(T) 01299 822600
Profile: **FT:** Coarse; **WN:** Severn; **WT:** River (Moving) **W. Size:** 225 Metres.
Ref: FH4183

SEVERN (RIVER)

River Severn, Ribbesford, Bewdley, **WORCESTERSHIRE**, DY12, **England**.
Contact/s: **Mr John Williams** (Secretary), Birmingham Anglers Association, 100 Icknield Port Rd, Rotton Park, Birmingham, B16 0AP.
(T) 0121 4549111
Profile: **FT:** Coarse; **WN:** Severn; **WT:** River (Moving) **W. Size:** 1600 Metres. **Location:** **Nr. Rd:** Bewdley to Stourport-on-Severn; **Main Rd:** B4194.
Ref: FH4184

SEVERN (RIVER)

River Severn, Harbour Inn, Upper Arley, Bewdley, **WORCESTERSHIRE**, DY12, **England**.
Contact/s: **Mr Neil Scriven**.
(T) 01299 401204
Profile: **FT:** Coarse; **WN:** Severn; **WT:** River (Moving) **W. Size:** 500 Metres. **Location:** **Nr. Rd:** B4190; **Main Rd:** B4190 to Button Oak, left to Upper Arley.
Ref: FH4185

SEVERN (RIVER)

River Severn, Northwood Bewdley, Bewdley, **WORCESTERSHIRE**, DY12, **England**.
Contact/s: **Mr Stan Lewis** (Manager), S Lewis Fishing Tackle, 2 Severnside South, Bewdley, Worcestershire, DY12 2DX.
(T) 01299 403358
Profile: **FT:** Combination; **WN:** Severn; **WT:** River (Moving) **W. Size:** 2250 Metres. **Location:** **Rail:** Bewdley.
Ref: FH4186

SEVERN (RIVER)

River Severn, Belvere Lock, Worcester, **WORCESTERSHIRE**, WR, **England**.
Contact/s: Fishery Manager.
(T) 01905 640275
Profile: **FT:** Coarse; **WN:** Severn; **WT:** River (Moving).
Ref: FH4187

SEVERN (RIVER)

River Severn, Beauchamp Court, Worcester, **WORCESTERSHIRE**, WR, **England**.
Contact/s: **Mr Dave Beresford** (Manager), Allans Fishing Tackle, 26-30 Malvern Rd, Worcester, Worcestershire, WR2 4LG.
(T) 01905 422107 **(F)** 01905 422107
Mr John Wells (Chairman), Worcester and District United Angling Association, Poplar Cottages, Poplar Rd, Whichenford, WR6 6YF.
(T) 01886 888459
Profile: **FT:** Coarse; **WN:** Severn; **WT:** River (Moving). **Location:** **Nr. Rd:** B4424, Lower Ferry Lane; **Main Rd:** A38, A449. **£Fr**
Ref: FH4188

SEVERN (RIVER)

River Severn, Holt Fleet, Worcester, **WORCESTERSHIRE**, WR6, **England**.
Contact/s: **Mr Andy Portman** (Fishery Manager).
(T) 01905 620218
Mr Dave Beresford (Manager), Allans Fishing Tackle, 26-30 Malvern Rd, Worcester, Worcestershire, WR2 4LG.
(T) 01905 422107 **(F)** 01905 422107
Profile: **FT:** Coarse; **WN:** Severn; **WT:** River (Moving). **Location:** **Nr. Rd:** A4133; **Main Rd:** A449 to Ombersley.
Ref: FH4189

SEVERN (RIVER)

River Severn, Newhalls Meadow, Stourport-on-Severn, **WORCESTERSHIRE**, DY13, **England**.
Profile: **FT:** Coarse; **WN:** Severn; **WT:** River (Moving).
Ref: FH4190

SEVERN (RIVER)

River Severn, Upton-upon-Severn, Worcester, **WORCESTERSHIRE**, WR8, **England**.
Contact/s: **Mr John Williams** (Secretary), Birmingham Anglers Association, 100 Icknield Port Rd, Rotton Park, Birmingham, B16 0AP.
(T) 0121 4549111
Profile: **FT:** Coarse; **WN:** Severn; **WT:** River (Moving) **W. Size:** 800 Metres. **Location:** **Nr. Rd:** A38; **Main Rd:** B4211 to Great Malvern. **£Fr**
Ref: FH4191

SEVERN (RIVER)

River Severn, Ripple, Upton-upon-Severn, Worcester, **WORCESTERSHIRE**, WR8, **England**.
Contact/s: **Mr Alan Churchward** (Area Manager), Environment Agency, Lower Severn Area Office, Riversmeet House, Newtown Industrial Estate, Tewkesbury GL20 8JG.
(T) 01684 850951 **(F)** 01684 293599
Profile: **FT:** Coarse; **WN:** Severn; **WT:** River (Moving) **W. Size:** 1909 Metres.
Ref: FH4192

SEVERN (RIVER)

River Severn, East Diglis, Worcester, **WORCESTERSHIRE**, WR, **England**.
Mr John Wells (Chairman), Worcester and District United Angling Association, Poplar Cottages, Poplar Rd, Whichenford, WR6 6YF.
(T) 01886 888459
Profile: **FT:** Coarse; **WN:** Severn; **WT:** River (Moving) **W. Size:** 350 Metres.
Ref: FH4193

SEVERN (RIVER)

River Severn, Holt Fleet Weir, Worcester, **WORCESTERSHIRE**, WR, **England**.
Contact/s: **Mr D.B. Law** (owner), Holt Fleet Restaurant, Holt Heath, Worcester, Worcestershire, WR6 6NL.
(T) 01905 620286
Profile: **FT:** Coarse; **WN:** Severn; **WT:** River (Moving) **W. Size:** 550 Metres. **Location:** **Nr. Rd:** Holt Fleet; **Main Rd:** A443 to Holt Heath.
Ref: FH4194

SEVERN (RIVER)

River Severn, The Ham, Upton-upon-Severn, Worcester, **WORCESTERSHIRE**, WR8, **England**.
Contact/s: **Mr Geoff Shinn** (Shop Keeper), Fishing Tackle Shop, 21-23 Old St, Upton-upon-Severn, Worcester, WR8 0HN.
(T) 01684 592012
Mr John Williams (Secretary), Birmingham Anglers Association, 100 Icknield Port Rd, Rotton Park, Birmingham, B16 0AP.
(T) 0121 4549111
Profile: **FT:** Coarse; **WN:** Severn; **WT:** River (Moving) **W. Size:** 800 Metres. **Location:** **Nr. Rd:** B4211; **Main Rd:** A48 to Tewkesbury. **£Fr**
Ref: FH4195

SEVERN (RIVER)

River Severn, Kempsey, Worcester, **WORCESTERSHIRE**, WR, **England**.
Contact/s: Fishery Manager.
(T) 01384 77204
Profile: **FT:** Coarse; **WN:** Severn; **WT:** River (Moving) **W. Size:** 350 Metres.
Ref: FH4196

SEVERN (RIVER)

River Severn, Wharf Inn, Worcester, **WORCESTERSHIRE**, WR, **England**.
Contact/s: Manager, The Wharf Inn, Holt Heath, Worcester, Worcestershire, WR6 6NN.
(T) 01905 620289 **(F)** 01905 620140
Profile: **FT:** Coarse; **WN:** Severn; **WT:** River (Moving).
Ref: FH4197

SEVERN ON THE HAM

Severn On The Ham, Tewkesbury, **GLOUCESTERSHIRE**, GL20, **England**.
Contact/s: **Mr Rob Danter** (Manager), Tewkesbury Fishing Tackle, 3 Barton St, Tewkesbury, Shropshire, GL20 1PR.
(T) 01684 293234
Profile: **FT:** Coarse; **WN:** Severn; **WT:** River (Moving).
Ref: FH4198

SEVINGTON LAKES FISHERY

Sevington Lakes Fishery, Wellfield House, Park House Lane, Keynsham, Bristol, BS31 2SG, **England**.
Contact/s: **Mr R J Pope** (Owner).
(T) 01179 861841
Profile: **FT:** Coarse; **WN:** Sevington; **WT:** Lake (Still) **W. Size:** 2 Acres.
Ref: FH4199

SHAFTESBURY LAKE

Shaftesbury Lake, Shaftesbury Avenue, Swindon, **WILTSHIRE**, SN, **England**.
Contact/s: Secretary, Shaftesbury Lake Angling Club, 19 Beaufort Green, Swindon, SN3 2AE.
Mr John Sage.
(T) 01793 536103
Profile: **FT:** Coarse; **WN:** Shaftesbury; **WT:** Lake (Still) **W. Size:** 2 Acres. **Location:** **Nr. Rd:** Shaftesbury Avenue.
Ref: FH4200

SHAFTOS LAKE

Shaftos Lake, Whitworth Park, Spennymoor, **COUNTY DURHAM**, DL16, **England**.
Contact/s: Manager, Shaftos Inn, Whitworth Park Estate, Whitworth, Spennymoor, DL16 7QX.
(T) 01388 819737 **(F)** 01388 815899
Mr Barry Hignett (Secretary), Ferryhill and District Angling Club, 74 Grasmere Rd, Garden Farm Estate, Chester-le-Street, County Durham.

(T) 0191 3883557
Profile: **FT:** Coarse; **WN:** Shafto; **WT:** Lake (Still).
Ref: FH4201

SHAKERLEY MERE

Shakerley Mere, Allostock, Northwich, **CHESHIRE**, CW, **England**.
Contact/s: **Mr Neil Jupp** (Club Secretary), Lymm Angling Club, PO Box 350, Warrington, Cheshire, WA2 9FB.
(T) 01925 411774
Profile: **FT:** Coarse; **WN:** Shakerley Mere; **WT:** Lake (Still); **F. Size:** 25 Acres; **W. Size:** 17 Acres. **Location:** **Nr. Rd:** B5082; **Main Rd:** M6.
Ref: FH4202

SHAKESPEARE MOORLANDS FARM

Shakespeare Moorlands Farm, Manor Lane, Hartlebury, Kidderminster, **WORCESTERSHIRE**, DY11 7XN, **England**.
Contact/s: **Mr John Talbot** (Moorlands Farm Manager).
(T) 01299 250427
Profile: **FT:** Coarse; **WN:** Meadow Pool; **WT:** Lake (Still). **Location:** **Main Rd:** A449 to Worcester; **Rail:** Hartlebury.
Ref: FH4203

SHALFORD RESERVOIRS

Shalford Reservoirs, Shalford Church, Braintree, **ESSEX**, CM7, **England**.
Contact/s: **Mr Derek Howard** (Hon Treasurer), Billericay and District Angling Club, 4 Long Meadow Drive, Wickford, Essex, SS11 8AX.
(T) 01268 734468
Profile: **FT:** Coarse; **WN:** Shalford; **WT:** Reservoir (Still); **F. Size:** 2 Acres; **W. Size:** 2 Acres. **Location:** **Nr. Rd:** Salford Church; **Main Rd:** B1053; **Rail:** Braintree.
Ref: FH4204

SHALLOW BROOK LAKES

Shallow Brook Lakes, Bridge Farm, Costessey, Norwich, **NORFOLK**, NR, **England**.
Contact/s: **Mr Martin Green**.
(T) 01603 741123
Mr Robin O'Brien (Bailiff).
(T) 01603 744680
Profile: **FT:** Coarse; **WN:** Shallow Brook; **WT:** Lake (Still) **W. Size:** 2 Acres.
Ref: FH4205

SHAMFOLD FARM FISHERY

Shamfold Farm Fishery, Rye, **SUSSEX (EAST)**, TN31, **England**.
Contact/s: **Mr Dennis Hilsdon** (Manager).
(T) 01323 768490
Profile: **FT:** Coarse; **WN:** Shamfold Farm Fishery; **WT:** Lake (Still).
Ref: FH4206

SHANDY KEV FISHERIES

Shandy Kev Fisheries, Dykes Cottage, Chapel Hill, Tattershall, Lincoln, **LINCOLNSHIRE**, LN4 4PX, **England**.
Contact/s: **Mr N Dolby** (Fishery Manager).
(T) 01526 343315
Mrs A L Dolby (Fishery Manager).
(T) 01526 343315
Profile: **FT:** Coarse; **WN:** Shandy Kev Fisheries; **WT:** Pond (Still) **W. Size:** 1 Acre. **Location:** **Main Rd:** Sleaford to Skegness Road; **Rail:** Boston.
Ref: FH4207

SHANNON (UPPER) (RIVER)

River Upper Shannon, Drumshanbo, **COUNTY LEITRIM**, **Ireland**.
(W) www.dbo.ie
Contact/s: **Mr Brian McGourty** (Fishing Expert), Lough Allen Conservation Assocaiation, Drumshanbo, County Leitrim, Ireland.
(T) 078 41648 (F) 078 41577
(E) dec@iol.ie
Mr Sean Wynne (Secretary), Lough Allen Conservation Assocaiation, Drumshanbo, County Leitrim, Ireland.
(T) 078 41564
Profile: **FT:** Game; **WN:** Upper Shannon; **WT:** River (Moving) **W. Size:** 50 Metres. **Location:** **Nr. Rd:** N4 from Dublin (110 miles); **Main Rd:** N4.
Ref: FH4208

SHARKEYS PIT

Sharkeys Pit, Strawberry Lane, Joppa, Hayle, **CORNWALL**, TR27, **England**.
Contact/s: **Mr Dave Burn**.
Profile: **FT:** Coarse; **WN:** Sharkeys Pit; **WT:** Lake (Still) **W. Size:** 2 Acres. **Location:** **Nr. Rd:** Strawberry Lane; **Main Rd:** A30.
Ref: FH4209

SHARNFOLD FARM FISHERY

Sharnfold Farm Fishery, Hailsham Rd, Stone Cross, Pevensey, **SUSSEX (EAST)**, BN24 5BU, **England**.
Contact/s: **Mr Dennis Hilsdon** (Manager).
(T) 01323 768490
Profile: **FT:** Coarse; **WN:** Sharnfold Farm Fishery; **WT:** Lake (Still); **F. Size:** 10 Acres; **W. Size:** 2 Acres. **Location:** **Nr. Rd:** B2104; **Main Rd:** A27; **Rail:** Polegate.
Ref: FH4210

SHARPLEY WATERS

Sharpley Waters, Sunderland, Cockermouth, **CUMBRIA**, CA13, **England**.
Contact/s: **Mr Weightman**.
(T) 0191 5818045
Profile: **FT:** Game; **WN:** Sharpley Waters; **WT:** Lake (Still). **Location:** **Main Rd:** A591.
Ref: FH4211

SHATTERFORD FISHERY

Shatterford Fishery And Wildlife Sanctuary, Bridgnorth Rd, Shatterford, Kidderminster, **WORCESTERSHIRE**, DY12 1TW, **England**.
Contact/s: **Mr Eric Lloyd** (Shatterford Fishery Manager).
(T) 01299 861597
Profile: **FT:** Coarse; **WN:** Shatterford Fishery And Wildlife Sanctuary; **WT:** Lake (Still); **F. Size:** 75 Acres; **W. Size:** 13 Acres. **Location:** **Nr. Rd:** Kidderminster to Bridgnorth; **Main Rd:** A442; **Rail:** Kidderminster.
Ref: FH4212

SHAWFIELDS LAKES

Shawfields Lakes, Ash, **SURREY**, **England**.
Contact/s:
(T) 01483 234054
Profile: **FT:** Coarse; **WN:** Shawfields Lakes; **WT:** Lake (Still).
Ref: FH4213

SHAWS LAKE

Shaws Lake, Armagh, **COUNTY ARMAGH**, BT60, **Northern Ireland**.
Contact/s: **Dessie Cartmill** (Manager), Armagh Fisheries Ltd, G I Stores, 5 Dobbin St, Armagh, County Armagh.
(T) 028 37522335 (F) 028 37522335
Mr Peter McKinney (Project Manager), Armagh Fisheries Ltd, 50 Ballynahonemore Rd, Armagh, County Armagh, BT60 1HY.
(T) 028 37511738 (M) 07775 805670
Profile: **FT:** Game; **WN:** Shaw's; **WT:** Lake (Still) **W. Size:** 40 Acres.
Ref: FH4214

SHAWS LAKE

Shaws Lake, Glenanne, Armagh, **COUNTY ARMAGH**, BT60, **Northern Ireland**.
Contact/s: **Cathal Doyle** (Secretary), Armagh Fisheries Ltd, 6 Knockamell Park, Armagh, County Armagh, BT61 7HJ.
(T) 028 37522068after6pm
Mr Dessie Cartmill (Sub Treasurer), Armagh Fisheries Ltd, G I Stores, 5 Dobbin St, Armagh, County Armagh.
(T) 028 37522335 (F) 028 37522335
Profile: **FT:** Game; **WN:** Shaw; **WT:** Lake (Still) **W. Size:** 40 Acres. **Location:** **Rail:** Newry.
Ref: FH4215

SHEAR WATER

Shear Water, Warminster, **WILTSHIRE**, BA12, **England**.
Contact/s: **Mr Nick Robbins**.
(T) 01985 844496 (F) 01985 844885
Profile: **FT:** Coarse; **WN:** Shear; **WT:** Lake (Still) **W. Size:** 38 Acres. **Location:** **Nr. Rd:** A350; **Main Rd:** B3414 to Warminster.
Ref: FH4216

SHEEPHOUSE FARM TROUT FISHERY

Sheephouse Farm Trout Fishery, Sheephouse Farm, Sheephouse Rd, Maidenhead, **BERKSHIRE**, SL6 8HJ, **England**.
Contact/s: **Mr Robert Amos** (Fishery Manager).
(T) 01628 771446
Profile: **FT:** Game; **WN:** Sheephouse Farm Trout Fishery; **WT:** Gravel Pit (Still) **W. Size:** 7 Acres. **Location:** **Nr. Rd:** Sheephouse Road; **Main Rd:** M4, junction 7 or M40, junction 3 or 4.
Ref: FH4217

SHEEPWALK LAKE

Sheepwalk Lake, Sheepwalk Lane, Shepperton, London, **LONDON (GREATER)**, TW17, **England**.
Contact/s: **Mr Alan Sivyer**.
(T) 01784 240013
Mrs V Sivyer (Secretary), Feltham Piscatorial Society, 96 Raleigh Rd, Feltham, Middlesex, TW13 4LP.
(T) 01818 909005
Profile: **FT:** Coarse; **WN:** Sheepwalk; **WT:** Lake (Still); **F. Size:** 2 Acres; **W. Size:** 2 Acres. **Location:** **Main Rd:** A316; **Rail:** Ashford International.
Ref: FH4218

SHEEPY MAGNA LAKE

Sheepy Magna Lake, Atherstone, **WARWICKSHIRE**, CV9, **England**.
Contact/s: Sheepy Magna.
(T) 01827 880242or872660
Profile: **FT:** Coarse; **WN:** Sheepy Magna; **WT:** Lake (Still) **W. Size:** 6 Acres.
Ref: FH4219

SHEFFIELD & S YORKS NAVIGATION

Sheffield And South Yorkshire Navigation, Kilnhurst, Rotherham, **YORKSHIRE (SOUTH)**, S, **England**.
Contact/s: **M Read**.
(T) 01709 584590
Profile: **FT:** Coarse; **WN:** Sheffield and South Yorkshire Navigation; **WT:** Canal (Still) **W. Size:** 1000 Metres.
Ref: FH4220

SHEFFIELD & S YORKS NAVIGATION

Sheffield And South Yorkshire Navigation, Swinton Bridge, Mexborough, **YORKSHIRE (SOUTH)**, S64, **England**.
Contact/s: **M Read**.
(T) 01709 584590
Profile: **FT:** Coarse; **WN:** Sheffield and South Yorkshire Navigation; **WT:** Canal (Still) **W. Size:** 1000 Metres. **Location:** **Nr. Rd:** Swinton Bridge to Ferryboat Locks.
Ref: FH4221

SHEFFIELD CANAL

Sheffield Canal, Plumper's, Sheffield, **YORKSHIRE (SOUTH)**, S, **England**.
Contact/s: Manager, Swale Angling Ctre, 738 Attercliffe Rd, Sheffield, Yorkshire (South), S9 3RQ.
(T) 0114 2436218 (F) 0114 2442398
Profile: **FT:** Coarse; **WN:** Sheffield; **WT:** Canal (Still). **Location:** **Nr. Rd:** A6178; **Main Rd:** Sheffield.
Ref: FH4222

SHEFFIELD CANAL

Sheffield Canal, Avesta Length, Sheffield, **YORKSHIRE (SOUTH)**, S, **England**.
Contact/s: Fishery Contact, Brian Mandley Avesta Sports Club, Bawtry Rd, Sheffield.

Mr Brian Cashmore.
(T) 01709 324672
Profile: **FT:** Coarse; **WN:** Sheffield; **WT:** Canal (Still). **Location:** **Nr. Rd:** Tinsley Park Road, park; **Main Rd:** M1, junction 34, then A6178.
Ref: FH4223

SHELFLEYS LAKE

Shelfleys Lake, Northampton, **NORTHAMPTONSHIRE**, NN, **England**.
Contact/s: Fishery Manager.
(T) 01327 705092
Profile: **FT:** Coarse; **WN:** Shelfley's; **WT:** Lake (Still).
Ref: FH4224

SHELL FRESH LAKE

Shell Fresh Lake, Hinckley, **LEICESTERSHIRE**, LE10, **England**.
Contact/s: Office Manager.
(T) 01455 619009
Profile: **FT:** Coarse; **WN:** Shell Fresh; **WT:** Lake (Still) **W. Size:** 1 Acre.
Ref: FH4225

SHELLOW FARM POOLS

Shellow Farm Pools, Shellow Farm, Nr. Warren, Congleton, **CHESHIRE**, **England**.
Contact/s: **Mr John Turner** (Hon Secretary), Prince Albert Angling Society, 15 Pexhill Drive, Macclesfield, Cheshire, SK10 3LP.
(T) 01625 422010
Profile: **FT:** Coarse; **WN:** Shellow Pools; **WT:** Pool (Still); **F. Size:** 3 Acres; **W. Size:** 2 Acres. **Location:** **Nr. Rd:** Shellow Lane; **Main Rd:** A536; **Rail:** Congleton.
Ref: FH4226

SHELMORE TROUT FISHERY

Shelmore Trout Fishery, Norbury Junction, Norbury, Stafford, **STAFFORDSHIRE**, ST20 0PN, **England**.
Contact/s: **Mr Eddie Brassington** (Fishery Manager).
(T) 01785 284886
Profile: **FT:** Game; **WN:** Shelmore; **WT:** Lake (Still).
Ref: FH4227

SHELSWELL LAKE

Shelswell Lake, Buckingham, **BUCKINGHAMSHIRE**, MK18, **England**.
Profile: **FT:** Coarse; **WN:** Shelswell; **WT:** Lake (Still).
Ref: FH4228

SHEPHERDS WAY

Shepherds Way, Brookmans Park, Hatfield, **HERTFORDSHIRE**, AL9, **England**.
(W) www.badac.co.uk
Contact/s: **Mr D Porter** (Secretary), 72 Rivington Cres, Mill Hill, London, NW7 2LF.
(T) 020 84401303
Profile: **FT:** Coarse; **WN:** Shepherds Way; **WT:** Lake (Still) **W. Size:** 2 Acres. **Location:** **Nr. Rd:** A1000; **Main Rd:** M25, junction 24.
Ref: FH4229

SHEPPERTON LAKE

Shepperton Lake, Penny Lane, Walton Bridge, Shepperton, London, **LONDON (GREATER)**, TW17, **England**.
(W) www.rmcangling.co.uk
Contact/s: **Mr Ian Welch** (Angling Manager), RMC Angling, The Square, Lightwater, Surrey, GU18 5SS.
(T) 01276 453300 **(F)** 01276 456611
(E) info@rmcangling.co.uk
Profile: **FT:** Coarse; **WN:** Shepperton; **WT:** Gravel Pit (Still) **W. Size:** 16 Acres. **Location:** **Nr. Rd:** Penny Lane; **Main Rd:** M25, A244 Walton Bridge Road.
Ref: FH4230

SHEPPERTON LAKES

Shepperton Lakes, Skibbereen, **COUNTY CORK**, **Ireland**.
(W) www.swrfb.ie
Contact/s: Area Manager, South West Regional Fisheries Board, 1 Nevilles Trce, Macroom, County Cork, Ireland.
(T) 026 41221
(E) swrfb@swrfb.ie
Mr N Connolly (Manager).
(T) 028 33328
Profile: **FT:** Game; **WN:** Shepperton; **WT:** Lake (Still) **W. Size:** 50 Acres. **Location:** **Nr. Rd:** Leap Road.
Ref: FH4231

SHEPPERTON LOCK

Shepperton Lock, Chertsey Rd, Shepperton, London, **LONDON (GREATER)**, TW17, **England**.
Contact/s: Fishery Contact.
(T) 01932 221840
Recreational Manager, The Environment Agency, Kings Meadow Rd, Reading, Berkshire, RG1 8DQ.
(T) 0118 9535000 **(F)** 0118 9500388
Profile: **FT:** Combination; **WN:** Shepperton; **WT:** Lock (Still). **Location:** **Nr. Rd:** Chertsey Road.
Ref: FH4232

SHERBORNE LAKE

Sherborne Lake, Sherborne, **DORSET**, DT9, **England**.
Contact/s: **Mr Alex Murray** (Secretary), Sherbourne Angling Association, 134 Westfield Gr, Yeovil, Somerset, BA21 3DN.
(T) 01935 425864
Profile: **FT:** Coarse; **WN:** Sherborne; **WT:** Lake (Still).
Ref: FH4233

SHERWOOD FOREST FISHERY

Sherwood Forest Farm Park Fishery, Edwinstowe, Mansfield, **NOTTINGHAMSHIRE**, NG21, **England**.
(W) www.anglersnet.co.uk
Contact/s: **Mr Brian Dale**.
(T) 01623 843077
Mr Mick Langton, 173 Sherwood St, Warsop, Mansfield, Nottinghamshire, NG20 0HG.
(T) 01623 842617 **(F)** 01623 842617 **(M)** 07721 316334
(E) mickyfish@totalise.co.uk
Profile: **FT:** Coarse; **WN:** Sherwood Forest Farm Park Fishery; **WT:** Lake (Still); **F. Size:** 10 Acres; **W. Size:** 10 Acres. **Location:** **Nr. Rd:** B6075; **Main Rd:** M1; **Rail:** Mansfield Woodhouse.
Ref: FH4234

SHIELD FISHERY

Shield Fishery, Bedale, **YORKSHIRE (NORTH)**, DL8, **England**.
Contact/s: **Mr Andrew Shield**, Burtree Farm, Crakhall, Bedale, Yorkshire (North), DL8 1LB.
(T) 01677 422833
Profile: **FT:** Combination; **WN:** Shield Fishery; **WT:** Pond (Still) **W. Size:** 1 Acre. **Location:** **Nr. Rd:** Little Crakehall to Hackforth.
Ref: FH4235

SHIELD TROUT FISHERY

Shield Trout Fishery, Bedale, Ripon, **YORKSHIRE (NORTH)**, HG4, **England**.
Contact/s: **Mr John Shield** (Manager).
(T) 01677 422833
Profile: **FT:** Game; **WN:** Shield; **WT:** Lake (Still) **W. Size:** 2 Acres.
Ref: FH4236

SHIFFORD LOCK

Shifford Lock, Aston, Bampton, **OXFORDSHIRE**, OX18, **England**.
Contact/s: Recreational Manager, The Environment Agency, Kings Meadow Rd, Reading, Berkshire, RG1 8DQ.
(T) 0118 9535000 **(F)** 0118 9500388
Profile: **FT:** Combination; **WN:** Thames; **WT:** River (Moving). **Location:** **Main Rd:** B449.
Ref: FH4237

SHILLAMILL LAKES COUNTRY PARK

Shillamill Lakes Country Park, Lanreath, Looe, **CORNWALL**, PL13 2PE, **England**.
Contact/s: **Mr Rick Pearce**.
(T) 01503 220886
Profile: **FT:** Coarse; **WN:** Shillamill; **WT:** Lake (Still) **W. Size:** 5 Acres. **Location:** **Nr. Rd:** Looe to Toldstwithiel; **Main Rd:** B3359.
Ref: FH4238

SHIMANO FELINDRE

Shimano Felindre Trout Fishery, Blae-Nant-Du Manor, Felindre, Swansea, SA5 7ND, **Wales**.
Contact/s: **Mr Jud Hamblin** (Manager).
(T) 01792 796584
Profile: **FT:** Game; **WN:** Shimano Felindre Trout Fishery; **WT:** Lake (Still). **Location:** **Nr. Rd:** M4 junctions 46 or 47.
Ref: FH4239

SHIMNA (RIVER)

River Shimna, Newcastle, **COUNTY DOWN**, BT33, **Northern Ireland**.
Contact/s: Ranger, Rangers Office, Tollymore Forest Park, 176 Tullybrannigan Rd, Newcastle, County Down, BT33 0PW.
(T) 028 43722428
Mr Ian Watts (Hon Secretary), 17 Ben Crom Park, Newcastle, County Down, BT33 0HU.
(T) 028 43722793
Mr Martin McKibben (Hon Treasurer), 19 Marguerite Avenue, Newcastle, County Down.
(T) 028 43722290
Profile: **FT:** Game; **WN:** Shimna; **WT:** River (Moving) **W. Size:** 4800 Metres.
Ref: FH4240

SHIPBROOK FLASH

Shipbrook Flash, Rudheath, Northwich, **CHESHIRE**, **England**.
Contact/s: **Mr John Turner** (Hon Secretary), Prince Albert Angling Society, 15 Pexhill Drive, Macclesfield, Cheshire, SK10 3LP.
(T) 01625 422010
Profile: **FT:** Coarse; **WN:** Shipbrook Flash; **WT:** Pit (Still); **F. Size:** 6 Acres; **W. Size:** 5 Acres. **Location:** **Nr. Rd:** Manor Lane; **Main Rd:** A530; **Rail:** Northwich.
Ref: FH4241

SHIPLAKE LOCK

Shiplake Lock, Mill Lane, Shiplake, Henley-on-Thames, **OXFORDSHIRE**, RG9, **England**.
Contact/s: Fishery Contact.
(T) 0118 9403350
Recreational Manager, The Environment Agency, Kings Meadow Rd, Reading, Berkshire, RG1 8DQ.
(T) 0118 9535000 **(F)** 0118 9500388
Profile: **FT:** Combination; **WN:** Thames; **WT:** River (Moving). **Location:** **Nr. Rd:** Mill Lane; **Main Rd:** A4155 to Lower Shiplake.
Ref: FH4242

SHIREOAKS PARK

Shireoaks Park, Shireoaks, Worksop, **YORKSHIRE (SOUTH)**, S8, **England**.
Contact/s: **Mr Kaz Godlewski**.
(T) 01909 500979
Profile: **FT:** Coarse; **WN:** Shireoaks; **WT:** Lake (Still). **Location:** **Nr. Rd:** Worksop to Thorpe Salvin; **Main Rd:** A57.
Ref: FH4243

SHOBROOKE PARK

Shobrooke Park, Shobrooke Estate, South Molton, **DEVON**, EX36 4AA, **England**.
Contact/s: Manager, Ladd DDV, Downes Mill House, Downes Mill, Crediton, EX17 3PW.
(T) 01363 772666
Profile: **FT:** Coarse; **WN:** Shobrooke; **WT:** Lake (Still) **W. Size:** 9 Acres. **Location:** **Nr. Rd:** South Street.
Ref: FH4244

SHOEBURY PARK

Shoebury Park, Elm Rd, Shoeburyness, Southend-on-Sea, **ESSEX**, SS, **England**.

Profile: FT: Coarse; WN: Shoebury Park; WT: Lake (Still) W. Size: 2 Acres. Location: Nr. Rd: B1016; Main Rd: A127.
Ref: FH4245

SHORNE COUNTRY PARK LAKES

Shorne Country Park Lakes, Shorne, Gravesend, **KENT**, DA12, **England**.
Profile: FT: Coarse; WN: Shorne; WT: Lake (Still).
Ref: FH4246

SHORT PLANTATION LAKE

Short Plantation Lake, Hevingham, Norwich, **NORFOLK**, NR10, **England**.
Contact/s: Fishery Manager.
Profile: FT: Coarse; WN: Short Plantation; WT: Lake (Still).
Ref: FH4247

SHOTTON COLLIERY LAKE

Shotton Colliery Lake, Hartlepool, **CLEVELAND**, TS24, **England**.
Contact/s: **Mr Ian Proudfoot** (Secretary), 19 Lincoln Walk, Great Lumley, Chester-le-Street.
(T) 0191 3982325after6pm
Mr Mark Arrow-Smith (Membership Secretary), Angler's Services, 27 Park Rd, Hartlepool, Cleveland, TS24 7PW.
(T) 01429 274844or266522
Profile: FT: Coarse; WN: Shotton Colliery; WT: Lake (Still) W. Size: 4 Acres. Location: Main Rd: A19, north to Peterlee junction.
Ref: FH4248

SHOTTON POND

Shotton Pond, Shotton Colliery, Shotton, Peterlee, **COUNTY DURHAM**, SR8, **England**.
Contact/s: **Mr Ian Proudfoot**, Shotton Colliery Angling Club, 19 Lincoln Walk, Lumley, Chester-le-Street.
Mr Mark Arrow-Smith (Membership Secretary), Angler's Services, 27 Park Rd, Hartlepool, Cleveland, TS24 7PW.
(T) 01429 274844 or 266522
Mr Steve Maitland (Membership Secretary), 2 Whitehouse Cres, Shotton Colliery, County Durham, DH6 2NQ.
Profile: FT: Coarse; WN: Shotton; WT: Lake (Still) W. Size: 4 Acres. Location: Nr. Rd: B1280; Main Rd: A19.
Ref: FH4249

SHROPSHIRE UNION CANAL

Shropshire Union Canal, Newport, NP20, **Wales**.
Contact/s: Secretary.
(T) 01952 811828
Profile: FT: Coarse; WN: Shropshire Union; WT: Canal (Still) W. Size: 315 Metres.
Ref: FH4250

SHROPSHIRE UNION CANAL

Shropshire Union Canal, Ellesmere Port To Audlem, Audlem, Crewe, **CHESHIRE**, CW3, **England**.
Contact/s: **Mr Griffiths** (Fishery Manager).
(T) 01606 723800
Profile: FT: Coarse; WN: Shropshire Union; WT: Canal (Still).
Ref: FH4251

SHROPSHIRE UNION CANAL

Shropshire Union Canal, Montgomery Branch, Aston Locks To Berriew, Berriew, Welshpool, **POWYS**, **Wales**.
Contact/s: **Mr John Turner** (Hon Secretary), Prince Albert Angling Society, 15 Pexhill Drive, Macclesfield, Cheshire, SK10 3LP.
(T) 01625 422010
Profile: FT: Coarse; WN: Shropshire Union; WT: Canal (Still). Location: Nr. Rd: A483; Rail: Welshpool.
Ref: FH4252

SHROPSHIRE UNION CANAL

Shropshire Union Canal, Market Drayton, **SHROPSHIRE**, TF9, **England**.
Contact/s: **David Watkins** (Secretary), Hodnet Angling Club, 57 Salisbury Hill View, Market Drayton, Shropshire, TF9 1DL.
(T) 01630 654130
Profile: FT: Coarse; WN: Shropshire Union; WT: Canal (Still).
Ref: FH4253

SHROPSHIRE UNION CANAL

Shropshire Union Canal, Pendeford, Wolverhampton, **STAFFORDSHIRE**, WV8, **England**.
Contact/s: **Mr Bill Turner** (Secretary).
(T) 01902 457906
Profile: FT: Coarse; WN: Shorpshire Union; WT: Canal (Still) W. Size: 2250 Metres. Location: Nr. Rd: Pendeford.
Ref: FH4254

SHROPSHIRE UNION CANAL

Shropshire Union Canal, Brewood, Stafford, **STAFFORDSHIRE**, ST19, **England**.
Contact/s: **Mr J Stanhope** (Secretary), Swan Angling Club, 4 High Rd, Lane Head, Willenhall, WV12 4JQ.
(T) 01902 630110
Profile: FT: Coarse; WN: Shropshire Union; WT: Canal (Still) W. Size: 800 Metres.
Ref: FH4255

SHROPSHIRE UNION CANAL

Shropshire Union Canal, Cowley, Gnosall, Stafford, **STAFFORDSHIRE**, ST20, **England**.
Contact/s: **Mr Keith Clarke**.
(T) 01785 663565
Profile: FT: Coarse; WN: Shropshire Union; WT: Canal (Still).
Ref: FH4256

SHROPSHIRE UNION CANAL

Shropshire Union Canal, Brewood, Stafford, **STAFFORDSHIRE**, ST19, **England**.
Contact/s: **Mr Mick Tuff** (Secretary), Dawley Angling Society, 68 Coronation St, Madley, Telford, TF7 5EH.
(T) 01952 590348
Profile: FT: Coarse; WN: Shropshire Union; WT: Canal (Still).
Ref: FH4257

SHROPSHIRE UNION CANAL

Shropshire Union Canal, Little Onn, Stafford, **STAFFORDSHIRE**, ST20 0, **England**.
Contact/s: Secretary.
(T) 01785 222014
Mr Andy Holt (Manager), Holt's Fishing Tackle, 122 Marston Rd, Stafford, Staffordshire, ST16 3BX.
(T) 01785 251073
Profile: FT: Coarse; WN: Shropshire Union; WT: Canal (Still) W. Size: 3750 Metres. Location: Nr. Rd: Little Onn.
Ref: FH4258

SHROPSHIRE UNION CANAL

Shropshire Union Canal, Wheaton Aston, Stafford, **STAFFORDSHIRE**, ST19, **England**.
Profile: FT: Coarse; WN: Shropshire Union; WT: Canal (Still) W. Size: 1600 Metres.
Ref: FH4259

SHROPSHIRE UNION CANAL

Shropshire Union Canal, Norbury Junction, Gnosall To Grubb St, Gnosall, Stafford, **STAFFORDSHIRE**, ST20, **England**.
Contact/s: **Mr Eric Gardener**.
(T) 01782 818380
Profile: FT: Coarse; WN: Shropshire Union; WT: Canal (Still).
Ref: FH4260

SHRUGGS WOOD FISHERY

Shruggs Wood Fishery, West Paddock, Leyland, Preston, **LANCASHIRE**, PR5, **England**.
Contact/s: Manager, Stones Quality Fishing Tackle, 13 Golden Hill Lane, Leyland, Preston, PR5 2NP.
(T) 01772 421953
Profile: FT: Coarse; WN: Shruggs Wood; WT: Lake (Still).
Ref: FH4261

SHUSTOKE FLY FISHERS

Shustoke Reservoir (Upper), Bixhill Lane, Shustock, Coleshill, Birmingham, **MIDLANDS (WEST)**, B46 2BE, **England**.
(W) www.troutfishing.fsbusiness.co.uk
Mr Phill Turner (Membership Secretary).
(T) 0121 7472845 (F) 01676 533091
(E) philip.turner@care4free.net
Profile: FT: Game; WN: Shustoke; WT: Reservoir (Still). Location: Main Rd: B4114.
Ref: FH4262

SIBLYBACK LAKE

Siblyback Lake, Liskeard, **CORNWALL**, PL14, **England**.
Contact/s: **Mr Peter Whitehead** (Ranger), Watersports Ctre, Siblyback, Common Moor, Liskeard, PL14 6.
(T) 01579 342366
Profile: FT: Game; WN: Siblyback; WT: Lake (Still) W. Size: 140 Acres.
Ref: FH4263

SIBSON FISHERIES

Sibson Fisheries, New Lane, Stibbington, Peterborough, **CAMBRIDGESHIRE**, PE8 6LW, **England**.
Contact/s: **Ms Louise Bradshaw** (Owner).
(T) 01780 782621 (F) 01780 783694
Profile: FT: Coarse; WN: Sibson Fisheries; WT: Lake (Still); F. Size: 28 Acres. Location: Main Rd: A1; Rail: Peterborough.
Ref: FH4264

SIDEWAY OVERFLOW

Sideway, Sideway, Stoke-on-Trent, **STAFFORDSHIRE**, ST3, **England**.
(W) www.fentondas.co.uk
Contact/s: **Mr C Yates** (Club Secretary), The Puzzles, 5 Gatley Gr, Meir Park, Stoke-on-Trent, Staffordshire ST3 7SH.
(T) 01782 396913
Profile: FT: Coarse; WN: Sideway; WT: Lake (Still); F. Size: 2 Acres; W. Size: 2 Acres. Location: Main Rd: A500 or A50; Rail: Stoke Station.
Ref: FH4265

SILKSWORTH SPORTS COMPLEX

Silksworth Sports Complex, New Silksworth, Sunderland, **TYNE AND WEAR**, SR, **England**.
Contact/s: **Mr Tony Kidd**, 25 Toronto Cl, Sunderland, Tyne and Wear, SR3.
(T) 0191 5229070
Profile: FT: Coarse; WN: Silksworth; WT: Lake (Still).
Ref: FH4266

SILLIGROVE FISHERY

Silligrove Fishery, Meaton Lane, Kinlet, Bewdley, **WORCESTERSHIRE**, DY14 8NT, **England**.
Contact/s: **Mrs Jan Freeman**.
(T) 01299 841426 (F) 01299 841551
(E) silligrove@iclway.co.uk
Profile: FT: Combination; WN: Silligrove Fishery; WT: Lake (Still) W. Size: 3 Acres. Location: Nr. Rd: A4117; Main Rd: A4117; Rail: Kidderminster.
Ref: FH4267

SILVER END PIT

Silver End Pit, Silver End, Witham, **ESSEX**, CM8, **England**.
Profile: FT: Coarse; WN: Silver End Pit; WT: Gravel Pit (Still) W. Size: 2 Acres. Location: Nr. Rd: B1018; Main Rd: A12 or A131.
Ref: FH4268

SILVER LAKE

Silver Lake, Syresham Rd, Wappenham, Towcester, **NORTHAMPTONSHIRE**, NN12, **England**.
Contact/s: **Mr Terry Rodhouse** (Secretary), Castle Angling Association, 12 Somerville Rd, Daventry, Northamptonshire, NN11 4RT.
(T) 01327 705692
Profile: FT: Coarse; WN: Silver; WT: Lake (Still) W. Size: 2 Acres. Location: Main Rd:

A43, Towcester to Brackley Road; **Rail:** Milton Keynes.
Ref: FH4269

SILVER SPRINGS FISHERY

Silver Springs Fishery, Bramble Reed Lane, Matfield, Tonbridge, **KENT**, TN12, **England**.
Contact/s: **Mr Ronnie Briggs**.
(T) 01892 722700 **(M)** 07961 842549
Profile: **FT:** Coarse; **WN:** Silver Springs Fishery; **WT:** Pool (Still). **Location:** **Nr. Rd:** Bramble Reed Lane to Matfield; **Main Rd:** B2160 to Paddock Wood.
Ref: FH4270

SILVER STREET MILL

Silver Street Mill, Cambridge, **CAMBRIDGESHIRE**, CB, **England**.
Profile: **FT:** Coarse; **WN:** Silver Street Mill; **WT:** Pond (Still). **Location:** **Nr. Rd:** Silver Street or Queens Road. £Fr
Ref: FH4271

SILVERLANDS LAKE

Silverlands Lake, Wick Farm, Lacock, Chippenham, **WILTSHIRE**, SN15 2LU, **England**.
Contact/s: **Mr Philip King** (Owner).
(T) 01249 730244 **(F)** 01249 730072
Mrs Susan King (Owner).
Profile: **FT:** Coarse; **WN:** Silverlands; **WT:** Gravel Pit (Still) **W. Size:** 3 Acres. **Location:** **Nr. Rd:** A350; **Main Rd:** A350; **Rail:** Chippenham.
Ref: FH4272

SILVERWING LAKE

Silverwing Lake, Amersham, **BUCKINGHAMSHIRE**, HP7, **England**.
(W) www.blenheim-angling.ic24.net
Contact/s: **Mr Fred Lancaster** (Secretary), Blenheim Angling Society, Brairwood, Burtons Lane, Chalfont St Giles, Buckinghamshire, HP8 4BB.
(T) 01494 764977
(E) blenheim.angling@ntlworld.com
Profile: **FT:** Coarse; **WN:** Silverwing; **WT:** Lake (Still) **W. Size:** 60 Acres. **Location:** **Nr. Rd:** B376; **Main Rd:** M25; **Rail:** Wraysbury.
Ref: FH4273

SIMPSON VALLEY FISHERY

Simpson Valley Fishery, Simpson Farm, Holsworthy, **DEVON**, EX22 6JW, **England**.
Contact/s: **Mr Sexton** (Owner), Simpson Valley Farm, Simpson Barton, Holsworthy, Devon, EX22 6JW.
(T) 01409 253593
Profile: **FT:** Coarse; **WN:** Simpson Valley Fishery; **WT:** Lake (Still) **W. Size:** 4 Acres. **Location:** **Nr. Rd:** Holsworthy to Hatherleigh; **Main Rd:** A3072.
Ref: FH4274

SINDON MILL FARM

Sindon Mill Farm, Malvern, **WORCESTERSHIRE**, WR14, **England**.
Contact/s: Manager.
(T) 01886 884550
Profile: **FT:** Game; **WN:** Sindon; **WT:** Lake (Still).
Ref: FH4275

SINGLETON LAKE

Singleton Lake, Buxsford Lane, Singleton, Ashford, **KENT**, TN2, **England**.
Contact/s: **Mr Alan Sandom** (Fisheries Officer), 39 Belmore Park, Ashford, Kent, TN24 8UW. **(M)** 07703 531359
Profile: **FT:** Coarse; **WN:** Singleton; **WT:** Lake (Still) **W. Size:** 4 Acres. **Location:** **Nr. Rd:** Buxsford Lane; **Main Rd:** A28, M20; **Rail:** Ashford International.
Ref: FH4276

SINKS PIT

Sinks Pit, Main Rd, Kesgrave, Ipswich, **SUFFOLK**, **England**.
Contact/s: **Mr Roger Oliver** (Owner, Ipswich Angling Centre), 154 Felixtowe Rd, Ipswich, Suffolk, IP3 8EF.
(T) 01473 728004
Profile: **FT:** Coarse; **WN:** Sinks; **WT:** Pit (Still); **F. Size:** 5 Acres; **W. Size:** 2 Acres. **Location:** **Main Rd:** A1214; **Rail:** Ipswich.
Ref: FH4277

SINNINGTON (RIVER)

River Sinnington, Sinnington, York, **YORKSHIRE (NORTH)**, YO62, **England**.
Contact/s: **Mrs B J Stansfield** (Secretary), Sun Seven, Sinnington, Yorkshire, YO6 6RZ.
Profile: **FT:** Game; **WN:** Sinnington; **WT:** River (Moving) **W. Size:** 4000 Metres.
Ref: FH4278

SION FARM FISHERIES

Sion Farm Fisheries, Hill Pool, Chaddesley Corbett, Kidderminster, **WORCESTERSHIRE**, DY10 4PF, **England**.
Contact/s: **Mr Robert Stephens** (Fishery Manager).
(T) 01562 730386or730444
Profile: **FT:** Coarse; **WN:** Sion Farm Fisheries; **WT:** Lake (Still); **F. Size:** 10 Acres; **W. Size:** 4 Acres. **Location:** **Main Rd:** A450 Worcester Road; **Rail:** Blakedown.
Ref: FH4279

SIRHOWY (RIVER)

River Sirhowy, Tredegar, **BLAENAU GWENT**, NP22, **Wales**.
Contact/s: **Mr Alfred Stevenson** (Hon Secretary), 58 James St, Markham, Blackwood, Gwent, NP2 0QP.
(T) 01495 226331
Profile: **FT:** Game; **WN:** Sirhowy; **WT:** River (Moving). **Location:** **Nr. Rd:** Tredegar to Argoed.
Ref: FH4280

SIRHOWY (RIVER)

River Sirhowy, Blackwood, **CAERPHILLY**, NP12, **Wales**.
Contact/s: **Mr Hubert Meller** (Hon Secretary), 7 Penllwyn St, Cwmfelinfach, Gwent, NP1 7HE.
(T) 01495 200357
Profile: **FT:** Game; **WN:** Sirhowy; **WT:** River (Moving). **Location:** **Nr. Rd:** Crosskeys to Blackwood.
Ref: FH4281

SITTINGBOURNE LAKES

Sittingbourne Lakes, 5 Sunnybanks, Murston, Sittingbourne, **KENT**, ME, **England**.
Contact/s: **C Brown**.
Profile: **FT:** Coarse; **WN:** Sittingbourne; **WT:** Gravel Pit (Still).
Ref: FH4282

SIX MILE WATER

Six Mile Water, Doagh, Antrim, **COUNTY ANTRIM**, BT41, **Northern Ireland**.
Contact/s: **Mr R Kirk**, 15 Fernwood Park, Glenburn, Muckamore, BT41 1QF.
(T) 028 94465144after5pm,01849463333daytime
Mr V Harkness (Manager), Country Sports and Tackle, 9 Rough Lane, Antrim, County Antrim, BT41 2QG.
(T) 028 94467378daytime **(F)** 028 94463703
Profile: **FT:** Game; **WN:** Six Mile Water; **WT:** River (Moving) **W. Size:** 16000 Metres. **Location:** **Nr. Rd:** Doagh Road.
Ref: FH4283

SIX MILE WATER

Six Mile Water, Ballynure, **COUNTY ANTRIM**, BT39, **Northern Ireland**.
Contact/s: **Mr John Arneil** (Secretary), 17 Collinview Drive, Ballyclare, BT39 9PG.
(T) 028 93324716after6pm
Profile: **FT:** Game; **WN:** Six Mile Water; **WT:** River (Moving) **W. Size:** 16000 Metres.
Ref: FH4284

SKEGNESS WATER LEISURE PARK

Skegness Water Leisure Park, Walls Lane, Ingoldmells, Skegness, **LINCOLNSHIRE**, PE25 1JF, **England**.
Contact/s: **Mr Harvey Firth**.
(T) 01754 769019 **(F)** 01754 769019
(E) skegwept@aol.com
Profile: **FT:** Coarse; **WN:** Skegness Water Leisure Park; **WT:** Lake (Still) **W. Size:** 4 Acres. **Location:** **Nr. Rd:** Walls Lane; **Main Rd:** A52; **Rail:** Skegness.
Ref: FH4285

SKELL (RIVER)

River Skell, Waterskellgate, Ripon, **YORKSHIRE (NORTH)**, HG4, **England**.
Profile: **FT:** Game; **WN:** Skell; **WT:** River (Moving). **Location:** **Nr. Rd:** Waterskellgate; **Main Rd:** A1.
Ref: FH4286

SKELMORLIE FISHERIES

Skelmorlie Fisheries, Upper Reservoir, Skelmorlie, **AYRSHIRE (NORTH)**, PA17 5HA, **Scotland**.
Contact/s: **Mr Jim Mackenzie**.
(T) 01475 520925
Profile: **FT:** Game; **WN:** Skelmorlie Fisheries; **WT:** Reservoir (Still).
Ref: FH4287

SKELSMERGH LAKE

Skelsmergh Lake, Kendal, **CUMBRIA**, LA, **England**.
Profile: **FT:** Coarse; **WN:** Skelsmergh; **WT:** Lake (Still).
Ref: FH4288

SKERTON FISHERY

Skerton Fishery, Greenup Cottage, Hornby Rd, Caton, Lancaster, **LANCASHIRE**, LA2, **England**.
Profile: **FT:** Game; **WN:** Lune; **WT:** River (Moving).
Ref: FH4289

SKETEWAN BEAT

Sketewan Beat, Aberfeldy, **PERTH AND KINROSS**, PH15, **Scotland**.
(W) www.fishingnet.com/beats/sketewan.htm
Contact/s: **Ms Em Honeyman** (Manager), Wade Newsagents, 31 Bank St, Aberfeldy, Perth and Kinross, PH15 2BB.
(T) 01887 820397
Profile: **FT:** Combination; **WN:** Birch, Sketewan and East Mains; **WT:** Pool (Still).
Ref: FH4290

SKIRFARE (RIVER)

River Skirfare, Skipton, **YORKSHIRE (NORTH)**, BD23, **England**.
Contact/s: **Mr Robin Miller** (Manager), Falcon Inn, Arncliffe, Skipton, Yorkshire (North), BD23 5QE.
(T) 01756 770205
Profile: **FT:** Game; **WN:** Skirfare; **WT:** River (Moving).
Ref: FH4291

SLADE RESERVOIRS

Slade Reservoirs, Slade, Ilfracombe, **DEVON**, EX34, **England**.
Contact/s: Manager, Slade Post Office, 80 Slade Rd, Ilfracombe, Devon, EX34 8LQ.
(T) 01271 862257
Mr Nick Laws (Manager), Summerlands Tackle, 3 Golf Links Rd, 16-20 Nelson Rd, Westward Ho!, Devon EX39 1LH.
(T) 01237 471291
Profile: **FT:** Coarse; **WN:** Slade; **WT:** Reservoir (Still) **W. Size:** 10 Acres. **Location:** **Nr. Rd:** B3231 from Ilfracombe.
Ref: FH4292

SLALFORD LAKES

Slalford Lakes, Wasing Estate, Reading, **BERKSHIRE**, RG7 4NG, **England**.
Contact/s: **Mr Kevin Rolls** (Fishery Manager).
(T) 0118 9714281
Mr Patrick Todd (Estate Manager), Wasing Estate Farm Office, Wasing Park, Aldermaston, Reading, RG7 4NG.
(T) 0118 9714140 **(F)** 0118 9713251
Profile: **FT:** Combination; **WN:** Slalford

Lakes; **WT:** Lake (Still). **Location:** **Main Rd:** A4; **Rail:** Midgham.
Ref: FH4293

SLAPTON LEY

Slapton Ley National Nature Reserve, Field Studies Council, Slapton Ley Field Ctre, Slapton, Kingsbridge, **DEVON**, TQ7 2QP, **England**.
Contact/s: **Mr Chris Riley**.
(T) 01548 580685 (F) 01548 580123
Profile: **FT:** Coarse; **WN:** Slapton Ley National Nature Reserve; **WT:** Lake (Still); **F. Size:** 600 Acres; **W. Size:** 180 Acres. **Location:** **Main Rd:** A379; **Rail:** Totnes.
Ref: FH4294

SLATEHOUSE LOCH

Slatehouse Loch, Buccleuch Estates Ltd, Drumlanrig Mains, Thornhill, **DUMFRIES AND GALLOWAY**, DG3 4AG, **Scotland**.
Contact/s: **Mr N A G Waugh**.
(T) 01848 600283 (F) 01848 600244
Profile: **FT:** Game; **WN:** Slatehouse; **WT:** Loch (Still). **Location:** **Nr. Rd:** A76; **Rail:** Sanquhar.
Ref: FH4295

SLAUGHAM MILL POND

Slaugham Mill Pond, Haywards Heath, **SUSSEX (WEST)**, RH17, **England**.
Contact/s: Manager, Burgess Hill Angling Centre Limited, 143 Lower Church Rd, Burgess Hill, Sussex (West), RH15 9AA.
(T) 01444 232287 (F) 01444 232287
Profile: **FT:** Coarse; **WN:** Slaugham Mill; **WT:** Lake (Still).
Ref: FH4296

SLAUGHTERFORD FARM

Slaughterford Farm, Partridge Green, Horsham, **SUSSEX (WEST)**, RH13, **England**.
Contact/s: Fishery Manager.
(T) 01403 730328
Profile: **FT:** Coarse; **WN:** Slaughterford Farm; **WT:** Pond (Still).
Ref: FH4297

SLEIGHTS (RIVER)

River Sleights, Whitby, **YORKSHIRE (NORTH)**, YO2, **England**.
Profile: **FT:** Game; **WN:** Sleights River; **WT:** River (Moving).
Ref: FH4298

SLIPE LANE PITS

Slipe Lane Pits, Turnford Marsh, Slipe Lane, Wormley, Broxbourne, **HERTFORDSHIRE**, EN10, **England**.
Contact/s: Information Officer, Lee Valley Park Information Ctre, Abbey Gardens, Waltham Abbey, Essex, EN9 1XQ.
(T) 01992 702200
Mr Krizim Seltham (Angling Manager), Lee Valley Regional Park Authority, Myddleton House, Bulls Cross, Enfield, EN2 9HG.
(T) 01992 709832
(E) garysmith@leevalleypark.org.uk
Profile: **FT:** Coarse; **WN:** Slipe Lane; **WT:** Gravel Pit (Still) **W. Size:** 25 Acres. **Location:** **Nr. Rd:** A1010 High Street; **Main Rd:** A10; **Rail:** Broxbourne.
Ref: FH4299

SLIVER FISHERY

Sliver Fishery, Hatfield Water Park, Hatfield, Doncaster, **YORKSHIRE (SOUTH)**, DN7 6EQ, **England**.
Contact/s: **Mr Robin Goforth** (Manager), Hayfield Lodge, Hayfield Lane, Auckley, Doncaster, DN9 3NP.
(T) 01302 864555 (F) 01302 863419
Profile: **FT:** Coarse; **WN:** Sliver Fishery; **WT:** Lake (Still) **W. Size:** 20 Acres. **Location:** **Nr. Rd:** Old Thorne Road; **Main Rd:** A614.
Ref: FH4300

SLOUGH HOUSE LAKE

Slough House Lake, China Lane, Bulphan, Upminster, **ESSEX**, RM14, **England**.
Contact/s: **Mr Richard Banbury**, Basildon Angling Ctre, 402 Whitmore Way, Basildon, Essex, SS14 2HB.
(T) 01268 520144 (F) 01268 450260
Profile: **FT:** Coarse; **WN:** Slough House; **WT:** Lake (Still) **W. Size:** 5 Acres. **Location:** **Nr. Rd:** A128 China Lane; **Main Rd:** M25, junction 29, A127; **Rail:** West Horndon.
Ref: FH4301

SLOUGH HOUSE WATER

Slough House Water, Heybridge, Maldon, **ESSEX**, CM9, **England**.
Contact/s: **Mr David Western**, Chigboro Fisheries, Chigborough Farm, Chigborough Rd, Heybridge, Maldon, Essex CM9 7RE.
(T) 01621 857368 (F) 01621 855563
(E) djw@chigboro.co.uk
Profile: **FT:** Game; **WN:** Slough House Water; **WT:** Lake (Still). **Location:** **Nr. Rd:** Heybridge.
Ref: FH4302

SLOWING RIVERS FARM

Slowing Rivers Farm, Craigavon, **COUNTY ARMAGH**, BT63, **Northern Ireland**.
Contact/s: Manager, 49A Tullylish Rd, Gilford, Craigavon, County Armagh, BT63 6DP.
(T) 028 38831941
Profile: **FT:** Coarse; **WN:** Slowing Rivers Farm; **WT:** River (Moving).
Ref: FH4303

SMEATONS LAKES

Smeatons Lakes, Great North Rd, Newark, **NOTTINGHAMSHIRE**, NG23 6ED, **England**.
Contact/s: **Mrs Christine Price**.
(T) 01636 605088 (F) 01636 704076
Profile: **FT:** Coarse; **WN:** Smeatons Lakes; **WT:** Combination (Still & Moving) **W. Size:** 180 Metres. **Location:** **Nr. Rd:** A6065, A616; **Main Rd:** Great North Road, A46; **Rail:** Newark Midland.
Ref: FH4304

SMITH POOL

Smith Pool, Stoke-on-Trent, **STAFFORDSHIRE**, ST6, **England**.
Contact/s: Ranger Service.
(T) 01782 536920
Profile: **FT:** Coarse; **WN:** Smith; **WT:** Pool (Still) **W. Size:** 2 Acres.
Ref: FH4305

SMITHIES RESERVOIR

Smithies Reservoir, Smithies Lane, Barnsley, **YORKSHIRE (SOUTH)**, S7, **England**.
Contact/s: Area Manager, Environment Agency, Ridings Area Office, Phoenix House, Global Avenue, Leeds, LS11 8PG.
(T) 0113 2440191or2314834 (F) 0113 2134609
Mr Dave Saunderson.
(T) 01226 383203
Profile: **FT:** Coarse; **WN:** Smithies; **WT:** Reservoir (Still).
Ref: FH4306

SMITHPOOL LAKE

Smithpool Lake, Stoke-on-Trent, **STAFFORDSHIRE**, **England**.
(W) www.fentondas.co.uk
Contact/s: **Mr C Yates** (Club Secretary), The Puzzles, 5 Gatley Gr, Meir Park, Stoke-on-Trent, Staffordshire ST3 7SH.
(T) 01782 396913
Profile: **FT:** Coarse; **WN:** Smithpool; **WT:** Lake (Still); **F. Size:** 2 Acres. **Location:** **Rail:** Stoke Station.
Ref: FH4307

SNAILBEACH POOL

Snailbeach Pool, Minsterley, Shrewsbury, **SHROPSHIRE**, SY5, **England**.
Contact/s: Manager, Sundorne Fishng Tackle, 1 Sundorne Avenue, Shrewsbury, Shropshire, SY1 4JW.
(T) 01743 361804
Mr Mick Argue (Owner), Phoenix Tackle, Unit 1, 198 Whitchurch Rd, Shrewsbury, Shropshire, SY1 4EY.
(T) 01743 446759 (F) 01743 446759
Profile: **FT:** Coarse; **WN:** Snailbeach; **WT:** Pool (Still).
Ref: FH4308

SNETTERTON PITS

Snetterton Pits, Snetterton, Norwich, **NORFOLK**, NR16, **England**.
Contact/s: Fishery Manager.
(T) 01842 764312
Profile: **FT:** Coarse; **WN:** Snetterton; **WT:** Gravel Pit (Still).
Ref: FH4309

SNEYD POOL

Sneyd Pool, Bloxwich, Walsall, **MIDLANDS (WEST)**, WS3 3, **England**.
Contact/s: **Mr J Stanhope** (Secretary), Swan Angling Club, 4 High Rd, Lane Head, Willenhall, WV12 4JQ.
(T) 01902 630110
Profile: **FT:** Coarse; **WN:** Sneyd; **WT:** Pool (Still) **W. Size:** 1 Acre.
Ref: FH4310

SNIBSON COLLIERY CARP LAKE

Snibson Colliery Carp Lake, Coalville, **LEICESTERSHIRE**, LE67, **England**.
Contact/s: Snibson Discovery Park Manager.
(T) 01530 510851
Profile: **FT:** Coarse; **WN:** Snibson Colliery Carp Lake; **WT:** Lake (Still) **W. Size:** 2 Acres.
Ref: FH4311

SNITTERFIELD FRUIT FARM

Snitterfield Fruit Farm, Stratford-upon-Avon, **WARWICKSHIRE**, CV37, **England**.
Contact/s: **Mr Ernie Archer** (Secretary), Royal Lemington Spa Angling Association, 9 Southway, Leamington Spa, Warwickshire, CV31 2PG.
(T) 01926 334185
Profile: **FT:** Coarse; **WN:** Snitterfield Fruit Farm; **WT:** Lake (Still). **Location:** **Main Rd:** A439 to Warwick.
Ref: FH4312

SNOWBERRY

Snowberry, Bletchley, Milton Keynes, **BUCKINGHAMSHIRE**, MK, **England**.
Contact/s: Manager, Fourways Fishery, Poplars Nursery, Harlington Rd, Toddington, LU5 6HE.
(T) 01525 55590or876166
Profile: **FT:** Coarse; **WN:** Snowberry; **WT:** Lake (Still) **W. Size:** 3 Acres. **Location:** **Nr. Rd:** located just off A5.
Ref: FH4313

SNUFF MILL POOL

Snuff Mill Pool, Bewdley Works, Bewdley, **WORCESTERSHIRE**, DY12 2OX, **England**.
Contact/s: **Mr Stan Lewis** (Manager), S Lewis Fishing Tackle, 2 Severnside South, Bewdley, Worcestershire, DY12 2DX.
(T) 01299 403358
Profile: **FT:** Coarse; **WN:** Snuff Mill Pool; **WT:** Lake (Still); **F. Size:** 4 Acres; **W. Size:** 3 Acres. **Location:** **Nr. Rd:** Bewdley to Stourport; **Rail:** Bewdley.
Ref: FH4314

SOAR (RIVER)

River Soar, Kegworth Bridge, Kegworth, Derby, **DERBYSHIRE**, DE74, **England**.
Contact/s: **Mr Dennis Neale**.
(T) 01332 830229
Profile: **FT:** Coarse; **WN:** Soar (Kegworth Bridge to Radcliffe Lock); **WT:** River (Moving).
Ref: FH4315

SOAR (RIVER)

River Soar, Cotesmill, Loughborough, Leicester, **LEICESTERSHIRE**, LE11, **England**.
Contact/s: **Mr Stan Sharpe** (Secretary).
(T) 0402 305132
Profile: **FT:** Coarse; **WN:** Soar (Cotesmill to Hathern); **WT:** River (Moving) **W. Size:** 12800 Metres.
Ref: FH4316

SOAR (RIVER)

River Soar, Barrow Upon Soar, Loughborough,

Leicester, **LEICESTERSHIRE**, LE12, **England**.
Contact/s: Fishery Manager.
(T) 0116 2764680
Profile: **FT:** Coarse; **WN:** Soar; **WT:** River (Moving).
Ref: FH4317

SOAR (RIVER)

River Soar, Mountsorrel, Loughborough, **LEICESTERSHIRE**, LE12, **England**.
Contact/s: Fishery Manager.
(T) 0116 2665579
Profile: **FT:** Coarse; **WN:** Soar; **WT:** River (Moving).
Ref: FH4318

SOAR (RIVER)

River Soar, Thurmaston, Leicester, **LEICESTERSHIRE**, LE4 8, **England**.
Profile: **FT:** Coarse; **WN:** Soar; **WT:** River (Moving) **W. Size:** 990 Metres.
Ref: FH4319

SOHAM BY-PASS LAKE

Soham By-Pass Lake, Soham, Cambridge, **CAMBRIDGESHIRE**, CB, **England**.
Profile: **FT:** Coarse; **WN:** Soham By-Pass; **WT:** Gravel Pit (Still).
Ref: FH4320

SOHO LOOP CANAL

Soho Loop Canal, Winson Green, Birmingham, **MIDLANDS (WEST)**, B16 9, **England**.
Contact/s: **Mr Tony Troth** (Manager).
(T) 0121 7336398
Profile: **FT:** Coarse; **WN:** Soho Loop; **WT:** Canal (Still).
Ref: FH4321

SOMERLEY LAKES

Somerley Lakes, Blashford, Ringwood, **HAMPSHIRE**, BH24, **England**.
Contact/s: Manager.
(T) 01202 733110
Mr R J Andrews (Club Secretary), Christchurch Angling Club, 4 Marley Cl, New Milton, BH25 5LL.
(T) 01425 638502
Mr Steve Richards (Secretary), Christchurch Angling Club, 4 Marley Cl, New Milton, Hampshire, BH25 5LL.
(T) 01425 279710
Profile: **FT:** Coarse; **WN:** Somerley; **WT:** Lake (Still); **F. Size:** 25 Acres; **W. Size:** 20 Acres. Location: **Nr. Rd:** A338; **Main Rd:** A338; **Rail:** Bournemouth.
Ref: FH4322

SOMERS FISHERY

Somers Fishery, Meriden, Coventry, **MIDLANDS (WEST)**, CV7, **England**.
Contact/s: **Lord C H Guernsey** (Manager), Packington Fisheries, Broadwater, Maxstoke Lane, Meriden, CV7 7HR.
(T) 01676 522754 (F) 01676 523399
Profile: **FT:** Coarse; **WN:** Somers Fishery; **WT:** Lake (Still).
Ref: FH4323

SOMERSWOOD LAKE

Somerswood Lake, Brent Mill Farm, South Brent, **DEVON**, TQ10 9JD, **England**.
Contact/s: **Mrs S Goodman** (Owner).
(T) 01364 72154
Profile: **FT:** Game; **WN:** Somerswood; **WT:** Lake (Still) **W. Size:** 2 Acres.
Ref: FH4324

SOMERTON RESERVOIR

Somerton Reservoir, Newport, **ISLE OF WIGHT**, PO30, **England**.
(W) www.isleofwight.co.uk
Contact/s: **Mr A P Scott** (Manager), Scotties Fishing Tackle, 11 Lugley St, Newport, Isle of Wight, PO30 5HD.
(T) 01983 522115 (F) 01983 522115
Mr Alan Bravery (Manager), Scotties Tackle Shop, 11 Lugley St, Newport, Isle of Wight, PO30 5HD.
(T) 01983 522115 (F) 01983 522115
Mr Derek Holmes (Secretary).
(T) 01983 523230
(E) dkhiow@madasafish.com
Mr Paul Johnson (Manager), Scotties Sandown, 22 Fitzroy St, Sandown, Isle of Wight, PO36 8HZ.
(T) 01983 404555
Mr R J Kirby (Hon Secretary), 125 Furrlongs, Pan Estate, Newport, Isle of Wight, PO30 2BN.
(T) 01983 529617
Profile: **FT:** Coarse; **WN:** Somerton; **WT:** Reservoir (Still). Location: **Nr. Rd:** A3020.
Ref: FH4325

SONNING EYE

Sonning Eye, Sonning Common, Reading, **BERKSHIRE**, RG4, **England**.
Contact/s: **Mr Dusty Millar** (Associate members secretary), 238 Elgar Road South, Reading, Berkshire, RG3 0BW.
(T) 0118 9874882
Mr Mick Cox (Chief Bailiff), Dorstans, Hatch Lane, Brimpton Village, Reading, RG7 4TR.
(T) 0118 9714917
Profile: **FT:** Coarse; **WN:** Sonning Eye; **WT:** Gravel Pit (Still) **W. Size:** 80 Acres.
Ref: FH4326

SOPLEY FARM

Ringwood angling club, Sopley farm, Sopley, Christchurch, **DORSET**, BH23, **England**.
Contact/s: **Mr Graham Lavender** (Fishery Manager).
(T) 01425 403733
Profile: **FT:** Coarse; **WN:** Ringwood angling club; **WT:** Lake (Still) **W. Size:** 8 Acres.
Ref: FH4327

SOULSEAT LOCH

Soulseat Loch, Stranraer, **DUMFRIES AND GALLOWAY**, DG9, **Scotland**.
Contact/s: **Mr Eric McLean** (Manager), The Sports Shop, 88 George St, Stranraer, Dumfries and Galloway, DG9 7JS.
(T) 01776 702705
Profile: **FT:** Game; **WN:** Soulseat; **WT:** Loch (Still).
Ref: FH4328

SOUTH FIELD PARK

South Field Park, Ringmead Rd, Hanworth, **BERKSHIRE**, **England**.
Contact/s: **Mr Kevin Hiscock** (Match Secretary), Bracknell Angling Ctre, 2a Fowlers Lane, Bracknell, Berkshire, RG42 1XP.
(T) 01344 425130
Profile: **FT:** Coarse; **WN:** South Field Park; **WT:** Lake (Still) **W. Size:** 2 Acres. Location: **Nr. Rd:** Ringmead Road; **Main Rd:** M3 junction 3, A332.
Ref: FH4329

SOUTH HAY FARM

South Hay Farm, Shebbear, Beaworthy, **DEVON**, EX21, **England**.
Contact/s: **Mr Nigel Brown**.
Profile: **FT:** Combination; **WN:** South Hay Farm; **WT:** Lake (Still) **W. Size:** 2 Acres.
Location: **Main Rd:** A3079.
Ref: FH4330

SOUTH HILL PARK LAKE

South Hill Park Lake, North Lake, Birch Hill, Bracknell, **BERKSHIRE**, RG, **England**.
Contact/s: **Mr Kevin Hiscock** (Match Secretary), Bracknell Angling Ctre, 2a Fowlers Lane, Bracknell, Berkshire, RG42 1XP.
(T) 01344 425130
Profile: **FT:** Coarse; **WN:** Sout Hill Park; **WT:** Lake (Still) **W. Size:** 2 Acres. Location: **Nr. Rd:** Ringmead; **Main Rd:** A322.
Ref: FH4331

SOUTH HOLLAND DRAIN

South Holland Drain, Foreman's Bridge Caravan Park, Ambridge, Sutton Rd, Sutton St James, Spalding, **LINCOLNSHIRE**, PE12 0HU, **England**.
Contact/s: **Mrs Alison Strahan** (Manager).
(T) 01945 440346 (F) 01945 440346
Profile: **FT:** Coarse; **WN:** South Holland; **WT:** Drain (Still). Location: **Nr. Rd:** B1390; **Main Rd:** A17.
Ref: FH4332

SOUTH LAGOON

South Lagoon, Wyboston Pits, Wyboston, Bedford, **BEDFORDSHIRE**, MK44 3, **England**.
Contact/s: **Mr David Edwards** (Membership Secretary).
(T) 01582 728114
Profile: **FT:** Coarse; **WN:** South Lagoon; **WT:** Gravel Pit (Still).
Ref: FH4333

SOUTH LAKE

South Lake, Reading, **BERKSHIRE**, RG, **England**.
Contact/s: **Mr Williams** (Secretary), 24 Duncan Rd, Woodley, Reading, Berkshire.
Profile: **FT:** Combination; **WN:** South; **WT:** Lake (Still).
Ref: FH4334

SOUTH NORWOOD LAKE

South Norwood Lake, Woodvale, South Norwood, London, **LONDON (GREATER)**, SE25, **England**.
Profile: **FT:** Coarse; **WN:** South Norwood; **WT:** Lake (Still) **W. Size:** 2 Acres. Location: **Nr. Rd:** A213, A215; **Main Rd:** A23.
Ref: FH4335

SOUTH PARK

South Park, Macclesfield, **CHESHIRE**, SK11, **England**.
Contact/s: Fishery Manager.
(T) 01625 21955
Profile: **FT:** Coarse; **WN:** South Park; **WT:** Lake (Still).
Ref: FH4336

SOUTH POPLARS

South Poplars, Newlands Lane, Heath Hayes, Cannock, **STAFFORDSHIRE**, WS12 5HH, **England**.
Contact/s: **Mr Steven Haywood** (Manager).
(T) 01543 277999
Profile: **FT:** Coarse; **WN:** South Populars; **WT:** Pool (Still). Location: **Nr. Rd:** Newlands Lane; **Main Rd:** A5, A460, A5190.
Ref: FH4337

SOUTH REED LAKE

South Reed Fisheries Carp Lake, Boasley Cross, Bratton Clovelly, Okehampton, **DEVON**, EX20 4JJ, **England**.
Profile: **FT:** Coarse; **WN:** South Reed; **WT:** Lake (Still) **W. Size:** 3 Acres. Location: **Nr. Rd:** B3218 Okehampton to Halwill Road.
Ref: FH4338

SOUTH STRATFORD CANAL

South Stratford Canal, Stratford-upon-Avon, **WARWICKSHIRE**, CV37, **England**.
Contact/s: Manager, Dave Jones Angling Ctre, 17 Evesham Rd, Stratford-upon-Avon, Warwickshire, CV37 9AA.
(T) 01789 293950
Mr A Bruce (Secretary), Stratford-upon-Avon Angling Club, 42 Cherry Orchard, Stratford-upon-Avon, Warwickshire, CV37 9AP.
(T) 01789 205700
Profile: **FT:** Coarse; **WN:** Shropshire Union; **WT:** Canal (Still) **W. Size:** 7500 Metres.
Ref: FH4339

SOUTH TYNE (RIVER)

River South Tyne, Alston, **CUMBRIA**, CA9, **England**.
Profile: **FT:** Game; **WN:** South Tyne; **WT:** River (Moving).
Ref: FH4340

SOUTH TYNE (RIVER)

River South Tyne, Haltwhistle, **NORTHUMBERLAND**, NE49, **England**.
Contact/s: Manager, Greggs Sports, Market Sq, Haltwhistle, Northumberland, NE49 0BG.

(T) 01434 320255 (F) 01434 320255
Mr Chris Wilson, Melkridge House, Melkridge, Haltwhistle, NE49 0LT.
(T) 01434 320942
Profile: **FT:** Game; **WN:** South Tyne; **WT:** River (Moving) **W. Size:** 10000 Metres. **Location:** **Nr. Rd:** A69; **Main Rd:** A69; **Rail:** Haltwhistle.
Ref: FH4341

SOUTH UIST ESTATES

South Uist Estates Limited, Grogarry Lodge, Grogarry, Lochboisdale, **WESTERN ISLES**, HS8 5RR, **Scotland**.
Contact/s: **Mr John Kennedy** (Manager).
(T) 01878 700332
Profile: **FT:** Coarse; **WN:** South Uist Estates Limited; **WT:** Lake (Still).
Ref: FH4342

SOUTH VIEW FARM CARP FISHERY

South View Farm Carp Fishery, Irthlingborough Rd, Wellingborough, **NORTHAMPTONSHIRE**, NN8 1RQ, **England**.
Contact/s: **Mr R Sumner**.
(T) 01933 650457 (M) 07860 113977
Profile: **FT:** Coarse; **WN:** South View Farm Carp Fishery; **WT:** Lake (Still).
Ref: FH4343

SOUTH VIEW FARM FISHERY

South View Farm Fishery, Shillingford, St George, Exeter, **DEVON**, EX2 9UP, **England**.
Contact/s: **Mr Keith Gorton** (Owner).
(T) 01392 832278
Profile: **FT:** Coarse; **WN:** South View Farm Fishery; **WT:** Pond (Still); **F. Size:** 6 Acres; **W. Size:** 4 Acres. **Location:** **Nr. Rd:** Minor Road; **Main Rd:** A38, M5; **Rail:** Exeter, St Davids.
Ref: FH4344

SOUTH WEST WATER FISHERY

South West Water Fishery, Bideford, **DEVON**, EX39, **England**.
Contact/s: **Mr Gerry Tyzack** (Owner), Torridge Angling Ctre, 7 Allhalland St, Bideford, Devon, EX39 2JD.
(T) 01237 470043
Mrs B Tyzack (Owner), The Kingfisher Tackle Shop, 22 Castle St, Barnstaple, Devon, EX31 1DR.
(T) 01271 344919
Profile: **FT:** Coarse; **WN:** South West; **WT:** Lake (Still).
Ref: FH4345

SOUTHBOURNE LAKE

Southbourne Lake, Eastbourne Miniature Railway Park, Lottbridge Drove, Eastbourne, **SUSSEX (EAST)**, BN23 6NS, **England**.
Contact/s: **Mr Mike Wadey** (Owner).
(T) 01323 520229
Profile: **FT:** Coarse; **WN:** Southbourne; **WT:** Lake (Still); **F. Size:** 25 Acres; **W. Size:** 6 Acres. **Location:** **Nr. Rd:** Lottbridge Drove; **Main Rd:** A259, A22; **Rail:** Eastbourne.
Ref: FH4349

SOUTHFIELD RESERVOIRS

Southfield Reservoirs, Colwick Ponds, Doncaster, **YORKSHIRE (SOUTH)**, DN, **England**.
Contact/s: **Mr Maurice Tate** (Secretary), Doncaster and District Angling Association, 28 Holmescarr Rd, New Rossington, Doncaster, DN11 0QF.
(T) 01302 865482
W Sams (Secretary), Doncaster and District Angling Association, 28 Pipering Lane, Scawthorpe, Doncaster.
(T) 01302 780271
Profile: **FT:** Coarse; **WN:** Southfield; **WT:** Reservoir (Still) **W. Size:** 60 Acres.
Ref: FH4350

SOUTHLEIGH LAKE

Southleigh Lake, Cockerton 'Out Of Town' Shopping Ctre, Cockerton, Warminster, **WILTSHIRE**, BA12 8AP, **England**.
Contact/s: **Mr J Shiner**.
(T) 01985 846424
Profile: **FT:** Coarse; **WN:** Southleigh; **WT:** Lake (Still) **W. Size:** 2 Acres.
Ref: FH4351

SOUTHMINSTER FISHERIES

Southminster Fisheries, Goldsands Rd, Southminster, **ESSEX**, CM0, **England**.
Contact/s: **Mr Derek Howard** (Hon Treasurer), Billericay and District Angling Club, 4 Long Meadow Drive, Wickford, Essex, SS11 8AX.
(T) 01268 734468
Profile: **FT:** Coarse; **WN:** Southminster Fisheries; **WT:** Gravel Pit (Still); **F. Size:** 20 Acres; **W. Size:** 10 Acres. **Location:** **Nr. Rd:** Goldsands Road; **Main Rd:** B1020; **Rail:** Southminster.
Ref: FH4352

SOVAL ESTATE

Soval Estate, Kinloch Loch, Kinloch, Stornoway, **WESTERN ISLES**, HS1, **Scotland**.
Contact/s: **Mr Iain MacLeed** (Keeper), Valtos Cottage, Soval Estate, Kinloch, Isle of Lewis.
Mrs M Kershaw (Owner), Heyrose House, Old Hall Lane, Over Tabley, Knutsford, Cheshire, WA16 0HY.
(T) 01565 733483
Profile: **FT:** Game; **WN:** Laxay; **WT:** Combination (Still & Moving); **F. Size:** 35000 Acres; **W. Size:** 1000 Acres. **Location:** **Nr. Rd:** A859; **Main Rd:** A859.
Ref: FH4353

SOVEREIGN LAKES

Sovereign Lakes, Narborough, King's Lynn, **NORFOLK**, PE32, **England**.
Contact/s: **Mr John Barron**.
(T) 01760 337288or227228
Profile: **FT:** Coarse; **WN:** Sovereign; **WT:** Lake (Still). **Location:** **Nr. Rd:** Entrance by Narborough bypass; **Main Rd:** A47 King Lynn to Swaffham.
Ref: FH4354

SOW (RIVER)

River Sow, Great Bridgeford Hall Farm, Great Bridgeford, Stafford, **STAFFORDSHIRE**, ST, **England**.
Contact/s: **Mr Albert Perkins** (Hon Secretary), 63 Fowlers Lane, Light Oaks, Stoke-on-Trent, Staffordshire, ST2 7NB.
Ms Liz Hayes (Manager).
(T) 01625 251262
Profile: **FT:** Coarse; **WN:** Sow; **WT:** River (Moving) **W. Size:** 1500 Metres. **Location:** **Nr. Rd:** A5013; **Main Rd:** M6; **Rail:** Stafford.
Ref: FH4355

SPADE MILL RESERVOIR NO.2

Spade Mill Reservoir No.2, Longridge, Preston, **LANCASHIRE**, PR3, **England**.
Contact/s: Secretary, 100 Powis Rd, Preston, Lancashire, PR2 1AE.
Profile: **FT:** Game; **WN:** Spade Mill; **WT:** Reservoir (Still). **Location:** **Main Rd:** B5268, Longridge to Blackburn.
Ref: FH4356

SPADE OAK LAKE

Spade Oak Lake, High Wycombe, **BUCKINGHAMSHIRE**, HP11, **England**.
Contact/s: **Mr J Woodhouse** (Secretary), Marlow Angling Club, Conifers, Ash Rd, High Wycombe, Buckinghamshire, HP12 4SW.
(T) 01494 523988
Profile: **FT:** Coarse; **WN:** Spade Oak; **WT:** Lake (Still).
Ref: FH4357

SPARKS FARM FISHERY

Sparks Farm Fishery, Cuckfield Golf Course, Staplefield Rd, Cuckfield, Haywards Heath, **SUSSEX (WEST)**, RH17 5HY, **England**.
Contact/s: **Mr Andrew Ponsford** (Manager).
(T) 01444 459999
Profile: **FT:** Coarse; **WN:** Sparks Farm Fishery; **WT:** Pond (Still); **F. Size:** 5 Acres; **W. Size:** 2 Acres. **Location:** **Nr. Rd:** B2114; **Main Rd:** A23; **Rail:** Haywards Heath.
Ref: FH4358

SPARROWS POND

Sparrows Pond, Gosfield, Halstead, **ESSEX**, CO9, **England**.
Contact/s: **Mr P Emson** (Secretary), Emson and Son Tackle Shop, 88 High St, Earls Colne, Colchester, CO6 2QX.
(T) 01787 223331
Profile: **FT:** Coarse; **WN:** Sparrows Pond; **WT:** Pond (Still). **Location:** **Nr. Rd:** Yeldham to Halstead.
Ref: FH4359

SPARTH RESERVOIR

Sparth Reservoir, Park Gate Rd, Marsden, Huddersfield, **YORKSHIRE (WEST)**, HD7, **England**.
Contact/s: **Mr D Rushforth** (Membership Secretary), 122 Longwood Gate, Longwood, Huddersfield, Yorkshire (West), HD3 4US.
(T) 01484 651028
Mr R Carter (Bailiff), 10 Varley Rd, Slaithwaite, Yorkshire (West).
(T) 01484 843163
Profile: **FT:** Coarse; **WN:** Sparth; **WT:** Reservoir (Still) **W. Size:** 3 Acres. **Location:** **Nr. Rd:** Park Gate Road; **Main Rd:** A62 Manchester Road.
Ref: FH4360

SPEECH HOUSE LAKE

Speech House Lake, Forest Of Dean, Coleford, **GLOUCESTERSHIRE**, GL16, **England**.
Contact/s: **Mr Alex Bloxham** (Manager).
(T) 01531 821126
Profile: **FT:** Coarse; **WN:** Speech House; **WT:** Lake (Still).
Ref: FH4361

SPERRINGBROOK SEWER

Sperringbrook Sewer, Snargate, Romney Marsh, **KENT**, TN29, **England**.
Contact/s: **Mr Tony Jenkinson** (Secretary).
(T) 01737 643821
Profile: **FT:** Coarse; **WN:** Sperringbrook; **WT:** Stream (Moving).
Ref: FH4362

SPEY (RIVER)

River Spey, Tulchan Lodge, Advie, Grantown On Spey, **HIGHLAND**, PH26 3PW, **Scotland**.
Contact/s: **Mr C Excell** (Manager).
(T) 01807 510200
Profile: **FT:** Game; **WN:** Spey; **WT:** River (Moving) **W. Size:** 12800 Metres.
Ref: FH4363

SPEY (RIVER)

River Spey, Kingussie, **HIGHLAND**, PH21 1, **Scotland**.
Contact/s: **Mr Clive Freshwater** (Managing Director), Loch Insh Watersports Ctre, Insh Hall, Kincraig, Highland, PH21 1NU.
(T) 01540 651272 (F) 01540 651280
Profile: **FT:** Combination; **WN:** Spey; **WT:** River (Moving) **W. Size:** 4800 Metres. **Location:** **Nr. Rd:** B970; **Main Rd:** A9; **Rail:** Aviemore.
Ref: FH4364

SPIRES LAKES

Spires Lakes, Riverside, Fore St, North Tawton, Okehampton, **DEVON**, EX20 2ED, **England**.
Contact/s: **Mr Barry Ware** (Owner).
(T) 01837 82499
Profile: **FT:** Coarse; **WN:** Spires; **WT:** Lake (Still) **W. Size:** 3 Acres. **Location:** **Nr. Rd:** A3072; **Main Rd:** B3215.
Ref: FH4365

SPORTSMANS PIT

Sportsmans Pit, Swaffham Prior, **CAMBRIDGESHIRE**, **England**.
Contact/s: .
(T) 01223 234616

Profile: FT: Coarse; WN: Sportsmans Pit; WT: Pit (Still).
Ref: FH4366

SPRING GRANGE FISHERY

Spring Grange Fishery, Pumphouse, Croxton Rd, Beeby, Leicester, **LEICESTERSHIRE**, LE7 3BH, **England**.
Contact/s: Fishery Manager.
(T) 0116 2595338
Profile: FT: Coarse; WN: Spring Grange Fishery; WT: Lake (Still).
Ref: FH4367

SPRING HILL TROUT WATERS

Spring Hill Trout Waters, Albans Barn, Romford Rd, Pembury, Tunbridge Wells, **KENT**, TN2 4BB, **England**.
Contact/s: Mr Mark Wilding (Manager).
(T) 01892 822423
Profile: FT: Game; WN: Spring Hill Trout Waters; WT: Lake (Still). **Location:** Nr. Rd: Romford Road.
Ref: FH4368

SPRING LEE

Spring Lee, Hanwood, Shrewsbury, **SHROPSHIRE**, SY5, **England**.
Contact/s: Manager, Shrewsbury Bait Ctre, Unit 1, 198 Whitchurch Rd, Shrewsbury, Shropshire, SY1 4EY.
(T) 01743 446759 (F) 01743 446759
Mr Trevor Potter.
(T) 01743 860972
Profile: FT: Coarse; WN: Spring Lee; WT: Pool (Still). **Location:** Nr. Rd: Lea Cross; Main Rd: A488.
Ref: FH4369

SPRING POOL

Spring Pool, Antrobus, Northwich, **CHESHIRE**, CW9, **England**.
Contact/s: Mr Neil Jupp (Club Secretary), Lymm Angling Club, PO Box 350, Warrington, Cheshire, WA2 9FB.
(T) 01925 411774
Profile: FT: Coarse; WN: Spring; WT: Pool (Still). **Location:** Nr. Rd: Lake Lane; Main Rd: A559.
Ref: FH4370

SPRING VALLEY WATERS

Spring Valley Waters, Wakefield, **YORKSHIRE (WEST)**, WF, **England**.
Contact/s: Mr Ryan Kenny.
(T) 0113 2777474
Profile: FT: Coarse; WN: Spring Valley; WT: Lake (Still). **Location:** Nr. Rd: Green Lane; Main Rd: M1, junction 40.
Ref: FH4371

SPRING WOOD FISHERY AND FARM

Spring Wood Fishery And Farm, Stonecrouch Cottage, Flimwell, Wadhurst, **SUSSEX (EAST)**, TN5 7QA, **England**.
Contact/s: Mr Joe Benbenich.
(T) 01580 879525
Profile: FT: Combination; WN: Spring Wood Fishery And Farm; WT: Combination (Still). **Location:** Nr. Rd: A21; Main Rd: A21; Rail: Wadhurst.
Ref: FH4372

SPRINGLAKES

Springlakes, Ash Vale, Aldershot, **HAMPSHIRE**, GU12 5, **England**.
Contact/s: Mr Paul Biscombe (Manager).
(T) 01252 336333
Profile: FT: Coarse; WN: Springlakes; WT: Lake (Still).
Ref: FH4373

SPRINGWATER FISHERY

Springwater Fishery, Drumgabs Farm, Dalrymple, Ayr, **AYRSHIRE (SOUTH)**, KA6 6AW, **Scotland**.
Contact/s: Mr Danny Wilson (Owner).
(T) 01292 560343 (F) 01292 560343 (M) 07779 956428
(E) springwaterfishery@fsbusiness.co.uk
Mr David McPhail (Manager).
Profile: FT: Game; WN: Springwater; WT: Loch (Still) W. Size: 10 Acres. **Location:** Nr. Rd: Dalrymple; Main Rd: A77; Rail: Ayr.
Ref: FH4374

SPRINGWATER LAKES

Springwater Lakes, Harford, Llanwrda, **CARMARTHENSHIRE**, SA19 8DT, **Wales**.
Contact/s: Mr Malcolm Bexon.
(T) 01558 650788
Ms Shirley Bexon.
(T) 01558 650788
Profile: FT: Combination; WN: Springwaters; WT: Lake (Still); F. Size: 20 Acres; W. Size: 6 Acres. **Location:** Nr. Rd: A482; Main Rd: A482; Rail: Llanwrda.
Ref: FH4375

SPRINGWATER MEADOW

Springwater Meadow, 17A Cockhill Rd, Maze, Lisburn, **COUNTY ANTRIM**, BT27 5RS, **Northern Ireland**.
Contact/s: Mr Jim Fleming.
Mr John Lewis (Owner).
(T) 028 92622220 (F) 028 92622220
Profile: FT: Game; WN: Springwater Meadow; WT: Lake (Still); F. Size: 7 Acres; W. Size: 4 Acres. **Location:** Nr. Rd: Cockhill Road; Main Rd: A3, Moira Road; Rail: Lisburn.
Ref: FH4376

SPRINGWOOD POOL

Springwood Pool, Mobberley, Knutsford, **CHESHIRE**, WA16, **England**.
Contact/s: Mr Nigel Bours (Hon Secretary), Congleton AS, 8 Norfolk Rd, Congleton, Cheshire, CW12 1NY.
(T) 01260 277284
Profile: FT: Coarse; WN: Springwood Pool; WT: Pond (Still).
Ref: FH4377

SPRINT (RIVER)

River Sprint, Kendal, **CUMBRIA**, LA9 6, **England**.
Contact/s: Mr Chris Green (Secretary), Burneside Angling Association, Millside, Hall Rd, Burneside, LA9 6QE. (F) 01539 818486 (M) 07788 854539
Profile: FT: Combination; WN: Sprint; WT: River (Moving). **Location:** Rail: Burneside Station. £Fr
Ref: FH4378

SQUABMOOR RESERVOIR

Squabmoor Reservoir, Budleigh Salterton, Exeter, **DEVON**, EX, **England**.
Contact/s: Manager, Exmouth Tackle and Sports, 20 The Strand, Exmouth, Devon, EX8 1AF.
(T) 01395 274918
Mr Reg England (Manager), Peninsula Coarse Fisheries, St Cleer Depot, Lewdown, Okehampton, Devon EX20 4QT.
(T) 01837 871565 (F) 01837 871534
Profile: FT: Coarse; WN: Squabmoor; WT: Reservoir (Still) W. Size: 4 Acres. **Location:** Nr. Rd: B3179; Main Rd: A377, Exeter to Exmouth.
Ref: FH4379

SQUARE LODGE

Square Lodge, Hindley, Wigan, **LANCASHIRE**, WN, **England**.
(W) www.wiganaa.f9.co.uk
Contact/s: Mr Gerry Wilson (Hon Secretary), Wigan and District Angling Association, 11 Guildford Avenue, Chorley, Lancashire, PR6 8TG.
(T) 01257 265905
(E) gerry@wiganna.freeserve.co.uk
Profile: FT: Coarse; WN: Square Lodge; WT: Pond (Still). **Location:** Nr. Rd: A58; Main Rd: A577.
Ref: FH4380

ST ALGARS FARM LAKE

St Algars Farm Lake, West Woodlands, Frome, **SOMERSET**, BA11 5ER, **England**.
Contact/s: Mr Angus Mackintosh.
(T) 01985 844233
Profile: FT: Game; WN: St Algars Farm; WT: Lake (Still) W. Size: 2 Acres. **Location:** Nr. Rd: B3092; Main Rd: A361.
Ref: FH4381

ST BENETS ABBEY (RIVER)

River St Benets Abbey, Bude, **CORNWALL**, EX23, **England**.
Contact/s: Mr C Wigg (Secretary), 3 Coppice Avenue, Norwich, NR6 5RB.
Profile: FT: Coarse; WN: St Benets Abbey; WT: River (Moving).
Ref: FH4382

ST CLERE LAKE

St Clere Lake, Clere Estate, Kemsing Rd, Wrotham, **KENT**, **England**.
(W) www.midkentfish.demon.co.uk
Contact/s: Mr Chris Logsdon (Fisheries Manager), Mid Kent Fisheries, Chilham Water Mill, Mill Lane, Chilham, CT4 8EE.
(T) 01227 730668
(E) chilham@midkentfisheries.co.uk
Profile: FT: Coarse; WN: St. Clere; WT: Lake (Still); F. Size: 5 Acres; W. Size: 2 Acres. **Location:** Nr. Rd: Kemsing Road; Main Rd: B2016; Rail: Maidstone.
Ref: FH4383

ST EAU FISHING SYNDICATE

St Eau Fishing Syndicate, Little Langley, Bardney Rd, Wragby, Market Rasen, **LINCOLNSHIRE**, LN8 5JE, **England**.
Contact/s: Mr R Gibson Bevan (Secretary).
Profile: FT: Game; WN: St Eau; WT: Stream (Moving) W. Size: 9600 Metres. **Location:** Nr. Rd: Louth to Boston; Main Rd: A16.
Ref: FH4384

ST ERTH FISHERY

St Erth Fishery, Little Mill Lane, St Erth, Penzance, **CORNWALL**, TR, **England**.
Contact/s: Manager, St Erth Sub Post Office, 1 School Lane, St Erth, Hayle, Cornwall, TR27 6HN.
(T) 01736 753154
Mr B Trevitt (Secretary), 6 Chyandaunce Cl, Gulval, Penzance.
(T) 01736 763721
Profile: FT: Coarse; WN: St Erth Fishery; WT: Lake (Still) W. Size: 2 Acres.
Ref: FH4385

ST GERMANS LAKE

St Germans Lake, St Germans, Saltash, **CORNWALL**, PL12, **England**.
Contact/s: Mr Carl Bovey, 39 Hilton Avenue, Manadon, Plymouth, Devon, Pl5 3HS.
(T) 01752 709339
Profile: FT: Coarse; WN: St Germans; WT: Lake (Still) W. Size: 2 Acres. **Location:** Main Rd: A38 Saltash to Liskeard.
Ref: FH4386

ST IVES COMPLEX

St Ives Complex, Fen Drayton, St Ives, Huntingdon, **CAMBRIDGESHIRE**, PE17, **England**.
Contact/s: Mr H Pace (Secretary), 48 Fairfields, St Ives, Huntingdon, Cambridgeshire, PE17 4QF.
(T) 01480 469254
Profile: FT: Coarse; WN: Lowy's, St Ives Lagoon, Andersons; WT: Lake (Still). **Location:** Nr. Rd: Meadow Lane; Main Rd: A1128.
Ref: FH4387

ST IVES FARM

St Ives Farm, Butcherfield Lane, Hartfield, **SUSSEX (EAST)**, TN7 4JX, **England**.
Contact/s: Mr D Chapman (Manager).
(T) 01892 770213
Profile: FT: Coarse; WN: St Ives Farm; WT: Pool (Still) W. Size: 2 Acres. **Location:** Nr. Rd: B2026; Main Rd: A22, B2110.
Ref: FH4388

ST JAMES SMALL PARK LAKE

Sharman Road Lake, Sharman Rd, St James, Northampton, **NORTHAMPTONSHIRE**, NN, **England**.
Contact/s: **Mr Terry Rodhouse** (Secretary), Castle Angling Association, 12 Somerville Rd, Daventry, Northamptonshire, NN11 4RT.
(T) 01327 705692
Profile: **FT:** Coarse; **WN:** Park Lake; **WT:** Lake (Still) **W. Size:** 2 Acres. Location: **Nr. Rd:** A45, A428; **Main Rd:** A45; **Rail:** Northampton.
Ref: FH4389

ST JOHNS LOCH

St Johns Loch, Dunnet, Thurso, **HIGHLAND**, KW14, **Scotland**.
Contact/s: **Mr Hugo Ross** (Fishing Tackle Specialist), 56 High St, Wick, Caithness, KW1 4BP.
(T) 01955 604200 **(F)** 01955 604200
Profile: **FT:** Game; **WN:** St Johns Loch; **WT:** Loch (Still); **F. Size:** 150 Acres; **W. Size:** 150 Acres. Location: **Main Rd:** A836; **Rail:** Wick.
Ref: FH4390

ST JOHNS POOL

St Johns Pool, Shimano Linear Fisheries (Oxford), Smiths Concrete Site, Hardwick Village, Witney, **OXFORDSHIRE**, OX8 7Q, **England**.
Contact/s: **Mr Len Gurd** (Owner), 10A Rackstraw Gr, Old Farm Park, Milton Keynes, Buckinghamshire, MK7 8PZ.
(T) 01908 645135 **(F)** 01908 645115
Profile: **FT:** Coarse; **WN:** St Johns; **WT:** Lake (Still); **F. Size:** 20 Acres; **W. Size:** 18 Acres. Location: **Nr. Rd:** B4449; **Main Rd:** A40; **Rail:** Oxford.
Ref: FH4391

ST LEONARDS FISHING LAKE

St Leonards Fishing Lake, St Leonards Equestrian Ctre, The Cyder House, Polson, Launceston, **CORNWALL**, PL15 9QR, **England**.
Contact/s: **Mr Andy Reeve**.
(T) 01566 775543
Profile: **FT:** Coarse; **WN:** St Leonards; **WT:** Lake (Still) **W. Size:** 2 Acres.
Ref: FH4392

ST MARYS LOCH

St Marys Loch And Loch O The Lowes, Yarrow, Selkirk, **SCOTTISH BORDERS**, TD7, **Scotland**.
Contact/s: **Mr Neil MacIntyre** (Club Secretary), St Mary's Loch Angling Club, 8 Rosetta Rd, Peebles, Scottish Borders, EH45 8JU.
(T) 01721 722278
Profile: **FT:** Game; **WN:** St Marys Loch, & Loch O The Lowes; **WT:** Loch (Still). Location: **Nr. Rd:** A708; **Main Rd:** A708.
Ref: FH4393

ST MICHAELS WYRESIDE FISHERY

St Michaels Wyreside Fishery, Jenkinson's Farm, Garstang Rd, St Michaels On Wyre, Preston, **LANCASHIRE**, PR3 0TD, **England**.
(W) www.wyresidefisheries.co.uk
Contact/s: **Mrs M Laledakis**.
(T) 01995 679695 **(F)** 01995 679695
Profile: **FT:** Coarse; **WN:** St Michaels Wyreside Fishery; **WT:** Lake (Still); **F. Size:** 6 Acres; **W. Size:** 4 Acres. Location: **Nr. Rd:** A586; **Main Rd:** A586; **Rail:** Preston.
Ref: FH4394

ST PATRICKS

St Patricks, Loddon Drive, Charvil, Twyford, Reading, **BERKSHIRE**, RG10, **England**.
(W) www.rmcangling.co.uk
Contact/s: **Mr Ian Welch** (Angling Manager), RMC Angling, The Square, Lightwater, Surrey, GU18 5SS.
(T) 01276 453300 **(F)** 01276 456611
(E) info@rmcangling.co.uk
Profile: **FT:** Coarse; **WN:** St Patricks; **WT:** Stream (Moving) **W. Size:** 1420 Metres. Location: **Nr. Rd:** Loddon Drive; **Main Rd:** A4, Reading to Maidenhead; **Rail:** Twyford.
Ref: FH4395

ST PATRICKS LANE CARP LAKES

St Patricks Lane Carp Lakes, Frensham, Farnham, **SURREY**, GU10, **England**.
Profile: **FT:** Coarse; **WN:** St Patricks Lane; **WT:** Lake (Still). Location: **Main Rd:** A287.
Ref: FH4396

ST TINNEY FARM HOLIDAYS

St Tinney Farm Holidays, Otterham, Camelford, **CORNWALL**, PL32 9TA, **England**.
Profile: **FT:** Coarse; **WN:** St Tinney Farm Holidays; **WT:** Lake (Still).
Ref: FH4397

STADDLETHORPE POND

Staddlethorpe Pond, Broad Lane, Station Rd, Gilberdyke, Brough, **LINCOLNSHIRE (NORTH)**, DN15, **England**.
Contact/s: **Mr Kirk Rudge** (Owner), Fishing Tackle Direct, 25 Westfield Avenue, Goole, DN14 6JY.
(T) 01405 720231office **(F)** 01405 720490office
Mr Kirk Rudge (Partner).
(T) 01405 720231office **(F)** 01405 720490office
Profile: **FT:** Coarse; **WN:** Staddlethorpe; **WT:** Pond (Still); **F. Size:** 10 Acres; **W. Size:** 3 Acres. Location: **Nr. Rd:** Station Road; **Main Rd:** B1230; **Rail:** Staddlethorpe.
Ref: FH4398

STAFFORD AND WORCESTER CANAL

Stafford And Worcester Canal, Gailey, Stafford, **STAFFORDSHIRE**, ST19 5, **England**.
Contact/s: **Mr Bill Turner** (Secretary).
(T) 01902 457906
Profile: **FT:** Coarse; **WN:** Stafford and Worcester Canal; **WT:** Canal (Still) **W. Size:** 11000 Metres. Location: **Nr. Rd:** Gailey.
Ref: FH4399

STAFFORD AND WORCESTER CANAL

Stafford And Worcester Canal, Milford, Stafford, **STAFFORDSHIRE**, ST17 0, **England**.
Contact/s: **Mr Andy Holt** (Manager), Holt's Fishing Tackle, 122 Marston Rd, Stafford, Staffordshire, ST16 3BX.
(T) 01785 251073
Mr Mark Wilton (Treasurer).
(T) 01785 227452
(E) markwilton@webfactory.co.uk
Mr Pat Hogan (Secretary).
(T) 01785 222014
Profile: **FT:** Coarse; **WN:** Stafford and Worcester; **WT:** Canal (Still) **W. Size:** 5000 Metres. Location: **Nr. Rd:** Cannock to Lichfield Road; **Main Rd:** A34; **Rail:** Stafford.
Ref: FH4400

STAFFORD AND WORCESTER CANAL

Stafford And Worcester Canal, Tixall, Stafford, **STAFFORDSHIRE**, ST, **England**.
Contact/s: Manager, Holt's Fishing Tackle, 122 Marston Rd, Stafford, Staffordshire, ST16 3BX.
(T) 01785 251073
Profile: **FT:** Coarse; **WN:** Stafford and Worcester; **WT:** Canal (Still) **W. Size:** 3200 Metres. Location: **Nr. Rd:** Stafford to Tixall Road.
Ref: FH4401

STAFFORD MOOR FISHERY

Stafford Moor Fishery, Toad Hall, Dolton, Winkleigh, **DEVON**, EX19 8PP, **England**.
Contact/s: **Mr Andy Seery** (Owner).
(T) 01805 804360
Profile: **FT:** Combination; **WN:** Woodpecker, Pine Tree, Tanners, & Beatties; **WT:** Lake (Still); **F. Size:** 60 Acres.
Ref: FH4402

STAFFORD TO WORCESTER CANAL

Stafford To Worcester Canal, Wombourne, Wolverhampton, **MIDLANDS (WEST)**, WV5, **England**.
Contact/s: **Mr Bill Turner** (Secretary).
(T) 01902 457906
Profile: **FT:** Coarse; **WN:** Stafford to Worcester; **WT:** Canal (Still) **W. Size:** 6500 Metres. Location: **Nr. Rd:** Wombourne.
Ref: FH4403

STAFFORD TO WORCESTER CANAL

Stafford To Worcester Canal, Dimmingsdale To Awbridge, Wolverhampton, **MIDLANDS (WEST)**, WV4 4, **England**.
Profile: **FT:** Coarse; **WN:** Stafford to Worcester; **WT:** Canal (Still).
Ref: FH4404

STAFFORD TO WORCESTER CANAL

Stafford To Worcester Canal, Stafford, **STAFFORDSHIRE**, ST17, **England**.
Contact/s: Secretary.
(T) 01785 222014
Mr Andy Holt (Manager), Holt's Fishing Tackle, 122 Marston Rd, Stafford, Staffordshire, ST16 3BX.
(T) 01785 251073
Profile: **FT:** Coarse; **WN:** Stafford - Worcester; **WT:** Canal (Still) **W. Size:** 5250 Metres. Location: **Nr. Rd:** Stafford to Worcester Road.
Ref: FH4405

STAFFORD TO WORCESTER CANAL

Stafford To Worcester Canal, Bone Mill Lane, Stourport-on-Severn, **WORCESTERSHIRE**, DY13, **England**.
Contact/s: **Mr John Williams** (Secretary), Birmingham Anglers Association, 100 Icknield Port Rd, Rotton Park, Birmingham, B16 0AP.
(T) 0121 4549111
Profile: **FT:** Coarse; **WN:** Stafford to Worcester; **WT:** Canal (Still). Location: **Nr. Rd:** Bone Mill Lane.
Ref: FH4406

STAINFORTH AND KEADBY CANAL

Stainforth And Kneadby Canal, Crowle, Worcester, **WORCESTERSHIRE**, WR7 4, **England**.
Contact/s: **Mr Joe Cuncliffe** (Manager), 13 Westley Rd, Kiverton Parl, Sheffield, S31 8RJ.
(T) 01909 772587
Profile: **FT:** Coarse; **WN:** Stainforth and Keadby; **WT:** Canal (Still) **W. Size:** 12000 Metres.
Ref: FH4407

STAINFORTH AND KEADBY CANAL

Stainforth And Keadby Canal, Crowle, Stainforth, Doncaster, **YORKSHIRE (SOUTH)**, DN7, **England**.
Contact/s: **Mr Joe Cuncliffe** (Manager), 13 Westley Rd, Kiverton Parl, Sheffield, S31 8RJ.
(T) 01909 772587
Profile: **FT:** Coarse; **WN:** Stainforth and Keadby; **WT:** Canal (Still) **W. Size:** 13600 Metres. Location: **Nr. Rd:** Althorpe to Keadby; **Main Rd:** M18, junction 2; **Rail:** Crowle.
Ref: FH4408

STAINFORTH AND KEADBY CANAL

Stainforth And Keadby Canal, South Bramwith, Kirk Bramwith, Doncaster, **YORKSHIRE (SOUTH)**, DN7, **England**.
Contact/s: **Mr Roger Baker**.
(T) 01302 881707
Profile: **FT:** Coarse; **WN:** Stainforth and Keadby; **WT:** Canal (Still). Location: **Nr. Rd:** South Bramwith to Kirk Bramwith; **Main Rd:** M18, junction 4.
Ref: FH4409

STAINFORTH AND KEADBY CANAL

Stainforth And Keadby Canal, Doncaster, **YORKSHIRE (SOUTH)**, DN, **England**.
Profile: **FT:** Coarse; **WN:** Stainforth and Keadby; **WT:** Canal (Still) **W. Size:** 4800 Metres.

Ref: FH4410

STAKEHILL LODGES

Stakehill Lodges, Stakehill Lane, Middleton, Manchester, **MANCHESTER (GREATER)**, M24, **England**.
Contact/s: Landlord, The New Inn, 34 Long St, Middleton, Manchester, M24 6UQ.
(T) 0161 6534421 (F) 0161 6534421
Mr Gary Leigh (Secretary), Middleton Angling Society, 151 Tennyson Rd, Boarshaw, Middleton, Manchester M24 2NS.
(T) 0161 6546253 (M) 07973 205280
Profile: FT: Coarse; WN: Stakehill Lodges; WT: Pond (Still) W. Size: 5 Acres. **Location:** Nr. Rd: Stake Hill Lane; Main Rd: A627M; Rail: Rochdale.
Ref: FH4411

STAMBRIDGE STARR FISHERIES

Stambridge Starr Fisheries, Stambridge Rd, Stambridge, Rochford, **ESSEX**, SS4 2AR, **England**.
Contact/s: Manager.
(T) 01702 258274
Profile: FT: Coarse; WN: Stambridge Starr Fisheries; WT: Lake (Still).
Ref: FH4412

STAMFORD PARK LAKES

Stamford Park Lakes, Mellor Rd, Ashton-under-Lyne, **MANCHESTER (GREATER)**, OL6 6 DL, **England**.
Mr Mark Porter (Supervisor).
(T) 0161 3382394
Profile: FT: Coarse; WN: Stamford; WT: Lake (Still). **Location:** Nr. Rd: Darnton Road; Main Rd: A635 Stamford Street.
Ref: FH4413

STANBOROUGH FISHERIES

Stanborough Fisheries, Smithies Lane, Barnsley, **YORKSHIRE (SOUTH)**, S7, **England**.
Contact/s: **Mr Allan Hanson** (Manager), Wicketts, Low lane, Stainborough, Barnsley, S75 3EP.
(T) 01226 292579
Profile: FT: Coarse; WN: Fleets; WT: Mill Dam (Still) W. Size: 10 Acres. **Location:** Nr. Rd: Smithies Lane; Main Rd: A61; Rail: Barnsley.
Ref: FH4414

STANBOROUGH LAKE

Stanborough Lake, Welwyn Garden City, **HERTFORDSHIRE**, AL7, **England**.
Contact/s: **Mr Dennis Jakes**.
(T) 01707 335636
Mr Dicky Lairman (Bailiff). (M) 07947 647523
Mr Peter Tilbury (Manager), Oakwood Angling, 12 Hall Rd, Welwyn Garden City, AL7 4PH.
(T) 01707 334462
Profile: FT: Coarse; WN: Stanborough Lake; WT: Gravel Pit (Still) W. Size: 20 Acres. **Location:** Nr. Rd: A6129; Main Rd: A1(M).
Ref: FH4415

STANBOROUGH POOL

Stanborough Pool, Stanborough House, Cheltenham, **GLOUCESTERSHIRE**, GL, **England**.
Contact/s: **Mr Terry Timony** (Site Manager).
(T) 01242 680327
Profile: FT: Coarse; WN: Stanborough Pool; WT: Lake (Still). **Location:** Nr. Rd: A4019; Main Rd: A38.
Ref: FH4416

STANFORD PIT

Stanford Pit, Shefford, Stanford, **BEDFORDSHIRE**, SG18, **England**.
Contact/s: **Mr J Leath** (Secretary), Shefford and District Angling Association, 3 Ivel Cl, Shefford, Bedfordshire, SG17 5JX.
(T) 01462 812323
Profile: FT: Coarse; WN: Stanford; WT: Gravel Pit (Still) W. Size: 1 Acre. **Location:** Main Rd: B658 Shefford to Biggleswade road.
Ref: FH4417

STANFORD-LE-HOPE

Stanford-Le-Hope, Wharfe Rd, Standford-Le-Hope, **ESSEX**, SS17, **England**.
(W) www.rmcangling.co.uk
Contact/s: **Mr Ian Welch** (Angling Manager), RMC Angling, The Square, Lightwater, Surrey, GU18 5SS.
(T) 01276 453300 (F) 01276 456611
(E) info@rmcangling.co.uk
Profile: FT: Coarse; WN: Standford-Le-Hope; WT: Gravel Pit (Still) W. Size: 7 Acres. **Location:** Nr. Rd: Wharf Road; Main Rd: A13.
Ref: FH4418

STANKLIN POOL

Stanklin Pool, Kidderminster, **WORCESTERSHIRE**, DY, **England**.
Profile: FT: Coarse; WN: Stanklin Pool; WT: Lake (Still) W. Size: 6 Acres. **Location:** Main Rd: A449.
Ref: FH4419

STANLEY PARK LAKE

Stanley Park Lake, Thornton-Cleveleys, **LANCASHIRE**, FY5, **England**.
Contact/s: Manager, Bobs Tackle Shop, 35 Beach Rd, Thornton-Cleveleys, Lancashire, FY5 1EG.
(T) 01253 860616
Profile: FT: Coarse; WN: Stanley Park Lake; WT: Pool (Still) W. Size: 22 Acres. **Location:** Nr. Rd: East Park Road; Main Rd: M55, exit at Blackpool Zoo, fishery opposite.
£Fr
Ref: FH4420

STANLEY PARK LAKE

Stanley Park Lake, Walton Lane, Liverpool, **MERSEYSIDE**, L, **England**.
Contact/s: Fishery Manager.
(T) 0151 2255910
Profile: FT: Coarse; WN: Stanley Park; WT: Lake (Still). **Location:** Nr. Rd: Walton Lane; Main Rd: A580. £Fr
Ref: FH4421

STANLEY RESERVOIR

Stanley Reservoir, Puddy Lane, Stanley, Nr. Stockton Brook, Stoke-on-Trent, **STAFFORDSHIRE**, **England**.
Profile: FT: Coarse; WN: Stanley Reservoir; WT: Reservoir (Still); F. Size: 30 Acres. **Location:** Nr. Rd: Puddy Lane, off Stanley Road; Main Rd: A53; Rail: Stoke-On-Trent.
Ref: FH4422

STANSTEAD ABBOTTS

Stanstead Abbotts, Marsh Lane, Stanstead Abbotts, Ware, **HERTFORDSHIRE**, SG12, **England**.
(W) www.rmcangling.co.uk
Contact/s: **Mr Ian Welch** (Angling Manager), RMC Angling, The Square, Lightwater, Surrey, GU18 5SS.
(T) 01276 453300 (F) 01276 456611
(E) info@rmcangling.co.uk
Profile: FT: Coarse; WN: Stanstead Abbotts; WT: Combination (Still & Moving) W. Size: 9 Acres. **Location:** Nr. Rd: Marsh Lane; Main Rd: A414 to Stanstead Abbotts; Rail: St Margarets.
Ref: FH4423

STANTONS FARM RESERVOIR

Stantons Farm Reservoir, Workhouse Green, Sudbury, **SUFFOLK**, CO10, **England**.
Contact/s: **Mr Rob Hayward** (Manager), Sudbury Angling Ctre, 1 Acton Sq, Sudbury, Suffolk, CO10 1HG.
(T) 01787 312118
Mr Trevor Fairless (Secretary), Sudbury and District Angling Association, 39 Pot Kiln Rd, Sudbury, Suffolk, CO10 0DG.
(T) 01787 312536
Profile: FT: Coarse; WN: Stanton's Farm; WT: Reservoir (Still) W. Size: 3 Acres. **Location:** Nr. Rd: B1508 Sudbury to Bures; Main Rd: Sudbury.
Ref: FH4424

STANWORTH RESERVOIR

Stanworth Reservoir, Blackburn, **LANCASHIRE**, BB, **England**.
Contact/s: **Mr Harwood**, 257 Pringle St, Blackburn, BB1 1TR.
(T) 01254 676732
Profile: FT: Coarse; WN: Stanworth; WT: Reservoir (Still). **Location:** Main Rd: A674.
Ref: FH4425

STAR BARTON PONDS

Star Barton Ponds, Cowley, Exeter, **DEVON**, EX, **England**.
Contact/s: Manager, Exeter Angling Ctre, Smythen St, Exeter, Devon, EX1 1BN.
(T) 01392 435591or436404 (F) 01392 433855
Manager, Drum Sports Limited, 47 Courtenay St, Newton Abbot, Devon, TQ12 2QN.
(T) 01626 205040
Profile: FT: Coarse; WN: Star Barton; WT: Pond (Still).
Ref: FH4426

STAR CARR TROUT FARM

Star Carr Trout Farm, Hempholme Lane, Brandesburton, Driffield, **HUMBERSIDE**, YO25 8NB, **England**.
Contact/s: **Mr Ray Howe**.
(T) 01964 543466
Profile: FT: Combination; WN: Star Carr Trout Farm; WT: Gravel Pit (Still) W. Size: 8 Acres. **Location:** Nr. Rd: A165; Main Rd: A1035; Rail: Beverley.
Ref: FH4427

STAR LANE

Star Lane, Wakering, Southend-on-Sea, **ESSEX**, SS, **England**.
Profile: FT: Coarse; WN: Starlane; WT: Lake (Still). **Location:** Main Rd: A127 or A130.
Ref: FH4428

STAR MOUNT

Star Mount, Radcliffe, Manchester, **MANCHESTER (GREATER)**, M26, **England**.
Contact/s: **Mr Dennis Eckersall** (Fishery Manager).
(T) 0161 7246981
Profile: FT: Coarse; WN: Star Mount; WT: Lake (Still).
Ref: FH4429

STARBURN LOCH

Starburn Loch, Buccleuch Estates Ltd, Drumlanrig Mains, Thornhill, **DUMFRIES AND GALLOWAY**, DG3 4AG, **Scotland**.
Contact/s: **Mr N A G Waugh**.
(T) 01848 600283 (F) 01848 600244
Profile: FT: Game; WN: Starburn; WT: Loch (Still) W. Size: 3 Acres. **Location:** Main Rd: A76; Rail: Sanquhar.
Ref: FH4430

STARFIELD PIT

Starfield Pit, Sudbury, **SUFFOLK**, CO10, **England**.
Contact/s: **Mr N Mealham** (Owner), 6 Springfield Trce, East St, Sudbury, Suffolk.
(T) 01787 377139
Profile: FT: Coarse; WN: Starfield; WT: Gravel Pit (Still).
Ref: FH4431

STARGATE PONDS

Stargate Ponds, Ryton, **TYNE AND WEAR**, NE40, **England**.
Contact/s: D Totten.
(T) 0191 4133451
Profile: FT: Coarse; WN: Stargate; WT: Gravel Pit (Still) W. Size: 2 Acres.
Ref: FH4432

STARMERS PIT

Starmers Pit, Tritton Rd, Lincoln, **LINCOLNSHIRE**, LN, **England**.
Contact/s: **Mr Colin Parker** (Secretary),

Lincoln and District Angling Association, 4 Pottergate Cl, Waddington, Lincoln, LN5 9LY.
(T) 01522 720777
Mr Frank Butler (Chairman).
(T) 01522 534174
Profile: FT: Coarse; **WN:** Starmers Pit; **WT:** Lake (Still); **F. Size:** 7 Acres; **W. Size:** 7 Acres. **Location: Nr. Rd:** B1003; **Main Rd:** A46; **Rail:** North Hykeham.
Ref: FH4433

STARMOUNT LODGES

Starmount Lodges, Bolton, **LANCASHIRE**, BL, **England**.
Contact/s: Mr Dennis Eckersall (Fishery Manager).
(T) 0161 7246981
Profile: FT: Coarse; **WN:** Starmount Lodges; **WT:** Pond (Still). **Location: Nr. Rd:** Radcliffe Moor Road to Browns Road; **Main Rd:** A58 to A65.
Ref: FH4434

STARTOPS RESERVOIR

Startops Reservoir, Tring Park Estate, Tring, **HERTFORDSHIRE**, HP23, **England**.
Contact/s: Mr Bernard Double (Bailiff).
(T) 01442 822379
Profile: FT: Coarse; **WN:** Startops; **WT:** Reservoir (Still).
Ref: FH4435

STATES LAGOON

States Lagoon, Hardwick, Bicester, **OXFORDSHIRE**, OX6, **England**.
Contact/s: Mr Graham State (Manager), States Fishing Tackle, 19 Fettiplace Rd, Witney, Oxfordshire, OX8 5AP.
(T) 01993 702587
Profile: FT: Coarse; **WN:** States Lagoon; **WT:** Lake (Still) **W. Size:** 12 Acres. **Location: Nr. Rd:** B4449; **Main Rd:** A415 from Witney.
Ref: FH4436

STATHAM POOL

Statham Pool, Lymm, Warrington, **CHESHIRE**, WA, **England**.
Contact/s: Mr Neil Jupp (Club Secretary), Lymm Angling Club, PO Box 350, Warrington, Cheshire, WA2 9FB.
(T) 01925 411774
Profile: FT: Coarse; **WN:** Stratham; **WT:** Pond (Still). **Location: Nr. Rd:** Pool Lane; **Main Rd:** B5158, Cherry Lane.
Ref: FH4437

STATHE DRAIN

Stathe Drain, St Ives, Bridgwater, **SOMERSET**, TA7, **England**.
Contact/s: Mr Mike Hewitson (Manager), Tauton Angling Association, 56 Parkfield Rd, Taunton, Somerset, TA1 4SE.
(T) 01823 271194
Profile: FT: Coarse; **WN:** Stathe; **WT:** Drain (Moving) **W. Size:** 3600 Metres. **Location: Main Rd:** A378.
Ref: FH4438

STATION FARM

Station Farm, Station Rd, Appledore, Ashford, **KENT**, TN26 2DG, **England**.
Contact/s: Mr D Smith (Manager).
(T) 01233 758710
Profile: FT: Game; **WN:** Station Farm; **WT:** River (Moving).
Ref: FH4439

STAUNTON COUNTRY PARK

Staunton Country Park, Middle Park Way, Havant, **HAMPSHIRE**, PO9 5HB, **England**.
Contact/s: Mr Allan Talley (Assistant Park Manager).
(T) 023 92453405
Profile: FT: Coarse; **WN:** Staunton Country Park; **WT:** Lake (Still) **W. Size:** 3 Acres.
Ref: FH4440

STAUNTON COURT LAKES

Staunton Court Lakes, Ledbury Rd, Staunton, Gloucester, **GLOUCESTERSHIRE**, GL19 3QS, **England**.
Contact/s: Mr Brian Hawker, Staunton Court, Ledbury Rd, Staunton, Gloucestershire, GL19 3QS.
(T) 01452 840230 **(F)** 01452 840798
(E) hawker@stauntoncourt.com
Mr Peter Sedge (Tackle Shop Manager), Staunton Angling Ctre, Ledbury Rd, Staunton, Gloucestershire, GL19 3QS.
(T) 01452 840048
Profile: FT: Coarse; **WN:** Staunton Court; **WT:** Lake (Still) **W. Size:** 2 Acres. **Location: Nr. Rd:** A417; **Main Rd:** M50, junction 2; **Rail:** Gloucester.
Ref: FH4441

STAUNTON HAROLD RESERVOIR

Staunton Harold Reservoir, Derby, **DERBYSHIRE**, DE73, **England**.
Contact/s: Mr A Williams, Melbourne Tackle and Gun, 64 Church St, Melbourne, Derbyshire, DE73 1EJ.
(T) 01332 862091
Profile: FT: Coarse; **WN:** Staunton Harold; **WT:** Reservoir (Still) **W. Size:** 3200 Metres.
Ref: FH4442

STAVELEY LAKES

Staveley Lakes, Birkenshaw, Bradford, **YORKSHIRE (WEST)**, BD, **England**.
Contact/s: Mr N Briggs (General Secretary), 4 Brown Hill Cl, Birkenshaw, Bradford, Yorkshire (West), BD11 2AS.
(T) 01274 684906
Profile: FT: Coarse; **WN:** Staveley; **WT:** Lake (Still) **W. Size:** 4 Acres. **Location: Rail:** Knaresborough.
Ref: FH4443

STEAM MILLS LAKE

Steam Mills Lake, Steam Mills, Forest Of Dean, Cinderford, **GLOUCESTERSHIRE**, GL14, **England**.
Contact/s: Mr Paul Reed (Secretary), Royal Forest of Dean Angling Club, 20 Abbey St, Cinderford, Gloucestershire, GR14 2NW.
(T) 01594 824413
Profile: FT: Coarse; **WN:** Steam Mills; **WT:** Lake (Still) **W. Size:** 5 Acres. **Location: Nr. Rd:** Brickworks Road; **Main Rd:** A4136, Cinderford to Monmouth.
Ref: FH4444

STEANBRIDGE FISHERY

Steanbridge Fishery, Slad, Stroud, **GLOUCESTERSHIRE**, GL, **England**.
Contact/s: Mr Mick Mills (Manager).
(T) 01453 766793
Profile: FT: Game; **WN:** Steanbridge Fishery; **WT:** Lake (Still) **W. Size:** 2 Acres.
Ref: FH4445

STEEPING (RIVER)

River Steeping, Wainfleet, Skegness, **LINCOLNSHIRE**, PE24 4, **England**.
Contact/s: Manager, Skegness Fishing Tackle, 155 Roman Bank, Skegness, Lincolnshire, PE25 1RY.
(T) 01754 611172
Profile: FT: Coarse; **WN:** Steeping; **WT:** River (Moving).
Ref: FH4446

STEEPLE LANGFORD LAKES

Steeple Langford Lakes, Steeple Langford, Salisbury, **WILTSHIRE**, SP3, **England**.
Contact/s: Mr Ron Hillier (Secretary), 29 New Zealand Avenue, Salisbury, Wiltshire, SP2 7JX.
(T) 01722 321164
Profile: FT: Coarse; **WN:** Steepleford Langford; **WT:** Lake (Still). **Location: Nr. Rd:** A36 north of Salisbury; **Rail:** Salisbury.
Ref: FH4447

STELLA LAKE

Stella Lake, Kidderminster, **WORCESTERSHIRE**, DY14, **England**.
Contact/s: Mr Eric Lloyd (Shatterford Fishery Manager).
(T) 01299 861597
Profile: FT: Coarse; **WN:** Stella; **WT:** Lake (Still) **W. Size:** 1 Acre.
Ref: FH4448

STEMBOROUGH MILL TROUT FARM

Stemborough Mill Trout Farm, Stemborough Lane, Leire, Lutterworth, **LEICESTERSHIRE**, LE17 5EY, **England**.
Contact/s: Mrs D M Cherry (Owner).
(T) 01455 209624
Profile: FT: Game; **WN:** Severn; **WT:** Tributary (Moving) **W. Size:** 4 Acres.
Ref: FH4449

STEPHENSON LAKE

Stephenson Lake, Hetton-Le-Hole, Houghton Le Spring, **TYNE AND WEAR**, DH5, **England**.
Profile: FT: Coarse; **WN:** Stephenson; **WT:** Lake (Still). **Location: Nr. Rd:** Hetton; **Main Rd:** B1285.
Ref: FH4450

STEPSTONES LAKES

Stepstones Lakes, Dumpford, Rogate, Petersfield, **HAMPSHIRE**, GU31, **England**.
Contact/s: Manager, Rods 'N' Reels of Farlington, 418 Havant Rd, Farlington, Portsmouth, PO6 1NF.
(T) 023 92789090
Mr B Smith (Secretary).
(T) 023 92472110
Profile: FT: Coarse; **WN:** Stepstones; **WT:** Lake (Still).
Ref: FH4451

STEVENSTONE LAKES

Stevenstone Lakes, Torrington, **DEVON**, EX38 7HY, **England**.
Contact/s: Mr A J Parnell.
(T) 01805 622102
Profile: FT: Coarse; **WN:** Stevenstone; **WT:** Lake (Still) **W. Size:** 3 Acres. **Location: Nr. Rd:** B3227 Umberleigh; **Main Rd:** A386; **Rail:** Barnstaple.
Ref: FH4452

STEW POND

Stew Pond, St Neots, Huntingdon, **CAMBRIDGESHIRE**, PE1, **England**.
Profile: FT: Coarse; **WN:** The Stew Pond; **WT:** Gravel Pit (Still) **W. Size:** 2 Acres. **Location: Main Rd:** A1.
Ref: FH4453

STEWARDS POOL

Stewards Pool, Kidderminster, **WORCESTERSHIRE**, DY14, **England**.
Contact/s: Mr Eric Lloyd (Shatterford Fishery Manager).
(T) 01299 861597
Profile: FT: Coarse; **WN:** Stewards; **WT:** Pool (Still) **W. Size:** 2 Acres.
Ref: FH4454

STICKNEY BRICKPONDS

Stickney Brickponds, Stickney, Boston, **LINCOLNSHIRE**, PE22 8, **England**.
Contact/s: Fishery Manager.
(T) 01205 480093
Profile: FT: Coarse; **WN:** Stickney; **WT:** Pond (Still) **W. Size:** 4 Acres. **Location: Main Rd:** A16; **Rail:** Sibsey.
Ref: FH4455

STILL WATERS TROUT FISHERY

Still Waters Trout Fishery, Yarcombe, Honiton, **DEVON**, EX14, **England**.
Contact/s: Mr Micheal Ford (Manager), Lower Morhayne Farm, Yarcombe, Honiton, Devon, EX14 0QN.
(T) 01404 861284
Profile: FT: Game; **WN:** Still Waters Trout Fishery; **WT:** Lake (Still).
Ref: FH4456

STINCHAR (RIVER)

River Stinchar, Diana's Pool, Ballantrae, Girvan, **AYRSHIRE (SOUTH)**, KA26, **Scotland**.
(W) www.crailoch.demon.co.uk
Contact/s: Mr Robert Dalrymple, Crailoch, Ballantrae, Girvan, Ayrshire (South), KA26 0LW.

(E) wwwbookings@crailoch.demon.co.uk
Profile: FT: Game; WN: Stinchar; WT: River (Moving).
Ref: FH4457

STIRCHLEY POOLS

Stirchley Pools, Dawley, Telford, **SHROPSHIRE**, TF4 2, **England**.
Contact/s: **Mr Mick Tuff** (Secretary), Dawley Angling Society, 68 Coronation St, Madley, Telford, TF7 5EH.
(T) 01952 590348
Profile: FT: Coarse; WN: Stirchley; WT: Pool (Still).
Ref: FH4458

STITHIANS RESERVOIR

Stithians Reservoir, Peninsula Watersports Ctre, Stithians, Truro, **CORNWALL**, TR3, **England**.
Contact/s: Fisheries Manager, South West Lake Trust, Head Office, Highcombe Park, Lewdown, Okehampton, EX20 1YZ.
Mr Adam Davis (Waterski Instructor).
(T) 01209 860301
Profile: FT: Game; WN: Stithians; WT: Reservoir (Still) W. Size: 247 Acres.
Ref: FH4459

STOCKBRIDGE POND

Stockbridge Pond, Tilford, **SURREY**, **England**.
Contact/s: .
(T) 01252 320871
Profile: FT: Coarse; WN: Stockbridge Pond; WT: Pond (Still).
Ref: FH4460

STOCKLEY ROAD LAKES

Stockley Road Lakes, Stockley Rd, West Drayton, London, **LONDON (GREATER)**, UB7, **England**.
Contact/s: **Mr Gordon Dasvis** (Manager), Boyer Leisure Ltd, Heron's Point Tackle Shop, Farlow's Lake, Ford Lane, Iver SL0 9LL.
(T) 01753 630302 or 01895444707 (F) 01753 630302
(E) info@boyer.co.uk
Profile: FT: Coarse; WN: Stockley Road; WT: Gravel Pit (Still) W. Size: 4 Acres.
Location: Nr. Rd: A4020; Main Rd: M4; Rail: West Drayton.
Ref: FH4461

STOCKPOND

Stockpond, Winsford, **CHESHIRE**, CW7, **England**.
Contact/s: **Mr Neil Jupp** (Club Secretary), Lymm Angling Club, PO Box 350, Warrington, Cheshire, WA2 9FB.
(T) 01925 411774
Profile: FT: Coarse; WN: Stock; WT: Pond (Still). Location: Nr. Rd: Dalesfords Lane; Main Rd: A49 to Whitchurch.
Ref: FH4462

STOCKS FLY FISHERY

Stocks Fly Fishery, Catlow Rd, Slaidburn, Clitheroe, **LANCASHIRE**, BB7 3AQ, **England**.
Contact/s: **Mrs Jan Dobson**, Bank House, Low Mill, Caton, Lancaster, LA2 9HX.
(T) 01200 446602or01524770412
Profile: FT: Game; WN: Stocks; WT: Reservoir (Still); F. Size: 400 Acres; W. Size: 320 Acres. Location: Nr. Rd: B6478 to Slaidburn; Main Rd: M6, junction 31, A59 to Clitheroe; Rail: Clitheroe.
Ref: FH4463

STOCKTON RESERVOIR

Stockton Reservoir, Blue Lias, Stockton, Rugby, **WARWICKSHIRE**, CV23, **England**.
Profile: FT: Coarse; WN: Stockton; WT: Reservoir (Still).
Ref: FH4464

STOKESBY (RIVER)

River Stokesby, Stokesby, Great Yarmouth, **NORFOLK**, NR29, **England**.
Profile: FT: Coarse; WN: Stokesby; WT: River (Moving).
Ref: FH4465

STONAR LAKE

Stonar Lake, Sandwich, **KENT**, CT13, **England**.
Contact/s: Fishery Manager.
(T) 01227 728289
Profile: FT: Coarse; WN: Stonar; WT: Lake (Still).
Ref: FH4466

STONE END FARM LAKES

Stone End Farm Lakes, Hartpury, Gloucester, **GLOUCESTERSHIRE**, GL19, **England**.
Contact/s: **Mr Richard Spry**.
(T) 01452 700254
Profile: FT: Coarse; WN: Stone End Farm Lakes; WT: Pond (Still). Location: Nr. Rd: B2411 Church Lane; Main Rd: Hartpury.
Ref: FH4467

STONE END LAKE

Stone End Lake, Charles St, Louth, **LINCOLNSHIRE**, LN11, **England**.
Contact/s: **Mr Rod Hutchinson** (Manager), Station Rd, Legbourne, Louth, Lincolnshire, LN11 8LL.
(T) 01507 609069 (F) 01507 609051
Profile: FT: Coarse; WN: Stone End; WT: Lake (Still). Location: Nr. Rd: Charles Street.
Ref: FH4468

STONE FARM QUARRY

Stone Farm Quarry, Stone Farm, Bridestowe, Okehampton, **DEVON**, EX20, **England**.
Profile: FT: Coarse; WN: Stone Farm; WT: Gravel Pit (Still). Location: Nr. Rd: A30.
Ref: FH4469

STONE YARD FISHERY

Stone Yard Fishery, Chewton Mendip, **SOMERSET**, **England**.
Contact/s: **Mr Rodney Miles** (Thatchers Tackle Shop), Thatchers Pet & Tackle Shop, 18 Queen St, Wells, Somerset, BA5 2DP.
(T) 01749 673513
Profile: FT: Coarse; WN: Stone Yard Fishery; WT: Pond (Still); F. Size: 2 Acres; W. Size: 2 Acres. Location: Main Rd: A39; Rail: Bristol.
Ref: FH4470

STONEBRIDGE LAKES

Stonebridge Lakes, Hergill, Little Fencote, Northallerton, **YORKSHIRE (NORTH)**, DL7 0RR, **England**.
(W) www.stonebridgetroutlakes.co.uk
Contact/s: **Mr Adam Dick** (Owner).
(T) 01609 748818 (F) 01609 748750
(E) adam@stonebridgetroutlakes.co.uk
Mr David Deacon (Fishery Manager).
(T) 01609 748818
Profile: FT: Game; WN: Stonebridge Lakes; WT: Lake (Still) W. Size: 10 Acres.
Location: Nr. Rd: Hergill; Main Rd: A1; Rail: Northallerton.
Ref: FH4471

STONEHAM LAKES

Stoneham Lakes, Stoneham Lane, Eastleigh, Southampton, **HAMPSHIRE**, SO, **England**.
Contact/s: **Mr Colin Watts** (Manager), Homestore Tackle, 68 High Rd, Southampton, Hampshire, SO16 2HZ.
(T) 023 80551974
Mr Dave Banks (Fishery Manager).
(T) 023 0619491
Mr J Remington (Secretary), Eastleigh and District Angling Club, 121 Desborough Rd, Eastleigh, Hampshire, SO50 5NP.
(T) 023 80635540
Profile: FT: Coarse; WN: Stoneham; WT: Lake (Still). Location: Nr. Rd: B3354; Main Rd: M3.
Ref: FH4472

STONEY LANE PONDS

Stoney Lane Ponds, Stoney Lane, Staddleholme, Northallerton, **YORKSHIRE (NORTH)**, DL6, **England**.
Contact/s: **Mr Jeff Whittaker** (Bailiff).
(T) 01609 882542 (M) 07885 776291
Profile: FT: Coarse; WN: Stoney Lane; WT: Pond (Still). Location: Nr. Rd: Stoney Lane.
Ref: FH4473

STONEY PIT RESERVOIR

Stoney Pit Reservoir, Black Bower Lane, Hyde, Stockport, **MANCHESTER (GREATER)**, SK, **England**.
Contact/s: **John Kenworthy** (Secretary), Tameside Fishing Association, 69 Pennine Rd, Woodley, Stockport, SK6 1JR.
(T) 0161 4942671
Profile: FT: Coarse; WN: Stoney; WT: Gravel Pit (Still) W. Size: 1 Acre. Location: Nr. Rd: A560; Main Rd: M67. £Fr
Ref: FH4474

STONEYFIELD LOCH

Stoneyfield Loch Trout Fishery, Stoneyfield House, Newmore, Invergordon, **HIGHLAND**, IV18 0PG, **Scotland**.
Contact/s: **Ms Jennifer Connell**.
(T) 01349 852632
Profile: FT: Game; WN: Stoneyfield; WT: Loch (Still); F. Size: 60 Acres; W. Size: 16 Acres. Location: Nr. Rd: Newmore Road; Main Rd: A9; Rail: Alness.
Ref: FH4475

STOUR (DORSET) (RIVER)

River Dorset Stour, Bryanston, Blandford Forum, **DORSET**, DT11 0, **England**.
Contact/s: **Mr Steve Richards** (Secretary), Christchurch Angling Club, 4 Marley Cl, New Milton, Hampshire, BH25 5LL.
(T) 01425 279710
Mr Tim Bawn (Secretary), Ringwood Angling Club, 65 Arnewood Rd, Southbourne, Bournemouth, BH6 5DN.
(T) 01202 427305
Profile: FT: Coarse; WN: Dorset Stour; WT: River (Moving).
Ref: FH4476

STOUR (DORSET) (RIVER)

River Dorset Stour, Stourpaine, Blandford Forum, **DORSET**, DT11, **England**.
Contact/s: **Mr Kevin Grozier** (Permit Secretary), 15 Greenfinch Walk, Hightown, Ringwood, Hampshire, BH24 3RJ.
(T) 01425 471466 (F) 01425 471466
Profile: FT: Coarse; WN: Stour; WT: River (Moving) W. Size: 2000 Metres. Location: Nr. Rd: Hod Drive; Main Rd: A350, Stourpaine.
Ref: FH4477

STOUR (DORSET) (RIVER)

River Dorset Stour, Littledown, Bournemouth, **DORSET**, BH5, **England**.
Contact/s: **Mr Kevin Grozier** (Permit Secretary), Ringwood and District Angling Association, 15 Greenfinch Walk, Hightown, Ringwood, Hampshire, BH24 3RJ.
(T) 01425 471466 (F) 01425 471466
Profile: FT: Coarse; WN: Dorset Stour; WT: River (Moving). Location: Main Rd: A3060.
Ref: FH4478

STOUR (DORSET) (RIVER)

River Dorset Stour, Highmead, Longham, Ferndown, **DORSET**, BH22, **England**.
Contact/s: **Mr Steve Richards** (Secretary), Christchurch Angling Club, 4 Marley Cl, New Milton, Hampshire, BH25 5LL.
(T) 01425 279710
Profile: FT: Coarse; WN: Dorset Stour; WT: River (Moving) W. Size: 800 Metres.
Location: Nr. Rd: Highmead Lane; Main Rd: A348, B3073.
Ref: FH4479

STOUR (DORSET) (RIVER)

River Dorset Stour, Manor Farm, Longham, Poole, **DORSET**, BH12, **England**.
Contact/s: **Mr Pete Reading** (Secretary), 17 Mayford Rd, Poole, Dorset, BH12 1PT.
(T) 01202 733110
Profile: FT: Coarse; WN: Dorset Stour; WT:

River (Moving). **Location:** **Nr. Rd:** Milham's road; **Main Rd:** A341.
Ref: FH4480

STOUR (DORSET) (RIVER)

River Dorset Stour, Longham, Ferndown, **DORSET**, BH22, **England**.
Profile: **FT:** Coarse; **WN:** Dorset Stour; **WT:** River (Moving) **W. Size:** 400 Metres.
Location: **Main Rd:** A31. **£Fr**
Ref: FH4481

STOUR (DORSET) (RIVER)

River Dorset Stour, Bound's Farm, Parley Green, Parley, Christchurch, **DORSET**, BH23, **England**.
Contact/s: **Mr Kevin Grozier** (Permit Secretary), 15 Greenfinch Walk, Hightown, Ringwood, Hampshire, BH24 3RJ.
(T) 01425 471466 **(F)** 01425 471466
Profile: **FT:** Combination; **WN:** Dorset Stour; **WT:** River (Moving) **W. Size:** 1600 Metres.
Location: **Nr. Rd:** Pass airport entrance by the golf course; **Main Rd:** B3073 to Hurn.
Ref: FH4482

STOUR (DORSET) (RIVER)

River Dorset Stour, Wick To Iford, Wick Lane, Christchurch, **DORSET**, BH23, **England**.
Contact/s: **Mr Pete Reading** (Secretary), 17 Mayford Rd, Poole, Dorset, BH12 1PT.
(T) 01202 733110
Profile: **FT:** Coarse; **WN:** Dorset Stour; **WT:** River (Moving). **Location:** **Nr. Rd:** Wick Lane; **Main Rd:** A35.
Ref: FH4483

STOUR (DORSET) (RIVER)

River Dorset Stour, Christchurch, **DORSET**, BH23, **England**.
Contact/s: **Mr Graham Pepler** (Manager), Davis Tackle Shop, 75 Bargates, Christchurch, Dorset, BH23 1QE.
(T) 01202 485169or395532 **(F)** 01202 474261
Profile: **FT:** Coarse; **WN:** Dorset Stour (Ilford to Wick); **WT:** River (Moving).
Ref: FH4484

STOUR (DORSET) (RIVER)

River Dorset Stour, Fiddleford, Blandford Forum, **DORSET**, **England**.
Contact/s: **Mr S Dimmer** (Secretary), Sturminster and Hinton Angling Association, 38 Grosvenor Rd, Stalbridge, Sturminster Newton, DT10 2PN.
(T) 01963 363291
Profile: **FT:** Coarse; **WN:** Dorset Stour; **WT:** River (Moving) **W. Size:** 6400 Metres.
Location: **Nr. Rd:** A357; **Main Rd:** B3082; **Rail:** Blandford.
Ref: FH4485

STOUR (DORSET) (RIVER)

River Dorset Stour, Stalbridge, Sturminster Newton, **DORSET**, DT10, **England**.
Contact/s: **Mr Tony Cairns**.
(T) 01963 363688
Profile: **FT:** Coarse; **WN:** Dorset Stour; **WT:** River (Moving) **W. Size:** 4000 Metres.
Location: **Nr. Rd:** King's Mill Bridge; **Main Rd:** A350 North.
Ref: FH4486

STOUR (DORSET) (RIVER)

River Dorset Stour, Blandford Forum, **DORSET**, DT11, **England**.
Contact/s: **Mr C J Gorden** (President), Arthur Conyers, 3 West St, Blandford, Dorset.
(T) 01258 452307
Profile: **FT:** Coarse; **WN:** Dorset Stour; **WT:** River (Moving) **W. Size:** 6400 Metres.
Ref: FH4487

STOUR (DORSET) (RIVER)

River Dorset Stour, Hurn Beat One, Throop, Bournemouth, **DORSET**, BH, **England**.
Contact/s: **Mr Kevin Grozier** (Permit Secretary), Ringwood and District Angling Association, 15 Greenfinch Walk, Hightown, Ringwood, Hampshire, BH24 3RJ.
(T) 01425 471466 **(F)** 01425 471466
Profile: **FT:** Coarse; **WN:** Dorset Stour; **WT:** River (Moving) **W. Size:** 1600 Metres.
Location: **Nr. Rd:** Throop Road; **Main Rd:** A338, A3060.
Ref: FH4488

STOUR (DORSET) (RIVER)

River Dorset Stour, Shillingstone, Blandford Forum, **DORSET**, DT11, **England**.
Contact/s: **Mr Bill Lucy** (Secretary), Dorchester and District Angling Society, 7 Celtic Cresent, Dorcester, Dorset, DT1 2QJ.
(T) 01305 264873
Mr John Parkes (Membership Secretary), Dorchester and District Angling Society, 5 Malta Cl, Dorcester, Dorset, DT1 2QA.
(T) 01305 262813
Profile: **FT:** Coarse; **WN:** Dorset Stour; **WT:** River (Moving) **W. Size:** 4000 Metres.
Location: **Nr. Rd:** A357; **Main Rd:** A357; **Rail:** Sherborne.
Ref: FH4489

STOUR (DORSET) (RIVER)

River Dorset Stour, Hampreston, Wimborne, **DORSET**, BH21, **England**.
Contact/s: **Mr Kevin Grozier** (Permit Secretary), Ringwood and District Angling Association, 15 Greenfinch Walk, Hightown, Ringwood, Hampshire, BH24 3RJ.
(T) 01425 471466 **(F)** 01425 471466
Profile: **FT:** Coarse; **WN:** Dorset Stour; **WT:** River (Moving) **W. Size:** 2400 Metres.
Location: **Nr. Rd:** Stapehill Road (opposite); **Main Rd:** A31, B3073.
Ref: FH4490

STOUR (RIVER)

River Dorset Stour, Brecon Cl, Muscliff, Bournemouth, **DORSET**, BH, **England**.
Contact/s: Manager, Bournemouth Fishing Lodge, 904 Wimborne Rd, Bournemouth, Dorset, BH9 2DW.
(T) 01202 514345 **(F)** 01202 514345
Profile: **FT:** Coarse; **WN:** Stour; **WT:** River (Moving) **W. Size:** 1200 Metres. **Location:** **Nr. Rd:** Granby Road then Brecon Close; **Main Rd:** A338 to Ringwood. **£Fr**
Ref: FH4491

STOUR (RIVER)

River Stour, Sturminster Newton, **DORSET**, DT10, **England**.
Contact/s: **Mr R Wylde**, 10 Hillside, Manston, Sturminster Newton, Dorset, DT10 1EY.
(T) 01258 473391
Mr S Dimmer (Secretary), Sturminster and Hinton Angling Association, 38 Grosvenor Rd, Stalbridge, Sturminster Newton, DT10 2PN.
(T) 01963 363291
Profile: **FT:** Coarse; **WN:** Stour; **WT:** River (Moving) **W. Size:** 22400 Metres.
Ref: FH4492

STOUR (RIVER)

River Stour, Wimborne, **DORSET**, BH21, **England**.
Contact/s: **Mr Ron Hillier** (Secretary), 29 New Zealand Avenue, Salisbury, Wiltshire, SP2 7JX.
(T) 01722 321164
Profile: **FT:** Coarse; **WN:** Stour; **WT:** River (Moving). **Location:** **Rail:** Salisbury.
Ref: FH4493

STOUR (RIVER)

River Stour, Blandford Forum, **DORSET**, DT11, **England**.
Contact/s: **C Light**, 4 Water Lane, Durweston, Blandford.
Mr V Bell.
(T) 01258 451317
Profile: **FT:** Coarse; **WN:** Stour; **WT:** River (Moving) **W. Size:** 3200 Metres. **Location:** **Main Rd:** A354.
Ref: FH4494

STOUR (RIVER)

River Stour, Stratford St Mary, Colchester, **ESSEX**, CO7, **England**.
Contact/s: **Mr Paul Acres** (Secretary), Colchester Angling Preservation Society, PO Box 1286, Colchester, CO2 8PG.
(T) 01206 272918
Profile: **FT:** Coarse; **WN:** Stour; **WT:** River (Moving) **W. Size:** 1200 Metres. **Location:** **Nr. Rd:** Colchester to Ipswich; **Main Rd:** A12, north of Colchester.
Ref: FH4495

STOUR (RIVER)

River Stour, Lavel, Ringwood, **HAMPSHIRE**, BH24, **England**.
Contact/s: **Mr Kevin Grozier** (Permit Secretary), 15 Greenfinch Walk, Hightown, Ringwood, Hampshire, BH24 3RJ.
(T) 01425 471466 **(F)** 01425 471466
Mr Richard Middleton (Manager), Ringwood Tackle, 5 The Bridges, Ringwood, Hampshire, BH24 1EA.
(T) 01425 475155
Profile: **FT:** Combination; **WN:** Stour; **WT:** River (Moving). **Location:** **Nr. Rd:** Lavel to Stourpaine.
Ref: FH4496

STOUR (RIVER)

River Stour, Canterbury, **KENT**, CT, **England**.
Contact/s: **Mr Barten** (Secretary), Canterbury and District Angling Association, Riversdale, 14 Mill Rd, Sturry, Canterbury, CT2 0AF.
(T) 01227 710830
Profile: **FT:** Coarse; **WN:** Stour; **WT:** River (Moving).
Ref: FH4497

STOUR (RIVER)

Stour (River), Vauxhall Rd, Canterbury, **KENT**, **England**.
(W) www.midkentfish.co.uk
Contact/s: **Mr Chris Logsdon** (Fisheries Manager), Mid Kent Fisheries, Chilham Water Mill, Mill Lane, Chilham, CT4 8EE.
(T) 01227 730668
(E) chilham@midkentfisheries.co.uk
Profile: **FT:** Coarse; **WN:** Stour; **WT:** River (Moving). **Location:** **Nr. Rd:** Vauxhall Road; **Main Rd:** A257; **Rail:** Canterbury.
Ref: FH4498

STOUR (RIVER)

Stour (River), Thannington, Canterbury, **KENT**, **England**.
(W) www.midkentfish.co.uk
Contact/s: **Mr Chris Logsdon** (Fisheries Manager), Mid Kent Fisheries, Chilham Water Mill, Mill Lane, Chilham, CT4 8EE.
(T) 01227 730668
(E) chilham@midkentfisheries.co.uk
Profile: **FT:** Coarse; **WN:** Stour; **WT:** River (Moving). **Location:** **Main Rd:** A2; **Rail:** Canterbury.
Ref: FH4499

STOUR (RIVER)

River Stour, Henny St, Sudbury, **SUFFOLK**, CO10, **England**.
(W) www.bdac.co.uk
Contact/s: **Mr Derek Howard** (Hon Treasurer), Billericay and District Angling Club, 4 Long Meadow Drive, Wickford, Essex, SS11 8AX.
(T) 01268 734468
Profile: **FT:** Coarse; **WN:** Stour; **WT:** River (Moving) **W. Size:** 1600 Metres. **Location:** **Main Rd:** A131; **Rail:** Sudbury.
Ref: FH4500

STOUR (RIVER)

Rourbridge, Rourbridge Picnic Area, Long Melford, Sudbury, **SUFFOLK**, CO10, **England**.
Contact/s: **Mr Rob Hayward** (Manager), Sudbury Angling Ctre, 1 Acton Sq, Sudbury, Suffolk, CO10 1HG.
(T) 01787 312118
Mr Trevor Fairless (Secretary), Sudbury and District Angling Association, 39 Pot Kiln Rd, Sudbury, Suffolk, CO10 0DG.
(T) 01787 312536

Profile: FT: Coarse; WN: Stour (Suffolk); WT: River (Moving) W. Size: 500 Metres. Location: Nr. Rd: A134 Bury St Edmunds; Main Rd: A134; Rail: Sudbury.
Ref: FH4501

STOUR (SUFFOLK) (RIVER)

Suffolk Stour, Nayland, Colchester, **ESSEX**, CO6, **England**.
Contact/s: **Mr Paul Acres** (Secretary), Colchester Angling Preservation Society, PO Box 1286, Colchester, CO2 8PG.
(T) 01206 272918
Profile: FT: Coarse; WN: Stour (Suffolk); WT: River (Moving) W. Size: 400 Metres. **Location:** Nr. Rd: Horkesley Road; Main Rd: A134, Sudbury to Colchester.
Ref: FH4502

STOUR (SUFFOLK) (RIVER)

Suffolk Stour, Ipswich, **SUFFOLK**, IP, **England**.
Contact/s: **Mr Richard Harbach**.
(T) 01206 394452
Profile: FT: Coarse; WN: Stour (Suffolk); WT: River (Moving).
Ref: FH4503

STOUR (WARWICKSHIRE)

Warwickshire Stour, Stratford-upon-Avon, **WARWICKSHIRE**, CV37, **England**.
Contact/s: **Mr A Bruce** (Secretary), Stratford-upon-Avon Angling Club, 42 Cherry Orchard, Stratford-upon-Avon, Warwickshire, CV37 9AP.
(T) 01789 720603
Profile: FT: Coarse; WN: Warwickshire Stour; WT: River (Moving) W. Size: 2400 Metres. **Location:** Nr. Rd: Shipston-on-Stour to Stratford-upon-Avon; Main Rd: A3400.
Ref: FH4504

STOUR FARM FISHERY

Stour Farm Fishery, Billingsmoor Farm, Butterleigh, Cullompton, **DEVON**, EX15, **England**.
Contact/s: **Mr E Berry**.
Profile: FT: Coarse; WN: Stour Farm Fishery; WT: Pond (Still). **Location:** Main Rd: M5, junction 28.
Ref: FH4505

STOUR LAKE

Stour Lake, Shalmsford St, Chartham, Canterbury, **KENT**, CT4, **England**.
Contact/s: **Mr Chris Logsdon** (Manager), Mid Kent Fisheries, Chilham Water Mill, Mill Lane, Chilham, CT4 8EE.
(T) 01227 730668
Profile: FT: Coarse; WN: Stour; WT: Lake (Still); F. Size: 30 Acres; W. Size: 20 Acres. **Location:** Nr. Rd: Shalmsford Street; Main Rd: A28; Rail: Canterbury.
Ref: FH4506

STOUTING LAKE

Stouting Lake, Canterbury, **KENT**, CT4 6, **England**.
Contact/s: **Mr Micheal** (Manager), 3 Watery Lane, Stouting, Kent, CT4 6RJ.
(T) 01227 700871
Profile: FT: Game; WN: Stouting; WT: Lake (Still) W. Size: 3 Acres.
Ref: FH4507

STOW (RIVER)

Friars Meadow, Sudbury, **SUFFOLK**, CO10, **England**.
Contact/s: **Mr Trevor Fairless** (Secretary), Sudbury and District Angling Association, 39 Pot Kiln Rd, Sudbury, Suffolk, CO10 0DG.
(T) 01787 312536
Profile: FT: Coarse; WN: Stow (Suffolk); WT: River (Moving) W. Size: 375 Metres. **Location:** Nr. Rd: Town Centre; Main Rd: A131; Rail: Sudbury.
Ref: FH4508

STOW (RIVER)

Mill Meadows, The Common Lands, Sudbury, **SUFFOLK**, CO10, **England**.
Contact/s: **Mr Trevor Fairless** (Secretary), Sudbury and District Angling Association, 39 Pot Kiln Rd, Sudbury, Suffolk, CO10 0DG.
(T) 01787 312536
Profile: FT: Coarse; WN: Stow (Suffolk); WT: River (Moving) W. Size: 1500 Metres. **Location:** Nr. Rd: A134 to Bury Road; Main Rd: A134; Rail: Sudbury.
Ref: FH4509

STOW (RIVER)

Pecks Meadow, Sudbury, **SUFFOLK**, CO10, **England**.
Contact/s: **Mr Trevor Fairless** (Secretary), Sudbury and District Angling Association, 39 Pot Kiln Rd, Sudbury, Suffolk, CO10 0DG.
(T) 01787 312536
Profile: FT: Coarse; WN: Stow (Suffolk); WT: River (Moving) W. Size: 40 Metres. **Location:** Nr. Rd: B1508; Main Rd: A131; Rail: Sudbury.
Ref: FH4510

STOW (RIVER)

Kiplings Meadow, Sudbury, **SUFFOLK**, CO10, **England**.
Contact/s: **Mr Trevor Fairless** (Secretary), Sudbury and District Angling Association, 39 Pot Kiln Rd, Sudbury, Suffolk, CO10 0DG.
(T) 01787 312536
Profile: FT: Coarse; WN: Stow; WT: River (Moving); F. Size: 20 Acres; W. Size: 750 Metres. **Location:** Nr. Rd: Bury St Edmunds; Main Rd: A134; Rail: Sudbury.
Ref: FH4511

STOW (RIVER)

Rookery And Long Meadow, The Rookery, The Sports Ground, Nayland Rd, Bures, **SUFFOLK**, CO8, **England**.
Contact/s: **Mr Rob Hayward** (Manager), Sudbury Angling Ctre, 1 Acton Sq, Sudbury, Suffolk, CO10 1HG.
(T) 01787 312118
Mr Trevor Fairless (Secretary), Sudbury and District Angling Association, 39 Pot Kiln Rd, Sudbury, Suffolk, CO10 0DG.
(T) 01787 312536
Profile: FT: Coarse; WN: Stour (Suffolk); WT: River (Moving) W. Size: 750 Metres. **Location:** Nr. Rd: Nayland Road; Main Rd: A134, A12; Rail: Bures.
Ref: FH4512

STOWFORD GRANGE FISHERIES

Stowford Grange Fisheries, Lewdown, Launceston, **CORNWALL**, PL15, **England**.
Contact/s: **Mr Brian Sherring**.
(T) 01566 777230
Mrs Ashworth (Owner), Pets on Prde, Unit 8, Whitehart Arcade, Launceston, Cornwall, PL15 8AA.
(T) 01566 777230 (M) 07718 708723
Profile: FT: Coarse; WN: Stowford Grange Fisheries; WT: Lake (Still) W. Size: 5 Acres. **Location:** Nr. Rd: A30; Main Rd: A338.
Ref: FH4513

STOWTING TROUT LAKE

Stowting Trout Lake, Water Farm, Stowting, Ashford, **KENT**, TN25 6BA, **England**.
Contact/s: **Mr Colin Cole**.
(T) 01303 862401
Mrs Carole Cole.
(T) 01303 862401
Profile: FT: Game; WN: Stowting Trout; WT: Lake (Still); F. Size: 3 Acres; W. Size: 2 Acres. **Location:** Nr. Rd: B2068; Main Rd: M20, A20; Rail: Ashford International.
Ref: FH4514

STRADBALLY (RIVER)

River Stradbally, Athy, **COUNTY KILDARE**, **Ireland**.
Contact/s: Manager, Griffin Hawe Limited, 22 Duke St, Athy, County Kildare, Ireland.
(T) 050 731221 (F) 050 733885
(E) griffinhawe@tinet.ie
Profile: FT: Game; WN: Stradbally; WT: River (Moving) W. Size: 9600 Metres.
Ref: FH4515

STRAID FISHERY

Straid Fishery, 21 Castletown Rd, Ballynure, Ballyclare, **COUNTY ANTRIM**, BT39 9PU, **Northern Ireland**.
Contact/s: **Mr Jim Smallwoods** (Manager).
(T) 028 93340099 (F) 028 93322434
(E) straidfishery@hotmail.com
Mr Marcus Malley (Owner).
(T) 028 93322434 (F) 028 93322434
Profile: FT: Game; WN: Straid; WT: Lake (Still); F. Size: 28 Acres; W. Size: 24 Acres. **Location:** Nr. Rd: Castletown Road; Main Rd: A8; Rail: Larne.
Ref: FH4516

STRAIGHT MILE FISHERY

Straight Mile Fishery, Common Rd, Anston, Brampton-En-Le-Morten, Sheffield, **YORKSHIRE (SOUTH)**, S31 7AH, **England**.
Contact/s: **Mr John Cox** (Owner). (M) 07771 995331
Profile: FT: Coarse; WN: Straight Mile; WT: Lake (Still) W. Size: 5 Acres. **Location:** Nr. Rd: Common Road; Main Rd: M1, junction 31.
Ref: FH4517

STRAITS MILL

Straits Mill, Convent Lane, Bocking, Braintree, **ESSEX**, CM7, **England**.
Contact/s: **Mr Derek Howard** (Hon Treasurer), Billericay and District Angling Club, 4 Long Meadow Drive, Wickford, Essex, SS11 8AX.
(T) 01268 734468
Profile: FT: Coarse; WN: Straits Mill; WT: Combination (Still); F. Size: 10 Acres; W. Size: 6 Acres. **Location:** Nr. Rd: Convent Lane; Main Rd: B1053; Rail: Braintree.
Ref: FH4518

STRATHCLYDE LOCH

Strathclyde Loch, Motherwell, **LANARKSHIRE (NORTH)**, ML1, **Scotland**.
Contact/s: **Mr Ronnie Macleod** (Manager), MacLeod's Fishing Tackle, 176 High St, Motherwell, Lanarkshire, ML1 5JQ.
(T) 01698 860530
Profile: FT: Coarse; WN: Strathclyde; WT: Loch (Still).
Ref: FH4519

STRATHMANAIRD LOCHS

Strathmanaird Lochs, Strathmanaird, Ullapool, **HIGHLAND**, IV26, **Scotland**.
Contact/s: **Mr A Scott** (Secretary).
(T) 01854 613081
Profile: FT: Game; WN: Strathmanaird; WT: Lake (Still). **Location:** Nr. Rd: A835.
Ref: FH4520

STRATHY (RIVER)

River Strathy, Forsinard, **HIGHLAND**, KW13 6YT, **Scotland**.
(W) www.bowside.co.uk
Contact/s: **Mr Jack Patterson** (Manager), The Halladale Inn, Melvich, Thurso, Caithness, KW14 7YJ.
(T) 01641 531282
Profile: FT: Game; WN: Strathy; WT: River (Moving).
Ref: FH4521

STRATTON LODGE

Stratton Lodge, 52 Bath St, Abingdon, **OXFORDSHIRE**, OX1, **England**.
Profile: FT: Coarse; WN: Thames; WT: River (Moving).
Ref: FH4522

STRETHAM BASIN

Stretham Basin, Old West River, Stretham, Ely, **CAMBRIDGESHIRE**, CB6, **England**.
Contact/s: **Mr R Gentle** (Secretary).
(T) 01223 426711
Profile: FT: Coarse; WN: Old West; WT: River (Moving).
Ref: FH4523

STRETHAM LAKE

Stretham Lake, Stretham, Ely, **CAMBRIDGESHIRE**, CB6 3, **England**.
Contact/s: Fishery Manager.
(T) 01353 649375
Profile: FT: Coarse; WN: Stretham; WT: Lake (Still) W. Size: 2 Acres. **Location:** Main Rd: A10.
Ref: FH4524

STRETTON WATER

Stretton Water, Stretton, Warrington, **CHESHIRE**, **England**.
(W) www.baymalton-anglingclub.org
Contact/s: **Mr Stewart Godber** (Club Secretary), 38 Edenfield Rd, Mobberley, Cheshire, WA16 7HE.
(T) 01565 872582
Profile: FT: Coarse; WN: Stretton Water; WT: Pool (Still); F. Size: 1 Acre; W. Size: 1 Acre. **Location:** Main Rd: B5356; Rail: Warrington.
Ref: FH4525

STRIP PONDS

Strip Ponds, Lakeside Fisheries, Ranskill, Retford, **NOTTINGHAMSHIRE**, DN22, **England**.
Contact/s: **Mr Nigel Hawke**.
(T) 01777 818524
Profile: FT: Coarse; WN: Strip; WT: Pond (Still).
Ref: FH4526

STROUDWATER CANAL

Stroudwater Canal, Bridgend, CF31, **Wales**.
Mr Dale Gardener (Owner), Lobbys Tackle, 58a High St, Stonehouse, Gloucestershire, GL10 2NA.
(T) 01453 791417
Profile: FT: Coarse; WN: Stroudwater; WT: Canal (Still).
Ref: FH4527

STROUDWATER CANAL

Stroudwater Canal, Stonehouse, **GLOUCESTERSHIRE**, GL10, **England**.
Contact/s: Manager, Lobbys Tackle, 58a High St, Stonehouse, Gloucestershire, GL10 2NA.
(T) 01453 791417
Profile: FT: Coarse; WN: Stroudwater (Ryford to Bridgend); WT: Canal (Still). **Location:** Nr. Rd: A419 Ryford to Bridgend.
Ref: FH4528

STRULE (RIVER)

River Strule, Omagh, **COUNTY TYRONE**, BT78, **Northern Ireland**.
Contact/s: Fishing Manager, Sperrin Tourism Partnership, 50 Ballyronan Rd, Magherafelt, BT45 6EN.
(T) 028 7934570
Profile: FT: Coarse; WN: Strule; WT: River (Moving).
Ref: FH4529

STRULE (RIVER)

River Strule, Omagh, **COUNTY TYRONE**, BT78, **Northern Ireland**.
Contact/s: **Mr Ca Anderson** (Secretary), Omagh Angling Association, 64 Market St, Omagh, County Tyrone, BT78 1EN.
(E) andersonca@lineone.net
Mr Stephen Martin (License Distributor).
(T) 028 82242311 (F) 028 82249539 (M) 07776 343600
Profile: FT: Game; WN: Strule; WT: River (Moving) W. Size: 16000 Metres. **Location:** Nr. Rd: A5; Main Rd: A5.
Ref: FH4530

STUBPOND FISHERIES

Stubpond Fisheries, East Grinstead, **SUSSEX (WEST)**, RH19, **England**.
Contact/s: **Mr Robert Harman**.
(T) 07703 464046 (M) 07703 464046
Profile: FT: Coarse; WN: Stubpond; WT: Pond (Still).
Ref: FH4531

STUDIO AND BROADWATER

Studio And Broadwater, Shepperton, London, **LONDON (GREATER)**, TW17, **England**.
(W) www.calpac.bizland.com
Contact/s: **Mr Colin Trafford** (General Secretary).
(T) 020 82242617
Mrs Diane Wheeler (Secretary), 314 Old Lodge Lane, Purley, Surrey, CR8 4AQ.
(T) 020 86602766
Profile: FT: Coarse; WN: Studio and Broadwater; WT: Combination (Still & Moving). **Location:** Nr. Rd: Studios Road; Main Rd: A224.
Ref: FH4532

SUDBROOK POND

Sudbrook Pond, Sudbrook Hall Farm, Sudbrook, Lincoln, **LINCOLNSHIRE**, LN2, **England**.
Contact/s: **Mr J E Tolson**.
(T) 01400 230388
Profile: FT: Coarse; WN: Sudbrook; WT: Pond (Still) W. Size: 2 Acres. **Location:** Nr. Rd: Rookery Lane; Main Rd: A153, Sleaford to Grantham.
Ref: FH4533

SUIE

Suie, Crianlarich, **STIRLING**, FK20, **Scotland**.
(W) www.fishingnet.com/beats/dochart/suie.htm
Contact/s: **Mr P J Shoulders** (Owner), Suie Lodge Hotel, Luib, Crianlarich, Perth and Kinross, FK20 8QT.
(T) 01567 820417
Mrs V Hunter (Owner).
Profile: FT: Combination; WN: Suie; WT: Pool (Still).
Ref: FH4534

SUIR (RIVER)

Suir (River), Knocklofty, Clonmel, **COUNTY TIPPERARY**, **Ireland**.
Contact/s: Manager, Knocklofty House Hotel, Knocklofty, Clonmel, County Tipperary, Ireland.
(T) 052 38222
Profile: FT: Game; WN: Suir; WT: River (Moving).
Ref: FH4535

SUIR (RIVER)

River Suir, Cashel, **COUNTY TIPPERARY**, **Ireland**.
Contact/s: **Mrs Ryan** (Manager), Tackle Shop, Friar St, Cashel, County Tipperary, Ireland.
Profile: FT: Game; WN: Suir; WT: River (Moving) W. Size: 12800 Metres.
Ref: FH4536

SUIR (RIVER)

Suir (River), Clonmel, **COUNTY TIPPERARY**, **Ireland**.
Contact/s: **Mr Jean Loup Trautner**, Marlfield Fisheries, Marlfield Lodge, Clonmel, County Tipperary, Ireland.
(T) 052 255340
Profile: FT: Game; WN: Suir; WT: River (Moving).
Ref: FH4537

SUIR (RIVER)

River Suir, Cahir, **COUNTY TIPPERARY**, **Ireland**.
Contact/s: Manager, Suir Tackle, The Square, Cahir, County Tipperary, Ireland.
Manager, Kilcoran Lodge, Cahir, County Tipperary, Ireland.
(T) 052 41288 (F) 052 41994
Profile: FT: Game; WN: Suir; WT: River (Moving) W. Size: 12800 Metres.
Ref: FH4538

SUIR (RIVER)

Suir (River), Clonmel, **COUNTY TIPPERARY**, **Ireland**.
Contact/s: **Mr John Kavanagh** (Manager), John Kavanagh's Sports Shop, Westgate, Clonmel, County Tipperary, Ireland.
Profile: FT: Game; WN: Suir; WT: River (Moving).
Ref: FH4539

SUIR (RIVER)

River Suir, Coolnamuck Fisheries, Carrick-on-Suir, **COUNTY TIPPERARY**, **Ireland**.
Contact/s: **Mr J O'Keeffe** (Manager), OK Sports, New St, Carrick-on-Suir, County Tipperary, Ireland.
(T) 051 40626
Profile: FT: Game; WN: Suir; WT: River (Moving) W. Size: 4800 Metres.
Ref: FH4540

SUIR (RIVER)

River Suir, Ardfinnan, **COUNTY TIPPERARY**, **Ireland**.
Contact/s: **Mrs B Morrissey** (Secretary), Cahir and District Angling Association, Castle St, Ardfinnan, County Tipperary, Ireland.
Profile: FT: Game; WN: Suir; WT: River (Moving).
Ref: FH4541

SUIR (RIVER)

River Suir, Ardfinnan, **COUNTY TIPPERARY**, **Ireland**.
Contact/s: **Mrs B Morrissey** (Secretary), Cahir and District Angling Association, Castle St, Ardfinnan, County Tipperary, Ireland.
Profile: FT: Game; WN: Suir; WT: River (Moving).
Ref: FH4542

SUIR (RIVER)

Suir (River), Clonmel, **COUNTY TIPPERARY**, **Ireland**.
Profile: FT: Game; WN: Suir; WT: River (Moving).
Ref: FH4543

SUIR (RIVER)

River Suir, Thurles, **COUNTY TIPPERARY**, **Ireland**.
Contact/s: **J Grene** (Manager), Farm Guesthouse, Cappamurra House, Dundrum, County Tipperary, Ireland.
(T) 062 71127
Mr Jimmy Purcell (Secretary), Thurles, Hollycross and Ballycamas Angling Association, Rathcannon, Holycross, Thurles, County Tipperary, Ireland.
Profile: FT: Game; WN: Suir; WT: River (Moving).
Ref: FH4544

SUIR (RIVER)

Suir (River), Clonmel, **COUNTY TIPPERARY**, **Ireland**.
Contact/s: **J Carroll** (Secretary), Clonmel and District Angling Club, 3 New Quay, Clonmel, County Tipperary.
Profile: FT: Game; WN: Suir; WT: River (Moving) W. Size: 1600 Metres.
Ref: FH4545

SUIR (RIVER)

River Suir, Ardfinnan, **COUNTY TIPPERARY**, **Ireland**.
Contact/s: Manager, Shamrock Lodge, Ardfinnan, County Tipperary, Ireland.
Manager, Suir Tackle, The Square, Cahir, County Tipperary, Ireland.
Profile: FT: Game; WN: Suir; WT: River (Moving).
Ref: FH4546

SUIR (RIVER)

River Suir, Ardfinnan, **COUNTY TIPPERARY**, **Ireland**.
Contact/s: **Mrs B Morrissey** (Secretary), Cahir and District Angling Association, Castle St, Ardfinnan, County Tipperary, Ireland.
Profile: FT: Game; WN: Suir; WT: River (Moving).
Ref: FH4547

SUIR (RIVER)

River Suir, Carrick-on-Suir, **COUNTY TIPPERARY**, **Ireland**.

Contact/s: **Mr J O'Keeffe** (Manager), OK Sports, New St, Carrick-on-Suir, County Tipperary, Ireland.
(T) 051 40626
Profile: **FT:** Game; **WN:** Suir; **WT:** River (Moving). **Location:** **Nr. Rd:** Miloko to Duffcastle.
Ref: FH4548

SUIR (RIVER)

River Suir, Kilsheelin, **COUNTY TIPPERARY**, **Ireland**.
Contact/s: **Ms Maura Long**, Glencastle, Kilnasheen, County Tipperary, Ireland.
(T) 052 33287
Profile: **FT:** Game; **WN:** Suir; **WT:** River (Moving) **W. Size:** 42400 Metres.
Ref: FH4549

SUIR VALLEY FISHERY

Suir Valley Fishery, 11 Auburn Cl, Clonmel, **COUNTY TIPPERARY**, **Ireland**.
Contact/s: **Mr Jean Loup Trautner**, Marlfield Fisheries, Marlfield Lodge, Clonmel, County Tipperary, Ireland.
(T) 052 255340
Profile: **FT:** Game; **WN:** Suir; **WT:** River (Moving) **W. Size:** 1700 Metres.
Ref: FH4550

SULBY RESERVOIR

Sulby Reservoir, Welford, Northampton, **NORTHAMPTONSHIRE**, NN6, **England**.
Contact/s: Manager, MEM Fisheries Management Ltd, Bufton House, Walcote Lutterworth, Leicestershire, LE17 4JS.
Southern Region Manager, British Waterways, Hemel Hempstead.
(T) 01442 278717
Profile: **FT:** Coarse; **WN:** Sulby; **WT:** Reservoir (Still).
Ref: FH4551

SUMMERFIELDS TROUT FISHERY

Summerfields Trout Fishery, Haynes Turn, Haynes, Bedford, **BUCKINGHAMSHIRE**, MK4, **England**.
Contact/s: **Mr Graham Cole** (Manager).
(T) 01462 811266/0374460987
Profile: **FT:** Game; **WN:** Summerfields Trout Fishery; **WT:** Lake (Still). **Location:** **Nr. Rd:** A600; **Main Rd:** Bedford to Shefford.
Ref: FH4552

SUMMERHAYES

Summerhayes, Huntworth, Bridgwater, **SOMERSET**, TA, **England**.
Contact/s: Manager, Somerset Angling, 74 Bath Rd, Bridgwater, Somerset, TA6 4PL.
(T) 01278 431777or786934 **(F)** 01278 792397
Mr Mike Long.
(T) 01278 781565
Profile: **FT:** Coarse; **WN:** Summerhayes; **WT:** Lake (Still) **W. Size:** 2 Acres. **Location:** **Nr. Rd:** North Petherton to Bridgwater; **Main Rd:** A38.
Ref: FH4553

SUMMERLEAZE POND

Summerleaze Pond, Summerleaze Farm, Kilmington, Axminster, **DEVON**, EX13 7RA, **England**.
Contact/s: **Mr M Collier** (Fishery Manager).
(T) 01297 323390
Profile: **FT:** Coarse; **WN:** Summerleaze; **WT:** Pond (Still). **Location:** **Rail:** Axminster.
Ref: FH4554

SUMMERVILLE LOUGH

Summerville Lough, Claremorris, **COUNTY GALWAY**, **Ireland**.
Contact/s: **Mr Danny Goldrick** (Angling Officer), The Western Regional Fisheries Board, Weir Lodge, Earl's Island, Galway City, County Galway.
(T) 091 563118 **(F)** 091 566335
(E) wrfb@iol.ie
Profile: **FT:** Coarse; **WN:** Summerville; **WT:** Lough (Still) **W. Size:** 40 Acres.
Ref: FH4555

SUNDRIDGE LAKES

Sundridge Lakes, 4 Shoreham Lane, Rivehead, Sevenoaks, **KENT**, TN, **England**.
Profile: **FT:** Coarse; **WN:** Sundridge; **WT:** Gravel Pit (Still).
Ref: FH4556

SUNRIDGE FISHERY

Sunridge Fishery, Sundridge Nurseries, Worston, Yealmpton, Plymouth, **DEVON**, PL8 2LN, **England**.
Mr R M Hammett.
(T) 01752 880438 **(F)** 01752 880438 **(M)** 07779 445168
Profile: **FT:** Coarse; **WN:** Sunridge; **WT:** Lake (Still). **Location:** **Nr. Rd:** A379; **Main Rd:** A38; **Rail:** Plymouth.
Ref: FH4557

SURRENDEN LAKES

Surrenden Lakes, Old Surrenden Manor Rd, Bethersden, Ashford, **KENT**, TN2, **England**.
Contact/s: **Mr Alan Sandom** (Fisheries Officer), 39 Belmore Park, Ashford, Kent, TN24 8UW. **(M)** 07703 531359
Mr Dale Lee (Booking Secretary).
(T) 01303 812388
Mr Mick Ladley.
(T) 01233 627813
Profile: **FT:** Coarse; **WN:** Surrenden; **WT:** Lake (Still); **F. Size:** 14 Acres; **W. Size:** 8 Acres. **Location:** **Nr. Rd:** Old Surrenden Manor Road; **Main Rd:** A28 or M20; **Rail:** Ashford International.
Ref: FH4558

SUTTON AT HONE LAKE TWO

Sutton At Hone Lake Two, Devon Rd, Sutton At Hone, South Darenth, Dartford, **KENT**, DA, **England**.
(W) www.rmcangling.co.uk
Contact/s: **Mr Ian Welch** (Angling Manager), RMC Angling, The Square, Lightwater, Surrey, GU18 5SS.
(T) 01276 453300 **(F)** 01276 456611
(E) info@rmcangling.co.uk
Profile: **FT:** Coarse; **WN:** Sutton at Hone 2; **WT:** Gravel Pit (Still) **W. Size:** 4 Acres. **Location:** **Nr. Rd:** Devon Road; **Main Rd:** A1.
Ref: FH4559

SUTTON AT HONE LAKES 1 & 3

Sutton At Hone Lakes One And Three, Devon Rd, Sutton At Hone, South Darenth, Dartford, **KENT**, DA, **England**.
(W) www.rmcangling.co.uk
Contact/s: **Mr Ian Welch** (Angling Manager), RMC Angling, The Square, Lightwater, Surrey, GU18 5SS.
(T) 01276 453300 **(F)** 01276 456611
(E) info@rmcangling.co.uk
Profile: **FT:** Coarse; **WN:** Sutton at Hone; **WT:** Gravel Pit (Still) **W. Size:** 9 Acres. **Location:** **Nr. Rd:** Devon Road; **Main Rd:** A225.
Ref: FH4560

SUTTON BINGHAM RESERVOIR

Sutton Bingham Fishing Lodge, Netherton Lane, Clonworth, Yeovil, **SOMERSET**, BA22 9QL, **England**.
Contact/s: Customer Services, Wessex Water, Billing Ctre, Clevedon Walk, Nailsea, Bristol, BS48 1WW.
(T) 01179 290611 **(F)** 01275 810519
Mr I Tinsley (Ranger).
(T) 01935 872389
Profile: **FT:** Game; **WN:** Sutton Bingham; **WT:** Reservoir (Still) **W. Size:** 142 Acres. **Location:** **Main Rd:** A37, Dorchester Road.
Ref: FH4561

SUTTON BROOK

Sutton Brook, Burntheath, Hilton, **DERBYSHIRE**, **England**.
(W) www.fentondas.co.uk
Contact/s: **Mr C Yates** (Club Secretary), The Puzzles, 5 Gatley Gr, Meir Park, Stoke-on-Trent, Staffordshire ST3 7SH.
(T) 01782 396913
Profile: **FT:** Combination; **WN:** Sutton; **WT:** Brook (Moving) **W. Size:** 3218 Metres. **Location:** **Nr. Rd:** A511; **Main Rd:** A50; **Rail:** Tutbury.
Ref: FH4562

SUTTON LAWN DAM

Sutton Lawn Dam, Sutton-In-Ashfield, Mansfield, **NOTTINGHAMSHIRE**, **England**.
Contact/s: **Mr Allan Warren**.
(T) 01623 554645
Profile: **FT:** Coarse**WT:** (Still).
Ref: FH4563

SUTTON PARK

Sutton Park, Visitors Ctre, Park Rd, Sutton Coldfield, **MIDLANDS (WEST)**, B74 2YT, **England**.
Contact/s: Manager.
(T) 0121 3556370
Profile: **FT:** Coarse; **WN:** Sutton Park; **WT:** Lake (Still).
Ref: FH4564

SUTTON RESERVOIR

Sutton Reservoir, Runcorn, Sutton, Macclesfield, **CHESHIRE**, SK11, **England**.
Contact/s: **Mr Griffiths** (Fishery Manager).
(T) 01606 723800
Profile: **FT:** Coarse; **WN:** Sutton; **WT:** Reservoir (Still).
Ref: FH4565

SUTTON VENY ESTATE

Sutton Veny Estate (The), Eastleigh Farm, Bishopstrow, Warminster, **WILTSHIRE**, BA12 7BE, **England**.
Contact/s: **Mr Alex Walker**.
(T) 01985 219191 **(F)** 01985 219191 **(M)** 07836 294633
Profile: **FT:** Game; **WN:** Wylye; **WT:** Stream (Moving) **W. Size:** 6500 Metres. **Location:** **Nr. Rd:** A36; **Main Rd:** A36; **Rail:** Warminster.
Ref: FH4566

SWALE (RIVER)

River Swale, Boroughbridge Rd, Helperby, York, **YORKSHIRE (NORTH)**, YO61, **England**.
Contact/s: **Mr Mark Faulkner** (Farmer), Thornton Bridge, Boroughbridge Rd, Helperby, York, YO6 12PD. **(F)** 01423 360402 **(M)** 07710 784016
Profile: **FT:** Coarse; **WN:** Swale; **WT:** River (Moving) **W. Size:** 1280 Metres. **Location:** **Nr. Rd:** Boroughbridge Road; **Main Rd:** A1, A19; **Rail:** Thirsk.
Ref: FH4567

SWALE (RIVER)

River Swale, Easby, Richmond, **YORKSHIRE (NORTH)**, DL10, **England**.
Contact/s: **Mr Peter Bennet**.
(T) 01748 824894
Profile: **FT:** Coarse; **WN:** Swale; **WT:** River (Moving).
Ref: FH4568

SWALE (RIVER)

River Swale, Fawdington, York, **YORKSHIRE (NORTH)**, YO61, **England**.
Mr F Marrison (Hon Secretary), Helperby and Brafferton Angling Club, Gardeners Cottage, York Rd, Helperby, YO61 2PQ.
(T) 01423 360632
Mr J Gott (Owner), Elm Cotttage Bed and Breakfast, Humberton Gates, Helperby, Yorkshire, YO61 2RX.
(T) 01423 360213
Mr Jim Giles (Tackle Shop Owner), Fish' In ' Things, 5 Horsefair, Boroughbridge, YO51 9LS.
(T) 01423 324776
Mr Paul Weetman, The Oak Tree, Raskeolf Rd, Helperby, W061 2PH.
(T) 01423 360268
Mr Stuart Tate (Fishery Manager).
(T) 01347 821831 **(F)** 01347 821831 **(M)** 07801 126677

Mrs Wendy Bramley (Secretary), 23 Kirkby Rd, Ripon, Yorkshire (North), HG4 2EY.
(T) 01765 607343
Profile: **FT:** Coarse; **WN:** Swale; **WT:** River (Moving) **W. Size:** 2000 Metres. **Location:** **Main Rd:** A19; **Rail:** Thirsk.
Ref: FH4569

SWALE (RIVER)

River Swale, Catterick, Richmond, **YORKSHIRE (NORTH)**, DL10, **England**.
Contact/s: Manager, Richmond Angling Ctre, 8 Temple Sq, Craven Gate, Richmond, DL10 4ED.
(T) 01748 822989
Mr Derek Taylor (Secretary), Leeds ADASA, 75 Stoney Rock Lane, Beckett St, Leeds, LS29 7TB.
(T) 0113 2482373
Profile: **FT:** Combination; **WN:** Swale; **WT:** River (Moving) **W. Size:** 22400 Metres.
Ref: FH4570

SWALE (RIVER)

River Swale, Baldersby, Skipton-on-Swale, Thirsk, **YORKSHIRE (NORTH)**, YO7, **England**.
Contact/s: **Mr Derek Stratton** (President), Thirsk Angling Ctre, 7 Sowerby Rd, Thirsk, YO7 1HR.
(T) 01845 524684 **(F)** 01845 525549
Profile: **FT:** Coarse; **WN:** Swale; **WT:** River (Moving) **W. Size:** 1600 Metres. **Location:** **Main Rd:** A61 Topcliffe to Skipton-Upon-Swale.
Ref: FH4571

SWALE (RIVER)

River Swale, Asenby, Thirsk, **YORKSHIRE (NORTH)**, YO7, **England**.
Contact/s: **Mr Derek Taylor** (Secretary), Leeds ADASA, 75 Stoney Rock Lane, Beckett St, Leeds, LS29 7TB.
(T) 0113 2482373
Profile: **FT:** Coarse; **WN:** Swale; **WT:** River (Moving) **W. Size:** 923 Metres. **Location:** **Nr. Rd:** A168; **Main Rd:** A168.
Ref: FH4572

SWALE (RIVER)

River Swale, Richmond, **YORKSHIRE (NORTH)**, DL10, **England**.
Contact/s: **Mr B Thackrey** (Secretary).
(T) 01423 866695
Mr G Hinds (Chairman).
(T) 01423 869647
Mr Norman Edward (Vice Chairman), 125 The Avenue, Starbeck, Harrogate, HG1 4QG.
(T) 01423 885399
Profile: **FT:** Coarse; **WN:** Swale; **WT:** River (Moving). **Location:** **Main Rd:** A1.
Ref: FH4573

SWALE (RIVER)

River Swale, Topcliffe Mill To Topcliffe Bridge, Thirsk, **YORKSHIRE (NORTH)**, YO7, **England**.
Contact/s: **Mr Derek Taylor** (Secretary), Leeds ADASA, 75 Stoney Rock Lane, Beckett St, Leeds, LS29 7TB.
(T) 0113 2482373
Profile: **FT:** Coarse; **WN:** Swale; **WT:** River (Moving) **W. Size:** 330 Metres. **Location:** **Main Rd:** A168.
Ref: FH4574

SWALE (RIVER)

River Swale, Myton Grange, Myton-on-Swale, York, **YORKSHIRE (NORTH)**, YO61, **England**.
Contact/s: **Mr Derek Taylor** (Secretary), Leeds ADASA, 75 Stoney Rock Lane, Beckett St, Leeds, LS29 7TB.
(T) 0113 2482373
Profile: **FT:** Coarse; **WN:** Swale; **WT:** River (Moving). **Location:** **Nr. Rd:** Myton-on-Swale; **Main Rd:** A19, Shipton to Thirsk Road.
Ref: FH4575

SWALE (RIVER)

River Swale, Fawdington, Cundall, York, **YORKSHIRE (NORTH)**, YO61, **England**.
Profile: **FT:** Coarse; **WN:** Swale; **WT:** River (Moving) **W. Size:** 2200 Metres. **Location:** **Main Rd:** A168, A1.
Ref: FH4576

SWALE (RIVER)

River Swale, Cundall Hall, Cundall, York, **YORKSHIRE (NORTH)**, YO61, **England**.
Contact/s: **Mr W Thorpe**, Hall Cottage, Swale Aveue, Cundall, Helperby, YO61 2RP.
(T) 01423 360678
Profile: **FT:** Coarse; **WN:** Swale (Weir to Fordington); **WT:** River (Moving) **W. Size:** 8046 Metres. **Location:** **Nr. Rd:** Helperby to Topcliffe; **Main Rd:** A168; **Rail:** Thirsk.
Ref: FH4577

SWALE (RIVER)

River Swale, Topcliffe Bridge, Topcliffe, Thirsk, **YORKSHIRE (NORTH)**, YO7, **England**.
Mr Ted Reeder (Water Bailiff), Black Bull Caravan Park, Topcliffe, Thirsk, Yorkshire (West), YO7 3PB.
(T) 01845 577900
Profile: **FT:** Coarse; **WN:** Swale; **WT:** River (Moving). **Location:** **Main Rd:** A1 to A19.
Ref: FH4578

SWALE (RIVER)

River Swale, Maunby, Thirsk, **YORKSHIRE (NORTH)**, YO7, **England**.
Contact/s: **John Sparkson**.
Profile: **FT:** Coarse; **WN:** Swale; **WT:** River (Moving). **Location:** **Nr. Rd:** Manuby to Bradford.
Ref: FH4579

SWALE (RIVER)

River Swale, Skipton-on-Swale, Thirsk, **YORKSHIRE (NORTH)**, YO7, **England**.
Contact/s: **Mr D Noble** (Secretary), Brighouse Angling Association, 1a Church Lane, Brighouse, Yorkshire (West), HD6 1AT.
(T) 01484 717034
Mr R P Charnock (Treasurer), 110 Dewsbury Rd, Brighouse, Yorkshire (West), HD6 3QB.
(T) 01422 378280
Profile: **FT:** Coarse; **WN:** Swale; **WT:** River (Moving) **W. Size:** 2000 Metres. **Location:** **Main Rd:** A61 between Ripon and Thirsk.
Ref: FH4580

SWALE (RIVER)

River Swale, Richmond, **YORKSHIRE (NORTH)**, DL10, **England**.
Contact/s: Fishery Manager.
(T) 01748 823767
Profile: **FT:** Coarse; **WN:** Swale; **WT:** River (Moving).
Ref: FH4581

SWALE (RIVER)

River Swale, Crakehill, Skipton-on-Swale, Thirsk, **YORKSHIRE (NORTH)**, YO7, **England**.
Contact/s: **Mr Derek Stratton** (President), Thirsk Angling Ctre, 7 Sowerby Rd, Thirsk, YO7 1HR.
(T) 01845 524684 **(F)** 01845 525549
Profile: **FT:** Coarse; **WN:** Swale; **WT:** River (Moving) **W. Size:** 1200 Metres. **Location:** **Main Rd:** A61 between Ripon and Thirsk.
Ref: FH4582

SWALE (RIVER)

River Swale, Brafferton, Helperby, York, **YORKSHIRE (NORTH)**, YO61, **England**.
Contact/s: **Mr F Marrison** (Hon Secretary), Helperby and Brafferton Angling Club, Gardeners Cottage, York Rd, Helperby, YO61 2PQ.
(T) 01423 360632
Profile: **FT:** Coarse; **WN:** Swale; **WT:** River (Moving). **Location:** **Main Rd:** Brafferton to Helperby.
Ref: FH4583

SWALE (RIVER)

River Swale, Great Langton, Northallerton, **YORKSHIRE (NORTH)**, DL7, **England**.
Contact/s: **Mr Peter Bennet**.
(T) 01748 824894
Profile: **FT:** Coarse; **WN:** Swale; **WT:** River (Moving) **W. Size:** 1600 Metres. **Location:** **Nr. Rd:** B6271; **Main Rd:** A1.
Ref: FH4584

SWALE (RIVER)

River Swale, Morton Bridge, Morton On Swale, Northallerton, **YORKSHIRE (NORTH)**, DL7, **England**.
Contact/s: Fisheries Information Contact, Morton Auto Services, Morton-on-Swale, Northallerton, Yorkshire (North), DL7 9RJ.
(T) 01609 775342
Mr Rex Dale.
(T) 01609 771117
Profile: **FT:** Combination; **WN:** Swale; **WT:** River (Moving) **W. Size:** 4800 Metres. **Location:** **Main Rd:** A684.
Ref: FH4585

SWALE (RIVER)

River Swale, Helperby, **YORKSHIRE (NORTH)**, YO61, **England**.
Contact/s: **Mr Derek Taylor** (Secretary), Leeds ADASA, 75 Stoney Rock Lane, Beckett St, Leeds, LS29 7TB.
(T) 0113 2482373
Mr Stuart Tate (Fishery Manager).
(T) 01347 821831
Profile: **FT:** Coarse; **WN:** Swale; **WT:** River (Moving). **Location:** **Nr. Rd:** Boroughbridge to Cundall; **Main Rd:** Helperby.
Ref: FH4586

SWALE (RIVER)

River Swale, Swale Lane, Catterick, Richmond, **YORKSHIRE (NORTH)**, DL10, **England**.
Mr Derek Taylor (Secretary), Leeds ADASA, 75 Stoney Rock Lane, Beckett St, Leeds, LS29 7TB.
(T) 0113 2482373
Profile: **FT:** Combination; **WN:** Swale; **WT:** River (Moving). **Location:** **Main Rd:** A1.
Ref: FH4587

SWALE PIT

Swale Pit, Woodbridge, Ipswich, **SUFFOLK**, IP, **England**.
Contact/s: Manager, The Rod and Gun Shop, 18 Church St, Woodbridge, Suffolk, IP12.
Profile: **FT:** Coarse; **WN:** Swale; **WT:** Gravel Pit (Still).
Ref: FH4588

SWAN LAKE

Swan Lake, Tansor, Oundle, Peterborough, **CAMBRIDGESHIRE**, PE8 5HN, **England**.
Contact/s: **Mr Tony Bridgefoot** (Owner).
(T) 01832 226042
Profile: **FT:** Coarse; **WN:** Swan; **WT:** Lake (Still); **F. Size:** 108 Acres; **W. Size:** 15 Acres. **Location:** **Nr. Rd:** Tansor to Fotheringhay; **Main Rd:** A605; **Rail:** Peterborough.
Ref: FH4589

SWAN LAKE

Swan Lake, Connah's Quay, Connahs Quay, **FLINTSHIRE**, CH5, **Wales**.
Contact/s: **Mr P Ryan** (Secretary), Connahs Quay District Angling Club, 118 Wepre Park, Connah's Quay, Clwyd, CH5 4HW.
Profile: **FT:** Coarse; **WN:** Swan; **WT:** Lake (Still) **W. Size:** 5 Acres.
Ref: FH4590

SWAN LAKE

Swan Lake, Howfield Lane, Chartham Hatch, Canterbury, **KENT**, **England**.
(W) www.midkentfish.demon.co.uk
Contact/s: **Mr Chris Logsdon** (Fisheries Manager), Mid Kent Fisheries, Chilham Water Mill, Mill Lane, Chilham, CT4 8EE.
(T) 01227 730668
(E) chilham@midkentfisheries.co.uk
Profile: **FT:** Coarse; **WN:** Swan; **WT:** Lake (Still); **F. Size:** 30 Acres; **W. Size:** 4 Acres. **Location:** **Nr. Rd:** Howfield Lane; **Main Rd:** A28; **Rail:** Canterbury.
Ref: FH4591

SWAN LAKE

Swan Lake, Culvert Rd, Wainfleet, Skegness, **LINCOLNSHIRE**, PE24 4NJ, **England**.
(W) www.swan-lake.co.uk
Contact/s: **Mr Will Cayton** (Fishery Manager), Swan Lake, Culvert Rd, Wainfleet, Skegness, Lincolnshire, PE24 4NJ.
(T) 01754 881456
(E) swan.lake@talk21.com
Profile: **FT:** Coarse; **WN:** Swan; **WT:** Lake (Still); **F. Size:** 5 Acres; **W. Size:** 2 Acres.
Location: **Nr. Rd:** Culvert Road; **Main Rd:** B1195; **Rail:** Thorpe Culvert.
Ref: FH4592

SWAN LODGE

Swan Lodge, Radcliffe, Manchester, **MANCHESTER (GREATER)**, M26, **England**.
Contact/s: **Mr Barry Gregory** (Owner), Elton Tackle, 47 Church Street West, Radcliffe, Manchester, M26 2SP.
(T) 0161 7245425
Profile: **FT:** Coarse; **WN:** Swan Lodge; **WT:** Lake (Still). Location: **Main Rd:** A56 North of Manchester.
Ref: FH4593

SWAN PIT POOL

Swan Pit Pool, Swan Pit Farm, Swan Pit, Gnosall, Stafford, **STAFFORDSHIRE**, ST20 0EE, **England**.
Contact/s: **G McMaster**.
(T) 01785 822221
N Buckley-Robins (Bailiff).
(T) 01785 823826
Profile: **FT:** Coarse; **WN:** Swan Pit; **WT:** Pool (Still) **W. Size:** 4 Acres. Location: **Nr. Rd:** Stafford to Newport Road; **Main Rd:** A518; **Rail:** Stafford.
Ref: FH4594

SWAN POOL

Swan Pool, Sandwell Valley Country Park, West Bromwich, **MIDLANDS (WEST)**, B70, **England**.
Mr Ken Duffell (Manager), Sandwell Valley Country Park, Salters Lane, West Bromwich, B71 4BG.
(T) 0121 5530220 (F) 0121 5259435
Profile: **FT:** Coarse; **WN:** Swan; **WT:** Pool (Still) **W. Size:** 15 Acres.
Ref: FH4595

SWAN VALLEY

Swan Valley, Darby Green, Sandhurst, **BERKSHIRE**, GU47, **England**.
Contact/s: **Mr Chris Hill** (Fishery Information), Academy Angling, 80 High St, Sandhurst, Berkshire, GU47 8ED.
(T) 01252 871452
Profile: **FT:** Coarse; **WN:** Swan Valley; **WT:** Lake (Still) **W. Size:** 10 Acres. Location: **Main Rd:** B3272 Reading Road; **Rail:** Sandhurst.
Ref: FH4596

SWANBOROUGH LAKES

Swanborough Lakes, Swanborough Farm, Iford, Lewes, **SUSSEX (EAST)**, BN7 3PF, **England**.
(W) www.fishing.co.uk
Contact/s: **Mr W Greenwood**.
(T) 01273 472232or477388
(E) will.green@brinternet.com
Profile: **FT:** Coarse; **WN:** Swanborough; **WT:** Lake (Still); **F. Size:** 17 Acres; **W. Size:** 12 Acres. Location: **Nr. Rd:** A27 turn off at Newhaven Road; **Main Rd:** A27; **Rail:** Lewes.
Ref: FH4597

SWANGEY LAKES

Swangey Lakes, West Carr, Attleborough, **NORFOLK**, NR17, **England**.
Contact/s: **Ray**.
(T) 01953 452907
Profile: **FT:** Coarse; **WN:** Swangey; **WT:** Lake (Still) **W. Size:** 20 Acres. Location: **Nr. Rd:** B1077; **Main Rd:** A11, Norwich to Attleborough.
Ref: FH4598

SWANLEY

Swanley, Knutsford, **CHESHIRE**, **England**.
(W) www.baymalton-anglingclub.org
Contact/s: **Mr Stewart Godber** (Club Secretary), 38 Edenfield Rd, Mobberley, Cheshire, WA16 7HE.
(T) 01565 872582
Profile: **FT:** Coarse; **WN:** Swanley; **WT:** Lake (Still); **F. Size:** 1 Acre; **W. Size:** 1 Acre.
Ref: FH4599

SWANSWATER FISHERY

Swanswater Fishery, Sauchieburn, Stirling, FK7 9QB, **Scotland**.
Contact/s: **Mr Alasdair Lohoar**.
(T) 01786 814805 (F) 01786 814805
(E) morna.swans@virgin.net
Ms Morna Lohoar.
(T) 01786 814805 (F) 01786 814805
Profile: **FT:** Game; **WN:** Swanswater; **WT:** Loch (Still); **F. Size:** 15 Acres; **W. Size:** 12 Acres. Location: **Main Rd:** A872 Glasgow road; **Rail:** Stirling.
Ref: FH4600

SWANTLEY LAKE

Swantley Lake, Swantley, Morecambe, **LANCASHIRE**, LA3, **England**.
Contact/s: Manager, Gerry's of Morecambe, 5-7 Parliament St, Morecambe, Lancashire, LA3 1RQ.
(T) 01524 422146 (F) 01524 422146
Profile: **FT:** Coarse; **WN:** Swantley; **WT:** Lake (Still) **W. Size:** 4 Acres. Location: **Nr. Rd:** Swantley.
Ref: FH4601

SWANTON MORLEY FISHERY

Swanton Morley Fishery, Dereham, **NORFOLK**, NR, **England**.
Contact/s: **Mr David Appleby** (Secretary), Dereham and District Angling Club, 6 Rump Cl, Swanton Morley, Dereham, NR20 4NH.
(T) 01362 637591 or 01362692975
Profile: **FT:** Coarse; **WN:** Swanton Morley Fishery; **WT:** Gravel Pit (Still) **W. Size:** 30 Acres. Location: **Nr. Rd:** B1147; **Main Rd:** A47; **Rail:** Norwich. £Fr
Ref: FH4602

SWARBORN (RIVER)

Swarborn (River), Wychnor Estate, Alrewas, **STAFFORDSHIRE**, **England**.
Contact/s: **Mr John Turner** (Hon Secretary), Prince Albert Angling Society, 15 Pexhill Drive, Macclesfield, Cheshire, SK10 3LP.
(T) 01625 422010
Profile: **FT:** Coarse; **WN:** Swarborn; **WT:** River (Moving) **W. Size:** 3000 Metres.
Location: **Main Rd:** A513.
Ref: FH4603

SWARKESTONE GRAVEL PITS

Swarkestone Gravel Pits, Swarkestone, Derby, **DERBYSHIRE**, DE, **England**.
Contact/s: Secretary, Derby Angling Association, 4 Randolphe Rd, Derby, Derbyshire.
Profile: **FT:** Coarse; **WN:** Swarkestone; **WT:** Gravel Pit (Still) **W. Size:** 67 Acres.
Location: **Nr. Rd:** A541 South West of Derby.
Ref: FH4604

SWAY LAKES

Sway Lakes, Barrows Lane, Sway, Lymington, **HAMPSHIRE**, SO41 6DD, **England**.
Contact/s: **Mr Richard Carpenter** (Manager).
(T) 01590 682010 (F) 01590 682341
Mr Shaun Clark (Owner).
(T) 01590 682010
Profile: **FT:** Coarse; **WN:** Sway; **WT:** Lake (Still); **F. Size:** 10 Acres; **W. Size:** 3 Acres.
Location: **Nr. Rd:** Barrows Lane; **Rail:** Sway.
Ref: FH4605

SWEENEYCLIFFE HOUSE FISHERY

Sweeneycliffe House Fishery, Coalport, Ironbridge, Telford, **SHROPSHIRE**, TF8, **England**.
Contact/s: **Mr Stan Harris** (Secretary), Telford Angling Association, 73 Burnside, Brookside, Telford, TF3 1DA.
(T) 01952 590605
Profile: **FT:** Combination; **WN:** Severn; **WT:** River (Moving) **W. Size:** 700 Metres.
Location: **Nr. Rd:** Coalport Road; **Main Rd:** A442; **Rail:** Telford Central.
Ref: FH4606

SWEETHEDGES FARM FISHERY

Sweethedges Farm Fishery, Allexton Rd, Stockerston, Oakham, **RUTLAND**, LE15 9AD, **England**.
(W) www.a1tourism.com
Contact/s: **Mr Brian Bray** (Owner).
(T) 01572 717398
Profile: **FT:** Coarse; **WN:** Sweethedges Farm Fishery; **WT:** Lake (Still); **F. Size:** 7 Acres; **W. Size:** 2 Acres. Location: **Nr. Rd:** Field Roas Allexton to Stockerston; **Main Rd:** A47; **Rail:** Oakham.
Ref: FH4607

SWEETHOPE LOUGHS

Sweethope Loughs, Lough House, Harle, Newcastle Upon Tyne, **TYNE AND WEAR**, NE19 2PN, **England**.
Contact/s: **Mr Steve Thompson** (Estate Manager).
(T) 01830 540349 (M) 07730 058815
Profile: **FT:** Game; **WN:** Sweethope Loughs; **WT:** Lake (Still) **W. Size:** 160 Acres.
Location: **Nr. Rd:** A68; **Main Rd:** A696; **Rail:** Hexham.
Ref: FH4608

SWILLINGTON PARK

Swillington Park, Garden Cottage, Coach Rd, Leeds, **YORKSHIRE (WEST)**, LS26 8QA, **England**.
Contact/s: **Mr Andy Cartwright** (Manager).
(T) 0113 2869129or07970037475
Profile: **FT:** Coarse; **WN:** Swillington Park; **WT:** Lake (Still). Location: **Nr. Rd:** Woodlesford to Swillington; **Main Rd:** A642; **Rail:** Woodlesford.
Ref: FH4609

SWIMBRIDGE POOL

Swimbridge Pool, Swimbridge, Barnstaple, **DEVON**, EX3, **England**.
Profile: **FT:** Coarse; **WN:** Swimbridge Pool; **WT:** Gravel Pit (Still). Location: **Main Rd:** A361.
Ref: FH4610

SWINDEN RESERVOIR

Swinden Reservoir, Burnley, **LANCASHIRE**, BB, **England**.
Contact/s: **Mr D Thornton** (Secretary), 13 Church St, Briercliffe, Burnley, BB10 2HU.
Mr Roy Rhodes (Conservation, Access and Recreation Manager), Rivington Water Treatment Works, Bolton Rd, Horwich, Bolton, BL6 7RN.
(T) 01204 664300
Profile: **FT:** Game; **WN:** Swinden; **WT:** Reservoir (Still).
Ref: FH4611

SWINSTY & FEWSTON

Swinsty And Fewston Reservoirs, Blubberhouses, Otley, **YORKSHIRE (WEST)**, LS21, **England**.
Contact/s: **Mr Gore Brown**.
(T) 01943 880568
Profile: **FT:** Game; **WN:** Swinsty and Fewston; **WT:** Reservoir (Still).
Ref: FH4612

SWINTON ESTATE TROUT FISHERY

Swinton Estate Trout Fishery, Healey, Ripon, **YORKSHIRE (NORTH)**, HG4, **England**.
Profile: **FT:** Game; **WN:** Leighton; **WT:** Reservoir (Still).
Ref: FH4613

SWISS FARM LAKE

Swiss Farm Lake, Henley-on-Thames, **OXFORDSHIRE**, RG9, **England**.
Contact/s: Mr Borlase (Fishery Manager).
(T) 01491 573419
Profile: FT: Coarse; **WN:** Swiss Farm Lake; **WT:** Lake (Still).
Ref: FH4614

SWISS VALLEY

Swiss Valley, Upper Lliedi, Llanelli, **CARMARTHENSHIRE**, SA15 3AP, **Wales**.
Contact/s: Mr David Bannister (Parks Open Spaces Manager).
(T) 01554 747500
Profile: FT: Game; **WN:** Upper Lliedi; **WT:** River (Moving).
Ref: FH4615

SWITHLAND RESERVOIR

Swithland Reservoir, Swithland, **LEICESTERSHIRE**, **England**.
Profile: FT: Coarse; **WN:** Swithland**WT:** Reservoir.
Ref: FH4616

SWYERS LAKE

Swyers Lake, Hounslow, London, **LONDON (GREATER)**, TW5 9, **England**.
Contact/s: Mrs V Sivyer (Secretary), Feltham Piscatorial Society, 96 Raleigh Rd, Feltham, Middlesex, TW13 4LP.
(T) 020 8909005
Profile: FT: Coarse; **WN:** Swyers; **WT:** Lake (Still).
Ref: FH4617

SYCAMORE FISHING LAKES

Sycamore Fishing Lakes, Skegness Rd, Burgh-Le-Marsh, Skegness, **LINCOLNSHIRE**, PE24 5LN, **England**.
Contact/s: Mr Jose Giraldez.
(T) 01754 811411
Mrs Joy Giraldez (Proprietor).
(T) 01754 811411 **(M)** 07940 393915
Profile: FT: Coarse; **WN:** Sycamore Complex; **WT:** Clay Pit (Still); **F. Size:** 15 Acres; **W. Size:** 6 Acres. **Location: Nr. Rd:** A158; **Main Rd:** A158; **Rail:** Skegness.
Ref: FH4618

SYDNOPE FISHERIES

Sydnope Fisheries, Sydnope Hall Farm, 2 Dales, Matlock, **DERBYSHIRE**, DE4 5LN, **England**.
Contact/s: Mr Antony Salt (Manager).
(T) 01629 732641
Profile: FT: Game; **WN:** Sydnope Fisheries; **WT:** Lake (Still) **W. Size:** 1 Acre. **Location: Nr. Rd:** Dales.
Ref: FH4619

SYKEHOUSE RESERVOIRS

Sykehouse Reservoirs, Goole, **HUMBERSIDE**, DN14, **England**.
Contact/s: Mr Tony Green (Manager), Peg Two Tackle, 27 King St, Thorne, Yorkshire (South), DN8 5AU.
(T) 01405 814417
Profile: FT: Coarse; **WN:** Sykehouse; **WT:** Reservoir (Still).
Ref: FH4620

SYON PARK FISHERY

Syon Park Fishery, Syon Park, Brentford, London, **LONDON (GREATER)**, TW8 8JF, **England**.
(W) www.alburyestate.com
Contact/s: Mr Andrew Allen (Manager).
(T) 020 85686354 **(F)** 020 85680936 **(M)** 07956 378138
(E) andysyonfishery@eggconnect.net
Profile: FT: Game; **WN:** Syon Park Fishery; **WT:** Lake (Still); **F. Size:** 200 Acres; **W. Size:** 6 Acres. **Location: Nr. Rd:** Park Road; **Main Rd:** A315; **Rail:** Syon.
Ref: FH4621

SYSTON PARK TROUT LAKE

Syston Park Trout Lake, Grantham, **LINCOLNSHIRE**, NG, **England**.
Contact/s: Mr Paul Clegg (Manager).
(T) 01400 250000or01400250378
Profile: FT: Game; **WN:** Syston Park; **WT:** Lake (Still) **W. Size:** 10 Acres.
Ref: FH4622

SYWELL RESERVOIR

Sywell Reservoir, Wellingborough, **NORTHAMPTONSHIRE**, NN, **England**.
Contact/s: Dave.
(T) 01933 674263
Mr Richard Blenkharn (Secretary).
(T) 01604 820380
Profile: FT: Coarse; **WN:** Sywell; **WT:** Reservoir (Still).
Ref: FH4623

T P POND DAM

T P Pond Dam, Gledholt Bank, Gledholt, Huddersfield, **YORKSHIRE (WEST)**, HD1, **England**.
Contact/s: Mr J D Jones (Bailiff), 16 Malvern Rd, Nemsome, Huddesfield, Yorkshire (West).
(T) 01484 308948
Profile: FT: Coarse; **WN:** TP Pond; **WT:** Pond (Still). **Location: Nr. Rd:** Gledholt Bank; **Main Rd:** A62.
Ref: FH4624

TABLEY MERE

Tabley Mere, Knutsford, **CHESHIRE**, WA16, **England**.
Contact/s: Mr Neil Jupp (Club Secretary), Lymm Angling Club, PO Box 350, Warrington, Cheshire, WA2 9FB.
(T) 01925 411774
Profile: FT: Coarse; **WN:** Tabley; **WT:** Mere (Still) **W. Size:** 47 Acres. **Location: Nr. Rd:** A556; **Main Rd:** M6, south junction 19.
Ref: FH4625

TABLEY MOAT

Tabley Moat, Knutsford, **CHESHIRE**, WA16, **England**.
Contact/s: Mr Neil Jupp (Club Secretary), Lymm Angling Club, PO Box 350, Warrington, Cheshire, WA2 9FB.
(T) 01925 411774
Profile: FT: Coarse; **WN:** Tabley; **WT:** Moat (Still). **Location: Nr. Rd:** A556; **Main Rd:** M6, south junction 19.
Ref: FH4626

TAF (RIVER)

River Taf, St Clears, Carmarthen, **CARMARTHENSHIRE**, SA3, **Wales**.
Contact/s: Mr David J Bryan (Hon Secretary), St Clears Angling Association, Madras Cottage, Laugharne, Carmarthen, Dyfed, SA33 4NU.
(T) 01994 427331
Profile: FT: Game; **WN:** Taf; **WT:** River (Moving) **W. Size:** 8000 Metres. **Location: Nr. Rd:** St Clears to Pont-y-Fenni Tunnel.
Ref: FH4627

TAF (RIVER)

River Taf, Carmarthen, **CARMARTHENSHIRE**, SA3, **Wales**.
Contact/s: Mr C J Jenkins (President).
(T) 01994 230456
Mr David J Bryan (Hon Secretary), St Clears Angling Association, Madras Cottage, Laugharne, Carmarthen, SA33 4NU.
(T) 01994 427331
Profile: FT: Combination; **WN:** Taf; **WT:** River (Moving) **W. Size:** 8000 Metres. **Location: Nr. Rd:** A40; **Main Rd:** A4777; **Rail:** Carmarthen.
Ref: FH4628

TAF (RIVER)

River Taf, Whitland, **CARMARTHENSHIRE**, SA34, **Wales**.
Contact/s: Mr Ithel Parri-Roberts (Club Treasurer), Whitland Post Office, King Edward St, Whitland, Carmarthenshire, SA34 0AA.
(T) 01994 240236
Mr J Seedley, 9 St John St, Whitland, Carmarthenshire.
(T) 01994 240800
Mr Peter Hunt (Treasurer), White House Mill, Lampeter Velfrey, Whitland, Carmarthenshire, SA34 0RB.
(T) 01834 831304
Profile: FT: Game; **WN:** Taf; **WT:** River (Moving) **W. Size:** 7200 Metres. **Location: Nr. Rd:** Church Bridge; **Main Rd:** A40.
Ref: FH4629

TAFF (RIVER)

River Taff, Cardiff, CF24, **Wales**.
Contact/s: Mr S G Allen (Hon Secretary), 37 Aberporth Rd, Gabalfa, Cardiff, CF4 2RX.
(T) 029 20618579
Profile: FT: Game; **WN:** Taff; **WT:** River (Moving) **W. Size:** 4800 Metres.
Ref: FH4630

TAFF (RIVER)

River Taff, Cardiff, CF, **Wales**.
Contact/s: Mr J S Wilmot (Hon Secretary), 4 Clydesmuir Rd, Tremorfa, Cardiff, CF2 2QA.
(T) 029 20460697
Profile: FT: Game; **WN:** Taff; **WT:** River (Moving) **W. Size:** 3200 Metres. **Location: Nr. Rd:** Llystalybont Gate to Hailey Park.
Ref: FH4631

TAFF (RIVER)

River Taff, Pontsticill, Merthyr Tydfil, **GLAMORGAN (VALE OF)**, CF48, **Wales**.
Contact/s: Mr Frank Thompson (Information Contact).
(T) 01685 386730
Mr Gary Davis (Information Contact).
(T) 01685 371981
Mr Nigel Morgan (Manager), 20 James St, Merthyr, Glamorgan (Vale of).
(T) 01685 377848
Mr Tony Rees (Club Treasurer), 13 Alexandra Avenue, Merthyr Tydfil, CF47 9AE.
(T) 01685 723520
Profile: FT: Game; **WN:** Taff; **WT:** River (Moving). **Location: Nr. Rd:** Pontsticill Reservoir to Quakers Yard Bridge.
Ref: FH4632

TAFF BARGOED

Taff Bargoed, Bedlinog Rd, Treharris, **GLAMORGAN (VALE OF)**, CF46, **Wales**.
Contact/s: Mr Alan Humphreys (Chairman), 15 Mary St, Bedlinog, Treharris, Glamorgan (Vale of), CF46 6RS.
(T) 01443 710777
Mr Chris Hutchins.
(T) 01443 710346
Mr E J Jones (Hon Secretary), 52 Hylton Trce, Bedlinog, Treharris, Glamorgan (Vale of), CF46 6RG.
(T) 01443 710515
Profile: FT: Game; **WN:** Taff Bargoed; **WT:** River (Moving) **W. Size:** 10400 Metres. **Location: Nr. Rd:** Bedlinog Road; **Rail:** Edwardsville.
Ref: FH4633

TALKIN TARN

Talkin Tarn, Brampton, **CUMBRIA**, CA8, **England**.
Contact/s: Mr Bob Irving (Club Secretary).
(T) 01228 592459
Profile: FT: Coarse; **WN:** Talkin; **WT:** Tarn (Still).
Ref: FH4634

TALLA RESERVOIR

Talla Reservoir, Tweedsmuir, Biggar, **LANARKSHIRE (SOUTH)**, ML12, **Scotland**.
Contact/s: Mrs Bell (Manager), Crook Inn, Tweedsmuir, Biggar, Lanarkshire, ML12 6QN.
(T) 01899 880272 **(F)** 01899 880294
Profile: FT: Game; **WN:** Talla; **WT:** Reservoir (Still).
Ref: FH4635

TALLINGTON FISHERY

Tallington Fishery, Tallington, Stamford, **LINCOLNSHIRE**, PE9, **England**.
Contact/s: Fishery Manager.
(T) 01780 740815

KEY: **(w)**: Web address **(T)**: Telephone number **(F)**: Fax Number **(M)**: Mobile Number **(E)**: E-mail Address
F. Size: Fishery Size **FT:** Fisherytype **WN:** WaterName/s **WT:** WaterType **W. Size:** Water Size **£Fr**: Free Fishing

Profile: FT: Coarse; WN: Tallington Fishery; WT: Lake (Still).
Ref: FH4636

TALT (LOUGH)

Lough Talt, Bunnyconnellan, **COUNTY MAYO**, **Ireland**.
Contact/s: Angling Officer, North Western Regional Fisheries Board, Ardnaree House, Abbey St, Ballina, County Mayo.
(T) 096 22623 (F) 096 70543
Profile: FT: Game; WN: Talt; WT: Lough (Still) W. Size: 1640 Acres. **Location:** Nr. Rd: Ballina to Tubercurry Road; Main Rd: R294.
Ref: FH4637

TALYBONT RESERVOIR

Talybont Reservoir, Brecon Beacons, Talybont, **CEREDIGION**, SY24, **Wales**.
Contact/s: **Mr C Hatch** (Area Manager), Hamdden Ltd, Sluvad Treatment Works, Llandegfedd Reservoir, New Inn, Pontypool, Gwent NP4 0TA.
(T) 01495 769281 (F) 01495 769283
Profile: FT: Game; WN: Talybont; WT: Reservoir (Still) W. Size: 318 Acres.
Ref: FH4638

TALYLLN LAKE FISHERY

Talylln Lake Fishery, Towyn, Abergele, **CONWY**, LL22, **Wales**.
Contact/s: **Mr T W Rolands** (General Manager), Tyn-y-Cornel Hotel, Talyllyn, Tywyn, Gwynedd, LL36 9AJ.
(T) 01654 782282
Profile: FT: Game; WN: Tallylln; WT: Lake (Still).
Ref: FH4639

TALYLLYN LAKE

Talyllyn Lake, Tywyn, **GWYNEDD**, LL36, **Wales**.
Contact/s: **Mr Edwyn Jones** (Fishery Officer), Tyn-y-Cornel Hotel, Talyllyn, Tywyn, Gwynedd, LL36 9AJ.
(T) 01654 782282 (F) 01654 782679
Profile: FT: Game; WN: Talylln; WT: Lake (Still) W. Size: 220 Acres. **Location:** Nr. Rd: B4405; Main Rd: A487; Rail: Tywyn.
Ref: FH4640

TAMAR (RIVER)

River Tamar, Launceston, **CORNWALL**, PL15, **England**.
Contact/s: **Mr F E Broad** (Farmer), Lower Dutson Farm, Launceston, Cornwall, PL15 9SP.
(T) 01566 776456 (F) 01566 776456
Profile: FT: Combination; WN: Tamar; WT: River (Moving) W. Size: 800 Metres.
Location: Nr. Rd: Holsworthy; Main Rd: A388, North; Rail: Liskeard.
Ref: FH4641

TAMAR (RIVER)

River Tamar, Milton Abbot, Tavistock, **DEVON**, PL19, **England**.
Contact/s: **Mr Bob Wellard** (Manager), Endsleigh Fishing Club, Endsleigh House, Milton Abbot, Tavistock, PL19 0PQ.
(T) 01822 870248
Ms Melanie Healy (Bookings Administrator), Endsleigh Fishing Club, 52 Strode Rd, Fulham, London, SW6 6BN.
(T) 020 76101982
Profile: FT: Game; WN: Tamar; WT: River (Moving) W. Size: 19200 Metres. **Location:** Nr. Rd: B3362; Main Rd: A386; Rail: Exeter.
Ref: FH4642

TAMAR (RIVER)

River Tamar, Arundell Arms Hotel, Lifton, **DEVON**, PL16, **England**.
Contact/s: **Ms Anne Voss-Bank** (Manager), Arundell Arms Hotel, Fore St, Lifton, Devon, PL16 0AA.
(T) 01566 784666 (F) 01566 784494
Profile: FT: Game; WN: Tamar; WT: Combination (Still & Moving) W. Size: 3 Acres. **Location:** Main Rd: A30.
Ref: FH4643

TAMAR LAKE (LOWER)

Tamar Lake (Lower), Rydon Lane, Exeter, **DEVON**, EX2 7HR, **England**.
Contact/s: Fishery Manager.
(T) 01392 443362
Ranger, South West Water, Leisure Services, Highercoombe Park, Lewdown, Okehampton EX20 4QT.
(T) 01288 321262
Profile: FT: Game; WN: Tamar (Lower); WT: Lake (Still) W. Size: 81 Acres.
Ref: FH4644

TAMAR LAKE (UPPER)

Tamar Lake (Upper), Kilkhampton, Bude, **CORNWALL**, EX23, **England**.
Contact/s: Manager, Clive's Tackle and Bait, 182 Exeter St, Plymouth, Devon, PL4 0NQ.
(T) 01752 228940 (F) 01752 603001
Mr Nick Laws (Manager), Summerlands Tackle, 3 Golf Links Rd, 16-20 Nelson Rd, Westward Ho!, Devon EX39 1LS.
(T) 01237 471291
Mr Reg England (Manager), Peninsula Coarse Fisheries, St Cleer Depot, Lewdown, Okehampton, Devon EX20 4QT.
(T) 01837 871565 (F) 01837 871534
Profile: FT: Coarse; WN: Upper Tamar; WT: Lake (Still) W. Size: 81 Acres. **Location:** Main Rd: A39 to Kirkhampton.
Ref: FH4645

TAME (RIVER)

River Tame, Royal George Mill Complex, Friezland, Greenfield, Oldham, **MANCHESTER (GREATER)**, OL, **England**.
Contact/s: **Mr Ian Baxter** (Membership Secretary), 6 Bagnall Cl, Uppermill, Oldham, Lancashire, OL3 6DW.
(T) 01457 875818 (M) 07973 345128
Profile: FT: Combination; WN: Tame; WT: River (Moving) W. Size: 300 Metres.
Location: Nr. Rd: Hole Road; Main Rd: A635 Ashton under Lyne to Holmfirth; Rail: Greenfield.
Ref: FH4646

TAME (RIVER)

Tame (River), Salters Bridge, Alrewas, **STAFFORDSHIRE**, **England**.
Contact/s: **Mr John Turner** (Hon Secretary), Prince Albert Angling Society, 15 Pexhill Drive, Macclesfield, Cheshire, SK10 3LP.
(T) 01625 422010
Profile: FT: Coarse; WN: Tame; WT: River (Moving) W. Size: 1200 Metres. **Location:** Nr. Rd: A38; Rail: Burton-upon-Trent.
Ref: FH4647

TAME VALLEY CANAL

Tame Valley Canal, Perry Park, Birmingham, **MIDLANDS (WEST)**, B, **England**.
Contact/s: **Mr Phil Brown**.
(T) 0121 6811276
Profile: FT: Coarse; WN: Tame Valley; WT: Canal (Still) W. Size: 400 Metres. **Location:** Nr. Rd: Birmingham to Walsall; Main Rd: A34, North.
Ref: FH4648

TAN LLAN

Tan Llan, Pontybodkin, Ffrith, Wrexham, LL11 5, **Wales**.
Contact/s: **Mr Roger Roberts**.
(T) 01352 770296
Profile: FT: Coarse; WN: Tan Llan; WT: Pool (Still) W. Size: 2 Acres. **Location:** Nr. Rd: A5104.
Ref: FH4649

TANAT (RIVER)

River Tanat, Llangedwyn, Oswestry, **SHROPSHIRE**, SY10, **England**.
Contact/s: **Mr G Greenham** (Manager), Green Inn, Llangedwyn, Oswestry, Shropshire, SY10 9JW.
(T) 01691 828234
Profile: FT: Game; WN: Tanat; WT: River (Moving) W. Size: 750 Metres.
Ref: FH4650

TANFIELD LAKE

Tanfield Lake, Tanfield, Ripon, **YORKSHIRE (NORTH)**, HG4, **England**.
Contact/s: **Mr Christopher Bourne-Arton** (Manager), Tan Field Lodge, West Tanfield, Ripon, Yorkshire (North), HG4 5LE.
(T) 01677 470385 (F) 01677 470385
Profile: FT: Game; WN: Tanfield; WT: Lake (Still) W. Size: 12 Acres. **Location:** Rail: Thirsk.
Ref: FH4651

TANHOUSE FARM LAKE

Tanhouse Farm Lake, Tanhouse Farm, Yate, Bristol, BS37 7QL, **England**.
Contact/s: **Mrs C E James** (Owner).
(T) 01454 228280
Profile: FT: Coarse; WN: Tanhouse Farm; WT: Lake (Still) W. Size: 5 Acres. **Location:** Nr. Rd: Bury Hill Lane; Main Rd: B4060; Rail: Yate.
Ref: FH4652

TANNERS DAM

Tanners Dam, Greenfield, Sadleworth, Oldham, **MANCHESTER (GREATER)**, OL, **England**.
Contact/s: **Mr Ian Baxter** (Membership Secretary), 6 Bagnall Cl, Uppermill, Oldham, Lancashire, OL3 6DW.
(T) 01457 875818 (M) 07973 345128
Profile: FT: Coarse; WN: Tanner's; WT: Mill Dam (Still) W. Size: 2 Acres. **Location:** Nr. Rd: A635; Main Rd: A635; Rail: Greenfield.
£Fr
Ref: FH4653

TANYARD FISHERIES

Tanyard Fisheries, Tanyard Lane, Furners Green, Danehill, Uckfield, **SUSSEX (EAST)**, TN22 3RL, **England**.
Contact/s: **Mr Bernie Brown**.
(T) 01825 791010 (F) 01825 791116
Mr Steve Boreham.
(T) 01825 791010 (F) 01825 791116
Profile: FT: Coarse; WN: Tanyard Fisheries; WT: Lake (Still); F. Size: 20 Acres; W. Size: 8 Acres. **Location:** Nr. Rd: Tanyard Lane; Main Rd: A22; Rail: Haywards Heath.
Ref: FH4654

TAN-Y-COED FISHERY

Tan-Y-Coed Fishery, Pentre Cwrt, Newcastle Emlyn, **CARMARTHENSHIRE**, SA38, **Wales**.
(W) www.fishing-in-wales.co.uk/llandysul-aa/beat13a
Contact/s: **Mr Artie Jones** (Hon Secretary), Llandysul Angling Association, Glas-y-Dorlan, Llyn-y-Fran Rd, Llandysul, SA44 4JW.
(T) 01559 362317
Profile: FT: Game; WN: Teifi; WT: River (Moving). **Location:** Nr. Rd: A486 Pentrecwrt to Llandsul Road.
Ref: FH4655

TANYGRISIAU RESERVOIR

Tanygrisiau Reservoir, Blaenau Ffestiniog, **GWYNEDD**, LL41, **Wales**.
Contact/s: **Mr F W Roberts** (Manager), Fishing Tackle, 32 Church St, Blaenau Ffestiniog, Gwynedd, LL41 3HD.
(T) 01766 830607
Profile: FT: Game; WN: Tanygrisiau; WT: Reservoir (Still) W. Size: 95 Acres.
Ref: FH4656

TAN-Y-MYNYDD TROUT LAKES

Tan-Y-Mynydd Trout Lakes, Moelfre, Abergele, **CONWY**, LL22 9RF, **Wales**.
Contact/s: **Mr Mike Watkins** (Manager).
(T) 01745 823691
Profile: FT: Game; WN: Tan-y-Mynydd; WT: Lake (Still). **Location:** Nr. Rd: B5381 to St Asaph; Main Rd: A55 to Abergele.
Ref: FH4657

TAR (RIVER)

River Tar, Forteuse Cross, Exeter, **DEVON**, EX6 6, **England**.
Contact/s: **Mr Roddy Rae**, Half Stone Sporting Agency, 6 Hescane Park, Cheriton Bishop, Exeter, EX6 6JP.
(T) 01647 24643 **(F)** 01647 24643
Profile: **FT:** Game; **WN:** Tar; **WT:** River (Moving) **W. Size:** 1600 Metres. Location: **Nr. Rd:** Forteuse Cross.
Ref: FH4658

TAR STREAM

Tar Stream, Clonmel, **COUNTY TIPPERARY**, **Ireland**.
Contact/s: **Mr Andrew Ryan** (Manager), Clonanav Angling Ctre, Ballymacabry, Clonmel, County Tipperary, Ireland.
(T) 052 36141
Profile: **FT:** Game; **WN:** Tar; **WT:** Stream (Moving).
Ref: FH4659

TARGET LAKE

Target Lake, Barton-upon-Humber, **LINCOLNSHIRE (NORTH)**, DN18, **England**.
Contact/s: Fishery Manager.
(T) 01482 634154
Profile: **FT:** Coarse; **WN:** Target; **WT:** Lake (Still).
Ref: FH4660

TARVIE LOCHS FISHERY

Tarvie Lochs Fishery, Inchdrean, Tarvie, Strathpeffer, **HIGHLAND**, IV14 9EJ, **Scotland**.
Contact/s: **Mr Gerry Breau** (Manager).
(T) 01997 421250 **(F)** 01997 421250
Profile: **FT:** Game; **WN:** Tarvie; **WT:** Loch (Still); **F. Size:** 45 Acres. Location: **Nr. Rd:** Inverness to Ullapool Road; **Main Rd:** A835; **Rail:** Garve.
Ref: FH4661

TASWOOD LAKES

Taswood Lakes Fish Farm And Fishery, Mill Rd, Flordon, Norwich, **NORFOLK**, NR15 1LX, **England**.
Contact/s: **Mr Richard Ellis** (Owner).
(T) 01508 470919
Mrs S Ellis (Owner).
(T) 01508 470919
Profile: **FT:** Coarse; **WN:** Taswood Lakes Fish Farm And Fishery; **WT:** Lake (Still). Location: **Nr. Rd:** Fork right to Flordon, left to Tasburgh; **Main Rd:** A140, Norwich to Newton Flotman.
Ref: FH4662

TATTERSHALL LEISURE PARK

Tattershall Leisure Park, Sleaford Rd, Tattershall, Lincoln, **LINCOLNSHIRE**, LN4 4LR, **England**.
Contact/s: **Mr G Faulkner** (Site Manager).
(T) 01526 343193 **(F)** 01526 343008
Profile: **FT:** Coarse; **WN:** Bain; **WT:** Lake (Still); **F. Size:** 45 Acres; **W. Size:** 28 Acres. Location: **Nr. Rd:** A153; **Main Rd:** A153; **Rail:** Lincoln.
Ref: FH4663

TATTON MERE

Tatton Mere, Tatton Park, Knutsford, **CHESHIRE**, WA16 6QN, **England**.
(W) www.tattonpark.org.uk
Contact/s: **S.D Jones** (Ranger).
(T) 01625 534400 **(F)** 01625 534403
(E) tatton@cheshire.gov.uk
Profile: **FT:** Coarse; **WN:** Tatton; **WT:** Mere (Still). Location: **Nr. Rd:** A556; **Main Rd:** M6; **Rail:** Knutsford.
Ref: FH4664

TAUNTON AND BRIDGWATER CANAL

Taunton And Bridgwater Canal, Boat And Anchor, Bridgwater, **SOMERSET**, TA, **England**.
Contact/s: Manager, Somerset Angling, 74 Bath Rd, Bridgwater, Somerset, TA6 4PL.
(T) 01278 431777or786934
Profile: **FT:** Coarse; **WN:** Taunton and Bridgwater; **WT:** Canal (Still).
Ref: FH4665

TAUNTON ROAD PONDS

Taunton Road Ponds, Taunton Rd, Bridgwater, **SOMERSET**, TA, **England**.
Contact/s: **Mr Phil Dodds**.
(T) 01278 444145
Profile: **FT:** Coarse; **WN:** Taunton Road; **WT:** Pond (Still) **W. Size:** 4 Acres. Location: **Nr. Rd:** A38 Taunton Road; **Main Rd:** A38.
Ref: FH4666

TAUNTON TO BRIDGWATER CANAL

Taunton To Bridgwater Canal, Huntworth Bridge, Bridgwater, **SOMERSET**, TA7, **England**.
Contact/s: **Mr Phil Dodds**.
(T) 01278 444145
Profile: **FT:** Coarse; **WN:** Taunton to Bridgwater; **WT:** Canal (Still). Location: **Nr. Rd:** Huntworth Bridge; **Main Rd:** A38 to Bridgwater.
Ref: FH4667

TAVERHAM

Taverham, Ringland Lane, Old Costessey, Norwich, **NORFOLK**, NR, **England**.
(W) www.rmcangling.co.uk
Contact/s: **Mr Ian Welch** (Angling Manager), RMC Angling, The Square, Lightwater, Surrey, GU18 5SS.
(T) 01276 453300 **(F)** 01276 456611
(E) info@rmcangling.co.uk
Profile: **FT:** Coarse; **WN:** Taverham; **WT:** Combination (Still & Moving) **W. Size:** 9 Acres. Location: **Nr. Rd:** Ringland Lane; **Main Rd:** A47.
Ref: FH4668

TAVERHAM MILLS FISHERY

Taverham Mills Fishery, Taverham Mills Fishing Lodge, Costessey Rd, Taverham, Norwich, **NORFOLK**, NR8 6TA, **England**.
Contact/s: **Ms Jo Cottingham** (Recreational Manager), Taverham Mills Fishing Lodge, Costessey Rd, Taverham, Norfolk, NR8 6TA.
(T) 01603 861014 **(F)** 01603 861014
(E) jcottingham@anglianwater.co.uk
Profile: **FT:** Coarse; **WT:** Combination (Still & Moving); **F. Size:** 60 Acres; **W. Size:** 20 Acres. Location: **Nr. Rd:** Costessey Road; **Main Rd:** A1067; **Rail:** Norwich. **£Fr**
Ref: FH4669

TAVISTOCK TROUT FISHERY

Tavistock Trout Fishery, Parkwood Rd, Tavistock, **DEVON**, PL19 9JW, **England**.
(W) www.tavistocktroutfishery.co.uk
Contact/s: **Ms Abigail Underhill** (Trout Farmer).
(T) 01822 615441 **(F)** 01822 615401
(E) abigail@tavistocktroutfishery.co.uk
Profile: **FT:** Game; **WN:** Tavistock Trout Fishery; **WT:** Lake (Still); **F. Size:** 40 Acres; **W. Size:** 4 Acres. Location: **Nr. Rd:** Parkwood Road; **Main Rd:** A386; **Rail:** Gunnislake.
Ref: FH4670

TAVY (RIVER)

River Tavy, Tavistock, **DEVON**, PL19, **England**.
Contact/s: Manager, Barkells, 15 Duke St, Tavistock, Devon, PL19 0BA.
(T) 01822 612198
Mr D L Owen (Secretary), Plymouth and District Freshwater Angling Association, 39 Burnett Rd, Crownhill, Plymouth, PL6 5BH.
(T) 01752 705033
Profile: **FT:** Game; **WN:** Tavy; **WT:** River (Moving).
Ref: FH4671

TAW (RIVER)

River Taw, Barnstaple, **DEVON**, EX3, **England**.
Contact/s: **Mr Gerry Tyzack** (Manager), The Kingfisher Tackle Shop, 22 Castle St, Barnstaple, Devon, EX31 1DR.
(T) 01271 344919
Profile: **FT:** Game; **WN:** Taw; **WT:** River (Moving).
Ref: FH4672

TAW (RIVER)

River Taw, Tawbridge, Crediton, **DEVON**, EX17, **England**.
Profile: **FT:** Game; **WN:** Taw; **WT:** River (Moving).
Ref: FH4673

TAW FISHING CLUB

Taw Fishing Club, Coldridge, Crediton, **DEVON**, EX17, **England**.
Contact/s: **Mr J D V Michie** (Hon Secretary).
Profile: **FT:** Game; **WN:** Taw; **WT:** River (Moving) **W. Size:** 4900 Metres. Location: **Rail:** Eggesford.
Ref: FH4674

TAWE (RIVER)

River Tawe, Pontardawe, Swansea, SA8, **Wales**.
Contact/s: **Mr Mike Matthews** (Hon Secretary), 32 Farm Rd, Briton Ferry, Neath, Glamorgan (Vale of), SA11 2TA.
(T) 01639 632070
Profile: **FT:** Game; **WN:** Tawe; **WT:** River (Moving). Location: **Nr. Rd:** Pontardawe Road Bridge.
Ref: FH4675

TAWE (RIVER)

River Tawe, Ystradgynlais, Swansea, SA9, **Wales**.
Contact/s: **Mr John Glynn Davis** (Manager), Fieldsports, 3-7 Station Rd, Ystradgynlais, Wales, SA9 1NT. **(F)** 01639 843194
Profile: **FT:** Game; **WN:** Tawe; **WT:** River (Moving).
Ref: FH4676

TAX MERE

Tax Mere, Sandbach, **CHESHIRE**, CW11, **England**.
Contact/s: **Mr Ernie Shufflebottom**.
(T) 0161 9695210
Mr Stewart Godber, 38 Edenfield Rd, Mobberley, Knutsford, Cheshire, WA16 7HE.
(T) 01565 872582
Profile: **FT:** Coarse; **WN:** Tax Mere; **WT:** Lake (Still) **W. Size:** 9 Acres. Location: **Nr. Rd:** A50; **Main Rd:** M6, junction 17, A534. **£Fr**
Ref: FH4677

TAY (RIVER)

River Tay, Dunkeld, **PERTH AND KINROSS**, PH8, **Scotland**.
Contact/s: **Mr Archie Steele** (Secretary), Dunkeld and Birnam Angling Association, 21 Willow Bank, Birnam, Perth and Kinross.
(T) 01350 727428
Profile: **FT:** Game; **WN:** Tay; **WT:** River (Moving) **W. Size:** 8000 Metres. Location: **Nr. Rd:** A9; **Main Rd:** A9; **Rail:** Birnam.
Ref: FH4678

TAYLORS POOL

Taylors Pool, Scholar Green, Stoke-on-Trent, **STAFFORDSHIRE**, ST7, **England**.
Profile: **FT:** Coarse; **WN:** Taylors; **WT:** Pool (Still). Location: **Nr. Rd:** Scholars Green; **Main Rd:** Station Road.
Ref: FH4679

TEARDROP LAKES

Teardrop Lakes, Loughton Lakes, Milton Keynes, **BUCKINGHAMSHIRE**, MK, **England**.
Profile: **FT:** Coarse; **WN:** Teardrop; **WT:** Lake (Still) **W. Size:** 6 Acres.
Ref: FH4680

TEASDALE POND

Teasdale Pond, Tursdale, Coxhoe, Durham, **COUNTY DURHAM**, DH6, **England**.
Contact/s: **Mr Barry Hignett** (Secretary), Ferryhill and District Angling Club, 74 Grasmere Rd, Garden Farm Estate, Chester-le-Street, County Durham.

KEY: **(w)**: Web address **(T)**: Telephone number **(F)**: Fax Number **(M)**: Mobile Number **(E)**: E-mail Address
F. Size: Fishery Size **FT:** Fisherytype **WN:** WaterName/s **WT:** WaterType **W. Size:** Water Size **£Fr**: Free Fishing

(T) 0191 3883557
Profile: **FT:** Coarse; **WN:** Teasdale; **WT:** Pond (Still).
Ref: FH4681

TEDDINGTON LOCK

Teddington Lock, Teddington, London, **LONDON (GREATER)**, TW11, **England**.
Contact/s: **Mr Mac McEndoo**, Acton Angling Ctre, 185 Old Oak Rd, London, W3 7HH.
(T) 020 87433381 (F) 020 87434482
Profile: **FT:** Coarse; **WN:** Thames; **WT:** River (Moving) **W. Size:** 800 Metres.
Ref: FH4682

TEES (RIVER)

River Tees, Thornaby, Stockton-on-Tees, **CLEVELAND**, TS17, **England**.
Contact/s: **Mr Frank Flynn** (Owner), F Flynn Tackle Shop, 12 Varo Terr, Stockton-on-Tees, Cleveland, TS18 1 JY.
(T) 01642 676473
Profile: **FT:** Coarse; **WN:** Tees; **WT:** River (Moving).
Ref: FH4683

TEES (RIVER)

River Tees, Low Dinsdale, Darlington, **COUNTY DURHAM**, DL2, **England**.
Contact/s: **Mr Ron Thompson** (Secretary), 25 Endsleigh Drive, Acklam, Middlesbrough, TS5 4RG.
(T) 01642 863067
Profile: **FT:** Combination; **WN:** Tees; **WT:** River (Moving) **W. Size:** 2800 Metres.
Location: **Nr. Rd:** A1 Girsby to Neasham; **Main Rd:** Hurworth.
Ref: FH4684

TEES (RIVER)

River Tees, Durham Bank, Neasham, Darlington, **COUNTY DURHAM**, DL2, **England**.
Profile: **FT:** Combination; **WN:** Tees; **WT:** River (Moving). **Location:** **Nr. Rd:** Village green; **Main Rd:** A167. £Fr
Ref: FH4685

TEES (RIVER)

River Tees, Middleton One Row, Darlington, **COUNTY DURHAM**, DL2, **England**.
Profile: **FT:** Combination; **WN:** Tees; **WT:** River (Moving).
Ref: FH4686

TEES (RIVER)

River Tees, Barnard Castle, **COUNTY DURHAM**, DL12, **England**.
Profile: **FT:** Game; **WN:** Tees; **WT:** River (Moving). **Location:** **Nr. Rd:** Abbey Bridge Wood; **Main Rd:** A66, A688.
Ref: FH4687

TEES (RIVER)

River Tees, Gainsford, Piercebridge, Darlington, **COUNTY DURHAM**, DL2, **England**.
Contact/s: Manager, Raby Estate, Middleton, Teesdale.
(T) 01833 660207
Profile: **FT:** Combination; **WN:** Tees; **WT:** River (Moving). **Location:** **Main Rd:** A67.
Ref: FH4688

TEES (RIVER)

River Tees, Middleton-In-Teesdale, Barnard Castle, **COUNTY DURHAM**, DL12, **England**.
Profile: **FT:** Combination; **WN:** Tees; **WT:** River (Moving). **Location:** **Main Rd:** A19.
Ref: FH4689

TEES (RIVER)

River Tees, Middleton-one-Row, Middleton-St-George, Darlington, **COUNTY DURHAM**, DL17, **England**.
Contact/s: **Mr Barry Hignett** (Secretary), Ferryhill and District Angling Club, 74 Grasmere Rd, Garden Farm Estate, Chester-le-Street, County Durham.
(T) 0191 3883557
Mr S Kent (Membership Secretary), 4 Belsay Cl, Ferryhill, County Durham, DL17 8SX.
Profile: **FT:** Combination; **WN:** Tees; **WT:** River (Moving) **W. Size:** 800 Metres.
Location: **Main Rd:** A67; **Rail:** Dinsdale.
Ref: FH4690

TEES (RIVER)

River Tees, Hurworth Pl, Darlington, **COUNTY DURHAM**, DL2, **England**.
Profile: **FT:** Combination; **WN:** Tees; **WT:** River (Moving). **Location:** **Nr. Rd:** Skerne Mouth and Croft Bridge; **Main Rd:** A167 South of Darlington. £Fr
Ref: FH4691

TEES (RIVER)

River Tees, Blackwell, Darlington, **COUNTY DURHAM**, DL, **England**.
Contact/s: **Mr Clive Cloke** (Secretary).
(T) 01325 481818
Profile: **FT:** Coarse; **WN:** Tees (Blackwell); **WT:** River (Moving) **W. Size:** 4800 Metres.
Ref: FH4692

TEES (RIVER)

River Tees, Stone Bridge, Barnard Castle, **COUNTY DURHAM**, DL12, **England**.
Profile: **FT:** Combination; **WN:** Tees; **WT:** River (Moving). **Location:** **Nr. Rd:** Stone Bridge to Thorngate footbridge. £Fr
Ref: FH4693

TEES (RIVER)

River Tees, Barforth Wath, Gainford, Darlington, **COUNTY DURHAM**, DL2, **England**.
Contact/s: Fishery Contact, Gainford Post Office, Gainford, Darlington, County Durham.
(T) 01325 730201
Profile: **FT:** Combination; **WN:** Tees; **WT:** River (Moving). **Location:** **Nr. Rd:** St Mary's Well; **Main Rd:** A67.
Ref: FH4694

TEES (RIVER)

River Tees, Neasham, Darlington, **COUNTY DURHAM**, DL2, **England**.
Contact/s: **Mr Steve Maitland** (Manager (Anglers Services)).
(T) 01429 274844
Profile: **FT:** Coarse; **WN:** Tees; **WT:** River (Moving).
Ref: FH4695

TEES (RIVER)

River Tees, Croft On Tees, Darlington, **COUNTY DURHAM**, DL2, **England**.
Contact/s: **Mr Frank Flynn**, 12 Varo Trce, Stockton on Tees.
(T) 01642 676473
Mr Lol Bulmer.
(T) 01642 671531
Profile: **FT:** Combination; **WN:** Tees; **WT:** River (Moving). **Location:** **Main Rd:** A167, South of Darlington.
Ref: FH4696

TEES (RIVER)

River Tees, Egglestone, Middleton-In-Teesdale, Barnard Castle, **COUNTY DURHAM**, DL12, **England**.
(W) www.bishopaucklandanddistrictanglingclub.com
Contact/s: **Mr John Winter** (Secretary), Bishop Auckland and District Angling Club, 7 Royal Gr, Crook, County Durham, DL15 9ER.
(T) 01388 762538 (F) 01388 767762
(E) bacc@talk21.com
Profile: **FT:** Combination; **WN:** Tees; **WT:** River (Moving) **W. Size:** 4800 Metres.
Location: **Main Rd:** A167, A68; **Rail:** Bishop Auckland.
Ref: FH4697

TEES (RIVER)

River Tees, Yarm, **TYNE AND WEAR**, TS15, **England**.
Contact/s: **Mr Frank Flynn**, 12 Varo Trce, Stockton on Tees.
(T) 01642 676473
Profile: **FT:** Combination; **WN:** Tees; **WT:** River (Moving) **W. Size:** 4800 Metres.
Location: **Main Rd:** A19.
Ref: FH4698

TEES (RIVER)

River Tees, Yarm Road Bridge, Yarm, **TYNE AND WEAR**, TS15, **England**.
Contact/s: Manager.
(T) 01642 787969
Profile: **FT:** Coarse; **WN:** Tees; **WT:** River (Moving) **W. Size:** 1600 Metres. **Location:** **Nr. Rd:** Yarm High Street; **Main Rd:** A67. £Fr
Ref: FH4699

TEGGSNOSE RESERVOIR

Teggsnose Reservoir, Suttons Lane End, Langley, Macclesfield, **CHESHIRE**, SK11, **England**.
Contact/s: **Mr M Bowyer** (Secretary), 7 Ullswater, Macclesfield, Cheshire.
(T) 01625 434806
Mr Peter Sharples (Conservation, Access and Recreation Manager), North West Water Ltd, Woodhead Rd, Tintwhistle, Hadfiled via Hyde, SK14 7HR.
(T) 01457 864187
Profile: **FT:** Coarse; **WN:** Teggsnose; **WT:** Reservoir (Still).
Ref: FH4700

TEGLAN LAKE

Teglan Lake, Lampeter, **CEREDIGION**, SA48 8, **Wales**.
Contact/s: **Mr Mark Owen**, Ystryd Y Llun, Crilau Aeron, Lampeter, SA48 8DA.
(T) 01570 471115
Profile: **FT:** Coarse; **WN:** Teglan; **WT:** Lake (Still) **W. Size:** 2 Acres.
Ref: FH4701

TEIFI (RIVER

River Teifi, Faerdre Fawr, Llandysul, **CEREDIGION**, SA44 4PB, **Wales**.
Contact/s: **Mr Mike Grayson** (Manager).
(T) 01559 362177
Profile: **FT:** Game; **WN:** Teifi; **WT:** River (Moving) **W. Size:** 800 Metres.
Ref: FH4702

TEIFI (RIVER)

River Teifi, Newcastle Emlyn, **CARMARTHENSHIRE**, SA38, **Wales**.
Contact/s: **Mr Artie Jones** (Hon Secretary), Llandysul Angling Association, Glas-y-Dorlan, Llyn-y-Fran Rd, Llandysul, SA44 4JW.
(T) 01559 362317
Profile: **FT:** Game; **WN:** Teifi; **WT:** River (Moving) **W. Size:** 46400 Metres. **Location:** **Nr. Rd:** Newcastle Emlyn to Llanfair Clydogau.
Ref: FH4703

TEIFI (RIVER)

River Teifi, Llanybydder, **CARMARTHENSHIRE**, SA40, **Wales**.
Contact/s: **Mr Andrew Morgan** (Secretary).
(T) 01570 480980dayticketsonly
Mr Bill Wilkins (Hon Secretary), Maes-y-Fedw, Llanybydder, Carmarthenshire, SA40 9UG.
(T) 01570 480038
Mr D Morgan.
(T) 01570 480643
Profile: **FT:** Game; **WN:** Teifi; **WT:** River (Moving) **W. Size:** 8000 Metres.
Ref: FH4704

TEIFI (RIVER)

River Teifi, Llanybydder, **CARMARTHENSHIRE**, SA40, **Wales**.
Contact/s: **Mr D A Morgan**.
Profile: **FT:** Game; **WN:** Teifi; **WT:** River (Moving) **W. Size:** 4000 Metres. **Location:** **Rail:** Carmarthen.
Ref: FH4705

TEIFI (RIVER)

River Teifi, Cardigan, **CEREDIGION**, SA43, **Wales**.
Contact/s: **Mr Brian Gore** (Hon Secretary), Cwm Broch, Bribwll, Cardigan, Carmarthenshire, SA43 3DG.
(T) 01239 841332
Profile: **FT:** Game; **WN:** Teifi; **WT:** River (Moving) **W. Size:** 24000 Metres.
Ref: FH4706

TEIFI (RIVER)

River Teifi, Neuaddlas, Tregaron, **CEREDIGION**, SY25, **Wales**.
Contact/s: **Mr Will Davis** (Manager), Neuaddlas Country Guest House, Neuaddlas, Tregaron, Ceredigion, SY25 6LG.
(T) 01974 298905 **(F)** 01974 298905
Profile: **FT:** Game; **WN:** Teifi; **WT:** River (Moving).
Ref: FH4707

TEIFI (RIVER)

River Teifi, Llandysul, **CEREDIGION**, SA44, **Wales**.
Contact/s: **Mr Artie Jones** (Hon Secretary), Llandysul Angling Association, Glas-y-Dorlan, Llyn-y-Fran Rd, Llandysul, SA44 4JW.
(T) 01559 362317
Profile: **FT:** Game; **WN:** Teifi; **WT:** River (Moving) **W. Size:** 49500 Metres. **Location:** **Rail:** Carmarthen.
Ref: FH4708

TEIFI (RIVER)

River Teifi, Lampeter, **CEREDIGION**, SA48, **Wales**.
Contact/s: **Mr Alan Williams** (Manager), Lampeter Angling, 57 Bridge St, Lampeter, Carmarthenshire, SA48 7.
(T) 01570 422985
Profile: **FT:** Game; **WN:** Teifi; **WT:** River (Moving).
Ref: FH4709

TEIFI (RIVER)

River Teifi, Tregaron, **CEREDIGION**, SY25, **Wales**.
Contact/s: **Mr M J Morgan Obe** (Hon Secretary), Ivegoran Angling Association, Swyn Teifi, Pontrhydfendigaid, Ystrad Meurig, Carmarthenshire, SY25 6EF.
(T) 01974 831316 **(F)** 01974 831316
Profile: **FT:** Game; **WN:** Teifi; **WT:** River (Moving) **W. Size:** 27200 Metres.
Ref: FH4710

TEIFI (RIVER)

Teiffi (River), Dol-Llan Farm, Llandysul, **CEREDIGION**, **Wales**.
Contact/s: **Mr John Turner** (Hon Secretary), Prince Albert Angling Society, 15 Pexhill Drive, Macclesfield, Cheshire, SK10 3LP.
(T) 01625 422010
Profile: **FT:** Game; **WN:** Teifi; **WT:** River (Moving) **W. Size:** 1000 Metres. **Location:** **Nr. Rd:** B4476; **Main Rd:** A475.
Ref: FH4711

TEIFI (RIVER)

Teifi (River), Brongest & Coedmore Hall, Lampeter, **CEREDIGION**, **Wales**.
Contact/s: **Mr John Turner** (Hon Secretary), Prince Albert Angling Society, 15 Pexhill Drive, Macclesfield, Cheshire, SK10 3LP.
(T) 01625 422010
Profile: **FT:** Game; **WN:** Teifi; **WT:** River (Moving) **W. Size:** 500 Metres. **Location:** **Nr. Rd:** A482; **Rail:** Llandovery.
Ref: FH4712

TEIFI POOLS

Teifi Pools, Ystrad Meurig, **CEREDIGION**, SY25, **Wales**.
Contact/s: **Mr M J Morgan Obe** (Hon Secretary), Ivegoran Angling Association, Swyn Teifi, Pontrhydfendigaid, Ystrad Meurig, Carmarthenshire, SY25 6EF.
(T) 01974 831316 **(F)** 01974 831316
Profile: **FT:** Game; **WN:** Teifi; **WT:** Pool (Still).
Ref: FH4713

TEIFI VALLEY FISH

Teifi Valley Fish, Ty Mawr, Llanybydder, **CARMARTHENSHIRE**, SA40 9RE, **Wales**.
Contact/s: **Mr Peter Jarrams**.
(T) 01570 480789
Profile: **FT:** Combination; **WN:** Teifi Valley Fish; **WT:** Lake (Still).
Ref: FH4714

TEIFY POOLS FISHERY

Teify Pools Fishery, Tregaron, **CEREDIGION**, SY25 6EF, **Wales**.
Contact/s: **Mr M J Morgan Obe** (Hon Secretary), Ivegoran Angling Association, Swyn Teifi, Pontrhydfendigaid, Ystrad Meurig, Carmarthenshire, SY25 6EF.
(T) 01974 831316 **(F)** 01974 831316
Profile: **FT:** Game; **WN:** Teify; **WT:** River (Moving); **F. Size:** 120 Acres; **W. Size:** 25500 Metres. **Location:** **Nr. Rd:** Mountain Road; **Rail:** Aberystwyth.
Ref: FH4715

TEIGN

Teign, Exeter, **DEVON**, EX, **England**.
Contact/s: **Mr John Getliff** (Secretary), 22 The Square, Chagford, Devon.
Profile: **FT:** Game; **WN:** Teign; **WT:** River (Moving) **W. Size:** 12800 Metres.
Ref: FH4716

TEIGN (RIVER)

River Teign, Llangollen, **DENBIGHSHIRE**, LL20, **Wales**.
Contact/s: **Mr John Pugh** (owner), Golden Pheasant Hotel, Glyn Ceirog, Llangollen, Clwyd, LL20 7BB.
(T) 01691 718281
Profile: **FT:** Game; **WN:** Teirn; **WT:** River (Moving).
Ref: FH4717

TEIGN (RIVER)

River Teign, Newton Abbot, **DEVON**, TQ1, **England**.
Contact/s: Manager, Drum Sports Limited, 47 Courtenay St, Newton Abbot, Devon, TQ12 2QN.
(T) 01626 205042
Profile: **FT:** Game; **WN:** Teign; **WT:** River (Moving).
Ref: FH4718

TEIGN (RIVER)

River Teign, Ryecroft, Christow, Chudleigh, Newton Abbot, **DEVON**, TQ13, **England**.
Contact/s: **Mr Kevin Salisbury** (Manager), Exeter Angling Ctre, Smythen St, Exeter, Devon, EX1 1BN.
(T) 01392 435591or436404 **(F)** 01392 433855
Profile: **FT:** Game; **WN:** Teign; **WT:** River (Moving) **W. Size:** 1600 Metres.
Ref: FH4719

TEISE (RIVER)

River Teise, Court Lodge Down Fishery, Hawkenbury, Bells Yew Green, Tunbridge Wells, **KENT**, TN3 9BJ, **England**.
Contact/s: **Mr Ray Wadey** (Manager).
(T) 01892 616424 **(M)** 07802 429284
Profile: **FT:** Combination; **WN:** Teise; **WT:** River (Moving) **W. Size:** 1000 Metres. **Location:** **Main Rd:** A21; **Rail:** Frant.
Ref: FH4720

TELFORD TOWN PARK

Telford Town Park, Telford, **SHROPSHIRE**, TF4 2, **England**.
Contact/s: **Mr Stan Harris** (Secretary), Telford Angling Association, 73 Burnside, Brookside, Telford, TF3 1DA.
(T) 01952 590605
Profile: **FT:** Coarse; **WN:** Telford Town Park; **WT:** Pool (Still).
Ref: FH4721

TEME (RIVER)

River Teme, Ludlow, **SHROPSHIRE**, SY8, **England**.
Contact/s: **Mr Dave Bastin** (Chairman), Ludlow Angling Club, 96 Greenacres, Ludlow, Shropshire, SY8 1LZ.
(T) 01584 873577
Profile: **FT:** Coarse; **WN:** Teme; **WT:** River (Moving) **W. Size:** 1000 Metres. **Location:** **Nr. Rd:** A49; **Main Rd:** A49; **Rail:** Ludlow.
Ref: FH4722

TEME (RIVER)

River Teme, Saltmore, Ludlow, **SHROPSHIRE**, SY8, **England**.
Contact/s: **Mr Dave Bastin** (Chairman), Ludlow Angling Club, 96 Greenacres, Ludlow, Shropshire, SY8 1LZ.
(T) 01584 873577
Profile: **FT:** Coarse; **WN:** Teme; **WT:** River (Moving) **W. Size:** 500 Metres. **Location:** **Nr. Rd:** A49; **Main Rd:** A49; **Rail:** Ludlow.
Ref: FH4723

TEME (RIVER)

River Teme, Tenbury Wells, **WORCESTERSHIRE**, WR15, **England**.
Contact/s: **Mr W E Drew** (Chairman), 7 Remans Cottage, Berrington Rd, Worcestershire, WE15 8EL.
(T) 01584 810828
Mrs L M Rickett (Secretary), Tenbury Fishing Association, The Post House, Borrington Rd, Tenbury Wells, WR15 8EN.
(T) 01584 810345
Profile: **FT:** Combination; **WN:** Teme; **WT:** Combination (Moving). **Location:** **Nr. Rd:** A456; **Rail:** Ludlow.
Ref: FH4724

TEME (RIVER)

Teme (River), Ham Bridge & Ham Bridge Farm, Martley, **WORCESTERSHIRE**, **England**.
Contact/s: **Mr John Turner** (Hon Secretary), Prince Albert Angling Society, 15 Pexhill Drive, Macclesfield, Cheshire, SK10 3LP.
(T) 01625 422010
Profile: **FT:** Coarse; **WN:** Teme; **WT:** River (Moving) **W. Size:** 3000 Metres. **Location:** **Nr. Rd:** B4204; **Rail:** Worcester.
Ref: FH4725

TEME (RIVER)

River Teme, Stanford Bridge, Worcester, **WORCESTERSHIRE**, WR6, **England**.
Contact/s: **Mr John Williams** (Secretary), Birmingham Anglers Association, 100 Icknield Port Rd, Rotton Park, Birmingham, B16 0AP.
(T) 0121 4549111
Profile: **FT:** Coarse; **WN:** Teme; **WT:** River (Moving) **W. Size:** 1600 Metres. **Location:** **Nr. Rd:** B4203; **Main Rd:** Worcester.
Ref: FH4726

TEME (RIVER)

River Teme, Knightwick, Bewdley, **WORCESTERSHIRE**, DY12, **England**.
Contact/s: **Mr Dave Beresford** (Manager), Allans Fishing Tackle, 26-30 Malvern Rd, Worcester, Worcestershire, WR2 4LG.
(T) 01905 422107 **(F)** 01905 422107
Mr John Wells (Chairman), Worcester and District United Angling Association, Poplar Cottages, Poplar Rd, Whichenford, WR6 6YF.
(T) 01886 888459
Profile: **FT:** Coarse; **WN:** Teme; **WT:** River (Moving) **W. Size:** 2500 Metres.
Ref: FH4727

TEME (RIVER)

River Teme, Cotheridge, Worcester, **WORCESTERSHIRE**, WR, **England**.
Contact/s: **Mr John Williams** (Secretary), Birmingham Anglers Association, 100 Icknield Port Rd, Rotton Park, Birmingham, B16 0AP.
(T) 0121 4549111
Profile: **FT:** Combination; **WN:** Teme; **WT:** River (Moving). **Location:** **Nr. Rd:** A44 to Broadwas.

Ref: FH4728

TEME (RIVER)

River Teme, Westbrook Farm, Little Hereford, Tenbury Wells, **WORCESTERSHIRE**, WR15, **England**.
Contact/s: Farmhouse Manager.
(T) 01584 711280weekdaysonly
Profile: **FT:** Coarse; **WN:** Teme; **WT:** River (Moving) **W. Size:** 500 Metres.
Ref: FH4729

TEME (RIVER)

River Teme, Knightwick, Worcester, **WORCESTERSHIRE**, WR6 5PH, **England**.
Contact/s: Manager, The Talbot, Bromyard Rd, Knightwick, Worcester, WR6 5PH.
(T) 01886 821235 (F) 01886 821060
Profile: **FT:** Coarse; **WN:** Teme; **WT:** River (Moving) **W. Size:** 135 Metres.
Ref: FH4730

TEME (RIVER)

River Teme, Peacock Waters, Boraston, Tenbury Wells, **WORCESTERSHIRE**, WR15, **England**.
Contact/s: **Mr Jim Goddard**.
(T) 01584 881411
Profile: **FT:** Combination; **WN:** Teme; **WT:** River (Moving) **W. Size:** 900 Metres.
Location: **Main Rd:** A456 to Bewdley.
Ref: FH4731

TEME (RIVER)

Knightwick, Martley Works, Bewdley, **WORCESTERSHIRE**, DY12 2DX, **England**.
Contact/s: **Mr Stan Lewis** (Manager), S Lewis Fishing Tackle, 2 Severnside South, Bewdley, Worcestershire, DY12 2DX.
(T) 01299 403358
Profile: **FT:** Combination; **WN:** Teme; **WT:** River (Moving) **W. Size:** 1500 Metres.
Location: **Nr. Rd:** Martley Works.
Ref: FH4732

TEME (RIVER)

River Teme, Mill Lane, Eardiston, Tenbury Wells, **WORCESTERSHIRE**, WR15, **England**.
Contact/s: **Mr John Williams** (Secretary), Birmingham Anglers Association, 100 Icknield Port Rd, Rotton Park, Birmingham, B16 0AP.
(T) 0121 4549111
Profile: **FT:** Coarse; **WN:** Teme; **WT:** River (Moving). Location: **Main Rd:** Tenbury Wells road, west of Worcester.
Ref: FH4733

TEMPLE SPRINGS

Temple Springs, Smithills Dean Rd, Bolton, **LANCASHIRE**, BL, **England**.
Contact/s: Manager, Bolton Angling Ctre, 177 St Helens Rd, Bolton, Lancashire, BL3 3PZ.
(T) 01204 658989
Mr Terence A McKee (Secretary), Bolton and District Angling Association, 1 Lever Edge Lane, Bolton, Lancashire, BL3 3BU.
(T) 01204 393726
Profile: **FT:** Coarse; **WN:** Temple Springs; **WT:** Pond (Still). Location: **Nr. Rd:** A58, A666 South of Blackburn; **Main Rd:** M61.
Ref: FH4734

TEMPLE TROUT FISHERY

Temple Trout Fishery, Temple Rd, Temple, Bodmin, **CORNWALL**, PL30 4HW, **England**.
Contact/s: **Mr Julian Jones** (Manager).
(T) 01208 871730 (M) 07787 704966
(E) julian@fish43.freeserve.uk
Profile: **FT:** Game; **WN:** Temple Trout Fishery; **WT:** Clay Pit (Still) **W. Size:** 7 Acres.
Location: **Nr. Rd:** Bodmin Road; **Main Rd:** A30; **Rail:** Bodmin Parkway.
Ref: FH4735

TEMPO (RIVER)

River Tempo, Maguiresbridge, **COUNTY FERMANAGH**, BT94, **Northern Ireland**.
Contact/s: **Mr Patrick Trotter** (Secretary), 7 Tattinderry Estate, Maguiresbridge, County Fermanagh.
(T) 028 67721877
Profile: **FT:** Game; **WN:** Tempo; **WT:** Tributary (Moving) **W. Size:** 4800 Metres.
Ref: FH4736

TEN MILE BANK

Ten Mile Bank, Engine Rd, Downham Market, **NORFOLK**, PE38, **England**.
Contact/s: **K Allen** (Chairman), Mole Cottage, 15 Ten Mile Bank, Littleport, CB6 1EE.
(T) 01383 860936
Mr G Baker (Owner), The Tackle Box, 38 Tower St, King's Lynn, Norfolk, PE30 1EJ.
(T) 01553 761293
Mr Martin Allen (Owner), Anglers Corner, 55 London Rd, King's Lynn, Norfolk, PE30 5QH.
(T) 01553 775852
Mr Mick Grief (Secretary), King's Lynn Angling Association, 67 Peckover Way, South Wootton, King's Lynn, PE30 3UE.
(T) 01553 671545
Profile: **FT:** Coarse; **WN:** Great Ouse; **WT:** Stream (Moving). Location: **Nr. Rd:** Engine Road; **Main Rd:** A10.
Ref: FH4737

TENTERDEN TROUT WATERS

Tenterden Trout Waters, Coombe Farm, Chennell Park Rd, Tenterden, **KENT**, TN30 6XA, **England**.
(W) www.tenterden-trout-waters.co.uk
Contact/s: Fishery Manager.
(T) 01580 754420
(E) enquiries@tenterden-trout-waters.co.uk
Mr Barry Evans.
(T) 01580 763201
Mrs Audrey Evans.
(T) 01580 763201
Profile: **FT:** Game; **WN:** Tenterden Trout Waters; **WT:** Lake (Still); **F. Size:** 10 Acres; **W. Size:** 5 Acres. Location: **Nr. Rd:** Chennell Park Road; **Main Rd:** A28; **Rail:** Headcorn.
Ref: FH4738

TERN (RIVER)

River Tern, Tern Fisheries, Broomhall Grange, Peatswood, Market Drayton, **SHROPSHIRE**, TF9 2PA, **England**.
Contact/s: **Mr R J Sparrow**.
(T) 01630 653222 (F) 01630 657444
Profile: **FT:** Game; **WN:** Tern; **WT:** River (Moving) **W. Size:** 3200 Metres.
Ref: FH4739

TERN (RIVER)

Tern (River), Stoke Grange Farm, Ternhill, Market Drayton, **SHROPSHIRE**, **England**.
Contact/s: **Mr John Turner** (Hon Secretary), Prince Albert Angling Society, 15 Pexhill Drive, Macclesfield, Cheshire, SK10 3LP.
(T) 01625 422010
Profile: **FT:** Combination; **WN:** Tern; **WT:** River (Moving) **W. Size:** 1000 Metres.
Location: **Nr. Rd:** A41; **Rail:** Market Drayton.
Ref: FH4740

TERN (RIVER)

Tern (River), Market Drayton, **SHROPSHIRE**, TF9, **England**.
Contact/s: Manager, Environment Agency, Upper Severn Area Office, Hafren House, Welshpool Rd, Shelton SY3 8BB.
(T) 01743 272828 (F) 01743 272138
Profile: **FT:** Coarse; **WN:** Tern; **WT:** River (Moving) **W. Size:** 1207 Metres.
Ref: FH4741

TERN (RIVER)

River Tern, Isombridge Farm, Wellington, Telford, **SHROPSHIRE**, TF1, **England**.
Contact/s: **Mr Stan Harris** (Secretary), Telford Angling Association, 73 Burnside, Brookside, Telford, TF3 1DA.
(T) 01952 590605
Profile: **FT:** Coarse; **WN:** Tern; **WT:** River (Moving) **W. Size:** 1200 Metres.
Ref: FH4742

TERN FISHERIES

Tern Fisheries Ltd, Broomhall Grange, Peatswood, Market Drayton, **SHROPSHIRE**, TF9 2PA, **England**.
Contact/s: **Mr R J Sparrow**.
(T) 01630 653222 (F) 01630 657444
Profile: **FT:** Game; **WN:** Tern Fisheries Ltd; **WT:** River (Moving) **W. Size:** 4800 Metres.
Ref: FH4743

TEST (RIVER)

River Test, Broadlands Park, Romsey, **HAMPSHIRE**, SO51 9ZE, **England**.
Contact/s: **Mr John Dennis** (Bailiff/Fishery Manager), Estate Office, Broadlands, Romsey, Hampshire, SO51 9ZE.
(T) 01794 518885
Profile: **FT:** Combination; **WN:** Test; **WT:** River (Moving).
Ref: FH4744

TEST (RIVER)

River Test, Stockbridge, **HAMPSHIRE**, SO20, **England**.
Contact/s: **Mr R Skaron** (Owner), The Greyhound Hotel, 31 High St, Stockbridge, Hampshire, SO20 6EY.
(T) 01264 810833
Ms Judith Thornton (Manager).
(T) 01264 349519 (F) 01264 349505
Profile: **FT:** Game; **WN:** Test; **WT:** River (Moving) **W. Size:** 700 Metres. Location: **Nr. Rd:** A30; **Rail:** Andover.
Ref: FH4745

TESTWOOD SALMON FISHERIES

Testwood Salmon Fisheries Ltd, Fishing Cottage, Testwood Lane, Totton, Southampton, **HAMPSHIRE**, SO40 3QS, **England**.
Contact/s: **Mr Alan Kilkenny** (Director).
(T) 023 80867508
Profile: **FT:** Game; **WN:** Testwood Salmon Fisheries Ltd; **WT:** Lake (Still).
Ref: FH4746

TETTON FLASH

Tetton Flash, Tetton, Middlewich, **CHESHIRE**, CW10, **England**.
Contact/s: Fishery Manager.
(T) 01606 842287
Profile: **FT:** Coarse; **WN:** Tetton Flash; **WT:** Dam (Still).
Ref: FH4748

TETTON LAKE

Tetton Lake, Middlewich, **CHESHIRE**, CW10, **England**.
Contact/s: **Mr Colin Wyatt** (Secretary).
(T) 01606 832257 (M) 07976 329952
Profile: **FT:** Coarse; **WN:** Tetton; **WT:** Lake (Still) **W. Size:** 3 Acres.
Ref: FH4749

TEVIOT (RIVER)

River Teviot, Eckford Angling Association, The Buccleuch Estates Ltd, The Estate Office, Bowhill, Selkirk, **SCOTTISH BORDERS**, TD7 5ES, **Scotland**.
Contact/s: **Mr J Crosbie** (Per The Factor Ghillie).
(T) 01750 20753or32334 (F) 01750 22172
(E) jcrosbie@buccleuch.com
Profile: **FT:** Game; **WN:** Teviot; **WT:** River (Moving). Location: **Nr. Rd:** A698; **Main Rd:** A68; **Rail:** Edinburgh or Berwick-upon-Tweed.
Ref: FH4750

TEVIOT (RIVER)

River Teviot, Hawick, **SCOTTISH BORDERS**, TD9, **Scotland**.
Contact/s: **Mr Eric Stewart** (Secretary/Treasurer), Hawick Angling Club, 5 Sandbed, Hawick, Scottish Borders, TD9 0HE.
(T) 01450 373771
Profile: **FT:** Combination; **WN:** Teviot; **WT:** River (Moving) **W. Size:** 19200 Metres.
Location: **Main Rd:** A7; **Rail:** Carlisle.
Ref: FH4751

TEWITFIELDS TROUT FISHERY

Tewitfields Trout Fishery, Burton Rd, Tewitfields, Carnforth, **CUMBRIA**, LA6 1JH, **England**.
Contact/s: H J Clarke.
(T) 01253 725126
Mr L Bratby. **(F)** 01253 348714 **(M)** 07711 669976
Tommy Kay.
(T) 01524 730331 **(F)** 01253 348714
Profile: FT: Combination; **WN:** Tewitfields Trout Fishery; **WT:** Gravel Pit (Still); **F. Size:** 27 Acres; **W. Size:** 9 Acres. **Location: Nr. Rd:** A6070; **Main Rd:** A6, M6, junction 35; **Rail:** Carnforth.
Ref: FH4752

THAME (RIVER)

River Thame, Shabbington, Aylesbury, **BUCKINGHAMSHIRE**, HP18 9, **England**.
(W) www.uxbridge-rovers.fsnet.co.uk
Contact/s: Mr L Dalton (Secretary), Uxbridge Rovers Angling and Conservation Society, PO Box 253, Harrow, Middlesex, HA3 8XN.
(T) 01814 281739
Profile: FT: Coarse; **WN:** Thame; **WT:** River (Moving) **W. Size:** 2400 Metres. **Location: Nr. Rd:** A418; **Main Rd:** M40.
Ref: FH4753

THAME (RIVER)

River Thame, Chearsley, Tring, **HERTFORDSHIRE**, HP23, **England**.
(W) www.tringanglers.club24.co.uk
Contact/s: Mr Stuart Riddle (Secretary), The Tring Anglers, PO Box 1947, Tring, Hertfordshire, HP23 5LZ.
(T) 01442 826148
Profile: FT: Coarse; **WN:** Thame; **WT:** River (Moving).
Ref: FH4754

THAME (RIVER)

River Thame, Shabbington Island, Tring, **HERTFORDSHIRE**, HP23, **England**.
(W) www.tringanglers.club24.co.uk
Contact/s: Mr Stuart Riddle (Secretary), The Tring Anglers, PO Box 1947, Tring, Hertfordshire, HP23 5LZ.
(T) 01442 826148
Profile: FT: Coarse; **WN:** Thame; **WT:** River (Moving).
Ref: FH4755

THAME (RIVER)

River Thame, Ickford, Tring, **HERTFORDSHIRE**, HP23, **England**.
(W) www.tringanglers.club24.co.uk
Contact/s: Mr Stuart Riddle (Secretary), The Tring Anglers, PO Box 1947, Tring, Hertfordshire, HP23 5LZ.
(T) 01442 826148
Profile: FT: Coarse; **WN:** Thame; **WT:** River (Moving).
Ref: FH4756

THAME (RIVER)

River Thame, Ickford, **OXFORDSHIRE**, OX, **England**.
Contact/s: Mr J Woodhouse (Secretary), Marlow Angling Club, Conifers, Ash Rd, High Wycombe, Buckinghamshire, HP12 4SW.
(T) 01494 523988
Profile: FT: Coarse; **WN:** Thame; **WT:** River (Moving).
Ref: FH4757

THAME (RIVER)

River Thame, Henley-on-Thames, **OXFORDSHIRE**, RG9, **England**.
Contact/s: Mr R Hall (Secretary), Warborough and Shillingford Angling Club, 67 St Nicholas Rd, Wallingford, Oxfordshire, OX10 8HX.
(T) 01491 201852
Profile: FT: Coarse; **WN:** Thame; **WT:** River (Moving).
Ref: FH4758

THAME (RIVER)

River Thame, Berinsfield, Wallingford, **OXFORDSHIRE**, OX10, **England**.
Contact/s: Mr M Marriot (Secretary).
(T) 01865 341184
Profile: FT: Coarse; **WN:** Thame; **WT:** River (Moving).
Ref: FH4759

THAMES (RIVER)

River Thames, Old Windsor Weir To Albert Bridge, Windsor, **BERKSHIRE**, SL4, **England**.
Contact/s: Mr Alan Beaven (Secretary), Old Windsor Angling Club, 88 St Andrew's Way, Slough, Berkshire, SL1 5LJ.
(T) 01628 602537 **(M)** 07887 770630
Profile: FT: Coarse; **WN:** Thames; **WT:** River (Moving).
Ref: FH4760

THAMES (RIVER)

River Thames, Hurley Lock Island, Reading, **BERKSHIRE**, RG7 4, **England**.
Contact/s: Recreational Manager, The Environment Agency, Kings Meadow Rd, Reading, Berkshire, RG1 8DQ.
(T) 0118 9535000 **(F)** 0118 9500388
The Lock Keeper.
(T) 01628 824334
Profile: FT: Coarse; **WN:** Thames; **WT:** River (Moving).
Ref: FH4761

THAMES (RIVER)

River Thames, Penton Hook, Reading, **BERKSHIRE**, RG7, **England**.
Contact/s: Recreational Manager, The Environment Agency, Kings Meadow Rd, Reading, Berkshire, RG1 8DQ.
(T) 0118 9535000 **(F)** 0118 9500388
Profile: FT: Coarse; **WN:** Thames; **WT:** River (Moving).
Ref: FH4762

THAMES (RIVER)

River Thames, Chazey Farm, Caversham, Reading, **BERKSHIRE**, RG, **England**.
Contact/s: Mr Dusty Millar (Associate members secretary), 238 Elgar Road South, Reading, Berkshire, RG3 0BW.
(T) 0118 9874882
Mr Mick Cox (Chief Bailiff), Dorstans, Hatch Lane, Brimpton Village, Reading, RG7 4TR.
(T) 0118 9714917
Profile: FT: Coarse; **WN:** Thames; **WT:** River (Moving). **Location: Nr. Rd:** Caversham.
Ref: FH4763

THAMES (RIVER)

River Thames, Donnington To Kennington, Newbury, **BERKSHIRE**, RG14, **England**.
Contact/s: Mr Martin Room (Secretary), Oxford and District Angling Association, 136 Oxford Rd, Cowley, Oxfordshire, OX4 2DU.
(T) 01865 711410
Profile: FT: Coarse; **WN:** Thames; **WT:** River (Moving).
Ref: FH4764

THAMES (RIVER)

River Thames, Bell Weir, Bray, **BERKSHIRE**, SL6, **England**.
Contact/s: Recreational Manager, The Environment Agency, Kings Meadow Rd, Reading, Berkshire, RG1 8DQ.
(T) 0118 9535000 **(F)** 0118 9500388
Profile: FT: Coarse; **WN:** Thames; **WT:** River (Moving).
Ref: FH4765

THAMES (RIVER)

River Thames, Hurley Farm, Littlewick Green, Maidenhead, **BERKSHIRE**, SL6, **England**.
Contact/s: Mr D Burfitt.
(T) 01628 823501
Profile: FT: Coarse; **WN:** Thames; **WT:** River (Moving) **W. Size:** 2640 Metres.
Ref: FH4766

THAMES (RIVER)

River Thames, Molesey Lock, Reading, **BERKSHIRE**, RG1, **England**.
Contact/s: Recreational Manager, The Environment Agency, Kings Meadow Rd, Reading, Berkshire, RG1 8DQ.
(T) 0118 9535000 **(F)** 0118 9500388
Profile: FT: Coarse; **WN:** Thames; **WT:** River (Moving).
Ref: FH4767

THAMES (RIVER)

River Thames, East Towney, Reading, **BERKSHIRE**, RG7, **England**.
Contact/s: Mr Mick Cox (Secretary), Dorstans, Hatch Lane, Brimpton Village, Reading, RG7 4TR.
(T) 0118 9714917
Ms Dusty Millar (Ticket Administrator), 238 Elgar Road South, Reading, Berkshire, RG3 0BW.
(T) 0118 9874882
Profile: FT: Coarse; **WN:** Thames; **WT:** River (Moving).
Ref: FH4768

THAMES (RIVER)

River Thames, Maidenhead To Bray, Maidenhead, **BERKSHIRE**, SL6, **England**.
Contact/s: Buzz (Manager), Boyer Leisure Ltd, Heron's Point Tackle Shop, Farlow's Lake, Ford Lane, Iver SL0 9LL.
(T) 01753 630302or01895444707 **(F)** 01753 630302
(E) info@boyer.co.uk
Profile: FT: Coarse; **WN:** Thames; **WT:** River (Moving).
Ref: FH4769

THAMES (RIVER)

River Thames, Cookham, Maidenhead, **BERKSHIRE**, SL6 9, **England**.
(W) www.uxbridge-rovers.fsnet.co.uk
Contact/s: Mr L Dalton (Secretary), Uxbridge Rovers Angling and Conservation Society, PO Box 253, Harrow, Middlesex, HA3 8XN.
(T) 01814 281739
Profile: FT: Coarse; **WN:** Thames; **WT:** River (Moving) **W. Size:** 1200 Metres.
Ref: FH4770

THAMES (RIVER)

River Thames, Sonning, Reading, **BERKSHIRE**, RG, **England**.
Contact/s: Mr Dusty Millar (Associate members secretary), 238 Elgar Road South, Reading, Berkshire, RG3 0BW.
(T) 0118 9874882
Mr Mick Cox (Chief Bailiff), Dorstans, Hatch Lane, Brimpton Village, Reading, RG7 4TR.
(T) 0118 9714917
Profile: FT: Coarse; **WN:** Thames; **WT:** River (Moving). **Location: Nr. Rd:** Sonning.
Ref: FH4771

THAMES (RIVER)

River Thames, Windsor, **BERKSHIRE**, SL4, **England**.
Contact/s: Mr Phyllis Symons (Secretary), Salt Hill Angling Society, 18 Wood Lane, Cippenham, Slough, Berkshire SL1 9EA.
Profile: FT: Coarse; **WN:** Thames; **WT:** River (Moving).
Ref: FH4772

THAMES (RIVER)

River Thames, Salmon Cut, Reading, **BERKSHIRE**, RG3, **England**.
Contact/s: Mr Mick Cox (Secretary), Dorstans, Hatch Lane, Brimpton Village, Reading, RG7 4TR.
(T) 0118 9714917
Ms Dusty Millar (Ticket Administrator), 238 Elgar Road South, Reading, Berkshire, RG3 0BW.
(T) 0118 9874882
Profile: FT: Coarse; **WN:** Thames; **WT:** River (Moving).
Ref: FH4773

THAMES (RIVER)

River Thames, Midgeham, Reading,

BERKSHIRE, RG3, **England**.
Contact/s: **Mr Mick Cox** (Secretary), Dorstans, Hatch Lane, Brimpton Village, Reading, RG7 4TR.
(T) 0118 9714917
Ms Dusty Millar (Ticket Administrator), 238 Elgar Road South, Reading, Berkshire, RG3 0BW.
(T) 0118 9874882
Profile: **FT:** Coarse; **WN:** Thames; **WT:** River (Moving).
Ref: FH4774

THAMES (RIVER)

River Thames, Bray Lock, Bray, **BERKSHIRE**, SL6, **England**.
Contact/s: Recreational Manager, The Environment Agency, Kings Meadow Rd, Reading, Berkshire, RG1 8DQ.
(T) 0118 9535000 **(F)** 0118 9500388
Profile: **FT:** Coarse; **WN:** Thames; **WT:** River (Moving).
Ref: FH4775

THAMES (RIVER)

River Thames, Purley Park, Reading, **BERKSHIRE**, RG7, **England**.
Contact/s: **Mr Mick Cox** (Secretary), Dorstans, Hatch Lane, Brimpton Village, Reading, RG7 4TR.
(T) 0118 9714917
Ms Dusty Millar (Ticket Administrator), 238 Elgar Road South, Reading, Berkshire, RG3 0BW.
(T) 0118 9874882
Profile: **FT:** Coarse; **WN:** Thames; **WT:** River (Moving).
Ref: FH4776

THAMES (RIVER)

River Thames, High Wycombe, **BUCKINGHAMSHIRE**, HP11, **England**.
Contact/s: **Mr J Woodhouse** (Secretary), Marlow Angling Club, Conifers, Ash Rd, High Wycombe, Buckinghamshire, HP12 4SW.
(T) 01494 523988
Profile: **FT:** Coarse; **WN:** Thames; **WT:** River (Moving).
Ref: FH4777

THAMES (RIVER)

River Thames, Marlow, **BUCKINGHAMSHIRE**, SL2, **England**.
Contact/s: Recreational Manager, The Environment Agency, Kings Meadow Rd, Reading, Berkshire, RG1 8DQ.
(T) 0118 9535000 **(F)** 0118 9500388
Profile: **FT:** Coarse; **WN:** Thames; **WT:** River (Moving).
Ref: FH4778

THAMES (RIVER)

River Thames, Marlow, **BUCKINGHAMSHIRE**, SL2, **England**.
Contact/s: **Mrs Helen Rathbone**, The Compleat Angling Hotel, Marlow, Buckinghamshire.
(T) 01628 484444
Profile: **FT:** Coarse; **WN:** Thames; **WT:** River (Moving).
Ref: FH4779

THAMES (RIVER)

River Thames, Medmenham, Marlow, **BUCKINGHAMSHIRE**, SL7 2, **England**.
Contact/s: **Mr J Woodhouse** (Secretary), Marlow Angling Club, Conifers, Ash Rd, High Wycombe, Buckinghamshire, HP12 4SW.
(T) 01494 523988
Profile: **FT:** Coarse; **WN:** Thames; **WT:** River (Moving).
Ref: FH4780

THAMES (RIVER)

River Thames, Lock Cut And Meadow, Slough, **BUCKINGHAMSHIRE**, SL1, **England**.
Contact/s: **Mr Alan Beaven** (Secretary), Old Windsor Angling Club, 88 St Andrew's Way, Slough, Berkshire, SL1 5LJ.
(T) 01628 602537
Profile: **FT:** Coarse; **WN:** Thames; **WT:** River (Moving).
Ref: FH4781

THAMES (RIVER)

River Thames, Marlow, **BUCKINGHAMSHIRE**, SL2, **England**.
Contact/s: **Mr J Woodhouse** (Secretary), Marlow Angling Club, Conifers, Ash Rd, High Wycombe, Buckinghamshire, HP12 4SW.
(T) 01494 523988
Profile: **FT:** Coarse; **WN:** Thames; **WT:** River (Moving).
Ref: FH4782

THAMES (RIVER)

River Thames, Thame Stream Bridge To Meadside Fence, Dorchester, **DORSET**, DT2, **England**.
Contact/s: **Mr Micheal Pinder**.
(T) 01865 340404
Mr Mick Marriot (Secretary), Dorchester Angling Club, 14 Shadwell Rd, Berinsfield, Wallingford, Oxfordshire OX10 7PN.
(T) 01865 341184
Profile: **FT:** Coarse; **WN:** Thames; **WT:** River (Moving).
Ref: FH4783

THAMES (RIVER)

River Thames, Duxford Farm, Cirencester, **GLOUCESTERSHIRE**, GL7, **England**.
Contact/s: **Mr Ray Daffon** (Secretary), South Cerney Angling Club, Broadway Lane, South Cerney, Cirencester, GL7 5UH.
(T) 01285 861876 **(M)** 07775 970643
Profile: **FT:** Coarse; **WN:** River Thames; **WT:** River (Moving).
Ref: FH4784

THAMES (RIVER)

River Thames, Kelmscott, Lechlade, **GLOUCESTERSHIRE**, GL7, **England**.
Contact/s: **Mr Ray Daffon** (Secretary), South Cerney Angling Club, Broadway Lane, South Cerney, Cirencester, GL7 5UH.
(T) 01285 861876 **(M)** 07775 970643
Profile: **FT:** Coarse; **WN:** Thames; **WT:** River (Moving) **W. Size:** 4000 Metres. Location: **Nr. Rd:** B4449 to A4095; **Main Rd:** B4449.
Ref: FH4785

THAMES (RIVER)

River Thames, Shepperton Weir, Shepperton, London, **LONDON (GREATER)**, TW14, **England**.
Contact/s: Recreational Manager, The Environment Agency, Kings Meadow Rd, Reading, Berkshire, RG1 8DQ.
(T) 0118 9535000 **(F)** 0118 9500388
Profile: **FT:** Coarse; **WN:** Thames; **WT:** River (Moving).
Ref: FH4786

THAMES (RIVER)

River Thames, Sunbury Creek, Hounslow, London, **LONDON (GREATER)**, TW5 9, **England**.
Contact/s: **Mrs V Sivyer** (Secretary), Feltham Piscatorial Society, 96 Raleigh Rd, Feltham, Middlesex, TW13 4LP.
(T) 020 8909005
Profile: **FT:** Coarse; **WN:** Thames; **WT:** River (Moving).
Ref: FH4787

THAMES (RIVER)

River Thames, Barnes, London, **LONDON (GREATER)**, SW13, **England**.
Contact/s: **Mr Phil Anderson** (Fishery Manager).
(T) 020 87487689
Profile: **FT:** Coarse; **WN:** Thames; **WT:** River (Moving).
Ref: FH4788

THAMES (RIVER)

River Thames, Canbury Gardens, London, **LONDON (GREATER)**, SW17 9, **England**.
Contact/s: Manager, Fishing Unlimited, 299 Mitcham Rd, London, SW17 9JQ.
(T) 020 86721699
Profile: **FT:** Coarse; **WN:** Thames; **WT:** River (Moving).
Ref: FH4789

THAMES (RIVER)

River Thames, Channel To Folly, Cowley, **OXFORDSHIRE**, OX4, **England**.
Contact/s: **Mr Martin Room** (Secretary), Oxford and District Angling Association, 136, Oxford Rd, Cowley, Oxfordshire, OX4 2DU.
(T) 01865 711410
Profile: **FT:** Coarse; **WN:** Thames; **WT:** River (Moving).
Ref: FH4790

THAMES (RIVER)

River Thames, Wallingford, **OXFORDSHIRE**, OX10, **England**.
Contact/s: **Mr Bill Brown-Lee** (Secretary), Reading and District Angling Association, 47 Calbourne Drive, Calcot, Reading, Berkshire, RG3 7DB.
(T) 0118 9417368
Profile: **FT:** Coarse; **WN:** Thames; **WT:** River (Moving).
Ref: FH4791

THAMES (RIVER)

River Thames, Bablock Hythe A & B, Northmoor, Witney, **OXFORDSHIRE**, OX8, **England**.
Contact/s: **Mr Dusty Millar** (Associate members secretary), 238 Elgar Road South, Reading, Berkshire, RG3 0BW.
(T) 0118 9874882
Mr Mick Cox (Chief Bailiff), Dorstans, Hatch Lane, Brimpton Village, Reading, RG7 4TR.
(T) 0118 9714917
Profile: **FT:** Coarse; **WN:** Thames; **WT:** River (Moving).
Ref: FH4792

THAMES (RIVER)

River Thames, Godstow Rd, Wolvercote, **OXFORDSHIRE**, OX2, **England**.
Contact/s: **Mr Andrew Crisp** (Secretary), North Oxford Angling Society, 4 Grove St, Summertown, Oxford, Oxfordshire OX3 7JT.
(T) 01865 553800
Profile: **FT:** Coarse; **WN:** Thames; **WT:** River (Moving). Location: **Nr. Rd:** Godstow Road.
Ref: FH4793

THAMES (RIVER)

River Thames, Wolvercote, Oxford, **OXFORDSHIRE**, OX2, **England**.
Contact/s: **Mr Andrew Crisp** (Secretary), North Oxford Angling Society, 4 Grove St, Summertown, Oxford, Oxfordshire OX3 7JT.
(T) 01865 553800
Profile: **FT:** Coarse; **WN:** Thames; **WT:** River (Moving) **W. Size:** 1200 Metres. Location: **Main Rd:** A40.
Ref: FH4794

THAMES (RIVER)

River Thames, Sandford Lane, Sandford-on-Thames, Oxford, **OXFORDSHIRE**, OX4, **England**.
Contact/s: **Mr Derek Button**.
(T) 01235 520517
Profile: **FT:** Coarse; **WN:** Thames; **WT:** River (Moving) **W. Size:** 1600 Metres. Location: **Nr. Rd:** Sandford Lane; **Main Rd:** Abingdon to Radley.
Ref: FH4795

THAMES (RIVER)

River Thames, Warborough, Henley-on-Thames, **OXFORDSHIRE**, RG9, **England**.
Contact/s: **Mr R Hall** (Secretary), Warborough and Shillingford Angling Club, 67 St Nicholas Rd, Wallingford, Oxfordshire, OX10 8HX.
(T) 01491 201852
Profile: **FT:** Game; **WN:** Thames; **WT:** River (Moving).
Ref: FH4796

THAMES (RIVER)

River Thames, Clifton Hampden, Abingdon,

OXFORDSHIRE, OX14, **England**.
Contact/s: **Mr Martin Room** (Secretary), Oxford and District Angling Association, 136 Oxford Rd, Cowley, Oxfordshire, OX4 2DU.
(T) 01865 711410
Profile: **FT:** Coarse; **WN:** Thames; **WT:** River (Moving).
Ref: FH4797

THAMES (RIVER)

River Thames, Rushey Weir, Bampton, **OXFORDSHIRE**, OX18, **England**.
Contact/s: **Mr Tom Gerring**.
(T) 01993 850594
Profile: **FT:** Coarse; **WN:** Thames; **WT:** River (Moving) **W. Size:** 1200 Metres. **Location:** **Nr. Rd:** Cross the Tadpole Bridge; **Main Rd:** Bampton to Buckland.
Ref: FH4798

THAMES (RIVER)

River Thames, Bampton, **OXFORDSHIRE**, OX18, **England**.
Contact/s: **Mr Doug Foreshaw** (Secretary), Clanfield Angling Club, 117 Farmers Cl, Witney, Oxfordshire, OX8 6NR.
(T) 01993 200371
Profile: **FT:** Coarse; **WN:** Thames; **WT:** River (Moving).
Ref: FH4799

THAMES (RIVER)

River Thames, Wallingford, **OXFORDSHIRE**, OX10, **England**.
Contact/s: **Mr R Hall** (Secretary), Warborough and Shillingford Angling Club, 67 St Nicholas Rd, Wallingford, Oxfordshire, OX10 8HX.
(T) 01491 201852
Profile: **FT:** Coarse; **WN:** Thames; **WT:** River (Moving).
Ref: FH4800

THAMES (RIVER)

River Thames, King's Weir To Eynsham Rd, Summertown, **OXFORDSHIRE**, OX, **England**.
Contact/s: **Mr Andrew Crisp** (Secretary), North Oxford Angling Society, 4 Grove St, Summertown, Oxford, Oxfordshire OX3 7JT.
(T) 01865 553800
Profile: **FT:** Coarse; **WN:** Thames; **WT:** River (Moving).
Ref: FH4801

THAMES (RIVER)

River Thames, Medley, Cowley, **OXFORDSHIRE**, OX4, **England**.
Contact/s: **Mr Martin Room** (Secretary), Oxford and District Angling Association, 136 Oxford Rd, Cowley, Oxfordshire, OX4 2DU.
(T) 01865 711410
Profile: **FT:** Coarse; **WN:** Thames; **WT:** River (Moving).
Ref: FH4802

THAMES (RIVER)

River Thames, Rowstock, Didcot, **OXFORDSHIRE**, OX11 OJ, **England**.
Contact/s: **Mr Julian Humm** (Secretary), Benson Angling Club, Rainbow Cottage, Stadhampton, Oxfordshire, OX44 7TZ.
(T) 01235 464099
Profile: **FT:** Coarse; **WN:** Thames; **WT:** River (Moving).
Ref: FH4803

THAMES (RIVER)

River Thames, Hampton Court, East Molesey, **SURREY**, KT8 9, **England**.
Profile: **FT:** Coarse; **WN:** Thames; **WT:** River (Moving).
Ref: FH4804

THAMES (RIVER)

River Thames, Water Eaton, Cricklade, Swindon, **WILTSHIRE**, SN6, **England**.
Contact/s: **Mr Peter Gilbert** (Chairman), 31 Havelock St, Swindon, Wiltshire, SN1 1SD.
(T) 01793 535396 **(F)** 01793 535396
Profile: **FT:** Coarse; **WN:** Thames; **WT:** River (Moving) **W. Size:** 3000 Metres. **Location:** **Main Rd:** A419.
Ref: FH4805

THEALE

Theale, Station Rd, Theale, Reading, **BERKSHIRE**, RG, **England**.
(W) www.rmcangling.co.uk
Contact/s: **Mr Ian Welch** (Angling Manager), RMC Angling, The Square, Lightwater, Surrey, GU18 5SS.
(T) 01276 453300 **(F)** 01276 456611
(E) info@rmcangling.co.uk
Profile: **FT:** Coarse; **WN:** Theale; **WT:** Lake (Still) **W. Size:** 52 Acres. **Location:** **Nr. Rd:** Station Road; **Main Rd:** M4; **Rail:** Theale.
Ref: FH4806

THEALE CANAL

Theale Canal, Kennet And Avon Canal, Theale, Reading, **BERKSHIRE**, RG, **England**.
Contact/s: **Mr Dusty Millar** (Associate members secretary), 238 Elgar Road South, Reading, Berkshire, RG3 0BW.
(T) 0118 9874882
Mr Mick Cox (Chief Bailiff), Dorstans, Hatch Lane, Brimpton Village, Reading, RG7 4TR.
(T) 0118 9714917
Profile: **FT:** Coarse; **WN:** Theale; **WT:** Canal (Still).
Ref: FH4807

THEALE LAGOON

Theale Lagoon, Theale, Reading, **BERKSHIRE**, RG, **England**.
Contact/s: **Mr Dusty Millar** (Associate members secretary), 238 Elgar Road South, Reading, Berkshire, RG3 0BW.
(T) 0118 9874882
Mr Mick Cox (Chief Bailiff), Dorstans, Hatch Lane, Brimpton Village, Reading, RG7 4TR.
(T) 0118 9714917
Profile: **FT:** Coarse; **WN:** Theale Lagoon; **WT:** Gravel Pit (Still) **W. Size:** 320 Acres. **Location:** **Nr. Rd:** Station Road; **Main Rd:** M4 junction 12, A4; **Rail:** Reading.
Ref: FH4808

THET (RIVER)

River Thet, Bridgeham, Thetford, **SUFFOLK**, IP2, **England**.
Contact/s: **Mr N Roberts** (Manager).
(T) 01223 836773
Profile: **FT:** Coarse; **WN:** Thet; **WT:** River (Moving). **Location:** **Main Rd:** A11; **Rail:** Thetford.
Ref: FH4809

THIRLMERE

Thirlmere, Allerdale, Keswick, **CUMBRIA**, CA12, **England**.
Contact/s: **Mr Roy Rhodes** (Conservation, Access and Recreation Manager), Rivington Water Treatment Works, Bolton Rd, Horwich, Bolton, BL6 7RN.
(T) 01204 664300
Profile: **FT:** Combination; **WN:** Thirlmere; **WT:** Lake (Still). **Location:** **Nr. Rd:** A591 Grasmere to Keswick Road; **Main Rd:** M6.
£Fr
Ref: FH4810

THORNBROUGH LAKE

Thornbrough Lake, Corbridge, **NORTHUMBERLAND**, NE45, **England**.
Contact/s: **Mr John Armstrong**, 55 Calder Walk, Sunneyside, Whickham, Newcastle upon Tyne.
(T) 0191 4886496
Profile: **FT:** Coarse; **WN:** Thornbrough; **WT:** Lake (Still) **W. Size:** 1 Acre. **Location:** **Main Rd:** A69, A68.
Ref: FH4811

THORNDEN POND

Thornden Pond, Ashburnham, Battle, **SUSSEX (EAST)**, TN33, **England**.
Contact/s: Fishery Manager.
(T) 01435 830586
Profile: **FT:** Coarse; **WN:** Thornden; **WT:** Pond (Still).
Ref: FH4812

THORNDON PARK LAKE

Thorndon Park Lake, Halway Lane, Brentwood, **ESSEX**, CM1, **England**.
Profile: **FT:** Coarse; **WN:** Thorndon Park; **WT:** Lake (Still) **W. Size:** 3 Acres. **Location:** **Main Rd:** A127.
Ref: FH4813

THORNE NORTH POND

Thorne North Pond, Thorne, Doncaster, **YORKSHIRE (SOUTH)**, DN8, **England**.
Contact/s: **Mr Tony Sprott**.
(T) 01302 880548
Profile: **FT:** Coarse; **WN:** Thorne North; **WT:** Pool (Still). **Location:** **Nr. Rd:** A618; **Main Rd:** M18, junction 6; **Rail:** Thorne.
Ref: FH4814

THORNEY LAKES

Thorney Lakes, Thorney Farm, Muchelney, Langport, **SOMERSET**, TA10 0DW, **England**.
Contact/s: **Mr Richard England**.
(T) 01458 250811
Ms Ann England.
(T) 01458 250811
Profile: **FT:** Coarse; **WN:** Thorney; **WT:** Lake (Still); **F. Size:** 12 Acres; **W. Size:** 4 Acres. **Location:** **Nr. Rd:** Langport to Crewkerne; **Main Rd:** A303; **Rail:** Yeovil.
Ref: FH4815

THORNEY POOL

Thorney Pool, Thorney Mill Rd, West Drayton, London, **LONDON (GREATER)**, UB7, **England**.
Contact/s: **Mr Gordon Davis** (Manager), Boyer Leisure Ltd, Heron's Point Tackle Shop, Farlow's Lake, Ford Lane, Iver SL0 9LL.
(T) 01753 630302 or 01895444707 **(F)** 01753 630302
(E) info@boyer.co.uk
Profile: **FT:** Coarse; **WN:** Thorney Pool; **WT:** Gravel Pit (Still) **W. Size:** 2 Acres. **Location:** **Nr. Rd:** Thorney Mill Road; **Main Rd:** M25, junction 15; **Rail:** West Drayton.
Ref: FH4816

THORNEYCROFT LAKES

Thorneycroft Lakes, Siddington, Macclesfield, **CHESHIRE**, SK11, **England**.
Contact/s: **Mr John Turner** (Hon Secretary), Prince Albert Angling Society, 15 Pexhill Drive, Macclesfield, Cheshire, SK10 3LP.
(T) 01625 422010
Profile: **FT:** Coarse; **WN:** Thorneycroft Hall; **WT:** Lake (Still); **F. Size:** 25 Acres; **W. Size:** 18 Acres. **Location:** **Nr. Rd:** Henshaw Lane; **Main Rd:** B5392 Pexhill Road; **Rail:** Macclesfield.
Ref: FH4817

THORNHILL POND

Thornhill Pond, Thornhill, Dewsbury, **YORKSHIRE (WEST)**, WF, **England**.
Contact/s: Area Manager, Environment Agency, Ridings Area Office, Phoenix House, Global Avenue, Leeds, LS11 8PG.
(T) 0113 2440191or2314834 **(F)** 0113 2134609
Mr Jim Morris.
(T) 01924 406712
Profile: **FT:** Coarse; **WN:** Thornhill; **WT:** Pond (Still). **Location:** **Main Rd:** A638.
Ref: FH4818

THORNTON BRIDGE

Thornton Bridge, Boroughbridge Rd, Helperby, York, **YORKSHIRE (NORTH)**, YO61 2PD, **England**.
Contact/s: **Mr Mark Falilkner** (Owner).
(M) 07710 784016
Profile: **FT:** Coarse; **WN:** Swale; **WT:** River (Moving). **Location:** **Nr. Rd:** Boroughbridge Road; **Main Rd:** A168.
Ref: FH4819

THORNTON RESERVOIR

Thornton Reservoir, Reservoir Rd, Bagworth, Thornton, Leicester, **LEICESTERSHIRE**, LE67 1AH, **England**.

Contact/s: Mr Ifor Jones (Owner).
(T) 01530 230807
Profile: **FT:** Game; **WN:** Thornton; **WT:** Reservoir (Still); **F. Size:** 100 Acres; **W. Size:** 75 Acres. **Location:** **Nr. Rd:** Reservoir Road; **Main Rd:** Main Street, Thornton; **Rail:** Leicester.
Ref: FH4820

THORNTON STEWARD RESERVOIR

Thornton Steward Reservoir, Bedale, Thornton Steward, Ripon, **YORKSHIRE (NORTH)**, HG4, **England**.
Contact/s: **Ms Joan Hainsworth** (Ticket Sales), Hargill House, Finghall, Leyburn, Wensleydale, DL8 5ND.
(T) 01677 450245
Profile: **FT:** Game; **WN:** Thornton Steward; **WT:** Reservoir (Still).
Ref: FH4821

THORPE HALL

Thorpe Hall, Rudston, Driffield, **HUMBERSIDE**, YO25, **England**.
Contact/s: **Mr Nick Smith**.
(T) 01262 674183
Profile: **FT:** Coarse; **WN:** Thorpe Hall; **WT:** Lake (Still) **W. Size:** 2 Acres. **Location:** **Nr. Rd:** B1253 Rudston to Bridlington; **Main Rd:** Rudston.
Ref: FH4822

THORPE LE VALE FISHERY

Thorpe Le Vale Fishery, Ludford, Louth, **LINCOLNSHIRE**, LN11, **England**.
Contact/s: **Mr G Wildsmith**.
(T) 01472 398978
Mr Kaye Smith.
(T) 01472 316828
Profile: **FT:** Game; **WN:** Thorpe Le Vale Fishery; **WT:** Lake (Still).
Ref: FH4823

THORPE PARK WATERSKI LAKE

Thorpe Park Waterski Lake, Leisure Sport Angling, Thorpe Park, Staines Rd, Chertsey, **SURREY**, KT16, **England**.
Contact/s: **Mr Peter May** (Manager), 6 Papermill Cl, Carshalton, Surrey, SM5 2AD.
(M) 07867 808293
Profile: **FT:** Coarse; **WN:** Thorpe Park Waterski Lake; **WT:** Lake (Still). **Location:** **Nr. Rd:** Staines Road.
Ref: FH4824

THORPE PERROW QUARRY

Thorpe Perrow Quarry, Bedale, **YORKSHIRE (NORTH)**, DL8, **England**.
Contact/s: **Mr Peter Bennet**.
(T) 01748 824894
Profile: **FT:** Coarse; **WN:** Thorpe Perrow Quarry; **WT:** Gravel Pit (Still). **Location:** **Main Rd:** B6268.
Ref: FH4825

THORPE UNDERWOOD

Thorpe Underwood, York, **YORKSHIRE (NORTH)**, YO, **England**.
Contact/s: **Mr Dave Almond**.
(T) 01423 331080
Profile: **FT:** Coarse; **WN:** Thorpe Underwood; **WT:** Lake (Still).
Ref: FH4826

THORPE WATERVILLE LAKE

Thorpe Waterville Lake, Thorpe Waterville, Kettering, **NORTHAMPTONSHIRE**, NN14, **England**.
Contact/s: **Mr D Garrett**, Kettering and Thrapston Angling Association, 17 Browning Avenue, Kettering, Northamptonshire, NN16 8NP.
(T) 01536 515547
Mr Mick Cardy, 50 Warmton Lane, Kettering, Northamptonshire.
(T) 01536 518178
Profile: **FT:** Coarse; **WN:** Thorpe Waterville; **WT:** Lake (Still). **Location:** **Main Rd:** A605, A604.
Ref: FH4827

THRAPSTON (RIVER)

River Thrapston, Thrapston, Kettering, **NORTHAMPTONSHIRE**, NN14, **England**.
Profile: **FT:** Coarse; **WN:** Thrapston; **WT:** River (Moving). **Location:** **Nr. Rd:** Thrapston to Denton.
Ref: FH4828

THRAPSTON LAKES

Thrapston Lakes, Thrapston, Kettering, **NORTHAMPTONSHIRE**, NN14, **England**.
Contact/s: **Mr D Garrett**, Kettering and Thrapston Angling Association, 17 Browning Avenue, Kettering, Northamptonshire, NN16 8NP.
(T) 01536 515547
Mr Mick Cardy (Owner), 50 Warmton Lane, Kettering, Northamptonshire.
(T) 01536 518178
Profile: **FT:** Coarse; **WN:** Thrapston Lakes; **WT:** Combination (Still & Moving) **W. Size:** 18000 Metres. **Location:** **Nr. Rd:** A604; **Main Rd:** A14.
Ref: FH4829

THREE LAKES

Three Lakes, Selby, **YORKSHIRE (NORTH)**, YO8, **England**.
Profile: **FT:** Coarse; **WN:** Three Lakes; **WT:** Lake (Still).
Ref: FH4830

THREE SISTERS

Three Sisters, Bryn, Wigan, **LANCASHIRE**, WN, **England**.
Contact/s: Fishery Manager.
(T) 01942 496806
Profile: **FT:** Coarse; **WN:** Three Sisters; **WT:** Lake (Still).
Ref: FH4831

THREIPMUIR RESERVOIRS

Threipmuir Reservoirs, Balerno, **EDINBURGH (CITY OF)**, EH14, **Scotland**.
Contact/s: **Mr A Flemming**, Flemmings Grocery Shop, 42 Main St, Balerno, Edinburgh, EH30 9TQ.
(T) 0131 4493833
Profile: **FT:** Game; **WN:** Threipmuir; **WT:** Reservoir (Still).
Ref: FH4832

THROCKLEY REIGH

Throckley Reigh, Newcastle Upon Tyne, **TYNE AND WEAR**, NE, **England**.
Contact/s: Warden, Tyne Anglers Alliance, PO Box 72, Heaton Rd, Newcastle upon Tyne.
(T) 0191 2681613
Profile: **FT:** Coarse; **WN:** Throckley Reigh; **WT:** Lake (Still).
Ref: FH4833

THROOP FISHERIES

Throop Fisheries, South Lodge, Holdenhurst Village, Bournemouth, **DORSET**, BH8 0EF, **England**.
Contact/s: **Mr Graham Pepler** (Manager), Davis Tackle Shop, 75 Bargates, Christchurch, Dorset, BH23 1QE.
(T) 01202 485169or395532 **(F)** 01202 474261
Mr Kevin Grozier (Permit Secretary), 15 Greenfinch Walk, Hightown, Ringwood, Hampshire, BH24 3RJ.
(T) 01425 471466 **(F)** 01425 471466
Mr Tim Bawn (Secretary), Ringwood Angling Club, 65 Arnewood Rd, Southbourne, Bournemouth, BH6 5DN.
(T) 01202 427305or0860337221
Profile: **FT:** Combination; **WN:** Dorset Stour; **WT:** River (Moving) **W. Size:** 17600 Metres. **Location:** **Main Rd:** A338.
Ref: FH4834

THRYBERGH COUNTRY PARK

Thrybergh Country Park, Doncaster Rd, Thrybergh, Rotherham, **YORKSHIRE (SOUTH)**, S65 4NU, **England**.
Contact/s: Area Manager, Environment Agency, Ridings Area Office, Phoenix House, Global Avenue, Leeds, LS11 8PG.
(T) 0113 2440191or2314834 **(F)** 0113 2134609
Mr Alan Duncan (Countryside Ranger), Thrybergh Country Park, Doncaster Rd, Thrybergh, Rotherham, S65 4NU.
(T) 01709 850353 **(F)** 01709 851532 **(M)** 07971 158692
(E) thrybergh32.freeserve.co.uk
Mr Ivan Machin (Senior Ranger), Thrybergh Country Park, Doncaster Rd, Thrybergh, Rotherham, S65 4NU.
(T) 01709 838317 **(F)** 01709 851532
(E) thrybergh32.freeserve.co.uk
Profile: **FT:** Game; **WN:** Thrybergh Country Park; **WT:** Lake (Still) **W. Size:** 35 Acres. **Location:** **Nr. Rd:** Doncaster Road; **Main Rd:** A630; **Rail:** Rotherham.
Ref: FH4835

THURLEYBEARE POND

Thurleybeare Pond, Taunton Show Ground, Taunton, **SOMERSET**, TA, **England**.
Contact/s: **Mr Peter Lantan** (Secretary), Marshalsea, Cottage Corner, Ilton, Ilminster.
(T) 01460 52519
Profile: **FT:** Coarse; **WN:** Thurleybeare; **WT:** Pond (Still) **W. Size:** 2 Acres. **Location:** **Main Rd:** Ilminster and Taunton.
Ref: FH4836

THURNE MOUTH (RIVER)

River Thurne Mouth, Thurne, Great Yarmouth, **NORFOLK**, NR29, **England**.
Contact/s: **Ms C Delf**, Hedera House, Potter Heigham, Great Yarmouth, Norfolk, NR29 5.
(T) 01692 670242
Profile: **FT:** Coarse; **WN:** Thurne Mouth; **WT:** River (Moving) **W. Size:** 800 Metres.
Ref: FH4837

THURSLAND HILL FARM

Thursland Hill Farm, Thurnham, Lancaster, **LANCASHIRE**, LA2 0AX, **England**.
Contact/s: **Mrs G N Kellet** (Owner/Manager).
(T) 01524 751076
Profile: **FT:** Coarse; **WN:** New Lake; **WT:** Lake (Still); **F. Size:** 4 Acres; **W. Size:** 1 Acre. **Location:** **Nr. Rd:** Moss Lane; **Main Rd:** M6; **Rail:** Lancaster.
Ref: FH4838

TIDBURY GREEN GOLF CLUB

Tidbury Green Golf Club, Tilehouse Lane, Tidbury Green, Solihull, **MIDLANDS (WEST)**, B90 1PT, **England**.
Contact/s: Manager.
(T) 01564 824460
Profile: **FT:** Coarse; **WN:** Tidbury Green Golf Club; **WT:** Lake (Still) **W. Size:** 2 Acres.
Ref: FH4839

TIDDENFOOT PIT

Tiddenfoot Pit, Mentmore Rd, Leighton Buzzard, **BEDFORDSHIRE**, LU7, **England**.
Contact/s: , Leighton Buzzard Angling Club, 54 Pebble Moor, Edlesborough, Leighton Buzzard, LU6 2HZ.
(T) 01582 696759
Profile: **FT:** Coarse; **WN:** Tiddenfoot; **WT:** Gravel Pit (Still) **W. Size:** 10 Acres. **Location:** **Nr. Rd:** Mentmore Road.
Ref: FH4840

TILARY LAKE

Tilary Lake, Flaxfleet, Hull, **HUMBERSIDE**, HU, **England**.
Contact/s: **Mr Bill Brame** (Secretary), Hull and District Angling Association, PO Box 188, Hull, HU9 1AN.
Mr Dave Harold (Fisheries Information Officer), 33 Jipdane Orchard Park, Hull, Yorkshire (East), HU6 9EE.
(T) 01482 809832
Profile: **FT:** Coarse; **WN:** Tilary; **WT:** Lake (Still); **F. Size:** 23 Acres; **W. Size:** 20 Acres. **Location:** **Nr. Rd:** Turn off the B1230,then carry on over railway crossing; **Main Rd:** B1230; **Rail:** Broomfleet.
Ref: FH4841

TILDARG FISHERY

Tildarg Fishery, Tildarg, Ballyclare, **COUNTY ANTRIM**, BT39, **Northern Ireland**.
Contact/s: Manager, Country Sport and Tackle, 9 Rough Lane, Antrim, County Antrim, BT41 2QG.
(T) 028 94467378
Profile: **FT:** Game; **WN:** Tildarg Fishery; **WT:** Combination (Still) **W. Size:** 17 Acres.
Ref: FH4842

TILERY LAKE

Tilery Lake, Wingate, Hartlepool, **CLEVELAND**, TS, **England**.
Profile: **FT:** Coarse; **WN:** Tilery; **WT:** Lake (Still) **W. Size:** 5 Acres. **Location:** **Nr. Rd:** B1280; **Main Rd:** A19.
Ref: FH4843

TILEYARD LANE

Tileyard Lane, Pasture Rd, Barton-upon-Humber, **LINCOLNSHIRE (NORTH)**, DN18, **England**.
Contact/s: **Mr Andy Kirby** (Match Secretary), 5 Queens Avenue, Barton-upon-Humber, Lincolnshire.
(T) 01652 636868day01652636243evening
Mr Tony Dukes (Secretary), 1 Orchard Cl, Barton-upon-Humber, Lincolnshire (North).
(T) 01652 635551
Profile: **FT:** Coarse; **WN:** Tileyard Lane; **WT:** Lake (Still) **W. Size:** 4 Acres. **Location:** **Nr. Rd:** Barrow Road; **Main Rd:** A1077; **Rail:** Waterside Road.
Ref: FH4844

TILGATE LAKES

Tilgate Lakes, Crawley, **SUSSEX (WEST)**, **England**.
Contact/s: .
(T) 01342 842174
Profile: **FT:** Coarse; **WN:** Tilgate Lakes; **WT:** Lake (Still).
Ref: FH4845

TILL (RIVER)

River Till, Saxilby, Lincoln, **LINCOLNSHIRE**, LN, **England**.
Contact/s: **Mr Colin Parker** (Secretary), Lincoln and District Angling Association, 4 Pottergate Cl, Waddington, Lincoln, LN5 9LY.
(T) 01522 720777
Mr Frank Butler (Chairman).
(T) 01522 534174 **(F)** 16/03/01
Profile: **FT:** Coarse; **WN:** Till; **WT:** River (Moving) **W. Size:** 800 Metres. **Location:** **Nr. Rd:** A57; **Main Rd:** A57; **Rail:** Saxilby.
Ref: FH4846

TILL (RIVER)

River Till, Tillbridge Lane, Sturton-By-Stow, Lincoln, **LINCOLNSHIRE**, LN, **England**.
Contact/s: **Mr Colin Parker** (Secretary), Lincoln and District Angling Association, 4 Pottergate Cl, Waddington, Lincoln, LN5 9LY.
(T) 01522 720777
Mr Frank Butler (Chairman).
(T) 01522 534174
Profile: **FT:** Coarse; **WN:** Till Tillbridge; **WT:** River (Moving) **W. Size:** 300 Metres. **Location:** **Nr. Rd:** Tillbridge Lane, A1500; **Main Rd:** A57, A15; **Rail:** Saxilby.
Ref: FH4847

TILTLESWORTH

Tiltlesworth, Meerbrook, Leek, **STAFFORDSHIRE**, ST13 8SH, **England**.
Contact/s: **Mr Dave Naylor**.
(T) 01538 300389
Profile: **FT:** Coarse; **WN:** Tiltlesworth; **WT:** Lake (Still).
Ref: FH4848

TIM HALL LAKE

Tim Hall Lake, Dorrington, Lincoln, **LINCOLNSHIRE**, LN4, **England**.
Contact/s: Fishery Manager.
(T) 01526 833100
Profile: **FT:** Coarse; **WN:** Tim Hall; **WT:** Lake (Still).
Ref: FH4849

TIN DENE FISHERY

Tin Dene Fishery, Bostrase, Millpool, Penzance, **CORNWALL**, TR20 9JG, **England**.
Contact/s: **Mr J Laity** (Owner).
(T) 01736 763486
Profile: **FT:** Coarse; **WN:** Tin Dene Fishery; **WT:** Pond (Still); **F. Size:** 6 Acres; **W. Size:** 2 Acres. **Location:** **Nr. Rd:** A394; **Main Rd:** A30.
Ref: FH4850

TINGRITH COARSE FISHERY

Tingrith Coarse Fishery, Tingrith, Dunstable, **BEDFORDSHIRE**, LU5, **England**.
Contact/s: **Ms Ann Freeman**.
(T) 01525 714012 **(F)** 01525 715255
(E) tingrithfishery@studiofish.co.uk
Profile: **FT:** Coarse; **WN:** Tingrith Coarse Fishery; **WT:** Lake (Still). **Location:** **Nr. Rd:** Flickwick to Tingrith; **Main Rd:** M1 junction12, A5120.
Ref: FH4851

TINGRITH LAKES

Tingrith Lakes, Tingrith, Milton Keynes, **BUCKINGHAMSHIRE**, MK17 9EW, **England**.
(W) www.tingrithfishery.co.uk
Contact/s: **Ms Ann Freeman** (Partner).
(T) 01525 714012 **(F)** 01525 715255 **(M)** 07775 694217
(E) tingrith.fishery@virgin.net
Profile: **FT:** Coarse; **WN:** Tingrith; **WT:** Lake (Still); **F. Size:** 20 Acres; **W. Size:** 11 Acres. **Location:** **Nr. Rd:** A5120; **Main Rd:** M1, junction 12; **Rail:** Harlington.
Ref: FH4852

TINGRITH MANOR LAKE

Tingrith Manor Lake, Tingrith, Dunstable, **BEDFORDSHIRE**, LU, **England**.
Contact/s: **Mr B Matthews** (Secretary), Vauxhall Motors Angling Club, 88 Langford Drive, Luton, Bedfordshire.
(T) 01582 419489
Profile: **FT:** Coarse; **WN:** Tingrith Manor; **WT:** Lake (Still) **W. Size:** 5 Acres. **Location:** **Main Rd:** M1.
Ref: FH4853

TINKERS PONDS

Tinkers Ponds, Woodstock Rd, Willow Bank, Barnsley, **YORKSHIRE (SOUTH)**, **England**.
Contact/s: **Mr Tony Eaton** (Club Secretary), 60 Walton St, Gawber, Barnsley, S75 2PD.
(T) 01226 203090 **(M)** 07979 970201
Profile: **FT:** Coarse; **WN:** Tinker; **WT:** Pond (Still). **Location:** **Nr. Rd:** Woodstock Road; **Main Rd:** A635; **Rail:** Barnsley.
Ref: FH4854

TINNEY WATERS

Tinney Waters, Pyworthy, Holsworthy, **DEVON**, EX22 6LF, **England**.
Contact/s: **Mr Jeff Mason** (Owner).
(T) 01409 271362
(E) jj.m.tinney@tinernet.com
Mrs Jane Mason (Owner).
(T) 01409 271362
(E) jj.m.tinney@tinernet.com
Profile: **FT:** Combination; **WN:** Tinney Waters; **WT:** Combination (Still & Moving). **Location:** **Nr. Rd:** A3072; **Rail:** Exeter.
Ref: FH4855

TINTO TROUT FISHERIES

Tinto Trout Fisheries, Lochlyoch Cottage, Thankerton, Biggar, **LANARKSHIRE (SOUTH)**, ML12 6NH, **Scotland**.
Contact/s: **Mr John Reid** (Owner).
(T) 01899 308697
Profile: **FT:** Game; **WN:** Lyoch; **WT:** Loch (Still); **F. Size:** 10 Acres; **W. Size:** 10 Acres. **Location:** **Nr. Rd:** A73; **Main Rd:** A73; **Rail:** Lanark.
Ref: FH4856

TITCHFIELD ABBEY LAKES

Titchfield Abbey Golf And Coarse Fishing Lakes, Mill Lane, Titchfield, Fareham, **HAMPSHIRE**, PO14, **England**.
Contact/s: **Mr Jimmy Harris** (Manager).
(T) 01329 846606
Profile: **FT:** Coarse; **WT:** Lake (Still).
Location: **Nr. Rd:** Mill Lane; **Main Rd:** A27.
Ref: FH4857

TITTESWORTH RESERVOIR

Tittesworth Reservoir, Tittesworth Fly Fishers Limited, The Fishing Lodge, Meerbrook, Leek, **STAFFORDSHIRE**, ST13 8SW, **England**.
Contact/s: **Mr Dave Naylor**.
(T) 01538 300389
Profile: **FT:** Game; **WN:** Tittesworth; **WT:** Reservoir (Still); **F. Size:** 220 Acres; **W. Size:** 190 Acres. **Location:** **Main Rd:** A53; **Rail:** Stoke-on-Trent.
Ref: FH4858

TOAD HALL FARM

Toad Hall Farm, Inskip, Preston, **LANCASHIRE**, PR4, **England**.
Contact/s: **Brian** (Manager), Lostock Tackle Box, 16 Watkin Lane, Lostock Hall, Preston, PR5 5RD.
(T) 01772 626585 **(F)** 01772 626584
Profile: **FT:** Coarse; **WN:** Toad Hall Farm; **WT:** Pond (Still).
Ref: FH4859

TOAD HALL FISHERY

Toad Hall Fishery, Harewood End, Hereford, **HEREFORDSHIRE**, HR2, **England**.
Contact/s: **Mr Neville Williams** (Manager), Pencoyd, St Own's Cross, Harewood, Herefordshire, HR2 8NG.
(T) 01989 730231
Profile: **FT:** Game; **WN:** Toad Hall; **WT:** Lake (Still).
Ref: FH4860

TOCKENHAM RESERVOIR

Tockenham Reservoir, Lyneham, Chippenham, **WILTSHIRE**, SN15 4, **England**.
Contact/s: **Mr Jeff Parker** (Secretary), Bristol, Bath and Wilts Amalgamation, 16 Lansdown View, Kingswood, Bristol, BS15 4AW.
(T) 01179 672977
Profile: **FT:** Coarse; **WN:** Tockenham; **WT:** Lake (Still) **W. Size:** 12 Acres. **Location:** **Main Rd:** A3102.
Ref: FH4861

TODBER MANOR

Todber Manor, Sturminster Newton, **DORSET**, DT10 1J, **England**.
(W) www.todbermanor.co.uk
Contact/s: **Mr John Candy** (Owner), Manor Farm, Todber, Sturminster Newton, Dorset, DT10 1JB.
(T) 01258 820384 **(F)** 01258 820384
(E) info@todbermanor.co.uk
Profile: **FT:** Coarse; **WN:** Todber; **WT:** Lake (Still) **W. Size:** 2 Acres. **Location:** **Nr. Rd:** B3052; **Main Rd:** A30.
Ref: FH4862

TODDBROOK RESERVOIR

Toddbrook Reservoir, Whaley Bridge, High Peak, **DERBYSHIRE**, SK23, **England**.
Contact/s: **Mr Griffiths** (Fishery Manager).
(T) 01606 723800
Profile: **FT:** Coarse; **WN:** Toddbrook; **WT:** Reservoir (Still).
Ref: FH4863

TOFT NEWTON TROUT FISHERY

Toft Newton Trout Fishery, Toft-Next-Newton, Market Rasen, **LINCOLNSHIRE**, LN8 3NE, **England**.
(W) www.toftnewton.freeserve.co.uk
Mr Andrew Hewitt (Bailiff).
(T) 01673 878453 **(M)** 07730 322191
Profile: **FT:** Game; **WN:** Toft Newton; **WT:** Reservoir (Still); **F. Size:** 60 Acres; **W. Size:** 40 Acres. **Location:** **Main Rd:** A15, A46; **Rail:** Market Rasen.
Ref: FH4864

TOFT POOL

Toft Pool, Toft Hall, Knutsford, **CHESHIRE**, WA16, **England**.
Contact/s: Secretary, Altrincham Angling Society, 37 Crossgates Avenue, Sharston, Manchester.
(T) 0161 2863952
Profile: FT: Coarse; **WN:** Toft Pool; **WT:** Lake (Still) **W. Size:** 400 Metres. **Location: Nr. Rd:** Knutsford to Holmes Chapel; **Main Rd:** A50.
Ref: FH4865

TOLL BAR POND

Toll Bar Pond, Adwick-Le-Street, Doncaster, **YORKSHIRE (SOUTH)**, DN6, **England**.
Contact/s: **Mr Franco Pezzulo** (Owner), Franco's Angling Supplies, 148 High St, Bentley, Doncaster, DN5 0AT.
(T) 01302 876124
Profile: FT: Coarse; **WN:** Toll Bar; **WT:** Pond (Still). **Location: Nr. Rd:** Adwick-le-Street; **Main Rd:** A19, Bentley to Tilts.
Ref: FH4866

TOLLERTON FISHING PONDS

Tollerton Fishing Ponds, Easingwold, Tollerton, York, **YORKSHIRE (NORTH)**, YO61, **England**.
Contact/s: **Mr Brian Pallister** (Owner).
(T) 01347 838115
Profile: FT: Coarse; **WN:** Tollerton; **WT:** Pond (Still) **W. Size:** 3 Acres. **Location: Nr. Rd:** Thirsk to York; **Main Rd:** A19.
Ref: FH4867

TOMBUIE BEAT

Tombuie Beat, Aberfeldy, **PERTH AND KINROSS**, PH15, **Scotland**.
(W) www.fishingnet.com/beats/killiechassie.htm
Contact/s: **Mr J Crystal**, Tombuie Farm House, Aberfeldy, Perth and Kinross, PH15 2JS.
(T) 01887 820127 (F) 01887 829625
Profile: FT: Combination; **WN:** See above; **WT:** Pool (Still).
Ref: FH4868

TONE (RIVER)

River Tone, New Bridge, North Curry, Taunton, **SOMERSET**, TA3, **England**.
Profile: FT: Coarse; **WN:** Tone; **WT:** River (Moving). **Location: Nr. Rd:** West Lyng to North Curry; **Main Rd:** M5, junction 25, then A361 to Othery.
Ref: FH4869

TONE (RIVER)

River Tone, Taunton, **SOMERSET**, TA, **England**.
Contact/s: **Mr I.J. Topp** (Manager), Topp Tackle, 63 Station Rd, Taunton, Somerset, TA1 1PA.
(T) 01823 282518
Profile: FT: Game; **WN:** Tone; **WT:** River (Moving).
Ref: FH4870

TONFORD LAKE

Tonford Lake, Tonford Lane, Chartham Hatch, Canterbury, **KENT**, **England**.
(W) www.midkentfish.demon.co.uk
Contact/s: **Mr Chris Logsdon** (Fisheries Manager), Mid Kent Fisheries, Chilham Water Mill, Mill Lane, Chilham, CT4 8EE.
(T) 01227 730668
(E) chilham@midkentfisheries.co.uk
Profile: FT: Coarse; **WN:** Tonford; **WT:** Lake (Still); **F. Size:** 30 Acres; **W. Size:** 4 Acres. **Location: Nr. Rd:** Tonford Lane; **Main Rd:** A28; **Rail:** Canterbury.
Ref: FH4871

TONG PARK DAM

Tong Park Dam, Baildon, Shipley, **YORKSHIRE (WEST)**, BD18, **England**.
Contact/s: **Mr W M Troman** (Ticket Secretary), Saltaire Angling Association, 7 Hall Royd, Shipley, Yorkshire (West), BD18 3ED.
(T) 01274 583088
Profile: FT: Game; **WN:** Tong Park; **WT:** Dam (Still) **W. Size:** 2 Acres. **Location: Nr. Rd:** A6038; **Main Rd:** A6038; **Rail:** Shipley.
Ref: FH4872

TONGUE OF BOMBIE LOCHAN

Tongue Of Bombie Lochan, Kirkcudbright, **DUMFRIES AND GALLOWAY**, DG6 4, **Scotland**.
Contact/s: **Mr Bradley** (Fishery Manager).
(T) 01557 500258
Profile: FT: Coarse; **WN:** Tongue Of Bombie Lochan; **WT:** Pond (Still).
Ref: FH4873

TONTINE LAKE

Tontine Lake, Osmotherly, Northallerton, **YORKSHIRE (NORTH)**, DL6, **England**.
Contact/s: Secretary.
(T) 01287 630687
Mr Andy Skaife (Secretary), Northallerton Angling Ctre, 3 East Rd, Northallerton, Yorkshire (North), DL6 1ND.
(T) 01609 779140 (F) 01609 779140
Profile: FT: Coarse; **WN:** Tontine; **WT:** Lake (Still). **Location: Main Rd:** A19.
Ref: FH4874

TOP BARN ANGLING CENTRE

Top Barn Angling Centre, Holt Heath, Worcester, **WORCESTERSHIRE**, WR6 6, **England**.
Contact/s: **Mr Brian Lammas**. **(M)** 07712 897109
Profile: FT: Coarse; **WN:** Top Barn Angling Centre; **WT:** Pool (Still). **Location: Nr. Rd:** A443.
Ref: FH4875

TOP FARM POOL

Top Farm Pool, Lymm, **CHESHIRE**, **England**.
(W) www.baymalton-anglingclub.org
Contact/s: **Mr Stewart Godber** (Club Secretary), 38 Edenfield Rd, Mobberley, Cheshire, WA16 7HE.
(T) 01565 872582
Profile: FT: Coarse; **WN:** Top Farm Pool; **WT:** Pool (Still); **F. Size:** 1 Acre; **W. Size:** 1 Acre. **Location: Main Rd:** A56; **Rail:** Warrington.
Ref: FH4876

TOPACRE LAKE

Topacre Lake, Alresford, Winchester, **HAMPSHIRE**, SO21, **England**.
Contact/s: **K Cayzer**, Keepers Cottage, New England Estate, Alresford, Hampshire, SO24.
(T) 01962 732837
Profile: FT: Coarse; **WN:** Topacre; **WT:** Pond (Still). **Location: Nr. Rd:** B3047, B3046; **Main Rd:** A31.
Ref: FH4878

TORHOUSEKIE AND KIRWAUGH

Torhousekie And Kirwaugh, Bladnoch Inn, Bladnoch Village, Wigtown, Newton Stewart, **DUMFRIES AND GALLOWAY**, DG8 9AB, **Scotland**.
Contact/s: **Mr Peter McLaughlin** (Owner).
(T) 01988 402200
(E) peter@bladnoch.freeserve.co.uk
Profile: FT: Game; **WN:** Bladnoch; **WT:** Combination (Still & Moving) **W. Size:** 3000 Metres. **Location: Nr. Rd:** B733; **Main Rd:** B733; **Rail:** Dumfries.
Ref: FH4879

TORNE (RIVER)

River Torne, Doncaster, **YORKSHIRE (SOUTH)**, DN11, **England**.
Contact/s: **Mr Maurice Tate** (Secretary), Doncaster and District Angling Association, 28 Holmescarr Rd, New Rossington, Doncaster, DN11 0QF.
(T) 01302 865482
Profile: FT: Coarse; **WN:** Torne; **WT:** River (Moving).
Ref: FH4880

TORNE (RIVER)

River Torne, Belton, Epworth, Doncaster, **YORKSHIRE (SOUTH)**, DN9 1, **Scotland**.
Contact/s: **Mr Maurice Tate** (Secretary), Doncaster and District Angling Association, 28 Holmescarr Rd, New Rossington, Doncaster, DN11 0QF.
(T) 01302 865482
W Sams (Secretary), Doncaster and District Angling Association, 28 Pipering Lane, Scawthorpe, Doncaster.
(T) 01302 780271
Profile: FT: Coarse; **WN:** Torne; **WT:** River (Moving) **W. Size:** 4800 Metres.
Ref: FH4881

TORRENT (RIVER)

River Torrent, Coalisland, Dungannon, **COUNTY TYRONE**, BT71, **Northern Ireland**.
Contact/s: **Mr Tony Kerr** (Secretary), Coalisland and District Angling Club, 9 Torrent Drive, Coalisland, County Tyrone, BT71 4SG.
(T) 028 87748447
Mr Walter Atkinson (Secretary), Newmills and District Angling Club, Roughan Rd, Newmills, County Tyrone.
(T) 028 87740492
Profile: FT: Game; **WN:** Torrent; **WT:** River (Moving) **W. Size:** 11200 Metres.
Ref: FH4882

TORRIDGE (RIVER)

River Torridge, Bideford, **DEVON**, EX39 4, **England**.
(W) www.riversdale-devon.com
Contact/s: **Mr Eddie Ellison**, Riversdale, Weare Giffard, Bideford, Devon, EX39 4QR.
(T) 01237 423676
(E) riversdale@connectfree.co.uk
Profile: FT: Game; **WN:** Torridge; **WT:** River (Moving) **W. Size:** 1250 Metres. **Location: Nr. Rd:** Weare Giffard; **Main Rd:** A368.
Ref: FH4883

TORRIDGE (RIVER)

River Torridge, Bideford, **DEVON**, EX39, **England**.
Contact/s: **Mr Nick Laws** (Manager), Summerlands Tackle, 3 Golf Links Rd, 16-20 Nelson Rd, Westward Ho!, Devon EX39 1LS.
(T) 01237 471291
Profile: FT: Game; **WN:** Torridge; **WT:** River (Moving).
Ref: FH4884

TORRIDGE (RIVER)

River Torridge, Haytown Beat, Holsworthy, **DEVON**, EX22 7, **England**.
Contact/s: **Mr Fred Cogdell** (Manager), 1 Bailey Trce, Holsworthy, Devon, EX22 7ER.
(T) 01288 381669 (F) 01288 381669
Profile: FT: Game; **WN:** Torridge; **WT:** River (Moving) **W. Size:** 800 Metres.
Ref: FH4885

TORWOOD HOUSE HOTEL

Torwood House Hotel, Glenluce, Newton Stewart, **DUMFRIES AND GALLOWAY**, DG8, **Scotland**.
Contact/s: Fishery Manager.
(T) 01581 300469
Profile: FT: Coarse; **WN:** Torwood House Hotel; **WT:** Lake (Still).
Ref: FH4886

TORY FARM LAKE

Tory Farm Lake, Ponsanooth, Truro, **CORNWALL**, TR3 7HN, **England**.
Contact/s: **Mr A Ayers**.
(T) 01209 861272
Profile: FT: Coarse; **WN:** Tory Farm; **WT:** Lake (Still) **W. Size:** 2 Acres. **Location: Nr. Rd:** Laity Moor Road; **Rail:** Penryn.
Ref: FH4887

TOTTENHILL PIT

Tottenhill Pit, Tottenhill, King's Lynn, **NORFOLK**, PE, **England**.
Contact/s: Manager, The Tackle Box, 38 Tower St, King's Lynn, Norfolk, PE30 1EJ.

(T) 01553 761293
K Allen (Chairman), Mole Cottage, 15 Ten Mile Bank, Littleport, CB6 1EE.
(T) 01383 860936
Martin (Manager), Anglers Corner, 55 London Rd, King's Lynn, Norfolk, PE30 5QH.
(T) 01553 775852
Mr Mick Grief (Secretary), King's Lynn Angling Association, 67 Peckover Way, South Wootton, King's Lynn, PE30 3UE.
(T) 01553 671545
Profile: FT: Coarse; WN: Tottenhill; WT: Gravel Pit (Still) W. Size: 2 Acres. Location: Nr. Rd: Willow Place; Main Rd: A10, South from Norwich.
Ref: FH4888

TOTTIFORD RESERVOIR

Tottiford Reservoir, Okehampton, **DEVON**, EX20, **England**.
Contact/s: Mr Reg England (Manager), Peninsula Coarse Fisheries, St Cleer Depot, Lewdown, Okehampton, Devon EX20 4QT.
(T) 01837 871565 (F) 01837 871534
Profile: FT: Game; WN: Tottiford; WT: Reservoir (Still).
Ref: FH4889

TOWEY (RIVER)

River Towey, Llandovery, **CARMARTHENSHIRE**, SA20 0DX, **Wales**.
Contact/s: Mr Mick Davies.
(T) 01550 720633
Profile: FT: Game; WN: Towey; WT: River (Moving) W. Size: 9600 Metres. Location: Main Rd: A40.
Ref: FH4890

TOWI (RIVER)

River Towi, Llanfynydd Rd, Carmarthen, **CARMARTHENSHIRE**, SA32 7, **Wales**.
Contact/s: Ms Hazel Hudson (Manager), Pantglas Hall, 2 Llanfynydd Rd, Carmarthen, Carmarthenshire, SA32 7BY.
(T) 01558 668741 (F) 01558 668018
Profile: FT: Game; WN: Towi; WT: River (Moving). Location: Nr. Rd: Llanfynydd Road.
Ref: FH4891

TOWN PARK LANE

Town Park Lane, Runcorn, **CHESHIRE**, WA7, **England**.
Profile: FT: Coarse; WN: Town Park Lane; WT: Lake (Still) W. Size: 3 Acres. Location: Nr. Rd: Near Norton Sports Centre.
Ref: FH4892

TOWN PARKS COARSE FISHERY

Town Parks Coarse Fishery, Totnes Rd, Paignton, **DEVON**, TQ4 7PY, **England**.
Contact/s: Mr Paul Gammin (Farmer).
(T) 01803 523133
Profile: FT: Coarse; WN: Town Parks Coarse Fishery; WT: Lake (Still); F. Size: 3 Acres; W. Size: 2 Acres. Location: Nr. Rd: A385; Main Rd: A385; Rail: Paignton.
Ref: FH4893

TOWNSEND FISHERY

Townsend Fishery, Alveley, Bridgnorth, **SHROPSHIRE**, WV15 6NG, **England**.
Contact/s: Mr Andrew Hinton (Assistant).
(T) 01746 762173
Mr Bert Richards (Owner).
(T) 01746 780551
Mr Roger Butler (Assistant).
(T) 01746 780551
Mr Tom Hopkins (Assistant).
(T) 01746 780551
Profile: FT: Coarse; WN: Townsend Fishery; WT: Pond (Still) W. Size: 1 Acre. Location: Nr. Rd: Alveley Fenn Green Road; Main Rd: A442 at Roadhouse.
Ref: FH4894

TOWY (RIVER)

River Towy, Llandeilo, **CARMARTHENSHIRE**, SA19, **Wales**.
Contact/s: Mr Robert James (Information Officer), Rutland Stationers, 68 Rhosmaen St, Llandeilo, SA19 6EN.
(T) 01558 822248
Profile: FT: Game; WN: Towy; WT: River (Moving) W. Size: 14400 Metres. Location: Nr. Rd: Llandeilo and Llanarthne.
Ref: FH4895

TOWY (RIVER)

River Towy, Nantgaredig, Carmarthen, **CARMARTHENSHIRE**, SA32, **Wales**.
Contact/s: Mr Ron Ratti (Hon Secretary), Rhydal Mount, The Parade, Carmarthen, Carmarthenshire.
(T) 01267 237362
Profile: FT: Game; WN: Towy; WT: River (Moving) W. Size: 22400 Metres.
Ref: FH4896

TOWY (RIVER)

River Towy, Carmarthen, **CARMARTHENSHIRE**, SA3, **Wales**.
Contact/s: Mr Herbert Evans (Hon Secretary), 25 Maple Cres, Carmarthen, Carmarthenshire.
(T) 01267 231945
Profile: FT: Game; WN: Towy; WT: River (Moving) W. Size: 6400 Metres.
Ref: FH4897

TOWY (RIVER)

River Towy, Llwynfortune, **CARMARTHENSHIRE**, SA, **Wales**.
Contact/s: Mr Pat Kiernan (Hon Secretary), 48 Waterloo Rd, Penygroes, Llanelli, Carmarthenshire.
(T) 01269 842083
Profile: FT: Game; WN: Towy; WT: River (Moving) W. Size: 1600 Metres. Location: Nr. Rd: Llwynfortune to Glantowy.
Ref: FH4898

TOWY (RIVER)

River Towy, Glynmyrddin Farm, Whitemill, Carmarthen, **CARMARTHENSHIRE**, SA32, **Wales**.
Contact/s: Mr Wyndham Gill (Hon Secretary), 6 Llwynant Drive, Cwmgors, Ammanford, Carmarthenshire, SA18 1RP.
(T) 01269 823648
Profile: FT: Game; WN: Towy; WT: River (Moving) W. Size: 1600 Metres. Location: Nr. Rd: Glynmyrddin Farm.
Ref: FH4899

TOWY (RIVER)

River Towy, Llandeilo, **CARMARTHENSHIRE**, SA19, **Wales**.
Contact/s: Mr Pat Kiernan (Hon Secretary), 48 Waterloo Rd, Penygroes, Llanelli, Carmarthenshire.
(T) 01269 842083
Profile: FT: Game; WN: Towy; WT: River (Moving) W. Size: 2400 Metres. Location: Nr. Rd: Llandeilo to Carmarthen.
Ref: FH4900

TOWY (RIVER)

River Towy, Brecon, **POWYS**, LD3, **Wales**.
Contact/s: , Golden Grove Fishery, Hamdden Ltd, Plas y Ffnnon, Cambrian Way, Brecon LD3 7HP.
(T) 01874 614657
Profile: FT: Game; WN: Towy; WT: River (Moving).
Ref: FH4901

TP WOODS POND

Tp Woods Pond, Eledholt Bank, Huddersfield, **YORKSHIRE (WEST)**, HD7, **England**.
Contact/s: Mr D Rushforth (Secretary), 122 Longwood Gate, Longwood, Huddersfield, Yorkshire (West), HD3 4US.
(T) 01484 651028
Mr R Carter (Bailiff), 10 Varley Rd, Slaithwaite, Yorkshire (West).
(T) 01484 843163
Profile: FT: Coarse; WN: TP Woods; WT: Pond (Still). Location: Nr. Rd: Eledholt Bank; Main Rd: A62; Rail: Huddersfield.
Ref: FH4902

TRAGO MILLS

Trago Mills, Bovey Tracey Rd, Liverton, Newton Abbot, **DEVON**, TQ12 6JD, **England**.
Contact/s: Sports Department Manager.
(T) 01626 821111
Profile: FT: Coarse; WN: Trago Mills; WT: Stream (Moving). Location: Main Rd: A38.
Ref: FH4903

TRANQUIL OTTER

Tranquil Otter (The), The Lough, Thurstonfield, Carlisle, **CUMBRIA**, CA5 6HB, **England**.
Contact/s: Mr Richard Wise.
(T) 01228 576661 (F) 01228 576662
(E) tranquilotter@aol.com
Profile: FT: Game; WN: Tranquil Otter (The); WT: Lake (Still); F. Size: 25 Acres; W. Size: 20 Acres. Location: Nr. Rd: B5307; Main Rd: A595; Rail: Carlisle.
Ref: FH4904

TRAWFFYNYDD RESERVOIR

Trawffynydd Reservoir, Liverpool House, Trawsfynydd, Blaenau Ffestiniog, **GWYNEDD**, LL41, **Wales**.
Contact/s: , Newsagent, Manchester House, Trawsfynydd, Gwynedd, LL41 4UB.
Mr Malcolm Atherton (Secretary).
(T) 01766 770276
Mr Mitch Atherton (Owner), 8 Pantycelyn, Trawsffynydd, Gwynedd, LL41 4UH.
(T) 01766 540435 (F) 01766 540435
(E) idwalwyn@idwal.freeserve.co.uk
Profile: FT: Combination; WN: Trawffynydd Reservoir; WT: Combination (Still & Moving) W. Size: 1200 Acres. Location: Nr. Rd: A4212; Main Rd: A470; Rail: Blaenau Ffestiniog.
Ref: FH4905

TREBEDW FISHERY

Trebedw Fishery, Llandyfriog, Newcastle Emlyn, **CARMARTHENSHIRE**, SA38, **Wales**.
(W) www.fishing-in-wales.co.uk/llandysul-aa/beat14a
Contact/s: Mr Artie Jones (Hon Secretary), Llandysul Angling Association, Glas-y-Dorlan, Llyn-y-Fran Rd, Llandysul, SA44 4JW.
(T) 01559 362317
Profile: FT: Game; WN: Teifi; WT: River (Moving). Location: Main Rd: B4334.
Ref: FH4906

TREBELLAN PARK LAKES

Trebellan Park Lakes, Cubert, Newquay, **CORNWALL**, TR8 5PY, **England**.
Contact/s: Mr Kevin Jago.
(T) 01637 830522
Profile: FT: Coarse; WN: Trebellan Park; WT: Lake (Still) W. Size: 2 Acres. Location: Nr. Rd: Newquay to Cubert; Main Rd: A3075.
Ref: FH4907

TREDIDON BARTON LAKE

Tredidon Barton Lake, Launceston, **CORNWALL**, PL15, **England**.
Contact/s: Mr G Jones.
(T) 01566 86463
Profile: FT: Coarse; WN: Tredidon Barton; WT: Lake (Still). Location: Main Rd: A395; Rail: Launceston.
Ref: FH4908

TREE MEADOW TROUT FISHERY

Tree Meadow Trout Fishery, Deveral Rd, Fraddam, Hayle, **CORNWALL**, TR27, **England**.
Contact/s: Mr John Hodge.
(T) 01736 850899or850583
Profile: FT: Game; WN: Tree Meadow Trout Fishery; WT: Lake (Still); F. Size: 10 Acres; W. Size: 4 Acres. Location: Nr. Rd: Deveral Road; Main Rd: B3302 Hale to Halston.
Ref: FH4909

TREE TOPS FLY FISHERY

Tree Tops Fly Fishery, Llanfynydd, Wrexham, LL11 5HR, **Wales**.
(W) www.walesselfcatering.co.uk

Contact/s: Mr Peter Price (Manager).
(T) 01352 770648
(E) treetopuk@aol.com
Profile: FT: Game; WN: Tree Tops; WT: Lake (Still) W. Size: 10 Acres. **Location:** Nr. Rd: B5101; Main Rd: A541.
Ref: FH4910

TREFALDU FISHERY

Trefaldu Fishery, Trefaldu Farm, Pen Y Clawdd, Monmouth, **MONMOUTHSHIRE**, NP25 4DQ, **Wales**.
Contact/s: Mr Roger Bennett.
(T) 01600 740251
Profile: FT: Coarse; WN: Trefaldu Fishery; WT: Lake (Still) W. Size: 4 Acres. **Location:** Nr. Rd: Monmouth; Main Rd: B4293 turn right to Mitchel Troy.
Ref: FH4911

TREFANT POOL

Trefant Pool, Conwy, LL, **Wales**.
Contact/s: Manager, The Tackle Box, 17 Greenfield Rd, Colwyn Bay, LL29 8EL.
(T) 01492 531104
Profile: FT: Coarse; WN: Trefant; WT: Pool (Still).
Ref: FH4912

TRENCH FISHERIES

Trench Fisheries, Trench Farm, Redhall Lane, Penley, Wrexham, LL13 0NA, **Wales**.
Contact/s: Mr M A Huntbach.
(T) 01978 710098
Profile: FT: Coarse; WN: Trench Fisheries; WT: Pool (Still).
Ref: FH4913

TRENCH POOL

Trench Pool, Telford, **SHROPSHIRE**, TF, **England**.
Contact/s: Manager.
(T) 01952 503550
Profile: FT: Coarse; WN: Trench; WT: Pool (Still).
Ref: FH4914

TRENCHFORD RESERVOIR

Trenchford Reservoir, Dartmoor National Park, Christow, Exeter, **DEVON**, EX6, **England**.
Contact/s: Mr Reg England (Manager), Peninsula Coarse Fisheries, St Cleer Depot, Lewdown, Okehampton, Devon EX20 4QT.
(T) 01837 871565 (F) 01837 871534
Profile: FT: Coarse; WN: Trenchford; WT: Reservoir (Still) W. Size: 33 Acres.
Ref: FH4915

TRENESTRALL LAKE

Trenestrall Lake, Trenestrall Farm, Trenestrall Lake, Ruan High Lanes, St Mawes, Truro, **CORNWALL**, TR2, **England**.
Contact/s: Mr W Palmer (Owner).
(T) 01872 501259
Profile: FT: Coarse; WN: Trenestrall; WT: Lake (Still) W. Size: 2 Acres.
Ref: FH4916

TRENT (RIVER)

River Trent, Whatstandwell, Matlock, **DERBYSHIRE**, DE4, **England**.
Contact/s: Mr A Bunting (Manager), Derwent Hotel, Derby Rd, Whatstandwell, Matlock, DE4 5HG.
(T) 01773 856616
Profile: FT: Game; WN: Trent; WT: River (Moving) W. Size: 400 Metres.
Ref: FH4917

TRENT (RIVER)

River Trent, Borrowash, Derby, **DERBYSHIRE**, DE72, **England**.
Contact/s: Mr O Handley (Secretary), Osprey House, Ogston, Higham, Alfreton, DE55 6EL.
Profile: FT: Coarse; WN: Trent; WT: River (Moving) W. Size: 8000 Metres. **Location:** Nr. Rd: Borrowash to Sawley.
Ref: FH4918

TRENT (RIVER)

River Trent, North Clifton, Trent Lane, Lincoln, **LINCOLNSHIRE**, LN, **England**.
Contact/s: Mr Colin Parker (Secretary), Lincoln and District Angling Association, 4 Pottergate Cl, Waddington, Lincoln, LN5 9LY.
(T) 01522 720777
Mr Frank Butler (Chairman).
(T) 01522 534174
Profile: FT: Coarse; WN: Trent; WT: River (Moving) W. Size: 1500 Metres. **Location:** Nr. Rd: Trent Lane; Main Rd: A1133, A57; Rail: Saxilby.
Ref: FH4919

TRENT (RIVER)

River Trent, Lincoln, **LINCOLNSHIRE**, LN1 2EJ, **England**.
Contact/s: N Barratt.
(T) 01427 718342
W Wrath.
(T) 01427 718342
Profile: FT: Coarse; WN: Trent; WT: River (Moving) W. Size: 200 Metres. **Location:** Main Rd: Lincoln to Gainsborough; Rail: Saxilby.
Ref: FH4920

TRENT (RIVER)

River Trent, Laugherton, Marsh Lane, Lincoln, **LINCOLNSHIRE**, LN, **England**.
Contact/s: Mr Colin Parker (Secretary), Lincoln and District Angling Association, 4 Pottergate Cl, Waddington, Lincoln, LN5 9LY.
(T) 01522 720777
Mr Frank Butler (Chairman).
(T) 01522 534174
Profile: FT: Coarse; WN: Trent; WT: River (Moving) W. Size: 1500 Metres. **Location:** Nr. Rd: A1133 access via Marsh Lane; Main Rd: A156; Rail: Saxilby.
Ref: FH4921

TRENT (RIVER)

River Trent, Osburton Estate, Littleborough, Marton, Gainsborough, **LINCOLNSHIRE**, DN21, **England**.
Contact/s: Mr Colin Parker (Secretary), Lincoln and District Angling Association, 4 Pottergate Cl, Waddington, Lincoln, LN5 9LY.
(T) 01522 720777
Mr Frank Butler (Chairman).
(T) 01522 534174
Mr P Robbinson (Bailiff), 37 Lincoln Rd, Fenton, LN1 2EP.
Profile: FT: Game; WN: Trent; WT: River (Moving) W. Size: 6400 Metres.
Ref: FH4922

TRENT (RIVER)

River Trent, Bob's Island, Newark, **NOTTINGHAMSHIRE**, NG, **England**.
Contact/s: Mr T Ratford (Manager), Newark Angling Ctre, 29 Albert St, Newark, Nottinghamshire, NG24 4BJ.
(T) 01636 686212 (F) 01636 686212
Profile: FT: Coarse; WN: Trent; WT: River (Moving).
Ref: FH4923

TRENT (RIVER)

River Trent, Long Higgin, West Bridgford, Nottingham, **NOTTINGHAMSHIRE**, NG, **England**.
Contact/s: Mr Dave Fallows (Secretary), Parkside Fishing Club, 27 Woodstock Avenue, Radford, Nottingham, NG7 5QP.
(T) 0115 9787350
Profile: FT: Coarse; WN: Trent; WT: River (Moving) W. Size: 1624 Metres. **Location:** Nr. Rd: A6011; Main Rd: A6011; Rail: Nottingham Midland.
Ref: FH4924

TRENT (RIVER)

River Trent, Retford, **NOTTINGHAMSHIRE**, DN22, **England**.
Contact/s: Manager, Autosport, 2 Mansfield Rd, Creswell, Worksop.
(T) 01909 721322
Profile: FT: Coarse; WN: Trent; WT: River (Moving) W. Size: 10400 Metres. **Location:** Nr. Rd: Lound to East Retford.
Ref: FH4925

TRENT (RIVER)

Trent (River), Main St, Fiskerton, Newark-on-Trent, **NOTTINGHAMSHIRE**, **England**.
Contact/s: Mr Tony Eaton (Club Secretary), 60 Walton St, Gawber, Barnsley, S75 2PD.
(T) 01226 203090 (M) 07979 970201
Profile: FT: Coarse; WN: Trent; WT: River (Moving) W. Size: 900 Metres. **Location:** Nr. Rd: Main Street; Main Rd: A612; Rail: Fiskerton.
Ref: FH4926

TRENT (RIVER)

River Trent, Colwick Country Park, River Rd, Nottingham, **NOTTINGHAMSHIRE**, NE4, **England**.
(W) www.boat86.freeserve.co.uk
Contact/s: Mr Mick Weaver (Park Warden), Colwick Country Park, Colwick Hall, Colwick, Nottingham, NG4 2DW.
(T) 0115 9870785
(E) rainbow@boat86.freeserve.co.uk
Profile: FT: Combination; WN: Trent; WT: River (Moving) W. Size: 1000 Metres. **Location:** Nr. Rd: River Road; Main Rd: A612 Nottingham to Southwell; Rail: Netherfield.
Ref: FH4927

TRENT (RIVER)

River Trent, Beeston, Attenborough, Nottingham, **NOTTINGHAMSHIRE**, NG9 5NB, **England**.
Contact/s: Mr Roy (Bailiff).
(T) 07790 543434
Mrs Taylor.
(T) 0115 9160544
Profile: FT: Coarse; WN: Trent; WT: River (Moving). **Location:** Nr. Rd: The Strand; Main Rd: A1; Rail: Attenborough.
Ref: FH4928

TRENT (RIVER)

River Trent, Stock Bardolth, Nottingham, **NOTTINGHAMSHIRE**, NG, **England**.
Contact/s: Mr William Belshaw (Secretary), 17 Spring Green, Clifton Estate, Nottingham, NG11 9EF.
(T) 0115 9216645
Profile: FT: Coarse; WN: Trent; WT: River (Moving) W. Size: 10000 Metres. **Location:** Nr. Rd: Stock Bardolth to Beton Joyce to Gunthorpe.
Ref: FH4929

TRENT (RIVER)

River Trent, Burton Joyce, Nottingham, **NOTTINGHAMSHIRE**, NG, **England**.
Contact/s: Mr Tim Aplin, Matchman Supplies, 4 Ella Rd, West Bridgford, Nottingham, NG2 5GW.
(T) 0115 9813834
Mr William Belshaw (Secretary), 17 Spring Green, Clifton Estate, Nottingham, NG11 9EF.
(T) 0115 9216645
Profile: FT: Coarse; WN: Trent; WT: River (Moving).
Ref: FH4930

TRENT (RIVER)

River Trent, Beeston, Nottingham, **NOTTINGHAMSHIRE**, NG9, **England**.
Contact/s: Mr I Foulds (Secretary), Nottingham Angling Association, 95 Ilkeston Rd, Nottingham, Nottinghamshire, NG7 3HA.
(T) 0115 9033881or9708080
Profile: FT: Coarse; WN: Trent; WT: River (Moving) W. Size: 200 Metres.
Ref: FH4931

TRENT (RIVER)

River Trent, Radcliffe, Nottingham, **NOTTINGHAMSHIRE**, NG, **England**.
Contact/s: Secretary, Nottingham Federation of Anglers, Matchman Supplies, 4 Ella Rd,

West Bridgford, NG2 5GW.
(T) 0115 9813834
Profile: FT: Coarse; WN: River Trent; WT: River (Moving).
Ref: FH4932

TRENT (RIVER)

River Trent, Craythorpe And Hoveringham Rd, Hoveringham, Nottingham, **NOTTINGHAMSHIRE**, NG14, **England**.
Contact/s: **Mr Jack Bradbury**, 19 Ethel Avenue, Hucknall, Nottinghamshire, NG14 8DB.
(T) 0115 9634487
Mrs I Cotah, 4 The Spinney, Bulcote, Nottinghamshire, NG14 5GX.
(T) 0115 9313668
Profile: FT: Coarse; WN: Trent; WT: River (Moving) W. Size: 2180 Metres. **Location:** Main Rd: A614; Rail: Lowdam.
Ref: FH4933

TRENT (RIVER)

River Trent, Nottingham, **NOTTINGHAMSHIRE**, NG, **England**.
Contact/s: **G R Dennis**, 11 First Avenue, Carlton, Nottingham, NG4 1PH.
Profile: FT: Coarse; WN: Trent; WT: River (Moving) W. Size: 50 Metres. **Location:** Main Rd: Radcliffe Road; Rail: Midland.
Ref: FH4934

TRENT (RIVER)

Trent (River), Wychnor Estate, Alrewas, **STAFFORDSHIRE**, **England**.
Contact/s: **Mr John Turner** (Hon Secretary), Prince Albert Angling Society, 15 Pexhill Drive, Macclesfield, Cheshire, SK10 3LP.
(T) 01625 422010
Profile: FT: Coarse; WN: Trent; WT: River (Moving) W. Size: 1000 Metres. **Location:** Main Rd: A513.
Ref: FH4935

TRENT (RIVER)

Trent (River), Willowbrook Farm, Alrewas, **STAFFORDSHIRE**, **England**.
Contact/s: **Mr John Turner** (Hon Secretary), Prince Albert Angling Society, 15 Pexhill Drive, Macclesfield, Cheshire, SK10 3LP.
(T) 01625 422010
Profile: FT: Coarse; WN: Trent; WT: River (Moving) W. Size: 500 Metres. **Location:** Nr. Rd: A38; Rail: Burton-upon-Trent.
Ref: FH4936

TRENT (RIVER)

River Trent, Stone, **STAFFORDSHIRE**, ST15, **England**.
Contact/s: Manager, Dales Tackle Shop, Albert Sq, Stone, Staffordshire, ST15 8 HQ.
(T) 01785 813708
Mr A Kenny (Secretary), Stone and District Angling Society, 24 Albert Avenue, Stone, Staffordshire, ST15.
(T) 01785 819035
Profile: FT: Game; WN: Trent; WT: River (Moving) W. Size: 750 Metres.
Ref: FH4937

TRENT (RIVER)

River Trent, Sheffield, **YORKSHIRE (SOUTH)**, S, **England**.
Contact/s: Secretary, Severn Trent Water plc, PO Box 218, Sheffield, Yorkshire, S1 1BU.
Profile: FT: Coarse; WN: Trent; WT: River (Moving).
Ref: FH4938

TRENT AND MERSEY CANAL

Trent And Mersey Canal, Sandbach, **CHESHIRE**, CW11, **England**.
Contact/s: Fishery Manager.
(T) 01270 215141
Profile: FT: Coarse; WN: Trent and Mersey; WT: Canal (Still).
Ref: FH4939

TRENT AND MERSEY CANAL

Trent And Mersey Canal, Egginton, Derby, **DERBYSHIRE**, DE65, **England**.
(W) www.angling-fishing.co.uk
Contact/s: Manager, Angler's Corner, 344 Osmaston Rd, Derby, Derbyshire, DE24 8AF.
(T) 01332 343870
Mr Alan Miller (Secretary), Pride of Derby Angling Association, 16 Mercia Drive, Willington, Derby, DE65 6DA.
(T) 01283 702701 (M) 07770 415541
(E) amiller@btinternet.co.uk
Profile: FT: Coarse; WN: Trent and Mersey; WT: Canal (Still) W. Size: 6500 Metres.
Location: Nr. Rd: A38 Derby to Burton-on-Trent.
Ref: FH4940

TRENT AND MERSEY CANAL

Trent And Mersey Canal, Hunts Lock To To Alrewas Village, Burton-on-Trent, **STAFFORDSHIRE**, DE13, **England**.
Contact/s: Manager.
(T) 01543 491228
Profile: FT: Coarse; WN: Trent and Mersey; WT: Canal (Still) W. Size: 3200 Metres.
Location: Nr. Rd: Fradley Road; Main Rd: A513.
Ref: FH4941

TRENT AND MERSEY CANAL

Trent And Mersey Canal, Church Lawton, Stoke-on-Trent, **STAFFORDSHIRE**, ST7, **England**.
Contact/s: Fishery Manager.
(T) 01270 882019
Profile: FT: Coarse; WN: Trent and Mersey; WT: Canal (Still).
Ref: FH4942

TRENT AND MERSEY CANAL

Trent And Mersey Canal, Harecastle Tunnel, Kidsgrove, Stoke-on-Trent, **STAFFORDSHIRE**, ST7, **England**.
Contact/s: Fishery Manager.
(T) 01829 732748
Profile: FT: Coarse; WN: Trent and Mersey; WT: Canal (Still).
Ref: FH4943

TRENT AND MERSEY CANAL

Trent And Mersey Canal, Rode Heath, Stoke-on-Trent, **STAFFORDSHIRE**, ST7, **England**.
Contact/s: Fishery Manager.
(T) 01782 851128
Profile: FT: Coarse; WN: Trent and Mersey; WT: Canal (Still).
Ref: FH4944

TRENT AND MERSEY CANAL

Trent And Mersey Canal, Hanley - Barlaston, Stoke-on-Trent, **STAFFORDSHIRE**, **England**.
(W) www.fentondas.co.uk
Contact/s: **Mr C Yates** (Club Secretary), The Puzzles, 5 Gatley Gr, Meir Park, Stoke-on-Trent, Staffordshire ST3 7SH.
(T) 01782 396913
Profile: FT: Coarse; WN: Trent and Mersey; WT: Canal (Still) W. Size: 11263 Metres.
Location: Nr. Rd: Various; Main Rd: A50; Rail: Stoke Station or Barlaston.
Ref: FH4945

TRENT COUNTRY PARK LAKES

Trent Country Park Lakes, Enfield, London, **LONDON (GREATER)**, EN, **England**.
Contact/s: **Mr Derek Green** (Fishery Manager).
(T) 020 84498706
Profile: FT: Coarse; WN: Trent Country Park Lakes; WT: Lake (Still).
Ref: FH4946

TRENT PARK LAKES

Trent Park Lakes, Cockfosters, London, **LONDON (GREATER)**, N14 4, **England**.
Contact/s: Park Ranger.
(T) 020 84498706
Profile: FT: Coarse; WN: Trent Park; WT: Lake (Still) W. Size: 8 Acres. **Location:** Nr. Rd: A111 to Cockfosters; Main Rd: M25, junction 24.
Ref: FH4947

TRENTHAM GARDENS

Trentham Gardens, Stone Rd, Trentham, Stoke-on-Trent, **STAFFORDSHIRE**, ST4 8AX, **England**.
Contact/s: **Mr Simon Johnson** (Fisheries Manager).
(T) 01782 657341
Profile: FT: Coarse; WN: Trentham Gardens; WT: Lake (Still) W. Size: 85 Acres.
Ref: FH4948

TRETHIGGEY FARM POND

Trethiggey Farm Pond, Quintral Dawns, Newquay, **CORNWALL**, TR, **England**.
Contact/s: **Mr Eustice**.
Profile: FT: Coarse; WN: Trethiggey Farm; WT: Pond (Still).
Ref: FH4949

TREVELLA PARK

Trevella Caravan And Camping Park, Crantock, Newquay, **CORNWALL**, TR, **England**.
Profile: FT: Coarse; WN: Trevella Caravan And Camping Park; WT: Lake (Still) W. Size: 2 Acres. **Location:** Main Rd: A30, A3075.
£Fr
Ref: FH4950

TRI NANT TROUT FARM

Tri Nant Trout Farm, Llantrisant, Pontyclun, **RHONDDA CYNON TAFF**, CF72 8LQ, **Wales**.
Contact/s: **Mrs Barbara Johnson** (Owner).
(T) 01443 228316
Profile: FT: Game; WN: Trinant; WT: Lake (Still) W. Size: 6 Acres. **Location:** Main Rd: Llantrisant.
Ref: FH4951

TRIANGLE LAKE

Triangle Lake, Shalmsford St, Canterbury, **KENT**, **England**.
(W) www.midkentfish.demon.co.uk
Contact/s: **Mr Chris Logsdon** (Fisheries Manager), Mid Kent Fisheries, Chilham Water Mill, Mill Lane, Chilham, CT4 8EE.
(T) 01227 730668
(E) chilham@midkentfisheries.co.uk
Profile: FT: Coarse; WN: Triangle; WT: Lake (Still); F. Size: 10 Acres; W. Size: 2 Acres.
Location: Main Rd: A28; Rail: Chartham.
Ref: FH4952

TRIANGS FISHERY

Triangs Fishery, Kirton Rd, Doncaster, **YORKSHIRE (SOUTH)**, DN, **England**.
Contact/s: **Mr Peter Turner**.
(T) 01405 816402
Profile: FT: Coarse; WN: Triang's; WT: Lake (Still). **Location:** Main Rd: A614.
Ref: FH4953

TRI-LAKES

Tri-Lakes, Yateley Rd, Sandhurst, **BERKSHIRE**, GU47 8JQ, **England**.
(W) www.trilakes.co.uk
Contact/s: **Mr Colin Homewood** (Fishery Manager), Tri-Lakes, Yateley Rd, Sandhurst, Berkshire, GU47 8jQ.
(T) 01252 873191
Profile: FT: Coarse; WN: Tri; WT: Lake (Still); F. Size: 13 Acres; W. Size: 8 Acres.
Location: Nr. Rd: A321; Main Rd: M3, junction 4 or 4a; Rail: Sandhurst Halt.
Ref: FH4954

TRIMDON POND

Trimdon Pond, Trimdon, Trimdon Station, **COUNTY DURHAM**, TS29, **England**.
Contact/s: **Mr Colin Houghton**.
(T) 01429 881645
Mr Ron McTeer.
(T) 01429 880027
Profile: FT: Coarse; WN: Trimdon; WT: Pond (Still) W. Size: 2 Acres.
Ref: FH4955

TRIMPLEY RESERVOIR

Trimpley Reservoir, Bewdley, **WORCESTERSHIRE**, DY12, **England**.
Profile: **FT**: Combination; **WN**: Trimpley; **WT**: Reservoir (Still).
Ref: FH4956

TRING RESERVOIRS

Tring Reservoirs, Reservoir House, Watery Lane, Startops End, Marsworth, Tring, **HERTFORDSHIRE**, HP23 4LY, **England**.
Contact/s: Manager, Waddesdon Estate, Queen St, Waddesdon, Aylesbury, Buckinghamshire, HP18 0JW.
Mr Bernard Double (Head Bailiff).
(T) 01442 822379
Profile: **FT**: Coarse; **WN**: Tring; **WT**: Reservoir (Still); **F. Size**: 300 Acres; **W. Size**: 220 Acres. **Location:** **Nr. Rd**: B489; **Main Rd**: A41; **Rail**: Tring.
Ref: FH4957

TROCHRY BEAT

Trochry Beat, Dunkeld, **PERTH AND KINROSS**, PH8, **Scotland**.
(W) www.fishingnet.com/beats/braan/trochry77a.htm
Contact/s: **Mrs Diana MacDonald** (Permit Contact).
Mrs Vicky Hammer (Owner), Kettles of Dunkeld, 15-17 Atholl St, Dunkeld, Perth and Kinross, PH8 0AR.
(T) 01350 727556
Profile: **FT**: Game; **WN**: Trochry Beat; **WT**: Pool (Still).
Ref: FH4958

TROED-Y-BRYN FISHERY

Troed-Y-Bryn Fishery, Troed-Y-Bryn, Cribyn, Lampeter, **CEREDIGION**, SA48 7QH, **Wales**.
Contact/s: **Mr Les Edwards** (Manager).
(T) 01570 470798
Profile: **FT**: Game; **WN**: Troed-Y-Bryn Fishery; **WT**: Lake (Still). **Location:** **Nr. Rd**: B4337; **Main Rd**: A475 to Llanwnen.
Ref: FH4959

TROTHY (RIVER)

River Trothy, Raglan, Usk, **MONMOUTHSHIRE**, NP15, **Wales**.
Contact/s: **Mr John Taylor** (Hon Secretary), 23 Adenfield Way, Rhoose, Glamorgan (Vale of), CF62 3EA.
(T) 01446 711216
Profile: **FT**: Game; **WN**: Trothy; **WT**: River (Moving). **Location:** **Nr. Rd**: Raglan to Monmouth; **Main Rd**: A40.
Ref: FH4960

TROUT POND BARN

Trout Pond Barn, Acklam, Malton, **YORKSHIRE (NORTH)**, YO17, **England**.
Contact/s: **Mr Phillips**.
(T) 01653 693088or658468
Profile: **FT**: Game; **WN**: Trout Pond Barn; **WT**: Pond (Still). **Location:** **Main Rd**: A64.
Ref: FH4961

TRYWERYN (RIVER)

River Tryweryn, Bala, **GWYNEDD**, LL23, **Wales**.
Contact/s: **Mr Gumbley** (Hon Secretary), Mawnog, Fach, Bala, Gwynedd.
(T) 01678 520816
Mr Dewi Evans (Secretary), Bala and District Angling Club, 33 High St, Bala, Gwynedd, LL23 7AF.
(T) 01678 520370 (F) 01678 520370
Profile: **FT**: Game; **WN**: Tryweryn; **WT**: Stream (Moving) **W. Size**: 3200 Metres. **Location:** **Nr. Rd**: A4212; **Rail**: Wrexham.
Ref: FH4962

TUCKING MILL

Tucking Mill, Midford Valley, Bath, **SOMERSET**, BA, **England**.
Contact/s: Customer Services, Wessex Water, Billing Ctre, Clevedon Walk, Nailsea, Bristol, BS48 1WW.
(T) 01179 290611 (F) 01275 810519
Mr H Morris (Secretary), 86 North St, Downend, Bristol, BS16 5SF.
Profile: **FT**: Coarse; **WN**: Tucking Mill; **WT**: Lake (Still). **Location:** **Main Rd**: A36.
£Fr
Ref: FH4963

TUFNELL MERE

Tufnell Mere, Broads Green, Great Waltham, Chelmsford, **ESSEX**, CM3, **England**.
Contact/s: **Mr Frank Wright** (Membership Secretary), Chelmsford Angling Association, 61 Readers Court, Great Baddow, Chelmsford, CM2 8EX.
(T) 01245 474246or264832
(E) frank@chelmsfordaa.freeserve.co.uk
Profile: **FT**: Coarse; **WN**: Tufnell; **WT**: Mere (Still).
Ref: FH4964

TULLICH FISHERY

Tullich Fishery, Tullich By Ballater, Ballater, **ABERDEENSHIRE**, AB35 5SB, **Scotland**.
Contact/s: **Mr Davie Gill** (Manager).
(T) 01339 755648
Profile: **FT**: Game; **WN**: Tullich; **WT**: Reservoir (Still) **W. Size**: 6 Acres.
Ref: FH4965

TULLNAWOOD LAKE

Tullnawood Lake, Darkley, Armagh, **COUNTY ARMAGH**, BT60, **Northern Ireland**.
Contact/s: **Cathal Doyle** (Secretary), Armagh Fisheries Ltd, 6 Knockamell Park, Armagh, County Armagh, BT61 7HJ.
(T) 028 37522068after6pm
Mr Dessie Cartmill (Sub Treasurer), Armagh Fisheries Ltd, G I Stores, 5 Dobbin St, Armagh, County Armagh.
(T) 028 37522335 (F) 028 37522335
Profile: **FT**: Game; **WN**: Tullnawood; **WT**: Lake (Still).
Ref: FH4966

TULLYGIVEN LOUGH

Tullygiven Lough, Caledon, **COUNTY TYRONE**, BT68 4, **Northern Ireland**.
Contact/s: **Mrs Liz Salter** (Manager), Aughnacloy Development Association, The McCreedy Mill Centre, Aughnacloy, County Tyrone, BT69 6AL.
(T) 028 85557002
Profile: **FT**: Coarse; **WN**: Tullygiven; **WT**: Lough (Still). **Location:** **Nr. Rd**: Dungannon to Caledon Road; **Main Rd**: B45.
Ref: FH4967

TULLYLAGAN (RIVER)

River Tullylagan, Cookstown, **COUNTY TYRONE**, BT80, **Northern Ireland**.
Contact/s: Manager, Tullylagan Country House Hotel, 40B Tullylagan Rd, Cookstown, County Tyrone, BT80 8UP.
(T) 028 86765100
Manager, Tullylagan Petrol Station, 135 Dungannon Rd, Cookstown, County Tyrone, BT80 9BD.
(T) 028 86765110
Profile: **FT**: Game; **WN**: Tullylagan; **WT**: River (Moving) **W. Size**: 1600 Metres.
Ref: FH4968

TULLYNAWOOD RESERVOIR

Tullynawood Reservoir, Armagh, **COUNTY ARMAGH**, BT60, **Northern Ireland**.
Contact/s: **Dessie Cartmill** (Manager), Armagh Fisheries Ltd, G I Stores, 5 Dobbin St, Armagh, County Armagh.
(T) 028 37522335 (F) 028 37522335
Mr Peter McKinney (Project Manager), Armagh Fisheries Ltd, 50 Ballynahonemore Rd, Armagh, County Armagh, BT60 1HY.
(T) 028 37511738 (M) 07775 805670
Profile: **FT**: Game; **WN**: Tullynawood; **WT**: Reservoir (Still) **W. Size**: 148 Acres.
Ref: FH4969

TULLYPOWRIE BEAT

Tullypowrie Beat, Strathtay, Pitlochry, **PERTH AND KINROSS**, PH9, **Scotland**.
(W) www.fishingnet.com/beats/tullypowrie.htm
Contact/s: **Mrs S Simon**, Tullypowrie, Grandtully, Strathtay, Perth and Kinross, PH9 0PG.
Profile: **FT**: Combination; **WN**: Falls, Tullypowrie, Hall and Church; **WT**: Pool (Still).
Ref: FH4970

TULLYWEST FISHERY

Tullywest Fishery, 6 Tullywest Rd, Saintfield, Ballynahinch, **COUNTY DOWN**, BT24 7LY, **Northern Ireland**.
Contact/s: Fishery Manager.
(T) 028 97519113
Profile: **FT**: Game; **WN**: Tullywest Fishery; **WT**: Lough (Still).
Ref: FH4971

TUNNEL BARN FARM

Tunnel Barn Farm, Shrewley Common, Shrewley, Warwick, **WARWICKSHIRE**, CV35 7AN, **England**.
(W) www.tunnelbarnfarm.com
Contact/s: **Mr Mike Hamlington**.
(T) 01926 842975 (F) 0121 5542438
Profile: **FT**: Combination; **WN**: Tunnel Barn Farm; **WT**: Combination (Still). **Location:** **Main Rd**: Old Warwick Road; **Rail**: Hatton.
Ref: FH4972

TUNSTALL RESERVOIR

Tunstall Reservoir, Wolsingham, Weardale, Bishop Auckland, **COUNTY DURHAM**, DL13, **England**.
Contact/s: **Mr Graham Peadon** (Manager).
(T) 01388 527293
Profile: **FT**: Game; **WN**: Tunstall; **WT**: Reservoir (Still).
Ref: FH4973

TURBARY HOUSE NURSARY

Turbary House Nursery, Whitestake, Preston, **LANCASHIRE**, **England**.
Contact/s:
(T) 01772 697337
Profile: **FT**: Coarse; **WN**: Turbary House Nursery; **WT**: Lake (Still).
Ref: FH4974

TURF CROFT FARM

Turf Croft Farm, Forest Rd, Burley, Ringwood, **HAMPSHIRE**, BH24, **England**.
Contact/s: **Mr Stewart Duell** (Fishery Manager).
(T) 01425 403743
Profile: **FT**: Coarse; **WN**: Turf Croft; **WT**: Lake (Still) **W. Size**: 2 Acres. **Location:** **Nr. Rd**: Forest Road; **Main Rd**: A31.
Ref: FH4975

TURFMOOR FISHERY

Turfmoor Fishery, Edgerley, Oswestry, **SHROPSHIRE**, SY10, **England**.
Contact/s: **Mr Maddocks** (Owner).
(T) 01743 741512
Profile: **FT**: Combination; **WN**: Turfmoor Fishery; **WT**: Pool (Still).
Ref: FH4976

TURKS HEAD LAKE

Turks Head Lake, Hunters Fen Pub, Smithy Fen, Cottenham, Cambridge, **CAMBRIDGESHIRE**, CB4, **England**.
Contact/s: **R T Norman**.
(T) 01954 250687
Profile: **FT**: Coarse; **WN**: Turk's Head; **WT**: Lake (Still).
Ref: FH4977

TURKS HEAD RESERVOIR

Turks Head Reservoir, Macclesfield, **CHESHIRE**, SK11, **England**.
Contact/s: **Mr A Jones** (Secretary), 10 Purley Avenue, Northenden, Manchester, Lancashire, M23.
Profile: **FT**: Coarse; **WN**: Turks Head; **WT**: Reservoir (Still).
Ref: FH4978

TURNAFACE TROUT FISHERY

Turnaface Trout Fishery, Moneymore, Magherafelt, **COUNTY LONDONDERRY**, BT45 7, **Northern Ireland**.
Contact/s: **Ms Betty Ball** (Manager).
(T) 028 86748211
Profile: FT: Game; **WN:** Turnaface; **WT:** Lake (Still) **W. Size:** 4 Acres.
Ref: FH4979

TURNAGROVE FISHERY

Turnagrove Fishery, The Dromes Road, Armoy, Ballymoney, **COUNTY ANTRIM**, BT53, **Northern Ireland**.
Contact/s: **Mr John Barr** (Manager), 2 Ballure Heights, Corkey, Ballymena, County Antrim, BT44 9HT.
(T) 028 27641766
Profile: FT: Game; **WN:** Turnagrove Fishery; **WT:** Lake (Still). **Location:** **Main Rd:** The Dromes Road.
Ref: FH4980

TURNERS PADDOCK LAKE

Turners Paddock Lake, Stourhead, Mere, Warminster, **WILTSHIRE**, BA12, **England**.
Contact/s: **Mr John Candy**, Manor Farm, Todber, Sturminster Newton, Dorset, DT10 1JB.
(T) 01258 820384
Mr Simon Hebditch (Hon Secretary), 5 Ham Court, Shaftsbury Rd, Gillingham, Dorset, SP8 4LU.
(T) 01747 824817
Profile: FT: Coarse; **WN:** Turners Paddock; **WT:** Lake (Still). **Location:** **Main Rd:** A303.
Ref: FH4981

TURNERS POOL

Turners Pool, Swythamley, Rushton Spencer, Macclesfield, **CHESHIRE**, SK11, **England**.
Contact/s: **Mr S W Wilshaw** (Owner).
(T) 01260 227225
Mrs Olive Wilshaw (Owner).
(T) 01260 227225
Profile: FT: Coarse; **WN:** Turners; **WT:** Pool (Still) **W. Size:** 4 Acres. **Location:** **Main Rd:** Wincle to Rushton Spencer Road.
Ref: FH4982

TURNSIDE POOL

Turnside Pool, Ferryhill, Durham, **COUNTY DURHAM**, DH, **England**.
Contact/s: **A Roxley** (Secretary), Ferryhill and District Angling Club, 60 Linden Rd, West Cornforth, County Durham.
(T) 0191 3883557
Profile: FT: Coarse; **WN:** Turnside; **WT:** Pool (Still) **W. Size:** 1 Acre. **Location:** **Nr. Rd:** A617; **Main Rd:** A1.
Ref: FH4983

TURSDALE POND

Tursdale Pond, Ferryhill, Coxhoe, Durham, **COUNTY DURHAM**, DH6, **England**.
Contact/s: **Mr Barry Hignett** (Secretary), Ferryhill and District Angling Club, 74 Grasmere Rd, Garden Farm Estate, Chester-le-Street, County Durham.
(T) 0191 3883557
Mr S Kent (Membership Secretary), 4 Belsay Cl, Ferryhill, County Durham, DL17 8SX.
Mr Steve Wilkinson (Manager).
(T) 0191 3839010
Profile: FT: Coarse; **WN:** Tursdale (Ferryhill); **WT:** Pond (Still). **Location:** **Main Rd:** A1, B6295.
Ref: FH4984

TURSDALE POND (LANGLEY PARK)

Tursdale Pond (Langley Park), Tursdale, Coxhoe, Durham, **COUNTY DURHAM**, DH6, **England**.
Contact/s: **Mr Colin Donnelly** (Chairman), Langley Park Angling Club, 10 South View, Langley Park, Durham, DH7 9YQ.
(T) 0191 3736325
Profile: FT: Coarse; **WN:** Tursdale (Langley Park); **WT:** Pond (Still). **Location:** **Nr. Rd:** Field Track; **Main Rd:** A1, B6295.
Ref: FH4985

TURTON & ENTWISTLE RESERVOIR

Turton And Entwistle Reservoir, Croston, Preston, **LANCASHIRE**, PR5, **England**.
Contact/s: **Mr I Rigby** (Secretary), 10 Wayoh Croft, Edgworth, Bolton, BL7 0DF.
(T) 01204 852049
Profile: FT: Game; **WN:** Turton and Entwistle; **WT:** Reservoir (Still). **Location:** **Nr. Rd:** Batridge Road; **Main Rd:** A666.
Ref: FH4986

TWEED (RIVER)

River Tweed, Glenmoriston, Inverness, **HIGHLAND**, IV63, **Scotland**.
Contact/s: **Mr J H Leeming**, Stichill House, Kelso, Scottish Borders, TD5 7TB.
(T) 01573 470280 (F) 01573 470259
Profile: FT: Game; **WN:** Tweed (Glenormiston); **WT:** River (Moving) **W. Size:** 3200 Metres. **Location:** **Nr. Rd:** A72 Innerleithen to Peebles Road; **Main Rd:** B7062 or B709.
Ref: FH4987

TWEED (RIVER)

River Tweed, Chatton, Alnwick, **NORTHUMBERLAND**, NE66, **England**.
Contact/s: Secretary, Chatton Angling Association, 10 Church Hill, Alnwick, Northumberland.
Profile: FT: Combination; **WN:** Tweed; **WT:** Tributary (Moving) **W. Size:** 9680 Metres.
Ref: FH4988

TWEED (RIVER)

River Tweed, Pedwell, Norham, Berwick-upon-Tweed, **NORTHUMBERLAND**, TD15, **England**.
Contact/s: **Mr J H Leeming**, Stichill House, Kelso, Scottish Borders, TD5 7TB.
(T) 01573 470280 (F) 01573 470258
Profile: FT: Game; **WN:** Tweed (Pedwell); **WT:** River (Moving) **W. Size:** 2400 Metres. **Location:** **Nr. Rd:** B6470; **Main Rd:** A698.
Ref: FH4989

TWEED (RIVER)

River Tweed, Berwick-upon-Tweed, **NORTHUMBERLAND**, TD15, **England**.
Contact/s: **Mr R G Wharton** (Secretary), Ladykirk and Norham Angling Association, 8 St Cuthberts Sq, Norham, Berwick-upon-Tweed, Northumberland TD15 2LE.
(T) 01289 382467
Profile: FT: Game; **WN:** Tweed; **WT:** River (Moving) **W. Size:** 6750 Metres. **Location:** **Nr. Rd:** Norham to Ladykirk; **Main Rd:** A1; **Rail:** Berwick-upon-Tweed. **£Fr**
Ref: FH4990

TWEED (RIVER)

River Tweed, West Learmouth, Coldstream, **NORTHUMBERLAND**, TD12, **England**.
Contact/s: **Mr J H Leeming**, Stichill House, Kelso, Scottish Borders, TD5 7TB.
(T) 01573 470280 (F) 01573 470259
Profile: FT: Game; **WN:** Tweed (West Learmouth); **WT:** River (Moving) **W. Size:** 1200 Metres. **Location:** **Nr. Rd:** B6350; **Main Rd:** A697.
Ref: FH4991

TWEED (RIVER)

River Tweed, Ladybird, Norham, Berwick-upon-Tweed, **NORTHUMBERLAND**, TD15, **England**.
Contact/s: **Mr J H Leeming**, Stichill House, Kelso, Scottish Borders, TD5 7TB.
(T) 01573 470280 (F) 01573 470259
Profile: FT: Game; **WN:** Tweed (Ladykirk); **WT:** River (Moving) **W. Size:** 4800 Metres. **Location:** **Nr. Rd:** B6470; **Main Rd:** A698 or B6437.
Ref: FH4992

TWEED (RIVER)

River Tweed, Tweedhill, Berwick-upon-Tweed, **NORTHUMBERLAND**, TD15, **England**.
Contact/s: **Mr J H Leeming**, Stichill House, Kelso, Sco
(T) 01573 470280
Profile: FT: Game; **WN:**
WT: River (Moving) **W. Size:**
Location: **Nr. Rd:** A6105 or A6
A1.
Ref: FH4993

TWEED (RIVER)

River Tweed, Ravenswood, Melrose, **SCOTTISH BORDERS**, TD6, **Scotland**.
Contact/s: **Mr J H Leeming**, Stichill House, Kelso, Scottish Borders, TD5 7TB.
(T) 01573 470280 (F) 01573 470259
Profile: FT: Game; **WN:** Tweed (Ravenswood); **WT:** River (Moving). **Location:** **Nr. Rd:** A6091; **Main Rd:** A86 or A72.
Ref: FH4994

TWEED (RIVER)

River Tweed, Boleside, Lindean Mill, Galashiels, **SCOTTISH BORDERS**, TD1, **Scotland**.
Contact/s: **Mr J H Leeming**, Stichill House, Kelso, Scottish Borders, TD5 7TB.
(T) 01573 470280 (F) 01573 470259
Profile: FT: Game; **WN:** Tweed; **WT:** River (Moving) **W. Size:** 3200 Metres. **Location:** **Nr. Rd:** B7060; **Main Rd:** A7 or A6091.
Ref: FH4995

TWEED (RIVER)

River Tweed, Bemersyde, Newtown St. Boswells, Melrose, **SCOTTISH BORDERS**, TD6, **Scotland**.
Contact/s: **Mr J H Leeming**, Stichill House, Kelso, Scottish Borders, TD5 7TB.
(T) 01573 470280 (F) 01573 470259
Profile: FT: Game; **WN:** Tweed (Bemersyde); **WT:** River (Moving) **W. Size:** 1600 Metres. **Location:** **Nr. Rd:** B6356; **Main Rd:** A68.
Ref: FH4996

TWEED (RIVER)

River Tweed, Hendersyde, Kelso, **SCOTTISH BORDERS**, TD5, **Scotland**.
Contact/s: **Mr J H Leeming**, Stichill House, Kelso, Scottish Borders, TD5 7TB.
(T) 01573 470280 (F) 01573 470259
Profile: FT: Game; **WN:** Tweed (Hendersyde); **WT:** River (Moving). **Location:** **Nr. Rd:** A698; **Main Rd:** A697.
Ref: FH4997

TWEED (RIVER)

River Tweed, Fairnilee, Galashiels, **SCOTTISH BORDERS**, TD1, **Scotland**.
Contact/s: **Mr J H Leeming**, Stichill House, Kelso, Scottish Borders, TD5 7TB.
(T) 01573 470280 (F) 01573 470259
Profile: FT: Game; **WN:** Tweed (Fairnilee); **WT:** River (Moving). **Location:** **Nr. Rd:** B6360; **Main Rd:** A7 or A707.
Ref: FH4998

TWEED (RIVER)

River Tweed, Peebles, **SCOTTISH BORDERS**, EH45, **Scotland**.
Contact/s: Secretary, Blackwood and Smith WS, 39 High St, Peebles, EH45 8AH.
Profile: FT: Game; **WN:** Tweed; **WT:** River (Moving) **W. Size:** 34500 Metres. **Location:** **Rail:** Edinburgh.
Ref: FH4999

TWEED (RIVER)

River Tweed, Duns, **SCOTTISH BORDERS**, TD11, **Scotland**.
Contact/s: **Mr Jerry Ponder** (Manager), Countryside Cottages, The Courtyard, Allanton, Duns, TD11 3PY.
(T) 01890 818460
Profile: FT: Game; **WN:** Tweed; **WT:** River (Moving).
Ref: FH5000

TWEED (RIVER)

River Tweed, Traquair, Innerleithen, **SCOTTISH BORDERS**, EH44, **Scotland**.
Contact/s: **Mr J H Leeming**, Stichill

...TB.
...59
...quair);
... Rd:

...

... Galashiels,
...tland.
..., Stichill
..., TD5 7TB.
...3 470259
Profile: ... ...ed (Peel); **WT:** River (Moving) **W. Si...** ...2 Metres. **Location:** **Nr. Rd:** A707 or B710; **Main Rd:** A72.
Ref: FH5002

TWENTY FOOT DRAIN

Twenty Foot Drain, Coates, Whittlesey, Peterborough, **CAMBRIDGESHIRE**, PE7, **England**.
Contact/s: , Whittlesey Angling Ctre, 14 High Causeway, Whittlesey, Peterborough, PE7 1AE.
Mr Dave Slack (manager).
(T) 01733 205775day
Profile: **FT:** Coarse; **WN:** Twenty Foot Drain; **WT:** Reservoir (Still). **Location:** **Nr. Rd:** A605 to Wisbech.
Ref: FH5003

TWIN LAKES TROUT FISHERY

Twin Lakes Trout Fishery, Brickcroft Lane, Croston, Preston, **LANCASHIRE**, PR5 7AA, **England**.
Contact/s: **Mr Graham Cooper** (Manager).
(T) 01772 601093 **(M)** 07971 273096
Profile: **FT:** Game; **WN:** Twin; **WT:** Lake (Still); **F. Size:** 20 Acres; **W. Size:** 12 Acres. **Location:** **Nr. Rd:** B5247, Brickcroft Lane; **Main Rd:** A581; **Rail:** Croston.
Ref: FH5004

TWINE VALLEY TROUT FISHERY

Twine Valley Trout Fishery, Ridinghead Lane, Bye Rd, Shuttleworth, Ramsbottom, Bury, **MANCHESTER (GREATER)**, BL0 0HH, **England**.
Contact/s: **Mr Hervey Magnall** (Owner).
(T) 01706 825314 **(F)** 01706 825314
Profile: **FT:** Combination; **WN:** Twine Valley Trout Fishery; **WT:** Combination (Still & Moving); **F. Size:** 50 Acres; **W. Size:** 5 Acres. **Location:** **Nr. Rd:** Riding Head Lane; **Main Rd:** M66; **Rail:** Bury.
Ref: FH5005

TWISS (RIVER)

River Twiss, Ingleton, Carnforth, **CUMBRIA**, LA6, **England**.
Contact/s: **Mr Ian Crack** (Secretary), Ingleton Angling Association, Khardains, Ingleton Carnforth, Lancashire, LA6 3BS.
(T) 01524 241171
Profile: **FT:** Game; **WN:** Twiss; **WT:** River (Moving) **W. Size:** 2400 Metres. **Location:** **Main Rd:** A65; **Rail:** High Bentham.
Ref: FH5006

TWRCH (RIVER)

River Twrch, Neath, **NEATH PORT TALBOT**, SA, **Wales**.
Contact/s: **Mr Mike Matthews** (Hon Secretary), 32 Farm Rd, Briton Ferry, Neath, Glamorgan (Vale of), SA11 2TA.
(T) 01639 632070
Profile: **FT:** Game; **WN:** Twrch; **WT:** River (Moving).
Ref: FH5007

TWYFORD BBONT

Twyford B.B.O.N.T., Old Bath Rd, Twyford, Reading, **BERKSHIRE**, RG, **England**.
(W) www.rmcangling.co.uk
Contact/s: **Mr Ian Welch** (Angling Manager), RMC Angling, The Square, Lightwater, Surrey, GU18 5SS.
(T) 01276 453300 **(F)** 01276 456611
(E) info@rmcangling.co.uk
Profile: **FT:** Coarse; **WN:** Loddon; **WT:** Combination (Still & Moving) **W. Size:** 34 Acres. **Location:** **Nr. Rd:** A321 Old Bath Road; **Main Rd:** A4; **Rail:** Twyford.
Ref: FH5008

TWYFORD FARM POOL

Twyford Farm Pool, Evesham, **WORCESTERSHIRE**, WR11 4TP, **England**.
Contact/s: Centre Manager.
(T) 01386 443348
Mr Stu Gottfried (Fishery Manager). **(M)** 07973 147323
Ms May Vince.
(T) 01789 778365evening
Profile: **FT:** Coarse; **WN:** Twyford Farm Pool; **WT:** Combination (Still & Moving) **W. Size:** 2 Acres. **Location:** **Nr. Rd:** A46; **Main Rd:** Evesham.
Ref: FH5009

TWYFORD WATERS

Twyford Waters, Hurst, Reading, **BERKSHIRE**, RG10, **England**.
(W) www.badac.co.uk
Contact/s: **Mr D Porter** (Secretary), 72 Rivington Cres, Mill Hill, London, NW7 2LF.
(T) 020 84401303
Profile: **FT:** Coarse; **WN:** Loddon; **WT:** Combination (Still & Moving) **W. Size:** 38 Acres. **Location:** **Rail:** Twyford.
Ref: FH5010

TWYMYN (RIVER)

River Twymyn, Llanbrynmair, **POWYS**, SY19, **Wales**.
Contact/s: **Mrs D R Lewis** (Secretary), Llanbrynmair Angling Club, Bryn-Llugwy, Llanbrynmair, Powys, SY19 7AA.
(T) 01650 521385
Profile: **FT:** Game; **WN:** Twymyn; **WT:** River (Moving) **W. Size:** 5 Metres.
Ref: FH5011

TWYNERSH FISHING COMPLEX

Twynersh Fishing Complex, Thorpe Rd, Chertsey, **SURREY**, KT16 9EJ, **England**.
Contact/s: **Mr Mills** (Fishery Manager), Lorretta Lodge, Tilley Lane, Headley, Nr Epsom, Surrey.
(T) 01932 570156
Mr Paul Rogers (Manager).
(T) 01932 570156
Profile: **FT:** Coarse; **WN:** Twynersh Fishing Complex; **WT:** Gravel Pit (Still); **F. Size:** 45 Acres; **W. Size:** 18 Acres. **Location:** **Nr. Rd:** B388; **Main Rd:** A320 or M25; **Rail:** Chertsey.
Ref: FH5012

TY HEN LAKE

Ty Hen Lake, Ty Hen Farm, Station Rd, Rhosneigr, **ISLE OF ANGLESEY**, LL64 5QZ, **Wales**.
Contact/s: **Mr Bernard Summerfield**.
(T) 01407 810331
Profile: **FT:** Coarse; **WN:** Ty Hen; **WT:** Pond (Still) **W. Size:** 2 Acres. **Location:** **Nr. Rd:** A4413; **Main Rd:** B4417.
Ref: FH5013

TY MAWR RESERVOIR

Ty Mawr Reservoir, Gresford, Wrexham, LL12, **Wales**.
Contact/s: Fishery Manager.
(T) 01978 840116
Mr Tony Jackson (Fisheries Manager), Dee Valley Service plc, Packsaddle, Wrexham Rd, Rhostyllen, Wrexham LL14 4DS.
(T) 01978 846946
Profile: **FT:** Game; **WN:** Ty Mawr; **WT:** Reservoir (Still) **W. Size:** 20 Acres.
Ref: FH5014

TYDDYN MAWR TROUT FARM

Tyddyn Mawr Trout Farm, Tyddyn Mawr, Roewen, Conwy, LL32 8YL, **Wales**.
Contact/s: **Mr Dewi G Jones** (Owner).
(T) 01492 650302 **(F)** 01492 650302
Ms Margaret E Jones (Owner).
(T) 01492 650302 **(F)** 01492 650302
Profile: **FT:** Game; **WN:** Tyddyn Mawr Trout Farm; **WT:** Lake (Still); **F. Size:** 4 Acres; **W. Size:** 2 Acres. **Location:** **Nr. Rd:** Conwy to Rowen; **Main Rd:** A55; **Rail:** Conwy.
Ref: FH5015

TYDDYN SARGENT

Tyddyn Sargent, Tynygongl, Benllech, Tyn-Y-Gongl, **ISLE OF ANGLESEY**, LL74, **Wales**.
Contact/s: **Mr K Twist** (Manager), Tyddyn Sargent, Tynygongl, Benllech, Isle of Anglesey, Wales.
(T) 01248 853024
(E) k.twist@ukonline.co.uk
Profile: **FT:** Coarse; **WN:** Tyddyn Sargent; **WT:** Lake (Still).
Ref: FH5016

TYNE (RIVER)

River Tyne, Alston, **CUMBRIA**, CA9, **England**.
Contact/s: **Ms Sandra Harrison**, Alston and District Angling Association, Newsagents, Front St, Alston.
(T) 01434 381462
Profile: **FT:** Game; **WN:** Tyne; **WT:** River (Moving) **W. Size:** 16000 Metres.
Ref: FH5017

TYNE (RIVER)

River Tyne, East Lothian, Haddington, **LOTHIAN (EAST)**, EH41, **Scotland**.
Contact/s: **Mr John Crombie** (Secretary), 10 St Lawrence, Haddington, EH41 3RL.
(T) 01620 822058
Profile: **FT:** Game; **WN:** Tyne; **WT:** River (Moving) **W. Size:** 30000 Metres. **Location:** **Nr. Rd:** A1; **Main Rd:** A1; **Rail:** Dunbar.
Ref: FH5018

TYNE (RIVER)

River Tyne, Hexham, **NORTHUMBERLAND**, NE, **England**.
Contact/s: Fisheries Manager, Tynedale Council, Department of Leisure and Tourism, Prospect House, Hexham, Northumberland 46 3NH.
(T) 01434 652200 **(F)** 01434 652425
(E) tourism_section@tynedale.gov.uk
Profile: **FT:** Game; **WN:** Tyne; **WT:** River (Moving) **W. Size:** 800 Metres. **Location:** **Nr. Rd:** Tyne Green to Hexham Bridge; **Main Rd:** A69.
Ref: FH5019

TYNE (RIVER)

River Tyne, Riverdale Hall Hotel, Bellingham, Hexham, **NORTHUMBERLAND**, NE48, **England**.
Contact/s: **Mr John Cocker** (Manager), Riverdale Hall Hotel, Bellingham, Northumberland, NE48 2JT.
(T) 01434 220254
Profile: **FT:** Game; **WN:** Tyne; **WT:** River (Moving) **W. Size:** 4800 Metres.
Ref: FH5020

TYNE (RIVER)

River Tyne, Ovington, Prudhoe, **NORTHUMBERLAND**, NE42, **England**.
Contact/s: **Mr Alan Bagnall** (Head Bailiff), Northumbrian Anglers Federation, Mill Thirston, Felton, Northumberland NE65 9EH, NE65 9EH.
(T) 01670 787663
Profile: **FT:** Coarse; **WN:** Tyne; **WT:** River (Moving).
Ref: FH5021

TYNE (RIVER)

River Tyne, Corbridge, **NORTHUMBERLAND**, NE45, **England**.
Profile: **FT:** Combination; **WN:** Tyne; **WT:** River (Moving).
Ref: FH5022

TYNE (RIVER)

River Tyne, Wylam, **NORTHUMBERLAND**, NE41, **England**.
Contact/s: **Mr John Armstrong**, 55

Calder Walk, Sunneyside, Whickham, Newcastle upon Tyne.
(T) 0191 4886496
Profile: **FT:** Combination; **WN:** Tyne; **WT:** River (Moving).
Ref: FH5023

TYNE (RIVER)

River Tyne, Mickley Sq, Prudhoe, **NORTHUMBERLAND**, NE42, **England**.
Contact/s: **Mr Dave Stafford** (Information Contact).
(T) 0191 2424441
Mr Gary Rutherford (Ticket Administrator).
(T) 01207 588633
Profile: **FT:** Coarse; **WN:** Tyne; **WT:** River (Moving) **W. Size:** 3200 Metres. **Location:** **Main Rd:** A695; **Rail:** Hexham.
Ref: FH5024

TYNE (RIVER)

River Tyne, Prudhoe, **NORTHUMBERLAND**, NE42, **England**.
Contact/s: Fishery Manager.
(T) 0191 2650098
Profile: **FT:** Combination; **WN:** Tyne; **WT:** River (Moving) **W. Size:** 2400 Metres. **Location:** **Nr. Rd:** Prudhoe to Ovingham; **Main Rd:** A695; **Rail:** Low Prudhoe.
Ref: FH5025

TYNE (RIVER)

River Tyne, Hexham, **NORTHUMBERLAND**, NE46, **England**.
Contact/s: Fishery Manager.
(T) 01434 605225
Profile: **FT:** Coarse; **WN:** Tyne; **WT:** River (Moving).
Ref: FH5026

TYNE (RIVER)

River Tyne, Ovington, Prudhoe, **NORTHUMBERLAND**, NE42, **England**.
Contact/s: **Mr Alan Bagnall** (Head Bailiff), Northumbrian Anglers Federation, Mill Thirston, Felton, Northumberland, NE65 9EH.
(T) 01670 787663
Profile: **FT:** Combination; **WN:** Tyne; **WT:** River (Moving) **W. Size:** 3200 Metres. **Location:** **Nr. Rd:** A695; **Main Rd:** Prudhoe.
Ref: FH5027

TYNE (RIVER)

River Tyne, Wylam, **NORTHUMBERLAND**, NE41, **England**.
Contact/s: **Mr John Armstrong** (Secretary), 55 Calder Walk, Sunneyside, Whickham, Newcastle upon Tyne.
(T) 0191 4886496evening
Profile: **FT:** Combination; **WN:** Tyne; **WT:** River (Moving).
Ref: FH5028

TYNE (RIVER)

River Tyne, Reeltime Fishing Services, Bywell, Stocksfield, **NORTHUMBERLAND**, NE43 7HP, **England**.
Profile: **FT:** Game; **WN:** Tyne; **WT:** River (Moving) **W. Size:** 4800 Metres.
Ref: FH5029

TYNE (RIVER)

River Tyne, Close House, Newcastle Upon Tyne, **TYNE AND WEAR**, NE, **England**.
Profile: **FT:** Combination; **WN:** Tyne; **WT:** River (Moving).
Ref: FH5030

TYNE (RIVER)

River Tyne, Newburn, Newcastle Upon Tyne, **TYNE AND WEAR**, NE15, **England**.
Contact/s: Warden, Tyne Anglers Alliance, PO Box 72, Heaton Rd, Newcastle upon Tyne.
(T) 0191 2681613
Profile: **FT:** Combination; **WN:** Tyne; **WT:** River (Moving). **Location:** **Main Rd:** A69.
Ref: FH5031

TYNE (RIVER)

River Tyne, Newcastle Upon Tyne, **TYNE AND WEAR**, NE, **England**.
Contact/s: **Mr Gavin Jobson** (Manager), The County House, 123-125 Clayton Street West, Newcastle-upon-Tyne, Northumberland, NE1 5EE.
(T) 0191 2616669 (F) 0191 2619996
Profile: **FT:** Game; **WN:** Tyne; **WT:** River (Moving).
Ref: FH5032

TYNE (RIVER)

River Tyne, Clara Vale, Ryton, **TYNE AND WEAR**, NE40, **England**.
Contact/s: **Mr Alan Bagnall** (Head Bailiff), Northumbrian Anglers Federation, Mill Thirston, Felton, Northumberland, NE65 9EH.
(T) 01670 787663
Profile: **FT:** Combination; **WN:** Tyne; **WT:** River (Moving). **Location:** **Main Rd:** A69.
Ref: FH5033

TYNE (RIVER)

River Tyne, Mickley, Ripon, **YORKSHIRE (NORTH)**, HG4, **England**.
Contact/s: **Mr Gary Rutherford** (Secretary), 21 Blagdon Trce, Seaton Burn, Newcastle-upon-Tyne, NE13 6EY.
(T) 0191 2366703
Profile: **FT:** Combination; **WN:** Tyne; **WT:** River (Moving) **W. Size:** 2800 Metres.
Ref: FH5034

TYRAM HALL

Tyram Hall, Bawtry Rd, Hatfield Woodhouse, Doncaster, **YORKSHIRE (SOUTH)**, DN7 6DR, **England**.
Contact/s: Manager.
(T) 01302 840886
Profile: **FT:** Coarse; **WN:** Tyram Hall; **WT:** Lake (Still). **Location:** **Nr. Rd:** Bawtry Road.
Ref: FH5035

TYRDREF FISHERY

Tyrdref Fishery, Llandysul, **CEREDIGION**, SA44, **Wales**.
(W) www.fishing-in-wales.co.uk/llandysul-aa/beat12
Contact/s: **Mr Artie Jones** (Hon Secretary), Llandysul Angling Association, Glas-y-Dorlan, Llyn-y-Fran Rd, Llandysul, SA44 4JW.
(T) 01559 362317
Profile: **FT:** Game; **WN:** Teifi; **WT:** River (Moving).
Ref: FH5036

TYRINGHAM ESTATE

Tyringham Estate, Tyringham Hall, Filgrave, Newport Pagnell, **BUCKINGHAMSHIRE**, MK16, **England**.
(W) www.rmcangling.co.uk
Contact/s: **Mr Ian Welch** (Angling Manager), RMC Angling, The Square, Lightwater, Surrey, GU18 5SS.
(T) 01276 453300 (F) 01276 456611
(E) info@rmcangling.co.uk
Profile: **FT:** Coarse; **WN:** Ouse; **WT:** River (Moving) **W. Size:** 3000 Metres. **Location:** **Nr. Rd:** B526; **Main Rd:** M1.
Ref: FH5037

UCKINGHALL POOL

Uckinghall Pool, Uckinghall, Upton-upon-Severn, Worcester, **WORCESTERSHIRE**, WR8, **England**.
Contact/s: **Mr John Williams** (Secretary), Birmingham Anglers Association, 100 Icknield Port Rd, Rotton Park, Birmingham, B16 0AP.
(T) 0121 4549111
Profile: **FT:** Coarse; **WN:** Uckinghall Pool; **WT:** Pool (Still) **W. Size:** 4 Acres. **Location:** **Main Rd:** A38, M50 junction 1.
Ref: FH5038

UFTON CANAL

Ufton Canal, Kennet And Avon Canal, Ufton, Reading, **BERKSHIRE**, RG, **England**.
Contact/s: **Mr Dusty Millar** (Associate members secretary), 238 Elgar Road South, Reading, Berkshire, RG3 0BW.
(T) 0118 9874882
Mr Mick Cox (Chief Bailiff), Dorstans, Hatch Lane, Brimpton Village, Reading, RG7 4TR.
(T) 0118 9714917
Profile: **FT:** Coarse; **WN:** Ufton; **WT:** Canal (Still) **W. Size:** 28800 Metres. **Location:** **Nr. Rd:** Ufton.
Ref: FH5039

ULLESKELF (RIVER)

River Ulleskelf, Ulleskelf, Tadcaster, **YORKSHIRE (NORTH)**, LS24, **England**.
Contact/s: Fishery Manager.
(T) 01937 832136
Profile: **FT:** Coarse; **WN:** Ulleskelf; **WT:** River (Moving).
Ref: FH5040

ULLEY RESERVOIR

Ulley Reservoir, Ulley Country Park, Pleasley Rd, Ulley, Sheffield, **YORKSHIRE (SOUTH)**, S31 0YL, **England**.
Contact/s: **Mr Ivan Machin** (Senior Ranger).
(T) 01709 365332
Profile: **FT:** Coarse; **WN:** Ulley; **WT:** Reservoir (Still) **W. Size:** 30 Acres. **Location:** **Nr. Rd:** Ulley Lane; **Main Rd:** A618.
Ref: FH5041

ULLSWATER LAKE

Ullswater Lake, Eamont, Penrith, **CUMBRIA**, CA10, **England**.
Profile: **FT:** Game; **WN:** Ullswater; **WT:** Lake (Still); **F. Size:** 2200 Acres. **Location:** **Rail:** Penrith. **£Fr**
Ref: FH5042

ULVERSTON CANAL

Ulverston Canal, Canal Tavern, Ulverston, **CUMBRIA**, LA12, **England**.
Contact/s: **Mr Nige Cooper** (Manager), Coppers Fishing Tackle, 1 White Hart Yard, Market Pl, Ulverston, Cumbria, LA12 7BB.
(T) 01229 580261
Profile: **FT:** Coarse; **WN:** Ulverston; **WT:** Canal (Still). **Location:** **Nr. Rd:** From Canal Tavern, Ulverston to the Bay Horse Inn; **Main Rd:** A590 to Canal Tavern.
Ref: FH5043

UNDERBANK RESERVOIR

Underbank Reservoir, Stocksbridge, Sheffield, **YORKSHIRE (SOUTH)**, S36, **England**.
Contact/s: Area Manager, Environment Agency, Ridings Area Office, Phoenix House, Global Avenue, Leeds, LS11 8PG.
(T) 0113 2440191or2314834 (F) 0113 2134609
Conservation and Recreation Manager.
(T) 0114 2592005
Profile: **FT:** Coarse; **WN:** Underbank; **WT:** Reservoir (Still) **W. Size:** 60 Acres.
Ref: FH5044

UNDERHILL LAKE

Underhill Lake, Maresfield, Uckfield, **SUSSEX (EAST)**, TN22, **England**.
Contact/s: **Mrs Walker** (Secretary), Crowborough and District Angling Association, Crowfield Tackle, Whitehall Rd, Crowborough, East Sussex TN6 1JU.
(T) 01892 661145
Profile: **FT:** Coarse; **WN:** Underhill; **WT:** Lake (Still).
Ref: FH5045

UNION CANAL

Union Canal, Tourist Office, The Cross, Linlithgow, **LOTHIAN (WEST)**, EH49 7AJ, **Scotland**.
Contact/s: **Mr Steve Clerkin** (Fishery Manager).
(T) 01592 642242
Profile: **FT:** Coarse; **WN:** Union; **WT:** Canal (Still).
Ref: FH5046

UNITY LAKE

Unity Lake, Shimano Linear Fisheries (Oxford), Smiths Concrete Site, Hardwick Village, Witney, **OXFORDSHIRE**, OX8 7Q, **England**.

Contact/s: **Mr Len Gurd** (Owner), 10A Rackstraw Gr, Old Farm Park, Milton Keynes, Buckinghamshire, MK7 8PZ.
(T) 01908 645135 **(F)** 01908 645115
Profile: **FT:** Coarse; **WN:** Unity; **WT:** Lake (Still); **F. Size:** 30 Acres; **W. Size:** 25 Acres. **Location:** **Nr. Rd:** B4449; **Main Rd:** A40; **Rail:** Oxford.
Ref: FH5047

UNIVERSITY BROAD

University Broad, Bluebell Rd, Norwich, **NORFOLK**, **England**.
(W) www.uea.ac.uk/~e419/ueasaac/welcome.html
Contact/s: **Mr Roger Humphrey** (Publicity Officer), Roger Humphrey, Electronics Workshop Supervisor, Electrical Safety Officer (ENV & MATHS), School of Environmental Sciences, University of East Anglia, Norwich NR4 7TJ England.
(T) 01603 592502
(E) r.humphrey@uea.ac.uk
Profile: **FT:** Coarse; **WN:** University Broad; **WT:** Pit (Still); **F. Size:** 20 Acres; **W. Size:** 18 Acres. **Location:** **Nr. Rd:** Bluebell Road; **Main Rd:** B1108; **Rail:** Norwich.
Ref: FH5048

UNWICKS FARM FISHERY

Unwicks Farm Fishery, Station Rd, Hartlebury, Stourport-on-Severn, **WORCESTERSHIRE**, DY11 7YJ, **England**.
Contact/s: **Mr Elwin Birchall** (Unwicks Farm Manager), Unwicks Farm Fishery, Station Rd, Hartlebury, Stourport On Severn, DY11 7YJ.
(T) 01299 250320
Profile: **FT:** Coarse; **WN:** Unwicks Farm Fishery; **WT:** Lake (Still) **W. Size:** 1 Acre. **Location:** **Nr. Rd:** Station Road; **Main Rd:** A449 (T); **Rail:** Hartlebury.
Ref: FH5049

UPHAM FARM PONDS

Upham Farm Ponds, Farringdon, Exeter, **DEVON**, EX5 2HZ, **England**.
Contact/s: **Mr James Willcocks** (Owner).
(T) 01395 232247 **(F)** 01395 232247 **(M)** 07971 827552
(E) cjjj@uphamfarm.freeserve.co.uk
Profile: **FT:** Coarse; **WN:** Upham Farm; **WT:** Pond (Still); **F. Size:** 2 Acres; **W. Size:** 2 Acres. **Location:** **Nr. Rd:** A3052; **Main Rd:** A3052; **Rail:** Exeter.
Ref: FH5050

UPPER BORLICK BEAT

Upper Borlick Beat, Aberfeldy, **PERTH AND KINROSS**, PH15, **Scotland**.
(W) www.fishingnet.com/beats/boltachan.htm
Contact/s: **Mr Roddy Kennedy**, Borlick Farm, Upper Borlick, Aberfeldy, Perth and Kinross, PH15 2JP.
(T) 01887 820463
Profile: **FT:** Combination; **WN:** Cuil, Upper Distillery and Cuil Allan; **WT:** Pool (Still).
Ref: FH5051

UPPER BURE (STREAM)

Upper Bure (Stream), Bure Valley Fishery, Oulton, Aylesham, **NORFOLK**, NR11 6NW, **England**.
Contact/s: **Mr Mike Smith** (Manager).
(T) 01263 587666
Profile: **FT:** Game; **WN:** Upper Bure; **WT:** Stream (Moving) **W. Size:** 850 Metres. **Location:** **Nr. Rd:** B1354; **Main Rd:** A140; **Rail:** Norwich.
Ref: FH5052

UPPER GORTON RESERVOIR

Upper Gorton Reservoir, Gorton, Manchester, **MANCHESTER (GREATER)**, M18, **England**.
Contact/s: Fisheries Manager, Manchester City Council, Recreation Services Department, Belle Vue Athletics, Pink Bank Lane, Manchester M12 5QN.
Profile: **FT:** Coarse; **WN:** Upper Gorton; **WT:** Reservoir (Still).
Ref: FH5053

UPPER KINNAIRD BEAT

Upper Kinnaird Beat, Perth, **PERTH AND KINROSS**, PH, **Scotland**.
(W) www.fishingnet.com/beats/upperkinnaird.htm
Contact/s: **Mr P D Malloch** (Manager), Fishing Tackle Shop, 259 Old High St, Perth, Perth and Kinross, PH1 5QN.
(T) 01738 632316
Profile: **FT:** Combination; **WN:** Eastertyre, Neck of Newton, Ash Tree and Sand Bank; **WT:** Pool (Still).
Ref: FH5054

UPPER LAKE

Upper Lake, Birkenhead Park, Birkenhead, **MERSEYSIDE**, CH, **England**.
Contact/s: **Mr Billing**.
(T) 0151 3343174
Profile: **FT:** Coarse; **WN:** Upper; **WT:** Lake (Still). **Location:** **Nr. Rd:** Birkenhead Park.
Ref: FH5055

UPPER NEUADD

Upper Neuadd, Merthyr Tydfil, **GLAMORGAN (VALE OF)**, CF48, **Wales**.
Contact/s: **Mr Nigel Morgan** (Manager), 20 James St, Merthyr, Glamorgan (Vale of).
(T) 01685 377848
Profile: **FT:** Game; **WN:** Neuadd Upper; **WT:** River (Moving).
Ref: FH5056

UPPER RIVINGTON RESERVOIR

Upper Rivington Reservoir, Horrobin Lane, Horwich, Bolton, **LANCASHIRE**, BL6, **England**.
Contact/s: **Mr Roy Rhodes** (Conservation, Access and Recreation Manager), Rivington Water Treatment Works, Bolton Rd, Horwich, Bolton, BL6 7RN.
(T) 01204 664300
Mr Stephen Ackroyd.
(T) 01254 832193
Profile: **FT:** Coarse; **WN:** Upper Rivington; **WT:** Reservoir (Still). **Location:** **Nr. Rd:** Horrobin Lane; **Main Rd:** A673; **Rail:** Adlington.
Ref: FH5057

UPPER RODDLESWORTH RESERVOIR

Upper Roddlesworth Reservoir, Belmont, Bolton, **LANCASHIRE**, BL7, **England**.
Contact/s: **Mr Colin Wilson** (Secretary), 10 Ramswell Brow, Bromley Cross, Bolton, Lancashire.
(T) 01204 307636
Mr Roy Rhodes (Conservation, Access and Recreation Manager), Rivington Water Treatment Works, Bolton Rd, Horwich, Bolton, BL6 7RN.
(T) 01204 664300
Profile: **FT:** Game; **WN:** Upper Roddlesworth; **WT:** Reservoir (Still) **W. Size:** 24 Acres.
Ref: FH5058

UPPER STOUR (RIVER)

River Upper Stour, Gillingham, **DORSET**, SP8, **England**.
Contact/s: **Mr P Stone** (Treasurer), The Time Piece Newbury, High St, Newbury, Gilllingham, SP8 4HZ.
(T) 01747 823339
Mr Simon Hebditch (Hon Secretary), 5 Ham Court, Shaftsbury Rd, Gillingham, Dorset, SP8 4LU.
(T) 01747 824817
Profile: **FT:** Coarse; **WN:** Upper Stour (Gilllingham to Marnhull); **WT:** River (Moving) **W. Size:** 11200 Metres.
Ref: FH5059

UPPER WITHAM (RIVER)

River (Upper) Witham, Lincoln, **LINCOLNSHIRE**, LN, **England**.
Contact/s: **Mr Colin Parker** (Secretary), Lincoln and District Angling Association, 4 Pottergate Cl, Waddington, Lincoln, LN5 9LY.
(T) 01522 720777
Mr Frank Butler (Chairman).
(T) 01522 534174
Profile: **FT:** Coarse; **WN:** Upper Witham; **WT:** River (Moving) **W. Size:** 144000 Metres. **Location:** **Nr. Rd:** B1003, A1434; **Main Rd:** A46, A57, A607; **Rail:** Lincoln.
Ref: FH5060

UPPER YEALM FISHERY

Upper Yealm Fishery, Lucas Wood, Cornwood, Ivybridge, **DEVON**, PL21 9PN, **England**.
Contact/s: Manager, Snowbee (UK) Limited, Unit 2a Parkway Industrial Estate, St Modwen Rd, Plymouth, PL6 8LH.
(T) 01752 672226 **(F)** 01752 667070
Profile: **FT:** Game; **WN:** Yealm; **WT:** River (Moving) **W. Size:** 1600 Metres. **Location:** **Nr. Rd:** Smithaleigh to Cornwood; **Main Rd:** A38; **Rail:** Plymouth.
Ref: FH5061

UPTON WARREN LAKE

Upton Warren Lake, Culm Valley, Cullompton, **DEVON**, EX15 1RA, **England**.
Contact/s: **Mr Chris Down**.
(T) 01884 33097 **(F)** 01884 33097
Profile: **FT:** Coarse; **WN:** Upton Lake; **WT:** Lake (Still) **W. Size:** 2 Acres. **Location:** **Nr. Rd:** Meadow Road; **Main Rd:** M5, junction 28, towards Cullompton; **Rail:** Tiverton Parkway.
Ref: FH5062

UPTON WARREN LAKE

Upton Warren Lake, Outdoor Education Ctre, Bromsgrove, **WORCESTERSHIRE**, B60, **England**.
Contact/s: Manager.
(T) 01527 861426
Profile: **FT:** Coarse; **WN:** Upton Warren; **WT:** Lake (Still) **W. Size:** 18 Acres. **Location:** **Nr. Rd:** B4085; **Main Rd:** M5, junction 5.
Ref: FH5063

URE (RIVER AND TRIBUTARIES)

River Ure And Tributaries, Hawes, **YORKSHIRE (NORTH)**, DL8, **England**.
Contact/s: **Mr G Phillips** (Secretary), Hawes and High Abbotside Anglers Association, Holmlands, Appersett, Hawes, DL8 3LN.
(T) 01969 667362
Profile: **FT:** Game; **WN:** Ure and Tributaries; **WT:** River (Moving) **W. Size:** 20000 Metres. **Location:** **Main Rd:** A694; **Rail:** Garsdale.
Ref: FH5064

URE (RIVER)

River Ure, Hull, **HUMBERSIDE**, HU11, **England**.
Contact/s: **M Burgess**, No.1 Bungalow, Littlethorpe Rd, Ripon, Yorkshire (North).
Mr Gary Lumsden.
(T) 01765 605520
Profile: **FT:** Coarse; **WN:** Ure; **WT:** River (Moving). **Location:** **Nr. Rd:** Alborough to Lower Dunsforth; **Main Rd:** B6265.
Ref: FH5065

URE (RIVER)

River Ure, Boroughbridge, York, **YORKSHIRE (NORTH)**, YO51, **England**.
Contact/s: **Mr Bernard Thain** (Manager), Ripon Angling Ctre, 58-59 North St, Ripon, Yorkshire (North), HG4 1EN.
(T) 01765 604666 **(F)** 01765 603933
Profile: **FT:** Coarse; **WN:** Ure; **WT:** River (Moving).
Ref: FH5066

URE (RIVER)

River Ure, Bainbridge, Leyburn, **YORKSHIRE (NORTH)**, DL8, **England**.
Profile: **FT:** Game; **WN:** Ure; **WT:** River (Moving).
Ref: FH5067

URE (RIVER)

River Ure, Newby Hall, Skelton, York,

YORKSHIRE (NORTH), YO30, **England**.
Contact/s: Manager, Newby Hall Estates, Estate Office, Ripon, Yorkshire (North), HG4 5AE.
(T) 01423 322583
Profile: **FT:** Coarse; **WN:** Ure; **WT:** River (Moving).
Ref: FH5068

URE (RIVER)

River Ure, Ripon, **YORKSHIRE (NORTH)**, HG4, **England**.
Contact/s: **Mr Bernard Thain** (Manager), Ripon Angling Ctre, 58-59 North St, Ripon, Yorkshire (North), HG4 1EN.
(T) 01765 604666 **(F)** 01765 603933
Profile: **FT:** Combination; **WN:** Ure; **WT:** River (Moving).
Ref: FH5069

URE (RIVER)

River Ure, Westwick Hall Farm, Roecliffe, York, **YORKSHIRE (NORTH)**, YO51, **England**.
Contact/s: Fishery Manager.
(T) 01765 677293
Profile: **FT:** Coarse; **WN:** Ure; **WT:** River (Moving) **W. Size:** 6646 Metres. **Location:** **Nr. Rd:** Roecliffe; **Main Rd:** Boroughbridge to Bishop Monkton and A61.
Ref: FH5070

URE (RIVER)

River Ure, Hawes, **YORKSHIRE (NORTH)**, DL8, **England**.
Contact/s: **Mr Eccles** (Director), Lowis Country Wear, Riverside House, Bridge End, Hawes, DL8 3NH.
(T) 01969 667443
Profile: **FT:** Game; **WN:** Ure; **WT:** River (Moving).
Ref: FH5071

URE (RIVER)

River Ure, Ripon, **YORKSHIRE (NORTH)**, HG4, **England**.
Contact/s: **Mr B Thackrey** (Secretary).
(T) 01423 866695
Mr G Hinds (Chairman).
(T) 01423 869647
Mr Norman Edward (Vice Chairman), 125 The Avenue, Starbeck, Harrogate, HG1 4QG.
(T) 01423 885399
Profile: **FT:** Combination; **WN:** Ure; **WT:** River (Moving).
Ref: FH5072

URE (RIVER)

River Ure, Middleham, **YORKSHIRE (NORTH)**, DL8, **England**.
Contact/s: .
(T) 0113 2499721
Profile: **FT:** Coarse; **WN:** Ure; **WT:** River (Moving). **Location:** **Nr. Rd:** A6108.
Ref: FH5073

URE (RIVER)

River Ure, Boroughbridge, York, **YORKSHIRE (NORTH)**, YO51, **England**.
Contact/s: Manager, Fish-N-Things, 5 Horsefair, Boroughbridge, York, YO51 9LF.
(T) 01423 324776 **(F)** 01423 324776
Profile: **FT:** Coarse; **WN:** Ure; **WT:** River (Moving).
Ref: FH5074

URE (RIVER)

River Ure, Worton, Leyburn, **YORKSHIRE (NORTH)**, DL8, **England**.
Contact/s: **Mrs P Thorpe** (Secretary), Grange Farm, High Birstwith, Harrogate, HG3 2ST.
Profile: **FT:** Game; **WN:** Ure; **WT:** River (Moving).
Ref: FH5075

URR (RIVER)

River Urr, Craignair, Dalbeattie, **DUMFRIES AND GALLOWAY**, DG5, **Scotland**.
Contact/s: **Mr John Moran** (Secretary), 12 Church Cres, Dalbeattie, Dumfries and Galloway, DG5 4BA.
(T) 01556 610026 **(M)** 07778 140569
Profile: **FT:** Game; **WN:** Urr; **WT:** River (Moving). **Location:** **Nr. Rd:** B711; **Main Rd:** A75; **Rail:** Dumfries.
Ref: FH5076

USK (RIVER)

River Usk, Usk, **MONMOUTHSHIRE**, NP15, **Wales**.
Contact/s: Manager, Sweet's Fishing Tackle, 14 Porthycarne St, Usk, Gwent, NP15 1RY.
(T) 01291 672552
Profile: **FT:** Game; **WN:** Usk; **WT:** River (Moving) **W. Size:** 3200 Metres. **Location:** **Nr. Rd:** Llanbadoc Church.
Ref: FH5077

USK (RIVER)

River Usk, Abergavenny, **MONMOUTHSHIRE**, NP7, **Wales**.
Contact/s: **Mr John Taylor** (Hon Secretary), 23 Adenfield Way, Rhoose, Glamorgan (Vale of), CF62 3EA.
(T) 01446 711216
Profile: **FT:** Game; **WN:** Usk; **WT:** River (Moving) **W. Size:** 9600 Metres. **Location:** **Nr. Rd:** Bridge Inn to Footbridge.
Ref: FH5078

USK (RIVER)

River Usk, Crickhowell, **POWYS**, NP8, **Wales**.
Contact/s: **Mr N S Brabner** (Manager), Gliffaes Country House Hotel, Gliffaes Rd, Crickhowell, Powys, NP8 1RH.
(T) 01874 730371
Profile: **FT:** Game; **WN:** Usk; **WT:** River (Moving) **W. Size:** 4000 Metres.
Ref: FH5079

USK RESERVOIR

Usk Reservoir, Senny Bridge, Brecon, **POWYS**, LD3, **Wales**.
Contact/s: **Mr C Hatch** (Area Manager), Hamdden Ltd, Sluvad Treatment Works, Llandegfedd Reservoir, New Inn, Pontypool, Gwent NP4 0TA.
(T) 01495 769281 **(F)** 01495 769283
Profile: **FT:** Game; **WN:** Usk; **WT:** Reservoir (Still) **W. Size:** 318 Acres. **Location:** **Nr. Rd:** Senny Bridge.
Ref: FH5080

VALE BRIDGE LAKE

Vale Bridge Lake, Haywards Heath, **SUSSEX (WEST)**, RH17, **England**.
Contact/s: Manager, Sporting Chance, Unit 2 Sheffield House, 29 Boltro Rd, Haywards Heath, RH16 1BP.
(T) 01444 454095
Mr J Kenward (Secretary), Haywards Heath and District Angling Society, 60 Franklyn Rd, Haywards Heath, Sussex (West), RH16 4DH.
(T) 01444 452572
Profile: **FT:** Coarse; **WN:** Vale Bridge; **WT:** Lake (Still). **Location:** **Nr. Rd:** Rocky Lane; **Main Rd:** B2112.
Ref: FH5081

VALE FARM FISHERY

Vale Farm Fishery, Nuns Walk, Longparish, Andover, **HAMPSHIRE**, SP11 6QW, **England**.
Contact/s: **Mr Nick Dunford** (Manager).
(T) 01264 720227or07712063210
Profile: **FT:** Game; **WN:** Test Water; **WT:** Lake (Still) **W. Size:** 2 Acres. **Location:** **Nr. Rd:** Nuns Walk; **Main Rd:** A34, A303.
Ref: FH5082

VALE OF HEATH POND

Vale Of Heath Pond, East Heath Rd, Hampstead Common, Hampstead, London, **LONDON (GREATER)**, NW3, **England**.
Contact/s: Ranger, Rangers Office, Parliament Hill Fields, High Gate Rd, Hampstead Heath.
(T) 020 74854491
Mr Bob Sharpe (Manager), Sharps Tackle, 162 Malden Rd, London, NW5 4BS.
(T) 020 74851759
Profile: **FT:** Coarse; **WN:** Vale of Heath; **WT:** Pond (Still) **W. Size:** 2 Acres. **Location:** **Nr. Rd:** East Heath Road; **Main Rd:** A502.
£Fr
Ref: FH5083

VALE ROYAL LOCKS

Vale Royal Locks, Northwich, **CHESHIRE**, CW, **England**.
Contact/s: Manager, PO Box 18, Northwich, Cheshire, CW9 5SE.
Mr Jimmy Clitheroe.
(T) 01606 35071
Profile: **FT:** Coarse; **WN:** Weaver; **WT:** River (Moving). **Location:** **Nr. Rd:** Hartford Bridge; **Main Rd:** A533 to Middlewich.
Ref: FH5084

VALENCE MOAT

Valence Moat, Becontree Avenue, Dagenham, **ESSEX**, **England**.
(W) www.becmain-as.dial.pipex.com
Contact/s: **Mr Leslie Ailey** (Club Secretary), 3 Meadow Rd, Rush Green, Romford, Essex, RM7 0LR.
(T) 01708 745985 **(M)** 07714 091884
(E) becmain-as@dial.pipex.com
Profile: **FT:** Coarse; **WN:** Valence; **WT:** Lake (Still); **F. Size:** 2 Acres; **W. Size:** 1 Acre. **Location:** **Nr. Rd:** Becontree Avenue; **Main Rd:** A1083; **Rail:** Dagenham.
Ref: FH5085

VALLEY DAM FISHERY

Valley Dam Fishery, Llanfihangel, Llanfyllin, **POWYS**, SY22 5JF, **Wales**.
Contact/s: Fishery Manager.
(T) 01691 649837
Profile: **FT:** Game; **WN:** Valley; **WT:** Dam (Still).
Ref: FH5086

VALLEY FARM FISHERY

Valley Farm Fishery, Peasenhall Rd, Walpole, Halesworth, **SUFFOLK**, IP19 9BQ, **England**.
Contact/s: **Mr Harry Murphy** (Owner).
(T) 01986 784488
Mr Paul Murphy (Owner).
Profile: **FT:** Coarse; **WN:** Valley Farm Fishery; **WT:** Pond (Still).
Ref: FH5087

VALLEY SPRINGS TROUT FISHERY

Valley Springs Trout Fishery, Valley Springs, Sherford, Kingsbridge, **DEVON**, TQ7 2BG, **England**.
Contact/s: **Mr John Bishop**.
(T) 01548 531574 **(F)** 01548 531574
Profile: **FT:** Combination; **WN:** Valley Spring; **WT:** Lake (Still) **W. Size:** 2 Acres. **Location:** **Nr. Rd:** A379; **Main Rd:** A386; **Rail:** Totnes.
Ref: FH5088

VALLEY VIEW FISHERY

Valley View Fishery, Tedburn, St Mary, Crediton, **DEVON**, EX17, **England**.
Contact/s: , Tiverton and District Angling Club, 21 Alstone Rd, Tiverton, Devon, EX16 4LH.
Profile: **FT:** Coarse; **WN:** Valley View Fishery; **WT:** Pond (Still) **W. Size:** 4 Acres. **Location:** **Main Rd:** M5, A377.
Ref: FH5089

VAUXHALL PIT

Vauxhall Pit, Leighton Buzzard, **BEDFORDSHIRE**, LU7 0SJ, **England**.
Contact/s: **Mr Roy Poulton** (Secretary), 20 Leaches Way, Cheddington, Leighton Buzzard, Bedfordshire, LU7 0SJ.
(T) 01296 668985
Profile: **FT:** Coarse; **WN:** Vauxhall; **WT:** Pit (Still).
Ref: FH5090

VENFORD RESERVOIR

Venford Reservoir, Ashburton, Newton Abbot, **DEVON**, TQ13, **England**.
Contact/s: **Mr Chris Hall** (Manager).
(T) 01837 871565 **(F)** 01837 871534
Profile: **FT:** Game; **WN:** Venford; **WT:** Reservoir (Still).
Ref: FH5091

VENN DOWN LAKES

Venn Down Lakes, Trebowen, Trevalga, Boscastle, **CORNWALL**, PL35 0E, **England**.
Contact/s: **Mr Ted Bowen** (Manager).
(T) 01840 250018
Profile: **FT:** Game; **WN:** Venn Down; **WT:** Lake (Still).
Ref: FH5092

VENN POOL

Venn Pool, Barnstaple, **DEVON**, EX3, **England**.
Contact/s: **Mr Martin Turner**, Barnstaple and District Angling Association, 67 Taw View, Freminton, Barnstaple.
Profile: **FT:** Coarse; **WN:** Venn Pool; **WT:** Gravel Pit (Still).
Ref: FH5093

VENTONTRISSICK FISHERY

Ventontrissick Fishery, Zelah, Truro, **CORNWALL**, TR, **England**.
Contact/s: **Mr Gerald Wright** (Manager).
(T) 01872 540497
Profile: **FT:** Game; **WN:** Ventontrissick; **WT:** Lake (Still). **Location:** **Nr. Rd:** Zelah.
Ref: FH5094

VIADUCT FISHERY

Viaduct Fishery, Cedar Gr, Somerton, **SOMERSET**, TA11 6LJ, **England**.
Contact/s: **Mr Ian Parsons**.
(T) 01458 274022
Mr Steve Long (Company Director).
(T) 01458 274022 **(F)** 01458 274698
Profile: **FT:** Coarse; **WN:** Viaduct Fishery; **WT:** Lake (Still); **F. Size:** 28 Acres; **W. Size:** 14 Acres. **Location:** **Nr. Rd:** Brockle Hill; **Main Rd:** A303, B3151 to Somerton; **Rail:** Yeovil.
Ref: FH5095

VICARAGE SPINNEY FISHERY

Vicarage Spinney Trout Fishery, Haversham Rd, Little Linford, Milton Keynes, **BUCKINGHAMSHIRE**, MK19 7EA, **England**.
Contact/s: Fishery Manager.
(T) 01908 612227
Mr Chris W Cansdale, Latimer Park Lakes, Chesham, Buckinghamshire, HP5 1TT.
(T) 01494 766333 **(F)** 01494 766555
Profile: **FT:** Game; **WN:** Vicarage Spinney Trout Fishery; **WT:** Lake (Still) **W. Size:** 8 Acres.
Ref: FH5096

VICKERS POND

Vickers Pond, The Fisheries, Main Rd, Saltfleetby, Louth, **LINCOLNSHIRE**, LN11 7SS, **England**.
Contact/s: **Mr Gc Vickers**.
(T) 01507 338272
Profile: **FT:** Coarse; **WN:** Vickers; **WT:** Clay Pit (Still) **W. Size:** 2 Acres. **Location:** **Nr. Rd:** B1200; **Main Rd:** A16; **Rail:** Grimsby.
Ref: FH5097

VILLAGE POOL

Village Pool, Whitley, Warrington, **CHESHIRE**, WA, **England**.
Contact/s: **Mr Neil Jupp** (Club Secretary), Lymm Angling Club, PO Box 350, Warrington, Cheshire, WA2 9FB.
(T) 01925 411774
Profile: **FT:** Coarse; **WN:** Village; **WT:** Pool (Still). **Location:** **Nr. Rd:** A559; **Main Rd:** M56, junction 10.
Ref: FH5098

VINEHALL SCHOOL LAKE

Vinehall School Lake, Johns Cross, Robertsbridge, **SUSSEX (EAST)**, TN32, **England**.
Contact/s: **Mr Peter Maclean** (Hon Secretary), 37 Collier Rd, Hastings, Sussex (East), TN34 3JR.
(T) 01424 715218
Profile: **FT:** Coarse; **WN:** Vinehall School; **WT:** Lake (Still) **W. Size:** 1 Acre. **Location:** **Nr. Rd:** Whatlington to John's Cross; **Main Rd:** A21.
Ref: FH5099

VIRGINIA LAKE

Virginia Lake, Virginia House, Smeeth Rd, Marshland St James, Wisbech, **CAMBRIDGESHIRE**, PE, **England**.
Contact/s: **Dennis** (Bailiff).
(T) 01945 430332 **(F)** 01945 430128
Mr Ray Malle (P.A.A (Resident Instructor)).
(M) 07710 341480
Mr Ted Grib.
(T) 01945 430332 **(F)** 01945 430128
Profile: **FT:** Coarse; **WN:** Virginia; **WT:** Lake (Still) **W. Size:** 2 Acres. **Location:** **Nr. Rd:** Smeeth Road; **Main Rd:** King's Lynn.
Ref: FH5100

VOWNOG FISH LAKE

Vownog Fish Lake, Vownog, Porth-Y-Waen, Oswestry, **SHROPSHIRE**, SY10 8LX, **England**.
Contact/s: **Mr Steve Ellis** (Manager).
(T) 01691 828474 **(F)** 01691 828374
Mrs Liz Dixon.
(T) 01691 828474 **(F)** 01691 828374
Profile: **FT:** Game; **WN:** Vownog; **WT:** Lake (Still); **F. Size:** 10 Acres; **W. Size:** 2 Acres. **Location:** **Nr. Rd:** A495; **Main Rd:** A483; **Rail:** Gobowen. **£Fr**
Ref: FH5101

VYRNWY (RIVER)

Vyrnwy (River), Rhandregynwen Farm, Four Crosses, Welshpool, **POWYS**, **Wales**.
Contact/s: **Mr John Turner** (Hon Secretary), Prince Albert Angling Society, 15 Pexhill Drive, Macclesfield, Cheshire, SK10 3LP.
(T) 01625 422010
Profile: **FT:** Combination; **WN:** Vyrnwy; **WT:** River (Moving) **W. Size:** 1200 Metres. **Location:** **Nr. Rd:** Domgay Lane; **Main Rd:** A483; **Rail:** Welshpool.
Ref: FH5102

VYRNWY (RIVER)

River Vyrnwy, Llandrinio, Llanymynech, **POWYS**, SY22, **Wales**.
Contact/s: **Mr Neil Jupp** (Club Secretary), Lymm Angling Club, PO Box 350, Warrington, Cheshire, WA2 9FB.
(T) 01925 411744
Profile: **FT:** Combination; **WN:** Vyrnwy; **WT:** River (Moving). **Location:** **Nr. Rd:** B4393; **Main Rd:** M53 to Wrexham, A483.
Ref: FH5103

VYRNWY (RIVER)

River Vyrnwy, Cilmawr, Welshpool, **POWYS**, SY21, **Wales**.
Contact/s: Manager, Cilmawr, Meiford, Welshpool, Powys.
(T) 01938 500307
Profile: **FT:** Game; **WN:** Vyrnwy; **WT:** River (Moving) **W. Size:** 1500 Metres.
Ref: FH5104

VYRNWY (RIVER)

River Vyrnwy, Llanymynech, **POWYS**, SY22, **Wales**.
Contact/s: **Mr J A Mobley** (Hon Secretary), 155 Greenhill Rd, Halesowen, Midlands (West), B62 8EZ.
(T) 0121 4221161
Profile: **FT:** Combination; **WN:** Vyrnwy; **WT:** River (Moving) **W. Size:** 1200 Metres.
Ref: FH5105

VYRNWY (RIVER)

River Vyrnwy, Llansantffraid, **POWYS**, SY22, **Wales**.
Contact/s: **Mr D Williams**, Bryn Vyrnwy, Llansantffriad, Welshpool.
Profile: **FT:** Game; **WN:** Vyrnwy; **WT:** River (Moving) **W. Size:** 1600 Metres.
Ref: FH5106

VYRNWY (RIVER)

Vyrnwy (River), Plas Derwyn, Llansantffraid, Welshpool, **POWYS**, **Wales**.
Contact/s: **Mr John Turner** (Hon Secretary), Prince Albert Angling Society, 15 Pexhill Drive, Macclesfield, Cheshire, SK10 3LP.
(T) 01625 422010
Profile: **FT:** Game; **WN:** Vyrnwy; **WT:** River (Moving) **W. Size:** 400 Metres. **Location:** **Nr. Rd:** B4393; **Rail:** Welshpool.
Ref: FH5107

VYRNWY (RIVER)

River Vyrnwy, Great Dufford Farm, Welshpool, **POWYS**, SY21, **Wales**.
Contact/s: **Mr Hulme** (Secretary), Montgomeryshire Angling Association, 306 Heol-y-Coleg, Vaynor Estate, Newtown, SY16 1RA.
(T) 01938 553867
Profile: **FT:** Coarse; **WN:** Vyrnwy; **WT:** River (Moving) **W. Size:** 750 Metres.
Ref: FH5108

VYRNWY (RIVER)

Vyrnwy (River), Pentreheylin Hall, Maesbrook, Oswestry, **SHROPSHIRE**, **England**.
Contact/s: **Mr John Turner** (Hon Secretary), Prince Albert Angling Society, 15 Pexhill Drive, Macclesfield, Cheshire, SK10 3LP.
(T) 01625 422010
Profile: **FT:** Combination; **WN:** Vyrnwy; **WT:** River (Moving) **W. Size:** 1500 Metres. **Location:** **Main Rd:** B4398; **Rail:** Oswestry.
Ref: FH5109

WADE LAKE

Wade Lake, Hill Ridware, Rugeley, **STAFFORDSHIRE**, **England**.
Contact/s: **Mr John Turner** (Hon Secretary), Prince Albert Angling Society, 15 Pexhill Drive, Macclesfield, Cheshire, SK10 3LP.
(T) 01625 422010
Profile: **FT:** Coarse; **WN:** Wade Lake; **WT:** Lake (Still); **F. Size:** 25 Acres; **W. Size:** 18 Acres. **Location:** **Nr. Rd:** Church Lane; **Main Rd:** B5014; **Rail:** Rugeley.
Ref: FH5110

WADSWORTH FISHERY

Wadsworth Fishery, Witton Park, Bishop Auckland, **COUNTY DURHAM**, DL1, **England**.
Contact/s: **Mr John Winter** (Secretary), Bishop Auckland and District Angling Club, 7 Royal Gr, Crook, County Durham, DL15 9ER.
(T) 01388 762538 **(F)** 01388 767762
Profile: **FT:** Coarse; **WN:** Wadsworth Fishery; **WT:** Gravel Pit (Still); **F. Size:** 40 Acres; **W. Size:** 11 Acres. **Location:** **Nr. Rd:** Witton Park to Escomb Village; **Main Rd:** A689, A690; **Rail:** Bishop Auckland.
Ref: FH5111

WAGGONERS WELLS

Waggoners Wells, Summerden North, Waggoners Wells, Grayshott, Hindhead, **SURREY**, GU26, **England**.
Contact/s: Fishery Manager.
(T) 01428 609309
Profile: **FT:** Combination; **WN:** Waggoners; **WT:** Lake (Still). **Location:** **Nr. Rd:** A287; **Main Rd:** A3.
Ref: FH5112

WAINSFORD RESERVOIR

Wainsford Reservoir, Lymington, **HAMPSHIRE**, SO41, **England**.
Contact/s: **Mr R J Andrews** (Club Secretary), Christchurch Angling Club, 4 Marley Cl, New Milton, BH25 5LL.
(T) 01425 638502
Profile: **FT:** Coarse; **WN:** Wainsford; **WT:** Reservoir (Still) **W. Size:** 3 Acres. **Location:** **Main Rd:** A337, South of Southampton.
Ref: FH5113

WAKE VALLEY POND

Wake Valley Pond, Epping New Rd, Loughton, **ESSEX**, IG10, **England**.
Mr A Clark (Secretary), Ilford and District Angling Club, 68 Huntsman Rd, Hainault,

Essex, IG6 3SX.
Profile: **FT:** Coarse; **WN:** Wake Valley; **WT:** Pond (Still). **Location:** **Nr. Rd:** A104; **Main Rd:** Epping New Road; **Rail:** Loughton.
Ref: FH5114

WAL GOCH FLY

Wal Goch Fly, Wal Goch Farm, Nannerch, Mold, **FLINTSHIRE**, CH7 5RP, **Wales**.
Contact/s: **Mr Philip Robinson** (Manager).
(T) 01352 741378
Profile: **FT:** Game; **WN:** Wal Goch; **WT:** Lake (Still) **W. Size:** 3 Acres.
Ref: FH5115

WALCOT EAST LAKE

Walcot East Lake, Rotton Park, Birmingham, **MIDLANDS (WEST)**, B16 0AP, **England**.
Contact/s: **Mr John Williams** (Secretary), Birmingham Anglers Association, 100 Icknield Port Rd, Rotton Park, Birmingham, B16 0AP.
(T) 0121 4549111
Profile: **FT:** Coarse; **WN:** Walcot East; **WT:** Lake (Still). **Location:** **Main Rd:** B4368.
Ref: FH5116

WALCOT WEST LAKE

Walcot West Lake, Walcot West Mansion, Lydbury North, Bishops Castle, **SHROPSHIRE**, SY9, **England**.
Contact/s: **Mr Dave Bastin** (Secretary), Ludlow Angling Club, 96 Greenacres, Ludlow, Shropshire, SY8 1LZ.
(T) 01584 873577
Profile: **FT:** Coarse; **WN:** Walcot West; **WT:** Lake (Still) **W. Size:** 16 Acres. **Location:** **Nr. Rd:** Estate Road; **Main Rd:** B4368; **Rail:** Ludlow.
Ref: FH5117

WALDENS FARM FISHERY

Waldens Farm Fishery, Walden Estate, West Grimstead, Salisbury, **WILTSHIRE**, SP5 3RJ, **England**.
Contact/s: **Mr David Wateridge** (Owner).
(T) 01722 710480
Mrs Jackie Wateridge (Owner).
(T) 01722 710480
Profile: **FT:** Coarse; **WN:** Waldens Farm Fishery; **WT:** Lake (Still); **F. Size:** 47 Acres; **W. Size:** 8 Acres. **Location:** **Nr. Rd:** Farley Road; **Main Rd:** A36 to Southampton.
Ref: FH5118

WALKERWOOD RESERVOIR

Walkerwood Reservoir, Tameside, Hyde, **CHESHIRE**, SK14, **England**.
Contact/s: **Mr John Winterbottom** (Secretary), 1 Hill Crest Cross, Hyde, Manchester.
(T) 0161 3683173
Mr Roy Rhodes (Conservation, Access and Recreation Manager), Rivington Water Treatment Works, Bolton Rd, Horwich, Bolton, BL6 7RN.
(T) 01204 664300
Profile: **FT:** Game; **WN:** Walkerwood; **WT:** Reservoir (Still) **W. Size:** 27 Acres.
Ref: FH5119

WALKERWOOD TROUT FISHERY

Walkerwood Trout Fishery, Brushes Rd, Stalybridge, **CHESHIRE**, SK15 5QP, **England**.
(W) www.walkerwood.free-online.co.uk
Contact/s: **Mr John Winterbottom** (Bailiff), 1 Hill Crest Cross, Hyde, Manchester.
(T) 0161 3683173
(E) mail@walkerwood.idps.co.uk
Profile: **FT:** Game; **WN:** Walkerwood; **WT:** Reservoir (Still) **W. Size:** 27 Acres.
Location: **Nr. Rd:** Brushes Road; **Main Rd:** B6175 Huddersfield Road.
Ref: FH5120

WALL POOL LODGE

Wall Pool Lodge, Gawsworth Hall, Church Lane, Macclesfield, **CHESHIRE**, SK11 9RQ, **England**.
Contact/s: **Mr John Birch** (Owner).
(T) 01206 223442 **(M)** 07780 538762
Profile: **FT:** Coarse; **WN:** Wall; **WT:** Pool (Still); **F. Size:** 10 Acres; **W. Size:** 8 Acres.
Location: **Nr. Rd:** Church Lane; **Main Rd:** A356; **Rail:** Macclesfield.
Ref: FH5121

WALLERS HAVEN

Wallers Haven, Hailsham, **SUSSEX (EAST)**, BN27, **England**.
Profile: **FT:** Coarse; **WN:** Wallers Haven; **WT:** Lake (Still) **W. Size:** 4 Acres.
Ref: FH5122

WALLERS HAVEN

Wallers Haven, Pevensey Marshes Drain, Pevensey, **SUSSEX (EAST)**, BN24, **England**.
Contact/s: **Mr Alex Heggie** (Membership Secretary), Little Lucy's Farmhouse, Lower St, Hildenborough, Tonbridge, TN11 8PT.
(T) 01732 832352 **(F)** 01732 832352
Profile: **FT:** Coarse; **WN:** Waller's Haven; **WT:** Drain (Moving). **Location:** **Main Rd:** A259.
Ref: FH5123

WALLYS LAKE

Wallys Lake, Osmington Mill Holidays Ltd, Ranch House, Osmington Mills, Weymouth, **DORSET**, DT3 6HB, **England**.
Mrs Louise Goucher (Owner), The Ranch House, Osmington Mills, Weymouth, Dorset, DT3 6HB.
(T) 01305 832311
Profile: **FT:** Coarse; **WN:** Wally's; **WT:** Lake (Still) **W. Size:** 1 Acre. **Location:** **Nr. Rd:** Mills Road; **Main Rd:** A353, Weymouth to Wareham; **Rail:** Weymouth.
Ref: FH5124

WALNUT FARM FISHERIES

Walnut Farm Fisheries, Silver St, Besthorpe, Attleborough, **NORFOLK**, NR17, **England**.
(W) www.thefisheries.freeserve.co.uk
Contact/s: **Mike**, J M P Tackle, Unit 26, Haverscroft Industrial Estate, London Rd, Attleborough, NR17 1YE.
(T) 01953 455282
Mr Paul Fulcher.
(T) 01953 860264
Mr Simon England.
(T) 01953 851945
Profile: **FT:** Coarse; **WN:** Walnut Farm Fisheries; **WT:** Combination (Still); **F. Size:** 3 Acres; **W. Size:** 2 Acres. **Location:** **Nr. Rd:** Silver Street; **Main Rd:** A11; **Rail:** Attleborough.
Ref: FH5125

WALROW PONDS

Walrow Ponds, Walrow Ponds, Walrow Rd, Highbridge, **SOMERSET**, TA9, **England**.
Contact/s: **Mr S Bonwick** (Secretary), 13 Tennyson Avenue, Clevedon, Somerset, BS21 7QQ.
(T) 01275 791933
Profile: **FT:** Coarse; **WN:** Walrow; **WT:** Pond (Still); **F. Size:** 6 Acres; **W. Size:** 5 Acres.
Location: **Nr. Rd:** Walrow Road; **Main Rd:** M5, junction 22, A38.
Ref: FH5126

WALSALL ARBORETUM

Walsall Arboretum, Walsall, **MIDLANDS (WEST)**, WS1, **England**.
Contact/s: **Mr Lunn**.
(T) 01922 65000
Profile: **FT:** Coarse; **WN:** Walsall Arboretum; **WT:** Lake (Still) **W. Size:** 5 Acres.
Ref: FH5127

WALSDEN PRINTING CO LODGES

Walsden Printing Co Lodges, Ramsden Wood Rd, Todmorden, **YORKSHIRE (WEST)**, OL14, **England**.
(W) www.todmorden-angling.fsnet.co.uk
Contact/s: **Mr Ray Barber** (Secretary), Todmorden Angling Society, 12 Grisedale Drive, Burnley, Lancashire, BB12 8AR.
(T) 01282 428780 **(M)** 07970 897849
Profile: **FT:** Combination; **WN:** Walsden Printing Co Lodges; **WT:** Dam (Still); **F. Size:** 3 Acres; **W. Size:** 2 Acres. **Location:** **Nr. Rd:** A6033; **Rail:** Todmorden.
Ref: FH5128

WALTHAMSTOW (NO 2 & NO 3)

Walthamstow Reservoir (No 2 And No 3), Tottenham, London, **LONDON (GREATER)**, N17, **England**.
Contact/s: **Mr Chris King**, Walthamstow Reservoir Group, Thames Water Gatehouse, 2 Forest Rd, Tottenham, London, N17 9NH.
(T) 020 88081527
Profile: **FT:** Coarse; **WN:** No 2 and No 3; **WT:** Reservoir (Still) **W. Size:** 35 Acres.
Location: **Nr. Rd:** Forest Road; **Main Rd:** A10, North London; **Rail:** Tottenham Hale Underground.
Ref: FH5131

WALTHAMSTOW (EAST WARWICK)

Walthamstow Reservoir (East Warwick), Tottenham, London, **LONDON (GREATER)**, N17, **England**.
Contact/s: **Mr Chris King**, Walthamstow Reservoir Group, Thames Water Gatehouse, 2 Forest Rd, Tottenham, London, N17 9NH.
(T) 020 88081527
Profile: **FT:** Combination; **WN:** East Warwick; **WT:** Reservoir (Still) **W. Size:** 40 Acres.
Location: **Nr. Rd:** Forest Road; **Main Rd:** A10, North London; **Rail:** Tottenham Hale Underground.
Ref: FH5129

WALTHAMSTOW (NO 4 TROUT)

Walthamstow Reservoir (No 4 Trout), Tottenham, London, **LONDON (GREATER)**, N17, **England**.
Contact/s: **Mr Chris King**, Walthamstow Reservoir Group, Thames Water Gatehouse, 2 Forest Rd, Tottenham, London, N17 9NH.
(T) 020 88081527
Profile: **FT:** Game; **WN:** No 4 Trout; **WT:** Reservoir (Still) **W. Size:** 40 Acres.
Location: **Nr. Rd:** Forest Road; **Main Rd:** A10, North London; **Rail:** Tottenham Hale Underground.
Ref: FH5132

WALTHAMSTOW (WEST WARWICK)

Walthamstow Reservoir (West Warwick), Tottenham, London, **LONDON (GREATER)**, N17, **England**.
Contact/s: **Mr Chris King**, Walthamstow Reservoir Group, Thames Water Gatehouse, 2 Forest Rd, Tottenham, London, N17 9NH.
(T) 020 88081527
Profile: **FT:** Combination; **WN:** West Warwick; **WT:** Reservoir (Still) **W. Size:** 45 Acres. **Location:** **Nr. Rd:** Forest Road; **Main Rd:** A10, North London; **Rail:** Tottenham Hale Underground.
Ref: FH5134

WALTHAMSTOW RESERVOIR (NO 1)

Walthamstow Reservoir (No 1), Tottenham, London, **LONDON (GREATER)**, N17, **England**.
Contact/s: **Mr Chris King**, Walthamstow Reservoir Group, Thames Water Gatehouse, 2 Forest Rd, Tottenham, London, N17 9NH.
(T) 020 88081527
Profile: **FT:** Coarse; **WN:** No 1; **WT:** Reservoir (Still) **W. Size:** 19 Acres.
Location: **Nr. Rd:** Ferry Lane; **Main Rd:** A10, North London; **Rail:** Blackhorse Road Tube.
Ref: FH5130

WALTHAMSTOW RESERVOIR (NO 5)

Walthamstow Reservoir (No 5), Tottenham, London, **LONDON (GREATER)**, N17, **England**.
Contact/s: **Mr Chris King**, Walthamstow Reservoir Group, Thames Water Gatehouse, 2 Forest Rd, Tottenham, London, N17 9NH.
(T) 020 88081527
Profile: **FT:** Game; **WN:** No 5; **WT:** Reservoir (Still) **W. Size:** 45 Acres. **Location:** **Nr. Rd:** Forest Road; **Main Rd:** A10, North London; **Rail:** Tottenham Hale Underground.
Ref: FH5133

WALTON HALL PARK

Walton Hall Park, Queens Drive, Liverpool, **MERSEYSIDE**, L, **England**.
Contact/s: Fishery Manager.
(T) 0151 2255910
Fishery Manager.
(T) 0151 7341943
Profile: FT: Coarse; **WN:** Walton Hall Park; **WT:** Lake (Still). **Location: Nr. Rd:** Queens Drive A5058; **Main Rd:** Walton Lane A580. £Fr
Ref: FH5135

WALTON HALL TROUT LAKE

Walton Hall Trout Lake, Wakefield, **YORKSHIRE (WEST)**, WF, **England**.
Contact/s: Fishery Manager.
(T) 01924 242990
Mr David Kaye (Manager), Waterton Park Hotel, Walton, Wakefield, Yorkshire (West), WF2 6PW.
(T) 01924 257911
Profile: FT: Game; **WN:** Walton Hall; **WT:** Lake (Still). **Location: Nr. Rd:** Walton Road.
Ref: FH5136

WALVERDEN RESERVOIR

Walverden Reservoir, Brunswick St, Nelson, **LANCASHIRE**, BB9, **England**.
(W) www.pearce81.freeserve.co.uk
Contact/s: Mr Terry Hartley (Outdoor Recreation Officer), Pendle Leisure Services, Crown Way, Colne, Lancashire, BB8 8NP.
(T) 01282 661230 (F) 01282 661137 (M) 07718 601881
(E) plc@leisureinpendle.co.uk
Profile: FT: Combination; **WN:** Walverden; **WT:** Reservoir (Still) **W. Size:** 7 Acres. **Location: Nr. Rd:** Brunswick Street; **Main Rd:** M65; **Rail:** Nelson.
Ref: FH5137

WANDSWORTH COMMON POND

Wandsworth Common Pond, Wandsworth Common, London, **LONDON (GREATER)**, SW18, **England**.
Contact/s: Manager, Wandsworth Borough Council, Town Hall, Wandsworth, SW18.
Profile: FT: Coarse; **WN:** Wandsworth; **WT:** Pond (Still). **Location: Nr. Rd:** A214; **Main Rd:** A3.
Ref: FH5138

WANSBECK (RIVER)

River Wansbeck, Morpeth, **NORTHUMBERLAND**, NE, **England**.
Contact/s: Mr Peter Wigham (Secretary), Wansbeck Angling Association, School House, Chantry School, Mitford Rd, Morpeth, NE61 1RQ.
(T) 01670 511480 (M) 07885 326891
Profile: FT: Game; **WN:** Wansbeck; **WT:** River (Moving) **W. Size:** 9600 Metres. **Location: Nr. Rd:** A1; **Main Rd:** A197; **Rail:** Morpeth.
Ref: FH5139

WANSBECK (RIVER)

River Wansbeck, Riverside Park, Ashington, **NORTHUMBERLAND**, NE63, **England**.
Contact/s: Mr John Watts (Manager).
(T) 01670 812323
Profile: FT: Game; **WN:** Wansbeck; **WT:** River (Moving).
Ref: FH5140

WANSBECK STREAM

Wansbeck Stream, Morpeth, **NORTHUMBERLAND**, NE, **England**.
Contact/s: Mr D Bell, 9 Biltons Court, Morpeth, Northumberland.
Profile: FT: Game; **WN:** Wansbeck; **WT:** Stream (Moving) **W. Size:** 8000 Metres.
Ref: FH5141

WANSFORD STREAM

Wansford Stream, Wansford, Peterborough, **CAMBRIDGESHIRE**, PE8, **England**.
Contact/s: Manager, Webbs Tackle, 196 Newark Avenue, Wansford, Peterborough, Cambridgeshire, PE1 4NP.
(T) 01733 566466
Profile: FT: Coarse; **WN:** Wansford; **WT:** Stream (Moving) **W. Size:** 2400 Metres. **Location: Nr. Rd:** Road Bridge; **Main Rd:** A1.
Ref: FH5142

WANSFORD TROUT LAKE

Wansford Trout Lake, Wansford Trout Farm, Wansford, Driffield, **HUMBERSIDE**, YO25, **England**.
Contact/s: Mr Simon Marsh, 108 Wansford Rd, Driffield, Yorkshire (East), YO25 7NN.
(T) 01377 255863
Profile: FT: Game; **WN:** Wansford; **WT:** Lake (Still). **Location: Nr. Rd:** B1249; **Main Rd:** A614.
Ref: FH5143

WANSTEAD AND WOODFORD PONDS

Wanstead And Woodford Ponds, Woodford, Wanstead, Ilford, **ESSEX**, IG8, **England**.
Contact/s: Mr Russel Hogg (Owner), A1 Angling, 176 High Rd, Woodford Green, Essex, IG8 9EF.
(T) 020 85044848
Profile: FT: Coarse; **WN:** Knighton, Eagle, Whipps Cross, & Hollow Lake; **WT:** Pond (Still). **Location: Main Rd:** A12. £Fr
Ref: FH5144

WANSTEAD PARK LAKES

Wanstead Park Lakes, Wanstead, London, **LONDON (GREATER)**, E11 2, **England**.
Contact/s: Manager.
(T) 020 85012003
Profile: FT: Coarse; **WN:** Wanstead Park Lakes; **WT:** Lake (Still). **Location: Nr. Rd:** Warren Road; **Main Rd:** A12; **Rail:** Manor Park.
Ref: FH5145

WAPPERWELL POND

Wapperwell Pond, Chudleigh, Newton Abbot, **DEVON**, TQ13, **England**.
Contact/s: Mr Mike Harper.
(T) 01803 328652
Profile: FT: Coarse; **WN:** Wapperwell; **WT:** Pond (Still) **W. Size:** 1 Acre. **Location: Nr. Rd:** Chudleigh; **Main Rd:** A380 to Exeter.
Ref: FH5146

WARDS POOLS

Wards Pools, Watery Lane, Congleton, **CHESHIRE**, CW12, **England**.
Profile: FT: Coarse; **WN:** Wards; **WT:** Pool (Still). **Location: Nr. Rd:** Watery Lane; **Main Rd:** A34, Newcastle Road.
Ref: FH5147

WARMWELL HOLIDAY PARK

Warmwell Holiday Park, Warmwell, Dorchester, **DORSET**, DT2, **England**.
Contact/s: Manager.
(T) 08002 42222
Mr John Alpin, Specialist Angling Supplies, 1 Athelstan Rd, Dorchester, DT1 1NR.
(T) 01305 266500 (M) 07889 680464
Profile: FT: Coarse; **WN:** Warmwell Holiday Park; **WT:** Lake (Still); **F. Size:** 40 Acres. **Location: Nr. Rd:** B3390.
Ref: FH5148

WARPING DRAIN

Warping Drain, Gainsborough, **LINCOLNSHIRE**, DN21, **England**.
Contact/s: Mr Maurice Tate (Secretary), Doncaster and District Angling Association, 28 Holmescarr Rd, New Rossington, Doncaster, DN11 0QF.
(T) 01302 865482
W Sams (Secretary), Doncaster and District Angling Association, 28 Pipering Lane, Scawthorpe, Doncaster.
(T) 01302 780271
Profile: FT: Coarse; **WN:** Warping; **WT:** Drain (Moving) **W. Size:** 9600 Metres.
Ref: FH5149

WARREN

Warren (The), Standford-Le-Hope, **ESSEX**, SS17, **England**.
Contact/s: Secretary, Shell Club AS, Springhouse Rd, Corringham, Stanford-le-Hope, Essex.
(T) 01375 640444
Mr Gordon Edwards.
(T) 01375 677166
Profile: FT: Coarse; **WN:** Warren; **WT:** Lake (Still). **Location: Nr. Rd:** A13 to Standford-le-Hope; **Main Rd:** M25 (London) to A13; **Rail:** Standford-le-Hope. £Fr
Ref: FH5150

WARREN MILL

Warren Mill, Pendoylan, Cowbridge, **GLAMORGAN (VALE OF)**, CF71, **Wales**.
Contact/s: Fishery Manager.
(T) 01446 781274
Profile: FT: Coarse; **WN:** Warren; **WT:** Mill Dam (Still).
Ref: FH5151

WARREN POND

Warren Pond, Warren Rd, North Somercotes, Louth, **LINCOLNSHIRE**, LN11, **England**.
Contact/s: Mr Lowis, Warren Rd, North Somercotes, Louth, LN11 7.
(T) 01507 358350
Profile: FT: Coarse; **WN:** Warren; **WT:** Pond (Still).
Ref: FH5152

WARWICK CANAL

Warwick Canal, Leamington Spa, **WARWICKSHIRE**, CV, **England**.
Contact/s: Mr Ernie Archer (Secretary), Royal Lemington Spa Angling Association, 9 Southway, Leamington Spa, Warwickshire, CV31 2PG.
(T) 01926 334185
Profile: FT: Coarse; **WN:** Warwick; **WT:** Canal (Still).
Ref: FH5153

WARWICKSHIRE & AVON

Common Road, Common Rd, Evesham, **WORCESTERSHIRE**, **England**.
Contact/s: Mr John Davis (Water Allocation Officer), 99 Evendale Rd, Evesham, Worcestershire, WR11 6QA.
(T) 01386 41273 (F) 01386 41273
Profile: FT: Coarse; **WN:** Common Road; **WT:** River (Moving) **W. Size:** 1000 Metres. **Location: Nr. Rd:** Common Road; **Main Rd:** A46; **Rail:** Evesham.
Ref: FH5154

WARWICKSHIRE AVON

Warwickshire Avon, Barton, Stratford-upon-Avon, **WARWICKSHIRE**, CV37, **England**.
Contact/s: Mr John Williams (Secretary), Birmingham Anglers Association, 100 Icknield Port Rd, Rotton Park, Birmingham, B16 0AP.
(T) 0121 4549111
Profile: FT: Coarse; **WN:** Warwickshire Avon; **WT:** River (Moving). **Location: Nr. Rd:** Dorsington Road; **Main Rd:** B439 towards Evesham.
Ref: FH5155

WARWICKSHIRE AVON

Warwickshire Avon, Wasperton, Warwick, **WARWICKSHIRE**, CV35, **England**.
Contact/s: Mr John Williams (Secretary), Birmingham Anglers Association, 100 Icknield Port Rd, Rotton Park, Birmingham, B16 0AP.
(T) 0121 4549111
Profile: FT: Game; **WN:** Avon (Warwickshire); **WT:** River (Moving).
Ref: FH5156

WARWICKSHIRE AVON

Warwickshire Avon, Lido Waters, Stratford-upon-Avon, **WARWICKSHIRE**, CV37, **England**.
Contact/s: Mr Ernie Archer (Secretary), Royal Lemington Spa Angling Association, 9 Southway, Leamington Spa, Warwickshire,

CV31 2PG.
(T) 01926 334185
Profile: **FT:** Coarse; **WN:** Warwickshire Avon; **WT:** River (Moving) **W. Size:** 3200 Metres.
Location: **Nr. Rd:** A439 to Warwick.
Ref: FH5157

WARWICKSHIRE AVON

Warwickshire Avon, Manor Farm Leisure, Anchor Lane, Harvington, Evesham, **WORCESTERSHIRE**, WR11, **England**.
(W) www.anglersnet.co.uk/fisheries/manor.htm
Contact/s: **Mr David Byrd** (Manager), Manor Farm Leisure, Herons Roost, Anchor Lane, Evesham, WR11 5NR.
(T) 01386 870039
(E) manorfarmleisure@btinternet.com
Profile: **FT:** Coarse; **WN:** Warwickshire Avon; **WT:** River (Moving) **W. Size:** 800 Metres.
Location: **Nr. Rd:** B4088 Evesham to Harvington; **Main Rd:** Anchor Lane.
Ref: FH5158

WARWICKSHIRE AVON

Warwickshire Avon, Evesham, **WORCESTERSHIRE**, WR11, **England**.
Contact/s: **Mrs Diana Raphael**.
(T) 01386 442458 (F) 01386 41270
(E) diana@raphael.wynel.com.uk
Profile: **FT:** Coarse; **WN:** Avon (Warwickshire); **WT:** River (Moving).
Ref: FH5160

WARWICKSHIRE AVON

Warwickshire Avon, Pershore Weir, Pershore, **WORCESTERSHIRE**, WR10, **England**.
Contact/s: **Nick** (Manager), Browns Ironmongers, 3 High St, Pershore, Worcestershire, WR10 1AD.
(T) 01386 552648
Profile: **FT:** Coarse; **WN:** Warwickshire Avon; **WT:** River (Moving). **Location:** **Nr. Rd:** Evesham to Worcester; **Main Rd:** A44.
Ref: FH5161

WASH PIT

Wash Pit, Ringwood, **HAMPSHIRE**, BH24, **England**.
Contact/s: **Mr Richard Middleton** (Manager), Ringwood Tackle, 5 The Bridges, Ringwood, Hampshire, BH24 1EA.
(T) 01425 475155
Profile: **FT:** Coarse; **WN:** Wash; **WT:** Gravel Pit (Still).
Ref: FH5162

WASH POOL

Wash Pool, Great Witley, Worcester, **WORCESTERSHIRE**, WR6, **England**.
Contact/s: **Mr Stan Lewis** (Manager), S Lewis Fishing Tackle, 2 Severnside South, Bewdley, Worcestershire, DY12 2DX.
(T) 01299 403358
Profile: **FT:** Coarse; **WN:** Wash; **WT:** Pool (Still). **Location:** **Nr. Rd:** A4133.
Ref: FH5163

WASHBURN VALLEY

Washburn Valley (Fewston And Swinsty), Yorkshire Water Services Fishing Office, Swinsty Moor Car Park, Fewston, Harrogate, **YORKSHIRE (NORTH)**, HG3 1ST, **England**.
Contact/s: **Mr D Welsh**.
(T) 01943 880658
Profile: **FT:** Game; **WN:** Washburn; **WT:** Combination (Still & Moving) **W. Size:** 300 Acres. **Location:** **Main Rd:** A59; **Rail:** Harrogate.
Ref: FH5164

WASING WOODS

Wasing Woods, Wasing Estate, Reading, **BERKSHIRE**, RG7 4NG, **England**.
Contact/s: **Mr Kevin Rolls** (Fishery Manager).
(T) 0118 9714281
Mr Patrick Todd (Estate Manager), Wasing Estate Farm Office, Wasing Park, Aldermaston, Reading, RG7 4NG.
(T) 0118 9714140 (F) 0118 9713251
Profile: **FT:** Coarse; **WN:** Wasing Woods; **WT:** Gravel Pit (Still) **W. Size:** 10 Acres.
Location: **Main Rd:** A4; **Rail:** Midgham.
Ref: FH5165

WASKERLEY RESERVOIR

Waskerley Reservoir, Wolsingham, Consett, **COUNTY DURHAM**, DH8, **England**.
Contact/s: Manager, Quali-Tye, 11 Station Rd, Consett, County Durham, DH8 5RL.
(T) 01207 508010
Profile: **FT:** Game; **WN:** Waskerley; **WT:** Reservoir (Still).
Ref: FH5166

WASSELL GROVE FISHERIES

Wassell Grove Fisheries, Wasell Grove Lane, Hagley, Stourbridge, **MIDLANDS (WEST)**, DY, **England**.
Contact/s: **Mr Mark Moseley**. **(M)** 07773 501333
Mr Ray Wheeler (Fisheries Manager). **(M)** 07870 494534
Profile: **FT:** Coarse; **WN:** Specimen, match, and Brook Lake; **WT:** Pond (Still); **F. Size:** 20 Acres. **Location:** **Nr. Rd:** Wassell Grove Lane; **Rail:** Stourbridge.
Ref: FH5167

WATCH RESERVOIR

Watch Reservoir, Longformacus, Duns, **SCOTTISH BORDERS**, TD11 3PE, **Scotland**.
Contact/s: **Mr J Clark** (Catering Manager).
(T) 01361 890331
Mr William Renton.
(T) 01361 890331
Profile: **FT:** Game; **WN:** Watch; **WT:** Reservoir (Still); **F. Size:** 300 Acres; **W. Size:** 119 Acres. **Location:** **Nr. Rd:** Berwick to Greenlaw; **Main Rd:** A6105 or A1; **Rail:** Berwick.
Ref: FH5168

WATENDLATH TROUT FISHERY

Watendlath Trout Fishery, Fold Head Farm, Borrowdale, Keswick, **CUMBRIA**, CA12 5UY, **England**.
Contact/s: **Mr Stan Edmondson** (Manager), Troutdale Cottage, Borrowdale, Keswick, Cumbria.
(T) 01768 777293 (F) 01768 777293
Profile: **FT:** Game; **WN:** Watendlath Trout Fishery; **WT:** Lake (Still); **F. Size:** 7 Acres; **W. Size:** 7 Acres. **Location:** **Nr. Rd:** B5289; **Main Rd:** A66; **Rail:** Penrith.
Ref: FH5169

WATER END FISHERY

Water End Fishery, Maulden, Ampthill, Bedford, **BEDFORDSHIRE**, MK45, **England**.
Contact/s: **Mr Robert Hinds**.
(T) 01525 403310 (M) 07850 406866
Profile: **FT:** Coarse; **WN:** Water End Fishery; **WT:** Lake (Still) **W. Size:** 1 Acre. **Location:** **Main Rd:** South on A6, right at Clophill.
Ref: FH5170

WATER MEADOW LAKES

Water Meadow Lakes, Pitt Farmhouse, North Perrott, Crewkerne, **SOMERSET**, TA18 7SX, **England**.
Contact/s: **Mr Pike** (Fishery Manager).
(T) 01460 72856
Profile: **FT:** Coarse; **WN:** Water Meadows; **WT:** Lake (Still).
Ref: FH5171

WATER MEADOWS FLY FISHERIES

Water Meadows Fly Fisheries, Ashington Trout Farm, Ashington, Pulborough, **SUSSEX (WEST)**, RH20, **England**.
Contact/s: Fishery Manager.
(T) 01903 892073
Profile: **FT:** Game; **WN:** Water Meadows; **WT:** Lake (Still).
Ref: FH5172

WATER SPRING FISHERY

Water Spring Fishery, Holme Lane, Messingham, Scunthorpe, **HUMBERSIDE**, DN17 3SG, **England**.
Contact/s: Fishery Manager.
(T) 01724 782424
Profile: **FT:** Coarse; **WN:** Water Spring Fishery; **WT:** Lake (Still).
Ref: FH5173

WATERCRESS FARM TROUT FISHERY

Watercress Farm Trout Fishery, Kerswell Springs, Chudleigh, Newton Abbot, **DEVON**, TQ13 0DW, **England**.
Contact/s: **Mr Cook** (Owner).
(T) 01626 852168
Mrs Cook (Owner).
Profile: **FT:** Game; **WN:** Watercress Farm Trout Fishery; **WT:** Lake (Still); **F. Size:** 10 Acres; **W. Size:** 4 Acres. **Location:** **Rail:** Newton Abbot.
Ref: FH5174

WATERFALL LODGE

Waterfall Lodge (The), The Fishing Lodge, Edentrillick Rd, Hillsborough, **COUNTY DOWN**, BT26 6PG, **Northern Ireland**.
Contact/s: **Mr Colin McKibbin**.
(T) 028 92682939
Profile: **FT:** Coarse; **WN:** Waterfall Lodge (The); **WT:** Lake (Still). **Location:** **Nr. Rd:** Edentrillick Road.
Ref: FH5175

WATERFRONT FISHING LAKE

Waterfront Fishing Lake, Bude, **CORNWALL**, **England**.
(W) www.waterfrontfishing.freeserve.co.uk
Contact/s: **Mr Simon Brett** (Owner), Waterfront Fishing, The Lower Wharf Fishing Centre, Bude, Cornwall..
(T) 01288 359606
Profile: **FT:** Coarse; **WN:** Waterfront Fishing Lake; **WT:** Lake (Still); **F. Size:** 2 Acres; **W. Size:** 1 Acre.
Ref: FH5176

WATERGROVE RESERVOIR

Watergrove Reservoir, Rochdale, **MANCHESTER (GREATER)**, OL, **England**.
Contact/s: Fishery Manager.
(T) 01706 379060
Mr Roy Rhodes (Conservation, Access and Recreation Manager), Rivington Water Treatment Works, Bolton Rd, Horwich, Bolton, BL6 7RN.
(T) 01204 664300
Profile: **FT:** Game; **WN:** Watergrove; **WT:** Reservoir (Still).
Ref: FH5177

WATERLEY BROOK

Waterley Brook, Berkeley, **GLOUCESTERSHIRE**, GL13, **England**.
Profile: **FT:** Coarse; **WN:** Waterley; **WT:** Brook (Moving) **W. Size:** 4800 Metres.
Location: **Nr. Rd:** Billow Brook.
Ref: FH5178

WATERLOO SCREENS

Waterloo Screens, Brierley, Forest Of Dean, Gloucester, **GLOUCESTERSHIRE**, GL, **England**.
Contact/s: **Mr Paul Reed** (Secretary), 20 Abbey St, Cinderford, Gloucestershire, GR14 2NW.
(T) 01594 824413
Profile: **FT:** Coarse; **WN:** Waterloo Screens; **WT:** Pond (Still). **Location:** **Nr. Rd:** A4136; **Main Rd:** A40, A48.
Ref: FH5179

WATERMEAD PARK LAKES

Watermead Park Lakes, Wanlip, Leicester, **LEICESTERSHIRE**, LE, **England**.
Contact/s: **Mr A Smith** (Secretary), 10 Lords Avenue, Leicester, Leicestershire, LE4 2HY.
(T) 0116 2357210 (M) 07976 328836
Mr G Taylor (Membership Secretary), Broome Angling Society, 100 New Romney Cres, Leicester.
(T) 0116 2417018
Profile: **FT:** Coarse; **WN:** Watermead Park; **WT:** Gravel Pit (Still) **W. Size:** 20 Acres.
Location: **Main Rd:** Leicester; **Rail:**

Leicester.
Ref: FH5180

WATERMEADOWS FISHERY

Watermeadows Fishery, Thorpe Underwood, York, **YORKSHIRE (NORTH)**, YO5 9TA, **England**.
Contact/s: **Mr Dave Almond** (Owner).
(T) 01423 331080
Profile: **FT:** Game; **WN:** Watermeadows; **WT:** Lake (Still) **W. Size:** 5 Acres. **Location:** **Nr. Rd:** A59; **Main Rd:** B6265; **Rail:** Cattal.
Ref: FH5181

WATERMILL LAKE

Watermill Lake, Mangerton Mill, Mangerton, Bridport, **DORSET**, DT6 3SG, **England**.
Contact/s: **Mr Harris** (Manager).
(T) 01308 485224
Profile: **FT:** Game; **WN:** Watermill; **WT:** Lake (Still). **Location:** **Main Rd:** A35.
Ref: FH5182

WATERSIDE FARM FISHERY

Waterside Farm Fishery, Glasgow Rd, Galston, **AYRSHIRE (EAST)**, KA4 8PB, **Scotland**.
Contact/s: **Mr Colin Thompson** (Owner).
(T) 01563 821186
Profile: **FT:** Game; **WN:** Waterside Farm Fishery; **WT:** Lake (Still).
Ref: FH5183

WATERSIDE LEISURE PARK

Waterside Leisure Park, Anchor Lane, Ingoldmells, Skegness, **LINCOLNSHIRE**, PE25 1LX, **England**.
Contact/s: **Mr John Crawford** (Manager).
(T) 01754 874837
Profile: **FT:** Coarse; **WN:** Waterside Leisure Park; **WT:** Lake (Still) **W. Size:** 2 Acres. **Location:** **Nr. Rd:** A52 Skegness to Chapel St. Leonards; **Main Rd:** Ingoldmells.
Ref: FH5184

WATERSMEET & GLENTHORNE

Watersmeet And Glenthorne Fisheries, Lynton, Lynmouth, **DEVON**, EX35, **England**.
Contact/s: **Mr Winston Singleton** (Warden).
Profile: **FT:** Game; **WN:** Lyn; **WT:** River (Moving).
Ref: FH5185

WATERSMEET LAKES

Watersmeet Lakes, Ledbury Rd, Hartpury, Gloucester, **GLOUCESTERSHIRE**, GL19 3BT, **England**.
Contact/s: **Mr Tom Ring**.
(T) 01452 700358 **(F)** 01452 700861
Profile: **FT:** Coarse; **WN:** Watersmeet; **WT:** Lake (Still); **F. Size:** 10 Acres; **W. Size:** 3 Acres. **Location:** **Nr. Rd:** A417 Gloucester to Ledbury Road; **Main Rd:** M50.
Ref: FH5186

WATERY GATE FISHERY

Watery Gate Fishery, Normanton Park, Thurlaston, Leicester, **LEICESTERSHIRE**, LE9 7TS, **England**.
Contact/s: **Mr W H Benbow**.
(T) 01455 888104
Profile: **FT:** Coarse; **WN:** Watery Gate; **WT:** Combination (Still & Moving) **W. Size:** 3 Acres. **Location:** **Nr. Rd:** Watergate Lane; **Main Rd:** A47; **Rail:** Narborough.
Ref: FH5187

WATTLEHURST FARM TROUT LAKES

Wattlehurst Farm Trout Lakes, Wattlehurst Farm, Kingsfold, Horsham, **SUSSEX (WEST)**, RH12 3SD, **England**.
Contact/s: **Mr John Nye** (Manager).
(T) 01306 627490
Profile: **FT:** Game; **WN:** Wattlehurst Farm; **WT:** Lake (Still) **W. Size:** 2 Acres. **Location:** **Nr. Rd:** A24.
Ref: FH5188

WATTS POOL

Watts Pool, Chalfont St Giles, **BUCKINGHAMSHIRE**, HP8, **England**.
(W) www.blenheim-angling.ic24.net
Contact/s: **Mr Fred Lancaster** (Secretary), Blenheim Angling Society, Brairwood, Burtons Lane, Chalfont St Giles, Buckinghamshire, HP8 4BB.
(T) 01494 764977
(E) blenheim.angling@ntlworld.com
Mr John Gill (Assistant Fisheries Officer).
(T) 020 85612993
Profile: **FT:** Coarse; **WN:** Watts; **WT:** Pond (Still) **W. Size:** 2 Acres. **Location:** **Nr. Rd:** B376; **Main Rd:** M25; **Rail:** Wraysbury.
Ref: FH5189

WAULKMILL FISHERIES

Waulkmill Fisheries, Waulkmill, New Deer, Turriff, **ABERDEENSHIRE**, AB53 6UP, **Scotland**.
Contact/s: **Mr George Davidson** (Manager).
(T) 01771 644357
Profile: **FT:** Game; **WN:** Waulkmill Fisheries; **WT:** Lake (Still).
Ref: FH5190

WAVENEY (RIVER)

River Waveney, Bungay, **SUFFOLK**, NR35, **England**.
Contact/s: **Mr Ian Gosling** (Hon Secretary), Bungay Cherry Tree Angling Club, 37 St Marys Trce, Flixton Rd, Bungay, NR35 1DN.
(T) 01986 892982
Profile: **FT:** Coarse; **WN:** Waveney; **WT:** River (Moving) **W. Size:** 11200 Metres. **Location:** **Nr. Rd:** Earsham; **Rail:** Beccles.
Ref: FH5191

WAVENEY VALLEY LAKES

Waveney Valley Lakes, Wortwell, Harleston, **SUFFOLK**, IP20 0EH, **England**.
Contact/s: **Mr Knox** (Manager).
(T) 01986 788676
Profile: **FT:** Coarse; **WN:** Waveney Valley; **WT:** Lake (Still) **W. Size:** 5 Acres. **Location:** **Main Rd:** A143.
Ref: FH5192

WAYOH RESERVOIR

Wayoh Reservoir, Blackburn, **LANCASHIRE**, BB, **England**.
Contact/s: **Mr A G R Brown** (Secretary), Northern Anglers, 10 Dale Rd, Golbourne, Warrington, WA3 3PN.
(T) 01942 726917
Mr Roy Rhodes (Conservation, Access and Recreation Manager), Rivington Water Treatment Works, Bolton Rd, Horwich, Bolton, BL6 7RN.
(T) 01204 664300
Profile: **FT:** Coarse; **WN:** Wayoh; **WT:** Reservoir (Still).
Ref: FH5193

WEALD COUNTRY PARK

Weald Country Park, The Parks Office, Weald Rd, South Weald, Brentwood, **ESSEX**, CM14 5QS, **England**.
Contact/s: Fishery Manager.
(T) 01277 216297 **(F)** 01277 202157
Profile: **FT:** Coarse; **WN:** Weald Country Park; **WT:** Lake (Still) **W. Size:** 10 Acres. **Location:** **Main Rd:** M25, junction 28, A1012, A12; **Rail:** Brentwood.
Ref: FH5194

WEAR (RIVER)

River Wear, Cong Burn, Chester-Le-Street, **COUNTY DURHAM**, DH, **England**.
Contact/s: **Mr G Curry** (Hon Secretary), 62 Newcastle Rd, Chester-le-Street, County Durham, DH3 3UF.
Profile: **FT:** Combination; **WN:** Wear; **WT:** River (Moving) **W. Size:** 4000 Metres. **Location:** **Nr. Rd:** Cong Burn to Chirton Avenue.
Ref: FH5195

WEAR (RIVER)

River Wear, Sunnybrow, Willington, Crook, **COUNTY DURHAM**, DL15, **England**.
Contact/s: Manager, Bonds Tackle Shop, 80 High St, Willington, Crook, DL15 0PE.
(T) 01388 746273
Profile: **FT:** Combination; **WN:** Wear; **WT:** River (Moving).
Ref: FH5196

WEAR (RIVER)

River Wear, Milburngate Bridge, Durham, **COUNTY DURHAM**, DH, **England**.
Profile: **FT:** Combination; **WN:** Wear; **WT:** River (Moving). **Location:** **Nr. Rd:** Milburngate Bridge to Sewage Works.
Ref: FH5197

WEAR (RIVER)

River Wear, Chester-Le-Street, **COUNTY DURHAM**, DH, **England**.
Contact/s: **Mr G Curry** (Hon Secretary), 62 Newcastle Rd, Chester-le-Street, County Durham, DH3 3UF.
(T) 0191 3882154
Profile: **FT:** Combination; **WN:** Wear; **WT:** River (Moving) **W. Size:** 19200 Metres. **Location:** **Main Rd:** A1, A167.
Ref: FH5198

WEAR (RIVER)

River Wear, Upper Weardale, Bishop Auckland, **COUNTY DURHAM**, DL13, **England**.
Contact/s: **Mr H C Lee** (Hon Secretary), 7 Westfall, Wearhead, Bishop Auckland, Durham, DL13 1BP.
Profile: **FT:** Game; **WN:** Wear; **WT:** River (Moving) **W. Size:** 9600 Metres. **Location:** **Nr. Rd:** Westgate to Cowshill.
Ref: FH5199

WEAR (RIVER)

River Wear, Shincliffe Hall, Shincliffe, Durham, **COUNTY DURHAM**, DH1, **England**.
Contact/s: Area Manager, Environment Agency, Northumbria Area Office, Tyneside House, Skinnerburn Rd, Newcastle Business Park, Newcastle upon Tyne NE4 7AR.
(T) 0191 2034000 **(F)** 0191 2034004
Mr John Hall (Secretary), 21 Northumbria Pl, Stanley, County Durham, DH9 0UB.
(T) 01207 232401
Profile: **FT:** Coarse; **WN:** Wear; **WT:** River (Moving) **W. Size:** 4000 Metres. **Location:** **Nr. Rd:** Teeside to Durham City; **Main Rd:** A177 to Teeside, river on outskirts.
Ref: FH5200

WEAR (RIVER)

River Wear, Franklands, Durham, **COUNTY DURHAM**, DH, **England**.
Contact/s: Fishery Manager.
(T) 0191 3847520
Profile: **FT:** Coarse; **WN:** Wear; **WT:** River (Moving) **W. Size:** 1600 Metres. **Location:** **Main Rd:** A691.
Ref: FH5201

WEAR (RIVER)

River Wear, Kepier Viaduct, Durham, **COUNTY DURHAM**, DH, **England**.
Contact/s: Manager, Anglers Services Ltd, 45 Claypath, Durham, County Durham, DH1 1QS.
(T) 0191 3847584
Profile: **FT:** Combination; **WN:** Wear; **WT:** River (Moving). **Location:** **Nr. Rd:** Kepier Viaduct area.
Ref: FH5202

WEAR (RIVER)

River Wear, Frankland Farm, Frankland, Durham, **COUNTY DURHAM**, DH, **England**.
Contact/s: **Mr John Hall** (Secretary), 21 Northumbria Pl, Stanley, County Durham, DH9 0UB.
(T) 01207 232401
Profile: **FT:** Combination; **WN:** Wear; **WT:** River (Moving).
Ref: FH5203

WEAR (RIVER)

River Wear, Kepier Farm, Durham, **COUNTY DURHAM**, DH, **England**.
Profile: **FT:** Combination; **WN:** Wear; **WT:** River (Moving).
Ref: FH5204

WEAR (RIVER)

River Wear, Croxdale, Durham, **COUNTY DURHAM**, DH6, **England**.
Contact/s: **Mr Barry Hignett** (Secretary), Ferryhill and District Angling Club, 74 Grasmere Rd, Garden Farm Estate, Chester-le-Street, County Durham.
(T) 0191 3883557
Profile: **FT:** Game; **WN:** Wear; **WT:** River (Moving). **Location:** **Nr. Rd:** Croxdale to Durham; **Main Rd:** A167; **Rail:** Croxdale.
Ref: FH5205

WEAR (RIVER)

River Wear, St John's Chapel, Bishop Auckland, **COUNTY DURHAM**, DL13, **England**.
Contact/s: **H C Lee**.
(T) 01388 537482
Profile: **FT:** Game; **WN:** Wear; **WT:** River (Moving). **Location:** **Main Rd:** A686.
Ref: FH5206

WEAR (RIVER)

River Wear, Hagbridge, Eastgate, Bishop Auckland, **COUNTY DURHAM**, DL13, **England**.
Contact/s: **Mr Bell**, West End Filling Station, Front St, Stanhope, Bishop Auckland, DL13 2NL.
(T) 01388 528414
Profile: **FT:** Game; **WN:** Wear; **WT:** River (Moving) **W. Size:** 12800 Metres. **Location:** **Nr. Rd:** Hagbridge; **Main Rd:** A686.
Ref: FH5207

WEAR (RIVER)

River Wear, Durham, **COUNTY DURHAM**, DH, **England**.
Contact/s: **Mr John Hall** (Secretary), 21 Northumbria Pl, Stanley, County Durham, DH9 0UB.
(T) 01207 232401
Mr Mark Arrowsmith (Manager), Anglers Services Ltd, 11 High Street North, Langley Moor, County Durham, DH7 8JG.
(T) 0191 3847584
Profile: **FT:** Game; **WN:** Wear; **WT:** River (Moving) **W. Size:** 800 Metres. **Location:** **Nr. Rd:** A690, Leazes Road; **Main Rd:** Durham. **£Fr**
Ref: FH5208

WEAR (RIVER)

River Wear, Bishop Auckland, **COUNTY DURHAM**, DL1, **England**.
(W) www.bishopaucklandanddistrictanglingclub.com
Contact/s: **Mr John Winter** (Secretary), Bishop Auckland and District Angling Club, 7 Royal Gr, Crook, County Durham, DL15 9ER.
(T) 01388 762538 **(F)** 01388 767762
(E) bacc@talk21.com
Profile: **FT:** Game; **WN:** Wear; **WT:** River (Moving) **W. Size:** 32000 Metres. **Location:** **Main Rd:** A167, A68; **Rail:** Bishop Auckland.
Ref: FH5209

WEAR (RIVER)

River Wear, Stanhope, Bishop Auckland, **COUNTY DURHAM**, DL13, **England**.
Contact/s: **J J Lee**, 1 East Croft, Stanhope, County Durham.
Profile: **FT:** Game; **WN:** Wear; **WT:** River (Moving) **W. Size:** 3200 Metres.
Ref: FH5210

WEAR (RIVER)

River Wear, Chester Moor, Chester-Le-Street, **COUNTY DURHAM**, DH, **England**.
Contact/s: **Mr John Hall** (Secretary), 21 Northumbria Pl, Stanley, County Durham, DH9 0UB.
(T) 01207 232401
Mr Phil Watson (Manager).
(T) 0191 3847520
Profile: **FT:** Combination; **WN:** Wear; **WT:** River (Moving) **W. Size:** 3200 Metres.
Location: **Nr. Rd:** A1M.
Ref: FH5211

WEAR (RIVER)

River Wear, Fatfield, Washington, **TYNE AND WEAR**, NE38, **England**.
Contact/s: **Mr Dave Hancock**.
(T) 0191 3857488
Profile: **FT:** Combination; **WN:** Wear; **WT:** River (Moving) **W. Size:** 2400 Metres.
Location: **Nr. Rd:** Washington Highway to Station Road; **Main Rd:** A182.
Ref: FH5212

WEAVER (RIVER)

River Weaver, Sutton Weaver, Frodsham, Warrington, **CHESHIRE**, WA6, **England**.
Contact/s: **Mr Griffiths** (Fishery Manager).
(T) 01606 723800
Profile: **FT:** Coarse; **WN:** Weaver; **WT:** River (Moving).
Ref: FH5213

WEAVER (RIVER)

River Weaver, Buglawton, Macclesfield, **CHESHIRE**, SK11, **England**.
Profile: **FT:** Coarse; **WN:** Weaver; **WT:** Tributary (Moving).
Ref: FH5214

WEAVER (RIVER)

River Weaver, Northwich Boatyard, Northwich, **CHESHIRE**, CW, **England**.
Contact/s: **Mr J Clitheroe** (Secretary), Northwich Angling Association, PO Box 18, Northwich, Cheshire, CW9 5SE.
(T) 01606 75132
Profile: **FT:** Coarse; **WN:** Weaver; **WT:** River (Moving) **W. Size:** 200 Metres. **Location:** **Nr. Rd:** Kingsmead Estate; **Main Rd:** A533.
Ref: FH5215

WEAVER (RIVER)

River Weaver, Middlewich, **CHESHIRE**, CW10, **England**.
Contact/s: **Mr J Stewart Bailey** (Hon Secretary), 22 Plover Avenue, Winsford, CW7 1LA.
Profile: **FT:** Game; **WN:** Weaver; **WT:** River (Moving). **Location:** **Nr. Rd:** Croxton Lane to Kings Street.
Ref: FH5216

WEAVER (RIVER)

River Weaver, Congleton, **CHESHIRE**, CW12, **England**.
Contact/s: **Mr Nigel Bours** (Hon Secretary), Congleton AS, 8 Norfolk Rd, Congleton, Cheshire, CW12 1NY.
(T) 01260 277284
Profile: **FT:** Game; **WN:** Weaver; **WT:** River (Moving) **W. Size:** 8000 Metres.
Ref: FH5217

WEAVER (RIVER)

River Weaver, Anderton Moor, Northwich, **CHESHIRE**, CW, **England**.
Contact/s: Fishery Manager.
(T) 01606 782841
Mr J Clitheroe (Secretary), Northwich Angling Association, PO Box 18, Northwich, Cheshire, CW9 5SE.
(T) 01606 75132
Profile: **FT:** Coarse; **WN:** Weaver; **WT:** River (Moving).
Ref: FH5218

WEAVER (RIVER)

River Weaver, The Marina, Winsford, Northwich, **CHESHIRE**, CW, **England**.
Contact/s: Fishery Manager.
(T) 01606 593902
Mr Jim Clitheroe, 62 Station Rd, Northwich, Cheshire.
(T) 01606 75131
Profile: **FT:** Coarse; **WN:** Weaver; **WT:** River (Moving). **Location:** **Nr. Rd:** A54.
Ref: FH5219

WEAVER (RIVER)

River Weaver, Hayhurst Bridge, Northwich, **CHESHIRE**, CW, **England**.
Contact/s: **Mr J Clitheroe** (Secretary), Northwich Angling Association, PO Box 18, Northwich, Cheshire, CW9 5SE.
(T) 01606 75132
Profile: **FT:** Coarse; **WN:** Weaver; **WT:** River (Moving). **Location:** **Main Rd:** A556.
Ref: FH5220

WEAVER NAVIGATION

Weaver Navigation, Winsford, **CHESHIRE**, CW7, **England**.
Contact/s: Fishery Manager.
(T) 01606 593902
Profile: **FT:** Coarse; **WN:** Weaver Navigation; **WT:** Canal (Still).
Ref: FH5221

WEDGEHILL PONDS

Wedgehill Ponds, Verwood, Ringwood, **HAMPSHIRE**, BH24, **England**.
Contact/s: **Mr R J Andrews** (Club Secretary), Christchurch Angling Club, 4 Marley Cl, New Milton, BH25 5LL.
(T) 01425 279710
Profile: **FT:** Coarse; **WN:** Wedgehill; **WT:** Pond (Still). **Location:** **Main Rd:** B3081 to Verwood.
Ref: FH5222

WEE GLEN AMOUR LOCH

Wee Glen Amour Loch, New Galloway Rd, Newton Stewart, **DUMFRIES AND GALLOWAY**, DG8, **Scotland**.
Contact/s: **Mr Tony Dickinson** (Shop Proprietor), Galloway Guns and Tackle, 36a Arthur St, Newton Stewart, Dumfries and Galloway, DG8 6DE.
(T) 01671 403404 **(F)** 01671 403404
Profile: **FT:** Game; **WN:** Wee Glen Amour; **WT:** Loch (Still). **Location:** **Nr. Rd:** A75; **Main Rd:** A75; **Rail:** Barrhill.
Ref: FH5223

WEEDON ROAD GRAVEL PIT

Weedon Road Gravel Pit, Northampton, **NORTHAMPTONSHIRE**, NN, **England**.
Contact/s: Fishery Manager.
(T) 01604 757589
Profile: **FT:** Coarse; **WN:** Weedon Road; **WT:** Gravel Pit (Still). **Location:** **Nr. Rd:** Weedon Road.
Ref: FH5224

WEELEY BRIDGE HOLIDAY PARK

Weeley Bridge Holiday Park, Clacton Rd, Weeley, Clacton-on-Sea, **ESSEX**, CO16 9DH, **England**.
Contact/s: Manager.
(T) 01255 830403 **(F)** 01255 831544
Profile: **FT:** Coarse; **WN:** Weeley Bridge Holiday Park; **WT:** Lake (Still). **Location:** **Main Rd:** A133.
Ref: FH5225

WEEM BEAT

Weem Beat, Aberfeldy, **PERTH AND KINROSS**, PH15, **Scotland**.
(W) www.fishingnet.com/beats/weem.htm
Contact/s: , Weem Hotel, Weem, Aberfeldy, Perth and Kinross, PH15 2LD.
Mr Tom Sharpe, Laigh of Cluny Steading, Edradynate, Aberfeldy, Perth and Kinross, PH15 2JU.
(T) 01887 840469 **(F)** 01887 840469
Profile: **FT:** Combination; **WN:** See above; **WT:** Pool (Still).
Ref: FH5226

WEIR WOOD FISHERY

Weir Wood Fishery, The Lodge, Forest Row, **SUSSEX (EAST)**, RH18 5HT, **England**.
Contact/s: **Mr Jerry** (Manager), Weir Wood Fly Fishery, The Lodge, Forest Row, Sussex (West), RH18 5HT.
(T) 01306 730449/07884167196

Profile: **FT:** Combination; **WN:** Wier Wood; **WT:** Reservoir (Still) **W. Size:** 280 Acres. **Location:** **Nr. Rd:** A22; **Main Rd:** M25.
Ref: FH5227

WELDON RESERVOIR

Weldon Reservoir, St Neots, Huntingdon, **CAMBRIDGESHIRE**, PE1, **England**.
Contact/s: **Mr Ian Benton** (Match Secretary).
(T) 01480 219706
Mr Ieuan Thomas (Bailiff).
(T) 01480 213115
Mrs Diane Linger (Secretary), Skenbridge Cottage, Great Paxton, St Neots, Cambridgeshire, PE19 4RA.
(T) 01480 216730
Profile: **FT:** Coarse; **WN:** Weldon Reservoir; **WT:** Reservoir (Still) **W. Size:** 10 Acres. **Location:** **Nr. Rd:** A428; **Main Rd:** A428, A1.
Ref: FH5228

WELFIELD POOLS

Welfield Pools, Highley, Kidderminster, **WORCESTERSHIRE**, DY, **England**.
Contact/s: **Mr Stan Lewis** (Manager), S Lewis Fishing Tackle, 2 Severnside South, Bewdley, Worcestershire, DY12 2DX.
(T) 01299 403358
Profile: **FT:** Coarse; **WN:** Welfield; **WT:** Lake (Still). **Location:** **Nr. Rd:** B4555; **Main Rd:** A442 Bewdley.
Ref: FH5229

WELFORD RESERVOIR

Welford Reservoir, Welford Grange Farm, Welford, Northampton, **NORTHAMPTONSHIRE**, NN6, **England**.
Contact/s: **Mr W Williams** (Bailiff).
(T) 01858 575394
Profile: **FT:** Coarse; **WN:** Welford; **WT:** Reservoir (Still) **W. Size:** 20 Acres.
Ref: FH5230

WELHAM LAKE

Welham Lake, Malton And Norton Golf Club, Welham, Pickering, **YORKSHIRE (NORTH)**, YO18, **England**.
Contact/s: **Mr Mike O' Donnell** (Owner).
(T) 01751 473101
Profile: **FT:** Coarse; **WN:** Welham; **WT:** Lake (Still); **F. Size:** 30 Acres; **W. Size:** 5 Acres. **Location:** **Nr. Rd:** Malton and Norton Golf Club; **Main Rd:** A170.
Ref: FH5231

WELLAND (RIVER)

River Welland, Coronation Channel, Spalding, **LINCOLNSHIRE**, PE11, **England**.
Contact/s: **Mr R Whitehead** (Secretary), Worksop and District Angling Association, 72 Dryden Walk, Worksop, Nottinghamshire.
(T) 01909 486350
Profile: **FT:** Coarse; **WN:** Welland; **WT:** River (Moving).
Ref: FH5232

WELLAND (RIVER)

River Welland, Spalding, **LINCOLNSHIRE**, PE12, **England**.
Contact/s: **Mr Howard Tidswell** (Manager), Tidswells Tackle, New Bungalow, Burr Lane, Spalding, PE12 6AZ.
(T) 01775 723640
Profile: **FT:** Coarse; **WN:** Welland; **WT:** River (Moving). **Location:** **Nr. Rd:** Town Centre; **Main Rd:** A16. **£Fr**
Ref: FH5233

WELLAND (RIVER)

River Welland, Spalding, **LINCOLNSHIRE**, PE, **England**.
Contact/s: Fishery Manager.
(T) 01775 723640
Profile: **FT:** Coarse; **WN:** Welland; **WT:** River (Moving).
Ref: FH5234

WELLAND (RIVER)

River Welland, Duddington, Oakham, **RUTLAND**, LE15, **England**.
Contact/s: **Mr G Taylor** (Membership Secretary), Broome Angling Society, 100 New Romney Cres, Leicester.
(T) 0116 2417018
Profile: **FT:** Game; **WN:** Welland; **WT:** River (Moving) **W. Size:** 1600 Metres.
Ref: FH5235

WELLAND (RIVER)

River Welland, Wakerley, Oakham, **RUTLAND**, LE15, **England**.
Contact/s: **Mr Graham Money** (Secretary).
(T) 01780 480209
Profile: **FT:** Coarse; **WN:** Welland; **WT:** River (Moving) **W. Size:** 2400 Metres. **Location:** **Nr. Rd:** Barrowden to Wakerley; **Main Rd:** A43.
Ref: FH5236

WELLAND LODGE FISHERY

Welland Lodge Fishery, Market Harborough, **LEICESTERSHIRE**, LE16, **England**.
Contact/s: Fishery Manager.
(T) 01858 466792
Profile: **FT:** Coarse; **WN:** Welland Lodge Fishery; **WT:** Lake (Still).
Ref: FH5237

WELLFIELD POND

Wellfield Pond, Moor Lane, Wingate, Peterlee, **COUNTY DURHAM**, SR8, **England**.
Contact/s: **Mr Alan Blackmore** (Secretary), 21 Station Road (South), Murton Seaham, Durham, SR7 9SE.
(T) 0191 5264545
Profile: **FT:** Coarse; **WN:** Wellfield; **WT:** Pond (Still). **Location:** **Nr. Rd:** B1280; **Main Rd:** A19; **Rail:** Durham.
Ref: FH5238

WELLFIELD POOLS

Wellfield Pools, Kinlet, Bewdley, **WORCESTERSHIRE**, DY12, **England**.
Contact/s: Fishery Manager.
(T) 01299 841264
Profile: **FT:** Coarse; **WN:** Wellfield; **WT:** Pool (Still).
Ref: FH5239

WELLINGTON BASIN

Wellington Basin, Wellington, **SOMERSET**, TA21, **England**.
Contact/s: **Mr Mike Hewitson** (Manager), Tauton Angling Association, 56 Parkfield Rd, Taunton, Somerset, TA1 4SE.
(T) 01823 271194
Profile: **FT:** Coarse; **WN:** Wellington Basin; **WT:** Pond (Still) **W. Size:** 1 Acre. **Location:** **Nr. Rd:** Coram's Lane; **Main Rd:** M5 junction 26, A38, B3187.
Ref: FH5240

WELLINGTON COUNTRY PARK

Wellington Country Park, Riseley, Reading, **BERKSHIRE**, RG7 1, **England**.
Contact/s: Park Staff.
(T) 0118 9326444
Profile: **FT:** Coarse; **WN:** Wellington Country Park; **WT:** Lake (Still) **W. Size:** 35 Acres.
Ref: FH5241

WENNING (RIVER)

Wenning (River), Robert Hall Estate, Wennington, Lancaster, **LANCASHIRE**, **England**.
Profile: **FT:** Game; **WN:** Wenning; **WT:** River (Moving) **W. Size:** 1500 Metres. **Location:** **Nr. Rd:** B6480; **Rail:** Lancaster.
Ref: FH5242

WENNING (RIVER)

Wenning (River), Hornby Castle Estate, Hornby, Lancaster, **LANCASHIRE**, **England**.
Profile: **FT:** Game; **WN:** Wenning; **WT:** River (Moving) **W. Size:** 1500 Metres. **Location:** **Nr. Rd:** A683; **Rail:** Lancaster.
Ref: FH5243

WENNING (RIVER)

River Wenning, Clapham, **LANCASHIRE**, **England**.
Contact/s: **Mr John A Farrer** (owner), Ingleborough Estate, Estate Office, Clapham, Lancaster, Lancashire LA2 8DR.
(T) 01524 251302 **(F)** 01524 251466
Profile: **FT:** Game; **WN:** Wenning; **WT:** River (Moving) **W. Size:** 5600 Metres.
Ref: FH5244

WENSUM (RIVER)

River Wensum, Norwich, **NORFOLK**, NR9, **England**.
(W) www.lenwade-bridge.com
Contact/s: **Mr Darren Emmett** (Owner), The Bridge Public House, 2 Fakenham Rd, Lenwade, Norfolk, NR9 5SE.
(T) 01603 872248
(E) redl2000@aol.uk
Mrs Clare Emmett (Owner), The Bridge Public House, 2 Fakenham Rd, Lenwade, Norfolk, NR9 5SE.
(T) 01603 872248
(E) redl2000@aol.uk
Profile: **FT:** Combination; **WN:** River Wensum; **WT:** River (Moving) **W. Size:** 300 Metres. **Location:** **Main Rd:** A1067; **Rail:** Norwich.
Ref: FH5245

WENSUM (RIVER)

River Wensum, Fakenham, **NORFOLK**, NR21, **England**.
Contact/s: **Mr Dave Playford** (Manager), Dave's Tackle Shop, 8 Millers Walk, Fakenham, Norfolk, NR21 9AP.
(T) 01328 862543
Profile: **FT:** Combination; **WN:** Wensum; **WT:** River (Moving) **W. Size:** 2400 Metres. **Location:** **Main Rd:** Norwich King's Lynn. **£Fr**
Ref: FH5246

WENSUM (RIVER)

River Wensum, Dereham, **NORFOLK**, NR, **England**.
Contact/s: **Mr David Appleby** (Secretary), Dereham and District Angling Club, 6 Rump Cl, Swanton Morley, Dereham, NR20 4NH.
(T) 01362 637591
Profile: **FT:** Coarse; **WN:** River Wensum; **WT:** River (Moving) **W. Size:** 800 Metres. **Location:** **Nr. Rd:** B1147; **Main Rd:** A47; **Rail:** Norwich. **£Fr**
Ref: FH5247

WENSUM (RIVER)

River Wensum, Elmham Mill, Walsingham, **NORFOLK**, NR22, **England**.
Contact/s: Fishery Manager.
(T) 01362 668107
Profile: **FT:** Coarse; **WN:** Wensum; **WT:** River (Moving).
Ref: FH5248

WENSUM (RIVER)

River Wensum, Hayes Lane, Fakenham, **NORFOLK**, NR21, **England**.
Contact/s: **Mr Dave Playford** (Manager), Dave's Tackle Shop, 8 Millers Walk, Fakenham, Norfolk, NR21 9AP.
(T) 01328 862543
Mr G Twite (Secretary), Fakenham Angling Club, 16 Back St, Hempton, Fakenham, NR21 7LR.
(T) 01328 863054
Profile: **FT:** Combination; **WN:** Wensum; **WT:** River (Moving) **W. Size:** 3000 Metres. **Location:** **Nr. Rd:** Fakenham by-pass; **Main Rd:** Fakenham by-pass; **Rail:** Kings Lynn.
Ref: FH5249

WENSUM (RIVER)

River Wensum, Hellesdon Meadow, Norwich, **NORFOLK**, NR, **England**.
Contact/s: **Mr Tom Boulton**.
(T) 01603 426834
Profile: **FT:** Coarse; **WN:** Wensum; **WT:** River (Moving). **Location:** **Nr. Rd:** Hellesdon

Mill to New Mills Yard. £Fr
Ref: FH5250

WENTWOOD RESERVOIR

Wentwood Reservoir, Llanvaches, Penhow, Newport, NP, **Wales**.
Contact/s: **Mr D G P Jones** (Hon Secretary), 123 Castle Lea, Caldicot, Gwent.
(T) 01291 425158
Profile: **FT:** Game; **WN:** Wentwood; **WT:** Reservoir (Still) **W. Size:** 41 Acres.
Location: **Main Rd:** A48; **Rail:** Chepstow.
Ref: FH5251

WENTWORTH FISHERY

Wentworth Fishery, Fitzwilliam Wentworth Amenity Trust Estate Office, Clayfields Lane, Wentworth, Rotherham, **YORKSHIRE (SOUTH)**, S62 7TD, **England**.
Profile: **FT:** Coarse; **WN:** Wentworth Fishery; **WT:** Lake (Still).
Ref: FH5252

WERRINGTON LAKE

Werrington Lake, Werrington, Peterborough, **CAMBRIDGESHIRE**, PE, **England**.
Contact/s: **Mr N Cesare**.
(T) 01733 570226
Profile: **FT:** Coarse; **WN:** Werrington; **WT:** Lake (Still).
Ref: FH5253

WESSEX TROUT LAKES

Wessex Fly Fishing Trout Lakes, Wessex Fly Fishing Trout Lakes, Lawrences Farm, Tolpuddle, Dorchester, **DORSET**, DT2 7HF, **England**.
(W) www.goflyfishing.co.uk
Contact/s: **Mr Richard Slocock** (Manager), Wessex Fly Fishing, Lawrences Farm, Tolpuddle, Dorset, DT2 7HF.
(T) 01305 848460 **(F)** 01305 849060
Profile: **FT:** Coarse; **WN:** Wessex Fly Fishing Trout Lakes; **WT:** Gravel Pit (Still); **F. Size:** 59 Acres; **W. Size:** 4 Acres. **Location:** **Nr. Rd:** A35; **Main Rd:** A35; **Rail:** Moreton.
Ref: FH5254

WESSEX WATER RESERVOIRS

Wessex Water Reservoirs, Poole, **DORSET**, BH17, **England**.
Contact/s: Production Manager (South), 2 Nuffield Rd, Poole, Dorset BH17 7RL.
Profile: **FT:** Coarse; **WN:** Wessex Water Reservoirs; **WT:** Reservoir (Still).
Ref: FH5255

WEST ATHESTON COARSE FISHERY

West Atheston Coarse Fishery, West Atheston, Valley Rd, Narberth, **PEMBROKESHIRE**, SA67 8BT, **Wales**.
Contact/s: **Mr Tim Bodfish** (Owner).
(T) 01834 860387
Profile: **FT:** Coarse; **WN:** West Atheston Coarse Fishery; **WT:** Pond (Still); **F. Size:** 3 Acres; **W. Size:** 2 Acres. **Location:** **Nr. Rd:** Valley Road; **Main Rd:** A478; **Rail:** Narberth.
Ref: FH5256

WEST COUNTRY WATER PARK

West Country Water Park, Winterbourne, Bristol, BS, **England**.
Contact/s: **Mr Mike Thompson**.
(T) 01454 773599
Profile: **FT:** Coarse; **WN:** West Country Water Park; **WT:** Lake (Still) **W. Size:** 2 Acres.
Ref: FH5257

WEST FARM LAKE

West Farm Lake, Sedgefield, Stockton-on-Tees, **COUNTY DURHAM**, TS21, **England**.
Contact/s: **Mr Bowes S** (Fishery Manager).
(T) 01740 631045
Profile: **FT:** Coarse; **WN:** West Farm; **WT:** Lake (Still). **Location:** **Main Rd:** A177.
Ref: FH5258

WEST FEN DRAIN

West Fen Drain, Frithville, Boston, **LINCOLNSHIRE**, PE21, **England**.
Contact/s: **Mr Brian Balderson**, Boston Angling Ctre, 11 Horncastle Rd, Boston, Lincolnshire, PE21 9BN.
(T) 01205 353436 **(F)** 01205 368666
Mrs B Clifton (Secretary).
(T) 01205 365406 **(F)** 01205 365406
Profile: **FT:** Coarse; **WN:** West Fen; **WT:** Drain (Moving) **W. Size:** 5000 Metres.
Location: **Nr. Rd:** B1183; **Main Rd:** A16; **Rail:** Boston. £Fr
Ref: FH5259

WEST HADDLESEY LAKE

West Haddlesey Lake, Birkin Rd, West Haddlesey, Selby, **YORKSHIRE (NORTH)**, YO8, **England**.
Contact/s: **Mr J Dowson** (Club Secretary), 3 Colonles Walk, Goole, Yorkshire (East), DN14 6HJ.
(T) 01405 762002
Profile: **FT:** Coarse; **WN:** West Haddlesey; **WT:** Lake (Still) **W. Size:** 6 Acres. **Location:** **Nr. Rd:** Birkin Road; **Main Rd:** A19; **Rail:** Selby.
Ref: FH5260

WEST HILLBOROUGH

West Hillborough, West Hillborough Farm, Cranhill, Bidford-on-Avon, Alcester, **WARWICKSHIRE**, B50, **England**.
Contact/s: **Mr Alan Stephens**.
(T) 01789 762200
Profile: **FT:** Coarse; **WN:** Avon; **WT:** River (Moving) **W. Size:** 1100 Metres. **Location:** **Nr. Rd:** B4390; **Rail:** Stratford.
Ref: FH5261

WEST LOOE (RIVER)

River West Looe, Looe, **CORNWALL**, PL13, **England**.
Profile: **FT:** Coarse; **WN:** West Looe; **WT:** River (Moving) **W. Size:** 11200 Metres.
Ref: FH5262

WEST LOOE (RIVER)

River West Looe, Sowden's Bridge, Liskeard, **CORNWALL**, PL14, **England**.
Contact/s: **Mr Bill Eliot** (Secretary), Liskeard and District Angling Club, 64 Portbyhan Rd, West Looe, Cornwall, PL13 2QN.
(T) 01503 264173
Profile: **FT:** Game; **WN:** West Looe; **WT:** Stream (Moving) **W. Size:** 2400 Metres.
Location: **Nr. Rd:** Sowden's Bridge to Herods Foot Village; **Rail:** Looe.
Ref: FH5263

WEST PITT FARM FISHERY

West Pitt Farm Fishery, Uplowman, Tiverton, **DEVON**, EX16 7DU, **England**.
Contact/s: **Ms Susan Westgate** (Owner).
(T) 01884 820296 **(F)** 01884 820818
Profile: **FT:** Coarse; **WN:** West Pitt Farm Fishery; **WT:** Lake (Still). **Location:** **Main Rd:** M5, junction 27 then A361; **Rail:** Tiverton Parkway.
Ref: FH5264

WEST RESERVOIR

West Reservoir, Stoke Newington, London, **LONDON (GREATER)**, N16, **England**.
Contact/s: **Mr Geoff Philby**.
(T) 020 84428116
Profile: **FT:** Coarse; **WN:** West; **WT:** Reservoir (Still) **W. Size:** 24 Acres.
Location: **Nr. Rd:** Manor House junction; **Main Rd:** A105.
Ref: FH5265

WEST STOW COUNTRY PARK

West Stow Country Park, Mildenhall Rd, Bury St Edmunds, **SUFFOLK**, IP, **England**.
Contact/s: **Mr N Bruton**.
(T) 01284 766074
Profile: **FT:** Coarse; **WN:** West Stow Country Park; **WT:** Lake (Still).
Ref: FH5266

WEST VIEW POND

West View Pond, Ottery, St Mary, Exeter, **DEVON**, EX, **England**.
Contact/s: **Mr Barry Lucas** (Hon Secretary), Mayfield, Gorwyn Lane, Cheriton Bishop, Exeter, EX6 6JL.
(T) 01647 24566
Profile: **FT:** Coarse; **WN:** West View; **WT:** Pond (Still) **W. Size:** 5 Acres. **Location:** **Main Rd:** M5.
Ref: FH5267

WEST WARWICK

West Warwick, Ferry Lane, Tottenham, London, **LONDON (GREATER)**, N17, **England**.
Contact/s: **Mr Chris King**, Walthamstow Reservoir Group, Thames Water Gatehouse, 2 Forest Rd, Tottenham, London, N17 9NH.
(T) 020 88081527
Profile: **FT:** Coarse; **WN:** West Warwick; **WT:** Lake (Still) **W. Size:** 34 Acres. **Location:** **Nr. Rd:** Ferry Lane; **Main Rd:** A10, North London.
Ref: FH5268

WEST WATER RESERVOIR

West Water Reservoir, West Linton, Peebles, **SCOTTISH BORDERS**, EH45, **Scotland**.
Contact/s: Manager.
(T) 0131 4456462
Profile: **FT:** Game; **WN:** West Water; **WT:** Reservoir (Still) **W. Size:** 93 Acres.
Ref: FH5269

WESTBROOK MERE

Westbrook Mere, Bourne End, Hemel Hempstead, **HERTFORDSHIRE**, HP1, **England**.
Contact/s: Fishery Manager.
(T) 01442 395143
Profile: **FT:** Coarse; **WN:** Westbrook Mere; **WT:** Lake (Still) **W. Size:** 4 Acres. **Location:** **Nr. Rd:** A41 to Hemel Hempstead; **Main Rd:** A41.
Ref: FH5270

WESTERLY LAKE

Westerly Lake, The Lodge, Wheldrake, York, **YORKSHIRE (NORTH)**, YO4 6AH, **England**.
Contact/s: **Mr E M Hairsine** (Owner).
(T) 01904 448500
Profile: **FT:** Coarse; **WN:** Westerly; **WT:** Lake (Still); **F. Size:** 4 Acres; **W. Size:** 2 Acres.
Location: **Nr. Rd:** Wheldrake Lane; **Main Rd:** A19 York to Selby; **Rail:** York.
Ref: FH5271

WESTERN CLEDDAU (RIVER)

River Western Cleddau, Glanafon Manor, Haverfordwest, **PEMBROKESHIRE**, SA, **Wales**.
Contact/s: **Mr N Bryce-Jones** (Manager), County Sports, 3 Old Bridge, Haverfordwest, Carmarthenshire, SA61 2EZ.
(T) 01437 763740 **(F)** 01437 763740
Mr Tony Summers (Chairman), 72 City Rd, Haverfordwest, SA61 2RR.
(T) 01437 763216
Profile: **FT:** Game; **WN:** Western Cleddau; **WT:** River (Moving) **W. Size:** 24000 Metres.
Location: **Nr. Rd:** Glanafon Manor to St Catherine's Bridge; **Main Rd:** Wolf's Castle.
Ref: FH5272

WESTERN CLEDDAU (RIVER)

River Western Cleddau, Treffgarne Gorge, Haverfordwest, **PEMBROKESHIRE**, SA62, **Wales**.
Contact/s: Manager, County Sports, 3 Old Bridge, Haverfordwest, Carmarthenshire, SA61 2EZ.
(T) 01437 763740 **(F)** 01437 763740
Mr Tony Summers (Chairman), 72 City Rd, Haverfordwest, SA61 2RR.
(T) 01437 763216
Profile: **FT:** Game; **WN:** Western Cleddau; **WT:** River (Moving) **W. Size:** 9600 Metres.
Location: **Nr. Rd:** Treffgarne Gorge to Wolfscastle.
Ref: FH5273

WESTERN ROTHER

Western Rother, Midhurst, **SUSSEX (WEST)**, GU29, **England**.
Contact/s: Manager, Backshalls Garage, Dodsley Lane, Easebourne, Midhurst, GU29

9BB.
Profile: FT: Coarse; WN: Rother; WT: Combination (Still & Moving).
Ref: FH5274

WESTERN ROTHER (RIVER)

River Western Rother, Petworth, **SUSSEX (WEST)**, GU28, **England**.
Contact/s: **Mr Richard Etherington**, South Dean, Tillington, Petworth, GU28 0RE.
(T) 01798 343111
Profile: FT: Coarse; WN: Western Rother; WT: River (Moving) W. Size: 8800 Metres.
Location: Nr. Rd: Coultershaw Mill to Shopham Bridge.
Ref: FH5275

WESTFIELD FARM

Westfield Farm, Westfield, Medmenham, Marlow, **BUCKINGHAMSHIRE**, SL7, **England**.
(W) www.rmcangling.co.uk
Contact/s: **Mr Ian Welch** (Angling Manager), RMC Angling, The Square, Lightwater, Surrey, GU18 5SS.
(T) 01276 453300 (F) 01276 456611
(E) info@rmcangling.co.uk
Profile: FT: Coarse; WN: Westfield Farm; WT: Combination (Still) W. Size: 1 Acre.
Location: Nr. Rd: Marlow to Henley Road; Main Rd: A4155.
Ref: FH5276

WESTFIELD LAKES

Westfield Lakes, Westfields Hotel, Far Ines Rd, Barton-upon-Humber, **LINCOLNSHIRE (NORTH)**, DN18 5RG, **England**.
Contact/s: Fishery Manager.
(T) 01625 632313
Profile: FT: Coarse; WN: Westfield; WT: Lake (Still). Location: Nr. Rd: A15.
Ref: FH5277

WESTGATE POOL

Westgate Pool, Lymm, Manchester, **MANCHESTER (GREATER)**, M, **England**.
Profile: FT: Coarse; WN: Westgate; WT: Pool (Still).
Ref: FH5278

WESTHAY

Westhay, Westhay, Glastonbury, **SOMERSET**, BA6, **England**.
Profile: FT: Coarse; WN: Westhay; WT: River (Moving). Location: Nr. Rd: Lyford to Westhay.
Ref: FH5279

WESTHAY LAKE

Westhay Lake, Bridgwater, **SOMERSET**, TA, **England**.
Contact/s: Fishery Manager.
(T) 01278 456429 (M) 07966 363413
Profile: FT: Coarse; WN: Westhay; WT: Lake (Still) W. Size: 4 Acres.
Ref: FH5280

WESTHORPE PARK LAKE

Westhorpe Park Lake, High Wycombe, **BUCKINGHAMSHIRE**, HP12, **England**.
Contact/s: **Mr J Woodhouse** (Secretary), Marlow Angling Club, Conifers, Ash Rd, High Wycombe, Buckinghamshire, HP12 4SW.
(T) 01494 523988
Profile: FT: Coarse; WN: Westhorpe Park Lake; WT: Lake (Still).
Ref: FH5281

WESTLAKE FISHERY

Westlake Fishery, Domgay Rd, Four Crosses, Llandrinio, Llanymynech, **POWYS**, SY22 6SJ, **Wales**.
Contact/s: **Mr Mel Jarvill**, West Lake Café, Domgay Rd, Four Crosses, Llandrinio, Llanymynech, SY22 6SL.
(T) 01691 831475 (F) 01691 831475
(E) meljarvill@ic24.net
Profile: FT: Combination; WN: Westlake Fishery; WT: Lake (Still) W. Size: 7 Acres.
Location: Nr. Rd: Domgay Road; Main Rd: A483; Rail: Shrewsbury.
Ref: FH5282

WESTLOW MERE

Westlow Mere Trout Fisheries, Westlow Mere, Congleton, **CHESHIRE**, CW12 2JJ, **England**.
Contact/s: **Mr Mick Webster** (Manager).
(T) 01260 270012
Profile: FT: Game; WN: Westlow; WT: Mere (Still) W. Size: 18 Acres. Location: Nr. Rd: Giantswood Lane; Main Rd: A34; Rail: Congleton.
Ref: FH5283

WESTON FISHERY

Weston Fishery, Albury, Guildford, **SURREY**, GU, **England**.
Contact/s: **Mr Tony Hern** (Manager), Albury Estate Fisheries, The Estate Office, Weston Yard, Guildford, GU5 9AF. (M) 07976 810737
Profile: FT: Game; WN: Weston Fishery; WT: River (Moving). Location: Nr. Rd: A248; Main Rd: A247.
Ref: FH5284

WESTON LAWN FISHERIES

Weston Lawn Fisheries, Bedworth Rd, Bedworth, **WARWICKSHIRE**, CV12 9JA, **England**.
(W) www.fisheries.co.uk/weston
Contact/s: **Mr Nick Wells**.
(T) 024 76315745 (F) 024 76643595 (M) 07803 048899
(E) nick.wells@virgin.net
Profile: FT: Coarse; WN: Weston Lawn Fisheries; WT: Pool (Still) W. Size: 5 Acres.
Location: Nr. Rd: B444; Main Rd: B444; Rail: Nuneaton.
Ref: FH5285

WESTON TERVELL RESERVOIR

Weston Tervell Reservoir, Holton, Prestwood, Great Missenden, **BUCKINGHAMSHIRE**, HP16, **England**.
Profile: FT: Coarse; WN: Weston Tervell; WT: Reservoir (Still) W. Size: 15 Acres.
Ref: FH5286

WESTONS LAKE

Westons Lake, Weston, Stevenage, **HERTFORDSHIRE**, SG, **England**.
Profile: FT: Coarse; WN: Weston's; WT: Lake (Still) W. Size: 3 Acres. Location: Main Rd: A1, junction 9.
Ref: FH5287

WESTWOOD COUNTRY PARK

Westwood Country Park, High Green, Chapeltown, Rotherham, **YORKSHIRE (SOUTH)**, S, **England**.
Mr Steve Hinson, 22a Eilam Cl, Rotherham, Yorkshire (South), S61 3QE.
(T) 01709 555225
Profile: FT: Coarse; WN: Westwood; WT: Lake (Still); F. Size: 4 Acres. Location: Main Rd: A616.
Ref: FH5288

WEY (RIVER)

River Wey, Wey Manor Rd, Addlestone, **FIFE**, KY15, **England**.
(W) www.rmcangling.co.uk
Contact/s: **Mr Ian Welch** (Angling Manager), RMC Angling, The Square, Lightwater, Surrey, GU18 5SS.
(T) 01276 453300 (F) 01276 456611
(E) info@rmcangling.co.uk
Profile: FT: Coarse; WN: Wey; WT: River (Moving) W. Size: 400 Metres. Location: Nr. Rd: Wey Manor Road; Main Rd: A318, Byfleet Road.
Ref: FH5289

WEY (RIVER)

River Wey, Godalming, **SURREY**, GU9, **England**.
Contact/s: **Mr Charles Stuart** (Secretary), Peper Harow Park Flyfishers Club, 6 Lynch Rd, Farnham, Surrey, GU9 8BZ.
(T) 01252 722947
(E) charles.stuart@ukgateway.net
Profile: FT: Game; WN: Wey; WT: River (Moving) W. Size: 2000 Metres. Location: Nr. Rd: B3001; Main Rd: A3; Rail: Godalming.
Ref: FH5290

WEY (RIVER)

River Wey, Byfleet, West Byfleet, **SURREY**, KT14, **England**.
Contact/s: **Mr Tod Slaughter**, 15 Ruston Rd, Byfleet, Surrey.
(T) 01932 348268
Profile: FT: Coarse; WN: Wey Navigation; WT: River (Moving) W. Size: 1600 Metres.
Location: Nr. Rd: Pavis Bridge to White Hart; Main Rd: A245.
Ref: FH5291

WEY NAVIGATION (RIVER)

River Wey Navigation, Pyrford Lock, Wisley Lane, Pyrford, Woking, **SURREY**, GU22, **England**.
Contact/s: **Mr Les Southam**, 15 Ruston Rd, Byfleet, Surrey.
(T) 01932 853090
Profile: FT: Coarse; WN: Wey Navigation; WT: River (Moving) W. Size: 3200 Metres.
Location: Nr. Rd: Anchor Pub at Pyrford Lock to Parvis Bridge; Main Rd: A245.
Ref: FH5292

WEYBREAD FISHERY

Weybread Fishery, Mill Lane Farm, Mill Lane, Weybread, Diss, **NORFOLK**, IP21 5TP, **England**.
Contact/s: **Mr Dennis Gartell** (Owner).
(T) 01379 588141
Mr T Harrowven (Manager), Waveney Angling, 5 London Rd, Harleston, Norfolk, IP20 9BH.
(T) 01379 854886
Profile: FT: Coarse; WN: Weybread Fishery; WT: Lake (Still) W. Size: 2 Acres. Location: Nr. Rd: B1116; Main Rd: A143, Diss to Beccles Road.
Ref: FH5293

WEYBREAD GRAVEL PITS

Weybread Gravel Pits, Weybread, Harleston, **NORTHAMPTONSHIRE**, SUFFOLK, **England**.
Contact/s: .
(T) 01379 588141
Profile: FT: Coarse; WN: Weybread Gravel PitsWT: (Still); F. Size: 150 Acres; W. Size: 130 Acres.
Ref: FH5294

WHARF POOL

Wharf Pool, Wharf Rd, Standford-Le-Hope, **ESSEX**, SS17, **England**.
(W) www.rmcangling.co.uk
Contact/s: **Mr Ian Welch** (Angling Manager), RMC Angling, The Square, Lightwater, Surrey, GU18 5SS.
(T) 01276 453300 (F) 01276 456611
(E) info@rmcangling.co.uk
Profile: FT: Coarse; WN: Wharf; WT: Gravel Pit (Still) W. Size: 6 Acres. Location: Nr. Rd: Wharf Road; Main Rd: A13.
Ref: FH5295

WHARFE (RIVER)

River Wharfe, Newton Kyme, Boston, **LINCOLNSHIRE**, PE2, **England**.
Contact/s: **A Waddington** (Secretary), Boston Spa Angling Club, The Cottage, 17 The Village, Thorpe Arch, Wetherby LS23 7AR.
(T) 01937 842664
Profile: FT: Coarse; WN: Wharfe; WT: River (Moving) W. Size: 3200 Metres.
Ref: FH5296

WHARFE (RIVER)

River Wharfe, Collingham, Newark, **NOTTINGHAMSHIRE**, NG2, **England**.
Contact/s: **Mr Pete Broxham** (Secretary), Wetherby and District Angling Club, 1 Eel Mires, Garth, Wetherby, West Yorkshire LS22 7TQ.
(T) 01937 585764

(E) ico100@aol.co.uk
Profile: **FT:** Coarse; **WN:** Wharfe; **WT:** River (Moving) **W. Size:** 650 Metres. **Location:** **Nr. Rd:** A58; **Main Rd:** A58; **Rail:** Harrogate.
Ref: FH5297

WHARFE (RIVER)

River Wharfe, Burnsall, Skipton, **YORKSHIRE (NORTH)**, BD23, **England**.
Contact/s: **Mr J Mackrell** (Secretary), Appletreewick Barden and Burnsall Angling Club, Mouldgreave, Oxenhope, Keighley, BD22 9RT.
(T) 01535 218336 **(F)** 01535 609748
Profile: **FT:** Game; **WN:** Wharfe; **WT:** River (Moving) **W. Size:** 10400 Metres. **Location:** **Nr. Rd:** Linton Stepping stones to Barden Bridge.
Ref: FH5298

WHARFE (RIVER)

River Wharfe, Bolton Abbey, Skipton, **YORKSHIRE (NORTH)**, BD23, **England**.
Contact/s: , The Trustees of the Chatsworth Settlement, Bolton Abbey, Skipton, Yorkshire (North), BD23 6EX.
(T) 01756 710227 **(F)** 01756 710535
Profile: **FT:** Game; **WN:** Wharfe; **WT:** River (Moving). **Location:** **Nr. Rd:** A59 to Bolton Abbey.
Ref: FH5299

WHARFE (RIVER)

River Wharfe, Healaugh Manor, Tadcaster, **YORKSHIRE (NORTH)**, LS24, **England**.
Contact/s: **Mr Doug Dalton** (Fishery Manager).
(T) 01904 692046
Profile: **FT:** Coarse; **WN:** Wharfe; **WT:** River (Moving) **W. Size:** 1600 Metres. **Location:** **Main Rd:** A64.
Ref: FH5300

WHARFE (RIVER)

River Wharfe, Easedyke, Tadcaster, **YORKSHIRE (NORTH)**, LS24, **England**.
Contact/s: Fishery Manager.
(T) 0113 22499721
Profile: **FT:** Coarse; **WN:** Wharfe; **WT:** River (Moving) **W. Size:** 2400 Metres. **Location:** **Nr. Rd:** York to Leeds; **Main Rd:** A659.
Ref: FH5301

WHARFE (RIVER)

River Wharfe, Linton, Grassington, Skipton, **YORKSHIRE (NORTH)**, BD23, **England**.
Contact/s: **Mr John S Gilpin**, Watercraft Products, 889 Harrogate Rd, Greengates, Bradford, BD10 0QY.
(T) 01274 620173 **(F)** 01484 421559
Mr W M Troman (Ticket Secretary), Saltaire Angling Association, 7 Hall Royd, Shipley, Yorkshire (West), BD18 3ED.
(T) 01274 583088
Profile: **FT:** Combination; **WN:** Wharfe; **WT:** River (Moving). **Location:** **Nr. Rd:** B6265; **Main Rd:** B6265; **Rail:** Skipton.
Ref: FH5302

WHARFE (RIVER)

River Wharfe, Grange Park, Boston Spa, Wetherby, **YORKSHIRE (WEST)**, LS23, **England**.
Contact/s: **Mr Mick Hope** (Manager), Lower Wharfe Angling Ctre, 236 High St, Boston Spa, Wetherby, LS23 6AD.
(T) 01937 844260 **(F)** 01937 844260
Mr Pete Broxham (Secretary), Wetherby and District Angling Club, 1 Eel Mires, Garth, Wetherby, West Yorkshire LS22 7TQ.
(T) 01937 585764
(E) ico100@aol.co.uk
Profile: **FT:** Coarse; **WN:** Wharfe; **WT:** River (Moving) **W. Size:** 1600 Metres.
Ref: FH5303

WHARFE (RIVER)

Wharfe (River), Pool, Leeds, **YORKSHIRE (WEST)**, **England**.
Contact/s: **Mr John Turner** (Hon Secretary), Prince Albert Angling Society, 15 Pexhill Drive, Macclesfield, Cheshire, SK10 3LP.
(T) 01625 422010
Profile: **FT:** Coarse; **WN:** Wharfe; **WT:** River (Moving) **W. Size:** 2500 Metres. **Location:** **Nr. Rd:** A659; **Main Rd:** A658; **Rail:** Leeds.
Ref: FH5304

WHARFE (RIVER)

River Wharfe, Crane House, Tadcaster, **YORKSHIRE (WEST)**, LS2, **England**.
Contact/s: **Mr D Ashton** (Secretary).
(T) 01937 832279
Mr D Noble (Secretary), Brighouse Angling Association, 1a Church Lane, Brighouse, Yorkshire (West), HD6 1AT.
(T) 01484 717034
Profile: **FT:** Coarse; **WN:** Wharfe; **WT:** River (Moving) **W. Size:** 1200 Metres.
Ref: FH5305

WHARFE (RIVER)

River Wharfe, Below Town Bridge, Tadcaster, **YORKSHIRE (WEST)**, LS2, **England**.
Contact/s: **Mr Tony Emmott** (Manager).
(T) 01937 833843
Profile: **FT:** Coarse; **WN:** Wharfe; **WT:** River (Moving). **Location:** **Main Rd:** A64.
Ref: FH5306

WHARFE (RIVER)

River Wharfe, Grimston Park, Tadcaster, **YORKSHIRE (WEST)**, LS2, **England**.
Contact/s: **A Emmett** (Secretary), Tadcaster Angling and Preservation Association, 3 Ingleby Drive, Tadcaster, LS24 8HW.
Mrs C Burton (Manager), 69 Leeds Rd, Tadcaster, Yorkshire (North), LS24 9LA.
(T) 01937 833262
Profile: **FT:** Coarse; **WN:** Wharfe; **WT:** River (Moving) **W. Size:** 2000 Metres.
Ref: FH5307

WHARFE (RIVER)

River Wharfe, Ilkley, **YORKSHIRE (WEST)**, LS29, **England**.
Contact/s: **Mr B Featherstone** (President).
(T) 01943 602619
Mr Moore B (Secretary).
(T) 01943 604653
Profile: **FT:** Combination; **WN:** Wharfe; **WT:** River (Moving). **Location:** **Nr. Rd:** New Brook Street Bridge, Ilkley to Ben Rhydding.
Ref: FH5308

WHARFE (RIVER)

River Wharfe, Three Cornered Field, Otley, **YORKSHIRE (WEST)**, LS2, **England**.
Contact/s: **J Hunter** (Manager).
(T) 01943 463575
Mr Tim Windross (Secretary), 43 Newall Carr Rd, Otley, LS21 2AF.
(T) 01943 466041
Profile: **FT:** Coarse; **WN:** Wharfe; **WT:** River (Moving).
Ref: FH5309

WHARFE (RIVER)

River Wharfe, Gregory Fishery, Wilderness Car Park, High St, Wetherby, **YORKSHIRE (WEST)**, LS22, **England**.
Contact/s: **Mr Pete Broxham** (Secretary), Wetherby and District Angling Club, 1 Eel Mires, Garth, Wetherby, West Yorkshire LS22 7TQ.
(T) 01937 585764
(E) ico100@aol.co.uk
Profile: **FT:** Combination; **WN:** Wharfe; **WT:** River (Moving) **W. Size:** 780 Metres. **Location:** **Nr. Rd:** A661; **Main Rd:** A1; **Rail:** Harrogate.
Ref: FH5310

WHARFE (RIVER)

River Wharfe, Wetherby Ings, Swimming Pool Lane, Boston Rd, Wetherby, **YORKSHIRE (WEST)**, LS22, **England**.
Contact/s: **Mr Pete Broxham** (Club Secretary), Wetherby and District Angling Club, 1 Eel Mires, Garth, Wetherby, West Yorkshire LS22 7TQ.
(T) 01937 585764
(E) ico100@aol.co.uk
Profile: **FT:** Combination; **WN:** Wharfe; **WT:** River (Moving) **W. Size:** 2000 Metres. **Location:** **Nr. Rd:** A58; **Main Rd:** A1; **Rail:** Harrogate.
Ref: FH5311

WHARFE INN POOL

Wharfe Inn Pool, Holt Fleet, Worcester, **WORCESTERSHIRE**, WR6, **England**.
Contact/s: Manager, The Wharf Inn, Holt Heath, Worcester, Worcestershire, WR6 6NN.
(T) 01905 620289 **(F)** 01905 620140
Profile: **FT:** Coarse; **WN:** Wharfe Inn; **WT:** Pool (Still). **Location:** **Nr. Rd:** Ombersley to A4133; **Main Rd:** Ombersley to Holt Fleet.
Ref: FH5312

WHARNCLIFFE FLY FISHERY

Wharncliffe Fly Fishery, Sheffield, **YORKSHIRE (SOUTH)**, S, **England**.
Contact/s: **Mr Ron Ogle** (Manager), 23 Carrhead Rd, Howbrook, Sheffield, Yorkshire (South), S35 7HG.
(T) 0114 2845759
Profile: **FT:** Game; **WN:** Wharncliffe; **WT:** Lake (Still).
Ref: FH5313

WHARTONS PARK COARSE FISHING

Whartons Park Coarse Fishing, New Whartons Farm, Longbank, Bewdley, **WORCESTERSHIRE**, DY12 2QW, **England**.
Contact/s: **Mr Alan Tillsley**, New Whartons Farm, Longbank, Bewdley, Worcestershire, DY12 2QW.
(T) 01299 401545
Mr Bill Brame (Secretary), Hull and District Angler's Association, PO Box 188, Hull, HU9 1AN.
Mrs Gill Tillsley (Manager), New Whartons Farm, Longbank, Bewdley, Worcestershire, DY12 2QW.
(T) 01299 401545
Profile: **FT:** Coarse; **WN:** Whartons Park Coarse Fishing; **WT:** Pool (Still) **W. Size:** 1 Acre. **Location:** **Nr. Rd:** Bewdley town centre; **Main Rd:** A456; **Rail:** Kidderminster.
Ref: FH5314

WHEAL GREY

Wheal Grey, Ashton, Helston, **CORNWALL**, **England**.
Contact/s: .
(T) 01736 763721
Profile: **FT:** Coarse; **WN:** Wheal Grey; **WT:** Lake (Still). **Location:** **Main Rd:** A394; **Rail:** Penzance.
Ref: FH5315

WHEAL RASHLEIGH PITS

Wheal Rashleigh Pits, Luxulyan, St Blazey, St Austell, **CORNWALL**, PL26, **England**.
Profile: **FT:** Coarse; **WN:** Wheal Rashleigh; **WT:** Gravel Pit (Still).
Ref: FH5316

WHEELER (RIVER)

River Wheeler, Afonwen, Mold, **FLINTSHIRE**, CH7, **Wales**.
Contact/s: **Mr C P Harness** (Membership Secretary), 8 Llwyn Menlli, Ruthin, Clwyd.
(T) 01824 705208
Profile: **FT:** Game; **WN:** Wheeler; **WT:** River (Moving) **W. Size:** 2400 Metres. **Location:** **Nr. Rd:** Afon Wen to Bodfari; **Main Rd:** A541.
Ref: FH5317

WHEELER (RIVER)

River Wheeler, Mold, **FLINTSHIRE**, CH7, **Wales**.
Contact/s: Manager, Grosvenor Pet and Garden Ctre, Grosvenor St, Mold, Clwyd, CH7 1EJ.
(T) 01352 754264
Profile: **FT:** Game; **WN:** Wheeler; **WT:** River (Moving).
Ref: FH5318

WHELFORD POOLS COARSE FISHERY

Whelford Pools Coarse Fishery, Whelford Rd, Fairford, **GLOUCESTERSHIRE**, GL7 4DT, **England**.
(W) www.fisheries.co.uk/whelford
Contact/s: **Mr Jerry Godden** (Owner).
(T) 01285 713649 (F) 01285 713649
(E) whelford@dialstrat.net
Ms Ros Godden (Owner).
(T) 01285 713649 (F) 01285 713649
(E) whelford@dialstrat.net
Profile: **FT:** Coarse; **WN:** Top Lake & Specimen Pool; **WT:** Lake (Still); **F. Size:** 12 Acres; **W. Size:** 6 Acres. **Location:** **Nr. Rd:** A417; **Main Rd:** A419; **Rail:** Swindon.
Ref: FH5319

WHETSTONE GORSE

Whetstone Gorse Fisheries & Caravan Club, Willoughby Waterlease, **LEICESTERSHIRE**, **England**.
(W) www.ridgeon-network.co.uk/fishing
Contact/s: **Mr Martin Kind** (Owner).
(T) 0116 2773796
(E) admin@ridgeon-network.co.uk
Profile: **FT:** Coarse; **WN:** Silver fish Lake, Carp Lake, Willoughby Lakes; **WT:** Lake (Still).
Ref: FH5320

WHINBURGH TROUT LAKE

Whinburgh Trout Lake, Dereham, **NORFOLK**, NR19 1QU, **England**.
Contact/s: **Mr David Potter**.
(T) 01362 850201
Ms J Carrick, Park Farm, Swanton Morley, Dereham, Norfolk, NR20 4JU.
(T) 01362 637457
Profile: **FT:** Game; **WN:** Whinburgh; **WT:** Lake (Still) **W. Size:** 4 Acres. **Location:** **Nr. Rd:** B1135.
Ref: FH5321

WHINNYGILL RESERVOIR

Whinnygill Reservoir, Skipton, **YORKSHIRE (NORTH)**, BD23, **England**.
Contact/s: **Mr Ronnie Noble**.
(T) 01756 795222
Profile: **FT:** Combination; **WN:** Whinnygill; **WT:** Reservoir (Still) **W. Size:** 7 Acres. **Location:** **Nr. Rd:** Whinnygill Road; **Main Rd:** Skipton town centre; **Rail:** Skipton.
Ref: FH5322

WHINS POND

Whins Pond, Edenhall, Penrith, **CUMBRIA**, CA11, **England**.
Contact/s: **Mrs Siddle** (Manager).
(T) 01768 862671
Profile: **FT:** Combination; **WN:** Whin's; **WT:** Pond (Still) **W. Size:** 21 Acres. **Location:** **Nr. Rd:** A686 to Alston; **Main Rd:** M6, junction 40.
Ref: FH5323

WHINWHISTLE COARSE FISHERY

Whinwhistle Coarse Fishery, Whinwhistle Rd, East Wellow, Romsey, **HAMPSHIRE**, S051, **England**.
(W) www.woodington.fsbusiness.co.uk
Contact/s: **Mr Dan Casey** (Owner).
(T) 020 84070981
(E) caseyd@globalnet.co.uk
Profile: **FT:** Coarse; **WN:** Whinwhistle; **WT:** Combination (Still & Moving); **F. Size:** 10 Acres; **W. Size:** 2 Acres. **Location:** **Nr. Rd:** Whinwhistle Road; **Main Rd:** A36; **Rail:** Romsey.
Ref: FH5324

WHIPLEY MANOR

Whipley Manor, Guildford, **SURREY**, GU, **England**.
Contact/s: **Mr Adrian Bewley** (Manager), Ashvale Fisheries, 69 Fortescue Rd, Wimbledon, London, SW19 2EA.
(T) 020 82873892
Profile: **FT:** Coarse; **WN:** Whipley Manor; **WT:** Combination (Still & Moving).
Ref: FH5325

WHIRLEY MERE

Whirley Mere, Henbury, Macclesfield, **CHESHIRE**, SK11, **England**.
Contact/s: **Mr John Turner** (Hon Secretary), Prince Albert Angling Society, 15 Pexhill Drive, Macclesfield, Cheshire, SK10 3LP.
(T) 01625 422010
Profile: **FT:** Coarse; **WN:** Whirley Mere; **WT:** Pit (Still); **F. Size:** 6 Acres; **W. Size:** 5 Acres. **Location:** **Nr. Rd:** Sandy Lane; **Main Rd:** A537; **Rail:** Macclesfield.
Ref: FH5326

WHIRLEY POOL

Whirley Pool, Henbury, Macclesfield, **CHESHIRE**, SK11, **England**.
Contact/s: **Mr John Turner** (Hon Secretary), Prince Albert Angling Society, 15 Pexhill Drive, Macclesfield, Cheshire, SK10 3LP.
(T) 01625 422010
Profile: **FT:** Game; **WN:** Whirley Pool; **WT:** Gravel Pit (Still). **Location:** **Nr. Rd:** Whirley Road; **Main Rd:** A537; **Rail:** Macclesfield.
Ref: FH5327

WHIRLWIND LAKE

Whirlwind Lake, Whirlwind Rise, Dudmore Lane, Christchurch, **DORSET**, BH23 6BQ, **England**.
Contact/s: **Mr Pillinger** (Owner).
(T) 01202 475255
Mr Graham Pepler (Manager), Davis Tackle Shop, 75 Bargates, Christchurch, Dorset, BH23 1QE.
(T) 01202 485169or395532 (F) 01202 474261
Profile: **FT:** Coarse; **WN:** Whirlwind; **WT:** Lake (Still).
Ref: FH5328

WHISBY GARDEN CENTRE

Whisby Garden Fishing Lake, Whisby Rd, Whisby Moor, Lincoln, **LINCOLNSHIRE**, LN6 9BY, **England**.
Contact/s: **Gary** (Bailiff).
(T) 01522 682208
Profile: **FT:** Coarse; **WN:** Whisby Garden Fishing Lake; **WT:** Lake (Still) **W. Size:** 5 Acres. **Location:** **Nr. Rd:** Whisby Road; **Main Rd:** A46; **Rail:** Swallow Beck.
Ref: FH5329

WHITCHURCH LAKE

Whitchurch Lake, Black Park, Whitchurch, **SHROPSHIRE**, SY13, **England**.
Contact/s: **J E Windsor**.
Profile: **FT:** Coarse; **WN:** Whitchurch; **WT:** Lake (Still).
Ref: FH5330

WHITE HART HILL LAKE

White Hart Hill Lake, Guestling, Hastings, **SUSSEX (EAST)**, TN35, **England**.
Contact/s: **Mr Peter Maclean** (Hon Secretary), 37 Collier Rd, Hastings, Sussex (East), TN34 3JR.
(T) 01424 715218
Profile: **FT:** Coarse; **WN:** White Hart Hill; **WT:** Lake (Still). **Location:** **Nr. Rd:** Hastings to Rye; **Main Rd:** A259.
Ref: FH5331

WHITE HORSE (RIVER)

River White Horse, Mountrath, **COUNTY TIPPERARY**, **Ireland**.
Contact/s: **Mr Tommy Watkins** (Hon Secretary), 9 St Fiach's Trce, Mountrath, County Laois, Ireland.
(T) 050 232540
Profile: **FT:** Combination; **WN:** White Horse and Nore; **WT:** River (Moving). **Location:** **Main Rd:** Dublin to Limerick Road; **Rail:** Clonmel.
Ref: FH5332

WHITE HORSE FISHERIES

White Horse Fisheries, East Ham, London, **LONDON (GREATER)**, E6, **England**.
Contact/s: Manager, 106 High Street South, London, E6 3RL.
(T) 020 85528859
Profile: **FT:** Coarse; **WN:** White Horse Fisheries; **WT:** Lake (Still).
Ref: FH5333

WHITE HORSE INN LAKE

White Horse Inn Lake, Minety, Malmesbury, **WILTSHIRE**, SN16, **England**.
Contact/s: Manager, White Horse Inn, Minety, Malmesbury.
(T) 01666 860284
Profile: **FT:** Coarse; **WN:** White Horse Inn; **WT:** Lake (Still).
Ref: FH5334

WHITE HOUSE MILL

White House Mill, Lampeter Velfrey, Whitland, **CARMARTHENSHIRE**, SA34 0RB, **Wales**.
Contact/s: **Mr Peter Hunt** (Manager).
(T) 01834 831304
(E) peter@whitehousemill.co.uk
Ms Barbara Hunt (Manageress).
(T) 01834 831304
Profile: **FT:** Game; **WN:** White House Mill; **WT:** Lake (Still) **W. Size:** 4 Acres. **Location:** **Nr. Rd:** Velfrey Road; **Main Rd:** A40; **Rail:** Whitland.
Ref: FH5335

WHITE HOUSE PREDATOR LAKE

White House Predator Lake, Baston Fen, **LINCOLNSHIRE**, **England**.
Contact/s: .
(T) 01778 341817
Profile: **FT:** Coarse; **WN:** White House; **WT:** Lake (Still).
Ref: FH5336

WHITE HOUSE TROUT FARM

White House Trout Farm, Crossroads, Bastan Fen, Market Deeping, Peterborough, **CAMBRIDGESHIRE**, PE6 9QA, **England**.
Contact/s: **Mr Rob Oliver**.
(T) 01778 342155
Profile: **FT:** Game; **WN:** White House Trout Farm; **WT:** Lake (Still). **Location:** **Nr. Rd:** Langhoft; **Main Rd:** A15, Peterborough to Bourne.
Ref: FH5337

WHITE HOUSE TROUT FARM

White House Trout Farm, Rotherwick, Hook, **HAMPSHIRE**, RG27 9BZ, **England**.
Contact/s: **Mr G A Patch**.
(T) 01256 763700
Profile: **FT:** Game; **WN:** White House Trout Farm; **WT:** Lake (Still).
Ref: FH5338

WHITE LOCH OF MYRTON

White Loch Of Myrton, Newton Stewart, **DUMFRIES AND GALLOWAY**, DG8, **Scotland**.
Contact/s: **Ms Clare McClymont** (Manager), Palakona Bait Supplies, 30-32 Queen St, Newton Stewart, Dumfries and Galloway, DG8 9NR.
(T) 01671 402323
(E) palakonswscot@cs.com
Profile: **FT:** Coarse; **WN:** White; **WT:** Loch (Still).
Ref: FH5339

WHITE LOUGH

White Lough, Aughnacloy, **COUNTY TYRONE**, BT69 6, **Northern Ireland**.
Contact/s: **Mrs Liz Salter** (Manager), Aughnacloy Development Association, The McCreedy Mill Centre, Aughnacloy, County Tyrone, BT69 6AL.
(T) 028 85557002
Profile: **FT:** Game; **WN:** White; **WT:** Lough (Still) **W. Size:** 23 Acres.
Ref: FH5340

WHITE SPRINGS LAKES

White Springs Lakes, Holiday Complex, Garnswllt Rd, Pentrebach, Pontardulais,

Swansea, SA4 1QG, **Wales**.
Contact/s: Mr Vince Lloyd (Owner).
(T) 01792 885699 **(F)** 01792 885699
Profile: FT: Combination; **WN:** White Spring; **WT:** Lake (Still); **F. Size:** 35 Acres; **W. Size:** 12 Acres. **Location: Nr. Rd:** Garnswllt; **Rail:** Pontarddulais.
Ref: FH5341

WHITE SWAN LAKE

White Swan Lake, Dinton Pastures Country Park, Davis St, Hurst, Wokingham, **BERKSHIRE**, RG10 0TH, **England**.
Contact/s: Mr Simon Bartlam (Fishery Manager).
(T) 0118 9342016
Profile: FT: Coarse; **WN:** White Swan Lake; **WT:** Combination (Still & Moving) **W. Size:** 24 Acres. **Location: Rail:** Winnersh.
Ref: FH5343

WHITEACRES COUNTRY PARK

Whiteacres Country Park, White Cross, Newquay, **CORNWALL**, TR8 4LW, **England**.
(W) www.whiteacres.co.uk
Contact/s: Reservations Line.
(T) 01726 860220
Mr Clint Elliott (Manager).
(T) 01726 862113 **(M)** 07768 316670
Profile: FT: Coarse; **WN:** Whiteacres Country Park; **WT:** Lake (Still) **W. Size:** 28 Acres. **Location: Nr. Rd:** White Cross, A392; **Main Rd:** A30.
Ref: FH5344

WHITEADDER (RIVER)

River Whiteadder, Berwick-upon-Tweed, **NORTHUMBERLAND**, TD15, **England**.
Contact/s: Mr David Cowan (Secretary), 129 Etal Rd, Tweedmouth, Berwick-Upon-Tweed, Northumberland, TD15 2DU.
(T) 01289 306985
(E) whiteadder@supanet.com
Profile: FT: Game; **WN:** Whiteadder; **WT:** River (Moving). **Location: Rail:** Berwick-upon-Tweed.
Ref: FH5345

WHITEADDER RESERVOIR

Whiteadder Reservoir, Haddington, **LOTHIAN (EAST)**, EH41 4QH, **Scotland**.
Contact/s: Mr Whitson.
(T) 01361 390362
Mr Douglas Muir (Manager), Gobun Ha' Hotel, Main St, Gifford, Lothian (East), EH41 4QH.
(T) 01620 810244
Profile: FT: Game; **WN:** Whiteadder; **WT:** Reservoir (Still) **W. Size:** 193 Acres.
Ref: FH5346

WHITEGATE POND

Whitegate Pond, Cromwell Avenue, Warrington, **CHESHIRE**, **England**.
(W) www.pohas.moonfruit.com
Contact/s: Mr Joe Worsley (Club Secretary), 54, Shackleton Close, Old Hall, Warrington, WA5 9QE.
(T) 01925 413750
(E) joseph.worsley@btinternet.com
Profile: FT: Coarse; **WN:** Whitegate Pond; **WT:** Pond (Still); **F. Size:** 1 Acre; **W. Size:** 1 Acre. **Location: Nr. Rd:** Cromwell Avenue; **Main Rd:** A57; **Rail:** Warrington.
Ref: FH5347

WHITEHOUSE CARAVAN PARK LAKE

Whitehouse Caravan Park Lake, Great Broughton, Stokesley, Middlesbrough, **CLEVELAND**, TS9, **England**.
Contact/s: Fishery Manager.
(T) 01642 7782238
Profile: FT: Coarse; **WN:** Whitehouse Lake; **WT:** Lake (Still).
Ref: FH5348

WHITELEY KNOWL RESERVOIR

Whiteley Knowl Reservoir, Moorland, Littleborough, **MANCHESTER (GREATER)**, OL15, **England**.
(W) www.todmorden-angling.fsnet.co.uk
Contact/s: Mr Ray Barber (Secretary), Todmorden Angling Society, 12 Grisedale Drive, Burnley, Lancashire, BB12 8AR.
(T) 01282 423780 **(M)** 07970 897849
Profile: FT: Combination; **WN:** Whiteley; **WT:** Reservoir (Still); **F. Size:** 5 Acres; **W. Size:** 3 Acres. **Location: Nr. Rd:** Clough Road.
Ref: FH5349

WHITEMERE

Whitemere, Ellesmere, **SHROPSHIRE**, SY12, **England**.
Profile: FT: Coarse; **WN:** Whitemere; **WT:** Lake (Still). **Location: Nr. Rd:** Shrewsbury Road.
Ref: FH5350

WHITEMOOR LAKE

Whitemoor Lake, Broom Hill, Wimborne, **DORSET**, BH21, **England**.
Contact/s: Mr Paul Miller.
(T) 01202 884478
Profile: FT: Coarse; **WN:** Whitemoor; **WT:** Lake (Still). **Location: Nr. Rd:** Broom Hill.
Ref: FH5351

WHITEMOOR RESERVOIR

Whitemoor Reservoir, Pendle, Nelson, **LANCASHIRE**, BB9, **England**.
Contact/s: Mr Griffiths (Fishery Manager).
(T) 01606 723800
Profile: FT: Coarse; **WN:** Whitemoor; **WT:** Reservoir (Still).
Ref: FH5352

WHITESHEET TROUT FISHERY

Whitesheet Trout Fishery, Whitesheet Farm, Holt, Wimborne, **DORSET**, BH21 7DB, **England**.
Contact/s: Mr P T Cook.
(T) 01202 883687
Profile: FT: Game; **WN:** Whitesheet Trout Fishery; **WT:** Lake (Still); **F. Size:** 55 Acres; **W. Size:** 7 Acres. **Location: Nr. Rd:** Broomhill Road; **Main Rd:** A31; **Rail:** Bournemouth.
Ref: FH5353

WHITEVANE POND

Whitevane Pond, Forest Grange, Horsham, **SURREY**, RH1, **England**.
Contact/s: Mr Derek Yates, Furnace House, Guildford Rd, Slinfold, Horsham, RH13 7QZ.
(T) 01403 791163 **(F)** 01403 791804
Profile: FT: Coarse; **WN:** Whitevane; **WT:** Pond (Still) **W. Size:** 9 Acres. **Location: Nr. Rd:** Forest Grange; **Main Rd:** M23, junction 11; **Rail:** Horsham.
Ref: FH5354

WHITEWATER (RIVER)

River Whitewater, Kilkeel, Newry, **COUNTY DOWN**, BT34, **Northern Ireland**.
Contact/s: Secretary, The Kilmorey Arms, 41 Greencastle St, Kilkeel, County Down, BT34 4BH.
(T) 028 41762220 **(F)** 028 41765399
Profile: FT: Game; **WN:** Whitewater; **WT:** River (Moving) **W. Size:** 11200 Metres.
Ref: FH5355

WHITEWATER (RIVER)

Whitewater (River), Heckfield, **HAMPSHIRE**, **England**.
Contact/s:
(T) 01483 234054
Profile: FT: Combination; **WN:** Whitewater (River); **WT:** River (Moving).
Ref: FH5356

WHITLEY POOL

Whitley Pool, Whitley, Warrington, **CHESHIRE**, WA4, **England**.
Contact/s: Mr Neil Jupp (Club Secretary), Lymm Angling Club, PO Box 350, Warrington, Cheshire, WA2 9FB.
(T) 01925 411774
Profile: FT: Coarse; **WN:** Whitley; **WT:** Pool (Still) **W. Size:** 4 Acres. **Location: Nr. Rd:** A49 to Whitchurch; **Main Rd:** M56 to Chester.
Ref: FH5357

WHITTLE BROOK RESERVOIR

Whittle Brook Reservoir, Old Clough Lane, Walkden, Worsley, Manchester, **MANCHESTER (GREATER)**, M28, **England**.
Contact/s: Mr Bob Fearnhead (Secretary), Farnworth and District Angling Association, 3 Windmill Rd, Walkden, Manchester (Greater), M28 3RP.
(T) 0161 7994242
Profile: FT: Coarse; **WN:** Whittle Brook; **WT:** Reservoir (Still); **F. Size:** 6 Acres; **W. Size:** 5 Acres. **Location: Nr. Rd:** Old Clough Road; **Main Rd:** A6 Manchester Road; **Rail:** Walkden.
Ref: FH5358

WHITTLE DEAN RESERVOIR

Whittle Dean Reservoir, The Fishery Lodge, Hallington Reservoir's, Colwell, Hexham, **NORTHUMBERLAND**, NE46 4TT, **England**.
Contact/s: Mr John Irving.
(T) 01434 681405 **(F)** 01434 681405
Profile: FT: Game; **WN:** Whittle Dean; **WT:** Reservoir (Still). **Location: Nr. Rd:** A69.
Ref: FH5359

WHITTLE DENE TROUT FISHERY

Whittle Dene Trout Fishery, Stamfordham, Newcastle Upon Tyne, **TYNE AND WEAR**, NE18 0LH, **England**.
Contact/s: Mr John Irving.
(T) 01434 681405 **(F)** 01434 681405
Profile: FT: Game; **WN:** Whittle Dene; **WT:** Reservoir (Still); **F. Size:** 87 Acres; **W. Size:** 45 Acres. **Location: Nr. Rd:** B6318; **Main Rd:** A69. **£Fr**
Ref: FH5360

WHITTLESEY DYKE/ BEVILLS LEAM

Whittlesey Dyke/ Bevills Leam, Whittlesey, Peterborough, **CAMBRIDGESHIRE**, PE, **England**.
Contact/s: Mr Dave Slack (Secretary).
(T) 01733 205775day
Mr Dave White (Chairman).
(T) 01733 204170
Mr J Warren (Secretary).
(T) 01733 203800
Mr Richard Marson (Bailiff), 57 Bellmans Rd, Whittlesey, Peterborough, Cambridgeshire, PE7 1TY.
Profile: FT: Coarse; **WN:** Whittlesey Dyke/ Bevills Leam; **WT:** River (Moving) **W. Size:** 31200 Metres. **Location: Main Rd:** A605; **Rail:** Whittlesey.
Ref: FH5361

WHITWELL PONDS

Whitwell Ponds, Whitwell, Ventnor, **ISLE OF WIGHT**, PO38, **England**.
Contact/s: Mrs J Morris.
(T) 01983 730783
Profile: FT: Coarse; **WN:** Whitwell; **WT:** Pond (Still).
Ref: FH5362

WICK MERE

Wick Mere, Church Rd, Uting, Maldon, **ESSEX**, CM9, **England**.
(W) www.chelmsfordaa.freeserve.co.uk
Contact/s: Mr Frank Wright (Membership Secretary), Chelmsford Angling Association, 61 Readers Court, Great Baddow, Chelmsford, CM2 8EX.
(T) 01245 474246or264832
(E) frank@chelmsfordaa.freeserve.co.uk
Ms Irene Lewis (Secretary), 60 Delamere Rd, Chelmsford, CM1 2TG.
(T) 01245 264832
Profile: FT: Coarse; **WN:** Wick Mere; **WT:** Lake (Still); **F. Size:** 6 Acres; **W. Size:** 6 Acres. **Location: Nr. Rd:** Church Road; **Main Rd:** A414; **Rail:** Hatfield Peverell.
Ref: FH5363

WICK WATER

Wick Water, South Cerney, Cirencester, **GLOUCESTERSHIRE**, GL7, **England**.

Contact/s: **Mr Dave Savage** (Manager), D and J Sports Limited, 75 Cricklake St, Cirencester, Gloucestershire, GL7 1HY.
(T) 01285 652227 **(F)** 01285 641615
Mr Ray Daffon (Secretary), South Cerney Angling Club, Broadway Lane, South Cerney, Cirencester, GL7 5UH.
(T) 01285 861876 **(M)** 07775 970643
Profile: **FT:** Coarse; **WN:** Wick Water; **WT:** Lake (Still). **Location:** **Nr. Rd:** Wick Water Lane; **Main Rd:** A419 to Swindon, B4696.
Ref: FH5364

WICKHAM MARKET RESERVOIRS

Wickham Market Reservoirs, Bridge Farm, Wickham Market, Woodbridge, **SUFFOLK**, IP, **England**.
Contact/s: Secretary, Framlingham and District Angling Club, Royal British Legion Club, 6 Albert Rd, Framlingham, Woodbridge IP13 9EQ.
(T) 01728 724179
Mr G Hayward.
(T) 01473 611116
Mr R Boon.
(T) 01473 611116
Profile: **FT:** Coarse; **WN:** Wickham Market; **WT:** Reservoir (Still); **F. Size:** 7 Acres; **W. Size:** 2 Acres. **Location:** **Nr. Rd:** B1078; **Main Rd:** A12; **Rail:** Camsey Ashe.
Ref: FH5365

WID (RIVER)

River Wid, Margaretting, Ingatestone, **ESSEX**, CM4, **England**.
Contact/s: **Mr Sid Hibbert** (Secretary), Basildon and District Angling Society, 15 Culverdown, Basildon, Essex, SS14 2AL.
(T) 01268 287798
Profile: **FT:** Coarse; **WN:** Wid; **WT:** River (Moving) **W. Size:** 4 Metres. **Location:** **Nr. Rd:** Whitesbridge Road; **Main Rd:** A12.
Ref: FH5366

WIDEHURST FARM

Widehurst Farm, Thron Rd, Marden, Tonbridge, **KENT**, TN12 9LL, **England**.
Contact/s: **Mr Richard Douglas Thompson**.
(T) 01622 831781
Profile: **FT:** Coarse; **WN:** Widehurst Farm; **WT:** Lake (Still); **F. Size:** 39 Acres; **W. Size:** 2 Acres. **Location:** **Nr. Rd:** Thorn Road; **Main Rd:** A229; **Rail:** Marden.
Ref: FH5367

WIDOWS FLASH

Widows Flash, Ince-In-Markerfield, Lower Ince, Wigan, **LANCASHIRE**, WN2, **England**.
Contact/s: Manager, North West Angling Ctre, Chapel St, Hindley, Wigan, WN2 3AD.
(T) 01942 255993
Profile: **FT:** Coarse; **WN:** Widows Flash; **WT:** Lake (Still). **Location:** **Nr. Rd:** Hindley to Ince; **Main Rd:** A577.
Ref: FH5368

WILDEN POOL

Wilden Pool, Wilden, Stourport-on-Severn, **WORCESTERSHIRE**, DY13, **England**.
Profile: **FT:** Coarse; **WN:** Wilden; **WT:** Pond (Still). **Location:** **Main Rd:** A451, A449.
Ref: FH5369

WILDEN RESERVOIR

Wilden Reservoir, St Neots, Huntingdon, **CAMBRIDGESHIRE**, PE1, **England**.
Contact/s: Secretary, St Neots and District Angling and FPS, Skenbridge Cottage, Great Paxton, St Neots, PE19 4RA.
(T) 01480 219706
Profile: **FT:** Coarse; **WN:** Wilden; **WT:** Reservoir (Still). **Location:** **Nr. Rd:** Nuffield down to Wray House.
Ref: FH5370

WILDERNESS LAKE

Wilderness Lake, Dormans Park, East Grinstead, **SUSSEX (WEST)**, RH19, **England**.
Profile: **FT:** Coarse; **WN:** Wilderness; **WT:** Lake (Still) **W. Size:** 6 Acres. **Location:** **Main Rd:** A22 or A264.
Ref: FH5371

WILLIES WELL

Willies Well, Sled Lane, Wylam, **NORTHUMBERLAND**, NE41, **England**.
Contact/s: Warden, Tyne Anglers Alliance, PO Box 72, Heaton Rd, Newcastle upon Tyne.
(T) 0191 2681613
Profile: **FT:** Coarse; **WN:** Willies Well; **WT:** Well (Still).
Ref: FH5372

WILLINGHURST COARSE FISHERY

Willinghurst Coarse Fishery, Willinghurst Estate, Shamley Green, Guildford, **SURREY**, GU5 0SU, **England**.
Contact/s: **Mr John Boyze** (Manager).
(T) 01483 271005
Mr Mark Syms (Owner).
(T) 01483 275048
Profile: **FT:** Coarse; **WN:** Willinghurst Coarse Fishery; **WT:** Lake (Still); **F. Size:** 125 Acres; **W. Size:** 30 Acres. **Location:** **Nr. Rd:** B2128; **Main Rd:** A281; **Rail:** Guildford.
Ref: FH5373

WILLINGHURST TROUT FISHERY

Willinghurst Trout Fishery, Willinghurst Estate, Shamley Green, Guildford, **SURREY**, GU, **England**.
Contact/s: **Mr Mark Syms** (Owner).
(T) 01483 275048
Profile: **FT:** Game; **WN:** Willinghurst Trout Fishery; **WT:** Lake (Still); **F. Size:** 125 Acres; **W. Size:** 4 Acres. **Location:** **Nr. Rd:** B2128; **Main Rd:** A281; **Rail:** Guildford.
Ref: FH5374

WILLINGTON LAKE

Willington Lake, Great Barford, Bedford, **BEDFORDSHIRE**, MK44, **England**.
Contact/s: **Mr J Leath** (Secretary), Shefford and District Angling Association, 3 Ivel Cl, Shefford, Bedfordshire, SG17 5JX.
(T) 01462 812323
Profile: **FT:** Coarse; **WN:** Willington; **WT:** Lake (Still).
Ref: FH5375

WILLITOFT FISH FARM

Willitoft Fish Farm, Willitoft Rd, Spaldington, Goole, **HUMBERSIDE**, DN14 7, **England**.
Contact/s: **Jeff** (Warden).
(T) 01757 288609
Mr Ted Slights, Lake View House, Spaldington, Goole, Yorkshire (East), DN14 7NP.
(T) 01757 288609
Profile: **FT:** Coarse; **WN:** Willitoft; **WT:** Lake (Still); **F. Size:** 8 Acres; **W. Size:** 3 Acres. **Location:** **Nr. Rd:** Willitoft Road; **Main Rd:** M62, junction 37; **Rail:** Howden.
Ref: FH5376

WILLOW BANK FISHERY

Willow Bank Fishery, Pasture Farm, Station Rd, Kirton Lindsey, Gainsborough, **LINCOLNSHIRE**, DN21 4BB, **England**.
Contact/s: **Mr Mick Sargent**.
(T) 01652 640512
Profile: **FT:** Coarse; **WN:** Willow Bank Fishery; **WT:** Lake (Still). **Location:** **Main Rd:** Station Road; **Rail:** Kirton. £Fr
Ref: FH5377

WILLOW CREEK

Willow Creek, Tansor, Oundle, Peterborough, **CAMBRIDGESHIRE**, PE8 5HN, **England**.
Contact/s: **Mr Tony Bridgefoot** (Owner).
(T) 01832 226042
Profile: **FT:** Coarse; **WN:** Willow Creek; **WT:** Stream (Moving); **F. Size:** 108 Acres; **W. Size:** 750 Metres. **Location:** **Nr. Rd:** Tansor to Fotheringhay; **Main Rd:** A605; **Rail:** Peterborough.
Ref: FH5378

WILLOW FARM

Willow Farm, Louth, **LINCOLNSHIRE**, LN11, **England**.
Contact/s: Fishery Manager.
(T) 01507 398978
Profile: **FT:** Coarse; **WN:** Willow Farm; **WT:** Lake (Still).
Ref: FH5379

WILLOW FARM

Willow Farm, Lenchwick, Evesham, **WORCESTERSHIRE**, WR11, **England**.
Contact/s: Fishery Manager.
(T) 01386 871011
Profile: **FT:** Coarse; **WN:** Willow Farm; **WT:** Combination (Still). **Location:** **Nr. Rd:** Lenchwick Village to Chadbury; **Main Rd:** A4184.
Ref: FH5380

WILLOW GARTH FISHERY

Willow Garth Fishery, Shaftholme Lane, Arksey, Doncaster, **YORKSHIRE (SOUTH)**, DN, **England**.
Contact/s: Manager.
(T) 01302 874258
Mr Franco Pezzulo (Manager), Franco's Angling Supplies, 148 High St, Bentley, Doncaster, DN5 0AT.
(T) 01302 874888
Profile: **FT:** Coarse; **WN:** Willow Garth Fishery; **WT:** Lake (Still). **Location:** **Nr. Rd:** Marsh Lane; **Main Rd:** A19 towards Askern.
Ref: FH5381

WILLOW LAKE

Willow Lake, Decoy Farm, Eastrea, Whittlesey, Peterborough, **CAMBRIDGESHIRE**, PE, **England**.
Contact/s: **Mr Peter Band**.
(T) 01733 202230
Profile: **FT:** Coarse; **WN:** Willow; **WT:** Lake (Still). **Location:** **Main Rd:** A605.
Ref: FH5382

WILLOW LAKES

Willow Lakes, Ashby Hill Top Farm, Grimsby, **HUMBERSIDE**, DN37 0RY, **England**.
Contact/s: **Joanne Butters** (Fishery Manager).
(T) 01472824429
Profile: **FT:** Combination; **WN:** Willow; **WT:** Lake (Still).
Ref: FH5383

WILLOW LAKES

Willow Lakes, Newark Rd, Foston, Grantham, **LINCOLNSHIRE**, NG32 2LF, **England**.
Contact/s: **Mr Geoff Chilton**.
(T) 01400 282190
Profile: **FT:** Coarse; **WN:** Willow; **WT:** Lake (Still). **Location:** **Nr. Rd:** Newark Road; **Main Rd:** A1, trunk Road; **Rail:** Grantham.
Ref: FH5384

WILLOW LAKES TROUT FISHERY

Willow Lakes Trout Fishery, Ash Farm, Chediston, Halesworth, **SUFFOLK**, IP19 0BB, **England**.
Contact/s: **Mr Pat Gregory** (Secretary).
(T) 01986 785392
Profile: **FT:** Game; **WN:** Willow; **WT:** Lake (Still); **F. Size:** 5 Acres; **W. Size:** 4 Acres. **Location:** **Nr. Rd:** Chediston Green; **Main Rd:** B1123; **Rail:** Halesworth.
Ref: FH5385

WILLOW MARSH

Willow Marsh, Shenstone, Kidderminster, **WORCESTERSHIRE**, **England**.
Contact/s: **Mr Mike Talbot** (Owner).
(T) 01562 777406
Profile: **FT:** Coarse; **WN:** Willow Marsh**WT:** (Still). **Location:** **Rail:** Kidderminster.
Ref: FH5386

WILLOW PARK

Willow Park, Youngs Drive, Shawfield Rd, Ash Vale, Aldershot, **HAMPSHIRE**, GU12 6RE, **England**.
Mr Ian Covey (Manager).
(T) 01252 325867
Mr Kenny Collings (Fishery Manager),

Willow Park Fisheries, Youngs Drive, Shawfield Rd, Ash Vale, Nr Aldershot, Hants GU12 6RE.
(T) 01252 325867
Profile: FT: Coarse; WN: Main Lake, Middle Lake, & Small Lake; WT: Lake (Still); F. Size: 25 Acres. Location: Nr. Rd: Youngs Drive; Main Rd: A3, A31, A323.
Ref: FH5387

WILLOW POOL

Willow Pool, Northwich, **CHESHIRE**, CW9, **England**.
Contact/s: Mr Neil Jupp (Club Secretary), Lymm Angling Club, PO Box 350, Warrington, Cheshire, WA2 9FB.
(T) 01925 411774
Profile: FT: Coarse; WN: Willow; WT: Pool (Still). Location: Nr. Rd: Pole Lane; Main Rd: A559.
Ref: FH5388

WILLOW POOLS

Willow Pools, Bickford, Penkridge, Stafford, **STAFFORDSHIRE**, ST19, **England**.
Contact/s: Fishery Manager.
(T) 01785 663575
Profile: FT: Coarse; WN: Willow; WT: Pool (Still).
Ref: FH5389

WILLOW SPRINGS

Willow Springs, Messingham, Scunthorpe, **HUMBERSIDE**, DN17, **England**.
Contact/s: Fishery Manager.
(T) 01724 782424
Profile: FT: Coarse; WN: Willow Springs; WT: Lake (Still). Location: Nr. Rd: Scunthorpe to Messingham; Main Rd: M180.
Ref: FH5390

WILLOW WATER

Willow Water, Pocklington, York, **YORKSHIRE (NORTH)**, YO42, **England**.
Contact/s: Fishery Manager.
(T) 01759 306585
Profile: FT: Coarse; WN: Willow Water; WT: Lake (Still).
Ref: FH5391

WILLOWCROFT FISHERY

Willowcroft, Common Rd, Pentney, King's Lynn, **NORFOLK**, PE32, **England**.
Contact/s: Gary. (M) 07901 923882
Tina.
(T) 01760 338293
Profile: FT: Coarse; WN: Willowcroft; WT: Lake (Still); F. Size: 300 Acres; W. Size: 160 Acres. Location: Nr. Rd: Common Road; Main Rd: A47 East of King's Lynn.
Ref: FH5392

WILLOWFIELD LAKE COTTAGES

Willowfield Lake Cottages, Gallowell Rd, Velator, Braunton, **DEVON**, EX33, **England**.
(W) www.willowfieldlakecottages.co.uk
Contact/s: Mr Michael Reed.
(T) 01271 814346 (F) 01271 815337
(E) info@willowfieldlakecottages.co.uk
Profile: FT: Coarse; WN: Willowfield; WT: Lake (Still); F. Size: 12 Acres; W. Size: 2 Acres. Location: Nr. Rd: A361; Main Rd: A361; Rail: Barnstaple. £Fr
Ref: FH5393

WILLOWGARTH LAKE

Arksey Willowgarth, Shaftholme Lane, Arksey, Nr Bentley, Doncaster, **YORKSHIRE (SOUTH)**, **England**.
Contact/s: Mr Keith Davies (Fishery Manager).
(T) 01302 874258
Profile: FT: Coarse; WN: Willowgarth; WT: Lake (Still); F. Size: 8 Acres; W. Size: 4 Acres. Location: Nr. Rd: Shaftholme Lane; Main Rd: A19; Rail: Bentley.
Ref: FH5394

WILLOWS

Willows (The), Little Braxted Lane, Little Braxted, Witham, **ESSEX**, CM8, **England**.
(W) www.chelmsfordaa.freeserve.co.uk
Contact/s: Mr Frank Wright (Membership Secretary), Chelmsford Angling Association, 61 Readers Court, Great Baddow, Chelmsford, CM2 8EX.
(T) 01245 474246or264832
(E) frank@chelmsfordaa.freeserve.co.uk
Ms Irene Lewis (Secretary), 60 Delamere Rd, Chelmsford, CM1 2TG.
(T) 01245 264832
Profile: FT: Coarse; WN: Willows (The); WT: Combination (Still & Moving) W. Size: 7 Acres. Location: Nr. Rd: Little Braxted Lane; Main Rd: A12; Rail: Chelmsford.
Ref: FH5395

WILLOWS

Willows (The), Hessay, York, **YORKSHIRE (NORTH)**, YO26, **England**.
Contact/s: Mrs C Gallagher.
(T) 01904 738206
Profile: FT: Coarse; WN: Willows; WT: Pond (Still). Location: Main Rd: A58 West of York.
Ref: FH5396

WILLOWS (THE)

Willows (The), Barmston, Washington, **TYNE AND WEAR**, **England**.
Contact/s: .
(T) 0191 3857488
Profile: FT: Coarse; WN: Willows (The); WT: Lake (Still).
Ref: FH5397

WILLOWS AND FIRS LAKES

Willows And Firs Lakes, Sessay, Thirsk, **YORKSHIRE (NORTH)**, YO7, **England**.
Contact/s: Mr David Kay (Fishery Manager).
(T) 01845 501321
Profile: FT: Coarse; WN: Willow; WT: Lake (Still).
Ref: FH5398

WILLOWS FARM FISHING

Willows Farm Fishing, Willows Farm, Wanlip Rd, Syston, Leicester, **LEICESTERSHIRE**, LE7 8PD, **England**.
Contact/s: Mr Mike Winterton (Manager).
(M) 07889 119695
Profile: FT: Coarse; WN: Willows Farm Fishing; WT: Combination (Still & Moving); F. Size: 150 Acres; W. Size: 45 Acres. Location: Main Rd: A46.
Ref: FH5399

WILLOWS LAKE

Willows Lake, Chelmsford, **ESSEX**, CM, **England**.
Contact/s: Mr Arthur Rush (Secretary).
(T) 01245 261408
Profile: FT: Coarse; WN: Willows; WT: Lake (Still).
Ref: FH5400

WILLOWS POOLS

Willows Pools, Bickford, Penkridge, **STAFFORDSHIRE**, ST19, **England**.
Contact/s: Mr Tony Gough (Fishery Manager).
(T) 01785 663575
Profile: FT: Coarse; WN: Willows Pools; WT: Lake (Still). Location: Main Rd: A449; Rail: Penkridge.
Ref: FH5401

WILLOWSIDE CARP LAKE

Willowside Carp Lake, Stewardstone, Chingford, London, **LONDON (GREATER)**, E4, **England**.
Contact/s: Mr Peter Roddick (Manager).
(T) 020 85291371
Profile: FT: Coarse; WN: Willowside Carp; WT: Lake (Still). Location: Nr. Rd: Daws Hill Road; Main Rd: A112 to Chingford.
Ref: FH5402

WILLSMORE WATER

Willsmore Water, Hayes Lane, Fakenham, **NORFOLK**, NR21, **England**.
Contact/s: Mr Dave Playford (Manager), Dave's Tackle Shop, 8 Millers Walk, Fakenham, Norfolk, NR21 9AP.
(T) 01328 862543
Mr G Twite (Secretary), Fakenham Angling Club, 16 Back St, Hempton, Fakenham, NR21 7LR.
(T) 01328 863054
Profile: FT: Coarse; WN: Willsmore Water; WT: Lake (Still); F. Size: 2 Acres; W. Size: 1 Acre. Location: Nr. Rd: A1065 Fakenham to Swaffham; Main Rd: Fakenham by-pass; Rail: King's Lynn.
Ref: FH5403

WILSTONE RESERVOIR

Wilstone Reservoir, Tring Park Estate, Tring, **HERTFORDSHIRE**, HP23, **England**.
Contact/s: Mr Bernard Double (Bailiff).
(T) 01442 822379
Profile: FT: Coarse; WN: Wilstone; WT: Reservoir (Still).
Ref: FH5404

WIMBLEBALL LAKE

Wimbleball Lake, Hill Farm Barn, Dulverton, **SOMERSET**, TA22, **England**.
Contact/s: Customer Services, Wessex Water, Billing Ctre, Clevedon Walk, Nailsea, Bristol, BS48 1WW. (M) 03453 00600
Mr Topp (Owner), Topp Tackle, 63 Station Rd, Taunton, Somerset, TA1 1PA.
(T) 01823 282518
Mrs Topp (Owner).
Profile: FT: Game; WN: Wimbleball; WT: Lake (Still).
Ref: FH5405

WIMBLINGTON MERE

Wimblington Mere, Wimblington, Wisbech, **CAMBRIDGESHIRE**, PE, **England**.
Contact/s: Mr Keith Bradshaw (Head Bailiff).
(T) 01354 740350evenings
Profile: FT: Coarse; WN: Wimblington Mere; WT: Gravel Pit (Still). Location: Main Rd: B1098.
Ref: FH5406

WINCHAM BROOK

Wincham Brook, Wincham, Northwich, **CHESHIRE**, CW9, **England**.
Contact/s: Mr Neil Jupp (Club Secretary), Lymm Angling Club, PO Box 350, Warrington, Cheshire, WA2 9FB.
(T) 01925 411744
Profile: FT: Combination; WN: Wincham; WT: Brook (Moving). Location: Nr. Rd: A556; Main Rd: M6, junction 19, A556 to Chester.
Ref: FH5407

WINDMILL FARM LAKES

Windmill Farm Lakes, Spalford, Newark, **NOTTINGHAMSHIRE**, NG, **England**.
Contact/s: Fishery Manager.
(T) 01522 778305
Profile: FT: Coarse; WN: Windmill Farm; WT: Lake (Still).
Ref: FH5408

WINDMILL LAKE

Manor Farm Leisure, Anchor Lane, Harvington, Evesham, **WORCESTERSHIRE**, WR11 8PA, **England**.
(W) www.anglersnet.co.uk/fisheries/manor.htm
Contact/s: Mr David Byrd (Manager), Manor Farm Leisure, Herons Roost, Anchor Lane, Evesham, WR11 5NR.
(T) 01386 870039
(E) manorfarmleisure@btinternet.com
Profile: FT: Coarse; WN: Windmill Lake and Wood Pool; WT: Lake (Still); F. Size: 3 Acres; W. Size: 2 Acres. Location: Nr. Rd: Evesham to Bidford-on-Avon; Main Rd: B4088.
Ref: FH5409

WINDRUSH (RIVER)

River Windrush, Burford, **OXFORDSHIRE**, OX18, **England**.
Contact/s: Mr Dave Cohen (Secretary),

Burford Angling Club, 117 High St, Burford, Oxfordshire, OX18 4RG.
(T) 01993 822136
Profile: **FT:** Combination; **WN:** Windrush; **WT:** River (Moving). **Location:** **Nr. Rd:** A361; **Main Rd:** Oxford, take A40 to Burford.
Ref: FH5410

WINDRUSH (RIVER)

River Windrush, Witney, **OXFORDSHIRE**, OX8, **England**.
(W) www.badac.co.uk
Contact/s: **Mr D Porter** (Secretary), 72 Rivington Cres, Mill Hill, London, NW7 2LF.
(T) 020 84401303
Profile: **FT:** Coarse; **WN:** Windrush; **WT:** River (Moving).
Ref: FH5411

WINDRUSH (RIVER)

River Windrush, Burford, **OXFORDSHIRE**, OX18, **England**.
Contact/s: **Mr Dave Cohen** (Secretary), Burford Angling Club, 117 High St, Burford, Oxfordshire, OX18 4RG.
(T) 01993 822136
Profile: **FT:** Coarse; **WN:** Windrush; **WT:** River (Moving).
Ref: FH5412

WINDRUSH (RIVER)

Windrush (River), Shimano Linear Fisheries (Oxford), Smiths Concrete Site, Hardwick Village, Witney, **OXFORDSHIRE**, OX8 7Q, **England**.
Contact/s: **Mr Len Gurd** (Owner), 10A Rackstraw Gr, Old Farm Park, Milton Keynes, Buckinghamshire, MK7 8PZ.
(T) 01908 645135 **(F)** 01908 645115
Profile: **FT:** Coarse; **WN:** Windrush; **WT:** River (Moving). **Location:** **Nr. Rd:** B4449; **Main Rd:** A40; **Rail:** Oxford.
Ref: FH5413

WINDTHORPE PITS

Windthorpe Pits, Sheffield, **YORKSHIRE (SOUTH)**, S, **England**.
Contact/s: **F Turner**, 30 Mather Walk, Sheffield, Yorkshire (South).
Profile: **FT:** Coarse; **WN:** Windthorpe; **WT:** Gravel Pit (Still).
Ref: FH5414

WINFIELD LAGOON

Winfield Lagoon, National Water Sports Ctre, Adbolton Lane, Holme Pierrepont, Nottingham, **NOTTINGHAMSHIRE**, NG12 2LU, **England**.
Contact/s: Water Sports Manager.
(T) 0115 9821212 **(F)** 0115 9811359
Profile: **FT:** Coarse; **WN:** Winfield; **WT:** Lake (Still) **W. Size:** 1 Acre.
Ref: FH5415

WINGERWORTH LIDO

Wingerworth Lido, Wingerworth, Chesterfield, **DERBYSHIRE**, S42 6, **England**.
Contact/s: Manager, Clay Cross Angling, 51 High St, Clay Cross, Chesterfield, S45 9DX.
(T) 01246 861888
Profile: **FT:** Coarse; **WN:** Wingerworth Lido; **WT:** Lake (Still) **W. Size:** 5 Acres. **Location:** **Nr. Rd:** A61; **Main Rd:** M1 junction 29.
Ref: FH5416

WINGHAM FISHERY

Wingham Specimen Carp & Coarse Fishery, 20 Downs Way, Sellindge, Ashford, **KENT**, TN25 6EZ, **England**.
(W) www.anglersnet.co.uk/fisheries/wingham.htm
Contact/s: **Mr Steve Burke** (Owner), Wingham Fishery, 20 Downs Way, Sellindge, Ashford, Kent, TN25 6EZ..
(T) 01303 813644
(E) steve@go-fishing.co.uk
Profile: **FT:** Coarse; **WN:** Wingham Specimen Carp & Coarse Fishery; **WT:** Gravel Pit (Still); **F. Size:** 65 Acres; **W. Size:** 55 Acres.
Ref: FH5417

WINKTON FISHERY

Winkton Fishery, Winkton, Christchurch, **DORSET**, BH23, **England**.
Contact/s: **Mr Graham Pepler** (Manager), Davis Tackle Shop, 75 Bargates, Christchurch, Dorset, BH23 1QE.
(T) 01202 485169or395532 **(F)** 01202 474261
Profile: **FT:** Combination; **WN:** Avon (Hampshire); **WT:** River (Moving) **W. Size:** 1600 Metres. **Location:** **Nr. Rd:** B3347; **Main Rd:** A35; **Rail:** Christchurch.
Ref: FH5418

WINKWORTH LAKES

Winkworth Lakes, National Trust, Winkworth, Godalming, **SURREY**, GU, **England**.
Profile: **FT:** Game; **WN:** Winkworth; **WT:** Lake (Still).
Ref: FH5419

WINNINGTON POOL

Winnington Pool, Winnington St, Northwich, **CHESHIRE**, CW8, **England**.
Profile: **FT:** Coarse; **WN:** Winnington; **WT:** Pool (Still). **Location:** **Nr. Rd:** Winnington Street; **Main Rd:** B5374, Moss Road.
Ref: FH5420

WINSFORD FLASH

Winsford Flash, Winsford, **CHESHIRE**, **England**.
Contact/s: .
(T) 01606 558475
Profile: **FT:** Coarse; **WN:** Winsford Flash; **WT:** Lake (Still).
Ref: FH5421

WINSTER (RIVER)

River Winster, Grange, Keswick, **CUMBRIA**, CA12, **England**.
(W) www.wiganaa.f9.co.uk
Contact/s: **Mr Gerry Wilson** (Hon Secretary), Wigan and District Angling Association, 11 Guildford Avenue, Chorley, Lancashire, PR6 8TG.
(T) 01257 265905
(E) gerry@wiganna.freeserve.co.uk
Profile: **FT:** Combination; **WN:** Winster; **WT:** River (Moving) **W. Size:** 3200 Metres. **Location:** **Nr. Rd:** B5289; **Main Rd:** A590.
Ref: FH5422

WINSTER (RIVER)

River Winster, Meathop, Grange-Over-Sands, **CUMBRIA**, LA11, **England**.
Contact/s: **Mr Neil Yates** (Secretary), Brookside, Underbarrow, Kendal, Cumbria, LA8 8HH.
(T) 01539 568843
Profile: **FT:** Combination; **WN:** Winster; **WT:** River (Moving). **Location:** **Main Rd:** A590 Kendal to Barrow.
Ref: FH5423

WINTER BROTHERS POND

Winter Brothers Pond, Marsh Lane, East Halton, Immingham, **LINCOLNSHIRE**, DN40, **England**.
Contact/s: **Mr Winter** (Owner), Winter Brothers Pond, Marsh Lane, East Halton, Lincolnshire.
(T) 01469 540238
Profile: **FT:** Coarse; **WN:** Winters Brothers; **WT:** Pond (Still) **W. Size:** 21 Acres.
Ref: FH5424

WINTERFOLD PARK FISHERIES

Winterfold Park Fisheries, Kidderminster, **WORCESTERSHIRE**, DY11, **England**.
Contact/s: Manager, Gardeners Cottage, Winterfold Farm, Chaddesley Corbett.
(T) 01562 777963
Profile: **FT:** Coarse; **WN:** Winterfold Park Fisheries; **WT:** Lake (Still) **W. Size:** 1 Acre.
Ref: FH5425

WINTERLEY POOL FISHERY

Winterley Pool Fishery, Pool Farm, Crewe Rd, Haslington, Crewe, **CHESHIRE**, CW1 5RD, **England**.
Contact/s: **Mr C D Manifold**.
(T) 01270 629999 **(F)** 01270 629999
Profile: **FT:** Coarse; **WN:** Winterley Pool Fishery; **WT:** Lake (Still) **W. Size:** 12 Acres. **Location:** **Nr. Rd:** Crewe Road; **Main Rd:** A534; **Rail:** Crewe.
Ref: FH5426

WINTERS LAKE

Winters Lake, East Halton, Immingham, **LINCOLNSHIRE**, DN40, **England**.
Contact/s: **Mr Winter**, Winter Brothers Pond, Marsh Lane, East Halton, Lincolnshire.
(T) 01469 540238
Profile: **FT:** Coarse; **WN:** Winter's; **WT:** Lake (Still) **W. Size:** 21 Acres. **Location:** **Nr. Rd:** Scunthorpe to Grimsby; **Main Rd:** A180.
Ref: FH5427

WINTERSETT RESERVOIR

Wintersett Reservoir, Wakefield, **YORKSHIRE (WEST)**, WF, **England**.
Contact/s:
(T) 01924 378878
Profile: **FT:** Coarse; **WN:** Wintersett; **WT:** Reservoir (Still).
Ref: FH5428

WINTERSHALL WATERS

Wintershall Waters, Bramley, Godalming, **SURREY**, GU, **England**.
Contact/s: **Mr Peter Cockwill** (Fishery Manager).
(T) 01483 205196
Profile: **FT:** Game; **WN:** Wintershall Waters; **WT:** Lake (Still).
Ref: FH5429

WINTERSHILL TROUT LAKE

Wintershill Trout Lake, Wintershill Farm, Wintershill Trout Lake, Durley, Southampton, **HAMPSHIRE**, SO32 2AH, **England**.
Contact/s: **Commander C J Balfour** (Owner).
(T) 023 80601421or01489860200
Profile: **FT:** Game; **WN:** Wintershill Trout; **WT:** Lake (Still); **F. Size:** 6 Acres; **W. Size:** 3 Acres. **Location:** **Rail:** Eastleigh.
Ref: FH5430

WINTHORPE LAKE

Winthorpe Lake, Sheffield, **YORKSHIRE (SOUTH)**, S, **England**.
Contact/s: Manager, 142-144 Princess St, Sheffield, Yorkshire (South).
Profile: **FT:** Coarse; **WN:** Winthorpe; **WT:** Gravel Pit (Still).
Ref: FH5431

WINTONS FISHERY

Wintons Fishery, Wintons Farm, Folders Lane, Burgess Hill, **SUSSEX (WEST)**, RH15 0DR, **England**.
Contact/s: **Mr Alan Etherington**.
(T) 01444 236493
Profile: **FT:** Coarse; **WN:** Mallard, Heron, and Kingfisher; **WT:** Lake (Still); **F. Size:** 25 Acres. **Location:** **Nr. Rd:** Gatwick Airport; **Main Rd:** M23, A23.
Ref: FH5432

WISCOMBE FISHERY

Wiscombe Fishery, Southleigh, Colyton, **DEVON**, EX13 6JE, **England**.
Contact/s: **Mr Mike Raynor**.
(T) 01404 871474 **(F)** 01404 871460 **(M)** 07860 222342
(E) michael@wiscombe.globalnet.co.uk
Ms S A K Chichester (Owner).
(T) 01404 871474 **(F)** 01404 871460
Profile: **FT:** Combination; **WN:** Wiscombe Fishery; **WT:** Lake (Still) **W. Size:** 2 Acres. **Location:** **Rail:** Honiton. **£Fr**
Ref: FH5433

WISHING TREE RESERVOIR

Wishing Tree Reservoir, Queensway, Hastings, **SUSSEX (EAST)**, TN38, **England**.
Contact/s: **Mr Peter Maclean** (Hon Secretary), 37 Collier Rd, Hastings, Sussex

(East), TN34 3JR.
(T) 01424 715218
Profile: FT: Coarse; **WN:** Wishing Tree; **WT:** Reservoir (Still) **W. Size:** 4 Acres. **Location:** **Nr. Rd:** Hastings to Crowhurst; **Main Rd:** B2092 to Battle; **Rail:** West St Leonards.
Ref: FH5434

WISSEY (RIVER)
River Wissey, Hilgay Village, King's Lynn, **NORFOLK**, PE, **England**.
Contact/s: **K Allen** (Chairman), Mole Cottage, 15 Ten Mile Bank, Littleport, CB6 1EE.
(T) 01383 860936
Mr Mick Grief (Secretary), King's Lynn Angling Association, 67 Peckover Way, South Wootton, King's Lynn, PE30 3UE.
(T) 01553 671545
Profile: FT: Coarse; **WN:** Wissey; **WT:** River (Moving) **W. Size:** 6400 Metres. **Location:** **Main Rd:** A10.
Ref: FH5435

WISTLANDPOUND RESERVOIR
Wistlandpound Reservoir, Challacombe, Barnstaple, **DEVON**, EX3, **England**.
Contact/s: Manager, Challacombe Post Office, Challacombe, Barnstaple, Devon, EX31 4TT.
(T) 01598 763229
Profile: FT: Game; **WN:** Wistlandpound; **WT:** Reservoir (Still).
Ref: FH5436

WITCOMBE WATERS
Witcombe Waters, Witcombe Farm, Great Witcombe, Gloucester, **GLOUCESTERSHIRE**, GL3 4TR, **England**.
Contact/s: **C Hicks-Beach**.
(T) 01452 864413 **(F)** 01452 863591
Mr Jim Hunter (Manager).
(T) 01452 864413or01242603940home
Profile: FT: Game; **WN:** Witcombe Waters; **WT:** Reservoir (Still) **W. Size:** 28 Acres. **Location:** **Nr. Rd:** A417; **Rail:** Cheltenham or Gloucester.
Ref: FH5437

WITHAM (RIVER)
River Witham, Moon Cottage, Cowbridge, Boston, **LINCOLNSHIRE**, PE22 7BA, **England**.
Contact/s: Fishery Manager.
(T) 01205 350478
Profile: FT: Coarse; **WN:** Witham; **WT:** River (Moving).
Ref: FH5438

WITHAM (RIVER)
River Witham, Grantham, **LINCOLNSHIRE**, NG31, **England**.
Profile: FT: Coarse; **WN:** Witham; **WT:** River (Moving). **Location:** **Nr. Rd:** B1174; **Main Rd:** A1. **£Fr**
Ref: FH5439

WITHAM (RIVER)
River Witham, Long Bennington, Newark, **NOTTINGHAMSHIRE**, NG23 5, **England**.
Contact/s: **Mr Jack Garland** (Manager).
(T) 01636 702962
Profile: FT: Coarse; **WN:** Witham; **WT:** River (Moving).
Ref: FH5440

WITHAM FRIARY LAKE
Witham Friary Lake, Witham Hall Farm, Witham Friary, Frome, **SOMERSET**, BA11 5HB, **England**.
Contact/s: **Mr Miles**.
(T) 01373 836239
Profile: FT: Coarse; **WN:** Witham Friary; **WT:** Lake (Still) **W. Size:** 2 Acres.
Ref: FH5441

WITHERINGTON FARM FISHING
Witherington Farm Fishing, New Cottage, Witherington Farm, Downton, Salisbury, **WILTSHIRE**, SP5 3QX, **England**.
Contact/s: **Mr Tony Beeny**.
(T) 01722 710021
Mrs Caroline Beeny.
(T) 01722 710021
Profile: FT: Coarse; **WN:** Witherington Farm Fishing; **WT:** Lake (Still).
Ref: FH5442

WITHERSLACK HALL TARN
Witherslack Hall Tarn, Witherslack, Grange-Over-Sands, **CUMBRIA**, LA11, **England**.
Contact/s: **Mr Tony Ryan**, 8 Hayfell Rise, Kendal, Cumbria.
Profile: FT: Coarse; **WN:** Witherslack; **WT:** Tarn (Still) **W. Size:** 2 Acres. **Location:** **Nr. Rd:** Next to Witherslack School; **Main Rd:** A590 Kendal to Barrow.
Ref: FH5443

WITHINS RESERVOIR
Withins Reservoir, Radcliffe, Manchester, **MANCHESTER (GREATER)**, M26, **England**.
Contact/s: Fishery Manager.
(T) 0161 7245089
Profile: FT: Coarse; **WN:** Withins; **WT:** Reservoir (Still).
Ref: FH5444

WITHNELL RESERVOIRS
Withnell Reservoirs, Withnell Fisheries Limited, Oakmere Avenue, Withnell, Chorley, **LANCASHIRE**, PR, **England**.
Contact/s: **Mr T F Hampson** (Managing Director), 279 Hulton Lane, Bolton, BL3 4LF.
(T) 01204 654307
Profile: FT: Coarse; **WN:** Withnell; **WT:** Reservoir (Still). **Location:** **Nr. Rd:** Oakmere Avenue.
Ref: FH5445

WITHY POOL
Withy Pool, Bedford Rd, Henlow Camp, Henlow, **BEDFORDSHIRE**, SG16 6EA, **England**.
Contact/s: **Mr Paul Selman** (Syndicate Manager).
(T) 01925 763572 **(F)** 01925 763572
(E) paulselman@lineone.net
Profile: FT: Coarse; **WN:** Withy; **WT:** Pool (Still); **F. Size:** 4 Acres; **W. Size:** 3 Acres. **Location:** **Nr. Rd:** Bedford Road; **Main Rd:** A600.
Ref: FH5446

WITHY POOL
Withy Pool, Wellington, Telford, **SHROPSHIRE**, TF1, **England**.
Contact/s: Manager.
(T) 01952 503550
Profile: FT: Coarse; **WN:** Withy; **WT:** Pool (Still).
Ref: FH5447

WITLEY FISHERY
Witley Fishery, Hazelhurst Farm, Little Witley, Worcester, **WORCESTERSHIRE**, WR6 6LF, **England**.
Contact/s: **Mr Frankie Colwill** (Owner).
(T) 01299 896600
Mrs Jackie Colwill (Owner).
(T) 01299 896600
Profile: FT: Coarse; **WN:** Witley Fishery; **WT:** Combination (Still). **Location:** **Nr. Rd:** B4196, Witley Court; **Main Rd:** A451.
Ref: FH5448

WITLEY POOLS
Witley Pools, Witley Court, Great Witley, Worcester, **WORCESTERSHIRE**, WR6, **England**.
Contact/s: **Mr Stan Lewis** (Manager), S Lewis Fishing Tackle, 2 Severnside South, Bewdley, Worcestershire, DY12 2DX.
(T) 01299 403358
Ms Pat Pain.
(T) 01299 896564
Profile: FT: Coarse; **WN:** Whitley; **WT:** Lake (Still); **F. Size:** 6 Acres; **W. Size:** 5 Acres. **Location:** **Nr. Rd:** A443, Stourport to Martley; **Main Rd:** B4194, A451.
Ref: FH5449

WITTON BROOK
Witton Brook, Northwich, **CHESHIRE**, CW9, **England**.
Contact/s: **Mr J Clitheroe** (Secretary), Northwich Angling Association, PO Box 18, Northwich, Cheshire, CW9 5SE.
(T) 01606 75132
Profile: FT: Coarse; **WN:** Witton; **WT:** Brook (Moving).
Ref: FH5450

WITTON CASTLE LAKES
Witton Castle Lakes, Bishop Auckland, **COUNTY DURHAM**, DL1, **England**.
Contact/s: **Mr John Winter** (Secretary), Bishop Auckland and District Angling Club, 7 Royal Gr, Crook, County Durham, DL15 9ER.
(T) 01388 762538 **(F)** 01388 767762
Profile: FT: Game; **WN:** Witton Castle; **WT:** Gravel Pit (Still); **F. Size:** 80 Acres; **W. Size:** 14 Acres. **Location:** **Main Rd:** A68; **Rail:** Bishop Auckland.
Ref: FH5451

WNION (RIVER)
Wnion (River), Hengwrt & Newmill, Rhydymain, Dolgellau, **GWYNEDD**, **Wales**.
Contact/s: **Mr John Turner** (Hon Secretary), Prince Albert Angling Society, 15 Pexhill Drive, Macclesfield, Cheshire, SK10 3LP.
(T) 01625 422010
Profile: FT: Game; **WN:** Wnion; **WT:** River (Moving) **W. Size:** 4000 Metres. **Location:** **Nr. Rd:** A494; **Rail:** Machynlleth.
Ref: FH5452

WNION (RIVER)
River Wnion, Ganllwyd, Dolgellau, **GWYNEDD**, LL40, **Wales**.
Contact/s: **Mr J**

Dolmelynllyn Hall Hotel Barkwith (Angling Manager), Dolmelynllyn Hall Hotel, Ganllwyd, Dolgellau, Gwynedd, LL40 2HP.
(T) 01341 440273
Profile: FT: Game; **WN:** Mawddach; **WT:** River (Moving) **W. Size:** 16000 Metres.
Ref: FH5453

WOBURN CLOSE LAKE
Woburn Close Lake, St Ives, Hemingford Grey, Huntingdon, **CAMBRIDGESHIRE**, PE17, **England**.
Contact/s: **Mr Jim Eggett**, Woburn Cl, Meadow Lane, Hemingford Grey, St Ives, Cambridgeshire.
(T) 01480 62623
Profile: FT: Coarse; **WN:** Woburn Close; **WT:** Gravel Pit (Still) **W. Size:** 3 Acres.
Ref: FH5454

WOBURN SANDS
Woburn Sands, 88 Langford Drive, Luton, **BEDFORDSHIRE**, LU, **England**.
Contact/s: **Mr B Matthews** (Secretary), Vauxhall Motors Angling Club, 88 Langford Drive, Luton, Bedfordshire.
(T) 01582 419489
Profile: FT: Coarse; **WN:** Woburn Sands; **WT:** Gravel Pit (Still) **W. Size:** 10 Acres. **Location:** **Main Rd:** B557.
Ref: FH5455

WOLVERTON LAKES
Wolverton Lakes, Stratford Rd, Wolverton, Milton Keynes, **BUCKINGHAMSHIRE**, MK, **England**.
Contact/s: **Mr Kv Osborne** (Secretary), Milton Keynes Angling Association, 11 Gilpin Way, Olney, Buckinghamshire, MK46 4DN.
(T) 01234 713144
Profile: FT: Coarse; **WN:** Wolverton; **WT:** Lake (Still) **W. Size:** 2 Acres.
Ref: FH5456

WOMBWELL DAM
Wombwell Dam, Wombwell, Barnsley, **YORKSHIRE (SOUTH)**, S73, **England**.
Contact/s: **Mr Allan Hanson** (Manager).
(T) 01226 292579

Profile: FT: Coarse; **WN:** Wombwell; **WT:** Mill Dam (Still).
Ref: FH5457

WOOD FARM CARAVAN PARK

Wood Farm Caravan Park, Charmouth, Bridport, **DORSET**, DT6, **England**.
Contact/s: Mr Ian Pointing.
(T) 01297 560697
Profile: FT: Coarse; **WN:** Wood Farm Caravan Park; **WT:** Pond (Still) **W. Size:** 1 Acre. **Location:** Nr. Rd: Charmouth roundabout; **Main Rd:** A35 to Bridport.
Ref: FH5458

WOOD POOL

Wood Pool, Tansor, Oundle, Peterborough, **CAMBRIDGESHIRE**, PE8 5HN, **England**.
Contact/s: Mr Tony Bridgefoot (Owner).
(T) 01832 226042
Profile: FT: Coarse; **WN:** Wood; **WT:** Pool (Still); **F. Size:** 108 Acres. **Location:** Nr. Rd: Tansor to Fotheringhay; **Main Rd:** A605; **Rail:** Peterborough.
Ref: FH5459

WOOD POOL

Wood Pool, Gawsworth Hall, Church Lane, Macclesfield, **CHESHIRE**, SK11 9RN, **England**.
Contact/s: Mr John Birch.
(T) 01260 223442
Profile: FT: Coarse; **WN:** Wood; **WT:** Pool (Still). **Location:** Nr. Rd: Church Lane; **Main Rd:** A536, Congleton Road.
Ref: FH5460

WOOD POOL

Wood Pool, Faversham, **KENT**, **England**.
(W) www.midkentfish.demon.co.uk
Contact/s: Mr Chris Logsdon (Fisheries Manager), Mid Kent Fisheries, Chilham Water Mill, Mill Lane, Chilham, CT4 8EE.
(T) 01227 730668
(E) chilham@midkentfisheries.co.uk
Profile: FT: Coarse; **WN:** Wod Pool; **WT:** Gravel Pit (Still); **F. Size:** 30 Acres; **W. Size:** 5 Acres. **Location:** Main Rd: A2; **Rail:** Faversham.
Ref: FH5461

WOOD POOL

Wood Pool, Anchor Lane, Harvington, Evesham, **WORCESTERSHIRE**, WR11 5NR, **England**.
Contact/s: Mr David Byrd (Fishery Manager), Manor Farm Leisure, Herons Roost, Anchor Lane, Evesham, WR11 5NR.
(T) 01386 870039
Profile: FT: Coarse; **WN:** Wood; **WT:** Pool (Still). **Location:** Nr. Rd: Anchor Lane; **Main Rd:** B4088.
Ref: FH5462

WOODA FARM FISHERY

Wooda Farm Fishery, Pancrasweek, Holsworthy, **DEVON**, EX22, **England**.
Contact/s: Mr P Brown.
(T) 01409 241292
Profile: FT: Game; **WN:** Wooda; **WT:** Lake (Still). **Location:** Nr. Rd: Pancrasweek.
Ref: FH5463

WOODACOTT ARMS

Woodacott Arms, Woodacott Cross, Thornbury, Holsworthy, **DEVON**, EX22 7BT, **England**.
Contact/s: Mr Len Sanders (Owner).
(T) 01409 261358 **(F)** 01409 261358
Profile: FT: Coarse; **WN:** Woodacott Arms; **WT:** Lake (Still) **W. Size:** 2 Acres. **Location:** Nr. Rd: Holsworthy to Thornbury; **Main Rd:** A3072.
Ref: FH5464

WOODALLS POND

Woodalls Pond, Newport, Brough, **HUMBERSIDE**, HU15, **England**.
Contact/s: Mr Woodall.
(T) 01430 441127
Profile: FT: Coarse; **WN:** Woodalls; **WT:** Pond (Still) **W. Size:** 2 Acres. **Location:** Nr. Rd: North Cave to Gilberdyke; **Main Rd:** M62, junction 38.
Ref: FH5465

WOODBANK PARK POOL

Woodbank Park Pool, Offerton, Stockport, **MANCHESTER (GREATER)**, SK2, **England**.
Profile: FT: Coarse; **WN:** Woodbank Park; **WT:** Pool (Still). **Location:** Nr. Rd: Offerton.
Ref: FH5466

WOODBOROUGH PARK LAKE

Woodborough Park Lake, Midsomer Morton, Bath, **SOMERSET**, BA3, **England**.
Contact/s: Mr Dave Crookes (Secretary).
(T) 01275 343928
Profile: FT: Coarse; **WN:** Woodborough; **WT:** Lake (Still). **Location:** Nr. Rd: Midsomer Morton; **Main Rd:** A367, Bath.
Ref: FH5467

WOODBURN ANGLING CLUB

Woodburn Angling Club, 544 Upper Rd, Woodburn, Carrickfergus, **COUNTY ANTRIM**, BT38, **Northern Ireland**.
Contact/s: Mr W Moore.
Profile: FT: Combination; **WN:** Woodburn Angling Club; **WT:** Combination (Still).
Ref: FH5468

WOODCHURCH TROUT FISHERY

Woodchurch Trout Fishery, Townland Farm, Front Rd, Woodchurch, Ashford, **KENT**, TN26 3SA, **England**.
Contact/s: Mr Ian Douglas.
(T) 01233 860253
Profile: FT: Game; **WN:** Woodchurch Trout Fishery; **WT:** Lake (Still) **W. Size:** 4 Acres. **Location:** Nr. Rd: Front Road; **Main Rd:** B2067.
Ref: FH5469

WOODCOTE HALL

Woodcote Hall, Telford, **SHROPSHIRE**, TF2 9JU, **England**.
Contact/s: Mr Alby Edwards.
(T) 01952 610497 **(F)** 01952 610497
Profile: FT: Coarse; **WN:** Woodcote Hall; **WT:** Pond (Still); **F. Size:** 8 Acres; **W. Size:** 4 Acres. **Location:** Nr. Rd: A41; **Main Rd:** A41; **Rail:** Telford.
Ref: FH5470

WOODEN LOCH

Wooden Loch, Eckford, Kelso, **SCOTTISH BORDERS**, TD5, **Scotland**.
Contact/s: Loch Keeper, The Cottage, Eckford, Crailing, Scottish Borders.
Profile: FT: Game; **WN:** Wooden; **WT:** Loch (Still). **Location:** Nr. Rd: A698; **Main Rd:** A68 from Jedburgh.
Ref: FH5471

WOODEND QUARRY POND

Woodend Quarry Pond, Worksop, **NOTTINGHAMSHIRE**, S80, **England**.
Contact/s: Mr R Pimlott (Secretary), Coventry and District Angling Association, 111 Lord Litton Avenue, Stoke, Coventry, CV2 5JT.
(T) 024 76454225
Profile: FT: Coarse; **WN:** Woodend; **WT:** Pond (Still) **W. Size:** 2 Acres.
Ref: FH5472

WOODFOLD FARM FISHERIES

Woodfold Farm Fisheries, Woodfold Farm, Whitechapel, Goosnargh, Preston, **LANCASHIRE**, PR3 2ES, **England**.
Contact/s: Mr John Cornthwaite.
(T) 01995 640347 **(F)** 01995 640347 **(M)** 07711 411 542
Profile: FT: Coarse; **WN:** Woodfold Farm Fisheries; **WT:** Pond (Still); **F. Size:** 9 Acres; **W. Size:** 6 Acres. **Location:** Nr. Rd: Bleasdale Road; **Main Rd:** A6; **Rail:** Preston.
Ref: FH5473

WOODFORD FISHERY

Woodford Fishery, Carrickfergus, **COUNTY ANTRIM**, BT38 8PX, **Northern Ireland**.
Contact/s: J F Reid, Woodford Fly and Bait Fishery and Tackle Shop, 12c Woodburn Rd, Carrickfergus, County Antrim, BT38 8PX.
(T) 028 93360225
Profile: FT: Game; **WN:** Woodford Fishery; **WT:** Combination (Still); **F. Size:** 20 Acres; **W. Size:** 9 Acres. **Location:** Nr. Rd: Woodburn Road; **Main Rd:** Belfast Road; **Rail:** Clipperstown.
Ref: FH5474

WOODHOUSE FISH FARM

Woodhouse Fish Farm, Woodhouse Farm, Swan Rd, Newton-Le-Willows, **MERSEYSIDE**, WA12 0EZ, **England**.
Contact/s: Mr Colin Wood (Manager).
(T) 01925 225200
Profile: FT: Game; **WN:** Woodhouse Fish Farm; **WT:** Lake (Still). **Location:** Nr. Rd: Swan Road.
Ref: FH5475

WOODINGTON FISHERY

Woodington Fishery, Romsey Rd, West Wellow, Romsey, **HAMPSHIRE**, S051, **England**.
(W) www.woodington.fsbusiness.co.uk
Contact/s: Mr Dan Casey (Owner).
(T) 020 84070981
(E) caseyd@globalnet.co.uk
Profile: FT: Game; **WN:** Kingfisher, Shearwater, Keepers, & Top Lake; **WT:** Lake (Still); **F. Size:** 30 Acres. **Location:** Nr. Rd: Whinwhistle Road; **Main Rd:** A36; **Rail:** Romsey.
Ref: FH5476

WOODLAKES FISHERY

Woodlakes Fishery, Woodlakes Leisure Park, Holme Rd, Stow Bridge, King's Lynn, **NORFOLK**, PE34 3PX, **England**.
Contact/s: Mr Andy Newman (Manager).
(T) 01553 810414 **(F)** 01553 810817
Profile: FT: Coarse; **WN:** Woodlakes Fishery; **WT:** Combination (Still); **F. Size:** 66 Acres; **W. Size:** 37 Acres. **Location:** Nr. Rd: Holme Road; **Main Rd:** A10; **Rail:** Downham Market.
Ref: FH5477

WOODLAND FARM

Woodland Farm, Grendon Underwood, Aylesbury, **HERTFORDSHIRE**, HP1, **England**.
Contact/s: Mr Alan Ditchburn (Fishery Manager).
(T) 01296 770072
Profile: FT: Coarse; **WN:** Woodland Farm; **WT:** Lake (Still).
Ref: FH5478

WOODLAND LAKES

Woodland Lakes, Cartlon Miniott, Thirsk, **YORKSHIRE (NORTH)**, YO7 4NJ, **England**.
Contact/s: Mr Robin Fletcher (Owner).
(T) 01845 527099 **(M)** 07831 824870
Profile: FT: Coarse; **WN:** Woodland; **WT:** Lake (Still) **W. Size:** 22 Acres. **Location:** Nr. Rd: A61; **Main Rd:** A61; **Rail:** Thirsk.
Ref: FH5479

WOODLAND PARK

Woodland Park (The), Brokerswood, Westbury, **WILTSHIRE**, BA13 4EH, **England**.
Contact/s: Mrs S H Capon.
(T) 01373 822238 **(F)** 01373 858474
Ms Trish Coley (Park Manager).
(T) 01373 822238 **(F)** 01373 858474
(E) woodland.park@virgin.net
Profile: FT: Coarse; **WN:** Woodland Park (The); **WT:** Dam (Still); **F. Size:** 6 Acres; **W. Size:** 5 Acres. **Location:** Main Rd: A36; **Rail:** Westbury.
Ref: FH5480

WOODLAND VIEW

Woodland View, Preston Innovations, Ombersley, Droitwich, **WORCESTERSHIRE**, TF1, **England**.
Contact/s: Mr Mike Mason (Fishery Manager).

(T) 01905 621521or620872
Profile: **FT:** Coarse; **WN:** Woodland View; **WT:** Pool (Still) **W. Size:** 5 Acres. **Location:** **Nr. Rd:** A4133; **Main Rd:** A4133.
Ref: FH5481

WOODLAND WATERS

Woodland Waters, Ancaster, Grantham, **LINCOLNSHIRE**, NG32, **England**.
Contact/s: **Mr Malcolm Corradine** (Owner).
(T) 01400 230888
Profile: **FT:** Coarse; **WN:** Woodland Waters; **WT:** Lake (Still); **F. Size:** 72 Acres; **W. Size:** 22 Acres. **Location:** **Main Rd:** A153.
Ref: FH5482

WOODLANDS FISHERY

Woodlands Fishery, Ashby Rd, Spilsby, **LINCOLNSHIRE**, PE23 5DW, **England**.
Contact/s: **Mr Chris Sibley**.
(T) 01709 754252
Profile: **FT:** Coarse; **WN:** Woodlands Fishery; **WT:** Lake (Still).
Ref: FH5483

WOODLANDS LAKE

Woodlands Lake, Allostock, Knutsford, **CHESHIRE**, WA16, **England**.
Contact/s: **J T Lovatt**.
Mr John Turner (Hon Secretary), Prince Albert Angling Society, 15 Pexhill Drive, Macclesfield, Cheshire, SK10 3LP.
(T) 01625 422010
Profile: **FT:** Coarse; **WN:** Woodlands; **WT:** Lake (Still) **W. Size:** 10 Acres. **Location:** **Main Rd:** M6.
Ref: FH5484

WOODLANDS LAKE

Woodlands Lake, Gainsborough, **LINCOLNSHIRE**, DN21, **England**.
Contact/s: Chief Bailiff.
(T) 01427 628356
Profile: **FT:** Coarse; **WN:** Woodlands; **WT:** Lake (Still) **W. Size:** 1 Acre.
Ref: FH5485

WOODLAY HOLIDAY LAKES

Woodlay Holiday Lakes, Herodsfoot, Liskeard, **CORNWALL**, PL14 4RB, **England**.
Mr K J Hawke.
(T) 01503 220221 (F) 01503 220802
Profile: **FT:** Coarse; **WN:** Woodlay; **WT:** Lake (Still); **F. Size:** 15 Acres; **W. Size:** 5 Acres. **Location:** **Nr. Rd:** B3359; **Main Rd:** B3359; **Rail:** Liskeard.
Ref: FH5486

WOODMANCOTE PLACE FISHERY

Woodmancote Place Fishery, Brighton, **SUSSEX (EAST)**, BN1, **England**.
Contact/s: Manager.
(T) 01273 492941
Profile: **FT:** Coarse; **WN:** Woodmancote Place Fishery; **WT:** Lake (Still).
Ref: FH5487

WOODMILL SALMON FISHERY

Woodmill Salmon Fishery, Woodmill Lane, Swaythling, Southampton, **HAMPSHIRE**, SO18 2JR, **England**.
Contact/s: **Mr Andrew Hawkins**.
(T) 023 80555993 (F) 023 80556641 (M) 07831 403792
Profile: **FT:** Game; **WN:** Itchen; **WT:** Combination (Moving); **F. Size:** 12 Acres; **W. Size:** 5 Acres. **Location:** **Nr. Rd:** Woodmill Lane; **Main Rd:** A335; **Rail:** Swaythling.
Ref: FH5488

WOODRISING WATER MEADOWS

Cranworth Carp Lakes, Cranworth, Thetford, **NORFOLK**, IP25, **England**.
Contact/s: **Mr Richard Bunning** (Manager).
(T) 01362 820702
Profile: **FT:** Coarse; **WN:** Woodrising; **WT:** Lake (Still) **W. Size:** 2 Acres. **Location:** **Main Rd:** B1108, Watton to Scoulton.
Ref: FH5489

WOODROW FISH POND

Woodrow Fish Pond, Forest Lane, Hanbury, Bromsgrove, **WORCESTERSHIRE**, B60 4HP, **England**.
Contact/s: **Mr P Platt**, Woodrow Farm, Hanbury, Bromsgrove, Worcestershire, B60 4BU.
(T) 01527 821204
Profile: **FT:** Coarse; **WN:** Woodrow; **WT:** Pond (Still) **W. Size:** 2 Acres. **Location:** **Nr. Rd:** B4091, Forest Lane; **Main Rd:** A38.
Ref: FH5490

WOODSEAT LAKE

Woodseat Lake, Uttoxeter, **STAFFORDSHIRE**, ST14, **England**.
Contact/s: Fishery Manager.
(T) 01889 593841
Profile: **FT:** Coarse; **WN:** Woodseat; **WT:** Lake (Still).
Ref: FH5491

WOODSETTS QUARRY POND

Woodsetts Quarry Pond, Worksop, **NOTTINGHAMSHIRE**, S81, **England**.
Contact/s: **Mr R Whitehead** (Secretary), Worksop and District Angling Association, 72 Dryden Walk, Worksop, Nottinghamshire.
(T) 01909 486350
Profile: **FT:** Coarse; **WN:** Woodsetts; **WT:** Pond (Still) **W. Size:** 8 Acres.
Ref: FH5492

WOODSIDE POOL

Woodside Pool, Runcorn, **CHESHIRE**, WA7, **England**.
Contact/s: **Mr Neil Jupp** (Club Secretary), Lymm Angling Club, PO Box 350, Warrington, Cheshire, WA2 9FB.
(T) 01925 411744
Profile: **FT:** Coarse; **WN:** Woodside; **WT:** Pool (Still) **W. Size:** 1 Acre. **Location:** **Nr. Rd:** A533 to Runcorn; **Main Rd:** A49 to Whitley.
Ref: FH5493

WOODSLEE POOL

Woodslee Pool, Brotherton Park, Spital, Bebington, Wirral, **MERSEYSIDE**, CH63, **England**.
Contact/s: **Mr Billing**.
(T) 0151 3343174
Profile: **FT:** Coarse; **WN:** Woodslee; **WT:** Pool (Still).
Ref: FH5494

WOODSTOCK POOL

Woodstock Pool, Cymbran, Newport, NP, **Wales**.
Contact/s: .
(T) 01633 6642231
L J Clarke, Newport Angling Association, 14 Allt-yr-yn- Avenue, Newport, Wales, NP9 5DB.
(T) 01633 212953
Profile: **FT:** Coarse; **WN:** Woodstock; **WT:** Pool (Still) **W. Size:** 2 Acres. **Location:** **Nr. Rd:** A4042.
Ref: FH5495

WOODSTON MANOR POOLS

Woodston Manor Pools, Lindridge, Tenbury Wells, **WORCESTERSHIRE**, WR15, **England**.
Contact/s: **Mr John Walker**.
(T) 01584 881223
Profile: **FT:** Coarse; **WN:** Woodston Manor; **WT:** Pool (Still) **W. Size:** 1 Acre. **Location:** **Nr. Rd:** Lindridge to Newham; **Main Rd:** A443.
Ref: FH5496

WOODTHORPE HALL LAKE

Woodthorpe Hall Lake, Alford, **LINCOLNSHIRE**, LN13, **England**.
Contact/s: Fishery Manager.
(T) 01507 450294
Profile: **FT:** Coarse; **WN:** Woodthorpe Hall; **WT:** Lake (Still).
Ref: FH5497

WOODY PARK FISHERY

Woody Park Fishery, Radfield, Willand, Cullompton, **DEVON**, EX15 2RB, **England**.
Contact/s: Fishery Manager.
(T) 01884 35515
Profile: **FT:** Coarse; **WN:** Woody Park Fishery; **WT:** Lake (Still).
Ref: FH5498

WOOLBRIDGE MANOR

Woolbridge Manor, Frome, **SOMERSET**, BA11, **England**.
Contact/s: **Mr Bowerman**, Morden Estate Office, Charbourgh Park, Wimborne, Dorset, BH21.
Profile: **FT:** Game; **WN:** Woolbridge Manor; **WT:** River (Moving) **W. Size:** 2000 Metres.
Ref: FH5499

WOOLPACK FISHERY

Woolpack Fishery, Cow Lane, Godmanchester, Huntingdon, **CAMBRIDGESHIRE**, PE18, **England**.
Contact/s: **Mr Stan J Binge** (Manager), Stanjay Fishing Tackle and Trophies, 7 Old Court Wall, Godmanchester, Huntingdon, PE18 8HS.
(T) 01480 453303
Profile: **FT:** Coarse; **WN:** Ouse; **WT:** Combination (Still & Moving); **F. Size:** 70 Acres; **W. Size:** 1200 Metres. **Location:** **Nr. Rd:** Cow Lane.
Ref: FH5500

WOOLWICH DOCKYARD

Woolwich Dockyard, Woolwich, London, **LONDON (GREATER)**, SE18 5, **England**.
Contact/s: **Mr D R Etherington**, Woolwich Dockyard Angling Club, 6 Maud Cashmore Way, Woolwich, London, SE18 5QS.
(T) 020 88557849 (M) 07932 384690
Mr Staurt Smith (Secretary), Woolwich Dockyard Angling Club, 1 Resolution Walk, Woolwich Dockyard, London, SE18 5QS.
Profile: **FT:** Coarse; **WN:** Woolwich Docks; **WT:** Lake (Still) **W. Size:** 2 Acres. **Location:** **Nr. Rd:** Woolwich Road; **Rail:** Woolwich Dockyard.
Ref: FH5501

WOONSMITH LAKE

Woonsmith Lake, Mancledra, Penzance, **CORNWALL**, TR, **England**.
Contact/s: **Dr C Franklin** (Fishery Manager), St Ives Freshwater Angling Society, Chy-Am-Meor, Westward Rd, St Ives, TR26 1JX.
(T) 01736 798251
Profile: **FT:** Coarse; **WN:** Woonsmith; **WT:** Lake (Still) **W. Size:** 2 Acres. **Location:** **Nr. Rd:** St Ives to Penzance; **Main Rd:** B3311; **Rail:** Penzance.
Ref: FH5502

WOOTTON BROOK LAKE

Wootton Brook Lake, Shelfleys, West Hunsbury, Northampton, **NORTHAMPTONSHIRE**, NN, **England**.
Contact/s: **Mr Terry Rodhouse** (Secretary), Castle Angling Association, 12 Somerville Rd, Daventry, Northamptonshire, NN11 4RT.
(T) 01327 705692
Profile: **FT:** Coarse; **WN:** Wootton Brook; **WT:** Lake (Still) **W. Size:** 3 Acres. **Location:** **Main Rd:** A45; **Rail:** Northampton.
Ref: FH5503

WORKSHOP POND

Workshop Pond, Alerton Bywater, Castleford, **YORKSHIRE (WEST)**, WF10, **England**.
Contact/s: Secretary.
(T) 01977 550809
Profile: **FT:** Coarse; **WN:** Workshop; **WT:** Pond (Still) **W. Size:** 5 Acres. **Location:** **Nr. Rd:** A1; **Main Rd:** Fairburn Ings.
Ref: FH5504

WORMLEBURY

Wormlebury, Wormleybury House, Church

Lane, Broxbourne, **HERTFORDSHIRE**, EN10, **England**.
Contact/s: **Mr Graham Barnes**.
Profile: **FT:** Coarse; **WN:** Wormlebury; **WT:** Lake (Still) **W. Size:** 5 Acres. Location: **Nr. Rd:** A1170; **Main Rd:** A10.
Ref: FH5505

WORSBOROUGH RESERVOIR

Worsborough Reservoir, Sheffield Rd, Worsborough, Barnsley, **YORKSHIRE (SOUTH)**, **England**.
Contact/s: **Mr Tony Eaton** (Club Secretary), 60 Walton St, Gawber, Barnsley, Yorkshire (South), S75 2PD.
(T) 01226 203090
Profile: **FT:** Coarse; **WN:** Worsborough; **WT:** Reservoir (Still); **F. Size:** 16 Acres; **W. Size:** 15 Acres. Location: **Nr. Rd:** Sheffield Road (A61); **Rail:** Barnsley.
Ref: FH5506

WORSBROUGH CANAL

Worsbrough Canal, Barnsley, **YORKSHIRE (SOUTH)**, S73, **England**.
Contact/s: Temporary Secretary, Wombwell Angling Ctre, 25 Barnsley Rd, Wombwell, Barnsley, S73 8HT.
(T) 01226 750659
Profile: **FT:** Coarse; **WN:** Worsbrough; **WT:** Canal (Still). Location: **Nr. Rd:** B6100; **Main Rd:** A61.
Ref: FH5507

WORSBROUGH RESERVOIR

Worsbrough Reservoir, Worsbrough Country Park, Barnsley, **YORKSHIRE (SOUTH)**, S70, **England**.
Contact/s: **Mr Tony Eaton** (Secretary), Barnsley and District Ammalgamated Angling Society, 60 Wolton St, Gawber, Barnsley, S75 2PD.
(T) 01226 203090
Profile: **FT:** Coarse; **WN:** Worsbrough; **WT:** Reservoir (Still) **W. Size:** 15 Acres. Location: **Main Rd:** Sheffield Road; **Rail:** Barnsley.
Ref: FH5508

WORTHENBURY BROOK

Worthenbury Brook, Worthenbury, Wrexham, LL13, **Wales**.
Contact/s: **Mr Frank Lythgoe** (Secretary), Warrington Angling Association, 52 Parker St, Warrington, Lancashire.
(T) 01928 716238 (F) 01928 713898
(E) info@warrington-anglers.org.uk
Profile: **FT:** Game; **WN:** Dee; **WT:** River (Moving) **W. Size:** 462 Metres.
Ref: FH5509

WORTHINGTON NO 1

Worthington No 1, Chorley, **LANCASHIRE**, PR, **England**.
(W) www.wiganaa.f9.co.uk
Contact/s: **Mr Gerry Wilson** (Hon Secretary), Wigan and District Angling Association, 11 Guildford Avenue, Chorley, Lancashire, PR6 8TG.
(T) 01257 265905
(E) gerry@wiganna.freeserve.co.uk
Mr Roy Rhodes (Conservation, Access and Recreation Manager), Rivington Water Treatment Works, Bolton Rd, Horwich, Bolton, BL6 7RN.
(T) 01204 664300
Profile: **FT:** Coarse; **WN:** Worthington No 1; **WT:** Lake (Still) **W. Size:** 5 Acres. Location: **Nr. Rd:** A5106; **Main Rd:** Junction 27, M6.
Ref: FH5510

WORTHINGTON NO 2

Worthington No 2, Chorley, **LANCASHIRE**, PR, **England**.
(W) www.wiganaa.f9.co.uk
Contact/s: **Mr Gerry Wilson** (Hon Secretary), Wigan and District Angling Association, 11 Guildford Avenue, Chorley, Lancashire, PR6 8TG.
(T) 01257 265905
Mr Roy Rhodes (Conservation, Access and Recreation Manager), Rivington Water Treatment Works, Bolton Rd, Horwich, Bolton, BL6 7RN.
(T) 01204 664300
(E) gerry@wiganna.freeserve.co.uk
Profile: **FT:** Coarse; **WN:** Worthington No 2; **WT:** Lake (Still) **W. Size:** 7 Acres. Location: **Nr. Rd:** A5106; **Main Rd:** Junction 27, M6.
Ref: FH5511

WORTHINGTON NO 3

Worthington No 3, Chorley, **LANCASHIRE**, PR, **England**.
(W) www.wiganaa.f9.co.uk
Contact/s: **Mr Gerry Wilson** (Hon Secretary), Wigan and District Angling Association, 11 Guildford Avenue, Chorley, Lancashire, PR6 8TG.
(T) 01257 265905
(E) gerry@wiganna.freeserve.co.uk
Mr Roy Rhodes (Conservation, Access and Recreation Manager), Rivington Water Treatment Works, Bolton Rd, Horwich, Bolton, BL6 7RN.
(T) 01204 664300
Profile: **FT:** Coarse; **WN:** Worthington No 3; **WT:** Lake (Still) **W. Size:** 3 Acres. Location: **Nr. Rd:** A5106; **Main Rd:** Junction 27, M6.
Ref: FH5512

WRAYSBURY ONE

Wraysbury One, Douglas Lane, Wraysbury, Staines, London, **LONDON (GREATER)**, TW19, **England**.
(W) www.rmcangling.co.uk
Contact/s: **Mr Ian Welch** (Angling Manager), RMC Angling, The Square, Lightwater, Surrey, GU18 5SS.
(T) 01276 453300 (F) 01276 456611
(E) info@rmcangling.co.uk
Profile: **FT:** Coarse; **WN:** Wraysbury; **WT:** Gravel Pit (Still) **W. Size:** 120 Acres. Location: **Nr. Rd:** B276, Douglas Lane; **Main Rd:** M25, junction 13; **Rail:** Wraysbury.
Ref: FH5513

WRAYSBURY TWO

Wraysbury Two, Station Rd, Wraysbury, Staines, London, **LONDON (GREATER)**, TW19, **England**.
(W) www.rmcangling.co.uk
Contact/s: **Mr Ian Welch** (Angling Manager), RMC Angling, The Square, Lightwater, Surrey, GU18 5SS.
(T) 01276 453300 (F) 01276 456611
(E) info@rmcangling.co.uk
Profile: **FT:** Coarse; **WN:** Wraysbury; **WT:** Gravel Pit (Still) **W. Size:** 140 Acres. Location: **Nr. Rd:** Station Road; **Main Rd:** M25, junction 14; **Rail:** Wraysbury.
Ref: FH5514

WREAKE (RIVER)

River Wreake, Melton Mowbray, **LEICESTERSHIRE**, LE13, **England**.
Contact/s: **Mr R Fossey** (Secretary), Leicester and District Amalgamated Society of Anglers, 431 Gleneagles Avenue, Rushley Mead, Leicester, LE67.
(T) 0116 2666911
Profile: **FT:** Coarse; **WN:** Wreake; **WT:** River (Moving) **W. Size:** 4500 Metres.
Ref: FH5515

WREIGH (RIVER)

River Wreigh, Thropton, **NORTHUMBERLAND**, **England**.
Contact/s: **Mr Colin Bell** (Treasurer), Rothbury and Thropton Angling Club, 1 Silverdale Cottages, Snitter, Morpeth, NE65 7EL.
(T) 01669 621083
Profile: **FT:** Game; **WN:** Wreigh; **WT:** River (Moving) **W. Size:** 1000 Metres. Location: **Nr. Rd:** B6344; **Main Rd:** A697; **Rail:** Morpeth.
Ref: FH5516

WRIGHTS FARM

Wrights Farm, Middleton Rd, Sudbury, **SUFFOLK**, CO10, **England**.
Contact/s: **Mr Rob Hayward** (Manager), Sudbury Angling Ctre, 1 Acton Sq, Sudbury, Suffolk, CO10 1HG.
(T) 01787 312118
Mr Trevor Fairless (Secretary), Sudbury and District Angling Association, 39 Pot Kiln Rd, Sudbury, Suffolk, CO10 0DG.
(T) 01787 312536
Profile: **FT:** Coarse; **WN:** Stour (Suffolk); **WT:** River (Moving) **W. Size:** 750 Metres. Location: **Nr. Rd:** Middleton Road; **Main Rd:** A131; **Rail:** Sudbury.
Ref: FH5517

WRITES LOUGH

Writes Lough, Castlewellan, **COUNTY DOWN**, BT31, **Northern Ireland**.
Contact/s: **Mr J L Harty**, 22 Larchfield Park, Newcastle, County Down.
(T) 028 43726017after5.30pm
Profile: **FT:** Game; **WN:** Writes; **WT:** Lake (Still).
Ref: FH5518

WROUGHTON RESERVOIR

Wroughton Reservoir, Wroughton, Swindon, **WILTSHIRE**, SN, **England**.
Contact/s: , 20 St Johns Rd, Wroughton, Swindon, Wiltshire, SN4 9ED.
Mr Martin Drury (Manager), 82 Wharf Rd, Wroughton, Wiltshire.
(T) 01793 814261
Mr T Moulton (Secretary), 70 Perry's Lane, Wroughton, Swindon, Wiltshire, SN4 9AP.
(T) 01793 813155
Profile: **FT:** Coarse; **WN:** Wroughton; **WT:** Reservoir (Still).
Ref: FH5519

WROXHAM BROAD

Wroxham Broad, 175 Drayton Rd, Norwich, **NORFOLK**, NR, **England**.
Contact/s: Manager, Wroxham Angling Ctre, Station Rd, Hoveton, Norwich, NR12 8UR.
(T) 01603 782453
Mr Glen Hubbard (Manager).
(T) 01603 426834
Mr R Westgate (Club Secretary), Wroxham and District Angling Club, 31 The Paddocks, Old Catton, Norwich, NR6 7HF.
(T) 01603 401062 (F) 01603 897122 **(M)** 07885 644262
(E) wroxham.angling@virgin.net
Profile: **FT:** Coarse; **WN:** Bure; **WT:** Canal (Still).
Ref: FH5520

WRYE (RIVER)

River Wrye, St Michaels On Wrye, Preston, **LANCASHIRE**, PR3, **England**.
Profile: **FT:** Coarse; **WN:** Wyre; **WT:** River (Moving) **W. Size:** 1600 Metres. Location: **Nr. Rd:** A586; **Main Rd:** A585, M6.
Ref: FH5521

WULLIESTRUTHER LOCH

Wulliestruther Loch, Hawick, **SCOTTISH BORDERS**, TD9, **Scotland**.
Contact/s: **Mr Penman** (Manager), Pet Store, 1 Union St, Hawick, Scottish Borders, TD9 9LF.
(T) 01450 373543 (F) 01450 373543
Mr Eric Stewart (Secretary/Treasurer), Hawick Angling Club, 5 Sandbed, Hawick, Scottish Borders, TD9 0HE.
(T) 01450 373771
Profile: **FT:** Game; **WN:** Wulliestruther; **WT:** Loch (Still) **W. Size:** 8 Acres. Location: **Main Rd:** A7; **Rail:** Carlisle.
Ref: FH5522

WYATTS LAKE

Wyatts Lake, Westbrook, Bromham, Chippenham, **WILTSHIRE**, SN15 2EB, **England**.
Contact/s: **L Beale**.
(T) 01380 859651
Profile: **FT:** Coarse; **WN:** Wyatts; **WT:** Lake (Still) **W. Size:** 2 Acres.
Ref: FH5523

WYCH BROOK

Wych Brook, Halghton Mill, Worthenbury, **WREXHAM**, **England**.
Contact/s: **Mr John Turner** (Hon Secretary), Prince Albert Angling Society, 15 Pexhill Drive, Macclesfield, Cheshire, SK10 3LP.
(T) 01625 422010
Profile: **FT:** Coarse; **WN:** Wych; **WT:** Brook (Moving) **W. Size:** 1000 Metres. **Location:** **Nr. Rd:** B5069; **Rail:** Wrexham.
Ref: FH5524

WYCH ELM FISHERY

Wych Elm Fishery, Milnthorpe Rd, Carnforth, **CUMBRIA**, LA6 1PX, **England**.
Contact/s: **Mr Ken Ghille** (Manager).
(T) 01520 781449
Profile: **FT:** Game; **WN:** Wych Elm; **WT:** Lake (Still). **Location:** **Nr. Rd:** Milthorpe Road; **Main Rd:** M6, junctions 35 or 36.
Ref: FH5525

WYCH LODGE LAKE

Wych Lodge Lake, Taunton, **SOMERSET**, TA, **England**.
Contact/s: Manager, Topp Tackle, 63 Station Rd, Taunton, Somerset, TA1 1PA.
(T) 01823 282518
Mr K Gregson (Chairman).
(T) 01823 271264
Profile: **FT:** Coarse; **WN:** Wych Lodge; **WT:** Lake (Still) **W. Size:** 5 Acres. **Location:** **Nr. Rd:** Chard to Staple Fitzpaine Road; **Main Rd:** M5.
Ref: FH5526

WYE (RIVER)

River Wye, Bakewell, **DERBYSHIRE**, DE45, **England**.
Contact/s: Manager, Haddon Hall Estate, Bakewell, Derbyshire, DE45 1LA.
(T) 01629 812855
Profile: **FT:** Game; **WN:** Wye; **WT:** River (Moving).
Ref: FH5527

WYE (RIVER)

River Wye, Bakewell, **DERBYSHIRE**, DE45, **England**.
Contact/s: **Mr David Oakley** (manager), Chatsworth and Monsal Dale Fishery, The Estate Office, Edensor, Bakewell, Derbyshire DE45 1PJ.
(T) 01246 565300
Profile: **FT:** Game; **WN:** Wye; **WT:** River (Moving).
Ref: FH5528

WYE (RIVER)

River Wye, Peacock Hotel, Rawsley, Matlock, **DERBYSHIRE**, DE4 2EB, **England**.
Contact/s: **Mr Roger Hudson** (Manager), The Peacock Hotel, Rowsley, Matlock, Derbyshire, DE4 2EB.
(T) 01629 733518
Profile: **FT:** Game; **WN:** Wye; **WT:** River (Moving).
Ref: FH5529

WYE (RIVER)

Wye (River), Huntsham Bridge, Whitchurch, Ross-on-Wye, **HEREFORDSHIRE**, **England**.
Contact/s: **Mr John Turner** (Hon Secretary), Prince Albert Angling Society, 15 Pexhill Drive, Macclesfield, Cheshire, SK10 3LP.
(T) 01625 422010
Profile: **FT:** Combination; **WN:** Wye; **WT:** River (Moving) **W. Size:** 1200 Metres. **Location:** **Nr. Rd:** B4229; **Main Rd:** A40; **Rail:** Ross-On-Wye.
Ref: FH5530

WYE (RIVER)

River Wye, Lower Lydbrook, Symonds Yat, Ross-on-Wye, **HEREFORDSHIRE**, HR9, **England**.
Contact/s: Fishery Manager.
(T) 01432 344644
Mr G H Crouch (Secretary), Newport Angling Association, Greenway Cottage, Stowefield Rd, Lower Lydbrook, Gloucestershire.
(T) 01594 60048
Profile: **FT:** Combination; **WN:** Wye; **WT:** River (Moving) **W. Size:** 2400 Metres. **Location:** **Nr. Rd:** Goodrich to Symonds Yat.
Ref: FH5531

WYE (RIVER)

River Wye, Letton, Hereford, **HEREFORDSHIRE**, HR3, **England**.
Contact/s: Fishery Manager.
(T) 01544 327294
Profile: **FT:** Coarse; **WN:** Wye; **WT:** River (Moving).
Ref: FH5532

WYE (RIVER)

River Wye, Road Bridge, Hereford, **HEREFORDSHIRE**, HR, **England**.
Contact/s: Manager, Hattons Tackle Shop, 64 St Owen St, Hereford, Herefordshire, HR1 2PU.
Profile: **FT:** Combination; **WN:** Wye; **WT:** River (Moving). **Location:** **Nr. Rd:** Road Bridge; **Main Rd:** A49 to Hereford.
Ref: FH5533

WYE (RIVER)

River Wye, Glasbury, Hereford, **HEREFORDSHIRE**, HR3, **England**.
Contact/s: **Mr A Lloyd** (Information Contact), Bridgend Cottage, Glasbury on Wye, Hereford, Herefordshire, HR3 5NP.
(T) 01497 847227
Profile: **FT:** Game; **WN:** Wye; **WT:** River (Moving) **W. Size:** 1600 Metres.
Ref: FH5534

WYE (RIVER)

River Wye, Hereford, **HEREFORDSHIRE**, HR, **England**.
Contact/s: Fishery Manager.
(T) 01432 274152
Profile: **FT:** Coarse; **WN:** Wye; **WT:** River (Moving) **W. Size:** 1600 Metres. **Location:** **Main Rd:** B4224.
Ref: FH5535

WYE (RIVER)

River Wye, Wilton Bridge, Ross-on-Wye, **HEREFORDSHIRE**, HR9, **England**.
Contact/s: **Mr Alex Bloxham** (Manager).
(T) 01531 821126
Mr Les Bullock (Manager), GB Sports, 10 Broad St, Ross-on-Wye, Herefordshire, HR9 7EA.
(T) 01989 563723
Profile: **FT:** Coarse; **WN:** Wye; **WT:** River (Moving).
Ref: FH5536

WYE (RIVER)

River Wye, Wye Bridge, Monmouth, **MONMOUTHSHIRE**, NP25, **Wales**.
Contact/s: **Mr Roger Hudson** (Manager), The Peacock Hotel, Rowsley, Matlock, Derbyshire, DE4 2EB.
(T) 01629 733518
R J Gething (Secretary), Kennels Cottage, Ganarew, Monmouth, NP5 3SR.
(T) 01600 890047
Profile: **FT:** Combination; **WN:** Wye; **WT:** River (Moving).
Ref: FH5537

WYE (RIVER)

River Wye, Glanrhos, Llanwrthwl, Llandrindod Wells, **POWYS**, LD1 6NT, **Wales**.
Contact/s: **Mr C Easton** (Information Contact), Glanrhos, Llanwrthwl, Llandrindod Wells, Powys, LD1 6NT.
(T) 01597 810277
Profile: **FT:** Game; **WN:** Wye; **WT:** River (Moving) **W. Size:** 1200 Metres. **Location:** **Main Rd:** A470; **Rail:** Llandrindod Wells.
Ref: FH5538

WYE (RIVER)

River Wye, Rhayader, **POWYS**, LD6, **Wales**.
Contact/s: **Mr J Price** (Manager), Nant Y Mynach Farm, Nantmel, Powys, Wales.
(T) 01597 810491
Profile: **FT:** Game; **WN:** Wye; **WT:** River (Moving).
Ref: FH5539

WYE (RIVER)

River Wye, Llandrindod Wells, **POWYS**, LD1, **Wales**.
Contact/s: Manager, Wayfarers, Station Cres, Llandrindod Wells, Powys, LD1 5BD.
(T) 01597 825100
Mr A D Owen (Manager), Severn Arms Hotel, Penybont, Llandrindod Wells, Powys, LD1 5UA.
(T) 01597 851224 (F) 01597 851693
Profile: **FT:** Game; **WN:** Wye; **WT:** Tributary (Moving) **W. Size:** 8000 Metres. **Location:** **Nr. Rd:** Disserth to Llanyre Bridges.
Ref: FH5540

WYE (RIVER)

River Wye, Builth Wells, **POWYS**, LD2, **Wales**.
Contact/s: **Mr Lance Burton** (Secretary), Angler House, Pentrosfa, Cresent, Llandrindod Wells, Powys.
(T) 01597 823119
Mr M Morgan (Secretary), Groe Park and Irfon Angling Club, 23 Garth Rd, Builth Wells, Powys, LD2 3AR.
(T) 01982 552759
Profile: **FT:** Combination; **WN:** Wye; **WT:** River (Moving) **W. Size:** 2400 Metres. **Location:** **Main Rd:** At Builth Wells; **Rail:** Builth Road.
Ref: FH5541

WYE (RIVER)

River Wye, Rhayader, **POWYS**, LD6, **Wales**.
Contact/s: **Mr David Evans** (Secretary), Rhayader Angling Association, 72 Brynheulog, Rhayader, Powys, LD6 5EG.
(T) 01597 811404
Profile: **FT:** Game; **WN:** Wye; **WT:** River (Moving) **W. Size:** 8000 Metres.
Ref: FH5542

WYE (RIVER)

River Wye, Benhall Green, Saxmundham, **SUFFOLK**, IP17, **England**.
Contact/s: **Mr T Gibson** (Hon Secretary), 10 Redwood Cl, Ross-on-Wye, Herefordshire, HR9 5UD.
(T) 01989 567775
Profile: **FT:** Game; **WN:** Wye; **WT:** River (Moving) **W. Size:** 8000 Metres.
Ref: FH5543

WYKEHAM LAKES

Wykeham Lakes, Wykeham, Scarborough, **YORKSHIRE (NORTH)**, YO13 9Q, **England**.
Contact/s: **Mr Angus Young** (Manager).
(T) 01723 863148
Profile: **FT:** Game; **WN:** Wykeham; **WT:** Lake (Still) **W. Size:** 25 Acres.
Ref: FH5544

WYLANDS CENTRE

Wylands International Angling Centre, Wyland's Farm, Powdermill Lane, Catsfield, Battle, **SUSSEX (EAST)**, TN33 0SU, **England**.
(W) www.fisheries.co.uk/wylands
Contact/s: **Mr Colin Bourner** (Partner).
(T) 01424 893394 (F) 01424 893316
Mr Keith Harding (Partner).
(T) 01424 893394 (F) 01424 893316
(E) vg86@dial.pipex.com
Profile: **FT:** Game; **WN:** Wylands International Angling Centre; **WT:** Combination (Still); **F. Size:** 154 Acres; **W. Size:** 30 Acres. **Location:** **Nr. Rd:** A2100; **Main Rd:** A21; **Rail:** Battle.
Ref: FH5545

WYLIES LAKE

Wylies Lake, Thatcham, Newbury, **BERKSHIRE**, RG, **England**.
Contact/s: **Mr Dusty Millar** (Associate members secretary), 238 Elgar Road South,

Reading, Berkshire, RG3 0BW.
(T) 0118 9874882
Mr Mick Cox (Chief Bailiff), Dorstans, Hatch Lane, Brimpton Village, Reading, RG7 4TR.
(T) 0118 9714917
Profile: **FT:** Coarse; **WN:** Wylies; **WT:** Gravel Pit (Still) **W. Size:** 20 Acres. Location: **Nr. Rd:** Newbury to Thatcham; **Main Rd:** M4, junction 13.
Ref: FH5546

WYPHURST AND HYHURST LAKES

Wyphurst And Hyhurst Lakes, Amletts Lane, Cranleigh, **SURREY**, GU6, **England**.
Contact/s: Fishery Manager.
(T) 01483 271240
Mr Nick Bamford (Publicity Officer), Cranleigh Angling Club, 20 High St, Cranleigh, Surrey, GU6 8AE.
(T) 01483 274566
Mrs Sue Buxton, 5 Gingers Cl, Cranleigh, Surrey, GU6 7JL.
Profile: **FT:** Coarse; **WN:** Wyphurst and Hyhurst; **WT:** Lake (Still) **W. Size:** 1 Acre. Location: **Nr. Rd:** Amletts Lane; **Main Rd:** B2128; **Rail:** Guildford.
Ref: FH5547

WYRE (RIVER)

River Wyre, Fleetwood, **LANCASHIRE**, FY7, **England**.
Contact/s: **Mr Darren Fisher** (Manager), Bobs Tackle Shop, 35 Beach Rd, Thornton-Cleveleys, Lancashire, FY5 1EG.
(T) 01253 860616
Profile: **FT:** Coarse; **WN:** Wyre; **WT:** River (Moving).
Ref: FH5548

WYRE (RIVER)

Wrye (River), Ratten Row, Nr Great Eccleston, Kirkham, **LANCASHIRE**, **England**.
Contact/s: **Mr John Turner** (Hon Secretary), Prince Albert Angling Society, 15 Pexhill Drive, Macclesfield, Cheshire, SK10 3LP.
(T) 01625 422010
Profile: **FT:** Combination; **WN:** Wyre; **WT:** River (Moving) **W. Size:** 2000 Metres. Location: **Nr. Rd:** Rawcliffe Road; **Main Rd:** A586; **Rail:** Kirkham.
Ref: FH5549

WYRESIDE LAKES

Wyreside Lakes Fishery And Lodgings, Sunnyside Farm, Bay Horse, Lancaster, **LANCASHIRE**, LA2 9DG, **England**.
(W) www.wyresidelakes.co.uk
Contact/s: **Mr Bob Birkin** (Manager).
(T) 01524 792093
(E) info@wyresidelakes.co.uk
Profile: **FT:** Combination; **WN:** Wyreside Lakes Fishery And Lodgings; **WT:** Lake (Still) **W. Size:** 11 Acres. Location: **Nr. Rd:** Dolphinholme.
Ref: FH5550

WYRLEY ESSINGTON CANAL

Wyrley Essington Canal, Wednesfield, Wolverhampton, **SHROPSHIRE**, WV11, **England**.
Contact/s: **Mr J Stanhope** (Secretary), Swan Angling Club, 4 High Rd, Lane Head, Willenhall, WV12 4JQ.
(T) 01902 630110
Profile: **FT:** Coarse; **WN:** Wyrley Essington; **WT:** Canal (Still) **W. Size:** 6000 Metres.
Ref: FH5551

WYTHERINGTON FARM

Wytherington Farm, Salisbury, **WILTSHIRE**, SP, **England**.
Contact/s: **Mr Tony Beeny**.
(T) 01722 710021
Profile: **FT:** Coarse; **WN:** Wytherington Farm; **WT:** Lake (Still).
Ref: FH5552

Y2K LAKE

Y2K Lake, Wykeham, Scarborough, **YORKSHIRE (NORTH)**, YO13 9QP, **England**.
Contact/s: Fishery Manager.
(T) 01723 863148
Mr Angus (Bailiff). **(M)** 07901 647076
Mr Chris Tedman.
(T) 01723 866600
Profile: **FT:** Coarse; **WN:** Wykeham; **WT:** Lake (Still). Location: **Main Rd:** A170.
Ref: FH5553

YAR (A) (RIVER)

River Yar (A), Alverstone, Sandown, **ISLE OF WIGHT**, PO36, **England**.
(W) www.isleofwight.co.uk
Contact/s: **Mr Derek Holmes** (Secretary).
(T) 01983 523230
(E) dkhiow@madasafish.com
Mr R J Kirby (Hon Secretary), 125 Furrlongs, Pan Estate, Newport, Isle of Wight, PO30 2BN.
(T) 01983 529617
Profile: **FT:** Coarse; **WN:** Yar (a); **WT:** River (Moving). Location: **Main Rd:** A3068, A3055.
Ref: FH5554

YAR (RIVER)

River Yar (B), Brading, Sandown, **ISLE OF WIGHT**, PO36, **England**.
(W) www.isleofwight.co.uk
Contact/s: **Mr Derek Holmes** (Secretary).
(T) 01983 523230
(E) dkhiow@madasafish.com
Mr R J Kirby (Hon Secretary), 125 Furrlongs, Pan Estate, Newport, Isle of Wight, PO30 2BN.
(T) 01983 529617
Profile: **FT:** Coarse; **WN:** Yar; **WT:** River (Moving). Location: **Nr. Rd:** A3055 Brading to Sandown.
Ref: FH5555

YARE (RIVER)

River Yare, Thorpe End, Norwich, **NORFOLK**, NR13, **England**.
Contact/s: **Mr Griffin Marine**.
(T) 01603 433253
Profile: **FT:** Coarse; **WN:** Yare; **WT:** River (Moving).
Ref: FH5556

YARE (RIVER)

River Yare, Beauchamp Arms, Norwich, **NORFOLK**, NR7 8, **England**.
Contact/s: **Mr Keith Ford**, 2 Parana Rd, Norwich, Norfolk, NR7 8BG.
(T) 01603 483923 **(M)** 07979 001351
Profile: **FT:** Coarse; **WN:** Yare; **WT:** River (Moving). Location: **Main Rd:** A146.
Ref: FH5557

YARWELL MILL LAKE

Yarwell Mill Lake, Wansford, Peterborough, **CAMBRIDGESHIRE**, PE8, **England**.
Contact/s: Manager, Webbs Tackle, 196 Newark Avenue, Wansford, Peterborough, Cambridgeshire, PE1 4NP.
(T) 01733 566466
Mr K Usher.
(T) 01780 221860
Profile: **FT:** Coarse; **WN:** Yarwell Mill; **WT:** Lake (Still).
Ref: FH5558

YEADON TARN

Yeadon Tarn, Cemetery Rd, Yeadon, Bradford, **YORKSHIRE (WEST)**, BD, **England**.
Contact/s: Manager, Headingley Angling Ctre, 58 North Lane, Headingley, Leeds, LS6 3HU.
(T) 0113 2784445
Mr David Scott.
(T) 0113 2296930
Profile: **FT:** Coarse; **WN:** Yeadon; **WT:** Tarn (Still) **W. Size:** 30 Acres. Location: **Nr. Rd:** Cemetery Road; **Main Rd:** A658 to Harrogate.
Ref: FH5559

YEAVELEY ESTATE TROUT FISHERY

Yeaveley Estate Trout Fishery, Yeaveley, Ashbourne, **DERBYSHIRE**, DE6 2DT, **England**.
Contact/s: **Mr Guy Field** (Manager).
(T) 01335 330247 **(F)** 01335 330102
Profile: **FT:** Game; **WN:** Estate Lake; **WT:** Lake (Still); **F. Size:** 2 Acres; **W. Size:** 2 Acres. Location: **Nr. Rd:** Off A515; **Main Rd:** A515; **Rail:** Derby.
Ref: FH5560

YEO (RIVER)

River Yeo, Crediton, **DEVON**, EX17, **England**.
Contact/s: **Mr Howard Thresher** (Treasurer), Crediton and Fly Fishing Club, 30 Tuckers Meadow, Crediton, Devon, EX17 3NX.
(T) 01363 774926
Profile: **FT:** Game; **WN:** Yeo; **WT:** River (Moving) **W. Size:** 6400 Metres. Location: **Main Rd:** A377 to Exeter.
Ref: FH5561

YEO (RIVER)

River Yeo, Crediton, **DEVON**, EX17, **England**.
Contact/s: Manager, Ladd DDV, Downes Mill House, Downes Mill, Crediton, EX17 3PW.
(T) 01363 772666
Mr Howard Thresher (Treasurer), Crediton and Fly Fishing Club, 30 Tuckers Meadow, Crediton, Devon, EX17 3NX.
(T) 01363 774926
Profile: **FT:** Game; **WN:** Yeo; **WT:** Tributary (Moving) **W. Size:** 4800 Metres.
Ref: FH5562

YEO (RIVER)

River Yeo, Congresbury, Bristol, **SOMERSET**, BS49, **England**.
Contact/s: **Mr S Bonwick** (Secretary), 13 Tennyson Avenue, Clevedon, Somerset, BS21 7QQ.
(T) 01275 791933
Profile: **FT:** Coarse; **WN:** Yeo (Congresbury); **WT:** River (Moving) **W. Size:** 1200 Metres. Location: **Main Rd:** A370, Bristol to Weston-Super-Mare.
Ref: FH5563

YEO (RIVER)

River Yeo, Ilchester, Yeovil, **SOMERSET**, BA22, **England**.
Contact/s: **Mr M Barnes**, Ilchester and District Angling Club, 44 Marsh Lane, Yeovil, Somerset, BA21 3B.
Profile: **FT:** Coarse; **WN:** Yeo; **WT:** River (Moving).
Ref: FH5564

YEOMANS LAKE

Yeomans Lake, Shimano Linear Fisheries (Oxford), Smiths Concrete Site, Hardwick Village, Witney, **OXFORDSHIRE**, OX8 7Q, **England**.
Contact/s: **Mr Len Gurd** (Owner), 10A Rackstraw Gr, Old Farm Park, Milton Keynes, Buckinghamshire, MK7 8PZ.
(T) 01908 645135 **(F)** 01908 645115
Profile: **FT:** Coarse; **WN:** Yeomans; **WT:** Lake (Still); **F. Size:** 20 Acres; **W. Size:** 15 Acres. Location: **Nr. Rd:** B4449; **Main Rd:** A40; **Rail:** Oxford.
Ref: FH5565

YET-Y-GORS FISHERY

Yet-Y-Gors Fishery, Old Ferry Rd, Manorowen, Fishguard, **PEMBROKESHIRE**, SA65 9RE, **Wales**.
Contact/s: **Mr Hans Verhart** (Manager).
(T) 01348 873497
Profile: **FT:** Combination; **WN:** Yet-y-Gors; **WT:** Lake (Still). Location: **Nr. Rd:** Old Ferry Road; **Main Rd:** A40, A4219.
Ref: FH5566

YEW TREE FISHERIES

Yew Tree Fisheries, Harleston, **SUFFOLK**, **England**.
(W) www.tmikoi.com/fishing_complexes.htm
Contact/s:
(T) 01438 718558 **(F)** 01438 840096
Profile: **FT:** Coarse; **WN:** Yew Tree Lake, and Marsh Lake; **WT:** Lake (Still).
Ref: FH5567

YEW TREE POOL

Yew Tree Pool, Northwich, **CHESHIRE**, CW9, **England**.
Contact/s: **Mr Neil Jupp** (Club Secretary), Lymm Angling Club, PO Box 350, Warrington, Cheshire, WA2 9FB.
(T) 01925 411774
Profile: **FT:** Coarse; **WN:** Yew Tree; **WT:** Pool (Still) **W. Size:** 1 Acre. **Location:** **Nr. Rd:** Pole Lane; **Main Rd:** A559.
Ref: FH5568

YEW TREE TARN

Yew Tree Tarn, Coniston, **CUMBRIA**, LA21, **England**.
Contact/s: **Mr Colin Knipe** (Secretary), Coniston and Trover Angling Association, 8 Old Furness Rd, Coniston, Cumbria, LA21 8HU.
(T) 01539 441572
Profile: **FT:** Game; **WN:** Yew Tree Tarn; **WT:** Lake (Still).
Ref: FH5569

YEW TREE TROUT FISHERY

Yew Tree Trout Fishery, Yew Tree Lane, Rotherfield, Crowborough, **SUSSEX (EAST)**, TN6 3QP, **England**.
Contact/s: **Mr John Schumacher**.
(T) 01892 662983
Profile: **FT:** Game; **WN:** Yew Tree Trout Fishery; **WT:** Lake (Still); **F. Size:** 30 Acres; **W. Size:** 6 Acres. **Location:** **Nr. Rd:** Yew Tree Lane; **Main Rd:** A257; **Rail:** Jarvis Brook, Crowborough.
Ref: FH5570

YNYS-Y-FRO RESERVOIR

Ynys-Y-Fro Reservoir, Rogerstone, Newport, NP, **Wales**.
Contact/s: **Mr Nigel Jones** (Records Officer), Newport Reservoir Fly-Fishing Association, 2 Brynheulog St, Penybryn, Hengold, Glamorgan (Vale of).
(T) 01443 812440 **(M)** 07967 234716
(E) troutmaster2@lineone.net
Profile: **FT:** Game; **WN:** Ynys-Y-Fro; **WT:** Reservoir (Still) **W. Size:** 26 Acres. **Location:** **Nr. Rd:** Risca Road; **Main Rd:** M4; **Rail:** Newport.
Ref: FH5571

YORKSHIRE OUSE

Yorkshire Ouse, Beningbrough, York, **YORKSHIRE (NORTH)**, YO30, **England**.
Contact/s: Manager, Acomb Fishing Tackle, 227 Hamilton Drive West, York, Yorkshire (North), YO24 4PL.
(T) 01904 785237 **(F)** 01904 785237
Mr Doug Dalton (Fishery Manager).
(T) 01904 692046
Mr Walter Brown.
(T) 01904 794962
Profile: **FT:** Coarse; **WN:** Yorkshire Ouse; **WT:** River (Moving). **Location:** **Nr. Rd:** Beningbrough; **Main Rd:** A19, north to Shipton.
Ref: FH5572

YORKSHIRE OUSE

Yorkshire Ouse, Newton-on-Ouse, York, **YORKSHIRE (NORTH)**, YO30, **England**.
Contact/s: **Mr Martin Dukes**.
(T) 01347 848392
Profile: **FT:** Coarse; **WN:** Yorkshire Ouse; **WT:** River (Moving). **Location:** **Nr. Rd:** Linton; **Main Rd:** A19.
Ref: FH5573

YSTWYTH (RIVER)

River Ystwyth, Aberystwyth, **CEREDIGION**, SY23, **Wales**.
Contact/s: Manager, Llanilar Angling Association, Dryslwyn, Llanafan, Aberystwyth, SY23 4AX.
Mr John H Astill (Secretary).
(T) 01974 261237
Mr Peredur Eklund (Hon Secretary), 42 Erwgoch, Waunfawr, Aberystwyth, Carmarthenshire, SY23 3AZ.
(T) 01970 623021
Profile: **FT:** Game; **WN:** Ystwyth; **WT:** River (Moving) **W. Size:** 26400 Metres. **Location:** **Nr. Rd:** B4340; **Rail:** Aberystwyth.
Ref: FH5574

YTHAN FISHERY

Ythan Fishery, Newburgh, Ellon, **ABERDEENSHIRE**, AB41 6BN, **Scotland**.
Contact/s: **Mrs Audrey Forbes** (Manager), 3 Lea Cottages, 130 Main St, Newburgh, Ellon, AB41 6BN.
(T) 01358 789297 **(F)** 01358 789297
Profile: **FT:** Game; **WN:** Ythan; **WT:** River (Moving) **W. Size:** 59200 Metres. **Location:** **Nr. Rd:** Main Street; **Rail:** Aberdeen.
Ref: FH5575

YTHAN VALLEY FISHERY

Ythan Valley Fishery, 78 Aalesund Rd, Ardlethen, Ellon, **ABERDEENSHIRE**, AB41 8EF, **Scotland**.
Contact/s: **Mr Alastair Martin**, Ythan Valley Fishery, 78 Aalesund Rd, Ardlethen, Ellon, AB41 8EF.
(T) 01779 472560
(E) ythan-valley@lineone.net
Profile: **FT:** Game; **WN:** Ythan Valley Fishery; **WT:** Lake (Still) **W. Size:** 11 Acres. **Location:** **Nr. Rd:** B9005; **Main Rd:** Ellon to Tarves; **Rail:** Aberdeen.
Ref: FH5576

ZEALS TROUT FISHERY

Zeals Trout Fishery, Greenstones, Wolverton, Zeals, Warminster, **WILTSHIRE**, BA12, **England**.
Contact/s: **Mr Stewart Canham** (Manager).
(T) 01747 840573
Profile: **FT:** Game; **WN:** Zeals Trout Fishery; **WT:** Combination (Still & Moving).
Ref: FH5577

by County by Town

SECTION 2

This section helps you to locate Fisheries in a County or Town of your choice. The Counties are all split into different Countries.

eg. England, Somerset, Frome.

Once you have located a Fishery you can either look up further details in Section 1 or use the other sections to find what else the Fishery may have to offer.

Angling Times Fishooked Directory

BEDFORDSHIRE

ARLESEY

- ARLESEY LAKE
- GREEN LAGOON

BEDFORD

- AMPTHILL RESERVOIR
- BECKERINGS PARK FARM RESERVOIR
- BRIARWOOD FISHERY
- BROGBOROUGH NO.1 PIT
- FELMERSHAM (RIVER)
- FELMERSHAM GRAVEL PITS
- FIR COUNTRY PARK
- GREAT OUSE (RIVER)
- HAROLD FISHERY
- MARSTON PITS
- OUSE (RIVER)
- PRIORY COUNTRY PARK
- RADWELL COMPLEX
- SOUTH LAGOON
- WATER END FISHERY
- WILLINGTON LAKE

BIGGLESWADE

- IVEL (RIVER)
- LANGFORD MILL
- MANOR FARM LEISURE

DUNSTABLE

- HOUGHTON REGIS QUARRY
- TINGRITH COARSE FISHERY
- TINGRITH MANOR LAKE

ELSTOW

- ELSTOW PITS

HENLOW

- HENLOW GRANGE
- IVEL (RIVER)
- WITHY POOL

LEIGHTON BUZZARD

- CLAYDON LAKE
- JONES PIT
- LAKESIDE TROUT AND COARSE FISHERY
- LEDBURN ROAD
- RACKLEY HILLS PIT
- TIDDENFOOT PIT
- VAUXHALL PIT

LUTON

- WOBURN SANDS

SANDY

- LITTLE HEATH FARM TROUT FISHERY

STANFORD

- BROOM
- STANFORD PIT

BERKSHIRE

BRACKNELL

- ALLSMOOR POND
- FARLEYMOOR LAKE
- FELIX FARM TROUT FISHERY
- MILL POND
- SAVERNAKE POND
- SOUTH HILL PARK LAKE

BRAY

- THAMES (RIVER)

CROWTHORNE

- HOLME GRANGE

FINCHAMPSTEAD

- LONGMOOR FARM FISHING LAKE

HANWORTH

- SOUTH FIELD PARK

HUNGERFORD

- BARTON COURT FISHERY
- FROXFIELD A AND B

MAIDENHEAD

- AMERDEN POOL
- BRAY LAKE
- BRAY LOCK
- HURLEY LOCK
- PONDWOOD CARP LAKES
- SHEEPHOUSE FARM TROUT FISHERY
- THAMES (RIVER)

NEWBURY

- BENS LAKE
- BISHOPS GREEN FARM LAKE
- FORBURY FARM LAKES
- FROBURY FARM SPORTING CLUB
- HAMBRIDGE LANE
- KENNET (RIVER)
- NEWBURY TROUT LAKES
- THAMES (RIVER)
- WYLIES LAKE

READING

- ALDERMASTON
- BRIMPTON LAKE
- BURGHFIELD
- BURGHFIELD BLUE POOL
- BURGHFIELD CANAL
- BURGHFIELD MATCH LAKE
- COTTAGE LANE
- COURT FARM
- DINTON PASTURES COUNTRY PARK
- EAST TOWNEY
- ENGLEFIELD LAGOON
- FARNHAM FLINT
- HOLYBROOK
- KENNET (RIVER)
- KENNET AND AVON CANAL
- KENNET AND ENTORNE (RIVERS)
- LODDON (RIVER)
- LOWER BENYONS
- MAPLEDURHAM A AND B
- MATCH AND BLUE POOLS
- MOATLANDS POOL
- OLD MILL
- PANG VALLEY TROUT LAKE
- PINGEWOOD LAGOON
- PURLEY
- REDLANDS LAKE
- SEACOURT (STREAM)
- SLALFORD LAKES
- SONNING EYE
- SOUTH LAKE
- ST PATRICKS
- THAMES (RIVER)
- THEALE
- THEALE CANAL
- THEALE LAGOON
- TWYFORD BBONT
- TWYFORD WATERS
- UFTON CANAL
- WASING WOODS
- WELLINGTON COUNTRY PARK

SANDHURST

- CHURCH FARM
- MILL LANE
- SWAN VALLEY
- TRI-LAKES

WINDSOR

- ALBERT BRIDGE
- PRIORY WATER
- ROMNEY ISLAND AND MEADOW
- ROYAL BERKSHIRE FISHERY
- THAMES (RIVER)

WOKINGHAM

- ASHRIDGE MANOR
- JINGLES FARM
- LODDON (RIVER)
- LONGMOOR LAKE
- WHITE SWAN LAKE

BRISTOL

- ABBOTS POOL
- AVON (BRISTOL) (RIVER)
- AVON (RIVER)
- BAGWOOD LAKE
- BITTERWELL LAKE
- BRISTOL AVON
- BRISTOL DOCKS
- CHEW (RIVER)
- FISHPONDS LIDO
- FROME (RIVER)
- HAM GREEN LAKE
- HENLEAZE LAKE
- ROUNDWOOD POND
- SEVINGTON LAKES FISHERY
- TANHOUSE FARM LAKE
- WEST COUNTRY WATER PARK

BUCKINGHAMSHIRE

AMERSHAM

- CHESS (RIVER)
- SILVERWING LAKE

AYLESBURY

- THAME (RIVER)

BEDFORD

- BEDFORD BOATING LAKE
- HARROLD ODELL COUNTRY PARK
- KEMPSTONE HARDWICK
- MILTON KEYNES LAKES
- OUSE (RIVER)
- SUMMERFIELDS TROUT FISHERY

BUCKINGHAM

- BOURTON FISHERIES
- CLAYDON LAKE
- GALLOWS POOL
- HYDE LANE LAKES
- SHELSWELL LAKE

CHALFONT ST GILES

- WATTS POOL

CHESHAM

- CHESS (RIVER)
- LATIMER PARK FLY FISHERY

GERRARDS CROSS

- COMMON POND

GREAT LINFORD

- GREAT LINFORD LAKES

GREAT MISSENDEN

- WESTON TERVELL RESERVOIR

HIGH WYCOMBE

- HILL WOOD POND
- SPADE OAK LAKE
- THAMES (RIVER)
- WESTHORPE PARK LAKE

IVER

- BILLET LANE
- BLACK PARK
- CALVES LANE LAKE
- FARLOWS LAKE
- OLD SLADE LANE LAKE

MARLOW

- BACKWATER
- THAMES (RIVER)
- WESTFIELD FARM

MILTON KEYNES

- ALDERS FARM TROUT FISHERY
- CHURCH HILL FISHERY
- COSGROVE LEISURE PARK
- DOVECOTE LAKE FISHERY
- FURZTON LAKE
- GRAND UNION CANAL
- GREAT OUSE (RIVER)
- KINGFISHER GOLF CLUB
- LODGE LAKES
- LOUGHTON LODGE LAKE
- OUSE (RIVER)
- OUZEL (RIVER)
- SNOWBERRY
- TEARDROP LAKES
- TINGRITH LAKES
- VICARAGE SPINNEY TROUT FISHERY
- WOLVERTON LAKES

NEWPORT PAGNELL
- NEWPORT PAGNELL GRAVEL PITS
- TYRINGHAM ESTATE

OLNEY
- BOWLERS CANAL
- GREAT OUSE (RIVER)
- OUSE (RIVER)

SLOUGH
- COLNBROOK WEST
- COLNEBROOK (RIVER)
- CRAYFISH POOL
- GILBRATAR LAKE
- HORTON BOAT POOL
- HORTON CHURCH LAKE
- KINGSMEAD 1
- KINGSMEAD ISLAND LAKE
- MAYFIELDS LAKE
- ORLITTS LAKES
- THAMES (RIVER)

CAMBRIDGESHIRE

CAMBRIDGE
- BARNWELL PIT
- BURNSIDE LAKE
- BURWELL LODE
- CAM (RIVER)
- DICKERSONS PIT
- FEN DRAYTON COMPLEX
- FEN DRAYTON LAKE
- HATTON PARK POND
- MAGPIE LAKE
- MILTON COUNTRY PARK
- MILTON PITS
- OLD WEST (RIVER)
- SILVER STREET MILL
- SOHAM BY-PASS LAKE
- TURKS HEAD LAKE

ELY
- BARWAY LAKE
- BLOCK FEN COMPLEX
- CAM (RIVER)
- GREAT OUSE (RIVER)
- HIGH FLYER LAKE
- LARK (RIVER)
- MEPAL PIT
- OLD WEST (RIVER)
- RANDALLS LAKE
- ROSWELL PITS
- STRETHAM BASIN
- STRETHAM LAKE

HUNTINGDON
- BRACKHILL LAKE
- CHAWSTON LAKES
- CLEARWATERS COARSE FISHERY
- EARITH FISHERY
- EATON SOCON LAKE
- FENLAND FISHERIES
- GINGERBREAD LAKE AND DRIFT
- GODMANCHESTER (RIVER)
- GRAFHAM WATER
- GREAT OUSE (RIVER)
- HINCHINGBROOKE COUNTRY PARK
- HOLME FEN FISHING
- HUNDRED FOOT (RIVER)
- HUNTINGDON (RIVER)
- LEES BROOK
- LILY PARK LAKES
- LITTLE PAXTON FISHERY
- LONG REACH
- NORTH HOUSE LAKE
- OFFORD CLUNY
- OFFORD WEIRPOOL
- OLD NENE (RIVER)
- OLD WEST (RIVER)
- OVER MAIN DRAIN
- PAXTON LAKE
- ST IVES COMPLEX
- STEW POND
- WELDON RESERVOIR
- WILDEN RESERVOIR
- WOBURN CLOSE LAKE
- WOOLPACK FISHERY

MARCH
- FIELDS END WATER

PETERBOROUGH
- BARNWELL COUNTRY PARK
- BIGGIN LAKE
- BLUEBELL LAKE
- COTTERSTOCK RIVER
- CROWLAND ANGLING CLUB LAKES
- DECOY LAKE
- ELDERNELL LAKE
- FERRY MEADOWS
- GERARDS CARP LAKE
- GUNWADE LAKE
- KINGFISHER LAKE
- KINGSLAND RESERVOIRS
- MALEY GRAVEL PITS
- NENE (RIVER)
- NENE NORTH BANK (RIVER)
- NORTH BANK TROUT FISHERY
- NORTHEY PARK FISHERY
- OUNDLE (RIVER)
- PERIO MILL
- RAILWAY LAKES
- REDLANDS PITS
- SAND MARTIN LAKE
- SIBSON FISHERIES
- SWAN LAKE
- TWENTY FOOT DRAIN
- WANSFORD STREAM
- WERRINGTON LAKE
- WHITE HOUSE TROUT FARM
- WHITTLESEY DYKE/ BEVILLS LEAM
- WILLOW CREEK
- WILLOW LAKE
- WOOD POOL
- YARWELL MILL LAKE

RAMSEY
- RAVELEY DRAIN

SWAFFHAM PRIOR
- SPORTSMANS PIT

WHITTLESEY
- EAST DELPH LAKES

WISBECH
- MIDDLE LEVEL DRAIN
- PISCES CARAVAN PARK AND FISHERY
- VIRGINIA LAKE
- WIMBLINGTON MERE

CHESHIRE

ALTRINCHAM
- ASHLEY POOL
- MOBBERLEY POOL

CHEADLE HULME
- ABNEY PARK

CHESTER
- BOLESWORTH CASTLE
- CHESHIRE FISHING
- GOWY (RIVER)
- GOWY FISHERY
- LLOYDS MEADOW FISHERIES
- MEADOW FISHERY
- MILTON GREEN
- MOULDSWORTH MERE

CONGLETON
- ASTBURY MERE
- BRERETON HEATH COUNTRY PARK
- CRABTREE MOSS FARM POOL
- DANE (RIVER)
- GODWINS POOL
- MACCLESFIELD CANAL
- MORETON MERE FISHERY
- NORTH FIELD POOL
- PECK POOL
- SHELLOW FARM POOLS
- WARDS POOLS
- WEAVER (RIVER)
- WESTLOW MERE

CREWE
- BETLEY MERE
- BORDER FISHERIES
- BROOKSIDE FISHERIES
- DOODLESPOOL FARM LAKE
- DUKES POOL
- GORSTY HALL
- LAKEMORE COUNTRY PARK
- SHROPSHIRE UNION CANAL
- WINTERLEY POOL FISHERY

DUKINFIELD
- PEAK FOREST CANAL

HOLMES CHAPEL
- BROOK BANK POOL
- CATCHPENNY POOL
- DANE (RIVER)

HYDE
- OLDHAMS WATER
- WALKERWOOD RESERVOIR

KNUTSFORD
- ASTLE POOL
- BOLLIN (RIVER)
- BOUNDARY WATER PARK
- BRIGHOUSE POOL
- CICELY MILL POOL
- CLAY LANE FISHERY
- DOVEMERE, SANDMERE AND WOODLANDS
- FINGERPOST POOL
- LITTLE REEDS MERE
- MANOR POOL
- SAND MERE LAKE
- SPRINGWOOD POOL
- SWANLEY
- TABLEY MERE
- TABLEY MOAT
- TATTON MERE
- TOFT POOL
- WOODLANDS LAKE

LYMM
- ANTROBUS LAKES
- MOOR POOL
- MOSS POOLS
- MOSSBANK POOL
- NORBURY POOL
- TOP FARM POOL

MACCLESFIELD
- ASHLEY (RIVER)
- BOSLEY RESERVOIR
- BOTTOMS RESERVOIR
- CAPESTHORNE HALL STOCK POND
- CAPESTHORNE MAIN POOL
- CAPESTHORNE TOP POOL
- DANE (RIVER)
- DANEBRIDGE FISHERIES
- FANSHAWE LANE POOL
- HORSECOPPICE RESERVOIR
- JARMAN FARM POOL
- KAZAKO PONDS
- KNIGHTS POOL
- LAMALOAD RESERVOIR
- LEADBEATERS RESERVOIR
- MACCLESFIELD CANAL
- MARTON HEATH COARSE POOL
- MARTON HEATH TROUT POOLS
- MILL LODGE
- PARK POOL
- REDESMERE
- RIDGEGATE RESERVOIR
- SOUTH PARK
- SUTTON RESERVOIR
- TEGGSNOSE RESERVOIR
- THORNEYCROFT LAKES
- TURKS HEAD RESERVOIR
- TURNERS POOL
- WALL POOL LODGE
- WEAVER (RIVER)
- WHIRLEY MERE
- WHIRLEY POOL
- WOOD POOL

MALPAS
- EGERTON LAKE
- HAMPTON SPRINGS

MIDDLEWICH
- BRERTON QUARRY
- BYLEY FISHERIES
- DANE (RIVER)
- TETTON FLASH
- TETTON LAKE
- WEAVER (RIVER)

NANTWICH
- BADDILEY RESERVOIR
- BREAM HOLE
- HACK GREEN LAKE
- HARTHILL
- LLANGOLLEN CANAL
- MIDDLEWICH BRANCH CANAL
- REASEHEATH COLLEGE LAKE

NESTON
- BURTON MERE FISHERIES

NORTHWICH
- BELMONT POOL
- BILLINGE GREEN
- BLAKEMERE
- BUDWORTH MERE
- CANAL PIT
- CISTERNS
- DANE RIVERSIDE FISHERY
- FARM POOL
- FLUSHING MEADOWS FISHERY
- FOUNDERS POOL
- FRIARS POOL
- GREAT BUDWORTH MERE LAKE
- MONKS MOAT
- NEW POOL
- OAK POOL
- PETTY POOL
- ROOKERY POOL
- SHAKERLEY MERE
- SHIPBROOK FLASH
- SPRING POOL
- VALE ROYAL LOCKS
- WEAVER (RIVER)
- WILLOW POOL
- WINCHAM BROOK
- WINNINGTON POOL
- WITTON BROOK
- YEW TREE POOL

RUNCORN
- BRIDGEWATER CANAL
- RUNCORN PARK LAKE
- SANKEY ST HELENS CANAL
- TOWN PARK LANE
- WOODSIDE POOL

SALE
- BRIDGEWATER CANAL
- SALE WATER PARK

SANDBACH
- BULLS POOL
- CRABMILL FLASH
- PLEX FLASH
- RODE POOL
- SANDYBANK POOL
- TAX MERE
- TRENT AND MERSEY CANAL

STALYBRIDGE
- HUDDERSFIELD NARROW CANAL
- WALKERWOOD TROUT FISHERY

TARPORLEY
- BENTLEY TROUT POOL
- HOLMSTON HALL FISHERY
- LITTLE BUDWORTH
- LITTLE MILL
- OULTON MILL POOL

WARRINGTON
- ACKERS PIT
- APPLETON RESERVOIR
- BATE MILL
- BLUNDELLS FARM FISHERY
- BRIDGEWATER CANAL
- BROOKSIDE LAKES
- BROWNLEES POND
- GOLDEN POND
- GREY MIST MERE
- GRIMESDITCH MILL POOL
- GRIMSDITCH MILL POOL
- HAYDAN FISHERY
- LONGBARN POOL
- LYMM DAM
- MARY ANN POND
- MEADOW VIEW FISHERY
- MICKS LAKE
- MOORE QUARRY
- OLD QUAY CANAL
- ORFORD PARK POND
- PARTRIDGE LAKES
- STATHAM POOL
- STRETTON WATER
- VILLAGE POOL
- WEAVER (RIVER)
- WHITEGATE POND
- WHITLEY POOL

WHITCHURCH
- MARBURY MERE

WIDNES
- SANKEY ST HELENS CANAL
- SANKEY ST HELENS CANAL (LAC)

WILMSLOW
- BLACK LAKE
- DEAN (RIVER)
- ROSSMERE

WINSFORD
- LYMM VALE
- NEW BRIDGE POOL
- OCEAN POOL
- STOCKPOND
- WEAVER NAVIGATION
- WINSFORD FLASH

CLEVELAND

GUISBOROUGH
- LOCKWOOD BECK RESERVOIR
- PRIORY COTTAGE LAKE
- SCALING DAM

HARTLEPOOL
- HART RESERVOIR
- LOCH KENNY
- ROSSMERE PARK LAKE
- SHOTTON COLLIERY LAKE
- TILERY LAKE

MIDDLESBROUGH
- ASCOTT PONDS
- CHARLTONS PONDS
- HEMLINGTON LAKE
- LOCKE PARK
- WHITEHOUSE CARAVAN PARK LAKE

REDCAR
- NEW MARSKE RESERVOIR

STOCKTON-ON-TEES
- HARTBURN BRICK PIT
- HARTLEPOOL RESERVOIR
- ISLAND WATERS
- TEES (RIVER)

YARM
- HUTTON RUDBY PONDS

CORNWALL

BODMIN
- BUTTERWELL
- CAMEL (RIVER)
- COOMBE MILL
- EAST ROSE FARM
- FENWICK TROUT FISHERY
- FOWEY (RIVER)
- LAKEVIEW COUNTRY CLUB
- PRINCE PARK
- TEMPLE TROUT FISHERY

BOSCASTLE
- VENN DOWN LAKES

BUDE
- BUDE CANAL
- FORDA HOLIDAY LODGES
- NEETS VALLEY PARK
- ST BENETS ABBEY (RIVER)
- TAMAR LAKE (UPPER)
- WATERFRONT FISHING LAKE

CAMBORNE
- GWITHIAN BROOK

CAMELFORD
- CROWDY RESERVOIR
- ST TINNEY FARM HOLIDAYS

CRAWLEY
- BUCHAN PARK FISHERIES
- CRAYFISH FARM
- MILTON MOUNT LAKE
- ROWFANT HOUSE FISHERY

DELABOLE
- FERNDALE

FALMOUTH
- COLLEGE RESERVOIR
- CONSTANTINE BROOK
- MYLOR ANGLING LAKES

HAYLE
- BILLS POOL
- HAYLE CAUSEWAY
- SHARKEYS PIT
- TREE MEADOW TROUT FISHERY

HELSTON
- MIDDLE BOSWIN FARM
- POLCOVERACK FARM
- WHEAL GREY

LAUNCESTON
- AVALLON HOLIDAY PARK
- BRAGGS WOOD TROUT FISHERY
- DUTSON WATER
- ELMFIELD FARM COARSE FISHERY
- EMFIELD COARSE FISHERY
- HIDDEN VALLEY
- ROSE PARK FISHERY
- ST LEONARDS FISHING LAKE
- STOWFORD GRANGE FISHERIES
- TAMAR (RIVER)
- TREDIDON BARTON LAKE

LISKEARD
- BADHAM FARM LAKE
- COLLIFORD LAKE
- FOWEY (RIVER)
- INNY (RIVER)
- LYNHER (RIVER)
- SEATON (RIVER)
- SIBLYBACK LAKE
- WEST LOOE (RIVER)
- WOODLAY HOLIDAY LAKES

LOOE
- FOWEY (RIVER)
- SHILLAMILL LAKES COUNTRY PARK
- WEST LOOE (RIVER)

LOSTWITHIEL
- FOWEY (RIVER)

NEWQUAY
- FULL BAG FISHERY
- GWINEAR POOLS COARSE FISHERY
- GWINNEAR POOLS
- MELANHYL LAKE
- OAKSIDE FISHERY
- PENVOSE FARM
- PORTH RESERVOIR
- TREBELLAN PARK LAKES
- TRETHIGGEY FARM POND
- TREVELLA CARAVAN AND CAMPING PARK

- WHITEACRES COUNTRY PARK

PENRYN
- ARGAL RESERVOIR
- LAKE PENRYN

PENZANCE
- AMALWHIDDEN FARM
- BOSCATHNOE RESERVOIR
- CHOONE FARM
- CHYRAISE LODGE HOTEL
- DRIFT RESERVOIR
- MILLPOOL FISHERIES
- ST ERTH FISHERY
- TIN DENE FISHERY
- WOONSMITH LAKE

PERRANPORTH
- BOLINGEY LAKE

SALTASH
- BAKE FISHING LAKES
- BUSH LAKES FARM
- PORT ELLIOT LAKE
- ST GERMANS LAKE

ST AUSTELL
- ELECTRICITY POOL
- GLENLEIGH FARM FISHERY
- ORVIS INNIS COUNTRY CLUB AND FLY FISHERY
- WHEAL RASHLEIGH PITS

ST COLUMB
- MEADOWSIDE COARSE FISHERY
- RETALLACK WATERS

ST IVES
- BUSSOW RESERVOIR
- NANCE LAKES

TORPOINT
- CRAFTHOLE LAKE
- MILLBROOK COARSE FISHERY

TRURO
- GOONHAVERN COARSE FISHING LAKE
- GWARNICK MILL TROUT FISHERY
- LANGARTH POOLS
- MELLONWATTS MILL
- ROSEWATER LAKE
- STITHIANS RESERVOIR
- TORY FARM LAKE
- TRENESTRALL LAKE
- VENTONTRISSICK FISHERY

WADEBRIDGE
- CAMEL (RIVER)

COUNTY DURHAM

BARNARD CASTLE
- BLACKTON RESERVOIR
- COW GREEN WILD BROWN TROUT FISHERY
- GRASSHOLME RESERVOIR
- HURY RESERVOIR
- SELSET RESERVOIR
- TEES (RIVER)

BISHOP AUCKLAND
- FIELDSONS POND
- FLYLANDS POND
- TUNSTALL RESERVOIR
- WADSWORTH FISHERY
- WEAR (RIVER)
- WITTON CASTLE LAKES

CHESTER-LE-STREET
- EDMONDSLEY POND
- WEAR (RIVER)

CONSETT
- DERWENT (RIVER)
- DERWENT RESERVOIR
- KNITSLEY MILL TROUT FISHERIES AND STUD FARM
- WASKERLEY RESERVOIR

CROOK
- WEAR (RIVER)

DARLINGTON
- BURNHOPE FISHERY
- FIGHTING COCKS RESERVOIR
- HALNEBY LAKE
- HURWORTH BURN RESERVOIR
- JUBILEE LAKES
- LANGSDALE LAKE
- MIDDLETON WATER PARK
- RABY ESTATES WATER
- TEES (RIVER)

DURHAM
- BRASSIDE POND
- BROWNEY (RIVER)
- DURHAM BECK
- FINCHALE ABBEY FARM
- TEASDALE POND
- TURNSIDE POOL
- TURSDALE POND
- TURSDALE POND (LANGLEY PARK)
- WEAR (RIVER)

FERRYHILL
- KELLOW LAW POND
- MAINSFORTH POND

NEWTON AYCLIFFE
- AYCLIFFE LAKE

PETERLEE
- SHOTTON POND
- WELLFIELD POND

SPENNYMOOR
- BYERS GREEN
- SHAFTOS LAKE

STANLEY
- BEAMISH LAKE FLY FISHERY
- GREENCROFT POND

STOCKTON-ON-TEES
- WEST FARM LAKE

TRIMDON STATION
- TRIMDON POND

WINGATE
- BEAUMONT FISHERIES

CUMBRIA

ALSTON
- PRYHEAD FISHERY
- SOUTH TYNE (RIVER)
- TYNE (RIVER)

AMBLESIDE
- BLELHAM TARN
- BRATHAY (RIVER)
- CODALE TARN
- DRUNKEN DUCK TARN FISHERY
- EASEDALE TARN
- ESTHWAITE WATER
- GRASMERE COARSE FISHERY
- GRIZEDALE BECK
- HAWESWATER RESERVOIR
- HAWKSHEAD TROUT FISHING
- HAYESWATER RESERVOIR
- HIGH ARNSIDE TARN
- LOUGHRIGG TARN
- MOSS ECCLES TARN
- ROTHAY (RIVER)
- RYDAL WATER

APPLEBY-IN-WESTMORLAND
- EDEN (RIVER)
- SANDFORD ARMS

BARROW-IN-FURNESS
- BARROW-IN-FURNESS RESERVOIR
- ORMSGILL LOWER RESERVOIR
- POAKA BECK
- ROANHEAD FISHERIES

BOWNESS ON WINDERMERE
- DUBBS RESERVOIR
- GHYLL HEAD

BRAMPTON
- NEW HILLS TROUT FARM FISHERY
- TALKIN TARN

BROUGHTON-IN-FURNESS
- LICKLE (RIVER)

CARLISLE
- BARN LAKE
- BRAYTON POND
- CALDEW (RIVER)
- CARLETON HILL
- EAST VIEW FISHERY
- EDEN (RIVER)
- LIDDEL WATER
- LONSDALE COUNTRY PARK
- LOUGHSIDE FISHERY
- NETHERBY ESTATE
- OAKBANK LAKES
- TRANQUIL OTTER

CARNFORTH
- BARBON BECK
- BORWICK LAKE
- DOE (RIVER)
- GOODENBURGH TARN
- GRETA (RIVER)
- HALLMORE FISHERIES
- REDWELL FISHERIES
- TEWITFIELDS TROUT FISHERY
- TWISS (RIVER)
- WYCH ELM FISHERY

CLEATOR MOOR
- MEADLEY RESERVOIR

COCKERMOUTH
- BRIGHAM (RIVER)
- BUTTERMERE LAKE
- COGRA MOSS
- CRUMMOCK WATER LAKE
- DERWENT (RIVER)
- ELLERBECK FARM AND FISHERY
- LOWESWATER LAKE
- MOCKERKIN TARN
- SHARPLEY WATERS

CONISTON
- CONISTON WATER
- YEW TREE TARN

DALTON-IN-FURNESS
- BURLINGTON POND
- HARLOCK RESERVOIR
- PENNINIGTON RESERVOIR

EGREMONT
- EHEN (RIVER)
- ENNERDALE LAKE FISHERY

GRANGE-OVER-SANDS
- WINSTER (RIVER)
- WITHERSLACK HALL TARN

HOLMROOK
- IRT (RIVER)
- MEDKLIN TARN FISHERY

KENDAL
- BANKS POND
- FISHER TARN
- FISHER TARN ANGLERS
- KENT (RIVER)
- KILLINGTON RESERVOIR
- RATHER HEATH TARN
- SKELSMERGH LAKE
- SPRINT (RIVER)

KESWICK
- BASSENTHWAITE LAKE
- BORROWDALE FISHERIES
- DERWENT (RIVER)
- THIRLMERE
- WATENDLATH TROUT FISHERY
- WINSTER (RIVER)

KIRKBY STEPHEN
- BESSY BECK TROUT FARM

- EDEN (RIVER)
- EDEN VALLEY TROUT LAKE
- LITTLE MUSGRAVE

MARYPORT

- ELLEN (RIVER)
- KNOTT END TARN

MILLOM

- ANNAS (RIVER)
- ANNAS STREAM
- BAYSTONE BANK RESERVIOR
- LAZY (RIVER)

MILNTHORPE

- BELA STREAM

PENRITH

- AIRA BECK
- BLENCARN LAKE
- CROSSFIELD FISHERY
- DACRE BECK
- EAMONT (RIVER)
- HAWESWATER
- KENTMERE FISHERY
- KIRKBY THORE (RIVER)
- LOWTHER (RIVER)
- LUNE (RIVER)
- PINFOLD LAKE
- ULLSWATER LAKE
- WHINS POND

RAVENGLASS

- DEVOKE WATER
- ESK (RIVER)

SEDBERGH

- CLOUGH (RIVER)
- DEE (RIVER)
- LOW GILL
- LUNE (RIVER)
- RAWTHEY (RIVER)

SEDBURGH

- LUNE (RIVER)
- RAWTHEY (RIVER)

ULVERSTON

- BIGLAND HALL LAKE
- ULVERSTON CANAL

WIGTON

- MOORHOUSE TARN

WINDERMERE

- ATKINSONS TARN COARSE FISHERY
- BLENHEIM LODGE HOTEL
- BORRANS RESERVOIR
- CLEABARROW TARN
- DUBBS TROUT FISHERY
- GHYLL HEAD TROUT FISHERY
- HIGH NEWTON RESERVOIR
- HOLEHIRD TARN
- LAKE WINDERMERE
- SCHOOL KNOTT TARN

DERBYSHIRE

ALFRETON

- HIGHAM FARM COARSE FISHING

ASHBOURNE

- ALDAMORE POOL
- CARSINGTON WATER
- DOVE (RIVER)
- HENMORE (RIVER)
- YEAVELEY ESTATE TROUT FISHERY

BAKEWELL

- DERWENT (RIVER)
- DUKE OF RUTLAND ESTATE
- HADDON ESTATE FISHERIES
- MONSAL DALE FISHERY
- WYE (RIVER)

BELPER

- BELPER POND
- CODNOR PARK RESERVOIR
- DERBYSHIRE TROUT FISHERY
- DERWENT (RIVER)
- POSSY LODGE PONDS

CHESTERFIELD

- BARLOW FISHERIES
- CHAPEL WHEEL DAM
- HARLESTHORPE DAM
- LINACRE RESERVOIRS
- MOSS BROOK
- OGSTON RESERVOIR
- PRESS MANOR
- RINGWOOD LAKE
- WINGERWORTH LIDO

DERBY

- ALLESTREE LAKE
- ALVASTON LAKE
- ASHGROVE LAKE
- DERWENT (RIVER)
- DERWENT VALLEY FISHERY
- FOREMARK TROUT FISHERY
- KEGWORTH DEEP LOCK
- LOCHO PARK LAKE
- MARKEATON LAKE
- MELBOURNE POOL
- SOAR (RIVER)
- STAUNTON HAROLD RESERVOIR
- SWARKESTONE GRAVEL PITS
- TRENT (RIVER)
- TRENT AND MERSEY CANAL

GLOSSOP

- ARNFIELD RESERVOIR

HEANOR

- COPPICE LAKE

HIGH PEAK

- COMBS RESERVOIR
- COTE LODGE RESERVOIR
- ERRWOOD RESERVOIR
- GOYT (RIVER)
- TODDBROOK RESERVOIR

HILTON

- SUTTON BROOK

HOPE VALLEY

- LADYBOWER RESERVOIR

ILKESTON

- MAPPERLEY RESERVOIR

MATLOCK

- ALTON MANOR FARM
- DERWENT (RIVER)
- SYDNOPE FISHERIES
- TRENT (RIVER)
- WYE (RIVER)

RIPLEY

- BUTTERLEY RESERVOIR
- CONDOR PARK RESERVOIR

SHEFFIELD

- FOXTON DAM
- NETHERMOOR LAKE

SWADLINCOTE

- BEEHIVE FARM WOODLANDS LAKES
- CATTON PARK LAKE
- DONKHILL FISHERIES

DEVON

AXMINSTER

- AXE (RIVER)
- SUMMERLEAZE POND

BARNSTAPLE

- BLAKEWELL FISHERIES
- RIVERTON HOUSE AND LAKES
- SWIMBRIDGE POOL
- TAW (RIVER)
- VENN POOL
- WISTLANDPOUND RESERVOIR

BEAWORTHY

- ANGLERS ELDORADO
- ANGLERS PARADISE
- ANGLERS SHANGRILA
- GREENACRE TROUT LAKES
- HIGHAMPTON TROUT LAKES
- KINGLAKE FISHERY
- LEGGE FARM COARSE FISHERY
- SOUTH HAY FARM

BIDEFORD

- BULWORTHY FISHERY
- CLOVELLY LAKES
- FOSFELLE COUNTRY HOUSE HOTEL
- GAMMATON RESERVOIRS
- HARTLAND FOREST FISHERY GOLF CLUB
- JENNETTS RESERVOIR
- LITTLE WEACH
- MELBURY RESERVOIR
- PYEWELL FARM
- SOUTH WEST WATER FISHERY
- TORRIDGE (RIVER)

BODMIN

- CAMEL (RIVER)
- INNIS MOORE TROUT FISHERY

BRAUNTON

- LITTLE COMFORT FARM
- WILLOWFIELD LAKE COTTAGES

BRIXHAM

- CHANNELL FISHERIES

BUCKFASTLEIGH

- DART (RIVER)

BUDE

- EXEMOOR FARM
- LEWORTHY FARM

CHULMLEIGH

- EGGESFORD COUNTRY HOTEL WATERS

COLYTON

- AXE (RIVER)
- HIGHER COWNHAYNE LAKES
- WISCOMBE FISHERY

CREDITON

- CREEDY (RIVER)
- CREEDY LAKES
- GLYNDWR FISHERY
- LOWER HALLACOMBE FISHERY
- OLDBOROUGH FISHING RETREAT
- SALMONHUTCH COARSE FISHERY
- TAW (RIVER)
- TAW FISHING CLUB
- VALLEY VIEW FISHERY
- YEO (RIVER)

CULLOMPTON

- BILLINGSMOOR FARM
- CLAYHIDON (RIVER)
- GOODIFORD MILL TROUT FISHERY
- GRAND WESTERN CANAL
- HARTSMOOR FISHERIES
- KINGSMEAD CENTRE
- MILLHAYES
- NEWCOURT PONDS
- PADBROOK PARK
- STOUR FARM FISHERY
- UPTON WARREN LAKE
- WOODY PARK FISHERY

DARTMOUTH

- OLD MILL RESERVOIR

DAWLISH

- ASHCOMBE FISHERY
- COFTON PARK FARM

EXETER

- CREEDY (RIVER)
- CULM (RIVER)
- EXE (RIVER)
- EXETER CANAL
- EXETER SHIP CANAL
- FENECK POND
- FOUR PONDS
- HOGSBROOK LAKES
- HOME FARM FISHERY

- KENNICK RESERVOIR
- LUCCOMBES PONDS
- PICFRESH
- SOUTH VIEW FARM FISHERY
- SQUABMOOR RESERVOIR
- STAR BARTON PONDS
- TAMAR LAKE (LOWER)
- TAR (RIVER)
- TEIGN
- TRENCHFORD RESERVOIR
- UPHAM FARM PONDS
- WEST VIEW POND

HOLSWORTHY

- CLAWFORD VINEYARD AND FISHERIES
- EASTCOTT FARM AND LODGES
- MILL LEAT TROUT FISHERY
- SIMPSON VALLEY FISHERY
- TINNEY WATERS
- TORRIDGE (RIVER)
- WOODA FARM FISHERY
- WOODACOTT ARMS

HONITON

- DEER PARK COUNTRY HOTEL
- FISHPONDS HOUSE
- HOLLIES TROUT FARM AND FISHERY
- MILTON FARM PONDS
- OTTER (RIVER)
- OTTER FALLS FISHERY
- STILL WATERS TROUT FISHERY

ILFRACOMBE

- BERRYNARBOR MILL POND
- LONGLANDS FARM
- LOWER SLADE RESERVOIR
- MILL PARK COARSE FISHING LAKE
- SLADE RESERVOIRS

IVYBRIDGE

- UPPER YEALM FISHERY

KINGSBRIDGE

- AVETON GIFFORD STREAM
- AVON (RIVER)
- BICKERTON FARM FISHERY
- COOMBE WATER FISHERY
- LODDISWELL STREAM
- SLAPTON LEY NATIONAL NATURE RESERVE
- VALLEY SPRINGS TROUT FISHERY

LIFTON

- TAMAR (RIVER)

LYNMOUTH

- LYN (RIVER)
- WATERSMEET AND GLENTHORNE FISHERIES

NEWTON ABBOT

- ABBROOK POND
- DORES POND - RACKERHAYES
- EDDISON POND
- FERNWORTHY RESERVOIR
- FINLAKE PONDS
- INDIO POND
- ISLAND POND - RACKERHAYES
- NEWTON ABBOT SPRING PONDS
- ROCOMBE PONDS
- RUB - A - DUB POND
- SAWMILLS LAKE
- TEIGN (RIVER)
- TRAGO MILLS
- VENFORD RESERVOIR
- WAPPERWELL POND
- WATERCRESS FARM TROUT FISHERY

OKEHAMPTON

- ALDER LAKE
- BLUE LAKE
- MELDON RESERVOIR
- ROADFORD RESERVOIR
- SOUTH REED FISHERIES CARP LAKE
- SPIRES LAKES
- STONE FARM QUARRY
- TOTTIFORD RESERVOIR

PAIGNTON

- NEW BARN ANGLING CENTRE
- TOWN PARKS COARSE FISHERY

PLYMOUTH

- BURRATOR RESERVOIR
- CADOVER BRIDGE PITS
- DRAKELANDS GAME FISHERY
- PLYM (RIVER)
- SUNRIDGE FISHERY

SOUTH BRENT

- HATCHLAND TROUT FISHERY
- LITTLE ALLERS COARSE FISHERY
- MILL
- SOMERSWOOD LAKE

SOUTH MOLTON

- DUNSLEY FARM
- OAKTREE FISHERY
- SHOBROOKE PARK

TAVISTOCK

- COOMBE FISHERIES
- MILEMEAD FISHERIES
- TAMAR (RIVER)
- TAVISTOCK TROUT FISHERY
- TAVY (RIVER)

TIVERTON

- BELLBROOK VALLEY TROUT FISHERY
- COOMBE FARM FISHPONDS
- DELBROOK VALLEY TROUT FISHERY
- EXE (RIVER)
- GRAND WESTERN CANAL
- HATSWELL
- POUND POND FARM
- SAMPFORD PEVERAL PONDS
- WEST PITT FARM FISHERY

TORQUAY

- CHARLECOMBE

TORRINGTON

- BAKERS FARM
- DARRACOTT RESERVOIR
- STEVENSTONE LAKES

TOTNES

- AVON DAM
- NEWHOUSE FISHERY

UMBERLEIGH

- MOLE (RIVER)

WINKLEIGH

- LITTLE WARHAM FISHERY
- STAFFORD MOOR FISHERY

DORSET

BLANDFORD FORUM

- STOUR (DORSET) (RIVER)
- STOUR (RIVER)

BOURNEMOUTH

- STOUR (DORSET) (RIVER)
- STOUR (RIVER)
- THROOP FISHERIES

BRIDPORT

- BRIT (RIVER)
- CHAR STREAM
- WATERMILL LAKE
- WOOD FARM CARAVAN PARK

BUCKLAND NEWTON

- KNAPP HILL FARM LAKES

CHRISTCHURCH

- AVON (RIVER)
- AVON TYRRELL LAKES
- BLASHFORD LAKES
- CHRISTCHURCH LOWER STOUR
- CROW POOL
- GOLDEN SPRINGS LAKES
- HAMPSHIRE AVON (RIVER)
- HARROW POND
- LIFELANDS FISHERY
- MUDEFORD WOOD LAKE
- NEW MEADOWS LAKE
- ROYALTY FISHERY
- SOPLEY FARM
- STOUR (DORSET) (RIVER)
- WHIRLWIND LAKE
- WINKTON FISHERY

DORCHESTER

- CLUB LAKE
- FLOWERS FARM TROUT LAKES
- FROME (RIVER)
- HERMITAGE LAKES
- KINGCOMBE COARSE FARM
- KINGCOMBE LAKE
- LAWRENCES FARM
- LUCKFIELD LAKE FISHERY
- LYONS GATE CARAVAN PARK
- PALLINGTON LAKES
- PIDDLE (RIVER)
- RAWLSBURY WATERS
- REVELS FISHERY
- THAMES (RIVER)
- WARMWELL HOLIDAY PARK
- WESSEX FLY FISHING TROUT LAKES

FERNDOWN

- STOUR (DORSET) (RIVER)

GILLINGHAM

- CULVERS FARM FISHERIES
- UPPER STOUR (RIVER)

LYME REGIS

- AMHERST LODGE FISHERY

POOLE

- HAMWORTHY LAKE
- STOUR (DORSET) (RIVER)
- WESSEX WATER RESERVOIRS

SHERBORNE

- BERKELEY FARM
- SHERBORNE LAKE

STURMINSTER NEWTON

- MAPPOWDER COURT
- STOUR (DORSET) (RIVER)
- STOUR (RIVER)
- TODBER MANOR

WAREHAM

- DORSET FROME
- FROME (RIVER)
- HYDE LAKE
- PIDDLE (RIVER)

WEYMOUTH

- OSMINGTON MILLS
- RADIPOLE LAKE
- WALLYS LAKE

WIMBORNE

- CRANBOURNE FRUIT FARM
- CRANEBROOK TROUT FISHERY
- FROME AND PIDDLE (RIVERS)
- GOLD OAK FISH FARM
- HILLVIEW FARM LAKE
- HOLT WOOD PONDS
- MARTINS FARM
- STOUR (DORSET) (RIVER)
- STOUR (RIVER)
- WHITEMOOR LAKE
- WHITESHEET TROUT FISHERY

ESSEX

BARKING

- MAYSBROOK LAKES

BASILDON

- BURROWS FARM
- GLOUCESTER PARK LAKE
- MOATHOUSE LAKE
- NORTHLANDS PARK
- PIPPS HILL FISHERIES

BILLERICAY
- BARLEYLANDS RESERVOIR
- GREEN OAKS TROUT FISHERY
- KENNEL LANE
- LAKE MEADOWS

BRAINTREE
- BLACKWATER (RIVER)
- FENNES FISHERIES
- PANT (RIVER)
- RAYNE LODGE FARM
- RECTORY FARM POND
- SHALFORD RESERVOIRS
- STRAITS MILL

BRENTWOOD
- BRICKHOUSE FARM FISHERIES
- CHURCH LAKE
- CHURCHWOOD FISHERIES
- CROW GREEN FISHERY
- THORNDON PARK LAKE
- WEALD COUNTRY PARK

CHELMSFORD
- BLACKWATER (RIVER)
- BLASFORD HILL FISHERIES
- BLUNTS AND CANTS MERES
- BOREHAM FISHERY
- BOREHAM MERES
- BOVINGTON MERE 1
- BOVINGTON MERE 2
- BROAD GREEN AND TUFNELL MERE
- CENTRAL PARK LAKE
- CHELMER (RIVER)
- CHELMER AND BLACKWATER NAVIGATION CANAL
- DANBURY COUNTRY PARK
- EWSONS WATER
- HANNINGFIELD TROUT FISHERY
- JACKLETTS FARM
- MARCONIS PIT
- NEWLAND HALL CARP FISHERY
- PARSONAGE FARM
- TUFNELL MERE
- WILLOWS LAKE

CHIGWELL
- HAINAULT FOREST COUNTRY PARK
- RODING VALLEY LAKE

CLACTON-ON-SEA
- WEELEY BRIDGE HOLIDAY PARK

COLCHESTER
- ARDLEIGH RESERVOIR
- BLACKWATER (RIVER)
- BROOKHALL FISHERY
- COLNE (RIVER)
- DEDHAM MILL
- DONYLANDS LAKES
- HOUCHINS RESERVOIRS
- LAYER PIT
- MANNINGTREE RIVER POOLS
- OLD HALL FARM TROUT FISHERY
- OLIVERS LAKE
- PRESTONS LAKE
- STOUR (RIVER)
- STOUR (SUFFOLK) (RIVER)

DAGENHAM
- CHASE FISHERY
- VALENCE MOAT

DUNMOW
- ARMIGERS FARM
- LAUNDRY LAKE
- LITTLE EASTON FISHERIES
- LITTLE EASTON MANOR

GARNON
- GARNISH HALL

GRAYS
- ARENA LAKE
- GRANGE WATER

HALSTEAD
- GOSFIELD LAKE RESORT
- SPARROWS POND

HORNCHURCH
- ALBYNS LAKE

ILFORD
- FAIRLOP WATERS
- WANSTEAD AND WOODFORD PONDS

INGATESTONE
- BLACKMORE WOOD
- CARP FARM FRYERNING FISHERIES
- DODDS FARM
- MILLENNIUM LAKES
- WID (RIVER)

LOUGHTON
- CONNAUGHT WATER
- WAKE VALLEY POND

MALDON
- BLACKWATER (RIVER)
- BOG GROVE
- CHELMER AND BLACKWATER NAVIGATION CANAL
- CHIGBOROUGH
- CHIGBOROUGH FISHERIES
- SLOUGH HOUSE WATER
- WICK MERE

ONGAR
- BIRDS GREEN
- GREAT MYLES LAKE
- RODING (RIVER)

RAINHAM
- BERWICK PONDS

RAYLEIGH
- HOCKLEY LAKES

ROCHFORD
- DOGGETTS FARM FISHERY
- ROCHFORD RESERVOIR
- STAMBRIDGE STARR FISHERIES

ROMFORD
- AVELEY LAKES
- BEDFORDS PARK LAKE
- CHERPONT
- FAIRLOP EAST LAKE
- MAYBRAND FISHERY
- NORTON FISHERY
- NUPERS FARM
- RAPHAELS PARK
- RODING (RIVER)

SAFFRON WALDEN
- BORDEAUX PIT
- CLAVERING TROUT LAKE
- HOME FARM FISHERY
- ROCKELLS FARM

SOUTH OCKENDON
- ESSEX CARP FISHERY

SOUTHEND-ON-SEA
- MILL BARN FISHERY
- PRIORY PARK LAKES
- SHOEBURY PARK
- STAR LANE

SOUTHMINSTER
- ASHELDHAM FISHERY
- SOUTHMINSTER FISHERIES

STANDFORD-LE-HOPE
- COBBLERS MEAD LAKE
- JIMMYS LAKE
- STANFORD-LE-HOPE
- WARREN
- WHARF POOL

UPMINSTER
- BULPHAN PARK FISHERIES
- HARWOOD HALL LAKE
- PEA LANE FISHERY
- SLOUGH HOUSE LAKE

WALTHAM ABBEY
- CLAVERHAMBURY LAKE
- CROWN NETHERHALL
- FISHERS GREEN
- HOLYFIELD FISHERY
- HOOKS MARSH
- JOHNS LAKE FISHERIES
- KNIGHTS PIT
- LEA (RIVER)
- LEE FLOOD RELIEF CHANNEL
- MAGIC LAKE
- NAZEING MEADS
- PICKS COTTAGE CARP LAKES

WEST HORNDON
- PAR

WITHAM
- BLACKWATER (RIVER)
- BRAXTED HALL ESTATE
- CANTS MERE
- LITTLE BRAXTED FARM ESTATE
- SILVER END PIT
- WILLOWS

FIFE

ADDLESTONE
- WEY (RIVER)

EAST MOLESEY
- EMBER (RIVER)

GLOUCESTERSHIRE

BERKELEY
- WATERLEY BROOK

CHELTENHAM
- AVON (RIVER)
- BOURTON ON THE WATER GRAVEL PIT NO1
- BURLEY FIELDS LAKE
- DONNINGTON TROUT FISHERY
- MORETON PITS
- SANTHILL FISHERY
- STANBOROUGH POOL

CINDERFORD
- LIGHTMOOR POOL
- STEAM MILLS LAKE

CIRENCESTER
- ASHTON KEYNES POOL
- BRADLEYS PIT
- CHURN POOL TROUT FISHERY
- COKES PIT
- COLN (RIVER)
- COTSWOLD HOBURNE
- COTSWOLD WATER PARK
- FARMHOUSE LAKE (THE)
- HAM POOL
- ISIS NO 1 LAKE 19
- KEYNES COUNTRY PARK
- KEYNES PARK TOP LAKE
- LAKE NUMBER ONE (LAKE19)
- MILL LAKE (NO 44)
- NEIGH BRIDGE LAKE
- NETHERWOOD LAKE
- RAINBOW LAKES
- THAMES (RIVER)
- WICK WATER

COLEFORD
- MARIONS POOL
- SPEECH HOUSE LAKE

DURSLEY
- GREAT BURROWS TROUT FISHERY

DYMOCK
- SEVERN (RIVER)

FAIRFORD
- CLAYDON PARK FISHERY
- COLN (RIVER)
- MILESTONE FISHERY
- WHELFORD POOLS COARSE FISHERY

FOREST OF DEAN
- CANNOP PONDS

GLOUCESTER
- BROOK FARM TROUT FISHERY

GARDNERS POOL
GLOUCESTER AND SHARPNESS CANAL
GLOUCESTER CANAL
HIGHNAM COURT LAKE
HUNTLEY CARP POOLS
MEADOW POND
MEADOWCLIFFE POOL
NORTON FRUIT FARM
RED LION FISHERY
SEVERN (RIVER)
STAUNTON COURT LAKES
STONE END FARM LAKES
WATERLOO SCREENS
WATERSMEET LAKES
WITCOMBE WATERS

LECHLADE
BUSHYLEAZE TROUT FISHERY
HORSESHOE LAKE
LECHLADE TROUT FISHERY
THAMES (RIVER)

LYDNEY
LYDNEY BOATING LAKE

MITCHELDEAN
PLUMP HILL POOL

MORETON-IN-MARSH
COURT FARM
LEMINGTON LAKES

STONEHOUSE
STROUDWATER CANAL

STOW ON THE WOLD
ADLESTROP LAKE

STROUD
FROME STREAM
STEANBRIDGE FISHERY

TEWKESBURY
APPERLEY POOLS
BREDONS HARDWICK
CHURCH END TROUT FISHERY
ENVIRONMENT AGENCY
HILL VIEW LAKES
HILLVIEW FISHERY
MILL AVON
MYTHE POOL
SEVERN (RIVER)
SEVERN ON THE HAM

HAMPSHIRE

ALDERSHOT
FRENSHAM GREAT AND LITTLE PONDS
GOLD VALLEY LAKES
LAKESIDE
SPRINGLAKES
WILLOW PARK

ALRESFORD
CANDOVER BROOK

ANDOVER
ABBOTTS WORTHY
ANTON (RIVER)
ANTON LAKE
CHARLTON PITS
FOXCOTTE LAKE
GOLDEN POND FISHERY
KIMBRIDGE
PERIL LAKE
ROOKSBURY MILL TROUT FISHERIES
VALE FARM FISHERY

BASINGSTOKE
BASINGSTOKE CANAL

BROCKENHURST
HATCHET POND

CAMBERLEY
HAWLEY LAKE

EASTLEIGH
LAKESIDE COUNTRY PARK

FAREHAM
CARRON ROW FARM PONDS
CHIPHALL LAKE TROUT FISHERY
FUNTLEY POND
RIVER FARM
TITCHFIELD ABBEY GOLF AND COARSE FISHING LAKES

FARNBOROUGH
CUTT MILL
FRIMLEY LAKES
HOLLYBUSH LANE LAKES

FORDINGBRIDGE
AVON RIVER FISHERIES
HAMPSHIRE AVON (RIVER)
HUCKLESBROOK LAKE
LAKE FARM
LAPSLEYS FISHERY
NEW FOREST WATER PARK
ROCKBOURNE TROUT FISHERY

HAVANT
STAUNTON COUNTRY PARK

HECKFIELD
WHITEWATER (RIVER)

HOOK
BASINGSTOKE CANAL
ROTHERWICK AND NIGHTINGALE LAKES
WHITE HOUSE TROUT FARM

LEE-ON-THE-SOLENT
QUEENS ROAD POND

LIPHOOK
COOKS POND

LISS
BARONS PONDS (NEW SITE)
MBK LEISURE BARRONS POND

LYMINGTON
SWAY LAKES
WAINSFORD RESERVOIR

LYNDHURST
JANESMOOR POND
LEOMINSTEAD MILL POND
LEOMINSTEAD TROUT FISHERY
LYNDHURST LAKE
MILL POND LAKE

NEW MILTON
HORDLE LAKES
ORCHARD LAKES

PETERSFIELD
MEON SPRINGS FLY FISHERY
PETERSFIELD HEATH LAKE
STEPSTONES LAKES

PORTSMOUTH
BAFFINS POND
BROCKHURST MOAT
BROWNWICH POND
HILSEA MOATS
HMS DRYAD LAKE

RINGWOOD
AVON (RIVER)
BEECHES BROOK FISHERY
BICKERLEY MILLSTREAM
BROADLANDS LAKES
CROOKED WILLOWS
EAST MOORS LAKE
HALF PIT
HAMPSHIRE AVON
HAMPSHIRE AVON (RIVER)
HIGHTOWN LAKE
HURST POND
IBSLEY POOLS
MOORS VALLEY COUNTRY PARK
NORTHFIELD LAKES
ROCKFORD LAKE
SOMERLEY LAKES
STOUR (RIVER)
TURF CROFT FARM
WASH PIT
WEDGEHILL PONDS

ROMSEY
AWBRIDGE DANES LAKE
BROADLANDS MAIN LAKE
GREENRIDGE FARM LAKES
HOLBURY LAKES
LONGBRIDGE LAKES
LOWER ITCHEN FISHERY
PARSONAGE (RIVER) TEST
TEST (RIVER)
WHINWHISTLE COARSE FISHERY
WOODINGTON FISHERY

SOUTHAMPTON
BILCOMBES POND
DARK LANE PONDS
FIVE OAKS TROUT LAKE
FOREST LODGE HOME FARM
HOLBURY MANOR POND
ITCHEN NAVIGATION
KINGFISHER LAKE (A)
LAKESIDE
MOORHEN FARM TROUT LAKE
MOPLEY POND
STONEHAM LAKES
TESTWOOD SALMON FISHERIES
WINTERSHILL TROUT LAKE
WOODMILL SALMON FISHERY

STOCKBRIDGE
JOHN OGAUNTS FISHERY
NETHER WALLOP FLY FISHING SCHOOL
TEST (RIVER)

WINCHESTER
AVINGTON TROUT FISHERIES
DEVER SPRINGS TROUT FISHERY
ITCHEN (RIVER)
TOPACRE LAKE

YATELEY
FIRGROVE LAKES
NUTRABAITS YATELEY COMPLEX
NUTRABAITS YATELEY SOUTH LAKE

HEREFORDSHIRE

BROMYARD
KINGFISHER TROUT LAKE
MUNDERFIELD HAROLD

HEREFORD
ASHPERTON MOAT
CHURCH POOL
COPPICE TROUT FISHERY
COURT FARM
HAYCASTLE WATER
HERRIOTS POOL
HUNDRED POOL
LLYNFI (RIVER)
LUGG (RIVER)
MARLIAS (RIVER)
MARSH HOUSE FARM
MILLPOND
MOCCAS FISHERY
MONNOW (RIVER)
MONTE BISHOP
ROTHERWAS LONG POOL
ROYAL OAK POOL
TOAD HALL FISHERY
WYE (RIVER)

LEDBURY
BETULA WATERS
CASTLEMORTON
EASTNOR CASTLE
EVESBATCH TOP LAKE
GOLDEN VALLEY
LILY AND WILLOW POOLS
PIXLEY POOL
PRIDEWOOD LAKE
RED BANK POOLS
RUSSELLS END RESERVOIR

LEOMINSTER

- DOCKLOW POOLS

ROSS-ON-WYE

- BIDDLESTONE LAKE
- BULLEY LANE FISHERY
- CARADOC FISHERY
- DRUMMOND DUB
- INGESTONE FISHERY
- REDMIRE POOL
- WYE (RIVER)

HERTFORDSHIRE

ARLESEY

- BLUE LAGOON
- OLDFIELD

AYLESBURY

- AYLESBURY ARM CANAL
- BIERTON FISHING LAKES
- OAKFIELD FISHERY
- WOODLAND FARM

BERKHAMSTED

- GRAND UNION CANAL

BISHOPS STORTFORD

- HATFIELD FOREST LAKE
- LEE NAVIGATION

BOREHAMWOOD

- ALDENHAM RESERVOIR

BROXBOURNE

- CARTHAGENA FISHERY
- KINGS WEIR FISHERY
- LEA NAVIGATION
- LEE NAVIGATION
- OLD MILL AND MEADOWS
- SLIPE LANE PITS
- WORMLEBURY

HATFIELD

- HATFIELD BROADWATER
- SHEPHERDS WAY

HEMEL HEMPSTEAD

- BOXMOOR TROUT FISHERY
- PIXIES MERE
- WESTBROOK MERE

HERTFORD

- LEE NAVIGATION

HITCHIN

- DURRANTS LAKE
- OUGHTON (RIVER)

HODDESDON

- ADMIRALS WALK LAKE
- BROXBOURNE
- DOBBS WEIR FISHERY
- FEILDES WEIR
- LEA (RIVER)

KINGS LANGLEY

- GAYWOODS
- MERCHANT TAYLORS SCL LAKES

POTTERS BAR

- HOOK LAKE

RICKMANSWORTH

- BATCHWORTH LAKE
- COLNE (RIVER)
- CROXLEY HALL TROUT FISHERY
- INNS LAKE

ROYSTON

- RYEMEADS

ST ALBANS

- BOWMANS LAKES
- BROAD COLNEY LAKES
- COLNEY HEATH LAKE
- GRAND UNION CANAL
- LOWBELL LANE

STEVENAGE

- FAIRLANDS VALLEY PARK
- WESTONS LAKE

TRING

- AYLESBURY ARM CANAL
- GRAND UNION CANAL
- MARSWORTH RESERVOIR
- RISLIP LAKE
- STARTOPS RESERVOIR
- THAME (RIVER)
- TRING RESERVOIRS
- WILSTONE RESERVOIR

WALTHAM CROSS

- BOWYERS WATER
- BROOKFIELD LAKE
- CHESHUNT SOUTH RESERVOIR
- LEE NAVIGATION
- NORTH MET PIT
- OLD LEE (RIVER)
- PAYNES LANE PIT

WARE

- AMWELL LAKES
- LEE NAVIGATION
- NEW RIVER
- RIB VALLEY FISHING LAKE
- STANSTEAD ABBOTTS

WATFORD

- GADE (RIVER)
- GRAND UNION CANAL

WELWYN GARDEN CITY

- HOLWELL HYDE LAKE
- LEA (RIVER)
- STANBOROUGH LAKE

WORMLEY

- LEA (RIVER)
- OLD LEE (RIVER)

HUMBERSIDE

BEVERLEY

- BEVERLEY CANAL
- DRIFFIELD CANAL
- FOSSEHILL LAKES
- HULL (RIVER)
- LAKEMINSTER PARK
- LEVEN CANAL
- LEVEN PARK LAKE

BRIDLINGTON

- FISHPONDS FARM AND FISHERY

BROUGH

- BRICKYARD POND
- BROOMFLEET PONDS
- FISH TRADES POND
- MOTORWAY POND
- REDFERNS POND
- WOODALLS POND

CLEETHORPES

- CLEETHORPES COUNTRY PARK

DRIFFIELD

- BEVERLEY AND BARMSTON DRAIN
- BILLABONG WATER SPORTS AND CARAVAN PARK
- BRANDESBURTON
- BURSHILL A POND
- DACRE LAKESIDE PARK
- EMMOTLAND PONDS
- FAR GRANGE CARAVAN AND COUNTRY PARK
- FARM PONDS
- HUMBERSIDE FISHERIES
- LANGHOLME FISHERIES
- STAR CARR TROUT FARM
- THORPE HALL
- WANSFORD TROUT LAKE

GOOLE

- AIRE (RIVER)
- AIRE AND CALDER CANAL
- BIG HOLE PIT
- DERWENT (RIVER)
- GOWDALL LAKES
- MARKET WEIGHTON CANAL
- OAKLANDS WATER
- OUSE (RIVER)
- SYKEHOUSE RESERVOIRS
- WILLITOFT FISH FARM

GRIMSBY

- ESK (RIVER)
- LOUGH NAVIGATION
- NORTH THORESBY FISHERIES
- TETNEY LOCK ANGLING CLUB
- WILLOW LAKES

HULL

- BEVERLEY BECK
- BLUE LAGOON
- BRANDES BURTON 3 AND 4
- BURSTWICK SKI LAKE
- BURTON CONSTABLE COUNTRY PARK
- DERWENT (RIVER)
- EAST PARK LAKE
- HALSHAM POND
- LAMBWATH LAKES
- LEVEN CANAL
- NODDLE HILL LAKE
- RUSH LYVARS LAKE
- TILARY LAKE
- URE (RIVER)

SCUNTHORPE

- HOLME LAKE FISHERY
- NEST
- WATER SPRING FISHERY
- WILLOW SPRINGS

ISLE OF WIGHT

NEWPORT

- GILLEES POND
- GUNVILLE LAKE
- HALE MANOR LAKES
- ISLAND FISH FARM AND MEADOW LAKES
- MERSTONE FISHERIES
- SOMERTON RESERVOIR

SANDOWN

- BRADING LAKE
- MORTON FARM
- YAR (A) (RIVER)
- YAR (RIVER)

VENTNOR

- NETTLECOMBE FARMS
- ROOKLEY COUNTRY PARK
- WHITWELL PONDS

KENT

ASHFORD

- CACKLE HILL LAKES
- CHEQUERTREE TROUT AND COARSE FISHERY
- CONNINGBROOK
- EUREKA
- HOOKSTEAD LAKE
- NACCOLT LAKE
- SINGLETON LAKE
- STATION FARM
- STOWTING TROUT LAKE
- SURRENDEN LAKES
- WINGHAM FISHERY
- WOODCHURCH TROUT FISHERY

BEXLEYHEATH

- DANSON PARK LAKE

BROMLEY

- HAYES TROUT FISHERY
- ROOKERY LAKE

CANTERBURY

- BLUE LAGOON LAKE
- BRITTON COURT FARM
- BYWATER LAKE
- CALIBER COARSE AND CARP LAKES
- CHILHAM LAKE
- FORDWICH LAKE
- HANDLE LAKE
- HERONSVIEW FISHERIES

LONGSHAW FARM FISHING LAKES
MID KENT FISHERIES
MILTON PAN LAKE
NOOK & CRANNY LAKE
REED LAKE
STOUR (RIVER)
STOUR LAKE
STOUTING LAKE
SWAN LAKE
TONFORD LAKE
TRIANGLE LAKE

CHILHAM

MATCH LAKE

CRANBROOK

EASTERN ROTHER (RIVER)
HARTLEY LANDS FARM
HAWKHURST FISH FARM

DARTFORD

BROOKLANDS LAKE
COTTON FARM FISHERY
CRAYFORD (RIVER)
DARENT (RIVER)
DARENTH FISHING COMPLEX
HORTON KIRBY
SUTTON AT HONE LAKE TWO
SUTTON AT HONE LAKES ONE AND THREE

DEAL

COTTINGTON LAKES TROUT AND COARSE FISHERY
ROUKES DRIFT FARM

EAST PECKHAM

MEDWAY (RIVER)

EDENBRIDGE

CHIDDINGSTONE CASTLE LAKE
EDEN (RIVER)
LITTLE CANSIRON FISHING LAKES
SCARLETTS LAKE

FAVERSHAM

BYSINGWOOD
LAVENDER FARM
MILL POOL
SCHOOL POOL
WOOD POOL

GILLINGHAM

CAPSTONE FARM COUNTRY PARK

GRAVESEND

SHORNE COUNTRY PARK LAKES

HYTHE

BROCKHILL COUNTRY PARK

KENNARDINGTON

ROYAL MILITARY CANAL

LAMBERHURST

BEWL WATER
HOATHLEY FISHERY

LARKFIELD

ALDERS LAKES

MAIDSTONE

ABBEYCOURT LAKE
BLUEBELL FISHING PONDS
BURNHAM RESERVOIR
EAST FARLEIGH
GEDGES LAKES
LARKFIELD LAKES
MEDWAY (RIVER)
MOTE PARK FISHERY
RIVERFIELD CARP FARM

ORPINGTON

DARENT (RIVER)
RUXLEY PITS

ROCHESTER

ABBOTTS COURT
ALLHALLOWS LEISURE PARK
HOO LAKES

ROMNEY MARSH

DUNGENESS LONG PIT
ROYAL MILITARY CANAL
SPERRINGBROOK SEWER

SANDWICH

STONAR LAKE

SEVENOAKS

CHIPSTEAD LAKES
LONGFORD LAKE
SEPHAM TROUT FISHERY
SUNDRIDGE LAKES

SITTINGBOURNE

BROOMBANKS PITS
SITTINGBOURNE LAKES

TENTERDEN

BIDDENDEN LAKE
HEXDEN CHANNEL
ROTHER (RIVER)
TENTERDEN TROUT WATERS

TONBRIDGE

BALLAST PIT
BARDEN LAKE
BOUGH BEECH RESERVOIR
EDEN (RIVER)
GRANGE POOL
HAYSDEN COUNTRY PARK
LONGFIELD LAKE
MEDWAY (RIVER)
MONK LAKE FISHERIES
MOUSEHOLE LAKE
PIPPINS FARM LAKE
PITTLANDS LAKES
SILVER SPRINGS FISHERY
WIDEHURST FARM

TUNBRIDGE WELLS

BARTLEY MILL FISHERY
BIRCHDEN FARM FISHERY
CHALYBEATE SPRINGS TROUT FISHERY
DUNDALE LAKE
FORDCOMBE
FRANT LAKES
MEDWAY (RIVER)
SPRING HILL TROUT WATERS
TEISE (RIVER)

WROTHAM

ST CLERE LAKE

LANCASHIRE

ACCRINGTON

DEAN CLOUGH RESERVOIR
HAGGS RESERVOIR
KEARNS ALLEN LODGES
MITCHELLS HOUSE RESERVOIR
PARSONAGE RESERVOIR

BLACKBURN

CALDER (RIVER)
DICKENS STREET LODGE
EARNSDALE RESERVOIR
ENTWHISTLES RESERVOIR
HODDER (RIVER)
HODDLESDEN LAKE
RIBBLE (RIVER)
RISHTON RESERVOIR
STANWORTH RESERVOIR
WAYOH RESERVOIR

BOLTON

ADLINGTON RESERVOIR
BOLTON CANAL
BRADFORD RESERVOIR
BRADSHAW HALL FISHERIES
BRYAN HEY RESERVOIR
CHURCH GARDEN
CLOWBRIDGE RESERVOIR
CROMPTON LODGE
DINGLE RESERVOIR
DIXON GREEN RESERVOIR
DOFFCOCKER LODGE
DUNSCAR SHORE LODGE
EAGLEY WATERS
FIRWOOD LODGE AND THE BUNK
GLEAVES RESERVOIR
HULTON PARK LAKE
JUMBLES RESERVOIR
MANCHESTER, BOLTON AND BURY CANAL
MELCHES POND
RUMWORTH LODGE RESERVOIR
STARMOUNT LODGES
TEMPLE SPRINGS
UPPER RIVINGTON RESERVOIR
UPPER RODDLESWORTH RESERVOIR

BROUGHTON-IN-FURNESS

DUDDON (RIVER)

BURNLEY

CALDER (RIVER)
CANT CLOUGH RESERVOIR
CLIVIGER FISH PONDS
COLDWELL (LOWER) RESERVOIR
LANESHAW RESERVOIR
LEEDS TO LIVERPOOL CANAL
LOWER COLDWELL RESERVOIR
LOWER HOUSE LODGE
PORTSMOUTH RESERVIOR
ROWLEY PARK LAKE
SWINDEN RESERVOIR

BURSCOUGH

LATHOM FISHERIES

CHORLEY

BIRKACRE LODGES
BRINSCALL LODGE
CHARITY FARM FISHERY
COTTAGE GREEN GARDEN CENTRE
CROFT FISHERIES
DRAKESHEAD FLY FISHERY
FOUNDRY LODGE
HEAPEY NO 1
HEAPEY NO 2
HEAPEY NO 3
HEAPEY NO 6
HESKIN OLD FARM FISHERY
LANCASTER HOUSE
LEEDS TO LIVERPOOL CANAL
LOWER RIVINGTON RESERVOIR
LOWER RODDLESWORTH RESERVOIR
RAKE BROOK RESERVOIR
WITHNELL RESERVOIRS
WORTHINGTON NO 1
WORTHINGTON NO 2
WORTHINGTON NO 3

CLAPHAM

WENNING (RIVER)

CLITHEROE

EDISFORD AND BRUNGERLEY PARK
HODDER (RIVER)
PINE LODGE FISHERIES
RIBBLE (RIVER)
SABDEN RESERVOIR
STOCKS FLY FISHERY

COLNE

BALL GROVE LAKE
BROWNHILL RESERVOIR
COLNE WATER
FOULRIDGE RESERVOIR
HULLDOWN TROUT FISHERY

DARWEN

DEAN RESERVOIR
HODDLESDEN RESERVOIR

FLEETWOOD

WYRE (RIVER)

HEYWOOD

QUEENS PARK LAKE

KIRKHAM
- WYRE (RIVER)

LANCASTER
- BANK HOUSE FLY FISHERY
- BENTHAM STREAM
- BENTHAM TROUT FISHERY
- CONDER VALLEY FLY FISHERY
- HALTON FISHERY
- LANCASTER CANAL
- LUNE (RIVER)
- SKERTON FISHERY
- THURSLAND HILL FARM
- WENNING (RIVER)
- WYRESIDE LAKES FISHERY AND LODGINGS

MORECAMBE
- LITTLE DALE HALL COARSE FISHERY
- SWANTLEY LAKE

NELSON
- BARROWFORD RESERVOIR
- BLACKMOSS RESERVOIR
- INGS FARM TROUT FISHERY
- PENDLE WATER
- ROUGHLEE TROUT FISHERY
- WALVERDEN RESERVOIR
- WHITEMOOR RESERVOIR

ORMSKIRK
- BARRETTS FARM FISHERY
- BURSCOUGH BRICKWORKS LAKE
- GREEN LANE PONDS
- LEEDS TO LIVERPOOL CANAL
- PLATTS LANE LAKE
- RUFFORD CANAL

PRESTON
- BANNISTER HALL FARM
- BARNSFOLD WATERS
- BRIARCROFT FISHERY
- CHURN CLOUGH RESERVOIR
- CLAYLANDS CARAVAN SITE
- CLEVELEY BRIDGE FISHERY
- COPTHORNE COARSE FISHERIES
- CUERDEN VALLEY LAKE
- DERWENT (RIVER)
- DILWORTH (UPPER) RESERVOIR
- ERIC FISHWICK NATURE RESERVE
- FARINGTON LODGES
- GREAT BIRCH WOOD PONDS
- GREENHALGH LODGE FISHERY
- GRIMSARGH RESERVOIR
- GRIZEDALE LEA RESERVOIR
- HUDSONS FARM
- IRWELL (RIVER)
- KNIGHT BOTTOMS LAKE
- LANCASTER CANAL
- LEEDS TO LIVERPOOL CANAL
- LEISURE LAKES
- LONGTON BRICKCROFT
- LYNDHURST FARM LAKE
- MANOR HOUSE FISHERY
- MARTIN HALL FARM
- RED ROCKS FISHERY
- RIBBLE (RIVER)
- ROACH BRIDGE FISHERY
- RUSHYVARS LAKES
- SHRUGGS WOOD FISHERY
- SPADE MILL RESERVOIR NO.2
- ST MICHAELS WYRESIDE FISHERY
- TOAD HALL FARM
- TURBARY HOUSE NURSARY
- TURTON AND ENTWISTLE RESERVOIR
- TWIN LAKES TROUT FISHERY
- WOODFOLD FARM FISHERIES
- WRYE (RIVER)

ROSSENDALE
- FISHMOOR RESERVOIR
- HOLDEN WOOD RESERVOIR
- LANCASTER HOUSE FARM FISHERY
- LOVECLOUGH TROUT FISHERY
- OGDEN RESERVOIR

SKELMERSDALE
- ABBEY LAKES

THORNTON-CLEVELEYS
- STANLEY PARK LAKE

WIGAN
- ANGLEZARKE RESERVOIR
- ASHTON CANAL
- BICKERSHAW WATERS
- BRYN FLASH
- DEEP PIT
- DOUGLAS (RIVER)
- FAN LODGE
- FIR TREE LODGE
- FORSTERS LODGES
- HIGHER HALL FLASH
- HORROCKS FLASH
- HOUGHTONS LODGE
- INCE MOSS FISHERIES
- INCE PARK LAKE
- ISLAND DAM
- MELLINGS NO 1
- ORRELL WATER PARK
- POLLYS FLASH
- SCOT LANE PONDS
- SQUARE LODGE
- THREE SISTERS
- WIDOWS FLASH

LEICESTERSHIRE

COALVILLE
- SNIBSON COLLIERY CARP LAKE

HINCKLEY
- BAXTERS GARDEN FARM LAKE
- LAKESIDE FISHING
- LYNCHGATE LANE FISHERY
- MANOR FARM POOLS
- PARKLANDS FISHERY
- SHELL FRESH LAKE

LEICESTER
- BROOME FISHERIES
- CHARNWOOD WATER
- FRISBY LAKES
- GROBY FISHING LAKES
- LAKESIDE SPORTING
- LAUNDE ABBEY LAKES
- LEICESTER CANAL
- LEICESTER GRAND UNION CANAL
- MALLORY PARK FISHERIES
- MONNOW (RIVER)
- NANPANTAN RESERVOIR
- PROCTORS PLEASURE PARK
- SOAR (RIVER)
- SPRING GRANGE FISHERY
- THORNTON RESERVOIR
- WATERMEAD PARK LAKES
- WATERY GATE FISHERY
- WILLOWS FARM FISHING

LOUGHBOROUGH
- LOUGHBOROUGH SOAR CANAL
- SOAR (RIVER)

LUTTERWORTH
- C J FISHERIES
- HALL FARM
- HOLLY FARM FISHERY
- MANOR FARM
- MILL FARM FISHERY
- PEATLING POOLS (1-6)
- STEMBOROUGH MILL TROUT FARM

MARKET HARBOROUGH
- BROOK MEADOW FISHERY
- EYEBROOK TROUT FISHERY
- FOLLY POND
- WELLAND LODGE FISHERY

MELTON MOWBRAY
- BROOKSBY COLLEGE
- HALL FARM FISHING
- HOLWELL WORKS RESERVOIR
- WREAKE (RIVER)

RUTLAND
- RUTLAND WATER

SWITHLAND
- SWITHLAND RESERVOIR

WILLOUGHBY WATERLEASE
- WHETSTONE GORSE

LINCOLNSHIRE

ALFORD
- ABY POND
- OHAM LAKES
- WOODTHORPE HALL LAKE

BASTON FEN
- WHITE HOUSE PREDATOR LAKE

BOSTON
- HOBHOLE DRAIN
- LAKE HELEN
- ROSSWAYS WATER
- STICKNEY BRICKPONDS
- WEST FEN DRAIN
- WHARFE (RIVER)
- WITHAM (RIVER)

BOURNE
- BASTON FEN FISHERY
- GRIMSTHORPE LAKE

GAINSBOROUGH
- DAIWA GULL POOL
- TRENT (RIVER)
- WARPING DRAIN
- WILLOW BANK FISHERY
- WOODLANDS LAKE

GRANTHAM
- BELVOIR CASTLE
- BRICKYARD POND
- BUCKMINSTER PARK LAKE
- CULVERTHORPE LAKES
- DENTON RESERVOIR
- KINPTON RESERVOIR
- SYSTON PARK TROUT LAKE
- WILLOW LAKES
- WITHAM (RIVER)
- WOODLAND WATERS

HORNCASTLE
- ASHBY PARK FISHERIES
- BELLS YARD LAKE
- REVESBY RESERVOIR

IMMINGHAM
- EAST HALTON FISHING LAKES
- HOMESTEAD LAKE
- WINTER BROTHERS POND
- WINTERS LAKE

LINCOLN
- BOULTHAM PARK LAKE
- DYKES COTTAGE LAKES
- HARTSHOLME PARK LAKE
- HYKEHAM PIT
- LAKESIDE
- MARRIS LAKES
- OAKHILL LEISURE
- RICHMOND LAKES
- SHANDY KEV FISHERIES
- STARMERS PIT
- SUDBROOK POND
- TATTERSHALL LEISURE PARK
- TILL (RIVER)
- TIM HALL LAKE
- TRENT (RIVER)
- UPPER WITHAM (RIVER)
- WHISBY GARDEN CENTRE
- WHITE SWAN ANGLING CLUB

LOUTH
- ALVINGHAM FISHERIES
- BELLEAU BRIDGE FARM LAKE
- BRICKYARD FISHERY
- CHARLES STREET POND
- LINDEN WALK POND
- OASIS LAKES
- OLSTEN FISHERY

- STONE END LAKE
- THORPE LE VALE FISHERY
- VICKERS POND
- WARREN POND
- WILLOW FARM

MABLETHORPE

- GRANGE FARM LEISURE

MARKET RASEN

- CLAYBRIDGE TROUT LAKES
- FISH POND FARM
- GOLTHO LAKE
- HATTON TROUT LAKE
- LOBBY FIELD PONDS
- NORTH KELSEY PARK
- ST EAU FISHING SYNDICATE
- TOFT NEWTON TROUT FISHERY

SKEGNESS

- DENNIS RAINWATER LAKE
- GROOBYS PIT
- HERONS MEAD
- HILL VIEW LAKES
- HOLLAND PARK
- LAKESIDE LEISURE PARK
- MILL HILL LAKES
- MILL ROAD LAKES
- ROACH FARM PARK
- ROD AND LINE CARAVAN PARK
- SKEGNESS WATER LEISURE PARK
- STEEPING (RIVER)
- SWAN LAKE
- SYCAMORE FISHING LAKES
- WATERSIDE LEISURE PARK

SLEAFORD

- HAVERHOLME PARK

SPALDING

- LAKE ROSS FISHERY
- SOUTH HOLLAND DRAIN
- WELLAND (RIVER)

SPILSBY

- KEAL COATES FISHERY
- WOODLANDS FISHERY

STAMFORD

- BURGHLEY PARK LAKE
- TALLINGTON FISHERY

TATTERSHALL

- MOON LAKE

WOODHALL SPA

- PEACOCK LAKE

LINCOLNSHIRE (NORTH)

BARTON-UPON-HUMBER

- BARTON BROADS LAKE
- HOE HILL POND
- MARSHLANDS
- PASTURE HOUSE FISHERY
- PELICAN POND
- TARGET LAKE
- TILEYARD LANE
- WESTFIELD LAKES

BRIGG

- KINGFISHER LODGE
- OLD ANCHOLME (RIVER)

BROUGH

- STADDLETHORPE POND

SCUNTHORPE

- ORCHARD POND

LONDON (GREATER)

LONDON

- ALEXANDRA PALACE LAKE
- ALEXANDRA PARK LAKE
- ASHMERE FISHERIES
- ASHVALE FISHERIES
- BEDFONT LAKE
- BIRCHMERE
- BOXERS LAKE
- BROXBOURNE MEADOWS FISHERY
- BURES LAKE
- CARGILL LAKE
- CLAPHAM COMMON POND
- COLNE (RIVER)
- COPPER MILLSTREAM
- COWLEY LAKE
- CUTTING LAKE
- EAST WARWICK
- ENFIELD LOCK
- FLAKE STREAM
- FORTY HALL LAKE
- FROGMORE LAKE
- FURNACE POND
- GRAND UNION CANAL
- GREENHAMS
- HALLIFORD MERE LAKES
- HAMPSTEAD HEATH
- HAREFIELD CARP LAKE
- HEATH VALE POND
- HENRY STREETER LAKE
- HIGH MAYNARD RESERVOIR
- HIGHAMS PARK LAKE
- HIGHGATE PONDS
- HOLLOW PONDS
- HORSEMILL STREAM
- KINGFISHER LAKE
- KNIGHTSCOTE PONDS
- KORDA LAKE
- LEA NAVIGATION
- LEE NAVIGATION
- LITTLE BRITAIN LAKE
- LIZARD LAKES
- LOCKWOOD RESERVOIR
- LOW MAYNARD RESERVOIR
- MARCOA LAKE
- MULGROVE POND
- NEW CUT
- NORTH TROY LAKE AND COLNE (RIVER)
- NORWOOD LAKE
- OLD LEE (RIVER)
- OSTERLEY PARK MIDDLE LAKE
- PENTON HOOK LOCK
- PERCH POND
- PONDERS END
- POTOMAC POND
- REGENTS CANAL
- RODNEY MEADOW
- SAVAY LAKE
- SHEEPWALK LAKE
- SHEPPERTON LAKE
- SHEPPERTON LOCK
- SOUTH NORWOOD LAKE
- STOCKLEY ROAD LAKES
- STUDIO AND BROADWATER
- SWYERS LAKE
- SYON PARK FISHERY
- TEDDINGTON LOCK
- THAMES (RIVER)
- THORNEY POOL
- TRENT COUNTRY PARK LAKES
- TRENT PARK LAKES
- VALE OF HEATH POND
- WALTHAMSTOW RESERVOIR (EAST WARWICK)
- WALTHAMSTOW RESERVOIR (NO 1)
- WALTHAMSTOW RESERVOIR (NO 2 AND NO 3)
- WALTHAMSTOW RESERVOIR (NO 4 TROUT)
- WALTHAMSTOW RESERVOIR (NO 5)
- WALTHAMSTOW RESERVOIR (WEST WARWICK)
- WANDSWORTH COMMON POND
- WANSTEAD PARK LAKES
- WEST RESERVOIR
- WEST WARWICK
- WHITE HORSE FISHERIES
- WILLOWSIDE CARP LAKE
- WOOLWICH DOCKYARD
- WRAYSBURY ONE
- WRAYSBURY TWO

ORPINGTON

- BROOMWOOD LAKE

MANCHESTER (GREATER)

ASHTON-UNDER-LYNE

- CRIME LAKE
- STAMFORD PARK LAKES

BURY

- BURRS LODGE
- CARCUS WATERS
- CLARENCE RECREATION GROUND
- CROMPTONS WATER
- CROWN POOLS
- ELTON RESERVOIR
- ENDCROFTS POND
- FIELD LODGE POND
- FISHERMANS RETREAT
- IRWELL (RIVER)
- ISLAND AND CARTWHEEL LODGES
- MANCHESTER, BOLTON AND BURY CANAL
- TWINE VALLEY TROUT FISHERY

HEYWOOD

- PILSWORTH FISHERY COMPLEX

LEIGH

- FIR TREE FLASH
- FIRS PARK LAKE
- LEEDS TO LIVERPOOL CANAL
- LEIGH BRANCH CANAL
- PENNINGTON FLASH

LITTLEBOROUGH

- CLEGG HALL LAKES
- CROFT HEAD FISHERY
- GROVE LODGE
- HOLLINGWORTH LAKE COUNTRY PARK
- LOWER TOWN HOUSE FISHERY
- WHITELEY KNOWL RESERVOIR

MANCHESTER

- ASHENHURST LAKES
- BEEFOLD LODGE
- BLACKLEACH RESERVOIR
- BOGGART HOLE CLOUGH
- BOWKER LAKES
- BRIDGEWATER CANAL
- CHORLTON WATER PARK
- DEBDALE RESERVOIRS
- DINGLE LODGE
- DOUBLEWOODS
- FARM LODGE
- GEIGYS WATER
- GORSE PIT RESERVOIR
- GORTON (LOWER) RESERVOIR
- GORTON (UPPER) RESERVOIR
- HEATON PARK
- KING GEORGE V POOL
- KING WILLIAM IV RESERVOIR
- LANKYS MILL POND
- LEEKES WATER
- MANCHESTER CANAL
- MANCHESTER, BOLTON AND BURY CANAL
- MYRTLE ROAD LODGES
- OLD IRWELL
- PAINSWICK PARK LAKE
- PLATT FIELDS
- RHODES LODGE
- SANDY BEACH
- STAKEHILL LODGES
- STAR MOUNT
- SWAN LODGE
- UPPER GORTON RESERVOIR
- WESTGATE POOL
- WHITTLE BROOK RESERVOIR
- WITHINS RESERVOIR

MILLOM

- BLACK BECK (RIVER)

OLDHAM

- ALEXANDRA PARK
- BLACK MOSS RESERVOIR

- BRUN CLOUGH RESERVOIR
- DOWRY AND NEW YEARS BRIDGE RESERVOIR
- HUDDERSFIELD NARROW CANAL
- KITCLIFFE RESERVOIR
- LITTLE SEA RESERVOIR
- LOWER CASTLESHAW RESERVOIR
- OLDHAM FLY FISHING
- REDBROOK RESERVOIR
- ROYAL GEORGE MILL COMPLEX
- TAME (RIVER)
- TANNERS DAM

ROCHDALE

- BUCKLEY WOOD RESERVOIR
- DOCTOR DAM FISHERY
- OGDEN LOWER RESERVOIR
- PENNINE TROUT FISHERY
- PIETHORNE RESERVOIR
- ROCHDALE CANAL
- WATERGROVE RESERVOIR

SALFORD

- CLIFTON MARINA
- CLOWES PARK LAKE
- SALFORD QUAYS

STOCKPORT

- BOLLINHURST RESERVOIR
- DAVENPORT
- LUDWORTH RESERVOIR
- MACCLESFIELD CANAL
- NEW HOUSE FARM POOL
- PEAK FOREST CANAL
- POYNTON POOL
- REDDISH VALE MILL PONDS
- ROMAN LAKE LEISURE PARK
- STONEY PIT RESERVOIR
- WOODBANK PARK POOL

MERSEYSIDE

BIRKENHEAD

- BIRKENHEAD LOWER PARK LAKE
- LOWER LAKE
- UPPER LAKE

LIVERPOOL

- CALDERSTONES PARK LAKE
- FOOTBALL PIT
- GREENBANK PARK LAKE
- LEEDS TO LIVERPOOL
- LEEDS TO LIVERPOOL CANAL
- MILL HOUSE FISHERY
- NEWSHAM PARK
- PRINCES PARK LAKE
- STANLEY PARK LAKE
- WALTON HALL PARK

NEWTON-LE-WILLOWS

- WOODHOUSE FISH FARM

PRESCOT

- CARR LANE POOL

ST HELENS

- CARR MILL DAM
- LEG OMUTTON DAM
- PADDOCK DAM

WIRRAL

- ARROWE PARK LAKE
- CENTRAL PARK LAKE
- EVE A LYN FARM
- MORETON MERE
- POULTON RECREATION FIELD POOL
- RODEE MERE
- WOODSLEE POOL

MIDLANDS (WEST)

BIRMINGHAM

- ALVECHURCH FISHERIES
- EDGBASTON RESERVOIR
- SHUSTOKE FLY FISHERS
- SOHO LOOP CANAL
- TAME VALLEY CANAL
- WALCOT EAST LAKE

BRIDGNORTH

- ASTBURY FALLS FISH FARM
- KINGSNORDLEY
- NORDLEY POOLS
- POOL HALL
- SEVERN (RIVER)

COVENTRY

- AVON (RIVER)
- BLYTHE (RIVER)
- COOMBE ABBEY LAKE
- COOMBE POOL
- HOPSFORD HALL FISHERY
- LAVENDER HALL
- MEADOWLANDS
- PACKINGTON SOMERS FISHERY
- PACKINGTON TROUT FISHERY
- ROYAL BRITISH LEGION POOLS
- RYTON POOLS COUNTRY PARK
- SOMERS FISHERY

HALESOWEN

- BULL FISHERY
- DAYHOUSE FARM

PELSALL

- CANNOCK EXTENSION CANAL

SOLIHULL

- BLYTHE WATERS
- EARLSWOOD LAKES
- GRAND UNION CANAL
- GREY MILL FARM
- KINGSHURST LAKE
- TIDBURY GREEN GOLF CLUB

STOURBRIDGE

- WASSELL GROVE FISHERIES

SUTTON COLDFIELD

- CUTTLE MILL CARP FISHERY
- KINGSBURY WATER PARK
- PENNS HALL LAKE
- SUTTON PARK

WALSALL

- FOXHILLS FISHERY
- HEATHFIELD POOL
- RUSHALL CANAL
- SNEYD POOL
- WALSALL ARBORETUM

WARWICK

- AVON (RIVER)

WEST BROMWICH

- DARTMOUTH PARK
- SWAN POOL

WOLVERHAMPTON

- BRIDGE POOL
- CHURCH POOL
- HERON BROOK FISHERY
- HIMLEY ISLAND POOL
- LINCOMB LOCK
- PATSHULL PARK
- POOLE HALL FARM
- STAFFORD TO WORCESTER CANAL

NORFOLK

ATTLEBOROUGH

- ABBEY WATERS
- MANOR LAKE
- MILL FARM FISHERY
- PECK MEADOW POND
- SWANGEY LAKES
- WALNUT FARM FISHERIES

AYLESHAM

- BURE VALLEY LAKES
- UPPER BURE (STREAM)

CROMER

- FELBRIGG HALL LAKE
- GUNTON PARK LAKE

DEREHAM

- BARTLES LODGE
- BILNEY LAKES
- NORFOLK AND SUFFOLK FLY FISHERIES LAKE
- RAILWAY LAKE
- ROOSTING HILLS
- SALMON AND TROUT ASSOCIATION LAKES
- SWANTON MORLEY FISHERY
- WENSUM (RIVER)
- WHINBURGH TROUT LAKE

DISS

- DISS MERE
- HINDERCLAY LAKES
- WEYBREAD FISHERY

DOWNHAM MARKET

- DENTS OF HILGAY
- GREAT OUSE (RIVER)
- HILGAY (RIVER)
- LAKESIDE CARAVAN PARK
- TEN MILE BANK

EAST DEREHAM

- BILLINGFORD PIT
- BRIDGE FARM FISHERIES

EYE

- DOVE BROOK

FAKENHAM

- WENSUM (RIVER)
- WILLSMORE WATER

GREAT YARMOUTH

- BURE (RIVER)
- DECOY FARM
- FRITTON LAKE
- HALL FARM LAKES
- MARTHAM PITS
- ORMESBY ROLLESBY
- STOKESBY (RIVER)
- THURNE MOUTH (RIVER)

HOLT

- FELGRIGG LAKE
- LETHERINGSETT FISHERY
- SALTHOUSE BROAD

KING'S LYNN

- BABINGLEY (RIVER)
- BRADMOOR LAKES
- CASTLE RISING STREAM
- CUT OFF CHANNEL
- FOSTERS END PIT
- GATTON WATER CARAVAN SITE
- GREAT OUSE RELIEF CHANNEL
- LAKESIDE
- LITTLE DUNHAM CARP LAKES
- LITTLE OUSE (RIVER)
- MEADOW LAKE
- NAR (RIVER)
- NAR STREAM
- NARBOROUGH TROUT FARM
- PENTNEY LAKES
- RELIEF CHANNEL
- SOVEREIGN LAKES
- TOTTENHILL PIT
- WILLOWCROFT FISHERY
- WISSEY (RIVER)
- WOODLAKES FISHERY

LENWADE

- BRIDGE INN FISHERY

MELTON CONSTABLE

- GUNTHORPE HALL LAKE

NORWICH

- ABBOTS HALL
- ACLE (RIVER)
- BARFORD LAKES FISHERY
- BARNINGHAM HALL LAKE
- BAWBURGH LAKES
- BLICKLING PARK LAKE
- BOOTON CLAY PIT
- BORE VALLEY LAKES
- BURE (RIVER)
- CANTLEY (RIVER)
- CANTLEY SUGAR FACTORY
- CATCH 22 FISHERY
- CHAPEL ROAD LAKE

- CHARITY LAKES
- COBBLEACRES LAKES
- COLTON LAKE
- COSTESSEY PITS
- DRAYTON GREEN (RIVER)
- FELMINGHAM MILL LAKES
- FELTHORPE LAKE
- GIMINGHAM LAKES
- GLEN MERE
- GREAT MELTON FISHERY
- HADDISCOE PIT
- HARDLEY MARSHES
- HAVERINGLAND HALL PARK
- HEVINGHAM LAKES
- HICKLING BROAD
- HINGHAM FISHMERE
- HORNING (RIVER)
- KINGFISHER LAKES
- LENWADE COMMON LAKES
- LENWADE TROUT FISHERY
- LYNG PIT
- MILL FARM FISHERY
- PARK LIME PIT
- RACKHEATH SPRINGS
- RECTORY FARM FISHERY
- REEPHAM FISHERY
- RINGLAND LAKES
- RINGLAND PITS
- ROCKLAND BROAD
- RUSTON REACHES
- SCOULTON MERE
- SHALLOW BROOK LAKES
- SHORT PLANTATION LAKE
- SNETTERTON PITS
- TASWOOD LAKES FISH FARM AND FISHERY
- TAVERHAM
- TAVERHAM MILLS FISHERY
- UNIVERSITY BROAD
- WENSUM (RIVER)
- WROXHAM BROAD
- YARE (RIVER)

SWAFFHAM
- DUNHAM CARP AND TENCH LAKES

SWANNINGTON
- NATURES HAVEN LAKES

THETFORD
- BUCKENHAM PITS
- MIDDLE HARLING LAKE
- WOODRISING WATER MEADOWS

THUXTON
- RAILWAY LAKE

WALSINGHAM
- WENSUM (RIVER)

WATTON
- LOCH NEATON

WELLS-NEXT-THE-SEA
- HOLKHAM LAKE

NORTHAMPTONSHIRE

CORBY
- CORBY BOATING LAKE
- LYNN POOL FISHERY

DAVENTRY
- BODDINGTON RESERVOIR
- CANONS ASHBY LAKES
- CASTLE ANGLING ASSOCIATION
- DAVENTRY COUNTRY PARK
- DRAYTON RESERVOIR
- FLECKNOE FARM FISHERIES
- OXFORD CANAL

HARLESTON
- WEYBREAD GRAVEL PITS

KETTERING
- ALDWINCLE PITS
- BARKERS LAKE
- ELINOR COARSE LAKE
- ELINOR TROUT FISHERY
- ISE (RIVER)
- ISLIP NATURE LAKE
- NENE (RIVER)
- RINGSTEAD GRANGE TROUT FISHERY
- RINGSTEAD ISLAND
- THORPE WATERVILLE LAKE
- THRAPSTON (RIVER)
- THRAPSTON LAKES

NORTHAMPTON
- ABINGDON PARK LAKE
- BILLING AQUADROME
- BLUE LAGOON
- CASTLE ASHBY LAKES
- CRESCENT LAKE
- DELEPRE PARK LAKE
- DUSTON RESERVOIR
- ECTON GRAVEL PITS
- FOXHOLES FISHERIES
- GLEBE LAKE
- GRAND UNION CANAL
- GRENDON LAKES
- HARDWATER LAKE
- HEYFORD FISHERY
- HOLLOWELL RESERVOIR
- MENAGERIE POND
- NASEBY RESERVOIR
- NENE (RIVER)
- NORTHAMPTON JUNCTION CANAL
- PITSFORD RESERVOIR
- RAVENSTHORPE TROUT FISHERY
- SHELFLEYS LAKE
- ST JAMES SMALL PARK LAKE
- SULBY RESERVOIR
- WEEDON ROAD GRAVEL PIT
- WELFORD RESERVOIR
- WOOTTON BROOK LAKE

RUSHDEN
- LAKESIDE COUNTRY CLUB

TOWCESTER
- GREEN FARM LAKES
- SILVER LAKE

WELLINGBOROUGH
- BLUNHAM PITS
- CHESTER FARM LAKE
- DITCHFORD PITS
- LITTLE IRCHESTER COMPLEX
- PINE TREES LAKES
- SOUTH VIEW FARM CARP FISHERY
- SYWELL RESERVOIR

NORTHUMBERLAND

ALNWICK
- ALN (RIVER)
- TWEED (RIVER)

ASHINGTON
- QUEEN ELIZABETH II COUNTRY PARK
- WANSBECK (RIVER)

BERWICK-UPON-TWEED
- TWEED (RIVER)
- WHITEADDER (RIVER)

BLYTH
- HORTON GRANGE LAKE

COLDSTREAM
- LEET (RIVER)
- LYNE (RIVER)
- TWEED (RIVER)

CORBRIDGE
- HALLINGTON RESERVOIRS
- THORNBROUGH LAKE
- TYNE (RIVER)

HALTWHISTLE
- GILSLAND LAKE
- IRTHING (RIVER)
- SOUTH TYNE (RIVER)

HEXHAM
- GIBBS HILL TROUT FISHERY
- HADRIAN LODGE
- HEXHAM FISHERIES
- KIELDER WATER
- LANGLEY DAM FISHERIES
- LINNEL WOOD LAKE
- NORTH TYNE (RIVER)
- REDE (RIVER)
- TYNE (RIVER)
- WHITTLE DEAN RESERVOIR

MORPETH
- COQUET (RIVER)
- FELTON FENCE FARM PONDS
- FONTBURN RESERVOIR
- PLESSEY WOODS
- WANSBECK (RIVER)
- WANSBECK STREAM

PRUDHOE
- TYNE (RIVER)

STOCKSFIELD
- TYNE (RIVER)

THROPTON
- WREIGH (RIVER)

WYLAM
- TYNE (RIVER)
- WILLIES WELL

NOTTINGHAMSHIRE

GRANTHAM
- LAKESIDE FARM

MANSFIELD
- HARWICK HALL LAKES
- L-LAKE FISHERY
- MAUN (RIVER)
- SHERWOOD FOREST FARM PARK FISHERY
- SUTTON LAWN DAM

NEWARK
- A1 PITS
- CRANWELL LANE TROUT FISHERY
- CROMWELL LAKE TROUT FISHERY
- FLEET (RIVER)
- SAPPHIRE LAKES
- SMEATONS LAKES
- TRENT (RIVER)
- WHARFE (RIVER)
- WINDMILL FARM LAKES
- WITHAM (RIVER)

NEWARK-ON-TRENT
- TRENT (RIVER)

NOTTINGHAM
- ATTENBOROUGH GRAVEL PITS
- BESTWOOD POND
- COLWICK COUNTRY PARK
- COVERT SPRINGS FISHERIES
- CRANFLEET CANAL
- DOLAR POND
- EASTWOOD ANGLERS
- ENVIRONMENT AGENCY
- EREWASH CANAL
- GRANTHAM CANAL
- HOLME PIERPOINT
- IRONMONGERS POND
- NOTTINGHAM CANAL
- NOTTINGHAM CASTLE MARINA
- PINDERS PONDS
- TRENT (RIVER)
- WINFIELD LAGOON

RETFORD
- CHESTERFIELD CANAL
- DANESHILL LAKES
- HALLCROFT FISHERIES
- LAKESIDE FISHERY
- LOUND WINDSURF LAKE
- STRIP PONDS
- TRENT (RIVER)

SUTTON-IN-ASHFIELD
- KINGS MILL RESERVOIR

WORKSOP
- CLUMBER LAKE
- LANGOLD LAKES
- OWDY LANE TROUT FISHERY
- SANDHILL LAKE
- WOODEND QUARRY POND
- WOODSETTS QUARRY POND

OLDHAM
- CASTLESHAW (LOWER) RESERVOIR

OXFORDSHIRE

ABINGDON
- BULLFIELD LAKE
- CLIFTON LOCK
- DAYS LOCK
- MARLBOROUGH POOL
- MILLETS FARM TROUT FISHERY
- STRATTON LODGE
- THAMES (RIVER)

BAMPTON
- GRAFTON LOCK
- RUSHEY WEIR
- SHIFFORD LOCK
- THAMES (RIVER)

BANBURY
- CHEYNEY MANOR FISHERY
- CLATTERCOTE RESERVOIR
- COLLEGE FARM FISHING
- GRIMSBURY RESERVOIR
- HEART OF ENGLAND FISHERY
- HORSE AND GROOM LAKES
- NELL BRIDGE FISHERY
- OXFORD CANAL

BICESTER
- CHERWELL (RIVER)
- GLEBE COURT LAKE
- MANOR LAKE
- OXFORD CANAL
- PIMLICO FARM LAKES
- ROYAL PIONEER CORPS ANGLING ASSOCIATION WATER
- STATES LAGOON

BULBOURNE
- GRAND UNION CANAL

BURFORD
- WINDRUSH (RIVER)

CHIPPING NORTON
- BUTLERS HILL FARM
- CHAD LAKES
- CORNBURY PARK FISHERY
- SALFORD TROUT LAKES

COWLEY
- THAMES (RIVER)

DIDCOT
- THAMES (RIVER)

FARINGDON
- BUSCOT LOCK
- FARINGDON LAKE
- RADCOT LOCK
- RUSHEY LOCK

HENLEY-ON-THAMES
- MARSH LOCK
- SHIPLAKE LOCK
- SWISS FARM LAKE
- THAME (RIVER)
- THAMES (RIVER)

ICKFORD
- THAME (RIVER)

KIDLINGTON
- CHERWELL (RIVER)
- OXFORD CANAL

OXFORD
- BARNES TROUT LAKES
- BEIRTON LAKES
- CHERWELL (RIVER)
- FARMOOR TROUT FISHERY
- GOLDFISH BOWL (THE)
- GRAND UNION CANAL
- MANOR HOUSE
- MILTON POOLS FARM
- OXFORD CANAL
- ROLFS LAKE
- SANDFORD LOCK
- SEVERALLS FARM A AND B
- THAMES (RIVER)

SUMMERTOWN
- THAMES (RIVER)

WALLINGFORD
- BENSON LOCK
- DORCHESTER LAGOON
- ORCHID LAKES
- THAME (RIVER)
- THAMES (RIVER)

WANTAGE
- CLEARWATER FISH FARM
- LOCKINGE TROUT FISHERY

WITNEY
- CHRISTCHURCH LAKE
- DARLOW LAKE
- EYNSHAM LOCK
- FARMOOR 1 RESERVOIR
- GAUNTS LAKE
- HARDWICK LAKE AND SMITHS POOL
- HEYFORD LAKES
- HUNTS CORNER
- LINCH HILL FISHERY
- MANOR FARM LAKE
- OXLEASE LAKE
- ST JOHNS POOL
- THAMES (RIVER)
- UNITY LAKE
- WINDRUSH (RIVER)
- YEOMANS LAKE

WOLVERCOTE
- THAMES (RIVER)

WOODSTOCK
- BLADON LAKE
- BLENHEIM LAKE
- CHERWELL (RIVER)

RUTLAND

OAKHAM
- NORMANTON FISHING LODGE
- SWEETHEDGES FARM FISHERY
- WELLAND (RIVER)

SHROPSHIRE

BASCHURCH
- PERRY (RIVER)

BISHOPS CASTLE
- WALCOT WEST LAKE

BRIDGNORTH
- BOLDINGS POOLS
- HAMPTON LOCK
- MONKHALL FISHERIES
- SEVERN (RIVER)
- TOWNSEND FISHERY

BROSELEY
- BENTHALL LAKE
- BIRMINGHAM TO WORCESTER CANAL

CRAVEN ARMS
- DELBURY HALL TROUT FISHERY

ELLESMERE
- COLEMERE COUNTRY PARK
- CROSEMERE
- WHITEMERE

LUDLOW
- ONNY (RIVER)
- TEME (RIVER)

MARKET DRAYTON
- BACHE POOL
- MILL HOUSE LAKES
- SHROPSHIRE UNION CANAL
- TERN (RIVER)
- TERN FISHERIES

MUCH WELOCK
- LOWER HILL FARM

MUCH WENLOCK
- BROCKTON GRANGE
- SEVERN (RIVER)

NEWPORT
- AQUALATE MERE
- MEESE (RIVER)

OSWESTRY
- LAKE VYRNWY
- LLORAN GANOL FARM
- PERRY (RIVER)
- SEVERN (RIVER)
- TANAT (RIVER)
- TURFMOOR FISHERY
- VOWNOG FISH LAKE
- VYRNWY (RIVER)

SHIFNAL
- ACTON BURNELL
- BAYLIS POOLS

SHREWSBURY
- BIRCH GROVE
- COUND TROUT FISHERY
- ENVIRONMENT AGENCY
- FOLLY FARM POOL
- HAWKSTONE PARK LAKE
- ISLE LAKE
- RIVER (TERN)
- SEVEN OAKS LOG CABIN PARK
- SEVERN (RIVER)
- SNAILBEACH POOL
- SPRING LEE

TELFORD
- APLEY POOLS
- BEECHES POOL
- BLUE POOL
- ELLERDINE LAKES
- HINKSHAY POOLS
- HOLMER LAKE
- HORESHAY POOL
- LITTLE DAWLEY POOLS
- MIDDLE POOL
- NEWPORT CANAL
- SEVERN (RIVER)
- STIRCHLEY POOLS
- SWEENEYCLIFFE HOUSE FISHERY
- TELFORD TOWN PARK
- TERN (RIVER)
- TRENCH POOL
- WITHY POOL
- WOODCOTE HALL

WHITCHURCH
- BLAKEMERE
- DEARNFORD HALL TROUT FISHERY
- OSS MERE
- WHITCHURCH LAKE

WOLVERHAMPTON
- MILLRIDE FISHERY
- WYRLEY ESSINGTON CANAL

SOMERSET

BATH
- AVON (BRISTOL) (RIVER)
- AVON (RIVER)
- BRISTOL AVON
- DANDYS LAKE AND KNIGHTINGALE LAKE
- EMBOROUGH POND
- FROME (RIVER)
- HUNSTRETE LAKE COMPLEX
- KENNET AND AVON CANAL
- NEWTON PARK
- TUCKING MILL

- WOODBOROUGH PARK LAKE

BRIDGWATER
- BROWNES POND
- COMBWICH PONDS
- DUNWEAR LAKES
- DURLEIGH RESERVOIR
- FOLLY FOOT FARM
- FOLLYFOOT FARM
- HAWKRIDGE RESERVOIR
- HUNTSPILL (RIVER)
- KING SEDGEMOOR DRAIN
- PARRETT (RIVER)
- PAWLETT PONDS
- QUANTOCK FISHERIES
- SCREECH OWL PONDS
- SEDGES
- STATHE DRAIN
- SUMMERHAYES
- TAUNTON AND BRIDGWATER CANAL
- TAUNTON ROAD PONDS
- TAUNTON TO BRIDGWATER CANAL
- WESTHAY LAKE

BRISTOL
- BARROW RESERVOIRS
- BLAGDON LAKE
- CAMELEY TROUT LAKES
- CHEW VALLEY LAKE
- KENNET AND AVON CANAL
- LITTON RESERVOIR
- PAULTON LAKES
- YEO (RIVER)

BURNHAM-ON-SEA
- APEX LAKE

CHARD
- CHARD RESERVOIR
- HOWLEY STREET POND

CHEDDAR
- CHEDDAR RESERVOIR

CHEWTON MENDIP
- STONE YARD FISHERY

CLEVEDON
- BULLOCKS FARM FISHING LAKES
- KENN (RIVER)
- PLANTATIONS LAKES

CREWKERNE
- HIGHLANDS DAIRY LAKE
- PARRET (RIVER)
- WATER MEADOW LAKES

DULVERTON
- BARLE (RIVER)
- EXE (RIVER)
- EXE VALLEY FISHERY
- HADDOE TROUT FISHERY
- LAKESIDE
- LITTLE EXE
- WIMBLEBALL LAKE

EMBOROUGH
- EMBORUGH LAKE

FROME
- AVON (RIVER)
- EDNEYS FISHERIES
- FROME (RIVER)
- MARSTON LAKE
- MELLS PIT
- ST ALGARS FARM LAKE
- WITHAM FRIARY LAKE
- WOOLBRIDGE MANOR

GLASTONBURY
- AVALON FISHERIES
- GLASTONBURY
- GODNEY MOOR PONDS
- WESTHAY

HIGHBRIDGE
- BASON BRIDGE
- BRUE (RIVER)
- EMERALD POOL FISHERY
- KENN (RIVER)
- MARK (RIVER)
- NEWTOWN LAKE
- WALROW PONDS

LANGPORT
- COOMBE LAKE
- ISLE (RIVER)
- PARRETT (RIVER)
- THORNEY LAKES

MARTOCK
- ASHMEAD LAKES

MINEHEAD
- HORNER WATER

SOMERTON
- MINERS PONDS
- VIADUCT FISHERY

STOKE-SUB-HAMDON
- PARRETT (RIVER)

STREET
- BRUE (RIVER)
- BUTLEIGH ROAD PONDS

TAUNTON
- CLATWORTHY RESERVOIR
- LOWER LOVELYNCH FISHERIES
- OTTERHEAD LAKES
- OXENLEAZE FARM CARAVANS AND COARSE FISHERY
- THURLEYBEARE POND
- TONE (RIVER)
- WYCH LODGE LAKE

WEDMORE
- HORSESHOE LAKE
- LANDS END FARM
- LANDS END FISHERIES

WELLINGTON
- LANGFORD LAKES
- WELLINGTON BASIN

WELLS
- EMBOROUGH POOL

WESTON-SUPER-MARE
- HUTON POND
- PARRETT (RIVER)

YEOVIL
- OLD MILL FISHERY
- SUTTON BINGHAM RESERVOIR
- YEO (RIVER)

STAFFORDSHIRE

ALREWAS
- SWARBORN (RIVER)
- TAME (RIVER)
- TRENT (RIVER)

ALTON
- CHURNET (RIVER)

BURTON-ON-TRENT
- DOVE (RIVER)
- FRADLEY CANAL
- HARTSHORNE DAMS
- TRENT AND MERSEY CANAL

CANNOCK
- SOUTH POPLARS

DUDLEY
- HIMLEY HALL AND PARK LAKE
- PARKES HALL

LEEK
- BASFORD COARSE FISHERY
- BLACKSHAW FARM LAKES
- CHURNET (RIVER)
- DEEP HAYES COUNTRY PARK
- HAMPS (RIVER)
- HORSEBRIDGE POOL
- RUDYARD LAKE
- TILTLESWORTH
- TITTESWORTH RESERVOIR

LICHFIELD
- FISHERWICK LAKES
- MIDLAND GAME FISHERIES

LOGGERHEADS
- ASHLEY POOLS

LONGNOR
- DOVE (RIVER)

NEWCASTLE-UNDER-LYME
- BROWNING CUDMORE FISHERY
- LAWTON HALL POOL
- MADELEY POOL

PENKRIDGE
- PILLATON POOLS
- WILLOWS POOLS

RUGELEY
- BLITHFIELD RESERVOIR
- HAMSTALL FISHERY
- HEDNESFORD ROAD LAKE
- HORNS
- LITTLETONS AND MIDDLE POOL
- WADE LAKE

STAFFORD
- BADEN HALL FISHERY
- ELLENHALL NINE POOLS
- GAILEY TROUT AND PIKE FISHERY
- HERONBROOK FISHERY
- IZAAK WALTON FISHERY
- LOYNTON TROUT FISHERIES
- SHELMORE TROUT FISHERY
- SHROPSHIRE UNION CANAL
- SOW (RIVER)
- STAFFORD AND WORCESTER CANAL
- STAFFORD TO WORCESTER CANAL
- SWAN PIT POOL
- WILLOW POOLS

STOKE-ON-TRENT
- BIDDULPH GRANGE
- BLACK LAKE
- BLACKWOOD POOL
- CANAL RESERVOIRS
- CONSALL NATURE PARK
- DILHORNE HALL POOLS
- HANCHURCH FISHERIES
- HOLDEN LANE POOL
- KNYPERSLEY RESERVOIR
- MACCLESFIELD CANAL
- PARK HALL FARM
- PHOENIX ANGLING CLUB
- RISING TROUT FISHERY
- SIDEWAY OVERFLOW
- SMITH POOL
- SMITHPOOL LAKE
- STANLEY RESERVOIR
- TAYLORS POOL
- TRENT AND MERSEY CANAL
- TRENTHAM GARDENS

STONE
- TRENT (RIVER)

TAMWORTH
- ANKER (RIVER)
- BONEHILL MILL
- BORROWPIT LAKE
- COVENTRY CANAL
- DRAYTON BRIDGE
- PINE POOL
- POOL HOUSE FARM
- PRETTY PIGS FISHERY

UTTOXETER
- BLITHE (RIVER)
- CHURNET (RIVER)
- DOVE (RIVER)
- WOODSEAT LAKE

WOLVERHAMPTON
- ALBRIGHTON MOAT PROJECT
- SHROPSHIRE UNION CANAL

SUFFOLK

ALDEBURGH

- ALDE (RIVER)

BECCLES

- ALDEBY HALL FARM PITS
- BARSHAM DRAIN
- BECCLES QUAY
- HENHAM DAIRY POND

BRANDON

- LARK (RIVER)

BUNGAY

- BROOME PITS
- BUNGAY (RIVER)
- CLUB PIT
- DITCHINGHAM PIT
- HOMERSFIELD (RIVER)
- WAVENEY (RIVER)

BURES

- CLICKETTS HILL AND PLANTATION
- LITTLE BEVILLS ESTATE
- STOW (RIVER)

BURY ST EDMUNDS

- BLUE WATERS
- CROSS GREEN FLY FISHERY
- HATCHERY HOUSE TROUT LAKES
- LARK (RIVER)
- LARKWOOD TROUT FISHERY
- WEST STOW COUNTRY PARK

CLARE

- MILLERS LAKE

HALESWORTH

- HOLTON PIT
- VALLEY FARM FISHERY
- WILLOW LAKES TROUT FISHERY

HARLESTON

- CAMELOT LAKE
- HIGHFIELD FISHERY
- HOMERSFIELD LAKE
- WAVENEY VALLEY LAKES
- YEW TREE FISHERIES

HAVERHILL

- FLOOD PARK
- MELDUM WASHLANDS (FLOODPARK)

HOCKWOLD

- CROSS DROVE

IPSWICH

- ALDERSONS LAKES
- ALTON WATER RESERVOIR
- BARHAM A PIT
- BARHAM B PIT
- BOSMERE LAKE
- CAUSEWAY LAKES
- GIPPING (RIVER)
- NEEDHAM LAKE
- SINKS PIT
- STOUR (SUFFOLK) (RIVER)
- SWALE PIT

LOWESTOFT

- FLIXTON DECOY
- GUNTON HALL LAKE
- OULTON BROAD
- OULTON DYKE

SAXMUNDHAM

- ALDE (RIVER)
- GUNSSONS LAKE
- MARSH FARM LAKES
- WYE (RIVER)

SOUTHWOLD

- BUSS CREEK
- RAYDON PONDS
- REYDON LAKES

STOWMARKET

- BAKERS LAKE
- LAKESIDE
- RATTLE (RIVER)

SUDBURY

- CHESTERFORD FISHERIES
- CLARE PARK LAKE
- HOME FARM FISHERIES
- LAYZELLS FARM
- NORTH MEADOWS
- STANTONS FARM RESERVOIR
- STARFIELD PIT
- STOUR (RIVER)
- STOW (RIVER)
- WRIGHTS FARM

THETFORD

- LITTLE OUSE (RIVER)
- THET (RIVER)

WOODBRIDGE

- BREAKAWAY PIT
- BRIDGE FARM RESERVOIRS
- DEBEN (RIVER)
- LOAM POND
- MELTON LAKE
- PETTISTREE LAKES
- WICKHAM MARKET RESERVOIRS

SURREY

ASH

- SHAWFIELDS LAKES

CHERTSEY

- ATTENBOROUGH SOUTH
- CHERTSEY
- THORPE PARK WATERSKI LAKE
- TWYNERSH FISHING COMPLEX

COBHAM

- MANOR POND
- PAINSHILL PARK LAKE

CRANLEIGH

- ALDERBROOK LAKE
- ALFORD ROAD FISHERIES
- EAST WHIPLEY RESERVOIR
- FISHERIES THE
- FURZE FARM
- NAVIES HOLE
- WYPHURST AND HYHURST LAKES

DORKING

- BURY HILL FISHERIES
- GATTON MANOR LAKES
- HENFOLD LAKES FISHERY
- MILL POND
- MOLE (RIVER)
- PUDDENHOLE POND

EAST MOLESEY

- BUSHEY PARK
- HOME PARK
- MOLESEY LOCK
- THAMES (RIVER)

EGHAM

- BELL WEIR LOCK

EPSOM

- EPSOM STEW POND

FARNHAM

- BADSHOT LEA
- CROSSWATER MILL FISHERY
- FRENSHAM TROUT FISHERY
- RUSHMOOR LAKES
- ST PATRICKS LANE CARP LAKES

GODALMING

- BROADWATER LAKE
- ENTON LAKES TROUT FISHERY
- WEY (RIVER)
- WINKWORTH LAKES
- WINTERSHALL WATERS

GUILDFORD

- ALBURY ESTATE FISHERIES
- BRITTENS POND
- DEE (RIVER)
- POWDER MILLS FISHERY
- WESTON FISHERY
- WHIPLEY MANOR
- WILLINGHURST COARSE FISHERY
- WILLINGHURST TROUT FISHERY

HASLEMERE

- KINGFISHER FISHERY

HEATH END

- LAKESIDE

HINDHEAD

- WAGGONERS WELLS

HORSHAM

- HAWKINS POND
- PULBOROUGH LAKE
- ROOSTHOLE
- WHITEVANE POND

LEATHERHEAD

- LONG COPSE PONDS

LINGFIELD

- BEAVER FARM FISHERY

MILFORD

- BUSBRIDGE LAKE
- JOHNSONS LAKE

MITCHAM

- ONE ISLAND POND
- SEVEN ISLANDS

OXTED

- COLTSFORD MILL FISHERY

TILFORD

- STOCKBRIDGE POND

WALTON-ON-THAMES

- MOLE (RIVER)

WEST BYFLEET

- WEY (RIVER)

WOKING

- BOLDERMERE
- GOLDSWORTH WATER PARK
- PAPERCOURT FISHERY
- SEND PIT
- WEY NAVIGATION (RIVER)

SUSSEX (EAST)

BATTLE

- ASHBOURNE TROUT FISHERY
- BROOMHAM FISHERY
- CLAREMONT LAKE
- MOOR HALL POOL
- OLIVES FARM FISHERY
- POWDERMILL (GREAT SANDERS) WATER
- THORNDEN POND
- WYLANDS INTERNATIONAL ANGLING CENTRE

BEXHILL-ON-SEA

- BRICKYARD LAKE

BRIGHTON

- WOODMANCOTE PLACE FISHERY

CROWBOROUGH

- HOLTS LAKES
- KINGS STANDING LAKES
- PENNY BRIDGE
- SCALAND WOOD
- YEW TREE TROUT FISHERY

EASTBOURNE

- MICHELHAM PRIORY MOAT
- SOUTHBOURNE LAKE

ETCHINGHAM

- LAKEDOWN TROUT FISHERY

FOREST ROW

- WEIR WOOD FISHERY

HAILSHAM

- BELFREY COARSE FISHERY
- BRICK FARM LAKE
- CUCKMERE (RIVER)

- FALKENVIL FISHERY
- FURNACE BROOK FISHERY
- LEABRIDGE FARM
- PEVENSEY HAVEN
- WALLERS HAVEN

HARTFIELD
- BALLS GREEN LAKES
- ST IVES FARM

HASTINGS
- ALEXANDRA PARK WATERS
- CLIVE VALE RESERVOIRS
- COGHURST HALL
- ECCLESBOURNE RESERVOIR
- HASTINGS LAKE
- PETT POOLS
- RYE NOOK FISHERY
- WHITE HART HILL LAKE
- WISHING TREE RESERVOIR

HEATHFIELD
- BOJO FISHERIES
- HORAM MANOR FISHERY
- ROSEBANK FARM FISHERY

LEWES
- BARCOMBE RESERVOIR
- BEVERN STREAM
- DECOY LAKE
- OLD IRON (RIVER)
- OLD MILL
- OUSE (RIVER)
- SWANBOROUGH LAKES

PEVENSEY
- SHARNFOLD FARM FISHERY
- WALLERS HAVEN

POLEGATE
- ARLINGTON TROUT FISHERY
- CUCKMERE (RIVER)

ROBERTSBRIDGE
- DARWELL WATER
- ROTHER (RIVER)
- VINEHALL SCHOOL LAKE

RYE
- IDEN WOOD FISHERY
- SHAMFOLD FARM FISHERY

SEAFORD
- CUCKMERE (RIVER)

UCKFIELD
- BORINGWHEEL TROUT FISHERY
- BUXTED OAST FISHERY
- BUXTED PARK FISHERY
- COLIN GODMANS TROUTING
- CYPRUS WOOD TROUT FISHERY
- FRAMFIELD PARK FISHERIES
- HONEYS GREEN COARSE FISHERY
- ISFIELD (RIVER)
- LOWER HONEYS GREEN FARM
- PIPPINGFORD PARK ESTATE LAKES
- TANYARD FISHERIES
- UNDERHILL LAKE

WADHURST
- SPRING WOOD FISHERY AND FARM

SUSSEX (WEST)

ARUNDEL
- ARUN (RIVER)
- CASTLE TROUT POND
- CHALK SPRINGS TROUT FISHERY

BILLINGHURST
- DOUNHURST FARM FISHERY

BOGNOR REGIS
- ARUN (RIVER)

BURGESS HILL
- WINTONS FISHERY

CHICHESTER
- CHICESTER CANAL
- HAMBROOK TROUT FISHERY

CRAWLEY
- TILGATE LAKES

EAST GRINSTEAD
- BOLEBROOK CASTLE
- DAYLANDS FARM
- STUBPOND FISHERIES
- WILDERNESS LAKE

HAYWARDS HEATH
- ARDINGLY RESERVOIR
- BALCOMBE LAKE
- BORDE HILL GARDEN LAKES
- CUCKFIELD FISHERY
- HAYWARDS HEATH RIVER
- PILTDOWN POND
- SLAUGHAM MILL POND
- SPARKS FARM FISHERY
- VALE BRIDGE LAKE

HENFIELD
- ADUR (RIVER)

HORSHAM
- ARUN (RIVER)
- DOCTORS LAKE
- FURNACE LAKES
- HAZELCOPSE LAKES
- LENNOX WOOD LAKE
- MENARDS LAKE
- NEWELLS SPECIMEN CARP AND COARSE FISHERIES
- SLAUGHTERFORD FARM
- WATTLEHURST FARM TROUT LAKES

LANCING
- PASSIES PONDS

LITTLEHAMPTON
- ARUN (RIVER)
- OUSE (RIVER)

MIDHURST
- NEW POND
- ROTHER (RIVER)
- ROTHERFIELD POND
- WESTERN ROTHER

PETWORTH
- ARUN (RIVER)
- BLACKWOOL TROUT FISHERY
- BURTON MILL POND
- DUNCTON MILL
- LECONFIELD ESTATE
- WESTERN ROTHER (RIVER)

PULBOROUGH
- ARUN (RIVER)
- DUNCANS POND
- HURSTON LANE
- LAYBROOK LAKES
- MILL FARM FISHERY
- WATER MEADOWS FLY FISHERIES

STEYNING
- ADUR (RIVER)
- ALDERWOOD PONDS

TYNE AND WEAR

GATESHEAD
- FELLGATE PONDS

HOUGHTON LE SPRING
- STEPHENSON LAKE

JARROW
- FELLGATE FISHERIES

NEWCASTLE UPON TYNE
- BIG WATERS
- BOLAM LAKE COUNTRY PARK
- BRENKLEY POND
- DISSINGTON POND
- ENVIRONMENT AGENCY
- KILLINGWORTH LAKE
- LEAZES PARK LAKE
- LITTLE BIG WATER
- MAIN TYNE
- MARDEN QUARRY
- MILKHOPE POND
- RED BARNS POND
- REDE (RIVER)
- SWEETHOPE LOUGHS
- THROCKLEY REIGH
- TYNE (RIVER)
- WHITTLE DENE TROUT FISHERY

ROWLANDS GILL
- DERWENT (RIVER)

RYTON
- STARGATE PONDS
- TYNE (RIVER)

SUNDERLAND
- SILKSWORTH SPORTS COMPLEX

WASHINGTON
- MOUNT PLEASANT LAKE
- WEAR (RIVER)
- WILLOWS (THE)

YARM
- LEVEN (RIVER)
- TEES (RIVER)

WARWICKSHIRE

ALCESTER
- ADAMS POOL
- WEST HILLBOROUGH

ATHERSTONE
- RIDDINGS FISHERY
- SHEEPY MAGNA LAKE

BEDWORTH
- BRAMCOTE MAINS FISHERY
- HAWKESBURY FISHERY
- MAKIN FISHERIES
- MONKS POOL
- WESTON LAWN FISHERIES

LEAMINGTON SPA
- BISHOPS BOWL LAKES
- CHESTERTON MILL POOL TROUT FISHERY
- GRAND UNION CANAL
- LEAM (RIVER)
- OXFORD CANAL
- WARWICK CANAL

NUNEATON
- ASHBY CANAL
- BOSWORTH PARK LAKE
- BOSWORTH WATER TRUST AND FRIEZELAND POOLS
- COVENTRY CANAL
- GARDEN FARM FISHERIES

RUGBY
- AVON (RIVER)
- BANKS (THE)
- CLIFTON LAKES FISHERY
- DRAYCOTE WATER
- LANNYS LAGOON
- MILL POOL
- NEWBOLD QUARRY
- NORTH OXFORD CANAL
- OXFORD CANAL
- STOCKTON RESERVOIR

SOUTHAM
- HIGH CLAYS FARM
- NAPTON RESERVOIR
- NORTH FARM FISHERY

STRATFORD-UPON-AVON
- AVON (RIVER)
- BLACK HILL POOLS
- SNITTERFIELD FRUIT FARM
- SOUTH STRATFORD CANAL
- STOUR (WARWICKSHIRE)
- WARWICKSHIRE AVON

WARWICK

- ARDENCOTE MANOR HOTEL AND COUNTRY CLUB
- GRAND UNION CANAL
- HEATHCOTE LAKE
- KINGSTON POOLS
- OAKHAM FARM POOLS
- PARK FARM
- TUNNEL BARN FARM
- WARWICKSHIRE AVON

WILTSHIRE

BRADFORD-ON-AVON

- BRISTOL AVON
- KENNET AND AVON CANAL

CALNE

- BLACKLAND LAKES HOLIDAY AND LEISURE CENTRE
- BOWOOD LAKE
- HIGH PENN
- SABRE AND SWORDS LAKES

CHIPPENHAM

- AVON (BRISTOL) (RIVER)
- AVON (RIVER)
- BRISTOL AVON
- IVY HOUSE FARM
- SILVERLANDS LAKE
- TOCKENHAM RESERVOIR
- WYATTS LAKE

DEVIZES

- ERLESTOKE LAKE
- KENNET AND AVON CANAL
- MILL FARM TROUT LAKES

MALMESBURY

- BURTON HILL LAKE
- LOWER MOOR FISHERY
- WHITE HORSE INN LAKE

MARLBOROUGH

- KENNET AND AVON CANAL

MELKSHAM

- AVON (BRISTOL) (RIVER)
- AVON (RIVER)
- AVON ANGLING CLUB
- BRISTOL AVON
- BURBROOKS RESERVOIR
- KENNET AND AVON CANAL

PEWSEY

- KENNET AND AVON CANAL

SALISBURY

- AVON (BRISTOL) (RIVER)
- AVON (RIVER)
- AVON SPRINGS FISHERY
- BRITFORD FISHERY
- HAMPSHIRE AVON (RIVER)
- LANGFORD FISHERIES
- LONGHOUSE LAKES
- MILLBROOK TROUT FARM
- NADDER (RIVER)
- OLD WARDOUR
- PETERS FINGER LAKES
- STEEPLE LANGFORD LAKES
- WALDENS FARM FISHERY
- WITHERINGTON FARM FISHING
- WYTHERINGTON FARM

SWINDON

- COATE WATER COUNTRY PARK
- DORKHAM STORMWATER
- LAWNS (THE)
- LIDEN LAGOON
- MANOR BROOK LAKE
- PEARMOOR LAKE
- PEATMOOR LAGOON
- PEMBROKE POND
- PLAUMS PIT
- PURTON LAKE
- RAY (RIVER)
- RODBOURNE LAGOON
- SHAFTESBURY LAKE
- THAMES (RIVER)
- WROUGHTON RESERVOIR

TROWBRIDGE

- BISS (RIVER)
- KENNET AND AVON CANAL
- ROOD ASHTON LAKE

WARMINSTER

- AVON (RIVER)
- CROCKERTON POND
- HUNTERS MOON
- LONGLEAT LAKES
- SHEAR WATER
- SOUTHLEIGH LAKE
- SUTTON VENY ESTATE
- TURNERS PADDOCK LAKE
- ZEALS TROUT FISHERY

WESTBURY

- CLIVEY PONDS
- CUCKOOS REST
- WOODLAND PARK

WORCESTERSHIRE

BEWDLEY

- CURTISS POOL
- DEXTER POOL
- DOWLES BROOK
- HAYE FARM FISHERY
- MILL POOL
- SEVERN (RIVER)
- SILLIGROVE FISHERY
- SNUFF MILL POOL
- TEME (RIVER)
- TRIMPLEY RESERVOIR
- WELLFIELD POOLS
- WHARTONS PARK COARSE FISHING

BROMSGROVE

- BIRMINGHAM TO WORCESTER CANAL
- BROAD ACRES LAKE
- UPTON WARREN LAKE
- WOODROW FISH POND

DROITWICH

- ASTWOOD FISHERY
- DROITWICH CANAL
- ELMBRIDGE LAKES
- WOODLAND VIEW

EVESHAM

- ABBOTS SALFORD PARK
- ANCHOR MEADOWS FISHERY
- AVON (RIVER)
- BLACK MONK TROUT LAKES
- HARVINGTON MANOR FISHERY
- HUXLEYS HAMPTON FERRY FISHERIES
- LENCHES LAKES
- RED BECK LAKE
- TWYFORD FARM POOL
- WARWICKSHIRE & AVON
- WARWICKSHIRE AVON
- WILLOW FARM
- WINDMILL LAKE
- WOOD POOL

KIDDERMINSTER

- BEWDLEY POOL
- CAPTAINS POOL
- ERICS POOL
- FURNACE MILL FISHERY
- HURCOTT POOL
- MASTERS (THE)
- MOORLANDS FARM
- MOORS POOL
- POOLE HALL FISHERY
- SALWARPE (RIVER)
- SHAKESPEARE MOORLANDS FARM
- SHATTERFORD FISHERY AND WILDLIFE SANCTUARY
- SION FARM FISHERIES
- STANKLIN POOL
- STELLA LAKE
- STEWARDS POOL
- WELFIELD POOLS
- WILLOW MARSH
- WINTERFOLD PARK FISHERIES

MALVERN

- CASTLE GREEN POOLS
- LEIGH SINTON FISHING LAKES
- SINDON MILL FARM

MARTLEY

- TEME (RIVER)

PERSHORE

- AVON (RIVER)
- FOREST FARM
- WARWICKSHIRE AVON

REDDITCH

- ARROW VALLEY LAKE
- BROCKHILL FARM TROUT POOLS
- LODGE PARK LAKE

STOURPORT-ON-SEVERN

- BANKES POOL
- MAVER LARFORD
- SEVERN (RIVER)
- STAFFORD TO WORCESTER CANAL
- UNWICKS FARM FISHERY
- WILDEN POOL

TENBURY WELLS

- LEDWYCHE BROOK
- TEME (RIVER)
- WOODSTON MANOR POOLS

WORCESTER

- ACR FISHERIES
- BENNETTS POOL
- BIRMINGHAM TO WORCESTER CANAL
- BRAKE MILL POOL
- BRANSFORD GAME FISHERY
- BROCKAMIN POOLS
- EVESBATCH FISHERIES
- GROVE FARM
- HARVEY POOL
- HOLT FLEET POOL
- LENCHFORD
- LOWER BROADHEATH POOLS
- SEVERN (RIVER)
- STAINFORTH AND KEADBY CANAL
- TEME (RIVER)
- TOP BARN ANGLING CENTRE
- UCKINGHALL POOL
- WASH POOL
- WHARFE INN POOL
- WITLEY FISHERY
- WITLEY POOLS

WREXHAM

BANGOR-ON-DEE

- CLYWEDOG (RIVER)
- DEE (RIVER)

WORTHENBURY

- EMRAL BROOK
- WYCH BROOK

YORKSHIRE (NORTH)

BEDALE

- CLAY PIT
- NEWTON RIVER
- SHIELD FISHERY
- THORPE PERROW QUARRY

CARWOOD

- FAIRVIEW LAKE

CLIFTON

- CLIFTON MOOR LAKE

HARROGATE

- HIGH MOOR FARM PARK
- KINGSLEY CARP LAKE
- NIDD (RIVER)
- NIDD BRIDGE
- PROSPECT FARM POND
- RIPLEY CASTLE
- WASHBURN VALLEY (FEWSTON AND SWINSTY)

HAWES

- BLACKBURN FARM TROUT FISHERY
- SEMERWATER
- URE (RIVER AND TRIBUTARIES)
- URE (RIVER)

HELPERBY

- OUSE (RIVER)
- SWALE (RIVER)

KNARESBOROUGH

- FARMIRE TROUT FISHERY
- HAY-A-PARK
- NIDD (RIVER)

LEYBURN

- BAIN (RIVER)
- URE (RIVER)

MALTON

- ABBIE POND
- BIRKDALE FISHERY
- BRICKYARD FARM LAKE
- MANOR FARM POND
- OUSE (RIVER)
- RICCAL (RIVER)
- RYE (RIVER)
- RYE AND SEVEN (RIVERS)
- SELLEY BRIDGE LAKE
- TROUT POND BARN

MIDDLEHAM

- URE (RIVER)

NORTHALLERTON

- BEDALE BECK
- CORNHILL PONDS
- HAZEL HALL FARM FISHING
- HOLLINGWOOD FISHERY
- KIPLIN TROUT FISHERY
- LANGTON POND
- LEEMING (RIVER)
- PARKLANDS
- ROLIETH FISHERY
- STONEBRIDGE LAKES
- STONEY LANE PONDS
- SWALE (RIVER)
- TONTINE LAKE

PICKERING

- HAZELHEAD LAKE
- PICKERING PARK FISHING LAKE
- PICKERING TROUT LAKE
- WELHAM LAKE

RICHMOND

- BROKEN BREA FISHERY
- CATTERICK LAKES
- CRABTREE ANGLING LAKE
- ELLERTON PARK
- LAKESIDE FISHERIES
- SWALE (RIVER)

RIPON

- BELLFLASK TROUT FISHERY
- BRICKYARD FISHERY
- FARMIRE
- KINLIN HALL TROUT FARM
- LAVER (RIVER)
- LEIGHTON RESERVOIR
- NEWBY HALL FISHERIES
- QUEEN MARYS POND
- RACECOURSE LAKE
- RIPON CANAL
- RIPON RACECOURSE LAKE
- ROGERS POND
- SCAR HOUSE RESERVOIR
- SHIELD TROUT FISHERY
- SKELL (RIVER)
- SWINTON ESTATE TROUT FISHERY
- TANFIELD LAKE
- THORNTON STEWARD RESERVOIR
- TYNE (RIVER)
- URE (RIVER)

SCARBOROUGH

- BLEA TARN
- BROOKLANDS
- DERWENT (RIVER)
- SCARBOROUGH MERE
- WYKEHAM LAKES
- Y2K LAKE

SELBY

- BARLOW COMMON NATURE RESERVE
- BUBWITH (RIVER)
- CAWOOD HOLIDAY PARK
- DRAX LAKE
- MUNBY POND
- NEWHAY DAY TICKET LAKE
- NEWHAY SPECIMEN LAKE
- SELBY 3 LAKES
- SELBY CANAL
- THREE LAKES
- WEST HADDLESEY LAKE

SKIPTON

- BOLTON ABBEY FISHERIES
- EMBSAY RESERVOIR
- KILNSEY PARK AND TROUT FARM
- OUSE (RIVER)
- SKIRFARE (RIVER)
- WHARFE (RIVER)
- WHINNYGILL RESERVOIR

TADCASTER

- BACON FACTORY POND
- ULLESKELF (RIVER)
- WHARFE (RIVER)

THIRSK

- ALDERS LAKE
- CARLTON LODGE LAKE
- COD BECK
- KAYS LAKES
- LOW OSGOODBY LAKE
- MOULTON LANE POND
- OAKS FISHERY
- RIVER VIEW COTTAGE
- SWALE (RIVER)
- WILLOWS AND FIRS LAKES
- WOODLAND LAKES

WHITBY

- DANBY (RIVER)
- EGTON BRIDGE (RIVER)
- EGTON ESTATE BEAT
- ESK (RIVER)
- GLAISDALE (RIVER)
- RUSWARP (RIVER)
- SLEIGHTS (RIVER)

YORK

- ALDWARK BRIDGE
- BRAFFERTON COARSE FISHERY
- CARP VALE
- CASTLE HOWARD GREAT LAKE
- CHAPMANS POND
- CLAXTON BRICKWORKS
- CUNDALL LODGE FISHERY
- DERWENT (RIVER)
- EAST COTTINGWITH WATERS
- ELLERTON LANDING
- ELVINGTON LAKE
- ENVIRONMENT AGENCY
- FLETCHERS POND
- FOGGLESKYTE WATERS
- FOSS (RIVER)
- GRAFTON MERE
- HESSAY POND
- HOXNE FARM PONDS
- KILBURN POND
- LAKEHOUSE LAKE
- LAKESIDE LODGES
- LINGCROFT FARM POND
- LOWER DUNSFORTH (RIVER)
- MARKET WEIGHTON CANAL
- MARSTON WYSE TROUT FARM
- MILBY CUT
- MOORLANDS FARM PONDS
- NIDD (RIVER)
- NORTHINGALES FISHERY
- NUN MONKTON (RIVER)
- OAK MERE FISHERY
- OAKTREE LEISURE
- ORCHARD FARM PONDS
- OUSE (RIVER)
- POCKLINGTON CANAL
- POOL BRIDGE FARM LAKES
- POPPLETON (RIVER)
- POTTERY LAKE
- RAKER LAKES
- RASKELF LAKE
- REDHOUSE LAGOON
- RYE (RIVER)
- SINNINGTON (RIVER)
- SWALE (RIVER)
- THORNTON BRIDGE
- THORPE UNDERWOOD
- TOLLERTON FISHING PONDS
- URE (RIVER)
- WATERMEADOWS FISHERY
- WESTERLY LAKE
- WILLOW WATER
- WILLOWS
- YORKSHIRE OUSE

YORKSHIRE (SOUTH)

BARNBY DUN

- DON (RIVER)

BARNSLEY

- ATHERSLEY MEMORIAL LAKE
- BARNSLEY CANAL
- BRAMPTON CANAL
- DEARNE VALLEY PARK LAKE
- ELSECAR CANAL
- ELSECAR RESERVOIR
- FLEETS DAM
- MILTON PONDS
- NETHERWOOD COUNTRY PARK
- SALLY WALSHES DAM
- SMITHIES RESERVOIR
- STANBOROUGH FISHERIES
- TINKERS PONDS
- WOMBWELL DAM
- WORSBOROUGH RESERVOIR
- WORSBROUGH CANAL
- WORSBROUGH RESERVOIR

DONCASTER

- ARKSEY STATION POND
- ASKERN LAKE
- BEEDOMS FISHERY
- BULL HOLE
- CAMPSALL COUNTRY PARK
- CUSWORTH HALL LAKE
- DELVES FISH PONDS
- DELVES LAKES
- DON (RIVER)
- FINA HAYFIELD LAKES
- HAVEN
- IDLE (RIVER)
- LONG POND
- MICKS PLACE
- MISSION LINEBANK PONDS
- NEW JUNCTION CANAL
- PRESTON INNOVATIONS SILVER FISHERY
- RAILWAY POND
- ROSSINGTON BRICK POND
- SANDERSONS POND
- SLIVER FISHERY
- SOUTH YORKSHIRE NAVIGATION CANAL
- SOUTHFIELD RESERVOIRS
- STAINFORTH AND KEADBY CANAL
- THORNE NORTH POND
- TOLL BAR POND
- TORNE (RIVER)
- TRIANGS FISHERY
- TYRAM HALL
- WILLOW GARTH FISHERY
- WILLOWGARTH LAKE

MEXBOROUGH

- DEARNE (RIVER)
- MEXBOROUGH CANAL
- OLD DEARNE (RIVER)

- SHEFFIELD AND SOUTH YORKSHIRE NAVIGATION

ROTHERHAM

- BRICKYARD PONDS
- CUMWELL LANE
- FITZWILLIAM CANAL
- GREASBROUGH DAMS
- NEWBIGGIN POND
- SHEFFIELD AND SOUTH YORKSHIRE NAVIGATION
- THRYBERGH COUNTRY PARK
- WENTWORTH FISHERY
- WESTWOOD COUNTRY PARK

SHEFFIELD

- CHESTERFIELD CANAL
- CROOKES VALLEY PARK LAKE
- DAM FLASK RESERVOIR
- ECCLESFIELD POND
- HORSESHOE LAKE TROUT FISHERY
- HOWBROOK RESERVOIR
- KIVETON HALL
- KJS FISHERIES
- MORE HALL RESERVOIR
- NANCY POND
- NORWOOD FISHERIES
- PEBLEY RESERVOIR
- SCOUT DYKE RESERVOIR
- SHEFFIELD CANAL
- STRAIGHT MILE FISHERY
- TRENT (RIVER)
- ULLEY RESERVOIR
- UNDERBANK RESERVOIR
- WHARNCLIFFE FLY FISHERY
- WINDTHORPE PITS
- WINTHORPE LAKE

WORKSOP

- CHESTERFIELD CANAL
- DUKERIES LAKES
- HARTHILL RESERVIORS
- SHIREOAKS PARK

YORKSHIRE (WEST)

BATLEY

- LONGBOTTOMS DAM

BINGLEY

- COPPICE POND

BRADFORD

- CALDER (RIVER)
- DOE PARK RESERVOIR
- DYEHOUSE POND
- ROYDS HALL DAM
- STAVELEY LAKES
- YEADON TARN

BRIGHOUSE

- CALDER AND HEBBLE CANAL

CASTLEFORD

- LOWTHER LAKE
- WORKSHOP POND

DEWSBURY

- THORNHILL POND

HALIFAX

- BRIGHOUSE
- BROOKFOOT LAKE
- CLEARWATER LAKE
- ROCHDALE CANAL

HEBDEN BRIDGE

- CALDER AND HEBBLE CANAL
- ROCHDALE CANAL

HUDDERSFIELD

- BOTTOMS DAM
- CALDER (RIVER)
- COLNE (RIVER)
- HILL TOP RESERVOIR
- HOLME (RIVER)
- HOLME MILL DAM (SQUARE DAM)
- HORNSEA MERE
- HUDDERSFIELD BROAD CANAL
- NARROW CANAL
- OAKS SCAR RESERVOIR
- PINFOLD DAMS
- PUSH DAM
- ROWLEY DAM
- SPARTH RESERVOIR
- T P POND DAM
- TP WOODS POND

ILKLEY

- WHARFE (RIVER)

KEIGHLEY

- AIRE (RIVER)
- RAYGILL FISHERY
- ROBERTS POND

LEEDS

- AIRE (RIVER)
- BILLING DAM
- CLAYTON WOOD PONDS
- ENVIRONMENT AGENCY
- KIPPAX POND
- LEEDS TO LIVERPOOL CANAL
- MILLRACE
- ROUNDHAY PARK LAKES
- SWILLINGTON PARK
- WHARFE (RIVER)

MIRFIELD

- HOPTON WATERS

OTLEY

- KNOTFORD LAGOON
- SWINSTY AND FEWSTON RESERVOIRS
- WHARFE (RIVER)

OULTON

- AIRE AND CALDER CANAL

PONTEFRACT

- ACKTON POND
- HOYLE MILL DAM
- PONTEFRACT PARK LAKE

SHIPLEY

- AIRE (RIVER)
- LEEDS AND LIVERPOOL CANAL
- LEEDS TO LIVERPOOL CANAL
- TONG PARK DAM

TADCASTER

- WHARFE (RIVER)

TODMORDEN

- CALDER (RIVER)
- NEW MILL DAM
- ROCHDALE CANAL
- WALSDEN PRINTING CO LODGES

WAKEFIELD

- FLANSHAW DAM
- HORBURY LAGOON
- NOSTELL PRIORY LAKE
- PUGNEYS COUNTRY PARK
- SPRING VALLEY WATERS
- WALTON HALL TROUT LAKE
- WINTERSETT RESERVOIR

WETHERBY

- BOSTON SPA
- OUSE (RIVER)
- WHARFE (RIVER)

COUNTY CARLOW

CARLOW

- BURREN (RIVER)
- DOUGLAS (RIVER)
- GREESE (RIVER)
- LERR (RIVER)

GRAIGHUENAMANAGH

- BARROW (RIVER)

COUNTY CAVAN

BAILIEBOROUGH

- BAILIEBORO LAKES

BELTURBET

- ARDAN GRANGE GUEST HOUSE AND ANGLING CENTRE

VIRGINIA

- LOUGH RAMOR

COUNTY CLARE

AILLBRACK

- AILLBRACK LOUGH

COROFIN

- DROMORE AND BALLYLINE

ENNIS

- ALLARD FISHERIES

KILFENARA

- LICKEEN LAKE

COUNTY CORK

BALLINEEN

- BANDON (RIVER)
- MANCH HOUSE FISHERY

BANDON

- BANDON (RIVER)

BANTRY

- LOUGH BOFINNE

CAPPOQUIN

- BLACKWATER (RIVER)
- DROMANA LAKE
- FINISK (RIVER)
- OWENSHED (RIVER)

CASTLELYONS

- BLACKWATER SALMON FISHERY

CASTLETOWNBERE

- DERRYVEGALL LAKE

CONNA

- BLACKWATER (RIVER)

CORK

- BALLINCOLLIG RESERVOIR
- CORK LOUGH

DRIMOLEAGUE

- DRIMINIDY LAKE

DUNMANWAY

- BANDON (RIVER)
- CAHA (RIVER)
- CHAPEL LAKE
- CURRAGHALICKEY LAKE
- GARRANES LAKE
- LOUGH ATARRIFF
- LOUGH BALLYNACARRIGA
- LOUGH COOLKEELURE
- LOUGH CULLENAGH
- LOUGH NEASKIN

ENNISKEANE

- BANDON (RIVER)
- KILCOLEMAN FISHERY

FERMOY

- BLACKWATER (RIVER)
- BLACKWATER FLY FISHING
- CAREYSVILLE
- MUNSTER BLACKWATER (RIVER) (GHILLIE COTTAGE)

GLENGARIFF

- GLENGARIFF (RIVER)
- LOUGH AVAUL (LOWER)
- LOUGH AVAUL (UPPER)

INNISCARRA

- INNISCARRA LAKE

MALLOW

- BLACKWATER (RIVER)

MIDLETON

- LOUGH ADERRA

SCHULL

- SCHULL RESERVOIR

SKIBBEREEN

- ILEN (RIVER)
- SHEPPERTON LAKES

WATERFALL

- BALLYMAQUIRK FISHERY AND LODGE

YOUGHAL

- LOUGH ADERRY

COUNTY DONEGAL

BALLYBOFEY

- GLENMORE FISHERY

BALLYSHANNON

- ASSAROE LAKE

BEAGH

- LOUGH BEAGH

BURTONPORT

- ROSSES FISHERY

CLOGHAN

- CLOGHAN LODGE ESTATE FISHERY
- FINN (RIVER)

COUNTY DUBLIN

DUBLIN

- BROSNA (TRIBUTARY)
- CENTRAL FISHERIES BOARD

COUNTY GALWAY

BALLYCONNEELY

- DOOHULLA

CLAREMORRIS

- ACLAUREEN (LOUGH)
- CASTLEREAGH LOUGHS
- CLARE LOUGH
- CLOONDROON LAKE
- MAYFIELD LAKE
- NANANNAGH (LOUGH)
- SUMMERVILLE LOUGH

CLONBUR

- LOUGH COOLIN
- LOUGH MASK

CONNEMARA

- KYLEMORE HOUSE FISHERY
- SCREEBE FISHERY

COONEMARA

- CRUMLIN FISHERIES

COSTELLO

- COSTELLO AND FERMOYLE FISHERY

GALWAY

- GALWAY FISHERY

LEENANE

- DELPHI FISHERY
- ERRIFF FISHERY

MAAM CROSS

- TOP WATERS BALLYNAHINCH FISHERY

MOYCULLEN

- BALLINDOOLY LOUGH AND POND
- LOUGH ACEELAGH
- LOUGH ARORAM
- LOUGH BALLYLUIRKE
- LOUGH CORRIB
- LOUGH DOWN
- LOUGH DOWNBEG
- LOUGH HEMUSHMACONRY
- LOUGH PARKYFLAHERTY
- LOUGH POLLALHY
- NANEVIN (LOUGH)
- ROSS LAKE

RECESS

- BALLYNAHINCH CASTLE FISHERY

RENVYLE

- CULFIN FISHERY

COUNTY KERRY

CASTLEGREGORY

- LOUGH CAUM

GLENCAR

- CARAGH FISHERY

KENMARE

- LAKE HOUSE HOTEL
- LOUGH BARFINNIHY

KERRY

- BLACKWATER FISHERY

KILLARNEY

- ANGLERS PARADISE
- LAKES OF KILLARNEY

KILLORGLIN

- LOUGH NAKIRKA

SNEEM

- LOUGH FADDA

WATERVILLE

- KERRYFISHERIES

COUNTY KILDARE

ATHY

- BARROW (RIVER)
- BOHERBAUN (RIVER)
- GRAND CANAL (BARROW TRACK)
- GREESE (RIVER)
- STRADBALLY (RIVER)

BALLYTORE

- GREESE (RIVER)

MAYNOOTH

- CLANE ANGLING ASSOCIATION

PROSPEROUS

- GRAND CANAL

RATHANGON

- GRAND CANAL (BARROW BRANCH)

ROBERTSTOWN

- GRAND CANAL

COUNTY KILKENNY

INISTIOGE

- COTTERELL FISHERY
- NORE (RIVER)

KILKENNY

- BALLINAKILL LAKE
- DININ (RIVER)
- ERKINA (RIVER)
- KINGS (RIVER)
- NORE (RIVER)

KILMACOW

- BLACKWATER (RIVER)

THOMASTOWN

- COOLMORE ESTATE FISHERY

MOUNT JULIET FISHERY
NORE (RIVER)

COUNTY LAOIS

ABBEYLEIX

NORE (RIVER)

PORTARLINGTON

BARROW (RIVER)
BARROW (UPPER) (RIVER)
CUSHINA (RIVER)
FIGILE (RIVER)

PORTLAOISE

GRANSTOWN LAKE

RATHDOWNEY

ERKINA (RIVER)

COUNTY LEITRIM

DROMAHAIR

DROMAHAIR LODGE FISHERY

DRUMSHANBO

LOUGH ALLEN
SHANNON (UPPER) (RIVER)

KINLOUGH

DUFF ANGLING SYNDICATE

ROSSINVER

LOUGH MELVIN

COUNTY LIMERICK

CASTLECONNELL

CASTLECONNELL SALMON FISHERY

COUNTY LOUTH

DROGHEDA

BARNATTIN RESERVOIR
BOYNE (RIVER)
KILLINEER RESERVOIR

DUNDALK

BALLYMASCANLON (RIVER)
CASTLETON (RIVER)
FANE (RIVER)

COUNTY MAYO

BALLINA

BROHLY (LOUGH)
MOUNT FALCON SALMON FISHERY
MOY FISHERY

BOHOLA

GWEESTION (RIVER)

BUNNYCONNELLAN

TALT (LOUGH)

CASTLEBAR

CASTLEBAR LAKES

CHARLESTOWN

MULLAGHANOE (RIVER)
OWENGARVE (RIVER)

CONG

LOUGH CORRIB (UPPER)

CROSSMOLINA

CLOONAMOYNE FISHERY

FOXFORD

ARMSTRONG FISHERY
BEAL EASE FISHERY
CALLOW LAKES
CLOONGEE FISHERY
FOXFORD FISHERY
LECKEE FISHERY
LOUGHS COY CULLIN
MOY (RIVER)
MUCK (LOUGH)

KILTAMAGH

GLORE (RIVER)
POLLAGH (RIVER)

LOUISBURGH

CARROWNISKY
LOUGH NAMUCKA

NEWPORT

BURRISHOOLE FISHERY

WESTPORT

LOUGH CARRA

COUNTY MEATH

DUNSHAUGHLIN

RATHBEGGAN LAKES

KELLS

BOYNE (RIVER)

NAVAN

BOYNE (RIVER)

SLANE

BOYNE (RIVER)

COUNTY MONAGHAN

CLONES

EMY LAKE FISHERY

COUNTY OFFALY

EDENDERRY

EDENDERRY OFFALY EIRE
GRAND CANAL

COUNTY ROSCOMMON

BALLAGHADERREN

BREEDOGE LOUGH
LOUGH CLOONACOLLY
LOUGH CLOONAGH
LOUGH NASOOL
LOUGH URLAUR
LUNG RIVER

BOYLE

BOYLE (RIVER)
LOUGH ARROW
LOUGH GARA
LOUGH KEY

COUNTY SLIGO

CASTLEBALDWIN

LAKE NA LEIBE
LOUGH AUGH
LOUGH BO
LOUGH KEY

COUNTY TIPPERARY

ARDFINNAN

SUIR (RIVER)

CAHIR

SUIR (RIVER)

CARRICK-ON-SUIR

COOLNAMUCK FISHERIES
LINGAUN (RIVER)
SUIR (RIVER)

CASHEL

ATHRY FISHERY
SUIR (RIVER)

CLONMEL

CLONANAU FLY FISHING CENTRE
DUAG ANNER STREAM
NIRE (RIVER)
NIRE STREAM
SUIR (RIVER)
SUIR VALLEY FISHERY
TAR STREAM

DUNDRUM

MARL LAKE

KILSHEELIN

CLODIAGH (RIVER)
COUMSHINGAUN LOUGH
CROTTYS LOUGH
SUIR (RIVER)

MOUNTRATH

NORE (RIVER)
WHITE HORSE (RIVER)

NENAGH

DERG (LOUGH)

THURLES

CLODIAGH (RIVER)
DRISH (RIVER)
SUIR (RIVER)

TIPPERARY TOWN

ARA (RIVER)

COUNTY WATERFORD

LISMORE

BLACKWATER (RIVER)

PORTLAW CLODIAGH

BLACKWATER (RIVER)

TALLOW

BLACKWATER (RIVER)
FORT WILLIAM FISHERY

UPPER BALLYDUFF

BLACKWATER (RIVER)
BLACKWATER LODGE HOTEL AND FISHERY
KILBARRY FISHERY

WATERFORD

BALLINAROONE LODGE FISHERY
BALLYSHUNNOCK
KNOCKDERRY
MOCOLLOP FISHERY

COUNTY WESTMEATH

MULLINGAR

BALLINAFID LAKE
DOOLIN POND
GALMOYLESTOWN LAKE
LOUGH ENNEL FISHERY

COUNTY ANTRIM

ANTRIM
- BANN (LOWER) NAVIGATIONAL CANAL
- MAINE (RIVER)
- SIX MILE WATER

BALLYCASTLE
- CAREY (RIVER)
- GLENSHESK (RIVER)
- MARGEY (RIVER)

BALLYCLARE
- STRAID FISHERY
- TILDARG FISHERY

BALLYMENA
- BANN (LOWER) (RIVER)
- BRAID (RIVER)
- CLADY (RIVER)
- CLOGHWATER (RIVER)
- CLOUGH (RIVER)
- GLENARM (RIVER)
- KELLSWATER (RIVER)
- LOWER BANN (RIVER)
- MAINE (RIVER)
- RALOO TROUT FISHERIES

BALLYMONEY
- CRANOGUE FISHERY
- TURNAGROVE FISHERY

BALLYNURE
- SIX MILE WATER

BELFAST
- LAGAN (RIVER)

BUSHMILLS
- BUSH (RIVER)

CARRICKFERGUS
- WOODBURN ANGLING CLUB
- WOODFORD FISHERY

CRUMLIN
- CRUMLIN (RIVER)

CUSHENDALL
- DALL (RIVER)
- DUN (RIVER)
- GLENARRIFF (RIVER)

LARNE
- INVER (RIVER)
- MCCAMMANS LAKE

LISBURN
- SPRINGWATER MEADOW

MOVANAGHER
- BANN (LOWER) NAVIGATIONAL CANAL

PORTNA
- BANN (LOWER) NAVIGATIONAL CANAL

RANDALSTOWN
- MAINE (RIVER)

COUNTY ARMAGH

ARMAGH
- BLACKWATER (RIVER)
- CALLAN (RIVER)
- LOUGHGALL COARSE FISHERY
- LOWRYS LAKE
- SEAGAHAN RESERVOIR DAM
- SHAWS LAKE
- TULLNAWOOD LAKE
- TULLYNAWOOD RESERVOIR

CRAIGAVON
- BANN (UPPER) (RIVER)
- LAGAN (RIVER)
- LOUGH NEAGH
- SLOWING RIVERS FARM

COUNTY DOWN

BALLYNAHINCH
- CARRICKMANNON FISHERY
- DAIRY FISHERY
- LOUGH INAGH FISHERY
- TULLYWEST FISHERY

BANBRIDGE
- BANN (UPPER) (RIVER)

CASTLEWELLAN
- BALLYLOUGH
- WRITES LOUGH

DONAGHADEE
- BRIDGEWATER FISHERY

DOWNPATRICK
- QUOILE (RIVER)
- RINGDUFFERIN ESTUARY

DROMORE
- LAGAN (RIVER)
- MILL LODGE FISHERY
- OWENREAGH (RIVER)

HILLSBOROUGH
- WATERFALL LODGE

NEWCASTLE
- MONEYCARRAGH (RIVER)
- SHIMNA (RIVER)

NEWRY
- BANN (UPPER) AND TRIBUTARIES
- CLANRYE (RIVER)
- CLEGGAN (RIVER)
- CULLY (RIVER)
- FANE (RIVER)
- FORKHILL (RIVER)
- KILKEEL (RIVER)
- LOUGH CASHEL
- LOUGH GLASSDRUMMAN
- LOUGH KILTYBAINE
- LOUGH MULLAGHABAN
- NEWRY CANAL
- WHITEWATER (RIVER)

NEWTOWNARDS
- BALLY GRANGE FISHERY
- INLER (RIVER)
- LOUGH COWEY FISHERY

POYNTSPASS
- MCCOURTS LAKE

RATHFRILAND
- BANN (UPPER) (RIVER)

COUNTY FERMANAGH

BALLINAMALLARD
- KNOCKBRACKEN TROUT LAKES

BELLEEK
- ERNE (RIVER)
- LOUGH KEENAGHAN

ENNISKILLEN
- BALLINAMALLARD (RIVER)
- COLEBROOKE PARK
- COOLYERMER LOUGH FISHERY
- ERNE (RIVER)
- LOUGH ERNE
- LOWER LOUGH ERNE
- MILL LOUGH BELLANALECK

GARRISON
- LOUGH MELVIN

MAGUIRESBRIDGE
- COLEBROOKE (RIVER)
- TEMPO (RIVER)

COUNTY LONDONDERRY

COLERAINE
- AGIVEY (RIVER)
- BANN (LOWER) (RIVER)
- MACOSQUIN (RIVER)
- MOORBROOK LODGE

DERRY
- FOYLE FISHERIES COMMISSION

LIMAVADY
- ROE (RIVER)

LONDONDERRY
- CREGGAN RESERVOIRS
- ENAGH TROUT FISHERY
- FAUGHAN (RIVER)
- PADDY MCNAMARAS LAKE
- ROSE (RIVER)

MAGHERA
- MOYOLA (RIVER)

MAGHERAFELT
- LOWER BANN (RIVER)
- TURNAFACE TROUT FISHERY

COUNTY TYRONE

AUGHER
- LOUGHMORE

AUGHNACLOY
- BALLYGAWLEY (RIVER)
- CARRICK LOUGH
- CRANS LOUGH
- GREEVE LOUGH
- WHITE LOUGH

CALEDON
- TULLYGIVEN LOUGH

CASTLEDERG
- DERG (RIVER)

CLOGHER
- BLACKWATER (RIVER)

COOKSTOWN
- BALLINDERRY (RIVER)
- LOUGH FEA
- TULLYLAGAN (RIVER)

DUNGANNON
- ALTMORE FISHERIES
- ANNAGINNY STILL WATER TROUT AND COARSE FISHERY
- BRANTRY LOUGH
- DUNGANNON PARK FISHERY
- LOUGH ENAGH
- LOUGH MACRONAN
- OONA RIVER
- PARK LAKE TROUT FISHERY
- PLUCK MILL FISH FARM
- QUIET WATERS
- ROUGHAN LOUGH
- TORRENT (RIVER)

FIVEMILETOWN
- BLESSINGBOURNE LAKE
- ROUND LAKE

NEWTOWNSTEWART
- GLENELLY (RIVER)
- MOURNE (RIVER)
- OWENKILLEW (RIVER)

OMAGH
- BARONSCOURT LAKES
- CAMOWEN (RIVER)
- DERG (RIVER)
- DRUMRAGH (RIVER)
- FAIRY WATER
- FINN (RIVER)
- GLEMELAG (RIVER)
- MOURNE (RIVER)
- OWENKILLEW (RIVER)
- STRULE (RIVER)

STRABANE
- BURN DENNET (RIVER)
- BURN DENNETT (RIVER)
- DERG (RIVER)
- FINN (RIVER)
- FOYLE (RIVER)
- MOURNE (RIVER)

ABERDEENSHIRE

ABERDEEN
- ABERDEEN BOX POOL

BALLATER
- TULLICH FISHERY

ELLON
- MILL OF ELRICK FISHERY
- YTHAN FISHERY
- YTHAN VALLEY FISHERY

HUNTLY
- BOGNIE AND MOUNTBLAIRY FISHING

INSCH
- LOCH INSCH FISHERY

LAURENCEKIRK
- LOCH SAUGH

MACDUFF
- BACKHILL FISHERY

PETERHEAD
- PITFOUR LAKE

STONEHAVEN
- CARRON (RIVER)

TURRIFF
- WAULKMILL FISHERIES

ANGUS

BLAIRGOWRIE
- ISLA (RIVER)

BRECHIN
- GLEN ESK CARAVAN PARK

CARNOUSTIE
- CROMBIE RESERVOIR

DUNDEE
- CLATIO LOCH
- DEAN (RIVER)
- KINGENNIE FISHINGS
- PIPERDAM GOLF AND COUNTRY PARK
- PIPERDAM HOLDINGS
- RESCOBIE LOCH

KIRRIEMUIR
- LOCH OF LINTRATHEN

MONTROSE
- MILL OF CRIGGIE TROUT FISHERY

ARGYLL AND BUTE

BRIDGE OF ORCHY
- ORCHY (RIVER)

DUNOON
- CUR (RIVER)
- DUNOON RESERVOIR
- FINNART (RIVER)
- LOCH LOSKIN (THE LOCHAN)
- LOCH TARSAN
- MASSAN (RIVER)
- RUEL (RIVER)

HELENSBOURGH
- CLYDE ESTUARY
- FRUIN (RIVER)

INVERARAY
- LOCH GLASHAN

OBAN
- ARDTORNISH ESTATE LOCHS
- AWE DISTRICT SALMON FISHERY BOARD
- LOCH AVICH
- LOCH AWE
- LOCH NANT

ROTHESAY
- LOCH FAD
- LOCH QUIEN

TAYNUILT
- INVERAWE FISHERIES

TIGHNABRUAICH
- MILL HOUSE FISHERIES

AYRSHIRE (EAST)

GALSTON
- COWANS LAW TROUT FISHERY
- WATERSIDE FARM FISHERY

AYRSHIRE (NORTH)

BRODICK
- PORT-NA-LOCHAN

IRVINE
- EGLINGTON LOCH

KILBIRNIE
- CAMPHILL RESERVOIR

KILWINNING
- GOOSELOAN POND

LARGS
- HAYLIE FISHERY
- MIDDLETON FISHERY

SKELMORLIE
- SKELMORLIE FISHERIES

AYRSHIRE (SOUTH)

AYR
- AYR (RIVER)
- COYLE WATER FISHERY
- DALVENNAN COUNTRY SPORTS FISHERY
- DOON (RIVER)
- DOON DISTRICT SALMON FISHERY BOARD
- SPRINGWATER FISHERY

GIRVAN
- LOCH DORNAL
- LOCH MAYBERRY
- STINCHAR (RIVER)

KILMARNOCK
- CRAUFURDLAND FISHERY

PRESTWICK
- CRAITH RESERVOIR

CLACKMANNANSHIRE

ALLOA
- GARTMORN DAM FISHERY

DOLLAR
- GLENSHERRUP FISHERIES

GLENDEVON
- EASTER BALADO TROUT FISHERY (KINROSS)

DUMFRIES AND GALLOWAY

ANNAN
- ANNAN (RIVER)
- BROOM FISHERIES
- KELHEAD WATER
- KINMOUNT LAKE

CANONBIE
- ESK (RIVER)
- LOWER LIDDLE (RIVER)

CASTLE DOUGLAS
- BARSCOBE LOCH
- BRACK LOCH
- EARLSTOUN LOCH
- KEN (RIVER)
- LAIRDMANNOCH LOCH
- LOCH ROAN
- LOCH SKERROW
- LOCH WHINYEON
- LOCHENBRECK LOCH
- LOCHINVAR LOCH
- NEWTON LOCHAN

DALBEATTIE
- BUITTLE RESERVOIR
- DALBEATTIE RESERVOIR
- PORTLING FISHERIES
- URR (RIVER)

DUMFRIES
- COWANS FARM
- GLENKILN RESERVOIR
- JERICHO LOCHS
- LOCH KEN
- NEW ABBEY DOW

GRETNA
- KIRTLE WATER STREAM
- SARK STREAM

KIRKCUDBRIGHT
- TONGUE OF BOMBIE LOCHAN

LANGHOLM
- ESK (RIVER)

LOCKERBIE
- ANNAN (RIVER)
- BLACK ESK RESERVOIR
- CASTLE LOCH
- DORMONT LAKE COARSE FISHERY
- HODDOM WATER
- KIRKWOOD WATER
- PURDOMSTONE RESERVOIR

MOFFAT
- MOFFAT FISHERIES

NEWTON STEWART
- BLACK LOCH
- BLADNOCH (RIVER)
- BRUNTIS LOCH
- CLATTERINGSHAWS LOCH
- CRAIGHLAW
- CREE (RIVER)
- CULSCADDEN FARM POND
- FYNTALLOCH LOCH
- GALLOWAY FOREST PARK
- GLENDARROCH LOCH
- KIRKCHRIST
- KIRRIEREOCH LOCH
- LILLIES LOCH
- LOCH BARNBARROCH
- LOCH BRADAN
- LOCH BRECKBOWIE
- LOCH DEE
- LOCH ELDRIG
- LOCH HERON
- LOCH MONREITH
- LOCH RONALD
- LOCH WHITEFIELD
- MAINS OF PENNINGHAM FISHERY
- NAHINE LOCH
- OCHILTREE LOCH
- TORHOUSEKIE AND KIRWAUGH
- TORWOOD HOUSE HOTEL
- WEE GLEN AMOUR LOCH
- WHITE LOCH OF MYRTON

STRANRAER
- DINDINNIE RESERVOIR
- DUNSKEY LOCHS
- KNOCKQUASSEN RESERVOIR
- LABRAX FISHING
- LOCHNAW
- PENWHIRN RESERVOIR
- SOULSEAT LOCH

THORNHILL
- MORTON LOCH
- MORTON POND
- NITH (RIVER)
- SLATEHOUSE LOCH
- STARBURN LOCH

EDINBURGH (CITY OF)

BALERNO
- HARLAW RESERVOIR
- THREIPMUIR RESERVOIRS

EDINBURGH
- CLUBBIEDEAN RESERVOIR
- DUDDINGSTON LOCH

FALKIRK
- CENTRAL SCOTLAND TROUT FISHERY
- LOCH EARN
- MILLHALL RESERVOIR

CALLANDER
- LOCH FINLAS
- LOCH VENACHAR

FIFE

BURNTISLAND
- KINGHORN LOCH

CUPAR
- GOLDEN LOCH
- LINDORES LOCH

DUNFERMLINE
- CRAIGLUSCAR RESERVOIR
- LOCH FITTY TROUT FISHERY

GLENROTHES
- BALLO RESERVOIR
- HOLL RESERVOIR

KIRKCALDY
- RAITH LAKE FISHERY

LOCHGELLY
- LOCH ORE
- LOCHMORE MEADOWS

NEWPORT-ON-TAY
- NEWTON FARM FISHERY

ST ANDREWS
- CAMERON RESERVOIR
- CLUTTO LOCH

GLASGOW (CITY OF)

GLASGOW
- BALGRAVE RESERVOIR
- CAMPS RESERVOIR
- CLYDE (RIVER)
- CULCREUCH CASTLE POND
- FORTH AND CLYDE CANAL
- LOCH ARKLET
- NEILSTON TROUT FISHERY

STRATHCLYDE
- DAER RESERVOIR

HIGHLAND

ACHNASHEEN
- LOCH DAMH
- LOCH MAREE

AVIEMORE
- LOCH MORLICH

BALLACHULISH
- GLENCOE LOCHAN
- HOSPITAL LOCHAN

BEAULY
- GLASS (RIVER)

BRORA
- LOCH BRORA

DALWHINNIE
- LOCH ERICHT
- LOCH LAGGAN

DINGWALL
- CONON (RIVER)
- GLASS (RIVER)
- LOCH ACHANALT
- LOCH ACHONACHIE
- LOCH CHUILIN
- LOCH USSIE

DORNOCH
- DORNOCH LOCHANS

FORSINARD
- STRATHY (RIVER)

FORT AUGUSTUS
- LOCH NESS

FORT WILLIAM
- LOCH ARKAIG
- LOCH LOCHY
- LOCH SHIEL

GAIRLOCH
- LOCH BAD A CROTHA

GARVE
- LOCH GLASCARNOCH

GOLSPIE
- BRORA DISTRICT SALMON FISHERY BOARD
- LOCH HORN
- LOCH LUNDIE

GRANTOWN ON SPEY
- SPEY (RIVER)

INVERGARRY
- GARRY UPPER (RIVER)
- LOCH GARRY
- LOCH INCH LAGGAN
- LOCH OICH
- LOCH POULARY
- LOCH QUOICH

INVERGORDON
- STONEYFIELD LOCH TROUT FISHERY

INVERNESS
- AVIELOCHAN
- BEAULY (RIVER)
- LOCH AFFRIC
- LOCH BENEVEAN
- LOCH KNOCKIE
- LOCH LOYNE
- LOCH MULLARDOCH
- LOCH RUTHVEN
- NESS (RIVER)
- TWEED (RIVER)

ISLE ORNSAY
- LOCH BARAVAIG

KINBRACE
- LOCH BADANLOCH

KINGUSSIE
- LOCH ALVIE
- LOCH INSH
- SPEY (RIVER)

LAIRG
- LOCH ASSYNT
- LOCH BEANNACH
- LOCH BORRALAN
- LOCH BORRALIE
- LOCH CRAGGIE
- LOCH CULAG
- LOCH DOLA
- LOCH HOPE
- LOCH LOYAL
- LOCH MERKLAND
- LOCH NAVER
- LOCH SHIN
- SCOURIE HOTEL

MALLAIG
- LOCH MORAR

MUIR OF ORD
- LOCH BEANNACHAIRAN

NAIRN
- NAIRN (RIVER)

PORTREE
- BRAES SALMON STATION
- LOCH CONNAN
- LOCH DUAGRAICH

STRATHPEFFER
- LOCH ACHILITY
- LOCH FANNICH
- LOCH GARVE
- LOCH MEIG
- LOCH RUITH A PHUILL
- LOCH TARVIE
- TARVIE LOCHS FISHERY

THURSO
- FORSINARD
- HALLADALE SALMON FISHERY
- LOCH AKRAN
- LOCH MEADIE
- SALMON FISHING STATION
- ST JOHNS LOCH

ULLAPOOL
- LOCH SIONASCAIG
- STRATHMANAIRD LOCHS

WICK
- LOCH TOFTINGALL
- LOCH WATTEN

INVERCLYDE

GREENOCK
- ARDGOWAN TROUT FISHERY
- CLYDE (RIVER)
- LOCH THOM

KILMACOLM
- GRYFFE (RIVER)
- LAWFIELD TROUT FISHERY
- PINEWOOD TROUT FISHERY

LANARKSHIRE (NORTH)

AIRDRIE
- HILLEND LOCH
- LILY LOCH

COATBRIDGE
- MONKLAND CANAL

MOTHERWELL
- STRATHCLYDE LOCH

WISHAW
- CLYDE (RIVER)

LANARKSHIRE (SOUTH)

BIGGAR
- FRUID RESERVOIR
- TALLA RESERVOIR
- TINTO TROUT FISHERIES

HAMILTON
- QUARTER FISHERY

LANARK
- LANARK LOCH
- NEWMILL TROUT AND DEER FARM

LARKHALL
- AVON (RIVER)

LOTHIAN (EAST)

EAST LINTON
- MARKLE FISHERIES

HADDINGTON
- GIFFORD HOPES RESERVOIR
- MALTINGS FISHERY
- TYNE (RIVER)
- WHITEADDER RESERVOIR

LOTHIAN (MID)

PENICUIK
- GLADHOUSE RESERVOIR
- LOGANLEA TROUT FISHERY
- PORTMORE LOCH
- ROSLYNLEE FISHERY

LOTHIAN (WEST)

BROXBURN
- HOPETOUN FISHERY

LINLITHGOW
- BEECRAIGS LOCH
- BOWDEN SPRINGS FISHERY

- LINLITHGOW LOCH
- PARKLEY FISHERY
- UNION CANAL

LIVINGSTON

- CROSSWOOD RESERVOIR
- MORTON FISHERIES
- SELM MUIR FISHERY

SOUTH QUEENSFERRY

- ALMOND (RIVER)

WEST CALDER

- ALLANDALE TARN

MORAY

ABERLOUR

- GLEN OF ROTHES TROUT FISHERY

ELGIN

- BROOM OF MOY
- GLEN LATTERACH RESERVOIR
- LOCH NA BO
- MILLBUIES LOCH

FORRES

- LOCH DALLAS
- LOCH OF BLAIRS

PERTH AND KINROSS

ABERFELDY

- ABERFELDY ASSOCIATION BEAT
- BOLFRACKS BEAT
- CASTLE BEAT
- CASTLE MENZIES BEAT
- CLOCHFOLDICH BEAT
- COSHIEVILLE FARM
- CUILALUINN BEAT
- DERCULICH BEAT
- FARLEYER BEAT
- FINDYNATE BEAT
- HAUGH OF GRANDTULLY BEAT
- KENMORE BEAT
- LOCH TAY
- LOWER FARLEYER BEAT
- MAINS OF MURTHLY
- PITCASTLE BEAT
- PITNACREE BEAT
- SKETEWAN BEAT
- TOMBUIE BEAT
- UPPER BORLICK BEAT
- WEEM BEAT

AUCHTERARDER

- LOWER ABERUTHVEN FISHINGS

CRIEFF

- DRUMMOND FISHERIES
- DRUMMOND LOCH

DUNBLANE

- ORCHILL LOCH TROUT FISHERY

DUNKELD

- ALMOND (RIVER)
- AMULREE BEAT
- BRAAN (RIVER)
- BUTTERSTONE LOCH
- LOCH FREUCHIE
- RUMBLING BRIDGE
- TAY (RIVER)
- TROCHRY BEAT

KINROSS

- HEATHERYFORD FISHERY
- LOCH LEVEN FISHERIES
- LOWER FRANDY

PERTH

- ALMOND (RIVER)
- GLENFARG FISHERY
- LOWER SCONE BEAT
- MONTAGUE RESERVOIR
- NEWTON OF LOGIERAIT BEAT
- SANDYKNOWES FISHING
- SEAMAW LOCH
- UPPER KINNAIRD BEAT

PITLOCHRY

- BALLECHIN BEAT
- DUNALASTAIR LOCH
- EASTERTYRE BEAT
- LOCH BHAC
- LOCH EIGHEACH
- LOCH FASKALLY
- LOCH RANNOCH
- LOGIERAIT BEAT
- PITLOCHRY BOATING STATION AND LOCHSIDE CAFÉ
- TULLYPOWRIE BEAT

RENFREWSHIRE

BRIDGE OF WEIR

- BRIDGE OF WEIR
- GRYFFE (RIVER)

JOHNSTONE

- HOWWOOD TROUT FISHERY

LOCHGILPHEAD

- CARN LOCH
- CLACHAIG (LOCH)
- COILLE BHAR (LOCH)
- GLEAN LOCH
- LEIPEIG (LOCH)
- LOCH BARNLUASGAN
- LOCH DHU
- LOCH-AN-ADD
- LOCH-NA-BRIC
- LOCH-NA-FAOILINN
- NEW LOCH

LOCHWINNOCH

- MAICH WATERS

SCOTTISH BORDERS

DUNS

- BLACKADDER WATER
- TWEED (RIVER)
- WATCH RESERVOIR

EARLSTON

- LEADER (RIVER)

EYEMOUTH

- COLDINGHAM LOCH

GALASHIELS

- TWEED (RIVER)

HAWICK

- ACREKNOWE RESERVOIR
- AKERMOOR LOCH
- ALEMOOR RESERVOIR
- HELLMOOR LOCH
- TEVIOT (RIVER)
- WULLIESTRUTHER LOCH

INNERLEITHEN

- TWEED (RIVER)

JEDBURGH

- JED (RIVER)

KELSO

- BAILEY (RIVER)
- TWEED (RIVER)
- WOODEN LOCH

MELROSE

- CLERKLAND FLY FISHERY
- TWEED (RIVER)

NEWCASTLETON

- ESK AND LIDDLE FISHERIES
- LIDDLE (RIVER)

PEEBLES

- KAILZIE GARDENS FISHERY
- TWEED (RIVER)
- WEST WATER RESERVOIR

SELKIRK

- BUCCLEUCH ESTATES
- ETTERICK (RIVER)
- ETTRICK AND YARROW (RIVER)
- HEADSHAW FISHERY
- LINDEAN RESERVOIR
- MEGGET RESERVOIR
- ST MARYS LOCH
- TEVIOT (RIVER)

WEST LINTON

- MACBIEHILL ESTATE

SHETLAND ISLANDS

SHETLAND

- GOSSA WATER
- LOCH OF BROUGH
- LOCH OF COLVISTER
- LOCH OF CULLIVOE
- LOCH OF GUTCHER
- LOCH OF LUMBISTER
- LOCH OF PAPIL
- LOCH OF VOLLISTER
- MUSKRA LOCH

STIRLING

- HOWIETOUN FISHERY
- LAKE OF MENTEITH FISHERIES
- LOCH ACHRAY
- LOCH ARD
- LOCH ARKLET
- LOCH DRUNKIE
- LOCH GLENFINGLAS
- LOCH KATRINE
- NORTH THIRD TROUT FISHERY
- SWANSWATER FISHERY

CALLANDER

- KILLIN BREADALBANE ANGLING CLUB WATERS
- LOCH LUBNAIG

CRIANLARICH

- AUCHESSON BEAT
- PORTNELLAN
- SUIE

DOUNE

- LOCH KATRINE

GLASGOW

- BLAIRMORE FISHERY
- ENDRICK (RIVER)
- KILLEARN HOUSE FISHERY
- LOCH LOMOND

KILLIN

- BARNCROFT
- BORELAND
- CRAIGNAVIE
- DOCHART (RIVER)
- FINLARIG
- KINNEL
- LESKINE
- LOCH TAY HIGHLAND LODGES
- LOCHAN NA LARAIG
- LOCHAY (RIVER)

LOCHEARNHEAD

- BALVAIG (RIVER)
- LOCH VOIL

WESTERN ISLES

HARRIS

- CEANN-AN-ORA FISHERY
- LACASDALE LOCHS

LEVERBURGH

- OBBE FISHINGS

LOCHBOISDALE

- SOUTH UIST ESTATES

STORNOWAY

- GRIMERSTA LODGE
- SOVAL ESTATE

YORKSHIRE (SOUTH)

DONCASTER

- BANK END COARSE FISHERIES
- HAYFIELD LAKES
- LINDHOLME LEISURE LAKES FISHERIES (1)
- LINDHOLME LEISURE LAKES FISHERIES (2)
- LINDHOLME LEISURE LAKES FISHERIES (3)

LINDHOLME LEISURE LAKES FISHERIES (4)
TORNE (RIVER)

BLAENAU GWENT

EBBW VALE
- BLUE LAKE
- BOAT POND
- LYMOOR POOL 1 AND 2
- MACHINE POND

TREDEGAR
- BUTE TOWN RESERVOIR
- HAYRICK LAKES
- SIRHOWY (RIVER)

BRIDGEND
- GARW (RIVER)
- KENFIG LAKE
- OGMORE (RIVER)
- STROUDWATER CANAL

MAESTEG
- LLYNFI (RIVER)

CAERPHILLY
- CAERPHILLY CASTLE LAKES

BARGOED
- OGILVIE LAKE

BLACKWOOD
- EBBW (RIVER)
- SIRHOWY (RIVER)

HENGOED
- RIVERSIDE TROUT FISHERY

CARDIFF
- CEFN MABLEY
- EAST DOCK
- HENDRE LAKE
- TAFF (RIVER)

CARMARTHENSHIRE

AMMANFORD
- COTHI (RIVER)
- LLWCHWR (RIVER)
- LOUGHOR (RIVER)
- LOUGHOR VALLEY FISHERY

CARMARTHEN
- BRO TYWI FISHERIES
- COTHI (RIVER)
- COWIN (RIVER)
- CYNIN (RIVER)
- DUAD (RIVER)
- GWILI (RIVER)
- LLANLLAWDDOG FISHERY
- PANT Y BEDW FISHING LAKES
- PEWI FACH (RIVER)
- TAF (RIVER)
- TOWI (RIVER)
- TOWY (RIVER)

KIDWELLY
- GWENDRAETH FACH (RIVER)
- RIVER GWENLLIAN FISHERY

LLANBOIDY
- GLAS LLYN FISHERY

LLANDEILO
- EDWINSFORD FISHERY
- TOWY (RIVER)

LLANDOVERY
- COTHI (RIVER)
- TOWEY (RIVER)

LLANELLI
- GARNFFRWD FISHERY
- GWENDRAETH AND MORIASIS FISHERY
- GWENDRAETH FACH (RIVER)
- LLEIDI RESERVIORS
- SWISS VALLEY

LLANWRDA
- SPRINGWATER LAKES

LLANYBYDDER
- DOLGWM MILL FISHERY
- HENDY FISHERY
- MAES-ISAF FISHERY
- TEIFI (RIVER)
- TEIFI VALLEY FISH

LLWYNFORTUNE
- TOWY (RIVER)

NEWCASTLE EMLYN
- DOL WATTS FISHERY
- PENBEILI FISHERY
- RHYDFACH FISHERY
- TAN-Y-COED FISHERY
- TEIFI (RIVER)
- TREBEDW FISHERY

PENCADER
- BRYNHAWC FISHERY
- CHURCH FARM FISHERY

WHITLAND
- GLAS-LLYN FISHERY
- LLYN CARFAN
- TAF (RIVER)
- WHITE HOUSE MILL

CEREDIGION

ABERAERON
- AERON (RIVER)

ABERYSTWYTH
- CWM RHEIDOL FISHERY
- DINA FISHERY
- DINAS RESERVOIR
- FRON FARM FISHERY
- GEORGE BORROW HOTEL
- LAKE BLAENMELINDWR
- LAKE CRAIGYPISTYLL
- LAKE FRONGOCH
- LAKE LLYGAD
- LAKE PENDHAM
- LAKE RHEIDOL
- LAKE RHOSGOCH
- LAKE RHOSRHYDD
- NANT Y MOCH RESERVOIR
- RHEIDOL (RIVER)
- YSTWYTH (RIVER)

CARDIGAN
- CYCH (RIVER)
- LLWYNDURIS MANSION FISHERY
- TEIFI (RIVER)

LAMPETER
- BAYLIAU FISHERY
- CEFN-BRYN FISHERY
- CELLAN FISHERY
- GLWYDWERN TROUT FISHERY
- LAMPETER FISHERY
- LLETYTWPA FISHERY
- PENTRE FARM FISHERY
- RALLT FISHERY
- TEGLAN LAKE
- TEIFI (RIVER)
- TROED-Y-BRYN FISHERY

LLANARTH
- LLANARTH FISHERY
- NINE OAKS

LLANDYSUL
- ARTRO (RIVER)
- CASTELL-PYR FISHERY
- CWMMACKWITH FISHERY
- LLYN MAENOG TROUT FISHERY
- RHYDLEWIS TROUT FISHERY
- RHYDYGALFE FISHERY
- TEIFI (RIVER
- TEIFI (RIVER)
- TYRDREF FISHERY

TALYBONT
- TALYBONT RESERVOIR

TREGARON
- LLYN BERWYN
- NEUADDLAS COUNTRY GUEST HOUSE
- PANT TROUT POOL
- TEIFI (RIVER)
- TEIFY POOLS FISHERY

YSTRAD MEURIG
- LLYN BERWEN
- TEIFI POOLS

CONWY
- CONWY (RIVER)
- CONWY VALLEY FISHERIES
- LLYN NANT-Y-CERRIG
- TREFANT POOL
- TYDDYN MAWR TROUT FARM

ABERGELE
- ELWY (RIVER)
- TALYLLN LAKE FISHERY
- TAN-Y-MYNYDD TROUT LAKES

BETWS-Y-COED
- CONWY (RIVER)
- GILER ARMS LAKE

DENBIGH
- ALED (RIVER)
- CLWYD (RIVER)
- ELWY (RIVER)
- LLYN ALED

DOLWYDDELAN
- LLEDR (RIVER)

LLANRWST
- CONWY (RIVER)

PENMAENMAWR
- GRAIGLWYD SPRINGS FISHERY

TREFRIW
- LLYN CRAFNANT FISHERIES

DENBIGHSHIRE

CORWEN
- ALWEN (RIVER)
- ALWEN RESERVOIR
- BRENIG RESERVOIR
- DRAGONFLY FISHERIES
- GWYDDELWERN POOL
- LLYN BRENIG

LLANGOLLEN
- ABBEY FISHERY
- CEIRIOG (RIVER)
- DEE (RIVER)
- TEIGN (RIVER)

RHYL
- FELIN-Y-GORS FISHERIES
- LLYN COWLYD AND HILL LAKES

RUTHIN
- CEIRW STREAM
- CLWYD (RIVER)
- CLYWEDOG (RIVER)
- DEE (RIVER)
- LLYN ALWEN

ST ASAPH
- CLWYD (RIVER)
- DOLWEN AND PLAS UCHAF
- ELWY (RIVER)

WREXHAM
- CEIRIOG (RIVER)
- DEE (RIVER)
- MONKS POOL
- PANT GLAS RESERVOIR

FLINTSHIRE

BUCKLEY
- BUCKLEY TRAP POOL

CONNAHS QUAY
- SWAN LAKE

HOLYWELL
- FOREST HILL TROUT FARM
- GYRN CASTLE FISHERY

MOLD
- ALLTAMI CLAY PITS
- ALYN (RIVER)
- CLAWDD OFFAS DYKE
- CLWYD (RIVER)

DEE (RIVER)
GWERYD LAKES FISHING
NANT-Y-GAIN FISHERY
PADESWOOD POOL
SARN MILL FISHERIES
SEVEN SPRINGS TROUT FARM AND FISHERIES
WAL GOCH FLY
WHEELER (RIVER)

GLAMORGAN (VALE OF)

COWBRIDGE

HAZELCOURT PONDS
WARREN MILL

DINAS POWYS

BARRY RESERVOIR

MERTHYR TYDFIL

PENTWYN RESERVOIR
PENYWERN PONDS
PONTSTICILL RESERVOIR
TAFF (RIVER)
UPPER NEUADD

NEATH

MELLTE (STREAM)

TREHARRIS

LLYWN-ON RESERVOIR
TAFF BARGOED

GWYNEDD

BALA

CWM PRYSOR LAKE
DEE (RIVER)
LLYN CELYN FISHERY
LLYN TEGID (BALA LAKE)
PORTH WATERS FISHERY
TRYWERYN (RIVER)

BANGOR

OGWEN (RIVER)

BLAENAU FFESTINIOG

DWYRYD (RIVER)
FFESTINIOG FISHERY
TANYGRISIAU RESERVOIR
TRAWFFYNYDD RESERVOIR

CAERNARFON

AFON LLYFNI (RIVER)
AFON SEIONT (RIVER)
BONTNEWYDD FISHERY
CWM SILYN LAKE
DWYTHWCH LAKE
DYWARCHEN RESERVOIR
GWYRFAI (RIVER)
LLYN CWELLYN RESERVOIR
LLYN DINAS
LLYN GADAIR
LLYN NANTLLE
LLYN PADARN
NANTLLE LAKE

CRAIG-Y-TAN

LLIW (RIVER)

CRICCIETH

DWYFACH (RIVER)
DWYFAWR (RIVER)
GWYNEDD (RIVER)

DOLGELLAU

CREGENNAN LAKES
DUGOED (RIVER)
EDEN (RIVER)
GREGANNAN LAKES
GWERNAN LAKE FISHERY
LLYN CYNWCH LAKE
MAWDDACH (RIVER)
MAWDDACH AND WNION (RIVERS)
WNION (RIVER)

LLANRWST

CONWY (RIVER)

PENRHYNDEUDRAETH

GLASLYN (RIVER)

PORTHMADOG

GLAN MORFA MAWR FISHERY
LLYN CWMYSTRADLLYN
LLYN DDU (BLACK LAKE)
LLYN GLAN MOFA MAWR

PWLLHELI

BRON EIFION FISHERIES
CLWYD (RIVER)
ERCH (RIVER)
RHYDHIR (RIVER)

TALYBONT

LERI (RIVER)

TYWYN

DYSYNNI (RIVER)
LLYN BUGEILYN
TALYLLYN LAKE

ISLE OF ANGLESEY

AMLWCH

PLAS-Y-NANT TROUT FISHERY

ANGLESEY

LLYN DEWI
LLYN NANT ANOG
LLYN TACAN

BENLLECH

LAKE HOUSE HOLIDAYS

HOLYHEAD

BREAKWATER PARK
LLYN ALAN

LLANERCHYMEDD

LLYN LLWYDIARTH FAWR
PARC NEWYDD TROUT FISHERY

LLANFAIR PWLLGWYNGYLL

LLYN BRYNTIRION

LLANGEFNI

CEFNI RESERVOIR
LLYN CORON

MENAI BRIDGE

LLYN JANE FISHERY
LLYN Y GORS

RHOSNEIGR

TY HEN LAKE

TYN-Y-GONGL

TYDDYN SARGENT

MONMOUTHSHIRE

ABERGAVENNY

GROVE FARM FISHERY
MONNOW (RIVER)
USK (RIVER)

ABERTILLERY

CWMCELYN POND
CWMTILLERY RESERVOIR

CHEPSTOW

FAIROAK FISHERY
RAVENSNEST FISHERY

MONMOUTH

FIVE TREES
TREFALDU FISHERY
WYE (RIVER)

USK

OLWAY BROOK
TROTHY (RIVER)
USK (RIVER)

NEATH PORT TALBOT

NEATH

DULAIS (RIVER)
HEPSTE (STREAM)
NEATH (RIVER)
TWRCH (RIVER)

PORT TALBOT

ABERNANT FARM FISHERY
AFAN STREAM
EGLWYS NUNYDD RESERVOIR
GLYNCORRWG PONDS FISHERY
MARGRAM PARK FISHERY

NEWPORT

DEE (RIVER)
LLISWERRY POND
MONMOUTHSHIRE AND BRECON CANAL
NEVERN (RIVER)
PETERSTONE TROUT LAKE
SHROPSHIRE UNION CANAL
WENTWOOD RESERVOIR
WOODSTOCK POOL
YNYS-Y-FRO RESERVOIR

NORFOLK

HOLT

DEE (RIVER)

PEMBROKESHIRE

FISHGUARD

MILLBROOK FISHERY
YET-Y-GORS FISHERY

HAVERFORDWEST

EASTERN CLEDDAU (RIVER)
HAYCASTLE TROUT FISHERY
HAYSCASTLE TROUT FISHERY
LLYS Y FRAN RESERVOIR AND COUNTRY PARK
ROSEBUSH RESERVOIR
WESTERN CLEDDAU (RIVER)

LLANYCEFN

EASTERN CLEDDAU (RIVER)

MILFORD HAVEN

EWENNY (RIVER)
SABRE TOOTH

NARBERTH

EASTERN CLEDDAU (RIVER)
HOLGAN TROUT FARM FISHERY
IAN HEAPS PREMIER FISHERIES AND SCHOOL OF ANGLING
LUDCHURCH LAKE
ROADSIDE FARM
WEST ATHESTON COARSE FISHERY

TENBY

PENHOYLE FISHING PARK

POWYS

BRECON

BEACONS FISHERY
BEGUEILIN LAKE
CANTEF RESERVOIR
CRAI RESERVOIR
GLUDY LAKE
LLANGORSE LAKE
TOWY (RIVER)
USK RESERVOIR

BUILTH WELLS

BOATSIDE FARM
CAER BERIS MANOR HOTEL
IRFON (RIVER)
LLYN ALARCH
LLYSWEN CARP POOLS
WYE (RIVER)

CRICKHOWELL

USK (RIVER)

LLANBRYNMAIR

GWYDDIOR LAKE
LLYN-COCH HWYAD
TWYMYN (RIVER)

LLANDRINDOD WELLS

ITHON (RIVER)
NEW INN
WYE (RIVER)

LLANFYLLIN

VALLEY DAM FISHERY

LLANGAMMARCH WELLS

- IRFON (RIVER)
- RIVERSIDE CARAVAN PARK

LLANIDLOES

- CLYNWEDOG RESERVOIR
- CLYWEDOG (RIVER)
- DOL LLYS FARM
- DULAS (RIVER)
- LLYN CLYWEDOG
- SEVERN (RIVER)

LLANSANTFFRAID

- VYRNWY (RIVER)

LLANWRTYD WELLS

- IRFON (RIVER)

LLANYMYNECH

- DEE (RIVER)
- ERCH (RIVER)
- LLANDRINIO WEST LAKE
- MAERDY BROOK
- SEVERN (RIVER)
- VYRNWY (RIVER)
- WESTLAKE FISHERY

MACHYNLLETH

- DULAS (RIVER)
- DYFI (RIVER)

MONTGOMERY

- MONTGOMERY CANAL

NEWTOWN

- FACHWEN POOL
- LAKE MOCHDRE
- MULE (RIVER)
- SEVERN (RIVER)

RHAYADER

- CLAERWEN RESERVOIR
- ELAN (RIVER)
- ELAN VALLEY RESERVOIR
- LLNGWYN FISHERY
- LLYNGWYN LAKE
- WYE (RIVER)

WELSHPOOL

- BANWY (RIVER)
- SEVERN (RIVER)
- SHROPSHIRE UNION CANAL
- VYRNWY (RIVER)

RHONDDA CYNON TAFF

PONTYCLUN

- ELY (RIVER)
- LLYN ALAW
- SEVEN OAKS FISHERY
- TRI NANT TROUT FARM

PONTYPRIDD

- BROOKFIELD FISHERY

TREORCHY

- CMPRAC (RIVER)
- LLYN FAWR FISHERY
- RHONDDA (RIVER)

SWANSEA

- FENDROD LAKE
- GOWERTON COARSE FISHERY
- LOWER LLIW
- MAES GWYN FISHERY
- SHIMANO FELINDRE TROUT FISHERY
- TAWE (RIVER)
- WHITE SPRINGS LAKES

TORFAEN

CWMBRAN

- CWMBRAN BOATING LAKE
- MORGANS POND

PONTYPOOL

- BEACONS RESERVOIRS
- CANTREF RESERVOIR
- LISVANE RESERVOIR
- LLANDEGFEDD RESERVOIR
- LLANISHEN RESERVOIR
- LLWYN ON RESERVOIR
- LLYN ON RESERVOIR
- LLYWD (RIVER)

WREXHAM

- ALYN (RIVER)
- ARGAE LAKE
- BODIDRIS GAME FISHERY
- DEE (RIVER)
- DEE ABBEY FISHERIES
- FLASH
- LLANDEGLA TROUT FISHERY
- LLAY RESERVOIR
- LLYN CYFYNWY SPORT TROUT FISHERY
- PENYCAE LOWER RESERVOIR
- PENYCAE UPPER RESERVOIR
- PONKY POOL
- TAN LLAN
- TREE TOPS FLY FISHERY
- TRENCH FISHERIES
- TY MAWR RESERVOIR
- WORTHENBURY BROOK

BANGOR-ON-DEE

- DEE (RIVER)

WORTHENBURY

- DEE (RIVER)

by Nearest Location

SECTION 3

Sometimes you may know the name of a location but not know which Town or County it is in. This section helps you to search by various nearest locations.

e.g What Fisheries are near Bosley?

Once you have located a Fishery you can either look up further details in Section 1 or use the other sections to find what else the Fishery may have to offer.

Angling Times Fishooked Directory

ABBERLEY
- **WHARFE INN POOL** Worcestershire

ABINGDON
- **CLUB LAKE** Dorset
- **BULLFIELD LAKE** Oxfordshire
- **CLIFTON LOCK** Oxfordshire
- **DAYS LOCK** Oxfordshire
- **MARLBOROUGH POOL** Oxfordshire
- **MILLETS FARM TROUT FISHERY** Oxfordshire
- **ORCHID LAKES** Oxfordshire
- **STRATTON LODGE** Oxfordshire
- **THAMES (RIVER)** Oxfordshire

ABINGTON
- **MARLBOROUGH POOL** Oxfordshire
- **MILLETS FARM TROUT FISHERY** Oxfordshire

ABRIDGE
- **RODING (RIVER)** Essex

ACCRINGTON
- **DEAN CLOUGH RESERVOIR** Lancashire
- **HAGGS RESERVOIR** Lancashire
- **KEARNS ALLEN LODGES** Lancashire
- **MITCHELLS HOUSE RESERVOIR** Lancashire
- **PARSONAGE RESERVOIR** Lancashire

ACLE
- **ACLE (RIVER)** Norfolk

ADDERBURY
- **NELL BRIDGE FISHERY** Oxfordshire

ADDLESTONE
- **WEY (RIVER)** Fife

ALCESTER
- **ADAMS POOL** Warwickshire
- **WEST HILLBOROUGH** Warwickshire

ALDEBURGH
- **ALDE (RIVER)** Suffolk

ALDERMASTON
- **OLD MILL** Berkshire

ALDERSHOT
- **BASINGSTOKE CANAL** Hampshire
- **FRENSHAM GREAT AND LITTLE PONDS** Hampshire
- **GOLD VALLEY LAKES** Hampshire
- **LAKESIDE** Hampshire
- **SPRINGLAKES** Hampshire
- **WILLOW PARK** Hampshire

ALDHAM
- **COLNE (RIVER)** Essex

ALDRIDGE
- **FOXHILLS FISHERY** Midlands (West)

ALDRIGHT
- **RUSHALL CANAL** Midlands (West)

ALDWARK
- **LOWER DUNSFORTH (RIVER)** Yorkshire (North)
- **SWALE (RIVER)** Yorkshire (North)

ALFORD
- **ABY POND** Lincolnshire
- **OHAM LAKES** Lincolnshire
- **ST EAU FISHING SYNDICATE** Lincolnshire
- **WOODTHORPE HALL LAKE** Lincolnshire

ALFRETON
- **HIGHAM FARM COARSE FISHING** Derbyshire

ALFRISTON
- **CUCKMERE (RIVER)** Sussex (East)

ALLHALLOWS-ON-SEA
- **ALLHALLOWS LEISURE PARK** Kent

ALNWICK
- **ALN (RIVER)** Northumberland
- **TWEED (RIVER)** Northumberland

ALRESFORD
- **CANDOVER BROOK** Hampshire

ALREWAS
- **SWARBORN (RIVER)** Staffordshire
- **TAME (RIVER)** Staffordshire
- **TRENT (RIVER)** Staffordshire

ALSTON
- **PRYHEAD FISHERY** Cumbria
- **SOUTH TYNE (RIVER)** Cumbria
- **TYNE (RIVER)** Cumbria

ALTON
- **CHURNET (RIVER)** Staffordshire

ALTRINCHAM
- **ASHLEY POOL** Cheshire
- **BRIDGEWATER CANAL** Cheshire
- **MOBBERLEY POOL** Cheshire

ALVELEY
- **TOWNSEND FISHERY** Shropshire

AMBERLEY
- **ARUN (RIVER)** Sussex (West)

AMBLESIDE
- **BLELHAM TARN** Cumbria
- **BRATHAY (RIVER)** Cumbria
- **CODALE TARN** Cumbria
- **DRUNKEN DUCK TARN FISHERY** Cumbria
- **EASEDALE TARN** Cumbria
- **ESTHWAITE WATER** Cumbria
- **GRASMERE COARSE FISHERY** Cumbria
- **GRIZEDALE BECK** Cumbria
- **HAWESWATER RESERVOIR** Cumbria
- **HAWKSHEAD TROUT FISHING** Cumbria
- **HAYESWATER RESERVOIR** Cumbria
- **HIGH ARNSIDE TARN** Cumbria
- **LOUGHRIGG TARN** Cumbria
- **MOSS ECCLES TARN** Cumbria
- **ROTHAY (RIVER)** Cumbria
- **RYDAL WATER** Cumbria

AMERSHAM
- **CHESS (RIVER)** Buckinghamshire
- **SILVERWING LAKE** Buckinghamshire

AMPTHILL
- **BRIARWOOD FISHERY** Bedfordshire

ANDOVER
- **ABBOTTS WORTHY** Hampshire
- **ANTON (RIVER)** Hampshire
- **ANTON LAKE** Hampshire
- **CHARLTON PITS** Hampshire
- **FOXCOTTE LAKE** Hampshire
- **GOLDEN POND FISHERY** Hampshire
- **KIMBRIDGE** Hampshire
- **PERIL LAKE** Hampshire
- **ROOKSBURY MILL TROUT FISHERIES** Hampshire
- **VALE FARM FISHERY** Hampshire

APPLEBY
- **SANDFORD ARMS** Cumbria

APPLEBY-IN-WESTMORLAND
- **EDEN (RIVER)** Cumbria
- **SANDFORD ARMS** Cumbria

ARLESEY
- **ARLESEY LAKE** Bedfordshire
- **GREEN LAGOON** Bedfordshire
- **BLUE LAGOON** Hertfordshire
- **OLDFIELD** Hertfordshire

ARNCLIFFE
- **SKIRFARE (RIVER)** Yorkshire (North)

ARUNDEL
- **ARUN (RIVER)** Sussex (West)
- **CASTLE TROUT POND** Sussex (West)
- **CHALK SPRINGS TROUT FISHERY** Sussex (West)

ASENBY
- **SWALE (RIVER)** Yorkshire (North)

ASH
- **SHAWFIELDS LAKES** Surrey

ASHBOURNE
- **ALDAMORE POOL** Derbyshire
- **CARSINGTON WATER** Derbyshire
- **DOVE (RIVER)** Derbyshire
- **HENMORE (RIVER)** Derbyshire
- **YEAVELEY ESTATE TROUT FISHERY** Derbyshire

ASHBURTON
- **VENFORD RESERVOIR** Devon

ASHFORD
- **CACKLE HILL LAKES** Kent
- **CHEQUERTREE TROUT AND COARSE FISHERY** Kent
- **CONNINGBROOK** Kent
- **EUREKA** Kent
- **HOOKSTEAD LAKE** Kent
- **NACCOLT LAKE** Kent
- **ROYAL MILITARY CANAL** Kent
- **SINGLETON LAKE** Kent
- **STATION FARM** Kent
- **STOWTING TROUT LAKE** Kent
- **SURRENDEN LAKES** Kent
- **WINGHAM FISHERY** Kent
- **WOODCHURCH TROUT FISHERY** Kent

ASHFORD-IN-THE-WATER
- **MONSAL DALE FISHERY** Derbyshire

ASHINGTON
- **QUEEN ELIZABETH II COUNTRY PARK** Northumberland
- **WANSBECK (RIVER)** Northumberland
- **WANSBECK (RIVER)** Northumberland
- **WATER MEADOWS FLY FISHERIES** Sussex (West)

ASHTON-UNDER-LYNE
- **CRIME LAKE** Manchester (Greater)
- **STAMFORD PARK LAKES** Manchester (Greater)

ASHURST
- **DAYLANDS FARM** Sussex (West)

ASHVALE
- **LAKESIDE** Hampshire

ASKAM-IN-FURNESS
- **ULVERSTON CANAL** Cumbria

ASPATRIA
- **BRAYTON POND** Cumbria

ASTBURY
- **PECK POOL** Cheshire

ASTLEY ABBOTTS
- **BOLDINGS POOLS** Shropshire

ASTON
- **SHIFFORD LOCK** Oxfordshire

ATCHAM
- **SEVERN (RIVER)** Shropshire

ATHERSTONE
- RIDDINGS FISHERY Warwickshire
- SHEEPY MAGNA LAKE Warwickshire

ATTLEBOROUGH
- ABBEY WATERS Norfolk
- MANOR LAKE Norfolk
- MILL FARM FISHERY Norfolk
- PECK MEADOW POND Norfolk
- SCOULTON MERE Norfolk
- SWANGEY LAKES Norfolk
- WALNUT FARM FISHERIES Norfolk

AVON
- TUCKING MILL Somerset

AVONWICK
- MILL Devon

AXMINSTER
- AXE (RIVER) Devon
- SUMMERLEAZE POND Devon

AYLESBURY
- THAME (RIVER) Buckinghamshire
- AYLESBURY ARM CANAL Hertfordshire
- BIERTON FISHING LAKES Hertfordshire
- OAKFIELD FISHERY Hertfordshire
- WOODLAND FARM Hertfordshire

AYLESHAM
- BURE VALLEY LAKES Norfolk
- UPPER BURE (STREAM) Norfolk

AYLSHAM
- BURE VALLEY LAKES Norfolk
- UPPER BURE (STREAM) Norfolk

BABBACOMBE
- ROCOMBE PONDS Devon

BAILDON
- LEEDS TO LIVERPOOL CANAL Yorkshire (West)

BAINBRIDGE
- BAIN (RIVER) Yorkshire (North)
- URE (RIVER) Yorkshire (North)

BAKEWELL
- DERWENT (RIVER) Derbyshire
- DUKE OF RUTLAND ESTATE Derbyshire
- HADDON ESTATE FISHERIES Derbyshire
- MONSAL DALE FISHERY Derbyshire
- WYE (RIVER) Derbyshire

BAMFORD
- LADYBOWER RESERVOIR Derbyshire

BAMPTON
- FOUR PONDS Devon
- GRAFTON LOCK Oxfordshire
- RUSHEY WEIR Oxfordshire
- SHIFFORD LOCK Oxfordshire
- THAMES (RIVER) Oxfordshire

BAMPTON GRANGE
- LOWTHER (RIVER) Cumbria

BANBURY
- CANONS ASHBY LAKES Northamptonshire
- CHEYNEY MANOR FISHERY Oxfordshire
- CLATTERCOTE RESERVOIR Oxfordshire
- COLLEGE FARM FISHING Oxfordshire
- GRIMSBURY RESERVOIR Oxfordshire
- HEART OF ENGLAND FISHERY Oxfordshire
- HORSE AND GROOM LAKES Oxfordshire
- NELL BRIDGE FISHERY Oxfordshire
- OXFORD CANAL Oxfordshire

BANGOR-ON-DEE
- CLYWEDOG (RIVER) Wrexham
- DEE (RIVER) Wrexham

BARBON
- BARBON BECK Cumbria

BARBY
- BANKS (THE) Warwickshire

BARKING
- MAYSBROOK LAKES Essex

BARNARD CASTLE
- BLACKTON RESERVOIR County Durham
- COW GREEN WILD BROWN TROUT FISHERY County Durham
- GRASSHOLME RESERVOIR County Durham
- HURY RESERVOIR County Durham
- SELSET RESERVOIR County Durham
- TEES (RIVER) County Durham

BARNBY DUN
- DON (RIVER) Yorkshire (South)
- NEW JUNCTION CANAL Yorkshire (South)
- SOUTH YORKSHIRE NAVIGATION CANAL Yorkshire (South)

BARNES
- THAMES (RIVER) London (Greater)

BARNSLEY
- ATHERSLEY MEMORIAL LAKE Yorkshire (South)
- BARNSLEY CANAL Yorkshire (South)
- BRAMPTON CANAL Yorkshire (South)
- DEARNE VALLEY PARK LAKE Yorkshire (South)
- ELSECAR CANAL Yorkshire (South)
- ELSECAR RESERVOIR Yorkshire (South)
- FLEETS DAM Yorkshire (South)
- MILTON PONDS Yorkshire (South)
- NETHERWOOD COUNTRY PARK Yorkshire (South)
- NEWBIGGIN POND Yorkshire (South)
- SALLY WALSHES DAM Yorkshire (South)
- SMITHIES RESERVOIR Yorkshire (South)
- STANBOROUGH FISHERIES Yorkshire (South)
- TINKERS PONDS Yorkshire (South)
- WOMBWELL DAM Yorkshire (South)
- WORSBOROUGH RESERVOIR Yorkshire (South)
- WORSBROUGH CANAL Yorkshire (South)
- WORSBROUGH RESERVOIR Yorkshire (South)

BARNSTAPLE
- BLAKEWELL FISHERIES Devon
- LITTLE COMFORT FARM Devon
- RIVERTON HOUSE AND LAKES Devon
- SWIMBRIDGE POOL Devon
- TAW (RIVER) Devon
- VENN POOL Devon
- WISTLANDPOUND RESERVOIR Devon
- BARLE (RIVER) Somerset

BARROW
- POAKA BECK Cumbria

BARROW-IN-FURNESS
- BARROW-IN-FURNESS RESERVOIR Cumbria
- ORMSGILL LOWER RESERVOIR Cumbria
- POAKA BECK Cumbria
- ROANHEAD FISHERIES Cumbria

BARTON-UPON-HUMBER
- BARTON BROADS LAKE Lincolnshire (North)
- HOE HILL POND Lincolnshire (North)
- MARSHLANDS Lincolnshire (North)
- PASTURE HOUSE FISHERY Lincolnshire (North)
- PELICAN POND Lincolnshire (North)
- TARGET LAKE Lincolnshire (North)
- TILEYARD LANE Lincolnshire (North)
- WESTFIELD LAKES Lincolnshire (North)

BASCHURCH
- PERRY (RIVER) Shropshire

BASILDON
- BURROWS FARM Essex
- COBBLERS MEAD LAKE Essex
- GLOUCESTER PARK LAKE Essex
- MOATHOUSE LAKE Essex
- NORTHLANDS PARK Essex
- PIPPS HILL FISHERIES Essex
- WID (RIVER) Essex

BASINGSTOKE
- BASINGSTOKE CANAL Hampshire
- BASINGSTOKE CANAL Hampshire
- ROTHERWICK AND NIGHTINGALE LAKES Hampshire

BASTON FEN
- WHITE HOUSE PREDATOR LAKE Lincolnshire

BATH
- AVON (BRISTOL) (RIVER) Somerset
- AVON (RIVER) Somerset
- BRISTOL AVON Somerset
- DANDYS LAKE AND KNIGHTINGALE LAKE Somerset
- EMBOROUGH POND Somerset
- EMBORUGH LAKE Somerset
- FROME (RIVER) Somerset
- HUNSTRETE LAKE COMPLEX Somerset
- KENNET AND AVON CANAL Somerset
- KENNET AND AVON CANAL Somerset
- NEWTON PARK Somerset
- TUCKING MILL Somerset
- WOODBOROUGH PARK LAKE Somerset
- ROOD ASHTON LAKE Wiltshire

BATLEY
- LONGBOTTOMS DAM Yorkshire (West)

BATTLE
- ASHBOURNE TROUT FISHERY Sussex (East)
- BROOMHAM FISHERY Sussex (East)
- CLAREMONT LAKE Sussex (East)
- MOOR HALL POOL Sussex (East)
- OLIVES FARM FISHERY Sussex (East)
- POWDERMILL (GREAT SANDERS) WATER Sussex (East)
- THORNDEN POND Sussex (East)
- WYLANDS INTERNATIONAL ANGLING CENTRE Sussex (East)

BAWTRY
- LAKESIDE FISHERY Nottinghamshire
- IDLE (RIVER) Yorkshire (South)

BEAL
- AIRE (RIVER) Humberside

BEAUCHAMP ARMS
- YARE (RIVER) Norfolk

BEAULIEU
- LYNDHURST LAKE Hampshire

BEAWORTHY
- ANGLERS ELDORADO Devon
- ANGLERS PARADISE Devon
- ANGLERS SHANGRILA Devon
- GREENACRE TROUT LAKES Devon
- HIGHAMPTON TROUT LAKES Devon
- KINGLAKE FISHERY Devon
- LEGGE FARM COARSE FISHERY Devon
- SOUTH HAY FARM Devon

BEBINGTON
- POULTON RECREATION FIELD POOL Merseyside
- WOODSLEE POOL Merseyside

BECCLES
- HADDISCOE PIT Norfolk
- ALDEBY HALL FARM PITS Suffolk
- BARSHAM DRAIN Suffolk
- BECCLES QUAY Suffolk
- BUNGAY (RIVER) Suffolk
- HENHAM DAIRY POND Suffolk
- WAVENEY (RIVER) Suffolk

BEDALE
- CLAY PIT Yorkshire (North)
- NEWTON RIVER Yorkshire (North)
- SHIELD FISHERY Yorkshire (North)
- THORPE PERROW QUARRY Yorkshire (North)

BEDFORD
- AMPTHILL RESERVOIR Bedfordshire
- BECKERINGS PARK FARM RESERVOIR Bedfordshire
- BRIARWOOD FISHERY Bedfordshire
- BROGBOROUGH NO.1 PIT Bedfordshire
- FELMERSHAM (RIVER) Bedfordshire
- FELMERSHAM GRAVEL PITS Bedfordshire
- FIR COUNTRY PARK Bedfordshire
- GREAT OUSE (RIVER) Bedfordshire
- HAROLD FISHERY Bedfordshire
- MARSTON PITS Bedfordshire
- OUSE (RIVER) Bedfordshire
- PRIORY COUNTRY PARK Bedfordshire
- RADWELL COMPLEX Bedfordshire
- SOUTH LAGOON Bedfordshire
- WATER END FISHERY Bedfordshire
- WILLINGTON LAKE Bedfordshire
- BEDFORD BOATING LAKE Buckinghamshire
- HARROLD ODELL COUNTRY PARK Buckinghamshire
- KEMPSTONE HARDWICK Buckinghamshire
- MILTON KEYNES LAKES Buckinghamshire
- OUSE (RIVER) Buckinghamshire
- SUMMERFIELDS TROUT FISHERY Buckinghamshire

BEDWORTH
- LAKESIDE FISHING Leicestershire
- BRAMCOTE MAINS FISHERY Warwickshire
- HAWKESBURY FISHERY Warwickshire
- MAKIN FISHERIES Warwickshire
- MONKS POOL Warwickshire
- WESTON LAWN FISHERIES Warwickshire

BEEFORD
- DACRE LAKESIDE PARK Humberside

BEESTON
- ATTENBOROUGH GRAVEL PITS Nottinghamshire
- TRENT (RIVER) Nottinghamshire

BEETLEY
- ROOSTING HILLS Norfolk

BELLINGHAM
- KIELDER WATER Northumberland
- NORTH TYNE (RIVER) Northumberland
- TYNE (RIVER) Northumberland

BELLS YEW GREEN
- FRANT LAKES Kent
- TEISE (RIVER) Kent

BELMONT
- UPPER RODDLESWORTH RESERVOIR Lancashire

BELPER
- BELPER POND Derbyshire
- CODNOR PARK RESERVOIR Derbyshire
- DERBYSHIRE TROUT FISHERY Derbyshire
- DERWENT (RIVER) Derbyshire
- POSSY LODGE PONDS Derbyshire

BELSAY
- BOLAM LAKE COUNTRY PARK Tyne and Wear

BELTON
- SUDBROOK POND Lincolnshire

BENHALL
- WYE (RIVER) Suffolk

BENSON
- BENSON LOCK Oxfordshire

BENTLEY
- TOLL BAR POND Yorkshire (South)

BERKELEY
- WATERLEY BROOK Gloucestershire

BERKHAMSTED
- GRAND UNION CANAL Hertfordshire
- WESTBROOK MERE Hertfordshire

BERWICK-UPON-TWEED
- TWEED (RIVER) Northumberland
- WHITEADDER (RIVER) Northumberland

BEVERLEY
- BEVERLEY BECK Humberside
- BEVERLEY CANAL Humberside
- BRANDESBURTON Humberside
- DRIFFIELD CANAL Humberside
- FOSSEHILL LAKES Humberside
- HULL (RIVER) Humberside
- LAKEMINSTER PARK Humberside
- LEVEN CANAL Humberside
- LEVEN PARK LAKE Humberside
- STAR CARR TROUT FARM Humberside

BEWDLEY
- CURTISS POOL Worcestershire
- DEXTER POOL Worcestershire
- DOWLES BROOK Worcestershire
- HAYE FARM FISHERY Worcestershire
- MILL POOL Worcestershire
- SEVERN (RIVER) Worcestershire
- SILLIGROVE FISHERY Worcestershire
- SNUFF MILL POOL Worcestershire
- TEME (RIVER) Worcestershire
- TRIMPLEY RESERVOIR Worcestershire
- WELLFIELD POOLS Worcestershire
- WHARTONS PARK COARSE FISHING Worcestershire

BEWLEY
- TEME (RIVER) Worcestershire

BEXHILL-ON-SEA
- BRICKYARD LAKE Sussex (East)
- CLIVE VALE RESERVOIRS Sussex (East)
- MOOR HALL POOL Sussex (East)
- OLIVES FARM FISHERY Sussex (East)
- PETT POOLS Sussex (East)

BEXLEYHEATH
- DANSON PARK LAKE Kent

BICESTER
- CHERWELL (RIVER) Oxfordshire
- GLEBE COURT LAKE Oxfordshire
- MANOR LAKE Oxfordshire
- OXFORD CANAL Oxfordshire
- OXFORD CANAL Oxfordshire
- PIMLICO FARM LAKES Oxfordshire
- ROYAL PIONEER CORPS ANGLING ASSOCIATION WATER Oxfordshire
- STATES LAGOON Oxfordshire

BICKERSHAW
- FAN LODGE Lancashire

BICKNACRE
- JACKLETTS FARM Essex

BIDDULPH
- KNYPERSLEY RESERVOIR Staffordshire

BIDEFORD
- BULWORTHY FISHERY Devon
- CLOVELLY LAKES Devon
- FOSFELLE COUNTRY HOUSE HOTEL Devon
- GAMMATON RESERVOIRS Devon
- HARTLAND FOREST FISHERY GOLF CLUB Devon
- JENNETTS RESERVOIR Devon
- LITTLE WEACH Devon
- MELBURY RESERVOIR Devon
- PYEWELL FARM Devon
- SOUTH WEST WATER FISHERY Devon
- TORRIDGE (RIVER) Devon

BIGGLESWADE
- IVEL (RIVER) Bedfordshire
- LANGFORD MILL Bedfordshire
- LITTLE HEATH FARM TROUT FISHERY Bedfordshire
- MANOR FARM LEISURE Bedfordshire

BILLERICAY
- BARLEYLANDS RESERVOIR Essex
- GREEN OAKS TROUT FISHERY Essex
- KENNEL LANE Essex
- LAKE MEADOWS Essex

BILLINGE
- ISLAND DAM Lancashire

BILLINGHAM
- TRIMDON POND County Durham

BILLINGHURST
- DOUNHURST FARM FISHERY Sussex (West)

BINBROOK
- LOBBY FIELD PONDS Lincolnshire

BINGLEY
- COPPICE POND Yorkshire (West)

BINLEY
- COOMBE ABBEY LAKE Midlands (West)

BIRKENHEAD
- **BIRKENHEAD LOWER PARK LAKE** Merseyside
- **LOWER LAKE** Merseyside
- **UPPER LAKE** Merseyside

BIRMINGHAM
- **ALVECHURCH FISHERIES** Midlands (West)
- **BLYTHE WATERS** Midlands (West)
- **EDGBASTON RESERVOIR** Midlands (West)
- **GREY MILL FARM** Midlands (West)
- **KINGSBURY WATER PARK** Midlands (West)
- **SHUSTOKE FLY FISHERS** Midlands (West)
- **SOHO LOOP CANAL** Midlands (West)
- **SUTTON PARK** Midlands (West)
- **TAME VALLEY CANAL** Midlands (West)
- **WALCOT EAST LAKE** Midlands (West)

BIRSTALL
- **LONGBOTTOMS DAM** Yorkshire (West)

BISHOP AUCKLAND
- **FIELDSONS POND** County Durham
- **FLYLANDS POND** County Durham
- **TUNSTALL RESERVOIR** County Durham
- **TURNSIDE POOL** County Durham
- **WADSWORTH FISHERY** County Durham
- **WEAR (RIVER)** County Durham
- **WITTON CASTLE LAKES** County Durham

BISHOPS CASTLE
- **WALCOT EAST LAKE** Midlands (West)
- **WALCOT WEST LAKE** Shropshire

BISHOPS STORTFORD
- **HATFIELD FOREST LAKE** Hertfordshire
- **LEE NAVIGATION** Hertfordshire

BLACKBURN
- **CALDER (RIVER)** Lancashire
- **DICKENS STREET LODGE** Lancashire
- **DINGLE RESERVOIR** Lancashire
- **EARNSDALE RESERVOIR** Lancashire
- **ENTWHISTLES RESERVOIR** Lancashire
- **HODDER (RIVER)** Lancashire
- **HODDLESDEN LAKE** Lancashire
- **KNIGHT BOTTOMS LAKE** Lancashire
- **RIBBLE (RIVER)** Lancashire
- **RISHTON RESERVOIR** Lancashire
- **STANWORTH RESERVOIR** Lancashire
- **STOCKS FLY FISHERY** Lancashire
- **WAYOH RESERVOIR** Lancashire

BLACKPOOL
- **BRIARCROFT FISHERY** Lancashire
- **ST MICHAELS WYRESIDE FISHERY** Lancashire
- **STANLEY PARK LAKE** Lancashire
- **WYRE (RIVER)** Lancashire

BLACKROD
- **FORSTERS LODGES** Lancashire

BLANDFORD
- **STOUR (DORSET) (RIVER)** Dorset

BLANDFORD FORUM
- **MAPPOWDER COURT** Dorset
- **STOUR (DORSET) (RIVER)** Dorset
- **STOUR (RIVER)** Dorset

BLICKLING
- **BLICKLING PARK LAKE** Norfolk

BLISWORTH
- **GRAND UNION CANAL** Northamptonshire

BLUBBERHOUSES
- **SWINSTY AND FEWSTON RESERVOIRS** Yorkshire (West)

BLUHAM
- **OUSE (RIVER)** Bedfordshire

BLYTH
- **HORTON GRANGE LAKE** Northumberland

BODMIN
- **BUTTERWELL** Cornwall
- **CAMEL (RIVER)** Cornwall
- **COOMBE MILL** Cornwall
- **EAST ROSE FARM** Cornwall
- **FENWICK TROUT FISHERY** Cornwall
- **FOWEY (RIVER)** Cornwall
- **FOWEY (RIVER)** Cornwall
- **LAKEVIEW COUNTRY CLUB** Cornwall
- **PRINCE PARK** Cornwall
- **TEMPLE TROUT FISHERY** Cornwall
- **CAMEL (RIVER)** Devon
- **INNIS MOORE TROUT FISHERY** Devon

BODMIN MOOR
- **EAST ROSE FARM** Cornwall

BOGNOR REGIS
- **ARUN (RIVER)** Sussex (West)

BOLLINGTON
- **ASHLEY (RIVER)** Cheshire

BOLTON
- **ADLINGTON RESERVOIR** Lancashire
- **ANGLEZARKE RESERVOIR** Lancashire
- **BOLTON CANAL** Lancashire
- **BRADFORD RESERVOIR** Lancashire
- **BRADSHAW HALL FISHERIES** Lancashire
- **BRYAN HEY RESERVOIR** Lancashire
- **CHURCH GARDEN** Lancashire
- **CLOWBRIDGE RESERVOIR** Lancashire
- **CROMPTON LODGE** Lancashire
- **DINGLE RESERVOIR** Lancashire
- **DIXON GREEN RESERVOIR** Lancashire
- **DOFFCOCKER LODGE** Lancashire
- **DUNSCAR SHORE LODGE** Lancashire
- **EAGLEY WATERS** Lancashire
- **FIRWOOD LODGE AND THE BUNK** Lancashire
- **GLEAVES RESERVOIR** Lancashire
- **HULTON PARK LAKE** Lancashire
- **JUMBLES RESERVOIR** Lancashire
- **MANCHESTER, BOLTON AND BURY CANAL** Lancashire
- **MELCHES POND** Lancashire
- **RUMWORTH LODGE RESERVOIR** Lancashire
- **STARMOUNT LODGES** Lancashire
- **TEMPLE SPRINGS** Lancashire
- **UPPER RIVINGTON RESERVOIR** Lancashire
- **UPPER RODDLESWORTH RESERVOIR** Lancashire
- **BLACKLEACH RESERVOIR** Manchester (Greater)
- **DINGLE LODGE** Manchester (Greater)
- **FARM LODGE** Manchester (Greater)

BOLTON ABBEY
- **WHARFE (RIVER)** Yorkshire (North)

BOLVENTOR
- **COLLIFORD LAKE** Cornwall

BOOTLE
- **ANNAS (RIVER)** Cumbria
- **ANNAS STREAM** Cumbria

BOREHAMWOOD
- **ALDENHAM RESERVOIR** Hertfordshire

BOROUGHBRIDGE
- **SWALE (RIVER)** Yorkshire (North)
- **URE (RIVER)** Yorkshire (North)

BORROWASH
- **DERWENT (RIVER)** Derbyshire
- **TRENT (RIVER)** Derbyshire

BOSCASTLE
- **VENN DOWN LAKES** Cornwall
- **EXEMOOR FARM** Devon

BOSLEY
- **BOSLEY RESERVOIR** Cheshire

BOSTON
- **HOBHOLE DRAIN** Lincolnshire
- **LAKE HELEN** Lincolnshire
- **ROSSWAYS WATER** Lincolnshire
- **STICKNEY BRICKPONDS** Lincolnshire
- **WEST FEN DRAIN** Lincolnshire
- **WHARFE (RIVER)** Lincolnshire
- **WITHAM (RIVER)** Lincolnshire

BOSTON SPA
- **WHARFE (RIVER)** Lincolnshire
- **BOSTON SPA** Yorkshire (West)
- **OUSE (RIVER)** Yorkshire (West)

BOURNE
- **BASTON FEN FISHERY** Lincolnshire
- **GRIMSTHORPE LAKE** Lincolnshire

BOURNEMOUTH
- **CRANEBROOK TROUT FISHERY** Dorset
- **CROW POOL** Dorset
- **ROYALTY FISHERY** Dorset
- **STOUR (DORSET) (RIVER)** Dorset
- **STOUR (RIVER)** Dorset
- **THROOP FISHERIES** Dorset
- **EAST MOORS LAKE** Hampshire
- **ORCHARD LAKES** Hampshire

BOURTON-ON-THE-WATER
- **MORETON PITS** Gloucestershire

BOVEY TRACEY
- **INDIO POND** Devon

BOWNESS
- **CLEABARROW TARN** Cumbria

BOWNESS ON WINDERMERE
- **DUBBS RESERVOIR** Cumbria
- **GHYLL HEAD** Cumbria

BRACKNALL
- **ROYAL BERKSHIRE FISHERY** Berkshire

BRACKNELL
- **ALLSMOOR POND** Berkshire
- **FARLEYMOOR LAKE** Berkshire
- **FELIX FARM TROUT FISHERY** Berkshire
- **MILL POND** Berkshire
- **SAVERNAKE POND** Berkshire
- **SOUTH FIELD PARK** Berkshire
- **SOUTH HILL PARK LAKE** Berkshire

BRADFORD
- **SWALE (RIVER)** Yorkshire (North)
- **CALDER (RIVER)** Yorkshire (West)
- **CALDER AND HEBBLE CANAL** Yorkshire (West)
- **DOE PARK RESERVOIR** Yorkshire (West)

- DYEHOUSE POND Yorkshire (West)
- ROBERTS POND Yorkshire (West)
- ROCHDALE CANAL Yorkshire (West)
- ROYDS HALL DAM Yorkshire (West)
- STAVELEY LAKES Yorkshire (West)
- YEADON TARN Yorkshire (West)

BRADFORD-ON-AVON
- BRISTOL AVON Wiltshire
- KENNET AND AVON CANAL Wiltshire
- KENNET AND AVON CANAL Wiltshire

BRADWELL
- BLACKWATER (RIVER) Essex

BRAINTREE
- BLACKWATER (RIVER) Essex
- BLACKWATER (RIVER) Essex
- FENNES FISHERIES Essex
- HOUCHINS RESERVOIRS Essex
- LAUNDRY LAKE Essex
- PANT (RIVER) Essex
- RAYNE LODGE FARM Essex
- RECTORY FARM POND Essex
- SHALFORD RESERVOIRS Essex
- STRAITS MILL Essex

BRALINTON
- WILLOWFIELD LAKE COTTAGES Devon

BRAMPTON
- EDEN (RIVER) Cumbria
- NEW HILLS TROUT FARM FISHERY Cumbria
- TALKIN TARN Cumbria
- STRAIGHT MILE FISHERY Yorkshire (South)

BRANDESBURTON
- BEVERLEY AND BARMSTON DRAIN Humberside
- BRANDES BURTON 3 AND 4 Humberside
- BURSHILL A POND Humberside
- LEVEN CANAL Humberside

BRANDON
- LARK (RIVER) Suffolk

BRANSGROVE
- AVON TYRRELL LAKES Dorset

BRANSHOLME
- NODDLE HILL LAKE Humberside

BRAUNTON
- LITTLE COMFORT FARM Devon
- WILLOWFIELD LAKE COTTAGES Devon

BRAWBY VILLAGE
- RYE AND SEVEN (RIVERS) Yorkshire (North)

BRAY
- BRAY LAKE Berkshire
- THAMES (RIVER) Berkshire

BREDWARDINE
- MOCCAS FISHERY Herefordshire

BRENTFORD
- POTOMAC POND London (Greater)
- SYON PARK FISHERY London (Greater)

BRENTWOOD
- BRICKHOUSE FARM FISHERIES Essex
- CARP FARM FRYERNING FISHERIES Essex
- CHURCH LAKE Essex
- CHURCHWOOD FISHERIES Essex
- CROW GREEN FISHERY Essex
- MILLENNIUM LAKES Essex
- THORNDON PARK LAKE Essex
- WEALD COUNTRY PARK Essex

BRIDGNORTH
- ASTBURY FALLS FISH FARM Midlands (West)
- KINGSNORDLEY Midlands (West)
- NORDLEY POOLS Midlands (West)
- POOL HALL Midlands (West)
- SEVERN (RIVER) Midlands (West)
- BOLDINGS POOLS Shropshire
- HAMPTON LOCK Shropshire
- MONKHALL FISHERIES Shropshire
- SEVERN (RIVER) Shropshire
- TOWNSEND FISHERY Shropshire

BRIDGWATER
- BROWNES POND Somerset
- COMBWICH PONDS Somerset
- DUNWEAR LAKES Somerset
- DURLEIGH RESERVOIR Somerset
- EMERALD POOL FISHERY Somerset
- FOLLY FOOT FARM Somerset
- FOLLYFOOT FARM Somerset
- HAWKRIDGE RESERVOIR Somerset
- HUNTSPILL (RIVER) Somerset
- KING SEDGEMOOR DRAIN Somerset
- NEWTOWN LAKE Somerset
- PARRETT (RIVER) Somerset
- PAWLETT PONDS Somerset
- QUANTOCK FISHERIES Somerset
- SCREECH OWL PONDS Somerset
- SEDGES Somerset
- STATHE DRAIN Somerset
- SUMMERHAYES Somerset
- TAUNTON AND BRIDGWATER CANAL Somerset
- TAUNTON ROAD PONDS Somerset
- TAUNTON TO BRIDGWATER CANAL Somerset
- WESTHAY LAKE Somerset

BRIDLINGTON
- FISHPONDS FARM AND FISHERY Humberside

BRIDPORT
- BRIT (RIVER) Dorset
- CHAR STREAM Dorset
- KINGCOMBE COARSE FARM Dorset
- WATERMILL LAKE Dorset
- WOOD FARM CARAVAN PARK Dorset

BRIERLEY
- WATERLOO SCREENS Gloucestershire

BRIGG
- WILLOW SPRINGS Humberside
- KINGFISHER LODGE Lincolnshire (North)
- OLD ANCHOLME (RIVER) Lincolnshire (North)

BRIGHOUSE
- BRIGHOUSE Yorkshire (West)
- CALDER AND HEBBLE CANAL Yorkshire (West)

BRIGHTON
- SWANBOROUGH LAKES Sussex (East)
- WOODMANCOTE PLACE FISHERY Sussex (East)
- HURSTON LANE Sussex (West)

BRINKLOW
- LANNYS LAGOON Warwickshire

BRISTOL
- ABBOTS POOL Bristol
- AVON (BRISTOL) (RIVER) Bristol
- AVON (RIVER) Bristol
- BAGWOOD LAKE Bristol
- BITTERWELL LAKE Bristol
- BRISTOL AVON Bristol
- BRISTOL DOCKS Bristol
- CHEW (RIVER) Bristol
- FISHPONDS LIDO Bristol
- FROME (RIVER) Bristol
- HAM GREEN LAKE Bristol
- HENLEAZE LAKE Bristol
- ROUNDWOOD POND Bristol
- SEVINGTON LAKES FISHERY Bristol
- TANHOUSE FARM LAKE Bristol
- WEST COUNTRY WATER PARK Bristol
- BARROW RESERVOIRS Somerset
- BLAGDON LAKE Somerset
- CAMELEY TROUT LAKES Somerset
- CHEW VALLEY LAKE Somerset
- KENNET AND AVON CANAL Somerset
- LITTON RESERVOIR Somerset
- PAULTON LAKES Somerset
- STONE YARD FISHERY Somerset
- YEO (RIVER) Somerset

BRIXHAM
- CHANNELL FISHERIES Devon

BROAD OAK
- LAKEDOWN TROUT FISHERY Sussex (East)

BROCKAMIN
- BROCKAMIN POOLS Worcestershire

BROCKENHURST
- HATCHET POND Hampshire
- HURST POND Hampshire

BROGBOROUGH
- BROGBOROUGH NO.1 PIT Bedfordshire

BROMLEY
- HAYES TROUT FISHERY Kent
- ROOKERY LAKE Kent

BROMPTON-ON-SWALE
- LAKESIDE FISHERIES Yorkshire (North)

BROMSGROVE
- BIRMINGHAM TO WORCESTER CANAL Worcestershire
- BROAD ACRES LAKE Worcestershire
- UPTON WARREN LAKE Worcestershire
- WOODROW FISH POND Worcestershire

BROMYARD
- KINGFISHER TROUT LAKE Herefordshire
- MUNDERFIELD HAROLD Herefordshire
- TOAD HALL FISHERY Herefordshire

BROOK HOUSE
- LITTLE DALE HALL COARSE FISHERY Lancashire

BROOKMANS PARK
- SHEPHERDS WAY Hertfordshire

BROSELEY
- BENTHALL LAKE Shropshire
- BIRMINGHAM TO WORCESTER CANAL Shropshire
- SEVERN (RIVER) Shropshire

BROUGH
- BRICKYARD POND Humberside
- BROOMFLEET PONDS Humberside
- FISH TRADES POND Humberside
- MOTORWAY POND Humberside
- REDFERNS POND Humberside
- WOODALLS POND Humberside
- STADDLETHORPE POND Lincolnshire (North)

BROUGHTON CROSS
- BRIGHAM (RIVER) Cumbria

BROUGHTON IN FURNESS
- **LICKLE (RIVER)** Cumbria
- **DUDDON (RIVER)** Lancashire

BROUGHTON-IN-FURNESS
- **LICKLE (RIVER)** Cumbria
- **DUDDON (RIVER)** Lancashire

BROWNHILLS
- **SHROPSHIRE UNION CANAL** Staffordshire

BROXBOURNE
- **CARTHAGENA FISHERY** Hertfordshire
- **KINGS WEIR FISHERY** Hertfordshire
- **LEA NAVIGATION** Hertfordshire
- **LEE NAVIGATION** Hertfordshire
- **OLD MILL AND MEADOWS** Hertfordshire
- **SLIPE LANE PITS** Hertfordshire
- **WORMLEBURY** Hertfordshire

BRUE
- **BASON BRIDGE** Somerset
- **GLASTONBURY** Somerset
- **MARK (RIVER)** Somerset

BRYANSTON
- **STOUR (DORSET) (RIVER)** Dorset

BUBBENHALL
- **RYTON POOLS COUNTRY PARK** Midlands (West)

BUBWITH
- **BUBWITH (RIVER)** Yorkshire (North)
- **ELLERTON LANDING** Yorkshire (North)

BUCKFASTLEIGH
- **DART (RIVER)** Devon

BUCKINGHAM
- **BOURTON FISHERIES** Buckinghamshire
- **CLAYDON LAKE** Buckinghamshire
- **COSGROVE LEISURE PARK** Buckinghamshire
- **GALLOWS POOL** Buckinghamshire
- **HYDE LANE LAKES** Buckinghamshire
- **KINGFISHER GOLF CLUB** Buckinghamshire
- **SHELSWELL LAKE** Buckinghamshire

BUCKLAND NEWTON
- **KNAPP HILL FARM LAKES** Dorset

BUDE
- **BUDE CANAL** Cornwall
- **FORDA HOLIDAY LODGES** Cornwall
- **NEETS VALLEY PARK** Cornwall
- **ST BENETS ABBEY (RIVER)** Cornwall
- **TAMAR LAKE (UPPER)** Cornwall
- **WATERFRONT FISHING LAKE** Cornwall
- **EXEMOOR FARM** Devon
- **LEWORTHY FARM** Devon
- **TAMAR LAKE (LOWER)** Devon

BULBOURNE
- **GRAND UNION CANAL** Oxfordshire

BULPHAN
- **SLOUGH HOUSE LAKE** Essex

BUNGAY
- **BROOME PITS** Suffolk
- **BUNGAY (RIVER)** Suffolk
- **CAMELOT LAKE** Suffolk
- **CLUB PIT** Suffolk
- **DITCHINGHAM PIT** Suffolk
- **HOMERSFIELD (RIVER)** Suffolk
- **WAVENEY (RIVER)** Suffolk

BUNRESIDE
- **KENT (RIVER)** Cumbria
- **SPRINT (RIVER)** Cumbria

BURES
- **CLICKETTS HILL AND PLANTATION** Suffolk
- **LITTLE BEVILLS ESTATE** Suffolk
- **STOW (RIVER)** Suffolk

BURFORD
- **WINDRUSH (RIVER)** Oxfordshire

BURGESS HILL
- **WINTONS FISHERY** Sussex (West)

BURLEY
- **BEECHES BROOK FISHERY** Hampshire
- **ROCKFORD LAKE** Hampshire

BURNHAM
- **THAMES (RIVER)** Buckinghamshire

BURNHAM-ON-SEA
- **APEX LAKE** Somerset
- **WALROW PONDS** Somerset

BURNLEY
- **CALDER (RIVER)** Lancashire
- **CANT CLOUGH RESERVOIR** Lancashire
- **CLIVIGER FISH PONDS** Lancashire
- **CLOWBRIDGE RESERVOIR** Lancashire
- **COLDWELL (LOWER) RESERVOIR** Lancashire
- **LANESHAW RESERVOIR** Lancashire
- **LEEDS TO LIVERPOOL CANAL** Lancashire
- **LOVECLOUGH TROUT FISHERY** Lancashire
- **LOWER COLDWELL RESERVOIR** Lancashire
- **LOWER HOUSE LODGE** Lancashire
- **PENDLE WATER** Lancashire
- **PORTSMOUTH RESERVIOR** Lancashire
- **ROUGHLEE TROUT FISHERY** Lancashire
- **ROWLEY PARK LAKE** Lancashire
- **SWINDEN RESERVOIR** Lancashire

BURNSALL
- **WHARFE (RIVER)** Yorkshire (North)

BURSCOUGH
- **BURSCOUGH BRICKWORKS LAKE** Lancashire
- **LATHOM FISHERIES** Lancashire
- **RUFFORD CANAL** Lancashire

BURTON
- **BURTON MERE FISHERIES** Cheshire

BURTON-IN-LONSDALE
- **GOODENBURGH TARN** Cumbria

BURTON-ON-TRENT
- **CATTON PARK LAKE** Derbyshire
- **DOVE (RIVER)** Staffordshire
- **FRADLEY CANAL** Staffordshire
- **HARTSHORNE DAMS** Staffordshire
- **TRENT AND MERSEY CANAL** Staffordshire

BURTON-UPON-TRENT
- **SWARBORN (RIVER)** Staffordshire
- **TAME (RIVER)** Staffordshire
- **TRENT (RIVER)** Staffordshire

BURY
- **CHURCH GARDEN** Lancashire
- **BURRS LODGE** Manchester (Greater)
- **CARCUS WATERS** Manchester (Greater)
- **CLARENCE RECREATION GROUND** Manchester (Greater)
- **CROMPTONS WATER** Manchester (Greater)
- **CROWN POOLS** Manchester (Greater)
- **ELTON RESERVOIR** Manchester (Greater)
- **ENDCROFTS POND** Manchester (Greater)
- **FIELD LODGE POND** Manchester (Greater)
- **FISHERMANS RETREAT** Manchester (Greater)
- **IRWELL (RIVER)** Manchester (Greater)
- **ISLAND AND CARTWHEEL LODGES** Manchester (Greater)
- **MANCHESTER, BOLTON AND BURY CANAL** Manchester (Greater)
- **SWAN LODGE** Manchester (Greater)
- **TWINE VALLEY TROUT FISHERY** Manchester (Greater)

BURY ST EDMUNDS
- **BLUE WATERS** Suffolk
- **CROSS GREEN FLY FISHERY** Suffolk
- **HATCHERY HOUSE TROUT LAKES** Suffolk
- **LARK (RIVER)** Suffolk
- **LARKWOOD TROUT FISHERY** Suffolk
- **WEST STOW COUNTRY PARK** Suffolk

BUTTON OAK
- **SEVERN (RIVER)** Worcestershire

BUXTED
- **BUXTED OAST FISHERY** Sussex (East)

BUXTON
- **DANE (RIVER)** Cheshire
- **ERRWOOD RESERVOIR** Derbyshire
- **DOVE (RIVER)** Staffordshire

BYERS GREEN
- **BYERS GREEN** County Durham

BYFIELD
- **BODDINGTON RESERVOIR** Northamptonshire

BYWELL
- **TYNE (RIVER)** Northumberland

CALCOT
- **MOATLANDS POOL** Berkshire

CALNE
- **BLACKLAND LAKES HOLIDAY AND LEISURE CENTRE** Wiltshire
- **BOWOOD LAKE** Wiltshire
- **HIGH PENN** Wiltshire
- **SABRE AND SWORDS LAKES** Wiltshire

CAMBERLEY
- **CHURCH FARM** Berkshire
- **TRI-LAKES** Berkshire
- **FIRGROVE LAKES** Hampshire
- **HAWLEY LAKE** Hampshire

CAMBORNE
- **GWITHIAN BROOK** Cornwall

CAMBRIDGE
- **BARNWELL PIT** Cambridgeshire
- **BURNSIDE LAKE** Cambridgeshire
- **BURWELL LODE** Cambridgeshire
- **CAM (RIVER)** Cambridgeshire
- **CAM (RIVER)** Cambridgeshire
- **DICKERSONS PIT** Cambridgeshire
- **FEN DRAYTON COMPLEX** Cambridgeshire
- **FEN DRAYTON LAKE** Cambridgeshire
- **HATTON PARK POND** Cambridgeshire
- **HUNDRED FOOT (RIVER)** Cambridgeshire

- MAGPIE LAKE Cambridgeshire
- MILTON COUNTRY PARK Cambridgeshire
- MILTON PITS Cambridgeshire
- OLD WEST (RIVER) Cambridgeshire
- SILVER STREET MILL Cambridgeshire
- SOHAM BY-PASS LAKE Cambridgeshire
- STRETHAM LAKE Cambridgeshire
- TURKS HEAD LAKE Cambridgeshire
- MELDUM WASHLANDS (FLOODPARK) Suffolk

CAMDEN
- HAMPSTEAD HEATH London (Greater)

CAMELFORD
- CROWDY RESERVOIR Cornwall
- ST TINNEY FARM HOLIDAYS Cornwall

CANBURY GARDENS
- THAMES (RIVER) London (Greater)

CANNOCK
- GAILEY TROUT AND PIKE FISHERY Staffordshire
- HORNS Staffordshire
- LITTLETONS AND MIDDLE POOL Staffordshire
- SOUTH POPLARS Staffordshire

CANONBIE
- NETHERBY ESTATE Cumbria

CANTERBURY
- BLUE LAGOON LAKE Kent
- BRITTON COURT FARM Kent
- BYWATER LAKE Kent
- CALIBER COARSE AND CARP LAKES Kent
- CHILHAM LAKE Kent
- COTTINGTON LAKES TROUT AND COARSE FISHERY Kent
- FORDWICH LAKE Kent
- HANDLE LAKE Kent
- HERONSVIEW FISHERIES Kent
- LONGSHAW FARM FISHING LAKES Kent
- MATCH LAKE Kent
- MID KENT FISHERIES Kent
- MILTON PAN LAKE Kent
- NOOK & CRANNY LAKE Kent
- REED LAKE Kent
- STOUR (RIVER) Kent
- STOUR LAKE Kent
- STOUTING LAKE Kent
- SWAN LAKE Kent
- TONFORD LAKE Kent
- TRIANGLE LAKE Kent
- WINGHAM FISHERY Kent

CANTLEY
- CANTLEY (RIVER) Norfolk

CARLISLE
- BARN LAKE Cumbria
- BRAYTON POND Cumbria
- CALDEW (RIVER) Cumbria
- CARLETON HILL Cumbria
- EAST VIEW FISHERY Cumbria
- EDEN (RIVER) Cumbria
- LIDDEL WATER Cumbria
- LONSDALE COUNTRY PARK Cumbria
- LOUGHSIDE FISHERY Cumbria
- NETHERBY ESTATE Cumbria
- OAKBANK LAKES Cumbria
- TRANQUIL OTTER Cumbria

CARNFORTH
- BARBON BECK Cumbria
- BORWICK LAKE Cumbria
- DOE (RIVER) Cumbria
- GOODENBURGH TARN Cumbria
- GRETA (RIVER) Cumbria
- HALLMORE FISHERIES Cumbria
- REDWELL FISHERIES Cumbria
- TEWITFIELDS TROUT FISHERY Cumbria
- TWISS (RIVER) Cumbria
- WYCH ELM FISHERY Cumbria

CARWOOD
- FAIRVIEW LAKE Yorkshire (North)

CASTLEFORD
- ACKTON POND Yorkshire (West)
- AIRE AND CALDER CANAL Yorkshire (West)
- LOWTHER LAKE Yorkshire (West)
- WORKSHOP POND Yorkshire (West)

CATON
- HALTON FISHERY Lancashire

CATTERICK
- CLAY PIT Yorkshire (North)
- SWALE (RIVER) Yorkshire (North)
- SWALE (RIVER) Yorkshire (North)

CERNE ABBAS
- LYONS GATE CARAVAN PARK Dorset

CHADBURY
- WILLOW FARM Worcestershire

CHALFONT ST GILES
- WATTS POOL Buckinghamshire

CHAPEL-EN-LE-FRITH
- COMBS RESERVOIR Derbyshire

CHAPELTOWN
- HOWBROOK RESERVOIR Yorkshire (South)

CHARD
- CHARD RESERVOIR Somerset
- HOWLEY STREET POND Somerset

CHARFIELD
- WATERLEY BROOK Gloucestershire

CHARLTON
- MULGROVE POND London (Greater)

CHARMOUTH
- CHAR STREAM Dorset
- WOOD FARM CARAVAN PARK Dorset

CHATTERIS
- MEPAL PIT Cambridgeshire

CHATTON
- TWEED (RIVER) Northumberland

CHEADLE
- ABNEY PARK Cheshire

CHEADLE HULME
- ABNEY PARK Cheshire

CHEDDAR
- CHEDDAR RESERVOIR Somerset
- LANDS END FARM Somerset

CHELMSFORD
- BLACKWATER (RIVER) Essex
- BLASFORD HILL FISHERIES Essex
- BLUNTS AND CANTS MERES Essex
- BOREHAM FISHERY Essex
- BOREHAM MERES Essex
- BOVINGTON MERE 1 Essex
- BOVINGTON MERE 2 Essex
- BROAD GREEN AND TUFNELL MERE Essex
- CENTRAL PARK LAKE Essex
- CHELMER (RIVER) Essex
- CHELMER AND BLACKWATER NAVIGATION CANAL Essex
- DANBURY COUNTRY PARK Essex
- EWSONS WATER Essex
- GREAT MYLES LAKE Essex
- HANNINGFIELD TROUT FISHERY Essex
- JACKLETTS FARM Essex
- LITTLE BRAXTED FARM ESTATE Essex
- MARCONIS PIT Essex
- NEWLAND HALL CARP FISHERY Essex
- PARSONAGE FARM Essex
- STOUR (RIVER) Essex
- TUFNELL MERE Essex
- WICK MERE Essex
- WILLOWS Essex
- WILLOWS LAKE Essex

CHELTENHAM
- AVON (RIVER) Gloucestershire
- BOURTON ON THE WATER GRAVEL PIT NO1 Gloucestershire
- BURLEY FIELDS LAKE Gloucestershire
- DONNINGTON TROUT FISHERY Gloucestershire
- MORETON PITS Gloucestershire
- SANTHILL FISHERY Gloucestershire
- STANBOROUGH POOL Gloucestershire
- WITCOMBE WATERS Gloucestershire

CHEPSTOW
- LYDNEY BOATING LAKE Gloucestershire

CHERTSEY
- ATTENBOROUGH SOUTH Surrey
- CHERTSEY Surrey
- THORPE PARK WATERSKI LAKE Surrey
- TWYNERSH FISHING COMPLEX Surrey

CHESHAM
- CHESS (RIVER) Buckinghamshire
- LATIMER PARK FLY FISHERY Buckinghamshire

CHESHUNT
- BROOKFIELD LAKE Hertfordshire
- CHESHUNT SOUTH RESERVOIR Hertfordshire
- NORTH MET PIT Hertfordshire

CHESTER
- BENTLEY TROUT POOL Cheshire
- BOLESWORTH CASTLE Cheshire
- CHESHIRE FISHING Cheshire
- EGERTON LAKE Cheshire
- GOWY (RIVER) Cheshire
- GOWY FISHERY Cheshire
- HOLMSTON HALL FISHERY Cheshire
- LLOYDS MEADOW FISHERIES Cheshire
- MEADOW FISHERY Cheshire
- MILTON GREEN Cheshire
- MOULDSWORTH MERE Cheshire
- TABLEY MERE Cheshire
- TABLEY MOAT Cheshire

CHESTER MOOR
- WEAR (RIVER) County Durham

CHESTERFIELD
- BARLOW FISHERIES Derbyshire
- CHAPEL WHEEL DAM Derbyshire
- HARLESTHORPE DAM Derbyshire
- LINACRE RESERVOIRS Derbyshire
- MOSS BROOK Derbyshire
- OGSTON RESERVOIR Derbyshire
- PRESS MANOR Derbyshire
- RINGWOOD LAKE Derbyshire
- WINGERWORTH LIDO Derbyshire
- CHESTERFIELD CANAL Yorkshire (South)

CHESTER-LE-STREET
- EDMONDSLEY POND County Durham
- WEAR (RIVER) County Durham

CHESTNUT
- PAYNES LANE PIT Hertfordshire

CHEWTON MENDIP

- STONE YARD FISHERY Somerset

CHICHESTER

- CHICESTER CANAL Sussex (West)
- DUNCTON MILL Sussex (West)
- HAMBROOK TROUT FISHERY Sussex (West)

CHIGWELL

- BEDFORDS PARK LAKE Essex
- FAIRLOP EAST LAKE Essex
- HAINAULT FOREST COUNTRY PARK Essex
- RODING VALLEY LAKE Essex
- WANSTEAD PARK LAKES London (Greater)

CHILHAM

- MATCH LAKE Kent

CHINGFORD

- WILLOWSIDE CARP LAKE London (Greater)

CHIPPENHAM

- AVON (BRISTOL) (RIVER) Wiltshire
- AVON (BRISTOL) (RIVER) Wiltshire
- AVON (BRISTOL) (RIVER) Wiltshire
- AVON (RIVER) Wiltshire
- AVON (RIVER) Wiltshire
- BRISTOL AVON Wiltshire
- HIGH PENN Wiltshire
- IVY HOUSE FARM Wiltshire
- SILVERLANDS LAKE Wiltshire
- TOCKENHAM RESERVOIR Wiltshire
- WYATTS LAKE Wiltshire

CHIPPING NORTON

- BUTLERS HILL FARM Oxfordshire
- CHAD LAKES Oxfordshire
- CORNBURY PARK FISHERY Oxfordshire
- SALFORD TROUT LAKES Oxfordshire

CHIPPING SODBURY

- TANHOUSE FARM LAKE Bristol

CHORLEY

- BARRETTS FARM FISHERY Lancashire
- BIRKACRE LODGES Lancashire
- BRINSCALL LODGE Lancashire
- CHARITY FARM FISHERY Lancashire
- COTTAGE GREEN GARDEN CENTRE Lancashire
- CROFT FISHERIES Lancashire
- DRAKESHEAD FLY FISHERY Lancashire
- FOUNDRY LODGE Lancashire
- HEAPEY NO 1 Lancashire
- HEAPEY NO 2 Lancashire
- HEAPEY NO 3 Lancashire
- HEAPEY NO 6 Lancashire
- HESKIN OLD FARM FISHERY Lancashire
- LANCASTER HOUSE Lancashire
- LEEDS TO LIVERPOOL CANAL Lancashire
- LOWER RIVINGTON RESERVOIR Lancashire
- LOWER RODDLESWORTH RESERVOIR Lancashire
- RAKE BROOK RESERVOIR Lancashire
- STARMOUNT LODGES Lancashire
- TURTON AND ENTWISTLE RESERVOIR Lancashire
- TWIN LAKES TROUT FISHERY Lancashire
- WITHNELL RESERVOIRS Lancashire
- WORTHINGTON NO 1 Lancashire
- WORTHINGTON NO 2 Lancashire
- WORTHINGTON NO 3 Lancashire

CHORLTON

- CHORLTON WATER PARK Manchester (Greater)

CHRISTCHURCH

- AVON (RIVER) Dorset
- AVON TYRRELL LAKES Dorset
- BLASHFORD LAKES Dorset
- CHRISTCHURCH LOWER STOUR Dorset
- CROW POOL Dorset
- GOLDEN SPRINGS LAKES Dorset
- HAMPSHIRE AVON (RIVER) Dorset
- HARROW POND Dorset
- LIFELANDS FISHERY Dorset
- MUDEFORD WOOD LAKE Dorset
- NEW MEADOWS LAKE Dorset
- ROYALTY FISHERY Dorset
- SOPLEY FARM Dorset
- STOUR (DORSET) (RIVER) Dorset
- WHIRLWIND LAKE Dorset
- WINKTON FISHERY Dorset
- HAMPSHIRE AVON Hampshire

CHRISTOW

- FINLAKE PONDS Devon

CHUDLEIGH

- EDDISON POND Devon
- TEIGN (RIVER) Devon

CHULMLEIGH

- EGGESFORD COUNTRY HOTEL WATERS Devon

CHURT

- RUSHMOOR LAKES Surrey

CINDERFORD

- LIGHTMOOR POOL Gloucestershire
- STEAM MILLS LAKE Gloucestershire

CIRENCESTER

- ASHTON KEYNES POOL Gloucestershire
- BRADLEYS PIT Gloucestershire
- CHURN POOL TROUT FISHERY Gloucestershire
- COKES PIT Gloucestershire
- COLN (RIVER) Gloucestershire
- COTSWOLD HOBURNE Gloucestershire
- COTSWOLD WATER PARK Gloucestershire
- FARMHOUSE LAKE (THE) Gloucestershire
- HAM POOL Gloucestershire
- ISIS NO 1 LAKE 19 Gloucestershire
- KEYNES COUNTRY PARK Gloucestershire
- KEYNES PARK TOP LAKE Gloucestershire
- LAKE NUMBER ONE (LAKE19) Gloucestershire
- MILL LAKE (NO 44) Gloucestershire
- NEIGH BRIDGE LAKE Gloucestershire
- NETHERWOOD LAKE Gloucestershire
- RAINBOW LAKES Gloucestershire
- THAMES (RIVER) Gloucestershire
- WICK WATER Gloucestershire
- LOWER MOOR FISHERY Wiltshire
- MANOR BROOK LAKE Wiltshire

CLACTON-ON-SEA

- WEELEY BRIDGE HOLIDAY PARK Essex

CLANFIELD

- THAMES (RIVER) Gloucestershire
- GRAFTON LOCK Oxfordshire
- THAMES (RIVER) Oxfordshire

CLAPHAM

- WENNING (RIVER) Lancashire
- HAZEL HALL FARM FISHING Yorkshire (North)

CLARE

- MILLERS LAKE Suffolk

CLEATOR MOOR

- MEADLEY RESERVOIR Cumbria

CLEETHORPES

- CLEETHORPES COUNTRY PARK Humberside

CLEVEDON

- BULLOCKS FARM FISHING LAKES Somerset
- KENN (RIVER) Somerset
- PLANTATIONS LAKES Somerset

CLIFTON

- CLIFTON MOOR LAKE Yorkshire (North)

CLITHEROE

- EDISFORD AND BRUNGERLEY PARK Lancashire
- HODDER (RIVER) Lancashire
- PINE LODGE FISHERIES Lancashire
- RIBBLE (RIVER) Lancashire
- SABDEN RESERVOIR Lancashire
- STOCKS FLY FISHERY Lancashire

CLYST ST. GEORGE

- PICFRESH Devon

COALVILLE

- SNIBSON COLLIERY CARP LAKE Leicestershire

COBHAM

- MANOR POND Surrey
- PAINSHILL PARK LAKE Surrey

COCKERMOUTH

- BRIGHAM (RIVER) Cumbria
- BUTTERMERE LAKE Cumbria
- COGRA MOSS Cumbria
- CRUMMOCK WATER LAKE Cumbria
- DERWENT (RIVER) Cumbria
- ELLERBECK FARM AND FISHERY Cumbria
- LOWESWATER LAKE Cumbria
- MOCKERKIN TARN Cumbria
- SHARPLEY WATERS Cumbria

COGGESHALL

- BLACKWATER (RIVER) Essex

COLCHESTER

- ARDLEIGH RESERVOIR Essex
- BLACKWATER (RIVER) Essex
- BROOKHALL FISHERY Essex
- COLNE (RIVER) Essex
- DEDHAM MILL Essex
- DONYLANDS LAKES Essex
- HOUCHINS RESERVOIRS Essex
- LAYER PIT Essex
- MANNINGTREE RIVER POOLS Essex
- OLD HALL FARM TROUT FISHERY Essex
- OLIVERS LAKE Essex
- PRESTONS LAKE Essex
- SPARROWS POND Essex
- STOUR (RIVER) Essex
- STOUR (SUFFOLK) (RIVER) Essex
- STOW (RIVER) Suffolk

COLDSTREAM

- LEET (RIVER) Northumberland
- LYNE (RIVER) Northumberland
- TWEED (RIVER) Northumberland

COLEFORD

- LIGHTMOOR POOL Gloucestershire
- MARIONS POOL Gloucestershire
- SPEECH HOUSE LAKE Gloucestershire

COLESHILL

- SHUSTOKE FLY FISHERS Midlands (West)

COLLINGHAM
- **WHARFE (RIVER)** Nottinghamshire

COLNE
- **BALL GROVE LAKE** Lancashire
- **BROWNHILL RESERVOIR** Lancashire
- **COLNE WATER** Lancashire
- **FOULRIDGE RESERVOIR** Lancashire
- **HULLDOWN TROUT FISHERY** Lancashire

COLTISHALL
- **BURE (RIVER)** Norfolk

COLYTON
- **AXE (RIVER)** Devon
- **HIGHER COWNHAYNE LAKES** Devon
- **WISCOMBE FISHERY** Devon

CONGLETON
- **ASTBURY MERE** Cheshire
- **BRERETON HEATH COUNTRY PARK** Cheshire
- **CRABTREE MOSS FARM POOL** Cheshire
- **DANE (RIVER)** Cheshire
- **GODWINS POOL** Cheshire
- **MACCLESFIELD CANAL** Cheshire
- **MARTON HEATH COARSE POOL** Cheshire
- **MARTON HEATH TROUT POOLS** Cheshire
- **MORETON MERE FISHERY** Cheshire
- **NORTH FIELD POOL** Cheshire
- **PECK POOL** Cheshire
- **SHELLOW FARM POOLS** Cheshire
- **WARDS POOLS** Cheshire
- **WEAVER (RIVER)** Cheshire
- **WESTLOW MERE** Cheshire
- **BIDDULPH GRANGE** Staffordshire

CONGLTON
- **ASTBURY MERE** Cheshire

CONINSBY
- **HOBHOLE DRAIN** Lincolnshire

CONISTON
- **CONISTON WATER** Cumbria
- **YEW TREE TARN** Cumbria

CONSETT
- **DERWENT (RIVER)** County Durham
- **DERWENT RESERVOIR** County Durham
- **KNITSLEY MILL TROUT FISHERIES AND STUD FARM** County Durham
- **WASKERLEY RESERVOIR** County Durham

CORBRIDGE
- **HALLINGTON RESERVOIRS** Northumberland
- **THORNBROUGH LAKE** Northumberland
- **TYNE (RIVER)** Northumberland

CORBY
- **CORBY BOATING LAKE** Northamptonshire
- **LYNN POOL FISHERY** Northamptonshire

CORRINGHAM
- **JIMMYS LAKE** Essex

COSTESSEY
- **RINGLAND PITS** Norfolk

COTTENHAM
- **TURKS HEAD LAKE** Cambridgeshire

COTTERSTOCK
- **COTTERSTOCK RIVER** Cambridgeshire
- **NENE (RIVER)** Cambridgeshire

COVENTRY
- **AVON (RIVER)** Midlands (West)
- **BLYTHE (RIVER)** Midlands (West)
- **COOMBE ABBEY LAKE** Midlands (West)
- **COOMBE POOL** Midlands (West)
- **HOPSFORD HALL FISHERY** Midlands (West)
- **LAVENDER HALL** Midlands (West)
- **MEADOWLANDS** Midlands (West)
- **PACKINGTON SOMERS FISHERY** Midlands (West)
- **PACKINGTON TROUT FISHERY** Midlands (West)
- **ROYAL BRITISH LEGION POOLS** Midlands (West)
- **RYTON POOLS COUNTRY PARK** Midlands (West)
- **SOMERS FISHERY** Midlands (West)
- **HAWKESBURY FISHERY** Warwickshire
- **OXFORD CANAL** Warwickshire

COW COMMON
- **EMBER (RIVER)** Fife

COWBRIDGE
- **WITHAM (RIVER)** Lincolnshire

COWLEY
- **THAMES (RIVER)** Oxfordshire
- **SHROPSHIRE UNION CANAL** Staffordshire

COWSHILL
- **WEAR (RIVER)** County Durham

COXHOE
- **TURSDALE POND** County Durham

CRAMLINGTON
- **HORTON GRANGE LAKE** Northumberland
- **MILKHOPE POND** Tyne and Wear

CRANBOURNE
- **CRANBOURNE FRUIT FARM** Dorset
- **GOLD OAK FISH FARM** Dorset

CRANBROOK
- **EASTERN ROTHER (RIVER)** Kent
- **HARTLEY LANDS FARM** Kent
- **HAWKHURST FISH FARM** Kent

CRANLEIGH
- **ALDERBROOK LAKE** Surrey
- **ALFORD ROAD FISHERIES** Surrey
- **EAST WHIPLEY RESERVOIR** Surrey
- **FISHERIES THE** Surrey
- **FURZE FARM** Surrey
- **NAVIES HOLE** Surrey
- **WILLINGHURST COARSE FISHERY** Surrey
- **WILLINGHURST TROUT FISHERY** Surrey
- **WYPHURST AND HYHURST LAKES** Surrey

CRANWORTH
- **WOODRISING WATER MEADOWS** Norfolk

CRAVEN ARMS
- **DELBURY HALL TROUT FISHERY** Shropshire

CRAWLEY
- **BUCHAN PARK FISHERIES** Cornwall
- **CRAYFISH FARM** Cornwall
- **MILTON MOUNT LAKE** Cornwall
- **ROWFANT HOUSE FISHERY** Cornwall
- **TILGATE LAKES** Sussex (West)

CRAYFORD
- **DARENT (RIVER)** Kent

CREDITON
- **CREEDY (RIVER)** Devon
- **CREEDY LAKES** Devon
- **GLYNDWR FISHERY** Devon
- **LOWER HALLACOMBE FISHERY** Devon
- **OLDBOROUGH FISHING RETREAT** Devon
- **SALMONHUTCH COARSE FISHERY** Devon
- **TAW (RIVER)** Devon
- **TAW FISHING CLUB** Devon
- **VALLEY VIEW FISHERY** Devon
- **YEO (RIVER)** Devon

CREWE
- **BETLEY MERE** Cheshire
- **BORDER FISHERIES** Cheshire
- **BROOKSIDE FISHERIES** Cheshire
- **DOODLESPOOL FARM LAKE** Cheshire
- **DUKES POOL** Cheshire
- **GORSTY HALL** Cheshire
- **LAKEMORE COUNTRY PARK** Cheshire
- **SANDYBANK POOL** Cheshire
- **SHROPSHIRE UNION CANAL** Cheshire
- **WINTERLEY POOL FISHERY** Cheshire

CREWKERNE
- **HIGHLANDS DAIRY LAKE** Somerset
- **PARRET (RIVER)** Somerset
- **WATER MEADOW LAKES** Somerset

CRICKLADE
- **WICK WATER** Gloucestershire

CROFT
- **DENNIS RAINWATER LAKE** Lincolnshire

CROMER
- **FELBRIGG HALL LAKE** Norfolk
- **GUNTON PARK LAKE** Norfolk

CROOK
- **WEAR (RIVER)** County Durham

CROWBOROUGH
- **HOLTS LAKES** Sussex (East)
- **KINGS STANDING LAKES** Sussex (East)
- **PENNY BRIDGE** Sussex (East)
- **SCALAND WOOD** Sussex (East)
- **YEW TREE TROUT FISHERY** Sussex (East)

CROWLE
- **STAINFORTH AND KEADBY CANAL** Yorkshire (South)

CROWTHORNE
- **HOLME GRANGE** Berkshire

CROXDALE
- **BROWNEY (RIVER)** County Durham
- **WEAR (RIVER)** County Durham

CROYDON
- **ROOKERY LAKE** Kent
- **SOUTH NORWOOD LAKE** London (Greater)
- **SEVEN ISLANDS** Surrey

CUCKFIELD
- **SPARKS FARM FISHERY** Sussex (West)

CULLOMPTON
- **BILLINGSMOOR FARM** Devon
- **CLAYHIDON (RIVER)** Devon
- **GOODIFORD MILL TROUT FISHERY** Devon
- **GRAND WESTERN CANAL** Devon
- **HARTSMOOR FISHERIES** Devon
- **KINGSMEAD CENTRE** Devon
- **MILLHAYES** Devon
- **NEWCOURT PONDS** Devon
- **PADBROOK PARK** Devon
- **STOUR FARM FISHERY** Devon

UPTON WARREN LAKE Devon
WOODY PARK FISHERY Devon

CUMBRIA

EHEN (RIVER) Cumbria

DAGENHAM

CHASE FISHERY Essex
VALENCE MOAT Essex

DALTON IN FURNESS

PENNINIGTON RESERVOIR Cumbria

DALTON-IN-FURNESS

BURLINGTON POND Cumbria
HARLOCK RESERVOIR Cumbria
PENNINIGTON RESERVOIR Cumbria

DANBURY

BLACKWATER (RIVER) Essex
DANBURY COUNTRY PARK Essex

DANBY

ESK (RIVER) Yorkshire (North)

DARENT

CRAYFORD (RIVER) Kent

DARLINGTON

BURNHOPE FISHERY County Durham
FIGHTING COCKS RESERVOIR County Durham
HALNEBY LAKE County Durham
HURWORTH BURN RESERVOIR County Durham
JUBILEE LAKES County Durham
LANGSDALE LAKE County Durham
MIDDLETON WATER PARK County Durham
RABY ESTATES WATER County Durham
TEES (RIVER) County Durham
CORNHILL PONDS Yorkshire (North)
CRABTREE ANGLING LAKE Yorkshire (North)
MOULTON LANE POND Yorkshire (North)

DARTFORD

ARENA LAKE Essex
BROOKLANDS LAKE Kent
COTTON FARM FISHERY Kent
CRAYFORD (RIVER) Kent
DARENT (RIVER) Kent
DARENTH FISHING COMPLEX Kent
HORTON KIRBY Kent
SUTTON AT HONE LAKE TWO Kent
SUTTON AT HONE LAKES ONE AND THREE Kent
TRENT PARK LAKES London (Greater)

DARTMOOR

FERNWORTHY RESERVOIR Devon

DARTMOUTH

OLD MILL RESERVOIR Devon

DARWEN

DEAN RESERVOIR Lancashire
DUNSCAR SHORE LODGE Lancashire
EARNSDALE RESERVOIR Lancashire
HODDLESDEN LAKE Lancashire
HODDLESDEN RESERVOIR Lancashire

DAVENTRY

BODDINGTON RESERVOIR Northamptonshire
CANONS ASHBY LAKES Northamptonshire
DAVENTRY COUNTRY PARK Northamptonshire
DRAYTON RESERVOIR Northamptonshire
FLECKNOE FARM FISHERIES Northamptonshire
OXFORD CANAL Northamptonshire

DAWLISH

ASHCOMBE FISHERY Devon
COFTON PARK FARM Devon

DEAL

COTTINGTON LAKES TROUT AND COARSE FISHERY Kent
ROUKES DRIFT FARM Kent

DEDDINGTON

CHEYNEY MANOR FISHERY Oxfordshire

DEE

RAWTHEY (RIVER) Cumbria

DELABOLE

FERNDALE Cornwall

DENSHAW

DOWRY AND NEW YEARS BRIDGE RESERVOIR Manchester (Greater)

DENTON

DENTON RESERVOIR Lincolnshire

DERBY

ALLESTREE LAKE Derbyshire
ALVASTON LAKE Derbyshire
ASHGROVE LAKE Derbyshire
BEEHIVE FARM WOODLANDS LAKES Derbyshire
BELPER POND Derbyshire
CODNOR PARK RESERVOIR Derbyshire
DERWENT (RIVER) Derbyshire
DERWENT VALLEY FISHERY Derbyshire
FOREMARK TROUT FISHERY Derbyshire
HIGHAM FARM COARSE FISHING Derbyshire
KEGWORTH DEEP LOCK Derbyshire
LOCHO PARK LAKE Derbyshire
MARKEATON LAKE Derbyshire
MELBOURNE POOL Derbyshire
SOAR (RIVER) Derbyshire
STAUNTON HAROLD RESERVOIR Derbyshire
SUTTON BROOK Derbyshire
SWARKESTONE GRAVEL PITS Derbyshire
TRENT (RIVER) Derbyshire
TRENT AND MERSEY CANAL Derbyshire

DEREHAM

BARTLES LODGE Norfolk
BILNEY LAKES Norfolk
NORFOLK AND SUFFOLK FLY FISHERIES LAKE Norfolk
RAILWAY LAKE Norfolk
ROOSTING HILLS Norfolk
SALMON AND TROUT ASSOCIATION LAKES Norfolk
SWANTON MORLEY FISHERY Norfolk
WENSUM (RIVER) Norfolk
WHINBURGH TROUT LAKE Norfolk

DERWENT HAUGH

DERWENT (RIVER) Tyne and Wear

DEVIZES

ERLESTOKE LAKE Wiltshire
KENNET AND AVON CANAL Wiltshire
MILL FARM TROUT LAKES Wiltshire

DEVON

AVETON GIFFORD STREAM Devon
CLAYHIDON (RIVER) Devon

DEWSBURY

THORNHILL POND Yorkshire (West)

DIDCOT

LOCKINGE TROUT FISHERY Oxfordshire
THAMES (RIVER) Oxfordshire

DIMMINGSDALE

STAFFORD TO WORCESTER CANAL Midlands (West)

DISHFORTH

CUNDALL LODGE FISHERY Yorkshire (North)

DISLEY

BOLLINHURST RESERVOIR Manchester (Greater)

DISS

DISS MERE Norfolk
HINDERCLAY LAKES Norfolk
WEYBREAD FISHERY Norfolk
HIGHFIELD FISHERY Suffolk
HOMERSFIELD LAKE Suffolk

DITCHINGHAM

DITCHINGHAM PIT Suffolk

DOFFCOCKER

DOFFCOCKER LODGE Lancashire

DONCASTER

HALLCROFT FISHERIES Nottinghamshire
SELBY CANAL Yorkshire (North)
ARKSEY STATION POND Yorkshire (South)
ASKERN LAKE Yorkshire (South)
BEEDOMS FISHERY Yorkshire (South)
BULL HOLE Yorkshire (South)
CAMPSALL COUNTRY PARK Yorkshire (South)
CUSWORTH HALL LAKE Yorkshire (South)
DELVES FISH PONDS Yorkshire (South)
DELVES LAKES Yorkshire (South)
DON (RIVER) Yorkshire (South)
FINA HAYFIELD LAKES Yorkshire (South)
HAVEN Yorkshire (South)
IDLE (RIVER) Yorkshire (South)
LONG POND Yorkshire (South)
MICKS PLACE Yorkshire (South)
MISSION LINEBANK PONDS Yorkshire (South)
NEW JUNCTION CANAL Yorkshire (South)
PRESTON INNOVATIONS SILVER FISHERY Yorkshire (South)
RAILWAY POND Yorkshire (South)
ROSSINGTON BRICK POND Yorkshire (South)
SANDERSONS POND Yorkshire (South)
SLIVER FISHERY Yorkshire (South)
SOUTH YORKSHIRE NAVIGATION CANAL Yorkshire (South)
SOUTHFIELD RESERVOIRS Yorkshire (South)
STAINFORTH AND KEADBY CANAL Yorkshire (South)
THORNE NORTH POND Yorkshire (South)
TOLL BAR POND Yorkshire (South)
TORNE (RIVER) Yorkshire (South)
TRIANGS FISHERY Yorkshire (South)
TYRAM HALL Yorkshire (South)
WILLOW GARTH FISHERY Yorkshire (South)
WILLOWGARTH LAKE Yorkshire (South)

DORCHESTER

- **CLUB LAKE** Dorset
- **FLOWERS FARM TROUT LAKES** Dorset
- **FROME (RIVER)** Dorset
- **HERMITAGE LAKES** Dorset
- **KINGCOMBE COARSE FARM** Dorset
- **KINGCOMBE LAKE** Dorset
- **KNAPP HILL FARM LAKES** Dorset
- **LAWRENCES FARM** Dorset
- **LUCKFIELD LAKE FISHERY** Dorset
- **LYONS GATE CARAVAN PARK** Dorset
- **PALLINGTON LAKES** Dorset
- **PIDDLE (RIVER)** Dorset
- **RAWLSBURY WATERS** Dorset
- **REVELS FISHERY** Dorset
- **THAMES (RIVER)** Dorset
- **WARMWELL HOLIDAY PARK** Dorset
- **WESSEX FLY FISHING TROUT LAKES** Dorset

DORKING

- **BURY HILL FISHERIES** Surrey
- **GATTON MANOR LAKES** Surrey
- **HENFOLD LAKES FISHERY** Surrey
- **MILL POND** Surrey
- **MOLE (RIVER)** Surrey
- **PUDDENHOLE POND** Surrey

DOWNHAM MARKET

- **DENTS OF HILGAY** Norfolk
- **GREAT OUSE (RIVER)** Norfolk
- **HILGAY (RIVER)** Norfolk
- **LAKESIDE CARAVAN PARK** Norfolk
- **TEN MILE BANK** Norfolk

DRAYCOTT IN THE CLAY

- **DOVE (RIVER)** Derbyshire

DRAYTON

- **DRAYTON GREEN (RIVER)** Norfolk

DRIFFIELD

- **BEVERLEY AND BARMSTON DRAIN** Humberside
- **BILLABONG WATER SPORTS AND CARAVAN PARK** Humberside
- **BRANDESBURTON** Humberside
- **BURSHILL A POND** Humberside
- **DACRE LAKESIDE PARK** Humberside
- **EMMOTLAND PONDS** Humberside
- **FAR GRANGE CARAVAN AND COUNTRY PARK** Humberside
- **FARM PONDS** Humberside
- **FISHPONDS FARM AND FISHERY** Humberside
- **HUMBERSIDE FISHERIES** Humberside
- **LANGHOLME FISHERIES** Humberside
- **STAR CARR TROUT FARM** Humberside
- **THORPE HALL** Humberside
- **WANSFORD TROUT LAKE** Humberside

DROITWICH

- **HERRIOTS POOL** Herefordshire
- **ASTWOOD FISHERY** Worcestershire
- **DROITWICH CANAL** Worcestershire
- **ELMBRIDGE LAKES** Worcestershire
- **SEVERN (RIVER)** Worcestershire
- **UPTON WARREN LAKE** Worcestershire
- **WASH POOL** Worcestershire
- **WOODLAND VIEW** Worcestershire
- **WOODROW FISH POND** Worcestershire

DUDDINGTON

- **WELLAND (RIVER)** Rutland

DUDLEY

- **HIMLEY HALL AND PARK LAKE** Staffordshire
- **PARKES HALL** Staffordshire

DUKINFIELD

- **PEAK FOREST CANAL** Cheshire

DULVERTON

- **DUNSLEY FARM** Devon
- **BARLE (RIVER)** Somerset
- **EXE (RIVER)** Somerset
- **EXE VALLEY FISHERY** Somerset
- **HADDOE TROUT FISHERY** Somerset
- **LAKESIDE** Somerset
- **LITTLE EXE** Somerset
- **WIMBLEBALL LAKE** Somerset

DUNMOW

- **ARMIGERS FARM** Essex
- **LAUNDRY LAKE** Essex
- **LITTLE EASTON FISHERIES** Essex
- **LITTLE EASTON MANOR** Essex

DUNSDALE

- **NEW MARSKE RESERVOIR** Cleveland

DUNSTABLE

- **HOUGHTON REGIS QUARRY** Bedfordshire
- **TINGRITH COARSE FISHERY** Bedfordshire
- **TINGRITH MANOR LAKE** Bedfordshire
- **WOBURN SANDS** Bedfordshire

DURHAM

- **BEAUMONT FISHERIES** County Durham
- **BRASSIDE POND** County Durham
- **BROWNEY (RIVER)** County Durham
- **DURHAM BECK** County Durham
- **FINCHALE ABBEY FARM** County Durham
- **TEASDALE POND** County Durham
- **TEES (RIVER)** County Durham
- **TURNSIDE POOL** County Durham
- **TURSDALE POND** County Durham
- **TURSDALE POND (LANGLEY PARK)** County Durham
- **WEAR (RIVER)** County Durham

DURHAM CITY

- **WEAR (RIVER)** County Durham

DURSLEY

- **GREAT BURROWS TROUT FISHERY** Gloucestershire

DYMOCK

- **SEVERN (RIVER)** Gloucestershire

EALING

- **GRAND UNION CANAL** London (Greater)

EAMONT

- **EAMONT (RIVER)** Cumbria

EARDISTON

- **TEME (RIVER)** Worcestershire

EARITH

- **HOLME FEN FISHING** Cambridgeshire
- **LILY PARK LAKES** Cambridgeshire
- **OLD WEST (RIVER)** Cambridgeshire

EASINGTON

- **STEPHENSON LAKE** Tyne and Wear

EASINGWOLD

- **RASKELF LAKE** Yorkshire (North)

EAST DEREHAM

- **BILLINGFORD PIT** Norfolk
- **BRIDGE FARM FISHERIES** Norfolk
- **WHINBURGH TROUT LAKE** Norfolk

EAST GRINSTEAD

- **BEAVER FARM FISHERY** Surrey
- **BALLS GREEN LAKES** Sussex (East)
- **ST IVES FARM** Sussex (East)
- **TANYARD FISHERIES** Sussex (East)
- **WEIR WOOD FISHERY** Sussex (East)
- **BOLEBROOK CASTLE** Sussex (West)
- **DAYLANDS FARM** Sussex (West)
- **STUBPOND FISHERIES** Sussex (West)
- **WILDERNESS LAKE** Sussex (West)

EAST HALTON

- **WINTER BROTHERS POND** Lincolnshire
- **WINTERS LAKE** Lincolnshire

EAST MOLESEY

- **EMBER (RIVER)** Fife
- **BUSHEY PARK** Surrey
- **HOME PARK** Surrey
- **MOLESEY LOCK** Surrey
- **THAMES (RIVER)** Surrey

EAST PECKHAM

- **MEDWAY (RIVER)** Kent

EAST RETFORD

- **LOUND WINDSURF LAKE** Nottinghamshire

EAST TUDDENHAM

- **NORFOLK AND SUFFOLK FLY FISHERIES LAKE** Norfolk

EASTBOURNE

- **ARLINGTON TROUT FISHERY** Sussex (East)
- **MICHELHAM PRIORY MOAT** Sussex (East)
- **SHARNFOLD FARM FISHERY** Sussex (East)
- **SOUTHBOURNE LAKE** Sussex (East)

EASTGATE

- **WEAR (RIVER)** County Durham

EASTLEIGH

- **LAKESIDE COUNTRY PARK** Hampshire
- **STONEHAM LAKES** Hampshire

ECCLESHALL

- **BADEN HALL FISHERY** Staffordshire

ECKINGTON

- **FOXTON DAM** Derbyshire
- **MOSS BROOK** Derbyshire

EDEN

- **EDEN (RIVER)** Cumbria

EDEN HALL

- **WHINS POND** Cumbria

EDENBRIDGE

- **CHIDDINGSTONE CASTLE LAKE** Kent
- **EDEN (RIVER)** Kent
- **LITTLE CANSIRON FISHING LAKES** Kent
- **SCARLETTS LAKE** Kent

EDGBASTON

- **EDGBASTON RESERVOIR** Midlands (West)

EDMONTON

- **HIGHGATE PONDS** London (Greater)
- **LEE NAVIGATION** London (Greater)
- **VALE OF HEATH POND** London (Greater)
- **WEST RESERVOIR** London (Greater)

EGHAM

- **BELL WEIR LOCK** Surrey

EGREMONT

- **EHEN (RIVER)** Cumbria

ENNERDALE LAKE FISHERY Cumbria

ELLESMERE

COLEMERE COUNTRY PARK Shropshire
CROSEMERE Shropshire
WHITEMERE Shropshire

ELSTOW

ELSTOW PITS Bedfordshire

ELVINGTON

DERWENT (RIVER) Yorkshire (North)

ELWICK

HURWORTH BURN RESERVOIR County Durham

ELY

BARWAY LAKE Cambridgeshire
BLOCK FEN COMPLEX Cambridgeshire
BRACKHILL LAKE Cambridgeshire
CAM (RIVER) Cambridgeshire
CAM (RIVER) Cambridgeshire
GREAT OUSE (RIVER) Cambridgeshire
HIGH FLYER LAKE Cambridgeshire
LARK (RIVER) Cambridgeshire
MEPAL PIT Cambridgeshire
OLD WEST (RIVER) Cambridgeshire
RANDALLS LAKE Cambridgeshire
ROSWELL PITS Cambridgeshire
STRETHAM BASIN Cambridgeshire
STRETHAM LAKE Cambridgeshire

EMBOROUGH

EMBORUGH LAKE Somerset

ENFIELD

BOXERS LAKE London (Greater)
FORTY HALL LAKE London (Greater)
HORSEMILL STREAM London (Greater)
LEA NAVIGATION London (Greater)
TRENT COUNTRY PARK LAKES London (Greater)

EPPING

GARNISH HALL Essex

EPSOM

EPSOM STEW POND Surrey

ESSINGTON

MILLRIDE FISHERY Shropshire

ETCHINGHAM

LAKEDOWN TROUT FISHERY Sussex (East)

EVESHAM

ABBOTS SALFORD PARK Worcestershire
ANCHOR MEADOWS FISHERY Worcestershire
AVON (RIVER) Worcestershire
BLACK MONK TROUT LAKES Worcestershire
FOREST FARM Worcestershire
HARVINGTON MANOR FISHERY Worcestershire
HUXLEYS HAMPTON FERRY FISHERIES Worcestershire
LENCHES LAKES Worcestershire
RED BECK LAKE Worcestershire
TWYFORD FARM POOL Worcestershire
WARWICKSHIRE & AVON worcestershire
WARWICKSHIRE AVON Worcestershire
WILLOW FARM Worcestershire
WINDMILL LAKE Worcestershire
WOOD POOL Worcestershire

EXETER

BERRYNARBOR MILL POND Devon
BILLINGSMOOR FARM Devon
BULWORTHY FISHERY Devon
COFTON PARK FARM Devon
CREEDY (RIVER) Devon
CREEDY (RIVER) Devon
CULM (RIVER) Devon
EXE (RIVER) Devon
EXETER CANAL Devon
EXETER SHIP CANAL Devon
FENECK POND Devon
FOUR PONDS Devon
GRAND WESTERN CANAL Devon
HOGSBROOK LAKES Devon
HOME FARM FISHERY Devon
KENNICK RESERVOIR Devon
LUCCOMBES PONDS Devon
PICFRESH Devon
SAMPFORD PEVERAL PONDS Devon
SOMERSWOOD LAKE Devon
SOUTH VIEW FARM FISHERY Devon
SQUABMOOR RESERVOIR Devon
STAR BARTON PONDS Devon
TAMAR LAKE (LOWER) Devon
TAR (RIVER) Devon
TAW FISHING CLUB Devon
TEIGN Devon
TRENCHFORD RESERVOIR Devon
UPHAM FARM PONDS Devon
VALLEY VIEW FISHERY Devon
WATERCRESS FARM TROUT FISHERY Devon
WEST VIEW POND Devon
YEO (RIVER) Devon

EXMINSTER

LUCCOMBES PONDS Devon

EYE

DOVE BROOK Norfolk

EYNSHAM

EYNSHAM LOCK Oxfordshire

FAIRFORD

CLAYDON PARK FISHERY Gloucestershire
COLN (RIVER) Gloucestershire
MILESTONE FISHERY Gloucestershire
WHELFORD POOLS COARSE FISHERY Gloucestershire

FAKENHAM

WENSUM (RIVER) Norfolk
WILLSMORE WATER Norfolk

FALMOUTH

COLLEGE RESERVOIR Cornwall
CONSTANTINE BROOK Cornwall
MYLOR ANGLING LAKES Cornwall

FAR FOREST

SILLIGROVE FISHERY Worcestershire

FAREHAM

CARRON ROW FARM PONDS Hampshire
CHIPHALL LAKE TROUT FISHERY Hampshire
FUNTLEY POND Hampshire
QUEENS ROAD POND Hampshire
RIVER FARM Hampshire
TITCHFIELD ABBEY GOLF AND COARSE FISHING LAKES Hampshire

FARINGDON

BUSCOT LOCK Oxfordshire
FARINGDON LAKE Oxfordshire
RADCOT LOCK Oxfordshire
RUSHEY LOCK Oxfordshire

FARINGTON

FARINGTON LODGES Lancashire

FARNBOROUGH

CUTT MILL Hampshire
FRIMLEY LAKES Hampshire
HOLLYBUSH LANE LAKES Hampshire
OXFORD CANAL Oxfordshire

FARNHAM

BADSHOT LEA Surrey
CROSSWATER MILL FISHERY Surrey
FRENSHAM TROUT FISHERY Surrey
RUSHMOOR LAKES Surrey
ST PATRICKS LANE CARP LAKES Surrey

FARNWORTH

CROMPTON LODGE Lancashire

FARRINGDON

UPHAM FARM PONDS Devon

FAVERSHAM

BYSINGWOOD Kent
LAVENDER FARM Kent
MILL POOL Kent
SCHOOL POOL Kent
WOOD POOL Kent

FAWLEY

BILCOMBES POND Hampshire

FELMERSHAM

FELMERSHAM GRAVEL PITS Bedfordshire

FELTON

COQUET (RIVER) Northumberland

FENSTANTON

FEN DRAYTON COMPLEX Cambridgeshire
FEN DRAYTON LAKE Cambridgeshire

FERNDOWN

STOUR (DORSET) (RIVER) Dorset
STOUR (DORSET) (RIVER) Dorset

FERRYHILL

KELLOW LAW POND County Durham
MAINSFORTH POND County Durham

FINCHAMPSTEAD

JINGLES FARM Berkshire
LONGMOOR FARM FISHING LAKE Berkshire

FINCHLEY

ALEXANDRA PALACE LAKE London (Greater)

FIRBANK

LOW GILL Cumbria

FLEET

WHITE HOUSE TROUT FARM Hampshire

FLEETWOOD

WYRE (RIVER) Lancashire

FLITWICK

BECKERINGS PARK FARM RESERVOIR Bedfordshire

FORDINGBRIDGE

AVON RIVER FISHERIES Hampshire
HAMPSHIRE AVON (RIVER) Hampshire
HUCKLESBROOK LAKE Hampshire
LAKE FARM Hampshire
LAPSLEYS FISHERY Hampshire
NEW FOREST WATER PARK Hampshire
ROCKBOURNE TROUT FISHERY Hampshire

FOREST OF DEAN

CANNOP PONDS Gloucestershire

FOREST ROW
- WEIR WOOD FISHERY Sussex (East)

FORMBY
- MILL HOUSE FISHERY Merseyside

FOULRIDGE
- BROWNHILL RESERVOIR Lancashire
- FOULRIDGE RESERVOIR Lancashire

FOY
- INGESTONE FISHERY Herefordshire

FRAMLINGHAM
- BRIDGE FARM RESERVOIRS Suffolk

FRIMLEY
- FRIMLEY LAKES Hampshire

FRISBY
- FRISBY LAKES Leicestershire
- HOLWELL WORKS RESERVOIR Leicestershire

FROME
- AVON (RIVER) Somerset
- EDNEYS FISHERIES Somerset
- FROME (RIVER) Somerset
- MARSTON LAKE Somerset
- MELLS PIT Somerset
- ST ALGARS FARM LAKE Somerset
- WITHAM FRIARY LAKE Somerset
- WOOLBRIDGE MANOR Somerset
- LONGLEAT LAKES Wiltshire

GAINSBOROUGH
- DAIWA GULL POOL Lincolnshire
- TRENT (RIVER) Lincolnshire
- TRENT (RIVER) Lincolnshire
- WARPING DRAIN Lincolnshire
- WILLOW BANK FISHERY Lincolnshire
- WOODLANDS LAKE Lincolnshire

GARFORTH
- WORKSHOP POND Yorkshire (West)

GARNON
- GARNISH HALL Essex

GARRARDS CROSS
- KNIGHTSCOTE PONDS London (Greater)

GARSTANG
- COPTHORNE COARSE FISHERIES Lancashire
- MANOR HOUSE FISHERY Lancashire

GATESHEAD
- FELLGATE FISHERIES Tyne and Wear
- FELLGATE PONDS Tyne and Wear

GERRARDS CROSS
- COMMON POND Buckinghamshire

GILLINGHAM
- CULVERS FARM FISHERIES Dorset
- TODBER MANOR Dorset
- UPPER STOUR (RIVER) Dorset
- CAPSTONE FARM COUNTRY PARK Kent

GILLLINGHAM
- UPPER STOUR (RIVER) Dorset

GLASBURY
- LLYNFI (RIVER) Herefordshire
- WYE (RIVER) Herefordshire

GLASTONBURY
- AVALON FISHERIES Somerset
- GLASTONBURY Somerset
- GODNEY MOOR PONDS Somerset
- WESTHAY Somerset

GLEWSTONE
- BIDDLESTONE LAKE Herefordshire

GLOSSOP
- ARNFIELD RESERVOIR Derbyshire

GLOUCESTER
- BROOK FARM TROUT FISHERY Gloucestershire
- GARDNERS POOL Gloucestershire
- GLOUCESTER AND SHARPNESS CANAL Gloucestershire
- GLOUCESTER CANAL Gloucestershire
- HIGHNAM COURT LAKE Gloucestershire
- HUNTLEY CARP POOLS Gloucestershire
- MEADOW POND Gloucestershire
- MEADOWCLIFFE POOL Gloucestershire
- NORTON FRUIT FARM Gloucestershire
- RED LION FISHERY Gloucestershire
- SEVERN (RIVER) Gloucestershire
- STAUNTON COURT LAKES Gloucestershire
- STONE END FARM LAKES Gloucestershire
- WATERLOO SCREENS Gloucestershire
- WATERSMEET LAKES Gloucestershire
- WITCOMBE WATERS Gloucestershire

GNOSALL
- SHROPSHIRE UNION CANAL Staffordshire
- SWAN PIT POOL Staffordshire

GODALMING
- BROADWATER LAKE Surrey
- BUSBRIDGE LAKE Surrey
- ENTON LAKES TROUT FISHERY Surrey
- WEY (RIVER) Surrey
- WINKWORTH LAKES Surrey
- WINTERSHALL WATERS Surrey

GODMANCHESTER
- GODMANCHESTER (RIVER) Cambridgeshire

GOOLE
- AIRE (RIVER) Humberside
- AIRE AND CALDER CANAL Humberside
- BIG HOLE PIT Humberside
- DERWENT (RIVER) Humberside
- GOWDALL LAKES Humberside
- MARKET WEIGHTON CANAL Humberside
- OAKLANDS WATER Humberside
- OUSE (RIVER) Humberside
- SYKEHOUSE RESERVOIRS Humberside
- WILLITOFT FISH FARM Humberside
- STADDLETHORPE POND Lincolnshire (North)

GORTON
- UPPER GORTON RESERVOIR Manchester (Greater)

GRANGE
- WINSTER (RIVER) Cumbria

GRANGE-OVER-SANDS
- WINSTER (RIVER) Cumbria
- WITHERSLACK HALL TARN Cumbria

GRANTHAM
- BELVOIR CASTLE Lincolnshire
- BRICKYARD POND Lincolnshire
- BUCKMINSTER PARK LAKE Lincolnshire
- CULVERTHORPE LAKES Lincolnshire
- DENTON RESERVOIR Lincolnshire
- KINPTON RESERVOIR Lincolnshire
- SYSTON PARK TROUT LAKE Lincolnshire
- WILLOW LAKES Lincolnshire
- WITHAM (RIVER) Lincolnshire
- WOODLAND WATERS Lincolnshire
- LAKESIDE FARM Nottinghamshire

GRASMERE
- CODALE TARN Cumbria
- EASEDALE TARN Cumbria

GRASSINGTON
- OUSE (RIVER) Yorkshire (North)
- WHARFE (RIVER) Yorkshire (North)

GRAVESEND
- SHORNE COUNTRY PARK LAKES Kent

GRAYS
- ARENA LAKE Essex
- GRANGE WATER Essex

GREAT DUNMOW
- LITTLE EASTON FISHERIES Essex
- LITTLE EASTON MANOR Essex

GREAT LANGTON
- KIPLIN TROUT FISHERY Yorkshire (North)

GREAT LINFORD
- GREAT LINFORD LAKES Buckinghamshire

GREAT LUMLEY
- EDMONDSLEY POND County Durham

GREAT MISSENDEN
- WESTON TERVELL RESERVOIR Buckinghamshire

GREAT OUSEBURN
- ALDWARK BRIDGE Yorkshire (North)

GREAT TORRINGTON
- STEVENSTONE LAKES Devon

GREAT YARMOUTH
- BURE (RIVER) Norfolk
- DECOY FARM Norfolk
- FRITTON LAKE Norfolk
- HALL FARM LAKES Norfolk
- MARTHAM PITS Norfolk
- ORMESBY ROLLESBY Norfolk
- STOKESBY (RIVER) Norfolk
- THURNE MOUTH (RIVER) Norfolk

GREATER LONDON
- MAYSBROOK LAKES Essex

GREATER MANCHESTER
- ELTON RESERVOIR Manchester (Greater)

GREEN HAMMERTON
- NIDD (RIVER) Yorkshire (North)

GRENDON VILLAGE
- RIDDINGS FISHERY Warwickshire

GRESFORD
- MILTON GREEN Cheshire

GRIMSBY
- ESK (RIVER) Humberside
- LOUGH NAVIGATION Humberside
- NORTH THORESBY FISHERIES Humberside
- WILLOW LAKES Humberside

GUESTLING
- WHITE HART HILL LAKE Sussex (East)

GUILDFORD
- ALBURY ESTATE FISHERIES Surrey
- BRITTENS POND Surrey

DEE (RIVER) Surrey
ENTON LAKES TROUT FISHERY Surrey
FURZE FARM Surrey
POWDER MILLS FISHERY Surrey
WESTON FISHERY Surrey
WHIPLEY MANOR Surrey
WILLINGHURST COARSE FISHERY Surrey
WILLINGHURST TROUT FISHERY Surrey

GUILFORD
EAST WHIPLEY RESERVOIR Surrey
NAVIES HOLE Surrey

GUISBOROUGH
LOCKWOOD BECK RESERVOIR Cleveland
PRIORY COTTAGE LAKE Cleveland
SCALING DAM Cleveland

HAILSHAM
BELFREY COARSE FISHERY Sussex (East)
BRICK FARM LAKE Sussex (East)
CUCKMERE (RIVER) Sussex (East)
FALKENVIL FISHERY Sussex (East)
FURNACE BROOK FISHERY Sussex (East)
LEABRIDGE FARM Sussex (East)
MICHELHAM PRIORY MOAT Sussex (East)
PEVENSEY HAVEN Sussex (East)
WALLERS HAVEN Sussex (East)

HAINAULT
HAINAULT FOREST COUNTRY PARK Essex

HALESOWEN
BULL FISHERY Midlands (West)
DAYHOUSE FARM Midlands (West)

HALESWOOD
BULL FISHERY Midlands (West)

HALESWORTH
HOLTON PIT Suffolk
VALLEY FARM FISHERY Suffolk
WILLOW LAKES TROUT FISHERY Suffolk

HALIFAX
BRIGHOUSE Yorkshire (West)
BROOKFOOT LAKE Yorkshire (West)
CLEARWATER LAKE Yorkshire (West)
ROCHDALE CANAL Yorkshire (West)

HALSTEAD
GOSFIELD LAKE RESORT Essex
SPARROWS POND Essex
CLICKETTS HILL AND PLANTATION Suffolk

HALTWHISTLE
GILSLAND LAKE Northumberland
IRTHING (RIVER) Northumberland
SOUTH TYNE (RIVER) Northumberland

HAM BROOK
HAMBROOK TROUT FISHERY Sussex (West)

HAMBLETON
WRYE (RIVER) Lancashire

HAMBRIDGE
ISLE (RIVER) Somerset

HAMPSTEAD
REGENTS CANAL London (Greater)

HAMPTON COURT
THAMES (RIVER) Surrey

HAMPTON LOADE
HAMPTON LOCK Shropshire

HAMWORTH
GREENHAMS London (Greater)

HANWORTH
SOUTH FIELD PARK Berkshire

HAREFIELD
HAREFIELD CARP LAKE London (Greater)
NORTH TROY LAKE AND COLNE (RIVER) London (Greater)

HARLESTON
WEYBREAD FISHERY Norfolk
WEYBREAD GRAVEL PITS Northamptonshire
CAMELOT LAKE Suffolk
HIGHFIELD FISHERY Suffolk
HOMERSFIELD LAKE Suffolk
WAVENEY VALLEY LAKES Suffolk
YEW TREE FISHERIES Suffolk

HARLOW
HOLYFIELD FISHERY Essex
BROXBOURNE Hertfordshire

HARROGATE
HIGH MOOR FARM PARK Yorkshire (North)
KINGSLEY CARP LAKE Yorkshire (North)
NIDD (RIVER) Yorkshire (North)
NIDD BRIDGE Yorkshire (North)
PROSPECT FARM POND Yorkshire (North)
RIPLEY CASTLE Yorkshire (North)
WASHBURN VALLEY (FEWSTON AND SWINSTY) Yorkshire (North)

HART
HART RESERVOIR Cleveland

HARTFIELD
LITTLE CANSIRON FISHING LAKES Kent
BALLS GREEN LAKES Sussex (East)
ST IVES FARM Sussex (East)

HARTLAND
WOODACOTT ARMS Devon

HARTLEPOOL
HART RESERVOIR Cleveland
LOCH KENNY Cleveland
ROSSMERE PARK LAKE Cleveland
SHOTTON COLLIERY LAKE Cleveland
TILERY LAKE Cleveland

HASLEMERE
KINGFISHER FISHERY Surrey
WAGGONERS WELLS Surrey

HASLINGDEN
FISHMOOR RESERVOIR Lancashire
LANCASTER HOUSE FARM FISHERY Lancashire

HASLINGDON
HOLDEN WOOD RESERVOIR Lancashire

HASTINGS
ALEXANDRA PARK WATERS Sussex (East)
CLIVE VALE RESERVOIRS Sussex (East)
COGHURST HALL Sussex (East)
DARWELL WATER Sussex (East)
ECCLESBOURNE RESERVOIR Sussex (East)
HASTINGS LAKE Sussex (East)
IDEN WOOD FISHERY Sussex (East)
PETT POOLS Sussex (East)

POWDERMILL (GREAT SANDERS) WATER Sussex (East)
RYE NOOK FISHERY Sussex (East)
VINEHALL SCHOOL LAKE Sussex (East)
WHITE HART HILL LAKE Sussex (East)
WISHING TREE RESERVOIR Sussex (East)
WYLANDS INTERNATIONAL ANGLING CENTRE Sussex (East)

HATFIELD
HATFIELD BROADWATER Hertfordshire
SHEPHERDS WAY Hertfordshire
BULL HOLE Yorkshire (South)
DELVES LAKES Yorkshire (South)
SLIVER FISHERY Yorkshire (South)

HATFIELD WOODHOUSE
MICKS PLACE Yorkshire (South)

HAVANT
STAUNTON COUNTRY PARK Hampshire

HAVERHILL
FLOOD PARK Suffolk
MELDUM WASHLANDS (FLOODPARK) Suffolk

HAWES
BLACKBURN FARM TROUT FISHERY Yorkshire (North)
SEMERWATER Yorkshire (North)
URE (RIVER AND TRIBUTARIES) Yorkshire (North)
URE (RIVER) Yorkshire (North)

HAWKHURST
ROTHER (RIVER) Sussex (East)

HAWKSHEAD
BLELHAM TARN Cumbria
GRIZEDALE BECK Cumbria
MOSS ECCLES TARN Cumbria

HAWORTH
AIRE (RIVER) Yorkshire (West)

HAYDON BRIDGE
LANGLEY DAM FISHERIES Northumberland

HAYLE
BILLS POOL Cornwall
HAYLE CAUSEWAY Cornwall
SHARKEYS PIT Cornwall
TREE MEADOW TROUT FISHERY Cornwall

HAYLE AND CAMBORNE
BILLS POOL Cornwall

HAY-ON-WYE
HAYCASTLE WATER Herefordshire

HAYWARDS HEATH
ARDINGLY RESERVOIR Sussex (West)
BALCOMBE LAKE Sussex (West)
BORDE HILL GARDEN LAKES Sussex (West)
CUCKFIELD FISHERY Sussex (West)
HAYWARDS HEATH RIVER Sussex (West)
PILTDOWN POND Sussex (West)
SLAUGHAM MILL POND Sussex (West)
SPARKS FARM FISHERY Sussex (West)
VALE BRIDGE LAKE Sussex (West)

HEANOR
COPPICE LAKE Derbyshire

HEATH END
LAKESIDE Surrey

HEATHFIELD
- **BOJO FISHERIES** Sussex (East)
- **HORAM MANOR FISHERY** Sussex (East)
- **ROSEBANK FARM FISHERY** Sussex (East)

HEBDEN BRIDGE
- **CALDER AND HEBBLE CANAL** Yorkshire (West)
- **ROCHDALE CANAL** Yorkshire (West)

HECKFIELD
- **WHITEWATER (RIVER)** Hampshire

HEDON
- **BURSTWICK SKI LAKE** Humberside

HELPERBY
- **BRAFFERTON COARSE FISHERY** Yorkshire (North)
- **OUSE (RIVER)** Yorkshire (North)
- **SWALE (RIVER)** Yorkshire (North)
- **SWALE (RIVER)** Yorkshire (North)
- **THORNTON BRIDGE** Yorkshire (North)

HELSTON
- **BOSCATHNOE RESERVOIR** Cornwall
- **MIDDLE BOSWIN FARM** Cornwall
- **POLCOVERACK FARM** Cornwall
- **WHEAL GREY** Cornwall

HEMEL HEMPSTEAD
- **BOXMOOR TROUT FISHERY** Hertfordshire
- **DURRANTS LAKE** Hertfordshire
- **PIXIES MERE** Hertfordshire
- **WESTBROOK MERE** Hertfordshire

HEMYOCK
- **HARTSMOOR FISHERIES** Devon

HENFIELD
- **ADUR (RIVER)** Sussex (West)

HENLEY-ON-THAMES
- **MARSH LOCK** Oxfordshire
- **SHIPLAKE LOCK** Oxfordshire
- **SWISS FARM LAKE** Oxfordshire
- **THAME (RIVER)** Oxfordshire
- **THAMES (RIVER)** Oxfordshire

HENLOW
- **HENLOW GRANGE** Bedfordshire
- **IVEL (RIVER)** Bedfordshire
- **WITHY POOL** Bedfordshire

HEREFORD
- **ASHPERTON MOAT** Herefordshire
- **CHURCH POOL** Herefordshire
- **COPPICE TROUT FISHERY** Herefordshire
- **COURT FARM** Herefordshire
- **DOCKLOW POOLS** Herefordshire
- **HAYCASTLE WATER** Herefordshire
- **HERRIOTS POOL** Herefordshire
- **HUNDRED POOL** Herefordshire
- **LLYNFI (RIVER)** Herefordshire
- **LUGG (RIVER)** Herefordshire
- **MARLIAS (RIVER)** Herefordshire
- **MARSH HOUSE FARM** Herefordshire
- **MILLPOND** Herefordshire
- **MOCCAS FISHERY** Herefordshire
- **MONNOW (RIVER)** Herefordshire
- **MONTE BISHOP** Herefordshire
- **ROTHERWAS LONG POOL** Herefordshire
- **ROYAL OAK POOL** Herefordshire
- **TOAD HALL FISHERY** Herefordshire
- **WYE (RIVER)** Herefordshire

HERTFORD
- **LEE NAVIGATION** Hertfordshire

HEXHAM
- **GIBBS HILL TROUT FISHERY** Northumberland
- **HADRIAN LODGE** Northumberland
- **HEXHAM FISHERIES** Northumberland
- **KIELDER WATER** Northumberland
- **LANGLEY DAM FISHERIES** Northumberland
- **LINNEL WOOD LAKE** Northumberland
- **NORTH TYNE (RIVER)** Northumberland
- **REDE (RIVER)** Northumberland
- **TYNE (RIVER)** Northumberland
- **WHITTLE DEAN RESERVOIR** Northumberland

HEYBRIDGE
- **CHIGBOROUGH FISHERIES** Essex

HEYWOOD
- **QUEENS PARK LAKE** Lancashire
- **PILSWORTH FISHERY COMPLEX** Manchester (Greater)

HIGH FIELD
- **EAST COTTINGWITH WATERS** Yorkshire (North)

HIGH PEAK
- **COMBS RESERVOIR** Derbyshire
- **COTE LODGE RESERVOIR** Derbyshire
- **ERRWOOD RESERVOIR** Derbyshire
- **GOYT (RIVER)** Derbyshire
- **TODDBROOK RESERVOIR** Derbyshire

HIGH WYCOMBE
- **HILL WOOD POND** Buckinghamshire
- **SPADE OAK LAKE** Buckinghamshire
- **THAMES (RIVER)** Buckinghamshire
- **WESTHORPE PARK LAKE** Buckinghamshire

HIGHAM ON THE HILL
- **ASHBY CANAL** Warwickshire

HIGHBRIDGE
- **BASON BRIDGE** Somerset
- **BRUE (RIVER)** Somerset
- **EMERALD POOL FISHERY** Somerset
- **HUNTSPILL (RIVER)** Somerset
- **KENN (RIVER)** Somerset
- **KING SEDGEMOOR DRAIN** Somerset
- **MARK (RIVER)** Somerset
- **NEWTOWN LAKE** Somerset
- **WALROW PONDS** Somerset

HILGAY
- **HILGAY (RIVER)** Norfolk

HILL
- **BRICKYARD POND** Humberside

HILLINGDON
- **THORNEY POOL** London (Greater)

HILLMORTON
- **OXFORD CANAL** Warwickshire

HILTON
- **SUTTON BROOK** Derbyshire

HINCKLEY
- **BAXTERS GARDEN FARM LAKE** Leicestershire
- **LAKESIDE FISHING** Leicestershire
- **LYNCHGATE LANE FISHERY** Leicestershire
- **MANOR FARM POOLS** Leicestershire
- **PARKLANDS FISHERY** Leicestershire
- **SHELL FRESH LAKE** Leicestershire
- **MAKIN FISHERIES** Warwickshire

HINDHEAD
- **WAGGONERS WELLS** Surrey

HINDLEY
- **DEEP PIT** Lancashire
- **SQUARE LODGE** Lancashire

HINKLEY
- **LYNCHGATE LANE FISHERY** Leicestershire
- **MANOR FARM POOLS** Leicestershire

HITCHIN
- **WITHY POOL** Bedfordshire
- **DURRANTS LAKE** Hertfordshire
- **OLDFIELD** Hertfordshire
- **OUGHTON (RIVER)** Hertfordshire

HOCKWOLD
- **CROSS DROVE** Suffolk

HODDESDON
- **CROWN NETHERHALL** Essex
- **ADMIRALS WALK LAKE** Hertfordshire
- **BROXBOURNE** Hertfordshire
- **CARTHAGENA FISHERY** Hertfordshire
- **DOBBS WEIR FISHERY** Hertfordshire
- **FEILDES WEIR** Hertfordshire
- **LEA (RIVER)** Hertfordshire
- **WORMLEBURY** Hertfordshire

HOLCOT
- **HOLLOWELL RESERVOIR** Northamptonshire
- **PITSFORD RESERVOIR** Northamptonshire

HOLLINS GREEN
- **BLUNDELLS FARM FISHERY** Cheshire

HOLLWORTHY
- **EASTCOTT FARM AND LODGES** Devon

HOLME
- **WYCH ELM FISHERY** Cumbria

HOLMES CHAPEL
- **BOUNDARY WATER PARK** Cheshire
- **BROOK BANK POOL** Cheshire
- **CATCHPENNY POOL** Cheshire
- **DANE (RIVER)** Cheshire
- **DUKES POOL** Cheshire

HOLMFIRTH
- **BOTTOMS DAM** Yorkshire (West)

HOLMROOK
- **IRT (RIVER)** Cumbria
- **MEDKLIN TARN FISHERY** Cumbria

HOLSWORTHY
- **CLAWFORD VINEYARD AND FISHERIES** Devon
- **EASTCOTT FARM AND LODGES** Devon
- **MILL LEAT TROUT FISHERY** Devon
- **SIMPSON VALLEY FISHERY** Devon
- **TINNEY WATERS** Devon
- **TORRIDGE (RIVER)** Devon
- **WOODA FARM FISHERY** Devon
- **WOODACOTT ARMS** Devon

HOLT
- **FELGRIGG LAKE** Norfolk
- **LETHERINGSETT FISHERY** Norfolk
- **SALTHOUSE BROAD** Norfolk

HOLT HEATH
- **TOP BARN ANGLING CENTRE** Worcestershire

HOLTON
- **ROLFS LAKE** Oxfordshire

HOLYWELL
- **TREBELLAN PARK LAKES** Cornwall

HOMROOK
- **MEDKLIN TARN FISHERY** Cumbria

HONITON
- **DEER PARK COUNTRY HOTEL** Devon
- **FISHPONDS HOUSE** Devon
- **HOLLIES TROUT FARM AND FISHERY** Devon
- **MILTON FARM PONDS** Devon
- **OTTER (RIVER)** Devon
- **OTTER FALLS FISHERY** Devon
- **STILL WATERS TROUT FISHERY** Devon
- **WISCOMBE FISHERY** Devon

HOOK
- **BASINGSTOKE CANAL** Hampshire
- **ROTHERWICK AND NIGHTINGALE LAKES** Hampshire
- **WHITE HOUSE TROUT FARM** Hampshire

HOPE VALLEY
- **LADYBOWER RESERVOIR** Derbyshire

HORAM
- **HORAM MANOR FISHERY** Sussex (East)

HORNCASTLE
- **ASHBY PARK FISHERIES** Lincolnshire
- **BELLS YARD LAKE** Lincolnshire
- **REVESBY RESERVOIR** Lincolnshire

HORNCHURCH
- **ALBYNS LAKE** Essex

HORNSEA
- **FARM PONDS** Humberside
- **HORNSEA MERE** Yorkshire (West)

HORSHAM
- **HAWKINS POND** Surrey
- **PULBOROUGH LAKE** Surrey
- **ROOSTHOLE** Surrey
- **WHITEVANE POND** Surrey
- **ARUN (RIVER)** Sussex (West)
- **DOCTORS LAKE** Sussex (West)
- **FURNACE LAKES** Sussex (West)
- **HAZELCOPSE LAKES** Sussex (West)
- **LENNOX WOOD LAKE** Sussex (West)
- **MENARDS LAKE** Sussex (West)
- **NEWELLS SPECIMEN CARP AND COARSE FISHERIES** Sussex (West)
- **SLAUGHTERFORD FARM** Sussex (West)
- **WATTLEHURST FARM TROUT LAKES** Sussex (West)

HORSMONDEN
- **PITTLANDS LAKES** Kent

HORTON
- **HILLVIEW FARM LAKE** Dorset

HORWICH
- **LOWER RIVINGTON RESERVOIR** Lancashire
- **UPPER RIVINGTON RESERVOIR** Lancashire

HOUGHTON LE SPRING
- **STEPHENSON LAKE** Tyne and Wear

HOUNSLOW
- **HENRY STREETER LAKE** London (Greater)
- **SWYERS LAKE** London (Greater)
- **THAMES (RIVER)** London (Greater)

HOWDEN
- **WILLITOFT FISH FARM** Humberside

HOXNE
- **DOVE BROOK** Norfolk

HUDDERSFIELD
- **BOTTOMS DAM** Yorkshire (West)
- **CALDER (RIVER)** Yorkshire (West)
- **COLNE (RIVER)** Yorkshire (West)
- **HILL TOP RESERVOIR** Yorkshire (West)
- **HOLME (RIVER)** Yorkshire (West)
- **HOLME MILL DAM (SQUARE DAM)** Yorkshire (West)
- **HORNSEA MERE** Yorkshire (West)
- **HUDDERSFIELD BROAD CANAL** Yorkshire (West)
- **NARROW CANAL** Yorkshire (West)
- **OAKS SCAR RESERVOIR** Yorkshire (West)
- **PINFOLD DAMS** Yorkshire (West)
- **PUSH DAM** Yorkshire (West)
- **ROWLEY DAM** Yorkshire (West)
- **SPARTH RESERVOIR** Yorkshire (West)
- **T P POND DAM** Yorkshire (West)
- **TP WOODS POND** Yorkshire (West)

HULL
- **BEVERLEY BECK** Humberside
- **BLUE LAGOON** Humberside
- **BRANDES BURTON 3 AND 4** Humberside
- **BURSTWICK SKI LAKE** Humberside
- **BURTON CONSTABLE COUNTRY PARK** Humberside
- **DERWENT (RIVER)** Humberside
- **EAST PARK LAKE** Humberside
- **HALSHAM POND** Humberside
- **LAMBWATH LAKES** Humberside
- **LEVEN CANAL** Humberside
- **MOTORWAY POND** Humberside
- **NODDLE HILL LAKE** Humberside
- **RUSH LYVARS LAKE** Humberside
- **TILARY LAKE** Humberside
- **URE (RIVER)** Humberside
- **BARTON BROADS LAKE** Lincolnshire (North)
- **PICKERING PARK FISHING LAKE** Yorkshire (North)

HUNGERFORD
- **BARTON COURT FISHERY** Berkshire
- **FROXFIELD A AND B** Berkshire

HUNTINGDON
- **BRACKHILL LAKE** Cambridgeshire
- **CHAWSTON LAKES** Cambridgeshire
- **CLEARWATERS COARSE FISHERY** Cambridgeshire
- **EARITH FISHERY** Cambridgeshire
- **EATON SOCON LAKE** Cambridgeshire
- **FENLAND FISHERIES** Cambridgeshire
- **GINGERBREAD LAKE AND DRIFT** Cambridgeshire
- **GODMANCHESTER (RIVER)** Cambridgeshire
- **GRAFHAM WATER** Cambridgeshire
- **GREAT OUSE (RIVER)** Cambridgeshire
- **HINCHINGBROOKE COUNTRY PARK** Cambridgeshire
- **HOLME FEN FISHING** Cambridgeshire
- **HUNDRED FOOT (RIVER)** Cambridgeshire
- **HUNTINGDON (RIVER)** Cambridgeshire
- **LEES BROOK** Cambridgeshire
- **LILY PARK LAKES** Cambridgeshire
- **LITTLE PAXTON FISHERY** Cambridgeshire
- **LONG REACH** Cambridgeshire
- **NORTH HOUSE LAKE** Cambridgeshire
- **OFFORD CLUNY** Cambridgeshire
- **OFFORD WEIRPOOL** Cambridgeshire
- **OLD NENE (RIVER)** Cambridgeshire
- **OLD WEST (RIVER)** Cambridgeshire
- **OVER MAIN DRAIN** Cambridgeshire
- **PAXTON LAKE** Cambridgeshire
- **ST IVES COMPLEX** Cambridgeshire
- **STEW POND** Cambridgeshire
- **WELDON RESERVOIR** Cambridgeshire
- **WILDEN RESERVOIR** Cambridgeshire
- **WOBURN CLOSE LAKE** Cambridgeshire
- **WOOLPACK FISHERY** Cambridgeshire

HUNTWORTH
- **SCREECH OWL PONDS** Somerset

HURST
- **DINTON PASTURES COUNTRY PARK** Berkshire
- **LODDON (RIVER)** Berkshire
- **TWYFORD WATERS** Berkshire

HYDE
- **OLDHAMS WATER** Cheshire
- **WALKERWOOD RESERVOIR** Cheshire

HYTHE
- **BROCKHILL COUNTRY PARK** Kent

IBSLEY
- **IBSLEY POOLS** Hampshire

ICKFORD
- **THAME (RIVER)** Oxfordshire

ILFORD
- **FAIRLOP WATERS** Essex
- **WANSTEAD AND WOODFORD PONDS** Essex
- **PERCH POND** London (Greater)

ILFRACOMBE
- **BERRYNARBOR MILL POND** Devon
- **LONGLANDS FARM** Devon
- **LOWER SLADE RESERVOIR** Devon
- **MILL PARK COARSE FISHING LAKE** Devon
- **SLADE RESERVOIRS** Devon

ILKESTON
- **MAPPERLEY RESERVOIR** Derbyshire

ILKLEY
- **WHARFE (RIVER)** Yorkshire (West)

IMMINGHAM
- **EAST HALTON FISHING LAKES** Lincolnshire
- **HOMESTEAD LAKE** Lincolnshire
- **WINTER BROTHERS POND** Lincolnshire
- **WINTERS LAKE** Lincolnshire

INDIAN QUEENS
- **OAKSIDE FISHERY** Cornwall

INGATESTONE
- **MOCKERKIN TARN** Cumbria
- **BLACKMORE WOOD** Essex
- **CARP FARM FRYERNING FISHERIES** Essex
- **DODDS FARM** Essex
- **MILLENNIUM LAKES** Essex
- **WID (RIVER)** Essex

INGOLDMELLS
- **WATERSIDE LEISURE PARK** Lincolnshire

INGWORTH
- **ABBOTS HALL** Norfolk

INSTOW
- **PYEWELL FARM** Devon

IPSWICH
- **ALDERSONS LAKES** Suffolk
- **ALTON WATER RESERVOIR** Suffolk
- **BARHAM A PIT** Suffolk
- **BARHAM B PIT** Suffolk
- **BOSMERE LAKE** Suffolk
- **CAUSEWAY LAKES** Suffolk
- **GIPPING (RIVER)** Suffolk
- **NEEDHAM LAKE** Suffolk
- **SINKS PIT** Suffolk
- **STOUR (SUFFOLK) (RIVER)** Suffolk
- **SWALE PIT** Suffolk
- **WICKHAM MARKET RESERVOIRS** Suffolk

IRONBRIDGE
- **LITTLE DAWLEY POOLS** Shropshire
- **SEVERN (RIVER)** Shropshire

ISFIELD
- **COLIN GODMANS TROUTING** Sussex (East)

ITCHEN
- **ITCHEN NAVIGATION** Hampshire

IVER
- **BILLET LANE** Buckinghamshire
- **BLACK PARK** Buckinghamshire
- **CALVES LANE LAKE** Buckinghamshire
- **FARLOWS LAKE** Buckinghamshire
- **OLD SLADE LANE LAKE** Buckinghamshire
- **COLNE (RIVER)** London (Greater)

IVYBRIDGE
- **UPPER YEALM FISHERY** Devon

JARROW
- **FELLGATE FISHERIES** Tyne and Wear

KEGWORTH
- **KEGWORTH DEEP LOCK** Derbyshire
- **SOAR (RIVER)** Derbyshire

KEIGHLEY
- **WHINNYGILL RESERVOIR** Yorkshire (North)
- **AIRE (RIVER)** Yorkshire (West)
- **COPPICE POND** Yorkshire (West)
- **RAYGILL FISHERY** Yorkshire (West)
- **ROBERTS POND** Yorkshire (West)

KELVEDON
- **BROOKHALL FISHERY** Essex

KEMPSTON
- **AMPTHILL RESERVOIR** Bedfordshire
- **MARSTON PITS** Bedfordshire
- **OUSE (RIVER)** Buckinghamshire

KENDAL
- **BANKS POND** Cumbria
- **DEE (RIVER)** Cumbria
- **DUBBS RESERVOIR** Cumbria
- **FISHER TARN** Cumbria
- **GHYLL HEAD** Cumbria
- **KENT (RIVER)** Cumbria
- **KILLINGTON RESERVOIR** Cumbria
- **LUNE (RIVER)** Cumbria
- **LUNE (RIVER)** Cumbria
- **RATHER HEATH TARN** Cumbria
- **RAWTHEY (RIVER)** Cumbria
- **SKELSMERGH LAKE** Cumbria
- **SPRINT (RIVER)** Cumbria

KENNARDINGTON
- **ROYAL MILITARY CANAL** Kent

KENNICK
- **KENNICK RESERVOIR** Devon

KENNINGTON
- **SANDFORD LOCK** Oxfordshire

KENTCHURCH
- **MONNOW (RIVER)** Herefordshire

KENTON
- **HOME FARM FISHERY** Devon
- **MARCOA LAKE** London (Greater)

KESWICK
- **BASSENTHWAITE LAKE** Cumbria
- **BORROWDALE FISHERIES** Cumbria
- **BUTTERMERE LAKE** Cumbria
- **CRUMMOCK WATER LAKE** Cumbria
- **DERWENT (RIVER)** Cumbria
- **THIRLMERE** Cumbria
- **WATENDLATH TROUT FISHERY** Cumbria
- **WINSTER (RIVER)** Cumbria

KETTERING
- **ALDWINCLE PITS** Northamptonshire
- **BARKERS LAKE** Northamptonshire
- **ELINOR COARSE LAKE** Northamptonshire
- **ELINOR TROUT FISHERY** Northamptonshire
- **ISE (RIVER)** Northamptonshire
- **ISLIP NATURE LAKE** Northamptonshire
- **NENE (RIVER)** Northamptonshire
- **RINGSTEAD GRANGE TROUT FISHERY** Northamptonshire
- **RINGSTEAD ISLAND** Northamptonshire
- **THORPE WATERVILLE LAKE** Northamptonshire
- **THRAPSTON (RIVER)** Northamptonshire
- **THRAPSTON LAKES** Northamptonshire

KEYNSHAM
- **AVON (RIVER)** Bristol
- **CHEW (RIVER)** Bristol

KIDDERMINSTER
- **POOL HALL** Midlands (West)
- **SEVERN (RIVER)** Shropshire
- **BEWDLEY POOL** Worcestershire
- **BRAKE MILL POOL** Worcestershire
- **CAPTAINS POOL** Worcestershire
- **ERICS POOL** Worcestershire
- **FURNACE MILL FISHERY** Worcestershire
- **HURCOTT POOL** Worcestershire
- **MASTERS (THE)** Worcestershire
- **MOORLANDS FARM** Worcestershire
- **MOORS POOL** Worcestershire
- **POOLE HALL FISHERY** Worcestershire
- **SALWARPE (RIVER)** Worcestershire
- **SEVERN (RIVER)** Worcestershire
- **SHAKESPEARE MOORLANDS FARM** Worcestershire
- **SHATTERFORD FISHERY AND WILDLIFE SANCTUARY** Worcestershire
- **SION FARM FISHERIES** Worcestershire
- **STANKLIN POOL** Worcestershire
- **STELLA LAKE** Worcestershire
- **STEWARDS POOL** Worcestershire
- **TEME (RIVER)** Worcestershire
- **WELFIELD POOLS** Worcestershire
- **WILLOW MARSH** Worcestershire
- **WINTERFOLD PARK FISHERIES** Worcestershire

KIDLINGTON
- **CHERWELL (RIVER)** Oxfordshire
- **CHERWELL (RIVER)** Oxfordshire
- **OXFORD CANAL** Oxfordshire

KIDSGROVE
- **WARDS POOLS** Cheshire
- **TAYLORS POOL** Staffordshire

KILBURN
- **LOW OSGOODBY LAKE** Yorkshire (North)

KILLERTON
- **EXE (RIVER)** Devon

KINETON
- **PARK FARM** Warwickshire

KINGCOMBE
- **RAWLSBURY WATERS** Dorset

KINGS LANGLEY
- **GAYWOODS** Hertfordshire
- **MERCHANT TAYLORS SCL LAKES** Hertfordshire

KING'S LYNN
- **BABINGLEY (RIVER)** Norfolk
- **BRADMOOR LAKES** Norfolk
- **CASTLE RISING STREAM** Norfolk
- **CUT OFF CHANNEL** Norfolk
- **FOSTERS END PIT** Norfolk
- **GATTON WATER CARAVAN SITE** Norfolk
- **GREAT OUSE RELIEF CHANNEL** Norfolk
- **LAKESIDE** Norfolk
- **LITTLE DUNHAM CARP LAKES** Norfolk
- **LITTLE OUSE (RIVER)** Norfolk
- **MEADOW LAKE** Norfolk
- **NAR (RIVER)** Norfolk
- **NAR STREAM** Norfolk
- **NARBOROUGH TROUT FARM** Norfolk
- **PENTNEY LAKES** Norfolk
- **RELIEF CHANNEL** Norfolk
- **SOVEREIGN LAKES** Norfolk
- **TEN MILE BANK** Norfolk
- **TOTTENHILL PIT** Norfolk
- **WILLOWCROFT FISHERY** Norfolk
- **WISSEY (RIVER)** Norfolk
- **WOODLAKES FISHERY** Norfolk

KING'S NYMPTON
- **MOLE (RIVER)** Devon

KINGSBRIDGE
- **AVETON GIFFORD STREAM** Devon
- **AVON (RIVER)** Devon
- **BICKERTON FARM FISHERY** Devon
- **COOMBE WATER FISHERY** Devon
- **LODDISWELL STREAM** Devon
- **SLAPTON LEY NATIONAL NATURE RESERVE** Devon
- **VALLEY SPRINGS TROUT FISHERY** Devon

KINGSNORTH
- **HOOKSTEAD LAKE** Kent

KINGSTON
- **HALLIFORD MERE LAKES** London (Greater)
- **TEDDINGTON LOCK** London (Greater)

KINGSTON UPON HULL
- **PASTURE HOUSE FISHERY** Lincolnshire (North)

KINGSTON UPON THAMES
- **BUSHEY PARK** Surrey
- **HOME PARK** Surrey

KINOULTON
- **GRANTHAM CANAL** Nottinghamshire

KIRKBRIDE
- **LOUGHSIDE FISHERY** Cumbria

KIRKBY STEPHEN
- **BESSY BECK TROUT FARM** Cumbria
- **EDEN (RIVER)** Cumbria
- **EDEN VALLEY TROUT LAKE** Cumbria
- **LITTLE MUSGRAVE** Cumbria

KIRKHAM
- **GREENHALGH LODGE FISHERY** Lancashire
- **WYRE (RIVER)** Lancashire

KITTERFORD CROSS
- **LITTLE ALLERS COARSE FISHERY** Devon

KNARESBOROUGH
- **FARMIRE TROUT FISHERY** Yorkshire (North)
- **HAY-A-PARK** Yorkshire (North)
- **MILBY CUT** Yorkshire (North)
- **NIDD (RIVER)** Yorkshire (North)
- **YORKSHIRE OUSE** Yorkshire (North)
- **STAVELEY LAKES** Yorkshire (West)

KNUTSFORD
- **ASTLE POOL** Cheshire
- **BOLLIN (RIVER)** Cheshire
- **BOUNDARY WATER PARK** Cheshire
- **BRIGHOUSE POOL** Cheshire
- **CICELY MILL POOL** Cheshire
- **CLAY LANE FISHERY** Cheshire
- **DOVEMERE, SANDMERE AND WOODLANDS** Cheshire
- **FINGERPOST POOL** Cheshire
- **LITTLE REEDS MERE** Cheshire
- **MANOR POOL** Cheshire
- **MOBBERLEY POOL** Cheshire
- **MOSS POOLS** Cheshire
- **MOSSBANK POOL** Cheshire
- **NORBURY POOL** Cheshire
- **SAND MERE LAKE** Cheshire
- **SPRINGWOOD POOL** Cheshire
- **SWANLEY** Cheshire
- **TABLEY MERE** Cheshire
- **TABLEY MOAT** Cheshire
- **TATTON MERE** Cheshire
- **TOFT POOL** Cheshire
- **WOODLANDS LAKE** Cheshire

LAMBERHURST
- **BEWL WATER** Kent
- **HOATHLEY FISHERY** Kent

LANCASTER
- **DOE (RIVER)** Cumbria
- **GRETA (RIVER)** Cumbria
- **TEWITFIELDS TROUT FISHERY** Cumbria
- **TWISS (RIVER)** Cumbria
- **BANK HOUSE FLY FISHERY** Lancashire
- **BENTHAM STREAM** Lancashire
- **BENTHAM TROUT FISHERY** Lancashire
- **CLAYLANDS CARAVAN SITE** Lancashire
- **CLEVELEY BRIDGE FISHERY** Lancashire
- **CONDER VALLEY FLY FISHERY** Lancashire
- **ERIC FISHWICK NATURE RESERVE** Lancashire
- **GRIZEDALE LEA RESERVOIR** Lancashire
- **HALTON FISHERY** Lancashire
- **LANCASTER CANAL** Lancashire
- **LUNE (RIVER)** Lancashire
- **SKERTON FISHERY** Lancashire
- **THURSLAND HILL FARM** Lancashire
- **WENNING (RIVER)** Lancashire
- **WYRESIDE LAKES FISHERY AND LODGINGS** Lancashire

LANCING
- **PASSIES PONDS** Sussex (West)

LANGDON BECK
- **COW GREEN WILD BROWN TROUT FISHERY** County Durham

LANGFORD
- **LANGFORD MILL** Bedfordshire

LANGPORT
- **COOMBE LAKE** Somerset
- **ISLE (RIVER)** Somerset
- **PARRETT (RIVER)** Somerset
- **PARRETT (RIVER)** Somerset
- **THORNEY LAKES** Somerset

LANHYDROCK
- **FOWEY (RIVER)** Cornwall

LARKFIELD
- **ALDERS LAKES** Kent

LAUNCESTON
- **AVALLON HOLIDAY PARK** Cornwall
- **BRAGGS WOOD TROUT FISHERY** Cornwall
- **DUTSON WATER** Cornwall
- **ELMFIELD FARM COARSE FISHERY** Cornwall
- **EMFIELD COARSE FISHERY** Cornwall
- **HIDDEN VALLEY** Cornwall
- **ROSE PARK FISHERY** Cornwall
- **ST LEONARDS FISHING LAKE** Cornwall
- **STOWFORD GRANGE FISHERIES** Cornwall
- **TAMAR (RIVER)** Cornwall
- **TREDIDON BARTON LAKE** Cornwall

LAYCOCK
- **BRISTOL AVON** Somerset
- **BRISTOL AVON** Wiltshire

LEAMINGTON SPA
- **BISHOPS BOWL LAKES** Warwickshire
- **CHESTERTON MILL POOL TROUT FISHERY** Warwickshire
- **GRAND UNION CANAL** Warwickshire
- **LEAM (RIVER)** Warwickshire
- **OXFORD CANAL** Warwickshire
- **WARWICK CANAL** Warwickshire

LEATHERHEAD
- **LONG COPSE PONDS** Surrey

LECHLADE
- **BUSHYLEAZE TROUT FISHERY** Gloucestershire
- **HORSESHOE LAKE** Gloucestershire
- **LECHLADE TROUT FISHERY** Gloucestershire
- **MILESTONE FISHERY** Gloucestershire
- **THAMES (RIVER)** Gloucestershire

LEDBURY
- **STONE END FARM LAKES** Gloucestershire
- **BETULA WATERS** Herefordshire
- **CASTLEMORTON** Herefordshire
- **EASTNOR CASTLE** Herefordshire
- **EVESBATCH TOP LAKE** Herefordshire
- **GOLDEN VALLEY** Herefordshire
- **LILY AND WILLOW POOLS** Herefordshire
- **PIXLEY POOL** Herefordshire
- **PRIDEWOOD LAKE** Herefordshire
- **RED BANK POOLS** Herefordshire
- **RUSSELLS END RESERVOIR** Herefordshire

LEEDS
- **AIRE (RIVER)** Yorkshire (West)
- **BILLING DAM** Yorkshire (West)
- **CLAYTON WOOD PONDS** Yorkshire (West)
- **KIPPAX POND** Yorkshire (West)
- **LEEDS TO LIVERPOOL CANAL** Yorkshire (West)
- **MILLRACE** Yorkshire (West)
- **ROUNDHAY PARK LAKES** Yorkshire (West)
- **SWILLINGTON PARK** Yorkshire (West)
- **WHARFE (RIVER)** Yorkshire (West)

LEEK
- **BASFORD COARSE FISHERY** Staffordshire
- **BLACKSHAW FARM LAKES** Staffordshire
- **CHURNET (RIVER)** Staffordshire
- **CONSALL NATURE PARK** Staffordshire
- **DEEP HAYES COUNTRY PARK** Staffordshire
- **HAMPS (RIVER)** Staffordshire
- **HORSEBRIDGE POOL** Staffordshire
- **RUDYARD LAKE** Staffordshire
- **TILTLESWORTH** Staffordshire
- **TITTESWORTH RESERVOIR** Staffordshire

LEEMING
- **BEDALE BECK** Yorkshire (North)

LEE-ON-THE-SOLENT
- **QUEENS ROAD POND** Hampshire

LEICESTER
- **BROOME FISHERIES** Leicestershire
- **C J FISHERIES** Leicestershire
- **CHARNWOOD WATER** Leicestershire
- **FRISBY LAKES** Leicestershire
- **GROBY FISHING LAKES** Leicestershire
- **HALL FARM** Leicestershire
- **HOLLY FARM FISHERY** Leicestershire
- **LAKESIDE SPORTING** Leicestershire
- **LAUNDE ABBEY LAKES** Leicestershire
- **LEICESTER CANAL** Leicestershire
- **LEICESTER GRAND UNION CANAL** Leicestershire
- **MALLORY PARK FISHERIES** Leicestershire
- **MANOR FARM** Leicestershire
- **MILL FARM FISHERY** Leicestershire
- **MONNOW (RIVER)** Leicestershire
- **NANPANTAN RESERVOIR** Leicestershire
- **PROCTORS PLEASURE PARK** Leicestershire
- **SOAR (RIVER)** Leicestershire
- **SPRING GRANGE FISHERY** Leicestershire
- **THORNTON RESERVOIR** Leicestershire
- **WATERMEAD PARK LAKES** Leicestershire
- **WATERY GATE FISHERY** Leicestershire
- **WHETSTONE GORSE** Leicestershire
- **WILLOWS FARM FISHING** Leicestershire
- **BOSWORTH WATER TRUST AND FRIEZELAND POOLS** Warwickshire

LEIGH
- **EDEN (RIVER)** Kent
- **POLLYS FLASH** Lancashire
- **FIR TREE FLASH** Manchester (Greater)
- **FIRS PARK LAKE** Manchester (Greater)
- **LEEDS TO LIVERPOOL CANAL** Manchester (Greater)
- **LEIGH BRANCH CANAL** Manchester (Greater)
- **PENNINGTON FLASH** Manchester (Greater)

LEIGHTON BUZZARD
- **CLAYDON LAKE** Bedfordshire

JONES PIT Bedfordshire
LAKESIDE TROUT AND COARSE FISHERY Bedfordshire
LEDBURN ROAD Bedfordshire
RACKLEY HILLS PIT Bedfordshire
TIDDENFOOT PIT Bedfordshire
VAUXHALL PIT Bedfordshire
ALDERS FARM TROUT FISHERY Buckinghamshire

LEMINGTON SPA

GRAND UNION CANAL Warwickshire

LENWADE

BRIDGE INN FISHERY Norfolk
WENSUM (RIVER) Norfolk

LEOMINSTER

DOCKLOW POOLS Herefordshire

LETCHWORTH

HENLOW GRANGE Bedfordshire

LEWES

BARCOMBE RESERVOIR Sussex (East)
BEVERN STREAM Sussex (East)
DECOY LAKE Sussex (East)
OLD IRON (RIVER) Sussex (East)
OLD MILL Sussex (East)
OUSE (RIVER) Sussex (East)
SWANBOROUGH LAKES Sussex (East)
OUSE (RIVER) Sussex (West)

LEYBURN

BAIN (RIVER) Yorkshire (North)
SHIELD FISHERY Yorkshire (North)
URE (RIVER) Yorkshire (North)

LEYLAND

BRINSCALL LODGE Lancashire
MARTIN HALL FARM Lancashire
SHRUGGS WOOD FISHERY Lancashire

LICHFIELD

FISHERWICK LAKES Staffordshire
MIDLAND GAME FISHERIES Staffordshire

LIFTON

TAMAR (RIVER) Devon

LIMBER HILL

ESK (RIVER) Humberside

LIMPLEY STOKE

KENNET AND AVON CANAL Somerset

LINCHFIELD

SOUTH POPLARS Staffordshire

LINCOLN

BOULTHAM PARK LAKE Lincolnshire
DYKES COTTAGE LAKES Lincolnshire
HARTSHOLME PARK LAKE Lincolnshire
HYKEHAM PIT Lincolnshire
LAKESIDE Lincolnshire
MARRIS LAKES Lincolnshire
OAKHILL LEISURE Lincolnshire
RICHMOND LAKES Lincolnshire
SHANDY KEV FISHERIES Lincolnshire
STARMERS PIT Lincolnshire
SUDBROOK POND Lincolnshire
TATTERSHALL LEISURE PARK Lincolnshire
TILL (RIVER) Lincolnshire
TIM HALL LAKE Lincolnshire
TOFT NEWTON TROUT FISHERY Lincolnshire
TRENT (RIVER) Lincolnshire
UPPER WITHAM (RIVER) Lincolnshire
WHISBY GARDEN CENTRE Lincolnshire

PELICAN POND Lincolnshire (North)

LINDRIDGE

WOODSTON MANOR POOLS Worcestershire

LINGFIELD

BEAVER FARM FISHERY Surrey

LINTHWAITE

COLNE (RIVER) Yorkshire (West)
NARROW CANAL Yorkshire (West)

LINTON-ON-OUSE

OUSE (RIVER) Yorkshire (North)

LIPHOOK

COOKS POND Hampshire

LISKEARD

BADHAM FARM LAKE Cornwall
COLLIFORD LAKE Cornwall
FOWEY (RIVER) Cornwall
INNY (RIVER) Cornwall
LYNHER (RIVER) Cornwall
SEATON (RIVER) Cornwall
SIBLYBACK LAKE Cornwall
WEST LOOE (RIVER) Cornwall
WOODLAY HOLIDAY LAKES Cornwall

LISS

BARONS PONDS (NEW SITE) Hampshire
MBK LEISURE BARRONS POND Hampshire

LITTLE MELTON

GREAT MELTON FISHERY Norfolk

LITTLE PAXTON

LITTLE PAXTON FISHERY Cambridgeshire

LITTLE WITTENHAM

DAYS LOCK Oxfordshire

LITTLEBOROUGH

TRENT (RIVER) Lincolnshire
CLEGG HALL LAKES Manchester (Greater)
CROFT HEAD FISHERY Manchester (Greater)
GROVE LODGE Manchester (Greater)
HOLLINGWORTH LAKE COUNTRY PARK Manchester (Greater)
LOWER TOWN HOUSE FISHERY Manchester (Greater)
WHITELEY KNOWL RESERVOIR Manchester (Greater)

LITTLEHAMPTON

ARUN (RIVER) Sussex (West)
OUSE (RIVER) Sussex (West)

LITTLEPORT

GREAT OUSE (RIVER) Cambridgeshire
GREAT OUSE (RIVER) Norfolk

LIVERPOOL

CALDERSTONES PARK LAKE Merseyside
CARR MILL DAM Merseyside
FOOTBALL PIT Merseyside
GREENBANK PARK LAKE Merseyside
LEEDS TO LIVERPOOL Merseyside
LEEDS TO LIVERPOOL CANAL Merseyside
MILL HOUSE FISHERY Merseyside
NEWSHAM PARK Merseyside
PRINCES PARK LAKE Merseyside
STANLEY PARK LAKE Merseyside
WALTON HALL PARK Merseyside

LLANGEDWYN

TANAT (RIVER) Shropshire

LODDON

HARDLEY MARSHES Norfolk

LOGGERHEADS

ASHLEY POOLS Staffordshire

LONDON

LEE NAVIGATION Hertfordshire
ALEXANDRA PALACE LAKE London (Greater)
ALEXANDRA PARK LAKE London (Greater)
ASHMERE FISHERIES London (Greater)
ASHVALE FISHERIES London (Greater)
BEDFONT LAKE London (Greater)
BIRCHMERE London (Greater)
BOXERS LAKE London (Greater)
BROXBOURNE MEADOWS FISHERY London (Greater)
BURES LAKE London (Greater)
CARGILL LAKE London (Greater)
CLAPHAM COMMON POND London (Greater)
COLNE (RIVER) London (Greater)
COPPER MILLSTREAM London (Greater)
COWLEY LAKE London (Greater)
CUTTING LAKE London (Greater)
EAST WARWICK London (Greater)
ENFIELD LOCK London (Greater)
FLAKE STREAM London (Greater)
FORTY HALL LAKE London (Greater)
FROGMORE LAKE London (Greater)
FURNACE POND London (Greater)
GRAND UNION CANAL London (Greater)
GREENHAMS London (Greater)
HALLIFORD MERE LAKES London (Greater)
HAMPSTEAD HEATH London (Greater)
HAREFIELD CARP LAKE London (Greater)
HEATH VALE POND London (Greater)
HENRY STREETER LAKE London (Greater)
HIGH MAYNARD RESERVOIR London (Greater)
HIGHAMS PARK LAKE London (Greater)
HIGHGATE PONDS London (Greater)
HOLLOW PONDS London (Greater)
HORSEMILL STREAM London (Greater)
KINGFISHER LAKE London (Greater)
KNIGHTSCOTE PONDS London (Greater)
KORDA LAKE London (Greater)
LEA NAVIGATION London (Greater)
LEE NAVIGATION London (Greater)
LITTLE BRITAIN LAKE London (Greater)
LIZARD LAKES London (Greater)
LOCKWOOD RESERVOIR London (Greater)
LOW MAYNARD RESERVOIR London (Greater)
MARCOA LAKE London (Greater)
MULGROVE POND London (Greater)
NEW CUT London (Greater)
NORTH TROY LAKE AND COLNE (RIVER) London (Greater)
NORWOOD LAKE London (Greater)
OLD LEE (RIVER) London (Greater)
OSTERLEY PARK MIDDLE LAKE London (Greater)
PENTON HOOK LOCK London (Greater)
PERCH POND London (Greater)
PONDERS END London (Greater)
POTOMAC POND London (Greater)
REGENTS CANAL London (Greater)
RODNEY MEADOW London (Greater)
SAVAY LAKE London (Greater)
SHEEPWALK LAKE London (Greater)
SHEPPERTON LAKE London (Greater)

- SHEPPERTON LOCK London (Greater)
- SOUTH NORWOOD LAKE London (Greater)
- STOCKLEY ROAD LAKES London (Greater)
- STUDIO AND BROADWATER London (Greater)
- SWYERS LAKE London (Greater)
- SYON PARK FISHERY London (Greater)
- TEDDINGTON LOCK London (Greater)
- THAMES (RIVER) London (Greater)
- THORNEY POOL London (Greater)
- TRENT COUNTRY PARK LAKES London (Greater)
- TRENT PARK LAKES London (Greater)
- VALE OF HEATH POND London (Greater)
- WALTHAMSTOW RESERVOIR (EAST WARWICK) London (Greater)
- WALTHAMSTOW RESERVOIR (NO 1) London (Greater)
- WALTHAMSTOW RESERVOIR (NO 2 AND NO 3) London (Greater)
- WALTHAMSTOW RESERVOIR (NO 4 TROUT) London (Greater)
- WALTHAMSTOW RESERVOIR (NO 5) London (Greater)
- WALTHAMSTOW RESERVOIR (WEST WARWICK) London (Greater)
- WANDSWORTH COMMON POND London (Greater)
- WANSTEAD PARK LAKES London (Greater)
- WEST RESERVOIR London (Greater)
- WEST WARWICK London (Greater)
- WHITE HORSE FISHERIES London (Greater)
- WILLOWSIDE CARP LAKE London (Greater)
- WOOLWICH DOCKYARD London (Greater)
- WRAYSBURY ONE London (Greater)
- WRAYSBURY TWO London (Greater)
- BOLDERMERE Surrey

LONG BENNINGTON

- LAKESIDE FARM Nottinghamshire
- WITHAM (RIVER) Nottinghamshire

LONG EATON

- TRENT (RIVER) Nottinghamshire

LONG FRAMLINGTON

- FELTON FENCE FARM PONDS Northumberland

LONG MARTON

- KIRKBY THORE (RIVER) Cumbria

LONGHAM

- STOUR (DORSET) (RIVER) Dorset

LONGNOR

- DOVE (RIVER) Staffordshire

LONGRIDGE

- DILWORTH (UPPER) RESERVOIR Lancashire
- SPADE MILL RESERVOIR NO.2 Lancashire

LONGSTRATTON

- MILL FARM FISHERY Norfolk

LONGTON

- BLACK LAKE Staffordshire

LOOE

- FOWEY (RIVER) Cornwall
- SHILLAMILL LAKES COUNTRY PARK Cornwall
- WEST LOOE (RIVER) Cornwall
- WEST LOOE (RIVER) Cornwall

LOSTWITHIEL

- FOWEY (RIVER) Cornwall

LOUGHBOROUGH

- CHARNWOOD WATER Leicestershire
- LAKESIDE SPORTING Leicestershire
- LOUGHBOROUGH SOAR CANAL Leicestershire
- PROCTORS PLEASURE PARK Leicestershire
- SOAR (RIVER) Leicestershire
- SOAR (RIVER) Leicestershire

LOUGHTON

- CONNAUGHT WATER Essex
- WAKE VALLEY POND Essex

LOUTH

- ALVINGHAM FISHERIES Lincolnshire
- BELLEAU BRIDGE FARM LAKE Lincolnshire
- BRICKYARD FISHERY Lincolnshire
- CHARLES STREET POND Lincolnshire
- LINDEN WALK POND Lincolnshire
- OASIS LAKES Lincolnshire
- OLSTEN FISHERY Lincolnshire
- STONE END LAKE Lincolnshire
- THORPE LE VALE FISHERY Lincolnshire
- VICKERS POND Lincolnshire
- WARREN POND Lincolnshire
- WILLOW FARM Lincolnshire

LOWER DUNSFORTH

- URE (RIVER) Humberside

LOWESTOFT

- FLIXTON DECOY Suffolk
- GUNTON HALL LAKE Suffolk
- OULTON BROAD Suffolk
- OULTON DYKE Suffolk

LOWESWATER

- LOWESWATER LAKE Cumbria

LOXLEY

- OAKHAM FARM POOLS Warwickshire

LUDHAM

- ST BENETS ABBEY (RIVER) Cornwall

LUDLOW

- DELBURY HALL TROUT FISHERY Shropshire
- ONNY (RIVER) Shropshire
- TEME (RIVER) Shropshire
- WALCOT WEST LAKE Shropshire

LUTON

- WOBURN SANDS Bedfordshire
- TINGRITH LAKES Buckinghamshire
- NORTH HOUSE LAKE Cambridgeshire

LUTTERWORTH

- C J FISHERIES Leicestershire
- HALL FARM Leicestershire
- HOLLY FARM FISHERY Leicestershire
- MANOR FARM Leicestershire
- MILL FARM FISHERY Leicestershire
- PEATLING POOLS (1-6) Leicestershire
- STEMBOROUGH MILL TROUT FARM Leicestershire

LYDNEY

- LYDNEY BOATING LAKE Gloucestershire

LYME REGIS

- AMHERST LODGE FISHERY Dorset

LYMINGTON

- HATCHET POND Hampshire
- SWAY LAKES Hampshire
- WAINSFORD RESERVOIR Hampshire

LYMM

- ANTROBUS LAKES Cheshire
- MOOR POOL Cheshire
- MOSS POOLS Cheshire
- MOSSBANK POOL Cheshire
- NORBURY POOL Cheshire
- TOP FARM POOL Cheshire

LYNDHURST

- HAMPSHIRE AVON (RIVER) Dorset
- JANESMOOR POND Hampshire
- LEOMINSTEAD MILL POND Hampshire
- LEOMINSTEAD TROUT FISHERY Hampshire
- LYNDHURST LAKE Hampshire
- MILL POND LAKE Hampshire

LYNEHAM

- TOCKENHAM RESERVOIR Wiltshire

LYNMOUTH

- LYN (RIVER) Devon
- WATERSMEET AND GLENTHORNE FISHERIES Devon

MABLETHORPE

- GRANGE FARM LEISURE Lincolnshire

MACCLESFIELD

- ASHLEY (RIVER) Cheshire
- BOSLEY RESERVOIR Cheshire
- BOTTOMS RESERVOIR Cheshire
- CAPESTHORNE HALL STOCK POND Cheshire
- CAPESTHORNE MAIN POOL Cheshire
- CAPESTHORNE TOP POOL Cheshire
- DANE (RIVER) Cheshire
- DANEBRIDGE FISHERIES Cheshire
- FANSHAWE LANE POOL Cheshire
- HORSECOPPICE RESERVOIR Cheshire
- JARMAN FARM POOL Cheshire
- KAZAKO PONDS Cheshire
- KNIGHTS POOL Cheshire
- LAMALOAD RESERVOIR Cheshire
- LEADBEATERS RESERVOIR Cheshire
- MACCLESFIELD CANAL Cheshire
- MARTON HEATH COARSE POOL Cheshire
- MARTON HEATH TROUT POOLS Cheshire
- MILL LODGE Cheshire
- PARK POOL Cheshire
- REDESMERE Cheshire
- RIDGEGATE RESERVOIR Cheshire
- SOUTH PARK Cheshire
- SUTTON RESERVOIR Cheshire
- TEGGSNOSE RESERVOIR Cheshire
- THORNEYCROFT LAKES Cheshire
- TURKS HEAD RESERVOIR Cheshire
- TURNERS POOL Cheshire
- WALL POOL LODGE Cheshire
- WEAVER (RIVER) Cheshire
- WHIRLEY MERE Cheshire
- WHIRLEY POOL Cheshire
- WOOD POOL Cheshire

MADELEY

- SEVERN (RIVER) Shropshire

MAIDEN NEWTON

- KINGCOMBE LAKE Dorset

MAIDENHEAD

- AMERDEN POOL Berkshire
- BRAY LAKE Berkshire
- BRAY LOCK Berkshire
- HURLEY LOCK Berkshire

PONDWOOD CARP LAKES Berkshire
SHEEPHOUSE FARM TROUT FISHERY Berkshire
THAMES (RIVER) Berkshire

MAIDSTONE

ABBEYCOURT LAKE Kent
ALDERS LAKES Kent
BLUEBELL FISHING PONDS Kent
BURNHAM RESERVOIR Kent
EAST FARLEIGH Kent
GEDGES LAKES Kent
LARKFIELD LAKES Kent
MEDWAY (RIVER) Kent
MONK LAKE FISHERIES Kent
MOTE PARK FISHERY Kent
RIVERFIELD CARP FARM Kent
WIDEHURST FARM Kent

MALDON

ASHELDHAM FISHERY Essex
BLACKWATER (RIVER) Essex
BOG GROVE Essex
CHELMER AND BLACKWATER NAVIGATION CANAL Essex
CHIGBOROUGH Essex
CHIGBOROUGH FISHERIES Essex
SLOUGH HOUSE WATER Essex
SOUTHMINSTER FISHERIES Essex
WICK MERE Essex

MALMESBURY

BURTON HILL LAKE Wiltshire
LOWER MOOR FISHERY Wiltshire
WHITE HORSE INN LAKE Wiltshire

MALPAS

EGERTON LAKE Cheshire
HAMPTON SPRINGS Cheshire

MALTON

DERWENT (RIVER) Lancashire
ABBIE POND Yorkshire (North)
BIRKDALE FISHERY Yorkshire (North)
BRICKYARD FARM LAKE Yorkshire (North)
DERWENT (RIVER) Yorkshire (North)
MANOR FARM POND Yorkshire (North)
OUSE (RIVER) Yorkshire (North)
RICCAL (RIVER) Yorkshire (North)
RYE (RIVER) Yorkshire (North)
RYE AND SEVEN (RIVERS) Yorkshire (North)
SELLEY BRIDGE LAKE Yorkshire (North)
TROUT POND BARN Yorkshire (North)

MALVERN

CASTLE GREEN POOLS Worcestershire
LEIGH SINTON FISHING LAKES Worcestershire
SINDON MILL FARM Worcestershire

MANCHESTER

SALE WATER PARK Cheshire
ASHENHURST LAKES Manchester (Greater)
BEEFOLD LODGE Manchester (Greater)
BLACKLEACH RESERVOIR Manchester (Greater)
BOGGART HOLE CLOUGH Manchester (Greater)
BOWKER LAKES Manchester (Greater)
BRIDGEWATER CANAL Manchester (Greater)
CHORLTON WATER PARK Manchester (Greater)
CLIFTON MARINA Manchester (Greater)
DEBDALE RESERVOIRS Manchester (Greater)
DINGLE LODGE Manchester (Greater)
DOUBLEWOODS Manchester (Greater)
FARM LODGE Manchester (Greater)
GEIGYS WATER Manchester (Greater)
GORSE PIT RESERVOIR Manchester (Greater)
GORTON (LOWER) RESERVOIR Manchester (Greater)
GORTON (UPPER) RESERVOIR Manchester (Greater)
HEATON PARK Manchester (Greater)
KING GEORGE V POOL Manchester (Greater)
KING WILLIAM IV RESERVOIR Manchester (Greater)
LANKYS MILL POND Manchester (Greater)
LEEKES WATER Manchester (Greater)
MANCHESTER CANAL Manchester (Greater)
MANCHESTER, BOLTON AND BURY CANAL Manchester (Greater)
MYRTLE ROAD LODGES Manchester (Greater)
OLD IRWELL Manchester (Greater)
PAINSWICK PARK LAKE Manchester (Greater)
PLATT FIELDS Manchester (Greater)
RHODES LODGE Manchester (Greater)
SALFORD QUAYS Manchester (Greater)
SANDY BEACH Manchester (Greater)
STAKEHILL LODGES Manchester (Greater)
STAR MOUNT Manchester (Greater)
SWAN LODGE Manchester (Greater)
TWINE VALLEY TROUT FISHERY Manchester (Greater)
UPPER GORTON RESERVOIR Manchester (Greater)
WESTGATE POOL Manchester (Greater)
WHITTLE BROOK RESERVOIR Manchester (Greater)
WITHINS RESERVOIR Manchester (Greater)

MANNINGTREE

ALTON WATER RESERVOIR Suffolk

MANSFIELD

HARWICK HALL LAKES Nottinghamshire
L-LAKE FISHERY Nottinghamshire
MAUN (RIVER) Nottinghamshire
SHERWOOD FOREST FARM PARK FISHERY Nottinghamshire
SUTTON LAWN DAM Nottinghamshire

MARBLETHORPE

OHAM LAKES Lincolnshire

MARCH

FIELDS END WATER Cambridgeshire
VIRGINIA LAKE Cambridgeshire

MARHAMCHURCH

BUDE CANAL Cornwall

MARKET DRAYTON

BACHE POOL Shropshire
MILL HOUSE LAKES Shropshire
SHROPSHIRE UNION CANAL Shropshire
TERN (RIVER) Shropshire
TERN FISHERIES Shropshire
ASHLEY POOLS Staffordshire

MARKET HARBOROUGH

BROOK MEADOW FISHERY Leicestershire
EYEBROOK TROUT FISHERY Leicestershire
FOLLY POND Leicestershire
WELLAND LODGE FISHERY Leicestershire

MARKET RASEN

CLAYBRIDGE TROUT LAKES Lincolnshire
FISH POND FARM Lincolnshire
GOLTHO LAKE Lincolnshire
HATTON TROUT LAKE Lincolnshire
LOBBY FIELD PONDS Lincolnshire
NORTH KELSEY PARK Lincolnshire
ST EAU FISHING SYNDICATE Lincolnshire
TOFT NEWTON TROUT FISHERY Lincolnshire

MARKET WEIGHTON

MARKET WEIGHTON CANAL Yorkshire (North)

MARLBOROUGH

KENNET AND AVON CANAL Wiltshire
SABRE AND SWORDS LAKES Wiltshire

MARLIAS

MARLIAS (RIVER) Herefordshire

MARLOW

BACKWATER Buckinghamshire
THAMES (RIVER) Buckinghamshire
WESTFIELD FARM Buckinghamshire

MARSDEN

HOLME MILL DAM (SQUARE DAM) Yorkshire (West)

MARSTON

BUDWORTH MERE Cheshire

MARSWORTH

AYLESBURY ARM CANAL Hertfordshire
GRAND UNION CANAL Hertfordshire

MARTHAM

MARTHAM PITS Norfolk

MARTLEY

TEME (RIVER) Worcestershire
WITLEY POOLS Worcestershire

MARTOCK

ASHMEAD LAKES Somerset

MARYPORT

ELLEN (RIVER) Cumbria
KNOTT END TARN Cumbria

MASHAM

LEIGHTON RESERVOIR Yorkshire (North)

MATLOCK

ALTON MANOR FARM Derbyshire
DERWENT (RIVER) Derbyshire
SYDNOPE FISHERIES Derbyshire
TRENT (RIVER) Derbyshire
WYE (RIVER) Derbyshire

MELBOURNE

MELBOURNE POOL Derbyshire

MELKSHAM

AVON (BRISTOL) (RIVER) Wiltshire
AVON (RIVER) Wiltshire
BRISTOL AVON Wiltshire
BURBROOKS RESERVOIR Wiltshire
KENNET AND AVON CANAL Wiltshire

MELTON

BREAKAWAY PIT Suffolk

MELTON CONSTABLE

GUNTHORPE HALL LAKE Norfolk

MELTON MOWBRAY

BROOKSBY COLLEGE Leicestershire

- **HALL FARM FISHING** Leicestershire
- **HOLWELL WORKS RESERVOIR** Leicestershire
- **WREAKE (RIVER)** Leicestershire

MERE
- **TURNERS PADDOCK LAKE** Wiltshire

MEXBOROUGH
- **DEARNE (RIVER)** Yorkshire (South)
- **MEXBOROUGH CANAL** Yorkshire (South)
- **OLD DEARNE (RIVER)** Yorkshire (South)
- **SHEFFIELD AND SOUTH YORKSHIRE NAVIGATION** Yorkshire (South)

MICKLEY
- **TYNE (RIVER)** Yorkshire (North)

MIDDLEHAM
- **URE (RIVER)** Yorkshire (North)

MIDDLESBROUGH
- **ASCOTT PONDS** Cleveland
- **CHARLTONS PONDS** Cleveland
- **HEMLINGTON LAKE** Cleveland
- **HUTTON RUDBY PONDS** Cleveland
- **LOCKE PARK** Cleveland
- **WHITEHOUSE CARAVAN PARK LAKE** Cleveland
- **TEES (RIVER)** Tyne and Wear

MIDDLESEX
- **ENFIELD LOCK** London (Greater)

MIDDLETON
- **ALEXANDRA PARK** Manchester (Greater)
- **MYRTLE ROAD LODGES** Manchester (Greater)
- **RHODES LODGE** Manchester (Greater)
- **STAKEHILL LODGES** Manchester (Greater)

MIDDLETON IN TEESDALE
- **SELSET RESERVOIR** County Durham
- **TEES (RIVER)** County Durham

MIDDLETON ONE ROW
- **TEES (RIVER)** County Durham

MIDDLEWICH
- **BRERTON QUARRY** Cheshire
- **BYLEY FISHERIES** Cheshire
- **DANE (RIVER)** Cheshire
- **TETTON FLASH** Cheshire
- **TETTON LAKE** Cheshire
- **VALE ROYAL LOCKS** Cheshire
- **WEAVER (RIVER)** Cheshire

MIDENHALL
- **LARK (RIVER)** Suffolk

MIDFORD
- **AVON (RIVER)** Somerset

MIDHURST
- **NEW POND** Sussex (West)
- **ROTHER (RIVER)** Sussex (West)
- **ROTHERFIELD POND** Sussex (West)
- **WESTERN ROTHER** Sussex (West)

MILFORD
- **BUSBRIDGE LAKE** Surrey
- **JOHNSONS LAKE** Surrey

MILLOM
- **ANNAS (RIVER)** Cumbria
- **ANNAS STREAM** Cumbria
- **BAYSTONE BANK RESERVIOR** Cumbria
- **LAZY (RIVER)** Cumbria
- **BLACK BECK (RIVER)** Manchester (Greater)

MILNTHORPE
- **BELA STREAM** Cumbria

MILTON ABBOT
- **TAMAR (RIVER)** Devon

MILTON KEYNES
- **ALDERS FARM TROUT FISHERY** Buckinghamshire
- **BOURTON FISHERIES** Buckinghamshire
- **BOWLERS CANAL** Buckinghamshire
- **CHURCH HILL FISHERY** Buckinghamshire
- **COSGROVE LEISURE PARK** Buckinghamshire
- **DOVECOTE LAKE FISHERY** Buckinghamshire
- **FURZTON LAKE** Buckinghamshire
- **GRAND UNION CANAL** Buckinghamshire
- **GREAT OUSE (RIVER)** Buckinghamshire
- **KINGFISHER GOLF CLUB** Buckinghamshire
- **LODGE LAKES** Buckinghamshire
- **LOUGHTON LODGE LAKE** Buckinghamshire
- **OUSE (RIVER)** Buckinghamshire
- **OUZEL (RIVER)** Buckinghamshire
- **SNOWBERRY** Buckinghamshire
- **TEARDROP LAKES** Buckinghamshire
- **TINGRITH LAKES** Buckinghamshire
- **VICARAGE SPINNEY TROUT FISHERY** Buckinghamshire
- **WOLVERTON LAKES** Buckinghamshire
- **SILVER LAKE** Northamptonshire

MINEHEAD
- **WATERSMEET AND GLENTHORNE FISHERIES** Devon
- **HORNER WATER** Somerset

MINSTEAD
- **JANESMOOR POND** Hampshire

MIRFIELD
- **HOPTON WATERS** Yorkshire (West)

MITCHAM
- **ONE ISLAND POND** Surrey
- **SEVEN ISLANDS** Surrey

MITCHELDEAN
- **PLUMP HILL POOL** Gloucestershire

MOLESEY
- **MOLESEY LOCK** Surrey

MONMOUTH
- **STEAM MILLS LAKE** Gloucestershire

MONTFORD BRIDGE
- **SEVERN (RIVER)** Shropshire

MOOR MONKTON
- **NIDD (RIVER)** Yorkshire (North)

MOORDOWN
- **STOUR (DORSET) (RIVER)** Dorset

MORDIFORD
- **MONTE BISHOP** Herefordshire

MORECAMBE
- **LITTLE DALE HALL COARSE FISHERY** Lancashire
- **SWANTLEY LAKE** Lancashire

MORETON-IN-MARSH
- **COURT FARM** Gloucestershire
- **LEMINGTON LAKES** Gloucestershire

MORPETH
- **COQUET (RIVER)** Northumberland
- **FELTON FENCE FARM PONDS** Northumberland
- **FONTBURN RESERVOIR** Northumberland
- **PLESSEY WOODS** Northumberland
- **WANSBECK (RIVER)** Northumberland
- **WANSBECK STREAM** Northumberland

MOULTON
- **SHOBROOKE PARK** Devon

MUCH WELOCK
- **LOWER HILL FARM** Shropshire

MUCH WENLOCK
- **BROCKTON GRANGE** Shropshire
- **LOWER HILL FARM** Shropshire
- **SEVERN (RIVER)** Shropshire

MUNDESLEY
- **GIMINGHAM LAKES** Norfolk

MYLOR
- **MYLOR ANGLING LAKES** Cornwall

NABURN
- **OUSE (RIVER)** Yorkshire (North)

NAILBRIDGE
- **MEADOWCLIFFE POOL** Gloucestershire

NANTWICH
- **BADDILEY RESERVOIR** Cheshire
- **BETLEY MERE** Cheshire
- **BREAM HOLE** Cheshire
- **HACK GREEN LAKE** Cheshire
- **HARTHILL** Cheshire
- **LLANGOLLEN CANAL** Cheshire
- **MIDDLEWICH BRANCH CANAL** Cheshire
- **REASEHEATH COLLEGE LAKE** Cheshire
- **SWANLEY** Cheshire

NARBOROUGH
- **SOVEREIGN LAKES** Norfolk

NASEBY
- **NASEBY RESERVOIR** Northamptonshire

NAYLAND
- **STOUR (SUFFOLK) (RIVER)** Essex

NAZEING
- **NAZEING MEADS** Essex

NELSON
- **BARROWFORD RESERVOIR** Lancashire
- **BLACKMOSS RESERVOIR** Lancashire
- **INGS FARM TROUT FISHERY** Lancashire
- **PENDLE WATER** Lancashire
- **ROUGHLEE TROUT FISHERY** Lancashire
- **WALVERDEN RESERVOIR** Lancashire
- **WHITEMOOR RESERVOIR** Lancashire

NESTON
- **BURTON MERE FISHERIES** Cheshire

NETHERFIELD
- **TRENT (RIVER)** Nottinghamshire

NETTLEBED
- **THAME (RIVER)** Oxfordshire

NEW MILTON
- **HORDLE LAKES** Hampshire
- **ORCHARD LAKES** Hampshire

NEW ROMNEY
- **ROYAL MILITARY CANAL** Kent

NEWARK
- **A1 PITS** Nottinghamshire

- **CRANWELL LANE TROUT FISHERY** Nottinghamshire
- **CROMWELL LAKE TROUT FISHERY** Nottinghamshire
- **FLEET (RIVER)** Nottinghamshire
- **SAPPHIRE LAKES** Nottinghamshire
- **SMEATONS LAKES** Nottinghamshire
- **TRENT (RIVER)** Nottinghamshire
- **WHARFE (RIVER)** Nottinghamshire
- **WINDMILL FARM LAKES** Nottinghamshire
- **WITHAM (RIVER)** Nottinghamshire

NEWARK-ON-TRENT

- **TRENT (RIVER)** Nottinghamshire

NEWBURN

- **TYNE (RIVER)** Tyne and Wear
- **TYNE (RIVER)** Tyne and Wear

NEWBURY

- **BENS LAKE** Berkshire
- **BISHOPS GREEN FARM LAKE** Berkshire
- **FORBURY FARM LAKES** Berkshire
- **FROBURY FARM SPORTING CLUB** Berkshire
- **HAMBRIDGE LANE** Berkshire
- **KENNET (RIVER)** Berkshire
- **KENNET (RIVER)** Berkshire
- **KENNET AND AVON CANAL** Berkshire
- **NEWBURY TROUT LAKES** Berkshire
- **THAMES (RIVER)** Berkshire
- **WYLIES LAKE** Berkshire

NEWCASTLE UPON TYNE

- **TYNE (RIVER)** Northumberland
- **BIG WATERS** Tyne and Wear
- **BOLAM LAKE COUNTRY PARK** Tyne and Wear
- **BRENKLEY POND** Tyne and Wear
- **DISSINGTON POND** Tyne and Wear
- **KILLINGWORTH LAKE** Tyne and Wear
- **LEAZES PARK LAKE** Tyne and Wear
- **LITTLE BIG WATER** Tyne and Wear
- **MAIN TYNE** Tyne and Wear
- **MARDEN QUARRY** Tyne and Wear
- **MILKHOPE POND** Tyne and Wear
- **RED BARNS POND** Tyne and Wear
- **REDE (RIVER)** Tyne and Wear
- **SWEETHOPE LOUGHS** Tyne and Wear
- **THROCKLEY REIGH** Tyne and Wear
- **TYNE (RIVER)** Tyne and Wear
- **WHITTLE DENE TROUT FISHERY** Tyne and Wear

NEWCASTLE-UNDER-LYME

- **BROWNING CUDMORE FISHERY** Staffordshire
- **HANCHURCH FISHERIES** Staffordshire
- **LAWTON HALL POOL** Staffordshire
- **MADELEY POOL** Staffordshire

NEWICK

- **OUSE (RIVER)** Sussex (East)

NEWMARKET

- **LARK (RIVER)** Suffolk

NEWPORT

- **BROOMFLEET PONDS** Humberside
- **FISH TRADES POND** Humberside
- **REDFERNS POND** Humberside
- **WOODALLS POND** Humberside
- **GILLEES POND** Isle of Wight
- **GUNVILLE LAKE** Isle of Wight
- **HALE MANOR LAKES** Isle of Wight
- **ISLAND FISH FARM AND MEADOW LAKES** Isle of Wight
- **MERSTONE FISHERIES** Isle of Wight
- **SOMERTON RESERVOIR** Isle of Wight
- **AQUALATE MERE** Shropshire
- **MEESE (RIVER)** Shropshire
- **LOYNTON TROUT FISHERIES** Staffordshire

NEWPORT PAGNELL

- **GREAT LINFORD LAKES** Buckinghamshire
- **NEWPORT PAGNELL GRAVEL PITS** Buckinghamshire
- **TYRINGHAM ESTATE** Buckinghamshire
- **VICARAGE SPINNEY TROUT FISHERY** Buckinghamshire

NEWQUAY

- **AVALLON HOLIDAY PARK** Cornwall
- **FULL BAG FISHERY** Cornwall
- **GOONHAVERN COARSE FISHING LAKE** Cornwall
- **GWINEAR POOLS COARSE FISHERY** Cornwall
- **GWINNEAR POOLS** Cornwall
- **MELANHYL LAKE** Cornwall
- **OAKSIDE FISHERY** Cornwall
- **PENVOSE FARM** Cornwall
- **PORTH RESERVOIR** Cornwall
- **TREBELLAN PARK LAKES** Cornwall
- **TRETHIGGEY FARM POND** Cornwall
- **TREVELLA CARAVAN AND CAMPING PARK** Cornwall
- **WHITEACRES COUNTRY PARK** Cornwall

NEWTON

- **POPPLETON (RIVER)** Yorkshire (North)

NEWTON ABBOT

- **ABBROOK POND** Devon
- **DORES POND - RACKERHAYES** Devon
- **EDDISON POND** Devon
- **FERNWORTHY RESERVOIR** Devon
- **FINLAKE PONDS** Devon
- **INDIO POND** Devon
- **ISLAND POND - RACKERHAYES** Devon
- **NEWTON ABBOT SPRING PONDS** Devon
- **ROCOMBE PONDS** Devon
- **RUB - A - DUB POND** Devon
- **SAWMILLS LAKE** Devon
- **TEIGN (RIVER)** Devon
- **TRAGO MILLS** Devon
- **TRENCHFORD RESERVOIR** Devon
- **VENFORD RESERVOIR** Devon
- **WAPPERWELL POND** Devon
- **WATERCRESS FARM TROUT FISHERY** Devon

NEWTON AYCLIFFE

- **AYCLIFFE LAKE** County Durham

NEWTON-LE-WILLOWS

- **WOODHOUSE FISH FARM** Merseyside

NEWTOWN UPON DERWENT

- **DERWENT (RIVER)** Humberside

NIBLEY

- **GREAT BURROWS TROUT FISHERY** Gloucestershire

NORHAM

- **TWEED (RIVER)** Northumberland

NORTH CAMP

- **HOLLYBUSH LANE LAKES** Hampshire

NORTH FRODINGHAM

- **LANGHOLME FISHERIES** Humberside

NORTH HYKEHAM

- **WHISBY GARDEN CENTRE** Lincolnshire

NORTH KELSEY

- **NORTH KELSEY PARK** Lincolnshire

NORTH MUSKHAM

- **A1 PITS** Nottinghamshire

NORTH PETHERTON

- **SEDGES** Somerset
- **TAUNTON TO BRIDGWATER CANAL** Somerset

NORTH SOMERCOTES

- **WARREN POND** Lincolnshire

NORTH THORESBY

- **NORTH THORESBY FISHERIES** Humberside

NORTH TYNESIDE

- **KILLINGWORTH LAKE** Tyne and Wear

NORTH WOOTTON

- **BABINGLEY (RIVER)** Norfolk
- **CASTLE RISING STREAM** Norfolk

NORTHALLERTON

- **BEDALE BECK** Yorkshire (North)
- **CORNHILL PONDS** Yorkshire (North)
- **HAZEL HALL FARM FISHING** Yorkshire (North)
- **HOLLINGWOOD FISHERY** Yorkshire (North)
- **KIPLIN TROUT FISHERY** Yorkshire (North)
- **LANGTON POND** Yorkshire (North)
- **LEEMING (RIVER)** Yorkshire (North)
- **PARKLANDS** Yorkshire (North)
- **ROLIETH FISHERY** Yorkshire (North)
- **STONEBRIDGE LAKES** Yorkshire (North)
- **STONEY LANE PONDS** Yorkshire (North)
- **SWALE (RIVER)** Yorkshire (North)
- **TONTINE LAKE** Yorkshire (North)

NORTHAMPTON

- **ABINGDON PARK LAKE** Northamptonshire
- **BILLING AQUADROME** Northamptonshire
- **BLUE LAGOON** Northamptonshire
- **CASTLE ASHBY LAKES** Northamptonshire
- **CRESCENT LAKE** Northamptonshire
- **DELEPRE PARK LAKE** Northamptonshire
- **DUSTON RESERVOIR** Northamptonshire
- **ECTON GRAVEL PITS** Northamptonshire
- **FOXHOLES FISHERIES** Northamptonshire
- **GLEBE LAKE** Northamptonshire
- **GRAND UNION CANAL** Northamptonshire
- **GRENDON LAKES** Northamptonshire
- **HARDWATER LAKE** Northamptonshire
- **HEYFORD FISHERY** Northamptonshire
- **HOLLOWELL RESERVOIR** Northamptonshire
- **MENAGERIE POND** Northamptonshire
- **NASEBY RESERVOIR** Northamptonshire
- **NENE (RIVER)** Northamptonshire
- **NORTHAMPTON JUNCTION CANAL** Northamptonshire
- **PITSFORD RESERVOIR** Northamptonshire
- **RAVENSTHORPE TROUT FISHERY** Northamptonshire
- **SHELFLEYS LAKE** Northamptonshire
- **ST JAMES SMALL PARK LAKE** Northamptonshire

SULBY RESERVOIR Northamptonshire
SYWELL RESERVOIR Northamptonshire
WEEDON ROAD GRAVEL PIT Northamptonshire
WELFORD RESERVOIR Northamptonshire
WOOTTON BROOK LAKE Northamptonshire

NORTHMOOR

THAMES (RIVER) Oxfordshire

NORTHWICH

ANTROBUS LAKES Cheshire
BELMONT POOL Cheshire
BILLINGE GREEN Cheshire
BLAKEMERE Cheshire
BROOKSIDE LAKES Cheshire
BUDWORTH MERE Cheshire
BYLEY FISHERIES Cheshire
CANAL PIT Cheshire
CISTERNS Cheshire
DANE RIVERSIDE FISHERY Cheshire
FARM POOL Cheshire
FLUSHING MEADOWS FISHERY Cheshire
FOUNDERS POOL Cheshire
FRIARS POOL Cheshire
GREAT BUDWORTH MERE LAKE Cheshire
LYMM VALE Cheshire
MONKS MOAT Cheshire
NEW POOL Cheshire
OAK POOL Cheshire
PETTY POOL Cheshire
ROOKERY POOL Cheshire
SHAKERLEY MERE Cheshire
SHIPBROOK FLASH Cheshire
SPRING POOL Cheshire
VALE ROYAL LOCKS Cheshire
WEAVER (RIVER) Cheshire
WILLOW POOL Cheshire
WINCHAM BROOK Cheshire
WINNINGTON POOL Cheshire
WITTON BROOK Cheshire
YEW TREE POOL Cheshire

NORWICH

ABBOTS HALL Norfolk
ACLE (RIVER) Norfolk
BARFORD LAKES FISHERY Norfolk
BARNINGHAM HALL LAKE Norfolk
BARTLES LODGE Norfolk
BAWBURGH LAKES Norfolk
BILLINGFORD PIT Norfolk
BLICKLING PARK LAKE Norfolk
BOOTON CLAY PIT Norfolk
BORE VALLEY LAKES Norfolk
BURE (RIVER) Norfolk
CANTLEY (RIVER) Norfolk
CANTLEY SUGAR FACTORY Norfolk
CATCH 22 FISHERY Norfolk
CHAPEL ROAD LAKE Norfolk
CHARITY LAKES Norfolk
COBBLEACRES LAKES Norfolk
COLTON LAKE Norfolk
COSTESSEY PITS Norfolk
DISS MERE Norfolk
DRAYTON GREEN (RIVER) Norfolk
FELMINGHAM MILL LAKES Norfolk
FELTHORPE LAKE Norfolk
GIMINGHAM LAKES Norfolk
GLEN MERE Norfolk
GREAT MELTON FISHERY Norfolk
HADDISCOE PIT Norfolk
HARDLEY MARSHES Norfolk
HAVERINGLAND HALL PARK Norfolk
HEVINGHAM LAKES Norfolk
HICKLING BROAD Norfolk
HINGHAM FISHMERE Norfolk
HORNING (RIVER) Norfolk
KINGFISHER LAKES Norfolk
LENWADE COMMON LAKES Norfolk
LENWADE TROUT FISHERY Norfolk
LITTLE DUNHAM CARP LAKES Norfolk
LYNG PIT Norfolk
MILL FARM FISHERY Norfolk
NATURES HAVEN LAKES Norfolk
PARK LIME PIT Norfolk
RACKHEATH SPRINGS Norfolk
RAILWAY LAKE Norfolk
RECTORY FARM FISHERY Norfolk
REEPHAM FISHERY LAKES Norfolk
RINGLAND LAKES Norfolk
RINGLAND PITS Norfolk
ROCKLAND BROAD Norfolk
RUSTON REACHES Norfolk
SCOULTON MERE Norfolk
SHALLOW BROOK LAKES Norfolk
SHORT PLANTATION LAKE Norfolk
SNETTERTON PITS Norfolk
TASWOOD LAKES FISH FARM AND FISHERY Norfolk
TAVERHAM Norfolk
TAVERHAM MILLS FISHERY Norfolk
UNIVERSITY BROAD Norfolk
WENSUM (RIVER) Norfolk
WROXHAM BROAD Norfolk
YARE (RIVER) Norfolk

NOTTINGHAM

MAPPERLEY RESERVOIR Derbyshire
ATTENBOROUGH GRAVEL PITS Nottinghamshire
BESTWOOD POND Nottinghamshire
COLWICK COUNTRY PARK Nottinghamshire
COVERT SPRINGS FISHERIES Nottinghamshire
CRANFLEET CANAL Nottinghamshire
DOLAR POND Nottinghamshire
EREWASH CANAL Nottinghamshire
GRANTHAM CANAL Nottinghamshire
HOLME PIERPOINT Nottinghamshire
IRONMONGERS POND Nottinghamshire
NOTTINGHAM CANAL Nottinghamshire
NOTTINGHAM CASTLE MARINA Nottinghamshire
PINDERS PONDS Nottinghamshire
TRENT (RIVER) Nottinghamshire
WINFIELD LAGOON Nottinghamshire

NUN MONKTON

NUN MONKTON (RIVER) Yorkshire (North)

NUNEATON

ASHBY CANAL Warwickshire
BOSWORTH PARK LAKE Warwickshire
BOSWORTH WATER TRUST AND FRIEZELAND POOLS Warwickshire
COVENTRY CANAL Warwickshire
GARDEN FARM FISHERIES Warwickshire

NUTLEY

BORINGWHEEL TROUT FISHERY Sussex (East)
PIPPINGFORD PARK ESTATE LAKES Sussex (East)

OAKHAM

RUTLAND WATER Leicestershire
NORMANTON FISHING LODGE Rutland
SWEETHEDGES FARM FISHERY Rutland
WELLAND (RIVER) Rutland

OATFIELD

GLOUCESTER CANAL Gloucestershire

OATH

PARRETT (RIVER) Somerset

OFFORD

OFFORD CLUNY Cambridgeshire

OKEHAMPTON

ALDER LAKE Devon
ANGLERS ELDORADO Devon
ANGLERS PARADISE Devon
ANGLERS SHANGRILA Devon
BLUE LAKE Devon
LEGGE FARM COARSE FISHERY Devon
MELDON RESERVOIR Devon
ROADFORD RESERVOIR Devon
SOUTH HAY FARM Devon
SOUTH REED FISHERIES CARP LAKE Devon
SPIRES LAKES Devon
STONE FARM QUARRY Devon
TOTTIFORD RESERVOIR Devon

OLDHAM

BRADFORD RESERVOIR Lancashire
ALEXANDRA PARK Manchester (Greater)
BLACK MOSS RESERVOIR Manchester (Greater)
BRUN CLOUGH RESERVOIR Manchester (Greater)
DOWRY AND NEW YEARS BRIDGE RESERVOIR Manchester (Greater)
HUDDERSFIELD NARROW CANAL Manchester (Greater)
KITCLIFFE RESERVOIR Manchester (Greater)
LITTLE SEA RESERVOIR Manchester (Greater)
LOWER CASTLESHAW RESERVOIR Manchester (Greater)
OLDHAM FLY FISHING Manchester (Greater)
REDBROOK RESERVOIR Manchester (Greater)
ROYAL GEORGE MILL COMPLEX Manchester (Greater)
TAME (RIVER) Manchester (Greater)
TANNERS DAM Manchester (Greater)
CASTLESHAW (LOWER) RESERVOIR Oldham

OLNEY

GREAT OUSE (RIVER) Bedfordshire
OUSE (RIVER) Bedfordshire
BOWLERS CANAL Buckinghamshire
GREAT OUSE (RIVER) Buckinghamshire
OUSE (RIVER) Buckinghamshire

OMBERSLEY

SEVERN (RIVER) Worcestershire

ONGAR

BIRDS GREEN Essex
GREAT MYLES LAKE Essex
PARSONAGE FARM Essex
RODING (RIVER) Essex

ONLEY

OUSE (RIVER) Buckinghamshire

ORMSKIRK

BARRETTS FARM FISHERY Lancashire
BURSCOUGH BRICKWORKS LAKE Lancashire
GREEN LANE PONDS Lancashire
LEEDS TO LIVERPOOL CANAL Lancashire
PLATTS LANE LAKE Lancashire
RUFFORD CANAL Lancashire

ORPINGTON
- **DARENT (RIVER)** Kent
- **LONGFORD LAKE** Kent
- **RUXLEY PITS** Kent
- **BROOMWOOD LAKE** London (Greater)

ORRELL
- **ORRELL WATER PARK** Lancashire

ORTON
- **PINFOLD LAKE** Cumbria

OSBASTON
- **MONNOW (RIVER)** Leicestershire

OSSETT
- **WALTON HALL TROUT LAKE** Yorkshire (West)

OSWESTRY
- **LAKE VYRNWY** Shropshire
- **LLORAN GANOL FARM** Shropshire
- **PERRY (RIVER)** Shropshire
- **SEVERN (RIVER)** Shropshire
- **TANAT (RIVER)** Shropshire
- **TURFMOOR FISHERY** Shropshire
- **VOWNOG FISH LAKE** Shropshire
- **VYRNWY (RIVER)** Shropshire

OTLEY
- **KNOTFORD LAGOON** Yorkshire (West)
- **SWINSTY AND FEWSTON RESERVOIRS** Yorkshire (West)
- **WHARFE (RIVER)** Yorkshire (West)

OTTERBURN
- **REDE (RIVER)** Tyne and Wear

OULTON
- **OULTON DYKE** Suffolk
- **AIRE AND CALDER CANAL** Yorkshire (West)

OUNDLE
- **BARNWELL COUNTRY PARK** Cambridgeshire
- **NENE (RIVER)** Cambridgeshire
- **OUNDLE (RIVER)** Cambridgeshire
- **PERIO MILL** Cambridgeshire

OUTWELL
- **MIDDLE LEVEL DRAIN** Cambridgeshire

OXFORD
- **BARNES TROUT LAKES** Oxfordshire
- **BEIRTON LAKES** Oxfordshire
- **CHERWELL (RIVER)** Oxfordshire
- **CHRISTCHURCH LAKE** Oxfordshire
- **CORNBURY PARK FISHERY** Oxfordshire
- **FARMOOR TROUT FISHERY** Oxfordshire
- **GOLDFISH BOWL (THE)** Oxfordshire
- **GRAND UNION CANAL** Oxfordshire
- **MANOR HOUSE** Oxfordshire
- **MANOR LAKE** Oxfordshire
- **MILTON POOLS FARM** Oxfordshire
- **OXFORD CANAL** Oxfordshire
- **ROLFS LAKE** Oxfordshire
- **SANDFORD LOCK** Oxfordshire
- **SEVERALLS FARM A AND B** Oxfordshire
- **THAMES (RIVER)** Oxfordshire

OXTED
- **COLTSFORD MILL FISHERY** Surrey

PADDOCK WOOD
- **GEDGES LAKES** Kent
- **SILVER SPRINGS FISHERY** Kent

PAIGNTON
- **NEW BARN ANGLING CENTRE** Devon
- **TOWN PARKS COARSE FISHERY** Devon

PATELEY BRIDGE
- **SCAR HOUSE RESERVOIR** Yorkshire (North)

PATTERDALE
- **ULLSWATER LAKE** Cumbria

PELSALL
- **CANNOCK EXTENSION CANAL** Midlands (west)

PENDLE
- **COLDWELL (LOWER) RESERVOIR** Lancashire
- **LANESHAW RESERVOIR** Lancashire

PENKRIDGE
- **PILLATON POOLS** Staffordshire
- **WILLOWS POOLS** Staffordshire

PENRITH
- **AIRA BECK** Cumbria
- **BLENCARN LAKE** Cumbria
- **CROSSFIELD FISHERY** Cumbria
- **DACRE BECK** Cumbria
- **EAMONT (RIVER)** Cumbria
- **EDEN VALLEY TROUT LAKE** Cumbria
- **HAWESWATER** Cumbria
- **KENTMERE FISHERY** Cumbria
- **KIRKBY THORE (RIVER)** Cumbria
- **LOWTHER (RIVER)** Cumbria
- **LUNE (RIVER)** Cumbria
- **PINFOLD LAKE** Cumbria
- **ULLSWATER LAKE** Cumbria
- **WHINS POND** Cumbria

PENRYN
- **ARGAL RESERVOIR** Cornwall
- **CONSTANTINE BROOK** Cornwall
- **LAKE PENRYN** Cornwall

PENSHURST
- **EDEN (RIVER)** Kent

PENZANCE
- **AMALWHIDDEN FARM** Cornwall
- **BOSCATHNOE RESERVOIR** Cornwall
- **CHOONE FARM** Cornwall
- **CHYRAISE LODGE HOTEL** Cornwall
- **DRIFT RESERVOIR** Cornwall
- **MILLPOOL FISHERIES** Cornwall
- **ST ERTH FISHERY** Cornwall
- **ST TINNEY FARM HOLIDAYS** Cornwall
- **TIN DENE FISHERY** Cornwall
- **WOONSMITH LAKE** Cornwall

PERRANPORTH
- **BOLINGEY LAKE** Cornwall
- **ROSEWATER LAKE** Cornwall

PERSHORE
- **AVON (RIVER)** Worcestershire
- **FOREST FARM** Worcestershire
- **WARWICKSHIRE AVON** Worcestershire

PETERBOROUGH
- **BARNWELL COUNTRY PARK** Cambridgeshire
- **BIGGIN LAKE** Cambridgeshire
- **BLUEBELL LAKE** Cambridgeshire
- **COTTERSTOCK RIVER** Cambridgeshire
- **CROWLAND ANGLING CLUB LAKES** Cambridgeshire
- **DECOY LAKE** Cambridgeshire
- **ELDERNELL LAKE** Cambridgeshire
- **FERRY MEADOWS** Cambridgeshire
- **GERARDS CARP LAKE** Cambridgeshire
- **GUNWADE LAKE** Cambridgeshire
- **KINGFISHER LAKE** Cambridgeshire
- **KINGSLAND RESERVOIRS** Cambridgeshire
- **MALEY GRAVEL PITS** Cambridgeshire
- **NENE (RIVER)** Cambridgeshire
- **NENE NORTH BANK (RIVER)** Cambridgeshire
- **NORTH BANK TROUT FISHERY** Cambridgeshire
- **NORTHEY PARK FISHERY** Cambridgeshire
- **OUNDLE (RIVER)** Cambridgeshire
- **PERIO MILL** Cambridgeshire
- **RAILWAY LAKES** Cambridgeshire
- **REDLANDS PITS** Cambridgeshire
- **SAND MARTIN LAKE** Cambridgeshire
- **SIBSON FISHERIES** Cambridgeshire
- **SWAN LAKE** Cambridgeshire
- **TWENTY FOOT DRAIN** Cambridgeshire
- **WANSFORD STREAM** Cambridgeshire
- **WERRINGTON LAKE** Cambridgeshire
- **WHITE HOUSE TROUT FARM** Cambridgeshire
- **WHITTLESEY DYKE/ BEVILLS LEAM** Cambridgeshire
- **WILLOW CREEK** Cambridgeshire
- **WILLOW LAKE** Cambridgeshire
- **WOOD POOL** Cambridgeshire
- **YARWELL MILL LAKE** Cambridgeshire

PETERLEE
- **SHOTTON POND** County Durham
- **WELLFIELD POND** County Durham

PETERSFIELD
- **BARONS PONDS (NEW SITE)** Hampshire
- **MEON SPRINGS FLY FISHERY** Hampshire
- **MOORHEN FARM TROUT LAKE** Hampshire
- **PETERSFIELD HEATH LAKE** Hampshire
- **STEPSTONES LAKES** Hampshire

PETWORTH
- **ARUN (RIVER)** Sussex (West)
- **BLACKWOOL TROUT FISHERY** Sussex (West)
- **BURTON MILL POND** Sussex (West)
- **DUNCTON MILL** Sussex (West)
- **LECONFIELD ESTATE** Sussex (West)
- **WESTERN ROTHER (RIVER)** Sussex (West)

PEVENSEY
- **SHARNFOLD FARM FISHERY** Sussex (East)
- **WALLERS HAVEN** Sussex (East)

PEVENSEY BAY
- **PEVENSEY HAVEN** Sussex (East)

PEWSEY
- **KENNET AND AVON CANAL** Wiltshire
- **KENNET AND AVON CANAL** Wiltshire

PICKERING
- **HAZELHEAD LAKE** Yorkshire (North)
- **PICKERING PARK FISHING LAKE** Yorkshire (North)
- **PICKERING TROUT LAKE** Yorkshire (North)
- **WELHAM LAKE** Yorkshire (North)

PINNER
- **BATCHWORTH LAKE** Hertfordshire

PLATT BRIDGE
- **BRYN FLASH** Lancashire

PLYMOUTH
- **PORT ELLIOT LAKE** Cornwall
- **ST GERMANS LAKE** Cornwall

WOODLAY HOLIDAY LAKES Cornwall
ALDER LAKE Devon
BICKERTON FARM FISHERY Devon
BURRATOR RESERVOIR Devon
CADOVER BRIDGE PITS Devon
COOMBE FISHERIES Devon
DRAKELANDS GAME FISHERY Devon
PLYM (RIVER) Devon
SLAPTON LEY NATIONAL NATURE RESERVE Devon
SUNRIDGE FISHERY Devon
UPPER YEALM FISHERY Devon

POCKLINGTON

FOGGLESKYTE WATERS Yorkshire (North)
POCKLINGTON CANAL Yorkshire (North)

POLEGATE

ARLINGTON TROUT FISHERY Sussex (East)
CUCKMERE (RIVER) Sussex (East)
CUCKMERE (RIVER) Sussex (East)

POLESWORTH

ANKER (RIVER) Staffordshire

PONSANOOTH

TORY FARM LAKE Cornwall

PONTEFRACT

ACKTON POND Yorkshire (West)
HOYLE MILL DAM Yorkshire (West)
PONTEFRACT PARK LAKE Yorkshire (West)

PONTELAND

DISSINGTON POND Tyne and Wear

PONTESBURY

SPRING LEE Shropshire

POOLE

HAMWORTHY LAKE Dorset
STOUR (DORSET) (RIVER) Dorset
STOUR (DORSET) (RIVER) Dorset
WESSEX WATER RESERVOIRS Dorset

POPPLETON

NEWTON RIVER Yorkshire (North)

PORTSMOUTH

BAFFINS POND Hampshire
BROCKHURST MOAT Hampshire
BROWNWICH POND Hampshire
HILSEA MOATS Hampshire
HMS DRYAD LAKE Hampshire
ROOKLEY COUNTRY PARK Isle of Wight

POTTERS BAR

HOOK LAKE Hertfordshire

POYNTON

POYNTON POOL Manchester (Greater)

PRESCOT

CARR LANE POOL Merseyside

PRESTON

BANNISTER HALL FARM Lancashire
BARNSFOLD WATERS Lancashire
BLACKMOSS RESERVOIR Lancashire
BRIARCROFT FISHERY Lancashire
CHURN CLOUGH RESERVOIR Lancashire
CLAYLANDS CARAVAN SITE Lancashire
CLEVELEY BRIDGE FISHERY Lancashire
COPTHORNE COARSE FISHERIES Lancashire
COTTAGE GREEN GARDEN CENTRE Lancashire
CUERDEN VALLEY LAKE Lancashire
DERWENT (RIVER) Lancashire
DILWORTH (UPPER) RESERVOIR Lancashire
ERIC FISHWICK NATURE RESERVE Lancashire
FARINGTON LODGES Lancashire
GREAT BIRCH WOOD PONDS Lancashire
GREENHALGH LODGE FISHERY Lancashire
GRIMSARGH RESERVOIR Lancashire
GRIZEDALE LEA RESERVOIR Lancashire
HUDSONS FARM Lancashire
IRWELL (RIVER) Lancashire
KNIGHT BOTTOMS LAKE Lancashire
LANCASTER CANAL Lancashire
LEEDS TO LIVERPOOL CANAL Lancashire
LEISURE LAKES Lancashire
LONGTON BRICKCROFT Lancashire
LYNDHURST FARM LAKE Lancashire
MANOR HOUSE FISHERY Lancashire
MARTIN HALL FARM Lancashire
PARSONAGE RESERVOIR Lancashire
RED ROCKS FISHERY Lancashire
RIBBLE (RIVER) Lancashire
ROACH BRIDGE FISHERY Lancashire
RUSHYVARS LAKES Lancashire
SHRUGGS WOOD FISHERY Lancashire
SPADE MILL RESERVOIR NO.2 Lancashire
ST MICHAELS WYRESIDE FISHERY Lancashire
TOAD HALL FARM Lancashire
TURBARY HOUSE NURSARY Lancashire
TURTON AND ENTWISTLE RESERVOIR Lancashire
TWIN LAKES TROUT FISHERY Lancashire
WOODFOLD FARM FISHERIES Lancashire
WRYE (RIVER) Lancashire

PRUDHOE

TYNE (RIVER) Northumberland

PUDDLETOWN

WOOLBRIDGE MANOR Somerset

PULBOROUGH

ARUN (RIVER) Sussex (West)
DUNCANS POND Sussex (West)
HURSTON LANE Sussex (West)
LAYBROOK LAKES Sussex (West)
MILL FARM FISHERY Sussex (West)
WATER MEADOWS FLY FISHERIES Sussex (West)

QUEDGELEY

GLOUCESTER AND SHARPNESS CANAL Gloucestershire

QUEEN ADELAIDE

GREAT OUSE (RIVER) Cambridgeshire

RADWELL

GREAT OUSE (RIVER) Bedfordshire
RADWELL COMPLEX Bedfordshire

RAINHAM

ALBYNS LAKE Essex
BERWICK PONDS Essex

RAINWORTH

L-LAKE FISHERY Nottinghamshire

RAMSEY

OLD NENE (RIVER) Cambridgeshire
RAVELEY DRAIN Cambridgeshire

RAVENGLASS

DEVOKE WATER Cumbria
ESK (RIVER) Cumbria
KNOTT END TARN Cumbria

RAVENSTONE

GREAT OUSE (RIVER) Buckinghamshire

RAWCLIFFE

BIG HOLE PIT Humberside

RAWTENSTALL

OGDEN RESERVOIR Lancashire

RAYLEIGH

HOCKLEY LAKES Essex

READING

ALDERMASTON Berkshire
BRIMPTON LAKE Berkshire
BURGHFIELD Berkshire
BURGHFIELD BLUE POOL Berkshire
BURGHFIELD CANAL Berkshire
BURGHFIELD MATCH LAKE Berkshire
COTTAGE LANE Berkshire
COURT FARM Berkshire
DINTON PASTURES COUNTRY PARK Berkshire
EAST TOWNEY Berkshire
ENGLEFIELD LAGOON Berkshire
FARNHAM FLINT Berkshire
HOLYBROOK Berkshire
KENNET (RIVER) Berkshire
KENNET AND AVON CANAL Berkshire
KENNET AND ENTORNE (RIVERS) Berkshire
LODDON (RIVER) Berkshire
LOWER BENYONS Berkshire
MAPLEDURHAM A AND B Berkshire
MATCH AND BLUE POOLS Berkshire
MILL LANE Berkshire
MOATLANDS POOL Berkshire
OLD MILL Berkshire
PANG VALLEY TROUT LAKE Berkshire
PINGEWOOD LAGOON Berkshire
PURLEY Berkshire
REDLANDS LAKE Berkshire
SEACOURT (STREAM) Berkshire
SLALFORD LAKES Berkshire
SONNING EYE Berkshire
SOUTH LAKE Berkshire
ST PATRICKS Berkshire
THAMES (RIVER) Berkshire
THEALE Berkshire
THEALE CANAL Berkshire
THEALE LAGOON Berkshire
TWYFORD BBONT Berkshire
TWYFORD WATERS Berkshire
UFTON CANAL Berkshire
WASING WOODS Berkshire
WELLINGTON COUNTRY PARK Berkshire
TAVERHAM Norfolk

REDCAR

NEW MARSKE RESERVOIR Cleveland

REDDITCH

ALVECHURCH FISHERIES Midlands (West)
ARROW VALLEY LAKE Worcestershire
BROCKHILL FARM TROUT POOLS Worcestershire
LODGE PARK LAKE Worcestershire

REDRUTH

STITHIANS RESERVOIR Cornwall

REEPHAM
- **BOOTON CLAY PIT** Norfolk
- **REEPHAM FISHERY** Norfolk

RETFORD
- **CHESTERFIELD CANAL** Nottinghamshire
- **DANESHILL LAKES** Nottinghamshire
- **HALLCROFT FISHERIES** Nottinghamshire
- **LAKESIDE FISHERY** Nottinghamshire
- **LOUND WINDSURF LAKE** Nottinghamshire
- **STRIP PONDS** Nottinghamshire
- **TRENT (RIVER)** Nottinghamshire

RHODES VILLAGE
- **GEIGYS WATER** Manchester (Greater)

RIBCHESTER
- **RIBBLE (RIVER)** Lancashire

RICCALL
- **LAKEHOUSE LAKE** Yorkshire (North)

RICHMOND
- **BROKEN BREA FISHERY** Yorkshire (North)
- **CATTERICK LAKES** Yorkshire (North)
- **CRABTREE ANGLING LAKE** Yorkshire (North)
- **ELLERTON PARK** Yorkshire (North)
- **LAKESIDE FISHERIES** Yorkshire (North)
- **SWALE (RIVER)** Yorkshire (North)

RICKMANSWORTH
- **BATCHWORTH LAKE** Hertfordshire
- **COLNE (RIVER)** Hertfordshire
- **CROXLEY HALL TROUT FISHERY** Hertfordshire
- **INNS LAKE** Hertfordshire

RIDSDALE
- **SWEETHOPE LOUGHS** Tyne and Wear

RINGSTEAD
- **BARKERS LAKE** Northamptonshire

RINGWOOD
- **MARTINS FARM** Dorset
- **STOUR (DORSET) (RIVER)** Dorset
- **AVON (RIVER)** Hampshire
- **BEECHES BROOK FISHERY** Hampshire
- **BICKERLEY MILLSTREAM** Hampshire
- **BROADLANDS LAKES** Hampshire
- **CROOKED WILLOWS** Hampshire
- **EAST MOORS LAKE** Hampshire
- **HALF PIT** Hampshire
- **HAMPSHIRE AVON** Hampshire
- **HAMPSHIRE AVON (RIVER)** Hampshire
- **HIGHTOWN LAKE** Hampshire
- **HURST POND** Hampshire
- **IBSLEY POOLS** Hampshire
- **MOORS VALLEY COUNTRY PARK** Hampshire
- **NORTHFIELD LAKES** Hampshire
- **ROCKFORD LAKE** Hampshire
- **SOMERLEY LAKES** Hampshire
- **STOUR (RIVER)** Hampshire
- **TURF CROFT FARM** Hampshire
- **WASH PIT** Hampshire
- **WEDGEHILL PONDS** Hampshire

RIPLEY
- **BUTTERLEY RESERVOIR** Derbyshire
- **CONDOR PARK RESERVOIR** Derbyshire
- **PAPERCOURT FISHERY** Surrey
- **RIPLEY CASTLE** Yorkshire (North)

RIPON
- **BELLFLASK TROUT FISHERY** Yorkshire (North)
- **BRICKYARD FISHERY** Yorkshire (North)
- **FARMIRE** Yorkshire (North)
- **KINLIN HALL TROUT FARM** Yorkshire (North)
- **LAVER (RIVER)** Yorkshire (North)
- **LEIGHTON RESERVOIR** Yorkshire (North)
- **NEWBY HALL FISHERIES** Yorkshire (North)
- **NIDD BRIDGE** Yorkshire (North)
- **QUEEN MARYS POND** Yorkshire (North)
- **RACECOURSE LAKE** Yorkshire (North)
- **RIPON CANAL** Yorkshire (North)
- **RIPON RACECOURSE LAKE** Yorkshire (North)
- **ROGERS POND** Yorkshire (North)
- **SCAR HOUSE RESERVOIR** Yorkshire (North)
- **SHIELD TROUT FISHERY** Yorkshire (North)
- **SKELL (RIVER)** Yorkshire (North)
- **SWALE (RIVER)** Yorkshire (North)
- **SWINTON ESTATE TROUT FISHERY** Yorkshire (North)
- **TANFIELD LAKE** Yorkshire (North)
- **THORNTON STEWARD RESERVOIR** Yorkshire (North)
- **TYNE (RIVER)** Yorkshire (North)
- **URE (RIVER)** Yorkshire (North)

RIPPLE
- **SEVERN (RIVER)** Worcestershire

RISELEY
- **WELLINGTON COUNTRY PARK** Berkshire

RISHTON
- **RISHTON RESERVOIR** Lancashire

ROBERTSBRIDGE
- **DARWELL WATER** Sussex (East)
- **ROTHER (RIVER)** Sussex (East)
- **VINEHALL SCHOOL LAKE** Sussex (East)

ROCHDALE
- **BUCKLEY WOOD RESERVOIR** Manchester (Greater)
- **CLEGG HALL LAKES** Manchester (Greater)
- **DOCTOR DAM FISHERY** Manchester (Greater)
- **HOLLINGWORTH LAKE COUNTRY PARK** Manchester (Greater)
- **OGDEN LOWER RESERVOIR** Manchester (Greater)
- **PENNINE TROUT FISHERY** Manchester (Greater)
- **PIETHORNE RESERVOIR** Manchester (Greater)
- **ROCHDALE CANAL** Manchester (Greater)
- **WATERGROVE RESERVOIR** Manchester (Greater)

ROCHESTER
- **ABBOTTS COURT** Kent
- **ALLHALLOWS LEISURE PARK** Kent
- **HOO LAKES** Kent

ROCHFORD
- **DOGGETTS FARM FISHERY** Essex
- **ROCHFORD RESERVOIR** Essex
- **STAMBRIDGE STARR FISHERIES** Essex

ROECLIFFE
- **URE (RIVER)** Yorkshire (North)

ROGATE
- **STEPSTONES LAKES** Hampshire

ROMFORD
- **AVELEY LAKES** Essex
- **BEDFORDS PARK LAKE** Essex
- **FAIRLOP EAST LAKE** Essex
- **HARWOOD HALL LAKE** Essex
- **MAYBRAND FISHERY** Essex
- **NORTON FISHERY** Essex
- **NUPERS FARM** Essex
- **PEA LANE FISHERY** Essex
- **RAPHAELS PARK** Essex
- **RODING (RIVER)** Essex

ROMNEY MARSH
- **DUNGENESS LONG PIT** Kent
- **ROYAL MILITARY CANAL** Kent
- **SPERRINGBROOK SEWER** Kent

ROMSEY
- **AWBRIDGE DANES LAKE** Hampshire
- **BROADLANDS MAIN LAKE** Hampshire
- **GREENRIDGE FARM LAKES** Hampshire
- **HOLBURY LAKES** Hampshire
- **LONGBRIDGE LAKES** Hampshire
- **LOWER ITCHEN FISHERY** Hampshire
- **PARSONAGE (RIVER) TEST** Hampshire
- **TEST (RIVER)** Hampshire
- **WHINWHISTLE COARSE FISHERY** Hampshire
- **WOODINGTON FISHERY** Hampshire

ROSSENDALE
- **FISHMOOR RESERVOIR** Lancashire
- **HOLDEN WOOD RESERVOIR** Lancashire
- **LANCASTER HOUSE FARM FISHERY** Lancashire
- **LOVECLOUGH TROUT FISHERY** Lancashire
- **OGDEN RESERVOIR** Lancashire

ROSSINGTON
- **TORNE (RIVER)** Yorkshire (South)

ROSS-ON-WYE
- **BIDDLESTONE LAKE** Herefordshire
- **BULLEY LANE FISHERY** Herefordshire
- **CARADOC FISHERY** Herefordshire
- **DRUMMOND DUB** Herefordshire
- **INGESTONE FISHERY** Herefordshire
- **REDMIRE POOL** Herefordshire
- **WYE (RIVER)** Herefordshire

ROTHBURY
- **COQUET (RIVER)** Northumberland
- **FONTBURN RESERVOIR** Northumberland
- **WREIGH (RIVER)** Northumberland

ROTHERHAM
- **BRICKYARD PONDS** Yorkshire (South)
- **CUMWELL LANE** Yorkshire (South)
- **DON (RIVER)** Yorkshire (South)
- **FITZWILLIAM CANAL** Yorkshire (South)
- **GREASBROUGH DAMS** Yorkshire (South)
- **NEWBIGGIN POND** Yorkshire (South)
- **SHEFFIELD AND SOUTH YORKSHIRE NAVIGATION** Yorkshire (South)
- **THRYBERGH COUNTRY PARK** Yorkshire (South)
- **ULLEY RESERVOIR** Yorkshire (South)
- **WENTWORTH FISHERY** Yorkshire (South)
- **WESTWOOD COUNTRY PARK** Yorkshire (South)

ROWLANDS GILL
DERWENT (RIVER) Tyne and Wear

ROYSTON
RYEMEADS Hertfordshire

RUDGWICK
ARUN (RIVER) Sussex (West)
FURNACE LAKES Sussex (West)
HAZELCOPSE LAKES Sussex (West)

RUDHEATH
DANE RIVERSIDE FISHERY Cheshire

RUGBY
STEMBOROUGH MILL TROUT FARM Leicestershire
FOXHOLES FISHERIES Northamptonshire
GRAND UNION CANAL Northamptonshire
AVON (RIVER) Warwickshire
BANKS (THE) Warwickshire
CLIFTON LAKES FISHERY Warwickshire
DRAYCOTE WATER Warwickshire
LANNYS LAGOON Warwickshire
MILL POOL Warwickshire
NEWBOLD QUARRY Warwickshire
NORTH OXFORD CANAL Warwickshire
OXFORD CANAL Warwickshire
STOCKTON RESERVOIR Warwickshire

RUGELEY
BLITHFIELD RESERVOIR Staffordshire
HAMSTALL FISHERY Staffordshire
HEDNESFORD ROAD LAKE Staffordshire
HORNS Staffordshire
LITTLETONS AND MIDDLE POOL Staffordshire
WADE LAKE Staffordshire

RUNCORN
BRIDGEWATER CANAL Cheshire
RUNCORN PARK LAKE Cheshire
SANKEY ST HELENS CANAL Cheshire
TOWN PARK LANE Cheshire
WOODSIDE POOL Cheshire

RUSHDEN
LAKESIDE COUNTRY CLUB Northamptonshire

RUTLAND
RUTLAND WATER Leicestershire

RYE
IDEN WOOD FISHERY Sussex (East)
RYE NOOK FISHERY Sussex (East)
SHAMFOLD FARM FISHERY Sussex (East)

RYTON
STARGATE PONDS Tyne and Wear
TYNE (RIVER) Tyne and Wear

SAFFRON WALDEN
BORDEAUX PIT Essex
CLAVERING TROUT LAKE Essex
HOME FARM FISHERY Essex
ROCKELLS FARM Essex
CHESTERFORD FISHERIES Suffolk

SALE
BRIDGEWATER CANAL Cheshire
SALE WATER PARK Cheshire

SALFORD
BRIDGEWATER CANAL Manchester (Greater)
CLIFTON MARINA Manchester (Greater)
CLOWES PARK LAKE Manchester (Greater)
IRWELL (RIVER) Manchester (Greater)
SALFORD QUAYS Manchester (Greater)

SALISBURY
STOUR (RIVER) Dorset
AVON RIVER FISHERIES Hampshire
ROCKBOURNE TROUT FISHERY Hampshire
DANDYS LAKE AND KNIGHTINGALE LAKE Somerset
AVON (BRISTOL) (RIVER) Wiltshire
AVON (RIVER) Wiltshire
AVON SPRINGS FISHERY Wiltshire
BRITFORD FISHERY Wiltshire
HAMPSHIRE AVON (RIVER) Wiltshire
LANGFORD FISHERIES Wiltshire
LONGHOUSE LAKES Wiltshire
MILLBROOK TROUT FARM Wiltshire
NADDER (RIVER) Wiltshire
OLD WARDOUR Wiltshire
PETERS FINGER LAKES Wiltshire
STEEPLE LANGFORD LAKES Wiltshire
WALDENS FARM FISHERY Wiltshire
WITHERINGTON FARM FISHING Wiltshire
WYTHERINGTON FARM Wiltshire

SALTASH
BAKE FISHING LAKES Cornwall
BUSH LAKES FARM Cornwall
PORT ELLIOT LAKE Cornwall
ST GERMANS LAKE Cornwall

SALTFORD
AVON (BRISTOL) (RIVER) Bristol

SALTHAM
RUSTON REACHES Norfolk

SANDBACH
BULLS POOL Cheshire
CRABMILL FLASH Cheshire
PLEX FLASH Cheshire
RODE POOL Cheshire
SANDYBANK POOL Cheshire
TAX MERE Cheshire
TRENT AND MERSEY CANAL Cheshire

SANDHURST
CHURCH FARM Berkshire
MILL LANE Berkshire
SWAN VALLEY Berkshire
TRI-LAKES Berkshire

SANDIWAY
PETTY POOL Cheshire

SANDLING
ABBEYCOURT LAKE Kent

SANDOWN
BRADING LAKE Isle of Wight
MORTON FARM Isle of Wight
YAR (A) (RIVER) Isle of Wight
YAR (RIVER) Isle of Wight

SANDWICH
STONAR LAKE Kent

SANDY
LITTLE HEATH FARM TROUT FISHERY Bedfordshire
BLUNHAM PITS Northamptonshire

SAXMUNDHAM
ALDE (RIVER) Suffolk
GUNSSONS LAKE Suffolk
MARSH FARM LAKES Suffolk
WYE (RIVER) Suffolk

SCARBOROUGH
THORPE HALL Humberside
BLEA TARN Yorkshire (North)
BROOKLANDS Yorkshire (North)
DERWENT (RIVER) Yorkshire (North)
SCARBOROUGH MERE Yorkshire (North)
WYKEHAM LAKES Yorkshire (North)
Y2K LAKE Yorkshire (North)

SCORTON
ELLERTON PARK Yorkshire (North)

SCRUTON
STONEBRIDGE LAKES Yorkshire (North)

SCUNTHORPE
HOLME LAKE FISHERY Humberside
NEST Humberside
WATER SPRING FISHERY Humberside
WILLOW SPRINGS Humberside
DAIWA GULL POOL Lincolnshire
WILLOW BANK FISHERY Lincolnshire
KINGFISHER LODGE Lincolnshire (North)
OLD ANCHOLME (RIVER) Lincolnshire (North)
ORCHARD POND Lincolnshire (North)

SEAFORD
CUCKMERE (RIVER) Sussex (East)

SEDBERGH
CLOUGH (RIVER) Cumbria
DEE (RIVER) Cumbria
LOW GILL Cumbria
LUNE (RIVER) Cumbria
RAWTHEY (RIVER) Cumbria

SEDBURGH
LUNE (RIVER) Cumbria
RAWTHEY (RIVER) Cumbria

SELBY
DERWENT (RIVER) Humberside
BARLOW COMMON NATURE RESERVE Yorkshire (North)
BUBWITH (RIVER) Yorkshire (North)
CAWOOD HOLIDAY PARK Yorkshire (North)
DRAX LAKE Yorkshire (North)
FAIRVIEW LAKE Yorkshire (North)
MUNBY POND Yorkshire (North)
NEWHAY DAY TICKET LAKE Yorkshire (North)
NEWHAY SPECIMEN LAKE Yorkshire (North)
SELBY 3 LAKES Yorkshire (North)
SELBY CANAL Yorkshire (North)
THREE LAKES Yorkshire (North)
WEST HADDLESEY LAKE Yorkshire (North)

SELWORTHY
HORNER WATER Somerset

SEMINGTON
AVON (BRISTOL) (RIVER) Wiltshire

SEVENOAKS
CHIPSTEAD LAKES Kent
DARENT (RIVER) Kent
LONGFORD LAKE Kent
SEPHAM TROUT FISHERY Kent
SUNDRIDGE LAKES Kent

SGEGNESS
KEAL COATES FISHERY Lincolnshire

SHAFTESBURY
STOUR (DORSET) (RIVER) Dorset

SHALFORD
SHALFORD RESERVOIRS Essex

SHEEPWASH

GREENACRE TROUT LAKES Devon

SHEFFIELD

FOXTON DAM Derbyshire
NETHERMOOR LAKE Derbyshire
OWDY LANE TROUT FISHERY Nottinghamshire
CHESTERFIELD CANAL Yorkshire (South)
CROOKES VALLEY PARK LAKE Yorkshire (South)
DAM FLASK RESERVOIR Yorkshire (South)
ECCLESFIELD POND Yorkshire (South)
HORSESHOE LAKE TROUT FISHERY Yorkshire (South)
HOWBROOK RESERVOIR Yorkshire (South)
KIVETON HALL Yorkshire (South)
KJS FISHERIES Yorkshire (South)
MORE HALL RESERVOIR Yorkshire (South)
NANCY POND Yorkshire (South)
NORWOOD FISHERIES Yorkshire (South)
PEBLEY RESERVOIR Yorkshire (South)
SCOUT DYKE RESERVOIR Yorkshire (South)
SHEFFIELD CANAL Yorkshire (South)
STRAIGHT MILE FISHERY Yorkshire (South)
TRENT (RIVER) Yorkshire (South)
ULLEY RESERVOIR Yorkshire (South)
UNDERBANK RESERVOIR Yorkshire (South)
WESTWOOD COUNTRY PARK Yorkshire (South)
WHARNCLIFFE FLY FISHERY Yorkshire (South)
WINDTHORPE PITS Yorkshire (South)
WINTHORPE LAKE Yorkshire (South)

SHEFFORD

BROOM Bedfordshire
STANFORD PIT Bedfordshire

SHEPPERTON

ASHMERE FISHERIES London (Greater)
SHEPPERTON LOCK London (Greater)
STUDIO AND BROADWATER London (Greater)
THAMES (RIVER) London (Greater)

SHERBORNE

BERKELEY FARM Dorset
HERMITAGE LAKES Dorset
SHERBORNE LAKE Dorset

SHIFNAL

ACTON BURNELL Shropshire
BAYLIS POOLS Shropshire

SHILDON

FIELDSONS POND County Durham
JUBILEE LAKES County Durham

SHILLINGFORD

THAMES (RIVER) Oxfordshire

SHILLINGSTONE

STOUR (DORSET) (RIVER) Dorset

SHIPLAKE-ON-THAMES

SHIPLAKE LOCK Oxfordshire

SHIPLEY

AIRE (RIVER) Yorkshire (West)
LEEDS AND LIVERPOOL CANAL Yorkshire (West)
LEEDS TO LIVERPOOL CANAL Yorkshire (West)
TONG PARK DAM Yorkshire (West)

SHOREHAM-BY-SEA

PASSIES PONDS Sussex (West)

SHORNE

SHORNE COUNTRY PARK LAKES Kent

SHOTLEY BRIDGE

DERWENT (RIVER) County Durham

SHREWSBURY

BIRCH GROVE Shropshire
COUND TROUT FISHERY Shropshire
FOLLY FARM POOL Shropshire
HAWKSTONE PARK LAKE Shropshire
ISLE LAKE Shropshire
PERRY (RIVER) Shropshire
RIVER (TERN) Shropshire
SEVEN OAKS LOG CABIN PARK Shropshire
SEVERN (RIVER) Shropshire
SNAILBEACH POOL Shropshire
SPRING LEE Shropshire

SIBSEY

STICKNEY BRICKPONDS Lincolnshire

SIBTON

GUNSSONS LAKE Suffolk

SINNINGTON

SINNINGTON (RIVER) Yorkshire (North)

SITTINGBOURNE

BROOMBANKS PITS Kent
SITTINGBOURNE LAKES Kent

SKEGNESS

DENNIS RAINWATER LAKE Lincolnshire
GROOBYS PIT Lincolnshire
HERONS MEAD Lincolnshire
HILL VIEW LAKES Lincolnshire
HOLLAND PARK Lincolnshire
LAKESIDE LEISURE PARK Lincolnshire
MILL HILL LAKES Lincolnshire
MILL ROAD LAKES Lincolnshire
ROACH FARM PARK Lincolnshire
ROD AND LINE CARAVAN PARK Lincolnshire
SKEGNESS WATER LEISURE PARK Lincolnshire
STEEPING (RIVER) Lincolnshire
SWAN LAKE Lincolnshire
SYCAMORE FISHING LAKES Lincolnshire
WATERSIDE LEISURE PARK Lincolnshire

SKELMERSDALE

ABBEY LAKES Lancashire

SKERNE

HUMBERSIDE FISHERIES Humberside

SKIPSEA

FAR GRANGE CARAVAN AND COUNTRY PARK Humberside

SKIPTON

BOLTON ABBEY FISHERIES Yorkshire (North)
EMBSAY RESERVOIR Yorkshire (North)
KILNSEY PARK AND TROUT FARM Yorkshire (North)
OUSE (RIVER) Yorkshire (North)
SKIRFARE (RIVER) Yorkshire (North)
SWALE (RIVER) Yorkshire (North)
WHARFE (RIVER) Yorkshire (North)
WHINNYGILL RESERVOIR Yorkshire (North)
RAYGILL FISHERY Yorkshire (West)

SLAIDBURN

HODDER (RIVER) Lancashire

SLEAFORD

HAVERHOLME PARK Lincolnshire
MOON LAKE Lincolnshire
WITHAM (RIVER) Lincolnshire
WOODLAND WATERS Lincolnshire

SLOUGH

COLNBROOK WEST Buckinghamshire
COLNEBROOK (RIVER) Buckinghamshire
CRAYFISH POOL Buckinghamshire
GILBRATAR LAKE Buckinghamshire
HORTON BOAT POOL Buckinghamshire
HORTON CHURCH LAKE Buckinghamshire
KINGSMEAD 1 Buckinghamshire
KINGSMEAD ISLAND LAKE Buckinghamshire
MAYFIELDS LAKE Buckinghamshire
ORLITTS LAKES Buckinghamshire
THAMES (RIVER) Buckinghamshire
GRAND UNION CANAL London (Greater)
RODNEY MEADOW London (Greater)

SMETHWICK

SOHO LOOP CANAL Midlands (West)

SNAITH

GOWDALL LAKES Humberside

SOLIHULL

BLYTHE WATERS Midlands (West)
EARLSWOOD LAKES Midlands (West)
GRAND UNION CANAL Midlands (West)
GREY MILL FARM Midlands (West)
KINGSHURST LAKE Midlands (West)
TIDBURY GREEN GOLF CLUB Midlands (West)

SOMERFORD KEYNES

NEIGH BRIDGE LAKE Gloucestershire

SOMERTON

CHERWELL (RIVER) Oxfordshire
MINERS PONDS Somerset
VIADUCT FISHERY Somerset

SONNING COMMON

SONNING EYE Berkshire

SOPLEY

HAMPSHIRE AVON (RIVER) Dorset

SOUTH BRENT

HATCHLAND TROUT FISHERY Devon
LITTLE ALLERS COARSE FISHERY Devon
MILL Devon
SOMERSWOOD LAKE Devon

SOUTH CERNEY

RAINBOW LAKES Gloucestershire

SOUTH LAKELAND

HARLOCK RESERVOIR Cumbria

SOUTH MOLTN

WISTLANDPOUND RESERVOIR Devon

SOUTH MOLTON

DUNSLEY FARM Devon
OAKTREE FISHERY Devon
SHOBROOKE PARK Devon

SOUTH OCKENDON

ESSEX CARP FISHERY Essex

SOUTHAM

- HIGH CLAYS FARM Warwickshire
- NAPTON RESERVOIR Warwickshire
- NORTH FARM FISHERY Warwickshire

SOUTHAMPTON

- BILCOMBES POND Hampshire
- DARK LANE PONDS Hampshire
- FIVE OAKS TROUT LAKE Hampshire
- FOREST LODGE HOME FARM Hampshire
- HOLBURY MANOR POND Hampshire
- ITCHEN NAVIGATION Hampshire
- KINGFISHER LAKE (A) Hampshire
- LAKESIDE Hampshire
- LOWER ITCHEN FISHERY Hampshire
- MOORHEN FARM TROUT LAKE Hampshire
- MOPLEY POND Hampshire
- STONEHAM LAKES Hampshire
- SWAY LAKES Hampshire
- TESTWOOD SALMON FISHERIES Hampshire
- WINTERSHILL TROUT LAKE Hampshire
- WOODMILL SALMON FISHERY Hampshire

SOUTHEND-ON-SEA

- MILL BARN FISHERY Essex
- PRIORY PARK LAKES Essex
- SHOEBURY PARK Essex
- STAR LANE Essex

SOUTHMINSTER

- ASHELDHAM FISHERY Essex
- SOUTHMINSTER FISHERIES Essex

SOUTHPORT

- BANNISTER HALL FARM Lancashire

SOUTHWOLD

- BUSS CREEK Suffolk
- RAYDON PONDS Suffolk
- REYDON LAKES Suffolk

SPALDING

- LAKE ROSS FISHERY Lincolnshire
- SOUTH HOLLAND DRAIN Lincolnshire
- WELLAND (RIVER) Lincolnshire

SPENNYMOOR

- BYERS GREEN County Durham
- SHAFTOS LAKE County Durham

SPILSBY

- KEAL COATES FISHERY Lincolnshire
- WOODLANDS FISHERY Lincolnshire

ST ALBANS

- BOWMANS LAKES Hertfordshire
- BROAD COLNEY LAKES Hertfordshire
- COLNEY HEATH LAKE Hertfordshire
- GRAND UNION CANAL Hertfordshire
- LOWBELL LANE Hertfordshire

ST AUSTELL

- ELECTRICITY POOL Cornwall
- GLENLEIGH FARM FISHERY Cornwall
- ORVIS INNIS COUNTRY CLUB AND FLY FISHERY Cornwall
- WHEAL RASHLEIGH PITS Cornwall

ST COLUMB

- ELECTRICITY POOL Cornwall
- MEADOWSIDE COARSE FISHERY Cornwall
- RETALLACK WATERS Cornwall

ST HELENS

- CARR MILL DAM Merseyside
- LEG OMUTTON DAM Merseyside
- PADDOCK DAM Merseyside

ST IVES

- CLEARWATERS COARSE FISHERY Cambridgeshire
- EARITH FISHERY Cambridgeshire
- GREAT OUSE (RIVER) Cambridgeshire
- LONG REACH Cambridgeshire
- OLD WEST (RIVER) Cambridgeshire
- ST IVES COMPLEX Cambridgeshire
- WOBURN CLOSE LAKE Cambridgeshire
- WOOLPACK FISHERY Cambridgeshire
- AMALWHIDDEN FARM Cornwall
- BUSSOW RESERVOIR Cornwall
- NANCE LAKES Cornwall
- WOONSMITH LAKE Cornwall

ST JOHN'S CHAPEL

- WEAR (RIVER) County Durham

ST MARY CRAY

- RUXLEY PITS Kent

ST MAWES

- TRENESTRALL LAKE Cornwall

ST NEOTS

- CHAWSTON LAKES Cambridgeshire
- EATON SOCON LAKE Cambridgeshire
- GREAT OUSE (RIVER) Cambridgeshire
- PAXTON LAKE Cambridgeshire
- STEW POND Cambridgeshire
- WELDON RESERVOIR Cambridgeshire
- WILDEN RESERVOIR Cambridgeshire

STADDLEHOLME

- STONEY LANE PONDS Yorkshire (North)

STAFFORD

- BADEN HALL FISHERY Staffordshire
- ELLENHALL NINE POOLS Staffordshire
- GAILEY TROUT AND PIKE FISHERY Staffordshire
- HERONBROOK FISHERY Staffordshire
- IZAAK WALTON FISHERY Staffordshire
- LOYNTON TROUT FISHERIES Staffordshire
- SHELMORE TROUT FISHERY Staffordshire
- SHROPSHIRE UNION CANAL Staffordshire
- SOW (RIVER) Staffordshire
- STAFFORD AND WORCESTER CANAL Staffordshire
- STAFFORD TO WORCESTER CANAL Staffordshire
- SWAN PIT POOL Staffordshire
- WILLOW POOLS Staffordshire

STAINES

- PENTON HOOK LOCK London (Greater)
- SHEEPWALK LAKE London (Greater)
- WRAYSBURY ONE London (Greater)
- WRAYSBURY TWO London (Greater)
- MANOR POND Surrey
- TWYNERSH FISHING COMPLEX Surrey

STAINFORTH

- STAINFORTH AND KEADBY CANAL Yorkshire (South)

STALYBRIDGE

- HUDDERSFIELD NARROW CANAL Cheshire
- WALKERWOOD TROUT FISHERY Cheshire
- STAMFORD PARK LAKES Manchester (Greater)

STAMBRIDGE

- STAMBRIDGE STARR FISHERIES Essex

STAMFORD

- BURGHLEY PARK LAKE Lincolnshire
- TALLINGTON FISHERY Lincolnshire
- WELLAND (RIVER) Rutland

STAMFORDHAM

- WHITTLE DEAN RESERVOIR Northumberland

STANDFORD-LE-HOPE

- COBBLERS MEAD LAKE Essex
- JIMMYS LAKE Essex
- STANFORD-LE-HOPE Essex
- WARREN Essex
- WHARF POOL Essex

STANDISH

- WORTHINGTON NO 1 Lancashire
- WORTHINGTON NO 2 Lancashire
- WORTHINGTON NO 3 Lancashire

STANFORD

- BROOM Bedfordshire
- STANFORD PIT Bedfordshire

STANFORD-LE-HOPE

- STANFORD-LE-HOPE Essex
- WARREN Essex
- WHARF POOL Essex

STANHOPE

- WEAR (RIVER) County Durham

STANLEY

- BEAMISH LAKE FLY FISHERY County Durham
- GREENCROFT POND County Durham

STANSTEAD ABBOTTS

- AMWELL LAKES Hertfordshire
- STANSTEAD ABBOTTS Hertfordshire

STANTON HARCOURT

- DARLOW LAKE Oxfordshire

STAPLEFORD ABBOTTS

- NUPERS FARM Essex

STATHE

- STATHE DRAIN Somerset

STAUNTON

- RUSSELLS END RESERVOIR Herefordshire

STAVERTON

- AVON (RIVER) Gloucestershire

STEEPLE CLAYDON

- CLAYDON LAKE Buckinghamshire

STEVENAGE

- FAIRLANDS VALLEY PARK Hertfordshire
- WESTONS LAKE Hertfordshire

STEYNING

- ADUR (RIVER) Sussex (West)
- ALDERWOOD PONDS Sussex (West)

STIBBINGTON
- **NENE (RIVER)** Cambridgeshire

STOCKBRIDGE
- **JOHN OGAUNTS FISHERY** Hampshire
- **KIMBRIDGE** Hampshire
- **NETHER WALLOP FLY FISHING SCHOOL** Hampshire
- **TEST (RIVER)** Hampshire

STOCKPORT
- **BOLLINHURST RESERVOIR** Manchester (Greater)
- **DAVENPORT** Manchester (Greater)
- **LUDWORTH RESERVOIR** Manchester (Greater)
- **MACCLESFIELD CANAL** Manchester (Greater)
- **NEW HOUSE FARM POOL** Manchester (Greater)
- **PEAK FOREST CANAL** Manchester (Greater)
- **POYNTON POOL** Manchester (Greater)
- **REDDISH VALE MILL PONDS** Manchester (Greater)
- **ROMAN LAKE LEISURE PARK** Manchester (Greater)
- **STONEY PIT RESERVOIR** Manchester (Greater)
- **WOODBANK PARK POOL** Manchester (Greater)

STOCKSBRIDGE
- **UNDERBANK RESERVOIR** Yorkshire (South)

STOCKSFIELD
- **TYNE (RIVER)** Northumberland

STOCKTON
- **HARTLEPOOL RESERVOIR** Cleveland
- **NAPTON RESERVOIR** Warwickshire
- **STOCKTON RESERVOIR** Warwickshire

STOCKTON HEATH
- **ACKERS PIT** Cheshire

STOCKTON-ON-TEES
- **HARTBURN BRICK PIT** Cleveland
- **HARTLEPOOL RESERVOIR** Cleveland
- **ISLAND WATERS** Cleveland
- **TEES (RIVER)** Cleveland
- **WEST FARM LAKE** County Durham

STOKE SUB HAMDON
- **PARRETT (RIVER)** Somerset

STOKE-ON-TRENT
- **BIDDULPH GRANGE** Staffordshire
- **BLACK LAKE** Staffordshire
- **BLACKWOOD POOL** Staffordshire
- **CANAL RESERVOIRS** Staffordshire
- **CONSALL NATURE PARK** Staffordshire
- **DILHORNE HALL POOLS** Staffordshire
- **HANCHURCH FISHERIES** Staffordshire
- **HOLDEN LANE POOL** Staffordshire
- **KNYPERSLEY RESERVOIR** Staffordshire
- **MACCLESFIELD CANAL** Staffordshire
- **PARK HALL FARM** Staffordshire
- **RISING TROUT FISHERY** Staffordshire
- **SIDEWAY OVERFLOW** Staffordshire
- **SMITH POOL** Staffordshire
- **SMITHPOOL LAKE** Staffordshire
- **STANLEY RESERVOIR** Staffordshire
- **TAYLORS POOL** Staffordshire
- **TRENT AND MERSEY CANAL** Staffordshire
- **TRENTHAM GARDENS** Staffordshire

STOKESBY
- **STOKESBY (RIVER)** Norfolk

STOKESLEY
- **WHITEHOUSE CARAVAN PARK LAKE** Cleveland

STOKE-SUB-HAMDON
- **PARRETT (RIVER)** Somerset

STONE
- **STROUDWATER CANAL** Gloucestershire
- **TRENT (RIVER)** Staffordshire
- **TRENTHAM GARDENS** Staffordshire

STONEHOUSE
- **STROUDWATER CANAL** Gloucestershire

STOURBRIDGE
- **WASSELL GROVE FISHERIES** Midlands (West)

STOURPORT
- **MAVER LARFORD** Worcestershire
- **SEVERN (RIVER)** Worcestershire
- **STAFFORD TO WORCESTER CANAL** Worcestershire

STOURPORT-ON-SEVERN
- **HUNDRED POOL** Herefordshire
- **BANKES POOL** Worcestershire
- **MAVER LARFORD** Worcestershire
- **SEVERN (RIVER)** Worcestershire
- **SHAKESPEARE MOORLANDS FARM** Worcestershire
- **STAFFORD TO WORCESTER CANAL** Worcestershire
- **UNWICKS FARM FISHERY** Worcestershire
- **WILDEN POOL** Worcestershire
- **WITLEY FISHERY** Worcestershire

STOW ON THE WOLD
- **ADLESTROP LAKE** Gloucestershire
- **BOURTON ON THE WATER GRAVEL PIT NO1** Gloucestershire

STOWBRIDGE
- **RELIEF CHANNEL** Norfolk

STOWMARKET
- **BAKERS LAKE** Suffolk
- **LAKESIDE** Suffolk
- **RATTLE (RIVER)** Suffolk

STOW-ON-THE-WOLD
- **CHAD LAKES** Oxfordshire

STRATFORD
- **AVON (RIVER)** Warwickshire
- **WEST HILLBOROUGH** Warwickshire

STRATFORD-UPON-AVON
- **AVON (RIVER)** Warwickshire
- **BLACK HILL POOLS** Warwickshire
- **SNITTERFIELD FRUIT FARM** Warwickshire
- **SOUTH STRATFORD CANAL** Warwickshire
- **STOUR (WARWICKSHIRE)** Warwickshire
- **WARWICKSHIRE AVON** Warwickshire

STREET
- **BRUE (RIVER)** Somerset
- **BUTLEIGH ROAD PONDS** Somerset

STRETFORD
- **BRIDGEWATER CANAL** Manchester (Greater)

STROUD
- **FROME STREAM** Gloucestershire
- **STEANBRIDGE FISHERY** Gloucestershire

STURMINSTER
- **STOUR (RIVER)** Dorset

STURMINSTER NEWTON
- **MAPPOWDER COURT** Dorset
- **STOUR (DORSET) (RIVER)** Dorset
- **STOUR (DORSET) (RIVER)** Dorset
- **STOUR (RIVER)** Dorset
- **TODBER MANOR** Dorset

SUDBURY
- **CHESTERFORD FISHERIES** Suffolk
- **CLARE PARK LAKE** Suffolk
- **HOME FARM FISHERIES** Suffolk
- **LAYZELLS FARM** Suffolk
- **LITTLE BEVILLS ESTATE** Suffolk
- **NORTH MEADOWS** Suffolk
- **STANTONS FARM RESERVOIR** Suffolk
- **STARFIELD PIT** Suffolk
- **STOUR (RIVER)** Suffolk
- **STOW (RIVER)** Suffolk
- **WRIGHTS FARM** Suffolk

SUMMERTOWN
- **THAMES (RIVER)** Oxfordshire

SUNDERLAND
- **SHARPLEY WATERS** Cumbria
- **SILKSWORTH SPORTS COMPLEX** Tyne and Wear

SUSTEAD
- **GLEN MERE** Norfolk

SUTTERTON
- **LAKE HELEN** Lincolnshire

SUTTON
- **SUTTON RESERVOIR** Cheshire

SUTTON COLDFIELD
- **CUTTLE MILL CARP FISHERY** Midlands (West)
- **KINGSBURY WATER PARK** Midlands (West)
- **PENNS HALL LAKE** Midlands (West)
- **SUTTON PARK** Midlands (West)

SUTTON GREEN
- **DEE (RIVER)** Surrey

SUTTON-IN-ASHFIELD
- **KINGS MILL RESERVOIR** Nottinghamshire

SWADLINCOTE
- **BEEHIVE FARM WOODLANDS LAKES** Derbyshire
- **CATTON PARK LAKE** Derbyshire
- **DONKHILL FISHERIES** Derbyshire

SWAFFHAM
- **DUNHAM CARP AND TENCH LAKES** Norfolk
- **MEADOW LAKE** Norfolk

SWAFFHAM PRIOR
- **SPORTSMANS PIT** Cambridgeshire

SWAINBY
- **ASCOTT PONDS** Cleveland

SWALE
- **LEEMING (RIVER)** Yorkshire (North)

SWANNINGTON
- **NATURES HAVEN LAKES** Norfolk

SWINDON
- **BUSHYLEAZE TROUT FISHERY** Gloucestershire
- **COLN (RIVER)** Gloucestershire
- **LAKE NUMBER ONE (LAKE19)** Gloucestershire
- **LECHLADE TROUT FISHERY** Gloucestershire
- **MILL LAKE (NO 44)** Gloucestershire
- **COATE WATER COUNTRY PARK** Wiltshire

- DORKHAM STORMWATER Wiltshire
- IVY HOUSE FARM Wiltshire
- LAWNS (THE) Wiltshire
- LIDEN LAGOON Wiltshire
- MANOR BROOK LAKE Wiltshire
- PEARMOOR LAKE Wiltshire
- PEATMOOR LAGOON Wiltshire
- PEMBROKE POND Wiltshire
- PLAUMS PIT Wiltshire
- PURTON LAKE Wiltshire
- RAY (RIVER) Wiltshire
- RODBOURNE LAGOON Wiltshire
- SHAFTESBURY LAKE Wiltshire
- THAMES (RIVER) Wiltshire
- WROUGHTON RESERVOIR Wiltshire

SWINFORD

- BRISTOL AVON Bristol

SWITHLAND

- SWITHLAND RESERVOIR Leicestershire

SYMONDS YAT

- WYE (RIVER) Herefordshire

TADCASTER

- BACON FACTORY POND Yorkshire (North)
- ULLESKELF (RIVER) Yorkshire (North)
- WHARFE (RIVER) Yorkshire (North)
- WHARFE (RIVER) Yorkshire (West)

TAMESIDE

- WALKERWOOD TROUT FISHERY Cheshire

TAMWORTH

- CUTTLE MILL CARP FISHERY Midlands (West)
- ANKER (RIVER) Staffordshire
- BONEHILL MILL Staffordshire
- BORROWPIT LAKE Staffordshire
- COVENTRY CANAL Staffordshire
- DRAYTON BRIDGE Staffordshire
- PINE POOL Staffordshire
- POOL HOUSE FARM Staffordshire
- PRETTY PIGS FISHERY Staffordshire

TANNERS GREEN

- EARLSWOOD LAKES Midlands (West)

TARLETON

- LEEDS TO LIVERPOOL CANAL Lancashire

TARPORLEY

- BENTLEY TROUT POOL Cheshire
- HOLMSTON HALL FISHERY Cheshire
- LITTLE BUDWORTH Cheshire
- LITTLE MILL Cheshire
- OULTON MILL POOL Cheshire

TATTERSHALL

- MOON LAKE Lincolnshire
- SHANDY KEV FISHERIES Lincolnshire

TAUNTON

- SPIRES LAKES Devon
- CLATWORTHY RESERVOIR Somerset
- EXE VALLEY FISHERY Somerset
- LANGFORD LAKES Somerset
- LOWER LOVELYNCH FISHERIES Somerset
- OTTERHEAD LAKES Somerset
- OXENLEAZE FARM CARAVANS AND COARSE FISHERY Somerset
- QUANTOCK FISHERIES Somerset
- THURLEYBEARE POND Somerset
- TONE (RIVER) Somerset
- WYCH LODGE LAKE Somerset

TAVISTOCK

- COOMBE FISHERIES Devon
- MILEMEAD FISHERIES Devon
- TAMAR (RIVER) Devon
- TAVISTOCK TROUT FISHERY Devon
- TAVY (RIVER) Devon

TEESIDE

- WEAR (RIVER) County Durham

TEIGNMOUTH

- ASHCOMBE FISHERY Devon

TELFORD

- RABY ESTATES WATER County Durham
- APLEY POOLS Shropshire
- BAYLIS POOLS Shropshire
- BEECHES POOL Shropshire
- BLUE POOL Shropshire
- ELLERDINE LAKES Shropshire
- HINKSHAY POOLS Shropshire
- HOLMER LAKE Shropshire
- HORESHAY POOL Shropshire
- LITTLE DAWLEY POOLS Shropshire
- MIDDLE POOL Shropshire
- NEWPORT CANAL Shropshire
- SEVERN (RIVER) Shropshire
- SEVERN (RIVER) Shropshire
- STIRCHLEY POOLS Shropshire
- SWEENEYCLIFFE HOUSE FISHERY Shropshire
- TELFORD TOWN PARK Shropshire
- TERN (RIVER) Shropshire
- TRENCH POOL Shropshire
- WITHY POOL Shropshire
- WOODCOTE HALL Shropshire

TELLISFORD

- FROME (RIVER) Somerset

TENBURY WELLS

- LEDWYCHE BROOK Worcestershire
- TEME (RIVER) Worcestershire
- TEME (RIVER) Worcestershire
- WOODSTON MANOR POOLS Worcestershire

TENTERDEN

- BIDDENDEN LAKE Kent
- HEXDEN CHANNEL Kent
- ROTHER (RIVER) Kent
- TENTERDEN TROUT WATERS Kent

TEWKESBURY

- APPERLEY POOLS Gloucestershire
- BREDONS HARDWICK Gloucestershire
- CHURCH END TROUT FISHERY Gloucestershire
- HILL VIEW LAKES Gloucestershire
- HILLVIEW FISHERY Gloucestershire
- MILL AVON Gloucestershire
- MYTHE POOL Gloucestershire
- SEVERN (RIVER) Gloucestershire
- SEVERN ON THE HAM Gloucestershire
- UCKINGHALL POOL Worcestershire

THATCHAM

- KENNET (RIVER) Berkshire

THAXTED

- ARMIGERS FARM Essex

THEALE

- KENNET (RIVER) Berkshire

THETFORD

- BUCKENHAM PITS Norfolk
- MIDDLE HARLING LAKE Norfolk
- WOODRISING WATER MEADOWS Norfolk
- LITTLE OUSE (RIVER) Suffolk
- THET (RIVER) Suffolk

THIRSK

- ALDERS LAKE Yorkshire (North)
- CARLTON LODGE LAKE Yorkshire (North)
- COD BECK Yorkshire (North)
- KAYS LAKES Yorkshire (North)
- KILBURN POND Yorkshire (North)
- LOW OSGOODBY LAKE Yorkshire (North)
- MOULTON LANE POND Yorkshire (North)
- OAKS FISHERY Yorkshire (North)
- RIVER VIEW COTTAGE Yorkshire (North)
- ROLIETH FISHERY Yorkshire (North)
- SWALE (RIVER) Yorkshire (North)
- WILLOWS AND FIRS LAKES Yorkshire (North)
- WOODLAND LAKES Yorkshire (North)

THORGANBY

- DERWENT (RIVER) Yorkshire (North)

THORNE

- DELVES FISH PONDS Yorkshire (South)
- SOUTHFIELD RESERVOIRS Yorkshire (South)
- STAINFORTH AND KEADBY CANAL Yorkshire (South)
- THORNE NORTH POND Yorkshire (South)
- TRIANGS FISHERY Yorkshire (South)

THORNTON STEWARD

- THORNTON STEWARD RESERVOIR Yorkshire (North)

THORNTON-CLEVELEYS

- STANLEY PARK LAKE Lancashire
- WYRE (RIVER) Lancashire

THORPE GREEN

- YARE (RIVER) Norfolk

THRAPSTON

- ISLIP NATURE LAKE Northamptonshire
- NENE (RIVER) Northamptonshire
- THORPE WATERVILLE LAKE Northamptonshire
- THRAPSTON (RIVER) Northamptonshire

THROPTON

- WREIGH (RIVER) Northumberland

THURLESTONE

- AVON (RIVER) Devon

THURNE

- THURNE MOUTH (RIVER) Norfolk

THURROCK

- GRANGE WATER Essex

THUXTON

- RAILWAY LAKE Norfolk

TIDEFORD

- BAKE FISHING LAKES Cornwall

TILFORD

- STOCKBRIDGE POND Surrey

TITCHFIELD

- TITCHFIELD ABBEY GOLF AND COARSE FISHING LAKES Hampshire

TIVERTON

- BELLBROOK VALLEY TROUT FISHERY Devon
- COOMBE FARM FISHPONDS Devon
- CULM (RIVER) Devon
- DELBROOK VALLEY TROUT FISHERY Devon

- EXE (RIVER) Devon
- GRAND WESTERN CANAL Devon
- GRAND WESTERN CANAL Devon
- HATSWELL Devon
- POUND POND FARM Devon
- SAMPFORD PEVERAL PONDS Devon
- STOUR FARM FISHERY Devon
- WEST PITT FARM FISHERY Devon
- LAKESIDE Somerset

TIXALL
- STAFFORD AND WORCESTER CANAL Staffordshire

TODDINGTON
- TINGRITH COARSE FISHERY Bedfordshire

TODMORDEN
- PORTSMOUTH RESERVIOR Lancashire
- CALDER (RIVER) Yorkshire (West)
- NEW MILL DAM Yorkshire (West)
- ROCHDALE CANAL Yorkshire (West)
- WALSDEN PRINTING CO LODGES Yorkshire (West)

TOLLERTON
- TOLLERTON FISHING PONDS Yorkshire (North)

TOLPUDDLE
- PIDDLE (RIVER) Dorset
- WESSEX FLY FISHING TROUT LAKES Dorset

TONBRIDGE
- BALLAST PIT Kent
- BARDEN LAKE Kent
- BOUGH BEECH RESERVOIR Kent
- CHIDDINGSTONE CASTLE LAKE Kent
- EDEN (RIVER) Kent
- GRANGE POOL Kent
- HAYSDEN COUNTRY PARK Kent
- LONGFIELD LAKE Kent
- MEDWAY (RIVER) Kent
- MEDWAY (RIVER) Kent
- MONK LAKE FISHERIES Kent
- MOUSEHOLE LAKE Kent
- PIPPINS FARM LAKE Kent
- PITTLANDS LAKES Kent
- SILVER SPRINGS FISHERY Kent
- WIDEHURST FARM Kent

TORPOINT
- CRAFTHOLE LAKE Cornwall
- MILLBROOK COARSE FISHERY Cornwall

TORQUAY
- CHARLECOMBE Devon
- NEWTON ABBOT SPRING PONDS Devon

TORRINGTON
- BAKERS FARM Devon
- DARRACOTT RESERVOIR Devon
- STEVENSTONE LAKES Devon

TOTNES
- AVON DAM Devon
- NEWHOUSE FISHERY Devon

TOTTENHAM
- EAST WARWICK London (Greater)
- PONDERS END London (Greater)

TOTTINGTON
- CARCUS WATERS Manchester (Greater)

TOTTON
- BROADLANDS LAKES Hampshire

TOWCESTER
- GREEN FARM LAKES Northamptonshire
- SILVER LAKE Northamptonshire

TREMAINE
- ELMFIELD FARM COARSE FISHERY Cornwall

TRIMDON STATION
- TRIMDON POND County Durham

TRING
- THAME (RIVER) Buckinghamshire
- AYLESBURY ARM CANAL Hertfordshire
- GRAND UNION CANAL Hertfordshire
- MARSWORTH RESERVOIR Hertfordshire
- RISLIP LAKE Hertfordshire
- STARTOPS RESERVOIR Hertfordshire
- THAME (RIVER) Hertfordshire
- TRING RESERVOIRS Hertfordshire
- WILSTONE RESERVOIR Hertfordshire

TROWBRIDGE
- BISS (RIVER) Wiltshire
- CUCKOOS REST Wiltshire
- KENNET AND AVON CANAL Wiltshire
- ROOD ASHTON LAKE Wiltshire
- WOODLAND PARK Wiltshire

TRURO
- GOONHAVERN COARSE FISHING LAKE Cornwall
- GWARNICK MILL TROUT FISHERY Cornwall
- LANGARTH POOLS Cornwall
- MELLONWATTS MILL Cornwall
- ROSEWATER LAKE Cornwall
- STITHIANS RESERVOIR Cornwall
- TIN DENE FISHERY Cornwall
- TORY FARM LAKE Cornwall
- TRENESTRALL LAKE Cornwall
- VENTONTRISSICK FISHERY Cornwall
- CAMEL (RIVER) Devon

TUNBRIDGE WELLS
- BARTLEY MILL FISHERY Kent
- BIRCHDEN FARM FISHERY Kent
- CHALYBEATE SPRINGS TROUT FISHERY Kent
- DUNDALE LAKE Kent
- FORDCOMBE Kent
- FRANT LAKES Kent
- HAWKHURST FISH FARM Kent
- MEDWAY (RIVER) Kent
- SCARLETTS LAKE Kent
- SPRING HILL TROUT WATERS Kent
- TEISE (RIVER) Kent
- FRAMFIELD PARK FISHERIES Sussex (East)
- PENNY BRIDGE Sussex (East)
- YEW TREE TROUT FISHERY Sussex (East)

TURNFORD
- SLIPE LANE PITS Hertfordshire

TURSDALE
- TEASDALE POND County Durham

UCKFIELD
- BORINGWHEEL TROUT FISHERY Sussex (East)
- BUXTED OAST FISHERY Sussex (East)
- BUXTED PARK FISHERY Sussex (East)
- COLIN GODMANS TROUTING Sussex (East)
- CYPRUS WOOD TROUT FISHERY Sussex (East)
- FRAMFIELD PARK FISHERIES Sussex (East)
- HONEYS GREEN COARSE FISHERY Sussex (East)
- ISFIELD (RIVER) Sussex (East)
- LOWER HONEYS GREEN FARM Sussex (East)
- PIPPINGFORD PARK ESTATE LAKES Sussex (East)
- TANYARD FISHERIES Sussex (East)
- UNDERHILL LAKE Sussex (East)

ULLESKELF
- ULLESKELF (RIVER) Yorkshire (North)

ULVERSTON
- BIGLAND HALL LAKE Cumbria
- HIGH NEWTON RESERVOIR Cumbria
- ULVERSTON CANAL Cumbria

ULVERSTONE
- BIGLAND HALL LAKE Cumbria

UMBERLEIGH
- MOLE (RIVER) Devon

UPMINSTER
- BULPHAN PARK FISHERIES Essex
- HARWOOD HALL LAKE Essex
- PEA LANE FISHERY Essex
- SLOUGH HOUSE LAKE Essex

UPPER ARLEY
- DOWLES BROOK Worcestershire

UPPER MARHAM
- NAR (RIVER) Norfolk

UPPINGHAM
- EYEBROOK TROUT FISHERY Leicestershire
- SWEETHEDGES FARM FISHERY Rutland

UPTON
- HAMWORTHY LAKE Dorset
- SEVERN (RIVER) Worcestershire

UPTON UPON SEVERN
- SEVERN (RIVER) Worcestershire

UTTOXETER
- ALDAMORE POOL Derbyshire
- BLITHE (RIVER) Staffordshire
- CHURNET (RIVER) Staffordshire
- CHURNET (RIVER) Staffordshire
- DOVE (RIVER) Staffordshire
- WOODSEAT LAKE Staffordshire

UXBRIDGE
- BILLET LANE Buckinghamshire
- COLNE (RIVER) London (Greater)
- COWLEY LAKE London (Greater)
- CUTTING LAKE London (Greater)
- FLAKE STREAM London (Greater)
- GRAND UNION CANAL London (Greater)
- STOCKLEY ROAD LAKES London (Greater)

VENTNOR
- NETTLECOMBE FARMS Isle of Wight
- ROOKLEY COUNTRY PARK Isle of Wight
- WHITWELL PONDS Isle of Wight

WADEBRIDGE
- CAMEL (RIVER) Cornwall

WADHURST
- SPRING WOOD FISHERY AND FARM Sussex (East)

WAINFLEET ALL SAINTS
- GROOBYS PIT Lincolnshire

WAKEFIELD
- FLANSHAW DAM Yorkshire (West)
- HORBURY LAGOON Yorkshire (West)
- NOSTELL PRIORY LAKE Yorkshire (West)
- PUGNEYS COUNTRY PARK Yorkshire (West)
- SPRING VALLEY WATERS Yorkshire (West)

WALTON HALL TROUT LAKE Yorkshire (West)
WINTERSETT RESERVOIR Yorkshire (West)

WALLINGFORD

BENSON LOCK Oxfordshire
DORCHESTER LAGOON Oxfordshire
ORCHID LAKES Oxfordshire
THAME (RIVER) Oxfordshire
THAMES (RIVER) Oxfordshire

WALMERSLEY

LEEKES WATER Manchester (Greater)

WALSALL

CANNOCK EXTENSION CANAL Midlands (west)
FOXHILLS FISHERY Midlands (West)
HEATHFIELD POOL Midlands (west)
RUSHALL CANAL Midlands (West)
SNEYD POOL Midlands (West)
TAME VALLEY CANAL Midlands (West)
WALSALL ARBORETUM Midlands (West)
PARK LIME PIT Norfolk

WALSINGHAM

WENSUM (RIVER) Norfolk

WALTHAM ABBEY

CLAVERHAMBURY LAKE Essex
CROWN NETHERHALL Essex
FISHERS GREEN Essex
HOLYFIELD FISHERY Essex
HOOKS MARSH Essex
JOHNS LAKE FISHERIES Essex
KNIGHTS PIT Essex
LEA (RIVER) Essex
LEE FLOOD RELIEF CHANNEL Essex
MAGIC LAKE Essex
NAZEING MEADS Essex
PICKS COTTAGE CARP LAKES Essex
BOWYERS WATER Hertfordshire
OLD MILL AND MEADOWS Hertfordshire
OLD LEE (RIVER) London (Greater)

WALTHAM CROSS

BOWYERS WATER Hertfordshire
BROOKFIELD LAKE Hertfordshire
CHESHUNT SOUTH RESERVOIR Hertfordshire
LEE NAVIGATION Hertfordshire
NORTH MET PIT Hertfordshire
OLD LEE (RIVER) Hertfordshire
PAYNES LANE PIT Hertfordshire

WALTHAMSTOW

HIGHAMS PARK LAKE London (Greater)
HOLLOW PONDS London (Greater)

WALTON

NIDD (RIVER) Yorkshire (North)

WALTON-ON-THAMES

SHEPPERTON LAKE London (Greater)
MOLE (RIVER) Surrey

WANDSWORTH

WANDSWORTH COMMON POND London (Greater)

WANLIP

WATERMEAD PARK LAKES Leicestershire

WANSFORD

YARWELL MILL LAKE Cambridgeshire

WANSTEAD

WANSTEAD AND WOODFORD PONDS Essex

WANTAGE

CLEARWATER FISH FARM Oxfordshire
LOCKINGE TROUT FISHERY Oxfordshire

WARE

AMWELL LAKES Hertfordshire
LEE NAVIGATION Hertfordshire
NEW RIVER Hertfordshire
RIB VALLEY FISHING LAKE Hertfordshire
STANSTEAD ABBOTTS Hertfordshire

WAREHAM

DORSET FROME Dorset
FROME (RIVER) Dorset
HYDE LAKE Dorset
PIDDLE (RIVER) Dorset

WARMINSTER

AVON (RIVER) Wiltshire
CROCKERTON POND Wiltshire
HUNTERS MOON Wiltshire
LONGLEAT LAKES Wiltshire
SHEAR WATER Wiltshire
SOUTHLEIGH LAKE Wiltshire
SUTTON VENY ESTATE Wiltshire
TURNERS PADDOCK LAKE Wiltshire
ZEALS TROUT FISHERY Wiltshire

WARRINGTON

ACKERS PIT Cheshire
APPLETON RESERVOIR Cheshire
BELMONT POOL Cheshire
BLUNDELLS FARM FISHERY Cheshire
BRIDGEWATER CANAL Cheshire
BROOKSIDE LAKES Cheshire
BROWNLEES POND Cheshire
FRIARS POOL Cheshire
GREY MIST MERE Cheshire
GRIMESDITCH MILL POOL Cheshire
GRIMSDITCH MILL POOL Cheshire
HAYDAN FISHERY Cheshire
LONGBARN POOL Cheshire
LYMM DAM Cheshire
MARY ANN POND Cheshire
MEADOW VIEW FISHERY Cheshire
MICKS LAKE Cheshire
MONKS MOAT Cheshire
MOORE QUARRY Cheshire
OAK POOL Cheshire
OLD QUAY CANAL Cheshire
ORFORD PARK POND Cheshire
PARTRIDGE LAKES Cheshire
SANKEY ST HELENS CANAL Cheshire
STATHAM POOL Cheshire
STRETTON WATER Cheshire
TOP FARM POOL Cheshire
VILLAGE POOL Cheshire
WEAVER (RIVER) Cheshire
WHITEGATE POND Cheshire
WHITLEY POOL Cheshire
WILLOW POOL Cheshire
YEW TREE POOL Cheshire
DOUBLEWOODS Manchester (Greater)

WARSOP

MAUN (RIVER) Nottinghamshire

WARWICK

AVON (RIVER) Midlands (West)
ARDENCOTE MANOR HOTEL AND COUNTRY CLUB Warwickshire
GRAND UNION CANAL Warwickshire
HEATHCOTE LAKE Warwickshire
KINGSTON POOLS Warwickshire
OAKHAM FARM POOLS Warwickshire
PARK FARM Warwickshire
TUNNEL BARN FARM Warwickshire
WARWICKSHIRE AVON Warwickshire

WASHINGTON

MOUNT PLEASANT LAKE Tyne and Wear
WEAR (RIVER) Tyne and Wear
WILLOWS (THE) Tyne and Wear

WATENDLATH

BLEA TARN Yorkshire (North)

WATERBEACH

MAGPIE LAKE Cambridgeshire

WATFORD

ALDENHAM RESERVOIR Hertfordshire
GADE (RIVER) Hertfordshire
GRAND UNION CANAL Hertfordshire

WATTON

LOCH NEATON Norfolk

WEDMORE

HORSESHOE LAKE Somerset
LANDS END FARM Somerset
LANDS END FISHERIES Somerset

WEEL

HULL (RIVER) Humberside

WELFORD

WELFORD RESERVOIR Northamptonshire

WELLAND BANK

CROWLAND ANGLING CLUB LAKES Cambridgeshire

WELLINGBOROUGH

BLUNHAM PITS Northamptonshire
CHESTER FARM LAKE Northamptonshire
DITCHFORD PITS Northamptonshire
LITTLE IRCHESTER COMPLEX Northamptonshire
PINE TREES LAKES Northamptonshire
SOUTH VIEW FARM CARP FISHERY Northamptonshire
SYWELL RESERVOIR Northamptonshire

WELLINGTON

KINGSMEAD CENTRE Devon
MARSH HOUSE FARM Herefordshire
ELLERDINE LAKES Shropshire
SEVERN (RIVER) Shropshire
TERN (RIVER) Shropshire
LANGFORD LAKES Somerset
WELLINGTON BASIN Somerset

WELLS

EMBOROUGH POOL Somerset
HORSESHOE LAKE Somerset

WELLS-NEXT-THE-SEA

HOLKHAM LAKE Norfolk

WELSHAMPTON

COLEMERE COUNTRY PARK Shropshire

WELWYN GARDEN CITY

HOLWELL HYDE LAKE Hertfordshire
LEA (RIVER) Hertfordshire
STANBOROUGH LAKE Hertfordshire

WENNING

BENTHAM STREAM Lancashire

WEST BRIDGFORD

TRENT (RIVER) Nottinghamshire

WEST BROMWICH
- **DARTMOUTH PARK** Midlands (West)
- **SWAN POOL** Midlands (West)

WEST BYFLEET
- **WEY (RIVER)** Surrey

WEST DEEPING
- **REDLANDS PITS** Cambridgeshire

WEST DRAYTON
- **MAYFIELDS LAKE** Buckinghamshire
- **BEDFONT LAKE** London (Greater)
- **GRAND UNION CANAL** London (Greater)
- **LIZARD LAKES** London (Greater)

WEST GORTON
- **TURKS HEAD RESERVOIR** Cheshire

WEST HORNDON
- **PAR** Essex

WEST LONDON
- **OSTERLEY PARK MIDDLE LAKE** London (Greater)

WEST LOOE
- **FOWEY (RIVER)** Cornwall
- **FOWEY (RIVER)** Cornwall
- **INNY (RIVER)** Cornwall
- **LYNHER (RIVER)** Cornwall
- **SEATON (RIVER)** Cornwall

WEST TANFIELD
- **TANFIELD LAKE** Yorkshire (North)

WEST WOODBURN
- **REDE (RIVER)** Northumberland

WESTBURY
- **CLIVEY PONDS** Wiltshire
- **CUCKOOS REST** Wiltshire
- **WOODLAND PARK** Wiltshire

WESTHAY
- **AVALON FISHERIES** Somerset
- **WESTHAY** Somerset

WESTON-SUPER-MARE
- **HUTON POND** Somerset
- **PARRETT (RIVER)** Somerset
- **YEO (RIVER)** Somerset

WETHERBY
- **BOSTON SPA** Yorkshire (West)
- **OUSE (RIVER)** Yorkshire (West)
- **WHARFE (RIVER)** Yorkshire (West)

WEYBRIDGE
- **MOLE (RIVER)** Surrey

WEYMOUTH
- **OSMINGTON MILLS** Dorset
- **RADIPOLE LAKE** Dorset
- **WALLYS LAKE** Dorset
- **WARMWELL HOLIDAY PARK** Dorset

WHALLEY
- **RIBBLE (RIVER)** Lancashire

WHATSTANDWELL
- **TRENT (RIVER)** Derbyshire

WHETHERBY
- **NIDD (RIVER)** Yorkshire (North)

WHITBY
- **DANBY (RIVER)** Yorkshire (North)
- **EGTON BRIDGE (RIVER)** Yorkshire (North)
- **EGTON ESTATE BEAT** Yorkshire (North)
- **ESK (RIVER)** Yorkshire (North)
- **GLAISDALE (RIVER)** Yorkshire (North)
- **RUSWARP (RIVER)** Yorkshire (North)
- **SLEIGHTS (RIVER)** Yorkshire (North)

WHITCHURCH
- **MARBURY MERE** Cheshire
- **WHITLEY POOL** Cheshire
- **APLEY POOLS** Shropshire
- **BLAKEMERE** Shropshire
- **DEARNFORD HALL TROUT FISHERY** Shropshire
- **OSS MERE** Shropshire
- **WHITCHURCH LAKE** Shropshire

WHITEHAVEN
- **ENNERDALE LAKE FISHERY** Cumbria
- **ESK (RIVER)** Cumbria

WHITTLESEY
- **EAST DELPH LAKES** Cambridgeshire
- **ELDERNELL LAKE** Cambridgeshire
- **KINGSLAND RESERVOIRS** Cambridgeshire
- **TWENTY FOOT DRAIN** Cambridgeshire
- **WHITTLESEY DYKE/ BEVILLS LEAM** Cambridgeshire

WIDNES
- **SANKEY ST HELENS CANAL** Cheshire
- **SANKEY ST HELENS CANAL (LAC)** Cheshire

WIGAN
- **ANGLEZARKE RESERVOIR** Lancashire
- **ASHTON CANAL** Lancashire
- **BICKERSHAW WATERS** Lancashire
- **BRYN FLASH** Lancashire
- **DEEP PIT** Lancashire
- **DOUGLAS (RIVER)** Lancashire
- **FAN LODGE** Lancashire
- **FIR TREE LODGE** Lancashire
- **FORSTERS LODGES** Lancashire
- **HIGHER HALL FLASH** Lancashire
- **HORROCKS FLASH** Lancashire
- **HOUGHTONS LODGE** Lancashire
- **INCE MOSS FISHERIES** Lancashire
- **INCE PARK LAKE** Lancashire
- **ISLAND DAM** Lancashire
- **MELLINGS NO 1** Lancashire
- **ORRELL WATER PARK** Lancashire
- **POLLYS FLASH** Lancashire
- **SCOT LANE PONDS** Lancashire
- **SQUARE LODGE** Lancashire
- **THREE SISTERS** Lancashire
- **WIDOWS FLASH** Lancashire

WIGTON
- **MOORHOUSE TARN** Cumbria

WILLINGFORD
- **SEVERALLS FARM A AND B** Oxfordshire

WILLINGTON
- **WEAR (RIVER)** County Durham

WILLOUGHBY WATERLEASE
- **WHETSTONE GORSE** Leicestershire

WILMSLOW
- **BLACK LAKE** Cheshire
- **CAPESTHORNE HALL STOCK POND** Cheshire
- **CAPESTHORNE MAIN POOL** Cheshire
- **CAPESTHORNE TOP POOL** Cheshire
- **DEAN (RIVER)** Cheshire
- **FANSHAWE LANE POOL** Cheshire
- **REDESMERE** Cheshire
- **ROSSMERE** Cheshire

WILTON
- **AVON (RIVER)** Wiltshire

WIMBLEDON
- **ASHVALE FISHERIES** London (Greater)

WIMBORNE
- **CRANBOURNE FRUIT FARM** Dorset
- **CRANEBROOK TROUT FISHERY** Dorset
- **FROME AND PIDDLE (RIVERS)** Dorset
- **GOLD OAK FISH FARM** Dorset
- **HILLVIEW FARM LAKE** Dorset
- **HOLT WOOD PONDS** Dorset
- **MARTINS FARM** Dorset
- **STOUR (DORSET) (RIVER)** Dorset
- **STOUR (RIVER)** Dorset
- **WHITEMOOR LAKE** Dorset
- **WHITESHEET TROUT FISHERY** Dorset

WIMBORNE MINSTER
- **HOLT WOOD PONDS** Dorset

WINCHAM
- **WINCHAM BROOK** Cheshire

WINCHESTER
- **ABBOTTS WORTHY** Hampshire
- **AVINGTON TROUT FISHERIES** Hampshire
- **DEVER SPRINGS TROUT FISHERY** Hampshire
- **ITCHEN (RIVER)** Hampshire
- **NETHER WALLOP FLY FISHING SCHOOL** Hampshire
- **TEST (RIVER)** Hampshire
- **TOPACRE LAKE** Hampshire

WINDERMERE
- **ATKINSONS TARN COARSE FISHERY** Cumbria
- **BLENHEIM LODGE HOTEL** Cumbria
- **BORRANS RESERVOIR** Cumbria
- **CLEABARROW TARN** Cumbria
- **DUBBS TROUT FISHERY** Cumbria
- **GHYLL HEAD TROUT FISHERY** Cumbria
- **HIGH NEWTON RESERVOIR** Cumbria
- **HOLEHIRD TARN** Cumbria
- **LAKE WINDERMERE** Cumbria
- **SCHOOL KNOTT TARN** Cumbria

WINDSOR
- **ALBERT BRIDGE** Berkshire
- **PRIORY WATER** Berkshire
- **ROMNEY ISLAND AND MEADOW** Berkshire
- **ROYAL BERKSHIRE FISHERY** Berkshire
- **THAMES (RIVER)** Berkshire

WINGATE
- **BEAUMONT FISHERIES** County Durham

WINGERWORTH
- **PRESS MANOR** Derbyshire

WINKLEIGH
- **LITTLE WARHAM FISHERY** Devon
- **STAFFORD MOOR FISHERY** Devon

WINNERSH
- **WHITE SWAN LAKE** Berkshire

WINSFORD
- **LYMM VALE** Cheshire
- **NEW BRIDGE POOL** Cheshire
- **OCEAN POOL** Cheshire
- **STOCKPOND** Cheshire
- **WEAVER NAVIGATION** Cheshire
- **WINSFORD FLASH** Cheshire

WINSOR
- **THAMES (RIVER)** Berkshire

WIRRAL
- **ARROWE PARK LAKE** Merseyside
- **CENTRAL PARK LAKE** Merseyside
- **EVE A LYN FARM** Merseyside
- **MORETON MERE** Merseyside

- **POULTON RECREATION FIELD POOL** Merseyside
- **ROODEE MERE** Merseyside
- **WOODSLEE POOL** Merseyside

WISBECH

- **MIDDLE LEVEL DRAIN** Cambridgeshire
- **PISCES CARAVAN PARK AND FISHERY** Cambridgeshire
- **VIRGINIA LAKE** Cambridgeshire
- **WIMBLINGTON MERE** Cambridgeshire

WITHAM

- **BLACKWATER (RIVER)** Essex
- **BRAXTED HALL ESTATE** Essex
- **CANTS MERE** Essex
- **LITTLE BRAXTED FARM ESTATE** Essex
- **SILVER END PIT** Essex
- **WILLOWS** Essex

WITHERNSEA

- **HALSHAM POND** Humberside

WITHERSLACK

- **WITHERSLACK HALL TARN** Cumbria

WITHNELL

- **WITHNELL RESERVOIRS** Lancashire

WITNEY

- **BARNES TROUT LAKES** Oxfordshire
- **CHRISTCHURCH LAKE** Oxfordshire
- **DARLOW LAKE** Oxfordshire
- **EYNSHAM LOCK** Oxfordshire
- **FARMOOR 1 RESERVOIR** Oxfordshire
- **GAUNTS LAKE** Oxfordshire
- **HARDWICK LAKE AND SMITHS POOL** Oxfordshire
- **HEYFORD LAKES** Oxfordshire
- **HUNTS CORNER** Oxfordshire
- **LINCH HILL FISHERY** Oxfordshire
- **MANOR FARM LAKE** Oxfordshire
- **OXLEASE LAKE** Oxfordshire
- **ST JOHNS POOL** Oxfordshire
- **STATES LAGOON** Oxfordshire
- **THAMES (RIVER)** Oxfordshire
- **UNITY LAKE** Oxfordshire
- **WINDRUSH (RIVER)** Oxfordshire
- **YEOMANS LAKE** Oxfordshire

WIVELISCOMBE

- **CLATWORTHY RESERVOIR** Somerset
- **OXENLEAZE FARM CARAVANS AND COARSE FISHERY** Somerset

WOKING

- **BOLDERMERE** Surrey
- **BRITTENS POND** Surrey
- **GOLDSWORTH WATER PARK** Surrey
- **PAPERCOURT FISHERY** Surrey
- **SEND PIT** Surrey
- **WEY (RIVER)** Surrey
- **WEY NAVIGATION (RIVER)** Surrey

WOKINGHAM

- **ASHRIDGE MANOR** Berkshire
- **HOLME GRANGE** Berkshire
- **JINGLES FARM** Berkshire
- **LODDON (RIVER)** Berkshire
- **LONGMOOR FARM FISHING LAKE** Berkshire
- **LONGMOOR LAKE** Berkshire
- **WHITE SWAN LAKE** Berkshire

WOLSINGHAM

- **TUNSTALL RESERVOIR** County Durham

WOLVERCOTE

- **THAMES (RIVER)** Oxfordshire

WOLVERHAMPTON

- **BRIDGE POOL** Midlands (West)
- **CHURCH POOL** Midlands (West)
- **HERON BROOK FISHERY** Midlands (West)
- **HIMLEY ISLAND POOL** Midlands (West)
- **LINCOMB LOCK** Midlands (West)
- **PATSHULL PARK** Midlands (West)
- **POOLE HALL FARM** Midlands (West)
- **STAFFORD TO WORCESTER CANAL** Midlands (West)
- **MILLRIDE FISHERY** Shropshire
- **WYRLEY ESSINGTON CANAL** Shropshire
- **ALBRIGHTON MOAT PROJECT** Staffordshire
- **HIMLEY HALL AND PARK LAKE** Staffordshire
- **SHROPSHIRE UNION CANAL** Staffordshire

WOLVERTON

- **OUSE (RIVER)** Buckinghamshire

WOMBOURNE

- **HIMLEY ISLAND POOL** Midlands (West)

WOODBRIDGE

- **BREAKAWAY PIT** Suffolk
- **BRIDGE FARM RESERVOIRS** Suffolk
- **DEBEN (RIVER)** Suffolk
- **LOAM POND** Suffolk
- **MELTON LAKE** Suffolk
- **PETTISTREE LAKES** Suffolk
- **SWALE PIT** Suffolk
- **WICKHAM MARKET RESERVOIRS** Suffolk

WOODHALL SPA

- **PEACOCK LAKE** Lincolnshire

WOODSTOCK

- **BLADON LAKE** Oxfordshire
- **BLENHEIM LAKE** Oxfordshire
- **CHERWELL (RIVER)** Oxfordshire
- **CHERWELL (RIVER)** Oxfordshire

WOODVILLE

- **HARTSHORNE DAMS** Staffordshire

WOOLFARDISWORTHY

- **CLOVELLY LAKES** Devon

WOOLWICH

- **WOOLWICH DOCKYARD** London (Greater)

WORCESTER

- **ACR FISHERIES** Worcestershire
- **BENNETTS POOL** Worcestershire
- **BIRMINGHAM TO WORCESTER CANAL** Worcestershire
- **BIRMINGHAM TO WORCESTER CANAL** Worcestershire
- **BRAKE MILL POOL** Worcestershire
- **BRANSFORD GAME FISHERY** Worcestershire
- **BROCKAMIN POOLS** Worcestershire
- **CASTLE GREEN POOLS** Worcestershire
- **EVESBATCH FISHERIES** Worcestershire
- **GROVE FARM** Worcestershire
- **HARVEY POOL** Worcestershire
- **HOLT FLEET POOL** Worcestershire
- **LEIGH SINTON FISHING LAKES** Worcestershire
- **LENCHFORD** Worcestershire
- **LOWER BROADHEATH POOLS** Worcestershire
- **SALWARPE (RIVER)** Worcestershire
- **SEVERN (RIVER)** Worcestershire
- **STAINFORTH AND KEADBY CANAL** Worcestershire
- **TEME (RIVER)** Worcestershire
- **TEME (RIVER)** Worcestershire
- **TEME (RIVER)** Worcestershire
- **TOP BARN ANGLING CENTRE** Worcestershire
- **UCKINGHALL POOL** Worcestershire
- **WARWICKSHIRE AVON** Worcestershire
- **WASH POOL** Worcestershire
- **WHARFE INN POOL** Worcestershire
- **WITLEY FISHERY** Worcestershire
- **WITLEY POOLS** Worcestershire

WORKSOP

- **CLUMBER LAKE** Nottinghamshire
- **LANGOLD LAKES** Nottinghamshire
- **OWDY LANE TROUT FISHERY** Nottinghamshire
- **SANDHILL LAKE** Nottinghamshire
- **WOODEND QUARRY POND** Nottinghamshire
- **WOODSETTS QUARRY POND** Nottinghamshire
- **CHESTERFIELD CANAL** Yorkshire (South)
- **DUKERIES LAKES** Yorkshire (South)
- **HARTHILL RESERVIORS** Yorkshire (South)
- **SHIREOAKS PARK** Yorkshire (South)

WORMLEY

- **KINGS WEIR FISHERY** Hertfordshire
- **LEA (RIVER)** Hertfordshire
- **LEA NAVIGATION** Hertfordshire
- **OLD LEE (RIVER)** Hertfordshire

WORTHENBURY

- **EMRAL BROOK** Wrexham
- **WYCH BROOK** Wrexham

WORTHING

- **ADUR (RIVER)** Sussex (West)
- **ADUR (RIVER)** Sussex (West)
- **MILL FARM FISHERY** Sussex (West)

WORTON

- **URE (RIVER)** Yorkshire (North)

WORTWELL

- **WAVENEY VALLEY LAKES** Suffolk

WRAGBY

- **GOLTHO LAKE** Lincolnshire
- **HATTON TROUT LAKE** Lincolnshire

WRAYSBURY

- **COLNEBROOK (RIVER)** Buckinghamshire
- **SILVERWING LAKE** Buckinghamshire
- **WATTS POOL** Buckinghamshire
- **CARGILL LAKE** London (Greater)

WREXHAM

- **CLYWEDOG (RIVER)** Wrexham
- **DEE (RIVER)** Wrexham
- **EMRAL BROOK** Wrexham
- **WYCH BROOK** Wrexham

WROTHAM

- **ST CLERE LAKE** Kent

WROXHAM

- **BURE (RIVER)** Norfolk
- **HORNING (RIVER)** Norfolk
- **WROXHAM BROAD** Norfolk

WYLAM

- **TYNE (RIVER)** Northumberland
- **WILLIES WELL** Northumberland

YALDING

- **MEDWAY (RIVER)** Kent

YARCOMBE

- **STILL WATERS TROUT FISHERY** Devon

YARE

- **TASWOOD LAKES FISH FARM AND FISHERY** Norfolk

YARM

- **HUTTON RUDBY PONDS** Cleveland
- **LEVEN (RIVER)** Tyne and Wear
- **TEES (RIVER)** Tyne and Wear

YATELEY

- **FIRGROVE LAKES** Hampshire
- **NUTRABAITS YATELEY COMPLEX** Hampshire
- **NUTRABAITS YATELEY SOUTH LAKE** Hampshire

YEADON

- **YEADON TARN** Yorkshire (West)

YEALMPTON

- **SUNRIDGE FISHERY** Devon

YELVERTON

- **BURRATOR RESERVOIR** Devon

YEOVIL

- **FLOWERS FARM TROUT LAKES** Dorset
- **OLD MILL FISHERY** Somerset
- **SUTTON BINGHAM RESERVOIR** Somerset
- **THORNEY LAKES** Somerset
- **YEO (RIVER)** Somerset

YORK

- **ALDWARK BRIDGE** Yorkshire (North)
- **BIRKDALE FISHERY** Yorkshire (North)
- **BRAFFERTON COARSE FISHERY** Yorkshire (North)
- **CARP VALE** Yorkshire (North)
- **CASTLE HOWARD GREAT LAKE** Yorkshire (North)
- **CHAPMANS POND** Yorkshire (North)
- **CLAXTON BRICKWORKS** Yorkshire (North)
- **CUNDALL LODGE FISHERY** Yorkshire (North)
- **DERWENT (RIVER)** Yorkshire (North)
- **EAST COTTINGWITH WATERS** Yorkshire (North)
- **ELLERTON LANDING** Yorkshire (North)
- **ELVINGTON LAKE** Yorkshire (North)
- **FLETCHERS POND** Yorkshire (North)
- **FOGGLESKYTE WATERS** Yorkshire (North)
- **FOSS (RIVER)** Yorkshire (North)
- **GRAFTON MERE** Yorkshire (North)
- **HESSAY POND** Yorkshire (North)
- **HOXNE FARM PONDS** Yorkshire (North)
- **KILBURN POND** Yorkshire (North)
- **LAKEHOUSE LAKE** Yorkshire (North)
- **LAKESIDE LODGES** Yorkshire (North)
- **LINGCROFT FARM POND** Yorkshire (North)
- **LOWER DUNSFORTH (RIVER)** Yorkshire (North)
- **MARKET WEIGHTON CANAL** Yorkshire (North)
- **MARSTON WYSE TROUT FARM** Yorkshire (North)
- **MILBY CUT** Yorkshire (North)
- **MOORLANDS FARM PONDS** Yorkshire (North)
- **NIDD (RIVER)** Yorkshire (North)
- **NORTHINGALES FISHERY** Yorkshire (North)
- **NUN MONKTON (RIVER)** Yorkshire (North)
- **OAK MERE FISHERY** Yorkshire (North)
- **OAKTREE LEISURE** Yorkshire (North)
- **ORCHARD FARM PONDS** Yorkshire (North)
- **OUSE (RIVER)** Yorkshire (North)
- **OUSE (RIVER)** Yorkshire (North)
- **POCKLINGTON CANAL** Yorkshire (North)
- **POOL BRIDGE FARM LAKES** Yorkshire (North)
- **POPPLETON (RIVER)** Yorkshire (North)
- **POTTERY LAKE** Yorkshire (North)
- **RAKER LAKES** Yorkshire (North)
- **RASKELF LAKE** Yorkshire (North)
- **REDHOUSE LAGOON** Yorkshire (North)
- **RYE (RIVER)** Yorkshire (North)
- **SINNINGTON (RIVER)** Yorkshire (North)
- **SWALE (RIVER)** Yorkshire (North)
- **THORNTON BRIDGE** Yorkshire (North)
- **THORPE UNDERWOOD** Yorkshire (North)
- **TOLLERTON FISHING PONDS** Yorkshire (North)
- **URE (RIVER)** Yorkshire (North)
- **WATERMEADOWS FISHERY** Yorkshire (North)
- **WESTERLY LAKE** Yorkshire (North)
- **WILLOW WATER** Yorkshire (North)
- **WILLOWS** Yorkshire (North)
- **YORKSHIRE OUSE** Yorkshire (North)

by Water Type by County

SECTION 4

This section allows you to search for Fisheries with certain water types, lakes, brooks, rivers, dams etc.

e.g Find lochs in Scotland, Highland

Once you have located a Fishery you can either look up further details in Section 1 or use the other sections to find what else the Fishery may have to offer.

BROOKS

CHESHIRE

- WINCHAM BROOK Northwich
- WITTON BROOK Northwich

DERBYSHIRE

- SUTTON BROOK Hilton

GLOUCESTERSHIRE

- WATERLEY BROOK Berkeley

HAMPSHIRE

- CANDOVER BROOK Alresford

WORCESTERSHIRE

- DOWLES BROOK Bewdley

WREXHAM

- EMRAL BROOK Worthenbury
- WYCH BROOK Worthenbury

CANALS

BERKSHIRE

- BURGHFIELD CANAL Reading
- EAST TOWNEY Reading
- FROXFIELD A AND B Hungerford
- KENNET AND AVON CANAL Reading
- THEALE CANAL Reading
- UFTON CANAL Reading

BUCKINGHAMSHIRE

- BOWLERS CANAL Olney
- GRAND UNION CANAL Milton Keynes

CAMBRIDGESHIRE

- OFFORD CLUNY Huntingdon

CHESHIRE

- BREAM HOLE Nantwich
- BRIDGEWATER CANAL Runcorn
- BRIDGEWATER CANAL Sale
- BRIDGEWATER CANAL Warrington
- HUDDERSFIELD NARROW CANAL Stalybridge
- LLANGOLLEN CANAL Nantwich
- MACCLESFIELD CANAL Congleton
- MACCLESFIELD CANAL Macclesfield
- MIDDLEWICH BRANCH CANAL Nantwich
- OLD QUAY CANAL Warrington
- OLDHAMS WATER Hyde
- PEAK FOREST CANAL Dukinfield
- SANKEY ST HELENS CANAL Runcorn
- SANKEY ST HELENS CANAL Widnes
- SANKEY ST HELENS CANAL (LAC) Widnes
- SHROPSHIRE UNION CANAL Crewe
- TRENT AND MERSEY CANAL Sandbach
- WEAVER NAVIGATION Winsford

CORNWALL

- BUDE CANAL Bude

CUMBRIA

- ULVERSTON CANAL Ulverston

DERBYSHIRE

- TRENT AND MERSEY CANAL Derby

DEVON

- EXETER CANAL Exeter
- EXETER SHIP CANAL Exeter
- GRAND WESTERN CANAL Cullompton
- GRAND WESTERN CANAL Tiverton

ESSEX

- CHELMER AND BLACKWATER NAVIGATION CANAL Chelmsford
- CHELMER AND BLACKWATER NAVIGATION CANAL Maldon

GLOUCESTERSHIRE

- GLOUCESTER AND SHARPNESS CANAL Gloucester
- GLOUCESTER CANAL Gloucester
- STROUDWATER CANAL Stonehouse

HAMPSHIRE

- BASINGSTOKE CANAL Basingstoke
- BASINGSTOKE CANAL Hook
- ITCHEN NAVIGATION Southampton

HERTFORDSHIRE

- AYLESBURY ARM CANAL Aylesbury
- AYLESBURY ARM CANAL Tring
- DOBBS WEIR FISHERY Hoddesdon
- GRAND UNION CANAL Berkhamsted
- GRAND UNION CANAL St Albans
- GRAND UNION CANAL Tring
- GRAND UNION CANAL Watford

HUMBERSIDE

- AIRE AND CALDER CANAL Goole
- BEVERLEY CANAL Beverley
- LEVEN CANAL Beverley
- LEVEN CANAL Hull
- MARKET WEIGHTON CANAL Goole

KENT

- ROYAL MILITARY CANAL Kennardington

LANCASHIRE

- ASHTON CANAL Wigan
- BOLTON CANAL Bolton
- HORROCKS FLASH Wigan
- LANCASTER CANAL Lancaster
- LANCASTER CANAL Preston
- LEEDS TO LIVERPOOL CANAL Burnley
- LEEDS TO LIVERPOOL CANAL Chorley
- LEEDS TO LIVERPOOL CANAL Ormskirk
- LEEDS TO LIVERPOOL CANAL Preston
- MANCHESTER, BOLTON AND BURY CANAL Bolton
- RUFFORD CANAL Ormskirk

LEICESTERSHIRE

- LEICESTER CANAL Leicester
- LEICESTER GRAND UNION CANAL Leicester
- LOUGHBOROUGH SOAR CANAL Loughborough

LONDON (GREATER)

- GRAND UNION CANAL London
- LEA NAVIGATION London
- REGENTS CANAL London

MANCHESTER (GREATER)

- BRIDGEWATER CANAL Manchester
- HUDDERSFIELD NARROW CANAL Oldham
- LEEDS TO LIVERPOOL CANAL Leigh
- LEIGH BRANCH CANAL Leigh
- MACCLESFIELD CANAL Stockport
- MANCHESTER CANAL Manchester
- MANCHESTER, BOLTON AND BURY CANAL Bury
- MANCHESTER, BOLTON AND BURY CANAL Manchester
- PEAK FOREST CANAL Stockport
- ROCHDALE CANAL Rochdale

MERSEYSIDE

- LEEDS TO LIVERPOOL Liverpool
- LEEDS TO LIVERPOOL CANAL Liverpool

MIDLANDS (WEST)

- CANNOCK EXTENSION CANAL Pelsall
- GRAND UNION CANAL Solihull
- RUSHALL CANAL Walsall
- SOHO LOOP CANAL Birmingham
- STAFFORD TO WORCESTER CANAL Wolverhampton
- TAME VALLEY CANAL Birmingham

NORFOLK

- ABBOTS HALL Norwich
- SALTHOUSE BROAD Holt
- WROXHAM BROAD Norwich

NORTHAMPTONSHIRE

- GRAND UNION CANAL Northampton
- NORTHAMPTON JUNCTION CANAL Northampton
- OXFORD CANAL Daventry

NOTTINGHAMSHIRE

- CHESTERFIELD CANAL Retford
- CRANFLEET CANAL Nottingham
- EREWASH CANAL Nottingham
- GRANTHAM CANAL Nottingham
- NOTTINGHAM CANAL Nottingham
- NOTTINGHAM CASTLE MARINA Nottingham

OXFORDSHIRE

- GRAND UNION CANAL Bulbourne
- GRAND UNION CANAL Oxford
- OXFORD CANAL Banbury
- OXFORD CANAL Bicester
- OXFORD CANAL Kidlington
- OXFORD CANAL Oxford

SHROPSHIRE

- BIRMINGHAM TO WORCESTER CANAL Broseley
- HAMPTON LOCK Bridgnorth
- NEWPORT CANAL Telford
- SHROPSHIRE UNION CANAL Market Drayton
- WYRLEY ESSINGTON CANAL Wolverhampton

SOMERSET

- KENNET AND AVON CANAL Bath
- KENNET AND AVON CANAL Bristol
- TAUNTON AND BRIDGWATER CANAL Bridgwater
- TAUNTON TO BRIDGWATER CANAL Bridgwater

STAFFORDSHIRE

- COVENTRY CANAL Tamworth
- DRAYTON BRIDGE Tamworth
- FRADLEY CANAL Burton-on-Trent
- MACCLESFIELD CANAL Stoke-on-Trent
- SHROPSHIRE UNION CANAL Stafford
- SHROPSHIRE UNION CANAL Wolverhampton
- STAFFORD AND WORCESTER CANAL Stafford
- STAFFORD TO WORCESTER CANAL Stafford
- TRENT AND MERSEY CANAL Burton-on-Trent
- TRENT AND MERSEY CANAL Stoke-on-Trent

SUSSEX (WEST)

- CHICESTER CANAL Chichester

WARWICKSHIRE

- ASHBY CANAL Nuneaton
- BANKS (THE) Rugby
- COVENTRY CANAL Nuneaton
- GRAND UNION CANAL Leamington Spa
- GRAND UNION CANAL Warwick
- NORTH OXFORD CANAL Rugby

OXFORD CANAL Leamington Spa
OXFORD CANAL Rugby
SOUTH STRATFORD CANAL Stratford-upon-Avon
WARWICK CANAL Leamington Spa

WILTSHIRE
KENNET AND AVON CANAL Bradford-on-Avon
KENNET AND AVON CANAL Devizes
KENNET AND AVON CANAL Marlborough
KENNET AND AVON CANAL Melksham
KENNET AND AVON CANAL Pewsey
KENNET AND AVON CANAL Trowbridge

WORCESTERSHIRE
BIRMINGHAM TO WORCESTER CANAL Bromsgrove
BIRMINGHAM TO WORCESTER CANAL Worcester
DROITWICH CANAL Droitwich
STAFFORD TO WORCESTER CANAL Stourport-on-Severn
STAINFORTH AND KEADBY CANAL Worcester

YORKSHIRE (NORTH)
MARKET WEIGHTON CANAL York
POCKLINGTON CANAL York
RIPON CANAL Ripon
SELBY CANAL Selby

YORKSHIRE (SOUTH)
BARNSLEY CANAL Barnsley
BRAMPTON CANAL Barnsley
CHESTERFIELD CANAL Sheffield
CHESTERFIELD CANAL Worksop
ELSECAR CANAL Barnsley
FITZWILLIAM CANAL Rotherham
MEXBOROUGH CANAL Mexborough
NEW JUNCTION CANAL Doncaster
SHEFFIELD AND SOUTH YORKSHIRE NAVIGATION Mexborough
SHEFFIELD AND SOUTH YORKSHIRE NAVIGATION Rotherham
SHEFFIELD CANAL Sheffield
SOUTH YORKSHIRE NAVIGATION CANAL Doncaster
STAINFORTH AND KEADBY CANAL Doncaster
WORSBROUGH CANAL Barnsley

YORKSHIRE (WEST)
AIRE AND CALDER CANAL Oulton
CALDER AND HEBBLE CANAL Brighouse
CALDER AND HEBBLE CANAL Hebden Bridge
HUDDERSFIELD BROAD CANAL Huddersfield
LEEDS AND LIVERPOOL CANAL Shipley
LEEDS TO LIVERPOOL CANAL Leeds
LEEDS TO LIVERPOOL CANAL Shipley
NARROW CANAL Huddersfield
ROCHDALE CANAL Halifax
ROCHDALE CANAL Hebden Bridge
ROCHDALE CANAL Todmorden

CLAY PITS

BERKSHIRE
FROBURY FARM SPORTING CLUB Newbury

CHESHIRE
MOOR POOL Lymm

CORNWALL
TEMPLE TROUT FISHERY Bodmin

COUNTY DURHAM
BEAUMONT FISHERIES Wingate

HUMBERSIDE
BIG HOLE PIT Goole
MOTORWAY POND Brough

KENT
NACCOLT LAKE Ashford

LINCOLNSHIRE
BRICKYARD FISHERY Louth
SYCAMORE FISHING LAKES Skegness
VICKERS POND Louth

NORTHAMPTONSHIRE
FOXHOLES FISHERIES Northampton

SHROPSHIRE
BACHE POOL Market Drayton

SUSSEX (EAST)
BRICK FARM LAKE Hailsham

YORKSHIRE (NORTH)
LAKEHOUSE LAKE York

COMBINATIONS

BEDFORDSHIRE
HAROLD FISHERY Bedford
HENLOW GRANGE Henlow
MANOR FARM LEISURE Biggleswade

BERKSHIRE
BURGHFIELD Reading
CHURCH FARM Sandhurst
DINTON PASTURES COUNTRY PARK Reading
OLD MILL Reading
PONDWOOD CARP LAKES Maidenhead
TWYFORD BBONT Reading
TWYFORD WATERS Reading
WHITE SWAN LAKE Wokingham

BRISTOL
BRISTOL DOCKS

BUCKINGHAMSHIRE
CHURCH HILL FISHERY Milton Keynes
COSGROVE LEISURE PARK Milton Keynes
DOVECOTE LAKE FISHERY Milton Keynes
LATIMER PARK FLY FISHERY Chesham
OLD SLADE LANE LAKE Iver
WESTFIELD FARM Marlow

CAMBRIDGESHIRE
PISCES CARAVAN PARK AND FISHERY Wisbech
WOOLPACK FISHERY Huntingdon

CHESHIRE
BROOKSIDE FISHERIES Crewe
DANE RIVERSIDE FISHERY Northwich
GOWY FISHERY Chester

CORNWALL
FENWICK TROUT FISHERY Bodmin

CUMBRIA
HAWESWATER Penrith

DERBYSHIRE
CATTON PARK LAKE Swadlincote

DEVON
DEER PARK COUNTRY HOTEL Honiton
HATCHLAND TROUT FISHERY South Brent
MILL LEAT TROUT FISHERY Holsworthy
NEWHOUSE FISHERY Totnes
OTTER FALLS FISHERY Honiton
TAMAR (RIVER) Lifton
TINNEY WATERS Holsworthy

ESSEX
BLACKWATER (RIVER) Maldon
BLASFORD HILL FISHERIES Chelmsford
BLUNTS AND CANTS MERES Chelmsford
BROAD GREEN AND TUFNELL MERE Chelmsford
COLNE (RIVER) Colchester
FENNES FISHERIES Braintree
FISHERS GREEN Waltham Abbey
LITTLE BRAXTED FARM ESTATE Witham
STRAITS MILL Braintree
WILLOWS Witham

GLOUCESTERSHIRE
RED LION FISHERY Gloucester

HAMPSHIRE
AVINGTON TROUT FISHERIES Winchester
DEVER SPRINGS TROUT FISHERY Winchester
HOLBURY LAKES Romsey
MEON SPRINGS FLY FISHERY Petersfield
NETHER WALLOP FLY FISHING SCHOOL Stockbridge
NUTRABAITS YATELEY COMPLEX Yateley
ROCKBOURNE TROUT FISHERY Fordingbridge
ROOKSBURY MILL TROUT FISHERIES Andover
WHINWHISTLE COARSE FISHERY Romsey
WOODMILL SALMON FISHERY Southampton

HEREFORDSHIRE
DOCKLOW POOLS Leominster
MOCCAS FISHERY Hereford
MUNDERFIELD HAROLD Bromyard

HERTFORDSHIRE
CARTHAGENA FISHERY Broxbourne
INNS LAKE Rickmansworth
KINGS WEIR FISHERY Broxbourne
OLD MILL AND MEADOWS Broxbourne
RYEMEADS Royston
STANSTEAD ABBOTTS Ware

HUMBERSIDE
DRIFFIELD CANAL Beverley

ISLE OF WIGHT
MORTON FARM Sandown

KENT
COTTINGTON LAKES TROUT AND COARSE FISHERY Deal
HAWKHURST FISH FARM Cranbrook
HAYSDEN COUNTRY PARK Tonbridge
MID KENT FISHERIES Canterbury

LANCASHIRE
ERIC FISHWICK NATURE RESERVE Preston
HUDSONS FARM Preston

LEICESTERSHIRE
MILL FARM FISHERY Lutterworth
NANPANTAN RESERVOIR Leicester
PROCTORS PLEASURE PARK Leicester

RUTLAND WATER Rutland
WATERY GATE FISHERY Leicester
WILLOWS FARM FISHING Leicester

LINCOLNSHIRE

BELVOIR CASTLE Grantham
LAKESIDE LEISURE PARK Skegness
OLSTEN FISHERY Louth

LONDON (GREATER)

HAMPSTEAD HEATH London
NORTH TROY LAKE AND COLNE (RIVER) London
STUDIO AND BROADWATER London

MANCHESTER (GREATER)

TWINE VALLEY TROUT FISHERY Bury

NORFOLK

COSTESSEY PITS Norwich
DISS MERE Diss
LENWADE COMMON LAKES Norwich
NARBOROUGH TROUT FARM King's Lynn
RINGLAND PITS Norwich
TAVERHAM Norwich
TAVERHAM MILLS FISHERY Norwich
WALNUT FARM FISHERIES Attleborough
WOODLAKES FISHERY King's Lynn

NORTHAMPTONSHIRE

BLUNHAM PITS Wellingborough
ELINOR TROUT FISHERY Kettering
LITTLE IRCHESTER COMPLEX Wellingborough
THRAPSTON LAKES Kettering

NOTTINGHAMSHIRE

A1 PITS Newark
HALLCROFT FISHERIES Retford
SMEATONS LAKES Newark

OXFORDSHIRE

CHEYNEY MANOR FISHERY Banbury
LOCKINGE TROUT FISHERY Wantage

SOMERSET

CAMELEY TROUT LAKES Bristol
KING SEDGEMOOR DRAIN Bridgwater
OLD MILL FISHERY Yeovil

STAFFORDSHIRE

BROWNING CUDMORE FISHERY Newcastle-under-Lyme
FISHERWICK LAKES Lichfield
HAMSTALL FISHERY Rugeley
HERONBROOK FISHERY Stafford
IZAAK WALTON FISHERY Stafford

SUFFOLK

NEEDHAM LAKE Ipswich

SURREY

ALBURY ESTATE FISHERIES Guildford
BEAVER FARM FISHERY Lingfield
CHERTSEY Chertsey
HENFOLD LAKES FISHERY Dorking
PAINSHILL PARK LAKE Cobham
WHIPLEY MANOR Guildford

SUSSEX (EAST)

FRAMFIELD PARK FISHERIES Uckfield
HORAM MANOR FISHERY Heathfield
IDEN WOOD FISHERY Rye
OLIVES FARM FISHERY Battle
ROSEBANK FARM FISHERY Heathfield
SPRING WOOD FISHERY AND FARM Wadhurst
WYLANDS INTERNATIONAL ANGLING CENTRE Battle

SUSSEX (WEST)

ADUR (RIVER) Henfield
WESTERN ROTHER Midhurst

WARWICKSHIRE

TUNNEL BARN FARM Warwick

WILTSHIRE

AVON (RIVER) Chippenham
AVON SPRINGS FISHERY Salisbury
HUNTERS MOON Warminster
LANGFORD FISHERIES Salisbury
ZEALS TROUT FISHERY Warminster

WORCESTERSHIRE

AVON (RIVER) Evesham
BRANSFORD GAME FISHERY Worcester
MAVER LARFORD Stourport-on-Severn
TEME (RIVER) Tenbury Wells
TWYFORD FARM POOL Evesham
WILLOW FARM Evesham
WITLEY FISHERY Worcester

YORKSHIRE (NORTH)

CLAXTON BRICKWORKS York
CUNDALL LODGE FISHERY York
RIVER VIEW COTTAGE Thirsk
WASHBURN VALLEY (FEWSTON AND SWINSTY) Harrogate

YORKSHIRE (WEST)

AIRE (RIVER) Shipley

DAMS

CHESHIRE

TETTON FLASH Middlewich

DERBYSHIRE

HARLESTHORPE DAM Chesterfield

MERSEYSIDE

LEG OMUTTON DAM St Helens
PADDOCK DAM St Helens

SUSSEX (EAST)

BUXTED OAST FISHERY Uckfield

WILTSHIRE

WOODLAND PARK Westbury

YORKSHIRE (WEST)

TONG PARK DAM Shipley
WALSDEN PRINTING CO LODGES Todmorden

DRAINS

CAMBRIDGESHIRE

MIDDLE LEVEL DRAIN Wisbech
OVER MAIN DRAIN Huntingdon
RAVELEY DRAIN Ramsey

CHESHIRE

CISTERNS Northwich

HUMBERSIDE

BEVERLEY AND BARMSTON DRAIN Driffield
BURTON CONSTABLE COUNTRY PARK Hull

LINCOLNSHIRE

HOBHOLE DRAIN Boston
SOUTH HOLLAND DRAIN Spalding
WARPING DRAIN Gainsborough
WEST FEN DRAIN Boston

SOMERSET

STATHE DRAIN Bridgwater

SUSSEX (EAST)

WALLERS HAVEN Pevensey

DYKES

SUFFOLK

OULTON DYKE Lowestoft

GRAVEL PITS

BEDFORDSHIRE

BROGBOROUGH NO.1 PIT Bedford
ELSTOW PITS Elstow
FELMERSHAM GRAVEL PITS Bedford
JONES PIT Leighton Buzzard
MARSTON PITS Bedford
RACKLEY HILLS PIT Leighton Buzzard
SOUTH LAGOON Bedford
STANFORD PIT Stanford
TIDDENFOOT PIT Leighton Buzzard
WOBURN SANDS Luton

BERKSHIRE

BURGHFIELD BLUE POOL Reading
COTTAGE LANE Reading
FELIX FARM TROUT FISHERY Bracknell
HAMBRIDGE LANE Newbury
MILL LANE Sandhurst
PINGEWOOD LAGOON Reading
PRIORY WATER Windsor
SHEEPHOUSE FARM TROUT FISHERY Maidenhead
SONNING EYE Reading
THEALE LAGOON Reading
WASING WOODS Reading
WYLIES LAKE Newbury

BUCKINGHAMSHIRE

COLNBROOK WEST Slough
FARLOWS LAKE Iver
HARROLD ODELL COUNTRY PARK Bedford
KINGSMEAD 1 Slough
KINGSMEAD ISLAND LAKE Slough
MAYFIELDS LAKE Slough
NEWPORT PAGNELL GRAVEL PITS Newport Pagnell

CAMBRIDGESHIRE

BARNWELL COUNTRY PARK Peterborough
BARNWELL PIT Cambridge
BLUEBELL LAKE Peterborough
BRACKHILL LAKE Huntingdon
DECOY LAKE Peterborough
DICKERSONS PIT Cambridge
FEN DRAYTON LAKE Cambridge
HATTON PARK POND Cambridge
LITTLE PAXTON FISHERY Huntingdon
LONG REACH Huntingdon
MALEY GRAVEL PITS Peterborough
MILTON COUNTRY PARK Cambridge
MILTON PITS Cambridge
NORTH BANK TROUT FISHERY Peterborough
NORTH HOUSE LAKE Huntingdon
SOHAM BY-PASS LAKE Cambridge
STEW POND Huntingdon
WIMBLINGTON MERE Wisbech
WOBURN CLOSE LAKE Huntingdon

CHESHIRE

ACKERS PIT Warrington
BRERETON HEATH COUNTRY PARK Congleton
BRERTON QUARRY Middlewich
CANAL PIT Northwich
KAZAKO PONDS Macclesfield
WHIRLEY POOL Macclesfield

CLEVELAND
- **HARTBURN BRICK PIT** Stockton-on-Tees

CORNWALL
- **ELECTRICITY POOL** St Austell
- **WHEAL RASHLEIGH PITS** St Austell

COUNTY DURHAM
- **WADSWORTH FISHERY** Bishop Auckland
- **WITTON CASTLE LAKES** Bishop Auckland

CUMBRIA
- **BARN LAKE** Carlisle
- **OAKBANK LAKES** Carlisle
- **ROANHEAD FISHERIES** Barrow-In-Furness
- **TEWITFIELDS TROUT FISHERY** Carnforth

DERBYSHIRE
- **SWARKESTONE GRAVEL PITS** Derby

DEVON
- **ABBROOK POND** Newton Abbot
- **BLUE LAKE** Okehampton
- **CADOVER BRIDGE PITS** Plymouth
- **ISLAND POND - RACKERHAYES** Newton Abbot
- **STONE FARM QUARRY** Okehampton
- **SWIMBRIDGE POOL** Barnstaple
- **VENN POOL** Barnstaple

DORSET
- **LUCKFIELD LAKE FISHERY** Dorchester
- **WESSEX FLY FISHING TROUT LAKES** Dorchester

ESSEX
- **ARENA LAKE** Grays
- **ASHELDHAM FISHERY** Southminster
- **BORDEAUX PIT** Saffron Walden
- **BOREHAM FISHERY** Chelmsford
- **BOVINGTON MERE 1** Chelmsford
- **BOVINGTON MERE 2** Chelmsford
- **CANTS MERE** Witham
- **CHASE FISHERY** Dagenham
- **DONYLANDS LAKES** Colchester
- **LAYER PIT** Colchester
- **MARCONIS PIT** Chelmsford
- **NAZEING MEADS** Waltham Abbey
- **NORTON FISHERY** Romford
- **PEA LANE FISHERY** Upminster
- **SILVER END PIT** Witham
- **SOUTHMINSTER FISHERIES** Southminster
- **STANFORD-LE-HOPE** Standford-Le-Hope
- **WHARF POOL** Standford-Le-Hope

GLOUCESTERSHIRE
- **BOURTON ON THE WATER GRAVEL PIT NO1** Cheltenham
- **BRADLEYS PIT** Cirencester
- **BREDONS HARDWICK** Tewkesbury
- **CLAYDON PARK FISHERY** Fairford
- **COKES PIT** Cirencester
- **COTSWOLD HOBURNE** Cirencester
- **GARDNERS POOL** Gloucester
- **HAM POOL** Cirencester
- **ISIS NO 1 LAKE 19** Cirencester
- **KEYNES COUNTRY PARK** Cirencester
- **KEYNES PARK TOP LAKE** Cirencester
- **LAKE NUMBER ONE (LAKE19)** Cirencester
- **MILL LAKE (NO 44)** Cirencester
- **MORETON PITS** Cheltenham
- **NEIGH BRIDGE LAKE** Cirencester
- **SANTHILL FISHERY** Cheltenham

HAMPSHIRE
- **CHARLTON PITS** Andover
- **FOXCOTTE LAKE** Andover
- **FRIMLEY LAKES** Farnborough
- **HALF PIT** Ringwood
- **HAWLEY LAKE** Camberley
- **HIGHTOWN LAKE** Ringwood
- **HOLLYBUSH LANE LAKES** Farnborough
- **KINGFISHER LAKE (A)** Southampton
- **LAKESIDE COUNTRY PARK** Eastleigh
- **NORTHFIELD LAKES** Ringwood
- **WASH PIT** Ringwood

HERTFORDSHIRE
- **ADMIRALS WALK LAKE** Hoddesdon
- **BLUE LAGOON** Arlesey
- **BOWMANS LAKES** St Albans
- **BOWYERS WATER** Waltham Cross
- **BROXBOURNE** Hoddesdon
- **CROXLEY HALL TROUT FISHERY** Rickmansworth
- **NORTH MET PIT** Waltham Cross
- **OLDFIELD** Arlesey
- **SLIPE LANE PITS** Broxbourne
- **STANBOROUGH LAKE** Welwyn Garden City

HUMBERSIDE
- **BILLABONG WATER SPORTS AND CARAVAN PARK** Driffield
- **BURSTWICK SKI LAKE** Hull
- **FARM PONDS** Driffield
- **STAR CARR TROUT FARM** Driffield

KENT
- **ABBOTTS COURT** Rochester
- **BROOMBANKS PITS** Sittingbourne
- **BYSINGWOOD** Faversham
- **COTTON FARM FISHERY** Dartford
- **DARENTH FISHING COMPLEX** Dartford
- **DUNGENESS LONG PIT** Romney Marsh
- **FORDWICH LAKE** Canterbury
- **HORTON KIRBY** Dartford
- **LONGFORD LAKE** Sevenoaks
- **MILL POOL** Faversham
- **MILTON PAN LAKE** Canterbury
- **RUXLEY PITS** Orpington
- **SITTINGBOURNE LAKES** Sittingbourne
- **SUNDRIDGE LAKES** Sevenoaks
- **SUTTON AT HONE LAKE TWO** Dartford
- **SUTTON AT HONE LAKES ONE AND THREE** Dartford
- **WINGHAM FISHERY** Ashford
- **WOOD POOL** Faversham

LANCASHIRE
- **DEEP PIT** Wigan

LEICESTERSHIRE
- **WATERMEAD PARK LAKES** Leicester

LINCOLNSHIRE
- **GROOBYS PIT** Skegness
- **OASIS LAKES** Louth

LONDON (GREATER)
- **ASHMERE FISHERIES** London
- **BURES LAKE** London
- **CARGILL LAKE** London
- **HAREFIELD CARP LAKE** London
- **KINGFISHER LAKE** London
- **KORDA LAKE** London
- **SAVAY LAKE** London
- **SHEPPERTON LAKE** London
- **STOCKLEY ROAD LAKES** London
- **THORNEY POOL** London
- **WRAYSBURY ONE** London
- **WRAYSBURY TWO** London

MANCHESTER (GREATER)
- **CLIFTON MARINA** Salford
- **DOUBLEWOODS** Manchester
- **STONEY PIT RESERVOIR** Stockport

MERSEYSIDE
- **FOOTBALL PIT** Liverpool

MIDLANDS (WEST)
- **CHURCH POOL** Wolverhampton
- **MEADOWLANDS** Coventry
- **PACKINGTON SOMERS FISHERY** Coventry

NORFOLK
- **BAWBURGH LAKES** Norwich
- **BOOTON CLAY PIT** Norwich
- **BRIDGE INN FISHERY** Lenwade
- **BUCKENHAM PITS** Thetford
- **BURE VALLEY LAKES** Aylesham
- **CATCH 22 FISHERY** Norwich
- **FOSTERS END PIT** King's Lynn
- **GATTON WATER CARAVAN SITE** King's Lynn
- **HADDISCOE PIT** Norwich
- **HALL FARM LAKES** Great Yarmouth
- **LYNG PIT** Norwich
- **MARTHAM PITS** Great Yarmouth
- **PENTNEY LAKES** King's Lynn
- **SNETTERTON PITS** Norwich
- **SWANTON MORLEY FISHERY** Dereham
- **TOTTENHILL PIT** King's Lynn

NORTHAMPTONSHIRE
- **ALDWINCLE PITS** Kettering
- **DITCHFORD PITS** Wellingborough
- **ECTON GRAVEL PITS** Northampton
- **RINGSTEAD GRANGE TROUT FISHERY** Kettering
- **WEEDON ROAD GRAVEL PIT** Northampton

NOTTINGHAMSHIRE
- **ATTENBOROUGH GRAVEL PITS** Nottingham
- **DOLAR POND** Nottingham
- **HOLME PIERPOINT** Nottingham
- **SAPPHIRE LAKES** Newark

OXFORDSHIRE
- **BULLFIELD LAKE** Abingdon
- **DARLOW LAKE** Witney
- **DORCHESTER LAGOON** Wallingford
- **HEYFORD LAKES** Witney
- **LINCH HILL FISHERY** Witney
- **MARLBOROUGH POOL** Abingdon

SOMERSET
- **HUTON POND** Weston-Super-Mare

SUFFOLK
- **ALDEBY HALL FARM PITS** Beccles
- **BARHAM A PIT** Ipswich
- **BLUE WATERS** Bury St Edmunds
- **BREAKAWAY PIT** Woodbridge
- **BROOME PITS** Bungay
- **CLUB PIT** Bungay
- **HOLTON PIT** Halesworth
- **STARFIELD PIT** Sudbury
- **SWALE PIT** Ipswich

SURREY
- **ATTENBOROUGH SOUTH** Chertsey
- **SEND PIT** Woking
- **TWYNERSH FISHING COMPLEX** Chertsey

SUSSEX (EAST)
- **RYE NOOK FISHERY** Hastings

TYNE AND WEAR
- **FELLGATE FISHERIES** Jarrow

MARDEN QUARRY Newcastle Upon Tyne
STARGATE PONDS Ryton

WILTSHIRE

HIGH PENN Calne
LOWER MOOR FISHERY Malmesbury
MANOR BROOK LAKE Swindon
SILVERLANDS LAKE Chippenham

YORKSHIRE (NORTH)

CLAY PIT Bedale
ELLERTON PARK Richmond
ELVINGTON LAKE York
HAY-A-PARK Knaresborough
LANGTON POND Northallerton
ROGERS POND Ripon
THORPE PERROW QUARRY Bedale

YORKSHIRE (SOUTH)

WINDTHORPE PITS Sheffield
WINTHORPE LAKE Sheffield

LAKES

BEDFORDSHIRE

ARLESEY LAKE Arlesey
BRIARWOOD FISHERY Bedford
BROOM Stanford
CLAYDON LAKE Leighton Buzzard
FIR COUNTRY PARK Bedford
GREEN LAGOON Arlesey
HOUGHTON REGIS QUARRY Dunstable
LAKESIDE TROUT AND COARSE FISHERY Leighton Buzzard
LEDBURN ROAD Leighton Buzzard
LITTLE HEATH FARM TROUT FISHERY Sandy
PRIORY COUNTRY PARK Bedford
RADWELL COMPLEX Bedford
TINGRITH COARSE FISHERY Dunstable
TINGRITH MANOR LAKE Dunstable
WATER END FISHERY Bedford
WILLINGTON LAKE Bedford

BERKSHIRE

ALDERMASTON Reading
AMERDEN POOL Maidenhead
ASHRIDGE MANOR Wokingham
BENS LAKE Newbury
BISHOPS GREEN FARM LAKE Newbury
BRAY LAKE Maidenhead
BRIMPTON LAKE Reading
BURGHFIELD MATCH LAKE Reading
COURT FARM Reading
ENGLEFIELD LAGOON Reading
FARLEYMOOR LAKE Bracknell
FARNHAM FLINT Reading
FORBURY FARM LAKES Newbury
HOLME GRANGE Crowthorne
JINGLES FARM Wokingham
LONGMOOR FARM FISHING LAKE Finchampstead
LONGMOOR LAKE Wokingham
MILL POND Bracknell
MOATLANDS POOL Reading
NEWBURY TROUT LAKES Newbury
PANG VALLEY TROUT LAKE Reading
REDLANDS LAKE Reading
ROYAL BERKSHIRE FISHERY Windsor
SLALFORD LAKES Reading
SOUTH FIELD PARK Hanworth
SOUTH HILL PARK LAKE Bracknell
SOUTH LAKE Reading
SWAN VALLEY Sandhurst
THEALE Reading
TRI-LAKES Sandhurst
WELLINGTON COUNTRY PARK Reading

BRISTOL

BAGWOOD LAKE
BITTERWELL LAKE
HAM GREEN LAKE
HENLEAZE LAKE
SEVINGTON LAKES FISHERY
TANHOUSE FARM LAKE
WEST COUNTRY WATER PARK

BUCKINGHAMSHIRE

BEDFORD BOATING LAKE Bedford
BLACK PARK Iver
CALVES LANE LAKE Iver
CLAYDON LAKE Buckingham
CRAYFISH POOL Slough
FURZTON LAKE Milton Keynes
GILBRATAR LAKE Slough
GREAT LINFORD LAKES Great Linford
HORTON BOAT POOL Slough
HORTON CHURCH LAKE Slough
HYDE LANE LAKES Buckingham
KEMPSTONE HARDWICK Bedford
KINGFISHER GOLF CLUB Milton Keynes
LODGE LAKES Milton Keynes
LOUGHTON LODGE LAKE Milton Keynes
MILTON KEYNES LAKES Bedford
ORLITTS LAKES Slough
SHELSWELL LAKE Buckingham
SILVERWING LAKE Amersham
SNOWBERRY Milton Keynes
SPADE OAK LAKE High Wycombe
SUMMERFIELDS TROUT FISHERY Bedford
TEARDROP LAKES Milton Keynes
TINGRITH LAKES Milton Keynes
VICARAGE SPINNEY TROUT FISHERY Milton Keynes
WESTHORPE PARK LAKE High Wycombe
WOLVERTON LAKES Milton Keynes

CAMBRIDGESHIRE

BARWAY LAKE Ely
BIGGIN LAKE Peterborough
BURNSIDE LAKE Cambridge
CHAWSTON LAKES Huntingdon
CLEARWATERS COARSE FISHERY Huntingdon
CROWLAND ANGLING CLUB LAKES Peterborough
EARITH FISHERY Huntingdon
EAST DELPH LAKES Whittlesey
EATON SOCON LAKE Huntingdon
ELDERNELL LAKE Peterborough
FEN DRAYTON COMPLEX Cambridge
FENLAND FISHERIES Huntingdon
FERRY MEADOWS Peterborough
FIELDS END WATER March
GERARDS CARP LAKE Peterborough
GINGERBREAD LAKE AND DRIFT Huntingdon
GUNWADE LAKE Peterborough
HIGH FLYER LAKE Ely
HINCHINGBROOKE COUNTRY PARK Huntingdon
HOLME FEN FISHING Huntingdon
KINGFISHER LAKE Peterborough
LILY PARK LAKES Huntingdon
MAGPIE LAKE Cambridge
MEPAL PIT Ely
NORTHEY PARK FISHERY Peterborough
PAXTON LAKE Huntingdon
RAILWAY LAKES Peterborough
RANDALLS LAKE Ely
REDLANDS PITS Peterborough
SAND MARTIN LAKE Peterborough
SIBSON FISHERIES Peterborough
ST IVES COMPLEX Huntingdon
STRETHAM LAKE Ely
SWAN LAKE Peterborough
TURKS HEAD LAKE Cambridge
VIRGINIA LAKE Wisbech
WERRINGTON LAKE Peterborough
WHITE HOUSE TROUT FARM Peterborough
WILLOW LAKE Peterborough
YARWELL MILL LAKE Peterborough

CHESHIRE

ABNEY PARK Cheadle Hulme
ANTROBUS LAKES Lymm
BLACK LAKE Wilmslow
BLAKEMERE Northwich
BLUNDELLS FARM FISHERY Warrington
BOLESWORTH CASTLE Chester
BOUNDARY WATER PARK Knutsford
BROOKSIDE LAKES Warrington
BUDWORTH MERE Northwich
BURTON MERE FISHERIES Neston
BYLEY FISHERIES Middlewich
CAPESTHORNE MAIN POOL Macclesfield
CAPESTHORNE TOP POOL Macclesfield
CHESHIRE FISHING Chester
CLAY LANE FISHERY Knutsford
CRABMILL FLASH Sandbach
DANEBRIDGE FISHERIES Macclesfield
DOODLESPOOL FARM LAKE Crewe
DOVEMERE, SANDMERE AND WOODLANDS Knutsford
EGERTON LAKE Malpas
FLUSHING MEADOWS FISHERY Northwich
GORSTY HALL Crewe
GREAT BUDWORTH MERE LAKE Northwich
GREY MIST MERE Warrington
HACK GREEN LAKE Nantwich
HAMPTON SPRINGS Malpas
HAYDAN FISHERY Warrington
HOLMSTON HALL FISHERY Tarporley
LAKEMORE COUNTRY PARK Crewe
LITTLE BUDWORTH Tarporley
LITTLE MILL Tarporley
LLOYDS MEADOW FISHERIES Chester
LYMM DAM Warrington
MARBURY MERE Whitchurch
MEADOW FISHERY Chester
MICKS LAKE Warrington
MILTON GREEN Chester
MOBBERLEY POOL Altrincham
OCEAN POOL Winsford
PARTRIDGE LAKES Warrington
PLEX FLASH Sandbach
REASEHEATH COLLEGE LAKE Nantwich
REDESMERE Macclesfield
RODE POOL Sandbach
ROSSMERE Wilmslow
RUNCORN PARK LAKE Runcorn
SALE WATER PARK Sale
SAND MERE LAKE Knutsford
SHAKERLEY MERE Northwich
SOUTH PARK Macclesfield
SWANLEY Knutsford
TAX MERE Sandbach
TETTON LAKE Middlewich
THORNEYCROFT LAKES Macclesfield
TOFT POOL Knutsford
TOWN PARK LANE Runcorn
WINSFORD FLASH Winsford
WINTERLEY POOL FISHERY Crewe
WOODLANDS LAKE Knutsford

CLEVELAND

HEMLINGTON LAKE Middlesbrough
ISLAND WATERS Stockton-on-Tees
LOCH KENNY Hartlepool

LOCKE PARK Middlesbrough
PRIORY COTTAGE LAKE Guisborough
ROSSMERE PARK LAKE Hartlepool
SHOTTON COLLIERY LAKE Hartlepool
TILERY LAKE Hartlepool
WHITEHOUSE CARAVAN PARK LAKE Middlesbrough

CORNWALL

AVALLON HOLIDAY PARK Launceston
BADHAM FARM LAKE Liskeard
BAKE FISHING LAKES Saltash
BOLINGEY LAKE Perranporth
BRAGGS WOOD TROUT FISHERY Launceston
BUCHAN PARK FISHERIES Crawley
BUSH LAKES FARM Saltash
CHOONE FARM Penzance
CHYRAISE LODGE HOTEL Penzance
COLLIFORD LAKE Liskeard
CRAFTHOLE LAKE Torpoint
CRAYFISH FARM Crawley
DUTSON WATER Launceston
EAST ROSE FARM Bodmin
ELMFIELD FARM COARSE FISHERY Launceston
EMFIELD COARSE FISHERY Launceston
FERNDALE Delabole
FULL BAG FISHERY Newquay
GLENLEIGH FARM FISHERY St Austell
GOONHAVERN COARSE FISHING LAKE Truro
GWARNICK MILL TROUT FISHERY Truro
GWINNEAR POOLS Newquay
HIDDEN VALLEY Launceston
LAKE PENRYN Penryn
LAKEVIEW COUNTRY CLUB Bodmin
MEADOWSIDE COARSE FISHERY St Columb
MELANHYL LAKE Newquay
MIDDLE BOSWIN FARM Helston
MILLPOOL FISHERIES Penzance
MILTON MOUNT LAKE Crawley
MYLOR ANGLING LAKES Falmouth
NANCE LAKES St Ives
NEETS VALLEY PARK Bude
OAKSIDE FISHERY Newquay
ORVIS INNIS COUNTRY CLUB AND FLY FISHERY St Austell
PENVOSE FARM Newquay
POLCOVERACK FARM Helston
PORT ELLIOT LAKE Saltash
PRINCE PARK Bodmin
RETALLACK WATERS St Columb
ROSE PARK FISHERY Launceston
ROSEWATER LAKE Truro
ROWFANT HOUSE FISHERY Crawley
SHARKEYS PIT Hayle
SHILLAMILL LAKES COUNTRY PARK Looe
SIBLYBACK LAKE Liskeard
ST ERTH FISHERY Penzance
ST GERMANS LAKE Saltash
ST LEONARDS FISHING LAKE Launceston
ST TINNEY FARM HOLIDAYS Camelford
STOWFORD GRANGE FISHERIES Launceston
TAMAR LAKE (UPPER) Bude
TORY FARM LAKE Truro
TREBELLAN PARK LAKES Newquay
TREDIDON BARTON LAKE Launceston
TREE MEADOW TROUT FISHERY Hayle
TRENESTRALL LAKE Truro
TREVELLA CARAVAN AND CAMPING PARK Newquay
VENN DOWN LAKES Boscastle
VENTONTRISSICK FISHERY Truro
WATERFRONT FISHING LAKE Bude
WHEAL GREY Helston
WHITEACRES COUNTRY PARK Newquay
WOODLAY HOLIDAY LAKES Liskeard
WOONSMITH LAKE Penzance

COUNTY DURHAM

AYCLIFFE LAKE Newton Aycliffe
BEAMISH LAKE FLY FISHERY Stanley
BRASSIDE POND Durham
EDMONDSLEY POND Chester-Le-Street
HALNEBY LAKE Darlington
JUBILEE LAKES Darlington
KNITSLEY MILL TROUT FISHERIES AND STUD FARM Consett
LANGSDALE LAKE Darlington
SHAFTOS LAKE Spennymoor
SHOTTON POND Peterlee
WEST FARM LAKE Stockton-on-Tees

CUMBRIA

BASSENTHWAITE LAKE Keswick
BESSY BECK TROUT FARM Kirkby Stephen
BIGLAND HALL LAKE Ulverston
BLELHAM TARN Ambleside
BLENCARN LAKE Penrith
BLENHEIM LODGE HOTEL Windermere
BORWICK LAKE Carnforth
BUTTERMERE LAKE Cockermouth
CARLETON HILL Carlisle
COGRA MOSS Cockermouth
CONISTON WATER Coniston
CROSSFIELD FISHERY Penrith
CRUMMOCK WATER LAKE Cockermouth
EDEN VALLEY TROUT LAKE Kirkby Stephen
ENNERDALE LAKE FISHERY Egremont
ESTHWAITE WATER Ambleside
GHYLL HEAD Bowness On Windermere
GRASMERE COARSE FISHERY Ambleside
HALLMORE FISHERIES Carnforth
HAWKSHEAD TROUT FISHING Ambleside
HOLEHIRD TARN Windermere
KENTMERE FISHERY Penrith
LAKE WINDERMERE Windermere
LITTLE MUSGRAVE Kirkby Stephen
LONSDALE COUNTRY PARK Carlisle
LOUGHSIDE FISHERY Carlisle
LOWESWATER LAKE Cockermouth
MOORHOUSE TARN Wigton
NEW HILLS TROUT FARM FISHERY Brampton
PINFOLD LAKE Penrith
PRYHEAD FISHERY Alston
REDWELL FISHERIES Carnforth
RYDAL WATER Ambleside
SHARPLEY WATERS Cockermouth
SKELSMERGH LAKE Kendal
THIRLMERE Keswick
TRANQUIL OTTER Carlisle
ULLSWATER LAKE Penrith
WATENDLATH TROUT FISHERY Keswick
WYCH ELM FISHERY Carnforth
YEW TREE TARN Coniston

DERBYSHIRE

ALDAMORE POOL Ashbourne
ALLESTREE LAKE Derby
ALTON MANOR FARM Matlock
ALVASTON LAKE Derby
ASHGROVE LAKE Derby
BARLOW FISHERIES Chesterfield
BEEHIVE FARM WOODLANDS LAKES Swadlincote
COPPICE LAKE Heanor
DERBYSHIRE TROUT FISHERY Belper
DERWENT VALLEY FISHERY Derby
DONKHILL FISHERIES Swadlincote
DUKE OF RUTLAND ESTATE Bakewell
FOXTON DAM Sheffield
HADDON ESTATE FISHERIES Bakewell
HIGHAM FARM COARSE FISHING Alfreton
LOCHO PARK LAKE Derby
MARKEATON LAKE Derby
NETHERMOOR LAKE Sheffield
RINGWOOD LAKE Chesterfield
SYDNOPE FISHERIES Matlock
WINGERWORTH LIDO Chesterfield
YEAVELEY ESTATE TROUT FISHERY Ashbourne

DEVON

ALDER LAKE Okehampton
ANGLERS ELDORADO Beaworthy
ANGLERS PARADISE Beaworthy
ANGLERS SHANGRILA Beaworthy
BAKERS FARM Torrington
BELLBROOK VALLEY TROUT FISHERY Tiverton
BLAKEWELL FISHERIES Barnstaple
BULWORTHY FISHERY Bideford
CHANNELL FISHERIES Brixham
CLAWFORD VINEYARD AND FISHERIES Holsworthy
CLOVELLY LAKES Bideford
COFTON PARK FARM Dawlish
COOMBE FISHERIES Tavistock
COOMBE WATER FISHERY Kingsbridge
CREEDY LAKES Crediton
DRAKELANDS GAME FISHERY Plymouth
EASTCOTT FARM AND LODGES Holsworthy
EXEMOOR FARM Bude
GLYNDWR FISHERY Crediton
GOODIFORD MILL TROUT FISHERY Cullompton
GREENACRE TROUT LAKES Beaworthy
HARTLAND FOREST FISHERY GOLF CLUB Bideford
HARTSMOOR FISHERIES Cullompton
HIGHAMPTON TROUT LAKES Beaworthy
HIGHER COWNHAYNE LAKES Colyton
HOGSBROOK LAKES Exeter
HOLLIES TROUT FARM AND FISHERY Honiton
HOME FARM FISHERY Exeter
KINGLAKE FISHERY Beaworthy
KINGSMEAD CENTRE Cullompton
LEGGE FARM COARSE FISHERY Beaworthy
LEWORTHY FARM Bude
LITTLE ALLERS COARSE FISHERY South Brent
LITTLE WEACH Bideford
LOWER HALLACOMBE FISHERY Crediton
LUCCOMBES PONDS Exeter
MILEMEAD FISHERIES Tavistock
MILL South Brent
MILL PARK COARSE FISHING LAKE Ilfracombe
MILLHAYES Cullompton
NEW BARN ANGLING CENTRE Paignton
OAKTREE FISHERY South Molton
PADBROOK PARK Cullompton

PICFRESH Exeter
SALMONHUTCH COARSE FISHERY Crediton
SAWMILLS LAKE Newton Abbot
SHOBROOKE PARK South Molton
SIMPSON VALLEY FISHERY Holsworthy
SLAPTON LEY NATIONAL NATURE RESERVE Kingsbridge
SOMERSWOOD LAKE South Brent
SOUTH HAY FARM Beaworthy
SOUTH REED FISHERIES CARP LAKE Okehampton
SOUTH WEST WATER FISHERY Bideford
SPIRES LAKES Okehampton
STAFFORD MOOR FISHERY Winkleigh
STEVENSTONE LAKES Torrington
STILL WATERS TROUT FISHERY Honiton
SUNRIDGE FISHERY Plymouth
TAMAR LAKE (LOWER) Exeter
TAVISTOCK TROUT FISHERY Tavistock
TOWN PARKS COARSE FISHERY Paignton
UPTON WARREN LAKE Cullompton
VALLEY SPRINGS TROUT FISHERY Kingsbridge
WATERCRESS FARM TROUT FISHERY Newton Abbot
WEST PITT FARM FISHERY Tiverton
WILLOWFIELD LAKE COTTAGES Braunton
WISCOMBE FISHERY Colyton
WOODA FARM FISHERY Holsworthy
WOODACOTT ARMS Holsworthy
WOODY PARK FISHERY Cullompton

DORSET

AMHERST LODGE FISHERY Lyme Regis
AVON TYRRELL LAKES Christchurch
BLASHFORD LAKES Christchurch
CLUB LAKE Dorchester
CRANBOURNE FRUIT FARM Wimborne
CRANEBROOK TROUT FISHERY Wimborne
CULVERS FARM FISHERIES Gillingham
FLOWERS FARM TROUT LAKES Dorchester
GOLD OAK FISH FARM Wimborne
GOLDEN SPRINGS LAKES Christchurch
HAMWORTHY LAKE Poole
HERMITAGE LAKES Dorchester
HILLVIEW FARM LAKE Wimborne
HYDE LAKE Wareham
KINGCOMBE COARSE FARM Dorchester
KINGCOMBE LAKE Dorchester
KNAPP HILL FARM LAKES Buckland Newton
LAWRENCES FARM Dorchester
LYONS GATE CARAVAN PARK Dorchester
MAPPOWDER COURT Sturminster Newton
MARTINS FARM Wimborne
MUDEFORD WOOD LAKE Christchurch
NEW MEADOWS LAKE Christchurch
OSMINGTON MILLS Weymouth
PALLINGTON LAKES Dorchester
RADIPOLE LAKE Weymouth
REVELS FISHERY Dorchester
SHERBORNE LAKE Sherborne
SOPLEY FARM Christchurch
TODBER MANOR Sturminster Newton
WALLYS LAKE Weymouth
WARMWELL HOLIDAY PARK Dorchester
WATERMILL LAKE Bridport
WHIRLWIND LAKE Christchurch
WHITEMOOR LAKE Wimborne
WHITESHEET TROUT FISHERY Wimborne

ESSEX

ALBYNS LAKE Hornchurch
ARMIGERS FARM Dunmow
AVELEY LAKES Romford
BEDFORDS PARK LAKE Romford
BIRDS GREEN Ongar
BLACKMORE WOOD Ingatestone
BOG GROVE Maldon
BOREHAM MERES Chelmsford
BRAXTED HALL ESTATE Witham
BRICKHOUSE FARM FISHERIES Brentwood
BROOKHALL FISHERY Colchester
BULPHAN PARK FISHERIES Upminster
BURROWS FARM Basildon
CARP FARM FRYERNING FISHERIES Ingatestone
CENTRAL PARK LAKE Chelmsford
CHIGBOROUGH Maldon
CHIGBOROUGH FISHERIES Maldon
CHURCH LAKE Brentwood
CHURCHWOOD FISHERIES Brentwood
CLAVERHAMBURY LAKE Waltham Abbey
CLAVERING TROUT LAKE Saffron Walden
COBBLERS MEAD LAKE Standford-Le-Hope
CONNAUGHT WATER Loughton
CROW GREEN FISHERY Brentwood
CROWN NETHERHALL Waltham Abbey
DANBURY COUNTRY PARK Chelmsford
DODDS FARM Ingatestone
DOGGETTS FARM FISHERY Rochford
ESSEX CARP FISHERY South Ockendon
EWSONS WATER Chelmsford
FAIRLOP EAST LAKE Romford
FAIRLOP WATERS Ilford
GARNISH HALL Garnon
GLOUCESTER PARK LAKE Basildon
GOSFIELD LAKE RESORT Halstead
GRANGE WATER Grays
GREAT MYLES LAKE Ongar
GREEN OAKS TROUT FISHERY Billericay
HAINAULT FOREST COUNTRY PARK Chigwell
HARWOOD HALL LAKE Upminster
HOCKLEY LAKES Rayleigh
HOLYFIELD FISHERY Waltham Abbey
HOME FARM FISHERY Saffron Walden
HOOKS MARSH Waltham Abbey
JACKLETTS FARM Chelmsford
JIMMYS LAKE Standford-Le-Hope
JOHNS LAKE FISHERIES Waltham Abbey
KENNEL LANE Billericay
KNIGHTS PIT Waltham Abbey
LAKE MEADOWS Billericay
LAUNDRY LANE Dunmow
LITTLE EASTON FISHERIES Dunmow
MAGIC LAKE Waltham Abbey
MAYBRAND FISHERY Romford
MAYSBROOK LAKES Barking
MILL BARN FISHERY Southend-on-Sea
MILLENNIUM LAKES Ingatestone
MOATHOUSE LAKE Basildon
NEWLAND HALL CARP FISHERY Chelmsford
NORTHLANDS PARK Basildon
NUPERS FARM Romford
OLD HALL FARM TROUT FISHERY Colchester
OLIVERS LAKE Colchester
PAR West Horndon
PARSONAGE FARM Chelmsford
PICKS COTTAGE CARP LAKES Waltham Abbey
PIPPS HILL FISHERIES Basildon
PRESTONS LAKE Colchester
PRIORY PARK LAKES Southend-on-Sea
RAPHAELS PARK Romford
RECTORY FARM POND Braintree
ROCKELLS FARM Saffron Walden
RODING VALLEY LAKE Chigwell
SHOEBURY PARK Southend-on-Sea
SLOUGH HOUSE LAKE Upminster
SLOUGH HOUSE WATER Maldon
STAMBRIDGE STARR FISHERIES Rochford
STAR LANE Southend-on-Sea
THORNDON PARK LAKE Brentwood
VALENCE MOAT Dagenham
WARREN Standford-Le-Hope
WEALD COUNTRY PARK Brentwood
WEELEY BRIDGE HOLIDAY PARK Clacton-on-Sea
WICK MERE Maldon
WILLOWS LAKE Chelmsford

GLOUCESTERSHIRE

ADLESTROP LAKE Stow On The Wold
APPERLEY POOLS Tewkesbury
ASHTON KEYNES POOL Cirencester
BROOK FARM TROUT FISHERY Gloucester
BUSHYLEAZE TROUT FISHERY Lechlade
COTSWOLD WATER PARK Cirencester
COURT FARM Moreton-In-Marsh
DONNINGTON TROUT FISHERY Cheltenham
FARMHOUSE LAKE (THE) Cirencester
GREAT BURROWS TROUT FISHERY Dursley
HIGHNAM COURT LAKE Gloucester
HILL VIEW LAKES Tewkesbury
HORSESHOE LAKE Lechlade
HUNTLEY CARP POOLS Gloucester
LECHLADE TROUT FISHERY Lechlade
LEMINGTON LAKES Moreton-In-Marsh
LYDNEY BOATING LAKE Lydney
MILESTONE FISHERY Fairford
MYTHE POOL Tewkesbury
NETHERWOOD LAKE Cirencester
NORTON FRUIT FARM Gloucester
RAINBOW LAKES Cirencester
SPEECH HOUSE LAKE Coleford
STANBOROUGH POOL Cheltenham
STAUNTON COURT LAKES Gloucester
STEAM MILLS LAKE Cinderford
STEANBRIDGE FISHERY Stroud
WATERSMEET LAKES Gloucester
WHELFORD POOLS COARSE FISHERY Fairford
WICK WATER Cirencester

HAMPSHIRE

ANTON LAKE Andover
AWBRIDGE DANES LAKE Romsey
BARONS PONDS (NEW SITE) Liss
BEECHES BROOK FISHERY Ringwood

BROADLANDS LAKES Ringwood
BROADLANDS MAIN LAKE Romsey
BROWNWICH POND Portsmouth
CHIPHALL LAKE TROUT FISHERY Fareham
CROOKED WILLOWS Ringwood
CUTT MILL Farnborough
EAST MOORS LAKE Ringwood
FIRGROVE LAKES Yateley
FIVE OAKS TROUT LAKE Southampton
FOREST LODGE HOME FARM Southampton
GOLD VALLEY LAKES Aldershot
GREENRIDGE FARM LAKES Romsey
HATCHET POND Brockenhurst
HMS DRYAD LAKE Portsmouth
HORDLE LAKES New Milton
HUCKLESBROOK LAKE Fordingbridge
JANESMOOR POND Lyndhurst
JOHN OGAUNTS FISHERY Stockbridge
LAKE FARM Fordingbridge
LAKESIDE Aldershot
LAKESIDE Southampton
LAPSLEYS FISHERY Fordingbridge
LEOMINSTEAD TROUT FISHERY Lyndhurst
LONGBRIDGE LAKES Romsey
LYNDHURST LAKE Lyndhurst
MILL POND LAKE Lyndhurst
MOORHEN FARM TROUT LAKE Southampton
MOORS VALLEY COUNTRY PARK Ringwood
NEW FOREST WATER PARK Fordingbridge
NUTRABAITS YATELEY SOUTH LAKE Yateley
ORCHARD LAKES New Milton
PERIL LAKE Andover
PETERSFIELD HEATH LAKE Petersfield
RIVER FARM Fareham
ROCKFORD LAKE Ringwood
SOMERLEY LAKES Ringwood
SPRINGLAKES Aldershot
STAUNTON COUNTRY PARK Havant
STEPSTONES LAKES Petersfield
STONEHAM LAKES Southampton
SWAY LAKES Lymington
TESTWOOD SALMON FISHERIES Southampton
TITCHFIELD ABBEY GOLF AND COARSE FISHING LAKES Fareham
TURF CROFT FARM Ringwood
VALE FARM FISHERY Andover
WHITE HOUSE TROUT FARM Hook
WILLOW PARK Aldershot
WINTERSHILL TROUT LAKE Southampton
WOODINGTON FISHERY Romsey

HEREFORDSHIRE

BETULA WATERS Ledbury
BIDDLESTONE LAKE Ross-on-Wye
BULLEY LANE FISHERY Ross-on-Wye
CASTLEMORTON Ledbury
COPPICE TROUT FISHERY Hereford
COURT FARM Hereford
DRUMMOND DUB Ross-on-Wye
EASTNOR CASTLE Ledbury
EVESBATCH TOP LAKE Ledbury
GOLDEN VALLEY Ledbury
KINGFISHER TROUT LAKE Bromyard
PRIDEWOOD LAKE Ledbury
TOAD HALL FISHERY Hereford

HERTFORDSHIRE

ALDENHAM RESERVOIR Borehamwood
AMWELL LAKES Ware
BATCHWORTH LAKE Rickmansworth
BIERTON FISHING LAKES Aylesbury
BOXMOOR TROUT FISHERY Hemel Hempstead
BROAD COLNEY LAKES St Albans
BROOKFIELD LAKE Waltham Cross
COLNEY HEATH LAKE St Albans
DURRANTS LAKE Hitchin
FAIRLANDS VALLEY PARK Stevenage
GAYWOODS Kings Langley
HATFIELD BROADWATER Hatfield
HATFIELD FOREST LAKE Bishops Stortford
HOLWELL HYDE LAKE Welwyn Garden City
HOOK LAKE Potters Bar
LOWBELL LANE St Albans
MERCHANT TAYLORS SCL LAKES Kings Langley
OAKFIELD FISHERY Aylesbury
PIXIES MERE Hemel Hempstead
RIB VALLEY FISHING LAKE Ware
RISLIP LAKE Tring
SHEPHERDS WAY Hatfield
WESTBROOK MERE Hemel Hempstead
WESTONS LAKE Stevenage
WOODLAND FARM Aylesbury
WORMLEBURY Broxbourne

HUMBERSIDE

BLUE LAGOON Hull
BRANDES BURTON 3 AND 4 Hull
BRANDESBURTON Driffield
BRICKYARD POND Brough
BURSHILL A POND Driffield
CLEETHORPES COUNTRY PARK Cleethorpes
DACRE LAKESIDE PARK Driffield
EAST PARK LAKE Hull
EMMOTLAND PONDS Driffield
FAR GRANGE CARAVAN AND COUNTRY PARK Driffield
FOSSEHILL LAKES Beverley
HOLME LAKE FISHERY Scunthorpe
HUMBERSIDE FISHERIES Driffield
LAKEMINSTER PARK Beverley
LAMBWATH LAKES Hull
LEVEN PARK LAKE Beverley
NEST Scunthorpe
NODDLE HILL LAKE Hull
NORTH THORESBY FISHERIES Grimsby
OAKLANDS WATER Goole
RUSH LYVARS LAKE Hull
THORPE HALL Driffield
TILARY LAKE Hull
WANSFORD TROUT LAKE Driffield
WATER SPRING FISHERY Scunthorpe
WILLITOFT FISH FARM Goole
WILLOW LAKES Grimsby
WILLOW SPRINGS Scunthorpe

ISLE OF WIGHT

BRADING LAKE Sandown
GUNVILLE LAKE Newport
HALE MANOR LAKES Newport
ISLAND FISH FARM AND MEADOW LAKES Newport
MERSTONE FISHERIES Newport
NETTLECOMBE FARMS Ventnor
ROOKLEY COUNTRY PARK Ventnor

KENT

ABBEYCOURT LAKE Maidstone
ALDERS LAKES Larkfield
ALLHALLOWS LEISURE PARK Rochester
BALLAST PIT Tonbridge
BARDEN LAKE Tonbridge
BARTLEY MILL FISHERY Tunbridge Wells
BIDDENDEN LAKE Tenterden
BLUE LAGOON LAKE Canterbury
BRITTON COURT FARM Canterbury
BROCKHILL COUNTRY PARK Hythe
BROOKLANDS LAKE Dartford
BYWATER LAKE Canterbury
CACKLE HILL LAKES Ashford
CALIBER COARSE AND CARP LAKES Canterbury
CAPSTONE FARM COUNTRY PARK Gillingham
CHALYBEATE SPRINGS TROUT FISHERY Tunbridge Wells
CHEQUERTREE TROUT AND COARSE FISHERY Ashford
CHIDDINGSTONE CASTLE LAKE Edenbridge
CHILHAM LAKE Canterbury
CHIPSTEAD LAKES Sevenoaks
CONNINGBROOK Ashford
DANSON PARK LAKE Bexleyheath
DUNDALE LAKE Tunbridge Wells
EAST FARLEIGH Maidstone
EUREKA Ashford
FORDCOMBE Tunbridge Wells
FRANT LAKES Tunbridge Wells
GEDGES LAKES Maidstone
HANDLE LAKE Canterbury
HAYES TROUT FISHERY Bromley
HERONSVIEW FISHERIES Canterbury
HOO LAKES Rochester
HOOKSTEAD LAKE Ashford
LARKFIELD LAKES Maidstone
LAVENDER FARM Faversham
LITTLE CANSIRON FISHING LAKES Edenbridge
LONGFIELD LAKE Tonbridge
LONGSHAW FARM FISHING LAKES Canterbury
MATCH LAKE Chilham
MONK LAKE FISHERIES Tonbridge
MOTE PARK FISHERY Maidstone
MOUSEHOLE LAKE Tonbridge
NOOK & CRANNY LAKE Canterbury
PIPPINS FARM LAKE Tonbridge
PITTLANDS LAKES Tonbridge
REED LAKE Canterbury
RIVERFIELD CARP FARM Maidstone
ROOKERY LAKE Bromley
SCARLETTS LAKE Edenbridge
SCHOOL POOL Faversham
SEPHAM TROUT FISHERY Sevenoaks
SHORNE COUNTRY PARK LAKES Gravesend
SINGLETON LAKE Ashford
SPRING HILL TROUT WATERS Tunbridge Wells
ST CLERE LAKE Wrotham
STONAR LAKE Sandwich
STOUR LAKE Canterbury
STOUTING LAKE Canterbury
STOWTING TROUT LAKE Ashford
SURRENDEN LAKES Ashford
SWAN LAKE Canterbury
TENTERDEN TROUT WATERS Tenterden
TONFORD LAKE Canterbury
TRIANGLE LAKE Canterbury
WIDEHURST FARM Tonbridge
WOODCHURCH TROUT FISHERY Ashford

LANCASHIRE

ABBEY LAKES Skelmersdale
BICKERSHAW WATERS Wigan
BIRKACRE LODGES Chorley
BRIARCROFT FISHERY Preston

BRINSCALL LODGE Chorley
BRYN FLASH Wigan
BURSCOUGH BRICKWORKS LAKE Ormskirk
CLEVELEY BRIDGE FISHERY Preston
CLIVIGER FISH PONDS Burnley
COPTHORNE COARSE FISHERIES Preston
CROFT FISHERIES Chorley
CROMPTON LODGE Bolton
CUERDEN VALLEY LAKE Preston
DICKENS STREET LODGE Blackburn
DOFFCOCKER LODGE Bolton
DRAKESHEAD FLY FISHERY Chorley
DUNSCAR SHORE LODGE Bolton
EAGLEY WATERS Bolton
ENTWHISTLES RESERVOIR Blackburn
FAN LODGE Wigan
FARINGTON LODGES Preston
FIR TREE LODGE Wigan
FIRWOOD LODGE AND THE BUNK Bolton
FOUNDRY LODGE Chorley
GREENHALGH LODGE FISHERY Preston
HEAPEY NO 1 Chorley
HEAPEY NO 2 Chorley
HEAPEY NO 3 Chorley
HEAPEY NO 6 Chorley
HESKIN OLD FARM FISHERY Chorley
HIGHER HALL FLASH Wigan
HODDLESDEN LAKE Blackburn
HOUGHTONS LODGE Wigan
HULLDOWN TROUT FISHERY Colne
INCE PARK LAKE Wigan
INGS FARM TROUT FISHERY Nelson
ISLAND DAM Wigan
KEARNS ALLEN LODGES Accrington
KNIGHT BOTTOMS LAKE Preston
LANCASTER HOUSE Chorley
LANCASTER HOUSE FARM FISHERY Rossendale
LATHOM FISHERIES Burscough
LEISURE LAKES Preston
LITTLE DALE HALL COARSE FISHERY Morecambe
LOVECLOUGH TROUT FISHERY Rossendale
LOWER HOUSE LODGE Burnley
LYNDHURST FARM LAKE Preston
MARTIN HALL FARM Preston
MELLINGS NO 1 Wigan
ORRELL WATER PARK Wigan
PINE LODGE FISHERIES Clitheroe
PLATTS LANE LAKE Ormskirk
POLLYS FLASH Wigan
QUEENS PARK LAKE Heywood
RED ROCKS FISHERY Preston
ROACH BRIDGE FISHERY Preston
ROUGHLEE TROUT FISHERY Nelson
ROWLEY PARK LAKE Burnley
RUSHYVARS LAKES Preston
SHRUGGS WOOD FISHERY Preston
ST MICHAELS WYRESIDE FISHERY Preston
SWANTLEY LAKE Morecambe
THREE SISTERS Wigan
THURSLAND HILL FARM Lancaster
TURBARY HOUSE NURSARY Preston
TWIN LAKES TROUT FISHERY Preston
WIDOWS FLASH Wigan
WORTHINGTON NO 1 Chorley
WORTHINGTON NO 2 Chorley
WORTHINGTON NO 3 Chorley
WYRESIDE LAKES FISHERY AND LODGINGS Lancaster

LEICESTERSHIRE

BAXTERS GARDEN FARM LAKE Hinckley
BROOK MEADOW FISHERY Market Harborough
BROOME FISHERIES Leicester
C J FISHERIES Lutterworth
CHARNWOOD WATER Leicester
FRISBY LAKES Leicester
GROBY FISHING LAKES Leicester
HALL FARM Lutterworth
HOLLY FARM FISHERY Lutterworth
LAKESIDE FISHING Hinckley
LAKESIDE SPORTING Leicester
LAUNDE ABBEY LAKES Leicester
LYNCHGATE LANE FISHERY Hinckley
MALLORY PARK FISHERIES Leicester
MANOR FARM Lutterworth
PARKLANDS FISHERY Hinckley
SHELL FRESH LAKE Hinckley
SNIBSON COLLIERY CARP LAKE Coalville
SPRING GRANGE FISHERY Leicester
WELLAND LODGE FISHERY Market Harborough
WHETSTONE GORSE Willoughby Waterlease

LINCOLNSHIRE

ALVINGHAM FISHERIES Louth
ASHBY PARK FISHERIES Horncastle
BASTON FEN FISHERY Bourne
BELLEAU BRIDGE FARM LAKE Louth
BELLS YARD LAKE Horncastle
BOULTHAM PARK LAKE Lincoln
BUCKMINSTER PARK LAKE Grantham
BURGHLEY PARK LAKE Stamford
CLAYBRIDGE TROUT LAKES Market Rasen
CULVERTHORPE LAKES Grantham
DENNIS RAINWATER LAKE Skegness
DYKES COTTAGE LAKES Lincoln
EAST HALTON FISHING LAKES Immingham
GOLTHO LAKE Market Rasen
GRANGE FARM LEISURE Mablethorpe
GRIMSTHORPE LAKE Bourne
HARTSHOLME PARK LAKE Lincoln
HATTON TROUT LAKE Market Rasen
HAVERHOLME PARK Sleaford
HERONS MEAD Skegness
HILL VIEW LAKES Skegness
HOMESTEAD LAKE Immingham
HYKEHAM PIT Lincoln
KEAL COATES FISHERY Spilsby
LAKE HELEN Boston
LAKE ROSS FISHERY Spalding
LAKESIDE Lincoln
MARRIS LAKES Lincoln
MILL HILL LAKES Skegness
MILL ROAD LAKES Skegness
MOON LAKE Tattershall
NORTH KELSEY PARK Market Rasen
OAKHILL LEISURE Lincoln
OHAM LAKES Alford
PEACOCK LAKE Woodhall Spa
RICHMOND LAKES Lincoln
ROACH FARM PARK Skegness
ROD AND LINE CARAVAN PARK Skegness
ROSSWAYS WATER Boston
SKEGNESS WATER LEISURE PARK Skegness
STARMERS PIT Lincoln
STONE END LAKE Louth
SWAN LAKE Skegness
SYSTON PARK TROUT LAKE Grantham
TALLINGTON FISHERY Stamford
TATTERSHALL LEISURE PARK Lincoln
THORPE LE VALE FISHERY Louth
TIM HALL LAKE Lincoln
WATERSIDE LEISURE PARK Skegness
WHISBY GARDEN CENTRE Lincoln
WHITE HOUSE PREDATOR LAKE Baston Fen
WILLOW BANK FISHERY Gainsborough
WILLOW FARM Louth
WILLOW LAKES Grantham
WINTERS LAKE Immingham
WOODLAND WATERS Grantham
WOODLANDS FISHERY Spilsby
WOODLANDS LAKE Gainsborough
WOODTHORPE HALL LAKE Alford

LINCOLNSHIRE (NORTH)

BARTON BROADS LAKE Barton-upon-Humber
MARSHLANDS Barton-upon-Humber
PASTURE HOUSE FISHERY Barton-upon-Humber
TARGET LAKE Barton-upon-Humber
TILEYARD LANE Barton-upon-Humber
WESTFIELD LAKES Barton-upon-Humber

LONDON (GREATER)

ALEXANDRA PARK LAKE London
ASHVALE FISHERIES London
BEDFONT LAKE London
BOXERS LAKE London
BROOMWOOD LAKE Orpington
COWLEY LAKE London
CUTTING LAKE London
EAST WARWICK London
FORTY HALL LAKE London
FROGMORE LAKE London
GREENHAMS London
HALLIFORD MERE LAKES London
HENRY STREETER LAKE London
HIGHAMS PARK LAKE London
HOLLOW PONDS London
LITTLE BRITAIN LAKE London
LIZARD LAKES London
MARCOA LAKE London
MULGROVE POND London
NORWOOD LAKE London
OSTERLEY PARK MIDDLE LAKE London
PERCH POND London
RODNEY MEADOW London
SHEEPWALK LAKE London
SOUTH NORWOOD LAKE London
SWYERS LAKE London
SYON PARK FISHERY London
TRENT COUNTRY PARK LAKES London
TRENT PARK LAKES London
WANSTEAD PARK LAKES London
WEST WARWICK London
WHITE HORSE FISHERIES London
WILLOWSIDE CARP LAKE London
WOOLWICH DOCKYARD London

MANCHESTER (GREATER)

ALEXANDRA PARK Oldham
ASHENHURST LAKES Manchester
BEEFOLD LODGE Manchester
BOGGART HOLE CLOUGH Manchester
BOWKER LAKES Manchester
CARCUS WATERS Bury
CHORLTON WATER PARK Manchester
CLARENCE RECREATION GROUND Bury
CLEGG HALL LAKES Littleborough
CLOWES PARK LAKE Salford
CRIME LAKE Ashton-under-Lyne

CROMPTONS WATER Bury
DAVENPORT Stockport
DINGLE LODGE Manchester
FARM LODGE Manchester
FIR TREE FLASH Leigh
FIRS PARK LAKE Leigh
HEATON PARK Manchester
HOLLINGWORTH LAKE COUNTRY PARK Littleborough
ISLAND AND CARTWHEEL LODGES Bury
LEEKES WATER Manchester
PAINSWICK PARK LAKE Manchester
PENNINE TROUT FISHERY Rochdale
PENNINGTON FLASH Leigh
PILSWORTH FISHERY COMPLEX Heywood
PLATT FIELDS Manchester
POYNTON POOL Stockport
ROMAN LAKE LEISURE PARK Stockport
ROYAL GEORGE MILL COMPLEX Oldham
SANDY BEACH Manchester
STAMFORD PARK LAKES Ashton-under-Lyne
STAR MOUNT Manchester
SWAN LODGE Manchester

MERSEYSIDE

ARROWE PARK LAKE Wirral
BIRKENHEAD LOWER PARK LAKE Birkenhead
CALDERSTONES PARK LAKE Liverpool
CENTRAL PARK LAKE Wirral
EVE A LYN FARM Wirral
GREENBANK PARK LAKE Liverpool
LOWER LAKE Birkenhead
MILL HOUSE FISHERY Liverpool
PRINCES PARK LAKE Liverpool
RODDEE MERE Wirral
STANLEY PARK LAKE Liverpool
UPPER LAKE Birkenhead
WALTON HALL PARK Liverpool
WOODHOUSE FISH FARM Newton-Le-Willows

MIDLANDS (WEST)

ASTBURY FALLS FISH FARM Bridgnorth
BLYTHE WATERS Solihull
COOMBE ABBEY LAKE Coventry
CUTTLE MILL CARP FISHERY Sutton Coldfield
DARTMOUTH PARK West Bromwich
EARLSWOOD LAKES Solihull
HEATHFIELD POOL Walsall
HERON BROOK FISHERY Wolverhampton
HOPSFORD HALL FISHERY Coventry
KINGSBURY WATER PARK Sutton Coldfield
KINGSHURST LAKE Solihull
LAVENDER HALL Coventry
PACKINGTON TROUT FISHERY Coventry
PATSHULL PARK Wolverhampton
PENNS HALL LAKE Sutton Coldfield
POOLE HALL FARM Wolverhampton
SOMERS FISHERY Coventry
SUTTON PARK Sutton Coldfield
TIDBURY GREEN GOLF CLUB Solihull
WALCOT EAST LAKE Birmingham
WALSALL ARBORETUM Walsall

NORFOLK

ABBEY WATERS Attleborough
BARFORD LAKES FISHERY Norwich
BARNINGHAM HALL LAKE Norwich
BARTLES LODGE Dereham
BILLINGFORD PIT East Dereham
BILNEY LAKES Dereham
BLICKLING PARK LAKE Norwich
BORE VALLEY LAKES Norwich
BRADMOOR LAKES King's Lynn
BRIDGE FARM FISHERIES East Dereham
CANTLEY SUGAR FACTORY Norwich
CHAPEL ROAD LAKE Norwich
CHARITY LAKES Norwich
COBBLEACRES LAKES Norwich
COLTON LAKE Norwich
DECOY FARM Great Yarmouth
DENTS OF HILGAY Downham Market
DUNHAM CARP AND TENCH LAKES Swaffham
FELBRIGG HALL LAKE Cromer
FELGRIGG LAKE Holt
FELMINGHAM MILL LAKES Norwich
FELTHORPE LAKE Norwich
FRITTON LAKE Great Yarmouth
GIMINGHAM LAKES Norwich
GLEN MERE Norwich
GREAT MELTON FISHERY Norwich
GUNTHORPE HALL LAKE Melton Constable
GUNTON PARK LAKE Cromer
HARDLEY MARSHES Norwich
HAVERINGLAND HALL PARK Norwich
HEVINGHAM LAKES Norwich
HINDERCLAY LAKES Diss
HINGHAM FISHMERE Norwich
HOLKHAM LAKE Wells-Next-The-Sea
KINGFISHER LAKES Norwich
LAKESIDE King's Lynn
LAKESIDE CARAVAN PARK Downham Market
LENWADE TROUT FISHERY Norwich
LETHERINGSETT FISHERY Holt
LITTLE DUNHAM CARP LAKES King's Lynn
LOCH NEATON Watton
MANOR LAKE Attleborough
MEADOW LAKE King's Lynn
MIDDLE HARLING LAKE Thetford
MILL FARM FISHERY Attleborough
MILL FARM FISHERY Norwich
NATURES HAVEN LAKES Swannington
NORFOLK AND SUFFOLK FLY FISHERIES LAKE Dereham
PECK MEADOW POND Attleborough
RACKHEATH SPRINGS Norwich
RAILWAY LAKE Dereham
RAILWAY LAKE Thuxton
RECTORY FARM FISHERY Norwich
REEPHAM FISHERY Norwich
RINGLAND LAKES Norwich
ROOSTING HILLS Dereham
RUSTON REACHES Norwich
SALMON AND TROUT ASSOCIATION LAKES Dereham
SHALLOW BROOK LAKES Norwich
SHORT PLANTATION LAKE Norwich
SOVEREIGN LAKES King's Lynn
SWANGEY LAKES Attleborough
TASWOOD LAKES FISH FARM AND FISHERY Norwich
WEYBREAD FISHERY Diss
WHINBURGH TROUT LAKE Dereham
WILLOWCROFT FISHERY King's Lynn
WILLSMORE WATER Fakenham
WOODRISING WATER MEADOWS Thetford

NORTHAMPTONSHIRE

ABINGDON PARK LAKE Northampton
BARKERS LAKE Kettering
BILLING AQUADROME Northampton
BLUE LAGOON Northampton
CANONS ASHBY LAKES Daventry
CASTLE ASHBY LAKES Northampton
CHESTER FARM LAKE Wellingborough
CORBY BOATING LAKE Corby
CRESCENT LAKE Northampton
DELEPRE PARK LAKE Northampton
ELINOR COARSE LAKE Kettering
FLECKNOE FARM FISHERIES Daventry
GLEBE LAKE Northampton
GREEN FARM LAKES Towcester
GRENDON LAKES Northampton
HARDWATER LAKE Northampton
HEYFORD FISHERY Northampton
ISLIP NATURE LAKE Kettering
LAKESIDE COUNTRY CLUB Rushden
PINE TREES LAKES Wellingborough
RAVENSTHORPE TROUT FISHERY Northampton
RINGSTEAD ISLAND Kettering
SHELFLEYS LAKE Northampton
SILVER LAKE Towcester
SOUTH VIEW FARM CARP FISHERY Wellingborough
ST JAMES SMALL PARK LAKE Northampton
THORPE WATERVILLE LAKE Kettering
WOOTTON BROOK LAKE Northampton

NORTHUMBERLAND

GIBBS HILL TROUT FISHERY Hexham
GILSLAND LAKE Haltwhistle
HADRIAN LODGE Hexham
HEXHAM FISHERIES Hexham
HORTON GRANGE LAKE Blyth
LANGLEY DAM FISHERIES Hexham
LINNEL WOOD LAKE Hexham
QUEEN ELIZABETH II COUNTRY PARK Ashington
THORNBROUGH LAKE Corbridge

NOTTINGHAMSHIRE

CLUMBER LAKE Worksop
COLWICK COUNTRY PARK Nottingham
COVERT SPRINGS FISHERIES Nottingham
CROMWELL LAKE TROUT FISHERY Newark
DANESHILL LAKES Retford
HARWICK HALL LAKES Mansfield
LAKESIDE FARM Grantham
LAKESIDE FISHERY Retford
LANGOLD LAKES Worksop
L-LAKE FISHERY Mansfield
LOUND WINDSURF LAKE Retford
OWDY LANE TROUT FISHERY Worksop
SANDHILL LAKE Worksop
SHERWOOD FOREST FARM PARK FISHERY Mansfield
WINDMILL FARM LAKES Newark
WINFIELD LAGOON Nottingham

OXFORDSHIRE

BARNES TROUT LAKES Oxford
BEIRTON LAKES Oxford
BLADON LAKE Woodstock
BLENHEIM LAKE Woodstock
BUTLERS HILL FARM Chipping Norton
CHAD LAKES Chipping Norton
CHRISTCHURCH LAKE Witney

COLLEGE FARM FISHING Banbury
CORNBURY PARK FISHERY Chipping Norton
FARINGDON LAKE Faringdon
FARMOOR TROUT FISHERY Oxford
GAUNTS LAKE Witney
GLEBE COURT LAKE Bicester
GOLDFISH BOWL (THE) Oxford
HARDWICK LAKE AND SMITHS POOL Witney
HEART OF ENGLAND FISHERY Banbury
HORSE AND GROOM LAKES Banbury
HUNTS CORNER Witney
MANOR FARM LAKE Witney
MANOR HOUSE Oxford
MANOR LAKE Bicester
MILLETS FARM TROUT FISHERY Abingdon
NELL BRIDGE FISHERY Banbury
ORCHID LAKES Wallingford
OXLEASE LAKE Witney
PIMLICO FARM LAKES Bicester
ROLFS LAKE Oxford
ROYAL PIONEER CORPS ANGLING ASSOCIATION WATER Bicester
SALFORD TROUT LAKES Chipping Norton
ST JOHNS POOL Witney
STATES LAGOON Bicester
SWISS FARM LAKE Henley-on-Thames
UNITY LAKE Witney
YEOMANS LAKE Witney

RUTLAND

NORMANTON FISHING LODGE Oakham
SWEETHEDGES FARM FISHERY Oakham

SHROPSHIRE

ACTON BURNELL Shifnal
AQUALATE MERE Newport
BENTHALL LAKE Broseley
BIRCH GROVE Shrewsbury
BLAKEMERE Whitchurch
BROCKTON GRANGE Much Wenlock
COLEMERE COUNTRY PARK Ellesmere
COUND TROUT FISHERY Shrewsbury
CROSEMERE Ellesmere
DEARNFORD HALL TROUT FISHERY Whitchurch
DELBURY HALL TROUT FISHERY Craven Arms
ELLERDINE LAKES Telford
HAWKSTONE PARK LAKE Shrewsbury
HOLMER LAKE Telford
ISLE LAKE Shrewsbury
LAKE VYRNWY Oswestry
LLORAN GANOL FARM Oswestry
LOWER HILL FARM Much Welock
MILL HOUSE LAKES Market Drayton
MONKHALL FISHERIES Bridgnorth
VOWNOG FISH LAKE Oswestry
WALCOT WEST LAKE Bishops Castle
WHITCHURCH LAKE Whitchurch
WHITEMERE Ellesmere

SOMERSET

APEX LAKE Burnham-on-Sea
ASHMEAD LAKES Martock
AVALON FISHERIES Glastonbury
BLAGDON LAKE Bristol
BULLOCKS FARM FISHING LAKES Clevedon
CHEW VALLEY LAKE Bristol
COOMBE LAKE Langport
DANDYS LAKE AND KNIGHTINGALE LAKE Bath
EDNEYS FISHERIES Frome
EMBOROUGH LAKE Emborough
EXE VALLEY FISHERY Dulverton
FOLLY FOOT FARM Bridgwater
HIGHLANDS DAIRY LAKE Crewkerne
HORSESHOE LAKE Wedmore
HUNSTRETE LAKE COMPLEX Bath
LANDS END FARM Wedmore
LANDS END FISHERIES Wedmore
LANGFORD LAKES Wellington
LOWER LOVELYNCH FISHERIES Taunton
MARSTON LAKE Frome
NEWTON PARK Bath
NEWTOWN LAKE Highbridge
OTTERHEAD LAKES Taunton
OXENLEAZE FARM CARAVANS AND COARSE FISHERY Taunton
PAULTON LAKES Bristol
PLANTATIONS LAKES Clevedon
QUANTOCK FISHERIES Bridgwater
SEDGES Bridgwater
ST ALGARS FARM LAKE Frome
SUMMERHAYES Bridgwater
THORNEY LAKES Langport
TUCKING MILL Bath
VIADUCT FISHERY Somerton
WATER MEADOW LAKES Crewkerne
WESTHAY LAKE Bridgwater
WIMBLEBALL LAKE Dulverton
WITHAM FRIARY LAKE Frome
WOODBOROUGH PARK LAKE Bath
WYCH LODGE LAKE Taunton

STAFFORDSHIRE

BIDDULPH GRANGE Stoke-on-Trent
BLACK LAKE Stoke-on-Trent
BLACKSHAW FARM LAKES Leek
BONEHILL MILL Tamworth
DEEP HAYES COUNTRY PARK Leek
DILHORNE HALL POOLS Stoke-on-Trent
HANCHURCH FISHERIES Stoke-on-Trent
HEDNESFORD ROAD LAKE Rugeley
HIMLEY HALL AND PARK LAKE Dudley
LAWTON HALL POOL Newcastle-under-Lyme
LOYNTON TROUT FISHERIES Stafford
MIDLAND GAME FISHERIES Lichfield
PARK HALL FARM Stoke-on-Trent
PRETTY PIGS FISHERY Tamworth
RISING TROUT FISHERY Stoke-on-Trent
RUDYARD LAKE Leek
SHELMORE TROUT FISHERY Stafford
SIDEWAY OVERFLOW Stoke-on-Trent
SMITHPOOL LAKE Stoke-on-Trent
TILTLESWORTH Leek
TRENTHAM GARDENS Stoke-on-Trent
WADE LAKE Rugeley
WILLOWS POOLS Penkridge
WOODSEAT LAKE Uttoxeter

SUFFOLK

ALDERSONS LAKES Ipswich
BAKERS LAKE Stowmarket
BOSMERE LAKE Ipswich
CAMELOT LAKE Harleston
CAUSEWAY LAKES Ipswich
CHESTERFORD FISHERIES Sudbury
CLARE PARK LAKE Sudbury
CROSS GREEN FLY FISHERY Bury St Edmunds
DITCHINGHAM PIT Bungay
FLIXTON DECOY Lowestoft
FLOOD PARK Haverhill
GUNSSONS LAKE Saxmundham
GUNTON HALL LAKE Lowestoft
HATCHERY HOUSE TROUT LAKES Bury St Edmunds
HIGHFIELD FISHERY Harleston
HOME FARM FISHERIES Sudbury
HOMERSFIELD LAKE Harleston
LAKESIDE Stowmarket
LARKWOOD TROUT FISHERY Bury St Edmunds
MARSH FARM LAKES Saxmundham
MELDUM WASHLANDS (FLOODPARK) Haverhill
MELTON LAKE Woodbridge
MILLERS LAKE Clare
OULTON BROAD Lowestoft
PETTISTREE LAKES Woodbridge
REYDON LAKES Southwold
WAVENEY VALLEY LAKES Harleston
WEST STOW COUNTRY PARK Bury St Edmunds
WILLOW LAKES TROUT FISHERY Halesworth
YEW TREE FISHERIES Harleston

SURREY

ALFORD ROAD FISHERIES Cranleigh
BADSHOT LEA Farnham
BOLDERMERE Woking
BROADWATER LAKE Godalming
BURY HILL FISHERIES Dorking
BUSBRIDGE LAKE Milford
COLTSFORD MILL FISHERY Oxted
CROSSWATER MILL FISHERY Farnham
ENTON LAKES TROUT FISHERY Godalming
FRENSHAM TROUT FISHERY Farnham
FURZE FARM Cranleigh
GATTON MANOR LAKES Dorking
GOLDSWORTH WATER PARK Woking
JOHNSONS LAKE Milford
LAKESIDE Heath End
NAVIES HOLE Cranleigh
PAPERCOURT FISHERY Woking
POWDER MILLS FISHERY Guildford
PULBOROUGH LAKE Horsham
ROOSTHOLE Horsham
RUSHMOOR LAKES Farnham
SHAWFIELDS LAKES Ash
ST PATRICKS LANE CARP LAKES Farnham
THORPE PARK WATERSKI LAKE Chertsey
WAGGONERS WELLS Hindhead
WILLINGHURST COARSE FISHERY Guildford
WILLINGHURST TROUT FISHERY Guildford
WINKWORTH LAKES Godalming
WINTERSHALL WATERS Godalming
WYPHURST AND HYHURST LAKES Cranleigh

SUSSEX (EAST)

BOJO FISHERIES Heathfield
BORINGWHEEL TROUT FISHERY Uckfield
BRICKYARD LAKE Bexhill-on-Sea
BROOMHAM FISHERY Battle
BUXTED PARK FISHERY Uckfield
CLAREMONT LAKE Battle
COGHURST HALL Hastings
COLIN GODMANS TROUTING Uckfield
CYPRUS WOOD TROUT FISHERY Uckfield
DECOY LAKE Lewes
FALKENVIL FISHERY Hailsham

FURNACE BROOK FISHERY Hailsham
HASTINGS LAKE Hastings
HOLTS LAKES Crowborough
HONEYS GREEN COARSE FISHERY Uckfield
KINGS STANDING LAKES Crowborough
LAKEDOWN TROUT FISHERY Etchingham
LEABRIDGE FARM Hailsham
PEVENSEY HAVEN Hailsham
PIPPINGFORD PARK ESTATE LAKES Uckfield
POWDERMILL (GREAT SANDERS) WATER Battle
SHAMFOLD FARM FISHERY Rye
SHARNFOLD FARM FISHERY Pevensey
SOUTHBOURNE LAKE Eastbourne
SWANBOROUGH LAKES Lewes
TANYARD FISHERIES Uckfield
UNDERHILL LAKE Uckfield
VINEHALL SCHOOL LAKE Robertsbridge
WALLERS HAVEN Hailsham
WHITE HART HILL LAKE Hastings
WOODMANCOTE PLACE FISHERY Brighton
YEW TREE TROUT FISHERY Crowborough

SUSSEX (WEST)

BALCOMBE LAKE Haywards Heath
BLACKWOOL TROUT FISHERY Petworth
BOLEBROOK CASTLE East Grinstead
BORDE HILL GARDEN LAKES Haywards Heath
CHALK SPRINGS TROUT FISHERY Arundel
CUCKFIELD FISHERY Haywards Heath
DOCTORS LAKE Horsham
DUNCTON MILL Petworth
FURNACE LAKES Horsham
HAMBROOK TROUT FISHERY Chichester
HAZELCOPSE LAKES Horsham
HURSTON LANE Pulborough
LAYBROOK LAKES Pulborough
LENNOX WOOD LAKE Horsham
MENARDS LAKE Horsham
MILL FARM FISHERY Pulborough
NEWELLS SPECIMEN CARP AND COARSE FISHERIES Horsham
SLAUGHAM MILL POND Haywards Heath
TILGATE LAKES Crawley
VALE BRIDGE LAKE Haywards Heath
WATER MEADOWS FLY FISHERIES Pulborough
WATTLEHURST FARM TROUT LAKES Horsham
WILDERNESS LAKE East Grinstead
WINTONS FISHERY Burgess Hill

TYNE AND WEAR

BIG WATERS Newcastle Upon Tyne
BOLAM LAKE COUNTRY PARK Newcastle Upon Tyne
KILLINGWORTH LAKE Newcastle Upon Tyne
LEAZES PARK LAKE Newcastle Upon Tyne
LITTLE BIG WATER Newcastle Upon Tyne
MILKHOPE POND Newcastle Upon Tyne
MOUNT PLEASANT LAKE Washington
SILKSWORTH SPORTS COMPLEX Sunderland
STEPHENSON LAKE Houghton Le Spring
SWEETHOPE LOUGHS Newcastle Upon Tyne
THROCKLEY REIGH Newcastle Upon Tyne
WILLOWS (THE) Washington

WARWICKSHIRE

ARDENCOTE MANOR HOTEL AND COUNTRY CLUB Warwick
BLACK HILL POOLS Stratford-upon-Avon
BOSWORTH PARK LAKE Nuneaton
BOSWORTH WATER TRUST AND FRIEZELAND POOLS Nuneaton
BRAMCOTE MAINS FISHERY Bedworth
CLIFTON LAKES FISHERY Rugby
HAWKESBURY FISHERY Bedworth
HIGH CLAYS FARM Southam
MILL POOL Rugby
NORTH FARM FISHERY Southam
PARK FARM Warwick
SHEEPY MAGNA LAKE Atherstone
SNITTERFIELD FRUIT FARM Stratford-upon-Avon

WILTSHIRE

BLACKLAND LAKES HOLIDAY AND LEISURE CENTRE Calne
BOWOOD LAKE Calne
BRITFORD FISHERY Salisbury
BURTON HILL LAKE Malmesbury
CUCKOOS REST Westbury
DORKHAM STORMWATER Swindon
ERLESTOKE LAKE Devizes
IVY HOUSE FARM Chippenham
LAWNS (THE) Swindon
LIDEN LAGOON Swindon
LONGHOUSE LAKES Salisbury
LONGLEAT LAKES Warminster
MILL FARM TROUT LAKES Devizes
OLD WARDOUR Salisbury
PEARMOOR LAKE Swindon
PEATMOOR LAGOON Swindon
PETERS FINGER LAKES Salisbury
PLAUMS PIT Swindon
PURTON LAKE Swindon
RODBOURNE LAGOON Swindon
ROOD ASHTON LAKE Trowbridge
SABRE AND SWORDS LAKES Calne
SHAFTESBURY LAKE Swindon
SHEAR WATER Warminster
SOUTHLEIGH LAKE Warminster
STEEPLE LANGFORD LAKES Salisbury
TOCKENHAM RESERVOIR Chippenham
TURNERS PADDOCK LAKE Warminster
WALDENS FARM FISHERY Salisbury
WHITE HORSE INN LAKE Malmesbury
WITHERINGTON FARM FISHING Salisbury
WYATTS LAKE Chippenham
WYTHERINGTON FARM Salisbury

WORCESTERSHIRE

ACR FISHERIES Worcester
ARROW VALLEY LAKE Redditch
BLACK MONK TROUT LAKES Evesham
BRAKE MILL POOL Worcester
BROAD ACRES LAKE Bromsgrove
BROCKHILL FARM TROUT POOLS Redditch
ELMBRIDGE LAKES Droitwich
EVESBATCH FISHERIES Worcester
FOREST FARM Pershore
FURNACE MILL FISHERY Kidderminster
GROVE FARM Worcester
HURCOTT POOL Kidderminster
LEIGH SINTON FISHING LAKES Malvern
LENCHES LAKES Evesham
LODGE PARK LAKE Redditch
MASTERS (THE) Kidderminster
RED BECK LAKE Evesham
SHAKESPEARE MOORLANDS FARM Kidderminster
SHATTERFORD FISHERY AND WILDLIFE SANCTUARY Kidderminster
SILLIGROVE FISHERY Bewdley
SINDON MILL FARM Malvern
SION FARM FISHERIES Kidderminster
SNUFF MILL POOL Bewdley
STANKLIN POOL Kidderminster
STELLA LAKE Kidderminster
UNWICKS FARM FISHERY Stourport-on-Severn
UPTON WARREN LAKE Bromsgrove
WELFIELD POOLS Kidderminster
WINDMILL LAKE Evesham
WINTERFOLD PARK FISHERIES Kidderminster
WITLEY POOLS Worcester

YORKSHIRE (NORTH)

ALDERS LAKE Thirsk
BARLOW COMMON NATURE RESERVE Selby
BELLFLASK TROUT FISHERY Ripon
BIRKDALE FISHERY Malton
BLACKBURN FARM TROUT FISHERY Hawes
BRAFFERTON COARSE FISHERY York
BRICKYARD FARM LAKE Malton
BRICKYARD FISHERY Ripon
BROKEN BREA FISHERY Richmond
BROOKLANDS Scarborough
CARLTON LODGE LAKE Thirsk
CASTLE HOWARD GREAT LAKE York
CATTERICK LAKES Richmond
CAWOOD HOLIDAY PARK Selby
CLIFTON MOOR LAKE Clifton
CRABTREE ANGLING LAKE Richmond
DRAX LAKE Selby
ELLERTON LANDING York
FAIRVIEW LAKE Carwood
FARMIRE Ripon
FOGGLESKYTE WATERS York
GRAFTON MERE York
HAZEL HALL FARM FISHING Northallerton
HAZELHEAD LAKE Pickering
HIGH MOOR FARM PARK Harrogate
HOLLINGWOOD FISHERY Northallerton
KAYS LAKES Thirsk
KILNSEY PARK AND TROUT FARM Skipton
KINGSLEY CARP LAKE Harrogate
KINLIN HALL TROUT FARM Ripon
KIPLIN TROUT FISHERY Northallerton
LAKESIDE FISHERIES Richmond
LAKESIDE LODGES York
LOW OSGOODBY LAKE Thirsk
MARSTON WYSE TROUT FARM York
MOORLANDS FARM PONDS York
NEWHAY DAY TICKET LAKE Selby
NEWHAY SPECIMEN LAKE Selby
OAKS FISHERY Thirsk
OAKTREE LEISURE York
PARKLANDS Northallerton
PICKERING PARK FISHING LAKE Pickering
PICKERING TROUT LAKE Pickering
POOL BRIDGE FARM LAKES York
POTTERY LAKE York
RACECOURSE LAKE Ripon

RAKER LAKES York
RASKELF LAKE York
REDHOUSE LAGOON York
RIPLEY CASTLE Harrogate
RIPON RACECOURSE LAKE Ripon
ROLIETH FISHERY Northallerton
SCARBOROUGH MERE Scarborough
SELBY 3 LAKES Selby
SELLEY BRIDGE LAKE Malton
SEMERWATER Hawes
SHIELD TROUT FISHERY Ripon
STONEBRIDGE LAKES Northallerton
TANFIELD LAKE Ripon
THORPE UNDERWOOD York
THREE LAKES Selby
TONTINE LAKE Northallerton
WATERMEADOWS FISHERY York
WELHAM LAKE Pickering
WEST HADDLESEY LAKE Selby
WESTERLY LAKE York
WILLOW WATER York
WILLOWS AND FIRS LAKES Thirsk
WOODLAND LAKES Thirsk
WYKEHAM LAKES Scarborough
Y2K LAKE Scarborough

YORKSHIRE (SOUTH)

ARKSEY STATION POND Doncaster
ASKERN LAKE Doncaster
ATHERSLEY MEMORIAL LAKE Barnsley
BEEDOMS FISHERY Doncaster
BULL HOLE Doncaster
CROOKES VALLEY PARK LAKE Sheffield
CUMWELL LANE Rotherham
CUSWORTH HALL LAKE Doncaster
DEARNE VALLEY PARK LAKE Barnsley
DELVES LAKES Doncaster
DUKERIES LAKES Worksop
FINA HAYFIELD LAKES Doncaster
HAVEN Doncaster
HORSESHOE LAKE TROUT FISHERY Sheffield
KIVETON HALL Sheffield
KJS FISHERIES Sheffield
MICKS PLACE Doncaster
NORWOOD FISHERIES Sheffield
PRESTON INNOVATIONS SILVER FISHERY Doncaster
RAILWAY POND Doncaster
SHIREOAKS PARK Worksop
SLIVER FISHERY Doncaster
STRAIGHT MILE FISHERY Sheffield
THRYBERGH COUNTRY PARK Rotherham
TRIANGS FISHERY Doncaster
TYRAM HALL Doncaster
WENTWORTH FISHERY Rotherham
WESTWOOD COUNTRY PARK Rotherham
WHARNCLIFFE FLY FISHERY Sheffield
WILLOW GARTH FISHERY Doncaster
WILLOWGARTH LAKE Doncaster

YORKSHIRE (WEST)

BOSTON SPA Wetherby
BOTTOMS DAM Huddersfield
BROOKFOOT LAKE Halifax
CLEARWATER LAKE Halifax
COPPICE POND Bingley
HOPTON WATERS Mirfield
HORNSEA MERE Huddersfield
KNOTFORD LAGOON Otley
LOWTHER LAKE Castleford
MILLRACE Leeds
NOSTELL PRIORY LAKE Wakefield
PINFOLD DAMS Huddersfield
PONTEFRACT PARK LAKE Pontefract
PUGNEYS COUNTRY PARK Wakefield
PUSH DAM Huddersfield
RAYGILL FISHERY Keighley
ROUNDHAY PARK LAKES Leeds
ROWLEY DAM Huddersfield
SPRING VALLEY WATERS Wakefield
STAVELEY LAKES Bradford
SWILLINGTON PARK Leeds
WALTON HALL TROUT LAKE Wakefield

LOCKS

BERKSHIRE

BRAY LOCK Maidenhead
HURLEY LOCK Maidenhead

ESSEX

DEDHAM MILL Colchester

HUMBERSIDE

LOUGH NAVIGATION Grimsby

LONDON (GREATER)

ENFIELD LOCK London
PENTON HOOK LOCK London
SHEPPERTON LOCK London

MIDLANDS (WEST)

LINCOMB LOCK Wolverhampton

OXFORDSHIRE

BENSON LOCK Wallingford
BUSCOT LOCK Faringdon
CLIFTON LOCK Abingdon
DAYS LOCK Abingdon
EYNSHAM LOCK Witney
GRAFTON LOCK Bampton
MARSH LOCK Henley-on-Thames

SURREY

BELL WEIR LOCK Egham
MOLESEY LOCK East Molesey

MERES

CHESHIRE

BETLEY MERE Crewe
MOULDSWORTH MERE Chester
TABLEY MERE Knutsford
TATTON MERE Knutsford
WESTLOW MERE Congleton

ESSEX

TUFNELL MERE Chelmsford

LONDON (GREATER)

BIRCHMERE London

NORFOLK

SCOULTON MERE Norwich

SHROPSHIRE

OSS MERE Whitchurch

MILL DAMS

BEDFORDSHIRE

LANGFORD MILL Biggleswade

CHESHIRE

MILL LODGE Macclesfield

CLEVELAND

SCALING DAM Guisborough

CORNWALL

COOMBE MILL Bodmin

DERBYSHIRE

CHAPEL WHEEL DAM Chesterfield

DEVON

AVON DAM Totnes

MANCHESTER (GREATER)

TANNERS DAM Oldham

MERSEYSIDE

CARR MILL DAM St Helens

STAFFORDSHIRE

HARTSHORNE DAMS Burton-on-Trent

YORKSHIRE (SOUTH)

FLEETS DAM Barnsley
GREASBROUGH DAMS Rotherham
SALLY WALSHES DAM Barnsley
STANBOROUGH FISHERIES Barnsley
WOMBWELL DAM Barnsley

YORKSHIRE (WEST)

BILLING DAM Leeds
FLANSHAW DAM Wakefield
HOYLE MILL DAM Pontefract
LONGBOTTOMS DAM Batley

MOATS

CHESHIRE

MONKS MOAT Northwich
TABLEY MOAT Knutsford

HAMPSHIRE

BROCKHURST MOAT Portsmouth
HILSEA MOATS Portsmouth

HEREFORDSHIRE

ASHPERTON MOAT Hereford

STAFFORDSHIRE

ALBRIGHTON MOAT PROJECT Wolverhampton

SUSSEX (EAST)

MICHELHAM PRIORY MOAT Eastbourne

PITS

BEDFORDSHIRE

VAUXHALL PIT Leighton Buzzard

CAMBRIDGESHIRE

BLOCK FEN COMPLEX Ely
ROSWELL PITS Ely
SPORTSMANS PIT Swaffham Prior

CHESHIRE

ASTBURY MERE Congleton
CATCHPENNY POOL Holmes Chapel
SHIPBROOK FLASH Northwich
WHIRLEY MERE Macclesfield

HERTFORDSHIRE

PAYNES LANE PIT Waltham Cross

LANCASHIRE

INCE MOSS FISHERIES Wigan

NORFOLK

UNIVERSITY BROAD Norwich

SUFFOLK

BARHAM B PIT Ipswich
SINKS PIT Ipswich

PONDS

BERKSHIRE

ALLSMOOR POND Bracknell
SAVERNAKE POND Bracknell

BRISTOL

ABBOTS POOL
FISHPONDS LIDO
ROUNDWOOD POND

BUCKINGHAMSHIRE

ALDERS FARM TROUT FISHERY Milton Keynes
COMMON POND Gerrards Cross
HILL WOOD POND High Wycombe
WATTS POOL Chalfont St Giles

CAMBRIDGESHIRE

- **OFFORD WEIRPOOL** Huntingdon
- **SILVER STREET MILL** Cambridge

CHESHIRE

- **BILLINGE GREEN** Northwich
- **BROWNLEES POND** Warrington
- **CAPESTHORNE HALL STOCK POND** Macclesfield
- **FANSHAWE LANE POOL** Macclesfield
- **GODWINS POOL** Congleton
- **GRIMESDITCH MILL POOL** Warrington
- **HARTHILL** Nantwich
- **MARY ANN POND** Warrington
- **MEADOW VIEW FISHERY** Warrington
- **ORFORD PARK POND** Warrington
- **SPRINGWOOD POOL** Knutsford
- **STATHAM POOL** Warrington
- **STOCKPOND** Winsford
- **WHITEGATE POND** Warrington

CLEVELAND

- **CHARLTONS PONDS** Middlesbrough
- **HUTTON RUDBY PONDS** Yarm

CORNWALL

- **FORDA HOLIDAY LODGES** Bude
- **LANGARTH POOLS** Truro
- **MELLONWATTS MILL** Truro
- **TIN DENE FISHERY** Penzance
- **TRETHIGGEY FARM POND** Newquay

COUNTY DURHAM

- **FIELDSONS POND** Bishop Auckland
- **FLYLANDS POND** Bishop Auckland
- **GREENCROFT POND** Stanley
- **KELLOW LAW POND** Ferryhill
- **MAINSFORTH POND** Ferryhill
- **TEASDALE POND** Durham
- **TRIMDON POND** Trimdon Station
- **TURSDALE POND** Durham
- **TURSDALE POND (LANGLEY PARK)** Durham
- **WELLFIELD POND** Peterlee

CUMBRIA

- **BANKS POND** Kendal
- **BRAYTON POND** Carlisle
- **BURLINGTON POND** Dalton-In-Furness
- **ELLERBECK FARM AND FISHERY** Cockermouth
- **WHINS POND** Penrith

DERBYSHIRE

- **POSSY LODGE PONDS** Belper

DEVON

- **ASHCOMBE FISHERY** Dawlish
- **BERRYNARBOR MILL POND** Ilfracombe
- **BICKERTON FARM FISHERY** Kingsbridge
- **BILLINGSMOOR FARM** Cullompton
- **CHARLECOMBE** Torquay
- **COOMBE FARM FISHPONDS** Tiverton
- **DORES POND - RACKERHAYES** Newton Abbot
- **DUNSLEY FARM** South Molton
- **EDDISON POND** Newton Abbot
- **FENECK POND** Exeter
- **FINLAKE PONDS** Newton Abbot
- **FISHPONDS HOUSE** Honiton
- **FOUR PONDS** Exeter
- **INDIO POND** Newton Abbot
- **LITTLE COMFORT FARM** Braunton
- **LONGLANDS FARM** Ilfracombe
- **MILTON FARM PONDS** Honiton
- **NEWCOURT PONDS** Cullompton
- **NEWTON ABBOT SPRING PONDS** Newton Abbot
- **POUND POND FARM** Tiverton
- **PYEWELL FARM** Bideford
- **ROCOMBE PONDS** Newton Abbot
- **RUB - A - DUB POND** Newton Abbot
- **SAMPFORD PEVERAL PONDS** Tiverton
- **SOUTH VIEW FARM FISHERY** Exeter
- **STAR BARTON PONDS** Exeter
- **STOUR FARM FISHERY** Cullompton
- **SUMMERLEAZE POND** Axminster
- **UPHAM FARM PONDS** Exeter
- **VALLEY VIEW FISHERY** Crediton
- **WAPPERWELL POND** Newton Abbot
- **WEST VIEW POND** Exeter

DORSET

- **BERKELEY FARM** Sherborne
- **CROW POOL** Christchurch
- **HARROW POND** Christchurch
- **HOLT WOOD PONDS** Wimborne
- **RAWLSBURY WATERS** Dorchester
- **WOOD FARM CARAVAN PARK** Bridport

ESSEX

- **BERWICK PONDS** Rainham
- **LITTLE EASTON MANOR** Dunmow
- **SPARROWS POND** Halstead
- **WAKE VALLEY POND** Loughton
- **WANSTEAD AND WOODFORD PONDS** Ilford

GLOUCESTERSHIRE

- **BURLEY FIELDS LAKE** Cheltenham
- **CANNOP PONDS** Forest Of Dean
- **HILLVIEW FISHERY** Tewkesbury
- **MEADOW POND** Gloucester
- **MEADOWCLIFFE POOL** Gloucester
- **PLUMP HILL POOL** Mitcheldean
- **STONE END FARM LAKES** Gloucester
- **WATERLOO SCREENS** Gloucester

HAMPSHIRE

- **BAFFINS POND** Portsmouth
- **BILCOMBES POND** Southampton
- **CARRON ROW FARM PONDS** Fareham
- **COOKS POND** Liphook
- **DARK LANE PONDS** Southampton
- **FRENSHAM GREAT AND LITTLE PONDS** Aldershot
- **FUNTLEY POND** Fareham
- **GOLDEN POND FISHERY** Andover
- **HOLBURY MANOR POND** Southampton
- **HURST POND** Ringwood
- **LEOMINSTEAD MILL POND** Lyndhurst
- **MBK LEISURE BARRONS POND** Liss
- **MOPLEY POND** Southampton
- **QUEENS ROAD POND** Lee-on-The-Solent
- **ROTHERWICK AND NIGHTINGALE LAKES** Hook
- **TOPACRE LAKE** Winchester
- **WEDGEHILL PONDS** Ringwood

HEREFORDSHIRE

- **CHURCH POOL** Hereford
- **MARSH HOUSE FARM** Hereford
- **MILLPOND** Hereford
- **RED BANK POOLS** Ledbury
- **REDMIRE POOL** Ross-on-Wye
- **ROYAL OAK POOL** Hereford

HUMBERSIDE

- **BROOMFLEET PONDS** Brough
- **FISH TRADES POND** Brough
- **FISHPONDS FARM AND FISHERY** Bridlington
- **GOWDALL LAKES** Goole
- **HALSHAM POND** Hull
- **LANGHOLME FISHERIES** Driffield
- **REDFERNS POND** Brough
- **WOODALLS POND** Brough

ISLE OF WIGHT

- **GILLEES POND** Newport
- **WHITWELL PONDS** Ventnor

KENT

- **BIRCHDEN FARM FISHERY** Tunbridge Wells
- **BLUEBELL FISHING PONDS** Maidstone
- **ROUKES DRIFT FARM** Deal

LANCASHIRE

- **BALL GROVE LAKE** Colne
- **BANK HOUSE FLY FISHERY** Lancaster
- **BARRETTS FARM FISHERY** Ormskirk
- **CLAYLANDS CARAVAN SITE** Preston
- **FORSTERS LODGES** Wigan
- **GREAT BIRCH WOOD PONDS** Preston
- **GREEN LANE PONDS** Ormskirk
- **HULTON PARK LAKE** Bolton
- **LONGTON BRICKCROFT** Preston
- **MANOR HOUSE FISHERY** Preston
- **MELCHES POND** Bolton
- **SCOT LANE PONDS** Wigan
- **SQUARE LODGE** Wigan
- **STARMOUNT LODGES** Bolton
- **TEMPLE SPRINGS** Bolton
- **TOAD HALL FARM** Preston
- **WOODFOLD FARM FISHERIES** Preston

LEICESTERSHIRE

- **BROOKSBY COLLEGE** Melton Mowbray
- **FOLLY POND** Market Harborough

LINCOLNSHIRE

- **ABY POND** Alford
- **BRICKYARD POND** Grantham
- **CHARLES STREET POND** Louth
- **FISH POND FARM** Market Rasen
- **HOLLAND PARK** Skegness
- **LINDEN WALK POND** Louth
- **LOBBY FIELD PONDS** Market Rasen
- **SHANDY KEV FISHERIES** Lincoln
- **STICKNEY BRICKPONDS** Boston
- **SUDBROOK POND** Lincoln
- **WARREN POND** Louth
- **WINTER BROTHERS POND** Immingham

LINCOLNSHIRE (NORTH)

- **HOE HILL POND** Barton-upon-Humber
- **KINGFISHER LODGE** Brigg
- **PELICAN POND** Barton-upon-Humber
- **STADDLETHORPE POND** Brough

LONDON (GREATER)

- **CLAPHAM COMMON POND** London
- **FURNACE POND** London
- **HEATH VALE POND** London
- **HIGHGATE PONDS** London
- **KNIGHTSCOTE PONDS** London
- **POTOMAC POND** London
- **VALE OF HEATH POND** London
- **WANDSWORTH COMMON POND** London

MANCHESTER (GREATER)

- **ENDCROFTS POND** Bury
- **FIELD LODGE POND** Bury
- **GEIGYS WATER** Manchester
- **GROVE LODGE** Littleborough
- **LANKYS MILL POND** Manchester
- **REDDISH VALE MILL PONDS** Stockport
- **RHODES LODGE** Manchester
- **STAKEHILL LODGES** Manchester

MIDLANDS (WEST)

- **WASSELL GROVE FISHERIES** Stourbridge

NORTHAMPTONSHIRE

- **MENAGERIE POND** Northampton

NORTHUMBERLAND

- **FELTON FENCE FARM PONDS** Morpeth

NOTTINGHAMSHIRE

- **BESTWOOD POND** Nottingham
- **IRONMONGERS POND** Nottingham
- **PINDERS PONDS** Nottingham
- **STRIP PONDS** Retford
- **WOODEND QUARRY POND** Worksop
- **WOODSETTS QUARRY POND** Worksop

OXFORDSHIRE

- **CLEARWATER FISH FARM** Wantage

SHROPSHIRE

- **SEVEN OAKS LOG CABIN PARK** Shrewsbury
- **TOWNSEND FISHERY** Bridgnorth
- **WOODCOTE HALL** Telford

SOMERSET

- **BROWNES POND** Bridgwater
- **BUTLEIGH ROAD PONDS** Street
- **COMBWICH PONDS** Bridgwater
- **DUNWEAR LAKES** Bridgwater
- **EMBOROUGH POND** Bath
- **EMERALD POOL FISHERY** Highbridge
- **GODNEY MOOR PONDS** Glastonbury
- **HOWLEY STREET POND** Chard
- **MELLS PIT** Frome
- **MINERS PONDS** Somerton
- **PAWLETT PONDS** Bridgwater
- **SCREECH OWL PONDS** Bridgwater
- **STONE YARD FISHERY** Chewton Mendip
- **TAUNTON ROAD PONDS** Bridgwater
- **THURLEYBEARE POND** Taunton
- **WALROW PONDS** Highbridge
- **WELLINGTON BASIN** Wellington

STAFFORDSHIRE

- **ELLENHALL NINE POOLS** Stafford
- **HORNS** Rugeley
- **HORSEBRIDGE POOL** Leek

SUFFOLK

- **HENHAM DAIRY POND** Beccles
- **LOAM POND** Woodbridge
- **RAYDON PONDS** Southwold
- **VALLEY FARM FISHERY** Halesworth

SURREY

- **ALDERBROOK LAKE** Cranleigh
- **BRITTENS POND** Guildford
- **BUSHEY PARK** East Molesey
- **EPSOM STEW POND** Epsom
- **FISHERIES THE** Cranleigh
- **HAWKINS POND** Horsham
- **HOME PARK** East Molesey
- **KINGFISHER FISHERY** Haslemere
- **LONG COPSE PONDS** Leatherhead
- **MANOR POND** Cobham
- **MILL POND** Dorking
- **ONE ISLAND POND** Mitcham
- **PUDDENHOLE POND** Dorking
- **SEVEN ISLANDS** Mitcham
- **STOCKBRIDGE POND** Tilford
- **WHITEVANE POND** Horsham

SUSSEX (EAST)

- **BALLS GREEN LAKES** Hartfield
- **BELFREY COARSE FISHERY** Hailsham
- **LOWER HONEYS GREEN FARM** Uckfield
- **PENNY BRIDGE** Crowborough
- **SCALAND WOOD** Crowborough
- **THORNDEN POND** Battle

SUSSEX (WEST)

- **ALDERWOOD PONDS** Steyning
- **BURTON MILL POND** Petworth
- **CASTLE TROUT POND** Arundel
- **DAYLANDS FARM** East Grinstead
- **DOUNHURST FARM FISHERY** Billinghurst
- **DUNCANS POND** Pulborough
- **NEW POND** Midhurst
- **PASSIES PONDS** Lancing
- **PILTDOWN POND** Haywards Heath
- **ROTHERFIELD POND** Midhurst
- **SLAUGHTERFORD FARM** Horsham
- **SPARKS FARM FISHERY** Haywards Heath
- **STUBPOND FISHERIES** East Grinstead

TYNE AND WEAR

- **BRENKLEY POND** Newcastle Upon Tyne
- **DISSINGTON POND** Newcastle Upon Tyne
- **FELLGATE PONDS** Gateshead
- **RED BARNS POND** Newcastle Upon Tyne

WARWICKSHIRE

- **ADAMS POOL** Alcester

WILTSHIRE

- **CLIVEY PONDS** Westbury
- **CROCKERTON POND** Warminster
- **PEMBROKE POND** Swindon

WORCESTERSHIRE

- **ABBOTS SALFORD PARK** Evesham
- **BANKES POOL** Stourport-on-Severn
- **BEWDLEY POOL** Kidderminster
- **HAYE FARM FISHERY** Bewdley
- **MOORS POOL** Kidderminster
- **WILDEN POOL** Stourport-on-Severn
- **WOODROW FISH POND** Bromsgrove

YORKSHIRE (NORTH)

- **ABBIE POND** Malton
- **BACON FACTORY POND** Tadcaster
- **CHAPMANS POND** York
- **CORNHILL PONDS** Northallerton
- **FLETCHERS POND** York
- **HESSAY POND** York
- **HOXNE FARM PONDS** York
- **LINGCROFT FARM POND** York
- **MANOR FARM POND** Malton
- **MOULTON LANE POND** Thirsk
- **MUNBY POND** Selby
- **NORTHINGALES FISHERY** York
- **OAK MERE FISHERY** York
- **ORCHARD FARM PONDS** York
- **PROSPECT FARM POND** Harrogate
- **QUEEN MARYS POND** Ripon
- **SHIELD FISHERY** Bedale
- **STONEY LANE PONDS** Northallerton
- **TOLLERTON FISHING PONDS** York
- **TROUT POND BARN** Malton
- **WILLOWS** York

YORKSHIRE (SOUTH)

- **BRICKYARD PONDS** Rotherham
- **CAMPSALL COUNTRY PARK** Doncaster
- **DELVES FISH PONDS** Doncaster
- **ECCLESFIELD POND** Sheffield
- **LONG POND** Doncaster
- **MILTON PONDS** Barnsley
- **MISSION LINEBANK PONDS** Doncaster
- **NANCY POND** Sheffield
- **NETHERWOOD COUNTRY PARK** Barnsley
- **NEWBIGGIN POND** Rotherham
- **ROSSINGTON BRICK POND** Doncaster
- **SANDERSONS POND** Doncaster
- **TINKERS PONDS** Barnsley
- **TOLL BAR POND** Doncaster

YORKSHIRE (WEST)

- **ACKTON POND** Pontefract
- **CLAYTON WOOD PONDS** Leeds
- **DYEHOUSE POND** Bradford
- **HOLME MILL DAM (SQUARE DAM)** Huddersfield
- **KIPPAX POND** Leeds
- **NEW MILL DAM** Todmorden
- **ROBERTS POND** Keighley
- **T P POND DAM** Huddersfield
- **THORNHILL POND** Dewsbury
- **TP WOODS POND** Huddersfield
- **WORKSHOP POND** Castleford

POOLS

BEDFORDSHIRE

- **WITHY POOL** Henlow

BERKSHIRE

- **MATCH AND BLUE POOLS** Reading

BUCKINGHAMSHIRE

- **GALLOWS POOL** Buckingham

CAMBRIDGESHIRE

- **WOOD POOL** Peterborough

CHESHIRE

- **ASHLEY POOL** Altrincham
- **ASTLE POOL** Knutsford
- **BELMONT POOL** Northwich
- **BENTLEY TROUT POOL** Tarporley
- **BORDER FISHERIES** Crewe
- **BRIGHOUSE POOL** Knutsford
- **BROOK BANK POOL** Holmes Chapel
- **BULLS POOL** Sandbach
- **CICELY MILL POOL** Knutsford
- **CRABTREE MOSS FARM POOL** Congleton
- **DUKES POOL** Crewe
- **FARM POOL** Northwich
- **FINGERPOST POOL** Knutsford
- **FOUNDERS POOL** Northwich
- **FRIARS POOL** Northwich
- **GRIMSDITCH MILL POOL** Warrington
- **JARMAN FARM POOL** Macclesfield
- **KNIGHTS POOL** Macclesfield
- **LITTLE REEDS MERE** Knutsford
- **LONGBARN POOL** Warrington
- **MANOR POOL** Knutsford
- **MARTON HEATH COARSE POOL** Macclesfield
- **MARTON HEATH TROUT POOLS** Macclesfield
- **MORETON MERE FISHERY** Congleton
- **MOSS POOLS** Lymm
- **MOSSBANK POOL** Lymm
- **NEW BRIDGE POOL** Winsford
- **NEW POOL** Northwich
- **NORBURY POOL** Lymm
- **NORTH FIELD POOL** Congleton
- **OAK POOL** Northwich
- **OULTON MILL POOL** Tarporley
- **PARK POOL** Macclesfield
- **PECK POOL** Congleton
- **PETTY POOL** Northwich
- **ROOKERY POOL** Northwich
- **SANDYBANK POOL** Sandbach
- **SHELLOW FARM POOLS** Congleton
- **SPRING POOL** Northwich
- **STRETTON WATER** Warrington
- **TOP FARM POOL** Lymm
- **TURNERS POOL** Macclesfield

VILLAGE POOL Warrington
WALL POOL LODGE Macclesfield
WARDS POOLS Congleton
WHITLEY POOL Warrington
WILLOW POOL Northwich
WINNINGTON POOL Northwich
WOOD POOL Macclesfield
WOODSIDE POOL Runcorn
YEW TREE POOL Northwich

CLEVELAND
ASCOTT PONDS Middlesbrough

CORNWALL
AMALWHIDDEN FARM Penzance
BILLS POOL Hayle
GWINEAR POOLS COARSE FISHERY Newquay

COUNTY DURHAM
TURNSIDE POOL Durham

CUMBRIA
BORROWDALE FISHERIES Keswick

DERBYSHIRE
BELPER POND Belper
MELBOURNE POOL Derby
PRESS MANOR Chesterfield

DEVON
RIVERTON HOUSE AND LAKES Barnstaple

ESSEX
MANNINGTREE RIVER POOLS Colchester
RAYNE LODGE FARM Braintree

GLOUCESTERSHIRE
CHURN POOL TROUT FISHERY Cirencester
LIGHTMOOR POOL Cinderford
MARIONS POOL Coleford

HAMPSHIRE
IBSLEY POOLS Ringwood

HEREFORDSHIRE
HERRIOTS POOL Hereford
HUNDRED POOL Hereford
LILY AND WILLOW POOLS Ledbury
PIXLEY POOL Ledbury
ROTHERWAS LONG POOL Hereford

HUMBERSIDE
FISHPONDS FARM AND FISHERY Bridlington

KENT
GRANGE POOL Tonbridge
SILVER SPRINGS FISHERY Tonbridge

LANCASHIRE
BANNISTER HALL FARM Preston
CHARITY FARM FISHERY Chorley
CHURCH GARDEN Bolton
COTTAGE GREEN GARDEN CENTRE Chorley
STANLEY PARK LAKE Thornton-Cleveleys

LEICESTERSHIRE
HALL FARM FISHING Melton Mowbray
MANOR FARM POOLS Hinckley
PEATLING POOLS (1-6) Lutterworth

LINCOLNSHIRE
DAIWA GULL POOL Gainsborough

LINCOLNSHIRE (NORTH)
ORCHARD POND Scunthorpe

LONDON (GREATER)
ALEXANDRA PALACE LAKE London

MANCHESTER (GREATER)
CROWN POOLS Bury
KING GEORGE V POOL Manchester
NEW HOUSE FARM POOL Stockport
WESTGATE POOL Manchester
WOODBANK PARK POOL Stockport

MERSEYSIDE
CARR LANE POOL Prescot
MORETON MERE Wirral
POULTON RECREATION FIELD POOL Wirral
WOODSLEE POOL Wirral

MIDLANDS (WEST)
ALVECHURCH FISHERIES Birmingham
BRIDGE POOL Wolverhampton
BULL FISHERY Halesowen
COOMBE POOL Coventry
DAYHOUSE FARM Halesowen
FOXHILLS FISHERY Walsall
HIMLEY ISLAND POOL Wolverhampton
KINGSNORDLEY Bridgnorth
NORDLEY POOLS Bridgnorth
POOL HALL Bridgnorth
ROYAL BRITISH LEGION POOLS Coventry
RYTON POOLS COUNTRY PARK Coventry
SNEYD POOL Walsall
SWAN POOL West Bromwich

NORFOLK
PARK LIME PIT Norwich

NORTHAMPTONSHIRE
LYNN POOL FISHERY Corby

OXFORDSHIRE
MILTON POOLS FARM Oxford

SHROPSHIRE
APLEY POOLS Telford
BAYLIS POOLS Shifnal
BEECHES POOL Telford
BLUE POOL Telford
BOLDINGS POOLS Bridgnorth
FOLLY FARM POOL Shrewsbury
HINKSHAY POOLS Telford
HORESHAY POOL Telford
LITTLE DAWLEY POOLS Telford
MIDDLE POOL Telford
MILLRIDE FISHERY Wolverhampton
SNAILBEACH POOL Shrewsbury
SPRING LEE Shrewsbury
STIRCHLEY POOLS Telford
TELFORD TOWN PARK Telford
TRENCH POOL Telford
TURFMOOR FISHERY Oswestry
WITHY POOL Telford

SOMERSET
EMBOROUGH POOL Wells
LAKESIDE Dulverton

STAFFORDSHIRE
ASHLEY POOLS Loggerheads
BADEN HALL FISHERY Stafford
BASFORD COARSE FISHERY Leek
BLACKWOOD POOL Stoke-on-Trent
BORROWPIT LAKE Tamworth
HOLDEN LANE POOL Stoke-on-Trent
LITTLETONS AND MIDDLE POOL Rugeley
MADELEY POOL Newcastle-under-Lyme
PARKES HALL Dudley
PILLATON POOLS Penkridge
PINE POOL Tamworth
POOL HOUSE FARM Tamworth
SMITH POOL Stoke-on-Trent
SOUTH POPLARS Cannock
SWAN PIT POOL Stafford
TAYLORS POOL Stoke-on-Trent
WILLOW POOLS Stafford

SUSSEX (EAST)
MOOR HALL POOL Battle
PETT POOLS Hastings
ST IVES FARM Hartfield

WARWICKSHIRE
BISHOPS BOWL LAKES Leamington Spa
CHESTERTON MILL POOL TROUT FISHERY Leamington Spa
KINGSTON POOLS Warwick
LANNYS LAGOON Rugby
MAKIN FISHERIES Bedworth
MONKS POOL Bedworth
OAKHAM FARM POOLS Warwick
RIDDINGS FISHERY Atherstone
WESTON LAWN FISHERIES Bedworth

WORCESTERSHIRE
ASTWOOD FISHERY Droitwich
BENNETTS POOL Worcester
BROCKAMIN POOLS Worcester
CAPTAINS POOL Kidderminster
CASTLE GREEN POOLS Malvern
CURTISS POOL Bewdley
DEXTER POOL Bewdley
ERICS POOL Kidderminster
HARVEY POOL Worcester
HOLT FLEET POOL Worcester
LOWER BROADHEATH POOLS Worcester
MILL POOL Bewdley
MOORLANDS FARM Kidderminster
POOLE HALL FISHERY Kidderminster
STEWARDS POOL Kidderminster
TOP BARN ANGLING CENTRE Worcester
UCKINGHALL POOL Worcester
WASH POOL Worcester
WELLFIELD POOLS Bewdley
WHARFE INN POOL Worcester
WHARTONS PARK COARSE FISHING Bewdley
WOOD POOL Evesham
WOODLAND VIEW Droitwich
WOODSTON MANOR POOLS Tenbury Wells

YORKSHIRE (NORTH)
CARP VALE York
KILBURN POND York

YORKSHIRE (SOUTH)
THORNE NORTH POND Doncaster

QUARRIES

CHESHIRE
LYMM VALE Winsford
MOORE QUARRY Warrington

CUMBRIA
EAST VIEW FISHERY Carlisle

DEVON
OLDBOROUGH FISHING RETREAT Crediton

WARWICKSHIRE
NEWBOLD QUARRY Rugby

YORKSHIRE (WEST)
HORBURY LAGOON Wakefield

QUAYS

MANCHESTER (GREATER)
SALFORD QUAYS Salford

RESERVOIRS

BEDFORDSHIRE

AMPTHILL RESERVOIR Bedford
BECKERINGS PARK FARM RESERVOIR Bedford

BUCKINGHAMSHIRE

BILLET LANE Iver
WESTON TERVELL RESERVOIR Great Missenden

CAMBRIDGESHIRE

GRAFHAM WATER Huntingdon
KINGSLAND RESERVOIRS Peterborough
TWENTY FOOT DRAIN Peterborough
WELDON RESERVOIR Huntingdon
WILDEN RESERVOIR Huntingdon

CHESHIRE

APPLETON RESERVOIR Warrington
BADDILEY RESERVOIR Nantwich
BOSLEY RESERVOIR Macclesfield
BOTTOMS RESERVOIR Macclesfield
HORSECOPPICE RESERVOIR Macclesfield
LAMALOAD RESERVOIR Macclesfield
LEADBEATERS RESERVOIR Macclesfield
RIDGEGATE RESERVOIR Macclesfield
SUTTON RESERVOIR Macclesfield
TEGGSNOSE RESERVOIR Macclesfield
TURKS HEAD RESERVOIR Macclesfield
WALKERWOOD RESERVOIR Hyde
WALKERWOOD TROUT FISHERY Stalybridge

CLEVELAND

HART RESERVOIR Hartlepool
HARTLEPOOL RESERVOIR Stockton-on-Tees
LOCKWOOD BECK RESERVOIR Guisborough
NEW MARSKE RESERVOIR Redcar

CORNWALL

ARGAL RESERVOIR Penryn
BOSCATHNOE RESERVOIR Penzance
BUSSOW RESERVOIR St Ives
COLLEGE RESERVOIR Falmouth
CROWDY RESERVOIR Camelford
DRIFT RESERVOIR Penzance
MILLBROOK COARSE FISHERY Torpoint
PORTH RESERVOIR Newquay
STITHIANS RESERVOIR Truro

COUNTY DURHAM

BLACKTON RESERVOIR Barnard Castle
BURNHOPE FISHERY Darlington
COW GREEN WILD BROWN TROUT FISHERY Barnard Castle
DERWENT RESERVOIR Consett
FIGHTING COCKS RESERVOIR Darlington
GRASSHOLME RESERVOIR Barnard Castle
HURWORTH BURN RESERVOIR Darlington
HURY RESERVOIR Barnard Castle
MIDDLETON WATER PARK Darlington
SELSET RESERVOIR Barnard Castle
TUNSTALL RESERVOIR Bishop Auckland
WASKERLEY RESERVOIR Consett

CUMBRIA

BARROW-IN-FURNESS RESERVOIR Barrow-In-Furness
BAYSTONE BANK RESERVIOR Millom
BORRANS RESERVOIR Windermere
DUBBS RESERVOIR Bowness On Windermere
DUBBS TROUT FISHERY Windermere
GHYLL HEAD TROUT FISHERY Windermere
HARLOCK RESERVOIR Dalton-In-Furness
HAWESWATER RESERVOIR Ambleside
HAYESWATER RESERVOIR Ambleside
HIGH NEWTON RESERVOIR Windermere
KILLINGTON RESERVOIR Kendal
LOW GILL Sedbergh
MEADLEY RESERVOIR Cleator Moor
ORMSGILL LOWER RESERVOIR Barrow-In-Furness
PENNINGTON RESERVOIR Dalton-In-Furness

DERBYSHIRE

ARNFIELD RESERVOIR Glossop
BUTTERLEY RESERVOIR Ripley
CARSINGTON WATER Ashbourne
CODNOR PARK RESERVOIR Belper
COMBS RESERVOIR High Peak
CONDOR PARK RESERVOIR Ripley
COTE LODGE RESERVOIR High Peak
ERRWOOD RESERVOIR High Peak
FOREMARK TROUT FISHERY Derby
LADYBOWER RESERVOIR Hope Valley
LINACRE RESERVOIRS Chesterfield
MAPPERLEY RESERVOIR Ilkeston
OGSTON RESERVOIR Chesterfield
STAUNTON HAROLD RESERVOIR Derby
TODDBROOK RESERVOIR High Peak

DEVON

BURRATOR RESERVOIR Plymouth
DARRACOTT RESERVOIR Torrington
DELBROOK VALLEY TROUT FISHERY Tiverton
FERNWORTHY RESERVOIR Newton Abbot
GAMMATON RESERVOIRS Bideford
JENNETTS RESERVOIR Bideford
KENNICK RESERVOIR Exeter
LOWER SLADE RESERVOIR Ilfracombe
MELBURY RESERVOIR Bideford
MELDON RESERVOIR Okehampton
OLD MILL RESERVOIR Dartmouth
ROADFORD RESERVOIR Okehampton
SLADE RESERVOIRS Ilfracombe
SQUABMOOR RESERVOIR Exeter
TOTTIFORD RESERVOIR Okehampton
TRENCHFORD RESERVOIR Exeter
VENFORD RESERVOIR Newton Abbot
WISTLANDPOUND RESERVOIR Barnstaple

DORSET

WESSEX WATER RESERVOIRS Poole

ESSEX

ARDLEIGH RESERVOIR Colchester
BARLEYLANDS RESERVOIR Billericay
HANNINGFIELD TROUT FISHERY Chelmsford
HOUCHINS RESERVOIRS Colchester
ROCHFORD RESERVOIR Rochford
SHALFORD RESERVOIRS Braintree

GLOUCESTERSHIRE

WITCOMBE WATERS Gloucester

HAMPSHIRE

WAINSFORD RESERVOIR Lymington

HEREFORDSHIRE

RUSSELLS END RESERVOIR Ledbury

HERTFORDSHIRE

CHESHUNT SOUTH RESERVOIR Waltham Cross
MARSWORTH RESERVOIR Tring
STARTOPS RESERVOIR Tring
TRING RESERVOIRS Tring
WILSTONE RESERVOIR Tring

HUMBERSIDE

SYKEHOUSE RESERVOIRS Goole

ISLE OF WIGHT

SOMERTON RESERVOIR Newport

KENT

BEWL WATER Lamberhurst
BOUGH BEECH RESERVOIR Tonbridge
BURNHAM RESERVOIR Maidstone
HARTLEY LANDS FARM Cranbrook

LANCASHIRE

ADLINGTON RESERVOIR Bolton
ANGLEZARKE RESERVOIR Wigan
BARNSFOLD WATERS Preston
BARROWFORD RESERVOIR Nelson
BLACKMOSS RESERVOIR Nelson
BRADFORD RESERVOIR Bolton
BRADSHAW HALL FISHERIES Bolton
BROWNHILL RESERVOIR Colne
BRYAN HEY RESERVOIR Bolton
CANT CLOUGH RESERVOIR Burnley
CHURN CLOUGH RESERVOIR Preston
CLOWBRIDGE RESERVOIR Bolton
COLDWELL (LOWER) RESERVOIR Burnley
CONDER VALLEY FLY FISHERY Lancaster
DEAN CLOUGH RESERVOIR Accrington
DEAN RESERVOIR Darwen
DILWORTH (UPPER) RESERVOIR Preston
DINGLE RESERVOIR Bolton
DIXON GREEN RESERVOIR Bolton
EARNSDALE RESERVOIR Blackburn
FISHMOOR RESERVOIR Rossendale
FOULRIDGE RESERVOIR Colne
GLEAVES RESERVOIR Bolton
GRIMSARGH RESERVOIR Preston
GRIZEDALE LEA RESERVOIR Preston
HAGGS RESERVOIR Accrington
HODDLESDEN RESERVOIR Darwen
HOLDEN WOOD RESERVOIR Rossendale
JUMBLES RESERVOIR Bolton

LANESHAW RESERVOIR Burnley
LOWER COLDWELL RESERVOIR Burnley
LOWER RIVINGTON RESERVOIR Chorley
LOWER RODDLESWORTH RESERVOIR Chorley
MITCHELLS HOUSE RESERVOIR Accrington
OGDEN RESERVOIR Rossendale
PARSONAGE RESERVOIR Accrington
PORTSMOUTH RESERVIOR Burnley
RAKE BROOK RESERVOIR Chorley
RISHTON RESERVOIR Blackburn
RUMWORTH LODGE RESERVOIR Bolton
SABDEN RESERVOIR Clitheroe
SPADE MILL RESERVOIR NO.2 Preston
STANWORTH RESERVOIR Blackburn
STOCKS FLY FISHERY Clitheroe
SWINDEN RESERVOIR Burnley
TURTON AND ENTWISTLE RESERVOIR Preston
UPPER RIVINGTON RESERVOIR Bolton
UPPER RODDLESWORTH RESERVOIR Bolton
WALVERDEN RESERVOIR Nelson
WAYOH RESERVOIR Blackburn
WHITEMOOR RESERVOIR Nelson
WITHNELL RESERVOIRS Chorley

LEICESTERSHIRE

EYEBROOK TROUT FISHERY Market Harborough
HOLWELL WORKS RESERVOIR Melton Mowbray
SWITHLAND RESERVOIR Swithland
THORNTON RESERVOIR Leicester

LINCOLNSHIRE

DENTON RESERVOIR Grantham
KINPTON RESERVOIR Grantham
REVESBY RESERVOIR Horncastle
TOFT NEWTON TROUT FISHERY Market Rasen

LONDON (GREATER)

HIGH MAYNARD RESERVOIR London
LOCKWOOD RESERVOIR London
LOW MAYNARD RESERVOIR London
WALTHAMSTOW RESERVOIR (EAST WARWICK) London
WALTHAMSTOW RESERVOIR (NO 1) London
WALTHAMSTOW RESERVOIR (NO 2 AND NO 3) London
WALTHAMSTOW RESERVOIR (NO 4 TROUT) London
WALTHAMSTOW RESERVOIR (NO 5) London
WALTHAMSTOW RESERVOIR (WEST WARWICK) London
WEST RESERVOIR London

MANCHESTER (GREATER)

BLACK MOSS RESERVOIR Oldham
BLACKLEACH RESERVOIR Manchester
BOLLINHURST RESERVOIR Stockport
BRUN CLOUGH RESERVOIR Oldham
BUCKLEY WOOD RESERVOIR Rochdale
BURRS LODGE Bury
CROFT HEAD FISHERY Littleborough
DEBDALE RESERVOIRS Manchester
DOCTOR DAM FISHERY Rochdale
DOWRY AND NEW YEARS BRIDGE RESERVOIR Oldham
ELTON RESERVOIR Bury
GORSE PIT RESERVOIR Manchester
GORTON (LOWER) RESERVOIR Manchester
GORTON (UPPER) RESERVOIR Manchester
KING WILLIAM IV RESERVOIR Manchester
KITCLIFFE RESERVOIR Oldham
LITTLE SEA RESERVOIR Oldham
LOWER CASTLESHAW RESERVOIR Oldham
LOWER TOWN HOUSE FISHERY Littleborough
LUDWORTH RESERVOIR Stockport
MYRTLE ROAD LODGES Manchester
OGDEN LOWER RESERVOIR Rochdale
PIETHORNE RESERVOIR Rochdale
REDBROOK RESERVOIR Oldham
UPPER GORTON RESERVOIR Manchester
WATERGROVE RESERVOIR Rochdale
WHITELEY KNOWL RESERVOIR Littleborough
WHITTLE BROOK RESERVOIR Manchester
WITHINS RESERVOIR Manchester

MIDLANDS (WEST)

EDGBASTON RESERVOIR Birmingham
SHUSTOKE FLY FISHERS Birmingham

NORTHAMPTONSHIRE

BODDINGTON RESERVOIR Daventry
DAVENTRY COUNTRY PARK Daventry
DRAYTON RESERVOIR Daventry
DUSTON RESERVOIR Northampton
HOLLOWELL RESERVOIR Northampton
NASEBY RESERVOIR Northampton
PITSFORD RESERVOIR Northampton
SULBY RESERVOIR Northampton
SYWELL RESERVOIR Wellingborough
WELFORD RESERVOIR Northampton

NORTHUMBERLAND

FONTBURN RESERVOIR Morpeth
HALLINGTON RESERVOIRS Corbridge
KIELDER WATER Hexham
WHITTLE DEAN RESERVOIR Hexham

NOTTINGHAMSHIRE

CRANWELL LANE TROUT FISHERY Newark
KINGS MILL RESERVOIR Sutton-In-Ashfield

OLDHAM

CASTLESHAW (LOWER) RESERVOIR

OXFORDSHIRE

CLATTERCOTE RESERVOIR Banbury
FARMOOR 1 RESERVOIR Witney
GRIMSBURY RESERVOIR Banbury

SOMERSET

BARROW RESERVOIRS Bristol
CHARD RESERVOIR Chard
CHEDDAR RESERVOIR Cheddar
CLATWORTHY RESERVOIR Taunton
DURLEIGH RESERVOIR Bridgwater
HAWKRIDGE RESERVOIR Bridgwater
LITTON RESERVOIR Bristol
SUTTON BINGHAM RESERVOIR Yeovil

STAFFORDSHIRE

BLITHFIELD RESERVOIR Rugeley
CANAL RESERVOIRS Stoke-on-Trent
GAILEY TROUT AND PIKE FISHERY Stafford
KNYPERSLEY RESERVOIR Stoke-on-Trent
STANLEY RESERVOIR Stoke-on-Trent
TITTESWORTH RESERVOIR Leek

SUFFOLK

ALTON WATER RESERVOIR Ipswich
BRIDGE FARM RESERVOIRS Woodbridge
STANTONS FARM RESERVOIR Sudbury
WICKHAM MARKET RESERVOIRS Woodbridge

SURREY

EAST WHIPLEY RESERVOIR Cranleigh

SUSSEX (EAST)

ALEXANDRA PARK WATERS Hastings
ARLINGTON TROUT FISHERY Polegate
BARCOMBE RESERVOIR Lewes
CLIVE VALE RESERVOIRS Hastings
DARWELL WATER Robertsbridge
ECCLESBOURNE RESERVOIR Hastings
WEIR WOOD FISHERY Forest Row
WISHING TREE RESERVOIR Hastings

SUSSEX (WEST)

ARDINGLY RESERVOIR Haywards Heath

TYNE AND WEAR

WHITTLE DENE TROUT FISHERY Newcastle Upon Tyne

WARWICKSHIRE

DRAYCOTE WATER Rugby
HEATHCOTE LAKE Warwick
NAPTON RESERVOIR Southam
STOCKTON RESERVOIR Rugby

WILTSHIRE

BURBROOKS RESERVOIR Melksham
COATE WATER COUNTRY PARK Swindon
WROUGHTON RESERVOIR Swindon

WORCESTERSHIRE

TRIMPLEY RESERVOIR Bewdley

YORKSHIRE (NORTH)

EMBSAY RESERVOIR Skipton
FARMIRE TROUT FISHERY Knaresborough
LEIGHTON RESERVOIR Ripon
SCAR HOUSE RESERVOIR Ripon
SWINTON ESTATE TROUT FISHERY Ripon
THORNTON STEWARD RESERVOIR Ripon
WHINNYGILL RESERVOIR Skipton

YORKSHIRE (SOUTH)

DAM FLASK RESERVOIR Sheffield

ELSECAR RESERVOIR Barnsley
HARTHILL RESERVIORS Worksop
HOWBROOK RESERVOIR Sheffield
MORE HALL RESERVOIR Sheffield
PEBLEY RESERVOIR Sheffield
SCOUT DYKE RESERVOIR Sheffield
SMITHIES RESERVOIR Barnsley
SOUTHFIELD RESERVOIRS Doncaster
ULLEY RESERVOIR Sheffield
UNDERBANK RESERVOIR Sheffield
WORSBOROUGH RESERVOIR Barnsley
WORSBROUGH RESERVOIR Barnsley

YORKSHIRE (WEST)

DOE PARK RESERVOIR Bradford
HILL TOP RESERVOIR Huddersfield
OAKS SCAR RESERVOIR Huddersfield
ROYDS HALL DAM Bradford
SPARTH RESERVOIR Huddersfield
SWINSTY AND FEWSTON RESERVOIRS Otley
WINTERSETT RESERVOIR Wakefield

RIVERS

BEDFORDSHIRE

FELMERSHAM (RIVER) Bedford
GREAT OUSE (RIVER) Bedford
IVEL (RIVER) Biggleswade
IVEL (RIVER) Henlow
OUSE (RIVER) Bedford

BERKSHIRE

ALBERT BRIDGE Windsor
BARTON COURT FISHERY Hungerford
HOLYBROOK Reading
KENNET (RIVER) Newbury
KENNET (RIVER) Reading
KENNET AND ENTORNE (RIVERS) Reading
LODDON (RIVER) Reading
LODDON (RIVER) Wokingham
LOWER BENYONS Reading
MAPLEDURHAM A AND B Reading
PURLEY Reading
ROMNEY ISLAND AND MEADOW Windsor
THAMES (RIVER) Bray
THAMES (RIVER) Maidenhead
THAMES (RIVER) Newbury
THAMES (RIVER) Reading
THAMES (RIVER) Windsor

BRISTOL

AVON (BRISTOL) (RIVER)
AVON (RIVER)
BRISTOL AVON
CHEW (RIVER)
FROME (RIVER)

BUCKINGHAMSHIRE

BACKWATER Marlow
BOURTON FISHERIES Buckingham
CHESS (RIVER) Amersham
CHESS (RIVER) Chesham
COLNEBROOK (RIVER) Slough
GREAT OUSE (RIVER) Milton Keynes
GREAT OUSE (RIVER) Olney
OUSE (RIVER) Bedford
OUSE (RIVER) Milton Keynes
OUSE (RIVER) Olney
OUZEL (RIVER) Milton Keynes
THAME (RIVER) Aylesbury
THAMES (RIVER) High Wycombe
THAMES (RIVER) Marlow
THAMES (RIVER) Slough
TYRINGHAM ESTATE Newport Pagnell

CAMBRIDGESHIRE

CAM (RIVER) Cambridge
CAM (RIVER) Ely
COTTERSTOCK RIVER Peterborough
GODMANCHESTER (RIVER) Huntingdon
GREAT OUSE (RIVER) Ely
GREAT OUSE (RIVER) Huntingdon
HUNDRED FOOT (RIVER) Huntingdon
HUNTINGDON (RIVER) Huntingdon
LARK (RIVER) Ely
NENE (RIVER) Peterborough
NENE NORTH BANK (RIVER) Peterborough
OLD NENE (RIVER) Huntingdon
OLD WEST (RIVER) Cambridge
OLD WEST (RIVER) Ely
OLD WEST (RIVER) Huntingdon
OUNDLE (RIVER) Peterborough
STRETHAM BASIN Ely
WHITTLESEY DYKE/ BEVILLS LEAM Peterborough

CHESHIRE

ASHLEY (RIVER) Macclesfield
BOLLIN (RIVER) Knutsford
DANE (RIVER) Congleton
DANE (RIVER) Holmes Chapel
DANE (RIVER) Macclesfield
DANE (RIVER) Middlewich
DEAN (RIVER) Wilmslow
GOWY (RIVER) Chester
VALE ROYAL LOCKS Northwich
WEAVER (RIVER) Congleton
WEAVER (RIVER) Middlewich
WEAVER (RIVER) Northwich
WEAVER (RIVER) Warrington

CLEVELAND

TEES (RIVER) Stockton-on-Tees

CORNWALL

BUTTERWELL Bodmin
CAMEL (RIVER) Bodmin
CAMEL (RIVER) Wadebridge
FOWEY (RIVER) Bodmin
FOWEY (RIVER) Liskeard
FOWEY (RIVER) Looe
FOWEY (RIVER) Lostwithiel
INNY (RIVER) Liskeard
LYNHER (RIVER) Liskeard
SEATON (RIVER) Liskeard
ST BENETS ABBEY (RIVER) Bude
TAMAR (RIVER) Launceston
WEST LOOE (RIVER) Looe

COUNTY DURHAM

BROWNEY (RIVER) Durham
BYERS GREEN Spennymoor
DERWENT (RIVER) Consett
FINCHALE ABBEY FARM Durham
RABY ESTATES WATER Darlington
TEES (RIVER) Barnard Castle
TEES (RIVER) Darlington
WEAR (RIVER) Bishop Auckland
WEAR (RIVER) Chester-Le-Street
WEAR (RIVER) Crook
WEAR (RIVER) Durham

CUMBRIA

AIRA BECK Penrith
ANNAS (RIVER) Millom
BRATHAY (RIVER) Ambleside
BRIGHAM (RIVER) Cockermouth
CALDEW (RIVER) Carlisle
CLOUGH (RIVER) Sedbergh
CODALE TARN Ambleside
DEE (RIVER) Sedbergh
DERWENT (RIVER) Cockermouth
DERWENT (RIVER) Keswick
DEVOKE WATER Ravenglass
DOE (RIVER) Carnforth
DRUNKEN DUCK TARN FISHERY Ambleside
EAMONT (RIVER) Penrith
EASEDALE TARN Ambleside
EDEN (RIVER) Appleby-In-Westmorland
EDEN (RIVER) Carlisle
EDEN (RIVER) Kirkby Stephen
EHEN (RIVER) Egremont
ELLEN (RIVER) Maryport
ESK (RIVER) Ravenglass
FISHER TARN Kendal
GRETA (RIVER) Carnforth
IRT (RIVER) Holmrook
KENT (RIVER) Kendal
KIRKBY THORE (RIVER) Penrith
LAZY (RIVER) Millom
LICKLE (RIVER) Broughton-In-Furness
LIDDEL WATER Carlisle
LOWTHER (RIVER) Penrith
LUNE (RIVER) Penrith
LUNE (RIVER) Sedbergh
LUNE (RIVER) Sedburgh
NETHERBY ESTATE Carlisle
RAWTHEY (RIVER) Sedbergh
RAWTHEY (RIVER) Sedburgh
ROTHAY (RIVER) Ambleside
SANDFORD ARMS Appleby-In-Westmorland
SOUTH TYNE (RIVER) Alston
SPRINT (RIVER) Kendal
TWISS (RIVER) Carnforth
TYNE (RIVER) Alston
WINSTER (RIVER) Grange-Over-Sands
WINSTER (RIVER) Keswick

DERBYSHIRE

DERWENT (RIVER) Bakewell
DERWENT (RIVER) Belper
DERWENT (RIVER) Derby
DERWENT (RIVER) Matlock
DOVE (RIVER) Ashbourne
GOYT (RIVER) High Peak
HENMORE (RIVER) Ashbourne
KEGWORTH DEEP LOCK Derby
MONSAL DALE FISHERY Bakewell
MOSS BROOK Chesterfield
SOAR (RIVER) Derby
TRENT (RIVER) Derby
TRENT (RIVER) Matlock
WYE (RIVER) Bakewell
WYE (RIVER) Matlock

DEVON

AVON (RIVER) Kingsbridge
AXE (RIVER) Axminster
AXE (RIVER) Colyton
CAMEL (RIVER) Bodmin
CLAYHIDON (RIVER) Cullompton
CREEDY (RIVER) Crediton
CREEDY (RIVER) Exeter
CULM (RIVER) Exeter
DART (RIVER) Buckfastleigh
EGGESFORD COUNTRY HOTEL WATERS Chulmleigh
EXE (RIVER) Exeter
EXE (RIVER) Tiverton
HATSWELL Tiverton
INNIS MOORE TROUT FISHERY Bodmin
LITTLE WARHAM FISHERY Winkleigh
LYN (RIVER) Lynmouth
MOLE (RIVER) Umberleigh
OTTER (RIVER) Honiton
PLYM (RIVER) Plymouth
TAMAR (RIVER) Tavistock
TAR (RIVER) Exeter
TAVY (RIVER) Tavistock
TAW (RIVER) Barnstaple
TAW (RIVER) Crediton
TAW FISHING CLUB Crediton
TEIGN Exeter
TEIGN (RIVER) Newton Abbot
TORRIDGE (RIVER) Bideford
TORRIDGE (RIVER) Holsworthy
UPPER YEALM FISHERY Ivybridge
WATERSMEET AND GLENTHORNE FISHERIES Lynmouth
YEO (RIVER) Crediton

DORSET

AVON (RIVER) Christchurch
BRIT (RIVER) Bridport
CHRISTCHURCH LOWER STOUR Christchurch
DORSET FROME Wareham
FROME (RIVER) Dorchester
FROME (RIVER) Wareham
FROME AND PIDDLE (RIVERS) Wimborne
HAMPSHIRE AVON (RIVER) Christchurch
LIFELANDS FISHERY Christchurch
PIDDLE (RIVER) Dorchester
PIDDLE (RIVER) Wareham
ROYALTY FISHERY Christchurch
STOUR (DORSET) (RIVER) Blandford Forum
STOUR (DORSET) (RIVER) Bournemouth
STOUR (DORSET) (RIVER) Christchurch
STOUR (DORSET) (RIVER) Ferndown
STOUR (DORSET) (RIVER) Poole
STOUR (DORSET) (RIVER) Sturminster Newton
STOUR (DORSET) (RIVER) Wimborne
STOUR (RIVER) Blandford Forum
STOUR (RIVER) Bournemouth
STOUR (RIVER) Sturminster Newton
STOUR (RIVER) Wimborne
THAMES (RIVER) Dorchester
THROOP FISHERIES Bournemouth
UPPER STOUR (RIVER) Gillingham
WINKTON FISHERY Christchurch

ESSEX

BLACKWATER (RIVER) Braintree
BLACKWATER (RIVER) Chelmsford
BLACKWATER (RIVER) Colchester
BLACKWATER (RIVER) Witham
CHELMER (RIVER) Chelmsford
COLNE (RIVER) Colchester
LEA (RIVER) Waltham Abbey
LEE FLOOD RELIEF CHANNEL Waltham Abbey
PANT (RIVER) Braintree
RODING (RIVER) Ongar
RODING (RIVER) Romford
STOUR (RIVER) Colchester
STOUR (SUFFOLK) (RIVER) Colchester
WID (RIVER) Ingatestone

FIFE

EMBER (RIVER) East Molesey
WEY (RIVER) Addlestone

GLOUCESTERSHIRE

AVON (RIVER) Cheltenham
CHURCH END TROUT FISHERY Tewkesbury
COLN (RIVER) Cirencester
COLN (RIVER) Fairford
MILL AVON Tewkesbury
SEVERN (RIVER) Gloucester
SEVERN (RIVER) Tewkesbury
SEVERN ON THE HAM Tewkesbury
THAMES (RIVER) Cirencester
THAMES (RIVER) Lechlade

HAMPSHIRE

ABBOTTS WORTHY Andover
ANTON (RIVER) Andover
AVON (RIVER) Ringwood
AVON RIVER FISHERIES Fordingbridge
BICKERLEY MILLSTREAM Ringwood
HAMPSHIRE AVON Ringwood
HAMPSHIRE AVON (RIVER) Fordingbridge
HAMPSHIRE AVON (RIVER) Ringwood
ITCHEN (RIVER) Winchester
KIMBRIDGE Andover
LOWER ITCHEN FISHERY Romsey
PARSONAGE (RIVER) TEST Romsey
STOUR (RIVER) Ringwood
TEST (RIVER) Romsey
TEST (RIVER) Stockbridge
WHITEWATER (RIVER) Heckfield

HEREFORDSHIRE

CARADOC FISHERY Ross-on-Wye
HAYCASTLE WATER Hereford
INGESTONE FISHERY Ross-on-Wye
LLYNFI (RIVER) Hereford
LUGG (RIVER) Hereford
MARLIAS (RIVER) Hereford
MONNOW (RIVER) Hereford
MONTE BISHOP Hereford
WYE (RIVER) Hereford
WYE (RIVER) Ross-on-Wye

HERTFORDSHIRE

COLNE (RIVER) Rickmansworth
GADE (RIVER) Watford
LEA (RIVER) Hoddesdon
LEA (RIVER) Welwyn Garden City
LEA (RIVER) Wormley
LEA NAVIGATION Broxbourne
LEE NAVIGATION Bishops Stortford
LEE NAVIGATION Broxbourne
LEE NAVIGATION Hertford
LEE NAVIGATION Waltham Cross
LEE NAVIGATION Ware
NEW RIVER Ware
OLD LEE (RIVER) Waltham Cross
OLD LEE (RIVER) Wormley
OUGHTON (RIVER) Hitchin
THAME (RIVER) Tring

HUMBERSIDE

AIRE (RIVER) Goole
DERWENT (RIVER) Goole
DERWENT (RIVER) Hull
ESK (RIVER) Grimsby
HULL (RIVER) Beverley
OUSE (RIVER) Goole
URE (RIVER) Hull

ISLE OF WIGHT

YAR (A) (RIVER) Sandown
YAR (RIVER) Sandown

KENT

CRAYFORD (RIVER) Dartford
DARENT (RIVER) Orpington
EASTERN ROTHER (RIVER) Cranbrook
EDEN (RIVER) Edenbridge
EDEN (RIVER) Tonbridge
HEXDEN CHANNEL Tenterden
MEDWAY (RIVER) East Peckham
MEDWAY (RIVER) Maidstone
MEDWAY (RIVER) Tonbridge
MEDWAY (RIVER) Tunbridge Wells
ROTHER (RIVER) Tenterden
ROYAL MILITARY CANAL Romney Marsh
STATION FARM Ashford
STOUR (RIVER) Canterbury
TEISE (RIVER) Tunbridge Wells

LANCASHIRE

BENTHAM TROUT FISHERY Lancaster
CALDER (RIVER) Blackburn
CALDER (RIVER) Burnley
COLNE WATER Colne
DERWENT (RIVER) Preston
DOUGLAS (RIVER) Wigan
DUDDON (RIVER) Broughton-In-Furness
EDISFORD AND BRUNGERLEY PARK Clitheroe
HALTON FISHERY Lancaster
HODDER (RIVER) Blackburn
HODDER (RIVER) Clitheroe
IRWELL (RIVER) Preston
LUNE (RIVER) Lancaster
PENDLE WATER Nelson
RIBBLE (RIVER) Blackburn
RIBBLE (RIVER) Clitheroe
RIBBLE (RIVER) Preston
SKERTON FISHERY Lancaster
WENNING (RIVER) Clapham
WENNING (RIVER) Lancaster
WRYE (RIVER) Preston
WYRE (RIVER) Fleetwood
WYRE (RIVER) Kirkham

LEICESTERSHIRE

MONNOW (RIVER) Leicester
SOAR (RIVER) Leicester
SOAR (RIVER) Loughborough
WREAKE (RIVER) Melton Mowbray

LINCOLNSHIRE

STEEPING (RIVER) Skegness
TILL (RIVER) Lincoln
TRENT (RIVER) Gainsborough
TRENT (RIVER) Lincoln
UPPER WITHAM (RIVER) Lincoln
WELLAND (RIVER) Spalding
WHARFE (RIVER) Boston
WITHAM (RIVER) Boston
WITHAM (RIVER) Grantham

LINCOLNSHIRE (NORTH)

OLD ANCHOLME (RIVER) Brigg

LONDON (GREATER)

BROXBOURNE MEADOWS FISHERY London
COLNE (RIVER) London
LEA NAVIGATION London
LEE NAVIGATION London
NEW CUT London
OLD LEE (RIVER) London
PONDERS END London
TEDDINGTON LOCK London
THAMES (RIVER) London

MANCHESTER (GREATER)

BLACK BECK (RIVER) Millom
FISHERMANS RETREAT Bury
IRWELL (RIVER) Bury
OLD IRWELL Manchester
OLDHAM FLY FISHING Oldham
TAME (RIVER) Oldham

MIDLANDS (WEST)

AVON (RIVER) Coventry
AVON (RIVER) Warwick
BLYTHE (RIVER) Coventry
GREY MILL FARM Solihull
SEVERN (RIVER) Bridgnorth

NORFOLK

ACLE (RIVER) Norwich
BABINGLEY (RIVER) King's Lynn
BURE (RIVER) Great Yarmouth
BURE (RIVER) Norwich
CANTLEY (RIVER) Norwich
CUT OFF CHANNEL King's Lynn
DRAYTON GREEN (RIVER) Norwich
GREAT OUSE (RIVER) Downham Market
GREAT OUSE RELIEF CHANNEL King's Lynn
HICKLING BROAD Norwich
HILGAY (RIVER) Downham Market
HORNING (RIVER) Norwich
LITTLE OUSE (RIVER) King's Lynn
NAR (RIVER) King's Lynn
RELIEF CHANNEL King's Lynn
ROCKLAND BROAD Norwich
STOKESBY (RIVER) Great Yarmouth
THURNE MOUTH (RIVER) Great Yarmouth
WENSUM (RIVER) Dereham
WENSUM (RIVER) Fakenham
WENSUM (RIVER) Norwich
WENSUM (RIVER) Walsingham
WISSEY (RIVER) King's Lynn
YARE (RIVER) Norwich

NORTHAMPTONSHIRE

- **ISE (RIVER)** Kettering
- **NENE (RIVER)** Kettering
- **NENE (RIVER)** Northampton
- **THRAPSTON (RIVER)** Kettering

NORTHUMBERLAND

- **ALN (RIVER)** Alnwick
- **COQUET (RIVER)** Morpeth
- **IRTHING (RIVER)** Haltwhistle
- **LEET (RIVER)** Coldstream
- **LYNE (RIVER)** Coldstream
- **NORTH TYNE (RIVER)** Hexham
- **PLESSEY WOODS** Morpeth
- **REDE (RIVER)** Hexham
- **SOUTH TYNE (RIVER)** Haltwhistle
- **TWEED (RIVER)** Berwick-upon-Tweed
- **TWEED (RIVER)** Coldstream
- **TYNE (RIVER)** Corbridge
- **TYNE (RIVER)** Hexham
- **TYNE (RIVER)** Prudhoe
- **TYNE (RIVER)** Stocksfield
- **TYNE (RIVER)** Wylam
- **WANSBECK (RIVER)** Ashington
- **WANSBECK (RIVER)** Morpeth
- **WHITEADDER (RIVER)** Berwick-upon-Tweed
- **WREIGH (RIVER)** Thropton

NOTTINGHAMSHIRE

- **FLEET (RIVER)** Newark
- **MAUN (RIVER)** Mansfield
- **TRENT (RIVER)** Newark
- **TRENT (RIVER)** Newark-on-Trent
- **TRENT (RIVER)** Nottingham
- **TRENT (RIVER)** Retford
- **WHARFE (RIVER)** Newark
- **WITHAM (RIVER)** Newark

OXFORDSHIRE

- **CHERWELL (RIVER)** Bicester
- **CHERWELL (RIVER)** Kidlington
- **CHERWELL (RIVER)** Oxford
- **CHERWELL (RIVER)** Woodstock
- **RADCOT LOCK** Faringdon
- **RUSHEY LOCK** Faringdon
- **RUSHEY WEIR** Bampton
- **SANDFORD LOCK** Oxford
- **SEVERALLS FARM A AND B** Oxford
- **SHIFFORD LOCK** Bampton
- **SHIPLAKE LOCK** Henley-on-Thames
- **STRATTON LODGE** Abingdon
- **THAME (RIVER)** Henley-on-Thames
- **THAME (RIVER)** Ickford
- **THAME (RIVER)** Wallingford
- **THAMES (RIVER)** Abingdon
- **THAMES (RIVER)** Bampton
- **THAMES (RIVER)** Cowley
- **THAMES (RIVER)** Didcot
- **THAMES (RIVER)** Henley-on-Thames
- **THAMES (RIVER)** Oxford
- **THAMES (RIVER)** Summertown
- **THAMES (RIVER)** Wallingford
- **THAMES (RIVER)** Witney
- **THAMES (RIVER)** Wolvercote
- **WINDRUSH (RIVER)** Burford
- **WINDRUSH (RIVER)** Witney

RUTLAND

- **WELLAND (RIVER)** Oakham

SHROPSHIRE

- **MEESE (RIVER)** Newport
- **ONNY (RIVER)** Ludlow
- **PERRY (RIVER)** Baschurch
- **PERRY (RIVER)** Oswestry
- **RIVER (TERN)** Shrewsbury
- **SEVERN (RIVER)** Bridgnorth
- **SEVERN (RIVER)** Much Wenlock
- **SEVERN (RIVER)** Oswestry
- **SEVERN (RIVER)** Shrewsbury
- **SEVERN (RIVER)** Telford
- **SWEENEYCLIFFE HOUSE FISHERY** Telford
- **TANAT (RIVER)** Oswestry
- **TEME (RIVER)** Ludlow
- **TERN (RIVER)** Market Drayton
- **TERN (RIVER)** Telford
- **TERN FISHERIES** Market Drayton
- **VYRNWY (RIVER)** Oswestry

SOMERSET

- **AVON (BRISTOL) (RIVER)** Bath
- **AVON (RIVER)** Bath
- **AVON (RIVER)** Frome
- **BARLE (RIVER)** Dulverton
- **BASON BRIDGE** Highbridge
- **BRISTOL AVON** Bath
- **BRUE (RIVER)** Highbridge
- **BRUE (RIVER)** Street
- **EXE (RIVER)** Dulverton
- **FOLLYFOOT FARM** Bridgwater
- **FROME (RIVER)** Bath
- **FROME (RIVER)** Frome
- **GLASTONBURY** Glastonbury
- **HADDOE TROUT FISHERY** Dulverton
- **HORNER WATER** Minehead
- **HUNTSPILL (RIVER)** Bridgwater
- **ISLE (RIVER)** Langport
- **KENN (RIVER)** Clevedon
- **KENN (RIVER)** Highbridge
- **LITTLE EXE** Dulverton
- **MARK (RIVER)** Highbridge
- **PARRET (RIVER)** Crewkerne
- **PARRETT (RIVER)** Bridgwater
- **PARRETT (RIVER)** Langport
- **PARRETT (RIVER)** Stoke-Sub-Hamdon
- **PARRETT (RIVER)** Weston-Super-Mare
- **TONE (RIVER)** Taunton
- **WESTHAY** Glastonbury
- **WOOLBRIDGE MANOR** Frome
- **YEO (RIVER)** Bristol
- **YEO (RIVER)** Yeovil

STAFFORDSHIRE

- **ANKER (RIVER)** Tamworth
- **BLITHE (RIVER)** Uttoxeter
- **CHURNET (RIVER)** Alton
- **CHURNET (RIVER)** Leek
- **CHURNET (RIVER)** Uttoxeter
- **DOVE (RIVER)** Burton-on-Trent
- **DOVE (RIVER)** Longnor
- **DOVE (RIVER)** Uttoxeter
- **HAMPS (RIVER)** Leek
- **SOW (RIVER)** Stafford
- **SWARBORN (RIVER)** Alrewas
- **TAME (RIVER)** Alrewas
- **TRENT (RIVER)** Alrewas
- **TRENT (RIVER)** Stone

SUFFOLK

- **ALDE (RIVER)** Aldeburgh
- **ALDE (RIVER)** Saxmundham
- **BARSHAM DRAIN** Beccles
- **BECCLES QUAY** Beccles
- **BUNGAY (RIVER)** Bungay
- **CLICKETTS HILL AND PLANTATION** Bures
- **DEBEN (RIVER)** Woodbridge
- **GIPPING (RIVER)** Ipswich
- **HOMERSFIELD (RIVER)** Bungay
- **LARK (RIVER)** Brandon
- **LARK (RIVER)** Bury St Edmunds
- **LAYZELLS FARM** Sudbury
- **LITTLE BEVILLS ESTATE** Bures
- **LITTLE OUSE (RIVER)** Thetford
- **NORTH MEADOWS** Sudbury
- **RATTLE (RIVER)** Stowmarket
- **STOUR (RIVER)** Sudbury
- **STOUR (SUFFOLK) (RIVER)** Ipswich
- **STOW (RIVER)** Bures
- **STOW (RIVER)** Sudbury
- **THET (RIVER)** Thetford
- **WAVENEY (RIVER)** Bungay
- **WRIGHTS FARM** Sudbury
- **WYE (RIVER)** Saxmundham

SURREY

- **DEE (RIVER)** Guildford
- **MOLE (RIVER)** Dorking
- **MOLE (RIVER)** Walton-on-Thames
- **THAMES (RIVER)** East Molesey
- **WESTON FISHERY** Guildford
- **WEY (RIVER)** Godalming
- **WEY (RIVER)** West Byfleet
- **WEY NAVIGATION (RIVER)** Woking

SUSSEX (EAST)

- **ASHBOURNE TROUT FISHERY** Battle
- **CUCKMERE (RIVER)** Hailsham
- **CUCKMERE (RIVER)** Polegate
- **CUCKMERE (RIVER)** Seaford
- **ISFIELD (RIVER)** Uckfield
- **OLD IRON (RIVER)** Lewes
- **OLD MILL** Lewes
- **OUSE (RIVER)** Lewes
- **ROTHER (RIVER)** Robertsbridge

SUSSEX (WEST)

- **ADUR (RIVER)** Henfield
- **ADUR (RIVER)** Steyning
- **ARUN (RIVER)** Arundel
- **ARUN (RIVER)** Bognor Regis
- **ARUN (RIVER)** Horsham
- **ARUN (RIVER)** Littlehampton
- **ARUN (RIVER)** Pulborough
- **HAYWARDS HEATH RIVER** Haywards Heath
- **LECONFIELD ESTATE** Petworth
- **OUSE (RIVER)** Littlehampton
- **ROTHER (RIVER)** Midhurst
- **WESTERN ROTHER (RIVER)** Petworth

TYNE AND WEAR

- **DERWENT (RIVER)** Rowlands Gill
- **LEVEN (RIVER)** Yarm
- **MAIN TYNE** Newcastle Upon Tyne
- **REDE (RIVER)** Newcastle Upon Tyne
- **TEES (RIVER)** Yarm
- **TYNE (RIVER)** Newcastle Upon Tyne
- **TYNE (RIVER)** Ryton
- **WEAR (RIVER)** Washington

WARWICKSHIRE

- **AVON (RIVER)** Rugby
- **AVON (RIVER)** Stratford-upon-Avon
- **LEAM (RIVER)** Leamington Spa
- **STOUR (WARWICKSHIRE)** Stratford-upon-Avon
- **WARWICKSHIRE AVON** Stratford-upon-Avon
- **WARWICKSHIRE AVON** Warwick
- **WEST HILLBOROUGH** Alcester

WILTSHIRE

- **AVON (BRISTOL) (RIVER)** Chippenham
- **AVON (BRISTOL) (RIVER)** Melksham
- **AVON (BRISTOL) (RIVER)** Salisbury
- **AVON (RIVER)** Chippenham
- **AVON (RIVER)** Melksham
- **AVON (RIVER)** Salisbury
- **AVON (RIVER)** Warminster
- **BISS (RIVER)** Trowbridge
- **BRISTOL AVON** Bradford-on-Avon
- **BRISTOL AVON** Chippenham
- **BRISTOL AVON** Melksham
- **HAMPSHIRE AVON (RIVER)** Salisbury
- **MILLBROOK TROUT FARM** Salisbury
- **NADDER (RIVER)** Salisbury
- **RAY (RIVER)** Swindon
- **THAMES (RIVER)** Swindon

WORCESTERSHIRE

- **ANCHOR MEADOWS FISHERY** Evesham
- **AVON (RIVER)** Evesham
- **AVON (RIVER)** Pershore
- **HARVINGTON MANOR FISHERY** Evesham
- **HUXLEYS HAMPTON FERRY FISHERIES** Evesham
- **LEDWYCHE BROOK** Tenbury Wells

LENCHFORD Worcester
SALWARPE (RIVER) Kidderminster
SEVERN (RIVER) Bewdley
SEVERN (RIVER) Stourport-on-Severn
SEVERN (RIVER) Worcester
TEME (RIVER) Bewdley
TEME (RIVER) Martley
TEME (RIVER) Tenbury Wells
TEME (RIVER) Worcester
WARWICKSHIRE & AVON Evesham
WARWICKSHIRE AVON Evesham
WARWICKSHIRE AVON Pershore

WREXHAM

CLYWEDOG (RIVER) Bangor-on-Dee
DEE (RIVER) Bangor-on-Dee

YORKSHIRE (NORTH)

ALDWARK BRIDGE York
BAIN (RIVER) Leyburn
BOLTON ABBEY FISHERIES Skipton
BUBWITH (RIVER) Selby
DANBY (RIVER) Whitby
DERWENT (RIVER) Scarborough
DERWENT (RIVER) York
EAST COTTINGWITH WATERS York
EGTON BRIDGE (RIVER) Whitby
EGTON ESTATE BEAT Whitby
ESK (RIVER) Whitby
FOSS (RIVER) York
GLAISDALE (RIVER) Whitby
LAVER (RIVER) Ripon
LEEMING (RIVER) Northallerton
LOWER DUNSFORTH (RIVER) York
MILBY CUT York
NEWBY HALL FISHERIES Ripon
NEWTON RIVER Bedale
NIDD (RIVER) Harrogate
NIDD (RIVER) Knaresborough
NIDD (RIVER) York
NIDD BRIDGE Harrogate
NUN MONKTON (RIVER) York
OUSE (RIVER) Helperby
OUSE (RIVER) York
POPPLETON (RIVER) York
RICCAL (RIVER) Malton
RUSWARP (RIVER) Whitby
RYE (RIVER) Malton
RYE (RIVER) York
RYE AND SEVEN (RIVERS) Malton
SINNINGTON (RIVER) York
SKELL (RIVER) Ripon
SKIRFARE (RIVER) Skipton
SLEIGHTS (RIVER) Whitby
SWALE (RIVER) Helperby
SWALE (RIVER) Northallerton
SWALE (RIVER) Richmond
SWALE (RIVER) Thirsk
SWALE (RIVER) York
THORNTON BRIDGE York
TYNE (RIVER) Ripon
ULLESKELF (RIVER) Tadcaster
URE (RIVER AND TRIBUTARIES) Hawes
URE (RIVER) Hawes
URE (RIVER) Leyburn
URE (RIVER) Middleham
URE (RIVER) Ripon
URE (RIVER) York
WHARFE (RIVER) Skipton
WHARFE (RIVER) Tadcaster
YORKSHIRE OUSE York

YORKSHIRE (SOUTH)

DEARNE (RIVER) Mexborough
DON (RIVER) Barnby Dun
DON (RIVER) Doncaster
IDLE (RIVER) Doncaster
OLD DEARNE (RIVER) Mexborough
TORNE (RIVER) Doncaster
TRENT (RIVER) Sheffield

YORKSHIRE (WEST)

AIRE (RIVER) Keighley
AIRE (RIVER) Leeds
BRIGHOUSE Halifax
CALDER (RIVER) Bradford
CALDER (RIVER) Huddersfield
CALDER (RIVER) Todmorden
COLNE (RIVER) Huddersfield
HOLME (RIVER) Huddersfield
WHARFE (RIVER) Ilkley
WHARFE (RIVER) Leeds
WHARFE (RIVER) Otley
WHARFE (RIVER) Tadcaster
WHARFE (RIVER) Wetherby

STREAMS

BERKSHIRE

SEACOURT (STREAM) Reading
ST PATRICKS Reading

CAMBRIDGESHIRE

PERIO MILL Peterborough
WANSFORD STREAM Peterborough
WILLOW CREEK Peterborough

CORNWALL

CONSTANTINE BROOK Falmouth
GWITHIAN BROOK Camborne
HAYLE CAUSEWAY Hayle
WEST LOOE (RIVER) Liskeard

COUNTY DURHAM

DURHAM BECK Durham

CUMBRIA

ANNAS STREAM Millom
BARBON BECK Carnforth
BELA STREAM Milnthorpe
DACRE BECK Penrith
GRIZEDALE BECK Ambleside
POAKA BECK Barrow-In-Furness

DEVON

AVETON GIFFORD STREAM Kingsbridge
FOSFELLE COUNTRY HOUSE HOTEL Bideford
LODDISWELL STREAM Kingsbridge
TRAGO MILLS Newton Abbot

DORSET

CHAR STREAM Bridport
HAMPSHIRE AVON (RIVER) Christchurch

GLOUCESTERSHIRE

FROME STREAM Stroud

HUMBERSIDE

BEVERLEY BECK Hull

KENT

SPERRINGBROOK SEWER Romney Marsh

LANCASHIRE

BENTHAM STREAM Lancaster

LINCOLNSHIRE

ST EAU FISHING SYNDICATE Market Rasen

LONDON (GREATER)

COPPER MILLSTREAM London
FLAKE STREAM London
HORSEMILL STREAM London

NORFOLK

CASTLE RISING STREAM King's Lynn
DOVE BROOK Eye
NAR STREAM King's Lynn
ORMESBY ROLLESBY Great Yarmouth
TEN MILE BANK Downham Market
UPPER BURE (STREAM) Aylesham

NORTHUMBERLAND

WANSBECK STREAM Morpeth

SUFFOLK

BUSS CREEK Southwold

SUSSEX (EAST)

BEVERN STREAM Lewes

WILTSHIRE

SUTTON VENY ESTATE Warminster

YORKSHIRE (NORTH)

BEDALE BECK Northallerton
COD BECK Thirsk

TARNS

CUMBRIA

ATKINSONS TARN COARSE FISHERY Windermere
CLEABARROW TARN Windermere
GOODENBURGH TARN Carnforth
HIGH ARNSIDE TARN Ambleside
KNOTT END TARN Maryport
LOUGHRIGG TARN Ambleside
MEDKLIN TARN FISHERY Holmrook
MOCKERKIN TARN Cockermouth
MOSS ECCLES TARN Ambleside
RATHER HEATH TARN Kendal
SCHOOL KNOTT TARN Windermere
TALKIN TARN Brampton
WITHERSLACK HALL TARN Grange-Over-Sands

YORKSHIRE (NORTH)

BLEA TARN Scarborough

YORKSHIRE (WEST)

YEADON TARN Bradford

TRIBUTARIES

CAMBRIDGESHIRE

BURWELL LODE Cambridge
LEES BROOK Huntingdon

CHESHIRE

WEAVER (RIVER) Macclesfield

CUMBRIA

EDEN (RIVER) Appleby-In-Westmorland

DEVON

EXE (RIVER) Exeter
YEO (RIVER) Crediton

GLOUCESTERSHIRE

SEVERN (RIVER) Dymock

KENT

DARENT (RIVER) Dartford
EDEN (RIVER) Tonbridge
HOATHLEY FISHERY Lamberhurst

LANCASHIRE

LUNE (RIVER) Lancaster

LEICESTERSHIRE

STEMBOROUGH MILL TROUT FARM Lutterworth

NORTHUMBERLAND

TWEED (RIVER) Alnwick

SUSSEX (WEST)

ARUN (RIVER) Petworth

YORKSHIRE (NORTH)

OUSE (RIVER) Malton
OUSE (RIVER) Skipton

YORKSHIRE (WEST)

OUSE (RIVER) Wetherby

WEIRS

HERTFORDSHIRE

FEILDES WEIR Hoddesdon

WELLS

NORTHUMBERLAND

WILLIES WELL Wylam

CANALS

COUNTY KILDARE

- **GRAND CANAL** Prosperous
- **GRAND CANAL** Robertstown
- **GRAND CANAL (BARROW BRANCH)** Rathangon
- **GRAND CANAL (BARROW TRACK)** Athy

COUNTY OFFALY

- **EDENDERRY OFFALY EIRE** Edenderry
- **GRAND CANAL** Edenderry

COMBINATIONS

COUNTY CLARE

- **ALLARD FISHERIES** Ennis

COUNTY CORK

- **BLACKWATER SALMON FISHERY** Castlelyons

COUNTY DONEGAL

- **CLOGHAN LODGE ESTATE FISHERY** Cloghan
- **ROSSES FISHERY** Burtonport

COUNTY GALWAY

- **BALLYNAHINCH CASTLE FISHERY** Recess
- **DOOHULLA** Ballyconneely
- **ERRIFF FISHERY** Leenane

COUNTY KERRY

- **KERRYFISHERIES** Waterville

COUNTY TIPPERARY

- **CLONANAU FLY FISHING CENTRE** Clonmel
- **NORE (RIVER)** Mountrath

LAKES

COUNTY CAVAN

- **ARDAN GRANGE GUEST HOUSE AND ANGLING CENTRE** Belturbet
- **BAILIEBORO LAKES** Bailieborough

COUNTY CLARE

- **DROMORE AND BALLYLINE** Corofin
- **LICKEEN LAKE** Kilfenara

COUNTY CORK

- **CHAPEL LAKE** Dunmanway
- **CURRAGHALICKEY LAKE** Dunmanway
- **DERRYVEGALL LAKE** Castletownbere
- **DRIMINIDY LAKE** Drimoleague
- **DROMANA LAKE** Cappoquin
- **GARRANES LAKE** Dunmanway
- **INNISCARRA LAKE** Inniscarra
- **SHEPPERTON LAKES** Skibbereen

COUNTY GALWAY

- **CLOONDROON LAKE** Claremorris
- **KYLEMORE HOUSE FISHERY** Connemara
- **MAYFIELD LAKE** Claremorris
- **ROSS LAKE** Moycullen
- **SCREEBE FISHERY** Connemara

COUNTY KERRY

- **LAKE HOUSE HOTEL** Kenmare
- **LAKES OF KILLARNEY** Killarney

COUNTY KILKENNY

- **BALLINAKILL LAKE** Kilkenny

COUNTY MAYO

- **CASTLEBAR LAKES** Castlebar
- **LOUGHS COY CULLIN** Foxford

COUNTY MEATH

- **RATHBEGGAN LAKES** Dunshaughlin

COUNTY SLIGO

- **LAKE NA LEIBE** Castlebaldwin

COUNTY TIPPERARY

- **MARL LAKE** Dundrum

COUNTY WESTMEATH

- **BALLINAFID LAKE** Mullingar
- **DOOLIN POND** Mullingar

LOCHS

COUNTY GALWAY

- **CRUMLIN FISHERIES** Coonemara

COUNTY KERRY

- **ANGLERS PARADISE** Killarney

LOUGHS

COUNTY CAVAN

- **LOUGH RAMOR** Virginia

COUNTY CLARE

- **AILLBRACK LOUGH** Aillbrack

COUNTY CORK

- **CORK LOUGH** Cork
- **LOUGH ADERRA** Midleton
- **LOUGH ADERRY** Youghal
- **LOUGH ATARRIFF** Dunmanway
- **LOUGH AVAUL (LOWER)** Glengariff
- **LOUGH AVAUL (UPPER)** Glengariff
- **LOUGH BALLYNACARRIGA** Dunmanway
- **LOUGH BOFINNE** Bantry
- **LOUGH COOLKEELURE** Dunmanway
- **LOUGH CULLENAGH** Dunmanway
- **LOUGH NEASKIN** Dunmanway

COUNTY DONEGAL

- **LOUGH BEAGH** Beagh

COUNTY GALWAY

- **ACLAUREEN (LOUGH)** Claremorris
- **BALLINDOOLY LOUGH AND POND** Moycullen
- **CASTLEREAGH LOUGHS** Claremorris
- **CLARE LOUGH** Claremorris
- **COSTELLO AND FERMOYLE FISHERY** Costello
- **LOUGH ACEELAGH** Moycullen
- **LOUGH ARORAM** Moycullen
- **LOUGH BALLYLUIRKE** Moycullen
- **LOUGH COOLIN** Clonbur
- **LOUGH CORRIB** Moycullen
- **LOUGH DOWN** Moycullen
- **LOUGH DOWNBEG** Moycullen
- **LOUGH HEMUSHMACONRY** Moycullen
- **LOUGH MASK** Clonbur
- **LOUGH PARKYFLAHERTY** Moycullen
- **LOUGH POLLALHY** Moycullen
- **NANANNAGH (LOUGH)** Claremorris
- **NANEVIN (LOUGH)** Moycullen
- **SUMMERVILLE LOUGH** Claremorris

COUNTY KERRY

- **LOUGH BARFINNIHY** Kenmare
- **LOUGH CAUM** Castlegregory
- **LOUGH FADDA** Sneem
- **LOUGH NAKIRKA** Killorglin

COUNTY LAOIS

- **GRANSTOWN LAKE** Portlaoise

COUNTY LEITRIM

- **DROMAHAIR LODGE FISHERY** Dromahair
- **LOUGH ALLEN** Drumshanbo
- **LOUGH MELVIN** Rossinver

COUNTY MAYO

- **BROHLY (LOUGH)** Ballina
- **BURRISHOOLE FISHERY** Newport
- **CALLOW LAKES** Foxford
- **CLOONAMOYNE FISHERY** Crossmolina
- **LOUGH CARRA** Westport
- **LOUGH CORRIB (UPPER)** Cong
- **LOUGH NAMUCKA** Louisburgh
- **MUCK (LOUGH)** Foxford
- **TALT (LOUGH)** Bunnyconnellan

COUNTY ROSCOMMON

- **BREEDOGE LOUGH** Ballaghaderren
- **LOUGH ARROW** Boyle
- **LOUGH CLOONACOLLY** Ballaghaderren
- **LOUGH CLOONAGH** Ballaghaderren
- **LOUGH GARA** Boyle
- **LOUGH KEY** Boyle
- **LOUGH NASOOL** Ballaghaderren
- **LOUGH URLAUR** Ballaghaderren

COUNTY SLIGO

- **LOUGH AUGH** Castlebaldwin
- **LOUGH BO** Castlebaldwin
- **LOUGH KEY** Castlebaldwin

COUNTY TIPPERARY

- **COUMSHINGAUN LOUGH** Kilsheelin
- **CROTTYS LOUGH** Kilsheelin
- **DERG (LOUGH)** Nenagh

COUNTY WATERFORD

- **BALLINAROONE LODGE FISHERY** Waterford

COUNTY WESTMEATH

- **LOUGH ENNEL FISHERY** Mullingar

MOATS

COUNTY WATERFORD

- **FORT WILLIAM FISHERY** Tallow

PONDS

COUNTY WESTMEATH

- **GALMOYLESTOWN LAKE** Mullingar

RESERVOIRS

COUNTY CORK

- **BALLINCOLLIG RESERVOIR** Cork
- **BALLYMAQUIRK FISHERY AND LODGE** Waterfall
- **SCHULL RESERVOIR** Schull

COUNTY KERRY

- **CARAGH FISHERY** Glencar

COUNTY LOUTH

- **BARNATTIN RESERVOIR** Drogheda
- **KILLINEER RESERVOIR** Drogheda

COUNTY MAYO

- **CLOONGEE FISHERY** Foxford

COUNTY WATERFORD

- **BALLYSHUNNOCK** Waterford
- **KNOCKDERRY** Waterford

RIVERS

COUNTY CARLOW

- **BARROW (RIVER)** Graighuenamanagh
- **BURREN (RIVER)** Carlow
- **DOUGLAS (RIVER)** Carlow
- **GREESE (RIVER)** Carlow
- **LERR (RIVER)** Carlow

COUNTY CORK

- **BANDON (RIVER)** Ballineen
- **BANDON (RIVER)** Bandon
- **BANDON (RIVER)** Dunmanway

BANDON (RIVER) Enniskeane
BLACKWATER (RIVER) Cappoquin
BLACKWATER (RIVER) Conna
BLACKWATER (RIVER) Fermoy
BLACKWATER (RIVER) Mallow
BLACKWATER FLY FISHING Fermoy
CAHA (RIVER) Dunmanway
CAREYSVILLE Fermoy
FINISK (RIVER) Cappoquin
GLENGARIFF (RIVER) Glengariff
ILEN (RIVER) Skibbereen
KILCOLEMAN FISHERY Enniskeane
MANCH HOUSE FISHERY Ballineen
MUNSTER BLACKWATER (RIVER) (GHILLIE COTTAGE) Fermoy
OWENSHED (RIVER) Cappoquin

COUNTY DONEGAL

ASSAROE LAKE Ballyshannon
FINN (RIVER) Cloghan
GLENMORE FISHERY Ballybofey

COUNTY GALWAY

DELPHI FISHERY Leenane
GALWAY FISHERY Galway
TOP WATERS BALLYNAHINCH FISHERY Maam Cross

COUNTY KERRY

BLACKWATER FISHERY Kerry

COUNTY KILDARE

BARROW (RIVER) Athy
BOHERBAUN (RIVER) Athy
GREESE (RIVER) Athy
GREESE (RIVER) Ballytore
STRADBALLY (RIVER) Athy

COUNTY KILKENNY

BLACKWATER (RIVER) Kilmacow
DININ (RIVER) Kilkenny
ERKINA (RIVER) Kilkenny
KINGS (RIVER) Kilkenny
MOUNT JULIET FISHERY Thomastown
NORE (RIVER) Inistioge
NORE (RIVER) Kilkenny
NORE (RIVER) Thomastown

COUNTY LAOIS

BARROW (RIVER) Portarlington
BARROW (UPPER) (RIVER) Portarlington
CUSHINA (RIVER) Portarlington
ERKINA (RIVER) Rathdowney
FIGILE (RIVER) Portarlington
NORE (RIVER) Abbeyleix

COUNTY LEITRIM

SHANNON (UPPER) (RIVER) Drumshanbo

COUNTY LIMERICK

CASTLECONNELL SALMON FISHERY Castleconnell

COUNTY LOUTH

BALLYMASCANLON (RIVER) Dundalk
BOYNE (RIVER) Drogheda
CASTLETON (RIVER) Dundalk
FANE (RIVER) Dundalk

COUNTY MAYO

ARMSTRONG FISHERY Foxford
BEAL EASE FISHERY Foxford
CARROWNISKY Louisburgh
FOXFORD FISHERY Foxford
GLORE (RIVER) Kiltamagh
GWEESTION (RIVER) Bohola
LECKEE FISHERY Foxford
MOUNT FALCON SALMON FISHERY Ballina
MOY (RIVER) Foxford
MOY FISHERY Ballina
MULLAGHANOE (RIVER) Charlestown
OWENGARVE (RIVER) Charlestown
POLLAGH (RIVER) Kiltamagh

COUNTY MEATH

BOYNE (RIVER) Kells
BOYNE (RIVER) Navan
BOYNE (RIVER) Slane

COUNTY MONAGHAN

EMY LAKE FISHERY Clones

COUNTY ROSCOMMON

BOYLE (RIVER) Boyle
LUNG RIVER Ballaghaderren

COUNTY TIPPERARY

ARA (RIVER) Tipperary Town
ATHRY FISHERY Cashel
CLODIAGH (RIVER) Kilsheelin
CLODIAGH (RIVER) Thurles
COOLNAMUCK FISHERIES Carrick-on-Suir
DRISH (RIVER) Thurles
LINGAUN (RIVER) Carrick-on-Suir
NIRE (RIVER) Clonmel
SUIR (RIVER) Ardfinnan
SUIR (RIVER) Cahir
SUIR (RIVER) Carrick-on-Suir
SUIR (RIVER) Cashel
SUIR (RIVER) Clonmel
SUIR (RIVER) Kilsheelin
SUIR (RIVER) Thurles
SUIR VALLEY FISHERY Clonmel
WHITE HORSE (RIVER) Mountrath

COUNTY WATERFORD

BLACKWATER (RIVER) Lismore
BLACKWATER (RIVER) Portlaw Clodiagh
BLACKWATER (RIVER) Tallow
BLACKWATER (RIVER) Upper Ballyduff
BLACKWATER LODGE HOTEL AND FISHERY Upper Ballyduff

STREAMS

COUNTY TIPPERARY

DUAG ANNER STREAM Clonmel
NIRE STREAM Clonmel
TAR STREAM Clonmel

TRIBUTARIES

COUNTY DUBLIN

BROSNA (TRIBUTARY) Dublin

CANALS

COUNTY ANTRIM

- **BANN (LOWER) NAVIGATIONAL CANAL** Antrim
- **BANN (LOWER) NAVIGATIONAL CANAL** Movanagher
- **BANN (LOWER) NAVIGATIONAL CANAL** Portna

COUNTY DOWN

- **NEWRY CANAL** Newry

COUNTY FERMANAGH

- **COLEBROOKE PARK** Enniskillen

COMBINATIONS

COUNTY ANTRIM

- **TILDARG FISHERY** Ballyclare
- **WOODBURN ANGLING CLUB** Carrickfergus
- **WOODFORD FISHERY** Carrickfergus

COUNTY FERMANAGH

- **ERNE (RIVER)** Belleek

LAKES

COUNTY ANTRIM

- **MCCAMMANS LAKE** Larne
- **SPRINGWATER MEADOW** Lisburn
- **STRAID FISHERY** Ballyclare
- **TURNAGROVE FISHERY** Ballymoney

COUNTY ARMAGH

- **LOWRYS LAKE** Armagh
- **SHAWS LAKE** Armagh
- **TULLNAWOOD LAKE** Armagh

COUNTY DOWN

- **BALLY GRANGE FISHERY** Newtownards
- **BALLYLOUGH** Castlewellan
- **LOUGH CASHEL** Newry
- **LOUGH GLASSDRUMMAN** Newry
- **LOUGH KILTYBAINE** Newry
- **LOUGH MULLAGHABAN** Newry
- **MCCOURTS LAKE** Poyntspass
- **MILL LODGE FISHERY** Dromore
- **RINGDUFFERIN ESTUARY** Downpatrick
- **WATERFALL LODGE** Hillsborough
- **WRITES LOUGH** Castlewellan

COUNTY FERMANAGH

- **KNOCKBRACKEN TROUT LAKES** Ballinamallard
- **LOUGH ERNE** Enniskillen

COUNTY LONDONDERRY

- **MOORBROOK LODGE** Coleraine
- **PADDY MCNAMARAS LAKE** Londonderry
- **TURNAFACE TROUT FISHERY** Magherafelt

COUNTY TYRONE

- **ALTMORE FISHERIES** Dungannon
- **ANNAGINNY STILL WATER TROUT AND COARSE FISHERY** Dungannon
- **BARONSCOURT LAKES** Omagh
- **BLESSINGBOURNE LAKE** Fivemiletown
- **DUNGANNON PARK FISHERY** Dungannon
- **PARK LAKE TROUT FISHERY** Dungannon
- **PLUCK MILL FISH FARM** Dungannon
- **QUIET WATERS** Dungannon
- **ROUND LAKE** Fivemiletown

LOCHS

COUNTY DOWN

- **CARRICKMANNON FISHERY** Ballynahinch

LOUGHS

COUNTY ANTRIM

- **RALOO TROUT FISHERIES** Ballymena

COUNTY ARMAGH

- **LOUGH NEAGH** Craigavon
- **LOUGHGALL COARSE FISHERY** Armagh

COUNTY DOWN

- **LOUGH COWEY FISHERY** Newtownards
- **TULLYWEST FISHERY** Ballynahinch

COUNTY FERMANAGH

- **COOLYERMER LOUGH FISHERY** Enniskillen
- **LOUGH MELVIN** Garrison
- **LOWER LOUGH ERNE** Enniskillen
- **MILL LOUGH BELLANALECK** Enniskillen

COUNTY TYRONE

- **BRANTRY LOUGH** Dungannon
- **CARRICK LOUGH** Aughnacloy
- **CRANS LOUGH** Aughnacloy
- **GREEVE LOUGH** Aughnacloy
- **LOUGH ENAGH** Dungannon
- **LOUGH FEA** Cookstown
- **LOUGH MACRONAN** Dungannon
- **LOUGHMORE** Augher
- **ROUGHAN LOUGH** Dungannon
- **TULLYGIVEN LOUGH** Caledon
- **WHITE LOUGH** Aughnacloy

RESERVOIRS

COUNTY ARMAGH

- **SEAGAHAN RESERVOIR DAM** Armagh
- **TULLYNAWOOD RESERVOIR** Armagh

COUNTY LONDONDERRY

- **CREGGAN RESERVOIRS** Londonderry

RIVERS

COUNTY ANTRIM

- **BANN (LOWER) (RIVER)** Ballymena
- **BRAID (RIVER)** Ballymena
- **BUSH (RIVER)** Bushmills
- **CLADY (RIVER)** Ballymena
- **CLOGHWATER (RIVER)** Ballymena
- **CRUMLIN (RIVER)** Crumlin
- **DUN (RIVER)** Cushendall
- **GLENARM (RIVER)** Ballymena
- **INVER (RIVER)** Larne
- **KELLSWATER (RIVER)** Ballymena
- **LAGAN (RIVER)** Belfast
- **LOWER BANN (RIVER)** Ballymena
- **MAINE (RIVER)** Antrim
- **MAINE (RIVER)** Ballymena
- **MAINE (RIVER)** Randalstown
- **MARGEY (RIVER)** Ballycastle
- **SIX MILE WATER** Antrim
- **SIX MILE WATER** Ballynure

COUNTY ARMAGH

- **BANN (UPPER) (RIVER)** Craigavon
- **BLACKWATER (RIVER)** Armagh
- **CALLAN (RIVER)** Armagh
- **LAGAN (RIVER)** Craigavon
- **SLOWING RIVERS FARM** Craigavon

COUNTY DOWN

- **BANN (UPPER) (RIVER)** Banbridge
- **BANN (UPPER) (RIVER)** Rathfriland
- **BANN (UPPER) AND TRIBUTARIES** Newry
- **CLANRYE (RIVER)** Newry
- **CLEGGAN (RIVER)** Newry
- **CULLY (RIVER)** Newry
- **DAIRY FISHERY** Ballynahinch
- **FANE (RIVER)** Newry
- **FORKHILL (RIVER)** Newry
- **INLER (RIVER)** Newtownards
- **KILKEEL (RIVER)** Newry
- **LAGAN (RIVER)** Dromore
- **LOUGH INAGH FISHERY** Ballynahinch
- **MONEYCARRAGH (RIVER)** Newcastle
- **OWENREAGH (RIVER)** Dromore
- **QUOILE (RIVER)** Downpatrick
- **SHIMNA (RIVER)** Newcastle
- **WHITEWATER (RIVER)** Newry

COUNTY FERMANAGH

- **BALLINAMALLARD (RIVER)** Enniskillen
- **COLEBROOKE (RIVER)** Maguiresbridge
- **ERNE (RIVER)** Enniskillen
- **LOUGH KEENAGHAN** Belleek

COUNTY LONDONDERRY

- **AGIVEY (RIVER)** Coleraine
- **BANN (LOWER) (RIVER)** Coleraine
- **FAUGHAN (RIVER)** Londonderry
- **LOWER BANN (RIVER)** Magherafelt
- **MOYOLA (RIVER)** Maghera
- **ROE (RIVER)** Limavady
- **ROSE (RIVER)** Londonderry

COUNTY TYRONE

- **BALLINDERRY (RIVER)** Cookstown
- **BALLYGAWLEY (RIVER)** Aughnacloy
- **BLACKWATER (RIVER)** Clogher
- **BURN DENNET (RIVER)** Strabane
- **BURN DENNETT (RIVER)** Strabane
- **CAMOWEN (RIVER)** Omagh
- **DERG (RIVER)** Castlederg
- **DERG (RIVER)** Omagh
- **DERG (RIVER)** Strabane
- **DRUMRAGH (RIVER)** Omagh
- **FAIRY WATER** Omagh
- **FINN (RIVER)** Omagh
- **FINN (RIVER)** Strabane
- **FOYLE (RIVER)** Strabane
- **GLEMELAG (RIVER)** Omagh
- **GLENELLY (RIVER)** Newtownstewart
- **MOURNE (RIVER)** Newtownstewart
- **MOURNE (RIVER)** Omagh
- **MOURNE (RIVER)** Strabane
- **OONA RIVER** Dungannon
- **OWENKILLEW (RIVER)** Newtownstewart
- **OWENKILLEW (RIVER)** Omagh
- **STRULE (RIVER)** Omagh
- **TORRENT (RIVER)** Dungannon
- **TULLYLAGAN (RIVER)** Cookstown

TRIBUTARIES

COUNTY ANTRIM

- **CAREY (RIVER)** Ballycastle
- **CLOUGH (RIVER)** Ballymena
- **DALL (RIVER)** Cushendall
- **GLENARRIFF (RIVER)** Cushendall
- **GLENSHESK (RIVER)** Ballycastle

COUNTY FERMANAGH

- **TEMPO (RIVER)** Maguiresbridge

COUNTY LONDONDERRY

- **MACOSQUIN (RIVER)** Coleraine

CANALS

GLASGOW (CITY OF)

FORTH AND CLYDE CANAL Glasgow

LANARKSHIRE (NORTH)

MONKLAND CANAL Coatbridge

LOTHIAN (WEST)

UNION CANAL Linlithgow

COMBINATIONS

ANGUS

PIPERDAM GOLF AND COUNTRY PARK Dundee

ARGYLL AND BUTE

INVERAWE FISHERIES Taynuilt
MILL HOUSE FISHERIES Tighnabruaich

DUMFRIES AND GALLOWAY

GALLOWAY FOREST PARK Newton Stewart
TORHOUSEKIE AND KIRWAUGH Newton Stewart

GLASGOW (CITY OF)

NEILSTON TROUT FISHERY Glasgow

LOTHIAN (WEST)

MORTON FISHERIES Livingston

MORAY

GLEN OF ROTHES TROUT FISHERY Aberlour

PERTH AND KINROSS

GLENFARG FISHERY Perth
PITLOCHRY BOATING STATION AND LOCHSIDE CAFÉ Pitlochry
SANDYKNOWES FISHING Perth

STIRLING

KILLIN BREADALBANE ANGLING CLUB WATERS Callander
PORTNELLAN Crianlarich

WESTERN ISLES

CEANN-AN-ORA FISHERY Harris
GRIMERSTA LODGE Stornoway
SOVAL ESTATE Stornoway

DAMS

RENFREWSHIRE

HOWWOOD TROUT FISHERY Johnstone
MAICH WATERS Lochwinnoch

ESTUARIES

ARGYLL AND BUTE

CLYDE ESTUARY Helensbourgh

GRAVEL PITS

ABERDEENSHIRE

PITFOUR LAKE Peterhead

DUMFRIES AND GALLOWAY

KELHEAD WATER Annan

PERTH AND KINROSS

HEATHERYFORD FISHERY Kinross

LAKES

ABERDEENSHIRE

WAULKMILL FISHERIES Turriff
YTHAN VALLEY FISHERY Ellon

ANGUS

GLEN ESK CARAVAN PARK Brechin
MILL OF CRIGGIE TROUT FISHERY Montrose

AYRSHIRE (EAST)

COWANS LAW TROUT FISHERY Galston
WATERSIDE FARM FISHERY Galston

AYRSHIRE (NORTH)

MIDDLETON FISHERY Largs

CLACKMANNANSHIRE

EASTER BALADO TROUT FISHERY (KINROSS) Glendevon
GARTMORN DAM FISHERY Alloa

DUMFRIES AND GALLOWAY

DORMONT LAKE COARSE FISHERY Lockerbie
JERICHO LOCHS Dumfries
KINMOUNT LAKE Annan
KIRKCHRIST Newton Stewart
LOCHNAW Stranraer
MOFFAT FISHERIES Moffat
PORTLING FISHERIES Dalbeattie
TORWOOD HOUSE HOTEL Newton Stewart

FALKIRK

CENTRAL SCOTLAND TROUT FISHERY

FIFE

LOCHMORE MEADOWS Lochgelly
NEWTON FARM FISHERY Newport-on-Tay

GLASGOW (CITY OF)

CULCREUCH CASTLE POND Glasgow

HIGHLAND

GLENCOE LOCHAN Ballachulish
STRATHMANAIRD LOCHS Ullapool

LANARKSHIRE (SOUTH)

NEWMILL TROUT AND DEER FARM Lanark
QUARTER FISHERY Hamilton

LOTHIAN (EAST)

MALTINGS FISHERY Haddington

LOTHIAN (MID)

LOGANLEA TROUT FISHERY Penicuik

SCOTTISH BORDERS

BUCCLEUCH ESTATES Selkirk
KAILZIE GARDENS FISHERY Peebles

SHETLAND ISLANDS

GOSSA WATER Shetland

STIRLING

KILLEARN HOUSE FISHERY Glasgow
LAKE OF MENTEITH FISHERIES

WESTERN ISLES

OBBE FISHINGS Leverburgh
SOUTH UIST ESTATES Lochboisdale

YORKSHIRE (SOUTH)

BANK END COARSE FISHERIES Doncaster
HAYFIELD LAKES Doncaster
LINDHOLME LEISURE LAKES FISHERIES (4) Doncaster

LOCHS

ABERDEENSHIRE

LOCH INSCH FISHERY Insch
LOCH SAUGH Laurencekirk
MILL OF ELRICK FISHERY Ellon

ANGUS

CLATIO LOCH Dundee
LOCH OF LINTRATHEN Kirriemuir
RESCOBIE LOCH Dundee

ARGYLL AND BUTE

ARDTORNISH ESTATE LOCHS Oban
LOCH AVICH Oban
LOCH AWE Oban
LOCH FAD Rothesay
LOCH GLASHAN Inveraray
LOCH LOSKIN (THE LOCHAN) Dunoon
LOCH NANT Oban
LOCH QUIEN Rothesay
LOCH TARSAN Dunoon

AYRSHIRE (NORTH)

EGLINGTON LOCH Irvine
HAYLIE FISHERY Largs
PORT-NA-LOCHAN Brodick

AYRSHIRE (SOUTH)

LOCH DORNAL Girvan
LOCH MAYBERRY Girvan
SPRINGWATER FISHERY Ayr

DUMFRIES AND GALLOWAY

BARSCOBE LOCH Castle Douglas
BLACK LOCH Newton Stewart
BRACK LOCH Castle Douglas
BROOM FISHERIES Annan
BRUNTIS LOCH Newton Stewart
CASTLE LOCH Lockerbie
CLATTERINGSHAWS LOCH Newton Stewart
COWANS FARM Dumfries
CRAIGHLAW Newton Stewart
DUNSKEY LOCHS Stranraer
EARLSTOUN LOCH Castle Douglas
FYNTALLOCH LOCH Newton Stewart
GLENDARROCH LOCH Newton Stewart
KIRRIEREOCH LOCH Newton Stewart
LAIRDMANNOCH LOCH Castle Douglas
LILLIES LOCH Newton Stewart
LOCH BARNBARROCH Newton Stewart
LOCH BRADAN Newton Stewart
LOCH BRECKBOWIE Newton Stewart
LOCH DEE Newton Stewart
LOCH ELDRIG Newton Stewart
LOCH HERON Newton Stewart
LOCH KEN Dumfries
LOCH MONREITH Newton Stewart
LOCH ROAN Castle Douglas
LOCH RONALD Newton Stewart
LOCH SKERROW Castle Douglas
LOCH WHINYEON Castle Douglas
LOCH WHITEFIELD Newton Stewart
LOCHENBRECK LOCH Castle Douglas
LOCHINVAR LOCH Castle Douglas
MAINS OF PENNINGHAM FISHERY Newton Stewart
MORTON LOCH Thornhill
NAHINE LOCH Newton Stewart
NEWTON LOCHAN Castle Douglas
OCHILTREE LOCH Newton Stewart
SLATEHOUSE LOCH Thornhill
SOULSEAT LOCH Stranraer
STARBURN LOCH Thornhill
WEE GLEN AMOUR LOCH Newton Stewart
WHITE LOCH OF MYRTON Newton Stewart

EDINBURGH (CITY OF)

DUDDINGSTON LOCH Edinburgh

FALKIRK

LOCH EARN
LOCH FINLAS Callander
LOCH VENACHAR Callander

FIFE

CLUTTO LOCH St Andrews
GOLDEN LOCH Cupar

KINGHORN LOCH Burntisland
LINDORES LOCH Cupar
LOCH FITTY TROUT FISHERY Dunfermline
LOCH ORE Lochgelly

GLASGOW (CITY OF)

LOCH ARKLET Glasgow

HIGHLAND

AVIELOCHAN Inverness
DORNOCH LOCHANS Dornoch
HOSPITAL LOCHAN Ballachulish
LOCH ACHANALT Dingwall
LOCH ACHILITY Strathpeffer
LOCH ACHONACHIE Dingwall
LOCH AFFRIC Inverness
LOCH AKRAN Thurso
LOCH ALVIE Kingussie
LOCH ARKAIG Fort William
LOCH ASSYNT Lairg
LOCH BAD A CROTHA Gairloch
LOCH BADANLOCH Kinbrace
LOCH BARAVAIG Isle Ornsay
LOCH BEANNACH Lairg
LOCH BEANNACHAIRAN Muir Of Ord
LOCH BENEVEAN Inverness
LOCH BORRALAN Lairg
LOCH BORRALIE Lairg
LOCH BRORA Brora
LOCH CHUILIN Dingwall
LOCH CONNAN Portree
LOCH CRAGGIE Lairg
LOCH CULAG Lairg
LOCH DAMH Achnasheen
LOCH DOLA Lairg
LOCH DUAGRAICH Portree
LOCH ERICHT Dalwhinnie
LOCH FANNICH Strathpeffer
LOCH GARRY Invergarry
LOCH GARVE Strathpeffer
LOCH GLASCARNOCH Garve
LOCH HOPE Lairg
LOCH HORN Golspie
LOCH INCH LAGGAN Invergarry
LOCH INSH Kingussie
LOCH KNOCKIE Inverness
LOCH LAGGAN Dalwhinnie
LOCH LOCHY Fort William
LOCH LOYAL Lairg
LOCH LOYNE Inverness
LOCH LUNDIE Golspie
LOCH MAREE Achnasheen
LOCH MEADIE Thurso
LOCH MEIG Strathpeffer
LOCH MERKLAND Lairg
LOCH MORAR Mallaig
LOCH MORLICH Aviemore
LOCH MULLARDOCH Inverness
LOCH NAVER Lairg
LOCH NESS Fort Augustus
LOCH OICH Invergarry
LOCH POULARY Invergarry
LOCH QUOICH Invergarry
LOCH RUITH A PHUILL Strathpeffer
LOCH RUTHVEN Inverness
LOCH SHIEL Fort William
LOCH SHIN Lairg
LOCH SIONASCAIG Ullapool
LOCH TARVIE Strathpeffer
LOCH TOFTINGALL Wick
LOCH USSIE Dingwall
LOCH WATTEN Wick
SCOURIE HOTEL Lairg
ST JOHNS LOCH Thurso
STONEYFIELD LOCH TROUT FISHERY Invergordon
TARVIE LOCHS FISHERY Strathpeffer

INVERCLYDE

ARDGOWAN TROUT FISHERY Greenock
LOCH THOM Greenock

LANARKSHIRE (NORTH)

HILLEND LOCH Airdrie
LILY LOCH Airdrie
STRATHCLYDE LOCH Motherwell

LANARKSHIRE (SOUTH)

LANARK LOCH Lanark
TINTO TROUT FISHERIES Biggar

LOTHIAN (EAST)

MARKLE FISHERIES East Linton

LOTHIAN (MID)

PORTMORE LOCH Penicuik

LOTHIAN (WEST)

BEECRAIGS LOCH Linlithgow
LINLITHGOW LOCH Linlithgow

MORAY

LOCH DALLAS Forres
LOCH NA BO Elgin
LOCH OF BLAIRS Forres
MILLBUIES LOCH Elgin

PERTH AND KINROSS

BUTTERSTONE LOCH Dunkeld
DRUMMOND FISHERIES Crieff
DRUMMOND LOCH Crieff
DUNALASTAIR LOCH Pitlochry
LOCH BHAC Pitlochry
LOCH EIGHEACH Pitlochry
LOCH FASKALLY Pitlochry
LOCH FREUCHIE Dunkeld
LOCH LEVEN FISHERIES Kinross
LOCH RANNOCH Pitlochry
LOCH TAY Aberfeldy
LOWER FRANDY Kinross
ORCHILL LOCH TROUT FISHERY Dunblane
SEAMAW LOCH Perth

RENFREWSHIRE

CARN LOCH Lochgilphead
CLACHAIG (LOCH) Lochgilphead
COILLE BHAR (LOCH) Lochgilphead
GLEAN LOCH Lochgilphead
LEIPEIG (LOCH) Lochgilphead
LOCH BARNLUASGAN Lochgilphead
LOCH DHU Lochgilphead
LOCH-AN-ADD Lochgilphead
LOCH-NA-BRIC Lochgilphead
LOCH-NA-FAOILINN Lochgilphead
NEW LOCH Lochgilphead

SCOTTISH BORDERS

AKERMOOR LOCH Hawick
BLACKADDER WATER Duns
CLERKLAND FLY FISHERY Melrose
COLDINGHAM LOCH Eyemouth
HEADSHAW FISHERY Selkirk
HELLMOOR LOCH Hawick
MACBIEHILL ESTATE West Linton
ST MARYS LOCH Selkirk
WOODEN LOCH Kelso
WULLIESTRUTHER LOCH Hawick

SHETLAND ISLANDS

LOCH OF BROUGH Shetland
LOCH OF COLVISTER Shetland
LOCH OF CULLIVOE Shetland
LOCH OF GUTCHER Shetland
LOCH OF LUMBISTER Shetland
LOCH OF PAPIL Shetland
LOCH OF VOLLISTER Shetland
MUSKRA LOCH Shetland

STIRLING

LOCH ACHRAY
LOCH ARD
LOCH ARKLET
LOCH DRUNKIE
LOCH GLENFINGLAS
LOCH KATRINE
LOCH KATRINE Doune
LOCH LOMOND Glasgow
LOCH LUBNAIG Callander
LOCH TAY HIGHLAND LODGES Killin
LOCH VOIL Lochearnhead
LOCHAN NA LARAIG Killin
SWANSWATER FISHERY

WESTERN ISLES

LACASDALE LOCHS Harris

MILL DAMS

ANGUS

PIPERDAM HOLDINGS Dundee

PONDS

KINGENNIE FISHINGS Dundee

AYRSHIRE (NORTH)

GOOSELOAN POND Kilwinning

DUMFRIES AND GALLOWAY

CULSCADDEN FARM POND Newton Stewart
MORTON POND Thornhill
TONGUE OF BOMBIE LOCHAN Kirkcudbright

INVERCLYDE

PINEWOOD TROUT FISHERY Kilmacolm

LOTHIAN (WEST)

HOPETOUN FISHERY Broxburn
PARKLEY FISHERY Linlithgow
SELM MUIR FISHERY Livingston

YORKSHIRE (SOUTH)

LINDHOLME LEISURE LAKES FISHERIES (1) Doncaster

POOLS

ABERDEENSHIRE

ABERDEEN BOX POOL Aberdeen

PERTH AND KINROSS

ABERFELDY ASSOCIATION BEAT Aberfeldy
AMULREE BEAT Dunkeld
BALLECHIN BEAT Pitlochry
BOLFRACKS BEAT Aberfeldy
CASTLE BEAT Aberfeldy
CASTLE MENZIES BEAT Aberfeldy
CLOCHFOLDICH BEAT Aberfeldy
COSHIEVILLE FARM Aberfeldy
CUILALUINN BEAT Aberfeldy
DERCULICH BEAT Aberfeldy
EASTERTYRE BEAT Pitlochry
FARLEYER BEAT Aberfeldy
FINDYNATE BEAT Aberfeldy
HAUGH OF GRANDTULLY BEAT Aberfeldy
KENMORE BEAT Aberfeldy
LOGIERAIT BEAT Pitlochry
LOWER FARLEYER BEAT Aberfeldy
LOWER SCONE BEAT Perth
MAINS OF MURTHLY Aberfeldy
NEWTON OF LOGIERAIT BEAT Perth
PITCASTLE BEAT Aberfeldy
PITNACREE BEAT Aberfeldy
RUMBLING BRIDGE Dunkeld
SKETEWAN BEAT Aberfeldy
TOMBUIE BEAT Aberfeldy
TROCHRY BEAT Dunkeld
TULLYPOWRIE BEAT Pitlochry
UPPER BORLICK BEAT Aberfeldy
UPPER KINNAIRD BEAT Perth
WEEM BEAT Aberfeldy

STIRLING

AUCHESSON BEAT Crianlarich
LESKINE Killin
SUIE Crianlarich

YORKSHIRE (SOUTH)

- **LINDHOLME LEISURE LAKES FISHERIES (2)** Doncaster
- **LINDHOLME LEISURE LAKES FISHERIES (3)** Doncaster

RESERVOIRS

ABERDEENSHIRE

- **TULLICH FISHERY** Ballater

ANGUS

- **CROMBIE RESERVOIR** Carnoustie

ARGYLL AND BUTE

- **DUNOON RESERVOIR** Dunoon

AYRSHIRE (NORTH)

- **CAMPHILL RESERVOIR** Kilbirnie
- **SKELMORLIE FISHERIES** Skelmorlie

AYRSHIRE (SOUTH)

- **CRAITH RESERVOIR** Prestwick

CLACKMANNANSHIRE

- **GLENSHERRUP FISHERIES** Dollar

DUMFRIES AND GALLOWAY

- **BLACK ESK RESERVOIR** Lockerbie
- **BUITTLE RESERVOIR** Dalbeattie
- **DALBEATTIE RESERVOIR** Dalbeattie
- **DINDINNIE RESERVOIR** Stranraer
- **GLENKILN RESERVOIR** Dumfries
- **KNOCKQUASSEN RESERVOIR** Stranraer
- **LABRAX FISHING** Stranraer
- **PENWHIRN RESERVOIR** Stranraer
- **PURDOMSTONE RESERVOIR** Lockerbie

EDINBURGH (CITY OF)

- **CLUBBIEDEAN RESERVOIR** Edinburgh
- **HARLAW RESERVOIR** Balerno
- **THREIPMUIR RESERVOIRS** Balerno

FALKIRK

- **MILLHALL RESERVOIR**

FIFE

- **BALLO RESERVOIR** Glenrothes
- **CAMERON RESERVOIR** St Andrews
- **CRAIGLUSCAR RESERVOIR** Dunfermline
- **HOLL RESERVOIR** Glenrothes

GLASGOW (CITY OF)

- **BALGRAVE RESERVOIR** Glasgow
- **CAMPS RESERVOIR** Glasgow
- **DAER RESERVOIR** Strathclyde

INVERCLYDE

- **LAWFIELD TROUT FISHERY** Kilmacolm

LANARKSHIRE (SOUTH)

- **FRUID RESERVOIR** Biggar
- **TALLA RESERVOIR** Biggar

LOTHIAN (EAST)

- **GIFFORD HOPES RESERVOIR** Haddington
- **WHITEADDER RESERVOIR** Haddington

LOTHIAN (MID)

- **GLADHOUSE RESERVOIR** Penicuik
- **ROSLYNLEE FISHERY** Penicuik

LOTHIAN (WEST)

- **BOWDEN SPRINGS FISHERY** Linlithgow
- **CROSSWOOD RESERVOIR** Livingston

MORAY

- **GLEN LATTERACH RESERVOIR** Elgin

PERTH AND KINROSS

- **MONTAGUE RESERVOIR** Perth

SCOTTISH BORDERS

- **ACREKNOWE RESERVOIR** Hawick
- **ALEMOOR RESERVOIR** Hawick
- **LINDEAN RESERVOIR** Selkirk
- **MEGGET RESERVOIR** Selkirk
- **WATCH RESERVOIR** Duns
- **WEST WATER RESERVOIR** Peebles

STIRLING

- **NORTH THIRD TROUT FISHERY**

RIVERS

ABERDEENSHIRE

- **BACKHILL FISHERY** Macduff
- **BOGNIE AND MOUNTBLAIRY FISHING** Huntly
- **CARRON (RIVER)** Stonehaven
- **YTHAN FISHERY** Ellon

ANGUS

- **DEAN (RIVER)** Dundee
- **ISLA (RIVER)** Blairgowrie

ARGYLL AND BUTE

- **CUR (RIVER)** Dunoon
- **FINNART (RIVER)** Dunoon
- **FRUIN (RIVER)** Helensbourgh
- **MASSAN (RIVER)** Dunoon
- **ORCHY (RIVER)** Bridge Of Orchy
- **RUEL (RIVER)** Dunoon

AYRSHIRE (SOUTH)

- **AYR (RIVER)** Ayr
- **COYLE WATER FISHERY** Ayr
- **CRAUFURDLAND FISHERY** Kilmarnock
- **DALVENNAN COUNTRY SPORTS FISHERY** Ayr
- **DOON (RIVER)** Ayr
- **STINCHAR (RIVER)** Girvan

DUMFRIES AND GALLOWAY

- **ANNAN (RIVER)** Annan
- **ANNAN (RIVER)** Lockerbie
- **BLADNOCH (RIVER)** Newton Stewart
- **CREE (RIVER)** Newton Stewart
- **ESK (RIVER)** Canonbie
- **ESK (RIVER)** Langholm
- **HODDOM WATER** Lockerbie
- **KEN (RIVER)** Castle Douglas
- **KIRKWOOD WATER** Lockerbie
- **LOWER LIDDLE (RIVER)** Canonbie
- **NEW ABBEY DOW** Dumfries
- **NITH (RIVER)** Thornhill
- **URR (RIVER)** Dalbeattie

FIFE

- **RAITH LAKE FISHERY** Kirkcaldy

GLASGOW (CITY OF)

- **CLYDE (RIVER)** Glasgow

HIGHLAND

- **BEAULY (RIVER)** Inverness
- **BRAES SALMON STATION** Portree
- **CONON (RIVER)** Dingwall
- **FORSINARD** Thurso
- **GARRY UPPER (RIVER)** Invergarry
- **GLASS (RIVER)** Beauly
- **GLASS (RIVER)** Dingwall
- **HALLADALE SALMON FISHERY** Thurso
- **NAIRN (RIVER)** Nairn
- **NESS (RIVER)** Inverness
- **SALMON FISHING STATION** Thurso
- **SPEY (RIVER)** Grantown On Spey
- **SPEY (RIVER)** Kingussie
- **STRATHY (RIVER)** Forsinard
- **TWEED (RIVER)** Inverness

INVERCLYDE

- **CLYDE (RIVER)** Greenock
- **GRYFFE (RIVER)** Kilmacolm

LANARKSHIRE (NORTH)

- **CLYDE (RIVER)** Wishaw

LANARKSHIRE (SOUTH)

- **AVON (RIVER)** Larkhall

LOTHIAN (EAST)

- **TYNE (RIVER)** Haddington

LOTHIAN (WEST)

- **ALMOND (RIVER)** South Queensferry

MORAY

- **BROOM OF MOY** Elgin

PERTH AND KINROSS

- **ALMOND (RIVER)** Dunkeld
- **ALMOND (RIVER)** Perth
- **BRAAN (RIVER)** Dunkeld
- **LOWER ABERUTHVEN FISHINGS** Auchterarder
- **TAY (RIVER)** Dunkeld

RENFREWSHIRE

- **BRIDGE OF WEIR** Bridge Of Weir
- **GRYFFE (RIVER)** Bridge Of Weir

SCOTTISH BORDERS

- **BAILEY (RIVER)** Kelso
- **ESK AND LIDDLE FISHERIES** Newcastleton
- **ETTERICK (RIVER)** Selkirk
- **ETTRICK AND YARROW (RIVER)** Selkirk
- **JED (RIVER)** Jedburgh
- **LEADER (RIVER)** Earlston
- **LIDDLE (RIVER)** Newcastleton
- **TEVIOT (RIVER)** Hawick
- **TEVIOT (RIVER)** Selkirk
- **TWEED (RIVER)** Duns
- **TWEED (RIVER)** Galashiels
- **TWEED (RIVER)** Innerleithen
- **TWEED (RIVER)** Kelso
- **TWEED (RIVER)** Melrose
- **TWEED (RIVER)** Peebles

STIRLING

- **BALVAIG (RIVER)** Lochearnhead
- **BARNCROFT** Killin
- **BLAIRMORE FISHERY** Glasgow
- **BORELAND** Killin
- **CRAIGNAVIE** Killin
- **DOCHART (RIVER)** Killin
- **ENDRICK (RIVER)** Glasgow
- **FINLARIG** Killin
- **HOWIETOUN FISHERY**
- **KINNEL** Killin
- **LOCHAY (RIVER)** Killin

YORKSHIRE (SOUTH)

- **TORNE (RIVER)** Doncaster

STREAMS

DUMFRIES AND GALLOWAY

- **KIRTLE WATER STREAM** Gretna
- **SARK STREAM** Gretna

TARNS

LOTHIAN (WEST)

- **ALLANDALE TARN** West Calder

BROOKS

MONMOUTHSHIRE
- OLWAY BROOK Usk

POWYS
- MAERDY BROOK Llanymynech

CANALS

BRIDGEND
- STROUDWATER CANAL

NEWPORT
- MONMOUTHSHIRE AND BRECON CANAL
- SHROPSHIRE UNION CANAL

POWYS
- MONTGOMERY CANAL Montgomery
- SHROPSHIRE UNION CANAL Welshpool

COMBINATIONS

GWYNEDD
- TRAWFFYNYDD RESERVOIR Blaenau Ffestiniog

RHONDDA CYNON TAFF
- SEVEN OAKS FISHERY Pontyclun

DAMS

CEREDIGION
- CWM RHEIDOL FISHERY Aberystwyth

POWYS
- VALLEY DAM FISHERY Llanfyllin

GRAVEL PITS

DENBIGHSHIRE
- MONKS POOL Wrexham

FLINTSHIRE
- ALLTAMI CLAY PITS Mold

LAKES

BLAENAU GWENT
- BLUE LAKE Ebbw Vale
- HAYRICK LAKES Tredegar

BRIDGEND
- KENFIG LAKE

CAERPHILLY
- CAERPHILLY CASTLE LAKES
- OGILVIE LAKE Bargoed
- RIVERSIDE TROUT FISHERY Hengoed

CARDIFF
- CEFN MABLEY
- HENDRE LAKE

CARMARTHENSHIRE
- EDWINSFORD FISHERY Llandeilo
- GARNFFRWD FISHERY Llanelli
- GLAS LLYN FISHERY Llanboidy
- GLAS-LLYN FISHERY Whitland
- GWENDRAETH AND MORIASIS FISHERY Llanelli
- LLANLLAWDDOG FISHERY Carmarthen
- LLYN CARFAN Whitland
- LOUGHOR VALLEY FISHERY Ammanford
- PANT Y BEDW FISHING LAKES Carmarthen
- SPRINGWATER LAKES Llanwrda
- TEIFI VALLEY FISH Llanybydder
- WHITE HOUSE MILL Whitland

CEREDIGION
- FRON FARM FISHERY Aberystwyth
- GLWYDWERN TROUT FISHERY Lampeter
- LAKE BLAENMELINDWR Aberystwyth
- LAKE CRAIGYPISTYLL Aberystwyth
- LAKE FRONGOCH Aberystwyth
- LAKE LLYGAD Aberystwyth
- LAKE PENDHAM Aberystwyth
- LAKE RHEIDOL Aberystwyth
- LAKE RHOSGOCH Aberystwyth
- LAKE RHOSRHYDD Aberystwyth
- LLANARTH FISHERY Llanarth
- LLYN BERWEN Ystrad Meurig
- LLYN BERWYN Tregaron
- NEUADDLAS COUNTRY GUEST HOUSE Tregaron
- NINE OAKS Llanarth
- RHYDLEWIS TROUT FISHERY Llandysul
- TEGLAN LAKE Lampeter
- TROED-Y-BRYN FISHERY Lampeter

CONWY
- CONWY VALLEY FISHERIES
- GILER ARMS LAKE Betws-Y-Coed
- LLYN CRAFNANT FISHERIES Trefriw
- LLYN NANT-Y-CERRIG
- TALYLLN LAKE FISHERY Abergele
- TAN-Y-MYNYDD TROUT LAKES Abergele
- TYDDYN MAWR TROUT FARM

DENBIGHSHIRE
- DRAGONFLY FISHERIES Corwen
- FELIN-Y-GORS FISHERIES Rhyl
- GWYDDELWERN POOL Corwen
- LLYN ALWEN Ruthin
- LLYN BRENIG Corwen
- LLYN COWLYD AND HILL LAKES Rhyl

FLINTSHIRE
- BUCKLEY TRAP POOL Buckley
- CLAWDD OFFAS DYKE Mold
- FOREST HILL TROUT FARM Holywell
- GWERYD LAKES FISHING Mold
- GYRN CASTLE FISHERY Holywell
- SWAN LAKE Connahs Quay
- WAL GOCH FLY Mold

GWYNEDD
- BRON EIFION FISHERIES Pwllheli
- CREGENNAN LAKES Dolgellau
- CWM PRYSOR LAKE Bala
- CWM SILYN LAKE Caernarfon
- DWYTHWCH LAKE Caernarfon
- GLAN MORFA MAWR FISHERY Porthmadog
- GREGANNAN LAKES Dolgellau
- GWERNAN LAKE FISHERY Dolgellau
- LLYN BUGEILYN Tywyn
- LLYN CELYN FISHERY Bala
- LLYN CWMYSTRADLLYN Porthmadog
- LLYN DDU (BLACK LAKE) Porthmadog
- LLYN DINAS Caernarfon
- LLYN GADAIR Caernarfon
- LLYN GLAN MOFA MAWR Porthmadog
- LLYN NANTLLE Caernarfon
- LLYN PADARN Caernarfon
- LLYN TEGID (BALA LAKE) Bala
- NANTLLE LAKE Caernarfon
- TALYLLYN LAKE Tywyn

ISLE OF ANGLESEY
- LAKE HOUSE HOLIDAYS Benllech
- LLYN BRYNTIRION Llanfair Pwllgwyngyll
- LLYN CORON Llangefni
- LLYN JANE FISHERY Menai Bridge
- LLYN LLWYDIARTH FAWR Llanerchymedd
- LLYN NANT ANOG Anglesey
- LLYN TACAN Anglesey
- LLYN Y GORS Menai Bridge
- PARC NEWYDD TROUT FISHERY Llanerchymedd
- PLAS-Y-NANT TROUT FISHERY Amlwch
- TYDDYN SARGENT Tyn-Y-Gongl

MONMOUTHSHIRE
- GROVE FARM FISHERY Abergavenny
- TREFALDU FISHERY Monmouth

NEATH PORT TALBOT
- GLYNCORRWG PONDS FISHERY Port Talbot
- MARGRAM PARK FISHERY Port Talbot

NEWPORT
- LLISWERRY POND
- PETERSTONE TROUT LAKE

PEMBROKESHIRE
- HAYCASTLE TROUT FISHERY Haverfordwest
- HAYSCASTLE TROUT FISHERY Haverfordwest
- HOLGAN TROUT FARM FISHERY Narberth
- IAN HEAPS PREMIER FISHERIES AND SCHOOL OF ANGLING Narberth
- LUDCHURCH LAKE Narberth
- MILLBROOK FISHERY Fishguard
- PENHOYLE FISHING PARK Tenby
- YET-Y-GORS FISHERY Fishguard

POWYS
- BEGUEILIN LAKE Brecon
- GLUDY LAKE Brecon
- GWYDDIOR LAKE Llanbrynmair
- LLANDRINIO WEST LAKE Llanymynech
- LLANGORSE LAKE Brecon
- LLYN ALARCH Builth Wells
- LLYN CLYWEDOG Llanidloes
- LLYN-COCH HWYAD Llanbrynmair
- LLYNGWYN LAKE Rhayader
- WESTLAKE FISHERY Llanymynech

RHONDDA CYNON TAFF
- BROOKFIELD FISHERY Pontypridd
- LLYN FAWR FISHERY Treorchy
- TRI NANT TROUT FARM Pontyclun

SWANSEA
- FENDROD LAKE
- SHIMANO FELINDRE TROUT FISHERY
- WHITE SPRINGS LAKES

TORFAEN
- CWMBRAN BOATING LAKE Cwmbran
- MORGANS POND Cwmbran

WREXHAM
- ARGAE LAKE
- BODIDRIS GAME FISHERY
- FLASH
- LLYN CYFYNWY SPORT TROUT FISHERY
- TREE TOPS FLY FISHERY

LOCKS

CARDIFF
- EAST DOCK

MILL DAMS

GLAMORGAN (VALE OF)
- WARREN MILL Cowbridge

PONDS

BLAENAU GWENT
- BOAT POND Ebbw Vale

BUTE TOWN RESERVOIR Tredegar
MACHINE POND Ebbw Vale

DENBIGHSHIRE

ABBEY FISHERY Llangollen

FLINTSHIRE

SARN MILL FISHERIES Mold
SEVEN SPRINGS TROUT FARM AND FISHERIES Mold

GLAMORGAN (VALE OF)

HAZELCOURT PONDS Cowbridge
PENYWERN PONDS Merthyr Tydfil

ISLE OF ANGLESEY

TY HEN LAKE Rhosneigr

MONMOUTHSHIRE

CWMCELYN POND Abertillery
FAIROAK FISHERY Chepstow
FIVE TREES Monmouth
RAVENSNEST FISHERY Chepstow

PEMBROKESHIRE

WEST ATHESTON COARSE FISHERY Narberth

SWANSEA

GOWERTON COARSE FISHERY
MAES GWYN FISHERY

POOLS

BLAENAU GWENT

LYMOOR POOL 1 AND 2 Ebbw Vale

CEREDIGION

PANT TROUT POOL Tregaron
TEIFI POOLS Ystrad Meurig

CONWY

TREFANT POOL

FLINTSHIRE

NANT-Y-GAIN FISHERY Mold
PADESWOOD POOL Mold

ISLE OF ANGLESEY

BREAKWATER PARK Holyhead
LLYN DEWI Anglesey

NEWPORT

WOODSTOCK POOL

POWYS

FACHWEN POOL Newtown
LLYSWEN CARP POOLS Builth Wells

WREXHAM

LLANDEGLA TROUT FISHERY
PONKY POOL
TAN LLAN
TRENCH FISHERIES

RESERVOIRS

CARMARTHENSHIRE

BRO TYWI FISHERIES Carmarthen
LLEIDI RESERVIORS Llanelli

CEREDIGION

DINA FISHERY Aberystwyth
DINAS RESERVOIR Aberystwyth
GEORGE BORROW HOTEL Aberystwyth
LLYN MAENOG TROUT FISHERY Llandysul
NANT Y MOCH RESERVOIR Aberystwyth
TALYBONT RESERVOIR Talybont

CONWY

GRAIGLWYD SPRINGS FISHERY Penmaenmawr
LLYN ALED Denbigh

DENBIGHSHIRE

ALWEN RESERVOIR Corwen
BRENIG RESERVOIR Corwen
DOLWEN AND PLAS UCHAF St Asaph
PANT GLAS RESERVOIR Wrexham

GLAMORGAN (VALE OF)

BARRY RESERVOIR Dinas Powys
LLYWN-ON RESERVOIR Treharris
PENTWYN RESERVOIR Merthyr Tydfil
PONTSTICILL RESERVOIR Merthyr Tydfil

GWYNEDD

DYWARCHEN RESERVOIR Caernarfon
FFESTINIOG FISHERY Blaenau Ffestiniog
LLYN CWELLYN RESERVOIR Caernarfon
LLYN CYNWCH LAKE Dolgellau
TANYGRISIAU RESERVOIR Blaenau Ffestiniog

ISLE OF ANGLESEY

CEFNI RESERVOIR Llangefni
LLYN ALAN Holyhead

MONMOUTHSHIRE

CWMTILLERY RESERVOIR Abertillery

NEATH PORT TALBOT

EGLWYS NUNYDD RESERVOIR Port Talbot

NEWPORT

WENTWOOD RESERVOIR
YNYS-Y-FRO RESERVOIR

PEMBROKESHIRE

LLYS Y FRAN RESERVOIR AND COUNTRY PARK Haverfordwest
ROADSIDE FARM Narberth
ROSEBUSH RESERVOIR Haverfordwest

POWYS

CANTEF RESERVOIR Brecon
CLAERWEN RESERVOIR Rhayader
CLYNWEDOG RESERVOIR Llanidloes
CRAI RESERVOIR Brecon
ELAN VALLEY RESERVOIR Rhayader
LAKE MOCHDRE Newtown
USK RESERVOIR Brecon

RHONDDA CYNON TAFF

LLYN ALAW Pontyclun

SWANSEA

LOWER LLIW

TORFAEN

BEACONS RESERVOIRS Pontypool
CANTREF RESERVOIR Pontypool
LISVANE RESERVOIR Pontypool
LLANDEGFEDD RESERVOIR Pontypool
LLANISHEN RESERVOIR Pontypool
LLWYN ON RESERVOIR Pontypool
LLYN ON RESERVOIR Pontypool

WREXHAM

LLAY RESERVOIR
PENYCAE LOWER RESERVOIR
PENYCAE UPPER RESERVOIR
TY MAWR RESERVOIR

RIVERS

BLAENAU GWENT

SIRHOWY (RIVER) Tredegar

BRIDGEND

GARW (RIVER)
LLYNFI (RIVER) Maesteg
OGMORE (RIVER)

CAERPHILLY

EBBW (RIVER) Blackwood
SIRHOWY (RIVER) Blackwood

CARDIFF

TAFF (RIVER)

CARMARTHENSHIRE

BRYNHAWC FISHERY Pencader
CHURCH FARM FISHERY Pencader
COTHI (RIVER) Ammanford
COTHI (RIVER) Carmarthen
COTHI (RIVER) Llandovery
COWIN (RIVER) Carmarthen
CYNIN (RIVER) Carmarthen
DOL WATTS FISHERY Newcastle Emlyn
DOLGWM MILL FISHERY Llanybydder
DUAD (RIVER) Carmarthen
GWENDRAETH FACH (RIVER) Kidwelly
GWENDRAETH FACH (RIVER) Llanelli
GWILI (RIVER) Carmarthen
HENDY FISHERY Llanybydder
LLWCHWR (RIVER) Ammanford
LOUGHOR (RIVER) Ammanford
MAES-ISAF FISHERY Llanybydder
PENBEILI FISHERY Newcastle Emlyn
PEWI FACH (RIVER) Carmarthen
RHYDFACH FISHERY Newcastle Emlyn
RIVER GWENLLIAN FISHERY Kidwelly
SWISS VALLEY Llanelli
TAF (RIVER) Carmarthen
TAF (RIVER) Whitland
TAN-Y-COED FISHERY Newcastle Emlyn
TEIFI (RIVER) Llanybydder
TEIFI (RIVER) Newcastle Emlyn
TOWEY (RIVER) Llandovery
TOWI (RIVER) Carmarthen
TOWY (RIVER) Carmarthen
TOWY (RIVER) Llandeilo
TOWY (RIVER) Llwynfortune
TREBEDW FISHERY Newcastle Emlyn

CEREDIGION

AERON (RIVER) Aberaeron
ARTRO (RIVER) Llandysul
BAYLIAU FISHERY Lampeter
CASTELL-PYR FISHERY Llandysul
CEFN-BRYN FISHERY Lampeter
CELLAN FISHERY Lampeter
CWMMACKWITH FISHERY Llandysul
CYCH (RIVER) Cardigan
LAMPETER FISHERY Lampeter
LLETYTWPA FISHERY Lampeter
LLWYNDURIS MANSION FISHERY Cardigan
PENTRE FARM FISHERY Lampeter
RALLT FISHERY Lampeter
RHEIDOL (RIVER) Aberystwyth
RHYDYGALFE FISHERY Llandysul
TEIFI (RIVER Llandysul
TEIFI (RIVER) Cardigan
TEIFI (RIVER) Lampeter
TEIFI (RIVER) Llandysul
TEIFI (RIVER) Tregaron
TEIFY POOLS FISHERY Tregaron
TYRDREF FISHERY Llandysul
YSTWYTH (RIVER) Aberystwyth

CONWY

ALED (RIVER) Denbigh
CLWYD (RIVER) Denbigh
CONWY (RIVER)
CONWY (RIVER) Betws-Y-Coed
CONWY (RIVER) Llanrwst
ELWY (RIVER) Abergele
ELWY (RIVER) Denbigh

LLEDR (RIVER) Dolwyddelan

DENBIGHSHIRE

ALWEN (RIVER) Corwen
CEIRIOG (RIVER) Llangollen
CEIRIOG (RIVER) Wrexham
CLWYD (RIVER) Ruthin
CLWYD (RIVER) St Asaph
CLYWEDOG (RIVER) Ruthin
DEE (RIVER) Llangollen
DEE (RIVER) Ruthin
DEE (RIVER) Wrexham
ELWY (RIVER) St Asaph
TEIGN (RIVER) Llangollen

FLINTSHIRE

ALYN (RIVER) Mold
CLWYD (RIVER) Mold
DEE (RIVER) Mold
WHEELER (RIVER) Mold

GLAMORGAN (VALE OF)

TAFF (RIVER) Merthyr Tydfil
TAFF BARGOED Treharris
UPPER NEUADD Merthyr Tydfil

GWYNEDD

AFON LLYFNI (RIVER) Caernarfon
AFON SEIONT (RIVER) Caernarfon
BONTNEWYDD FISHERY Caernarfon
CLWYD (RIVER) Pwllheli
CONWY (RIVER) Llanrwst
DEE (RIVER) Bala
DUGOED (RIVER) Dolgellau
DWYFACH (RIVER) Criccieth
DWYFAWR (RIVER) Criccieth
DWYRYD (RIVER) Blaenau Ffestiniog
DYSYNNI (RIVER) Tywyn
EDEN (RIVER) Dolgellau
ERCH (RIVER) Pwllheli
GLASLYN (RIVER) Penrhyndeudraeth
GWYRFAI (RIVER) Caernarfon
LERI (RIVER) Talybont
LLIW (RIVER) Craig-Y-Tan
MAWDDACH (RIVER) Dolgellau
MAWDDACH AND WNION (RIVERS) Dolgellau
OGWEN (RIVER) Bangor
PORTH WATERS FISHERY Bala
RHYDHIR (RIVER) Pwllheli
WNION (RIVER) Dolgellau

MONMOUTHSHIRE

MONNOW (RIVER) Abergavenny
TROTHY (RIVER) Usk
USK (RIVER) Abergavenny
USK (RIVER) Usk
WYE (RIVER) Monmouth

NEATH PORT TALBOT

ABERNANT FARM FISHERY Port Talbot
DULAIS (RIVER) Neath
NEATH (RIVER) Neath
TWRCH (RIVER) Neath

NEWPORT

DEE (RIVER)
NEVERN (RIVER)

NORFOLK

DEE (RIVER) Holt

PEMBROKESHIRE

EASTERN CLEDDAU (RIVER) Haverfordwest
EASTERN CLEDDAU (RIVER) Llanycefn
EASTERN CLEDDAU (RIVER) Narberth
EWENNY (RIVER) Milford Haven
SABRE TOOTH Milford Haven
WESTERN CLEDDAU (RIVER) Haverfordwest

POWYS

BANWY (RIVER) Welshpool
BEACONS FISHERY Brecon
BOATSIDE FARM Builth Wells
CAER BERIS MANOR HOTEL Builth Wells
CLYWEDOG (RIVER) Llanidloes
DEE (RIVER) Llanymynech
DOL LLYS FARM Llanidloes
DULAS (RIVER) Llanidloes
DULAS (RIVER) Machynlleth
DYFI (RIVER) Machynlleth
ELAN (RIVER) Rhayader
ERCH (RIVER) Llanymynech
IRFON (RIVER) Builth Wells
IRFON (RIVER) Llangammarch Wells
IRFON (RIVER) Llanwrtyd Wells
ITHON (RIVER) Llandrindod Wells
LLNGWYN FISHERY Rhayader
MULE (RIVER) Newtown
NEW INN Llandrindod Wells
RIVERSIDE CARAVAN PARK Llangammarch Wells
SEVERN (RIVER) Llanidloes
SEVERN (RIVER) Llanymynech
SEVERN (RIVER) Newtown
SEVERN (RIVER) Welshpool
TOWY (RIVER) Brecon
TWYMYN (RIVER) Llanbrynmair
USK (RIVER) Crickhowell
VYRNWY (RIVER) Llansantffraid
VYRNWY (RIVER) Llanymynech
VYRNWY (RIVER) Welshpool
WYE (RIVER) Builth Wells
WYE (RIVER) Llandrindod Wells
WYE (RIVER) Rhayader

RHONDDA CYNON TAFF

CMPRAC (RIVER) Treorchy
ELY (RIVER) Pontyclun
RHONDDA (RIVER) Treorchy

SWANSEA

TAWE (RIVER)

TORFAEN

LLYWD (RIVER) Pontypool

WREXHAM

ALYN (RIVER)
DEE (RIVER)
DEE (RIVER) Bangor-on-Dee
DEE (RIVER) Worthenbury
DEE ABBEY FISHERIES
WORTHENBURY BROOK

STREAMS

DENBIGHSHIRE

CEIRW STREAM Ruthin

GLAMORGAN (VALE OF)

MELLTE (STREAM) Neath

GWYNEDD

GWYNEDD (RIVER) Criccieth
TRYWERYN (RIVER) Bala

NEATH PORT TALBOT

AFAN STREAM Port Talbot
HEPSTE (STREAM) Neath

TRIBUTARIES

POWYS

WYE (RIVER) Llandrindod Wells

by Fishing Type by County

SECTION 5

This section allows you to search for Fisheries which are either coarse, game or combination types.

e.g Game Fisheries in Flintshire

Once you have located a Fishery you can either look up further details in Section 1 or use the other sections to find what else the Fishery may have to offer.

COARSE

BEDFORDSHIRE

- **AMPTHILL RESERVOIR** Bedford
- **ARLESEY LAKE** Arlesey
- **BECKERINGS PARK FARM RESERVOIR** Bedford
- **BRIARWOOD FISHERY** Bedford
- **BROGBOROUGH NO.1 PIT** Bedford
- **BROOM** Stanford
- **CLAYDON LAKE** Leighton Buzzard
- **ELSTOW PITS** Elstow
- **FELMERSHAM (RIVER)** Bedford
- **FELMERSHAM GRAVEL PITS** Bedford
- **FIR COUNTRY PARK** Bedford
- **GREAT OUSE (RIVER)** Bedford
- **GREEN LAGOON** Arlesey
- **HAROLD FISHERY** Bedford
- **HENLOW GRANGE** Henlow
- **HOUGHTON REGIS QUARRY** Dunstable
- **IVEL (RIVER)** Biggleswade
- **IVEL (RIVER)** Henlow
- **JONES PIT** Leighton Buzzard
- **LANGFORD MILL** Biggleswade
- **LEDBURN ROAD** Leighton Buzzard
- **MARSTON PITS** Bedford
- **OUSE (RIVER)** Bedford
- **PRIORY COUNTRY PARK** Bedford
- **RACKLEY HILLS PIT** Leighton Buzzard
- **RADWELL COMPLEX** Bedford
- **SOUTH LAGOON** Bedford
- **STANFORD PIT** Stanford
- **TIDDENFOOT PIT** Leighton Buzzard
- **TINGRITH COARSE FISHERY** Dunstable
- **TINGRITH MANOR LAKE** Dunstable
- **VAUXHALL PIT** Leighton Buzzard
- **WATER END FISHERY** Bedford
- **WILLINGTON LAKE** Bedford
- **WITHY POOL** Henlow
- **WOBURN SANDS** Luton

BERKSHIRE

- **ALBERT BRIDGE** Windsor
- **ALDERMASTON** Reading
- **ALLSMOOR POND** Bracknell
- **AMERDEN POOL** Maidenhead
- **ASHRIDGE MANOR** Wokingham
- **BENS LAKE** Newbury
- **BISHOPS GREEN FARM LAKE** Newbury
- **BRIMPTON LAKE** Reading
- **BURGHFIELD** Reading
- **BURGHFIELD BLUE POOL** Reading
- **BURGHFIELD CANAL** Reading
- **BURGHFIELD MATCH LAKE** Reading
- **CHURCH FARM** Sandhurst
- **COTTAGE LANE** Reading
- **COURT FARM** Reading
- **DINTON PASTURES COUNTRY PARK** Reading
- **EAST TOWNEY** Reading
- **ENGLEFIELD LAGOON** Reading
- **FARLEYMOOR LAKE** Bracknell
- **FARNHAM FLINT** Reading
- **FORBURY FARM LAKES** Newbury
- **FROBURY FARM SPORTING CLUB** Newbury
- **FROXFIELD A AND B** Hungerford
- **HAMBRIDGE LANE** Newbury
- **HOLME GRANGE** Crowthorne
- **HOLYBROOK** Reading
- **JINGLES FARM** Wokingham
- **KENNET (RIVER)** Reading
- **KENNET AND AVON CANAL** Reading
- **KENNET AND ENTORNE (RIVERS)** Reading
- **LODDON (RIVER)** Reading
- **LODDON (RIVER)** Wokingham
- **LONGMOOR FARM FISHING LAKE** Finchampstead
- **LONGMOOR LAKE** Wokingham
- **LOWER BENYONS** Reading
- **MAPLEDURHAM A AND B** Reading
- **MATCH AND BLUE POOLS** Reading
- **MILL LANE** Sandhurst
- **MILL POND** Bracknell
- **MOATLANDS POOL** Reading
- **OLD MILL** Reading
- **PINGEWOOD LAGOON** Reading
- **PONDWOOD CARP LAKES** Maidenhead
- **PRIORY WATER** Windsor
- **PURLEY** Reading
- **ROYAL BERKSHIRE FISHERY** Windsor
- **SAVERNAKE POND** Bracknell
- **SEACOURT (STREAM)** Reading
- **SONNING EYE** Reading
- **SOUTH FIELD PARK** Hanworth
- **SOUTH HILL PARK LAKE** Bracknell
- **ST PATRICKS** Reading
- **SWAN VALLEY** Sandhurst
- **THAMES (RIVER)** Bray
- **THAMES (RIVER)** Maidenhead
- **THAMES (RIVER)** Newbury
- **THAMES (RIVER)** Reading
- **THAMES (RIVER)** Windsor
- **THEALE** Reading
- **THEALE CANAL** Reading
- **THEALE LAGOON** Reading
- **TRI-LAKES** Sandhurst
- **TWYFORD BBONT** Reading
- **TWYFORD WATERS** Reading
- **UFTON CANAL** Reading
- **WASING WOODS** Reading
- **WELLINGTON COUNTRY PARK** Reading
- **WHITE SWAN LAKE** Wokingham
- **WYLIES LAKE** Newbury

BRISTOL

- **ABBOTS POOL**
- **AVON (BRISTOL) (RIVER)**
- **AVON (RIVER)**
- **BAGWOOD LAKE**
- **BITTERWELL LAKE**
- **BRISTOL AVON**
- **BRISTOL DOCKS**
- **CHEW (RIVER)**
- **FISHPONDS LIDO**
- **FROME (RIVER)**
- **HAM GREEN LAKE**
- **HENLEAZE LAKE**
- **ROUNDWOOD POND**
- **SEVINGTON LAKES FISHERY**
- **TANHOUSE FARM LAKE**
- **WEST COUNTRY WATER PARK**

BUCKINGHAMSHIRE

- **BACKWATER** Marlow
- **BEDFORD BOATING LAKE** Bedford
- **BILLET LANE** Iver
- **BLACK PARK** Iver
- **BOURTON FISHERIES** Buckingham
- **BOWLERS CANAL** Olney
- **CALVES LANE LAKE** Iver
- **CLAYDON LAKE** Buckingham
- **COLNBROOK WEST** Slough
- **COLNEBROOK (RIVER)** Slough
- **COMMON POND** Gerrards Cross
- **COSGROVE LEISURE PARK** Milton Keynes
- **CRAYFISH POOL** Slough
- **DOVECOTE LAKE FISHERY** Milton Keynes
- **FARLOWS LAKE** Iver
- **FURZTON LAKE** Milton Keynes
- **GALLOWS POOL** Buckingham
- **GILBRATAR LAKE** Slough
- **GRAND UNION CANAL** Milton Keynes
- **GREAT LINFORD LAKES** Great Linford
- **GREAT OUSE (RIVER)** Milton Keynes
- **GREAT OUSE (RIVER)** Olney
- **HARROLD ODELL COUNTRY PARK** Bedford
- **HILL WOOD POND** High Wycombe
- **HORTON BOAT POOL** Slough
- **HORTON CHURCH LAKE** Slough
- **HYDE LANE LAKES** Buckingham
- **KEMPSTONE HARDWICK** Bedford
- **KINGSMEAD 1** Slough
- **KINGSMEAD ISLAND LAKE** Slough
- **LODGE LAKES** Milton Keynes
- **LOUGHTON LODGE LAKE** Milton Keynes
- **MAYFIELDS LAKE** Slough
- **MILTON KEYNES LAKES** Bedford
- **NEWPORT PAGNELL GRAVEL PITS** Newport Pagnell
- **OLD SLADE LANE LAKE** Iver
- **ORLITTS LAKES** Slough
- **OUSE (RIVER)** Bedford
- **OUSE (RIVER)** Milton Keynes
- **OUSE (RIVER)** Olney
- **OUZEL (RIVER)** Milton Keynes
- **SHELSWELL LAKE** Buckingham
- **SILVERWING LAKE** Amersham
- **SNOWBERRY** Milton Keynes
- **SPADE OAK LAKE** High Wycombe
- **TEARDROP LAKES** Milton Keynes
- **THAME (RIVER)** Aylesbury
- **THAMES (RIVER)** High Wycombe
- **THAMES (RIVER)** Marlow
- **THAMES (RIVER)** Slough
- **TINGRITH LAKES** Milton Keynes
- **TYRINGHAM ESTATE** Newport Pagnell
- **WATTS POOL** Chalfont St Giles
- **WESTFIELD FARM** Marlow
- **WESTHORPE PARK LAKE** High Wycombe
- **WESTON TERVELL RESERVOIR** Great Missenden
- **WOLVERTON LAKES** Milton Keynes

CAMBRIDGESHIRE

- **BARNWELL COUNTRY PARK** Peterborough
- **BARNWELL PIT** Cambridge
- **BARWAY LAKE** Ely
- **BIGGIN LAKE** Peterborough
- **BLOCK FEN COMPLEX** Ely
- **BLUEBELL LAKE** Peterborough
- **BRACKHILL LAKE** Huntingdon
- **BURNSIDE LAKE** Cambridge
- **BURWELL LODE** Cambridge
- **CAM (RIVER)** Cambridge
- **CAM (RIVER)** Ely
- **CHAWSTON LAKES** Huntingdon
- **CLEARWATERS COARSE FISHERY** Huntingdon
- **COTTERSTOCK RIVER** Peterborough
- **CROWLAND ANGLING CLUB LAKES** Peterborough
- **DECOY LAKE** Peterborough
- **DICKERSONS PIT** Cambridge
- **EAST DELPH LAKES** Whittlesey
- **EATON SOCON LAKE** Huntingdon
- **ELDERNELL LAKE** Peterborough
- **FEN DRAYTON LAKE** Cambridge
- **FERRY MEADOWS** Peterborough
- **FIELDS END WATER** March
- **GERARDS CARP LAKE** Peterborough
- **GINGERBREAD LAKE AND DRIFT** Huntingdon
- **GODMANCHESTER (RIVER)** Huntingdon
- **GREAT OUSE (RIVER)** Ely
- **GREAT OUSE (RIVER)** Huntingdon
- **GUNWADE LAKE** Peterborough
- **HATTON PARK POND** Cambridge
- **HIGH FLYER LAKE** Ely
- **HINCHINGBROOKE COUNTRY PARK** Huntingdon
- **HOLME FEN FISHING** Huntingdon
- **HUNDRED FOOT (RIVER)** Huntingdon
- **HUNTINGDON (RIVER)** Huntingdon
- **KINGFISHER LAKE** Peterborough
- **KINGSLAND RESERVOIRS** Peterborough
- **LARK (RIVER)** Ely
- **LEES BROOK** Huntingdon
- **LILY PARK LAKES** Huntingdon

LITTLE PAXTON FISHERY Huntingdon
LONG REACH Huntingdon
MAGPIE LAKE Cambridge
MALEY GRAVEL PITS Peterborough
MEPAL PIT Ely
MIDDLE LEVEL DRAIN Wisbech
MILTON COUNTRY PARK Cambridge
MILTON PITS Cambridge
NENE (RIVER) Peterborough
NENE NORTH BANK (RIVER) Peterborough
NORTH HOUSE LAKE Huntingdon
NORTHEY PARK FISHERY Peterborough
OFFORD CLUNY Huntingdon
OFFORD WEIRPOOL Huntingdon
OLD NENE (RIVER) Huntingdon
OLD WEST (RIVER) Cambridge
OLD WEST (RIVER) Ely
OLD WEST (RIVER) Huntingdon
OUNDLE (RIVER) Peterborough
OVER MAIN DRAIN Huntingdon
PAXTON LAKE Huntingdon
PISCES CARAVAN PARK AND FISHERY Wisbech
RAILWAY LAKES Peterborough
RANDALLS LAKE Ely
RAVELEY DRAIN Ramsey
REDLANDS PITS Peterborough
ROSWELL PITS Ely
SAND MARTIN LAKE Peterborough
SIBSON FISHERIES Peterborough
SILVER STREET MILL Cambridge
SOHAM BY-PASS LAKE Cambridge
SPORTSMANS PIT Swaffham Prior
ST IVES COMPLEX Huntingdon
STEW POND Huntingdon
STRETHAM BASIN Ely
STRETHAM LAKE Ely
SWAN LAKE Peterborough
TURKS HEAD LAKE Cambridge
TWENTY FOOT DRAIN Peterborough
VIRGINIA LAKE Wisbech
WANSFORD STREAM Peterborough
WELDON RESERVOIR Huntingdon
WERRINGTON LAKE Peterborough
WHITTLESEY DYKE/ BEVILLS LEAM Peterborough
WILDEN RESERVOIR Huntingdon
WILLOW CREEK Peterborough
WILLOW LAKE Peterborough
WIMBLINGTON MERE Wisbech
WOBURN CLOSE LAKE Huntingdon
WOOD POOL Peterborough
WOOLPACK FISHERY Huntingdon
YARWELL MILL LAKE Peterborough

CHESHIRE

ABNEY PARK Cheadle Hulme
ACKERS PIT Warrington
ANTROBUS LAKES Lymm
ASHLEY POOL Altrincham
ASTBURY MERE Congleton
ASTLE POOL Knutsford
BELMONT POOL Northwich
BETLEY MERE Crewe
BILLINGE GREEN Northwich
BLACK LAKE Wilmslow
BLAKEMERE Northwich
BLUNDELLS FARM FISHERY Warrington
BOLESWORTH CASTLE Chester
BORDER FISHERIES Crewe
BOSLEY RESERVOIR Macclesfield
BOTTOMS RESERVOIR Macclesfield
BOUNDARY WATER PARK Knutsford
BREAM HOLE Nantwich
BRERETON HEATH COUNTRY PARK Congleton
BRERTON QUARRY Middlewich
BRIDGEWATER CANAL Runcorn
BRIDGEWATER CANAL Sale
BRIDGEWATER CANAL Warrington
BRIGHOUSE POOL Knutsford
BROOK BANK POOL Holmes Chapel
BROOKSIDE FISHERIES Crewe
BROOKSIDE LAKES Warrington
BROWNLEES POND Warrington
BUDWORTH MERE Northwich
BULLS POOL Sandbach
BURTON MERE FISHERIES Neston
BYLEY FISHERIES Middlewich
CANAL PIT Northwich
CAPESTHORNE HALL STOCK POND Macclesfield
CAPESTHORNE MAIN POOL Macclesfield
CAPESTHORNE TOP POOL Macclesfield
CICELY MILL POOL Knutsford
CISTERNS Northwich
CRABMILL FLASH Sandbach
CRABTREE MOSS FARM POOL Congleton
DANE (RIVER) Congleton
DANE (RIVER) Holmes Chapel
DANE (RIVER) Middlewich
DANE RIVERSIDE FISHERY Northwich
DEAN (RIVER) Wilmslow
DOODLESPOOL FARM LAKE Crewe
DOVEMERE, SANDMERE AND WOODLANDS Knutsford
DUKES POOL Crewe
EGERTON LAKE Malpas
FANSHAWE LANE POOL Macclesfield
FARM POOL Northwich
FINGERPOST POOL Knutsford
FLUSHING MEADOWS FISHERY Northwich
FOUNDERS POOL Northwich
FRIARS POOL Northwich
GODWINS POOL Congleton
GORSTY HALL Crewe
GOWY (RIVER) Chester
GREAT BUDWORTH MERE LAKE Northwich
GREY MIST MERE Warrington
GRIMESDITCH MILL POOL Warrington
GRIMSDITCH MILL POOL Warrington
HACK GREEN LAKE Nantwich
HAMPTON SPRINGS Malpas
HARTHILL Nantwich
HAYDAN FISHERY Warrington
HOLMSTON HALL FISHERY Tarporley
HUDDERSFIELD NARROW CANAL Stalybridge
JARMAN FARM POOL Macclesfield
KNIGHTS POOL Macclesfield
LAKEMORE COUNTRY PARK Crewe
LEADBEATERS RESERVOIR Macclesfield
LITTLE BUDWORTH Tarporley
LITTLE MILL Tarporley
LITTLE REEDS MERE Knutsford
LLANGOLLEN CANAL Nantwich
LLOYDS MEADOW FISHERIES Chester
LONGBARN POOL Warrington
LYMM DAM Warrington
LYMM VALE Winsford
MACCLESFIELD CANAL Congleton
MACCLESFIELD CANAL Macclesfield
MANOR POOL Knutsford
MARBURY MERE Whitchurch
MARTON HEATH COARSE POOL Macclesfield
MARY ANN POND Warrington
MEADOW VIEW FISHERY Warrington
MICKS LAKE Warrington
MIDDLEWICH BRANCH CANAL Nantwich
MILL LODGE Macclesfield
MILTON GREEN Chester
MOBBERLEY POOL Altrincham
MONKS MOAT Northwich
MOOR POOL Lymm
MOORE QUARRY Warrington
MORETON MERE FISHERY Congleton
MOSS POOLS Lymm
MOSSBANK POOL Lymm
MOULDSWORTH MERE Chester
NEW BRIDGE POOL Winsford
NEW POOL Northwich
NORBURY POOL Lymm
NORTH FIELD POOL Congleton
OAK POOL Northwich
OCEAN POOL Winsford
OLD QUAY CANAL Warrington
OLDHAMS WATER Hyde
ORFORD PARK POND Warrington
OULTON MILL POOL Tarporley
PARK POOL Macclesfield
PARTRIDGE LAKES Warrington
PEAK FOREST CANAL Dukinfield
PECK POOL Congleton
PETTY POOL Northwich
PLEX FLASH Sandbach
REASEHEATH COLLEGE LAKE Nantwich
REDESMERE Macclesfield
RODE POOL Sandbach
ROOKERY POOL Northwich
ROSSMERE Wilmslow
RUNCORN PARK LAKE Runcorn
SALE WATER PARK Sale
SAND MERE LAKE Knutsford
SANDYBANK POOL Sandbach
SANKEY ST HELENS CANAL Runcorn
SANKEY ST HELENS CANAL Widnes
SANKEY ST HELENS CANAL (LAC) Widnes
SHAKERLEY MERE Northwich
SHELLOW FARM POOLS Congleton
SHIPBROOK FLASH Northwich
SHROPSHIRE UNION CANAL Crewe
SOUTH PARK Macclesfield
SPRING POOL Northwich
SPRINGWOOD POOL Knutsford
STATHAM POOL Warrington
STOCKPOND Winsford
STRETTON WATER Warrington
SUTTON RESERVOIR Macclesfield
SWANLEY Knutsford
TABLEY MERE Knutsford
TABLEY MOAT Knutsford
TATTON MERE Knutsford
TAX MERE Sandbach
TEGGSNOSE RESERVOIR Macclesfield
TETTON FLASH Middlewich
TETTON LAKE Middlewich
THORNEYCROFT LAKES Macclesfield
TOFT POOL Knutsford
TOP FARM POOL Lymm
TOWN PARK LANE Runcorn
TRENT AND MERSEY CANAL Sandbach
TURKS HEAD RESERVOIR Macclesfield
TURNERS POOL Macclesfield
VALE ROYAL LOCKS Northwich
VILLAGE POOL Warrington
WALL POOL LODGE Macclesfield
WARDS POOLS Congleton
WEAVER (RIVER) Macclesfield
WEAVER (RIVER) Northwich
WEAVER (RIVER) Warrington
WEAVER NAVIGATION Winsford
WHIRLEY MERE Macclesfield
WHITEGATE POND Warrington
WHITLEY POOL Warrington
WILLOW POOL Northwich
WINNINGTON POOL Northwich

- **WINSFORD FLASH** Winsford
- **WINTERLEY POOL FISHERY** Crewe
- **WITTON BROOK** Northwich
- **WOOD POOL** Macclesfield
- **WOODLANDS LAKE** Knutsford
- **WOODSIDE POOL** Runcorn
- **YEW TREE POOL** Northwich

CLEVELAND

- **ASCOTT PONDS** Middlesbrough
- **CHARLTONS PONDS** Middlesbrough
- **HART RESERVOIR** Hartlepool
- **HARTBURN BRICK PIT** Stockton-on-Tees
- **HARTLEPOOL RESERVOIR** Stockton-on-Tees
- **HEMLINGTON LAKE** Middlesbrough
- **HUTTON RUDBY PONDS** Yarm
- **ISLAND WATERS** Stockton-on-Tees
- **LOCH KENNY** Hartlepool
- **LOCKE PARK** Middlesbrough
- **NEW MARSKE RESERVOIR** Redcar
- **PRIORY COTTAGE LAKE** Guisborough
- **ROSSMERE PARK LAKE** Hartlepool
- **SHOTTON COLLIERY LAKE** Hartlepool
- **TEES (RIVER)** Stockton-on-Tees
- **TILERY LAKE** Hartlepool
- **WHITEHOUSE CARAVAN PARK LAKE** Middlesbrough

CORNWALL

- **AMALWHIDDEN FARM** Penzance
- **ARGAL RESERVOIR** Penryn
- **AVALLON HOLIDAY PARK** Launceston
- **BADHAM FARM LAKE** Liskeard
- **BILLS POOL** Hayle
- **BOLINGEY LAKE** Perranporth
- **BOSCATHNOE RESERVOIR** Penzance
- **BUCHAN PARK FISHERIES** Crawley
- **BUDE CANAL** Bude
- **BUSSOW RESERVOIR** St Ives
- **CHOONE FARM** Penzance
- **CHYRAISE LODGE HOTEL** Penzance
- **COLLEGE RESERVOIR** Falmouth
- **COOMBE MILL** Bodmin
- **CRAFTHOLE LAKE** Torpoint
- **CRAYFISH FARM** Crawley
- **EAST ROSE FARM** Bodmin
- **ELECTRICITY POOL** St Austell
- **ELMFIELD FARM COARSE FISHERY** Launceston
- **EMFIELD COARSE FISHERY** Launceston
- **FERNDALE** Delabole
- **FORDA HOLIDAY LODGES** Bude
- **GLENLEIGH FARM FISHERY** St Austell
- **GOONHAVERN COARSE FISHING LAKE** Truro
- **GWINEAR POOLS COARSE FISHERY** Newquay
- **GWINNEAR POOLS** Newquay
- **GWITHIAN BROOK** Camborne
- **HAYLE CAUSEWAY** Hayle
- **HIDDEN VALLEY** Launceston
- **LAKEVIEW COUNTRY CLUB** Bodmin
- **LANGARTH POOLS** Truro
- **MEADOWSIDE COARSE FISHERY** St Columb
- **MELLONWATTS MILL** Truro
- **MIDDLE BOSWIN FARM** Helston
- **MILLBROOK COARSE FISHERY** Torpoint
- **MILLPOOL FISHERIES** Penzance
- **MILTON MOUNT LAKE** Crawley
- **MYLOR ANGLING LAKES** Falmouth
- **NANCE LAKES** St Ives
- **NEETS VALLEY PARK** Bude
- **OAKSIDE FISHERY** Newquay
- **PENVOSE FARM** Newquay
- **POLCOVERACK FARM** Helston
- **PORT ELLIOT LAKE** Saltash
- **PORTH RESERVOIR** Newquay
- **PRINCE PARK** Bodmin
- **RETALLACK WATERS** St Columb
- **ROSEWATER LAKE** Truro
- **ROWFANT HOUSE FISHERY** Crawley
- **SHARKEYS PIT** Hayle
- **SHILLAMILL LAKES COUNTRY PARK** Looe
- **ST BENETS ABBEY (RIVER)** Bude
- **ST ERTH FISHERY** Penzance
- **ST GERMANS LAKE** Saltash
- **ST LEONARDS FISHING LAKE** Launceston
- **ST TINNEY FARM HOLIDAYS** Camelford
- **STOWFORD GRANGE FISHERIES** Launceston
- **TAMAR LAKE (UPPER)** Bude
- **TIN DENE FISHERY** Penzance
- **TORY FARM LAKE** Truro
- **TREBELLAN PARK LAKES** Newquay
- **TREDIDON BARTON LAKE** Launceston
- **TRENESTRALL LAKE** Truro
- **TRETHIGGEY FARM POND** Newquay
- **TREVELLA CARAVAN AND CAMPING PARK** Newquay
- **WATERFRONT FISHING LAKE** Bude
- **WEST LOOE (RIVER)** Looe
- **WHEAL GREY** Helston
- **WHEAL RASHLEIGH PITS** St Austell
- **WHITEACRES COUNTRY PARK** Newquay
- **WOODLAY HOLIDAY LAKES** Liskeard
- **WOONSMITH LAKE** Penzance

COUNTY DURHAM

- **AYCLIFFE LAKE** Newton Aycliffe
- **BEAUMONT FISHERIES** Wingate
- **BRASSIDE POND** Durham
- **DERWENT RESERVOIR** Consett
- **DURHAM BECK** Durham
- **EDMONDSLEY POND** Chester-Le-Street
- **FIELDSONS POND** Bishop Auckland
- **FIGHTING COCKS RESERVOIR** Darlington
- **FLYLANDS POND** Bishop Auckland
- **GREENCROFT POND** Stanley
- **HALNEBY LAKE** Darlington
- **KELLOW LAW POND** Ferryhill
- **LANGSDALE LAKE** Darlington
- **MAINSFORTH POND** Ferryhill
- **MIDDLETON WATER PARK** Darlington
- **SHAFTOS LAKE** Spennymoor
- **SHOTTON POND** Peterlee
- **TEASDALE POND** Durham
- **TEES (RIVER)** Darlington
- **TRIMDON POND** Trimdon Station
- **TURNSIDE POOL** Durham
- **TURSDALE POND** Durham
- **TURSDALE POND (LANGLEY PARK)** Durham
- **WADSWORTH FISHERY** Bishop Auckland
- **WEAR (RIVER)** Durham
- **WELLFIELD POND** Peterlee
- **WEST FARM LAKE** Stockton-on-Tees

CUMBRIA

- **BANKS POND** Kendal
- **BARBON BECK** Carnforth
- **BARN LAKE** Carlisle
- **BARROW-IN-FURNESS RESERVOIR** Barrow-In-Furness
- **BIGLAND HALL LAKE** Ulverston
- **BLENHEIM LODGE HOTEL** Windermere
- **BORROWDALE FISHERIES** Keswick
- **BORWICK LAKE** Carnforth
- **BRAYTON POND** Carlisle
- **BRIGHAM (RIVER)** Cockermouth
- **BURLINGTON POND** Dalton-In-Furness
- **CALDEW (RIVER)** Carlisle
- **CARLETON HILL** Carlisle
- **CLEABARROW TARN** Windermere
- **DACRE BECK** Penrith
- **DUBBS RESERVOIR** Bowness On Windermere
- **EAST VIEW FISHERY** Carlisle
- **EDEN (RIVER)** Carlisle
- **ELLERBECK FARM AND FISHERY** Cockermouth
- **GHYLL HEAD** Bowness On Windermere
- **HALLMORE FISHERIES** Carnforth
- **HAWESWATER RESERVOIR** Ambleside
- **HOLEHIRD TARN** Windermere
- **KIRKBY THORE (RIVER)** Penrith
- **LITTLE MUSGRAVE** Kirkby Stephen
- **LONSDALE COUNTRY PARK** Carlisle
- **MOCKERKIN TARN** Cockermouth
- **MOORHOUSE TARN** Wigton
- **ORMSGILL LOWER RESERVOIR** Barrow-In-Furness
- **POAKA BECK** Barrow-In-Furness
- **RATHER HEATH TARN** Kendal
- **REDWELL FISHERIES** Carnforth
- **ROANHEAD FISHERIES** Barrow-In-Furness
- **RYDAL WATER** Ambleside
- **SKELSMERGH LAKE** Kendal
- **TALKIN TARN** Brampton
- **ULVERSTON CANAL** Ulverston
- **WITHERSLACK HALL TARN** Grange-Over-Sands

DERBYSHIRE

- **ALDAMORE POOL** Ashbourne
- **ALLESTREE LAKE** Derby
- **ALVASTON LAKE** Derby
- **ARNFIELD RESERVOIR** Glossop
- **ASHGROVE LAKE** Derby
- **BEEHIVE FARM WOODLANDS LAKES** Swadlincote
- **BELPER POND** Belper
- **BUTTERLEY RESERVOIR** Ripley
- **CATTON PARK LAKE** Swadlincote
- **CHAPEL WHEEL DAM** Chesterfield
- **CODNOR PARK RESERVOIR** Belper
- **COMBS RESERVOIR** High Peak
- **CONDOR PARK RESERVOIR** Ripley
- **COPPICE LAKE** Heanor
- **DERWENT (RIVER)** Belper
- **DERWENT (RIVER)** Derby
- **DERWENT VALLEY FISHERY** Derby
- **DOVE (RIVER)** Ashbourne
- **DUKE OF RUTLAND ESTATE** Bakewell
- **FOXTON DAM** Sheffield
- **HARLESTHORPE DAM** Chesterfield
- **HIGHAM FARM COARSE FISHING** Alfreton
- **KEGWORTH DEEP LOCK** Derby
- **LINACRE RESERVOIRS** Chesterfield
- **LOCHO PARK LAKE** Derby
- **MAPPERLEY RESERVOIR** Ilkeston
- **MARKEATON LAKE** Derby
- **MELBOURNE POOL** Derby
- **NETHERMOOR LAKE** Sheffield
- **POSSY LODGE PONDS** Belper
- **RINGWOOD LAKE** Chesterfield
- **SOAR (RIVER)** Derby
- **STAUNTON HAROLD RESERVOIR** Derby
- **SWARKESTONE GRAVEL PITS** Derby
- **TODDBROOK RESERVOIR** High Peak
- **TRENT (RIVER)** Derby
- **TRENT AND MERSEY CANAL** Derby
- **WINGERWORTH LIDO** Chesterfield

DEVON

- **ABBROOK POND** Newton Abbot
- **ANGLERS ELDORADO** Beaworthy
- **ANGLERS PARADISE** Beaworthy
- **ANGLERS SHANGRILA** Beaworthy
- **ASHCOMBE FISHERY** Dawlish
- **AVON DAM** Totnes
- **BAKERS FARM** Torrington
- **BERRYNARBOR MILL POND** Ilfracombe
- **BICKERTON FARM FISHERY** Kingsbridge
- **BILLINGSMOOR FARM** Cullompton
- **BLUE LAKE** Okehampton
- **CADOVER BRIDGE PITS** Plymouth
- **CHANNELL FISHERIES** Brixham
- **CHARLECOMBE** Torquay
- **CLAWFORD VINEYARD AND FISHERIES** Holsworthy
- **CLAYHIDON (RIVER)** Cullompton
- **CLOVELLY LAKES** Bideford
- **COFTON PARK FARM** Dawlish
- **COOMBE FARM FISHPONDS** Tiverton
- **COOMBE FISHERIES** Tavistock
- **COOMBE WATER FISHERY** Kingsbridge
- **CREEDY LAKES** Crediton
- **DARRACOTT RESERVOIR** Torrington
- **DORES POND - RACKERHAYES** Newton Abbot
- **DUNSLEY FARM** South Molton
- **EASTCOTT FARM AND LODGES** Holsworthy
- **EDDISON POND** Newton Abbot
- **EXE (RIVER)** Exeter
- **EXEMOOR FARM** Bude
- **EXETER CANAL** Exeter
- **EXETER SHIP CANAL** Exeter
- **FENECK POND** Exeter
- **FINLAKE PONDS** Newton Abbot
- **FISHPONDS HOUSE** Honiton
- **FOUR PONDS** Exeter
- **GLYNDWR FISHERY** Crediton
- **GRAND WESTERN CANAL** Cullompton
- **GRAND WESTERN CANAL** Tiverton
- **HARTLAND FOREST FISHERY GOLF CLUB** Bideford
- **HARTSMOOR FISHERIES** Cullompton
- **HOGSBROOK LAKES** Exeter
- **HOME FARM FISHERY** Exeter
- **INDIO POND** Newton Abbot
- **ISLAND POND - RACKERHAYES** Newton Abbot
- **JENNETTS RESERVOIR** Bideford
- **KINGSMEAD CENTRE** Cullompton
- **LEGGE FARM COARSE FISHERY** Beaworthy
- **LEWORTHY FARM** Bude
- **LITTLE ALLERS COARSE FISHERY** South Brent
- **LITTLE COMFORT FARM** Braunton
- **LITTLE WEACH** Bideford
- **LONGLANDS FARM** Ilfracombe
- **LOWER HALLACOMBE FISHERY** Crediton
- **LOWER SLADE RESERVOIR** Ilfracombe
- **LUCCOMBES PONDS** Exeter
- **MELBURY RESERVOIR** Bideford
- **MILEMEAD FISHERIES** Tavistock
- **MILL** South Brent
- **MILL PARK COARSE FISHING LAKE** Ilfracombe
- **MILLHAYES** Cullompton
- **MILTON FARM PONDS** Honiton
- **NEW BARN ANGLING CENTRE** Paignton
- **NEWCOURT PONDS** Cullompton
- **NEWTON ABBOT SPRING PONDS** Newton Abbot
- **OAKTREE FISHERY** South Molton
- **OLD MILL RESERVOIR** Dartmouth
- **OLDBOROUGH FISHING RETREAT** Crediton
- **PADBROOK PARK** Cullompton
- **PICFRESH** Exeter
- **POUND POND FARM** Tiverton
- **PYEWELL FARM** Bideford
- **RIVERTON HOUSE AND LAKES** Barnstaple
- **ROCOMBE PONDS** Newton Abbot
- **RUB - A - DUB POND** Newton Abbot
- **SALMONHUTCH COARSE FISHERY** Crediton
- **SAMPFORD PEVERAL PONDS** Tiverton
- **SAWMILLS LAKE** Newton Abbot
- **SHOBROOKE PARK** South Molton
- **SIMPSON VALLEY FISHERY** Holsworthy
- **SLADE RESERVOIRS** Ilfracombe
- **SLAPTON LEY NATIONAL NATURE RESERVE** Kingsbridge
- **SOUTH REED FISHERIES CARP LAKE** Okehampton
- **SOUTH VIEW FARM FISHERY** Exeter
- **SOUTH WEST WATER FISHERY** Bideford
- **SPIRES LAKES** Okehampton
- **SQUABMOOR RESERVOIR** Exeter
- **STAR BARTON PONDS** Exeter
- **STEVENSTONE LAKES** Torrington
- **STONE FARM QUARRY** Okehampton
- **STOUR FARM FISHERY** Cullompton
- **SUMMERLEAZE POND** Axminster
- **SUNRIDGE FISHERY** Plymouth
- **SWIMBRIDGE POOL** Barnstaple
- **TOWN PARKS COARSE FISHERY** Paignton
- **TRAGO MILLS** Newton Abbot
- **TRENCHFORD RESERVOIR** Exeter
- **UPHAM FARM PONDS** Exeter
- **UPTON WARREN LAKE** Cullompton
- **VALLEY VIEW FISHERY** Crediton
- **VENN POOL** Barnstaple
- **WAPPERWELL POND** Newton Abbot
- **WEST PITT FARM FISHERY** Tiverton
- **WEST VIEW POND** Exeter
- **WILLOWFIELD LAKE COTTAGES** Braunton
- **WOODACOTT ARMS** Holsworthy
- **WOODY PARK FISHERY** Cullompton

DORSET

- **AVON TYRRELL LAKES** Christchurch
- **BERKELEY FARM** Sherborne
- **BLASHFORD LAKES** Christchurch
- **CLUB LAKE** Dorchester
- **CRANBOURNE FRUIT FARM** Wimborne
- **CROW POOL** Christchurch
- **CULVERS FARM FISHERIES** Gillingham
- **DORSET FROME** Wareham
- **FROME (RIVER)** Wareham
- **GOLD OAK FISH FARM** Wimborne
- **HAMPSHIRE AVON (RIVER)** Christchurch
- **HAMWORTHY LAKE** Poole
- **HARROW POND** Christchurch
- **HILLVIEW FARM LAKE** Wimborne
- **HOLT WOOD PONDS** Wimborne
- **HYDE LAKE** Wareham
- **KINGCOMBE COARSE FARM** Dorchester
- **KINGCOMBE LAKE** Dorchester
- **KNAPP HILL FARM LAKES** Buckland Newton
- **LIFELANDS FISHERY** Christchurch
- **LUCKFIELD LAKE FISHERY** Dorchester
- **LYONS GATE CARAVAN PARK** Dorchester
- **MAPPOWDER COURT** Sturminster Newton
- **MARTINS FARM** Wimborne
- **MUDEFORD WOOD LAKE** Christchurch
- **NEW MEADOWS LAKE** Christchurch
- **OSMINGTON MILLS** Weymouth
- **PIDDLE (RIVER)** Wareham
- **RADIPOLE LAKE** Weymouth
- **REVELS FISHERY** Dorchester
- **SHERBORNE LAKE** Sherborne
- **SOPLEY FARM** Christchurch
- **STOUR (DORSET) (RIVER)** Blandford Forum
- **STOUR (DORSET) (RIVER)** Bournemouth
- **STOUR (DORSET) (RIVER)** Christchurch
- **STOUR (DORSET) (RIVER)** Ferndown
- **STOUR (DORSET) (RIVER)** Poole
- **STOUR (DORSET) (RIVER)** Sturminster Newton
- **STOUR (DORSET) (RIVER)** Wimborne
- **STOUR (RIVER)** Blandford Forum
- **STOUR (RIVER)** Bournemouth
- **STOUR (RIVER)** Sturminster Newton
- **STOUR (RIVER)** Wimborne
- **THAMES (RIVER)** Dorchester
- **TODBER MANOR** Sturminster Newton
- **UPPER STOUR (RIVER)** Gillingham
- **WALLYS LAKE** Weymouth
- **WARMWELL HOLIDAY PARK** Dorchester
- **WESSEX FLY FISHING TROUT LAKES** Dorchester
- **WESSEX WATER RESERVOIRS** Poole
- **WHIRLWIND LAKE** Christchurch
- **WHITEMOOR LAKE** Wimborne
- **WOOD FARM CARAVAN PARK** Bridport

ESSEX

- **ALBYNS LAKE** Hornchurch
- **ARDLEIGH RESERVOIR** Colchester
- **ARENA LAKE** Grays
- **ARMIGERS FARM** Dunmow
- **ASHELDHAM FISHERY** Southminster
- **AVELEY LAKES** Romford
- **BARLEYLANDS RESERVOIR** Billericay
- **BEDFORDS PARK LAKE** Romford
- **BERWICK PONDS** Rainham
- **BIRDS GREEN** Ongar
- **BLACKMORE WOOD** Ingatestone
- **BLACKWATER (RIVER)** Braintree
- **BLACKWATER (RIVER)** Chelmsford
- **BLACKWATER (RIVER)** Colchester
- **BLACKWATER (RIVER)** Maldon
- **BLACKWATER (RIVER)** Witham
- **BLASFORD HILL FISHERIES** Chelmsford
- **BOG GROVE** Maldon
- **BORDEAUX PIT** Saffron Walden
- **BOREHAM FISHERY** Chelmsford
- **BOREHAM MERES** Chelmsford
- **BOVINGTON MERE 1** Chelmsford
- **BOVINGTON MERE 2** Chelmsford
- **BRAXTED HALL ESTATE** Witham
- **BROAD GREEN AND TUFNELL MERE** Chelmsford
- **BROOKHALL FISHERY** Colchester
- **BULPHAN PARK FISHERIES** Upminster
- **BURROWS FARM** Basildon
- **CANTS MERE** Witham
- **CENTRAL PARK LAKE** Chelmsford
- **CHASE FISHERY** Dagenham
- **CHELMER (RIVER)** Chelmsford
- **CHELMER AND BLACKWATER NAVIGATION CANAL** Chelmsford
- **CHELMER AND BLACKWATER NAVIGATION CANAL** Maldon
- **CHIGBOROUGH** Maldon
- **CHURCH LAKE** Brentwood

CHURCHWOOD FISHERIES Brentwood
CLAVERHAMBURY LAKE Waltham Abbey
COBBLERS MEAD LAKE Standford-Le-Hope
COLNE (RIVER) Colchester
CONNAUGHT WATER Loughton
CROW GREEN FISHERY Brentwood
CROWN NETHERHALL Waltham Abbey
DANBURY COUNTRY PARK Chelmsford
DEDHAM MILL Colchester
DODDS FARM Ingatestone
DOGGETTS FARM FISHERY Rochford
DONYLANDS LAKES Colchester
ESSEX CARP FISHERY South Ockendon
EWSONS WATER Chelmsford
FAIRLOP EAST LAKE Romford
FAIRLOP WATERS Ilford
FENNES FISHERIES Braintree
FISHERS GREEN Waltham Abbey
GARNISH HALL Garnon
GLOUCESTER PARK LAKE Basildon
GOSFIELD LAKE RESORT Halstead
GRANGE WATER Grays
GREAT MYLES LAKE Ongar
HAINAULT FOREST COUNTRY PARK Chigwell
HARWOOD HALL LAKE Upminster
HOCKLEY LAKES Rayleigh
HOLYFIELD FISHERY Waltham Abbey
HOME FARM FISHERY Saffron Walden
HOOKS MARSH Waltham Abbey
HOUCHINS RESERVOIRS Colchester
JACKLETTS FARM Chelmsford
JIMMYS LAKE Standford-Le-Hope
JOHNS LAKE FISHERIES Waltham Abbey
KENNEL LANE Billericay
KNIGHTS PIT Waltham Abbey
LAKE MEADOWS Billericay
LAUNDRY LAKE Dunmow
LAYER PIT Colchester
LEA (RIVER) Waltham Abbey
LEE FLOOD RELIEF CHANNEL Waltham Abbey
LITTLE BRAXTED FARM ESTATE Witham
LITTLE EASTON FISHERIES Dunmow
LITTLE EASTON MANOR Dunmow
MAGIC LAKE Waltham Abbey
MANNINGTREE RIVER POOLS Colchester
MARCONIS PIT Chelmsford
MAYBRAND FISHERY Romford
MAYSBROOK LAKES Barking
MILL BARN FISHERY Southend-on-Sea
MILLENNIUM LAKES Ingatestone
MOATHOUSE LAKE Basildon
NAZEING MEADS Waltham Abbey
NEWLAND HALL CARP FISHERY Chelmsford
NORTHLANDS PARK Basildon
NUPERS FARM Romford
OLIVERS LAKE Colchester
PANT (RIVER) Braintree
PAR West Horndon
PARSONAGE FARM Chelmsford
PEA LANE FISHERY Upminster
PICKS COTTAGE CARP LAKES Waltham Abbey
PIPPS HILL FISHERIES Basildon
PRESTONS LAKE Colchester
PRIORY PARK LAKES Southend-on-Sea
RAPHAELS PARK Romford
RAYNE LODGE FARM Braintree
RECTORY FARM POND Braintree
ROCHFORD RESERVOIR Rochford
ROCKELLS FARM Saffron Walden
RODING (RIVER) Ongar
RODING (RIVER) Romford
RODING VALLEY LAKE Chigwell
SHALFORD RESERVOIRS Braintree
SHOEBURY PARK Southend-on-Sea
SILVER END PIT Witham
SLOUGH HOUSE LAKE Upminster
SOUTHMINSTER FISHERIES Southminster
SPARROWS POND Halstead
STAMBRIDGE STARR FISHERIES Rochford
STANFORD-LE-HOPE Standford-Le-Hope
STAR LANE Southend-on-Sea
STOUR (RIVER) Colchester
STOUR (SUFFOLK) (RIVER) Colchester
STRAITS MILL Braintree
THORNDON PARK LAKE Brentwood
TUFNELL MERE Chelmsford
VALENCE MOAT Dagenham
WAKE VALLEY POND Loughton
WANSTEAD AND WOODFORD PONDS Ilford
WARREN Standford-Le-Hope
WEALD COUNTRY PARK Brentwood
WEELEY BRIDGE HOLIDAY PARK Clacton-on-Sea
WHARF POOL Standford-Le-Hope
WICK MERE Maldon
WID (RIVER) Ingatestone
WILLOWS Witham
WILLOWS LAKE Chelmsford

FIFE

EMBER (RIVER) East Molesey
WEY (RIVER) Addlestone

GLOUCESTERSHIRE

ADLESTROP LAKE Stow On The Wold
APPERLEY POOLS Tewkesbury
ASHTON KEYNES POOL Cirencester
AVON (RIVER) Cheltenham
BOURTON ON THE WATER GRAVEL PIT NO1 Cheltenham
BRADLEYS PIT Cirencester
BREDONS HARDWICK Tewkesbury
BURLEY FIELDS LAKE Cheltenham
CANNOP PONDS Forest Of Dean
CLAYDON PARK FISHERY Fairford
COKES PIT Cirencester
COTSWOLD HOBURNE Cirencester
COTSWOLD WATER PARK Cirencester
FARMHOUSE LAKE (THE) Cirencester
GARDNERS POOL Gloucester
GLOUCESTER AND SHARPNESS CANAL Gloucester
GLOUCESTER CANAL Gloucester
HAM POOL Cirencester
HIGHNAM COURT LAKE Gloucester
HILL VIEW LAKES Tewkesbury
HILLVIEW FISHERY Tewkesbury
HORSESHOE LAKE Lechlade
ISIS NO 1 LAKE 19 Cirencester
KEYNES COUNTRY PARK Cirencester
KEYNES PARK TOP LAKE Cirencester
LAKE NUMBER ONE (LAKE19) Cirencester
LEMINGTON LAKES Moreton-In-Marsh
LIGHTMOOR POOL Cinderford
LYDNEY BOATING LAKE Lydney
MARIONS POOL Coleford
MEADOW POND Gloucester
MEADOWCLIFFE POOL Gloucester
MILL AVON Tewkesbury
MILL LAKE (NO 44) Cirencester
MORETON PITS Cheltenham
MYTHE POOL Tewkesbury
NEIGH BRIDGE LAKE Cirencester
NETHERWOOD LAKE Cirencester
PLUMP HILL POOL Mitcheldean
RED LION FISHERY Gloucester
SEVERN (RIVER) Gloucester
SEVERN (RIVER) Tewkesbury
SEVERN ON THE HAM Tewkesbury
SPEECH HOUSE LAKE Coleford
STANBOROUGH POOL Cheltenham
STAUNTON COURT LAKES Gloucester
STEAM MILLS LAKE Cinderford
STONE END FARM LAKES Gloucester
STROUDWATER CANAL Stonehouse
THAMES (RIVER) Cirencester
THAMES (RIVER) Lechlade
WATERLEY BROOK Berkeley
WATERLOO SCREENS Gloucester
WATERSMEET LAKES Gloucester
WHELFORD POOLS COARSE FISHERY Fairford
WICK WATER Cirencester

HAMPSHIRE

ANTON LAKE Andover
AWBRIDGE DANES LAKE Romsey
BAFFINS POND Portsmouth
BARONS PONDS (NEW SITE) Liss
BASINGSTOKE CANAL Basingstoke
BASINGSTOKE CANAL Hook
BEECHES BROOK FISHERY Ringwood
BICKERLEY MILLSTREAM Ringwood
BILCOMBES POND Southampton
BROADLANDS LAKES Ringwood
BROADLANDS MAIN LAKE Romsey
BROCKHURST MOAT Portsmouth
BROWNWICH POND Portsmouth
CARRON ROW FARM PONDS Fareham
CHARLTON PITS Andover
COOKS POND Liphook
CROOKED WILLOWS Ringwood
CUTT MILL Farnborough
DARK LANE PONDS Southampton
EAST MOORS LAKE Ringwood
FIRGROVE LAKES Yateley
FOREST LODGE HOME FARM Southampton
FOXCOTTE LAKE Andover
FRENSHAM GREAT AND LITTLE PONDS Aldershot
FUNTLEY POND Fareham
GOLD VALLEY LAKES Aldershot
GOLDEN POND FISHERY Andover
GREENRIDGE FARM LAKES Romsey
HALF PIT Ringwood
HAMPSHIRE AVON Ringwood
HAMPSHIRE AVON (RIVER) Fordingbridge
HAMPSHIRE AVON (RIVER) Ringwood
HATCHET POND Brockenhurst
HAWLEY LAKE Camberley
HIGHTOWN LAKE Ringwood
HILSEA MOATS Portsmouth
HMS DRYAD LAKE Portsmouth
HOLBURY MANOR POND Southampton
HOLLYBUSH LANE LAKES Farnborough
HORDLE LAKES New Milton
HUCKLESBROOK LAKE Fordingbridge
HURST POND Ringwood
IBSLEY POOLS Ringwood
ITCHEN NAVIGATION Southampton
JANESMOOR POND Lyndhurst
KINGFISHER LAKE (A) Southampton
LAKE FARM Fordingbridge

LAKESIDE Aldershot
LAKESIDE Southampton
LAKESIDE COUNTRY PARK Eastleigh
LAPSLEYS FISHERY Fordingbridge
LEOMINSTEAD MILL POND Lyndhurst
LONGBRIDGE LAKES Romsey
LYNDHURST LAKE Lyndhurst
MBK LEISURE BARRONS POND Liss
MILL POND LAKE Lyndhurst
MOORS VALLEY COUNTRY PARK Ringwood
MOPLEY POND Southampton
NEW FOREST WATER PARK Fordingbridge
NORTHFIELD LAKES Ringwood
NUTRABAITS YATELEY COMPLEX Yateley
NUTRABAITS YATELEY SOUTH LAKE Yateley
ORCHARD LAKES New Milton
PERIL LAKE Andover
PETERSFIELD HEATH LAKE Petersfield
QUEENS ROAD POND Lee-on-The-Solent
ROCKFORD LAKE Ringwood
ROTHERWICK AND NIGHTINGALE LAKES Hook
SOMERLEY LAKES Ringwood
SPRINGLAKES Aldershot
STAUNTON COUNTRY PARK Havant
STEPSTONES LAKES Petersfield
STONEHAM LAKES Southampton
SWAY LAKES Lymington
TITCHFIELD ABBEY GOLF AND COARSE FISHING LAKES Fareham
TOPACRE LAKE Winchester
TURF CROFT FARM Ringwood
WAINSFORD RESERVOIR Lymington
WASH PIT Ringwood
WEDGEHILL PONDS Ringwood
WHINWHISTLE COARSE FISHERY Romsey
WILLOW PARK Aldershot

HEREFORDSHIRE

ASHPERTON MOAT Hereford
BETULA WATERS Ledbury
BIDDLESTONE LAKE Ross-on-Wye
BULLEY LANE FISHERY Ross-on-Wye
CASTLEMORTON Ledbury
CHURCH POOL Hereford
COURT FARM Hereford
DRUMMOND DUB Ross-on-Wye
EASTNOR CASTLE Ledbury
EVESBATCH TOP LAKE Ledbury
GOLDEN VALLEY Ledbury
HERRIOTS POOL Hereford
HUNDRED POOL Hereford
LILY AND WILLOW POOLS Ledbury
LUGG (RIVER) Hereford
MARSH HOUSE FARM Hereford
MILLPOND Hereford
MOCCAS FISHERY Hereford
MONTE BISHOP Hereford
MUNDERFIELD HAROLD Bromyard
PIXLEY POOL Ledbury
PRIDEWOOD LAKE Ledbury
RED BANK POOLS Ledbury
REDMIRE POOL Ross-on-Wye
ROTHERWAS LONG POOL Hereford
ROYAL OAK POOL Hereford
RUSSELLS END RESERVOIR Ledbury
WYE (RIVER) Hereford
WYE (RIVER) Ross-on-Wye

HERTFORDSHIRE

ADMIRALS WALK LAKE Hoddesdon
ALDENHAM RESERVOIR Borehamwood
AMWELL LAKES Ware
AYLESBURY ARM CANAL Aylesbury
AYLESBURY ARM CANAL Tring
BATCHWORTH LAKE Rickmansworth
BIERTON FISHING LAKES Aylesbury
BLUE LAGOON Arlesey
BOWMANS LAKES St Albans
BOWYERS WATER Waltham Cross
BROAD COLNEY LAKES St Albans
BROOKFIELD LAKE Waltham Cross
BROXBOURNE Hoddesdon
CARTHAGENA FISHERY Broxbourne
CHESHUNT SOUTH RESERVOIR Waltham Cross
COLNE (RIVER) Rickmansworth
COLNEY HEATH LAKE St Albans
DOBBS WEIR FISHERY Hoddesdon
DURRANTS LAKE Hitchin
FAIRLANDS VALLEY PARK Stevenage
FEILDES WEIR Hoddesdon
GADE (RIVER) Watford
GAYWOODS Kings Langley
GRAND UNION CANAL Berkhamsted
GRAND UNION CANAL St Albans
GRAND UNION CANAL Tring
GRAND UNION CANAL Watford
HATFIELD BROADWATER Hatfield
HATFIELD FOREST LAKE Bishops Stortford
HOLWELL HYDE LAKE Welwyn Garden City
HOOK LAKE Potters Bar
INNS LAKE Rickmansworth
KINGS WEIR FISHERY Broxbourne
LEA (RIVER) Hoddesdon
LEA (RIVER) Welwyn Garden City
LEA (RIVER) Wormley
LEA NAVIGATION Broxbourne
LEE NAVIGATION Bishops Stortford
LEE NAVIGATION Broxbourne
LEE NAVIGATION Hertford
LEE NAVIGATION Waltham Cross
LEE NAVIGATION Ware
LOWBELL LANE St Albans
MARSWORTH RESERVOIR Tring
MERCHANT TAYLORS SCL LAKES Kings Langley
NORTH MET PIT Waltham Cross
OAKFIELD FISHERY Aylesbury
OLD MILL AND MEADOWS Broxbourne
OLDFIELD Arlesey
PAYNES LANE PIT Waltham Cross
PIXIES MERE Hemel Hempstead
RISLIP LAKE Tring
RYEMEADS Royston
SHEPHERDS WAY Hatfield
SLIPE LANE PITS Broxbourne
STANBOROUGH LAKE Welwyn Garden City
STANSTEAD ABBOTTS Ware
STARTOPS RESERVOIR Tring
THAME (RIVER) Tring
TRING RESERVOIRS Tring
WESTBROOK MERE Hemel Hempstead
WESTONS LAKE Stevenage
WILSTONE RESERVOIR Tring
WOODLAND FARM Aylesbury
WORMLEBURY Broxbourne

HUMBERSIDE

AIRE (RIVER) Goole
AIRE AND CALDER CANAL Goole
BEVERLEY AND BARMSTON DRAIN Driffield
BEVERLEY BECK Hull
BEVERLEY CANAL Beverley
BIG HOLE PIT Goole
BLUE LAGOON Hull
BRANDES BURTON 3 AND 4 Hull
BRANDESBURTON Driffield
BRICKYARD POND Brough
BROOMFLEET PONDS Brough
BURSHILL A POND Driffield
BURSTWICK SKI LAKE Hull
BURTON CONSTABLE COUNTRY PARK Hull
CLEETHORPES COUNTRY PARK Cleethorpes
DACRE LAKESIDE PARK Driffield
DERWENT (RIVER) Goole
DERWENT (RIVER) Hull
EAST PARK LAKE Hull
EMMOTLAND PONDS Driffield
FAR GRANGE CARAVAN AND COUNTRY PARK Driffield
FARM PONDS Driffield
FISHPONDS FARM AND FISHERY Bridlington
FOSSEHILL LAKES Beverley
GOWDALL LAKES Goole
HALSHAM POND Hull
HOLME LAKE FISHERY Scunthorpe
HULL (RIVER) Beverley
HUMBERSIDE FISHERIES Driffield
LAKEMINSTER PARK Beverley
LAMBWATH LAKES Hull
LEVEN CANAL Beverley
LEVEN CANAL Hull
LEVEN PARK LAKE Beverley
LOUGH NAVIGATION Grimsby
MARKET WEIGHTON CANAL Goole
MOTORWAY POND Brough
NEST Scunthorpe
NODDLE HILL LAKE Hull
OAKLANDS WATER Goole
OUSE (RIVER) Goole
REDFERNS POND Brough
RUSH LYVARS LAKE Hull
SYKEHOUSE RESERVOIRS Goole
THORPE HALL Driffield
TILARY LAKE Hull
URE (RIVER) Hull
WATER SPRING FISHERY Scunthorpe
WILLITOFT FISH FARM Goole
WILLOW SPRINGS Scunthorpe
WOODALLS POND Brough

ISLE OF WIGHT

BRADING LAKE Sandown
GILLEES POND Newport
GUNVILLE LAKE Newport
MERSTONE FISHERIES Newport
MORTON FARM Sandown
NETTLECOMBE FARMS Ventnor
ROOKLEY COUNTRY PARK Ventnor
SOMERTON RESERVOIR Newport
WHITWELL PONDS Ventnor
YAR (A) (RIVER) Sandown
YAR (RIVER) Sandown

KENT

ABBEYCOURT LAKE Maidstone
ABBOTTS COURT Rochester
ALDERS LAKES Larkfield
ALLHALLOWS LEISURE PARK Rochester
BALLAST PIT Tonbridge
BARDEN LAKE Tonbridge
BIDDENDEN LAKE Tenterden
BIRCHDEN FARM FISHERY Tunbridge Wells
BLUE LAGOON LAKE Canterbury
BLUEBELL FISHING PONDS Maidstone
BROCKHILL COUNTRY PARK Hythe
BROOKLANDS LAKE Dartford
BROOMBANKS PITS Sittingbourne
BURNHAM RESERVOIR Maidstone
BYSINGWOOD Faversham
BYWATER LAKE Canterbury
CACKLE HILL LAKES Ashford
CALIBER COARSE AND CARP LAKES Canterbury

CAPSTONE FARM COUNTRY PARK Gillingham
CHIDDINGSTONE CASTLE LAKE Edenbridge
CHILHAM LAKE Canterbury
CHIPSTEAD LAKES Sevenoaks
CONNINGBROOK Ashford
COTTON FARM FISHERY Dartford
CRAYFORD (RIVER) Dartford
DANSON PARK LAKE Bexleyheath
DARENT (RIVER) Dartford
DARENTH FISHING COMPLEX Dartford
DUNDALE LAKE Tunbridge Wells
DUNGENESS LONG PIT Romney Marsh
EAST FARLEIGH Maidstone
EASTERN ROTHER (RIVER) Cranbrook
EDEN (RIVER) Edenbridge
EDEN (RIVER) Tonbridge
EUREKA Ashford
FORDCOMBE Tunbridge Wells
FORDWICH LAKE Canterbury
FRANT LAKES Tunbridge Wells
GEDGES LAKES Maidstone
GRANGE POOL Tonbridge
HANDLE LAKE Canterbury
HARTLEY LANDS FARM Cranbrook
HAYSDEN COUNTRY PARK Tonbridge
HERONSVIEW FISHERIES Canterbury
HEXDEN CHANNEL Tenterden
HOO LAKES Rochester
HOOKSTEAD LAKE Ashford
HORTON KIRBY Dartford
LARKFIELD LAKES Maidstone
LAVENDER FARM Faversham
LITTLE CANSIRON FISHING LAKES Edenbridge
LONGFIELD LAKE Tonbridge
LONGFORD LAKE Sevenoaks
LONGSHAW FARM FISHING LAKES Canterbury
MATCH LAKE Chilham
MEDWAY (RIVER) East Peckham
MEDWAY (RIVER) Maidstone
MEDWAY (RIVER) Tonbridge
MEDWAY (RIVER) Tunbridge Wells
MILL POOL Faversham
MILTON PAN LAKE Canterbury
MONK LAKE FISHERIES Tonbridge
MOTE PARK FISHERY Maidstone
NACCOLT LAKE Ashford
NOOK & CRANNY LAKE Canterbury
PIPPINS FARM LAKE Tonbridge
PITTLANDS LAKES Tonbridge
REED LAKE Canterbury
RIVERFIELD CARP FARM Maidstone
ROOKERY LAKE Bromley
ROTHER (RIVER) Tenterden
ROUKES DRIFT FARM Deal
ROYAL MILITARY CANAL Kennardington
ROYAL MILITARY CANAL Romney Marsh
RUXLEY PITS Orpington
SCARLETTS LAKE Edenbridge
SCHOOL POOL Faversham
SHORNE COUNTRY PARK LAKES Gravesend
SILVER SPRINGS FISHERY Tonbridge
SINGLETON LAKE Ashford
SITTINGBOURNE LAKES Sittingbourne
SPERRINGBROOK SEWER Romney Marsh
ST CLERE LAKE Wrotham
STONAR LAKE Sandwich
STOUR (RIVER) Canterbury
STOUR LAKE Canterbury
SUNDRIDGE LAKES Sevenoaks
SURRENDEN LAKES Ashford
SUTTON AT HONE LAKE TWO Dartford
SUTTON AT HONE LAKES ONE AND THREE Dartford
SWAN LAKE Canterbury
TONFORD LAKE Canterbury
TRIANGLE LAKE Canterbury
WIDEHURST FARM Tonbridge
WINGHAM FISHERY Ashford
WOOD POOL Faversham

LANCASHIRE

ABBEY LAKES Skelmersdale
ASHTON CANAL Wigan
BALL GROVE LAKE Colne
BANNISTER HALL FARM Preston
BARRETTS FARM FISHERY Ormskirk
BARROWFORD RESERVOIR Nelson
BICKERSHAW WATERS Wigan
BIRKACRE LODGES Chorley
BOLTON CANAL Bolton
BRADFORD RESERVOIR Bolton
BRADSHAW HALL FISHERIES Bolton
BRIARCROFT FISHERY Preston
BRINSCALL LODGE Chorley
BRYAN HEY RESERVOIR Bolton
BRYN FLASH Wigan
BURSCOUGH BRICKWORKS LAKE Ormskirk
CHARITY FARM FISHERY Chorley
CHURCH GARDEN Bolton
CHURN CLOUGH RESERVOIR Preston
CLAYLANDS CARAVAN SITE Preston
CLEVELEY BRIDGE FISHERY Preston
CLIVIGER FISH PONDS Burnley
CLOWBRIDGE RESERVOIR Bolton
COPTHORNE COARSE FISHERIES Preston
COTTAGE GREEN GARDEN CENTRE Chorley
CROFT FISHERIES Chorley
CROMPTON LODGE Bolton
CUERDEN VALLEY LAKE Preston
DEEP PIT Wigan
DERWENT (RIVER) Preston
DICKENS STREET LODGE Blackburn
DINGLE RESERVOIR Bolton
DIXON GREEN RESERVOIR Bolton
DOFFCOCKER LODGE Bolton
DOUGLAS (RIVER) Wigan
DUNSCAR SHORE LODGE Bolton
EAGLEY WATERS Bolton
EDISFORD AND BRUNGERLEY PARK Clitheroe
FAN LODGE Wigan
FARINGTON LODGES Preston
FIR TREE LODGE Wigan
FIRWOOD LODGE AND THE BUNK Bolton
FISHMOOR RESERVOIR Rossendale
FORSTERS LODGES Wigan
FOULRIDGE RESERVOIR Colne
FOUNDRY LODGE Chorley
GREAT BIRCH WOOD PONDS Preston
GREEN LANE PONDS Ormskirk
GREENHALGH LODGE FISHERY Preston
HAGGS RESERVOIR Accrington
HEAPEY NO 1 Chorley
HEAPEY NO 2 Chorley
HEAPEY NO 3 Chorley
HEAPEY NO 6 Chorley
HESKIN OLD FARM FISHERY Chorley
HIGHER HALL FLASH Wigan
HODDLESDEN RESERVOIR Darwen
HOLDEN WOOD RESERVOIR Rossendale
HORROCKS FLASH Wigan
HOUGHTONS LODGE Wigan
HUDSONS FARM Preston
HULTON PARK LAKE Bolton
INCE MOSS FISHERIES Wigan
INCE PARK LAKE Wigan
IRWELL (RIVER) Preston
ISLAND DAM Wigan
JUMBLES RESERVOIR Bolton
KEARNS ALLEN LODGES Accrington
KNIGHT BOTTOMS LAKE Preston
LANCASTER CANAL Lancaster
LANCASTER CANAL Preston
LANCASTER HOUSE Chorley
LANCASTER HOUSE FARM FISHERY Rossendale
LATHOM FISHERIES Burscough
LEEDS TO LIVERPOOL CANAL Burnley
LEEDS TO LIVERPOOL CANAL Chorley
LEEDS TO LIVERPOOL CANAL Ormskirk
LEEDS TO LIVERPOOL CANAL Preston
LEISURE LAKES Preston
LITTLE DALE HALL COARSE FISHERY Morecambe
LONGTON BRICKCROFT Preston
LOWER HOUSE LODGE Burnley
LOWER RIVINGTON RESERVOIR Chorley
LOWER RODDLESWORTH RESERVOIR Chorley
LYNDHURST FARM LAKE Preston
MANCHESTER, BOLTON AND BURY CANAL Bolton
MANOR HOUSE FISHERY Preston
MARTIN HALL FARM Preston
MELCHES POND Bolton
MELLINGS NO 1 Wigan
ORRELL WATER PARK Wigan
PARSONAGE RESERVOIR Accrington
PINE LODGE FISHERIES Clitheroe
PLATTS LANE LAKE Ormskirk
POLLYS FLASH Wigan
PORTSMOUTH RESERVIOR Burnley
QUEENS PARK LAKE Heywood
RED ROCKS FISHERY Preston
RIBBLE (RIVER) Preston
RISHTON RESERVOIR Blackburn
ROACH BRIDGE FISHERY Preston
ROWLEY PARK LAKE Burnley
RUFFORD CANAL Ormskirk
RUMWORTH LODGE RESERVOIR Bolton
SCOT LANE PONDS Wigan
SHRUGGS WOOD FISHERY Preston
SQUARE LODGE Wigan
ST MICHAELS WYRESIDE FISHERY Preston
STANLEY PARK LAKE Thornton-Cleveleys
STANWORTH RESERVOIR Blackburn
STARMOUNT LODGES Bolton
SWANTLEY LAKE Morecambe
TEMPLE SPRINGS Bolton
THREE SISTERS Wigan
THURSLAND HILL FARM Lancaster
TOAD HALL FARM Preston
TURBARY HOUSE NURSARY Preston
UPPER RIVINGTON RESERVOIR Bolton
WAYOH RESERVOIR Blackburn
WHITEMOOR RESERVOIR Nelson
WIDOWS FLASH Wigan
WITHNELL RESERVOIRS Chorley
WOODFOLD FARM FISHERIES Preston
WORTHINGTON NO 1 Chorley
WORTHINGTON NO 2 Chorley
WORTHINGTON NO 3 Chorley
WRYE (RIVER) Preston
WYRE (RIVER) Fleetwood

LEICESTERSHIRE

BAXTERS GARDEN FARM LAKE Hinckley

BROOK MEADOW FISHERY Market Harborough
BROOKSBY COLLEGE Melton Mowbray
BROOME FISHERIES Leicester
C J FISHERIES Lutterworth
CHARNWOOD WATER Leicester
FOLLY POND Market Harborough
FRISBY LAKES Leicester
GROBY FISHING LAKES Leicester
HALL FARM Lutterworth
HALL FARM FISHING Melton Mowbray
HOLLY FARM FISHERY Lutterworth
HOLWELL WORKS RESERVOIR Melton Mowbray
LAKESIDE FISHING Hinckley
LAUNDE ABBEY LAKES Leicester
LEICESTER CANAL Leicester
LEICESTER GRAND UNION CANAL Leicester
LOUGHBOROUGH SOAR CANAL Loughborough
LYNCHGATE LANE FISHERY Hinckley
MALLORY PARK FISHERIES Leicester
MANOR FARM Lutterworth
MANOR FARM POOLS Hinckley
MILL FARM FISHERY Lutterworth
NANPANTAN RESERVOIR Leicester
PARKLANDS FISHERY Hinckley
PEATLING POOLS (1-6) Lutterworth
SHELL FRESH LAKE Hinckley
SNIBSON COLLIERY CARP LAKE Coalville
SOAR (RIVER) Leicester
SOAR (RIVER) Loughborough
SPRING GRANGE FISHERY Leicester
SWITHLAND RESERVOIR Swithland
WATERMEAD PARK LAKES Leicester
WATERY GATE FISHERY Leicester
WELLAND LODGE FISHERY Market Harborough
WHETSTONE GORSE Willoughby Waterlease
WILLOWS FARM FISHING Leicester
WREAKE (RIVER) Melton Mowbray

LINCOLNSHIRE

ABY POND Alford
ALVINGHAM FISHERIES Louth
ASHBY PARK FISHERIES Horncastle
BASTON FEN FISHERY Bourne
BELLEAU BRIDGE FARM LAKE Louth
BELLS YARD LAKE Horncastle
BELVOIR CASTLE Grantham
BOULTHAM PARK LAKE Lincoln
BRICKYARD FISHERY Louth
BRICKYARD POND Grantham
BURGHLEY PARK LAKE Stamford
CHARLES STREET POND Louth
CULVERTHORPE LAKES Grantham
DAIWA GULL POOL Gainsborough
DENNIS RAINWATER LAKE Skegness
DENTON RESERVOIR Grantham
DYKES COTTAGE LAKES Lincoln
EAST HALTON FISHING LAKES Immingham
FISH POND FARM Market Rasen
GOLTHO LAKE Market Rasen
GRIMSTHORPE LAKE Bourne
GROOBYS PIT Skegness
HARTSHOLME PARK LAKE Lincoln
HATTON TROUT LAKE Market Rasen
HAVERHOLME PARK Sleaford
HERONS MEAD Skegness
HILL VIEW LAKES Skegness
HOBHOLE DRAIN Boston
HOMESTEAD LAKE Immingham
HYKEHAM PIT Lincoln
KEAL COATES FISHERY Spilsby
KINPTON RESERVOIR Grantham
LAKE HELEN Boston
LAKE ROSS FISHERY Spalding
LAKESIDE Lincoln
LINDEN WALK POND Louth
LOBBY FIELD PONDS Market Rasen
MARRIS LAKES Lincoln
MILL HILL LAKES Skegness
MILL ROAD LAKES Skegness
MOON LAKE Tattershall
NORTH KELSEY PARK Market Rasen
OAKHILL LEISURE Lincoln
OASIS LAKES Louth
OHAM LAKES Alford
PEACOCK LAKE Woodhall Spa
REVESBY RESERVOIR Horncastle
RICHMOND LAKES Lincoln
ROACH FARM PARK Skegness
ROD AND LINE CARAVAN PARK Skegness
ROSSWAYS WATER Boston
SHANDY KEV FISHERIES Lincoln
SKEGNESS WATER LEISURE PARK Skegness
SOUTH HOLLAND DRAIN Spalding
STARMERS PIT Lincoln
STEEPING (RIVER) Skegness
STICKNEY BRICKPONDS Boston
STONE END LAKE Louth
SUDBROOK POND Lincoln
SWAN LAKE Skegness
SYCAMORE FISHING LAKES Skegness
TALLINGTON FISHERY Stamford
TATTERSHALL LEISURE PARK Lincoln
TILL (RIVER) Lincoln
TIM HALL LAKE Lincoln
TRENT (RIVER) Lincoln
UPPER WITHAM (RIVER) Lincoln
VICKERS POND Louth
WARPING DRAIN Gainsborough
WARREN POND Louth
WATERSIDE LEISURE PARK Skegness
WELLAND (RIVER) Spalding
WEST FEN DRAIN Boston
WHARFE (RIVER) Boston
WHISBY GARDEN CENTRE Lincoln
WHITE HOUSE PREDATOR LAKE Baston Fen
WILLOW BANK FISHERY Gainsborough
WILLOW FARM Louth
WILLOW LAKES Grantham
WINTER BROTHERS POND Immingham
WINTERS LAKE Immingham
WITHAM (RIVER) Boston
WITHAM (RIVER) Grantham
WOODLAND WATERS Grantham
WOODLANDS FISHERY Spilsby
WOODLANDS LAKE Gainsborough
WOODTHORPE HALL LAKE Alford

LINCOLNSHIRE (NORTH)

BARTON BROADS LAKE Barton-upon-Humber
HOE HILL POND Barton-upon-Humber
KINGFISHER LODGE Brigg
MARSHLANDS Barton-upon-Humber
OLD ANCHOLME (RIVER) Brigg
ORCHARD POND Scunthorpe
PASTURE HOUSE FISHERY Barton-upon-Humber
PELICAN POND Barton-upon-Humber
STADDLETHORPE POND Brough
TARGET LAKE Barton-upon-Humber
TILEYARD LANE Barton-upon-Humber
WESTFIELD LAKES Barton-upon-Humber

LONDON (GREATER)

ALEXANDRA PALACE LAKE London
ALEXANDRA PARK LAKE London
BEDFONT LAKE London
BIRCHMERE London
BOXERS LAKE London
BROOMWOOD LAKE Orpington
BROXBOURNE MEADOWS FISHERY London
BURES LAKE London
CARGILL LAKE London
CLAPHAM COMMON POND London
COLNE (RIVER) London
COPPER MILLSTREAM London
COWLEY LAKE London
CUTTING LAKE London
EAST WARWICK London
FLAKE STREAM London
FORTY HALL LAKE London
FROGMORE LAKE London
GRAND UNION CANAL London
GREENHAMS London
HAMPSTEAD HEATH London
HAREFIELD CARP LAKE London
HEATH VALE POND London
HENRY STREETER LAKE London
HIGH MAYNARD RESERVOIR London
HIGHAMS PARK LAKE London
HIGHGATE PONDS London
HOLLOW PONDS London
HORSEMILL STREAM London
KINGFISHER LAKE London
KNIGHTSCOTE PONDS London
KORDA LAKE London
LEA NAVIGATION London
LEE NAVIGATION London
LITTLE BRITAIN LAKE London
LIZARD LAKES London
LOCKWOOD RESERVOIR London
LOW MAYNARD RESERVOIR London
MARCOA LAKE London
MULGROVE POND London
NEW CUT London
NORTH TROY LAKE AND COLNE (RIVER) London
NORWOOD LAKE London
OLD LEE (RIVER) London
OSTERLEY PARK MIDDLE LAKE London
PERCH POND London
PONDERS END London
POTOMAC POND London
REGENTS CANAL London
RODNEY MEADOW London
SAVAY LAKE London
SHEEPWALK LAKE London
SHEPPERTON LAKE London
SOUTH NORWOOD LAKE London
STOCKLEY ROAD LAKES London
STUDIO AND BROADWATER London
SWYERS LAKE London
TEDDINGTON LOCK London
THAMES (RIVER) London
THORNEY POOL London
TRENT COUNTRY PARK LAKES London
TRENT PARK LAKES London
VALE OF HEATH POND London
WALTHAMSTOW RESERVOIR (NO 1) London
WALTHAMSTOW RESERVOIR (NO 2 AND NO 3) London
WANDSWORTH COMMON POND London
WANSTEAD PARK LAKES London
WEST RESERVOIR London
WEST WARWICK London
WHITE HORSE FISHERIES London
WILLOWSIDE CARP LAKE London
WOOLWICH DOCKYARD London

WRAYSBURY ONE London
WRAYSBURY TWO London

MANCHESTER (GREATER)

ALEXANDRA PARK Oldham
ASHENHURST LAKES Manchester
BEEFOLD LODGE Manchester
BLACK MOSS RESERVOIR Oldham
BLACKLEACH RESERVOIR Manchester
BOGGART HOLE CLOUGH Manchester
BOWKER LAKES Manchester
BRIDGEWATER CANAL Manchester
BRUN CLOUGH RESERVOIR Oldham
BUCKLEY WOOD RESERVOIR Rochdale
BURRS LODGE Bury
CARCUS WATERS Bury
CHORLTON WATER PARK Manchester
CLARENCE RECREATION GROUND Bury
CLIFTON MARINA Salford
CLOWES PARK LAKE Salford
CRIME LAKE Ashton-under-Lyne
CROFT HEAD FISHERY Littleborough
CROMPTONS WATER Bury
CROWN POOLS Bury
DAVENPORT Stockport
DEBDALE RESERVOIRS Manchester
DINGLE LODGE Manchester
DOCTOR DAM FISHERY Rochdale
DOUBLEWOODS Manchester
ELTON RESERVOIR Bury
ENDCROFTS POND Bury
FARM LODGE Manchester
FIELD LODGE POND Bury
FIR TREE FLASH Leigh
FIRS PARK LAKE Leigh
GEIGYS WATER Manchester
GORSE PIT RESERVOIR Manchester
GORTON (LOWER) RESERVOIR Manchester
GORTON (UPPER) RESERVOIR Manchester
GROVE LODGE Littleborough
HEATON PARK Manchester
HOLLINGWORTH LAKE COUNTRY PARK Littleborough
HUDDERSFIELD NARROW CANAL Oldham
IRWELL (RIVER) Bury
ISLAND AND CARTWHEEL LODGES Bury
KING GEORGE V POOL Manchester
KING WILLIAM IV RESERVOIR Manchester
LANKYS MILL POND Manchester
LEEDS TO LIVERPOOL CANAL Leigh
LEEKES WATER Manchester
LEIGH BRANCH CANAL Leigh
LITTLE SEA RESERVOIR Oldham
LOWER TOWN HOUSE FISHERY Littleborough
LUDWORTH RESERVOIR Stockport
MACCLESFIELD CANAL Stockport
MANCHESTER CANAL Manchester
MANCHESTER, BOLTON AND BURY CANAL Bury
MANCHESTER, BOLTON AND BURY CANAL Manchester
MYRTLE ROAD LODGES Manchester
NEW HOUSE FARM POOL Stockport
OGDEN LOWER RESERVOIR Rochdale
OLD IRWELL Manchester
PAINSWICK PARK LAKE Manchester
PEAK FOREST CANAL Stockport
PENNINGTON FLASH Leigh
PILSWORTH FISHERY COMPLEX Heywood
PLATT FIELDS Manchester
POYNTON POOL Stockport
REDBROOK RESERVOIR Oldham
REDDISH VALE MILL PONDS Stockport
RHODES LODGE Manchester
ROCHDALE CANAL Rochdale
ROMAN LAKE LEISURE PARK Stockport
ROYAL GEORGE MILL COMPLEX Oldham
SALFORD QUAYS Salford
SANDY BEACH Manchester
STAKEHILL LODGES Manchester
STAMFORD PARK LAKES Ashton-under-Lyne
STAR MOUNT Manchester
STONEY PIT RESERVOIR Stockport
SWAN LODGE Manchester
TANNERS DAM Oldham
UPPER GORTON RESERVOIR Manchester
WESTGATE POOL Manchester
WHITTLE BROOK RESERVOIR Manchester
WITHINS RESERVOIR Manchester
WOODBANK PARK POOL Stockport

MERSEYSIDE

ARROWE PARK LAKE Wirral
BIRKENHEAD LOWER PARK LAKE Birkenhead
CALDERSTONES PARK LAKE Liverpool
CARR LANE POOL Prescot
CARR MILL DAM St Helens
CENTRAL PARK LAKE Wirral
EVE A LYN FARM Wirral
FOOTBALL PIT Liverpool
GREENBANK PARK LAKE Liverpool
LEEDS TO LIVERPOOL Liverpool
LEEDS TO LIVERPOOL CANAL Liverpool
LEG OMUTTON DAM St Helens
LOWER LAKE Birkenhead
MILL HOUSE FISHERY Liverpool
MORETON MERE Wirral
NEWSHAM PARK Liverpool
PADDOCK DAM St Helens
POULTON RECREATION FIELD POOL Wirral
PRINCES PARK LAKE Liverpool
RODEE MERE Wirral
STANLEY PARK LAKE Liverpool
UPPER LAKE Birkenhead
WALTON HALL PARK Liverpool
WOODSLEE POOL Wirral

MIDLANDS (WEST)

ALVECHURCH FISHERIES Birmingham
AVON (RIVER) Coventry
AVON (RIVER) Warwick
BLYTHE (RIVER) Coventry
BLYTHE WATERS Solihull
BRIDGE POOL Wolverhampton
BULL FISHERY Halesowen
CANNOCK EXTENSION CANAL Pelsall
CHURCH POOL Wolverhampton
COOMBE ABBEY LAKE Coventry
COOMBE POOL Coventry
CUTTLE MILL CARP FISHERY Sutton Coldfield
DARTMOUTH PARK West Bromwich
DAYHOUSE FARM Halesowen
EARLSWOOD LAKES Solihull
EDGBASTON RESERVOIR Birmingham
FOXHILLS FISHERY Walsall
GRAND UNION CANAL Solihull
GREY MILL FARM Solihull
HEATHFIELD POOL Walsall
HERON BROOK FISHERY Wolverhampton
HIMLEY ISLAND POOL Wolverhampton
HOPSFORD HALL FISHERY Coventry
KINGSBURY WATER PARK Sutton Coldfield
KINGSHURST LAKE Solihull
KINGSNORDLEY Bridgnorth
LAVENDER HALL Coventry
LINCOMB LOCK Wolverhampton
MEADOWLANDS Coventry
NORDLEY POOLS Bridgnorth
PACKINGTON SOMERS FISHERY Coventry
PENNS HALL LAKE Sutton Coldfield
POOLE HALL FARM Wolverhampton
ROYAL BRITISH LEGION POOLS Coventry
RUSHALL CANAL Walsall
RYTON POOLS COUNTRY PARK Coventry
SEVERN (RIVER) Bridgnorth
SNEYD POOL Walsall
SOHO LOOP CANAL Birmingham
SOMERS FISHERY Coventry
STAFFORD TO WORCESTER CANAL Wolverhampton
SUTTON PARK Sutton Coldfield
SWAN POOL West Bromwich
TAME VALLEY CANAL Birmingham
TIDBURY GREEN GOLF CLUB Solihull
WALCOT EAST LAKE Birmingham
WALSALL ARBORETUM Walsall
WASSELL GROVE FISHERIES Stourbridge

NORFOLK

ABBEY WATERS Attleborough
ACLE (RIVER) Norwich
BABINGLEY (RIVER) King's Lynn
BARFORD LAKES FISHERY Norwich
BARNINGHAM HALL LAKE Norwich
BARTLES LODGE Dereham
BAWBURGH LAKES Norwich
BILLINGFORD PIT East Dereham
BILNEY LAKES Dereham
BLICKLING PARK LAKE Norwich
BOOTON CLAY PIT Norwich
BORE VALLEY LAKES Norwich
BRADMOOR LAKES King's Lynn
BRIDGE FARM FISHERIES East Dereham
BRIDGE INN FISHERY Lenwade
BUCKENHAM PITS Thetford
BURE (RIVER) Norwich
CANTLEY (RIVER) Norwich
CANTLEY SUGAR FACTORY Norwich
CASTLE RISING STREAM King's Lynn
CATCH 22 FISHERY Norwich
CHAPEL ROAD LAKE Norwich
CHARITY LAKES Norwich
COBBLEACRES LAKES Norwich
COLTON LAKE Norwich
COSTESSEY PITS Norwich
CUT OFF CHANNEL King's Lynn
DECOY FARM Great Yarmouth
DENTS OF HILGAY Downham Market
DISS MERE Diss
DOVE BROOK Eye
DRAYTON GREEN (RIVER) Norwich
DUNHAM CARP AND TENCH LAKES Swaffham
FELBRIGG HALL LAKE Cromer
FELGRIGG LAKE Holt
FELMINGHAM MILL LAKES Norwich
FELTHORPE LAKE Norwich
FOSTERS END PIT King's Lynn
FRITTON LAKE Great Yarmouth
GATTON WATER CARAVAN SITE King's Lynn

GIMINGHAM LAKES Norwich
GLEN MERE Norwich
GREAT MELTON FISHERY Norwich
GREAT OUSE (RIVER) Downham Market
GREAT OUSE RELIEF CHANNEL King's Lynn
GUNTHORPE HALL LAKE Melton Constable
GUNTON PARK LAKE Cromer
HADDISCOE PIT Norwich
HALL FARM LAKES Great Yarmouth
HARDLEY MARSHES Norwich
HAVERINGLAND HALL PARK Norwich
HEVINGHAM LAKES Norwich
HICKLING BROAD Norwich
HILGAY (RIVER) Downham Market
HINDERCLAY LAKES Diss
HINGHAM FISHMERE Norwich
HOLKHAM LAKE Wells-Next-The-Sea
HORNING (RIVER) Norwich
KINGFISHER LAKES Norwich
LAKESIDE King's Lynn
LAKESIDE CARAVAN PARK Downham Market
LENWADE COMMON LAKES Norwich
LETHERINGSETT FISHERY Holt
LITTLE DUNHAM CARP LAKES King's Lynn
LITTLE OUSE (RIVER) King's Lynn
LOCH NEATON Watton
LYNG PIT Norwich
MANOR LAKE Attleborough
MARTHAM PITS Great Yarmouth
MEADOW LAKE King's Lynn
MIDDLE HARLING LAKE Thetford
MILL FARM FISHERY Attleborough
MILL FARM FISHERY Norwich
NATURES HAVEN LAKES Swannington
ORMESBY ROLLESBY Great Yarmouth
PARK LIME PIT Norwich
PECK MEADOW POND Attleborough
PENTNEY LAKES King's Lynn
RACKHEATH SPRINGS Norwich
RAILWAY LAKE Dereham
RAILWAY LAKE Thuxton
RECTORY FARM FISHERY Norwich
REEPHAM FISHERY Norwich
RELIEF CHANNEL King's Lynn
RINGLAND LAKES Norwich
RINGLAND PITS Norwich
ROCKLAND BROAD Norwich
ROOSTING HILLS Dereham
RUSTON REACHES Norwich
SALTHOUSE BROAD Holt
SCOULTON MERE Norwich
SHALLOW BROOK LAKES Norwich
SHORT PLANTATION LAKE Norwich
SNETTERTON PITS Norwich
SOVEREIGN LAKES King's Lynn
STOKESBY (RIVER) Great Yarmouth
SWANGEY LAKES Attleborough
SWANTON MORLEY FISHERY Dereham
TASWOOD LAKES FISH FARM AND FISHERY Norwich
TAVERHAM Norwich
TAVERHAM MILLS FISHERY Norwich
TEN MILE BANK Downham Market
THURNE MOUTH (RIVER) Great Yarmouth
TOTTENHILL PIT King's Lynn
UNIVERSITY BROAD Norwich
WALNUT FARM FISHERIES Attleborough
WENSUM (RIVER) Dereham
WENSUM (RIVER) Norwich
WENSUM (RIVER) Walsingham
WEYBREAD FISHERY Diss
WILLOWCROFT FISHERY King's Lynn
WILLSMORE WATER Fakenham
WISSEY (RIVER) King's Lynn
WOODLAKES FISHERY King's Lynn
WOODRISING WATER MEADOWS Thetford
WROXHAM BROAD Norwich
YARE (RIVER) Norwich

NORTHAMPTONSHIRE

ABINGDON PARK LAKE Northampton
ALDWINCLE PITS Kettering
BARKERS LAKE Kettering
BILLING AQUADROME Northampton
BLUE LAGOON Northampton
BLUNHAM PITS Wellingborough
BODDINGTON RESERVOIR Daventry
CANONS ASHBY LAKES Daventry
CASTLE ASHBY LAKES Northampton
CHESTER FARM LAKE Wellingborough
CORBY BOATING LAKE Corby
CRESCENT LAKE Northampton
DAVENTRY COUNTRY PARK Daventry
DELEPRE PARK LAKE Northampton
DITCHFORD PITS Wellingborough
DRAYTON RESERVOIR Daventry
DUSTON RESERVOIR Northampton
ECTON GRAVEL PITS Northampton
ELINOR COARSE LAKE Kettering
FLECKNOE FARM FISHERIES Daventry
FOXHOLES FISHERIES Northampton
GLEBE LAKE Northampton
GRAND UNION CANAL Northampton
GREEN FARM LAKES Towcester
GRENDON LAKES Northampton
HARDWATER LAKE Northampton
HEYFORD FISHERY Northampton
HOLLOWELL RESERVOIR Northampton
ISE (RIVER) Kettering
ISLIP NATURE LAKE Kettering
LAKESIDE COUNTRY CLUB Rushden
LITTLE IRCHESTER COMPLEX Wellingborough
LYNN POOL FISHERY Corby
MENAGERIE POND Northampton
NASEBY RESERVOIR Northampton
NENE (RIVER) Kettering
NENE (RIVER) Northampton
NORTHAMPTON JUNCTION CANAL Northampton
OXFORD CANAL Daventry
PINE TREES LAKES Wellingborough
RINGSTEAD ISLAND Kettering
SHELFLEYS LAKE Northampton
SILVER LAKE Towcester
SOUTH VIEW FARM CARP FISHERY Wellingborough
ST JAMES SMALL PARK LAKE Northampton
SULBY RESERVOIR Northampton
SYWELL RESERVOIR Wellingborough
THORPE WATERVILLE LAKE Kettering
THRAPSTON (RIVER) Kettering
THRAPSTON LAKES Kettering
WEEDON ROAD GRAVEL PIT Northampton
WELFORD RESERVOIR Northampton
WEYBREAD GRAVEL PITS Harleston
WOOTTON BROOK LAKE Northampton

NORTHUMBERLAND

FELTON FENCE FARM PONDS Morpeth
GILSLAND LAKE Haltwhistle
HALLINGTON RESERVOIRS Corbridge
HORTON GRANGE LAKE Blyth
QUEEN ELIZABETH II COUNTRY PARK Ashington
THORNBROUGH LAKE Corbridge
TYNE (RIVER) Hexham
TYNE (RIVER) Prudhoe
WILLIES WELL Wylam

NOTTINGHAMSHIRE

A1 PITS Newark
ATTENBOROUGH GRAVEL PITS Nottingham
BESTWOOD POND Nottingham
CHESTERFIELD CANAL Retford
CLUMBER LAKE Worksop
COVERT SPRINGS FISHERIES Nottingham
CRANFLEET CANAL Nottingham
DANESHILL LAKES Retford
DOLAR POND Nottingham
EREWASH CANAL Nottingham
FLEET (RIVER) Newark
GRANTHAM CANAL Nottingham
HALLCROFT FISHERIES Retford
HARWICK HALL LAKES Mansfield
HOLME PIERPOINT Nottingham
IRONMONGERS POND Nottingham
KINGS MILL RESERVOIR Sutton-In-Ashfield
LANGOLD LAKES Worksop
L-LAKE FISHERY Mansfield
LOUND WINDSURF LAKE Retford
MAUN (RIVER) Mansfield
NOTTINGHAM CANAL Nottingham
NOTTINGHAM CASTLE MARINA Nottingham
PINDERS PONDS Nottingham
SANDHILL LAKE Worksop
SAPPHIRE LAKES Newark
SHERWOOD FOREST FARM PARK FISHERY Mansfield
SMEATONS LAKES Newark
STRIP PONDS Retford
SUTTON LAWN DAM Mansfield
TRENT (RIVER) Newark
TRENT (RIVER) Newark-on-Trent
TRENT (RIVER) Nottingham
TRENT (RIVER) Retford
WHARFE (RIVER) Newark
WINDMILL FARM LAKES Newark
WINFIELD LAGOON Nottingham
WITHAM (RIVER) Newark
WOODEND QUARRY POND Worksop
WOODSETTS QUARRY POND Worksop

OLDHAM

CASTLESHAW (LOWER) RESERVOIR

OXFORDSHIRE

BEIRTON LAKES Oxford
BLADON LAKE Woodstock
BLENHEIM LAKE Woodstock
BULLFIELD LAKE Abingdon
BUTLERS HILL FARM Chipping Norton
CHAD LAKES Chipping Norton
CHERWELL (RIVER) Bicester
CHERWELL (RIVER) Kidlington
CHERWELL (RIVER) Oxford
CHERWELL (RIVER) Woodstock
CHEYNEY MANOR FISHERY Banbury
CHRISTCHURCH LAKE Witney
CLATTERCOTE RESERVOIR Banbury
COLLEGE FARM FISHING Banbury
DORCHESTER LAGOON Wallingford
EYNSHAM LOCK Witney
FARINGDON LAKE Faringdon

GAUNTS LAKE Witney
GLEBE COURT LAKE Bicester
GOLDFISH BOWL (THE) Oxford
GRAND UNION CANAL Bulbourne
GRAND UNION CANAL Oxford
GRIMSBURY RESERVOIR Banbury
HARDWICK LAKE AND SMITHS POOL Witney
HEYFORD LAKES Witney
HORSE AND GROOM LAKES Banbury
HUNTS CORNER Witney
LINCH HILL FISHERY Witney
MANOR FARM LAKE Witney
MANOR HOUSE Oxford
MANOR LAKE Bicester
MARLBOROUGH POOL Abingdon
MILTON POOLS FARM Oxford
NELL BRIDGE FISHERY Banbury
ORCHID LAKES Wallingford
OXFORD CANAL Banbury
OXFORD CANAL Bicester
OXFORD CANAL Kidlington
OXFORD CANAL Oxford
OXLEASE LAKE Witney
PIMLICO FARM LAKES Bicester
ROLFS LAKE Oxford
ROYAL PIONEER CORPS ANGLING ASSOCIATION WATER Bicester
RUSHEY WEIR Bampton
SEVERALLS FARM A AND B Oxford
ST JOHNS POOL Witney
STATES LAGOON Bicester
STRATTON LODGE Abingdon
SWISS FARM LAKE Henley-on-Thames
THAME (RIVER) Henley-on-Thames
THAME (RIVER) Ickford
THAME (RIVER) Wallingford
THAMES (RIVER) Abingdon
THAMES (RIVER) Bampton
THAMES (RIVER) Cowley
THAMES (RIVER) Didcot
THAMES (RIVER) Oxford
THAMES (RIVER) Summertown
THAMES (RIVER) Wallingford
THAMES (RIVER) Witney
THAMES (RIVER) Wolvercote
UNITY LAKE Witney
WINDRUSH (RIVER) Burford
WINDRUSH (RIVER) Witney
YEOMANS LAKE Witney

RUTLAND

SWEETHEDGES FARM FISHERY Oakham
WELLAND (RIVER) Oakham

SHROPSHIRE

ACTON BURNELL Shifnal
APLEY POOLS Telford
AQUALATE MERE Newport
BACHE POOL Market Drayton
BAYLIS POOLS Shifnal
BEECHES POOL Telford
BENTHALL LAKE Broseley
BIRCH GROVE Shrewsbury
BIRMINGHAM TO WORCESTER CANAL Broseley
BLAKEMERE Whitchurch
BLUE POOL Telford
BROCKTON GRANGE Much Wenlock
COLEMERE COUNTRY PARK Ellesmere
CROSEMERE Ellesmere
FOLLY FARM POOL Shrewsbury
HAMPTON LOCK Bridgnorth
HAWKSTONE PARK LAKE Shrewsbury
HINKSHAY POOLS Telford
HOLMER LAKE Telford
HORESHAY POOL Telford
ISLE LAKE Shrewsbury
LITTLE DAWLEY POOLS Telford
LLORAN GANOL FARM Oswestry
LOWER HILL FARM Much Welock
MEESE (RIVER) Newport
MIDDLE POOL Telford
MILL HOUSE LAKES Market Drayton
MONKHALL FISHERIES Bridgnorth
NEWPORT CANAL Telford
OSS MERE Whitchurch
PERRY (RIVER) Baschurch
PERRY (RIVER) Oswestry
SEVEN OAKS LOG CABIN PARK Shrewsbury
SEVERN (RIVER) Bridgnorth
SEVERN (RIVER) Oswestry
SEVERN (RIVER) Shrewsbury
SEVERN (RIVER) Telford
SHROPSHIRE UNION CANAL Market Drayton
SNAILBEACH POOL Shrewsbury
SPRING LEE Shrewsbury
STIRCHLEY POOLS Telford
TELFORD TOWN PARK Telford
TEME (RIVER) Ludlow
TERN (RIVER) Market Drayton
TERN (RIVER) Telford
TOWNSEND FISHERY Bridgnorth
TRENCH POOL Telford
WALCOT WEST LAKE Bishops Castle
WHITCHURCH LAKE Whitchurch
WHITEMERE Ellesmere
WITHY POOL Telford
WOODCOTE HALL Telford
WYRLEY ESSINGTON CANAL Wolverhampton

SOMERSET

APEX LAKE Burnham-on-Sea
ASHMEAD LAKES Martock
AVALON FISHERIES Glastonbury
AVON (BRISTOL) (RIVER) Bath
AVON (RIVER) Frome
BASON BRIDGE Highbridge
BRISTOL AVON Bath
BROWNES POND Bridgwater
BRUE (RIVER) Highbridge
BULLOCKS FARM FISHING LAKES Clevedon
BUTLEIGH ROAD PONDS Street
CHARD RESERVOIR Chard
CHEDDAR RESERVOIR Cheddar
COMBWICH PONDS Bridgwater
COOMBE LAKE Langport
DANDYS LAKE AND KNIGHTINGALE LAKE Bath
DUNWEAR LAKES Bridgwater
DURLEIGH RESERVOIR Bridgwater
EDNEYS FISHERIES Frome
EMBOROUGH POND Bath
EMBOROUGH POOL Wells
EMBORUGH LAKE Emborough
EMERALD POOL FISHERY Highbridge
FOLLY FOOT FARM Bridgwater
FOLLYFOOT FARM Bridgwater
FROME (RIVER) Frome
GLASTONBURY Glastonbury
GODNEY MOOR PONDS Glastonbury
HIGHLANDS DAIRY LAKE Crewkerne
HORSESHOE LAKE Wedmore
HOWLEY STREET POND Chard
HUNSTRETE LAKE COMPLEX Bath
HUNTSPILL (RIVER) Bridgwater
HUTON POND Weston-Super-Mare
ISLE (RIVER) Langport
KENN (RIVER) Clevedon
KENN (RIVER) Highbridge
KENNET AND AVON CANAL Bath
KENNET AND AVON CANAL Bristol
KING SEDGEMOOR DRAIN Bridgwater
LAKESIDE Dulverton
LANDS END FARM Wedmore
LANDS END FISHERIES Wedmore
LANGFORD LAKES Wellington
LOWER LOVELYNCH FISHERIES Taunton
MARK (RIVER) Highbridge
MARSTON LAKE Frome
MELLS PIT Frome
NEWTON PARK Bath
NEWTOWN LAKE Highbridge
OLD MILL FISHERY Yeovil
OXENLEAZE FARM CARAVANS AND COARSE FISHERY Taunton
PARRETT (RIVER) Bridgwater
PARRETT (RIVER) Langport
PARRETT (RIVER) Stoke-Sub-Hamdon
PARRETT (RIVER) Weston-Super-Mare
PAULTON LAKES Bristol
PAWLETT PONDS Bridgwater
PLANTATIONS LAKES Clevedon
SCREECH OWL PONDS Bridgwater
SEDGES Bridgwater
STATHE DRAIN Bridgwater
STONE YARD FISHERY Chewton Mendip
SUMMERHAYES Bridgwater
TAUNTON AND BRIDGWATER CANAL Bridgwater
TAUNTON ROAD PONDS Bridgwater
TAUNTON TO BRIDGWATER CANAL Bridgwater
THORNEY LAKES Langport
THURLEYBEARE POND Taunton
TONE (RIVER) Taunton
TUCKING MILL Bath
VIADUCT FISHERY Somerton
WALROW PONDS Highbridge
WATER MEADOW LAKES Crewkerne
WELLINGTON BASIN Wellington
WESTHAY Glastonbury
WESTHAY LAKE Bridgwater
WITHAM FRIARY LAKE Frome
WOODBOROUGH PARK LAKE Bath
WYCH LODGE LAKE Taunton
YEO (RIVER) Bristol
YEO (RIVER) Yeovil

STAFFORDSHIRE

ALBRIGHTON MOAT PROJECT Wolverhampton
ANKER (RIVER) Tamworth
ASHLEY POOLS Loggerheads
BADEN HALL FISHERY Stafford
BASFORD COARSE FISHERY Leek
BIDDULPH GRANGE Stoke-on-Trent
BLACK LAKE Stoke-on-Trent
BLACKSHAW FARM LAKES Leek
BLACKWOOD POOL Stoke-on-Trent
BONEHILL MILL Tamworth
BORROWPIT LAKE Tamworth
BROWNING CUDMORE FISHERY Newcastle-under-Lyme
CANAL RESERVOIRS Stoke-on-Trent
CHURNET (RIVER) Alton
CHURNET (RIVER) Leek
CONSALL NATURE PARK Stoke-on-Trent
COVENTRY CANAL Tamworth
DEEP HAYES COUNTRY PARK Leek
DILHORNE HALL POOLS Stoke-on-Trent
DOVE (RIVER) Uttoxeter
DRAYTON BRIDGE Tamworth
ELLENHALL NINE POOLS Stafford
FRADLEY CANAL Burton-on-Trent
HAMSTALL FISHERY Rugeley
HARTSHORNE DAMS Burton-on-Trent
HEDNESFORD ROAD LAKE Rugeley
HERONBROOK FISHERY Stafford
HIMLEY HALL AND PARK LAKE Dudley
HOLDEN LANE POOL Stoke-on-Trent
HORNS Rugeley
HORSEBRIDGE POOL Leek

KNYPERSLEY RESERVOIR Stoke-on-Trent
LAWTON HALL POOL Newcastle-under-Lyme
LITTLETONS AND MIDDLE POOL Rugeley
MACCLESFIELD CANAL Stoke-on-Trent
MADELEY POOL Newcastle-under-Lyme
PARK HALL FARM Stoke-on-Trent
PARKES HALL Dudley
PILLATON POOLS Penkridge
PINE POOL Tamworth
POOL HOUSE FARM Tamworth
PRETTY PIGS FISHERY Tamworth
RUDYARD LAKE Leek
SHROPSHIRE UNION CANAL Stafford
SHROPSHIRE UNION CANAL Wolverhampton
SIDEWAY OVERFLOW Stoke-on-Trent
SMITH POOL Stoke-on-Trent
SMITHPOOL LAKE Stoke-on-Trent
SOUTH POPLARS Cannock
SOW (RIVER) Stafford
STAFFORD AND WORCESTER CANAL Stafford
STAFFORD TO WORCESTER CANAL Stafford
STANLEY RESERVOIR Stoke-on-Trent
SWAN PIT POOL Stafford
SWARBORN (RIVER) Alrewas
TAME (RIVER) Alrewas
TAYLORS POOL Stoke-on-Trent
TILTLESWORTH Leek
TRENT (RIVER) Alrewas
TRENT AND MERSEY CANAL Burton-on-Trent
TRENT AND MERSEY CANAL Stoke-on-Trent
TRENTHAM GARDENS Stoke-on-Trent
WADE LAKE Rugeley
WILLOW POOLS Stafford
WILLOWS POOLS Penkridge
WOODSEAT LAKE Uttoxeter

SUFFOLK

ALDE (RIVER) Saxmundham
ALDEBY HALL FARM PITS Beccles
ALDERSONS LAKES Ipswich
ALTON WATER RESERVOIR Ipswich
BAKERS LAKE Stowmarket
BARHAM A PIT Ipswich
BARHAM B PIT Ipswich
BARSHAM DRAIN Beccles
BECCLES QUAY Beccles
BLUE WATERS Bury St Edmunds
BOSMERE LAKE Ipswich
BREAKAWAY PIT Woodbridge
BRIDGE FARM RESERVOIRS Woodbridge
BROOME PITS Bungay
BUNGAY (RIVER) Bungay
BUSS CREEK Southwold
CAMELOT LAKE Harleston
CAUSEWAY LAKES Ipswich
CLARE PARK LAKE Sudbury
CLICKETTS HILL AND PLANTATION Bures
CLUB PIT Bungay
CROSS DROVE Hockwold
DEBEN (RIVER) Woodbridge
DITCHINGHAM PIT Bungay
FLIXTON DECOY Lowestoft
FLOOD PARK Haverhill
GIPPING (RIVER) Ipswich
GUNSSONS LAKE Saxmundham
GUNTON HALL LAKE Lowestoft
HENHAM DAIRY POND Beccles
HIGHFIELD FISHERY Harleston
HOLTON PIT Halesworth
HOME FARM FISHERIES Sudbury
HOMERSFIELD (RIVER) Bungay
HOMERSFIELD LAKE Harleston
LAKESIDE Stowmarket
LAYZELLS FARM Sudbury
LITTLE BEVILLS ESTATE Bures
LITTLE OUSE (RIVER) Thetford
LOAM POND Woodbridge
MARSH FARM LAKES Saxmundham
MELDUM WASHLANDS (FLOODPARK) Haverhill
MELTON LAKE Woodbridge
MILLERS LAKE Clare
NEEDHAM LAKE Ipswich
NORTH MEADOWS Sudbury
OULTON BROAD Lowestoft
OULTON DYKE Lowestoft
PETTISTREE LAKES Woodbridge
RATTLE (RIVER) Stowmarket
RAYDON PONDS Southwold
REYDON LAKES Southwold
SINKS PIT Ipswich
STANTONS FARM RESERVOIR Sudbury
STARFIELD PIT Sudbury
STOUR (RIVER) Sudbury
STOUR (SUFFOLK) (RIVER) Ipswich
STOW (RIVER) Bures
STOW (RIVER) Sudbury
SWALE PIT Ipswich
THET (RIVER) Thetford
VALLEY FARM FISHERY Halesworth
WAVENEY (RIVER) Bungay
WAVENEY VALLEY LAKES Harleston
WEST STOW COUNTRY PARK Bury St Edmunds
WICKHAM MARKET RESERVOIRS Woodbridge
WRIGHTS FARM Sudbury
YEW TREE FISHERIES Harleston

SURREY

ALDERBROOK LAKE Cranleigh
ALFORD ROAD FISHERIES Cranleigh
ATTENBOROUGH SOUTH Chertsey
BADSHOT LEA Farnham
BEAVER FARM FISHERY Lingfield
BOLDERMERE Woking
BRITTENS POND Guildford
BROADWATER LAKE Godalming
BURY HILL FISHERIES Dorking
BUSBRIDGE LAKE Milford
BUSHEY PARK East Molesey
CHERTSEY Chertsey
COLTSFORD MILL FISHERY Oxted
EAST WHIPLEY RESERVOIR Cranleigh
EPSOM STEW POND Epsom
FISHERIES THE Cranleigh
FURZE FARM Cranleigh
GATTON MANOR LAKES Dorking
GOLDSWORTH WATER PARK Woking
HAWKINS POND Horsham
HENFOLD LAKES FISHERY Dorking
HOME PARK East Molesey
JOHNSONS LAKE Milford
LAKESIDE Heath End
LONG COPSE PONDS Leatherhead
MANOR POND Cobham
MILL POND Dorking
MOLE (RIVER) Dorking
MOLE (RIVER) Walton-on-Thames
NAVIES HOLE Cranleigh
ONE ISLAND POND Mitcham
PAINSHILL PARK LAKE Cobham
PAPERCOURT FISHERY Woking
PUDDENHOLE POND Dorking
PULBOROUGH LAKE Horsham
ROOSTHOLE Horsham
RUSHMOOR LAKES Farnham
SEND PIT Woking
SEVEN ISLANDS Mitcham
SHAWFIELDS LAKES Ash
ST PATRICKS LANE CARP LAKES Farnham
STOCKBRIDGE POND Tilford
THAMES (RIVER) East Molesey
THORPE PARK WATERSKI LAKE Chertsey
TWYNERSH FISHING COMPLEX Chertsey
WEY (RIVER) West Byfleet
WEY NAVIGATION (RIVER) Woking
WHIPLEY MANOR Guildford
WHITEVANE POND Horsham
WILLINGHURST COARSE FISHERY Guildford
WYPHURST AND HYHURST LAKES Cranleigh

SUSSEX (EAST)

ALEXANDRA PARK WATERS Hastings
BALLS GREEN LAKES Hartfield
BELFREY COARSE FISHERY Hailsham
BEVERN STREAM Lewes
BOJO FISHERIES Heathfield
BRICKYARD LAKE Bexhill-on-Sea
BROOMHAM FISHERY Battle
BUXTED OAST FISHERY Uckfield
BUXTED PARK FISHERY Uckfield
CLAREMONT LAKE Battle
CLIVE VALE RESERVOIRS Hastings
COGHURST HALL Hastings
CUCKMERE (RIVER) Hailsham
CUCKMERE (RIVER) Polegate
CUCKMERE (RIVER) Seaford
DECOY LAKE Lewes
ECCLESBOURNE RESERVOIR Hastings
FALKENVIL FISHERY Hailsham
FRAMFIELD PARK FISHERIES Uckfield
FURNACE BROOK FISHERY Hailsham
HASTINGS LAKE Hastings
HOLTS LAKES Crowborough
HONEYS GREEN COARSE FISHERY Uckfield
IDEN WOOD FISHERY Rye
ISFIELD (RIVER) Uckfield
LEABRIDGE FARM Hailsham
LOWER HONEYS GREEN FARM Uckfield
MICHELHAM PRIORY MOAT Eastbourne
MOOR HALL POOL Battle
OLD IRON (RIVER) Lewes
OLIVES FARM FISHERY Battle
OUSE (RIVER) Lewes
PENNY BRIDGE Crowborough
PETT POOLS Hastings
PEVENSEY HAVEN Hailsham
PIPPINGFORD PARK ESTATE LAKES Uckfield
ROSEBANK FARM FISHERY Heathfield
RYE NOOK FISHERY Hastings
SCALAND WOOD Crowborough
SHAMFOLD FARM FISHERY Rye
SHARNFOLD FARM FISHERY Pevensey
SOUTHBOURNE LAKE Eastbourne
ST IVES FARM Hartfield
SWANBOROUGH LAKES Lewes
TANYARD FISHERIES Uckfield
THORNDEN POND Battle
UNDERHILL LAKE Uckfield
VINEHALL SCHOOL LAKE Robertsbridge
WALLERS HAVEN Hailsham
WALLERS HAVEN Pevensey
WHITE HART HILL LAKE Hastings
WISHING TREE RESERVOIR Hastings
WOODMANCOTE PLACE FISHERY Brighton
WYLANDS INTERNATIONAL ANGLING CENTRE Battle

SUSSEX (WEST)

ADUR (RIVER) Henfield
ADUR (RIVER) Steyning
ALDERWOOD PONDS Steyning
ARDINGLY RESERVOIR Haywards Heath
ARUN (RIVER) Arundel
ARUN (RIVER) Bognor Regis
ARUN (RIVER) Horsham
ARUN (RIVER) Pulborough
BALCOMBE LAKE Haywards Heath
BOLEBROOK CASTLE East Grinstead
BORDE HILL GARDEN LAKES Haywards Heath
BURTON MILL POND Petworth
CHICESTER CANAL Chichester
CUCKFIELD FISHERY Haywards Heath
DAYLANDS FARM East Grinstead
DOCTORS LAKE Horsham
DOUNHURST FARM FISHERY Billinghurst
DUNCANS POND Pulborough
FURNACE LAKES Horsham
HURSTON LANE Pulborough
LAYBROOK LAKES Pulborough
LENNOX WOOD LAKE Horsham
MENARDS LAKE Horsham
MILL FARM FISHERY Pulborough
NEW POND Midhurst
NEWELLS SPECIMEN CARP AND COARSE FISHERIES Horsham
PASSIES PONDS Lancing
PILTDOWN POND Haywards Heath
ROTHER (RIVER) Midhurst
ROTHERFIELD POND Midhurst
SLAUGHAM MILL POND Haywards Heath
SLAUGHTERFORD FARM Horsham
SPARKS FARM FISHERY Haywards Heath
STUBPOND FISHERIES East Grinstead
TILGATE LAKES Crawley
VALE BRIDGE LAKE Haywards Heath
WESTERN ROTHER Midhurst
WESTERN ROTHER (RIVER) Petworth
WILDERNESS LAKE East Grinstead
WINTONS FISHERY Burgess Hill

TYNE AND WEAR

BIG WATERS Newcastle Upon Tyne
BOLAM LAKE COUNTRY PARK Newcastle Upon Tyne
BRENKLEY POND Newcastle Upon Tyne
DISSINGTON POND Newcastle Upon Tyne
FELLGATE FISHERIES Jarrow
FELLGATE PONDS Gateshead
KILLINGWORTH LAKE Newcastle Upon Tyne
LEAZES PARK LAKE Newcastle Upon Tyne
LEVEN (RIVER) Yarm
LITTLE BIG WATER Newcastle Upon Tyne
MARDEN QUARRY Newcastle Upon Tyne
MILKHOPE POND Newcastle Upon Tyne
MOUNT PLEASANT LAKE Washington
RED BARNS POND Newcastle Upon Tyne
SILKSWORTH SPORTS COMPLEX Sunderland
STARGATE PONDS Ryton
STEPHENSON LAKE Houghton Le Spring
TEES (RIVER) Yarm
THROCKLEY REIGH Newcastle Upon Tyne
WILLOWS (THE) Washington

WARWICKSHIRE

ADAMS POOL Alcester
ASHBY CANAL Nuneaton
AVON (RIVER) Rugby
AVON (RIVER) Stratford-upon-Avon
BANKS (THE) Rugby
BISHOPS BOWL LAKES Leamington Spa
BLACK HILL POOLS Stratford-upon-Avon
BOSWORTH PARK LAKE Nuneaton
BOSWORTH WATER TRUST AND FRIEZELAND POOLS Nuneaton
BRAMCOTE MAINS FISHERY Bedworth
CLIFTON LAKES FISHERY Rugby
COVENTRY CANAL Nuneaton
GARDEN FARM FISHERIES Nuneaton
GRAND UNION CANAL Leamington Spa
GRAND UNION CANAL Warwick
HAWKESBURY FISHERY Bedworth
HIGH CLAYS FARM Southam
KINGSTON POOLS Warwick
LANNYS LAGOON Rugby
LEAM (RIVER) Leamington Spa
MILL POOL Rugby
MONKS POOL Bedworth
NAPTON RESERVOIR Southam
NEWBOLD QUARRY Rugby
NORTH FARM FISHERY Southam
NORTH OXFORD CANAL Rugby
OAKHAM FARM POOLS Warwick
OXFORD CANAL Leamington Spa
OXFORD CANAL Rugby
PARK FARM Warwick
RIDDINGS FISHERY Atherstone
SHEEPY MAGNA LAKE Atherstone
SNITTERFIELD FRUIT FARM Stratford-upon-Avon
SOUTH STRATFORD CANAL Stratford-upon-Avon
STOCKTON RESERVOIR Rugby
STOUR (WARWICKSHIRE) Stratford-upon-Avon
WARWICK CANAL Leamington Spa
WARWICKSHIRE AVON Stratford-upon-Avon
WEST HILLBOROUGH Alcester
WESTON LAWN FISHERIES Bedworth

WILTSHIRE

AVON (BRISTOL) (RIVER) Chippenham
AVON (BRISTOL) (RIVER) Melksham
AVON (BRISTOL) (RIVER) Salisbury
AVON (RIVER) Chippenham
AVON (RIVER) Melksham
AVON (RIVER) Salisbury
AVON (RIVER) Warminster
BISS (RIVER) Trowbridge
BLACKLAND LAKES HOLIDAY AND LEISURE CENTRE Calne
BOWOOD LAKE Calne
BRISTOL AVON Bradford-on-Avon
BRISTOL AVON Chippenham
BRISTOL AVON Melksham
BURBROOKS RESERVOIR Melksham
BURTON HILL LAKE Malmesbury
CLIVEY PONDS Westbury
COATE WATER COUNTRY PARK Swindon
CROCKERTON POND Warminster
CUCKOOS REST Westbury
DORKHAM STORMWATER Swindon
ERLESTOKE LAKE Devizes
HAMPSHIRE AVON (RIVER) Salisbury
HIGH PENN Calne
IVY HOUSE FARM Chippenham
KENNET AND AVON CANAL Bradford-on-Avon
KENNET AND AVON CANAL Devizes
KENNET AND AVON CANAL Marlborough
KENNET AND AVON CANAL Melksham
KENNET AND AVON CANAL Pewsey
KENNET AND AVON CANAL Trowbridge
LAWNS (THE) Swindon
LIDEN LAGOON Swindon
LONGHOUSE LAKES Salisbury
LONGLEAT LAKES Warminster
NADDER (RIVER) Salisbury
OLD WARDOUR Salisbury
PEARMOOR LAKE Swindon
PEATMOOR LAGOON Swindon
PEMBROKE POND Swindon
PETERS FINGER LAKES Salisbury
PLAUMS PIT Swindon
PURTON LAKE Swindon
RAY (RIVER) Swindon
RODBOURNE LAGOON Swindon
ROOD ASHTON LAKE Trowbridge
SABRE AND SWORDS LAKES Calne
SHAFTESBURY LAKE Swindon
SHEAR WATER Warminster
SILVERLANDS LAKE Chippenham
SOUTHLEIGH LAKE Warminster
STEEPLE LANGFORD LAKES Salisbury
THAMES (RIVER) Swindon
TOCKENHAM RESERVOIR Chippenham
TURNERS PADDOCK LAKE Warminster
WALDENS FARM FISHERY Salisbury
WHITE HORSE INN LAKE Malmesbury
WITHERINGTON FARM FISHING Salisbury
WOODLAND PARK Westbury
WROUGHTON RESERVOIR Swindon
WYATTS LAKE Chippenham
WYTHERINGTON FARM Salisbury

WORCESTERSHIRE

ABBOTS SALFORD PARK Evesham
ACR FISHERIES Worcester
ANCHOR MEADOWS FISHERY Evesham
ARROW VALLEY LAKE Redditch
ASTWOOD FISHERY Droitwich
AVON (RIVER) Evesham
AVON (RIVER) Pershore
BANKES POOL Stourport-on-Severn
BENNETTS POOL Worcester
BEWDLEY POOL Kidderminster
BIRMINGHAM TO WORCESTER CANAL Bromsgrove
BIRMINGHAM TO WORCESTER CANAL Worcester
BRAKE MILL POOL Worcester
BROAD ACRES LAKE Bromsgrove
BROCKAMIN POOLS Worcester
CAPTAINS POOL Kidderminster
CASTLE GREEN POOLS Malvern
CURTISS POOL Bewdley
DEXTER POOL Bewdley
DOWLES BROOK Bewdley
DROITWICH CANAL Droitwich
ELMBRIDGE LAKES Droitwich
ERICS POOL Kidderminster
EVESBATCH FISHERIES Worcester
FOREST FARM Pershore
FURNACE MILL FISHERY Kidderminster
GROVE FARM Worcester
HARVEY POOL Worcester
HARVINGTON MANOR FISHERY Evesham
HAYE FARM FISHERY Bewdley
HOLT FLEET POOL Worcester
HURCOTT POOL Kidderminster
LEIGH SINTON FISHING LAKES Malvern
LODGE PARK LAKE Redditch
LOWER BROADHEATH POOLS Worcester

MAVER LARFORD Stourport-on-Severn
MILL POOL Bewdley
MOORLANDS FARM Kidderminster
MOORS POOL Kidderminster
SALWARPE (RIVER) Kidderminster
SEVERN (RIVER) Bewdley
SEVERN (RIVER) Stourport-on-Severn
SEVERN (RIVER) Worcester
SHAKESPEARE MOORLANDS FARM Kidderminster
SHATTERFORD FISHERY AND WILDLIFE SANCTUARY Kidderminster
SION FARM FISHERIES Kidderminster
SNUFF MILL POOL Bewdley
STAFFORD TO WORCESTER CANAL Stourport-on-Severn
STAINFORTH AND KEADBY CANAL Worcester
STANKLIN POOL Kidderminster
STELLA LAKE Kidderminster
STEWARDS POOL Kidderminster
TEME (RIVER) Bewdley
TEME (RIVER) Martley
TEME (RIVER) Tenbury Wells
TEME (RIVER) Worcester
TOP BARN ANGLING CENTRE Worcester
TWYFORD FARM POOL Evesham
UCKINGHALL POOL Worcester
UNWICKS FARM FISHERY Stourport-on-Severn
UPTON WARREN LAKE Bromsgrove
WARWICKSHIRE & AVON Evesham
WARWICKSHIRE AVON Evesham
WARWICKSHIRE AVON Pershore
WASH POOL Worcester
WELFIELD POOLS Kidderminster
WELLFIELD POOLS Bewdley
WHARFE INN POOL Worcester
WHARTONS PARK COARSE FISHING Bewdley
WILDEN POOL Stourport-on-Severn
WILLOW FARM Evesham
WILLOW MARSH Kidderminster
WINDMILL LAKE Evesham
WINTERFOLD PARK FISHERIES Kidderminster
WITLEY FISHERY Worcester
WITLEY POOLS Worcester
WOOD POOL Evesham
WOODLAND VIEW Droitwich
WOODROW FISH POND Bromsgrove
WOODSTON MANOR POOLS Tenbury Wells

WREXHAM

CLYWEDOG (RIVER) Bangor-on-Dee
DEE (RIVER) Bangor-on-Dee
EMRAL BROOK Worthenbury
WYCH BROOK Worthenbury

YORKSHIRE (NORTH)

ABBIE POND Malton
ALDERS LAKE Thirsk
ALDWARK BRIDGE York
BACON FACTORY POND Tadcaster
BAIN (RIVER) Leyburn
BARLOW COMMON NATURE RESERVE Selby
BEDALE BECK Northallerton
BIRKDALE FISHERY Malton
BRAFFERTON COARSE FISHERY York
BRICKYARD FARM LAKE Malton
BRICKYARD FISHERY Ripon
BROKEN BREA FISHERY Richmond
BROOKLANDS Scarborough
BUBWITH (RIVER) Selby
CARLTON LODGE LAKE Thirsk
CARP VALE York
CASTLE HOWARD GREAT LAKE York
CATTERICK LAKES Richmond
CAWOOD HOLIDAY PARK Selby
CHAPMANS POND York
CLAXTON BRICKWORKS York
CLAY PIT Bedale
CLIFTON MOOR LAKE Clifton
COD BECK Thirsk
CORNHILL PONDS Northallerton
CUNDALL LODGE FISHERY York
DERWENT (RIVER) York
DRAX LAKE Selby
EAST COTTINGWITH WATERS York
ELLERTON LANDING York
ELLERTON PARK Richmond
ELVINGTON LAKE York
FAIRVIEW LAKE Carwood
FARMIRE Ripon
FLETCHERS POND York
FOGGLESKYTE WATERS York
FOSS (RIVER) York
GRAFTON MERE York
HAY-A-PARK Knaresborough
HAZEL HALL FARM FISHING Northallerton
HESSAY POND York
HIGH MOOR FARM PARK Harrogate
HOLLINGWOOD FISHERY Northallerton
HOXNE FARM PONDS York
KAYS LAKES Thirsk
KILBURN POND York
KINGSLEY CARP LAKE Harrogate
LAKEHOUSE LAKE York
LAKESIDE LODGES York
LANGTON POND Northallerton
LINGCROFT FARM POND York
LOWER DUNSFORTH (RIVER) York
MANOR FARM POND Malton
MARKET WEIGHTON CANAL York
MILBY CUT York
MOORLANDS FARM PONDS York
MOULTON LANE POND Thirsk
MUNBY POND Selby
NEWHAY DAY TICKET LAKE Selby
NEWHAY SPECIMEN LAKE Selby
NEWTON RIVER Bedale
NIDD (RIVER) Harrogate
NIDD (RIVER) York
NORTHINGALES FISHERY York
NUN MONKTON (RIVER) York
OAK MERE FISHERY York
OAKS FISHERY Thirsk
OAKTREE LEISURE York
ORCHARD FARM PONDS York
OUSE (RIVER) Helperby
OUSE (RIVER) Malton
OUSE (RIVER) York
PARKLANDS Northallerton
PICKERING PARK FISHING LAKE Pickering
POCKLINGTON CANAL York
POOL BRIDGE FARM LAKES York
POPPLETON (RIVER) York
POTTERY LAKE York
PROSPECT FARM POND Harrogate
QUEEN MARYS POND Ripon
RACECOURSE LAKE Ripon
RASKELF LAKE York
REDHOUSE LAGOON York
RIPLEY CASTLE Harrogate
RIPON CANAL Ripon
RIPON RACECOURSE LAKE Ripon
ROGERS POND Ripon
ROLIETH FISHERY Northallerton
SCARBOROUGH MERE Scarborough
SELBY 3 LAKES Selby
SELBY CANAL Selby
SELLEY BRIDGE LAKE Malton
STONEY LANE PONDS Northallerton
SWALE (RIVER) Helperby
SWALE (RIVER) Northallerton
SWALE (RIVER) Richmond
SWALE (RIVER) Thirsk
SWALE (RIVER) York
THORNTON BRIDGE York
THORPE PERROW QUARRY Bedale
THORPE UNDERWOOD York
THREE LAKES Selby
TOLLERTON FISHING PONDS York
TONTINE LAKE Northallerton
ULLESKELF (RIVER) Tadcaster
URE (RIVER) Middleham
URE (RIVER) York
WELHAM LAKE Pickering
WEST HADDLESEY LAKE Selby
WESTERLY LAKE York
WHARFE (RIVER) Tadcaster
WILLOW WATER York
WILLOWS York
WILLOWS AND FIRS LAKES Thirsk
WOODLAND LAKES Thirsk
Y2K LAKE Scarborough
YORKSHIRE OUSE York

YORKSHIRE (SOUTH)

ARKSEY STATION POND Doncaster
ASKERN LAKE Doncaster
ATHERSLEY MEMORIAL LAKE Barnsley
BARNSLEY CANAL Barnsley
BEEDOMS FISHERY Doncaster
BRAMPTON CANAL Barnsley
BRICKYARD PONDS Rotherham
BULL HOLE Doncaster
CAMPSALL COUNTRY PARK Doncaster
CHESTERFIELD CANAL Worksop
CROOKES VALLEY PARK LAKE Sheffield
CUMWELL LANE Rotherham
CUSWORTH HALL LAKE Doncaster
DAM FLASK RESERVOIR Sheffield
DEARNE (RIVER) Mexborough
DEARNE VALLEY PARK LAKE Barnsley
DELVES FISH PONDS Doncaster
DELVES LAKES Doncaster
DON (RIVER) Barnby Dun
DON (RIVER) Doncaster
DUKERIES LAKES Worksop
ECCLESFIELD POND Sheffield
ELSECAR CANAL Barnsley
ELSECAR RESERVOIR Barnsley
FINA HAYFIELD LAKES Doncaster
FITZWILLIAM CANAL Rotherham
FLEETS DAM Barnsley
GREASBROUGH DAMS Rotherham
HARTHILL RESERVIORS Worksop
HAVEN Doncaster
HOWBROOK RESERVOIR Sheffield
IDLE (RIVER) Doncaster
KIVETON HALL Sheffield
KJS FISHERIES Sheffield
LONG POND Doncaster
MEXBOROUGH CANAL Mexborough
MICKS PLACE Doncaster
MILTON PONDS Barnsley
MISSION LINEBANK PONDS Doncaster
NANCY POND Sheffield
NETHERWOOD COUNTRY PARK Barnsley
NEW JUNCTION CANAL Doncaster
NEWBIGGIN POND Rotherham
NORWOOD FISHERIES Sheffield
OLD DEARNE (RIVER) Mexborough
PEBLEY RESERVOIR Sheffield
PRESTON INNOVATIONS SILVER FISHERY Doncaster
RAILWAY POND Doncaster

- **ROSSINGTON BRICK POND** Doncaster
- **SALLY WALSHES DAM** Barnsley
- **SANDERSONS POND** Doncaster
- **SHEFFIELD AND SOUTH YORKSHIRE NAVIGATION** Mexborough
- **SHEFFIELD AND SOUTH YORKSHIRE NAVIGATION** Rotherham
- **SHEFFIELD CANAL** Sheffield
- **SHIREOAKS PARK** Worksop
- **SLIVER FISHERY** Doncaster
- **SMITHIES RESERVOIR** Barnsley
- **SOUTH YORKSHIRE NAVIGATION CANAL** Doncaster
- **SOUTHFIELD RESERVOIRS** Doncaster
- **STAINFORTH AND KEADBY CANAL** Doncaster
- **STANBOROUGH FISHERIES** Barnsley
- **STRAIGHT MILE FISHERY** Sheffield
- **THORNE NORTH POND** Doncaster
- **TINKERS PONDS** Barnsley
- **TOLL BAR POND** Doncaster
- **TORNE (RIVER)** Doncaster
- **TRENT (RIVER)** Sheffield
- **TRIANGS FISHERY** Doncaster
- **TYRAM HALL** Doncaster
- **ULLEY RESERVOIR** Sheffield
- **UNDERBANK RESERVOIR** Sheffield
- **WENTWORTH FISHERY** Rotherham
- **WESTWOOD COUNTRY PARK** Rotherham
- **WILLOW GARTH FISHERY** Doncaster
- **WILLOWGARTH LAKE** Doncaster
- **WINDTHORPE PITS** Sheffield
- **WINTHORPE LAKE** Sheffield
- **WOMBWELL DAM** Barnsley
- **WORSBOROUGH RESERVOIR** Barnsley
- **WORSBROUGH CANAL** Barnsley
- **WORSBROUGH RESERVOIR** Barnsley

YORKSHIRE (WEST)

- **ACKTON POND** Pontefract
- **AIRE (RIVER)** Leeds
- **AIRE AND CALDER CANAL** Oulton
- **BRIGHOUSE** Halifax
- **BROOKFOOT LAKE** Halifax
- **CALDER (RIVER)** Huddersfield
- **CALDER AND HEBBLE CANAL** Brighouse
- **CALDER AND HEBBLE CANAL** Hebden Bridge
- **CLAYTON WOOD PONDS** Leeds
- **CLEARWATER LAKE** Halifax
- **COPPICE POND** Bingley
- **DOE PARK RESERVOIR** Bradford
- **DYEHOUSE POND** Bradford
- **FLANSHAW DAM** Wakefield
- **HILL TOP RESERVOIR** Huddersfield
- **HOLME MILL DAM (SQUARE DAM)** Huddersfield
- **HOPTON WATERS** Mirfield
- **HORBURY LAGOON** Wakefield
- **HORNSEA MERE** Huddersfield
- **HOYLE MILL DAM** Pontefract
- **HUDDERSFIELD BROAD CANAL** Huddersfield
- **KIPPAX POND** Leeds
- **KNOTFORD LAGOON** Otley
- **LEEDS AND LIVERPOOL CANAL** Shipley
- **LEEDS TO LIVERPOOL CANAL** Leeds
- **LEEDS TO LIVERPOOL CANAL** Shipley
- **LONGBOTTOMS DAM** Batley
- **LOWTHER LAKE** Castleford
- **MILLRACE** Leeds
- **NARROW CANAL** Huddersfield
- **NOSTELL PRIORY LAKE** Wakefield
- **OAKS SCAR RESERVOIR** Huddersfield
- **PINFOLD DAMS** Huddersfield
- **PONTEFRACT PARK LAKE** Pontefract
- **PUGNEYS COUNTRY PARK** Wakefield
- **PUSH DAM** Huddersfield
- **ROBERTS POND** Keighley
- **ROCHDALE CANAL** Halifax
- **ROCHDALE CANAL** Hebden Bridge
- **ROCHDALE CANAL** Todmorden
- **ROUNDHAY PARK LAKES** Leeds
- **ROWLEY DAM** Huddersfield
- **ROYDS HALL DAM** Bradford
- **SPARTH RESERVOIR** Huddersfield
- **SPRING VALLEY WATERS** Wakefield
- **STAVELEY LAKES** Bradford
- **SWILLINGTON PARK** Leeds
- **T P POND DAM** Huddersfield
- **THORNHILL POND** Dewsbury
- **TP WOODS POND** Huddersfield
- **WHARFE (RIVER)** Leeds
- **WHARFE (RIVER)** Otley
- **WHARFE (RIVER)** Tadcaster
- **WHARFE (RIVER)** Wetherby
- **WINTERSETT RESERVOIR** Wakefield
- **WORKSHOP POND** Castleford
- **YEADON TARN** Bradford

GAME

BEDFORDSHIRE

- **LITTLE HEATH FARM TROUT FISHERY** Sandy

BERKSHIRE

- **BRAY LAKE** Maidenhead
- **FELIX FARM TROUT FISHERY** Bracknell
- **KENNET (RIVER)** Newbury
- **NEWBURY TROUT LAKES** Newbury
- **PANG VALLEY TROUT LAKE** Reading
- **SHEEPHOUSE FARM TROUT FISHERY** Maidenhead

BUCKINGHAMSHIRE

- **CHESS (RIVER)** Amersham
- **CHESS (RIVER)** Chesham
- **CHURCH HILL FISHERY** Milton Keynes
- **KINGFISHER GOLF CLUB** Milton Keynes
- **LATIMER PARK FLY FISHERY** Chesham
- **SUMMERFIELDS TROUT FISHERY** Bedford
- **VICARAGE SPINNEY TROUT FISHERY** Milton Keynes

CAMBRIDGESHIRE

- **GRAFHAM WATER** Huntingdon
- **NORTH BANK TROUT FISHERY** Peterborough
- **PERIO MILL** Peterborough
- **WHITE HOUSE TROUT FARM** Peterborough

CHESHIRE

- **BADDILEY RESERVOIR** Nantwich
- **BENTLEY TROUT POOL** Tarporley
- **CATCHPENNY POOL** Holmes Chapel
- **CLAY LANE FISHERY** Knutsford
- **DANE (RIVER)** Congleton
- **DANE (RIVER)** Macclesfield
- **DANEBRIDGE FISHERIES** Macclesfield
- **GOWY (RIVER)** Chester
- **HORSECOPPICE RESERVOIR** Macclesfield
- **LAMALOAD RESERVOIR** Macclesfield
- **MARTON HEATH TROUT POOLS** Macclesfield
- **MEADOW FISHERY** Chester
- **RIDGEGATE RESERVOIR** Macclesfield
- **WALKERWOOD RESERVOIR** Hyde
- **WALKERWOOD TROUT FISHERY** Stalybridge
- **WEAVER (RIVER)** Congleton
- **WEAVER (RIVER)** Middlewich
- **WESTLOW MERE** Congleton
- **WHIRLEY POOL** Macclesfield

CLEVELAND

- **LOCKWOOD BECK RESERVOIR** Guisborough
- **SCALING DAM** Guisborough

CORNWALL

- **BRAGGS WOOD TROUT FISHERY** Launceston
- **BUTTERWELL** Bodmin
- **CAMEL (RIVER)** Bodmin
- **CAMEL (RIVER)** Wadebridge
- **COLLIFORD LAKE** Liskeard
- **CONSTANTINE BROOK** Falmouth
- **CROWDY RESERVOIR** Camelford
- **DRIFT RESERVOIR** Penzance
- **FENWICK TROUT FISHERY** Bodmin
- **FOWEY (RIVER)** Bodmin
- **FOWEY (RIVER)** Liskeard
- **FOWEY (RIVER)** Looe
- **FOWEY (RIVER)** Lostwithiel
- **FULL BAG FISHERY** Newquay
- **GWARNICK MILL TROUT FISHERY** Truro
- **INNY (RIVER)** Liskeard
- **LAKE PENRYN** Penryn
- **LYNHER (RIVER)** Liskeard
- **MELANHYL LAKE** Newquay
- **ORVIS INNIS COUNTRY CLUB AND FLY FISHERY** St Austell
- **ROSE PARK FISHERY** Launceston
- **SEATON (RIVER)** Liskeard
- **SIBLYBACK LAKE** Liskeard
- **STITHIANS RESERVOIR** Truro
- **TEMPLE TROUT FISHERY** Bodmin
- **TREE MEADOW TROUT FISHERY** Hayle
- **VENN DOWN LAKES** Boscastle
- **VENTONTRISSICK FISHERY** Truro
- **WEST LOOE (RIVER)** Liskeard

COUNTY DURHAM

- **BEAMISH LAKE FLY FISHERY** Stanley
- **BLACKTON RESERVOIR** Barnard Castle
- **BURNHOPE FISHERY** Darlington
- **COW GREEN WILD BROWN TROUT FISHERY** Barnard Castle
- **DERWENT (RIVER)** Consett
- **GRASSHOLME RESERVOIR** Barnard Castle
- **HURY RESERVOIR** Barnard Castle
- **JUBILEE LAKES** Darlington
- **KNITSLEY MILL TROUT FISHERIES AND STUD FARM** Consett
- **SELSET RESERVOIR** Barnard Castle
- **TEES (RIVER)** Barnard Castle
- **TUNSTALL RESERVOIR** Bishop Auckland
- **WASKERLEY RESERVOIR** Consett
- **WEAR (RIVER)** Bishop Auckland
- **WEAR (RIVER)** Durham
- **WITTON CASTLE LAKES** Bishop Auckland

CUMBRIA

- **AIRA BECK** Penrith
- **ANNAS (RIVER)** Millom
- **ANNAS STREAM** Millom
- **BAYSTONE BANK RESERVIOR** Millom
- **BELA STREAM** Milnthorpe
- **BESSY BECK TROUT FARM** Kirkby Stephen
- **BLENCARN LAKE** Penrith
- **BORRANS RESERVOIR** Windermere
- **BRATHAY (RIVER)** Ambleside
- **CLOUGH (RIVER)** Sedbergh
- **CODALE TARN** Ambleside
- **COGRA MOSS** Cockermouth
- **CONISTON WATER** Coniston
- **CROSSFIELD FISHERY** Penrith

DEE (RIVER) Sedbergh
DERWENT (RIVER) Cockermouth
DERWENT (RIVER) Keswick
DEVOKE WATER Ravenglass
DOE (RIVER) Carnforth
DRUNKEN DUCK TARN FISHERY Ambleside
DUBBS TROUT FISHERY Windermere
EAMONT (RIVER) Penrith
EDEN (RIVER) Appleby-In-Westmorland
EDEN (RIVER) Kirkby Stephen
EDEN VALLEY TROUT LAKE Kirkby Stephen
EHEN (RIVER) Egremont
ELLEN (RIVER) Maryport
ENNERDALE LAKE FISHERY Egremont
ESK (RIVER) Ravenglass
FISHER TARN Kendal
GHYLL HEAD TROUT FISHERY Windermere
GRETA (RIVER) Carnforth
GRIZEDALE BECK Ambleside
HARLOCK RESERVOIR Dalton-In-Furness
HAWKSHEAD TROUT FISHING Ambleside
HAYESWATER RESERVOIR Ambleside
HIGH ARNSIDE TARN Ambleside
HIGH NEWTON RESERVOIR Windermere
IRT (RIVER) Holmrook
KENT (RIVER) Kendal
KENTMERE FISHERY Penrith
KNOTT END TARN Maryport
LAZY (RIVER) Millom
LICKLE (RIVER) Broughton-In-Furness
LIDDEL WATER Carlisle
LOUGHSIDE FISHERY Carlisle
LOW GILL Sedbergh
LOWTHER (RIVER) Penrith
LUNE (RIVER) Penrith
LUNE (RIVER) Sedbergh
LUNE (RIVER) Sedburgh
MEADLEY RESERVOIR Cleator Moor
MEDKLIN TARN FISHERY Holmrook
MOSS ECCLES TARN Ambleside
NETHERBY ESTATE Carlisle
NEW HILLS TROUT FARM FISHERY Brampton
OAKBANK LAKES Carlisle
PENNINIGTON RESERVOIR Dalton-In-Furness
PINFOLD LAKE Penrith
PRYHEAD FISHERY Alston
RAWTHEY (RIVER) Sedbergh
RAWTHEY (RIVER) Sedburgh
ROTHAY (RIVER) Ambleside
SANDFORD ARMS Appleby-In-Westmorland
SCHOOL KNOTT TARN Windermere
SHARPLEY WATERS Cockermouth
SOUTH TYNE (RIVER) Alston
TRANQUIL OTTER Carlisle
TWISS (RIVER) Carnforth
TYNE (RIVER) Alston
ULLSWATER LAKE Penrith
WATENDLATH TROUT FISHERY Keswick
WYCH ELM FISHERY Carnforth
YEW TREE TARN Coniston

DERBYSHIRE

ALTON MANOR FARM Matlock
CARSINGTON WATER Ashbourne
COTE LODGE RESERVOIR High Peak
DERBYSHIRE TROUT FISHERY Belper
DERWENT (RIVER) Bakewell
DERWENT (RIVER) Matlock
DONKHILL FISHERIES Swadlincote
DOVE (RIVER) Ashbourne
ERRWOOD RESERVOIR High Peak
FOREMARK TROUT FISHERY Derby
GOYT (RIVER) High Peak
HENMORE (RIVER) Ashbourne
LADYBOWER RESERVOIR Hope Valley
MONSAL DALE FISHERY Bakewell
MOSS BROOK Chesterfield
OGSTON RESERVOIR Chesterfield
SYDNOPE FISHERIES Matlock
TRENT (RIVER) Matlock
WYE (RIVER) Bakewell
WYE (RIVER) Matlock
YEAVELEY ESTATE TROUT FISHERY Ashbourne

DEVON

AVETON GIFFORD STREAM Kingsbridge
AVON (RIVER) Kingsbridge
AXE (RIVER) Axminster
AXE (RIVER) Colyton
BELLBROOK VALLEY TROUT FISHERY Tiverton
BLAKEWELL FISHERIES Barnstaple
BURRATOR RESERVOIR Plymouth
CAMEL (RIVER) Bodmin
DART (RIVER) Buckfastleigh
DELBROOK VALLEY TROUT FISHERY Tiverton
DRAKELANDS GAME FISHERY Plymouth
EGGESFORD COUNTRY HOTEL WATERS Chulmleigh
EXE (RIVER) Exeter
EXE (RIVER) Tiverton
FERNWORTHY RESERVOIR Newton Abbot
GAMMATON RESERVOIRS Bideford
GOODIFORD MILL TROUT FISHERY Cullompton
GREENACRE TROUT LAKES Beaworthy
HATSWELL Tiverton
HIGHAMPTON TROUT LAKES Beaworthy
HIGHER COWNHAYNE LAKES Colyton
HOLLIES TROUT FARM AND FISHERY Honiton
INNIS MOORE TROUT FISHERY Bodmin
KENNICK RESERVOIR Exeter
KINGLAKE FISHERY Beaworthy
LITTLE WARHAM FISHERY Winkleigh
LODDISWELL STREAM Kingsbridge
LYN (RIVER) Lynmouth
MELDON RESERVOIR Okehampton
MILL LEAT TROUT FISHERY Holsworthy
MOLE (RIVER) Umberleigh
NEWHOUSE FISHERY Totnes
PLYM (RIVER) Plymouth
ROADFORD RESERVOIR Okehampton
SOMERSWOOD LAKE South Brent
STILL WATERS TROUT FISHERY Honiton
TAMAR (RIVER) Lifton
TAMAR (RIVER) Tavistock
TAMAR LAKE (LOWER) Exeter
TAR (RIVER) Exeter
TAVISTOCK TROUT FISHERY Tavistock
TAVY (RIVER) Tavistock
TAW (RIVER) Barnstaple
TAW (RIVER) Crediton
TAW FISHING CLUB Crediton
TEIGN Exeter
TEIGN (RIVER) Newton Abbot
TORRIDGE (RIVER) Bideford
TORRIDGE (RIVER) Holsworthy
TOTTIFORD RESERVOIR Okehampton
UPPER YEALM FISHERY Ivybridge
VENFORD RESERVOIR Newton Abbot
WATERCRESS FARM TROUT FISHERY Newton Abbot
WATERSMEET AND GLENTHORNE FISHERIES Lynmouth
WISTLANDPOUND RESERVOIR Barnstaple
WOODA FARM FISHERY Holsworthy
YEO (RIVER) Crediton

DORSET

AMHERST LODGE FISHERY Lyme Regis
BRIT (RIVER) Bridport
CHAR STREAM Bridport
CRANEBROOK TROUT FISHERY Wimborne
FLOWERS FARM TROUT LAKES Dorchester
FROME (RIVER) Dorchester
LAWRENCES FARM Dorchester
PIDDLE (RIVER) Dorchester
RAWLSBURY WATERS Dorchester
WATERMILL LAKE Bridport
WHITESHEET TROUT FISHERY Wimborne

ESSEX

CLAVERING TROUT LAKE Saffron Walden
GREEN OAKS TROUT FISHERY Billericay
HANNINGFIELD TROUT FISHERY Chelmsford
NORTON FISHERY Romford
OLD HALL FARM TROUT FISHERY Colchester
SLOUGH HOUSE WATER Maldon

GLOUCESTERSHIRE

BROOK FARM TROUT FISHERY Gloucester
BUSHYLEAZE TROUT FISHERY Lechlade
CHURCH END TROUT FISHERY Tewkesbury
CHURN POOL TROUT FISHERY Cirencester
COLN (RIVER) Cirencester
COLN (RIVER) Fairford
DONNINGTON TROUT FISHERY Cheltenham
GREAT BURROWS TROUT FISHERY Dursley
LECHLADE TROUT FISHERY Lechlade
RAINBOW LAKES Cirencester
SANTHILL FISHERY Cheltenham
STEANBRIDGE FISHERY Stroud
WITCOMBE WATERS Gloucester

HAMPSHIRE

ABBOTTS WORTHY Andover
ANTON (RIVER) Andover
AVINGTON TROUT FISHERIES Winchester
CANDOVER BROOK Alresford
CHIPHALL LAKE TROUT FISHERY Fareham
DEVER SPRINGS TROUT FISHERY Winchester
FIVE OAKS TROUT LAKE Southampton
HOLBURY LAKES Romsey
ITCHEN (RIVER) Winchester
JOHN OGAUNTS FISHERY Stockbridge
KIMBRIDGE Andover
LEOMINSTEAD TROUT FISHERY Lyndhurst
MEON SPRINGS FLY FISHERY Petersfield
MOORHEN FARM TROUT LAKE Southampton
NETHER WALLOP FLY FISHING SCHOOL Stockbridge
PARSONAGE (RIVER) TEST Romsey

- **RIVER FARM** Fareham
- **ROCKBOURNE TROUT FISHERY** Fordingbridge
- **ROOKSBURY MILL TROUT FISHERIES** Andover
- **TEST (RIVER)** Stockbridge
- **TESTWOOD SALMON FISHERIES** Southampton
- **VALE FARM FISHERY** Andover
- **WHITE HOUSE TROUT FARM** Hook
- **WINTERSHILL TROUT LAKE** Southampton
- **WOODINGTON FISHERY** Romsey
- **WOODMILL SALMON FISHERY** Southampton

HEREFORDSHIRE

- **CARADOC FISHERY** Ross-on-Wye
- **COPPICE TROUT FISHERY** Hereford
- **INGESTONE FISHERY** Ross-on-Wye
- **KINGFISHER TROUT LAKE** Bromyard
- **LLYNFI (RIVER)** Hereford
- **LUGG (RIVER)** Hereford
- **MARLIAS (RIVER)** Hereford
- **MONNOW (RIVER)** Hereford
- **TOAD HALL FISHERY** Hereford
- **WYE (RIVER)** Hereford

HERTFORDSHIRE

- **BOXMOOR TROUT FISHERY** Hemel Hempstead
- **RIB VALLEY FISHING LAKE** Ware

HUMBERSIDE

- **ESK (RIVER)** Grimsby
- **WANSFORD TROUT LAKE** Driffield

KENT

- **BEWL WATER** Lamberhurst
- **BRITTON COURT FARM** Canterbury
- **CHALYBEATE SPRINGS TROUT FISHERY** Tunbridge Wells
- **DARENT (RIVER)** Orpington
- **HAYES TROUT FISHERY** Bromley
- **MOUSEHOLE LAKE** Tonbridge
- **ROTHER (RIVER)** Tenterden
- **SEPHAM TROUT FISHERY** Sevenoaks
- **SPRING HILL TROUT WATERS** Tunbridge Wells
- **STATION FARM** Ashford
- **STOUTING LAKE** Canterbury
- **STOWTING TROUT LAKE** Ashford
- **TENTERDEN TROUT WATERS** Tenterden
- **WOODCHURCH TROUT FISHERY** Ashford

LANCASHIRE

- **ADLINGTON RESERVOIR** Bolton
- **ANGLEZARKE RESERVOIR** Wigan
- **BANK HOUSE FLY FISHERY** Lancaster
- **BARNSFOLD WATERS** Preston
- **BENTHAM STREAM** Lancaster
- **BENTHAM TROUT FISHERY** Lancaster
- **BLACKMOSS RESERVOIR** Nelson
- **BROWNHILL RESERVOIR** Colne
- **CALDER (RIVER)** Blackburn
- **CALDER (RIVER)** Burnley
- **CANT CLOUGH RESERVOIR** Burnley
- **COLDWELL (LOWER) RESERVOIR** Burnley
- **COLNE WATER** Colne
- **CONDER VALLEY FLY FISHERY** Lancaster
- **DEAN CLOUGH RESERVOIR** Accrington
- **DEAN RESERVOIR** Darwen
- **DILWORTH (UPPER) RESERVOIR** Preston
- **DRAKESHEAD FLY FISHERY** Chorley
- **DUDDON (RIVER)** Broughton-In-Furness
- **EARNSDALE RESERVOIR** Blackburn
- **ENTWHISTLES RESERVOIR** Blackburn
- **GRIZEDALE LEA RESERVOIR** Preston
- **HODDER (RIVER)** Blackburn
- **HODDER (RIVER)** Clitheroe
- **HODDLESDEN LAKE** Blackburn
- **HULLDOWN TROUT FISHERY** Colne
- **INGS FARM TROUT FISHERY** Nelson
- **LOVECLOUGH TROUT FISHERY** Rossendale
- **LOWER COLDWELL RESERVOIR** Burnley
- **LUNE (RIVER)** Lancaster
- **MITCHELLS HOUSE RESERVOIR** Accrington
- **OGDEN RESERVOIR** Rossendale
- **RIBBLE (RIVER)** Blackburn
- **ROUGHLEE TROUT FISHERY** Nelson
- **SABDEN RESERVOIR** Clitheroe
- **SKERTON FISHERY** Lancaster
- **SPADE MILL RESERVOIR NO.2** Preston
- **STOCKS FLY FISHERY** Clitheroe
- **SWINDEN RESERVOIR** Burnley
- **TURTON AND ENTWISTLE RESERVOIR** Preston
- **TWIN LAKES TROUT FISHERY** Preston
- **UPPER RODDLESWORTH RESERVOIR** Bolton
- **WENNING (RIVER)** Clapham
- **WENNING (RIVER)** Lancaster

LEICESTERSHIRE

- **EYEBROOK TROUT FISHERY** Market Harborough
- **LAKESIDE SPORTING** Leicester
- **MONNOW (RIVER)** Leicester
- **STEMBOROUGH MILL TROUT FARM** Lutterworth
- **THORNTON RESERVOIR** Leicester

LINCOLNSHIRE

- **CLAYBRIDGE TROUT LAKES** Market Rasen
- **ST EAU FISHING SYNDICATE** Market Rasen
- **SYSTON PARK TROUT LAKE** Grantham
- **THORPE LE VALE FISHERY** Louth
- **TOFT NEWTON TROUT FISHERY** Market Rasen
- **TRENT (RIVER)** Gainsborough

LONDON (GREATER)

- **ASHMERE FISHERIES** London
- **ASHVALE FISHERIES** London
- **ENFIELD LOCK** London
- **HALLIFORD MERE LAKES** London
- **SYON PARK FISHERY** London
- **WALTHAMSTOW RESERVOIR (NO 4 TROUT)** London
- **WALTHAMSTOW RESERVOIR (NO 5)** London

MANCHESTER (GREATER)

- **BLACK BECK (RIVER)** Millom
- **FISHERMANS RETREAT** Bury
- **KITCLIFFE RESERVOIR** Oldham
- **LOWER CASTLESHAW RESERVOIR** Oldham
- **OLDHAM FLY FISHING** Oldham
- **PENNINE TROUT FISHERY** Rochdale
- **PIETHORNE RESERVOIR** Rochdale
- **WATERGROVE RESERVOIR** Rochdale

MERSEYSIDE

- **WOODHOUSE FISH FARM** Newton-Le-Willows

MIDLANDS (WEST)

- **PACKINGTON TROUT FISHERY** Coventry
- **SHUSTOKE FLY FISHERS** Birmingham

NORFOLK

- **ABBOTS HALL** Norwich
- **BURE (RIVER)** Great Yarmouth
- **LENWADE TROUT FISHERY** Norwich
- **NAR (RIVER)** King's Lynn
- **NAR STREAM** King's Lynn
- **NORFOLK AND SUFFOLK FLY FISHERIES LAKE** Dereham
- **SALMON AND TROUT ASSOCIATION LAKES** Dereham
- **UPPER BURE (STREAM)** Aylesham
- **WHINBURGH TROUT LAKE** Dereham

NORTHAMPTONSHIRE

- **PITSFORD RESERVOIR** Northampton
- **RAVENSTHORPE TROUT FISHERY** Northampton
- **RINGSTEAD GRANGE TROUT FISHERY** Kettering

NORTHUMBERLAND

- **ALN (RIVER)** Alnwick
- **COQUET (RIVER)** Morpeth
- **FONTBURN RESERVOIR** Morpeth
- **GIBBS HILL TROUT FISHERY** Hexham
- **HADRIAN LODGE** Hexham
- **HEXHAM FISHERIES** Hexham
- **IRTHING (RIVER)** Haltwhistle
- **KIELDER WATER** Hexham
- **LANGLEY DAM FISHERIES** Hexham
- **LEET (RIVER)** Coldstream
- **LINNEL WOOD LAKE** Hexham
- **LYNE (RIVER)** Coldstream
- **NORTH TYNE (RIVER)** Hexham
- **REDE (RIVER)** Hexham
- **SOUTH TYNE (RIVER)** Haltwhistle
- **TWEED (RIVER)** Berwick-upon-Tweed
- **TWEED (RIVER)** Coldstream
- **TYNE (RIVER)** Hexham
- **TYNE (RIVER)** Stocksfield
- **WANSBECK (RIVER)** Ashington
- **WANSBECK (RIVER)** Morpeth
- **WANSBECK STREAM** Morpeth
- **WHITEADDER (RIVER)** Berwick-upon-Tweed
- **WHITTLE DEAN RESERVOIR** Hexham
- **WREIGH (RIVER)** Thropton

NOTTINGHAMSHIRE

- **CRANWELL LANE TROUT FISHERY** Newark
- **CROMWELL LAKE TROUT FISHERY** Newark
- **LAKESIDE FARM** Grantham
- **OWDY LANE TROUT FISHERY** Worksop

OXFORDSHIRE

- **CLEARWATER FISH FARM** Wantage
- **CORNBURY PARK FISHERY** Chipping Norton
- **DARLOW LAKE** Witney
- **FARMOOR 1 RESERVOIR** Witney
- **FARMOOR TROUT FISHERY** Oxford
- **HEART OF ENGLAND FISHERY** Banbury
- **LOCKINGE TROUT FISHERY** Wantage
- **MILLETS FARM TROUT FISHERY** Abingdon
- **SALFORD TROUT LAKES** Chipping Norton
- **THAMES (RIVER)** Henley-on-Thames

RUTLAND

- **WELLAND (RIVER)** Oakham

SHROPSHIRE

- **COUND TROUT FISHERY** Shrewsbury

DEARNFORD HALL TROUT FISHERY Whitchurch
DELBURY HALL TROUT FISHERY Craven Arms
LAKE VYRNWY Oswestry
ONNY (RIVER) Ludlow
TANAT (RIVER) Oswestry
TERN (RIVER) Market Drayton
TERN FISHERIES Market Drayton
VOWNOG FISH LAKE Oswestry

SOMERSET

AVON (RIVER) Bath
BARLE (RIVER) Dulverton
BARROW RESERVOIRS Bristol
BLAGDON LAKE Bristol
CAMELEY TROUT LAKES Bristol
CHEW VALLEY LAKE Bristol
CLATWORTHY RESERVOIR Taunton
EXE (RIVER) Dulverton
EXE VALLEY FISHERY Dulverton
FROME (RIVER) Bath
HADDOE TROUT FISHERY Dulverton
HAWKRIDGE RESERVOIR Bridgwater
HORNER WATER Minehead
LITTLE EXE Dulverton
LITTON RESERVOIR Bristol
MINERS PONDS Somerton
OTTERHEAD LAKES Taunton
PARRET (RIVER) Crewkerne
QUANTOCK FISHERIES Bridgwater
ST ALGARS FARM LAKE Frome
SUTTON BINGHAM RESERVOIR Yeovil
TONE (RIVER) Taunton
WIMBLEBALL LAKE Dulverton
WOOLBRIDGE MANOR Frome

STAFFORDSHIRE

BLITHFIELD RESERVOIR Rugeley
CHURNET (RIVER) Leek
CHURNET (RIVER) Uttoxeter
DOVE (RIVER) Longnor
DOVE (RIVER) Uttoxeter
GAILEY TROUT AND PIKE FISHERY Stafford
LOYNTON TROUT FISHERIES Stafford
RISING TROUT FISHERY Stoke-on-Trent
SHELMORE TROUT FISHERY Stafford
TITTESWORTH RESERVOIR Leek
TRENT (RIVER) Stone

SUFFOLK

CROSS GREEN FLY FISHERY Bury St Edmunds
HATCHERY HOUSE TROUT LAKES Bury St Edmunds
LARKWOOD TROUT FISHERY Bury St Edmunds
WILLOW LAKES TROUT FISHERY Halesworth
WYE (RIVER) Saxmundham

SURREY

ALBURY ESTATE FISHERIES Guildford
CROSSWATER MILL FISHERY Farnham
DEE (RIVER) Guildford
ENTON LAKES TROUT FISHERY Godalming
FRENSHAM TROUT FISHERY Farnham
POWDER MILLS FISHERY Guildford
WESTON FISHERY Guildford
WEY (RIVER) Godalming
WILLINGHURST TROUT FISHERY Guildford
WINKWORTH LAKES Godalming
WINTERSHALL WATERS Godalming

SUSSEX (EAST)

ARLINGTON TROUT FISHERY Polegate
ASHBOURNE TROUT FISHERY Battle
BARCOMBE RESERVOIR Lewes
BORINGWHEEL TROUT FISHERY Uckfield
BRICK FARM LAKE Hailsham
COLIN GODMANS TROUTING Uckfield
CYPRUS WOOD TROUT FISHERY Uckfield
DARWELL WATER Robertsbridge
KINGS STANDING LAKES Crowborough
LAKEDOWN TROUT FISHERY Etchingham
POWDERMILL (GREAT SANDERS) WATER Battle
ROTHER (RIVER) Robertsbridge
YEW TREE TROUT FISHERY Crowborough

SUSSEX (WEST)

BLACKWOOL TROUT FISHERY Petworth
CASTLE TROUT POND Arundel
CHALK SPRINGS TROUT FISHERY Arundel
DUNCTON MILL Petworth
HAMBROOK TROUT FISHERY Chichester
HAYWARDS HEATH RIVER Haywards Heath
HAZELCOPSE LAKES Horsham
LECONFIELD ESTATE Petworth
OUSE (RIVER) Littlehampton
WATER MEADOWS FLY FISHERIES Pulborough
WATTLEHURST FARM TROUT LAKES Horsham

TYNE AND WEAR

DERWENT (RIVER) Rowlands Gill
REDE (RIVER) Newcastle Upon Tyne
SWEETHOPE LOUGHS Newcastle Upon Tyne
TYNE (RIVER) Newcastle Upon Tyne
WHITTLE DENE TROUT FISHERY Newcastle Upon Tyne

WARWICKSHIRE

ARDENCOTE MANOR HOTEL AND COUNTRY CLUB Warwick
CHESTERTON MILL POOL TROUT FISHERY Leamington Spa
DRAYCOTE WATER Rugby
HEATHCOTE LAKE Warwick
WARWICKSHIRE AVON Warwick

WILTSHIRE

AVON (RIVER) Salisbury
AVON SPRINGS FISHERY Salisbury
LANGFORD FISHERIES Salisbury
MILL FARM TROUT LAKES Devizes
MILLBROOK TROUT FARM Salisbury
SUTTON VENY ESTATE Warminster
ZEALS TROUT FISHERY Warminster

WORCESTERSHIRE

BLACK MONK TROUT LAKES Evesham
BRANSFORD GAME FISHERY Worcester
BROCKHILL FARM TROUT POOLS Redditch
LENCHES LAKES Evesham
MASTERS (THE) Kidderminster
RED BECK LAKE Evesham
SINDON MILL FARM Malvern

YORKSHIRE (NORTH)

BELLFLASK TROUT FISHERY Ripon
BLACKBURN FARM TROUT FISHERY Hawes
BOLTON ABBEY FISHERIES Skipton
CRABTREE ANGLING LAKE Richmond
DANBY (RIVER) Whitby
DERWENT (RIVER) Scarborough
EGTON BRIDGE (RIVER) Whitby
EGTON ESTATE BEAT Whitby
EMBSAY RESERVOIR Skipton
ESK (RIVER) Whitby
FARMIRE TROUT FISHERY Knaresborough
GLAISDALE (RIVER) Whitby
HAZELHEAD LAKE Pickering
KILNSEY PARK AND TROUT FARM Skipton
KINLIN HALL TROUT FARM Ripon
KIPLIN TROUT FISHERY Northallerton
LAKESIDE FISHERIES Richmond
LAVER (RIVER) Ripon
LEIGHTON RESERVOIR Ripon
LOW OSGOODBY LAKE Thirsk
MARSTON WYSE TROUT FARM York
NIDD (RIVER) Harrogate
OUSE (RIVER) Skipton
PICKERING TROUT LAKE Pickering
RICCAL (RIVER) Malton
RIVER VIEW COTTAGE Thirsk
RUSWARP (RIVER) Whitby
RYE (RIVER) York
SCAR HOUSE RESERVOIR Ripon
SHIELD TROUT FISHERY Ripon
SINNINGTON (RIVER) York
SKELL (RIVER) Ripon
SKIRFARE (RIVER) Skipton
SLEIGHTS (RIVER) Whitby
STONEBRIDGE LAKES Northallerton
SWINTON ESTATE TROUT FISHERY Ripon
TANFIELD LAKE Ripon
THORNTON STEWARD RESERVOIR Ripon
TROUT POND BARN Malton
URE (RIVER AND TRIBUTARIES) Hawes
URE (RIVER) Hawes
URE (RIVER) Leyburn
WASHBURN VALLEY (FEWSTON AND SWINSTY) Harrogate
WATERMEADOWS FISHERY York
WHARFE (RIVER) Skipton
WYKEHAM LAKES Scarborough

YORKSHIRE (SOUTH)

CHESTERFIELD CANAL Sheffield
HORSESHOE LAKE TROUT FISHERY Sheffield
MORE HALL RESERVOIR Sheffield
SCOUT DYKE RESERVOIR Sheffield
THRYBERGH COUNTRY PARK Rotherham
WHARNCLIFFE FLY FISHERY Sheffield

YORKSHIRE (WEST)

BILLING DAM Leeds
COLNE (RIVER) Huddersfield
HOLME (RIVER) Huddersfield
SWINSTY AND FEWSTON RESERVOIRS Otley
TONG PARK DAM Shipley
WALTON HALL TROUT LAKE Wakefield

COMBINATION

BEDFORDSHIRE

LAKESIDE TROUT AND COARSE FISHERY Leighton Buzzard
MANOR FARM LEISURE Biggleswade

BERKSHIRE

BARTON COURT FISHERY Hungerford
BRAY LOCK Maidenhead

HURLEY LOCK Maidenhead
KENNET (RIVER) Reading
KENNET AND AVON CANAL Reading
REDLANDS LAKE Reading
ROMNEY ISLAND AND MEADOW Windsor
SLALFORD LAKES Reading
SOUTH LAKE Reading

BUCKINGHAMSHIRE

ALDERS FARM TROUT FISHERY Milton Keynes

CAMBRIDGESHIRE

EARITH FISHERY Huntingdon
FEN DRAYTON COMPLEX Cambridge
FENLAND FISHERIES Huntingdon

CHESHIRE

APPLETON RESERVOIR Warrington
ASHLEY (RIVER) Macclesfield
BOLLIN (RIVER) Knutsford
CHESHIRE FISHING Chester
GOWY FISHERY Chester
KAZAKO PONDS Macclesfield
WINCHAM BROOK Northwich

CORNWALL

BAKE FISHING LAKES Saltash
BUSH LAKES FARM Saltash
DUTSON WATER Launceston
TAMAR (RIVER) Launceston

COUNTY DURHAM

BROWNEY (RIVER) Durham
BYERS GREEN Spennymoor
FINCHALE ABBEY FARM Durham
HURWORTH BURN RESERVOIR Darlington
RABY ESTATES WATER Darlington
TEES (RIVER) Barnard Castle
TEES (RIVER) Darlington
WEAR (RIVER) Chester-Le-Street
WEAR (RIVER) Crook
WEAR (RIVER) Durham

CUMBRIA

ATKINSONS TARN COARSE FISHERY Windermere
BASSENTHWAITE LAKE Keswick
BLELHAM TARN Ambleside
BUTTERMERE LAKE Cockermouth
CRUMMOCK WATER LAKE Cockermouth
EASEDALE TARN Ambleside
EDEN (RIVER) Appleby-In-Westmorland
ESTHWAITE WATER Ambleside
GOODENBURGH TARN Carnforth
GRASMERE COARSE FISHERY Ambleside
HAWESWATER Penrith
KENT (RIVER) Kendal
KILLINGTON RESERVOIR Kendal
LAKE WINDERMERE Windermere
LOUGHRIGG TARN Ambleside
LOWESWATER LAKE Cockermouth
RYDAL WATER Ambleside
SPRINT (RIVER) Kendal
TEWITFIELDS TROUT FISHERY Carnforth
THIRLMERE Keswick
WHINS POND Penrith
WINSTER (RIVER) Grange-Over-Sands
WINSTER (RIVER) Keswick

DERBYSHIRE

BARLOW FISHERIES Chesterfield
HADDON ESTATE FISHERIES Bakewell
PRESS MANOR Chesterfield
SUTTON BROOK Hilton

DEVON

ALDER LAKE Okehampton
BULWORTHY FISHERY Bideford
CREEDY (RIVER) Crediton
CREEDY (RIVER) Exeter
CULM (RIVER) Exeter
DEER PARK COUNTRY HOTEL Honiton
FOSFELLE COUNTRY HOUSE HOTEL Bideford
HATCHLAND TROUT FISHERY South Brent
OTTER (RIVER) Honiton
OTTER FALLS FISHERY Honiton
SOUTH HAY FARM Beaworthy
STAFFORD MOOR FISHERY Winkleigh
TINNEY WATERS Holsworthy
VALLEY SPRINGS TROUT FISHERY Kingsbridge
WISCOMBE FISHERY Colyton

DORSET

AVON (RIVER) Christchurch
CHRISTCHURCH LOWER STOUR Christchurch
FROME AND PIDDLE (RIVERS) Wimborne
GOLDEN SPRINGS LAKES Christchurch
HERMITAGE LAKES Dorchester
PALLINGTON LAKES Dorchester
ROYALTY FISHERY Christchurch
STOUR (DORSET) (RIVER) Christchurch
THROOP FISHERIES Bournemouth
WINKTON FISHERY Christchurch

ESSEX

BLUNTS AND CANTS MERES Chelmsford
BRICKHOUSE FARM FISHERIES Brentwood
CARP FARM FRYERNING FISHERIES Ingatestone
CHIGBOROUGH FISHERIES Maldon
PANT (RIVER) Braintree

GLOUCESTERSHIRE

COURT FARM Moreton-In-Marsh
FROME STREAM Stroud
HUNTLEY CARP POOLS Gloucester
MILESTONE FISHERY Fairford
NORTON FRUIT FARM Gloucester
SEVERN (RIVER) Dymock

HAMPSHIRE

AVON (RIVER) Ringwood
AVON RIVER FISHERIES Fordingbridge
FRIMLEY LAKES Farnborough
HAMPSHIRE AVON (RIVER) Fordingbridge
LOWER ITCHEN FISHERY Romsey
STOUR (RIVER) Ringwood
TEST (RIVER) Romsey
WHITEWATER (RIVER) Heckfield

HEREFORDSHIRE

DOCKLOW POOLS Leominster
HAYCASTLE WATER Hereford
WYE (RIVER) Hereford
WYE (RIVER) Ross-on-Wye

HERTFORDSHIRE

CROXLEY HALL TROUT FISHERY Rickmansworth
LEE NAVIGATION Bishops Stortford
NEW RIVER Ware
OLD LEE (RIVER) Waltham Cross
OLD LEE (RIVER) Wormley
OUGHTON (RIVER) Hitchin

HUMBERSIDE

BILLABONG WATER SPORTS AND CARAVAN PARK Driffield
DRIFFIELD CANAL Beverley
FISH TRADES POND Brough
LANGHOLME FISHERIES Driffield
NORTH THORESBY FISHERIES Grimsby
STAR CARR TROUT FARM Driffield
WILLOW LAKES Grimsby

ISLE OF WIGHT

HALE MANOR LAKES Newport
ISLAND FISH FARM AND MEADOW LAKES Newport

KENT

BARTLEY MILL FISHERY Tunbridge Wells
BOUGH BEECH RESERVOIR Tonbridge
CHEQUERTREE TROUT AND COARSE FISHERY Ashford
COTTINGTON LAKES TROUT AND COARSE FISHERY Deal
HAWKHURST FISH FARM Cranbrook
HOATHLEY FISHERY Lamberhurst
MID KENT FISHERIES Canterbury
TEISE (RIVER) Tunbridge Wells

LANCASHIRE

ERIC FISHWICK NATURE RESERVE Preston
GLEAVES RESERVOIR Bolton
GRIMSARGH RESERVOIR Preston
HALTON FISHERY Lancaster
LANESHAW RESERVOIR Burnley
PENDLE WATER Nelson
RAKE BROOK RESERVOIR Chorley
RIBBLE (RIVER) Clitheroe
RIBBLE (RIVER) Preston
RUSHYVARS LAKES Preston
WALVERDEN RESERVOIR Nelson
WYRE (RIVER) Kirkham
WYRESIDE LAKES FISHERY AND LODGINGS Lancaster

LEICESTERSHIRE

PROCTORS PLEASURE PARK Leicester
RUTLAND WATER Rutland

LINCOLNSHIRE

BUCKMINSTER PARK LAKE Grantham
GRANGE FARM LEISURE Mablethorpe
HOLLAND PARK Skegness
LAKESIDE LEISURE PARK Skegness
OLSTEN FISHERY Louth

LONDON (GREATER)

FURNACE POND London
PENTON HOOK LOCK London
SHEPPERTON LOCK London
WALTHAMSTOW RESERVOIR (EAST WARWICK) London
WALTHAMSTOW RESERVOIR (WEST WARWICK) London

MANCHESTER (GREATER)

BOLLINHURST RESERVOIR Stockport
CLEGG HALL LAKES Littleborough
DOWRY AND NEW YEARS BRIDGE RESERVOIR Oldham
TAME (RIVER) Oldham
TWINE VALLEY TROUT FISHERY Bury
WHITELEY KNOWL RESERVOIR Littleborough

MIDLANDS (WEST)

ASTBURY FALLS FISH FARM Bridgnorth
PATSHULL PARK Wolverhampton
POOL HALL Bridgnorth

NORFOLK

BURE VALLEY LAKES Aylesham
NARBOROUGH TROUT FARM King's Lynn
WENSUM (RIVER) Fakenham
WENSUM (RIVER) Norwich

NORTHAMPTONSHIRE

ELINOR TROUT FISHERY Kettering

NORTHUMBERLAND

NORTH TYNE (RIVER) Hexham

PLESSEY WOODS Morpeth
TWEED (RIVER) Alnwick
TYNE (RIVER) Corbridge
TYNE (RIVER) Prudhoe
TYNE (RIVER) Wylam

NOTTINGHAMSHIRE

COLWICK COUNTRY PARK Nottingham
LAKESIDE FISHERY Retford
TRENT (RIVER) Nottingham

OXFORDSHIRE

BARNES TROUT LAKES Oxford
BENSON LOCK Wallingford
BUSCOT LOCK Faringdon
CLIFTON LOCK Abingdon
DAYS LOCK Abingdon
GRAFTON LOCK Bampton
MARSH LOCK Henley-on-Thames
RADCOT LOCK Faringdon
RUSHEY LOCK Faringdon
SANDFORD LOCK Oxford
SHIFFORD LOCK Bampton
SHIPLAKE LOCK Henley-on-Thames
WINDRUSH (RIVER) Burford

RUTLAND

NORMANTON FISHING LODGE Oakham

SHROPSHIRE

BOLDINGS POOLS Bridgnorth
ELLERDINE LAKES Telford
MILLRIDE FISHERY Wolverhampton
RIVER (TERN) Shrewsbury
SEVERN (RIVER) Much Wenlock
SEVERN (RIVER) Shrewsbury
SWEENEYCLIFFE HOUSE FISHERY Telford
TERN (RIVER) Market Drayton
TURFMOOR FISHERY Oswestry
VYRNWY (RIVER) Oswestry

SOMERSET

AVON (RIVER) Bath
BRUE (RIVER) Street

STAFFORDSHIRE

BLITHE (RIVER) Uttoxeter
DOVE (RIVER) Burton-on-Trent
FISHERWICK LAKES Lichfield
HAMPS (RIVER) Leek
HANCHURCH FISHERIES Stoke-on-Trent
IZAAK WALTON FISHERY Stafford
MIDLAND GAME FISHERIES Lichfield

SUFFOLK

ALDE (RIVER) Aldeburgh
CHESTERFORD FISHERIES Sudbury
LARK (RIVER) Brandon
LARK (RIVER) Bury St Edmunds

SURREY

BELL WEIR LOCK Egham
KINGFISHER FISHERY Haslemere
MOLESEY LOCK East Molesey
WAGGONERS WELLS Hindhead

SUSSEX (EAST)

HORAM MANOR FISHERY Heathfield
OLD MILL Lewes
OUSE (RIVER) Lewes
SPRING WOOD FISHERY AND FARM Wadhurst
WEIR WOOD FISHERY Forest Row

SUSSEX (WEST)

ADUR (RIVER) Henfield
ADUR (RIVER) Steyning
ARUN (RIVER) Littlehampton
ARUN (RIVER) Petworth
ARUN (RIVER) Pulborough

TYNE AND WEAR

MAIN TYNE Newcastle Upon Tyne
TEES (RIVER) Yarm
TYNE (RIVER) Newcastle Upon Tyne
TYNE (RIVER) Ryton
WEAR (RIVER) Washington

WARWICKSHIRE

MAKIN FISHERIES Bedworth
TUNNEL BARN FARM Warwick

WILTSHIRE

BRITFORD FISHERY Salisbury
HUNTERS MOON Warminster
LOWER MOOR FISHERY Malmesbury
MANOR BROOK LAKE Swindon
NADDER (RIVER) Salisbury

WORCESTERSHIRE

HUXLEYS HAMPTON FERRY FISHERIES Evesham
LEDWYCHE BROOK Tenbury Wells
LENCHFORD Worcester
POOLE HALL FISHERY Kidderminster
SEVERN (RIVER) Bewdley
SILLIGROVE FISHERY Bewdley
TEME (RIVER) Bewdley
TEME (RIVER) Tenbury Wells
TEME (RIVER) Worcester
TRIMPLEY RESERVOIR Bewdley

YORKSHIRE (NORTH)

BLEA TARN Scarborough
LEEMING (RIVER) Northallerton
NEWBY HALL FISHERIES Ripon
NIDD (RIVER) Knaresborough
NIDD BRIDGE Harrogate
RAKER LAKES York
RYE (RIVER) Malton
RYE AND SEVEN (RIVERS) Malton
SEMERWATER Hawes
SHIELD FISHERY Bedale
SWALE (RIVER) Northallerton
SWALE (RIVER) Richmond
TYNE (RIVER) Ripon
URE (RIVER) Ripon
WHARFE (RIVER) Skipton
WHINNYGILL RESERVOIR Skipton

YORKSHIRE (WEST)

AIRE (RIVER) Keighley
AIRE (RIVER) Shipley
BOSTON SPA Wetherby
BOTTOMS DAM Huddersfield
CALDER (RIVER) Bradford
CALDER (RIVER) Todmorden
NEW MILL DAM Todmorden
OUSE (RIVER) Wetherby
RAYGILL FISHERY Keighley
WALSDEN PRINTING CO LODGES Todmorden
WHARFE (RIVER) Ilkley
WHARFE (RIVER) Wetherby

CANALS

COUNTY KILDARE

- **GRAND CANAL** Prosperous
- **GRAND CANAL** Robertstown
- **GRAND CANAL (BARROW BRANCH)** Rathangon
- **GRAND CANAL (BARROW TRACK)** Athy

COUNTY OFFALY

- **EDENDERRY OFFALY EIRE** Edenderry
- **GRAND CANAL** Edenderry

COMBINATIONS

COUNTY CLARE

- **ALLARD FISHERIES** Ennis

COUNTY CORK

- **BLACKWATER SALMON FISHERY** Castlelyons

COUNTY DONEGAL

- **CLOGHAN LODGE ESTATE FISHERY** Cloghan
- **ROSSES FISHERY** Burtonport

COUNTY GALWAY

- **BALLYNAHINCH CASTLE FISHERY** Recess
- **DOOHULLA** Ballyconneely
- **ERRIFF FISHERY** Leenane

COUNTY KERRY

- **KERRYFISHERIES** Waterville

COUNTY TIPPERARY

- **CLONANAU FLY FISHING CENTRE** Clonmel
- **NORE (RIVER)** Mountrath

LAKES

COUNTY CAVAN

- **ARDAN GRANGE GUEST HOUSE AND ANGLING CENTRE** Belturbet
- **BAILIEBORO LAKES** Bailieborough

COUNTY CLARE

- **DROMORE AND BALLYLINE** Corofin
- **LICKEEN LAKE** Kilfenara

COUNTY CORK

- **CHAPEL LAKE** Dunmanway
- **CURRAGHALICKEY LAKE** Dunmanway
- **DERRYVEGALL LAKE** Castletownbere
- **DRIMINIDY LAKE** Drimoleague
- **DROMANA LAKE** Cappoquin
- **GARRANES LAKE** Dunmanway
- **INNISCARRA LAKE** Inniscarra
- **SHEPPERTON LAKES** Skibbereen

COUNTY GALWAY

- **CLOONDROON LAKE** Claremorris
- **KYLEMORE HOUSE FISHERY** Connemara
- **MAYFIELD LAKE** Claremorris
- **ROSS LAKE** Moycullen
- **SCREEBE FISHERY** Connemara

COUNTY KERRY

- **LAKE HOUSE HOTEL** Kenmare
- **LAKES OF KILLARNEY** Killarney

COUNTY KILKENNY

- **BALLINAKILL LAKE** Kilkenny

COUNTY MAYO

- **CASTLEBAR LAKES** Castlebar
- **LOUGHS COY CULLIN** Foxford

COUNTY MEATH

- **RATHBEGGAN LAKES** Dunshaughlin

COUNTY SLIGO

- **LAKE NA LEIBE** Castlebaldwin

COUNTY TIPPERARY

- **MARL LAKE** Dundrum

COUNTY WESTMEATH

- **BALLINAFID LAKE** Mullingar
- **DOOLIN POND** Mullingar

LOCHS

COUNTY GALWAY

- **CRUMLIN FISHERIES** Coonemara

COUNTY KERRY

- **ANGLERS PARADISE** Killarney

LOUGHS

COUNTY CAVAN

- **LOUGH RAMOR** Virginia

COUNTY CLARE

- **AILLBRACK LOUGH** Aillbrack

COUNTY CORK

- **CORK LOUGH** Cork
- **LOUGH ADERRA** Midleton
- **LOUGH ADERRY** Youghal
- **LOUGH ATARRIFF** Dunmanway
- **LOUGH AVAUL (LOWER)** Glengariff
- **LOUGH AVAUL (UPPER)** Glengariff
- **LOUGH BALLYNACARRIGA** Dunmanway
- **LOUGH BOFINNE** Bantry
- **LOUGH COOLKEELURE** Dunmanway
- **LOUGH CULLENAGH** Dunmanway
- **LOUGH NEASKIN** Dunmanway

COUNTY DONEGAL

- **LOUGH BEAGH** Beagh

COUNTY GALWAY

- **ACLAUREEN (LOUGH)** Claremorris
- **BALLINDOOLY LOUGH AND POND** Moycullen
- **CASTLEREAGH LOUGHS** Claremorris
- **CLARE LOUGH** Claremorris
- **COSTELLO AND FERMOYLE FISHERY** Costello
- **LOUGH ACEELAGH** Moycullen
- **LOUGH ARORAM** Moycullen
- **LOUGH BALLYLUIRKE** Moycullen
- **LOUGH COOLIN** Clonbur
- **LOUGH CORRIB** Moycullen
- **LOUGH DOWN** Moycullen
- **LOUGH DOWNBEG** Moycullen
- **LOUGH HEMUSHMACONRY** Moycullen
- **LOUGH MASK** Clonbur
- **LOUGH PARKYFLAHERTY** Moycullen
- **LOUGH POLLALHY** Moycullen
- **NANANNAGH (LOUGH)** Claremorris
- **NANEVIN (LOUGH)** Moycullen
- **SUMMERVILLE LOUGH** Claremorris

COUNTY KERRY

- **LOUGH BARFINNIHY** Kenmare
- **LOUGH CAUM** Castlegregory
- **LOUGH FADDA** Sneem
- **LOUGH NAKIRKA** Killorglin

COUNTY LAOIS

- **GRANSTOWN LAKE** Portlaoise

COUNTY LEITRIM

- **DROMAHAIR LODGE FISHERY** Dromahair
- **LOUGH ALLEN** Drumshanbo
- **LOUGH MELVIN** Rossinver

COUNTY MAYO

- **BROHLY (LOUGH)** Ballina
- **BURRISHOOLE FISHERY** Newport
- **CALLOW LAKES** Foxford
- **CLOONAMOYNE FISHERY** Crossmolina
- **LOUGH CARRA** Westport
- **LOUGH CORRIB (UPPER)** Cong
- **LOUGH NAMUCKA** Louisburgh
- **MUCK (LOUGH)** Foxford
- **TALT (LOUGH)** Bunnyconnellan

COUNTY ROSCOMMON

- **BREEDOGE LOUGH** Ballaghaderren
- **LOUGH ARROW** Boyle
- **LOUGH CLOONACOLLY** Ballaghaderren
- **LOUGH CLOONAGH** Ballaghaderren
- **LOUGH GARA** Boyle
- **LOUGH KEY** Boyle
- **LOUGH NASOOL** Ballaghaderren
- **LOUGH URLAUR** Ballaghaderren

COUNTY SLIGO

- **LOUGH AUGH** Castlebaldwin
- **LOUGH BO** Castlebaldwin
- **LOUGH KEY** Castlebaldwin

COUNTY TIPPERARY

- **COUMSHINGAUN LOUGH** Kilsheelin
- **CROTTYS LOUGH** Kilsheelin
- **DERG (LOUGH)** Nenagh

COUNTY WATERFORD

- **BALLINAROONE LODGE FISHERY** Waterford

COUNTY WESTMEATH

- **LOUGH ENNEL FISHERY** Mullingar

MOATS

COUNTY WATERFORD

- **FORT WILLIAM FISHERY** Tallow

PONDS

COUNTY WESTMEATH

- **GALMOYLESTOWN LAKE** Mullingar

RESERVOIRS

COUNTY CORK

- **BALLINCOLLIG RESERVOIR** Cork
- **BALLYMAQUIRK FISHERY AND LODGE** Waterfall
- **SCHULL RESERVOIR** Schull

COUNTY KERRY

- **CARAGH FISHERY** Glencar

COUNTY LOUTH

- **BARNATTIN RESERVOIR** Drogheda
- **KILLINEER RESERVOIR** Drogheda

COUNTY MAYO

- **CLOONGEE FISHERY** Foxford

COUNTY WATERFORD

- **BALLYSHUNNOCK** Waterford
- **KNOCKDERRY** Waterford

RIVERS

COUNTY CARLOW

- **BARROW (RIVER)** Graighuenamanagh
- **BURREN (RIVER)** Carlow
- **DOUGLAS (RIVER)** Carlow
- **GREESE (RIVER)** Carlow
- **LERR (RIVER)** Carlow

COUNTY CORK

- **BANDON (RIVER)** Ballineen
- **BANDON (RIVER)** Bandon
- **BANDON (RIVER)** Dunmanway
- **BANDON (RIVER)** Enniskeane
- **BLACKWATER (RIVER)** Cappoquin
- **BLACKWATER (RIVER)** Conna
- **BLACKWATER (RIVER)** Fermoy
- **BLACKWATER (RIVER)** Mallow
- **BLACKWATER FLY FISHING** Fermoy
- **CAHA (RIVER)** Dunmanway
- **CAREYSVILLE** Fermoy
- **FINISK (RIVER)** Cappoquin
- **GLENGARIFF (RIVER)** Glengariff
- **ILEN (RIVER)** Skibbereen
- **KILCOLEMAN FISHERY** Enniskeane
- **MANCH HOUSE FISHERY** Ballineen

MUNSTER BLACKWATER (RIVER) (GHILLIE COTTAGE) Fermoy
OWENSHED (RIVER) Cappoquin

COUNTY DONEGAL

ASSAROE LAKE Ballyshannon
FINN (RIVER) Cloghan
GLENMORE FISHERY Ballybofey

COUNTY GALWAY

DELPHI FISHERY Leenane
GALWAY FISHERY Galway
TOP WATERS BALLYNAHINCH FISHERY Maam Cross

COUNTY KERRY

BLACKWATER FISHERY Kerry

COUNTY KILDARE

BARROW (RIVER) Athy
BOHERBAUN (RIVER) Athy
GREESE (RIVER) Athy
GREESE (RIVER) Ballytore
STRADBALLY (RIVER) Athy

COUNTY KILKENNY

BLACKWATER (RIVER) Kilmacow
DININ (RIVER) Kilkenny
ERKINA (RIVER) Kilkenny
KINGS (RIVER) Kilkenny
MOUNT JULIET FISHERY Thomastown
NORE (RIVER) Inistioge
NORE (RIVER) Kilkenny
NORE (RIVER) Thomastown

COUNTY LAOIS

BARROW (RIVER) Portarlington
BARROW (UPPER) (RIVER) Portarlington
CUSHINA (RIVER) Portarlington
ERKINA (RIVER) Rathdowney
FIGILE (RIVER) Portarlington
NORE (RIVER) Abbeyleix

COUNTY LEITRIM

SHANNON (UPPER) (RIVER) Drumshanbo

COUNTY LIMERICK

CASTLECONNELL SALMON FISHERY Castleconnell

COUNTY LOUTH

BALLYMASCANLON (RIVER) Dundalk
BOYNE (RIVER) Drogheda
CASTLETON (RIVER) Dundalk
FANE (RIVER) Dundalk

COUNTY MAYO

ARMSTRONG FISHERY Foxford
BEAL EASE FISHERY Foxford
CARROWNISKY Louisburgh
FOXFORD FISHERY Foxford
GLORE (RIVER) Kiltamagh
GWEESTION (RIVER) Bohola
LECKEE FISHERY Foxford
MOUNT FALCON SALMON FISHERY Ballina
MOY (RIVER) Foxford
MOY FISHERY Ballina
MULLAGHANOE (RIVER) Charlestown
OWENGARVE (RIVER) Charlestown
POLLAGH (RIVER) Kiltamagh

COUNTY MEATH

BOYNE (RIVER) Kells
BOYNE (RIVER) Navan
BOYNE (RIVER) Slane

COUNTY MONAGHAN

EMY LAKE FISHERY Clones

COUNTY ROSCOMMON

BOYLE (RIVER) Boyle
LUNG RIVER Ballaghaderren

COUNTY TIPPERARY

ARA (RIVER) Tipperary Town
ATHRY FISHERY Cashel
CLODIAGH (RIVER) Kilsheelin
CLODIAGH (RIVER) Thurles
COOLNAMUCK FISHERIES Carrick-on-Suir
DRISH (RIVER) Thurles
LINGAUN (RIVER) Carrick-on-Suir
NIRE (RIVER) Clonmel
SUIR (RIVER) Ardfinnan
SUIR (RIVER) Cahir
SUIR (RIVER) Carrick-on-Suir
SUIR (RIVER) Cashel
SUIR (RIVER) Clonmel
SUIR (RIVER) Kilsheelin
SUIR (RIVER) Thurles
SUIR VALLEY FISHERY Clonmel
WHITE HORSE (RIVER) Mountrath

COUNTY WATERFORD

BLACKWATER (RIVER) Lismore
BLACKWATER (RIVER) Portlaw Clodiagh
BLACKWATER (RIVER) Tallow
BLACKWATER (RIVER) Upper Ballyduff
BLACKWATER LODGE HOTEL AND FISHERY Upper Ballyduff

STREAMS

COUNTY TIPPERARY

DUAG ANNER STREAM Clonmel
NIRE STREAM Clonmel
TAR STREAM Clonmel

TRIBUTARIES

COUNTY DUBLIN

BROSNA (TRIBUTARY) Dublin

COARSE

COUNTY ANTRIM

- **BANN (LOWER) (RIVER)** Ballymena
- **BANN (LOWER) NAVIGATIONAL CANAL** Antrim
- **BANN (LOWER) NAVIGATIONAL CANAL** Movanagher
- **BANN (LOWER) NAVIGATIONAL CANAL** Portna
- **CLADY (RIVER)** Ballymena
- **LAGAN (RIVER)** Belfast
- **LOWER BANN (RIVER)** Ballymena

COUNTY ARMAGH

- **LOUGHGALL COARSE FISHERY** Armagh
- **SLOWING RIVERS FARM** Craigavon

COUNTY DOWN

- **MCCOURTS LAKE** Poyntspass
- **MILL LODGE FISHERY** Dromore
- **NEWRY CANAL** Newry
- **WATERFALL LODGE** Hillsborough

COUNTY LONDONDERRY

- **LOWER BANN (RIVER)** Magherafelt
- **PADDY MCNAMARAS LAKE** Londonderry

COUNTY TYRONE

- **BARONSCOURT LAKES** Omagh
- **BLESSINGBOURNE LAKE** Fivemiletown
- **CARRICK LOUGH** Aughnacloy
- **CRANS LOUGH** Aughnacloy
- **DUNGANNON PARK FISHERY** Dungannon
- **FAIRY WATER** Omagh
- **GREEVE LOUGH** Aughnacloy
- **LOUGH MACRONAN** Dungannon
- **QUIET WATERS** Dungannon
- **ROUGHAN LOUGH** Dungannon
- **ROUND LAKE** Fivemiletown
- **STRULE (RIVER)** Omagh
- **TULLYGIVEN LOUGH** Caledon

GAME

COUNTY ANTRIM

- **BANN (LOWER) (RIVER)** Ballymena
- **BRAID (RIVER)** Ballymena
- **BUSH (RIVER)** Bushmills
- **CAREY (RIVER)** Ballycastle
- **CLADY (RIVER)** Ballymena
- **CLOGHWATER (RIVER)** Ballymena
- **CLOUGH (RIVER)** Ballymena
- **CRANOGUE FISHERY** Ballymoney
- **CRUMLIN (RIVER)** Crumlin
- **DALL (RIVER)** Cushendall
- **DUN (RIVER)** Cushendall
- **GLENARM (RIVER)** Ballymena
- **GLENARRIFF (RIVER)** Cushendall
- **GLENSHESK (RIVER)** Ballycastle
- **INVER (RIVER)** Larne
- **KELLSWATER (RIVER)** Ballymena
- **MAINE (RIVER)** Antrim
- **MAINE (RIVER)** Ballymena
- **MAINE (RIVER)** Randalstown
- **MARGEY (RIVER)** Ballycastle
- **MCCAMMANS LAKE** Larne
- **RALOO TROUT FISHERIES** Ballymena
- **SIX MILE WATER** Antrim
- **SIX MILE WATER** Ballynure
- **SPRINGWATER MEADOW** Lisburn
- **STRAID FISHERY** Ballyclare
- **TILDARG FISHERY** Ballyclare
- **TURNAGROVE FISHERY** Ballymoney
- **WOODFORD FISHERY** Carrickfergus

COUNTY ARMAGH

- **BANN (UPPER) (RIVER)** Craigavon
- **CALLAN (RIVER)** Armagh
- **LAGAN (RIVER)** Craigavon
- **LOUGH NEAGH** Craigavon
- **LOWRYS LAKE** Armagh
- **SEAGAHAN RESERVOIR DAM** Armagh
- **SHAWS LAKE** Armagh
- **TULLNAWOOD LAKE** Armagh
- **TULLYNAWOOD RESERVOIR** Armagh

COUNTY DOWN

- **BALLY GRANGE FISHERY** Newtownards
- **BALLYLOUGH** Castlewellan
- **BANN (UPPER) (RIVER)** Banbridge
- **BANN (UPPER) (RIVER)** Rathfriland
- **BANN (UPPER) AND TRIBUTARIES** Newry
- **BRIDGEWATER FISHERY** Donaghadee
- **CARRICKMANNON FISHERY** Ballynahinch
- **CLEGGAN (RIVER)** Newry
- **CULLY (RIVER)** Newry
- **DAIRY FISHERY** Ballynahinch
- **FANE (RIVER)** Newry
- **FORKHILL (RIVER)** Newry
- **INLER (RIVER)** Newtownards
- **KILKEEL (RIVER)** Newry
- **LAGAN (RIVER)** Dromore
- **LOUGH CASHEL** Newry
- **LOUGH COWEY FISHERY** Newtownards
- **LOUGH GLASSDRUMMAN** Newry
- **LOUGH INAGH FISHERY** Ballynahinch
- **LOUGH KILTYBAINE** Newry
- **LOUGH MULLAGHABAN** Newry
- **MONEYCARRAGH (RIVER)** Newcastle
- **OWENREAGH (RIVER)** Dromore
- **QUOILE (RIVER)** Downpatrick
- **RINGDUFFERIN ESTUARY** Downpatrick
- **SHIMNA (RIVER)** Newcastle
- **TULLYWEST FISHERY** Ballynahinch
- **WHITEWATER (RIVER)** Newry
- **WRITES LOUGH** Castlewellan

COUNTY FERMANAGH

- **BALLINAMALLARD (RIVER)** Enniskillen
- **COLEBROOKE (RIVER)** Maguiresbridge
- **COLEBROOKE PARK** Enniskillen
- **COOLYERMER LOUGH FISHERY** Enniskillen
- **ERNE (RIVER)** Enniskillen
- **KNOCKBRACKEN TROUT LAKES** Ballinamallard
- **LOUGH ERNE** Enniskillen
- **LOUGH KEENAGHAN** Belleek
- **LOUGH MELVIN** Garrison
- **LOWER LOUGH ERNE** Enniskillen
- **MILL LOUGH BELLANALECK** Enniskillen
- **TEMPO (RIVER)** Maguiresbridge

COUNTY LONDONDERRY

- **AGIVEY (RIVER)** Coleraine
- **BANN (LOWER) (RIVER)** Coleraine
- **CREGGAN RESERVOIRS** Londonderry
- **ENAGH TROUT FISHERY** Londonderry
- **FAUGHAN (RIVER)** Londonderry
- **MACOSQUIN (RIVER)** Coleraine
- **MOORBROOK LODGE** Coleraine
- **MOYOLA (RIVER)** Maghera
- **ROE (RIVER)** Limavady
- **ROSE (RIVER)** Londonderry
- **TURNAFACE TROUT FISHERY** Magherafelt

COUNTY TYRONE

- **ALTMORE FISHERIES** Dungannon
- **BALLINDERRY (RIVER)** Cookstown
- **BALLYGAWLEY (RIVER)** Aughnacloy
- **BLACKWATER (RIVER)** Clogher
- **BRANTRY LOUGH** Dungannon
- **BURN DENNET (RIVER)** Strabane
- **BURN DENNETT (RIVER)** Strabane
- **CAMOWEN (RIVER)** Omagh
- **DERG (RIVER)** Castlederg
- **DERG (RIVER)** Omagh
- **DERG (RIVER)** Strabane
- **DRUMRAGH (RIVER)** Omagh
- **FINN (RIVER)** Omagh
- **FINN (RIVER)** Strabane
- **FOYLE (RIVER)** Strabane
- **GLEMELAG (RIVER)** Omagh
- **GLENELLY (RIVER)** Newtownstewart
- **LOUGH ENAGH** Dungannon
- **LOUGH FEA** Cookstown
- **LOUGHMORE** Augher
- **MOURNE (RIVER)** Newtownstewart
- **MOURNE (RIVER)** Omagh
- **MOURNE (RIVER)** Strabane
- **OONA RIVER** Dungannon
- **OWENKILLEW (RIVER)** Newtownstewart
- **OWENKILLEW (RIVER)** Omagh
- **PARK LAKE TROUT FISHERY** Dungannon
- **PLUCK MILL FISH FARM** Dungannon
- **STRULE (RIVER)** Omagh
- **TORRENT (RIVER)** Dungannon
- **TULLYLAGAN (RIVER)** Cookstown
- **WHITE LOUGH** Aughnacloy

COMBINATION

COUNTY ANTRIM

- **WOODBURN ANGLING CLUB** Carrickfergus

COUNTY ARMAGH

- **BLACKWATER (RIVER)** Armagh

COUNTY DOWN

- **CLANRYE (RIVER)** Newry

COUNTY FERMANAGH

- **ERNE (RIVER)** Belleek

COUNTY TYRONE

- **ANNAGINNY STILL WATER TROUT AND COARSE FISHERY** Dungannon

COARSE

ABERDEENSHIRE
- ABERDEEN BOX POOL Aberdeen

ANGUS
- CLATIO LOCH Dundee
- GLEN ESK CARAVAN PARK Brechin

AYRSHIRE (NORTH)
- EGLINGTON LOCH Irvine
- GOOSELOAN POND Kilwinning

AYRSHIRE (SOUTH)
- LOCH MAYBERRY Girvan

CLACKMANNANSHIRE
- GLENSHERRUP FISHERIES Dollar

DUMFRIES AND GALLOWAY
- CASTLE LOCH Lockerbie
- COWANS FARM Dumfries
- CRAIGHLAW Newton Stewart
- CULSCADDEN FARM POND Newton Stewart
- DORMONT LAKE COARSE FISHERY Lockerbie
- GLENDARROCH LOCH Newton Stewart
- KELHEAD WATER Annan
- KINMOUNT LAKE Annan
- KIRRIEREOCH LOCH Newton Stewart
- LOCH BARNBARROCH Newton Stewart
- LOCH ELDRIG Newton Stewart
- LOCH HERON Newton Stewart
- LOCH KEN Dumfries
- LOCH MONREITH Newton Stewart
- LOCH RONALD Newton Stewart
- LOCH WHITEFIELD Newton Stewart
- MORTON POND Thornhill
- NEWTON LOCHAN Castle Douglas
- PORTLING FISHERIES Dalbeattie
- TONGUE OF BOMBIE LOCHAN Kirkcudbright
- TORWOOD HOUSE HOTEL Newton Stewart
- WHITE LOCH OF MYRTON Newton Stewart

EDINBURGH (CITY OF)
- DUDDINGSTON LOCH Edinburgh

FALKIRK
- MILLHALL RESERVOIR

FIFE
- KINGHORN LOCH Burntisland

GLASGOW (CITY OF)
- CULCREUCH CASTLE POND Glasgow
- FORTH AND CLYDE CANAL Glasgow

HIGHLAND
- LOCH USSIE Dingwall

LANARKSHIRE (NORTH)
- MONKLAND CANAL Coatbridge
- STRATHCLYDE LOCH Motherwell

LANARKSHIRE (SOUTH)
- LANARK LOCH Lanark

LOTHIAN (EAST)
- MALTINGS FISHERY Haddington

LOTHIAN (WEST)
- MORTON FISHERIES Livingston
- UNION CANAL Linlithgow

RENFREWSHIRE
- HOWWOOD TROUT FISHERY Johnstone

STIRLING
- HOWIETOUN FISHERY

WESTERN ISLES
- SOUTH UIST ESTATES Lochboisdale

YORKSHIRE (SOUTH)
- BANK END COARSE FISHERIES Doncaster
- HAYFIELD LAKES Doncaster
- LINDHOLME LEISURE LAKES FISHERIES (1) Doncaster
- LINDHOLME LEISURE LAKES FISHERIES (2) Doncaster
- LINDHOLME LEISURE LAKES FISHERIES (4) Doncaster
- TORNE (RIVER) Doncaster

GAME

ABERDEENSHIRE
- BACKHILL FISHERY Macduff
- BOGNIE AND MOUNTBLAIRY FISHING Huntly
- CARRON (RIVER) Stonehaven
- LOCH INSCH FISHERY Insch
- LOCH SAUGH Laurencekirk
- MILL OF ELRICK FISHERY Ellon
- PITFOUR LAKE Peterhead
- TULLICH FISHERY Ballater
- WAULKMILL FISHERIES Turriff
- YTHAN FISHERY Ellon
- YTHAN VALLEY FISHERY Ellon

ANGUS
- CROMBIE RESERVOIR Carnoustie
- KINGENNIE FISHINGS Dundee
- LOCH OF LINTRATHEN Kirriemuir
- MILL OF CRIGGIE TROUT FISHERY Montrose
- PIPERDAM GOLF AND COUNTRY PARK Dundee
- PIPERDAM HOLDINGS Dundee
- RESCOBIE LOCH Dundee

ARGYLL AND BUTE
- ARDTORNISH ESTATE LOCHS Oban
- CLYDE ESTUARY Helensbourgh
- CUR (RIVER) Dunoon
- DUNOON RESERVOIR Dunoon
- FINNART (RIVER) Dunoon
- FRUIN (RIVER) Helensbourgh
- INVERAWE FISHERIES Taynuilt
- LOCH AVICH Oban
- LOCH FAD Rothesay
- LOCH GLASHAN Inveraray
- LOCH LOSKIN (THE LOCHAN) Dunoon
- LOCH NANT Oban
- LOCH QUIEN Rothesay
- LOCH TARSAN Dunoon
- MASSAN (RIVER) Dunoon
- MILL HOUSE FISHERIES Tighnabruaich
- ORCHY (RIVER) Bridge Of Orchy
- RUEL (RIVER) Dunoon

AYRSHIRE (EAST)
- COWANS LAW TROUT FISHERY Galston
- WATERSIDE FARM FISHERY Galston

AYRSHIRE (NORTH)
- CAMPHILL RESERVOIR Kilbirnie
- HAYLIE FISHERY Largs
- MIDDLETON FISHERY Largs
- PORT-NA-LOCHAN Brodick
- SKELMORLIE FISHERIES Skelmorlie

AYRSHIRE (SOUTH)
- AYR (RIVER) Ayr
- COYLE WATER FISHERY Ayr
- CRAITH RESERVOIR Prestwick
- CRAUFURDLAND FISHERY Kilmarnock
- DALVENNAN COUNTRY SPORTS FISHERY Ayr
- DOON (RIVER) Ayr
- LOCH DORNAL Girvan
- SPRINGWATER FISHERY Ayr
- STINCHAR (RIVER) Girvan

CLACKMANNANSHIRE
- EASTER BALADO TROUT FISHERY (KINROSS) Glendevon
- GARTMORN DAM FISHERY Alloa

DUMFRIES AND GALLOWAY
- ANNAN (RIVER) Annan
- ANNAN (RIVER) Lockerbie
- BARSCOBE LOCH Castle Douglas
- BLACK ESK RESERVOIR Lockerbie
- BLACK LOCH Newton Stewart
- BRACK LOCH Castle Douglas
- BRUNTIS LOCH Newton Stewart
- BUITTLE RESERVOIR Dalbeattie
- CLATTERINGSHAWS LOCH Newton Stewart
- CREE (RIVER) Newton Stewart
- DALBEATTIE RESERVOIR Dalbeattie
- DINDINNIE RESERVOIR Stranraer
- DUNSKEY LOCHS Stranraer
- EARLSTOUN LOCH Castle Douglas
- ESK (RIVER) Canonbie
- ESK (RIVER) Langholm
- FYNTALLOCH LOCH Newton Stewart
- GLENKILN RESERVOIR Dumfries
- HODDOM WATER Lockerbie
- JERICHO LOCHS Dumfries
- KEN (RIVER) Castle Douglas
- KIRKCHRIST Newton Stewart
- KIRKWOOD WATER Lockerbie
- KIRTLE WATER STREAM Gretna
- KNOCKQUASSEN RESERVOIR Stranraer
- LABRAX FISHING Stranraer
- LAIRDMANNOCH LOCH Castle Douglas
- LILLIES LOCH Newton Stewart
- LOCH BRADAN Newton Stewart
- LOCH BRECKBOWIE Newton Stewart
- LOCH DEE Newton Stewart
- LOCH SKERROW Castle Douglas
- LOCH WHINYEON Castle Douglas
- LOCHENBRECK LOCH Castle Douglas
- LOCHINVAR LOCH Castle Douglas
- LOCHNAW Stranraer
- LOWER LIDDLE (RIVER) Canonbie
- MAINS OF PENNINGHAM FISHERY Newton Stewart
- MOFFAT FISHERIES Moffat
- MORTON LOCH Thornhill
- NAHINE LOCH Newton Stewart
- NEW ABBEY DOW Dumfries
- NITH (RIVER) Thornhill
- OCHILTREE LOCH Newton Stewart
- PENWHIRN RESERVOIR Stranraer
- PURDOMSTONE RESERVOIR Lockerbie
- SARK STREAM Gretna
- SLATEHOUSE LOCH Thornhill
- SOULSEAT LOCH Stranraer
- STARBURN LOCH Thornhill
- TORHOUSEKIE AND KIRWAUGH Newton Stewart
- URR (RIVER) Dalbeattie
- WEE GLEN AMOUR LOCH Newton Stewart

EDINBURGH (CITY OF)
- CLUBBIEDEAN RESERVOIR Edinburgh
- HARLAW RESERVOIR Balerno
- THREIPMUIR RESERVOIRS Balerno

FALKIRK
- CENTRAL SCOTLAND TROUT FISHERY
- LOCH EARN
- LOCH FINLAS Callander
- LOCH VENACHAR Callander

FIFE
- BALLO RESERVOIR Glenrothes
- CAMERON RESERVOIR St Andrews

CLUTTO LOCH St Andrews
CRAIGLUSCAR RESERVOIR Dunfermline
GOLDEN LOCH Cupar
HOLL RESERVOIR Glenrothes
LINDORES LOCH Cupar
LOCH FITTY TROUT FISHERY Dunfermline
LOCH ORE Lochgelly
LOCHMORE MEADOWS Lochgelly
NEWTON FARM FISHERY Newport-on-Tay
RAITH LAKE FISHERY Kirkcaldy

GLASGOW (CITY OF)

BALGRAVE RESERVOIR Glasgow
CAMPS RESERVOIR Glasgow
CLYDE (RIVER) Glasgow
DAER RESERVOIR Strathclyde
LOCH ARKLET Glasgow
NEILSTON TROUT FISHERY Glasgow

HIGHLAND

AVIELOCHAN Inverness
BEAULY (RIVER) Inverness
BRAES SALMON STATION Portree
CONON (RIVER) Dingwall
DORNOCH LOCHANS Dornoch
FORSINARD Thurso
GARRY UPPER (RIVER) Invergarry
GLASS (RIVER) Beauly
GLASS (RIVER) Dingwall
GLENCOE LOCHAN Ballachulish
HALLADALE SALMON FISHERY Thurso
HOSPITAL LOCHAN Ballachulish
LOCH ACHANALT Dingwall
LOCH ACHILITY Strathpeffer
LOCH ACHONACHIE Dingwall
LOCH AFFRIC Inverness
LOCH AKRAN Thurso
LOCH ALVIE Kingussie
LOCH ARKAIG Fort William
LOCH ASSYNT Lairg
LOCH BAD A CROTHA Gairloch
LOCH BADANLOCH Kinbrace
LOCH BARAVAIG Isle Ornsay
LOCH BEANNACH Lairg
LOCH BEANNACHAIRAN Muir Of Ord
LOCH BENEVEAN Inverness
LOCH BORRALAN Lairg
LOCH BORRALIE Lairg
LOCH BRORA Brora
LOCH CHUILIN Dingwall
LOCH CONNAN Portree
LOCH CRAGGIE Lairg
LOCH CULAG Lairg
LOCH DAMH Achnasheen
LOCH DOLA Lairg
LOCH DUAGRAICH Portree
LOCH ERICHT Dalwhinnie
LOCH FANNICH Strathpeffer
LOCH GARRY Invergarry
LOCH GARVE Strathpeffer
LOCH GLASCARNOCH Garve
LOCH HOPE Lairg
LOCH HORN Golspie
LOCH INCH LAGGAN Invergarry
LOCH KNOCKIE Inverness
LOCH LAGGAN Dalwhinnie
LOCH LOCHY Fort William
LOCH LOYAL Lairg
LOCH LOYNE Inverness
LOCH LUNDIE Golspie
LOCH MAREE Achnasheen
LOCH MEADIE Thurso
LOCH MEIG Strathpeffer
LOCH MERKLAND Lairg
LOCH MORAR Mallaig
LOCH MORLICH Aviemore
LOCH MULLARDOCH Inverness
LOCH NAVER Lairg
LOCH NESS Fort Augustus
LOCH OICH Invergarry
LOCH POULARY Invergarry
LOCH QUOICH Invergarry
LOCH RUITH A PHUILL Strathpeffer
LOCH RUTHVEN Inverness
LOCH SHIEL Fort William
LOCH SHIN Lairg
LOCH SIONASCAIG Ullapool
LOCH TARVIE Strathpeffer
LOCH TOFTINGALL Wick
LOCH WATTEN Wick
NESS (RIVER) Inverness
SALMON FISHING STATION Thurso
SCOURIE HOTEL Lairg
SPEY (RIVER) Grantown On Spey
ST JOHNS LOCH Thurso
STONEYFIELD LOCH TROUT FISHERY Invergordon
STRATHMANAIRD LOCHS Ullapool
STRATHY (RIVER) Forsinard
TARVIE LOCHS FISHERY Strathpeffer
TWEED (RIVER) Inverness

INVERCLYDE

ARDGOWAN TROUT FISHERY Greenock
CLYDE (RIVER) Greenock
GRYFFE (RIVER) Kilmacolm
LAWFIELD TROUT FISHERY Kilmacolm
LOCH THOM Greenock
PINEWOOD TROUT FISHERY Kilmacolm

LANARKSHIRE (NORTH)

LILY LOCH Airdrie

LANARKSHIRE (SOUTH)

AVON (RIVER) Larkhall
FRUID RESERVOIR Biggar
NEWMILL TROUT AND DEER FARM Lanark
QUARTER FISHERY Hamilton
TALLA RESERVOIR Biggar
TINTO TROUT FISHERIES Biggar

LOTHIAN (EAST)

GIFFORD HOPES RESERVOIR Haddington
TYNE (RIVER) Haddington
WHITEADDER RESERVOIR Haddington

LOTHIAN (MID)

GLADHOUSE RESERVOIR Penicuik
LOGANLEA TROUT FISHERY Penicuik
PORTMORE LOCH Penicuik
ROSLYNLEE FISHERY Penicuik

LOTHIAN (WEST)

ALLANDALE TARN West Calder
ALMOND (RIVER) South Queensferry
BEECRAIGS LOCH Linlithgow
BOWDEN SPRINGS FISHERY Linlithgow
CROSSWOOD RESERVOIR Livingston
LINLITHGOW LOCH Linlithgow
PARKLEY FISHERY Linlithgow
SELM MUIR FISHERY Livingston

MORAY

BROOM OF MOY Elgin
GLEN LATTERACH RESERVOIR Elgin
GLEN OF ROTHES TROUT FISHERY Aberlour
LOCH DALLAS Forres
LOCH NA BO Elgin
LOCH OF BLAIRS Forres
MILLBUIES LOCH Elgin

PERTH AND KINROSS

ALMOND (RIVER) Perth
AMULREE BEAT Dunkeld
BOLFRACKS BEAT Aberfeldy
BRAAN (RIVER) Dunkeld
BUTTERSTONE LOCH Dunkeld
CASTLE BEAT Aberfeldy
CUILALUINN BEAT Aberfeldy
DRUMMOND FISHERIES Crieff
DRUMMOND LOCH Crieff
DUNALASTAIR LOCH Pitlochry
FARLEYER BEAT Aberfeldy
FINDYNATE BEAT Aberfeldy
GLENFARG FISHERY Perth
HEATHERYFORD FISHERY Kinross
KENMORE BEAT Aberfeldy
LOCH BHAC Pitlochry
LOCH FASKALLY Pitlochry
LOCH LEVEN FISHERIES Kinross
LOCH TAY Aberfeldy
LOWER FRANDY Kinross
MONTAGUE RESERVOIR Perth
ORCHILL LOCH TROUT FISHERY Dunblane
PITCASTLE BEAT Aberfeldy
RUMBLING BRIDGE Dunkeld
SANDYKNOWES FISHING Perth
SEAMAW LOCH Perth
TAY (RIVER) Dunkeld
TROCHRY BEAT Dunkeld

RENFREWSHIRE

BRIDGE OF WEIR Bridge Of Weir
CARN LOCH Lochgilphead
CLACHAIG (LOCH) Lochgilphead
COILLE BHAR (LOCH) Lochgilphead
GLEAN LOCH Lochgilphead
GRYFFE (RIVER) Bridge Of Weir
LEIPEIG (LOCH) Lochgilphead
LOCH BARNLUASGAN Lochgilphead
LOCH DHU Lochgilphead
LOCH-AN-ADD Lochgilphead
LOCH-NA-BRIC Lochgilphead
LOCH-NA-FAOILINN Lochgilphead
MAICH WATERS Lochwinnoch
NEW LOCH Lochgilphead

SCOTTISH BORDERS

ACREKNOWE RESERVOIR Hawick
AKERMOOR LOCH Hawick
ALEMOOR RESERVOIR Hawick
BAILEY (RIVER) Kelso
BLACKADDER WATER Duns
BUCCLEUCH ESTATES Selkirk
CLERKLAND FLY FISHERY Melrose
COLDINGHAM LOCH Eyemouth
ESK AND LIDDLE FISHERIES Newcastleton
ETTERICK (RIVER) Selkirk
ETTRICK AND YARROW (RIVER) Selkirk
HEADSHAW FISHERY Selkirk
HELLMOOR LOCH Hawick
JED (RIVER) Jedburgh
KAILZIE GARDENS FISHERY Peebles
LEADER (RIVER) Earlston
LIDDLE (RIVER) Newcastleton
LINDEAN RESERVOIR Selkirk
MACBIEHILL ESTATE West Linton
MEGGET RESERVOIR Selkirk
ST MARYS LOCH Selkirk
TEVIOT (RIVER) Selkirk
TWEED (RIVER) Duns
TWEED (RIVER) Galashiels
TWEED (RIVER) Innerleithen
TWEED (RIVER) Kelso
TWEED (RIVER) Melrose
TWEED (RIVER) Peebles
WATCH RESERVOIR Duns
WEST WATER RESERVOIR Peebles
WOODEN LOCH Kelso
WULLIESTRUTHER LOCH Hawick

SHETLAND ISLANDS

GOSSA WATER Shetland
LOCH OF BROUGH Shetland
LOCH OF COLVISTER Shetland
LOCH OF CULLIVOE Shetland
LOCH OF GUTCHER Shetland
LOCH OF LUMBISTER Shetland
LOCH OF PAPIL Shetland
LOCH OF VOLLISTER Shetland
MUSKRA LOCH Shetland

STIRLING

- **BALVAIG (RIVER)** Lochearnhead
- **BLAIRMORE FISHERY** Glasgow
- **DOCHART (RIVER)** Killin
- **ENDRICK (RIVER)** Glasgow
- **KILLEARN HOUSE FISHERY** Glasgow
- **KINNEL** Killin
- **LAKE OF MENTEITH FISHERIES**
- **LESKINE** Killin
- **LOCH ACHRAY**
- **LOCH ARD**
- **LOCH ARKLET**
- **LOCH DRUNKIE**
- **LOCH GLENFINGLAS**
- **LOCH KATRINE**
- **LOCH KATRINE** Doune
- **LOCH LUBNAIG** Callander
- **LOCH VOIL** Lochearnhead
- **LOCHAN NA LARAIG** Killin
- **NORTH THIRD TROUT FISHERY**
- **PORTNELLAN** Crianlarich
- **SWANSWATER FISHERY**

WESTERN ISLES

- **CEANN-AN-ORA FISHERY** Harris
- **GRIMERSTA LODGE** Stornoway
- **LACASDALE LOCHS** Harris
- **OBBE FISHINGS** Leverburgh
- **SOVAL ESTATE** Stornoway

YORKSHIRE (SOUTH)

- **LINDHOLME LEISURE LAKES FISHERIES (3)** Doncaster

COMBINATION

ANGUS

- **DEAN (RIVER)** Dundee
- **ISLA (RIVER)** Blairgowrie

ARGYLL AND BUTE

- **LOCH AWE** Oban

DUMFRIES AND GALLOWAY

- **BLADNOCH (RIVER)** Newton Stewart
- **BROOM FISHERIES** Annan
- **GALLOWAY FOREST PARK** Newton Stewart
- **LOCH ROAN** Castle Douglas

HIGHLAND

- **CONON (RIVER)** Dingwall
- **LOCH INSH** Kingussie
- **NAIRN (RIVER)** Nairn
- **SPEY (RIVER)** Kingussie

LANARKSHIRE (NORTH)

- **CLYDE (RIVER)** Wishaw
- **HILLEND LOCH** Airdrie

LOTHIAN (EAST)

- **MARKLE FISHERIES** East Linton

LOTHIAN (WEST)

- **HOPETOUN FISHERY** Broxburn

PERTH AND KINROSS

- **ABERFELDY ASSOCIATION BEAT** Aberfeldy
- **ALMOND (RIVER)** Dunkeld
- **BALLECHIN BEAT** Pitlochry
- **CASTLE MENZIES BEAT** Aberfeldy
- **CLOCHFOLDICH BEAT** Aberfeldy
- **COSHIEVILLE FARM** Aberfeldy
- **DERCULICH BEAT** Aberfeldy
- **EASTERTYRE BEAT** Pitlochry
- **HAUGH OF GRANDTULLY BEAT** Aberfeldy
- **LOCH EIGHEACH** Pitlochry
- **LOCH FREUCHIE** Dunkeld
- **LOCH RANNOCH** Pitlochry
- **LOGIERAIT BEAT** Pitlochry
- **LOWER ABERUTHVEN FISHINGS** Auchterarder
- **LOWER FARLEYER BEAT** Aberfeldy
- **LOWER SCONE BEAT** Perth
- **MAINS OF MURTHLY** Aberfeldy
- **NEWTON OF LOGIERAIT BEAT** Perth
- **PITLOCHRY BOATING STATION AND LOCHSIDE CAFÉ** Pitlochry
- **PITNACREE BEAT** Aberfeldy
- **SKETEWAN BEAT** Aberfeldy
- **TOMBUIE BEAT** Aberfeldy
- **TULLYPOWRIE BEAT** Pitlochry
- **UPPER BORLICK BEAT** Aberfeldy
- **UPPER KINNAIRD BEAT** Perth
- **WEEM BEAT** Aberfeldy

SCOTTISH BORDERS

- **TEVIOT (RIVER)** Hawick

STIRLING

- **AUCHESSON BEAT** Crianlarich
- **BARNCROFT** Killin
- **BORELAND** Killin
- **CRAIGNAVIE** Killin
- **DOCHART (RIVER)** Killin
- **FINLARIG** Killin
- **KILLIN BREADALBANE ANGLING CLUB WATERS** Callander
- **LOCH LOMOND** Glasgow
- **LOCH TAY HIGHLAND LODGES** Killin
- **LOCHAY (RIVER)** Killin
- **SUIE** Crianlarich

by **Fishing Type** in **Scotland**

Game - Combination

COARSE

BLAENAU GWENT
- **BLUE LAKE** Ebbw Vale
- **BOAT POND** Ebbw Vale
- **BUTE TOWN RESERVOIR** Tredegar
- **LYMOOR POOL 1 AND 2** Ebbw Vale
- **MACHINE POND** Ebbw Vale

BRIDGEND
- **KENFIG LAKE**
- **STROUDWATER CANAL**

CAERPHILLY
- **CAERPHILLY CASTLE LAKES**
- **OGILVIE LAKE** Bargoed

CARDIFF
- **EAST DOCK**
- **HENDRE LAKE**

CARMARTHENSHIRE
- **GLAS-LLYN FISHERY** Whitland

CEREDIGION
- **LLANARTH FISHERY** Llanarth
- **LLYN BERWEN** Ystrad Meurig
- **NINE OAKS** Llanarth
- **TEGLAN LAKE** Lampeter

CONWY
- **CONWY VALLEY FISHERIES**
- **GILER ARMS LAKE** Betws-Y-Coed
- **LLYN NANT-Y-CERRIG**
- **TREFANT POOL**

DENBIGHSHIRE
- **GWYDDELWERN POOL** Corwen
- **MONKS POOL** Wrexham

FLINTSHIRE
- **ALLTAMI CLAY PITS** Mold
- **BUCKLEY TRAP POOL** Buckley
- **CLAWDD OFFAS DYKE** Mold
- **GWERYD LAKES FISHING** Mold
- **GYRN CASTLE FISHERY** Holywell
- **PADESWOOD POOL** Mold
- **SWAN LAKE** Connahs Quay

GLAMORGAN (VALE OF)
- **BARRY RESERVOIR** Dinas Powys
- **HAZELCOURT PONDS** Cowbridge
- **PENTWYN RESERVOIR** Merthyr Tydfil
- **PENYWERN PONDS** Merthyr Tydfil
- **WARREN MILL** Cowbridge

GWYNEDD
- **LLYN TEGID (BALA LAKE)** Bala

ISLE OF ANGLESEY
- **BREAKWATER PARK** Holyhead
- **LLYN BRYNTIRION** Llanfair Pwllgwyngyll
- **LLYN DEWI** Anglesey
- **LLYN NANT ANOG** Anglesey
- **LLYN TACAN** Anglesey
- **LLYN Y GORS** Menai Bridge
- **TY HEN LAKE** Rhosneigr
- **TYDDYN SARGENT** Tyn-Y-Gongl

MONMOUTHSHIRE
- **CWMCELYN POND** Abertillery
- **FIVE TREES** Monmouth
- **GROVE FARM FISHERY** Abergavenny
- **TREFALDU FISHERY** Monmouth

NEWPORT
- **LLISWERRY POND**
- **MONMOUTHSHIRE AND BRECON CANAL**
- **SHROPSHIRE UNION CANAL**
- **WOODSTOCK POOL**

PEMBROKESHIRE
- **IAN HEAPS PREMIER FISHERIES AND SCHOOL OF ANGLING** Narberth
- **LUDCHURCH LAKE** Narberth
- **ROADSIDE FARM** Narberth
- **WEST ATHESTON COARSE FISHERY** Narberth

POWYS
- **CLAERWEN RESERVOIR** Rhayader
- **FACHWEN POOL** Newtown
- **LLANGORSE LAKE** Brecon
- **LLNGWYN FISHERY** Rhayader
- **LLYSWEN CARP POOLS** Builth Wells
- **MONTGOMERY CANAL** Montgomery
- **SEVERN (RIVER)** Newtown
- **SHROPSHIRE UNION CANAL** Welshpool
- **VYRNWY (RIVER)** Welshpool

SWANSEA
- **FENDROD LAKE**
- **GOWERTON COARSE FISHERY**

TORFAEN
- **CWMBRAN BOATING LAKE** Cwmbran
- **MORGANS POND** Cwmbran

WREXHAM
- **ARGAE LAKE**
- **FLASH**
- **LLAY RESERVOIR**
- **PONKY POOL**
- **TAN LLAN**
- **TRENCH FISHERIES**

GAME

BLAENAU GWENT
- **HAYRICK LAKES** Tredegar
- **SIRHOWY (RIVER)** Tredegar

BRIDGEND
- **GARW (RIVER)**
- **LLYNFI (RIVER)** Maesteg
- **OGMORE (RIVER)**

CAERPHILLY
- **EBBW (RIVER)** Blackwood
- **SIRHOWY (RIVER)** Blackwood

CARDIFF
- **TAFF (RIVER)**

CARMARTHENSHIRE
- **BRYNHAWC FISHERY** Pencader
- **CHURCH FARM FISHERY** Pencader
- **COTHI (RIVER)** Ammanford
- **COTHI (RIVER)** Carmarthen
- **COTHI (RIVER)** Llandovery
- **DOL WATTS FISHERY** Newcastle Emlyn
- **DOLGWM MILL FISHERY** Llanybydder
- **DUAD (RIVER)** Carmarthen
- **EDWINSFORD FISHERY** Llandeilo
- **GARNFFRWD FISHERY** Llanelli
- **GLAS LLYN FISHERY** Llanboidy
- **GWENDRAETH AND MORIASIS FISHERY** Llanelli
- **GWENDRAETH FACH (RIVER)** Kidwelly
- **GWENDRAETH FACH (RIVER)** Llanelli
- **GWILI (RIVER)** Carmarthen
- **HENDY FISHERY** Llanybydder
- **LLANLLAWDDOG FISHERY** Carmarthen
- **LLEIDI RESERVIORS** Llanelli
- **LLWCHWR (RIVER)** Ammanford
- **LOUGHOR (RIVER)** Ammanford
- **LOUGHOR VALLEY FISHERY** Ammanford
- **MAES-ISAF FISHERY** Llanybydder
- **PANT Y BEDW FISHING LAKES** Carmarthen
- **PENBEILI FISHERY** Newcastle Emlyn
- **RHYDFACH FISHERY** Newcastle Emlyn
- **RIVER GWENLLIAN FISHERY** Kidwelly
- **SWISS VALLEY** Llanelli
- **TAF (RIVER)** Carmarthen
- **TAF (RIVER)** Whitland
- **TAN-Y-COED FISHERY** Newcastle Emlyn
- **TEIFI (RIVER)** Llanybydder
- **TEIFI (RIVER)** Newcastle Emlyn
- **TOWEY (RIVER)** Llandovery
- **TOWI (RIVER)** Carmarthen
- **TOWY (RIVER)** Carmarthen
- **TOWY (RIVER)** Llandeilo
- **TOWY (RIVER)** Llwynfortune
- **TREBEDW FISHERY** Newcastle Emlyn
- **WHITE HOUSE MILL** Whitland

CEREDIGION
- **AERON (RIVER)** Aberaeron
- **ARTRO (RIVER)** Llandysul
- **BAYLIAU FISHERY** Lampeter
- **CASTELL-PYR FISHERY** Llandysul
- **CEFN-BRYN FISHERY** Lampeter
- **CELLAN FISHERY** Lampeter
- **CWM RHEIDOL FISHERY** Aberystwyth
- **CWMMACKWITH FISHERY** Llandysul
- **CYCH (RIVER)** Cardigan
- **DINA FISHERY** Aberystwyth
- **DINAS RESERVOIR** Aberystwyth
- **FRON FARM FISHERY** Aberystwyth
- **GEORGE BORROW HOTEL** Aberystwyth
- **GLWYDWERN TROUT FISHERY** Lampeter
- **LAKE BLAENMELINDWR** Aberystwyth
- **LAKE CRAIGYPISTYLL** Aberystwyth
- **LAKE FRONGOCH** Aberystwyth
- **LAKE LLYGAD** Aberystwyth
- **LAKE PENDHAM** Aberystwyth
- **LAKE RHEIDOL** Aberystwyth
- **LAKE RHOSGOCH** Aberystwyth
- **LAKE RHOSRHYDD** Aberystwyth
- **LAMPETER FISHERY** Lampeter
- **LLETYTWPA FISHERY** Lampeter
- **LLWYNDURIS MANSION FISHERY** Cardigan
- **LLYN BERWYN** Tregaron
- **LLYN MAENOG TROUT FISHERY** Llandysul
- **NANT Y MOCH RESERVOIR** Aberystwyth
- **NEUADDLAS COUNTRY GUEST HOUSE** Tregaron
- **PANT TROUT POOL** Tregaron
- **PENTRE FARM FISHERY** Lampeter
- **RALLT FISHERY** Lampeter
- **RHEIDOL (RIVER)** Aberystwyth
- **RHYDLEWIS TROUT FISHERY** Llandysul
- **RHYDYGALFE FISHERY** Llandysul
- **TALYBONT RESERVOIR** Talybont
- **TEIFI (RIVER** Llandysul
- **TEIFI (RIVER)** Cardigan
- **TEIFI (RIVER)** Lampeter
- **TEIFI (RIVER)** Llandysul
- **TEIFI (RIVER)** Tregaron
- **TEIFI POOLS** Ystrad Meurig
- **TEIFY POOLS FISHERY** Tregaron
- **TROED-Y-BRYN FISHERY** Lampeter
- **TYRDREF FISHERY** Llandysul
- **YSTWYTH (RIVER)** Aberystwyth

CONWY
- **ALED (RIVER)** Denbigh
- **CLWYD (RIVER)** Denbigh
- **CONWY (RIVER)** Betws-Y-Coed
- **CONWY (RIVER)** Llanrwst
- **ELWY (RIVER)** Abergele
- **ELWY (RIVER)** Denbigh
- **GRAIGLWYD SPRINGS FISHERY** Penmaenmawr
- **LLEDR (RIVER)** Dolwyddelan
- **LLYN CRAFNANT FISHERIES** Trefriw
- **TALYLLN LAKE FISHERY** Abergele
- **TAN-Y-MYNYDD TROUT LAKES** Abergele
- **TYDDYN MAWR TROUT FARM**

DENBIGHSHIRE
- **ABBEY FISHERY** Llangollen

ALWEN (RIVER) Corwen
ALWEN RESERVOIR Corwen
BRENIG RESERVOIR Corwen
CEIRIOG (RIVER) Llangollen
CEIRIOG (RIVER) Wrexham
CEIRW STREAM Ruthin
CLWYD (RIVER) Ruthin
CLWYD (RIVER) St Asaph
CLYWEDOG (RIVER) Ruthin
DEE (RIVER) Llangollen
DEE (RIVER) Ruthin
DEE (RIVER) Wrexham
DOLWEN AND PLAS UCHAF St Asaph
DRAGONFLY FISHERIES Corwen
ELWY (RIVER) St Asaph
FELIN-Y-GORS FISHERIES Rhyl
LLYN ALWEN Ruthin
LLYN BRENIG Corwen
LLYN COWLYD AND HILL LAKES Rhyl
PANT GLAS RESERVOIR Wrexham
TEIGN (RIVER) Llangollen

FLINTSHIRE

ALYN (RIVER) Mold
CLWYD (RIVER) Mold
DEE (RIVER) Mold
FOREST HILL TROUT FARM Holywell
NANT-Y-GAIN FISHERY Mold
SEVEN SPRINGS TROUT FARM AND FISHERIES Mold
WAL GOCH FLY Mold
WHEELER (RIVER) Mold

GLAMORGAN (VALE OF)

LLYWN-ON RESERVOIR Treharris
MELLTE (STREAM) Neath
TAFF (RIVER) Merthyr Tydfil
TAFF BARGOED Treharris
UPPER NEUADD Merthyr Tydfil

GWYNEDD

AFON LLYFNI (RIVER) Caernarfon
AFON SEIONT (RIVER) Caernarfon
BONTNEWYDD FISHERY Caernarfon
BRON EIFION FISHERIES Pwllheli
CLWYD (RIVER) Pwllheli
CONWY (RIVER) Llanrwst
CREGENNAN LAKES Dolgellau
CWM PRYSOR LAKE Bala
CWM SILYN LAKE Caernarfon
DEE (RIVER) Bala
DUGOED (RIVER) Dolgellau
DWYFACH (RIVER) Criccieth
DWYFAWR (RIVER) Criccieth
DWYRYD (RIVER) Blaenau Ffestiniog
DWYTHWCH LAKE Caernarfon
DYSYNNI (RIVER) Tywyn
DYWARCHEN RESERVOIR Caernarfon
EDEN (RIVER) Dolgellau
ERCH (RIVER) Pwllheli
FFESTINIOG FISHERY Blaenau Ffestiniog
GLAN MORFA MAWR FISHERY Porthmadog
GLASLYN (RIVER) Penrhyndeudraeth
GREGANNAN LAKES Dolgellau
GWERNAN LAKE FISHERY Dolgellau
GWYRFAI (RIVER) Caernarfon
LERI (RIVER) Talybont
LLIW (RIVER) Craig-Y-Tan
LLYN BUGEILYN Tywyn
LLYN CELYN FISHERY Bala
LLYN CWELLYN RESERVOIR Caernarfon
LLYN CWMYSTRADLLYN Porthmadog
LLYN CYNWCH LAKE Dolgellau
LLYN DDU (BLACK LAKE) Porthmadog
LLYN DINAS Caernarfon
LLYN GADAIR Caernarfon
LLYN GLAN MOFA MAWR Porthmadog
LLYN NANTLLE Caernarfon
LLYN PADARN Caernarfon
MAWDDACH (RIVER) Dolgellau
MAWDDACH AND WNION (RIVERS) Dolgellau
NANTLLE LAKE Caernarfon
OGWEN (RIVER) Bangor
PORTH WATERS FISHERY Bala
RHYDHIR (RIVER) Pwllheli
TALYLLYN LAKE Tywyn
TANYGRISIAU RESERVOIR Blaenau Ffestiniog
TRYWERYN (RIVER) Bala
WNION (RIVER) Dolgellau

ISLE OF ANGLESEY

CEFNI RESERVOIR Llangefni
LAKE HOUSE HOLIDAYS Benllech
LLYN ALAN Holyhead
LLYN CORON Llangefni
LLYN JANE FISHERY Menai Bridge
PARC NEWYDD TROUT FISHERY Llanerchymedd
PLAS-Y-NANT TROUT FISHERY Amlwch

MONMOUTHSHIRE

CWMTILLERY RESERVOIR Abertillery
FAIROAK FISHERY Chepstow
OLWAY BROOK Usk
RAVENSNEST FISHERY Chepstow
TROTHY (RIVER) Usk
USK (RIVER) Abergavenny
USK (RIVER) Usk

NEATH PORT TALBOT

ABERNANT FARM FISHERY Port Talbot
AFAN STREAM Port Talbot
DULAIS (RIVER) Neath
EGLWYS NUNYDD RESERVOIR Port Talbot
HEPSTE (STREAM) Neath
MARGRAM PARK FISHERY Port Talbot
NEATH (RIVER) Neath
TWRCH (RIVER) Neath

NEWPORT

DEE (RIVER)
NEVERN (RIVER)
WENTWOOD RESERVOIR
YNYS-Y-FRO RESERVOIR

PEMBROKESHIRE

EASTERN CLEDDAU (RIVER) Haverfordwest
EASTERN CLEDDAU (RIVER) Llanycefn
EASTERN CLEDDAU (RIVER) Narberth
EWENNY (RIVER) Milford Haven
HAYCASTLE TROUT FISHERY Haverfordwest
HAYSCASTLE TROUT FISHERY Haverfordwest
LLYS Y FRAN RESERVOIR AND COUNTRY PARK Haverfordwest
MILLBROOK FISHERY Fishguard
PENHOYLE FISHING PARK Tenby
ROSEBUSH RESERVOIR Haverfordwest
SABRE TOOTH Milford Haven
WESTERN CLEDDAU (RIVER) Haverfordwest

POWYS

BANWY (RIVER) Welshpool
BEACONS FISHERY Brecon
BEGUEILIN LAKE Brecon
BOATSIDE FARM Builth Wells
CAER BERIS MANOR HOTEL Builth Wells
CANTEF RESERVOIR Brecon
CLYNWEDOG RESERVOIR Llanidloes
CLYWEDOG (RIVER) Llanidloes
CRAI RESERVOIR Brecon
DEE (RIVER) Llanymynech
DOL LLYS FARM Llanidloes
DULAS (RIVER) Llanidloes
DULAS (RIVER) Machynlleth
DYFI (RIVER) Machynlleth
ELAN (RIVER) Rhayader
ELAN VALLEY RESERVOIR Rhayader
ERCH (RIVER) Llanymynech
GLUDY LAKE Brecon
GWYDDIOR LAKE Llanbrynmair
IRFON (RIVER) Builth Wells
IRFON (RIVER) Llangammarch Wells
IRFON (RIVER) Llanwrtyd Wells
LAKE MOCHDRE Newtown
LLYN ALARCH Builth Wells
LLYN CLYWEDOG Llanidloes
LLYN-COCH HWYAD Llanbrynmair
LLYNGWYN LAKE Rhayader
MULE (RIVER) Newtown
NEW INN Llandrindod Wells
SEVERN (RIVER) Llanidloes
SEVERN (RIVER) Newtown
TOWY (RIVER) Brecon
TWYMYN (RIVER) Llanbrynmair
USK (RIVER) Crickhowell
USK RESERVOIR Brecon
VALLEY DAM FISHERY Llanfyllin
VYRNWY (RIVER) Llansantffraid
VYRNWY (RIVER) Welshpool
WYE (RIVER) Llandrindod Wells
WYE (RIVER) Rhayader

RHONDDA CYNON TAFF

BROOKFIELD FISHERY Pontypridd
CMPRAC (RIVER) Treorchy
ELY (RIVER) Pontyclun
LLYN ALAW Pontyclun
LLYN FAWR FISHERY Treorchy
RHONDDA (RIVER) Treorchy
TRI NANT TROUT FARM Pontyclun

SWANSEA

LOWER LLIW
SHIMANO FELINDRE TROUT FISHERY
TAWE (RIVER)

TORFAEN

BEACONS RESERVOIRS Pontypool
CANTREF RESERVOIR Pontypool
LISVANE RESERVOIR Pontypool
LLANDEGFEDD RESERVOIR Pontypool
LLANISHEN RESERVOIR Pontypool
LLWYN ON RESERVOIR Pontypool
LLYN ON RESERVOIR Pontypool
LLYWD (RIVER) Pontypool

WREXHAM

ALYN (RIVER)
BODIDRIS GAME FISHERY
DEE (RIVER)
LLANDEGLA TROUT FISHERY
LLYN CYFYNWY SPORT TROUT FISHERY
PENYCAE LOWER RESERVOIR
PENYCAE UPPER RESERVOIR
TREE TOPS FLY FISHERY
TY MAWR RESERVOIR
WORTHENBURY BROOK

COMBINATION

CAERPHILLY

RIVERSIDE TROUT FISHERY Hengoed

CARDIFF

CEFN MABLEY

CARMARTHENSHIRE

BRO TYWI FISHERIES Carmarthen
COWIN (RIVER) Carmarthen
CYNIN (RIVER) Carmarthen
LLYN CARFAN Whitland
PEWI FACH (RIVER) Carmarthen
SPRINGWATER LAKES Llanwrda
TAF (RIVER) Carmarthen
TEIFI VALLEY FISH Llanybydder

CONWY

- **CONWY (RIVER)**
- **CONWY (RIVER)** Betws-Y-Coed
- **LLYN ALED** Denbigh

FLINTSHIRE

- **SARN MILL FISHERIES** Mold

GLAMORGAN (VALE OF)

- **PONTSTICILL RESERVOIR** Merthyr Tydfil

GWYNEDD

- **DEE (RIVER)** Bala
- **GWYNEDD (RIVER)** Criccieth
- **TRAWFFYNYDD RESERVOIR** Blaenau Ffestiniog

ISLE OF ANGLESEY

- **LLYN LLWYDIARTH FAWR** Llanerchymedd

MONMOUTHSHIRE

- **MONNOW (RIVER)** Abergavenny
- **WYE (RIVER)** Monmouth

NEATH PORT TALBOT

- **GLYNCORRWG PONDS FISHERY** Port Talbot

NEWPORT

- **PETERSTONE TROUT LAKE**

NORFOLK

- **DEE (RIVER)** Holt

PEMBROKESHIRE

- **HOLGAN TROUT FARM FISHERY** Narberth
- **YET-Y-GORS FISHERY** Fishguard

POWYS

- **IRFON (RIVER)** Builth Wells
- **ITHON (RIVER)** Llandrindod Wells
- **LLANDRINIO WEST LAKE** Llanymynech
- **MAERDY BROOK** Llanymynech
- **RIVERSIDE CARAVAN PARK** Llangammarch Wells
- **SEVERN (RIVER)** Llanymynech
- **SEVERN (RIVER)** Newtown
- **SEVERN (RIVER)** Welshpool
- **VYRNWY (RIVER)** Llanymynech
- **VYRNWY (RIVER)** Welshpool
- **WESTLAKE FISHERY** Llanymynech
- **WYE (RIVER)** Builth Wells

RHONDDA CYNON TAFF

- **SEVEN OAKS FISHERY** Pontyclun

SWANSEA

- **MAES GWYN FISHERY**
- **WHITE SPRINGS LAKES**

WREXHAM

- **DEE (RIVER)**
- **DEE (RIVER)** Bangor-on-Dee
- **DEE (RIVER)** Worthenbury
- **DEE ABBEY FISHERIES**

Facilities Available

SECTION 6

This section allows you to search for Fisheries with particular facilities available. This is useful to know before you choose to fish there.

e.g Café, Toilets and Tackle Hire.

Once you have located a Fishery you can either look up further details in Section 1 or use the other sections to find what else the Fishery may have to offer.

Fishing Facilities and Amenities

	Net Dips	Tackle Hire	Site Tackle Shop	Boats Available	Bait Sold	Adult Matches	Junior Matches	Half Day Fishing	Night Fishing	Tuition Given	Accommodation	Camping	Caravan Site	Male Toilets	Female Toilets	Disabled Toilets	Disabled Facilities	Hardcore Parking	Public Telephone	Showers	Washing Facilities	Restaurant	Hot Meals	Cafe	Refreshments	Day Lodge Available	Solid Based Swims	Easy Access Swims	Disabled Access Swims	Grass Swims	Tree Sheltered	Dogs Allowed	Fulltime Security	Rare Birdlife	Rare Wildlife	Spectators Allowed	Kids with Adults
ENGLAND																																					
BEDFORDSHIRE																																					
BRIARWOOD FISHERY (FH0619)									●																												
ELSTOW PITS (FH1573)									●																				●						●	●		
IVEL (RIVER) (FH2402)						●			●																												
IVEL (RIVER) (FH2401)										●																				●							
JONES PIT (FH2416)									●	●				●	●															●		●					
LAKESIDE (FH2597)										●																											
LEDBURN ROAD (FH2659)									●																												
LITTLE HEATH FARM (FH2753)				●																																	
MANOR FARM LEISURE (FH3163)	●	●	●		●				●	●				●	●		●	●	●		●			●	●	●	●	●	●	●			●	●	●	●	●
OUSE (RIVER) (FH3639)						●			●																					●		●					
OUSE (RIVER) (FH3638)										●																				●							
PRIORY COUNTRY PARK (FH3848)			●						●		●			●	●	●	●	●	●		●	●	●		●		●	●	●	●	●	●	●			●	
TINGRITH COARSE FISHERY (FH4851)		●	●		●				●					●	●	●							●	●	●												
VAUXHALL PIT (FH5090)									●																												
WITHY POOL (FH5446)														●	●			●		●	●						●				●			●	●		
BERKSHIRE																																					
AMERDEN POOL (FH0100)					●				●																		●	●		●							
BARTON COURT FISHERY (FH0338)						●	●			●				●	●			●									●	●		●				●	●		●
BENS LAKE (FH0385)		●			●									●	●	●													●		●						
BISHOPS GREEN FARM LAKE (FH0436)																		●										●		●	●			●	●		
BRAY LOCK (FH0607)				●		●	●				●	●	●	●	●	●	●		●		●							●	●		●	●	●	●	●	●	●
BURGHFIELD (FH0739)									●																					●		●					
BURGHFIELD BLUE POOL (FH0740)						●	●			●																	●	●	●	●							
BURGHFIELD CANAL (FH0741)						●	●																					●		●						●	
BURGHFIELD MATCH LAKE (FH0742)						●	●			●																	●	●	●							●	
COTTAGE LANE (FH1134)						●	●			●																		●	●	●							
COURT FARM (FH1141)														●	●																						
EAST TOWNEY (FH1514)						●	●																				●	●	●							●	
ENGLEFIELD LAGOON (FH1594)									●														●	●	●			●	●	●							
FARLEYMOOR LAKE (FH1667)																													●								
FARNHAM FLINT (FH1677)						●	●		●																			●	●	●	●			●		●	
FELIX FARM TROUT FISHERY (FH1684)		●		●		●				●				●	●								●	●			●		●		●					●	
FROBURY FARM SPORTING CLUB (FH1805)		●			●	●	●			●	●	●	●	●	●			●	●								●	●	●		●		●				●

Fishing Facilities and Amenities

Fishery	Net Dips	Tackle Hire	Site Tackle Shop	Boats Available	Bait Sold	Adult Matches	Junior Matches	Half Day Fishing	Night Fishing	Tuition Given	Accommodation	Camping	Caravan Site	Male Toilets	Female Toilets	Disabled Toilets	Disabled Facilities	Hardcore Parking	Public Telephone	Showers	Washing Facilities	Restaurant	Hot Meals	Cafe	Refreshments	Day Lodge Available	Solid Based Swims	Easy Access Swims	Disabled Access Swims	Grass Swims	Tree Sheltered	Dogs Allowed	Fulltime Security	Rare Birdlife	Rare Wildlife	Spectators Allowed	Kids with Adults
FROXFIELD A AND B (FH1815)						●	●																				●	●	●	●						●	
HAMBRIDGE LANE (FH2079)									●																			●	●	●				●			
HOLYBROOK (FH2277)																												●		●	●						
HURLEY LOCK (FH2345)														●	●																						
KENNET (RIVER) (FH2440)						●	●																					●		●						●	
KENNET (RIVER) (FH2438)														●	●															●							
KENNET (RIVER) (FH2442)						●	●																				●	●	●	●							
KENNET (RIVER) (FH2441)						●	●		●																			●		●						●	
KENNET (RIVER) (FH2443)						●	●																				●	●	●							●	
KENNET (RIVER) (FH2448)																		●											●								
KENNET (RIVER) (FH2435)						●	●																				●	●		●		●				●	
KENNET (RIVER) (FH2444)						●	●																					●		●							
KENNET (RIVER) (FH2446)						●	●																				●	●	●	●						●	
KENNET AND AVON CANAL (FH2452)						●	●																				●	●	●	●		●				●	
KENNET AND AVON CANAL (FH2455)						●	●																				●	●	●							●	
KENNET AND AVON CANAL (FH2454)						●	●																					●		●						●	
KENNET AND AVON CANAL (FH2450)						●																						●									
KENNET AND AVON CANAL (FH2451)						●	●																				●	●	●			●				●	
KENNET AND AVON CANAL (FH2449)						●																	●	●	●												
KENNET AND ENTORNE (RIVERS) (FH2468)									●	●																	●	●	●	●				●	●		
LONGMOOR FARM FISHING LAKE (FH2993)	●							●		●				●	●	●	●	●			●				●		●	●	●	●			●				
LOWER BENYONS (FH3073)						●	●																				●	●		●						●	
MAPLEDURHAM A AND B (FH3172)						●	●																					●	●	●						●	
MATCH AND BLUE POOLS (FH3207)						●																							●								
MILL LANE (FH3290)														●	●	●													●		●						
MILL POND (FH3298)			●			●	●			●				●	●	●	●					●			●			●	●		●						
MOATLANDS POOL (FH3331)						●	●																					●		●	●					●	
NEWBURY TROUT LAKES (FH3480)				●				●						●	●			●									●	●	●	●				●	●		
PADWORTH MILL (FH2447)						●	●																							●						●	
PADWORTH ROTA (FH2453)						●	●																				●	●	●							●	
PINGEWOOD LAGOON (FH3783)									●																			●	●	●				●	●		
PONDWOOD CARP LAKES (FH3814)								●						●	●			●										●	●	●	●			●	●	●	
PURLEY (FH3858)						●	●																					●		●						●	
ROMNEY ISLAND AND MEADOW (FH4001)						●																						●		●						●	
SHEEPHOUSE FARM TROUT FISHERY (FH4217)		●		●						●																			●								

Fishing Facilities and Amenities

Fishery	Kids with Adults	Spectators Allowed	Rare Wildlife	Rare Birdlife	Fulltime Security	Dogs Allowed	Tree Sheltered	Grass Swims	Disabled Access Swims	Easy Access Swims	Solid Based Swims	Day Lodge Available	Refreshments	Cafe	Hot Meals	Restaurant	Washing Facilities	Showers	Public Telephone	Hardcore Parking	Disabled Facilities	Disabled Toilets	Female Toilets	Male Toilets	Caravan Site	Camping	Accommodation	Tuition Given	Night Fishing	Half Day Fishing	Junior Matches	Adult Matches	Bait Sold	Boats Available	Site Tackle Shop	Tackle Hire	Net Dips
SLALFORD LAKES (FH4293)								●	●	●	●										●	●	●	●													
SONNING EYE (FH4326)		●						●	●	●																					●	●					
SOUTH FIELD PARK (FH4329)													●		●								●	●													
SOUTH HILL PARK LAKE (FH4331)						●					●		●							●	●	●	●	●				●			●	●			●		
ST PATRICKS (FH4395)								●																				●	●								
SWAN VALLEY (FH4596)			●	●		●		●		●										●								●	●		●	●					
THAMES (RIVER) (FH4763)		●						●	●	●																					●	●					
THAMES (RIVER) (FH4771)		●						●		●																					●	●					
THAMES (RIVER) (FH4761)									●																												
THEALE (FH4806)			●	●				●																				●									
THEALE CANAL (FH4807)		●						●	●	●	●																				●	●					
THEALE LAGOON (FH4808)			●	●				●	●	●																					●	●					
TRI-LAKES (FH4954)		●							●				●	●	●	●					●	●	●	●		●	●						●				
TWYFORD BBONT (FH5008)			●	●				●																				●	●								
TWYFORD WATERS (FH5010)				●			●	●			●									●								●									
UFTON CANAL (FH5039)								●	●	●	●																				●	●					
WASING WOODS (FH5165)			●	●				●	●	●	●																	●	●								
WHITE SWAN LAKE (FH5343)		●	●	●		●		●	●	●	●		●	●	●						●	●	●	●				●	●								
WYLIES LAKE (FH5546)		●						●	●	●	●								●												●	●					
BRISTOL																																					
AVON (BRISTOL) (RIVER) (FH0191)		●						●																					●								
BAGWOOD LAKE (FH0249)																													●								
BITTERWELL LAKE (FH0438)		●				●	●		●	●			●		●					●			●	●						●		●	●				
BRISTOL DOCKS (FH0655)		●	●					●		●	●		●						●			●	●	●					●		●	●		●			
FISHPONDS LIDO (FH1737)																●																					
TANHOUSE FARM LAKE (FH4652)							●	●		●													●	●													
BUCKINGHAMSHIRE																																					
ALDERS FARM TROUT FISHERY (FH0062)			●	●	●		●	●			●		●	●	●				●	●			●	●				●		●			●			●	●
BACKWATER (FH0242)																													●								
BILLET LANE (FH0417)									●																												●
BLACK PARK (FH0447)													●	●																							
BOURTON FISHERIES (FH0567)								●																					●								
CHURCH HILL FISHERY (FH0953)		●		●			●	●		●					●					●		●	●	●						●						●	
COLNBROOK WEST (FH1068)							●	●	●	●	●																		●								
COLNEBROOK (RIVER) (FH1076)			●	●				●			●									●									●								

Fishing Facilities and Amenities

Fishery	Kids with Adults	Spectators Allowed	Rare Wildlife	Rare Birdlife	Fulltime Security	Dogs Allowed	Tree Sheltered	Grass Swims	Disabled Access Swims	Easy Access Swims	Solid Based Swims	Day Lodge Available	Refreshments	Cafe	Hot Meals	Restaurant	Washing Facilities	Showers	Public Telephone	Hardcore Parking	Disabled Facilities	Disabled Toilets	Female Toilets	Male Toilets	Caravan Site	Camping	Accommodation	Tuition Given	Night Fishing	Half Day Fishing	Junior Matches	Adult Matches	Bait Sold	Boats Available	Site Tackle Shop	Tackle Hire	Net Dips
COSGROVE LEISURE PARK (FH1122)									●				●																				●			●	
CRAYFISH POOL (FH1171)								●																					●								
DOVECOTE LAKE FISHERY (FH1430)		●	●	●			●	●	●	●	●		●	●	●	●			●	●			●	●					●	●	●	●	●			●	
FARLOWS LAKE (FH1668)								●	●	●	●		●	●	●		●		●	●	●	●	●	●					●		●	●	●		●		
GILBRATAR LAKE (FH1854)							●			●	●																					●					
GREAT LINFORD LAKES (FH1982)										●			●	●	●			●		●		●	●	●					●						●		
GREAT OUSE (RIVER) (FH1988)																				●																	
HILL WOOD POND (FH2225)																													●								
HORTON BOAT POOL (FH2310)			●	●		●		●		●	●		●		●				●				●	●					●								
HORTON CHURCH LAKE (FH2311)			●	●		●		●		●	●		●		●				●		●		●	●					●								
KINGFISHER GOLF CLUB (FH2496)			●	●		●	●	●	●	●			●		●					●			●	●													
KINGSMEAD 1 (FH2514)			●	●		●		●		●	●		●		●				●		●		●	●				●	●								
KINGSMEAD ISLAND LAKE (FH2516)			●	●		●		●															●	●					●								
LATIMER PARK FLY FISHERY (FH2628)									●	●																								●			
LODGE LAKES (FH2978)		●					●			●	●									●																	
LOUGHTON LODGE LAKE (FH3063)																				●																	
MAYFIELDS LAKE (FH3216)							●	●		●	●									●									●		●	●					
OLD SLADE LANE LAKE (FH3599)																				●									●								
ORLITTS LAKES (FH3622)								●		●	●																		●		●	●					
OUSE (RIVER) (FH3642)	●	●	●	●	●	●	●	●												●											●	●					
OUSE (RIVER) KEMPSTON MILL (FH3641)		●						●		●	●																				●	●					
SHELSWELL LAKE (FH4228)																																		●			
SILVERWING LAKE (FH4273)			●	●				●			●									●									●								
SPADE OAK LAKE (FH4357)																													●								
THAMES (RIVER) (FH4782)																													●								
THAMES (RIVER) (FH4778)																													●								
THAMES (RIVER) (FH4780)																													●								
THAMES (RIVER) (FH4779)																													●								
THAMES (RIVER) (FH4777)																				●									●								
TINGRITH LAKES (FH4852)	●	●			●			●		●	●		●	●	●				●	●			●	●				●	●	●	●	●	●			●	●
TYRINGHAM ESTATE (FH5037)								●																					●								
VICARAGE SPINNEY FISHERY (FH5096)																																		●			
WATTS POOL (FH5189)			●	●				●			●									●									●								
WESTFIELD FARM (FH5276)								●	●	●																		●	●		●	●					
WESTHORPE PARK LAKE (FH5281)																													●								

Fishing Facilities and Amenities

Fishery	Net Dips	Tackle Hire	Site Tackle Shop	Boats Available	Bait Sold	Adult Matches	Junior Matches	Half Day Fishing	Night Fishing	Tuition Given	Accommodation	Camping	Caravan Site	Male Toilets	Female Toilets	Disabled Toilets	Disabled Facilities	Hardcore Parking	Public Telephone	Showers	Washing Facilities	Restaurant	Hot Meals	Cafe	Refreshments	Day Lodge Available	Solid Based Swims	Easy Access Swims	Disabled Access Swims	Grass Swims	Tree Sheltered	Dogs Allowed	Fulltime Security	Rare Birdlife	Rare Wildlife	Spectators Allowed	Kids with Adults
WESTON TERVELL RESERVOIR (FH5286)									●																												
WOLVERTON LAKES (FH5456)																		●																			
CAMBRIDGESHIRE																																					
BARNWELL COUNTRY PARK (FH0320)	●													●	●	●	●	●			●				●		●	●	●	●		●	●	●	●	●	
BARNWELL PIT (FH0321)																													●								
BLUEBELL LAKE (FH0513)	●	●	●	●	●			●	●	●		●	●	●	●		●	●	●			●	●	●	●	●	●	●	●	●	●	●	●	●	●	●	●
CAM (RIVER) (FH0807)														●	●									●													
CAM (RIVER) (FH0805)																		●										●	●	●		●				●	
CHAWSTON LAKES (FH0908)						●			●																		●			●		●				●	
ELDERNELL LAKE (FH1559)																		●									●				●						
FENLAND FISHERIES (FH1696)														●	●		●							●	●			●	●								
FERRY MEADOWS (FH1701)						●								●	●	●	●	●	●				●	●	●		●	●	●	●	●	●		●	●	●	
FIELDS END WATER (FH1704)					●	●	●	●						●	●										●		●	●			●	●		●	●	●	
GERARDS CARP LAKE (FH1849)						●																															
GRAFHAM WATER (FH1934)		●		●																		●															
GREAT OUSE (RIVER) (FH1991)						●	●	●	●								●	●									●	●	●	●		●	●	●	●	●	●
GREAT OUSE (RIVER) (FH1992)																		●										●	●								
GREAT OUSE (RIVER) (FH1994)						●			●																					●						●	
GREAT OUSE (RIVER) (FH1993)																									●												
GREAT OUSE (RIVER) (FH1996)						●	●		●								●	●	●			●	●	●				●	●	●	●	●				●	
GREAT OUSE (RIVER) (FH1995)						●			●																		●			●		●				●	
HINCHINGBROOKE COUNTRY PARK (FH2232)														●	●									●													
KINGFISHER LAKE (FH2497)				●	●	●	●	●	●					●	●			●	●			●	●	●			●	●	●	●	●	●		●	●	●	
KINGSLAND RESERVOIRS (FH2512)						●											●																				
LARK (RIVER) (FH2622)																		●																			
MAGPIE LAKE (FH3139)						●																									●						
MEPAL PIT (FH3256)									●																		●	●		●					●	●	
MILTON COUNTRY PARK (FH3318)									●					●	●	●	●	●							●		●	●	●			●				●	●
NENE (RIVER) (FH3445)						●	●		●																			●	●	●						●	
NENE (RIVER) (FH3446)	●	●	●	●	●			●	●	●		●	●	●	●		●	●	●			●	●	●	●	●	●	●	●	●	●	●	●	●	●	●	●
NENE (RIVER) (FH3441)						●	●	●																				●		●							
NENE (RIVER) (FH3440)														●	●									●	●												
NENE NORTH BANK (RIVER) (FH3449)						●	●											●										●		●							
NORTH BANK TROUT FISHERY (FH3526)		●		●		●	●							●	●	●	●		●				●		●		●	●	●					●	●		
NORTHEY PARK FISHERY (FH3543)									●					●	●														●								

Fishing Facilities and Amenities

Facility	OFFORD WEIRPOOL (FH3575)	OLD WEST (RIVER) (FH3602)	OVER MAIN DRAIN (FH3659)	RAVELEY DRAIN (FH3893)	ROSWELL PITS (FH4022)	SAND MARTIN LAKE (FH4091)	SIBSON FISHERIES (FH4264)	ST IVES COMPLEX (FH4387)	STEW POND (FH4453)	SWAN LAKE (FH4589)	TURKS HEAD LAKE (FH4977)	TWENTY FOOT DRAIN (FH5003)	VIRGINIA LAKE (FH5100)	WELDON RESERVOIR (FH5228)	WHITTLESEY DYKE/ BEVILLS LEAM (FH5361)	WILLOW CREEK (FH5378)	WOOD POOL (FH5459)	CHESHIRE	ASHLEY POOL (FH0164)	ASTBURY MERE (FH0176)	BELMONT POOL (FH0381)	BETLEY MERE (FH0396)	BLUNDELLS FARM FISHERY (FH0514)	BOLESWORTH CASTLE (FH0532)	BORDER FISHERIES (FH0546)	BOTTOMS RESERVOIR (FH0563)	BOUNDARY WATER PARK (FH0566)	BRERETON HEATH COUNTRY PARK (FH0616)	BRIGHOUSE POOL (FH0643)	BROOK BANK POOL (FH0676)	BROOKSIDE FISHERIES (FH0686)	BROOKSIDE LAKES (FH0687)	BROWNLEES POND (FH0703)	BULLS POOL (FH0729)	BURTON MERE FISHERIES (FH0761)
Kids with Adults																							●										●		
Spectators Allowed		●				●	●			●			●	●		●	●			●			●												
Rare Wildlife						●				●			●			●	●			●		●							●	●	●				●
Rare Birdlife				●		●	●			●			●			●	●			●		●		●					●	●	●				●
Fulltime Security																																			
Dogs Allowed						●	●			●			●	●		●	●			●															
Tree Sheltered						●	●			●						●	●					●	●	●	●		●			●	●		●		●
Grass Swims		●				●	●			●				●	●	●	●		●	●				●					●		●				●
Disabled Access Swims						●	●			●			●			●	●						●		●		●			●	●	●	●		●
Easy Access Swims		●		●		●	●			●			●		●	●	●			●		●	●		●	●				●	●		●		●
Solid Based Swims						●	●			●			●	●	●	●	●			●		●	●	●						●	●		●		●
Day Lodge Available																							●												
Refreshments													●														●				●	●			●
Cafe						●				●			●			●	●								●		●								●
Hot Meals						●				●						●	●										●				●				●
Restaurant						●				●			●			●	●			●															
Washing Facilities																				●			●												
Showers																																			
Public Telephone						●				●			●			●	●														●				●
Hardcore Parking	●				●	●	●			●						●	●			●		●	●	●		●	●			●	●			●	●
Disabled Facilities													●																						●
Disabled Toilets													●							●						●						●			●
Female Toilets						●				●	●		●			●	●			●			●	●	●	●	●	●			●	●			●
Male Toilets						●				●	●		●			●	●			●		●	●	●	●	●	●	●			●	●			●
Caravan Site																																			
Camping																																			
Accommodation																																			
Tuition Given													●																						●
Night Fishing			●			●	●		●	●				●		●	●			●	●	●		●			●								●
Half Day Fishing						●				●						●	●						●												●
Junior Matches						●	●			●					●	●	●						●										●		
Adult Matches						●	●			●		●	●	●	●	●	●						●	●	●						●	●			●
Bait Sold						●				●			●			●	●														●				●
Boats Available						●		●		●						●	●																		
Site Tackle Shop																																			
Tackle Hire													●																						●
Net Dips																							●												

Fishing Facilities and Amenities

Fishery	Net Dips	Tackle Hire	Site Tackle Shop	Boats Available	Bait Sold	Adult Matches	Junior Matches	Half Day Fishing	Night Fishing	Tuition Given	Accommodation	Camping	Caravan Site	Male Toilets	Female Toilets	Disabled Toilets	Disabled Facilities	Hardcore Parking	Public Telephone	Showers	Washing Facilities	Restaurant	Hot Meals	Cafe	Refreshments	Day Lodge Available	Solid Based Swims	Easy Access Swims	Disabled Access Swims	Grass Swims	Tree Sheltered	Dogs Allowed	Fulltime Security	Rare Birdlife	Rare Wildlife	Spectators Allowed	Kids with Adults
BYLEY FISHERIES (FH0783)														●	●		●																	●	●		
CAPESTHORNE HALL STOCK POND (FH0831)						●	●							●	●	●	●											●	●	●							
CAPESTHORNE MAIN POOL (FH0832)														●	●		●										●	●	●	●							
CAPESTHORNE TOP POOL (FH0833)									●					●	●			●									●			●	●			●	●		
CHESHIRE FISHING (FH0925)		●			●	●	●		●					●	●	●	●											●	●		●						
DANE (RIVER) (FH1255)																													●		●						
DANE RIVERSIDE FISHERY (FH1267)						●								●	●								●	●	●				●		●						
DANEBRIDGE FISHERIES (FH1268)		●				●	●	●						●	●			●	●								●	●	●	●	●			●	●	●	
DEAN (RIVER) (FH1286)											●											●			●					●				●	●		
EGERTON LAKE (FH1550)						●	●		●																			●	●	●	●					●	
FANSHAWE LANE POOL (FH1662)																														●							
FARM POOL (FH1671)									●																												
GOWY FISHERY (FH1932)								●										●									●			●						●	●
GRIMESDITCH MILL POOL (FH2020)						●	●		●									●									●	●	●		●					●	
GRIMSDITCH MILL POOL (FH2023)									●									●									●	●	●								
HAMPTON SPRINGS (FH2096)														●	●													●	●								
HARTHILL (FH2114)														●	●														●		●						
HOLMSTON HALL FISHERY (FH2270)					●			●						●	●		●	●									●	●	●							●	
JARMAN FARM POOL (FH2407)														●	●																						
KAZAKO PONDS (FH2421)					●																									●			●	●	●		
LAKEMORE COUNTRY PARK (FH2578)						●			●	●				●	●							●	●	●	●			●	●	●				●	●		
LAMALOAD RESERVOIR (FH2599)														●	●			●										●									
LITTLE REEDS MERE (FH2760)																														●	●			●	●		
LLOYDS MEADOW FISHERIES (FH2784)						●	●	●		●				●	●	●		●																			
LONGBARN POOL (FH2985)									●																										●		
LYMM DAM (FH3115)						●			●						●	●																					
LYMM VALE (FH3116)									●																												
MANOR POOL (FH3171)																											●			●	●			●	●		
MARBURY MERE (FH3175)														●	●	●																					
MARTON HEATH COARSE POOL (FH3202)								●						●				●									●	●			●						●
MARTON HEATH TROUT POOLS (FH3203)		●	●			●		●		●				●	●		●	●			●				●	●	●	●	●		●		●	●	●	●	●
MARY ANN POND (FH3204)							●																				●	●	●								●
MEADOW FISHERY (FH3222)		●				●		●						●	●	●	●	●							●		●	●	●	●	●					●	
MEADOW VIEW FISHERY (FH3225)						●	●	●						●	●	●	●	●							●		●	●	●		●						
MILL LODGE (FH3292)														●	●																						

www.fishooked.com

Fishing Facilities and Amenities

	Net Dips	Tackle Hire	Site Tackle Shop	Boats Available	Bait Sold	Adult Matches	Junior Matches	Half Day Fishing	Night Fishing	Tuition Given	Accommodation	Camping	Caravan Site	Male Toilets	Female Toilets	Disabled Toilets	Disabled Facilities	Hardcore Parking	Public Telephone	Showers	Washing Facilities	Restaurant	Hot Meals	Cafe	Refreshments	Day Lodge Available	Solid Based Swims	Easy Access Swims	Disabled Access Swims	Grass Swims	Tree Sheltered	Dogs Allowed	Fulltime Security	Rare Birdlife	Rare Wildlife	Spectators Allowed	Kids with Adults
MOORE QUARRY (FH3360)																		●																			
MORETON MERE FISHERY (FH3370)					●	●	●		●					●	●	●	●	●					●		●		●	●	●	●	●			●			
NEW POOL (FH3476)									●																				●								
OAK POOL (FH3559)									●																												
OLD QUAY CANAL (FH3598)									●																												
PARTRIDGE LAKES (FH3714)										●				●	●	●		●									●		●		●						
REASEHEATH COLLEGE LAKE (FH3904)														●	●	●	●						●	●	●		●	●	●	●							
REDESMERE (FH3916)									●									●							●					●	●			●	●		
SALE WATER PARK (FH4081)																						●			●												
SANKEY ST HELENS CANAL (FH4100)						●			●																												
SHAKERLEY MERE (FH4202)						●			●					●	●	●	●	●									●	●	●	●	●	●		●		●	
STOCKPOND (FH4462)									●																												
STRETTON WATER (FH4525)																											●							●	●		
SWANLEY (FH4599)																														●	●			●	●		
TABLEY MERE (FH4625)				●																																	
TABLEY MOAT (FH4626)						●			●																												
TATTON MERE (FH4664)						●	●							●	●	●		●	●		●							●		●		●	●	●	●	●	●
TAX MERE (FH4677)																															●						
TOFT POOL (FH4865)																													●		●						
TOP FARM POOL (FH4876)																															●						
TURNERS POOL (FH4982)																												●	●	●	●						
VALE ROYAL LOCKS (FH5084)																													●		●						
VILLAGE POOL (FH5098)									●																						●						
WALL POOL LODGE (FH5121)	●					●								●	●		●	●									●	●	●	●	●		●				●
WEAVER (RIVER) (FH5215)																	●																				
WESTLOW MERE (FH5283)				●			●	●		●				●	●			●			●				●	●		●	●	●	●	●	●				●
WHITEGATE POND (FH5347)							●																				●	●	●								●
WHITLEY POOL (FH5357)									●																												
WILLOW POOL (FH5388)									●																												
WINSFORD FLASH (FH5421)														●	●										●												
WINTERLEY POOL FISHERY (FH5426)						●	●		●					●	●			●									●	●		●	●					●	
YEW TREE POOL (FH5568)									●																												
CLEVELAND																																					
HART RESERVOIR (FH2112)																		●																			
HUTTON RUDBY PONDS (FH2351)																													●								

Fishing Facilities and Amenities

Facility	LOCH KENNY (FH2899)	LOCKE PARK (FH2971)	ROSSMERE PARK LAKE (FH4020)	TILERY LAKE (FH4843)	CORNWALL	ARGAL RESERVOIR (FH0134)	BAKE FISHING LAKES (FH0253)	BILLS POOL (FH0423)	BOLINGEY LAKE (FH0534)	BOSCATHNOE RESERVOIR (FH0556)	BRAGGS WOOD TROUT FISHERY (FH0594)	BUDE CANAL (FH0721)	BUSH LAKES FARM (FH0768)	BUSSOW RESERVOIR (FH0772)	BUTTERWELL (FH0779)	COLLEGE RESERVOIR (FH1064)	CRAFTHOLE LAKE (FH1157)	DRIFT RESERVOIR (FH1443)	DUTSON WATER (FH1487)	EAST ROSE FARM (FH1513)	ELECTRICITY POOL (FH1560)	ELMFIELD FARM COARSE FISHERY (FH1570)	FENWICK TROUT FISHERY (FH1698)	FERNDALE (FH1699)	FORDA HOLIDAY LODGES (FH1761)	FOWEY (RIVER) (FH1785)	FOWEY (RIVER) (FH1787)	FOWEY (RIVER) (FH1786)	FOWEY (RIVER) (FH1782)	FOWEY (RIVER) (FH1784)	GLENLEIGH FARM FISHERY (FH1892)	GOONHAVERN LAKE (FH1920)	GWARNICK MILL TROUT FISHERY (FH2040)	GWINEAR POOLS COARSE FISHERY (FH2049)	GWINNEAR POOLS (FH2050)
Kids with Adults							●													●				●							●	●		●	
Spectators Allowed							●												●	●				●							●	●	●	●	
Rare Wildlife							●				●				●				●	●						●	●	●	●		●				
Rare Birdlife							●				●				●			●	●	●						●	●	●	●	●	●				●
Fulltime Security																															●			●	
Dogs Allowed							●												●	●											●	●	●	●	
Tree Sheltered		●						●			●				●		●		●	●	●		●	●				●	●		●		●	●	●
Grass Swims	●			●			●												●									●		●	●	●		●	●
Disabled Access Swims		●					●	●		●	●		●	●					●	●	●	●						●		●	●		●	●	
Easy Access Swims	●			●			●			●					●			●	●	●				●				●		●	●	●	●	●	
Solid Based Swims							●												●	●											●	●		●	●
Day Lodge Available							●																											
Refreshments		●					●		●		●									●					●						●		●		
Cafe																				●													●		
Hot Meals															●					●													●		
Restaurant																				●													●		
Washing Facilities						●	●												●	●				●							●				
Showers																																		●	
Public Telephone																				●													●		
Hardcore Parking						●	●			●					●			●	●	●				●				●			●	●	●	●	●
Disabled Facilities			●				●												●	●										●	●		●		
Disabled Toilets		●				●	●		●		●									●		●											●		
Female Toilets		●				●	●		●		●		●		●				●	●		●		●							●		●	●	
Male Toilets		●				●	●		●		●	●	●		●				●	●		●		●							●	●	●	●	
Caravan Site																			●															●	
Camping																				●				●											
Accommodation																			●	●												●			
Tuition Given							●								●																				
Night Fishing															●	●			●							●	●	●	●	●	●	●	●		
Half Day Fishing																				●													●	●	
Junior Matches							●													●													●		●
Adult Matches							●													●													●	●	●
Bait Sold							●		●						●				●	●										●				●	
Boats Available																																	●		
Site Tackle Shop							●												●																
Tackle Hire							●		●						●			●		●				●									●		
Net Dips							●																	●							●	●		●	

FACILITIES AVAILABLE

England (by County)

Fishing Facilities and Amenities

Facility	HIDDEN VALLEY (FH2203)	INNY (RIVER) (FH2372)	LAKE PENRYN (FH2568)	LAKEVIEW COUNTRY CLUB (FH2598)	LANGARTH POOLS (FH2610)	LYNHER (RIVER) (FH3124)	MEADOWSIDE COARSE FISHERY (FH3228)	MIDDLE BOSWIN FARM (FH3264)	MILLBROOK COARSE FISHERY (FH3305)	MILTON MOUNT LAKE (FH3322)	NANCE LAKES (FH3414)	OAKSIDE FISHERY (FH3567)	ORVIS INNIS FLY FISHERY (FH3626)	PORTH RESERVOIR (FH3825)	RETALLACK WATERS (FH3931)	ROSE PARK FISHERY (FH4011)	ROSEWATER LAKE (FH4014)	SEATON (RIVER) (FH4127)	SHARKEYS PIT (FH4209)	SHILLAMILL LAKES COUNTRY PARK (FH4238)	ST ERTH FISHERY (FH4385)	STITHIANS RESERVOIR (FH4459)	STOWFORD GRANGE FISHERIES (FH4513)	TAMAR (RIVER) (FH4641)	TAMAR LAKE (UPPER) (FH4645)	TEMPLE TROUT FISHERY (FH4735)	TIN DENE FISHERY (FH4850)	TORY FARM LAKE (FH4887)	TREBELLAN PARK LAKES (FH4907)	TREDIDON BARTON LAKE (FH4908)	TREE MEADOW TROUT FISHERY (FH4909)	TREVELLA PARK (FH4950)	WEST LOOE (RIVER) (FH5263)	WHITEACRES COUNTRY PARK (FH5344)	WOONSMITH LAKE (FH5502)
Kids with Adults					●		●		●						●											●									
Spectators Allowed	●			●	●		●	●	●				●		●	●	●							●		●	●	●							●
Rare Wildlife	●	●		●	●	●	●		●						●	●		●						●		●	●				●		●		●
Rare Birdlife	●	●		●	●	●	●		●						●	●	●	●						●		●	●	●			●		●		●
Fulltime Security				●	●		●		●						●											●									
Dogs Allowed	●				●				●				●			●								●		●	●		●						
Tree Sheltered	●				●			●	●				●	●	●	●	●			●			●	●		●	●		●		●		●		●
Grass Swims	●			●	●			●	●						●									●		●		●	●						
Disabled Access Swims	●			●	●			●	●	●	●	●	●		●	●	●			●				●		●	●		●					●	●
Easy Access Swims	●			●	●		●	●	●	●	●		●		●		●		●					●		●	●	●	●	●	●		●		●
Solid Based Swims	●			●	●					●					●				●					●		●	●	●							●
Day Lodge Available																																			
Refreshments	●			●			●						●		●	●			●						●	●					●				
Cafe	●			●			●						●		●																●			●	
Hot Meals	●			●			●						●		●											●								●	
Restaurant				●									●		●																	●		●	
Washing Facilities				●																				●		●									
Showers									●						●																				
Public Telephone				●									●													●									
Hardcore Parking	●			●	●		●	●	●	●	●	●	●		●		●		●				●	●		●	●		●	●	●			●	
Disabled Facilities				●	●				●				●		●									●	●	●									●
Disabled Toilets				●	●		●						●		●					●						●			●					●	
Female Toilets	●			●	●		●		●		●	●	●	●	●	●	●		●	●				●	●	●			●	●	●			●	
Male Toilets	●			●	●		●		●		●	●	●	●	●	●	●		●	●				●	●	●			●	●	●			●	
Caravan Site							●								●									●					●	●					
Camping							●		●						●														●	●					
Accommodation																	●							●						●					
Tuition Given					●							●			●											●								●	
Night Fishing		●				●			●			●		●	●			●			●			●			●	●					●	●	
Half Day Fishing	●				●								●		●											●					●				
Junior Matches	●				●								●																					●	●
Adult Matches	●			●	●								●						●							●								●	●
Bait Sold	●			●			●	●							●		●		●					●		●								●	
Boats Available			●										●	●								●													
Site Tackle Shop				●											●		●		●	●				●		●									
Tackle Hire				●			●	●					●				●									●					●				
Net Dips				●	●		●		●						●																				●

www.fishooked.com

Fishing Facilities and Amenities

Fishery	Kids with Adults	Spectators Allowed	Rare Wildlife	Rare Birdlife	Fulltime Security	Dogs Allowed	Tree Sheltered	Grass Swims	Disabled Access Swims	Easy Access Swims	Solid Based Swims	Day Lodge Available	Refreshments	Cafe	Hot Meals	Restaurant	Washing Facilities	Showers	Public Telephone	Hardcore Parking	Disabled Facilities	Disabled Toilets	Female Toilets	Male Toilets	Caravan Site	Camping	Accommodation	Tuition Given	Night Fishing	Half Day Fishing	Junior Matches	Adult Matches	Bait Sold	Boats Available	Site Tackle Shop	Tackle Hire	Net Dips
COUNTY DURHAM																																					
AYCLIFFE LAKE (FH0235)									●																			●									
BEAUMONT FISHERIES (FH0358)	●		●	●	●		●		●	●	●	●	●	●	●		●			●			●	●				●		●	●	●	●			●	
BRASSIDE POND (FH0603)							●																														
BURNHOPE FISHERY (FH0749)																							●	●													
BYERS GREEN (FH0782)								●		●	●																		●		●	●					
DERWENT RESERVOIR (FH1360)													●		●								●	●									●				
FIELDSONS POND (FH1705)									●	●	●									●									●		●	●					
FINCHALE ABBEY FARM (FH1709)		●				●							●	●	●				●			●	●	●													
GREENCROFT POND (FH2006)							●		●				●																								
JUBILEE LAKES (FH2417)									●											●			●	●												●	
LANGSDALE LAKE (FH2617)							●		●														●	●													
MAINSFORTH POND (FH3149)																															●	●					
SHOTTON POND (FH4249)									●																												
TEES (RIVER) (FH4684)							●																														
TEES (RIVER) (FH4690)								●																								●					
TRIMDON POND (FH4955)									●																												
TURSDALE POND (FH4984)								●	●	●	●																	●			●	●					
WADSWORTH FISHERY (FH5111)							●	●	●	●	●									●									●								
WEAR (RIVER) (FH5200)													●																								
WEAR (RIVER) (FH5201)							●																														
WEAR (RIVER) (FH5209)			●	●																●								●	●								
WELLFIELD POND (FH5238)		●						●	●	●	●																		●		●	●					
WITTON CASTLE LAKES (FH5451)			●	●	●		●	●	●	●	●	●					●		●	●	●	●	●	●	●	●		●							●	●	
CUMBRIA																																					
ANNAS (RIVER) (FH0115)										●																			●								
BARN LAKE (FH0313)																							●	●													
BASSENTHWAITE LAKE (FH0344)																																		●			
BESSY BECK TROUT FARM (FH0394)	●	●		●	●	●		●	●	●	●	●	●	●	●		●			●	●	●	●	●				●		●			●	●		●	
BIGLAND HALL LAKE (FH0414)			●				●		●				●								●							●	●				●				
BLELHAM TARN (FH0495)							●	●																													
BLENCARN LAKE (FH0496)	●	●	●	●	●			●	●	●	●	●					●			●	●		●	●						●							
BORROWDALE FISHERIES (FH0553)		●	●	●			●			●				●	●				●				●	●									●			●	
BORWICK LAKE (FH0555)																					●																
BRAYTON POND (FH0608)														●																		●					

Angling Times Fishooked Directory

FACILITIES AVAILABLE

England (by County)

www.fishooked.com

Fishing Facilities and Amenities

	BUTTERMERE LAKE (FH0777)	CARLETON HILL (FH0842)	CROSSFIELD FISHERY (FH1193)	CRUMMOCK WATER LAKE (FH1206)	DERWENT (RIVER) (FH1345)	DOE (RIVER) (FH1390)	DRUNKEN DUCK TARN FISHERY (FH1454)	EAST VIEW FISHERY (FH1515)	EDEN (RIVER) (FH1535)	EDEN VALLEY TROUT LAKE (FH1543)	ELLEN (RIVER) (FH1563)	ELLERBECK FARM AND FISHERY (FH1565)	ENNERDALE LAKE FISHERY (FH1595)	ESK (RIVER) (FH1618)	ESK (RIVER) (FH1617)	ESTHWAITE WATER (FH1630)	GHYLL HEAD TROUT FISHERY (FH1851)	GRASMERE COARSE FISHERY (FH1976)	GRETA (RIVER) (FH2016)	HOLEHIRD TARN (FH2251)	IRT (RIVER) (FH2380)	KENT (RIVER) (FH2472)	KENT (RIVER) (FH2471)	KENTMERE FISHERY (FH2473)	LAKE WINDERMERE (FH2574)	LAZY (RIVER) (FH2641)	LICKLE (RIVER) (FH2714)	LIDDEL WATER (FH2715)	LONSDALE COUNTRY PARK (FH2997)	LOUGHRIGG TARN (FH3060)	LOUGHSIDE FISHERY (FH3062)	LOWESWATER LAKE (FH3096)	LUNE (RIVER) (FH3107)	MOSS ECCLES TARN (FH3378)	NEW HILLS TROUT FARM FISHERY (FH3465)
Kids with Adults	●			●							●	●											●									●	●		
Spectators Allowed	●			●		●		●		●	●	●	●			●			●				●									●	●		
Rare Wildlife	●		●	●		●					●	●				●			●				●						●			●	●		
Rare Birdlife	●		●	●		●					●	●				●			●				●						●			●	●		
Fulltime Security												●				●							●										●		
Dogs Allowed	●		●	●				●		●	●																					●			
Tree Sheltered	●			●		●		●		●	●	●				●	●		●	●					●					●		●	●	●	
Grass Swims								●								●													●	●					
Disabled Access Swims												●				●						●							●						
Easy Access Swims	●			●		●				●	●	●		●		●			●		●	●				●	●		●			●	●		
Solid Based Swims												●																	●						
Day Lodge Available												●																							
Refreshments						●				●		●				●			●										●				●		●
Cafe						●													●														●		
Hot Meals						●													●														●		●
Restaurant						●													●														●		●
Washing Facilities												●				●																			
Showers												●																							
Public Telephone						●		●			●								●										●				●		
Hardcore Parking	●			●		●		●		●	●	●	●		●	●			●						●			●				●	●		●
Disabled Facilities			●									●				●													●						
Disabled Toilets						●						●	●			●			●										●						●
Female Toilets						●		●				●	●			●			●										●						●
Male Toilets						●		●				●	●			●			●										●						●
Caravan Site											●	●											●										●		
Camping											●	●																					●		
Accommodation											●	●																					●		
Tuition Given									●							●																	●		
Night Fishing	●	●		●		●	●	●		●	●		●	●					●		●	●	●			●	●					●	●		
Half Day Fishing	●			●			●	●		●						●						●										●			
Junior Matches								●																											
Adult Matches								●								●													●						
Bait Sold																●													●						●
Boats Available	●			●	●											●		●						●	●						●	●			
Site Tackle Shop																●																			
Tackle Hire																●																			
Net Dips												●																							

Fishing Facilities and Amenities

Facility	OAKBANK LAKES (FH3560)	PRYHEAD FISHERY (FH3853)	RATHER HEATH TARN (FH3891)	SHARPLEY WATERS (FH4211)	SPRINT (RIVER) (FH4378)	TEWITFIELDS TROUT FISHERY (FH4752)	THIRLMERE (FH4810)	TRANQUIL OTTER (FH4904)	TWISS (RIVER) (FH5006)	ULLSWATER LAKE (FH5042)	ULVERSTON CANAL (FH5043)	WATENDLATH TROUT FISHERY (FH5169)	WHINS POND (FH5323)	WITHERSLACK HALL TARN (FH5443)	DERBYSHIRE	ALLESTREE LAKE (FH0078)	ALVASTON LAKE (FH0089)	ARNFIELD RESERVOIR (FH0140)	ASHGROVE LAKE (FH0162)	BARLOW FISHERIES (FH0312)	BEEHIVE FARM WOODLANDS LAKES (FH0371)	BUTTERLEY RESERVOIR (FH0776)	CARSINGTON WATER (FH0854)	CATTON PARK LAKE (FH0875)	COMBS RESERVOIR (FH1081)	CONDOR PARK RESERVOIR (FH1085)	COPPICE LAKE (FH1112)	DERBYSHIRE TROUT FISHERY (FH1334)	DONKHILL FISHERIES (FH1404)	ERRWOOD RESERVOIR (FH1616)	FOREMARK TROUT FISHERY (FH1764)	HARLESTHORPE DAM (FH2107)	HIGHAM FARM COARSE FISHING (FH2211)	LADYBOWER RESERVOIR (FH2549)	MARKEATON LAKE (FH3183)
Kids with Adults					●							●																	●						
Spectators Allowed	●				●				●			●											●		●				●	●	●				
Rare Wildlife	●				●	●		●	●			●									●		●	●					●	●	●	●			
Rare Birdlife	●				●	●		●	●			●						●			●		●	●					●	●	●	●			
Fulltime Security	●				●																								●						
Dogs Allowed	●							●																								●			
Tree Sheltered	●		●			●	●		●			●	●	●										●	●						●	●			
Grass Swims	●					●															●		●	●					●	●	●				
Disabled Access Swims	●		●	●		●		●				●	●							●	●	●		●		●	●	●				●		●	●
Easy Access Swims	●					●			●			●									●		●	●					●	●	●	●			
Solid Based Swims	●					●					●										●		●	●					●	●					
Day Lodge Available																													●						
Refreshments	●					●		●	●			●	●					●		●	●		●								●				
Cafe	●					●			●			●									●		●								●				
Hot Meals									●			●						●			●		●								●				
Restaurant									●														●				●								
Washing Facilities	●																												●						
Showers	●																																		
Public Telephone								●	●			●									●		●								●				
Hardcore Parking			●			●	●		●			●				●					●			●	●				●		●	●			●
Disabled Facilities	●			●															●		●		●								●			●	
Disabled Toilets	●							●	●												●		●								●	●		●	
Female Toilets	●	●				●	●	●	●			●						●	●	●	●		●	●					●	●	●	●		●	
Male Toilets	●	●				●	●	●	●			●				●	●	●	●	●	●		●	●					●	●	●	●		●	
Caravan Site	●				●																														
Camping	●											●																							
Accommodation												●																							
Tuition Given						●		●				●																	●						
Night Fishing	●				●				●																							●	●		
Half Day Fishing	●					●						●									●			●					●		●	●			
Junior Matches	●																				●				●						●				
Adult Matches	●					●					●										●		●	●	●						●	●			
Bait Sold	●												●																			●			
Boats Available								●		●		●						●					●								●	●		●	
Site Tackle Shop												●																							
Tackle Hire						●		●				●											●						●		●			●	
Net Dips																																			

www.fishooked.com

Fishing Facilities and Amenities

	MELBOURNE POOL (FH3243)	MONSAL DALE FISHERY (FH3352)	POSSY LODGE PONDS (FH3832)	RINGWOOD LAKE (FH3956)	SOAR (RIVER) (FH4315)	STAUNTON HAROLD RESERVOIR (FH4442)	SUTTON BROOK (FH4562)	TRENT (RIVER) (FH4917)	TRENT AND MERSEY CANAL (FH4940)	YEAVELEY ESTATE TROUT FISHERY (FH5560)	DEVON	ABBROOK POND (FH0012)	ALDER LAKE (FH0059)	ANGLERS ELDORADO (FH0106)	ANGLERS PARADISE (FH0108)	ANGLERS SHANGRILA (FH0109)	ASHCOMBE FISHERY (FH0159)	BAKERS FARM (FH0254)	BELLBROOK VALLEY (FH0377)	BICKERTON FARM FISHERY (FH0406)	BLUE LAKE (FH0509)	BULWORTHY FISHERY (FH0731)	CAMEL (RIVER) (FH0811)	CAMEL (RIVER) (FH0810)	CLAWFORD FISHERIES (FH0985)	CLOVELLY LAKES (FH1024)	COFTON PARK FARM (FH1052)	COOMBE FARM FISHPONDS (FH1105)	COOMBE FISHERIES (FH1106)	COOMBE WATER FISHERY (FH1110)	CREEDY (RIVER) (FH1175)	CREEDY (RIVER) (FH1174)	CREEDY LAKES (FH1176)	DARRACOTT RESERVOIR (FH1276)	DEER PARK COUNTRY HOTEL (FH1324)
Kids with Adults		●							●	●			●											●					●	●			●		
Spectators Allowed	●		●						●	●			●				●		●										●				●		●
Rare Wildlife		●							●										●				●	●	●				●				●		●
Rare Birdlife		●	●						●	●									●				●	●	●				●	●			●		●
Fulltime Security		●							●	●																							●		
Dogs Allowed	●								●				●																●						●
Tree Sheltered		●	●		●		●	●	●				●	●		●	●		●				●			●			●	●			●		●
Grass Swims	●	●	●				●		●	●		●	●	●	●	●			●						●				●	●		●	●		●
Disabled Access Swims	●					●			●	●					●	●	●								●	●				●			●		●
Easy Access Swims	●		●	●					●	●		●	●	●	●	●	●								●				●	●		●	●		●
Solid Based Swims	●			●					●	●			●		●										●					●			●		●
Day Lodge Available										●																									
Refreshments																		●	●						●		●						●		●
Cafe	●																		●						●										
Hot Meals																									●								●		●
Restaurant																									●										●
Washing Facilities										●																			●				●		
Showers																																			
Public Telephone																	●								●								●		●
Hardcore Parking		●	●	●					●	●			●	●	●	●							●	●					●	●			●		●
Disabled Facilities																				●					●								●		
Disabled Toilets															●										●	●							●		
Female Toilets										●					●		●		●		●				●	●			●	●			●		●
Male Toilets										●					●		●		●		●				●	●			●	●			●		●
Caravan Site																													●						
Camping													●																●						
Accommodation		●																												●			●		
Tuition Given			●				●			●									●						●						●				
Night Fishing	●								●			●	●								●		●	●				●	●	●				●	●
Half Day Fishing			●										●						●										●	●			●		●
Junior Matches																●														●					
Adult Matches									●							●			●						●					●					
Bait Sold	●									●					●										●				●				●		
Boats Available																						●													
Site Tackle Shop																																			
Tackle Hire										●					●				●																●
Net Dips																													●				●		

Fishing Facilities and Amenities

Fishery	Net Dips	Tackle Hire	Site Tackle Shop	Boats Available	Bait Sold	Adult Matches	Junior Matches	Half Day Fishing	Night Fishing	Tuition Given	Accommodation	Camping	Caravan Site	Male Toilets	Female Toilets	Disabled Toilets	Disabled Facilities	Hardcore Parking	Public Telephone	Showers	Washing Facilities	Restaurant	Hot Meals	Cafe	Refreshments	Day Lodge Available	Solid Based Swims	Easy Access Swims	Disabled Access Swims	Grass Swims	Tree Sheltered	Dogs Allowed	Fulltime Security	Rare Birdlife	Rare Wildlife	Spectators Allowed	Kids with Adults
DORES POND - RACKERHAYES (FH1413)																		●										●	●								
DRAKELANDS GAME FISHERY (FH1435)		●				●	●	●						●	●			●									●	●	●	●	●	●		●	●	●	
DUNSLEY FARM (FH1481)																															●						
EDDISON POND (FH1532)																															●						
EGGESFORD WATERS (FH1551)		●						●	●					●	●	●	●	●	●			●	●		●			●		●	●	●		●	●	●	
EXE (RIVER) (FH1643)														●	●	●								●	●		●		●								
EXE (RIVER) (FH1640)		●								●								●								●	●	●		●	●	●	●	●	●	●	●
EXE (RIVER) (FH1639)						●	●		●									●									●	●				●				●	
EXE (RIVER) (FH1642)		●							●	●																											
EXEMOOR FARM (FH1646)																															●						
EXETER CANAL (FH1647)														●	●		●							●													
EXETER SHIP CANAL (FH1648)						●	●		●									●									●	●	●	●		●				●	
FENECK POND (FH1695)						●	●		●									●									●	●		●		●				●	
FINLAKE PONDS (FH1713)														●	●	●													●		●						
FISHPONDS HOUSE (FH1736)	●	●				●	●	●			●	●	●	●	●	●	●	●	●	●	●	●	●	●	●		●	●	●	●		●	●	●	●	●	●
FOSFELLE COUNTRY HOUSE HOTEL (FH1774)								●						●	●			●				●	●	●	●						●	●				●	
FOUR PONDS (FH1781)									●																												
GRAND WESTERN CANAL (FH1967)						●	●							●	●	●	●	●					●	●	●		●	●	●	●	●			●	●	●	
HARTLAND FOREST FISHERY (FH2116)														●	●	●						●															
HARTSMOOR FISHERIES (FH2121)	●								●			●		●	●	●		●										●	●	●			●	●	●	●	●
HATCHLAND TROUT FISHERY (FH2129)		●				●								●	●													●	●					●		●	
HOGSBROOK LAKES (FH2246)									●																												
HOME FARM FISHERY (FH2280)	●	●	●		●							●		●			●	●	●						●		●	●	●	●	●		●			●	●
INDIO POND (FH2365)					●			●	●		●			●	●		●	●		●	●		●			●	●	●	●	●	●	●	●	●	●	●	●
ISLAND POND - RACKERHAYES (FH2391)																		●										●	●								
JENNETTS RESERVOIR (FH2409)														●	●																●						
KENNICK RESERVOIR (FH2469)				●													●																				
KINGSMEAD CENTRE (FH2515)			●						●	●	●	●	●	●	●	●		●		●	●							●	●					●	●		
LEGGE FARM COARSE FISHERY (FH2688)		●			●	●		●	●					●	●			●							●		●	●	●	●	●	●		●	●	●	
LITTLE ALLERS COARSE FISHERY (FH2739)																															●						
LITTLE COMFORT FARM (FH2746)														●	●																						
LITTLE WEACH (FH2763)														●	●																						●
LUCCOMBES PONDS (FH3101)	●					●	●			●				●	●			●			●						●	●	●	●	●	●	●	●	●	●	●
MELBURY RESERVOIR (FH3244)									●																												
MILEMEAD FISHERIES (FH3274)	●		●		●	●	●	●		●				●	●		●	●							●		●	●	●		●	●	●	●	●	●	

Fishing Facilities and Amenities

Fishery	Net Dips	Tackle Hire	Site Tackle Shop	Boats Available	Bait Sold	Adult Matches	Junior Matches	Half Day Fishing	Night Fishing	Tuition Given	Accommodation	Camping	Caravan Site	Male Toilets	Female Toilets	Disabled Toilets	Disabled Facilities	Hardcore Parking	Public Telephone	Showers	Washing Facilities	Restaurant	Hot Meals	Cafe	Refreshments	Day Lodge Available	Solid Based Swims	Easy Access Swims	Disabled Access Swims	Grass Swims	Tree Sheltered	Dogs Allowed	Fulltime Security	Rare Birdlife	Rare Wildlife	Spectators Allowed	Kids with Adults
MILL LEAT TROUT FISHERY (FH3291)		●						●						●	●	●		●										●	●	●	●	●		●	●	●	
MILL PARK COARSE FISHING LAKE (FH3297)					●	●	●	●						●	●			●	●				●		●			●	●	●	●	●		●	●	●	
MILLHAYES (FH3313)						●				●				●	●												●	●	●	●						●	
MILTON FARM PONDS (FH3319)																													●								
MOLE (RIVER) (FH3337)		●							●	●																											
NEW BARN ANGLING CENTRE (FH3461)			●		●					●	●			●	●	●	●	●							●		●	●	●								
NEWCOURT PONDS (FH3482)														●	●													●	●								
NEWHOUSE FISHERY (FH3486)		●				●		●		●				●	●		●	●					●	●	●		●	●	●	●	●			●	●	●	
OAKTREE FISHERY (FH3568)		●			●	●	●	●	●					●	●	●		●	●				●	●	●		●	●	●		●	●		●	●	●	
OLDBOROUGH FISHING RETREAT (FH3604)											●			●	●			●	●		●		●	●			●	●	●		●	●	●	●	●		●
OTTER (RIVER) (FH3630)					●			●		●	●			●	●		●	●	●	●	●	●	●	●	●	●		●		●		●	●	●	●	●	
OTTER FALLS FISHERY (FH3631)		●	●					●		●	●			●	●	●		●	●	●	●	●	●					●		●		●	●	●	●	●	●
PADBROOK PARK (FH3681)														●	●	●			●			●	●	●	●											●	
PICFRESH (FH3765)																		●																			
RIVERTON HOUSE AND LAKES (FH3970)	●	●			●	●	●	●	●	●	●	●	●	●	●		●	●			●		●		●		●	●	●	●		●	●	●	●	●	●
ROCOMBE PONDS (FH3986)																															●						
SALMONHUTCH COARSE FISHERY (FH4087)									●					●	●	●	●	●	●								●	●	●	●	●			●	●	●	
SAMPFORD PEVERAL PONDS (FH4090)						●	●		●									●									●	●				●				●	
SAWMILLS LAKE (FH4109)																													●		●						
SIMPSON VALLEY FISHERY (FH4274)														●	●	●													●		●				●		
SLADE RESERVOIRS (FH4292)									●																												
SLAPTON LEY (FH4294)				●				●						●	●	●		●																●	●		
SOUTH HAY FARM (FH4330)									●																												
SOUTH VIEW FARM FISHERY (FH4344)														●	●			●									●	●	●		●	●				●	
SPIRES LAKES (FH4365)														●	●			●																			
SQUABMOOR RESERVOIR (FH4379)									●																												
STAFFORD MOOR FISHERY (FH4402)		●																																			
STEVENSTONE LAKES (FH4452)																												●		●							
STILL WATERS TROUT FISHERY (FH4456)														●	●																						
SUMMERLEAZE POND (FH4554)																											●	●	●		●	●				●	
SUNRIDGE FISHERY (FH4557)						●	●	●	●		●		●	●	●			●		●	●						●	●		●	●			●	●	●	●
TAMAR (RIVER) (FH4643)										●				●	●	●			●				●	●	●					●	●	●					
TAMAR (RIVER) (FH4642)		●	●						●	●	●			●	●			●	●	●	●	●						●				●	●	●	●	●	
TAMAR LAKE (LOWER) (FH4644)				●																																	
TAR (RIVER) (FH4658)		●							●	●																											

Fishing Facilities and Amenities

Fishery	Kids with Adults	Spectators Allowed	Rare Wildlife	Rare Birdlife	Fulltime Security	Dogs Allowed	Tree Sheltered	Grass Swims	Disabled Access Swims	Easy Access Swims	Solid Based Swims	Day Lodge Available	Refreshments	Cafe	Hot Meals	Restaurant	Washing Facilities	Showers	Public Telephone	Hardcore Parking	Disabled Facilities	Disabled Toilets	Female Toilets	Male Toilets	Caravan Site	Camping	Accommodation	Tuition Given	Night Fishing	Half Day Fishing	Junior Matches	Adult Matches	Bait Sold	Boats Available	Site Tackle Shop	Tackle Hire	Net Dips
TAVISTOCK TROUT FISHERY (FH4670)	●	●			●				●	●		●	●		●		●			●	●	●	●	●			●	●		●					●	●	
TAW FISHING CLUB (FH4674)		●	●	●		●	●																						●								
TEIGN (FH4716)																												●	●							●	
TINNEY WATERS (FH4855)		●	●	●		●		●	●	●	●				●				●				●	●				●	●				●			●	
TORRIDGE (RIVER) (FH4883)	●	●	●	●						●							●			●			●	●			●		●								
TOWN PARKS COARSE FISHERY (FH4893)	●	●	●	●	●	●	●	●	●	●	●						●	●	●	●			●	●	●	●		●	●	●		●	●			●	●
TRENCHFORD RESERVOIR (FH4915)																				●														●			
UPHAM FARM PONDS (FH5050)		●			●	●	●	●	●	●										●	●	●	●	●	●	●			●								●
UPPER YEALM FISHERY (FH5061)		●	●	●			●			●			●							●				●					●	●							
UPTON WARREN LAKE (FH5062)							●			●													●	●							●	●					
VALLEY SPRINGS TROUT FISHERY (FH5088)	●	●	●	●	●	●	●	●	●	●										●			●	●			●	●				●	●			●	
WAPPERWELL POND (FH5146)							●																														
WATERCRESS FARM TROUT FISHERY (FH5174)			●	●			●	●	●	●	●		●	●						●	●	●	●	●						●		●				●	
WEST PITT FARM FISHERY (FH5264)		●					●	●	●	●	●									●			●	●													
WILLOWFIELD LAKE COTTAGES (FH5393)	●	●					●	●		●	●						●	●	●	●			●	●			●		●					●			
WISCOMBE FISHERY (FH5433)	●	●	●	●		●		●	●	●										●			●	●		●		●		●						●	
WOODA FARM FISHERY (FH5463)							●																														
WOODACOTT ARMS (FH5464)							●		●				●		●							●	●	●													
DORSET																																					
AMHERST LODGE FISHERY (FH0101)		●	●	●			●	●					●																							●	
AVON TYRRELL LAKES (FH0230)	●		●	●	●		●			●	●		●				●	●	●	●	●	●	●	●	●	●	●		●		●	●					●
BLASHFORD LAKES (FH0493)			●	●																																	
CHRISTCHURCH LOWER STOUR (FH0948)		●	●	●		●	●	●	●	●	●			●					●	●	●	●	●	●										●			
CRANBOURNE FRUIT FARM (FH1163)							●		●													●	●	●													
CROW POOL (FH1198)																					●																
DORSET FROME (FH1417)	●			●				●		●										●																	
FLOWERS FARM TROUT LAKES (FH1750)	●		●	●			●				●	●							●	●			●	●				●		●				●		●	●
GOLD OAK FISH FARM (FH1908)											●																		●	●	●	●					
HAMPSHIRE AVON (RIVER) (FH2084)									●																												
HAMPSHIRE AVON (RIVER) (FH2087)									●																												
HAMPSHIRE AVON (RIVER) (FH2085)							●																														
HAMPSHIRE AVON (RIVER) (FH2083)							●																														
HAMWORTHY LAKE (FH2098)													●										●	●													
HARROW POND (FH2111)							●																														
HERMITAGE LAKES (FH2189)	●	●			●	●	●	●	●	●										●	●		●	●	●					●							

Fishing Facilities and Amenities	Net Dips	Tackle Hire	Site Tackle Shop	Boats Available	Bait Sold	Adult Matches	Junior Matches	Half Day Fishing	Night Fishing	Tuition Given	Accommodation	Camping	Caravan Site	Male Toilets	Female Toilets	Disabled Toilets	Disabled Facilities	Hardcore Parking	Public Telephone	Showers	Washing Facilities	Restaurant	Hot Meals	Cafe	Refreshments	Day Lodge Available	Solid Based Swims	Easy Access Swims	Disabled Access Swims	Grass Swims	Tree Sheltered	Dogs Allowed	Fulltime Security	Rare Birdlife	Rare Wildlife	Spectators Allowed	Kids with Adults
HOLT WOOD PONDS (FH2272)														●	●		●												●		●						
HYDE LAKE (FH2353)									●																												
KINGCOMBE COARSE FARM (FH2492)								●	●	●		●	●	●	●			●										●		●		●		●	●	●	●
KINGCOMBE LAKE (FH2493)						●	●							●	●			●									●	●		●			●				●
LAWRENCES FARM (FH2636)								●	●	●																											
LUCKFIELD LAKE FISHERY (FH3102)									●									●							●				●		●						
MUDEFORD WOOD LAKE (FH3397)									●																				●		●						
NEW MEADOWS LAKE (FH3473)														●	●														●		●						
PALLINGTON LAKES (FH3687)	●	●	●		●	●	●	●	●					●	●		●	●		●	●	●	●	●	●		●	●	●	●	●		●	●	●	●	●
PIDDLE (RIVER) (FH3769)		●						●		●				●	●			●										●			●			●		●	
RADIPOLE LAKE (FH3875)				●					●																●						●			●			
REVEL'S FISHERY (FH3932)														●	●			●													●						
ROYALTY FISHERY (FH4049)				●				●						●	●			●									●	●	●	●	●					●	
STOUR (DORSET) (RIVER) (FH4478)																		●												●							
STOUR (DORSET) (RIVER) (FH4485)																													●								
STOUR (DORSET) (RIVER) (FH4490)																															●						
STOUR (DORSET) (RIVER) (FH4479)																															●						
STOUR (DORSET) (RIVER) (FH4489)						●	●											●										●		●				●	●		●
STOUR (DORSET) (RIVER) (FH4482)									●																												
STOUR (DORSET) (RIVER) (FH4486)						●																															
STOUR (DORSET) (RIVER) (FH4477)									●																						●						
STOUR (DORSET) (RIVER) (FH4483)									●																												
STOUR (RIVER) (FH4493)						●			●	●																	●	●	●	●							
STOUR (RIVER) (FH4491)																															●						
TODBER MANOR (FH4862)		●	●		●	●	●		●	●	●			●	●													●	●			●				●	
WALLYS LAKE (FH5124)									●					●	●												●					●				●	
WARMWELL HOLIDAY PARK (FH5148)									●					●	●			●				●			●												
WATERMILL LAKE (FH5182)														●	●	●							●	●												●	
WESSEX TROUT LAKES (FH5254)			●					●		●	●			●	●			●			●							●									●
WHITEMOOR LAKE (FH5351)									●	●				●	●														●								
WHITESHEET TROUT FISHERY (FH5353)								●						●	●			●													●			●	●		
WINKTON FISHERY (FH5418)																		●												●	●						
WOOD FARM CARAVAN PARK (FH5458)														●	●								●		●				●		●						
ESSEX																																					
ALBYNS LAKE (FH0053)										●							●												●								

Fishing Facilities and Amenities

Facility	ARDLEIGH RESERVOIR (FH0130)	ARMIGERS FARM (FH0138)	ASHELDHAM FISHERY (FH0160)	BARLEYLANDS RESERVOIR (FH0310)	BEDFORDS PARK LAKE (FH0365)	BERWICK PONDS (FH0393)	BIRDS GREEN (FH0428)	BLACKMORE WOOD (FH0452)	BLACKWATER (RIVER) (FH0477)	BLASFORD HILL FISHERIES (FH0492)	BLUNTS AND CANTS MERES (FH0516)	BOG GROVE (FH0523)	BORDEAUX PIT (FH0545)	BOREHAM FISHERY (FH0548)	BOREHAM MERES (FH0549)	BOVINGTON MERE 1 (FH0569)	BOVINGTON MERE 2 (FH0570)	BRAXTED HALL ESTATE (FH0605)	BRICKHOUSE FARM FISHERIES (FH0621)	BROAD GREEN AND TUFNELL MERE (FH0663)	BROOKHALL FISHERY (FH0682)	BULPHAN PARK FISHERIES (FH0730)	BURROWS FARM (FH0754)	CARP FARM FRYERNING FISHERIES (FH0845)	CHASE FISHERY (FH0907)	CHELMER & BLACKWATER (FH0913)	CHELMER (RIVER) (FH0911)	CHELMER (RIVER) (FH0910)	CHIGBOROUGH (FH0940)	CHIGBOROUGH FISHERIES (FH0941)	CLAVERHAMBURY LAKE (FH0982)	COLNE (RIVER) (FH1070)	CONNAUGHT WATER (FH1087)	CROWN NETHERHALL (FH1201)	DODDS FARM (FH1389)
Kids with Adults	●																													●					
Spectators Allowed																			●						●	●		●					●	●	
Rare Wildlife								●			●				●		●	●	●					●			●			●			●	●	●
Rare Birdlife	●							●			●				●		●	●	●					●			●			●			●	●	●
Fulltime Security																														●					
Dogs Allowed		●	●	●					●		●									●						●		●	●				●		
Tree Sheltered	●		●				●			●	●			●	●	●	●	●	●	●	●						●	●		●	●		●	●	●
Grass Swims	●							●			●		●		●			●	●		●			●	●	●	●		●	●	●		●	●	●
Disabled Access Swims	●						●	●		●	●			●		●	●	●	●					●					●	●	●	●	●		
Easy Access Swims	●		●	●				●		●	●		●		●	●	●	●	●	●	●			●	●	●	●		●	●	●		●	●	●
Solid Based Swims										●			●				●		●		●			●	●					●	●		●		●
Day Lodge Available	●																													●					
Refreshments					●		●															●													
Cafe							●												●			●								●					
Hot Meals																			●											●					
Restaurant																														●					
Washing Facilities	●																													●					
Showers																														●					
Public Telephone																																			
Hardcore Parking	●	●	●	●				●	●	●	●				●	●	●	●	●	●							●				●		●	●	●
Disabled Facilities								●			●							●												●		●			
Disabled Toilets			●		●		●	●			●							●	●											●	●				
Female Toilets	●		●		●		●	●			●							●	●			●		●						●	●			●	
Male Toilets	●		●		●		●	●			●							●	●		●	●		●						●	●			●	
Caravan Site																																			
Camping																														●					
Accommodation																																			
Tuition Given						●					●		●								●									●					
Night Fishing	●		●	●		●			●		●	●			●	●	●					●	●	●		●	●	●	●	●			●	●	
Half Day Fishing	●																		●		●									●					
Junior Matches	●							●		●	●				●			●								●	●								●
Adult Matches	●					●	●	●		●	●				●			●	●							●	●	●							●
Bait Sold																																			
Boats Available																														●					
Site Tackle Shop																																			
Tackle Hire																			●											●					
Net Dips																																			

www.fishooked.com

Fishing Facilities and Amenities

Facility	DONYLANDS LAKES (FH1406)	EWSONS WATER (FH1638)	FAIRLOP EAST LAKE (FH1653)	FENNES FISHERIES (FH1697)	FISHERS GREEN (FH1731)	GARNISH HALL (FH1837)	GLOUCESTER PARK LAKE (FH1900)	GOSFIELD LAKE RESORT (FH1926)	HAINAULT FOREST COUNTRY PARK (FH2063)	HANNINGFIELD TROUT FISHERY (FH2101)	HARWOOD HALL LAKE (FH2125)	HOCKLEY LAKES (FH2239)	HOLYFIELD FISHERY (FH2278)	HOME FARM FISHERY (FH2281)	HOOKS MARSH (FH2289)	HOUCHINS RESERVOIRS (FH2315)	JACKLETTS FARM (FH2405)	JOHNS LAKE FISHERIES (FH2414)
Kids with Adults																		
Spectators Allowed				●	●		●						●		●			●
Rare Wildlife	●				●				●	●	●				●	●		●
Rare Birdlife					●				●	●					●	●		●
Fulltime Security																		●
Dogs Allowed		●			●		●								●		●	
Tree Sheltered	●	●	●			●	●	●		●		●	●					●
Grass Swims	●				●		●	●		●								●
Disabled Access Swims			●	●	●		●				●	●	●		●		●	●
Easy Access Swims	●			●	●		●			●			●		●		●	●
Solid Based Swims	●			●	●		●			●					●		●	●
Day Lodge Available																		
Refreshments				●									●					●
Cafe							●	●		●			●					●
Hot Meals				●				●		●			●					
Restaurant								●		●								
Washing Facilities																		
Showers																		
Public Telephone										●			●					●
Hardcore Parking	●			●			●			●	●		●					●
Disabled Facilities				●	●				●	●								
Disabled Toilets					●		●			●			●		●			
Female Toilets				●	●	●	●	●		●			●		●			●
Male Toilets				●	●	●	●	●		●			●	●	●			●
Caravan Site																		
Camping																		
Accommodation																		
Tuition Given					●													
Night Fishing	●	●					●	●					●		●	●		
Half Day Fishing										●			●					
Junior Matches										●								●
Adult Matches				●				●		●		●						●
Bait Sold				●									●					
Boats Available										●								
Site Tackle Shop																		●
Tackle Hire										●								
Net Dips																		

Facility	KENNEL LANE (FH2434)	KNIGHTS PIT (FH2535)	LAKE MEADOWS (FH2562)	LAUNDRY LAKE (FH2630)	LAYER PIT (FH2639)	LITTLE BRAXTED FARM ESTATE (FH2742)	LITTLE EASTON FISHERIES (FH2750)	LITTLE EASTON MANOR (FH2751)	MAGIC LAKE (FH3138)	MARCONIS PIT (FH3177)	MAYBRAND FISHERY (FH3214)	MILL BARN FISHERY (FH3279)	MILLENNIUM LAKES (FH3309)	MOATHOUSE LAKE (FH3330)	NAZEING MEADS (FH3431)	NEWLAND HALL CARP FISHERY (FH3487)	NORTHLANDS PARK (FH3546)
Kids with Adults								●				●					
Spectators Allowed			●									●				●	●
Rare Wildlife	●					●		●				●		●			
Rare Birdlife	●					●		●				●		●	●		
Fulltime Security								●				●					
Dogs Allowed			●				●								●	●	●
Tree Sheltered	●			●		●	●	●			●	●	●	●		●	●
Grass Swims	●		●			●	●	●				●		●	●	●	●
Disabled Access Swims	●		●	●			●	●	●		●	●		●	●	●	
Easy Access Swims	●		●			●	●	●	●			●		●	●	●	●
Solid Based Swims	●					●						●		●	●		●
Day Lodge Available																	
Refreshments			●						●		●		●			●	●
Cafe			●						●							●	●
Hot Meals			●						●		●					●	●
Restaurant																	
Washing Facilities												●					
Showers																	
Public Telephone																	
Hardcore Parking	●		●		●	●	●	●						●		●	●
Disabled Facilities			●					●			●	●		●			●
Disabled Toilets			●											●			●
Female Toilets			●			●	●	●	●		●	●	●	●		●	●
Male Toilets			●			●	●	●	●		●		●	●		●	●
Caravan Site								●			●						
Camping											●						
Accommodation																	
Tuition Given											●	●					
Night Fishing	●	●								●	●				●	●	●
Half Day Fishing								●								●	
Junior Matches	●													●			
Adult Matches	●					●			●			●	●	●		●	
Bait Sold																	
Boats Available																	
Site Tackle Shop																	
Tackle Hire											●						
Net Dips												●					

Fishing Facilities and Amenities

Fishery	Net Dips	Tackle Hire	Site Tackle Shop	Boats Available	Bait Sold	Adult Matches	Junior Matches	Half Day Fishing	Night Fishing	Tuition Given	Accommodation	Camping	Caravan Site	Male Toilets	Female Toilets	Disabled Toilets	Disabled Facilities	Hardcore Parking	Public Telephone	Showers	Washing Facilities	Restaurant	Hot Meals	Cafe	Refreshments	Day Lodge Available	Solid Based Swims	Easy Access Swims	Disabled Access Swims	Grass Swims	Tree Sheltered	Dogs Allowed	Fulltime Security	Rare Birdlife	Rare Wildlife	Spectators Allowed	Kids with Adults
NUPERS FARM (FH3555)						●								●	●									●	●						●						
OLIVERS LAKE (FH3608)									●									●										●	●								
PANT (RIVER) (FH3689)						●	●							●	●			●														●					
PANT (RIVER) (FH3690)									●																							●					
PARSONAGE FARM (FH3712)																		●										●		●		●		●			
PEA LANE FISHERY (FH3722)									●					●	●			●											●								
PICKS COTTAGE CARP LAKES (FH3768)								●						●	●	●													●								
PRESTONS LAKE (FH3842)									●									●																			
RAPHAELS PARK (FH3888)														●	●	●							●		●				●								
RAYNE LODGE FARM (FH3903)																															●						
RECTORY FARM POND (FH3906)									●									●										●			●						
ROCKELLS FARM (FH3983)														●	●			●									●	●			●					●	
RODING (RIVER) (FH3991)									●									●														●					
RODING (RIVER) (FH3992)									●									●														●					
RODING (RIVER) (FH3993)									●									●														●					
RODING VALLEY LAKE (FH3994)									●																			●									
SHALFORD RESERVOIRS (FH4204)														●	●			●										●		●	●	●					
SLOUGH HOUSE LAKE (FH4301)								●		●				●	●												●				●		●			●	
SOUTHMINSTER FISHERIES (FH4352)						●	●		●					●	●			●									●	●	●		●	●					
STAMBRIDGE STARR FISHERIES (FH4412)		●							●	●				●	●	●						●															
STANFORD-LE-HOPE (FH4418)									●																			●		●							
STOUR (SUFFOLK) (RIVER) (FH4502)																															●						
STRAITS MILL (FH4518)						●	●							●	●			●										●			●	●					
VALENCE MOAT (FH5085)														●	●			●											●								
WAKE VALLEY POND (FH5114)									●									●										●		●	●	●		●	●	●	
WARREN (FH5150)						●																							●		●						
WEALD COUNTRY PARK (FH5194)														●	●	●	●	●						●				●	●		●					●	
WHARF POOL (FH5295)									●																			●		●							
WICK MERE (FH5363)																		●												●	●	●					
WID (RIVER) (FH5366)						●	●		●									●												●				●	●		
WILLOWS (FH5395)						●			●	●							●										●	●	●		●						
FIFE																																					
WEY (RIVER) (FH5289)									●																					●							
GLOUCESTERSHIRE																																					
ADLESTROP LAKE (FH0027)						●	●		●									●									●	●	●	●	●		●	●	●	●	●

Fishing Facilities and Amenities

Fishery	Kids with Adults	Spectators Allowed	Rare Wildlife	Rare Birdlife	Fulltime Security	Dogs Allowed	Tree Sheltered	Grass Swims	Disabled Access Swims	Easy Access Swims	Solid Based Swims	Day Lodge Available	Refreshments	Cafe	Hot Meals	Restaurant	Washing Facilities	Showers	Public Telephone	Hardcore Parking	Disabled Facilities	Disabled Toilets	Female Toilets	Male Toilets	Caravan Site	Camping	Accommodation	Tuition Given	Night Fishing	Half Day Fishing	Junior Matches	Adult Matches	Bait Sold	Boats Available	Site Tackle Shop	Tackle Hire	Net Dips
ASHTON KEYNES POOL (FH0171)									●																				●								
BOURTON-ON-THE-WATER PIT NO1 (FH0568)	●		●	●				●	●	●										●	●										●	●					●
BROOK FARM TROUT FISHERY (FH0677)	●		●		●								●				●			●			●	●				●									●
BURLEY FIELDS LAKE (FH0744)																													●			●					
BUSHYLEAZE TROUT FISHERY (FH0770)		●	●	●		●	●	●	●	●	●		●		●					●	●	●	●	●						●		●	●	●		●	
CANNOP PONDS (FH0823)									●	●													●	●													
CHURN POOL TROUT FISHERY (FH0959)									●																												
COKES PIT (FH1056)		●	●	●		●	●	●	●	●	●			●	●				●	●	●	●	●	●					●	●							
COLN (RIVER) (FH1067)									●																											●	
COLN (RIVER) (FH1066)										●						●														●							
COTSWOLD HOBURNE (FH1131)		●	●	●						●			●	●	●				●			●	●	●									●	●			
COURT FARM (FH1142)														●									●	●													
DONNINGTON TROUT FISHERY (FH1405)									●																			●									
GLOUCESTER & SHARPNESS (FH1897)									●				●																								
GREAT BURROWS TROUT FISHERY (FH1981)																												●								●	
HAM POOL (FH2078)									●														●	●													
HILL VIEW LAKES (FH2223)		●	●	●			●	●	●	●	●		●	●	●					●		●	●	●						●	●	●	●				
HILLVIEW FISHERY (FH2228)									●				●	●							●		●	●													
HORSESHOE LAKE (FH2307)																				●			●	●													
ISIS NO 1 LAKE 19 (FH2386)		●	●	●				●		●	●																		●		●	●					
KEYNES COUNTRY PARK (FH2475)	●	●	●	●		●	●	●	●	●	●			●	●				●	●	●	●	●	●					●	●							
KEYNES PARK TOP LAKE (FH2476)		●	●	●		●		●	●	●	●		●	●					●		●	●	●	●					●							●	
LAKE NUMBER ONE (LAKE19) (FH2565)		●		●			●	●	●	●	●									●									●		●	●					
LECHLADE TROUT FISHERY (FH2656)		●	●	●		●	●	●	●	●	●		●		●					●	●	●	●	●						●		●	●	●		●	
LEMINGTON LAKES (FH2696)									●				●	●	●							●	●	●								●					
LIGHTMOOR POOL (FH2719)		●				●			●	●											●										●	●					
MARIONS POOL (FH3181)		●	●	●		●		●		●	●																		●								
MEADOWCLIFFE POOL (FH3226)	●	●						●	●	●	●									●	●								●								
MILESTONE FISHERY (FH3275)									●				●																●				●				
MILL LAKE (NO 44) (FH3289)									●													●	●	●													
MORETON PITS (FH3371)									●																												
NEIGH BRIDGE LAKE (FH3437)		●	●	●		●		●	●	●	●										●		●	●					●								
NORTON FRUIT FARM (FH3548)									●	●										●			●	●						●							
PLUMP HILL POOL (FH3806)		●	●	●		●		●	●	●	●																										
RED LION FISHERY (FH3910)		●				●	●			●			●		●				●	●			●	●							●	●					

Fishing Facilities and Amenities

Fishery	Kids with Adults	Spectators Allowed	Rare Wildlife	Rare Birdlife	Fulltime Security	Dogs Allowed	Tree Sheltered	Grass Swims	Disabled Access Swims	Easy Access Swims	Solid Based Swims	Day Lodge Available	Refreshments	Cafe	Hot Meals	Restaurant	Washing Facilities	Showers	Public Telephone	Hardcore Parking	Disabled Facilities	Disabled Toilets	Female Toilets	Male Toilets	Caravan Site	Camping	Accommodation	Tuition Given	Night Fishing	Half Day Fishing	Junior Matches	Adult Matches	Bait Sold	Boats Available	Site Tackle Shop	Tackle Hire	Net Dips
SEVERN (RIVER) (FH4147)													●		●						●		●	●	●													
SEVERN (RIVER) (FH4146)							●																														
STANBOROUGH POOL (FH4416)										●			●								●		●	●					●								
STAUNTON COURT LAKES (FH4441)		●			●	●	●	●	●	●	●		●				●	●		●			●	●	●	●					●	●	●		●		●
STEAM MILLS LAKE (FH4444)		●	●	●		●		●	●	●	●																		●		●	●					
STONE END FARM LAKES (FH4467)									●													●	●	●													
THAMES (RIVER) (FH4785)							●		●																							●					
WATERLOO SCREENS (FH5179)		●	●	●		●		●		●	●																		●								
WATERSMEET LAKES (FH5186)							●		●	●			●		●	●			●	●		●	●	●					●								
WHELFORD POOLS COARSE FISHERY (FH5319)	●	●			●		●	●	●	●	●		●				●	●	●	●	●	●	●	●				●	●				●		●		●
WICK WATER (FH5364)									●																				●								
WITCOMBE WATERS (FH5437)			●	●			●	●	●	●			●							●			●	●				●		●		●		●		●	
HAMPSHIRE																																					
ABBOTTS WORTHY (FH0011)																							●	●													
ANTON LAKE (FH0118)							●																														
AVON RIVER FISHERIES (FH0228)		●					●			●	●									●																	
AWBRIDGE DANES LAKE (FH0231)							●																														
BASINGSTOKE CANAL (FH0342)							●																														
BROADLANDS LAKES (FH0664)		●		●			●	●	●	●	●		●						●	●	●	●	●	●					●		●	●	●			●	
BROADLANDS MAIN LAKE (FH0665)																															●	●					
CARRON ROW FARM PONDS (FH0852)							●		●												●		●	●													
CHIPHALL LAKE TROUT FISHERY (FH0943)		●	●	●			●	●	●	●			●		●					●	●		●	●						●		●				●	
COOKS POND (FH1100)							●	●	●	●																		●			●	●					
DARK LANE PONDS (FH1274)					●		●	●	●	●										●	●				●	●	●		●			●					●
DEVER SPRINGS TROUT FISHERY (FH1362)		●	●	●			●						●							●	●	●	●	●						●			●			●	
EAST MOORS LAKE (FH1511)	●		●	●					●	●										●			●	●					●								
FIRGROVE LAKES (FH1722)							●																														
FOXCOTTE LAKE (FH1789)							●		●				●		●							●	●	●													
FRIMLEY LAKES (FH1802)		●	●	●		●	●	●																													
FUNTLEY POND (FH1819)							●																														
GOLD VALLEY LAKES (FH1909)													●		●	●				●	●		●	●					●				●		●	●	●
GOLDEN POND FISHERY (FH1912)		●	●	●			●		●	●	●									●	●		●	●					●	●							
GREENRIDGE FARM LAKES (FH2009)	●	●	●	●	●		●	●	●	●	●	●	●				●			●	●		●	●	●	●			●	●	●	●	●				●
HAMPSHIRE AVON (FH2082)		●	●	●			●	●		●	●									●											●	●					
HAMPSHIRE AVON (RIVER) (FH2088)																													●								

Fishing Facilities and Amenities

Fishery	Net Dips	Tackle Hire	Site Tackle Shop	Boats Available	Bait Sold	Adult Matches	Junior Matches	Half Day Fishing	Night Fishing	Tuition Given	Accommodation	Camping	Caravan Site	Male Toilets	Female Toilets	Disabled Toilets	Disabled Facilities	Hardcore Parking	Public Telephone	Showers	Washing Facilities	Restaurant	Hot Meals	Cafe	Refreshments	Day Lodge Available	Solid Based Swims	Easy Access Swims	Disabled Access Swims	Grass Swims	Tree Sheltered	Dogs Allowed	Fulltime Security	Rare Birdlife	Rare Wildlife	Spectators Allowed	Kids with Adults
HAMPSHIRE AVON (RIVER) (FH2092)																											●			●				●	●		
HAMPSHIRE AVON (RIVER) (FH2089)																		●																			
HATCHET POND (FH2128)														●	●	●		●										●	●	●		●					
HILSEA MOATS (FH2229)						●								●	●		●	●											●		●					●	
HOLBURY LAKES (FH2247)						●		●		●				●	●	●		●	●		●					●		●	●		●		●	●	●	●	●
HOLLYBUSH LANE LAKES (FH2262)						●	●		●									●									●	●	●	●	●						
HORDLE LAKES (FH2296)														●	●			●																			
HUCKLESBROOK LAKE (FH2324)																															●						
HURST POND (FH2346)									●																		●	●	●	●	●						
IBSLEY POOLS (FH2357)														●	●	●													●								
ITCHEN (RIVER) (FH2397)																																		●	●		
JANESMOOR POND (FH2406)																														●				●			●
KIMBRIDGE (FH2488)														●	●																						
LAKE FARM (FH2556)																											●	●	●	●		●		●	●	●	
LAKESIDE (FH2580)																		●																			
LAKESIDE (FH2581)																	●												●		●						
LAKESIDE COUNTRY PARK (FH2589)						●	●			●				●	●	●	●		●						●		●	●	●	●		●		●		●	
LEOMINSTEAD MILL POND (FH2702)						●	●		●																				●		●						
LEOMINSTEAD TROUT FISHERY (FH2703)		●	●					●		●				●	●			●			●		●		●								●	●	●		●
LYNDHURST LAKE (FH3121)														●	●								●		●												
MEON SPRINGS FLY FISHERY (FH3255)		●						●						●	●			●													●	●				●	
MILL POND LAKE (FH3300)									●	●																	●			●		●		●		●	
MOORHEN FARM TROUT LAKE (FH3361)		●												●	●		●	●							●			●	●							●	
MOORS VALLEY COUNTRY PARK (FH3366)							●							●	●	●	●	●	●				●	●				●	●			●			●	●	
MOPLEY POND (FH3367)	●								●					●	●			●			●								●	●	●		●	●	●		
NETHER WALLOP (FH3452)		●						●						●	●			●							●						●						
NEW FOREST WATER PARK (FH3464)									●				●	●	●	●		●	●	●	●		●	●	●		●	●	●	●	●	●	●	●	●	●	●
NORTHFIELD LAKES (FH3544)									●																				●		●						
NUTRABAITS YATELEY COMPLEX (FH3556)									●	●				●	●		●										●	●	●	●							
NUTRABAITS YATELEY SOUTH LAKE (FH3557)									●					●	●	●							●		●				●		●						
ORCHARD LAKES (FH3616)						●	●	●										●									●	●	●		●					●	
PARSONAGE (RIVER) TEST (FH3711)										●				●	●			●								●		●			●	●		●	●		
PERIL LAKE (FH3752)														●	●	●													●		●						
PETERSFIELD HEATH LAKE (FH3757)														●	●														●		●						
QUEENS ROAD POND (FH3867)																									●												

Fishing Facilities and Amenities

	RIVER FARM (FH3964)	ROCKBOURNE TROUT FISHERY (FH3982)	ROOKSBURY MILL (FH4007)	ROTHERWICK & NIGHTINGALE (FH4032)	SOMERLEY LAKES (FH4322)	STONEHAM LAKES (FH4472)	SWAY LAKES (FH4605)	TEST (RIVER) (FH4745)	TITCHFIELD ABBEY LAKES (FH4857)	TURF CROFT FARM (FH4975)	WEDGEHILL PONDS (FH5222)	WHINWHISTLE COARSE FISHERY (FH5324)	WHITE HOUSE TROUT FARM (FH5338)	WILLOW PARK (FH5387)	WINTERSHILL TROUT LAKE (FH5430)	WOODINGTON FISHERY (FH5476)	WOODMILL SALMON FISHERY (FH5488)	HEREFORDSHIRE	BETULA WATERS (FH0397)	BIDDLESTONE LAKE (FH0408)	CASTLEMORTON (FH0868)	DOCKLOW POOLS (FH1386)	DRUMMOND DUB (FH1450)	EASTNOR CASTLE (FH1525)	EVESBATCH TOP LAKE (FH1636)	GOLDEN VALLEY (FH1914)	HAYCASTLE WATER (FH2150)	HUNDRED POOL (FH2337)	INGESTONE FISHERY (FH2366)	KINGFISHER TROUT LAKE (FH2502)	LILY AND WILLOW POOLS (FH2721)	MARSH HOUSE FARM (FH3192)	MILLPOND (FH3314)	MOCCAS FISHERY (FH3333)	MUNDERFIELD HAROLD (FH3402)
Kids with Adults																										●			●			●		
Spectators Allowed		●		●	●		●															●	●				●			●		●			●
Rare Wildlife	●	●		●	●							●					●										●			●		●			
Rare Birdlife	●	●	●	●	●			●				●					●					●				●	●			●					
Fulltime Security																						●								●			●		
Dogs Allowed								●							●												●			●					●
Tree Sheltered	●	●	●	●	●		●	●		●	●			●	●		●			●		●	●	●				●		●					
Grass Swims	●		●	●	●		●					●					●					●					●			●			●	●	
Disabled Access Swims	●	●		●	●	●				●		●	●	●			●				●	●			●		●	●	●	●		●	●		●
Easy Access Swims	●	●		●	●		●			●		●		●			●					●	●				●			●		●	●		●
Solid Based Swims					●		●							●	●		●					●					●			●		●			
Day Lodge Available																						●								●					
Refreshments		●	●					●						●		●						●								●		●		●	
Cafe		●												●		●						●								●					
Hot Meals		●						●														●								●		●		●	
Restaurant								●														●								●				●	
Washing Facilities														●																●			●		
Showers																						●											●		
Public Telephone								●									●					●											●		
Hardcore Parking	●	●		●	●	●	●	●		●		●		●	●	●	●					●	●				●			●			●		
Disabled Facilities					●									●			●													●		●	●		
Disabled Toilets					●									●			●													●		●	●		
Female Toilets	●	●	●		●	●		●		●		●		●	●	●	●					●								●	●	●	●	●	●
Male Toilets	●	●	●		●	●		●		●		●		●	●	●	●					●								●	●	●	●	●	●
Caravan Site																						●											●		
Camping																																	●		
Accommodation																						●													
Tuition Given																														●		●			
Night Fishing				●	●		●										●		●			●													
Half Day Fishing	●	●	●					●	●						●							●	●							●					
Junior Matches					●												●						●									●			●
Adult Matches				●	●									●						●		●	●							●	●	●	●		●
Bait Sold			●														●					●								●		●			
Boats Available			●																																
Site Tackle Shop														●								●								●					
Tackle Hire		●	●																											●		●			
Net Dips																														●			●		

FACILITIES AVAILABLE

England (by County)

Fishing Facilities and Amenities

	Net Dips	Tackle Hire	Site Tackle Shop	Boats Available	Bait Sold	Adult Matches	Junior Matches	Half Day Fishing	Night Fishing	Tuition Given	Accommodation	Camping	Caravan Site	Male Toilets	Female Toilets	Disabled Toilets	Disabled Facilities	Hardcore Parking	Public Telephone	Showers	Washing Facilities	Restaurant	Hot Meals	Cafe	Refreshments	Day Lodge Available	Solid Based Swims	Easy Access Swims	Disabled Access Swims	Grass Swims	Tree Sheltered	Dogs Allowed	Fulltime Security	Rare Birdlife	Rare Wildlife	Spectators Allowed	Kids with Adults
PIXLEY POOL (FH3797)							●		●																												
PRIDEWOOD LAKE (FH3844)						●			●																		●	●	●	●							
RED BANK POOLS (FH3907)														●	●														●								
ROYAL OAK POOL (FH4047)						●																															
RUSSELLS END RESERVOIR (FH4065)						●	●																														
WYE (RIVER) (FH5533)						●																															
HERTFORDSHIRE																																					
ADMIRALS WALK LAKE (FH0029)																														●		●		●	●		
ALDENHAM RESERVOIR (FH0058)				●		●		●	●					●	●	●	●	●	●			●			●		●	●	●	●				●	●		
AMWELL LAKES (FH0104)									●					●	●	●												●		●							
AYLESBURY ARM CANAL (FH0236)																													●								
BATCHWORTH LAKE (FH0346)									●					●	●													●	●								
BIERTON FISHING LAKES (FH0410)	●				●	●		●		●				●	●												●	●	●	●	●		●	●	●	●	●
BOWMANS LAKES (FH0574)			●		●	●		●	●			●	●	●	●	●	●	●		●	●		●	●			●	●	●	●			●	●	●	●	
BOWYERS WATER (FH0576)									●																		●	●				●		●	●		
BROAD COLNEY LAKES (FH0662)										●								●										●	●	●	●			●	●		
CARTHAGENA FISHERY (FH0855)																											●	●	●	●				●	●		
CROXLEY HALL TROUT FISHERY (FH1203)		●												●	●															●							
DOBBS WEIR FISHERY (FH1381)					●									●	●	●	●		●				●	●	●		●	●	●	●	●	●		●	●		
DURRANTS LAKE (FH1485)																									●				●		●						
FAIRLANDS VALLEY PARK (FH1652)						●								●	●	●								●					●								
GAYWOODS (FH1845)																		●										●	●								
GRAND UNION CANAL (FH1951)																												●	●								
GRAND UNION CANAL (FH1950)																												●	●								
GRAND UNION CANAL (FH1944)						●																					●	●		●							
GRAND UNION CANAL (FH1945)																												●	●								
GRAND UNION CANAL (FH1948)																													●								
GRAND UNION CANAL (FH1947)						●																					●	●		●							
GRAND UNION CANAL (FH1946)						●												●																			
HOLWELL HYDE LAKE (FH2275)																												●	●								
HOOK LAKE (FH2288)									●																							●					
INNS LAKE (FH2371)									●																												
KINGS WEIR FISHERY (FH2509)																													●		●						
LEA (RIVER) (FH2645)					●									●	●										●			●	●								
LEA (RIVER) (FH2644)														●	●										●			●	●								

Fishing Facilities and Amenities

Facility	LEE NAVIGATION (FH2668)	LEE NAVIGATION (FH2662)	LEE NAVIGATION (FH2666)	LEE NAVIGATION (FH2665)	LEE NAVIGATION (FH2663)	LOWBELL LANE (FH3069)	NEW RIVER (FH3477)	NORTH MET PIT (FH3532)	OAKFIELD FISHERY (FH3561)	OLD LEE (RIVER) (FH3589)	OLD LEE (RIVER) (FH3590)	OLD MILL AND MEADOWS (FH3594)	PAYNES LANE PIT (FH3721)	PIXIES MERE (FH3796)	RISLIP LAKE (FH3962)	RYEMEADS (FH4076)	SHEPHERDS WAY (FH4229)	SLIPE LANE PITS (FH4299)	STANBOROUGH LAKE (FH4415)	STANSTEAD ABBOTTS (FH4423)	STARTOPS RESERVOIR (FH4435)	THAME (RIVER) (FH4755)	TRING RESERVOIRS (FH4957)	WESTBROOK MERE (FH5270)	WESTONS LAKE (FH5287)	WOODLAND FARM (FH5478)	HUMBERSIDE	AIRE AND CALDER CANAL (FH0047)	BEVERLEY BECK (FH0399)	BEVERLEY CANAL (FH0400)	BIG HOLE PIT (FH0411)	BILLABONG PARK (FH0416)	BLUE LAGOON (FH0505)	BRANDES BURTON 3 AND 4 (FH0599)	BRANDESBURTON (FH0600)
Kids with Adults									●																			●			●				
Spectators Allowed		●							●			●								●			●					●			●				
Rare Wildlife								●	●					●		●		●		●			●					●			●				●
Rare Birdlife								●	●					●		●		●		●			●					●			●				●
Fulltime Security									●														●								●				
Dogs Allowed												●						●		●			●					●			●				
Tree Sheltered		●							●			●		●			●						●	●										●	
Grass Swims						●						●		●		●	●	●		●			●					●			●		●		●
Disabled Access Swims		●	●			●	●	●	●	●	●		●	●	●			●		●	●		●	●		●		●	●	●	●		●		
Easy Access Swims		●	●			●	●		●	●	●		●	●	●		●	●		●			●					●			●		●		●
Solid Based Swims		●				●		●	●			●		●			●	●		●			●					●			●		●		●
Day Lodge Available																																			
Refreshments												●		●									●												
Cafe		●																					●												
Hot Meals														●									●									●			
Restaurant																							●												
Washing Facilities																																			
Showers																																			
Public Telephone																							●												
Hardcore Parking	●	●							●					●			●						●					●							
Disabled Facilities		●							●			●		●						●								●			●				
Disabled Toilets		●										●																							
Female Toilets		●					●		●			●		●			●															●			
Male Toilets		●					●		●			●		●						●												●			
Caravan Site																																			
Camping																																			
Accommodation																																			
Tuition Given						●		●						●			●						●					●			●				
Night Fishing		●	●				●			●	●		●	●		●		●		●	●	●	●			●		●							●
Half Day Fishing																																			
Junior Matches		●						●						●				●										●			●				
Adult Matches		●		●	●				●					●			●	●							●			●			●				
Bait Sold																																			
Boats Available																			●																
Site Tackle Shop																																			
Tackle Hire																																			
Net Dips									●																										

Fishing Facilities and Amenities

Facility	BRICKYARD POND (FH0626)	BURSTWICK SKI LAKE (FH0758)	BURTON CONSTABLE COUNTRY PARK (FH0759)	DACRE LAKESIDE PARK (FH1244)	DERWENT (RIVER) (FH1351)	DRIFFIELD CANAL (FH1442)	EMMOTLAND PONDS (FH1587)	FAR GRANGE PARK (FH1663)	FARM PONDS (FH1670)	FISHPONDS FARM AND FISHERY (FH1735)	GOWDALL LAKES (FH1928)	HALSHAM POND (FH2075)	HULL (RIVER) (FH2332)	LANGHOLME FISHERIES (FH2614)	MOTORWAY POND (FH3382)	NODDLE HILL LAKE (FH3513)	OAKLANDS WATER (FH3564)	REDFERNS POND (FH3917)	STAR CARR TROUT FARM (FH4427)	THORPE HALL (FH4822)	TILARY LAKE (FH4841)	WILLITOFT FISH FARM (FH5376)	WILLOW SPRINGS (FH5390)	WOODALLS POND (FH5465)	ISLE OF WIGHT	GUNVILLE LAKE (FH2038)	ISLAND FISH FARM/MEADOW LAKES (FH2390)	MERSTONE FISHERIES (FH3258)	MORTON FARM (FH3373)	NETTLECOMBE FARMS (FH3457)	ROOKLEY COUNTRY PARK (FH4006)	KENT	ALDERS LAKES (FH0064)	BALLAST PIT (FH0259)	BARDEN LAKE (FH0304)
Kids with Adults			●				●	●											●			●					●								
Spectators Allowed		●	●					●								●			●								●	●			●				
Rare Wildlife	●	●	●				●								●	●			●		●	●						●	●						
Rare Birdlife	●	●	●				●								●	●			●		●					●	●	●	●						
Fulltime Security			●				●	●								●			●			●					●								
Dogs Allowed		●	●													●						●									●				
Tree Sheltered		●					●		●	●				●	●				●			●							●		●				●
Grass Swims							●								●	●			●		●	●				●	●	●	●		●			●	
Disabled Access Swims		●	●	●	●	●	●	●	●	●	●	●		●		●	●	●	●	●		●	●	●			●	●							●
Easy Access Swims		●	●				●	●		●						●		●	●			●				●	●	●	●		●			●	●
Solid Based Swims	●		●				●	●							●	●			●		●	●				●		●						●	
Day Lodge Available							●												●																
Refreshments			●			●	●	●				●	●						●			●									●				
Cafe								●																							●				
Hot Meals								●				●	●						●			●									●				
Restaurant								●				●																			●				
Washing Facilities			●				●	●											●								●								
Showers								●											●																
Public Telephone			●					●				●																			●				
Hardcore Parking			●				●	●		●						●			●		●	●					●		●	●	●				
Disabled Facilities			●				●	●		●						●	●														●				
Disabled Toilets			●					●		●				●													●				●			●	●
Female Toilets			●				●	●		●	●	●		●		●	●	●	●			●					●			●	●			●	●
Male Toilets			●				●	●		●	●	●		●		●	●	●	●			●					●			●	●		●	●	●
Caravan Site			●					●																											
Camping			●					●																											
Accommodation			●					●											●								●								
Tuition Given																●			●								●	●					●		
Night Fishing		●		●			●					●						●			●					●		●			●		●	●	
Half Day Fishing								●								●		●	●								●				●				
Junior Matches			●					●								●						●				●		●							
Adult Matches							●	●		●						●		●	●			●				●		●		●					
Bait Sold			●																			●					●								
Boats Available																			●																
Site Tackle Shop			●																●								●								
Tackle Hire																											●								
Net Dips								●											●																

Fishing Facilities and Amenities

Facility	BARTLEY MILL FISHERY (FH0336)	BEWL WATER (FH0403)	BIRCHDEN FARM FISHERY (FH0426)	BLUE LAGOON LAKE (FH0507)	BLUEBELL FISHING PONDS (FH0512)	BOUGH BEECH RESERVOIR (FH0564)	BYWATER LAKE (FH0785)	CACKLE HILL LAKES (FH0787)	CAPSTONE FARM COUNTRY PARK (FH0834)	CHALYBEATE SPRINGS (FH0892)	CHEQUERTREE FISHERY (FH0914)	CHIDDINGSTONE CASTLE LAKE (FH0939)	CHILHAM LAKE (FH0942)	CONNINGBROOK (FH1088)	COTTINGTON LAKES (FH1137)	DARENT (RIVER) (FH1272)	DARENTH FISHING COMPLEX (FH1273)	DUNDALE LAKE (FH1474)	EDEN (RIVER) (FH1539)	EDEN (RIVER) (FH1542)	FRANT LAKES (FH1798)	GRANGE POOL (FH1970)	HANDLE LAKE (FH2100)	HARTLEY LANDS FARM (FH2118)	HAWKHURST FISH FARM (FH2142)	HAYES TROUT FISHERY (FH2153)	HAYSDEN COUNTRY PARK (FH2160)	HOOKSTEAD LAKE (FH2290)	LARKFIELD LAKES (FH2625)	LITTLE CANSIRON FISHING LAKES (FH2745)	LONGFIELD LAKE (FH2988)	MATCH LAKE (FH3208)	MEDWAY (RIVER) (FH3236)	MEDWAY (RIVER) (FH3234)	MEDWAY (RIVER) (FH3231)
Kids with Adults		●																								●					●					
Spectators Allowed		●	●					●			●	●			●		●				●						●			●			●	
Rare Wildlife		●				●	●				●				●		●	●		●	●			●	●		●			●			●	
Rare Birdlife		●				●	●				●				●		●			●	●			●	●		●			●			●	
Fulltime Security		●																				●				●					●					
Dogs Allowed		●	●																																	
Tree Sheltered			●				●				●	●			●		●	●	●						●	●	●		●	●				●	●
Grass Swims		●		●		●	●				●				●		●	●		●	●				●	●	●		●	●	●	●	●		
Disabled Access Swims	●				●	●	●	●	●		●		●		●		●				●	●		●	●	●	●			●					●
Easy Access Swims		●	●	●		●	●	●	●		●		●		●		●				●		●		●	●	●			●		●		
Solid Based Swims						●	●								●		●				●				●		●			●					
Day Lodge Available		●																																		
Refreshments		●							●		●				●		●		●		●				●											
Cafe		●				●			●						●		●				●				●											
Hot Meals		●				●								●		●				●				●											
Restaurant		●														●																			
Washing Facilities		●																				●				●					●					
Showers		●																				●				●											
Public Telephone		●				●				●					●		●																			
Hardcore Parking		●	●	●		●	●	●			●				●		●	●			●		●		●	●	●	●		●		●		
Disabled Facilities		●				●	●								●		●				●				●	●	●			●					
Disabled Toilets		●				●			●						●		●				●				●		●									
Female Toilets	●	●	●	●	●	●	●	●	●		●		●	●	●	●	●				●		●	●	●	●	●			●		●		
Male Toilets	●	●	●	●	●	●	●	●	●		●		●	●	●	●	●				●		●	●	●	●	●			●		●		
Caravan Site											●											●													
Camping											●											●													
Accommodation											●																							
Tuition Given		●							●											●	●			●	●	●							●		
Night Fishing								●			●			●	●		●	●			●				●				●	●			●		
Half Day Fishing		●					●				●				●		●				●				●	●									
Junior Matches						●				●				●		●				●				●		●						●		
Adult Matches		●				●	●				●		●		●		●				●			●	●		●			●			●		
Bait Sold															●		●				●			●	●					●					
Boats Available		●				●																													
Site Tackle Shop		●																			●													
Tackle Hire		●									●				●									●											
Net Dips																					●				●					●					

Fishing Facilities and Amenities

	Net Dips	Tackle Hire	Site Tackle Shop	Boats Available	Bait Sold	Adult Matches	Junior Matches	Half Day Fishing	Night Fishing	Tuition Given	Accommodation	Camping	Caravan Site	Male Toilets	Female Toilets	Disabled Toilets	Disabled Facilities	Hardcore Parking	Public Telephone	Showers	Washing Facilities	Restaurant	Hot Meals	Cafe	Refreshments	Day Lodge Available	Solid Based Swims	Easy Access Swims	Disabled Access Swims	Grass Swims	Tree Sheltered	Dogs Allowed	Fulltime Security	Rare Birdlife	Rare Wildlife	Spectators Allowed	Kids with Adults
MEDWAY (RIVER) (FH3232)																		●																			
MEDWAY (RIVER) (FH3239)														●	●	●	●	●	●				●	●	●			●	●	●						●	
MEDWAY (RIVER) (FH3238)						●	●											●										●		●	●			●	●	●	
MEDWAY (RIVER) (FH3233)																		●																			
MID KENT FISHERIES (FH3263)		●			●	●	●	●	●					●	●	●	●	●	●						●		●	●	●	●	●	●		●	●	●	
MILL POOL (FH3301)														●	●			●										●									
MONK LAKE FISHERIES (FH3342)		●			●			●	●					●	●	●	●						●		●			●	●	●				●			
NACCOLT LAKE (FH3408)																		●										●		●							
NOOK & CRANNY LAKE (FH3514)														●	●			●										●									
REED LAKE (FH3923)														●	●			●										●		●							
ROOKERY LAKE (FH4004)																		●										●	●								
ROUKES DRIFT FARM (FH4035)						●								●	●			●									●	●	●		●			●	●		
ROYAL MILITARY CANAL (FH4046)						●												●																			
SCARLETTS LAKE (FH4114)						●	●	●																													
SILVER SPRINGS FISHERY (FH4270)														●	●	●															●						
SINGLETON LAKE (FH4276)						●	●			●							●		●								●	●	●			●				●	
ST CLERE LAKE (FH4383)																		●												●							
STOUR (RIVER) (FH4499)																		●																			
STOUR (RIVER) (FH4498)														●	●			●										●		●							
STOUR LAKE (FH4506)														●	●			●										●		●							
STOUTING LAKE (FH4507)				●										●	●								●		●												
STOWTING TROUT LAKE (FH4514)		●						●		●	●	●	●	●	●		●	●			●				●			●	●	●	●		●			●	●
SURRENDEN LAKES (FH4558)						●	●			●				●	●	●	●										●	●	●								
SUTTON AT HONE LAKE TWO (FH4559)														●	●													●		●							
SUTTON AT HONE LAKES 1 & 3 (FH4560)														●	●													●		●							
SWAN LAKE (FH4591)														●	●			●										●									
TEISE (RIVER) (FH4720)	●		●		●	●	●	●	●	●		●	●	●	●	●	●	●		●	●		●	●	●		●	●	●	●			●	●	●	●	
TENTERDEN TROUT WATERS (FH4738)		●	●							●				●	●			●			●				●	●		●	●		●	●	●	●			●
TONFORD LAKE (FH4871)														●	●			●										●									
TRIANGLE LAKE (FH4952)														●	●			●										●		●							
WIDEHURST FARM (FH5367)								●										●										●	●	●	●					●	
WOOD POOL (FH5461)														●	●			●										●		●							
LANCASHIRE																																					
ABBEY LAKES (FH0003)						●			●																						●						
ASHTON CANAL (FH0170)						●																															

Fishing Facilities and Amenities

	Net Dips	Tackle Hire	Site Tackle Shop	Boats Available	Bait Sold	Adult Matches	Junior Matches	Half Day Fishing	Night Fishing	Tuition Given	Accommodation	Camping	Caravan Site	Male Toilets	Female Toilets	Disabled Toilets	Disabled Facilities	Hardcore Parking	Public Telephone	Showers	Washing Facilities	Restaurant	Hot Meals	Cafe	Refreshments	Day Lodge Available	Solid Based Swims	Easy Access Swims	Disabled Access Swims	Grass Swims	Tree Sheltered	Dogs Allowed	Fulltime Security	Rare Birdlife	Rare Wildlife	Spectators Allowed	Kids with Adults
BALL GROVE LAKE (FH0258)						●		●	●					●	●		●	●			●						●	●	●	●			●			●	
BALL GROVE LAKE (FH0258)						●		●	●					●	●		●	●			●						●	●	●				●	●		●	
BANK HOUSE FLY FISHERY (FH0286)		●				●		●		●				●	●	●		●			●				●	●	●	●	●		●	●	●	●		●	●
BANNISTER HALL FARM (FH0300)																									●				●		●						
BARNSFOLD WATERS (FH0318)		●		●				●						●	●	●	●	●							●									●	●		
BOLTON CANAL (FH0540)																													●								
BRADSHAW HALL FISHERIES (FH0591)			●			●	●			●				●	●		●	●	●						●		●	●			●						
BRIARCROFT FISHERY (FH0618)						●	●										●																				
BRYAN HEY RESERVOIR (FH0711)						●								●	●				●				●	●													
BURSCOUGH BRICKWORKS LAKE (FH0756)																	●																				
CHARITY FARM FISHERY (FH0900)						●	●																														
CHURCH GARDEN (FH0952)																													●								
CLEVELEY BRIDGE FISHERY (FH1004)																	●																				
CLIVIGER FISH PONDS (FH1012)						●	●																				●	●		●		●		●	●	●	
COPTHORNE COARSE FISHERIES (FH1115)					●	●	●			●				●	●		●	●					●		●			●	●	●	●	●		●	●	●	
COTTAGE GREEN GARDEN CENTRE (FH1133)														●	●	●								●					●								
CROFT FISHERIES (FH1182)						●	●	●						●	●	●	●	●									●	●	●	●	●					●	
CROMPTON LODGE (FH1185)																											●			●				●	●		
DEEP PIT (FH1323)						●																															
DIXON GREEN RESERVOIR (FH1380)						●	●											●									●	●	●	●						●	
DOFFCOCKER LODGE (FH1392)						●	●																				●	●	●	●				●	●	●	
DRAKESHEAD FLY FISHERY (FH1436)								●						●	●			●													●						
DUNSCAR SHORE LODGE (FH1479)																													●		●						
EDISFORD AND BRUNGERLEY PARK (FH1546)														●	●	●	●	●					●	●				●	●								
ERIC FISHWICK NATURE RESERVE (FH1608)								●						●	●			●										●	●	●	●			●	●		
FIR TREE LODGE (FH1721)														●	●										●			●	●								
FOULRIDGE RESERVOIR (FH1778)						●												●									●	●		●				●	●	●	●
GLEAVES RESERVOIR (FH1876)																													●		●						
GREENHALGH LODGE FISHERY (FH2007)														●	●	●									●				●								
GRIMSARGH RESERVOIR (FH2021)																	●																				
HEAPEY NO 2 (FH2168)						●																															
HOLDEN WOOD RESERVOIR (FH2250)	●							●		●				●				●	●							●	●	●					●	●			●
JUMBLES RESERVOIR (FH2418)										●				●	●	●	●	●						●			●	●	●	●				●	●	●	
KNIGHT BOTTOMS LAKE (FH2534)									●					●	●	●							●		●				●								
LANCASTER CANAL (FH2603)						●											●																				

Fishing Facilities and Amenities

Fishery	Net Dips	Tackle Hire	Site Tackle Shop	Boats Available	Bait Sold	Adult Matches	Junior Matches	Half Day Fishing	Night Fishing	Tuition Given	Accommodation	Camping	Caravan Site	Male Toilets	Female Toilets	Disabled Toilets	Disabled Facilities	Hardcore Parking	Public Telephone	Showers	Washing Facilities	Restaurant	Hot Meals	Cafe	Refreshments	Day Lodge Available	Solid Based Swims	Easy Access Swims	Disabled Access Swims	Grass Swims	Tree Sheltered	Dogs Allowed	Fulltime Security	Rare Birdlife	Rare Wildlife	Spectators Allowed	Kids with Adults
LANCASTER HOUSE (FH2605)																																					●
LANESHAW RESERVOIR (FH2609)										●																								●	●		
LATHOM FISHERIES (FH2627)														●	●																						
LEEDS TO LIVERPOOL CANAL (FH2674)						●	●																					●	●								
LEEDS TO LIVERPOOL CANAL (FH2673)																													●								
LEISURE LAKES (FH2695)														●	●	●													●		●						
LITTLE DALE HALL (FH2747)	●				●	●	●	●										●									●	●			●		●	●	●	●	
LONGTON BRICKCROFT (FH2996)									●																												
LOVECLOUGH TROUT FISHERY (FH3065)	●					●	●	●		●				●	●			●	●		●			●	●	●	●	●	●			●	●	●	●	●	●
LOWER RIVINGTON RESERVOIR (FH3091)														●	●	●			●				●	●								●				●	
LUNE (RIVER) (FH3112)																																●	●	●	●	●	●
MARTIN HALL FARM (FH3200)																							●		●				●								
OGDEN RESERVOIR (FH3577)	●							●		●				●				●	●							●	●	●					●	●			●
ORRELL WATER PARK (FH3625)						●	●							●	●	●	●	●			●						●	●	●			●		●	●	●	●
PARSONAGE RESERVOIR (FH3713)																		●										●		●				●			
PINE LODGE FISHERIES (FH3777)																	●																				
PORTSMOUTH RESERVIOR (FH3831)																		●									●	●		●						●	●
RED ROCKS FISHERY (FH3911)						●								●	●	●													●								
ROUGHLEE TROUT FISHERY (FH4034)		●		●		●	●	●		●				●	●		●	●	●						●	●	●	●	●		●		●				
RUFFORD CANAL (FH4054)						●																															
RUSHYVARS LAKES (FH4064)														●	●														●								
SCOT LANE PONDS (FH4118)						●																															
ST MICHAELS WYRESIDE FISHERY (FH4394)					●			●	●					●	●	●	●	●	●				●	●	●		●	●	●		●	●				●	
STANLEY PARK LAKE (FH4420)														●	●	●													●								
STARMOUNT LODGES (FH4434)																													●		●						
STOCKS FLY FISHERY (FH4463)		●		●	●	●	●	●		●				●	●	●	●	●					●	●	●		●	●	●	●	●			●	●	●	
THURSLAND HILL FARM (FH4838)		●			●				●		●			●	●	●	●	●					●		●		●	●	●	●						●	●
TURBARY HOUSE NURSARY (FH4974)														●	●										●												
TWIN LAKES TROUT FISHERY (FH5004)		●	●	●				●		●				●	●			●			●		●	●	●	●	●	●					●			●	
UPPER RODDLESWORTH RESERVOIR (FH5058)				●						●																											
WALVERDEN RESERVOIR (FH5137)						●		●	●								●	●									●	●	●				●	●	●	●	
WIDOWS FLASH (FH5368)																													●								
WITHNELL RESERVOIRS (FH5445)																		●									●			●							
WOODFOLD FARM FISHERIES (FH5473)																		●									●	●			●			●	●		
WORTHINGTON NO 2 (FH5511)						●																															

Fishing Facilities and Amenities

	Net Dips	Tackle Hire	Site Tackle Shop	Boats Available	Bait Sold	Adult Matches	Junior Matches	Half Day Fishing	Night Fishing	Tuition Given	Accommodation	Camping	Caravan Site	Male Toilets	Female Toilets	Disabled Toilets	Disabled Facilities	Hardcore Parking	Public Telephone	Showers	Washing Facilities	Restaurant	Hot Meals	Cafe	Refreshments	Day Lodge Available	Solid Based Swims	Easy Access Swims	Disabled Access Swims	Grass Swims	Tree Sheltered	Dogs Allowed	Fulltime Security	Rare Birdlife	Rare Wildlife	Spectators Allowed	Kids with Adults
WYRESIDE LAKES (FH5550)											●			●	●	●		●							●		●	●		●				●	●		
LEICESTERSHIRE																																					
BROOME FISHERIES (FH0692)						●	●		●	●																	●	●	●	●							
C J FISHERIES (FH0786)																		●									●	●			●						
CHARNWOOD WATER (FH0906)																													●								
EYEBROOK TROUT FISHERY (FH1649)		●		●				●		●				●	●	●	●	●											●		●	●		●	●	●	
FRISBY LAKES (FH1803)						●	●		●								●	●									●	●	●	●		●			●		
GROBY FISHING LAKES (FH2027)																													●								
HALL FARM (FH2066)									●																			●		●							
HOLLY FARM FISHERY (FH2261)						●				●	●			●	●		●	●					●		●			●	●	●							
LAKESIDE FISHING (FH2593)						●								●	●		●											●	●		●						
LAKESIDE SPORTING (FH2596)										●																											
LEICESTER GRAND UNION CANAL (FH2690)																													●								
LOUGHBOROUGH SOAR CANAL (FH3055)																													●								
LYNCHGATE LANE FISHERY (FH3119)						●								●				●									●	●	●								●
MALLORY PARK FISHERIES (FH3152)						●								●	●	●		●									●	●	●		●			●	●		
MANOR FARM (FH3161)						●	●		●	●																	●	●	●	●							
MANOR FARM POOLS (FH3165)														●	●			●				●		●	●			●	●								
MILL FARM FISHERY (FH3280)					●	●	●	●	●					●	●	●	●	●					●	●			●	●	●		●					●	
NANPANTAN RESERVOIR (FH3417)						●	●							●	●	●	●	●									●	●	●	●	●			●	●	●	
PARKLANDS FISHERY (FH3704)																													●								
PEATLING POOLS (1-6) (FH3727)																													●								
PROCTORS PLEASURE PARK (FH3851)						●	●		●																			●	●	●	●	●				●	
RUTLAND WATER (FH4068)		●		●																		●															
SHELL FRESH LAKE (FH4225)																													●								
SNIBSON COLLIERY CARP LAKE (FH4311)						●																							●								
SOAR (RIVER) (FH4316)																													●								
THORNTON RESERVOIR (FH4820)		●		●		●	●	●						●	●	●	●	●	●					●	●			●	●	●	●	●		●		●	
WATERMEAD PARK LAKES (FH5180)						●			●								●	●									●	●	●	●	●	●		●	●	●	
WATERY GATE FISHERY (FH5187)						●	●							●	●										●			●	●	●						●	
WHETSTONE GORSE (FH5320)						●	●							●	●	●	●	●			●						●	●	●	●						●	
WILLOWS FARM FISHING (FH5399)									●									●										●		●	●			●	●		
LINCOLNSHIRE																																					
ASHBY PARK FISHERIES (FH0158)					●									●	●	●	●										●		●								
BELVOIR CASTLE (FH0383)																●												●	●	●				●			

www.fishooked.com

Fishing Facilities and Amenities

Fishery	Net Dips	Tackle Hire	Site Tackle Shop	Boats Available	Bait Sold	Adult Matches	Junior Matches	Half Day Fishing	Night Fishing	Tuition Given	Accommodation	Camping	Caravan Site	Male Toilets	Female Toilets	Disabled Toilets	Disabled Facilities	Hardcore Parking	Public Telephone	Showers	Washing Facilities	Restaurant	Hot Meals	Cafe	Refreshments	Day Lodge Available	Solid Based Swims	Easy Access Swims	Disabled Access Swims	Grass Swims	Tree Sheltered	Dogs Allowed	Fulltime Security	Rare Birdlife	Rare Wildlife	Spectators Allowed	Kids with Adults
BOULTHAM PARK LAKE (FH0565)						●	●	●						●	●			●	●												●					●	
BRICKYARD FISHERY (FH0623)								●				●	●	●	●			●		●	●						●	●		●		●				●	
DAIWA GULL POOL (FH1247)									●					●	●													●		●			●	●			●
DENNIS RAINWATER LAKE (FH1331)														●	●																						
FISH POND FARM (FH1725)																							●						●								
GOLTHO LAKE (FH1917)	●					●	●		●	●		●	●	●	●		●								●			●	●	●	●	●	●	●	●	●	●
GRANGE FARM LEISURE (FH1969)		●			●	●								●	●										●			●	●								
GROOBYS PIT (FH2028)														●	●	●													●								
HARTSHOLME PARK LAKE (FH2119)								●						●	●			●	●												●					●	
HATTON TROUT LAKE (FH2134)						●								●	●	●		●									●		●	●							
HAVERHOLME PARK (FH2137)														●	●		●																				
HILL VIEW LAKES (FH2224)	●	●	●		●	●		●			●	●	●	●	●	●	●	●	●		●		●	●	●		●	●	●	●	●		●	●	●		●
HOBHOLE DRAIN (FH2238)						●							●										●		●						●						
HOLLAND PARK (FH2255)		●						●						●	●			●	●									●		●	●						
KEAL COATES FISHERY (FH2422)																		●							●			●	●								
KINPTON RESERVOIR (FH2522)																													●								
LAKE HELEN (FH2558)		●	●		●				●		●	●	●		●		●	●									●	●	●	●	●		●	●	●	●	●
LAKE ROSS FISHERY (FH2572)						●		●			●	●	●	●	●	●		●	●						●		●	●	●		●					●	
LAKESIDE (FH2582)						●								●	●	●													●		●						
LAKESIDE LEISURE PARK (FH2594)		●			●	●	●	●						●	●			●					●	●	●		●	●	●			●		●		●	
LOBBY FIELD PONDS (FH2834)						●	●																				●	●	●	●				●		●	
MARRIS LAKES (FH3190)														●	●																						
MILL HILL LAKES (FH3285)														●			●																				
MILL ROAD LAKES (FH3304)					●	●	●	●						●	●	●	●	●					●	●	●		●	●			●	●		●		●	
MOON LAKE (FH3356)						●								●				●										●									●
OAKHILL LEISURE (FH3563)									●					●	●	●	●	●		●	●						●	●	●								
OASIS LAKES (FH3570)			●		●	●		●						●	●		●	●			●				●		●	●	●	●	●	●	●	●	●	●	●
OHAM LAKES (FH3583)			●		●			●				●		●	●		●	●			●			●	●		●	●	●	●	●	●	●	●	●	●	●
PEACOCK LAKE (FH3723)							●				●	●	●	●	●					●	●						●	●			●				●	●	
REVESBY RESERVOIR (FH3933)														●																							
ROACH FARM PARK (FH3972)			●											●	●		●																				
ROSSWAYS WATER (FH4021)											●			●	●			●	●									●		●	●						
SHANDY KEV FISHERIES (FH4207)						●	●	●									●	●									●	●	●	●	●					●	
SKEGNESS WATER LEISURE PARK (FH4285)														●	●	●			●			●	●	●	●			●		●		●		●	●	●	
SOUTH HOLLAND DRAIN (FH4332)																			●													●					

Fishing Facilities and Amenities

	Net Dips	Tackle Hire	Site Tackle Shop	Boats Available	Bait Sold	Adult Matches	Junior Matches	Half Day Fishing	Night Fishing	Tuition Given	Accommodation	Camping	Caravan Site	Male Toilets	Female Toilets	Disabled Toilets	Disabled Facilities	Hardcore Parking	Public Telephone	Showers	Washing Facilities	Restaurant	Hot Meals	Cafe	Refreshments	Day Lodge Available	Solid Based Swims	Easy Access Swims	Disabled Access Swims	Grass Swims	Tree Sheltered	Dogs Allowed	Fulltime Security	Rare Birdlife	Rare Wildlife	Spectators Allowed	Kids with Adults
STARMERS PIT (FH4433)								●	●					●	●	●	●		●				●	●							●	●				●	
STICKNEY BRICKPONDS (FH4455)									●					●	●	●												●	●								●
SUDBROOK POND (FH4533)																													●								
SWAN LAKE (FH4592)											●	●	●	●	●		●	●	●				●		●			●	●	●				●	●	●	
SYCAMORE FISHING LAKES (FH4618)	●	●	●		●	●	●	●			●	●	●	●	●		●	●	●	●	●		●	●	●	●	●	●	●	●	●	●	●	●	●	●	●
SYSTON PARK TROUT LAKE (FH4622)				●										●	●																						
TATTERSHALL LEISURE PARK (FH4663)	●	●	●	●	●	●	●		●	●	●	●	●	●	●	●	●	●	●	●	●	●	●	●	●	●	●	●	●	●	●	●	●	●	●	●	●
THORPE LE VALE FISHERY (FH4823)					●					●				●			●	●											●								
TILL (RIVER) (FH4846)								●	●									●														●				●	
TILL (RIVER) (FH4847)								●	●									●														●				●	
TOFT NEWTON TROUT FISHERY (FH4864)		●	●	●		●	●	●		●				●	●	●	●	●			●				●	●		●	●				●	●	●	●	●
TRENT (RIVER) (FH4919)						●	●	●	●									●										●				●				●	
TRENT (RIVER) (FH4921)						●	●	●	●									●														●				●	
TRENT (RIVER) (FH4920)						●	●											●									●	●		●		●				●	
UPPER WITHAM (RIVER) (FH5060)						●	●	●	●									●					●	●					●			●				●	
VICKERS POND (FH5097)												●	●	●	●		●	●		●	●				●		●	●	●	●	●	●				●	
WARREN POND (FH5152)																													●								
WELLAND (RIVER) (FH5233)																		●					●		●		●	●			●	●				●	
WEST FEN DRAIN (FH5259)									●																			●									
WHISBY GARDEN CENTRE (FH5329)			●						●					●	●	●								●	●				●						●		
WHITE HOUSE PREDATOR LAKE (FH5336)									●					●	●	●												●	●								
WHITE SWAN ANGLING CLUB (FH5342)						●	●											●									●	●		●		●				●	
WILLOW BANK FISHERY (FH5377)									●					●	●												●	●		●				●	●		
WILLOW LAKES (FH5384)						●	●							●	●			●									●	●	●								
WINTERS LAKE (FH5427)																													●								
WITHAM (RIVER) (FH5439)						●					●							●							●												
WOODLAND WATERS (FH5482)														●	●		●						●		●			●	●		●						
WOODLANDS FISHERY (FH5483)		●			●									●	●	●							●		●												
WOODLANDS LAKE (FH5485)																													●								
LINCOLNSHIRE (NORTH)																																					
BARTON BROADS LAKE (FH0337)						●	●		●			●	●	●	●			●										●	●		●		●				●
HOE HILL POND (FH2245)						●	●		●																		●	●	●								
KINGFISHER LODGE (FH2501)								●				●	●	●	●		●	●		●	●						●	●	●	●		●	●			●	
OLD ANCHOLME (RIVER) (FH3584)																									●				●		●						
ORCHARD POND (FH3617)																													●								

Fishing Facilities and Amenities

	Net Dips	Tackle Hire	Site Tackle Shop	Boats Available	Bait Sold	Adult Matches	Junior Matches	Half Day Fishing	Night Fishing	Tuition Given	Accommodation	Camping	Caravan Site	Male Toilets	Female Toilets	Disabled Toilets	Disabled Facilities	Hardcore Parking	Public Telephone	Showers	Washing Facilities	Restaurant	Hot Meals	Cafe	Refreshments	Day Lodge Available	Solid Based Swims	Easy Access Swims	Disabled Access Swims	Grass Swims	Tree Sheltered	Dogs Allowed	Fulltime Security	Rare Birdlife	Rare Wildlife	Spectators Allowed	Kids with Adults
PASTURE HOUSE FISHERY (FH3716)									●		●			●	●		●								●				●								
STADDLETHORPE POND (FH4398)						●	●											●										●	●				●				●
TILEYARD LANE (FH4844)						●	●																				●	●								●	
LONDON (GREATER)																																					
ALEXANDRA PALACE LAKE (FH0071)				●										●	●	●									●				●		●						
ALEXANDRA PARK LAKE (FH0073)				●										●	●														●								
ASHMERE FISHERIES (FH0167)		●		●						●				●	●			●	●												●			●			
BEDFONT LAKE (FH0363)					●	●	●		●					●	●			●					●	●	●			●	●	●							
BIRCHMERE (FH0427)									●					●	●																						
BOXERS LAKE (FH0577)																		●	●									●		●						●	
BROOMWOOD LAKE (FH0696)																		●										●	●								
CARGILL LAKE (FH0841)									●									●									●			●				●	●		
CLAPHAM COMMON POND (FH0973)						●	●			●				●	●								●		●			●	●								
COLNE (RIVER) (FH1072)									●																												
COPPER MILLSTREAM (FH1111)														●	●			●									●			●	●						
COWLEY LAKE (FH1152)						●											●												●								
CUTTING LAKE (FH1231)																													●								
FORTY HALL LAKE (FH1773)									●																			●	●								
GRAND UNION CANAL (FH1956)																	●	●									●	●				●	●			●	
GRAND UNION CANAL (FH1952)									●																												
GREENHAMS (FH2008)									●																				●								
HALLIFORD MERE LAKES (FH2071)		●		●	●	●		●		●				●	●		●	●	●			●			●			●	●	●	●			●	●	●	
HAMPSTEAD HEATH (FH2094)									●																●				●								
HAREFIELD CARP LAKE (FH2105)									●					●	●												●	●		●							
HIGH MAYNARD RESERVOIR (FH2207)						●								●	●			●										●		●						●	
HIGHAMS PARK LAKE (FH2213)								●	●									●										●	●	●		●	●			●	
HIGHGATE PONDS (FH2217)				●										●	●	●								●	●						●						
HOLLOW PONDS (FH2259)								●	●								●	●	●			●	●	●	●		●	●	●	●	●	●	●			●	
HORSEMILL STREAM (FH2306)									●																			●	●								
LEA NAVIGATION (FH2648)																									●												
LITTLE BRITAIN LAKE (FH2743)						●	●		●									●				●		●			●	●	●	●	●	●			●		
LIZARD LAKES (FH2766)						●	●		●					●	●		●						●	●			●	●	●	●	●						
LOCKWOOD RESERVOIR (FH2974)					●									●	●													●		●				●			
LOW MAYNARD RESERVOIR (FH3067)					●	●								●													●	●		●	●					●	
NORTH TROY LAKE & COLNE (FH3536)														●	●	●													●								

Fishing Facilities and Amenities

Venue	Kids with Adults	Spectators Allowed	Rare Wildlife	Rare Birdlife	Fulltime Security	Dogs Allowed	Tree Sheltered	Grass Swims	Disabled Access Swims	Easy Access Swims	Solid Based Swims	Day Lodge Available	Refreshments	Cafe	Hot Meals	Restaurant	Washing Facilities	Showers	Public Telephone	Hardcore Parking	Disabled Facilities	Disabled Toilets	Female Toilets	Male Toilets	Caravan Site	Camping	Accommodation	Tuition Given	Night Fishing	Half Day Fishing	Junior Matches	Adult Matches	Bait Sold	Boats Available	Site Tackle Shop	Tackle Hire	Net Dips
OSTERLEY PARK MIDDLE LAKE (FH3629)		●				●	●	●		●				●	●				●	●		●	●	●													
PENTON HOOK LOCK (FH3743)																								●													
PERCH POND (FH3751)		●		●		●	●	●		●	●		●	●	●					●	●	●	●	●					●		●	●					
POTOMAC POND (FH3833)							●		●																				●			●					
REGENTS CANAL (FH3928)		●				●			●	●	●																					●					
REGENTS CANAL (FH3925)									●																						●	●					
RODNEY MEADOW (FH3995)																													●								
SHEEPWALK LAKE (FH4218)		●				●	●		●	●																											
SHEPPERTON LAKE (FH4230)						●	●	●		●																		●	●								
SHEPPERTON LOCK (FH4232)																							●	●													
STOCKLEY ROAD LAKES (FH4461)								●			●																		●		●	●					
SWYERS LAKE (FH4617)									●																												
SYON PARK FISHERY (FH4621)		●			●			●		●										●	●							●		●							
TEDDINGTON LOCK (FH4682)																													●								
THORNEY POOL (FH4816)							●	●	●	●	●																		●		●	●					
TRENT COUNTRY PARK LAKES (FH4946)									●	●																											
TRENT PARK LAKES (FH4947)							●		●																												
VALE OF HEATH POND (FH5083)							●		●				●										●	●													
WALTHAMSTOW (NO 2 & NO 3) (FH5131)							●	●		●										●			●	●								●					
WALTHAMSTOW (EAST WARWICK) (FH5129)										●	●									●			●	●						●		●					
WALTHAMSTOW (NO 4 TROUT) (FH5132)										●	●									●			●	●						●							
WALTHAMSTOW (WEST WARWICK) (FH5134)				●				●		●										●																	
WALTHAMSTOW RESERVOIR (NO 1) (FH5130)		●					●	●	●	●	●									●			●	●							●	●					
WALTHAMSTOW RESERVOIR (NO 5) (FH5133)		●					●			●	●									●										●							
WANSTEAD PARK LAKES (FH5145)								●	●		●		●		●					●		●	●	●													
WEST RESERVOIR (FH5265)																					●		●	●													
WILLOWSIDE CARP LAKE (FH5402)									●														●	●					●			●					
WOOLWICH DOCKYARD (FH5501)		●	●	●	●				●	●	●	●					●			●	●	●	●	●				●	●	●	●	●					
WRAYSBURY ONE (FH5513)			●	●		●		●																					●								
WRAYSBURY TWO (FH5514)			●	●			●	●		●																			●								
MANCHESTER (GREATER)																																					
ALEXANDRA PARK (FH0072)									●		●		●		●					●			●	●													
BLACKLEACH RESERVOIR (FH0451)		●		●				●	●	●	●									●	●										●	●					
BOGGART HOLE CLOUGH (FH0524)							●		●				●	●	●							●	●	●													
BRIDGEWATER CANAL (FH0638)									●																							●					

Fishing Facilities and Amenities

	Net Dips	Tackle Hire	Site Tackle Shop	Boats Available	Bait Sold	Adult Matches	Junior Matches	Half Day Fishing	Night Fishing	Tuition Given	Accommodation	Camping	Caravan Site	Male Toilets	Female Toilets	Disabled Toilets	Disabled Facilities	Hardcore Parking	Public Telephone	Showers	Washing Facilities	Restaurant	Hot Meals	Cafe	Refreshments	Day Lodge Available	Solid Based Swims	Easy Access Swims	Disabled Access Swims	Grass Swims	Tree Sheltered	Dogs Allowed	Fulltime Security	Rare Birdlife	Rare Wildlife	Spectators Allowed	Kids with Adults
CHORLTON WATER PARK (FH0946)									●					●	●		●	●											●								
CLEGG HALL LAKES (FH1001)						●								●	●		●																				
CLIFTON MARINA (FH1008)						●			●					●	●		●											●			●						
CROFT HEAD FISHERY (FH1183)							●											●									●	●	●		●			●	●		●
DINGLE LODGE (FH1372)						●	●																				●	●		●							
DOUBLEWOODS (FH1418)																													●								
DOWRY & NEW YEARS BRIDGE (FH1433)						●	●											●																			●
FARM LODGE (FH1669)																															●						
FIR TREE FLASH (FH1720)									●									●										●	●		●						
GEIGYS WATER (FH1847)	●								●			●						●									●	●		●	●						
GORSE PIT RESERVOIR (FH1922)						●	●											●										●		●	●					●	
GORTON (LOWER) RESERVOIR (FH1924)																	●												●								
GROVE LODGE (FH2031)																		●									●	●		●	●	●				●	
HEATON PARK (FH2176)				●										●	●	●		●						●				●	●		●	●					
HOLLINGWORTH LAKE (FH2258)						●	●				●	●	●	●	●	●	●	●	●			●	●	●	●		●	●	●			●				●	●
HUDDERSFIELD NARROW CANAL (FH2328)						●	●																				●	●	●					●	●	●	
KING GEORGE V POOL (FH2489)						●								●	●		●						●		●			●	●		●						
LOWER TOWN HOUSE FISHERY (FH3095)							●											●									●	●	●		●			●	●		●
PAINSWICK PARK LAKE (FH3686)						●	●																														
PENNINE TROUT FISHERY (FH3737)		●				●		●	●					●				●					●		●			●	●		●			●	●	●	
PENNINGTON FLASH (FH3738)																																					●
PIETHORNE RESERVOIR (FH3771)						●	●			●							●																				
PLATT FIELDS (FH3800)				●																											●			●			
REDDISH VALE MILL PONDS (FH3913)						●				●				●	●	●								●				●									
RHODES LODGE (FH3936)						●	●		●			●						●							●		●	●	●	●	●		●	●		●	
ROMAN LAKE LEISURE PARK (FH4000)														●	●									●													
ROYAL GEORGE MILL COMPLEX (FH4044)						●	●																							●				●	●		
STAKEHILL LODGES (FH4411)	●								●									●									●			●							●
STAMFORD PARK LAKES (FH4413)				●				●	●					●	●			●						●							●	●					
TAME (RIVER) (FH4646)						●	●																							●				●	●		
TWINE VALLEY TROUT FISHERY (FH5005)				●		●	●	●						●	●		●	●	●			●	●		●		●	●	●		●			●	●	●	
WHITELEY KNOWL RESERVOIR (FH5349)																											●	●		●	●					●	●
WHITTLE BROOK RESERVOIR (FH5358)						●												●									●	●		●	●					●	
MERSEYSIDE																																					
BIRKENHEAD LOWER PARK LAKE (FH0431)														●	●	●							●		●				●								

Fishing Facilities and Amenities

	Net Dips	Tackle Hire	Site Tackle Shop	Boats Available	Bait Sold	Adult Matches	Junior Matches	Half Day Fishing	Night Fishing	Tuition Given	Accommodation	Camping	Caravan Site	Male Toilets	Female Toilets	Disabled Toilets	Disabled Facilities	Hardcore Parking	Public Telephone	Showers	Washing Facilities	Restaurant	Hot Meals	Cafe	Refreshments	Day Lodge Available	Solid Based Swims	Easy Access Swims	Disabled Access Swims	Grass Swims	Tree Sheltered	Dogs Allowed	Fulltime Security	Rare Birdlife	Rare Wildlife	Spectators Allowed	Kids with Adults
CALDERSTONES PARK LAKE (FH0799)																											●			●				●	●		
CARR MILL DAM (FH0848)																													●								
LOWER LAKE (FH3085)																	●																				
PRINCES PARK LAKE (FH3846)														●	●	●															●						
ROODEE MERE (FH4003)																	●																				
WOODSLEE POOL (FH5494)																	●																				
MIDLANDS (WEST)																																					
ALVECHURCH FISHERIES (FH0090)					●	●	●	●						●	●			●	●				●		●		●	●	●	●	●			●	●	●	
ASTBURY FALLS FISH FARM (FH0175)										●				●	●		●											●	●								
AVON (RIVER) (FH0208)																												●	●								
BLYTHE (RIVER) (FH0517)	●		●		●	●	●	●		●		●	●	●			●	●	●			●	●	●	●		●	●	●		●		●	●	●		
BLYTHE WATERS (FH0518)						●	●	●						●	●	●	●	●	●				●	●	●		●	●	●		●			●	●		
CANNOCK EXTENSION CANAL (FH0822)						●		●																						●							
CHURCH POOL (FH0956)									●					●	●		●						●	●	●		●	●		●				●	●		
COOMBE POOL (FH1109)						●																							●		●						
CUTTLE MILL CARP FISHERY (FH1232)					●			●						●	●	●	●	●	●			●	●	●	●		●	●	●	●	●						
DARTMOUTH PARK (FH1278)																													●								
DAYHOUSE FARM (FH1282)														●	●			●									●		●		●			●	●		
FOXHILLS FISHERY (FH1791)	●					●	●	●			●			●	●			●							●		●	●	●	●	●	●	●	●	●	●	
GRAND UNION CANAL (FH1957)						●																							●								
GREY MILL FARM (FH2017)					●																																
HEATHFIELD POOL (FH2175)						●												●									●	●	●								
HOPSFORD HALL FISHERY (FH2292)																													●								
KINGSBURY WATER PARK (FH2510)						●	●							●	●	●			●				●	●	●			●	●	●				●			
KINGSHURST LAKE (FH2511)																													●								
KINGSNORDLEY (FH2517)														●															●								
LAVENDER HALL (FH2632)						●	●		●					●	●	●	●	●				●	●	●	●		●	●	●								
MEADOWLANDS (FH3227)														●	●			●					●		●												
PACKINGTON SOMERS FISHERY (FH3679)	●		●		●	●	●	●	●	●		●	●	●			●	●	●			●	●	●	●		●	●	●		●		●	●	●		
PACKINGTON TROUT FISHERY (FH3680)		●	●	●		●				●				●	●			●							●	●		●						●	●		
PATSHULL PARK (FH3717)		●		●		●	●	●		●				●	●		●	●					●	●	●		●	●	●	●	●			●	●	●	
PENNS HALL LAKE (FH3740)									●		●			●	●	●		●					●	●	●		●				●			●	●	●	
POOL HALL (FH3819)						●	●							●	●		●						●		●				●								
POOLE HALL FARM (FH3821)									●					●	●								●		●				●		●						
ROYAL BRITISH LEGION POOLS (FH4043)																													●								

Fishing Facilities and Amenities

	RUSHALL CANAL (FH4059)	SHUSTOKE FLY FISHERS (FH4262)	STAFFORD TO WORCESTER CANAL (FH4403)	SWAN POOL (FH4595)	TIDBURY GREEN GOLF CLUB (FH4839)	WALCOT EAST LAKE (FH5116)	WALSALL ARBORETUM (FH5127)	WASSELL GROVE FISHERIES (FH5167)	NORFOLK	ABBEY WATERS (FH0004)	BARFORD LAKES FISHERY (FH0305)	BARNINGHAM HALL LAKE (FH0317)	BARTLES LODGE (FH0335)	BAWBURGH LAKES (FH0348)	BILNEY LAKES (FH0424)	BOOTON CLAY PIT (FH0543)	BRIDGE FARM FISHERIES (FH0629)	BRIDGE INN FISHERY (FH0631)	BUCKENHAM PITS (FH0717)	BURE (RIVER) (FH0736)	BURE VALLEY LAKES (FH0737)	CATCH 22 FISHERY (FH0872)	COLTON LAKE (FH1078)	COSTESSEY PITS (FH1125)	CUT OFF CHANNEL (FH1229)	DISS MERE (FH1376)	FELBRIGG HALL LAKE (FH1681)	FELTHORPE LAKE (FH1690)	FRITTON LAKE (FH1804)	GATTON WATER CARAVAN SITE (FH1843)	GIMINGHAM LAKES (FH1858)	GLEN MERE (FH1882)	GREAT MELTON FISHERY (FH1983)	GREAT OUSE (RIVER) (FH1997)	GREAT OUSE RELIEF CHANNEL (FH1999)
Kids with Adults		●										●	●				●	●		●	●								●				●		
Spectators Allowed		●									●				●	●		●		●	●	●							●						
Rare Wildlife												●			●					●	●	●					●		●				●		
Rare Birdlife		●										●			●			●		●	●	●					●		●	●			●		
Fulltime Security											●	●			●			●		●	●									●			●		
Dogs Allowed																					●														
Tree Sheltered						●					●	●	●		●	●		●		●	●	●		●		●	●		●				●		
Grass Swims												●			●	●		●		●	●	●			●		●		●	●			●		●
Disabled Access Swims		●	●	●	●		●	●			●	●	●		●	●			●	●	●	●		●					●		●		●		●
Easy Access Swims		●		●				●			●	●			●	●		●	●	●	●	●			●	●			●	●			●		●
Solid Based Swims				●				●			●	●			●	●		●		●	●	●								●			●	●	
Day Lodge Available																					●														
Refreshments					●			●			●		●		●		●	●		●	●	●							●	●					●
Cafe								●							●			●		●									●						
Hot Meals								●							●			●		●	●								●	●					
Restaurant																		●		●									●	●					
Washing Facilities		●													●			●		●	●														
Showers																														●					
Public Telephone																		●		●	●					●			●	●					
Hardcore Parking		●		●				●		●	●			●	●	●		●		●	●	●	●				●	●	●	●		●	●		
Disabled Facilities		●						●			●				●					●	●	●							●						
Disabled Toilets		●									●		●		●	●				●									●						
Female Toilets		●						●			●		●		●	●	●	●		●	●	●							●	●	●				●
Male Toilets		●		●				●			●		●		●	●	●	●		●	●	●							●	●	●				●
Caravan Site											●										●								●	●					
Camping															●						●									●					
Accommodation																		●		●	●								●						
Tuition Given											●						●				●												●		
Night Fishing				●										●	●	●		●		●	●	●		●					●				●	●	
Half Day Fishing		●									●	●						●											●						
Junior Matches										●	●				●					●			●		●	●			●				●		●
Adult Matches	●									●	●				●					●			●		●	●			●		●	●	●		●
Bait Sold											●				●		●	●			●	●													
Boats Available		●																		●	●								●						
Site Tackle Shop																				●	●														
Tackle Hire											●				●						●														
Net Dips												●			●			●			●														

Fishing Facilities and Amenities

Facility	GUNTON PARK LAKE (FH2037)	HALL FARM LAKES (FH2068)	HAVERINGLAND HALL PARK (FH2138)	HEVINGHAM LAKES (FH2197)	HINDERCLAY LAKES (FH2233)	HORNING (RIVER) (FH2299)	KINGFISHER LAKES (FH2500)	LAKESIDE (FH2583)	LAKESIDE CARAVAN PARK (FH2587)	LENWADE COMMON LAKES (FH2700)	LITTLE DUNHAM CARP LAKES (FH2749)	LITTLE OUSE (RIVER) (FH2757)	LOCH NEATON (FH2922)	MARTHAM PITS (FH3199)	MEADOW LAKE (FH3223)	MIDDLE HARLING LAKE (FH3265)	MILL FARM FISHERY (FH3282)	MILL FARM FISHERY (FH3281)	NARBOROUGH TROUT FARM (FH3424)	NATURES HAVEN LAKES (FH3429)	PARK LIME PIT (FH3700)	PECK MEADOW POND (FH3730)	PENTNEY LAKES (FH3742)	RACKHEATH SPRINGS (FH3872)	RAILWAY LAKE (FH3878)	RAILWAY LAKE (FH3877)	REEPHAM FISHERY (FH3924)	RINGLAND PITS (FH3953)	RUSTON REACHES (FH4066)	SCOULTON MERE (FH4119)	SHALLOW BROOK LAKES (FH4205)	SOVEREIGN LAKES (FH4354)	SWANGEY LAKES (FH4598)	SWANTON MORLEY FISHERY (FH4602)	TASWOOD LAKES (FH4662)
Kids with Adults				●																●	●			●					●					●	●
Spectators Allowed			●	●						●									●		●					●	●		●					●	
Rare Wildlife			●		●					●									●		●			●				●	●					●	
Rare Birdlife			●		●														●		●							●	●					●	
Fulltime Security																	●												●						
Dogs Allowed			●	●						●											●					●								●	
Tree Sheltered		●	●	●	●					●					●		●	●	●		●		●	●		●			●	●		●			●
Grass Swims			●	●						●		●					●		●					●			●	●						●	
Disabled Access Swims			●		●		●			●	●		●	●	●	●	●	●		●	●		●		●		●	●					●	●	●
Easy Access Swims			●	●	●				●	●	●	●	●			●	●		●	●								●	●					●	
Solid Based Swims			●							●							●		●	●				●										●	
Day Lodge Available																																			
Refreshments															●			●	●	●			●												
Cafe																		●																	
Hot Meals																				●															
Restaurant																																			
Washing Facilities				●																															
Showers				●			●																												
Public Telephone			●																●																
Hardcore Parking		●			●		●	●		●		●	●			●	●		●	●	●				●				●	●				●	
Disabled Facilities	●	●	●						●	●													●		●										
Disabled Toilets											●		●					●	●						●										
Female Toilets		●	●	●			●	●	●	●	●		●		●			●	●	●			●		●		●		●			●	●		●
Male Toilets		●	●	●			●	●	●	●	●		●		●			●	●	●			●		●		●		●			●	●		●
Caravan Site				●																															
Camping				●																															
Accommodation				●																									●						
Tuition Given																	●		●															●	
Night Fishing				●			●			●							●					●				●		●				●	●	●	●
Half Day Fishing																			●		●										●				
Junior Matches										●		●					●		●	●						●								●	
Adult Matches			●		●					●		●			●		●		●	●				●	●	●					●	●		●	
Bait Sold															●				●																
Boats Available						●											●							●											
Site Tackle Shop																							●												
Tackle Hire															●				●																
Net Dips																	●																		

Fishing Facilities and Amenities

Fishery	Kids with Adults	Spectators Allowed	Rare Wildlife	Rare Birdlife	Fulltime Security	Dogs Allowed	Tree Sheltered	Grass Swims	Disabled Access Swims	Easy Access Swims	Solid Based Swims	Day Lodge Available	Refreshments	Cafe	Hot Meals	Restaurant	Washing Facilities	Showers	Public Telephone	Hardcore Parking	Disabled Facilities	Disabled Toilets	Female Toilets	Male Toilets	Caravan Site	Camping	Accommodation	Tuition Given	Night Fishing	Half Day Fishing	Junior Matches	Adult Matches	Bait Sold	Boats Available	Site Tackle Shop	Tackle Hire	Net Dips
TAVERHAM (FH4668)																				●									●								
TAVERHAM MILLS FISHERY (FH4669)	●	●	●	●	●		●	●		●	●		●				●	●	●	●			●	●			●	●	●				●		●	●	●
TEN MILE BANK (FH4737)								●		●	●																				●	●					
TOTTENHILL PIT (FH4888)							●																								●						
UNIVERSITY BROAD (FH5048)							●				●									●									●		●	●					
UPPER BURE (STREAM) (FH5052)	●	●	●	●	●	●	●	●	●	●	●	●	●		●		●		●	●	●		●	●	●	●	●	●	●				●	●	●	●	●
WALNUT FARM FISHERIES (FH5125)	●	●	●	●	●		●	●	●	●	●									●	●							●		●		●					
WENSUM (RIVER) (FH5249)						●		●																					●								
WENSUM (RIVER) (FH5245)	●	●		●	●			●		●	●		●	●	●	●	●		●	●			●	●			●			●			●				●
WENSUM (RIVER) (FH5247)	●	●	●	●		●		●	●	●	●									●								●	●		●	●					
WEYBREAD FISHERY (FH5293)		●	●	●		●		●	●	●													●	●													
WILLOWCROFT FISHERY (FH5392)							●		●				●								●		●	●			●	●	●						●		
WILLSMORE WATER (FH5403)						●	●	●	●	●	●									●									●	●	●	●					
WISSEY (RIVER) (FH5435)								●		●	●												●	●							●	●					
WOODLAKES FISHERY (FH5477)		●	●			●	●	●		●	●								●	●			●	●					●	●		●					
WOODRISING WATER MEADOWS (FH5489)							●		●	●										●				●	●	●			●		●	●					
WROXHAM BROAD (FH5520)																																		●			
YARE (RIVER) (FH5556)																																		●			
NORTHAMPTONSHIRE																																					
BODDINGTON RESERVOIR (FH0521)		●	●	●				●															●	●							●	●					
CANONS ASHBY LAKES (FH0824)							●			●	●									●											●	●					
CASTLE ASHBY LAKES (FH0858)																															●	●					
CRESCENT LAKE (FH1179)		●								●	●																	●			●	●					
DAVENTRY COUNTRY PARK (FH1281)		●	●	●		●					●		●	●	●					●		●	●	●				●			●	●					
DRAYTON RESERVOIR (FH1441)		●		●			●		●	●	●		●	●	●	●				●			●	●							●	●	●				
DUSTON RESERVOIR (FH1486)		●		●			●	●	●	●	●			●	●	●				●										●	●	●					
ELINOR TROUT FISHERY (FH1562)		●	●	●			●	●		●			●							●			●	●					●	●			●	●		●	
FOXHOLES FISHERIES (FH1792)	●	●	●	●	●		●	●		●							●	●		●			●	●	●	●			●								
GRAND UNION CANAL (FH1959)		●	●	●		●	●	●	●	●	●									●									●	●	●	●					
GREEN FARM LAKES (FH2000)										●	●												●	●							●	●					
HEYFORD FISHERY (FH2200)		●					●	●	●	●	●		●	●	●				●	●	●	●	●	●							●	●	●				
ISE (RIVER) (FH2384)							●	●		●																											
ISLIP NATURE LAKE (FH2396)		●	●	●			●	●		●																		●			●	●					
LITTLE IRCHESTER COMPLEX (FH2754)		●						●																					●		●						
LYNN POOL FISHERY (FH3125)								●	●	●										●																	

Fishing Facilities and Amenities

	MENAGERIE POND (FH3253)	NENE (RIVER) (FH3448)	NENE (RIVER) (FH3447)	NORTHAMPTON JUNCTION CANAL (FH3542)	OXFORD CANAL (FH3667)	RINGSTEAD GRANGE (FH3954)	SILVER LAKE (FH4269)	ST JAMES SMALL PARK LAKE (FH4389)	THORPE WATERVILLE LAKE (FH4827)	THRAPSTON LAKES (FH4829)	WEYBREAD GRAVEL PITS (FH5294)	WOOTTON BROOK LAKE (FH5503)	NORTHUMBERLAND	ALN (RIVER) (FH0085)	COQUET (RIVER) (FH1116)	HORTON GRANGE LAKE (FH2312)	IRTHING (RIVER) (FH2381)	KIELDER WATER (FH2477)	LINNEL WOOD LAKE (FH2737)	NORTH TYNE (RIVER) (FH3538)	SOUTH TYNE (RIVER) (FH4341)	TWEED (RIVER) (FH4990)	TWEED (RIVER) (FH4992)	TWEED (RIVER) (FH4993)	TYNE (RIVER) (FH5027)	TYNE (RIVER) (FH5025)	WANSBECK (RIVER) (FH5139)	WHITEADDER (RIVER) (FH5345)	WREIGH (RIVER) (FH5516)	NOTTINGHAMSHIRE	A1 PITS (FH0001)	CHESTERFIELD CANAL (FH0930)	CLUMBER LAKE (FH1030)	COLWICK COUNTRY PARK (FH1080)	CRANFLEET CANAL (FH1165)
Kids with Adults			●			●																												●	
Spectators Allowed		●	●				●	●		●		●					●				●	●					●	●					●	●	
Rare Wildlife			●											●					●			●					●	●					●	●	
Rare Birdlife		●	●						●										●			●					●	●					●	●	
Fulltime Security			●			●																						●						●	
Dogs Allowed																																		●	
Tree Sheltered		●		●	●	●	●	●		●		●		●			●				●	●			●	●	●						●	●	
Grass Swims	●	●	●			●		●	●	●				●													●							●	
Disabled Access Swims		●				●	●	●		●	●																●				●	●	●	●	●
Easy Access Swims	●	●		●	●	●	●	●		●	●	●				●			●			●						●						●	
Solid Based Swims	●	●		●	●		●	●				●				●			●			●					●							●	
Day Lodge Available						●																													
Refreshments						●																●			●		●						●		
Cafe		●																				●					●						●		
Hot Meals		●																				●					●						●		
Restaurant		●																									●						●		
Washing Facilities																																		●	
Showers																																			
Public Telephone		●																				●			●		●						●		
Hardcore Parking		●	●	●	●	●	●	●				●		●			●				●	●					●						●	●	
Disabled Facilities			●			●	●																				●						●	●	
Disabled Toilets		●																				●					●						●	●	
Female Toilets		●				●		●											●						●		●						●	●	
Male Toilets		●				●		●											●			●			●		●						●	●	
Caravan Site						●																													
Camping						●																													
Accommodation																												●							
Tuition Given			●													●			●								●	●						●	
Night Fishing											●				●		●				●	●						●	●					●	
Half Day Fishing						●																												●	
Junior Matches		●	●	●	●		●			●						●				●		●					●								
Adult Matches		●	●	●	●		●			●						●				●		●					●						●		
Bait Sold																			●																
Boats Available						●												●	●				●	●										●	
Site Tackle Shop																																			
Tackle Hire						●													●																
Net Dips																																			

www.fishooked.com

FACILITIES AVAILABLE

England (by County)

Fishing Facilities and Amenities

Fishery	Net Dips	Tackle Hire	Site Tackle Shop	Boats Available	Bait Sold	Adult Matches	Junior Matches	Half Day Fishing	Night Fishing	Tuition Given	Accommodation	Camping	Caravan Site	Male Toilets	Female Toilets	Disabled Toilets	Disabled Facilities	Hardcore Parking	Public Telephone	Showers	Washing Facilities	Restaurant	Hot Meals	Cafe	Refreshments	Day Lodge Available	Solid Based Swims	Easy Access Swims	Disabled Access Swims	Grass Swims	Tree Sheltered	Dogs Allowed	Fulltime Security	Rare Birdlife	Rare Wildlife	Spectators Allowed	Kids with Adults
DANESHILL LAKES (FH1269)																													●								
DOLAR POND (FH1396)						●	●											●										●	●							●	
EREWASH CANAL (FH1607)																													●								
FLEET (RIVER) (FH1745)						●	●											●									●	●	●	●						●	
GRANTHAM CANAL (FH1975)						●	●	●									●										●	●	●	●			●	●	●	●	●
GRANTHAM CANAL (FH1973)																													●								
HALLCROFT FISHERIES (FH2070)					●	●	●	●						●	●	●	●	●	●				●	●	●			●	●			●				●	
HOLME PIERPOINT (FH2268)						●	●											●										●	●							●	
KINGS MILL RESERVOIR (FH2507)																													●								
LAKESIDE FISHERY (FH2592)	●					●	●		●	●				●	●	●	●	●		●	●		●	●	●	●	●	●	●				●			●	●
LANGOLD LAKES (FH2616)				●		●	●	●					●	●	●	●	●	●			●		●		●			●	●			●	●	●	●	●	
L-LAKE FISHERY (FH2767)														●	●	●													●		●						
MAUN (RIVER) (FH3209)	●					●	●			●				●	●		●	●			●		●	●	●		●	●	●	●		●	●			●	●
NOTTINGHAM CANAL (FH3552)																													●								
NOTTINGHAM CASTLE MARINA (FH3553)																	●		●						●		●	●	●	●			●				●
OWDY LANE TROUT FISHERY (FH3660)		●		●				●	●					●	●			●	●								●	●	●	●	●				●	●	
PINDERS PONDS (FH3776)																												●		●							
SAPPHIRE LAKES (FH4104)	●				●	●	●	●	●	●	●		●	●	●		●	●	●	●	●		●		●		●	●		●	●	●	●	●		●	●
SHERWOOD FOREST FISHERY (FH4234)	●					●	●			●				●	●		●	●	●		●		●	●	●		●	●	●	●		●				●	●
SMEATONS LAKES (FH4304)						●	●	●	●	●				●	●	●	●	●	●						●		●	●	●	●	●	●		●	●	●	
TRENT (RIVER) (FH4927)				●				●	●	●				●	●	●	●	●	●		●							●	●			●	●				●
TRENT (RIVER) (FH4929)						●	●											●										●	●							●	
TRENT (RIVER) (FH4926)						●												●																			
TRENT (RIVER) (FH4933)						●	●											●									●	●		●						●	
TRENT (RIVER) (FH4928)						●	●		●								●	●										●	●			●	●	●	●	●	
TRENT (RIVER) (FH4924)						●	●	●				●	●					●										●		●		●		●	●		●
TRENT (RIVER) (FH4934)						●	●											●										●		●		●		●		●	
WINFIELD LAGOON (FH5415)																													●								
OXFORDSHIRE																																					
BARNES TROUT LAKES (FH0316)		●				●		●	●	●				●	●			●							●	●		●									●
BEIRTON LAKES (FH0373)																	●												●								
BLADON LAKE (FH0486)				●																									●								
BLENHEIM LAKE (FH0497)				●																									●								
BUTLERS HILL FARM (FH0775)									●																												
CHAD LAKES (FH0890)	●		●		●			●	●	●				●	●	●	●	●			●				●		●	●	●	●	●		●				●

Fishing Facilities and Amenities

	CHERWELL (RIVER) (FH0920)	CHERWELL (RIVER) (FH0922)	CHERWELL (RIVER) (FH0924)	CHERWELL (RIVER) (FH0919)	CHEYNEY MANOR FISHERY (FH0937)	CHRISTCHURCH LAKE (FH0947)	CLATTERCOTE RESERVOIR (FH0979)	CLEARWATER FISH FARM (FH0997)	COLLEGE FARM FISHING (FH1063)	CORNBURY PARK FISHERY (FH1120)	DARLOW LAKE (FH1275)	EYNSHAM LOCK (FH1650)	FARMOOR 1 RESERVOIR (FH1675)	FARMOOR TROUT FISHERY (FH1676)	GAUNTS LAKE (FH1844)	GAUNTS LAKE (FH1844)	GLEBE COURT LAKE (FH1877)	GRAND UNION CANAL (FH1960)	HARDWICK LAKE AND SMITHS POOL (FH2104)	HEART OF ENGLAND FISHERY (FH2171)	HEYFORD LAKES (FH2201)	HORSE AND GROOM INN (FH2303)	HUNTS CORNER (FH2342)	LINCH HILL FISHERY (FH2725)	LOCKINGE TROUT FISHERY (FH2972)	MANOR FARM LAKE (FH3162)	MANOR HOUSE (FH3166)	MILTON POOLS FARM (FH3326)	NELL BRIDGE FISHERY (FH3439)	ORCHID LAKES (FH3618)	OXFORD CANAL (FH3671)	OXFORD CANAL (FH3672)	OXLEASE LAKE (FH3678)	PIMLICO FARM LAKES (FH3775)	RADCOT LOCK (FH3874)
Kids with Adults											●		●		●	●			●		●		●			●			●				●		
Spectators Allowed							●	●		●				●	●	●			●		●		●	●		●		●	●				●		
Rare Wildlife						●	●			●				●	●	●			●				●			●				●			●		
Rare Birdlife						●	●			●			●	●	●	●			●		●		●			●		●		●			●		
Fulltime Security								●							●	●			●				●			●			●	●			●		
Dogs Allowed								●		●					●	●			●		●		●			●							●		
Tree Sheltered		●		●			●			●					●	●			●		●	●	●	●	●	●					●		●		
Grass Swims											●				●	●			●		●	●	●	●		●		●	●				●		
Disabled Access Swims			●			●	●		●		●		●	●	●	●	●	●	●		●		●	●	●	●		●	●	●			●		
Easy Access Swims						●	●	●		●	●		●	●	●	●			●		●	●	●	●		●		●	●	●		●	●		
Solid Based Swims							●	●					●	●							●			●						●					
Day Lodge Available													●																	●					
Refreshments		●			●	●		●																	●					●	●				
Cafe						●																		●						●					
Hot Meals																								●											
Restaurant																									●										
Washing Facilities								●					●																	●					
Showers						●																		●						●					
Public Telephone								●					●												●					●					
Hardcore Parking						●	●	●		●	●		●	●	●	●			●		●		●	●	●	●			●	●			●		
Disabled Facilities														●	●	●			●		●		●	●		●				●			●		
Disabled Toilets						●							●	●										●						●					
Female Toilets		●			●	●	●	●		●	●	●	●	●	●	●			●	●	●		●	●	●	●		●	●	●			●		
Male Toilets		●			●	●	●	●		●	●	●	●	●	●	●			●	●	●		●	●	●	●		●	●	●			●		●
Caravan Site						●																													
Camping						●									●	●			●				●			●							●		
Accommodation																																			
Tuition Given								●		●	●		●		●	●			●				●			●		●		●			●	●	
Night Fishing	●		●		●		●		●						●	●			●		●		●	●		●	●			●		●	●		
Half Day Fishing										●			●	●																					
Junior Matches					●		●							●							●														
Adult Matches				●	●		●							●															●						
Bait Sold					●			●																						●					
Boats Available						●				●				●						●															
Site Tackle Shop													●																						
Tackle Hire								●		●				●																					
Net Dips															●	●			●		●		●			●				●			●		

www.fishooked.com

Fishing Facilities and Amenities

	Net Dips	Tackle Hire	Site Tackle Shop	Boats Available	Bait Sold	Adult Matches	Junior Matches	Half Day Fishing	Night Fishing	Tuition Given	Accommodation	Camping	Caravan Site	Male Toilets	Female Toilets	Disabled Toilets	Disabled Facilities	Hardcore Parking	Public Telephone	Showers	Washing Facilities	Restaurant	Hot Meals	Cafe	Refreshments	Day Lodge Available	Solid Based Swims	Easy Access Swims	Disabled Access Swims	Grass Swims	Tree Sheltered	Dogs Allowed	Fulltime Security	Rare Birdlife	Rare Wildlife	Spectators Allowed	Kids with Adults
RUSHEY LOCK (FH4061)														●																							
RUSHEY WEIR (FH4062)						●																															
SALFORD TROUT LAKES (FH4083)		●						●		●	●			●	●			●								●	●	●	●		●			●	●		
SEVERALLS FARM A AND B (FH4144)						●	●																					●		●						●	
ST JOHNS POOL (FH4391)	●								●	●		●		●	●		●	●										●	●	●	●	●	●	●	●	●	●
STATES LAGOON (FH4436)																													●		●						
SWISS FARM LAKE (FH4614)																													●								
THAME (RIVER) (FH4757)									●																												
THAMES (RIVER) (FH4794)									●									●										●	●		●						
THAMES (RIVER) (FH4798)																		●													●						
THAMES (RIVER) (FH4803)									●																												
THAMES (RIVER) (FH4792)						●	●																					●	●	●						●	
THAMES (RIVER) (FH4799)																													●								
UNITY LAKE (FH5047)	●								●	●		●		●	●		●	●										●	●	●	●	●	●	●	●	●	●
WINDRUSH (RIVER) (FH5413)	●								●	●		●		●	●		●	●										●	●	●	●	●	●	●	●	●	●
WINDRUSH (RIVER) (FH5411)										●																				●							
YEOMANS LAKE (FH5565)	●								●	●		●		●	●		●	●										●	●	●	●	●	●	●	●	●	●
RUTLAND																																					
SWEETHEDGES FARM FISHERY (FH4607)	●							●			●		●	●	●		●	●	●			●	●	●	●			●	●	●	●		●				●
SHROPSHIRE																																					
APLEY POOLS (FH0121)																						●	●		●				●		●						
AQUALATE MERE (FH0124)				●																										●				●	●		
BACHE POOL (FH0240)																		●										●									
BAYLIS POOLS (FH0351)									●																				●		●						
BEECHES POOL (FH0367)																		●							●		●				●			●	●		
BENTHALL LAKE (FH0387)																													●								
BIRCH GROVE (FH0425)									●					●	●						●						●	●			●			●	●		
BIRMINGHAM TO WORCESTER CANAL (FH0432)																													●								
BLUE POOL (FH0510)																													●								
BOLDINGS POOLS (FH0530)					●	●	●							●	●		●	●			●	●	●	●	●		●	●	●	●			●	●	●	●	●
COUND TROUT FISHERY (FH1140)		●		●		●		●	●					●	●	●		●	●			●	●	●	●			●	●		●	●		●	●	●	
DEARNFORD HALL TROUT FISHERY (FH1291)	●	●		●		●	●	●		●	●	●	●	●	●	●		●	●						●	●	●	●	●		●	●	●	●	●	●	●
DELBURY HALL TROUT FISHERY (FH1326)								●		●				●	●		●	●	●		●					●		●	●	●			●	●	●	●	●
ELLERDINE LAKES (FH1566)	●	●	●		●			●		●	●	●	●	●	●	●	●	●	●				●	●	●	●	●	●	●	●	●		●	●	●	●	●
HOLMER LAKE (FH2269)						●	●										●		●			●						●	●			●		●	●	●	

Fishing Facilities and Amenities

	Net Dips	Tackle Hire	Site Tackle Shop	Boats Available	Bait Sold	Adult Matches	Junior Matches	Half Day Fishing	Night Fishing	Tuition Given	Accommodation	Camping	Caravan Site	Male Toilets	Female Toilets	Disabled Toilets	Disabled Facilities	Hardcore Parking	Public Telephone	Showers	Washing Facilities	Restaurant	Hot Meals	Cafe	Refreshments	Day Lodge Available	Solid Based Swims	Easy Access Swims	Disabled Access Swims	Grass Swims	Tree Sheltered	Dogs Allowed	Fulltime Security	Rare Birdlife	Rare Wildlife	Spectators Allowed	Kids with Adults
ISLE LAKE (FH2395)														●	●			●																			
LAKE VYRNWY (FH2573)																													●								
LOWER HILL FARM (FH3081)											●	●	●	●	●			●			●		●		●		●		●								
MEESE (RIVER) (FH3240)																														●				●	●		
MIDDLE POOL (FH3267)																		●											●								
MILLRIDE FISHERY (FH3317)						●								●	●	●							●	●	●				●								
MONKHALL FISHERIES (FH3343)						●								●	●									●													
NEWPORT CANAL (FH3489)																													●								
ONNY (RIVER) (FH3613)																										●		●		●	●			●			●
PERRY (RIVER) (FH3755)																													●								
SEVERN (RIVER) (FH4162)						●			●					●	●	●	●	●	●			●	●	●	●					●				●	●		
SEVERN (RIVER) (FH4167)																															●						
SEVERN (RIVER) (FH4166)																													●								
SEVERN (RIVER) (FH4180)																															●						
SEVERN (RIVER) (FH4178)																		●												●				●	●		
SEVERN (RIVER) (FH4171)									●																												
SEVERN (RIVER) (FH4173)														●	●										●						●						
SEVERN (RIVER) (FH4169)																													●								
SEVERN (RIVER) (FH4177)																		●																			
SEVERN (RIVER) (FH4176)																		●																●	●		
SEVERN (RIVER) (FH4175)																		●																			
SEVERN (RIVER) (FH4172)														●	●			●																			
SEVERN (RIVER) (FH4182)						●			●																					●							
STIRCHLEY POOLS (FH4458)																													●								
TELFORD TOWN PARK (FH4721)																													●								
TEME (RIVER) (FH4723)						●	●																				●	●	●	●				●	●	●	●
TEME (RIVER) (FH4722)						●	●																				●	●	●	●				●	●	●	●
TERN (RIVER) (FH4740)																		●																			
TOWNSEND FISHERY (FH4894)						●	●							●	●										●		●	●	●	●							
VOWNOG FISH LAKE (FH5101)		●		●				●						●	●			●									●	●	●		●	●		●	●	●	
WALCOT WEST LAKE (FH5117)						●	●																				●	●	●	●				●	●	●	●
WOODCOTE HALL (FH5470)						●	●										●	●									●	●	●	●	●						
WYRLEY ESSINGTON CANAL (FH5551)																													●								
SOMERSET																																					
APEX LAKE (FH0120)						●																															

Fishing Facilities and Amenities

Fishery	Net Dips	Tackle Hire	Site Tackle Shop	Boats Available	Bait Sold	Adult Matches	Junior Matches	Half Day Fishing	Night Fishing	Tuition Given	Accommodation	Camping	Caravan Site	Male Toilets	Female Toilets	Disabled Toilets	Disabled Facilities	Hardcore Parking	Public Telephone	Showers	Washing Facilities	Restaurant	Hot Meals	Cafe	Refreshments	Day Lodge Available	Solid Based Swims	Easy Access Swims	Disabled Access Swims	Grass Swims	Tree Sheltered	Dogs Allowed	Fulltime Security	Rare Birdlife	Rare Wildlife	Spectators Allowed	Kids with Adults
AVALON FISHERIES (FH0186)					●	●	●		●					●	●	●	●	●			●			●	●		●	●	●	●	●	●	●	●	●	●	●
BARLE (RIVER) (FH0309)		●												●	●			●	●			●	●		●		●			●	●	●		●	●	●	
BARROW RESERVOIRS (FH0329)								●																			●						●	●	●		●
BLAGDON LAKE (FH0487)		●	●	●						●				●	●			●	●		●					●							●	●	●		●
BRISTOL AVON (FH0649)						●	●	●	●					●				●	●			●		●						●						●	●
BRISTOL AVON (FH0647)						●	●	●	●					●				●	●			●		●						●						●	●
BRISTOL AVON (FH0648)						●	●	●	●					●				●	●			●		●						●						●	●
BULLOCKS FARM FISHING LAKES (FH0728)						●	●	●		●				●	●		●	●									●	●	●		●				●	●	
CAMELEY TROUT LAKES (FH0812)														●	●																						
CHARD RESERVOIR (FH0899)														●	●														●		●						
CHEDDAR RESERVOIR (FH0909)						●	●											●									●	●						●	●	●	
CHEW VALLEY LAKE (FH0936)		●	●	●		●				●				●	●	●	●	●	●		●	●	●	●	●			●					●	●	●		●
CLATWORTHY RESERVOIR (FH0981)				●										●	●		●																	●	●		
COOMBE LAKE (FH1107)	●																	●									●	●	●	●	●					●	●
DANDYS & KNIGHTINGALE LAKES (FH1254)						●			●	●																	●	●	●	●							
DURLEIGH RESERVOIR (FH1484)														●	●														●					●	●		
EMBOROUGH POOL (FH1582)																													●		●						
EMBORUGH LAKE (FH1583)						●			●									●										●	●								
EMERALD POOL FISHERY (FH1585)		●			●	●	●	●	●		●			●	●	●	●	●					●	●	●		●	●	●		●	●				●	
EXE VALLEY FISHERY (FH1645)		●						●	●					●	●	●	●	●							●		●	●	●			●				●	
FOLLY FOOT FARM (FH1755)									●					●	●		●	●			●							●	●								
FOLLYFOOT FARM (FH1757)														●	●	●	●	●									●		●								
GODNEY MOOR PONDS (FH1906)																													●		●						
HAWKRIDGE RESERVOIR (FH2144)		●		●						●				●	●			●																			
HORSESHOE LAKE (FH2308)																		●										●		●	●			●	●	●	
HOWLEY STREET POND (FH2320)																															●						
HUNSTRETE LAKE COMPLEX (FH2338)										●				●	●												●		●								
KENN (RIVER) (FH2433)						●	●											●										●		●						●	
KENNET AND AVON CANAL (FH2457)																									●				●		●						
LANDS END FARM (FH2607)		●			●	●		●						●	●		●	●							●			●	●							●	
LANGFORD LAKES (FH2612)															●			●									●	●	●	●	●	●		●	●	●	
LITTON RESERVOIR (FH2765)														●	●			●										●						●	●		●
LOWER LOVELYNCH FISHERIES (FH3089)														●	●	●													●								
OLD MILL FISHERY (FH3595)						●	●							●	●	●		●									●	●	●	●	●					●	
OXENLEAZE FARM FISHERY (FH3666)																																				●	

Fishing Facilities and Amenities

	Net Dips	Tackle Hire	Site Tackle Shop	Boats Available	Bait Sold	Adult Matches	Junior Matches	Half Day Fishing	Night Fishing	Tuition Given	Accommodation	Camping	Caravan Site	Male Toilets	Female Toilets	Disabled Toilets	Disabled Facilities	Hardcore Parking	Public Telephone	Showers	Washing Facilities	Restaurant	Hot Meals	Cafe	Refreshments	Day Lodge Available	Solid Based Swims	Easy Access Swims	Disabled Access Swims	Grass Swims	Tree Sheltered	Dogs Allowed	Fulltime Security	Rare Birdlife	Rare Wildlife	Spectators Allowed	Kids with Adults
PARRETT (RIVER) (FH3708)						●	●											●												●							
PAWLETT PONDS (FH3719)						●												●									●	●	●	●	●			●	●	●	
PLANTATIONS LAKES (FH3798)																															●						
QUANTOCK FISHERIES (FH3862)		●						●		●				●	●		●	●			●					●		●		●	●			●	●	●	●
SEDGES (FH4128)						●								●	●	●													●								
ST ALGARS FARM LAKE (FH4381)								●																													
STONE YARD FISHERY (FH4470)						●												●																			
SUMMERHAYES (FH4553)														●	●	●													●								
SUTTON BINGHAM RESERVOIR (FH4561)										●				●	●		●																	●			
THORNEY LAKES (FH4815)	●							●				●	●	●	●			●										●		●	●	●		●	●	●	●
TUCKING MILL (FH4963)						●										●												●	●		●						
VIADUCT FISHERY (FH5095)	●	●	●		●	●	●	●	●	●				●	●			●			●				●		●	●		●	●		●	●	●	●	
WELLINGTON BASIN (FH5240)																												●	●		●						
WESTHAY LAKE (FH5280)									●																												
WYCH LODGE LAKE (FH5526)																		●										●	●	●	●			●	●		
STAFFORDSHIRE																																					
ALBRIGHTON MOAT PROJECT (FH0051)		●								●				●	●	●	●	●	●						●				●					●	●		
ASHLEY POOLS (FH0165)																															●						
BADEN HALL FISHERY (FH0245)	●	●			●	●	●		●					●	●	●	●	●	●	●	●	●	●	●	●	●	●	●	●	●			●	●	●	●	●
BASFORD COARSE FISHERY (FH0340)								●										●										●		●							
BIDDULPH GRANGE (FH0409)														●	●			●									●			●				●	●		
BLACK LAKE (FH0443)																											●				●						
BLACKWOOD POOL (FH0483)						●	●		●									●									●	●		●	●			●	●	●	●
BORROWPIT LAKE (FH0554)														●	●	●		●						●			●	●	●					●	●		
BROWNING CUDMORE FISHERY (FH0702)					●	●	●		●					●	●	●		●	●			●	●	●	●		●	●	●	●	●			●	●	●	
CHURNET (RIVER) (FH0961)																															●						
CHURNET (RIVER) (FH0963)												●	●					●										●						●	●		
CONSALL NATURE PARK (FH1091)														●	●	●		●			●						●			●		●		●	●		
COVENTRY CANAL (FH1145)																													●								
DEEP HAYES COUNTRY PARK (FH1322)								●						●	●	●		●			●						●			●		●	●	●	●		
DILHORNE HALL POOLS (FH1367)						●			●									●									●	●			●						
DOVE (RIVER) (FH1428)									●																					●							
DOVE (RIVER) (FH1427)						●			●																					●							
DRAYTON BRIDGE (FH1439)																													●								
ELLENHALL NINE POOLS (FH1564)						●	●																					●		●							

www.fishooked.com

Fishing Facilities and Amenities

Fishery	Net Dips	Tackle Hire	Site Tackle Shop	Boats Available	Bait Sold	Adult Matches	Junior Matches	Half Day Fishing	Night Fishing	Tuition Given	Accommodation	Camping	Caravan Site	Male Toilets	Female Toilets	Disabled Toilets	Disabled Facilities	Hardcore Parking	Public Telephone	Showers	Washing Facilities	Restaurant	Hot Meals	Cafe	Refreshments	Day Lodge Available	Solid Based Swims	Easy Access Swims	Disabled Access Swims	Grass Swims	Tree Sheltered	Dogs Allowed	Fulltime Security	Rare Birdlife	Rare Wildlife	Spectators Allowed	Kids with Adults
FISHERWICK LAKES (FH1732)		●		●	●	●	●	●		●				●	●			●							●		●	●		●	●			●	●		
GAILEY TROUT AND PIKE FISHERY (FH1828)	●	●	●	●		●		●		●	●	●	●	●	●			●	●						●	●		●	●	●		●	●	●	●	●	●
HAMSTALL FISHERY (FH2097)					●	●	●	●		●				●	●	●	●	●						●	●		●	●	●	●	●			●	●	●	
HANCHURCH FISHERIES (FH2099)					●	●	●							●	●	●	●	●	●						●		●	●	●	●	●						
HEDNESFORD ROAD LAKE (FH2177)																			●						●				●								
HERONBROOK FISHERY (FH2191)						●	●			●							●	●									●	●	●	●	●	●				●	
HIMLEY HALL AND PARK LAKE (FH2230)									●					●	●	●		●	●				●	●			●	●	●		●						
HORNS (FH2300)						●																			●				●		●						
HORSEBRIDGE POOL (FH2304)																														●							
IZAAK WALTON FISHERY (FH2404)	●				●	●	●			●		●	●	●	●	●	●	●	●		●			●	●		●	●	●	●	●	●	●	●		●	
KNYPERSLEY RESERVOIR (FH2544)														●	●													●	●								
LITTLETONS AND MIDDLE POOL (FH2764)																													●		●						
LOYNTON TROUT FISHERIES (FH3100)					●			●						●	●			●					●	●	●			●	●	●	●			●	●		
MADELEY POOL (FH3134)																													●								
MIDLAND GAME FISHERIES (FH3272)																													●								
PILLATON POOLS (FH3772)						●	●					●	●			●		●									●	●	●	●			●	●	●	●	●
PINE POOL (FH3778)														●	●														●								
POOL HOUSE FARM (FH3820)						●	●	●		●							●	●									●	●	●		●		●				●
RUDYARD LAKE (FH4052)								●																													
SHROPSHIRE UNION CANAL (FH4254)																													●								
SIDEWAY OVERFLOW (FH4265)						●																					●			●	●						
SMITH POOL (FH4305)																													●								
SMITHPOOL LAKE (FH4307)						●																					●				●						
SOW (RIVER) (FH4355)									●																					●							
STAFFORD AND WORCESTER CANAL (FH4400)						●											●	●										●	●	●	●	●		●	●	●	●
STAFFORD AND WORCESTER CANAL (FH4399)																													●								
STAFFORD TO WORCESTER CANAL (FH4405)																															●						
SWAN PIT POOL (FH4594)						●	●							●	●												●	●	●	●	●					●	
TITTESWORTH RESERVOIR (FH4858)				●										●	●	●	●	●					●	●							●			●	●		
TRENT AND MERSEY CANAL (FH4945)						●	●																					●		●							
TRENTHAM GARDENS (FH4948)																													●								
WILLOWS POOLS (FH5401)						●																					●				●			●	●		
SUFFOLK																																					
ALDERSONS LAKES (FH0065)														●	●	●													●		●						
ALTON WATER RESERVOIR (FH0088)		●				●	●							●	●	●	●	●			●		●	●	●			●	●	●			●	●	●	●	

Fishing Facilities and Amenities

	Net Dips	Tackle Hire	Site Tackle Shop	Boats Available	Bait Sold	Adult Matches	Junior Matches	Half Day Fishing	Night Fishing	Tuition Given	Accommodation	Camping	Caravan Site	Male Toilets	Female Toilets	Disabled Toilets	Disabled Facilities	Hardcore Parking	Public Telephone	Showers	Washing Facilities	Restaurant	Hot Meals	Cafe	Refreshments	Day Lodge Available	Solid Based Swims	Easy Access Swims	Disabled Access Swims	Grass Swims	Tree Sheltered	Dogs Allowed	Fulltime Security	Rare Birdlife	Rare Wildlife	Spectators Allowed	Kids with Adults
BARHAM B PIT (FH0307)									●									●									●			●							
BLUE WATERS (FH0511)																													●		●						
BREAKAWAY PIT (FH0609)									●					●	●		●																				
BRIDGE FARM RESERVOIRS (FH0630)																													●								
BROOME PITS (FH0693)						●	●																										●				
CAMELOT LAKE (FH0813)														●	●	●													●		●						
CAUSEWAY LAKES (FH0876)																	●																				
CHESTERFORD FISHERIES (FH0933)														●	●																						
CLARE PARK LAKE (FH0975)									●					●	●			●							●			●			●						
CLICKETTS HILL AND PLANTATION (FH1005)									●																			●		●	●			●	●		
CLUB PIT (FH1028)						●	●		●								●												●				●				
CROSS DROVE (FH1191)														●	●										●												
CROSS GREEN FLY FISHERY (FH1192)								●						●	●	●		●	●					●			●	●	●	●	●	●		●	●	●	
FLIXTON DECOY (FH1748)				●																																	
GIPPING (RIVER) (FH1862)																														●							
HIGHFIELD FISHERY (FH2216)																									●				●								
HOLTON PIT (FH2273)						●																									●						
HOMERSFIELD LAKE (FH2284)									●																						●			●	●		
LARK (RIVER) (FH2624)									●								●											●	●	●	●				●	●	
LARK (RIVER) (FH2623)																	●																				
LARKWOOD TROUT FISHERY (FH2626)		●	●			●		●		●				●	●			●							●		●	●	●	●			●	●			●
LAYZELLS FARM (FH2640)									●																			●		●				●	●		
LITTLE BEVILLS ESTATE (FH2740)						●	●		●																			●		●	●			●	●		
LITTLE OUSE (RIVER) (FH2758)						●	●											●									●	●	●	●	●					●	
LOAM POND (FH2833)																											●			●				●	●		
MARSH FARM LAKES (FH3191)	●					●	●					●	●	●	●			●			●							●	●	●	●		●	●	●	●	●
MELDUM WASHLANDS (FLOODPARK) (FH3247)						●	●											●										●		●				●	●		
NEEDHAM LAKE (FH3435)						●	●			●				●	●	●	●		●						●			●	●	●		●		●		●	
NORTH MEADOWS (FH3531)						●	●		●									●										●		●		●		●	●	●	
OULTON BROAD (FH3634)				●																									●								
SINKS PIT (FH4277)																		●									●				●						
STANTONS FARM RESERVOIR (FH4424)														●	●	●													●								
STOUR (RIVER) (FH4501)						●	●		●					●	●	●		●										●		●				●	●	●	
STOUR (RIVER) (FH4500)									●																					●		●					
STOW (RIVER) (FH4510)						●	●		●																		●	●	●	●	●			●	●	●	

Fishing Facilities and Amenities

Fishery	Kids with Adults	Spectators Allowed	Rare Wildlife	Rare Birdlife	Fulltime Security	Dogs Allowed	Tree Sheltered	Grass Swims	Disabled Access Swims	Easy Access Swims	Solid Based Swims	Day Lodge Available	Refreshments	Cafe	Hot Meals	Restaurant	Washing Facilities	Showers	Public Telephone	Hardcore Parking	Disabled Facilities	Disabled Toilets	Female Toilets	Male Toilets	Caravan Site	Camping	Accommodation	Tuition Given	Night Fishing	Half Day Fishing	Junior Matches	Adult Matches	Bait Sold	Boats Available	Site Tackle Shop	Tackle Hire	Net Dips
STOW (RIVER) (FH4512)							●	●		●										●									●		●	●					
STOW (RIVER) (FH4511)			●	●			●	●		●						●				●									●		●	●					
STOW (RIVER) (FH4508)		●				●		●	●	●				●	●				●	●		●	●	●					●		●	●	●				
STOW (RIVER) (FH4509)		●	●	●		●	●	●		●				●		●				●		●	●	●					●		●	●	●				
THET (RIVER) (FH4809)		●	●	●				●																													
WAVENEY (RIVER) (FH5191)					●			●																					●		●	●					
WAVENEY VALLEY LAKES (FH5192)													●		●								●	●					●				●				
WICKHAM MARKET RESERVOIRS (FH5365)			●	●			●	●	●	●																											
WILLOW LAKES TROUT FISHERY (FH5385)		●	●	●			●	●		●			●							●										●							
WRIGHTS FARM (FH5517)		●						●		●																			●		●	●					
YEW TREE FISHERIES (FH5567)									●	●								●		●	●	●	●	●													
SURREY																																					
ALBURY ESTATE FISHERIES (FH0052)			●	●	●		●	●	●	●		●	●		●	●	●		●	●	●		●	●			●	●		●					●	●	
ALDERBROOK LAKE (FH0060)							●		●																												
BEAVER FARM FISHERY (FH0359)		●	●	●	●	●	●	●	●	●	●		●	●	●				●	●	●	●	●	●				●	●	●	●	●				●	
BELL WEIR LOCK (FH0376)																							●	●													
BOLDERMERE (FH0529)							●						●	●	●								●	●					●								
BRITTENS POND (FH0658)							●		●																				●								
BURY HILL FISHERIES (FH0764)		●	●		●	●		●	●	●			●	●	●		●		●	●	●	●	●	●				●		●	●	●		●	●	●	●
BUSBRIDGE LAKE (FH0765)									●	●	●									●																	
BUSHEY PARK (FH0769)	●	●	●	●	●	●		●	●	●	●		●							●	●	●	●	●													
CHERTSEY (FH0916)						●		●																					●								
CROSSWATER MILL FISHERY (FH1194)	●	●	●	●		●	●	●	●	●	●	●								●	●		●	●	●	●	●	●		●		●			●	●	
ENTON LAKES TROUT FISHERY (FH1596)		●	●	●			●	●	●	●	●		●							●			●	●						●				●		●	
EPSOM STEW POND (FH1604)									●																				●								
FISHERIES THE (FH1729)									●																							●					
FRENSHAM TROUT FISHERY (FH1800)	●	●	●	●		●	●	●	●	●	●	●								●	●		●	●	●	●	●	●		●		●			●	●	
FURZE FARM (FH1824)							●		●																				●								
GATTON MANOR LAKES (FH1842)							●		●				●									●	●	●													
GOLDSWORTH WATER PARK (FH1916)							●						●																			●					
HENFOLD LAKES FISHERY (FH2182)		●				●	●	●	●	●	●		●	●	●				●	●			●	●				●		●	●	●	●				
HOME PARK (FH2282)	●	●	●	●	●	●		●	●	●	●		●							●	●	●	●	●													
JOHNSONS LAKE (FH2415)									●	●										●			●	●													
KINGFISHER FISHERY (FH2495)			●	●			●	●	●	●										●			●	●					●	●			●				
LAKESIDE (FH2586)									●	●			●	●									●	●													

Fishing Facilities and Amenities

Facility	MANOR POND (FH3170)	MOLE (RIVER) (FH3339)	MOLE (RIVER) (FH3338)	MOLESEY LOCK (FH3340)	NAVIES HOLE (FH3430)	PAINSHILL PARK LAKE (FH3685)	PAPERCOURT FISHERY (FH3694)	RUSHMOOR LAKES (FH4063)	SHAWFIELDS LAKES (FH4213)	ST PATRICKS LANE CARP LAKES (FH4396)	STOCKBRIDGE POND (FH4460)	TWYNERSH FISHING COMPLEX (FH5012)	WEY (RIVER) (FH5291)	WEY (RIVER) (FH5290)	WEY NAVIGATION (RIVER) (FH5292)	WHITEVANE POND (FH5354)	WILLINGHURST COARSE FISHERY (FH5373)	WILLINGHURST TROUT FISHERY (FH5374)	WYPHURST AND HYHURST LAKES (FH5547)	SUSSEX (EAST)	ALEXANDRA PARK WATERS (FH0074)	ARLINGTON TROUT FISHERY (FH0137)	BALLS GREEN LAKES (FH0272)	BARCOMBE RESERVOIR (FH0303)	BELFREY COARSE FISHERY (FH0375)	BEVERN STREAM (FH0401)	BORINGWHEEL TROUT FISHERY (FH0551)	BRICK FARM LAKE (FH0620)	BUXTED OAST FISHERY (FH0780)	CLIVE VALE RESERVOIRS (FH1010)	COGHURST HALL (FH1053)	CYPRUS WOOD TROUT FISHERY (FH1242)	DARWELL WATER (FH1279)	FALKENVIL FISHERY (FH1658)	FRAMFIELD PARK FISHERIES (FH1797)
Kids with Adults						●		●						●								●	●	●				●							
Spectators Allowed						●										●	●	●				●		●	●	●			●						●
Rare Wildlife						●	●	●						●		●	●	●				●		●		●		●					●		
Rare Birdlife						●		●						●		●	●	●				●		●	●	●		●					●		
Fulltime Security						●		●				●				●						●	●	●											
Dogs Allowed							●										●	●							●										
Tree Sheltered	●	●	●		●	●		●							●	●										●		●	●				●		●
Grass Swims						●	●	●				●		●		●	●	●				●	●		●	●		●	●						●
Disabled Access Swims			●			●	●	●	●		●	●	●		●		●	●			●				●			●		●					●
Easy Access Swims						●		●	●		●	●		●	●	●	●	●				●	●	●	●				●						●
Solid Based Swims						●	●	●				●		●		●						●						●							●
Day Lodge Available																●						●		●											
Refreshments							●									●	●	●				●		●					●			●	●		●
Cafe												●					●	●											●						
Hot Meals																●	●	●											●		●				
Restaurant															●		●	●													●				
Washing Facilities																●													●						
Showers																																			
Public Telephone																						●		●									●		
Hardcore Parking						●		●				●		●		●						●	●	●					●				●		●
Disabled Facilities												●																	●				●		
Disabled Toilets						●						●				●						●											●		
Female Toilets				●		●						●					●	●				●		●					●			●	●	●	●
Male Toilets				●		●						●				●	●	●				●		●					●			●	●	●	●
Caravan Site																																			
Camping																																			
Accommodation																																			
Tuition Given																	●	●				●		●				●							
Night Fishing						●	●	●				●		●		●	●	●			●				●										●
Half Day Fishing								●								●													●						●
Junior Matches								●									●	●							●										●
Adult Matches						●		●		●							●	●	●						●				●						●
Bait Sold																																●	●		●
Boats Available																						●					●						●		
Site Tackle Shop																						●													
Tackle Hire																						●										●	●		
Net Dips																																			

Fishing Facilities and Amenities

	Net Dips	Tackle Hire	Site Tackle Shop	Boats Available	Bait Sold	Adult Matches	Junior Matches	Half Day Fishing	Night Fishing	Tuition Given	Accommodation	Camping	Caravan Site	Male Toilets	Female Toilets	Disabled Toilets	Disabled Facilities	Hardcore Parking	Public Telephone	Showers	Washing Facilities	Restaurant	Hot Meals	Cafe	Refreshments	Day Lodge Available	Solid Based Swims	Easy Access Swims	Disabled Access Swims	Grass Swims	Tree Sheltered	Dogs Allowed	Fulltime Security	Rare Birdlife	Rare Wildlife	Spectators Allowed	Kids with Adults
HOLTS LAKES (FH2274)						●	●		●									●									●	●	●	●	●					●	
HONEYS GREEN COARSE FISHERY (FH2286)						●								●	●			●	●									●		●	●					●	
HORAM MANOR FISHERY (FH2294)	●		●		●	●	●	●	●	●		●	●	●	●		●	●	●	●	●		●	●	●			●	●	●	●	●	●	●	●	●	
IDEN WOOD FISHERY (FH2358)						●	●		●					●	●			●										●	●	●	●			●	●	●	
LEABRIDGE FARM (FH2650)						●								●	●	●													●		●						
MICHELHAM PRIORY MOAT (FH3260)														●	●	●	●	●	●			●	●	●	●			●	●	●	●					●	
MOOR HALL POOL (FH3357)						●	●											●										●		●							
OLD MILL (FH3593)																															●			●	●		
OLIVES FARM FISHERY (FH3609)						●	●		●									●										●		●				●	●		
OUSE (RIVER) (FH3645)																														●	●			●	●	●	
PENNY BRIDGE (FH3741)						●	●										●	●									●	●	●		●						
PIPPINGFORD PARK ESTATE LAKES (FH3786)									●			●						●									●				●		●	●	●	●	●
POWDERMILL (FH3838)		●	●	●				●		●				●	●	●	●	●	●		●				●	●					●		●	●	●		●
ROSEBANK FARM FISHERY (FH4012)						●	●	●	●					●	●			●										●		●	●	●				●	
RYE NOOK FISHERY (FH4075)						●	●		●					●	●			●						●			●	●	●	●				●	●	●	●
SCALAND WOOD (FH4110)									●																			●			●						
SHARNFOLD FARM FISHERY (FH4210)								●						●	●			●										●			●						
SOUTHBOURNE LAKE (FH4349)					●			●						●	●			●	●				●	●			●	●	●	●	●						
SPRING WOOD FISHERY AND FARM (FH4372)		●			●	●	●	●						●	●			●					●		●		●	●	●	●	●						
ST IVES FARM (FH4388)														●	●								●		●						●						
SWANBOROUGH LAKES (FH4597)						●	●	●	●					●	●		●	●									●	●	●	●	●						
TANYARD FISHERIES (FH4654)			●		●	●	●		●					●	●	●	●	●	●		●		●	●	●	●	●			●	●	●	●	●	●		
WEIR WOOD FISHERY (FH5227)		●		●			●							●	●			●		●							●										
WHITE HART HILL LAKE (FH5331)																									●												
WISHING TREE RESERVOIR (FH5434)									●																				●								
WYLANDS CENTRE (FH5545)					●	●	●		●	●				●	●	●	●	●	●				●	●	●		●	●	●	●	●	●		●	●	●	
YEW TREE TROUT FISHERY (FH5570)								●						●	●	●	●	●							●			●	●		●					●	
SUSSEX (WEST)																																					
ADUR (RIVER) (FH0033)																							●		●												
ALDERWOOD PONDS (FH0066)									●	●				●	●			●							●		●	●	●	●	●		●	●	●		●
ARDINGLY RESERVOIR (FH0129)				●		●		●	●	●				●	●	●	●	●	●	●	●			●	●					●	●	●	●	●		●	
ARUN (RIVER) (FH0152)						●		●	●									●										●		●							
ARUN (RIVER) (FH0151)														●	●										●												
ARUN (RIVER) (FH0148)																															●						
BALCOMBE LAKE (FH0256)																		●																			

Fishing Facilities and Amenities

Facility	BLACKWOOL TROUT FISHERY (FH0484)	BORDE HILL GARDEN LAKES (FH0544)	CHALK SPRINGS TROUT FISHERY (FH0891)	DUNCTON MILL (FH1473)	FURNACE LAKES (FH1821)	HAMBROOK TROUT FISHERY (FH2080)	HURSTON LANE (FH2347)	MENARDS LAKE (FH3254)	MILL FARM FISHERY (FH3283)	NEW POND (FH3475)	NEWELLS FISHERIES (FH3483)	PASSIES PONDS (FH3715)	ROTHER (RIVER) (FH4028)	ROTHERFIELD POND (FH4030)	SPARKS FARM FISHERY (FH4358)	STUBPOND FISHERIES (FH4531)	TILGATE LAKES (FH4845)	VALE BRIDGE LAKE (FH5081)	WATTLEHURST FARM TROUT LAKES (FH5188)	WINTONS FISHERY (FH5432)	TYNE AND WEAR	BOLAM LAKE COUNTRY PARK (FH0528)	DISSINGTON POND (FH1377)	KILLINGWORTH LAKE (FH2486)	LEAZES PARK LAKE (FH2655)	MILKHOPE POND (FH3276)	MOUNT PLEASANT LAKE (FH3387)	RED BARNS POND (FH3908)	STEPHENSON LAKE (FH4450)	SWEETHOPE LOUGHS (FH4608)	TEES (RIVER) (FH4699)	WEAR (RIVER) (FH5212)	WHITTLE DENE TROUT FISHERY (FH5360)	WARWICKSHIRE	ADAMS POOL (FH0026)
Kids with Adults	●				●										●							●								●					●
Spectators Allowed		●	●		●							●		●								●													●
Rare Wildlife		●		●	●							●										●				●				●					
Rare Birdlife		●	●	●	●							●										●								●					
Fulltime Security	●				●						●											●								●					●
Dogs Allowed		●																				●													
Tree Sheltered		●	●	●	●						●		●	●	●							●	●			●	●			●		●			●
Grass Swims	●	●	●	●	●				●	●	●	●	●	●	●							●													●
Disabled Access Swims	●	●	●	●	●		●			●	●	●	●	●		●	●	●				●	●		●	●	●	●	●	●	●				
Easy Access Swims	●	●	●	●	●					●	●	●	●	●	●		●			●		●				●				●					●
Solid Based Swims		●	●	●	●						●	●		●						●		●									●				●
Day Lodge Available	●				●	●																													
Refreshments	●	●	●	●	●	●						●				●	●			●										●	●	●			
Cafe		●										●			●							●													
Hot Meals	●	●										●			●													●			●				
Restaurant	●	●																	●													●			
Washing Facilities	●				●										●							●													
Showers																				●															
Public Telephone		●										●								●		●								●			●		●
Hardcore Parking	●	●	●	●	●				●		●	●	●	●	●							●								●					●
Disabled Facilities	●													●		●				●		●		●									●		
Disabled Toilets	●	●			●	●														●		●							●		●		●		
Female Toilets	●	●	●	●		●						●			●		●		●	●		●			●				●	●	●	●	●		
Male Toilets	●	●	●	●	●	●			●		●	●			●	●	●		●	●		●			●				●	●	●	●	●		
Caravan Site	●																																		
Camping	●																																		
Accommodation																																			
Tuition Given	●	●	●					●		●	●	●	●	●		●														●					●
Night Fishing					●			●		●	●			●		●				●					●										●
Half Day Fishing	●	●	●	●	●						●	●			●										●					●					
Junior Matches		●	●	●						●		●	●	●		●									●	●									
Adult Matches		●	●	●						●		●	●	●	●	●									●	●									
Bait Sold												●			●					●															
Boats Available		●																							●					●					
Site Tackle Shop												●								●										●					
Tackle Hire	●	●	●	●		●														●										●					
Net Dips											●																								

www.fishooked.com

Fishing Facilities and Amenities

	Net Dips	Tackle Hire	Site Tackle Shop	Boats Available	Bait Sold	Adult Matches	Junior Matches	Half Day Fishing	Night Fishing	Tuition Given	Accommodation	Camping	Caravan Site	Male Toilets	Female Toilets	Disabled Toilets	Disabled Facilities	Hardcore Parking	Public Telephone	Showers	Washing Facilities	Restaurant	Hot Meals	Cafe	Refreshments	Day Lodge Available	Solid Based Swims	Easy Access Swims	Disabled Access Swims	Grass Swims	Tree Sheltered	Dogs Allowed	Fulltime Security	Rare Birdlife	Rare Wildlife	Spectators Allowed	Kids with Adults
ARDENCOTE (FH0127)		●			●																		●	●	●				●								
BISHOPS BOWL LAKES (FH0435)						●			●					●	●	●							●	●	●				●		●						
BOSWORTH & FRIEZELAND (FH0561)				●					●					●	●	●	●	●	●				●	●				●	●		●	●				●	
CHESTERTON MILL (FH0934)								●	●					●	●	●		●							●		●	●	●	●	●	●		●	●	●	
CLIFTON LAKES FISHERY (FH1006)						●			●					●	●		●								●				●		●						
COVENTRY CANAL (FH1146)																													●								
DRAYCOTE WATER (FH1438)		●		●		●	●							●	●	●	●	●	●					●	●			●	●	●	●			●		●	
GRAND UNION CANAL (FH1962)																													●								
GRAND UNION CANAL (FH1965)																													●								
GRAND UNION CANAL (FH1966)																													●		●						
GRAND UNION CANAL (FH1963)																													●								
HAWKESBURY FISHERY (FH2141)														●	●																●						
KINGSTON POOLS (FH2518)						●	●		●					●	●												●	●	●	●				●	●		
LANNYS LAGOON (FH2620)						●								●	●	●													●		●						
MAKIN FISHERIES (FH3150)														●	●		●								●		●	●	●							●	
MONKS POOL (FH3347)														●	●								●	●	●				●		●						●
NAPTON RESERVOIR (FH3421)																		●																			
NORTH FARM FISHERY (FH3527)																													●								
NORTH OXFORD CANAL (FH3533)																															●						
OAKHAM FARM POOLS (FH3562)														●	●										●												
OXFORD CANAL (FH3677)						●												●	●									●	●		●	●	●			●	
PARK FARM (FH3697)						●																									●						
RIDDINGS FISHERY (FH3949)						●								●	●	●	●						●	●	●		●	●	●	●	●						
SHEEPY MAGNA LAKE (FH4219)																													●								
SNITTERFIELD FRUIT FARM (FH4312)																													●							●	
TUNNEL BARN FARM (FH4972)					●	●	●	●		●				●	●			●					●	●	●		●	●	●	●	●				●	●	
WARWICKSHIRE AVON (FH5157)																															●						
WARWICKSHIRE AVON (FH5155)																	●														●						
WEST HILLBOROUGH (FH5261)						●																					●	●		●	●						
WESTON LAWN FISHERIES (FH5285)						●	●		●			●		●	●	●	●	●			●		●	●	●		●	●	●	●		●	●	●	●	●	
WILTSHIRE																																					
AVON (BRISTOL) (RIVER) (FH0200)									●																												
AVON (BRISTOL) (RIVER) (FH0195)						●	●											●									●	●	●	●	●					●	
AVON (BRISTOL) (RIVER) (FH0199)																															●						
AVON (BRISTOL) (RIVER) (FH0196)																													●		●						

Fishing Facilities and Amenities

Facility	AVON (BRISTOL) (RIVER) (FH0197)	AVON (BRISTOL) (RIVER) (FH0194)	AVON (RIVER) (FH0218)	AVON (RIVER) (FH0216)	AVON (RIVER) (FH0220)	AVON ANGLING CLUB (FH0226)	AVON SPRINGS FISHERY (FH0229)	BLACKLAND LAKES (FH0450)	BRISTOL AVON (FH0650)	BRISTOL AVON (FH0651)	COATE WATER COUNTRY PARK (FH1046)	CUCKOOS REST (FH1211)	HIGH PENN (FH2210)	KENNET AND AVON CANAL (FH2463)	KENNET AND AVON CANAL (FH2465)	LANGFORD FISHERIES (FH2611)	LONGLEAT LAKES (FH2992)	LOWER MOOR FISHERY (FH3090)	MANOR BROOK LAKE (FH3160)	NADDER (RIVER) (FH3409)	PETERS FINGER LAKES (FH3756)	PURTON LAKE (FH3859)	ROOD ASHTON LAKE (FH4002)	SABRE AND SWORDS LAKES (FH4079)	SHAFTESBURY LAKE (FH4200)	SHEAR WATER (FH4216)	SILVERLANDS LAKE (FH4272)	STEEPLE LANGFORD LAKES (FH4447)	SUTTON VENY ESTATE (FH4566)	THAMES (RIVER) (FH4805)	WALDENS FARM FISHERY (FH5118)	WHITE HORSE INN LAKE (FH5334)	WOODLAND PARK (FH5480)	WROUGHTON RESERVOIR (FH5519)	WYATTS LAKE (FH5523)
Kids with Adults								●	●																		●				●				
Spectators Allowed			●			●	●	●	●				●		●		●	●					●		●		●		●	●	●		●		
Rare Wildlife							●	●								●	●	●							●		●								
Rare Birdlife							●	●								●	●	●							●		●						●		
Fulltime Security							●	●																			●				●				
Dogs Allowed								●																	●		●		●				●		
Tree Sheltered		●					●	●			●			●				●					●		●					●	●		●		
Grass Swims			●	●	●	●	●	●	●						●	●	●			●	●				●		●	●		●			●		
Disabled Access Swims					●		●	●			●	●			●	●				●	●		●	●	●	●		●			●				
Easy Access Swims			●	●	●		●	●							●	●	●	●		●	●		●		●	●	●	●		●	●		●		
Solid Based Swims				●	●		●	●							●	●				●	●				●			●		●	●		●		
Day Lodge Available							●																								●				
Refreshments			●					●			●					●	●							●		●					●	●	●		
Cafe			●					●	●							●	●																●		
Hot Meals								●								●	●															●	●		
Restaurant								●	●								●															●			
Washing Facilities							●	●																			●								
Showers								●																											
Public Telephone								●	●								●																●		
Hardcore Parking							●	●	●	●						●	●	●				●	●				●			●	●		●	●	
Disabled Facilities							●	●							●	●	●								●										
Disabled Toilets			●				●	●			●					●	●																●		
Female Toilets			●				●	●			●	●				●	●							●		●	●				●		●		
Male Toilets			●				●	●	●		●	●				●	●	●						●		●	●				●		●		
Caravan Site								●																			●				●		●		
Camping								●																			●				●		●		
Accommodation								●																			●						●		
Tuition Given					●		●													●	●							●			●				
Night Fishing	●		●	●	●	●		●	●						●		●		●	●	●					●	●	●			●	●			●
Half Day Fishing							●		●							●	●						●		●		●								
Junior Matches			●						●						●								●		●		●			●					
Adult Matches	●		●		●	●	●		●						●					●	●		●	●	●		●	●		●			●		
Bait Sold			●			●																									●				
Boats Available																●			●																
Site Tackle Shop							●																								●				
Tackle Hire			●				●									●		●											●		●				
Net Dips							●																				●				●				

www.fishooked.com

Fishing Facilities and Amenities

	Net Dips	Tackle Hire	Site Tackle Shop	Boats Available	Bait Sold	Adult Matches	Junior Matches	Half Day Fishing	Night Fishing	Tuition Given	Accommodation	Camping	Caravan Site	Male Toilets	Female Toilets	Disabled Toilets	Disabled Facilities	Hardcore Parking	Public Telephone	Showers	Washing Facilities	Restaurant	Hot Meals	Cafe	Refreshments	Day Lodge Available	Solid Based Swims	Easy Access Swims	Disabled Access Swims	Grass Swims	Tree Sheltered	Dogs Allowed	Fulltime Security	Rare Birdlife	Rare Wildlife	Spectators Allowed	Kids with Adults
WORCESTERSHIRE																																					
ABBOTS SALFORD PARK (FH0009)														●	●		●	●						●								●				●	●
ANCHOR MEADOWS FISHERY (FH0105)																													●								
ARROW VALLEY LAKE (FH0141)						●	●	●						●	●	●	●	●	●				●	●	●			●	●		●					●	
AVON (RIVER) (FH0223)						●																															
BIRMINGHAM TO WORCESTER CANAL (FH0434)																													●		●						
BIRMINGHAM TO WORCESTER CANAL (FH0433)																													●								
BRAKE MILL POOL (FH0596)						●																															
BRANSFORD GAME FISHERY (FH0601)		●						●		●				●	●		●	●					●	●	●				●			●				●	
BROAD ACRES LAKE (FH0661)														●	●													●	●								
BROCKAMIN POOLS (FH0667)																													●								
CAPTAINS POOL (FH0835)						●												●									●	●		●	●			●	●		●
CASTLE GREEN POOLS (FH0860)														●	●														●								
ELMBRIDGE LAKES (FH1569)						●	●	●						●	●	●								●					●								
ERICS POOL (FH1609)														●	●														●					●	●		
EVESBATCH FISHERIES (FH1635)																													●								
FOREST FARM (FH1765)														●	●	●													●		●						
FURNACE MILL FISHERY (FH1822)					●	●	●	●						●	●			●					●	●	●		●	●	●	●	●			●	●	●	
HAYE FARM FISHERY (FH2152)						●	●							●	●		●											●									
HOLT FLEET POOL (FH2271)																													●								
HUXLEYS HAMPTON FERRY FISHERY (FH2352)						●	●	●					●	●	●		●	●	●	●	●	●	●	●	●		●	●	●		●	●		●	●	●	●
LEIGH SINTON FISHING LAKES (FH2692)					●	●	●	●						●	●			●					●	●	●		●	●	●	●	●	●				●	●
LENCHES LAKES (FH2697)		●			●			●						●	●	●	●	●	●				●	●				●	●		●			●	●		
LENCHFORD (FH2698)						●			●		●	●	●					●									●	●		●	●			●	●		●
MASTERS (THE) (FH3206)																													●								
MAVER LARFORD (FH3210)						●								●	●									●							●						
MILL POOL (FH3303)																													●								
MOORLANDS FARM (FH3363)	●		●			●	●			●			●	●	●			●	●		●		●	●	●		●	●	●	●				●	●	●	●
MOORS POOL (FH3365)						●																															
POOLE HALL FISHERY (FH3822)																													●								
RED BECK LAKE (FH3909)																												●		●			●				●
SALWARPE (RIVER) (FH4089)																															●						
SEVERN (RIVER) (FH4186)					●	●	●											●				●	●	●	●		●	●		●	●			●	●	●	
SEVERN (RIVER) (FH4188)																															●						
SEVERN (RIVER) (FH4184)														●	●										●				●		●						

Fishing Facilities and Amenities

	SEVERN (RIVER) (FH4195)	SEVERN (RIVER) (FH4197)	SEVERN (RIVER) (FH4194)	SEVERN (RIVER) (FH4192)	SHAKESPEARE MOORLANDS FARM (FH4203)	SHATTERFORD FISHERY (FH4212)	SILLIGROVE FISHERY (FH4267)	SION FARM FISHERIES (FH4279)	SNUFF MILL POOL (FH4314)	STAINFORTH AND KEADBY CANAL (FH4407)	STELLA LAKE (FH4448)	STEWARDS POOL (FH4454)	TEME (RIVER) (FH4728)	TEME (RIVER) (FH4733)	TEME (RIVER) (FH4732)	TEME (RIVER) (FH4725)	TEME (RIVER) (FH4726)	TEME (RIVER) (FH4731)	TWYFORD FARM POOL (FH5009)	UCKINGHALL POOL (FH5038)	UNWICKS FARM FISHERY (FH5049)	UPTON WARREN LAKE (FH5063)	WARWICKSHIRE & AVON (FH5154)	WARWICKSHIRE AVON (FH5159)	WARWICKSHIRE AVON (FH5161)	WARWICKSHIRE AVON (FH5158)	WELFIELD POOLS (FH5229)	WHARFE INN POOL (FH5312)	WHARTONS PARK COARSE FISHING (FH5314)	WILDEN POOL (FH5369)	WILLOW FARM (FH5380)	WILLOW MARSH (FH5386)	WINDMILL LAKE (FH5409)	WINTERFOLD PARK FISHERIES (FH5425)	WITLEY FISHERY (FH5448)
Kids with Adults							●																									●			●
Spectators Allowed					●		●	●	●						●									●					●			●			
Rare Wildlife							●	●	●						●												●					●			
Rare Birdlife						●	●	●	●						●												●		●			●			
Fulltime Security							●																	●								●			
Dogs Allowed					●																		●	●											●
Tree Sheltered	●		●	●		●	●	●	●				●	●	●		●	●	●						●	●			●		●		●		●
Grass Swims						●			●						●														●			●			
Disabled Access Swims		●	●		●	●	●	●		●	●	●						●	●	●	●	●			●	●	●	●			●	●	●	●	●
Easy Access Swims					●	●	●		●														●	●					●			●			●
Solid Based Swims					●	●			●														●	●								●			●
Day Lodge Available							●																												
Refreshments	●						●													●			●	●				●	●		●				
Cafe					●	●									●				●																
Hot Meals					●	●	●								●					●								●							
Restaurant					●										●																				
Washing Facilities							●														●		●	●											
Showers																							●	●											
Public Telephone																							●	●											
Hardcore Parking					●	●	●	●	●							●				●	●		●	●					●			●			●
Disabled Facilities						●	●																●	●											
Disabled Toilets						●	●	●											●				●	●				●			●				
Female Toilets	●				●	●	●	●	●										●		●		●	●			●	●			●	●			
Male Toilets	●				●	●	●	●	●										●		●		●	●			●	●			●	●			
Caravan Site																							●	●		●							●		
Camping																							●	●		●							●		
Accommodation																							●	●											
Tuition Given							●																			●									
Night Fishing						●															●									●					●
Half Day Fishing					●	●	●	●															●	●					●			●			
Junior Matches				●	●	●	●	●	●											●			●	●								●			●
Adult Matches				●	●	●	●	●	●									●	●	●		●	●	●		●		●				●			●
Bait Sold					●	●									●																				
Boats Available																																			
Site Tackle Shop																																			
Tackle Hire					●		●																												
Net Dips							●																									●			

Fishing Facilities and Amenities

Facility	WITLEY POOLS (FH5449)	WOOD POOL (FH5462)	WOODLAND VIEW (FH5481)	WOODROW FISH POND (FH5490)	WOODSTON MANOR POOLS (FH5496)	WREXHAM	CLYWEDOG (RIVER) (FH1044)	EMRAL BROOK (FH1588)	YORKSHIRE (NORTH)	BARLOW COMMON NATURE RESERVE (FH0311)	BELLFLASK TROUT FISHERY (FH0379)	BIRKDALE FISHERY (FH0430)	BOLTON ABBEY FISHERIES (FH0539)	BRAFFERTON COARSE FISHERY (FH0593)	BRICKYARD FARM LAKE (FH0622)	BROKEN BREA FISHERY (FH0674)	BROOKLANDS (FH0683)	CARP VALE (FH0846)	CATTERICK LAKES (FH0874)	CAWOOD HOLIDAY PARK (FH0877)	CHAPMANS POND (FH0897)	CLAY PIT (FH0988)	COD BECK (FH1049)	CORNHILL PONDS (FH1121)	CRABTREE ANGLING LAKE (FH1155)	CUNDALL LODGE FISHERY (FH1223)	ELLERTON PARK (FH1568)	ELVINGTON LAKE (FH1575)	ESK (RIVER) (FH1627)	FAIRVIEW LAKE (FH1656)	FLETCHERS POND (FH1747)	FOGGLESKYTE WATERS (FH1753)	GRAFTON MERE (FH1936)	HAZELHEAD LAKE (FH2165)	HIGH MOOR FARM PARK (FH2208)
Kids with Adults			●											●				●									●								
Spectators Allowed	●	●		●									●	●				●		●					●			●						●	
Rare Wildlife	●	●								●			●	●											●			●							
Rare Birdlife	●	●		●						●			●	●									●		●		●	●							
Fulltime Security														●				●										●							
Dogs Allowed				●									●	●				●		●								●							
Tree Sheltered	●	●								●			●	●				●	●	●	●			●		●	●	●					●		●
Grass Swims	●			●									●	●									●				●	●							
Disabled Access Swims			●	●	●					●		●		●	●	●	●	●	●			●		●	●	●	●	●			●		●		●
Easy Access Swims	●		●	●	●					●			●	●		●		●		●			●				●	●		●					
Solid Based Swims				●						●				●		●	●	●										●		●					
Day Lodge Available																																			
Refreshments		●	●		●								●		●	●			●		●			●			●	●	●						●
Cafe			●										●			●			●	●								●							
Hot Meals			●										●						●	●				●				●						●	
Restaurant													●							●								●							
Washing Facilities			●																								●	●							
Showers																											●	●							
Public Telephone			●										●							●							●								
Hardcore Parking	●	●					●	●		●	●		●	●		●		●		●					●		●			●					
Disabled Facilities	●													●		●	●	●	●			●			●		●					●			
Disabled Toilets		●	●		●					●			●		●					●							●	●			●				●
Female Toilets		●	●		●					●			●		●	●	●			●		●		●	●		●	●		●	●	●			●
Male Toilets		●	●		●					●			●		●	●	●			●		●		●	●		●	●		●	●	●			●
Caravan Site																											●	●							
Camping																											●	●							
Accommodation														●		●																			
Tuition Given																●																			
Night Fishing																										●	●								
Half Day Fishing			●											●	●			●		●					●									●	
Junior Matches	●															●		●					●				●	●							
Adult Matches	●		●											●	●	●		●					●				●	●							
Bait Sold			●												●		●																		
Boats Available																											●								
Site Tackle Shop			●																																
Tackle Hire			●																									●							
Net Dips														●																					

Fishing Facilities and Amenities

	Net Dips	Tackle Hire	Site Tackle Shop	Boats Available	Bait Sold	Adult Matches	Junior Matches	Half Day Fishing	Night Fishing	Tuition Given	Accommodation	Camping	Caravan Site	Male Toilets	Female Toilets	Disabled Toilets	Disabled Facilities	Hardcore Parking	Public Telephone	Showers	Washing Facilities	Restaurant	Hot Meals	Cafe	Refreshments	Day Lodge Available	Solid Based Swims	Easy Access Swims	Disabled Access Swims	Grass Swims	Tree Sheltered	Dogs Allowed	Fulltime Security	Rare Birdlife	Rare Wildlife	Spectators Allowed	Kids with Adults
HOLLINGWOOD FISHERY (FH2257)										●				●	●												●	●	●								
HOXNE FARM PONDS (FH2322)													●	●	●																						
KILNSEY PARK AND TROUT FARM (FH2487)		●			●			●		●				●	●	●	●	●			●	●	●	●	●		●	●	●	●	●			●	●		●
KINGSLEY CARP LAKE (FH2513)						●	●	●										●									●	●	●		●		●	●	●	●	
LAKEHOUSE LAKE (FH2576)																															●						
LAKESIDE LODGES (FH2595)									●		●			●	●	●		●									●	●		●	●	●	●				●
LANGTON POND (FH2618)																															●						
LEIGHTON RESERVOIR (FH2693)						●	●		●	●				●	●			●										●						●	●		
LINGCROFT FARM POND (FH2735)																													●								
LOW OSGOODBY LAKE (FH3068)								●		●				●	●																●	●		●	●	●	
MARKET WEIGHTON CANAL (FH3185)						●																															
MARSTON WYSE TROUT FARM (FH3197)						●		●						●	●	●	●	●									●	●	●	●	●			●	●		
MILBY CUT (FH3273)						●																						●	●		●						
MUNBY POND (FH3401)						●	●																				●	●									
NEWHAY DAY TICKET LAKE (FH3484)									●					●	●			●									●	●	●		●						
NEWHAY SPECIMEN LAKE (FH3485)									●					●	●			●									●	●	●		●						
NIDD (RIVER) (FH3507)						●	●		●	●																		●		●	●						
NIDD (RIVER) (FH3503)						●	●		●	●																		●		●							
NIDD (RIVER) (FH3504)						●																									●						
NIDD (RIVER) (FH3506)						●	●		●																					●							
NORTHINGALES FISHERY (FH3545)														●	●																						
OAK MERE FISHERY (FH3558)														●	●														●								
OAKS FISHERY (FH3565)					●			●						●	●		●	●						●	●												●
OAKTREE LEISURE (FH3569)														●	●	●													●								
ORCHARD FARM PONDS (FH3615)																	●														●						
OUSE (RIVER) (FH3651)						●	●		●	●																		●		●							
PARKLANDS (FH3703)						●	●		●					●	●			●			●						●	●		●				●	●		●
PICKERING PARK FISHING LAKE (FH3766)	●					●	●	●		●				●	●	●	●	●	●		●				●			●	●		●	●	●	●	●	●	
POOL BRIDGE FARM LAKES (FH3818)																								●													
POTTERY LAKE (FH3834)	●					●	●	●	●			●						●										●	●		●		●	●	●	●	●
PROSPECT FARM POND (FH3852)						●	●		●					●	●	●												●	●		●	●				●	
RAKER LAKES (FH3884)	●					●	●	●	●	●			●	●	●	●		●		●							●	●	●	●	●		●				●
RASKELF LAKE (FH3889)																													●								
RIPON CANAL (FH3958)						●																															
RIPON RACECOURSE LAKE (FH3959)									●																												

Fishing Facilities and Amenities

Fishery	Net Dips	Tackle Hire	Site Tackle Shop	Boats Available	Bait Sold	Adult Matches	Junior Matches	Half Day Fishing	Night Fishing	Tuition Given	Accommodation	Camping	Caravan Site	Male Toilets	Female Toilets	Disabled Toilets	Disabled Facilities	Hardcore Parking	Public Telephone	Showers	Washing Facilities	Restaurant	Hot Meals	Cafe	Refreshments	Day Lodge Available	Solid Based Swims	Easy Access Swims	Disabled Access Swims	Grass Swims	Tree Sheltered	Dogs Allowed	Fulltime Security	Rare Birdlife	Rare Wildlife	Spectators Allowed	Kids with Adults
RUSWARP (RIVER) (FH4067)				●																				●				●		●		●					
RYE AND SEVEN (RIVERS) (FH4074)																															●						
SCARBOROUGH MERE (FH4113)														●	●										●				●								
SELBY 3 LAKES (FH4129)														●	●			●										●					●	●	●	●	
SELBY CANAL (FH4133)						●	●																					●		●		●		●	●	●	
SELBY CANAL (FH4132)														●	●														●								
SELBY CANAL (FH4131)																		●												●				●	●		
SELLEY BRIDGE LAKE (FH4134)														●	●		●	●											●								
SHIELD FISHERY (FH4235)																													●								
SHIELD TROUT FISHERY (FH4236)														●	●																						
STONEBRIDGE LAKES (FH4471)		●				●		●	●	●				●	●	●	●	●			●		●		●	●		●	●		●		●				●
SWALE (RIVER) (FH4569)						●	●			●	●							●	●									●		●	●					●	
SWALE (RIVER) (FH4576)						●																									●						
SWALE (RIVER) (FH4573)						●	●			●																				●							
SWALE (RIVER) (FH4567)						●												●										●		●	●	●		●	●	●	●
TANFIELD LAKE (FH4651)								●						●	●	●	●	●			●					●		●	●		●			●	●		●
THORPE PERROW QUARRY (FH4825)																		●																			
TOLLERTON FISHING PONDS (FH4867)									●					●	●	●													●		●						
URE (RIVER) (FH5070)														●	●																●						
URE (RIVER) (FH5072)						●	●			●																				●							
WASHBURN VALLEY (FH5164)						●								●	●	●	●	●	●									●	●		●	●		●	●	●	
WATERMEADOWS FISHERY (FH5181)				●		●		●						●	●		●	●									●	●	●		●			●	●	●	
WEST HADDLESEY LAKE (FH5260)					●				●									●									●	●	●	●			●				
WESTERLY LAKE (FH5271)						●	●	●						●	●										●			●	●							●	
WHARFE (RIVER) (FH5301)														●	●	●									●				●		●						
WHARFE (RIVER) (FH5302)																		●												●							●
WILLOWS (FH5396)														●	●														●								
WOODLAND LAKES (FH5479)		●	●		●	●	●			●				●	●	●	●	●	●		●	●	●	●	●		●	●	●	●			●	●	●	●	
WYKEHAM LAKES (FH5544)				●	●			●						●	●								●		●												
Y2K LAKE (FH5553)								●																													
YORKSHIRE OUSE (FH5572)																															●						
YORKSHIRE (SOUTH)																																					
ASKERN LAKE (FH0173)				●																									●								
BRAMPTON CANAL (FH0598)																		●																			
BULL HOLE (FH0725)						●																															

Fishing Facilities and Amenities

Facility	CAMPSALL COUNTRY PARK (FH0818)	CHESTERFIELD CANAL (FH0931)	CROOKES VALLEY PARK LAKE (FH1189)	CUSWORTH HALL LAKE (FH1228)	DAM FLASK RESERVOIR (FH1251)	DELVES LAKES (FH1330)	HORSESHOE LAKE TROUT FISHERY (FH2309)	HOWBROOK RESERVOIR (FH2318)	IDLE (RIVER) (FH2359)	KIVETON HALL (FH2531)	KJS FISHERIES (FH2532)	MICKS PLACE (FH3262)	NEWBIGGIN POND (FH3478)	PEBLEY RESERVOIR (FH3729)	RAILWAY POND (FH3880)	SALLY WALSHES DAM (FH4084)	SCOUT DYKE RESERVOIR (FH4121)	SHEFFIELD CANAL (FH4223)	SHEFFIELD CANAL (FH4222)	SHIREOAKS PARK (FH4243)	SLIVER FISHERY (FH4300)	STANBOROUGH FISHERIES (FH4414)	STRAIGHT MILE FISHERY (FH4517)	THORNE NORTH POND (FH4814)	THRYBERGH COUNTRY PARK (FH4835)	TINKERS PONDS (FH4854)	TOLL BAR POND (FH4866)	TORNE (RIVER) (FH4880)	ULLEY RESERVOIR (FH5041)	WESTWOOD COUNTRY PARK (FH5288)	WILLOW GARTH FISHERY (FH5381)	WILLOWGARTH LAKE (FH5394)	WORSBOROUGH RESERVOIR (FH5506)	WORSBROUGH RESERVOIR (FH5508)
Kids with Adults								●					●									●			●					●				
Spectators Allowed																	●				●	●			●									●
Rare Wildlife																	●					●			●									●
Rare Birdlife																	●					●			●									●
Fulltime Security																						●			●	●								
Dogs Allowed																	●				●	●			●									
Tree Sheltered		●	●	●		●				●								●	●			●		●	●						●			
Grass Swims																					●				●									●
Disabled Access Swims	●	●	●	●		●					●		●	●	●				●	●	●		●	●		●		●	●		●		●	●
Easy Access Swims		●											●								●	●			●								●	
Solid Based Swims		●						●					●								●	●			●	●							●	●
Day Lodge Available																									●									
Refreshments				●			●				●								●	●	●				●		●						●	
Cafe										●	●	●							●		●				●								●	●
Hot Meals							●				●									●	●				●								●	
Restaurant		●	●																		●													
Washing Facilities																						●			●									
Showers																									●									
Public Telephone																					●				●									
Hardcore Parking										●							●					●			●					●		●	●	
Disabled Facilities				●					●				●					●			●	●			●									
Disabled Toilets						●					●								●	●	●	●		●	●									
Female Toilets			●	●	●	●	●				●				●				●	●	●	●	●	●	●				●				●	●
Male Toilets			●	●	●	●	●				●				●	●			●	●	●	●	●	●	●				●				●	●
Caravan Site																									●									
Camping																									●									
Accommodation																									●									
Tuition Given		●																			●				●									
Night Fishing																●																●		
Half Day Fishing																																		
Junior Matches		●								●					●		●				●	●									●			
Adult Matches		●			●					●					●	●	●			●	●	●			●									●
Bait Sold																									●									
Boats Available																																		
Site Tackle Shop																									●									
Tackle Hire																																		
Net Dips																																		

YORKSHIRE (WEST)

FACILITIES AVAILABLE

Fishing Facilities and Amenities

Venue	Kids with Adults	Spectators Allowed	Rare Wildlife	Rare Birdlife	Fulltime Security	Dogs Allowed	Tree Sheltered	Grass Swims	Disabled Access Swims	Easy Access Swims	Solid Based Swims	Day Lodge Available	Refreshments	Cafe	Hot Meals	Restaurant	Washing Facilities	Showers	Public Telephone	Hardcore Parking	Disabled Facilities	Disabled Toilets	Female Toilets	Male Toilets	Caravan Site	Camping	Accommodation	Tuition Given	Night Fishing	Half Day Fishing	Junior Matches	Adult Matches	Bait Sold	Boats Available	Site Tackle Shop	Tackle Hire	Net Dips
ACKTON POND (FH0020)																													●								
AIRE (RIVER) (FH0045)													●										●	●													
AIRE (RIVER) (FH0043)	●	●		●	●		●	●		●										●											●	●					
AIRE AND CALDER CANAL (FH0048)									●	●										●																	
CALDER (RIVER) (FH0795)																					●																
CALDER (RIVER) (FH0794)							●	●																													
CALDER (RIVER) (FH0796)							●		●	●																						●					
COPPICE POND (FH1113)							●		●													●	●	●													
DYEHOUSE POND (FH1493)							●		●	●																						●					
HOLME (RIVER) (FH2263)							●																														
HOPTON WATERS (FH2293)									●														●	●				●									
HORNSEA MERE (FH2301)																																		●			
KIPPAX POND (FH2524)									●	●																											
KNOTFORD LAGOON (FH2542)							●		●																												
LEEDS AND LIVERPOOL CANAL (FH2671)									●	●																					●	●					
LEEDS TO LIVERPOOL CANAL (FH2682)		●					●		●	●										●												●					
LOWTHER LAKE (FH3099)	●	●	●	●	●	●		●			●																				●	●					
MILLRACE (FH3316)							●		●												●		●	●													
NEW MILL DAM (FH3474)		●					●	●	●	●	●									●	●							●			●						
NOSTELL PRIORY LAKE (FH3551)		●				●	●	●		●			●	●	●	●				●			●	●						●							
OAKS SCAR RESERVOIR (FH3566)		●																																			
PUGNEYS COUNTRY PARK (FH3855)		●		●		●		●	●	●									●		●	●	●	●													
RAYGILL FISHERY (FH3902)	●		●	●	●		●	●	●	●	●	●	●	●	●		●			●	●	●	●	●				●	●	●	●	●	●	●	●		●
ROBERTS POND (FH3976)								●													●																
ROCHDALE CANAL (FH3979)		●				●	●	●	●	●	●									●											●	●					
ROUNDHAY PARK LAKES (FH4037)														●																							
SPRING VALLEY WATERS (FH4371)									●				●		●							●	●	●													
STAVELEY LAKES (FH4443)	●		●	●	●		●	●	●	●	●									●	●																
SWILLINGTON PARK (FH4609)			●	●				●	●	●	●										●	●	●	●													
TONG PARK DAM (FH4872)	●				●		●	●	●												●							●									
WALSDEN PRINTING CO LODGES (FH5128)	●	●						●	●	●	●									●																	
WHARFE (RIVER) (FH5311)	●	●	●	●				●		●										●										●	●	●					
WHARFE (RIVER) (FH5310)	●	●	●	●				●	●	●				●						●										●							
WORKSHOP POND (FH5504)									●				●		●																						
YEADON TARN (FH5559)									●				●	●																							

Fishing Facilities and Amenities

	Net Dips	Tackle Hire	Site Tackle Shop	Boats Available	Bait Sold	Adult Matches	Junior Matches	Half Day Fishing	Night Fishing	Tuition Given	Accommodation	Camping	Caravan Site	Male Toilets	Female Toilets	Disabled Toilets	Disabled Facilities	Hardcore Parking	Public Telephone	Showers	Washing Facilities	Restaurant	Hot Meals	Cafe	Refreshments	Day Lodge Available	Solid Based Swims	Easy Access Swims	Disabled Access Swims	Grass Swims	Tree Sheltered	Dogs Allowed	Fulltime Security	Rare Birdlife	Rare Wildlife	Spectators Allowed	Kids with Adults
IRELAND																																					
COUNTY CAVAN																																					
LOUGH RAMOR (FH3053)						●	●		●													●						●	●			●		●	●	●	
COUNTY CLARE																																					
ALLARD FISHERIES (FH0077)				●					●									●										●		●	●						
DROMORE AND BALLYLINE (FH1449)				●																																	
LICKEEN LAKE (FH2713)				●										●	●																						
COUNTY CORK																																					
BLACKWATER FLY FISHING (FH0480)										●																											
CAREYSVILLE (FH0840)		●								●	●			●	●			●	●		●	●	●		●	●	●	●			●	●	●	●	●	●	●
CORK LOUGH (FH1119)																																		●			
DERRYVEGALL LAKE (FH1341)				●																																	
GARRANES LAKE (FH1838)				●																																	
ILEN (RIVER) (FH2362)									●									●											●		●			●	●	●	
LOUGH ADERRA (FH2999)				●																																	
LOUGH AVAUL (LOWER) (FH3006)				●																																	
LOUGH AVAUL (UPPER) (FH3007)				●																																	
LOUGH BOFINNE (FH3013)				●																																	
MANCH HOUSE FISHERY (FH3154)									●	●	●																	●						●	●	●	●
SHEPPERTON LAKES (FH4231)				●																																	
COUNTY DONEGAL																																					
ASSAROE LAKE (FH0174)				●	●	●	●																				●	●	●	●	●	●		●	●	●	
CLOGHAN LODGE ESTATE FISHERY (FH1016)		●	●		●			●	●		●	●	●	●	●			●	●		●				●	●	●	●		●		●	●	●	●		●
FINN (RIVER) (FH1715)		●	●		●			●	●		●	●	●	●	●			●	●		●				●	●	●	●		●		●	●	●	●		●
GLENMORE FISHERY (FH1893)								●										●									●	●			●						
LOUGH BEAGH (FH3011)				●																																	
ROSSES FISHERY (FH4017)		●	●	●		●	●	●	●	●	●	●	●	●	●		●	●	●	●	●	●	●	●	●			●	●		●	●	●	●	●	●	●
COUNTY GALWAY																																					
CASTLEREAGH LOUGHS (FH0869)																													●								
CLARE LOUGH (FH0974)																													●								
DOOHULLA (FH1408)				●					●																							●			●	●	
ERRIFF FISHERY (FH1615)				●																																	
KYLEMORE HOUSE FISHERY (FH2546)				●										●	●				●				●														
LOUGH BALLYLUIRKE (FH3008)																		●											●								
LOUGH COOLIN (FH3019)		●		●		●	●	●	●					●	●	●	●	●				●	●	●	●		●	●			●	●		●	●	●	

Fishing Facilities and Amenities

	Net Dips	Tackle Hire	Site Tackle Shop	Boats Available	Bait Sold	Adult Matches	Junior Matches	Half Day Fishing	Night Fishing	Tuition Given	Accommodation	Camping	Caravan Site	Male Toilets	Female Toilets	Disabled Toilets	Disabled Facilities	Hardcore Parking	Public Telephone	Showers	Washing Facilities	Restaurant	Hot Meals	Cafe	Refreshments	Day Lodge Available	Solid Based Swims	Easy Access Swims	Disabled Access Swims	Grass Swims	Tree Sheltered	Dogs Allowed	Fulltime Security	Rare Birdlife	Rare Wildlife	Spectators Allowed	Kids with Adults
LOUGH CORRIB (FH3021)		●		●	●				●					●	●		●	●	●			●	●		●		●	●	●	●				●	●	●	
LOUGH HEMUSHMACONRY (FH3034)																															●						
LOUGH MASK (FH3041)		●		●		●	●	●	●					●	●	●	●	●				●	●	●	●		●	●			●	●		●	●	●	
LOUGH PARKYFLAHERTY (FH3051)																															●						
LOUGH POLLALHY (FH3052)																															●						
ROSS LAKE (FH4016)				●																									●		●						
SUMMERVILLE LOUGH (FH4555)																													●								
COUNTY KERRY																																					
KERRYFISHERIES (FH2474)				●																																	
LAKE HOUSE HOTEL (FH2560)				●										●	●								●		●												
LAKES OF KILLARNEY (FH2579)		●												●	●	●	●	●					●	●												●	
LOUGH BARFINNIHY (FH3010)				●																								●									
LOUGH CAUM (FH3016)				●																																	
LOUGH FADDA (FH3030)				●																																	
COUNTY KILDARE																																					
GREESE (RIVER) (FH2012)									●													●	●								●	●				●	
COUNTY KILKENNY																																					
NORE (RIVER) (FH3518)									●					●	●	●	●	●	●			●	●	●	●						●	●		●	●	●	
COUNTY LAOIS																																					
BARROW (RIVER) (FH0327)						●	●	●	●									●	●						●			●		●	●			●	●	●	
GRANSTOWN LAKE (FH1972)						●	●	●	●		●	●					●	●									●	●	●		●			●	●		●
COUNTY LEITRIM																																					
LOUGH ALLEN (FH3001)					●	●								●	●	●	●			●	●														●		●
LOUGH MELVIN (FH3043)				●	●													●																			
COUNTY LIMERICK																																					
CASTLECONNELL SALMON FISHERY (FH0867)		●		●	●													●				●	●		●		●	●		●	●	●		●	●	●	
COUNTY LOUTH																																					
BALLYMASCANLON (RIVER) (FH0277)									●																			●								●	
CASTLETON (RIVER) (FH0871)									●																			●								●	
FANE (RIVER) (FH1661)									●																			●								●	
COUNTY MAYO																																					
BROHLY (LOUGH) (FH0673)				●																																	
CASTLEBAR LAKES (FH0866)				●																																	
CLOONGEE FISHERY (FH1021)										●				●	●		●		●		●										●		●	●	●	●	●
LOUGH CORRIB (UPPER) (FH3022)		●	●	●	●	●	●	●	●	●	●	●	●	●	●		●	●	●	●	●	●	●	●	●			●	●	●	●	●	●	●	●	●	

Fishing Facilities and Amenities

Facility	LOUGHS COY CULLIN (FH3061)	MOUNT FALCON SALMON FISHERY (FH3385)	MOY (RIVER) (FH3393)	MOY FISHERY (FH3394)	MUCK (LOUGH) (FH3396)	TALT (LOUGH) (FH4637)	COUNTY MEATH	RATHBEGGAN LAKES (FH3890)	COUNTY OFFALY	EDENDERRY OFFALY EIRE (FH1544)	GRAND CANAL (FH1940)	COUNTY ROSCOMMON	LOUGH ARROW (FH3003)	LOUGH GARA (FH3032)	LUNG RIVER (FH3113)	COUNTY SLIGO	LAKE NA LEIBE (FH2564)	COUNTY TIPPERARY	ARA (RIVER) (FH0125)	CLONANAU FLY FISHING CENTRE (FH1018)	DERG (LOUGH) (FH1336)	NORE (RIVER) (FH3523)	WHITE HORSE (RIVER) (FH5332)	COUNTY WATERFORD	BLACKWATER LODGE (FH0481)	KNOCKDERRY (FH2540)	COUNTY WESTMEATH	DOOLIN POND (FH1409)	GALMOYLESTOWN LAKE (FH1831)
Kids with Adults														●	●														
Spectators Allowed		●								●			●								●				●				
Rare Wildlife				●										●	●					●					●				
Rare Birdlife				●										●	●					●	●	●	●		●				
Fulltime Security											●																		
Dogs Allowed										●	●		●																
Tree Sheltered										●	●			●	●					●	●	●	●		●				
Grass Swims											●			●	●						●				●				
Disabled Access Swims										●	●			●	●										●				●
Easy Access Swims		●								●	●			●	●					●					●			●	●
Solid Based Swims										●	●														●				
Day Lodge Available																													
Refreshments				●						●	●			●	●					●	●	●	●		●				
Cafe				●						●				●	●										●				
Hot Meals				●						●	●			●	●					●	●	●	●		●				
Restaurant				●						●	●			●	●							●	●		●				
Washing Facilities																													
Showers																													
Public Telephone				●						●	●			●	●							●	●		●				
Hardcore Parking		●								●	●		●	●	●				●						●				
Disabled Facilities				●						●				●	●										●				
Disabled Toilets				●																					●				
Female Toilets				●				●												●		●	●		●				
Male Toilets				●				●												●		●	●		●				
Caravan Site														●	●														
Camping														●	●														
Accommodation											●			●	●														
Tuition Given								●						●	●														
Night Fishing										●	●		●						●	●		●	●		●				
Half Day Fishing						●							●							●									
Junior Matches										●	●		●	●	●							●	●						
Adult Matches										●	●		●	●	●							●	●						
Bait Sold	●	●	●	●						●	●														●				
Boats Available	●	●	●		●								●				●				●					●			
Site Tackle Shop																													
Tackle Hire	●	●	●								●		●							●		●	●		●				
Net Dips																													

Fishing Facilities and Amenities

	Net Dips	Tackle Hire	Site Tackle Shop	Boats Available	Bait Sold	Adult Matches	Junior Matches	Half Day Fishing	Night Fishing	Tuition Given	Accommodation	Camping	Caravan Site	Male Toilets	Female Toilets	Disabled Toilets	Disabled Facilities	Hardcore Parking	Public Telephone	Showers	Washing Facilities	Restaurant	Hot Meals	Cafe	Refreshments	Day Lodge Available	Solid Based Swims	Easy Access Swims	Disabled Access Swims	Grass Swims	Tree Sheltered	Dogs Allowed	Fulltime Security	Rare Birdlife	Rare Wildlife	Spectators Allowed	Kids with Adults
NORTHERN IRELAND																																					
COUNTY ANTRIM																																					
BUSH (RIVER) (FH0767)								●									●	●	●									●	●		●						
SPRINGWATER MEADOW (FH4376)		●						●	●					●	●			●	●						●		●	●	●	●	●	●		●	●	●	
STRAID FISHERY (FH4516)		●		●				●		●				●	●			●	●					●	●		●	●	●		●	●	●	●	●	●	
WOODFORD FISHERY (FH5474)		●		●	●									●	●		●		●				●	●	●						●						
COUNTY ARMAGH																																					
LOUGHGALL COARSE FISHERY (FH3056)		●	●		●	●					●			●	●	●	●	●	●	●	●				●	●	●	●	●		●	●		●	●	●	
LOWRYS LAKE (FH3097)																		●										●				●		●	●		●
SEAGAHAN RESERVOIR DAM (FH4125)				●														●										●									●
SHAWS LAKE (FH4215)																		●										●									●
TULLNAWOOD LAKE (FH4966)				●																																	
COUNTY DOWN																																					
BALLY GRANGE FISHERY (FH0273)														●	●								●		●												
CLANRYE (RIVER) (FH0972)									●	●																	●			●			●	●	●		●
INLER (RIVER) (FH2368)										●																											
MCCOURTS LAKE (FH3220)						●	●			●								●															●				
MILL LODGE FISHERY (FH3293)		●							●	●	●							●									●										
RINGDUFFERIN ESTUARY (FH3951)		●	●					●		●				●	●	●	●	●	●		●				●		●	●	●	●	●			●	●		●
COUNTY FERMANAGH																																					
COLEBROOKE PARK (FH1060)		●			●					●													●		●												
COOLYERMER LOUGH FISHERY (FH1103)		●	●	●		●	●	●	●	●				●	●		●	●								●		●	●			●	●	●	●	●	●
KNOCKBRACKEN TROUT LAKES (FH2539)														●	●	●													●								
LOUGH MELVIN (FH3042)		●	●	●	●			●		●	●	●	●	●	●	●	●	●	●	●	●	●	●	●	●			●	●	●		●	●	●	●	●	●
MILL LOUGH BELLANALECK (FH3294)				●																																	
COUNTY LONDONDERRY																																					
CREGGAN RESERVOIRS (FH1178)		●		●	●			●	●					●	●			●	●						●			●	●			●				●	
FAUGHAN (RIVER) (FH1678)									●																								●	●	●		
FAUGHAN (RIVER) (FH1679)									●									●										●	●	●	●			●	●		
MOORBROOK LODGE (FH3359)		●						●			●	●		●	●			●			●		●		●	●		●			●	●	●	●	●	●	●
MOYOLA (RIVER) (FH3395)		●			●			●	●	●	●	●	●				●	●	●			●	●	●	●	●	●	●			●		●	●	●	●	●
TURNAFACE TROUT FISHERY (FH4979)				●										●	●								●		●												
COUNTY TYRONE																																					
ALTMORE FISHERIES (FH0086)					●									●	●	●	●						●		●				●								
ANNAGINNY STILL WATER FISHERY (FH0112)	●	●	●		●	●	●	●		●		●	●	●	●	●	●	●	●	●	●			●	●	●	●	●	●	●	●	●	●	●	●	●	

Fishing Facilities and Amenities

	BARONSCOURT LAKES (FH0323)	BRANTRY LOUGH (FH0602)	CAMOWEN (RIVER) (FH0815)	DRUMRAGH (RIVER) (FH1453)	DUNGANNON PARK FISHERY (FH1475)	FINN (RIVER) (FH1716)	LOUGHMORE (FH3057)	OWENKILLEW (RIVER) (FH3662)	PARK LAKE TROUT FISHERY (FH3699)	ROUND LAKE (FH4036)	STRULE (RIVER) (FH4530)	WHITE LOUGH (FH5340)
Kids with Adults						●						
Spectators Allowed			●	●		●		●			●	
Rare Wildlife	●		●	●	●	●		●			●	
Rare Birdlife	●		●	●	●	●		●			●	
Fulltime Security			●	●		●		●			●	
Dogs Allowed												
Tree Sheltered					●							
Grass Swims			●	●	●	●		●			●	
Disabled Access Swims			●	●	●	●		●	●		●	
Easy Access Swims			●	●	●	●		●			●	
Solid Based Swims			●	●		●		●		●	●	
Day Lodge Available												
Refreshments	●				●							
Cafe												
Hot Meals												
Restaurant												
Washing Facilities												
Showers												
Public Telephone												
Hardcore Parking		●	●	●		●		●	●	●	●	
Disabled Facilities			●	●	●			●	●		●	
Disabled Toilets					●					●		
Female Toilets					●				●	●		
Male Toilets					●				●	●		
Caravan Site												
Camping												
Accommodation												
Tuition Given			●	●		●		●			●	
Night Fishing			●	●		●		●			●	
Half Day Fishing					●	●						
Junior Matches					●							
Adult Matches					●	●						
Bait Sold			●	●	●			●			●	
Boats Available	●	●			●		●		●			●
Site Tackle Shop			●	●				●		●	●	
Tackle Hire					●							
Net Dips												

Fishing Facilities and Amenities

	Net Dips	Tackle Hire	Site Tackle Shop	Boats Available	Bait Sold	Adult Matches	Junior Matches	Half Day Fishing	Night Fishing	Tuition Given	Accommodation	Camping	Caravan Site	Male Toilets	Female Toilets	Disabled Toilets	Disabled Facilities	Hardcore Parking	Public Telephone	Showers	Washing Facilities	Restaurant	Hot Meals	Cafe	Refreshments	Day Lodge Available	Solid Based Swims	Easy Access Swims	Disabled Access Swims	Grass Swims	Tree Sheltered	Dogs Allowed	Fulltime Security	Rare Birdlife	Rare Wildlife	Spectators Allowed	Kids with Adults
SCOTLAND																																					
ABERDEENSHIRE																																					
BOGNIE & MOUNTBLAIRY FISHING (FH0525)									●									●													●	●		●	●	●	
LOCH INSCH FISHERY (FH2894)		●	●		●	●	●	●		●		●	●	●	●	●	●	●							●	●		●	●		●	●	●	●		●	
MILL OF ELRICK FISHERY (FH3296)		●	●		●			●		●				●	●	●	●	●							●	●		●	●	●			●	●	●	●	●
TULLICH FISHERY (FH4965)														●	●																						
YTHAN FISHERY (FH5575)																																		●	●	●	
YTHAN VALLEY FISHERY (FH5576)		●				●				●				●				●							●							●		●		●	
ANGUS																																					
CLATIO LOCH (FH0978)						●																															
DEAN (RIVER) (FH1285)																												●									
ISLA (RIVER) (FH2387)																												●									
KINGENNIE FISHINGS (FH2494)	●	●	●		●	●		●		●	●			●	●	●	●	●	●	●			●		●	●		●	●		●	●	●	●	●	●	
MILL OF CRIGGIE TROUT FISHERY (FH3295)		●				●		●	●					●	●			●							●			●	●							●	
PIPERDAM (FH3784)		●		●	●			●		●				●	●	●	●	●	●			●	●	●	●							●		●	●	●	
ARGYLL AND BUTE																																					
CLYDE ESTUARY (FH1040)									●																												
FINNART (RIVER) (FH1718)				●																																	
FRUIN (RIVER) (FH1817)									●																												
INVERAWE FISHERIES (FH2374)		●				●	●	●		●				●	●	●	●	●	●				●	●	●						●	●		●	●	●	
LOCH AVICH (FH2847)		●		●					●	●	●	●						●	●													●	●	●	●	●	
LOCH AWE (FH2848)		●		●					●	●	●	●						●	●													●	●	●	●	●	
LOCH FAD (FH2879)		●		●	●	●	●	●		●				●	●	●		●	●		●				●		●	●		●	●	●	●	●	●	●	
LOCH QUIEN (FH2936)				●		●	●											●									●	●		●			●	●	●	●	
LOCH TARSAN (FH2948)				●																																	
MILL HOUSE FISHERIES (FH3286)																		●									●	●		●							
AYRSHIRE (EAST)																																					
COWANS LAW TROUT FISHERY (FH1150)				●						●				●	●								●		●												
AYRSHIRE (NORTH)																																					
CAMPHILL RESERVOIR (FH0816)				●														●																			
MIDDLETON FISHERY (FH3268)		●						●						●	●			●	●				●	●	●			●	●		●			●		●	
PORT-NA-LOCHAN (FH3829)		●	●		●			●	●	●	●			●	●	●	●	●	●		●				●	●		●	●		●		●		●		●
AYRSHIRE (SOUTH)																																					
CRAITH RESERVOIR (FH1162)																		●																		●	
DOON (RIVER) (FH1410)											●			●	●			●									●	●		●	●		●	●	●		●

Fishing Facilities and Amenities

	Net Dips	Tackle Hire	Site Tackle Shop	Boats Available	Bait Sold	Adult Matches	Junior Matches	Half Day Fishing	Night Fishing	Tuition Given	Accommodation	Camping	Caravan Site	Male Toilets	Female Toilets	Disabled Toilets	Disabled Facilities	Hardcore Parking	Public Telephone	Showers	Washing Facilities	Restaurant	Hot Meals	Cafe	Refreshments	Day Lodge Available	Solid Based Swims	Easy Access Swims	Disabled Access Swims	Grass Swims	Tree Sheltered	Dogs Allowed	Fulltime Security	Rare Birdlife	Rare Wildlife	Spectators Allowed	Kids with Adults
LOCH DORNAL (FH2872)				●																																	
LOCH MAYBERRY (FH2911)				●																																	
SPRINGWATER FISHERY (FH4374)		●			●	●	●	●	●	●				●	●	●	●	●	●		●		●	●	●	●	●	●	●	●			●	●	●	●	●
STINCHAR (RIVER) (FH4457)											●																					●					
CLACKMANNANSHIRE																																					
EASTER BALADO (KINROSS) (FH1519)				●						●				●	●								●		●												
DUMFRIES AND GALLOWAY																																					
ANNAN (RIVER) (FH0113)		●	●		●				●	●	●	●		●	●	●		●	●		●	●	●		●			●		●	●	●		●	●	●	●
BARSCOBE LOCH (FH0333)																														●							
BROOM FISHERIES (FH0689)		●	●			●	●			●		●		●	●			●							●		●	●	●		●	●	●	●	●		●
BUITTLE RESERVOIR (FH0723)				●		●	●	●				●	●															●					●	●	●	●	●
CLATTERINGSHAWS LOCH (FH0980)														●				●														●				●	
CRAIGHLAW (FH1159)					●				●		●	●					●	●									●	●	●			●		●		●	●
DORMONT LAKE COARSE FISHERY (FH1415)						●	●			●						●	●	●									●	●	●					●	●	●	
DUNSKEY LOCHS (FH1480)				●																																	
EARLSTOUN LOCH (FH1502)				●										●	●	●			●			●			●					●							
ESK (RIVER) (FH1620)									●																												
GALLOWAY FOREST PARK (FH1829)									●																					●	●			●	●	●	
GLENDARROCH LOCH (FH1887)																		●																			
HODDOM WATER (FH2244)									●					●	●			●									●	●			●	●				●	
KELHEAD WATER (FH2425)														●	●			●										●			●	●				●	
KEN (RIVER) (FH2429)																											●			●							
KINMOUNT LAKE (FH2520)																																		●	●		
KIRKCHRIST (FH2526)				●																																	
KIRKWOOD WATER (FH2527)									●									●										●			●	●		●	●		
KIRRIEREOCH LOCH (FH2528)																																		●	●	●	
KNOCKQUASSEN RESERVOIR (FH2541)									●									●																			●
LOCH ROAN (FH2939)				●																																	
LOCH WHINYEON (FH2958)				●						●								●													●			●	●		●
LOCHENBRECK LOCH (FH2964)				●						●								●													●			●	●		●
MAINS OF PENNINGHAM FISHERY (FH3148)				●						●																											
MOFFAT FISHERIES (FH3336)		●			●									●	●								●		●												
MORTON LOCH (FH3375)				●														●										●		●	●			●	●	●	
MORTON POND (FH3376)																		●										●		●	●			●	●	●	
NEW ABBEY DOW (FH3460)									●		●																	●		●	●	●		●	●	●	●

Fishing Facilities and Amenities

Fishery	Kids with Adults	Spectators Allowed	Rare Wildlife	Rare Birdlife	Fulltime Security	Dogs Allowed	Tree Sheltered	Grass Swims	Disabled Access Swims	Easy Access Swims	Solid Based Swims	Day Lodge Available	Refreshments	Cafe	Hot Meals	Restaurant	Washing Facilities	Showers	Public Telephone	Hardcore Parking	Disabled Facilities	Disabled Toilets	Female Toilets	Male Toilets	Caravan Site	Camping	Accommodation	Tuition Given	Night Fishing	Half Day Fishing	Junior Matches	Adult Matches	Bait Sold	Boats Available	Site Tackle Shop	Tackle Hire	Net Dips
NEWTON LOCHAN (FH3495)		●					●	●		●																			●								
NITH (RIVER) (FH3512)		●	●	●			●	●		●	●																										
OCHILTREE LOCH (FH3573)																																		●			
PURDOMSTONE RESERVOIR (FH3857)						●														●																	
SLATEHOUSE LOCH (FH4295)		●	●	●			●	●		●										●														●			
STARBURN LOCH (FH4430)		●	●	●			●	●		●										●														●			
TONGUE OF BOMBIE LOCHAN (FH4873)																				●																	
TORHOUSEKIE AND KIRWAUGH (FH4879)			●	●																								●						●			
URR (RIVER) (FH5076)	●		●	●	●																								●				●				
WEE GLEN AMOUR LOCH (FH5223)									●																												
FALKIRK																																					
C.SCOTLAND TROUT FISHERY (FH0889)													●		●							●	●														
LOCH FINLAS (FH2882)																																		●			
LOCH VENACHAR (FH2955)																																		●			
FIFE																																					
CRAIGLUSCAR RESERVOIR (FH1160)		●					●												●	●														●			
KINGHORN LOCH (FH2503)									●																												
LOCH FITTY TROUT FISHERY (FH2883)	●	●	●	●	●	●	●		●	●		●	●	●	●	●	●		●	●	●		●	●	●	●	●	●	●	●		●	●	●	●	●	
LOCH ORE (FH2934)			●	●																																	
NEWTON FARM FISHERY (FH3494)		●				●	●		●	●			●							●			●	●					●	●						●	
RAITH LAKE FISHERY (FH3882)	●	●	●	●	●	●	●	●	●	●	●	●	●	●	●	●	●		●	●	●		●	●			●	●	●	●	●	●		●	●	●	
GLASGOW (CITY OF)																																					
NEILSTON TROUT FISHERY (FH3438)		●	●	●					●	●			●	●					●	●	●		●	●					●	●				●			
HIGHLAND																																					
CONON (RIVER) (FH1089)	●	●	●	●		●			●	●										●	●				●	●	●	●		●	●	●			●	●	
GARRY UPPER (RIVER) (FH1839)		●	●	●		●									●	●			●				●	●										●			
GLASS (RIVER) (FH1873)		●	●	●		●	●			●						●			●	●									●	●						●	
GLENCOE LOCHAN (FH1886)		●	●	●	●	●	●		●	●										●	●													●			
LOCH BORRALAN (FH2858)		●	●	●		●			●	●			●		●	●			●	●	●	●	●	●						●	●	●		●			
LOCH GARRY (FH2885)		●	●	●		●									●	●			●				●	●										●			
LOCH INCH LAGGAN (FH2893)		●	●	●		●									●	●			●				●	●										●			
LOCH INSH (FH2895)	●	●	●	●	●		●		●	●	●		●	●	●	●	●	●	●	●	●	●	●	●			●	●		●					●	●	
LOCH POULARY (FH2935)		●	●	●		●									●	●			●				●	●										●			
LOCH QUOICH (FH2937)		●	●	●		●									●	●			●				●	●										●			
LOCH SHIN (FH2945)																																		●			

Fishing Facilities and Amenities

Facility	LOCH TOFTINGALL (FH2953)	LOCH USSIE (FH2954)	LOCH WATTEN (FH2957)	NAIRN (RIVER) (FH3412)	NESS (RIVER) (FH3450)	SCOURIE HOTEL (FH4120)	SPEY (RIVER) (FH4364)	ST JOHNS LOCH (FH4390)	STONEYFIELD LOCH (FH4475)	STRATHMANAIRD LOCHS (FH4520)	TARVIE LOCHS FISHERY (FH4661)	INVERCLYDE	ARDGOWAN TROUT FISHERY (FH0128)	PINEWOOD TROUT FISHERY (FH3780)	LANARKSHIRE (NORTH)	CLYDE (RIVER) (FH1039)	HILLEND LOCH (FH2226)
Kids with Adults					●		●						●				●
Spectators Allowed		●		●	●		●			●	●		●			●	●
Rare Wildlife	●	●	●			●	●	●			●					●	●
Rare Birdlife	●	●	●			●	●	●		●	●					●	●
Fulltime Security					●		●						●				●
Dogs Allowed	●	●	●	●	●	●				●	●						
Tree Sheltered		●					●		●		●						●
Grass Swims																●	●
Disabled Access Swims		●			●		●		●				●				●
Easy Access Swims		●			●		●		●				●				●
Solid Based Swims					●		●						●				●
Day Lodge Available													●				
Refreshments					●	●	●						●				●
Cafe					●		●						●				
Hot Meals					●	●	●										●
Restaurant					●	●	●										●
Washing Facilities					●		●				●						
Showers							●										
Public Telephone					●	●	●		●					●			●
Hardcore Parking	●	●	●		●		●	●	●		●		●				●
Disabled Facilities		●			●		●	●					●				●
Disabled Toilets					●		●		●				●				
Female Toilets					●	●	●		●		●		●	●			
Male Toilets					●	●	●		●		●		●	●			
Caravan Site		●			●												
Camping		●			●												
Accommodation		●			●		●										
Tuition Given		●					●				●		●				●
Night Fishing				●												●	
Half Day Fishing	●	●	●				●	●	●		●		●			●	
Junior Matches		●															●
Adult Matches		●							●								●
Bait Sold				●					●		●		●				
Boats Available	●		●			●	●	●			●		●				●
Site Tackle Shop		●					●						●				
Tackle Hire	●	●	●			●	●	●	●		●		●				
Net Dips																	●

Facility	LILY LOCH (FH2722)	MONKLAND CANAL (FH3344)	LANARKSHIRE (SOUTH)	TALLA RESERVOIR (FH4635)	TINTO TROUT FISHERIES (FH4856)	LOTHIAN (EAST)	MARKLE FISHERIES (FH3186)	TYNE (RIVER) (FH5018)	LOTHIAN (MID)	LOGANLEA TROUT FISHERY (FH2980)	LOTHIAN (WEST)	ALLANDALE TARN (FH0076)	HOPETOUN FISHERY (FH2291)	LINLITHGOW LOCH (FH2736)	PARKLEY FISHERY (FH3705)	SELM MUIR FISHERY (FH4135)	UNION CANAL (FH5046)
Kids with Adults					●									●			
Spectators Allowed	●	●					●			●		●	●	●		●	
Rare Wildlife	●				●		●			●			●	●	●	●	
Rare Birdlife	●				●		●			●			●		●	●	
Fulltime Security					●												
Dogs Allowed	●	●					●			●							
Tree Sheltered	●											●	●			●	
Grass Swims		●					●									●	
Disabled Access Swims		●					●					●	●	●		●	●
Easy Access Swims		●			●		●					●	●			●	
Solid Based Swims		●					●					●	●				
Day Lodge Available														●			
Refreshments					●		●			●		●	●		●	●	
Cafe										●		●				●	
Hot Meals												●					
Restaurant																	
Washing Facilities					●									●			
Showers																	
Public Telephone	●									●		●		●			
Hardcore Parking	●	●			●		●					●	●	●		●	
Disabled Facilities												●		●			
Disabled Toilets							●					●		●			
Female Toilets					●		●			●		●	●	●			
Male Toilets					●		●			●		●	●	●		●	
Caravan Site																	
Camping		●															
Accommodation					●												
Tuition Given					●					●							
Night Fishing	●	●					●	●		●		●	●		●	●	●
Half Day Fishing		●		●			●					●				●	
Junior Matches							●			●		●				●	
Adult Matches							●			●		●	●			●	
Bait Sold							●					●	●		●	●	
Boats Available	●			●						●				●			
Site Tackle Shop																	
Tackle Hire							●			●		●	●			●	
Net Dips																	

Fishing Facilities and Amenities

	Net Dips	Tackle Hire	Site Tackle Shop	Boats Available	Bait Sold	Adult Matches	Junior Matches	Half Day Fishing	Night Fishing	Tuition Given	Accommodation	Camping	Caravan Site	Male Toilets	Female Toilets	Disabled Toilets	Disabled Facilities	Hardcore Parking	Public Telephone	Showers	Washing Facilities	Restaurant	Hot Meals	Cafe	Refreshments	Day Lodge Available	Solid Based Swims	Easy Access Swims	Disabled Access Swims	Grass Swims	Tree Sheltered	Dogs Allowed	Fulltime Security	Rare Birdlife	Rare Wildlife	Spectators Allowed	Kids with Adults
MORAY																																					
BROOM OF MOY (FH0690)																																		●			
GLEN OF ROTHES TROUT FISHERY (FH1883)		●			●	●		●		●				●	●	●	●	●			●			●	●	●		●	●	●			●	●	●	●	●
PERTH AND KINROSS																																					
ABERFELDY ASSOCIATION BEAT (FH0014)									●																												
BOLFRACKS BEAT (FH0533)				●																											●						
BRAAN (RIVER) (FH0584)																											●					●	●	●	●	●	
CASTLE MENZIES BEAT (FH0863)									●																												
GLENFARG FISHERY (FH1889)		●			●	●	●	●	●					●	●	●	●	●	●				●	●	●			●	●					●	●	●	
HEATHERYFORD FISHERY (FH2174)		●				●		●		●	●			●	●	●	●	●	●		●	●	●		●			●	●						●	●	
KENMORE BEAT (FH2431)										●																			●		●						
LOCH BHAC (FH2857)				●																																	
LOCH EIGHEACH (FH2876)								●										●															●				●
LOCH FASKALLY (FH2881)				●																																	
LOCH LEVEN FISHERIES (FH2902)		●		●		●	●	●	●					●	●			●	●					●	●						●	●		●	●	●	
LOCH TAY (FH2950)				●				●			●																				●			●	●	●	
LOWER ABERUTHVEN FISHINGS (FH3070)								●	●																			●	●								
MONTAGUE RESERVOIR (FH3353)				●		●				●								●										●		●			●	●	●		●
ORCHILL LOCH TROUT FISHERY (FH3619)														●	●																						
PITLOCHRY BOATING STATION (FH3792)		●		●	●			●						●	●	●	●	●						●							●					●	
SANDYKNOWES FISHING (FH4099)		●				●	●	●						●	●	●	●	●						●	●		●	●	●		●	●		●	●	●	
SEAMAW LOCH (FH4126)				●		●				●								●										●		●			●	●	●		●
TAY (RIVER) (FH4678)						●	●																				●					●	●	●	●	●	
TOMBUIE BEAT (FH4868)									●																												
UPPER BORLICK BEAT (FH5051)									●																												
WEEM BEAT (FH5226)									●																												
RENFREWSHIRE																																					
CARN LOCH (FH0844)				●				●	●																							●		●	●	●	
CLACHAIG (LOCH) (FH0967)				●				●	●																							●		●	●	●	
COILLE BHAR (LOCH) (FH1055)				●				●	●																							●		●	●	●	
GLEAN LOCH (FH1875)				●				●	●																							●		●	●	●	
HOWWOOD TROUT FISHERY (FH2321)		●	●	●	●	●	●	●	●	●				●	●		●	●	●				●	●	●	●	●	●	●	●			●	●	●	●	
LEIPEIG (LOCH) (FH2694)				●				●	●																							●		●	●	●	
LOCH BARNLUASGAN (FH2853)				●				●	●																							●		●	●	●	
LOCH DHU (FH2870)				●				●	●																							●		●	●	●	

Fishing Facilities and Amenities

	Net Dips	Tackle Hire	Site Tackle Shop	Boats Available	Bait Sold	Adult Matches	Junior Matches	Half Day Fishing	Night Fishing	Tuition Given	Accommodation	Camping	Caravan Site	Male Toilets	Female Toilets	Disabled Toilets	Disabled Facilities	Hardcore Parking	Public Telephone	Showers	Washing Facilities	Restaurant	Hot Meals	Cafe	Refreshments	Day Lodge Available	Solid Based Swims	Easy Access Swims	Disabled Access Swims	Grass Swims	Tree Sheltered	Dogs Allowed	Fulltime Security	Rare Birdlife	Rare Wildlife	Spectators Allowed	Kids with Adults
LOCH-AN-ADD (FH2961)				●				●	●																							●		●	●	●	
LOCH-NA-BRIC (FH2967)				●				●	●																							●		●	●	●	
LOCH-NA-FAOILINN (FH2968)				●				●	●																							●		●	●	●	
MAICH WATERS (FH3140)			●	●				●		●				●	●	●	●	●	●		●			●	●		●	●	●		●		●	●		●	●
NEW LOCH (FH3471)				●				●	●																							●		●	●	●	
SCOTTISH BORDERS																																					
ACREKNOWE RESERVOIR (FH0024)				●																								●		●						●	
AKERMOOR LOCH (FH0049)				●																																●	
ALEMOOR RESERVOIR (FH0070)									●																					●				●	●	●	
BUCCLEUCH ESTATES (FH0715)				●																												●					
CLERKLAND FLY FISHERY (FH1003)		●		●		●								●	●														●								
COLDINGHAM LOCH (FH1057)				●										●	●								●		●												
ETTRICK AND YARROW (RIVER) (FH1632)																																●					
HEADSHAW FISHERY (FH2166)				●										●	●								●		●												
HELLMOOR LOCH (FH2178)									●																									●	●	●	
KAILZIE GARDENS FISHERY (FH2419)														●	●								●		●						●						
LINDEAN RESERVOIR (FH2727)				●				●																													
MACBIEHILL ESTATE (FH3127)		●		●				●	●	●				●		●	●	●			●	●	●		●	●		●	●					●	●		●
MEGGET RESERVOIR (FH3241)				●																					●												
ST MARYS LOCH (FH4393)				●																																	
TEVIOT (RIVER) (FH4750)																																●					
TWEED (RIVER) (FH4997)				●																																	
TWEED (RIVER) (FH4998)				●																																	
TWEED (RIVER) (FH4995)				●																																	
TWEED (RIVER) (FH4996)				●																											●						
WATCH RESERVOIR (FH5168)		●		●		●	●	●	●	●				●	●	●	●	●	●			●	●	●	●		●	●	●	●	●			●	●	●	
WEST WATER RESERVOIR (FH5269)				●										●	●																						
WULLIESTRUTHER LOCH (FH5522)									●																			●		●						●	
STIRLING																																					
BALVAIG (RIVER) (FH0280)				●																																	
BARNCROFT (FH0315)									●																												
DOCHART (RIVER) (FH1382)		●		●	●									●	●	●	●	●	●			●	●	●	●									●	●	●	
DOCHART (RIVER) (FH1385)								●	●																												
ENDRICK (RIVER) (FH1592)									●																												
KILLEARN HOUSE FISHERY (FH2482)		●			●			●						●				●						●	●		●	●	●		●	●		●	●	●	

Fishing Facilities and Amenities

	KILLIN BREADALBANE AC WATERS (FH2483)	LAKE OF MENTEITH FISHERIES (FH2566)	LOCH LOMOND (FH2904)	LOCH TAY HIGHLAND LODGES (FH2951)	LOCH VOIL (FH2956)	LOCHAN NA LARAIG (FH2960)	LOCHAY (RIVER) (FH2963)	NORTH THIRD TROUT FISHERY (FH3534)	PORTNELLAN (FH3830)	SUIE (FH4534)	SWANSWATER FISHERY (FH4600)	WESTERN ISLES	CEANN-AN-ORA FISHERY (FH0878)	GRIMERSTA LODGE (FH2019)	LACASDALE LOCHS (FH2548)	OBBE FISHINGS (FH3571)	SOVAL ESTATE (FH4353)	YORKSHIRE (SOUTH)	BANK END COARSE FISHERIES (FH0285)	HAYFIELD LAKES (FH2155)	LINDHOLME FISHERIES (1) (FH2729)	LINDHOLME FISHERIES (2) (FH2730)	LINDHOLME FISHERIES (3) (FH2731)	LINDHOLME FISHERIES 4) (FH2732)
Kids with Adults					●																●	●	●	●
Spectators Allowed	●		●	●		●	●								●	●				●				
Rare Wildlife	●	●	●	●	●	●	●	●	●						●	●	●				●	●	●	●
Rare Birdlife	●	●	●	●	●	●	●	●	●		●					●	●				●	●	●	●
Fulltime Security					●						●										●	●	●	●
Dogs Allowed		●	●	●											●	●	●							
Tree Sheltered	●	●	●																				●	
Grass Swims			●						●											●	●	●	●	●
Disabled Access Swims					●						●				●	●				●	●	●	●	●
Easy Access Swims					●				●		●		●			●				●	●	●	●	●
Solid Based Swims			●								●									●	●	●	●	●
Day Lodge Available					●						●													
Refreshments	●		●			●	●		●							●			●	●				
Cafe	●		●			●	●				●					●				●				
Hot Meals	●		●			●	●		●							●				●				
Restaurant	●		●			●	●									●				●				
Washing Facilities					●																●	●	●	●
Showers																								
Public Telephone	●		●	●		●	●		●							●				●				
Hardcore Parking	●	●	●	●	●	●	●	●	●		●				●	●	●		●		●	●	●	●
Disabled Facilities	●	●	●	●		●	●				●								●	●	●	●	●	●
Disabled Toilets	●	●	●	●		●	●				●									●				
Female Toilets	●	●	●	●	●	●	●	●	●		●			●					●	●	●	●	●	●
Male Toilets	●	●	●	●	●	●	●	●	●		●			●					●	●	●	●	●	●
Caravan Site					●																			
Camping					●																			
Accommodation					●																			
Tuition Given					●						●									●	●	●	●	●
Night Fishing			●							●			●		●	●				●				
Half Day Fishing		●	●	●	●						●		●		●						●	●	●	●
Junior Matches			●																	●	●	●	●	●
Adult Matches		●	●					●												●	●	●	●	●
Bait Sold	●		●			●	●																	
Boats Available	●	●		●	●	●	●	●	●		●			●	●	●	●							
Site Tackle Shop																							●	
Tackle Hire	●	●	●	●	●	●	●		●		●				●								●	
Net Dips																					●	●	●	●

Fishing Facilities and Amenities

	Net Dips	Tackle Hire	Site Tackle Shop	Boats Available	Bait Sold	Adult Matches	Junior Matches	Half Day Fishing	Night Fishing	Tuition Given	Accommodation	Camping	Caravan Site	Male Toilets	Female Toilets	Disabled Toilets	Disabled Facilities	Hardcore Parking	Public Telephone	Showers	Washing Facilities	Restaurant	Hot Meals	Cafe	Refreshments	Day Lodge Available	Solid Based Swims	Easy Access Swims	Disabled Access Swims	Grass Swims	Tree Sheltered	Dogs Allowed	Fulltime Security	Rare Birdlife	Rare Wildlife	Spectators Allowed	Kids with Adults
BLAENAU GWENT																																					
BUTE TOWN RESERVOIR (FH0773)						●	●																														
LYMOOR POOL 1 AND 2 (FH3117)																													●								
BRIDGEND																																					
GARW (RIVER) (FH1841)																		●											●								
OGMORE (RIVER) (FH3579)							●																														
CAERPHILLY																																					
OGILVIE LAKE (FH3578)														●	●	●													●								
CARMARTHENSHIRE																																					
COTHI (RIVER) (FH1127)														●	●							●															
COWIN (RIVER) (FH1151)							●		●																			●	●					●	●	●	
CYNIN (RIVER) (FH1241)							●		●																			●	●					●	●	●	
DOLGWM MILL FISHERY (FH1397)									●																						●						
GARNFFRWD FISHERY (FH1836)														●	●																						
GLAS-LLYN FISHERY (FH1870)														●	●																						
HENDY FISHERY (FH2181)									●																						●						
LLYN CARFAN (FH2798)	●	●							●			●		●	●			●			●		●		●		●	●	●	●	●	●		●	●	●	●
MAES-ISAF FISHERY (FH3137)									●																												
PANT Y BEDW FISHING LAKES (FH3693)						●	●	●						●	●	●	●	●									●	●	●	●	●			●	●		
PENBEILI FISHERY (FH3734)									●																						●						
PEWI FACH (RIVER) (FH3763)							●		●																			●	●					●	●	●	
SPRINGWATER LAKES (FH4375)		●			●	●	●	●	●	●				●	●	●	●	●	●								●	●	●	●	●	●		●	●	●	
TAF (RIVER) (FH4629)									●																										●		
TAF (RIVER) (FH4628)							●		●																			●	●					●	●	●	
TEIFI (RIVER) (FH4705)									●																						●			●	●		
TOWEY (RIVER) (FH4890)										●																											
TOWI (RIVER) (FH4891)														●	●							●															
WHITE HOUSE MILL (FH5335)		●								●	●			●	●	●	●	●			●				●	●		●	●	●	●	●	●	●	●	●	●
CEREDIGION																																					
ARTRO (RIVER) (FH0143)									●																												
BAYLIAU FISHERY (FH0350)																															●						
CELLAN FISHERY (FH0885)																															●						
CWMMACKWITH FISHERY (FH1238)									●																												
FRON FARM FISHERY (FH1814)	●	●			●	●	●	●	●	●	●			●	●			●			●				●	●		●	●	●			●	●	●		●
GEORGE BORROW HOTEL (FH1848)				●																			●		●												

Fishing Facilities and Amenities

	Net Dips	Tackle Hire	Site Tackle Shop	Boats Available	Bait Sold	Adult Matches	Junior Matches	Half Day Fishing	Night Fishing	Tuition Given	Accommodation	Camping	Caravan Site	Male Toilets	Female Toilets	Disabled Toilets	Disabled Facilities	Hardcore Parking	Public Telephone	Showers	Washing Facilities	Restaurant	Hot Meals	Cafe	Refreshments	Day Lodge Available	Solid Based Swims	Easy Access Swims	Disabled Access Swims	Grass Swims	Tree Sheltered	Dogs Allowed	Fulltime Security	Rare Birdlife	Rare Wildlife	Spectators Allowed	Kids with Adults
LAMPETER FISHERY (FH2601)																															●						
LLANARTH FISHERY (FH2768)	●	●	●		●	●				●				●	●	●	●	●			●						●	●	●	●			●	●	●	●	●
NANT Y MOCH RESERVOIR (FH3418)				●																																	
NEUADDLAS COUNTRY GUEST HOUSE (FH3458)														●	●								●		●												
NINE OAKS (FH3509)		●			●	●				●				●	●	●	●										●	●	●	●		●		●	●	●	
RALLT FISHERY (FH3885)																															●						
RHYDYGALFE FISHERY (FH3941)									●																												
TEGLAN LAKE (FH4701)																	●												●								
TEIFI (RIVER) (FH4707)														●	●								●		●												
TEIFI (RIVER) (FH4710)																													●								
TEIFI (RIVER) (FH4712)																																		●	●		
TEIFI (RIVER) (FH4708)						●			●	●				●	●	●																		●		●	
TEIFY POOLS FISHERY (FH4715)						●	●																					●	●	●	●			●	●	●	
TYRDREF FISHERY (FH5036)										●							●												●								
YSTWYTH (RIVER) (FH5574)									●									●	●									●			●			●	●		
CONWY																																					
CONWY VALLEY FISHERIES (FH1099)	●		●		●			●			●			●	●	●	●	●	●		●		●	●	●		●	●	●	●			●	●	●	●	●
GILER ARMS LAKE (FH1855)	●	●				●	●	●		●	●	●	●	●	●		●	●	●	●	●	●	●		●		●	●	●				●			●	●
LLEDR (RIVER) (FH2777)		●			●																																
LLYN ALED (FH2791)																												●		●						●	●
LLYN CRAFNANT FISHERIES (FH2803)				●																					●												
TYDDYN MAWR TROUT FARM (FH5015)		●						●						●	●			●									●	●		●	●	●				●	
DENBIGHSHIRE																																					
ABBEY FISHERY (FH0002)																																●		●	●	●	
ALWEN RESERVOIR (FH0093)			●															●										●		●		●	●	●		●	●
CEIRIOG (RIVER) (FH0882)		●		●										●	●	●						●			●				●					●	●		
CEIRW STREAM (FH0884)						●	●							●	●	●		●	●			●	●	●	●			●		●	●			●	●	●	
DEE (RIVER) (FH1311)						●	●							●	●	●		●	●			●	●	●	●			●		●	●			●	●	●	
DOLWEN AND PLAS UCHAF (FH1398)								●										●										●		●	●	●					●
FELIN-Y-GORS FISHERIES (FH1683)		●			●									●	●										●												
LLYN ALWEN (FH2792)						●	●							●	●	●		●	●			●	●	●	●			●		●	●			●	●	●	
LLYN BRENIG (FH2795)		●	●	●		●		●		●				●	●	●	●	●	●		●	●	●	●	●	●		●	●	●	●	●	●	●	●	●	●
FLINTSHIRE																																					
BUCKLEY TRAP POOL (FH0718)									●					●	●	●	●	●											●								
CLAWDD OFFAS DYKE (FH0984)						●	●							●	●		●	●									●	●	●		●			●	●	●	

Fishing Facilities and Amenities

	Net Dips	Tackle Hire	Site Tackle Shop	Boats Available	Bait Sold	Adult Matches	Junior Matches	Half Day Fishing	Night Fishing	Tuition Given	Accommodation	Camping	Caravan Site	Male Toilets	Female Toilets	Disabled Toilets	Disabled Facilities	Hardcore Parking	Public Telephone	Showers	Washing Facilities	Restaurant	Hot Meals	Cafe	Refreshments	Day Lodge Available	Solid Based Swims	Easy Access Swims	Disabled Access Swims	Grass Swims	Tree Sheltered	Dogs Allowed	Fulltime Security	Rare Birdlife	Rare Wildlife	Spectators Allowed	Kids with Adults
FOREST HILL TROUT FARM (FH1766)																															●						
GWERYD LAKES FISHING (FH2047)		●	●		●	●			●	●	●			●	●	●							●	●	●				●								
GYRN CASTLE FISHERY (FH2056)																									●												
NANT-Y-GAIN FISHERY (FH3420)																	●								●				●								
PADESWOOD POOL (FH3684)														●	●												●	●		●							
SARN MILL FISHERIES (FH4106)														●	●												●	●		●				●	●		
SEVEN SPRINGS FISHERIES (FH4143)		●						●						●	●			●	●										●		●	●				●	
GLAMORGAN (VALE OF)																																					
HAZELCOURT PONDS (FH2164)						●																							●		●						
MELLTE (STREAM) (FH3251)							●		●																		●	●		●				●	●	●	
PENYWERN PONDS (FH3750)																						●	●		●				●								
PONTSTICILL RESERVOIR (FH3817)						●																															
TAFF BARGOED (FH4633)					●	●	●																					●	●					●	●	●	
GWYNEDD																																					
AFON LLYFNI (RIVER) (FH0037)				●					●	●	●	●	●					●	●									●	●			●	●	●	●		●
AFON SEIONT (RIVER) (FH0038)				●					●	●	●	●	●					●	●									●	●		●		●	●	●		●
CONWY (RIVER) (FH1098)											●	●	●																								
CREGENNAN LAKES (FH1177)				●										●	●	●																	●	●	●		
CWM SILYN LAKE (FH1235)				●					●	●	●	●	●					●	●									●	●				●	●	●		●
DEE (RIVER) (FH1314)		●		●	●	●	●		●					●	●	●	●	●	●				●	●	●			●	●	●	●			●	●	●	
DWYFACH (RIVER) (FH1488)									●	●																											
DWYTHWCH LAKE (FH1492)				●					●	●	●	●	●					●	●									●	●			●	●	●	●		
DYSYNNI (RIVER) (FH1497)		●		●																																	
DYSYNNI (RIVER) (FH1496)									●									●										●						●	●	●	
DYWARCHEN RESERVOIR (FH1498)									●	●	●	●	●					●	●									●	●			●	●	●	●		●
EDEN (RIVER) (FH1538)				●	●	●	●	●						●	●	●	●	●	●			●	●	●			●	●	●	●	●	●		●	●	●	
ERCH (RIVER) (FH1605)					●				●									●									●	●					●	●	●	●	●
FFESTINIOG FISHERY (FH1702)														●	●			●					●	●				●								●	
GLAN MORFA MAWR FISHERY (FH1868)		●			●	●	●							●	●			●	●									●	●	●	●	●		●	●	●	
GWYRFAI (RIVER) (FH2055)				●					●	●	●	●	●					●	●									●	●		●		●	●	●		●
LLYN BUGEILYN (FH2797)		●		●																																	
LLYN CWELLYN RESERVOIR (FH2804)									●	●	●	●	●					●	●									●	●			●	●	●	●		●
LLYN CWMYSTRADLLYN (FH2805)																		●									●	●		●			●	●	●	●	
LLYN CYNWCH LAKE (FH2807)						●	●			●							●	●										●	●	●	●	●		●	●	●	
LLYN PADARN (FH2821)									●	●	●	●	●					●	●									●	●			●	●	●	●		●

Fishing Facilities and Amenities

	Net Dips	Tackle Hire	Site Tackle Shop	Boats Available	Bait Sold	Adult Matches	Junior Matches	Half Day Fishing	Night Fishing	Tuition Given	Accommodation	Camping	Caravan Site	Male Toilets	Female Toilets	Disabled Toilets	Disabled Facilities	Hardcore Parking	Public Telephone	Showers	Washing Facilities	Restaurant	Hot Meals	Cafe	Refreshments	Day Lodge Available	Solid Based Swims	Easy Access Swims	Disabled Access Swims	Grass Swims	Tree Sheltered	Dogs Allowed	Fulltime Security	Rare Birdlife	Rare Wildlife	Spectators Allowed	Kids with Adults
LLYN TEGID (BALA LAKE) (FH2823)						●	●		●					●	●							●	●	●			●	●	●		●	●					
MAWDDACH (RIVER) (FH3212)									●													●	●		●							●		●			
MAWDDACH AND WNION (RIVERS) (FH3213)						●	●			●							●	●										●	●	●	●	●		●	●	●	
NANTLLE LAKE (FH3419)				●					●	●	●	●	●					●	●									●	●		●		●	●	●		●
RHYDHIR (RIVER) (FH3939)					●				●									●									●	●					●	●	●	●	●
TALYLLYN LAKE (FH4640)		●	●	●		●	●	●		●	●			●	●			●	●		●	●	●			●	●	●		●	●	●	●	●	●	●	●
TRAWFFYNYDD RESERVOIR (FH4905)				●	●	●	●	●						●	●	●	●	●	●			●	●	●			●	●	●	●	●	●		●	●	●	
TRYWERYN (RIVER) (FH4962)		●		●	●	●	●		●					●	●	●		●	●				●	●	●			●	●	●	●			●	●	●	
ISLE OF ANGLESEY																																					
BREAKWATER PARK (FH0610)	●					●	●	●						●	●	●	●	●			●			●	●		●	●	●	●				●	●	●	●
CEFNI RESERVOIR (FH0881)				●						●				●	●	●									●												
LLYN ALAN (FH2788)				●																																	
LLYN CORON (FH2801)				●																																	
LLYN Y GORS (FH2824)					●	●	●		●					●	●			●	●						●		●	●	●	●	●	●		●	●	●	
PLAS-Y-NANT TROUT FISHERY (FH3799)		●																																			
TY HEN LAKE (FH5013)														●	●																						
MONMOUTHSHIRE																																					
CWMCELYN POND (FH1237)						●	●			●									●								●	●	●	●		●				●	
FAIROAK FISHERY (FH1655)		●	●			●		●		●				●	●	●		●			●		●	●		●		●	●	●	●		●			●	●
FIVE TREES (FH1740)																		●																			
MONNOW (RIVER) (FH3351)																			●			●			●			●			●					●	
RAVENSNEST FISHERY (FH3894)		●																																			
TREFALDU FISHERY (FH4911)														●	●			●									●				●						
NEATH PORT TALBOT																																					
EGLWYS NUNYDD RESERVOIR (FH1553)				●																																	
HEPSTE (STREAM) (FH2188)							●		●																		●	●		●	●			●	●	●	
NEATH (RIVER) (FH3434)							●		●									●									●			●	●			●	●	●	
NEWPORT																																					
SHROPSHIRE UNION CANAL (FH4250)																													●								
WENTWOOD RESERVOIR (FH5251)				●										●																							
WOODSTOCK POOL (FH5495)									●																												
YNYS-Y-FRO RESERVOIR (FH5571)				●										●	●						●							●					●				
PEMBROKESHIRE																																					
EASTERN CLEDDAU (RIVER) (FH1520)		●	●		●	●	●			●	●			●	●	●	●	●							●	●	●	●	●	●			●	●	●	●	●
EASTERN CLEDDAU (RIVER) (FH1521)								●	●									●									●	●		●	●			●	●		●

Fishing Facilities and Amenities

	Net Dips	Tackle Hire	Site Tackle Shop	Boats Available	Bait Sold	Adult Matches	Junior Matches	Half Day Fishing	Night Fishing	Tuition Given	Accommodation	Camping	Caravan Site	Male Toilets	Female Toilets	Disabled Toilets	Disabled Facilities	Hardcore Parking	Public Telephone	Showers	Washing Facilities	Restaurant	Hot Meals	Cafe	Refreshments	Day Lodge Available	Solid Based Swims	Easy Access Swims	Disabled Access Swims	Grass Swims	Tree Sheltered	Dogs Allowed	Fulltime Security	Rare Birdlife	Rare Wildlife	Spectators Allowed	Kids with Adults
HOLGAN TROUT FARM FISHERY (FH2252)		●												●	●													●	●								
IAN HEAPS PREMIER FISHERIES (FH2356)		●	●		●	●	●			●	●			●	●	●	●	●							●	●	●	●	●	●	●		●	●	●	●	●
LLYS Y FRAN RESERVOIR (FH2829)		●	●	●	●		●	●		●				●	●	●	●	●			●		●	●	●					●		●	●			●	●
LUDCHURCH LAKE (FH3103)				●		●	●							●	●												●	●	●	●		●		●	●	●	
ROADSIDE FARM (FH3974)									●																			●		●		●					
ROSEBUSH RESERVOIR (FH4013)				●																										●	●			●			●
WEST ATHESTON COARSE FISHERY (FH5256)									●									●										●	●		●	●		●	●	●	
YET-Y-GORS FISHERY (FH5566)														●	●								●		●												
POWYS																																					
BOATSIDE FARM (FH0520)														●	●			●																			
CAER BERIS MANOR HOTEL (FH0789)		●												●	●	●	●		●			●										●		●			
CLYNWEDOG RESERVOIR (FH1041)				●										●	●			●													●			●	●	●	
CLYWEDOG (RIVER) (FH1043)				●										●	●			●																●	●	●	
DULAS (RIVER) (FH1468)				●										●	●			●																●	●	●	
GWYDDIOR LAKE (FH2053)				●				●										●																●	●		
IRFON (RIVER) (FH2377)		●												●	●	●																●				●	
ITHON (RIVER) (FH2400)									●		●	●	●														●			●				●	●		●
LLANDRINIO WEST LAKE (FH2771)																								●					●								
LLANGORSE LAKE (FH2773)				●					●					●	●			●	●				●	●	●							●				●	
LLYN ALARCH (FH2789)		●															●	●										●	●		●			●	●		
LLYN CLYWEDOG (FH2800)				●																		●	●		●												
LLYN-COCH HWYAD (FH2825)				●														●															●	●	●		●
LLYNGWYN LAKE (FH2828)				●																																	
SEVERN (RIVER) (FH4160)																													●								
SEVERN (RIVER) (FH4156)																												●	●								
SEVERN (RIVER) (FH4157)																													●								
SEVERN (RIVER) (FH4153)				●										●	●			●																●	●	●	
USK (RIVER) (FH5079)										●				●	●				●			●	●		●						●						
VYRNWY (RIVER) (FH5104)																													●								
WESTLAKE FISHERY (FH5282)	●	●	●					●	●	●		●	●	●	●	●	●	●		●	●		●	●	●	●	●	●	●	●	●	●	●	●		●	●
WYE (RIVER) (FH5538)																		●																●	●	●	
WYE (RIVER) (FH5541)																		●													●			●	●	●	
RHONDDA CYNON TAFF																																					
LLYN ALAW (FH2790)			●	●	●	●	●							●	●	●	●	●							●	●	●	●	●	●	●	●	●	●	●	●	
SEVEN OAKS FISHERY (FH4141)	●	●	●		●	●	●	●		●				●	●	●	●	●	●		●				●	●	●	●	●	●	●		●	●	●	●	●

Fishing Facilities and Amenities

	Net Dips	Tackle Hire	Site Tackle Shop	Boats Available	Bait Sold	Adult Matches	Junior Matches	Half Day Fishing	Night Fishing	Tuition Given	Accommodation	Camping	Caravan Site	Male Toilets	Female Toilets	Disabled Toilets	Disabled Facilities	Hardcore Parking	Public Telephone	Showers	Washing Facilities	Restaurant	Hot Meals	Cafe	Refreshments	Day Lodge Available	Solid Based Swims	Easy Access Swims	Disabled Access Swims	Grass Swims	Tree Sheltered	Dogs Allowed	Fulltime Security	Rare Birdlife	Rare Wildlife	Spectators Allowed	Kids with Adults
SWANSEA																																					
FENDROD LAKE (FH1694)						●	●		●									●									●	●	●	●						●	
GOWERTON COARSE FISHERY (FH1929)	●				●	●	●							●	●	●	●	●	●		●	●	●	●	●		●	●	●					●	●		●
LOWER LLIW (FH3087)				●																																	
MAES GWYN FISHERY (FH3136)		●	●		●			●		●				●	●	●	●	●			●		●	●	●	●	●	●	●	●	●		●	●	●	●	●
SHIMANO FELINDRE (FH4239)														●	●	●							●		●												
WHITE SPRINGS LAKES (FH5341)		●			●	●	●	●	●					●	●	●	●	●	●			●	●		●		●	●	●	●	●	●		●	●	●	
TORFAEN																																					
CWMBRAN BOATING LAKE (FH1236)						●	●	●						●	●	●	●	●						●			●	●	●					●		●	
LLYN ON RESERVOIR (FH2820)				●																																	
WREXHAM																																					
ALYN (RIVER) (FH0096)																												●									
DEE (RIVER) (FH1303)														●	●				●			●	●		●												
DEE (RIVER) (FH1301)									●																												
LLANDEGLA TROUT FISHERY (FH2770)	●	●	●		●	●	●	●		●				●	●	●	●	●			●		●	●	●	●	●	●	●	●	●		●	●	●	●	●
TREE TOPS FLY FISHERY (FH4910)	●	●	●		●			●		●	●			●	●	●	●	●	●		●		●	●	●	●						●	●	●	●	●	●

Fishing Allowances

SECTION 7

This section allows you to view fishery allowances, so that you know what is and is not allowed before you get to the fishery with regard to baits and methods..

e.g Number of Rods allowed

Once you have located a Fishery you can either look up further details in Section 1 or use the other sections to find what else the Fishery may have to offer.

Fishing Allowances UK & Irish Fisheries

Fishery	Bank Fishing Only	Barbed Hooks	Boilies	Catch & Release	Kill All Fish Caught	Dead Bait	Live Bait	Dry Fly	Wet Fly	Electric Bait Boats	Sonar Boats	Fixed Weights Allowed	Floater Fish	Floating Bait	Floating Rings - Game	Ground Baiting	Hair Rigs	Keep Nets	More than one rod	Number of Rods Allowed	Particle Baits	Spinners	Unhooking Mats essential	Wading	Worms Only
ENGLAND																									
BEDFORDSHIRE																									
BRIARWOOD FISHERY (FH0619)			●																						
ELSTOW PITS (FH1573)			●									●					●		●						
IVEL (RIVER) (FH2401)		●																●			●				
IVEL (RIVER) (FH2402)		●	●				●						●	●		●		●	●		●				
JONES PIT (FH2416)		●	●				●			●	●		●	●		●		●	●		●	●	●		
LEDBURN ROAD (FH2659)																			●						
MANOR FARM LEISURE (FH3163)	●		●		●			●	●	●	●	●		●		●	●	●	●	2		●	●		
OUSE (RIVER) (FH3639)		●	●				●			●	●		●	●		●		●	●		●	●			
OUSE (RIVER) (FH3638)		●																●	●		●	●			
PRIORY COUNTRY PARK (FH3848)	●	●	●	●		●								●		●	●	●	●	2	●	●			
SOUTH LAGOON (FH4333)																●		●							
TINGRITH COARSE FISHERY (FH4851)																			●	2					
WITHY POOL (FH5446)			●														●		●	3			●		
BERKSHIRE																									
ALBERT BRIDGE (FH0050)		●														●		●							
AMERDEN POOL (FH0100)		●	●				●							●		●		●	●		●		●		
ASHRIDGE MANOR (FH0169)																			●						
BARTON COURT FISHERY (FH0338)	●	●				●	●					●		●		●	●		●	2	●	●	●		
BISHOPS GREEN FARM LAKE (FH0436)																			●		●				
BRAY LOCK (FH0607)	●	●	●	●	●	●	●	●	●			●		●		●	●	●	●	2	●	●	●	●	●
BURGHFIELD (FH0739)		●	●				●			●	●		●	●		●		●	●		●	●			
BURGHFIELD BLUE POOL (FH0740)																●			●						
BURGHFIELD MATCH LAKE (FH0742)																●			●						
CHURCH FARM (FH0950)																		●							
FELIX FARM TROUT FISHERY (FH1684)								●	●																
FROBURY FARM SPORTING CLUB (FH1805)	●			●				●	●			●		●		●	●		●	2	●		●		
FROXFIELD A AND B (FH1815)			●																						
JINGLES FARM (FH2412)																			●						
KENNET (RIVER) (FH2443)																			●						
KENNET (RIVER) (FH2438)		●	●				●									●		●	●		●	●	●		
LODDON (RIVER) (FH2977)			●										●					●	●		●	●	●		
LONGMOOR FARM FISHING LAKE (FH2993)																			●	2					
LONGMOOR LAKE (FH2994)			●										●	●		●		●	●		●		●		
MILL LANE (FH3290)			●			●								●		●									
MILL POND (FH3298)			●													●			●		●				
NEWBURY TROUT LAKES (FH3480)		●						●	●																
PANG VALLEY TROUT LAKE (FH3688)								●	●																
PONDWOOD CARP LAKES (FH3814)			●																●				●		
ROMNEY ISLAND AND MEADOW (FH4001)		●														●		●							
ROYAL BERKSHIRE FISHERY (FH4042)																		●	●	2			●		
SHEEPHOUSE FARM TROUT FISHERY (FH4217)								●	●																
SOUTH HILL PARK LAKE (FH4331)			●													●			●		●				
ST PATRICKS (FH4395)		●	●				●						●	●		●		●	●		●				
SWAN VALLEY (FH4596)	●					●	●						●	●		●	●		●	2	●	●	●		
THEALE (FH4806)		●	●				●			●	●		●	●		●		●	●		●	●			
THEALE LAGOON (FH4808)						●																●			
TRI-LAKES (FH4954)			●											●		●	●		●	2	●		●		
TWYFORD BBONT (FH5008)		●	●				●						●	●		●		●	●		●	●			
TWYFORD WATERS (FH5010)		●	●															●	●		●	●	●		
WASING WOODS (FH5165)			●											●		●			●				●		
WHITE SWAN LAKE (FH5343)			●					●	●				●	●		●		●	●		●		●		
BRISTOL																									
AVON (BRISTOL) (RIVER) (FH0191)		●	●													●		●	●		●				
BITTERWELL LAKE (FH0438)																		●	●				●		
BRISTOL DOCKS (FH0655)		●	●													●		●	●		●		●		
TANHOUSE FARM LAKE (FH4652)									●									●	●						
BUCKINGHAMSHIRE																									
ALDERS FARM TROUT FISHERY (FH0062)	●				●			●	●					●					●	2			●		
BOURTON FISHERIES (FH0567)		●	●				●							●		●			●		●		●		
CALVES LANE LAKE (FH0804)																							●		
CHESS (RIVER) (FH0928)									●																
CHURCH HILL FISHERY (FH0953)								●	●																
COLNBROOK WEST (FH1068)		●	●				●							●		●		●	●		●		●		
COLNEBROOK (RIVER) (FH1076)	●	●	●	●		●	●							●		●	●	●	●	2	●	●	●	●	●
CRAYFISH POOL (FH1171)		●	●				●			●	●		●	●		●			●	2	●	●	●		
DOVECOTE LAKE FISHERY (FH1430)			●				●						●					●	●		●	●			

Fishing Allowances UK & Irish Fisheries

	Bank Fishing Only	Barbed Hooks	Boilies	Catch & Release	Kill All Fish Caught	Dead Bait	Live Bait	Dry Fly	Wet Fly	Electric Bait Boats	Sonar Boats	Fixed Weights Allowed	Floater Fish	Floating Bait	Floating Rings - Game	Ground Baiting	Hair Rigs	Keep Nets	More than one rod	Number of Rods Allowed	Particle Baits	Spinners	Unhooking Mats essential	Wading	Worms Only
FARLOWS LAKE (FH1668)		●	●				●							●		●		●	●	2	●		●		
GILBRATAR LAKE (FH1854)													●					●			●				
GREAT LINFORD LAKES (FH1982)		●	●										●			●	●		●	2	●				
HORTON BOAT POOL (FH2310)		●	●				●			●	●		●	●		●		●	●	4	●	●	●		
HORTON CHURCH LAKE (FH2311)		●	●				●			●	●		●	●		●	●	●	●	3	●	●	●		
KINGFISHER GOLF CLUB (FH2496)																		●	●			●			
KINGSMEAD 1 (FH2514)		●	●				●			●	●		●	●		●		●	●	4	●	●	●		
KINGSMEAD ISLAND LAKE (FH2516)		●	●				●			●	●		●	●		●		●	●		●	●	●		
LATIMER PARK FLY FISHERY (FH2628)								●	●																
MAYFIELDS LAKE (FH3216)		●	●				●							●		●		●	●				●		
OLD SLADE LANE LAKE (FH3599)			●																●	4					
ORLITTS LAKES (FH3622)		●	●				●							●		●		●	●	4	●	●	●		
OUSE (RIVER) (FH3640)		●	●				●							●		●		●							
OUSE (RIVER) (FH3642)	●	●	●	●		●	●	●	●			●		●		●	●	●	●	2	●	●		●	●
OUSE (RIVER) KEMPSTON MILL (FH3641)		●												●		●		●	●		●		●		
SILVERWING LAKE (FH4273)	●	●	●	●		●	●							●		●	●	●	●		●	●	●	●	●
SPADE OAK LAKE (FH4357)																		●							
TINGRITH LAKES (FH4852)	●		●											●		●	●		●	2					●
TYRINGHAM ESTATE (FH5037)		●	●				●			●	●		●	●		●		●	●		●	●	●		
WATTS POOL (FH5189)	●	●	●	●		●	●							●		●	●	●	●	2	●	●	●	●	●
WESTFIELD FARM (FH5276)			●				●			●	●		●	●		●		●	●			●	●		
CAMBRIDGESHIRE																									
BARNWELL COUNTRY PARK (FH0320)	●		●	●		●						●		●		●	●	●			●	●			
BLUEBELL LAKE (FH0513)			●			●	●			●				●		●	●	●	●			●	●		●
CAM (RIVER) (FH0805)						●										●									
CHAWSTON LAKES (FH0908)		●	●							●			●	●		●		●	●		●		●		
DECOY LAKE (FH1295)																		●							
ELDERNELL LAKE (FH1559)																		●	●	2					
FENLAND FISHERIES (FH1696)																			●						
FERRY MEADOWS (FH1701)		●	●							●			●					●	●		●	●	●		
FIELDS END WATER (FH1704)																		●	●		●				
GREAT OUSE (RIVER) (FH1992)																●						●			
GREAT OUSE (RIVER) (FH1991)	●	●		●		●						●		●		●		●		2	●	●		●	●
GREAT OUSE (RIVER) (FH1996)		●	●				●	●	●				●	●		●		●	●		●	●	●		
GREAT OUSE (RIVER) (FH1995)		●	●							●			●	●		●		●	●		●		●		
GREAT OUSE (RIVER) (FH1990)		●	●				●	●	●	●	●		●	●		●		●	●		●	●	●		
GREAT OUSE (RIVER) (FH1994)							●									●		●							
KINGFISHER LAKE (FH2497)			●				●			●			●					●	●			●	●		
LARK (RIVER) (FH2622)																●									
MAGPIE LAKE (FH3139)																		●							
MEPAL PIT (FH3256)			●				●							●				●	●		●		●		
MILTON COUNTRY PARK (FH3318)	●		●	●		●						●		●		●	●	●	●	2		●	●		
NENE (RIVER) (FH3445)		●	●													●		●	●		●		●		
NENE (RIVER) (FH3441)		●					●											●	●		●	●			
NENE (RIVER) (FH3446)			●			●	●			●				●		●	●	●	●			●	●		●
NENE NORTH BANK (RIVER) (FH3449)		●	●															●	●		●	●			
NORTH BANK TROUT FISHERY (FH3526)		●						●	●																
NORTHEY PARK FISHERY (FH3543)																							●		
OFFORD WEIRPOOL (FH3575)													●												
OLD WEST (RIVER) (FH3602)																●		●	●						
OVER MAIN DRAIN (FH3659)																			●				●		
PERIO MILL (FH3753)								●	●																
ROSWELL PITS (FH4022)																		●							
SAND MARTIN LAKE (FH4091)			●				●			●			●					●	●			●	●		
SIBSON FISHERIES (FH4264)			●															●	●			●			
STRETHAM LAKE (FH4524)																●			●	2					
SWAN LAKE (FH4589)			●				●			●			●					●	●			●	●		
VIRGINIA LAKE (FH5100)			●							●	●								●		●		●		
WELDON RESERVOIR (FH5228)		●	●							●			●	●		●		●	●		●		●		
WHITTLESEY DYKE/ BEVILLS LEAM (FH5361)		●														●		●							
WILLOW CREEK (FH5378)			●				●			●			●					●	●			●	●		
WILLOW LAKE (FH5382)																		●							
WOOD POOL (FH5459)			●				●			●			●					●	●			●	●		
CHESHIRE																									
ASTBURY MERE (FH0176)	●	●	●	●		●	●									●	●		●	4	●	●	●		
BETLEY MERE (FH0396)	●	●	●	●		●	●			●			●	●		●	●		●	3	●	●	●		
BLUNDELLS FARM FISHERY (FH0514)	●			●								●		●			●	●	●	3	●	●			●
BOLESWORTH CASTLE (FH0532)		●	●											●		●	●	●	●	2	●		●		●

Fishing Allowances UK & Irish Fisheries

	Bank Fishing Only	Barbed Hooks	Boilies	Catch & Release	Kill All Fish Caught	Dead Bait	Live Bait	Dry Fly	Wet Fly	Electric Bait Boats	Sonar Boats	Fixed Weights Allowed	Floater Fish	Floating Bait	Floating Rings - Game	Ground Baiting	Hair Rigs	Keep Nets	More than one rod	Number of Rods Allowed	Particle Baits	Spinners	Unhooking Mats essential	Wading	Worms Only
BORDER FISHERIES (FH0546)																			●						
BOSLEY RESERVOIR (FH0557)																							●		
BOTTOMS RESERVOIR (FH0563)																						●			
BROOKSIDE FISHERIES (FH0686)							●												●		●				
BROOKSIDE LAKES (FH0687)																			●						
BULLS POOL (FH0729)	●		●										●				●		●			●			●
BURTON MERE FISHERIES (FH0761)		●	●					●	●					●		●			●				●		
BYLEY FISHERIES (FH0783)																			●						
CAPESTHORNE HALL STOCK POND (FH0831)			●											●		●			●		●		●		
CAPESTHORNE MAIN POOL (FH0832)		●	●				●			●				●		●		●	●		●	●	●		
CAPESTHORNE TOP POOL (FH0833)		●	●				●							●		●			●	2	●	●	●		
CATCHPENNY POOL (FH0873)								●	●																
DANE (RIVER) (FH1262)								●	●																
DANE (RIVER) (FH1257)								●	●																
DANE (RIVER) (FH1259)								●	●																
DANE (RIVER) (FH1265)								●	●																
DANEBRIDGE FISHERIES (FH1268)								●	●																
EGERTON LAKE (FH1550)			●																●						
FANSHAWE LANE POOL (FH1662)			●											●		●		●			●	●	●		
GOWY (RIVER) (FH1931)								●	●																
GOWY FISHERY (FH1932)	●			●				●	●																
GRIMESDITCH MILL POOL (FH2020)			●										●						●						
GRIMSDITCH MILL POOL (FH2023)			●										●				●								
HARTHILL (FH2114)																			●						
HOLMSTON HALL FISHERY (FH2270)													●						●						
KAZAKO PONDS (FH2421)		●	●																						
LAKEMORE COUNTRY PARK (FH2578)			●													●			●	3			●		
LAMALOAD RESERVOIR (FH2599)								●	●																
LLOYDS MEADOW FISHERIES (FH2784)													●	●		●		●	●		●	●	●		
MACCLESFIELD CANAL (FH3128)			●															●				●			
MARTON HEATH COARSE POOL (FH3202)																		●	●	2					
MARTON HEATH TROUT POOLS (FH3203)	●			●				●	●										●	2					
MEADOW FISHERY (FH3222)								●	●																
MOORE QUARRY (FH3360)																							●		
MORETON MERE FISHERY (FH3370)																		●	●		●		●		
PARTRIDGE LAKES (FH3714)																●			●	2					
REASEHEATH COLLEGE LAKE (FH3904)			●											●		●		●			●		●		
REDESMERE (FH3916)		●	●				●							●		●		●	●	2	●	●	●		
SHAKERLEY MERE (FH4202)			●																●		●				
TATTON MERE (FH4664)	●		●	●		●						●		●		●	●	●		2	●	●	●	●	
VALE ROYAL LOCKS (FH5084)																						●			
VILLAGE POOL (FH5098)																			●						
WALKERWOOD TROUT FISHERY (FH5120)								●	●																
WALL POOL LODGE (FH5121)			●															●	●	3	●		●		
WEAVER (RIVER) (FH5215)																●									
WEAVER (RIVER) (FH5220)																●									
WESTLOW MERE (FH5283)	●			●				●	●																
WHIRLEY POOL (FH5327)								●	●																
WINSFORD FLASH (FH5421)			●														●		●	3					
WINTERLEY POOL FISHERY (FH5426)		●	●							●			●					●	●		●	●	●		
CLEVELAND																									
HART RESERVOIR (FH2112)																●									
LOCH KENNY (FH2899)		●	●											●		●		●			●		●		
TILERY LAKE (FH4843)		●	●								●			●		●		●	●		●		●		
CORNWALL																									
ARGAL RESERVOIR (FH0134)			●																				●		
BAKE FISHING LAKES (FH0253)	●		●	●				●	●	●		●		●		●	●	●	●	2	●		●		
BOLINGEY LAKE (FH0534)																●			●						
BOSCATHNOE RESERVOIR (FH0556)			●																●	3			●		
BUSH LAKES FARM (FH0768)			●																						
BUSSOW RESERVOIR (FH0772)			●	●									●				●		●	2		●			●
CHOONE FARM (FH0945)																			●						
COLLIFORD LAKE (FH1065)								●	●																
CRAFTHOLE LAKE (FH1157)			●																●				●		
DRIFT RESERVOIR (FH1443)								●	●																
DUTSON WATER (FH1487)	●		●	●								●		●			●	●			●		●		
EAST ROSE FARM (FH1513)	●			●		●	●	●	●	●	●	●		●		●	●		●	2	●	●			
ELMFIELD FARM COARSE FISHERY (FH1570)																			●						

FISHING ALLOWANCES

England (by County)

Fishing Allowances UK & Irish Fisheries

	Bank Fishing Only	Barbed Hooks	Boilies	Catch & Release	Kill All Fish Caught	Dead Bait	Live Bait	Dry Fly	Wet Fly	Electric Bait Boats	Sonar Boats	Fixed Weights Allowed	Floater Fish	Floating Bait	Floating Rings - Game	Ground Baiting	Hair Rigs	Keep Nets	More than one rod	Number of Rods Allowed	Particle Baits	Spinners	Unhooking Mats essential	Wading	Worms Only
EMFIELD COARSE FISHERY (FH1586)																	●		●	2					●
FERNDALE (FH1699)				●													●	●	●	2	●				
FOWEY (RIVER) (FH1786)		●					●	●	●													●			
FOWEY (RIVER) (FH1787)	●			●	●			●	●													●		●	●
FOWEY (RIVER) (FH1785)	●			●	●			●	●													●		●	●
FOWEY (RIVER) (FH1782)		●					●	●	●													●			
FOWEY (RIVER) (FH1784)		●					●	●	●																
GLENLEIGH FARM FISHERY (FH1892)	●		●	●										●			●	●	●	2	●		●		
GOONHAVERN LAKE (FH1920)	●		●	●								●		●		●	●	●			●	●			
GWARNICK MILL TROUT FISHERY (FH2040)							●	●	●									●				●			
GWINEAR POOLS COARSE FISHERY (FH2049)	●		●	●										●		●	●	●	●	2	●		●		
GWINNEAR POOLS (FH2050)			●														●		●	2					●
HIDDEN VALLEY (FH2203)							●											●	●				●		
INNY (RIVER) (FH2372)	●			●	●			●	●													●		●	●
LAKEVIEW COUNTRY CLUB (FH2598)	●			●										●		●	●		●	2			●		
LANGARTH POOLS (FH2610)	●		●	●								●		●		●	●	●	●	2			●		
LYNHER (RIVER) (FH3124)	●			●	●			●	●													●		●	●
MEADOWSIDE COARSE FISHERY (FH3228)	●		●	●													●	●	●	2	●		●		
MIDDLE BOSWIN FARM (FH3264)			●										●						●				●		
MILLBROOK COARSE FISHERY (FH3305)			●													●	●	●	●	2			●		
MILTON MOUNT LAKE (FH3322)			●														●		●	2					
OAKSIDE FISHERY (FH3567)			●										●	●		●		●							
ORVIS INNIS FLY FISHERY (FH3626)		●						●	●										●						
POLCOVERACK FARM (FH3810)			●														●		●	2					●
PORTH RESERVOIR (FH3825)			●													●	●		●			●			●
PRINCE PARK (FH3845)																			●						
RETALLACK WATERS (FH3931)	●	●	●	●		●	●			●	●	●		●		●	●	●	●	3	●	●	●		
ROSE PARK FISHERY (FH4011)								●	●										●						
ROSEWATER LAKE (FH4014)			●																●	2					
SEATON (RIVER) (FH4127)	●			●	●			●	●													●		●	●
SHARKEYS PIT (FH4209)			●											●		●			●		●		●		
STITHIANS RESERVOIR (FH4459)								●	●																
TAMAR (RIVER) (FH4641)	●		●	●								●		●			●	●			●		●		
TEMPLE TROUT FISHERY (FH4735)	●			●	●							●		●			●				●	●			
TIN DENE FISHERY (FH4850)			●															●	●				●		
TORY FARM LAKE (FH4887)			●											●					●				●		
TREBELLAN PARK LAKES (FH4907)																			●						
TRETHIGGEY FARM POND (FH4949)																			●						
WEST LOOE (RIVER) (FH5263)		●						●	●																
WOODLAY HOLIDAY LAKES (FH5486)			●				●												●				●		
WOONSMITH LAKE (FH5502)	●		●	●								●		●		●	●	●	●	2	●	●			
COUNTY DURHAM																									
BEAUMONT FISHERIES (FH0358)	●			●										●					●	2			●		
BYERS GREEN (FH0782)								●	●									●			●				
LANGSDALE LAKE (FH2617)																			●						
TEES (RIVER) (FH4697)		●					●	●	●													●			
TEES (RIVER) (FH4690)																		●			●				
TURSDALE POND (FH4984)			●															●	●		●		●		
WADSWORTH FISHERY (FH5111)	●		●	●										●			●		●	3			●		
WEAR (RIVER) (FH5210)																						●			
WEAR (RIVER) (FH5209)	●	●				●	●	●	●			●										●		●	
WELLFIELD POND (FH5238)		●	●											●		●		●	●		●				
WITTON CASTLE LAKES (FH5451)	●			●				●	●																
CUMBRIA																									
ANNAS (RIVER) (FH0115)								●	●					●											
ATKINSONS TARN COARSE FISHERY (FH0181)													●												
BAYSTONE BANK RESERVIOR (FH0352)								●	●																
BESSY BECK TROUT FARM (FH0394)	●						●	●	●											20		●			
BLENCARN LAKE (FH0496)	●	●		●				●	●																
BORWICK LAKE (FH0555)																							●		
BUTTERMERE LAKE (FH0777)						●		●	●			●			●				●	3		●		●	
CLOUGH (RIVER) (FH1023)								●	●													●			
CROSSFIELD FISHERY (FH1193)			●											●		●			●		●				
CRUMMOCK WATER LAKE (FH1206)						●		●	●			●			●				●	3		●		●	
DEE (RIVER) (FH1305)								●	●													●			
DEE (RIVER) (FH1306)								●	●																
DOE (RIVER) (FH1390)								●	●													●			
DRUNKEN DUCK TARN FISHERY (FH1454)																			●						

FISHING ALLOWANCES

England (by County)

Fishing Allowances UK & Irish Fisheries

Fishery	Bank Fishing Only	Barbed Hooks	Boilies	Catch & Release	Kill All Fish Caught	Dead Bait	Live Bait	Dry Fly	Wet Fly	Electric Bait Boats	Sonar Boats	Fixed Weights Allowed	Floater Fish	Floating Bait	Floating Rings - Game	Ground Baiting	Hair Rigs	Keep Nets	More than one rod	Number of Rods Allowed	Particle Baits	Spinners	Unhooking Mats essential	Wading	Worms Only
DUBBS TROUT FISHERY (FH1458)								●	●																
EAST VIEW FISHERY (FH1515)				●																					
EDEN VALLEY TROUT LAKE (FH1543)		●						●	●																
ELLEN (RIVER) (FH1563)	●	●					●	●	●			●		●		●						●		●	
ELLERBECK FARM AND FISHERY (FH1565)	●			●										●		●		●	●	2	●				
ENNERDALE LAKE FISHERY (FH1595)		●					●	●	●													●			
ESK (RIVER) (FH1617)								●	●																
ESK (RIVER) (FH1618)								●	●					●											
ESTHWAITE WATER (FH1630)		●		●		●		●	●	●	●				●			●	●	2		●	●	●	●
GHYLL HEAD TROUT FISHERY (FH1851)								●	●																
GOODENBURGH TARN (FH1918)								●	●																
GRASMERE COARSE FISHERY (FH1976)																			●						
GRETA (RIVER) (FH2016)								●	●													●			
HAWESWATER RESERVOIR (FH2140)								●	●																
HIGH NEWTON RESERVOIR (FH2209)													●												
HOLEHIRD TARN (FH2251)			●																						
IRT (RIVER) (FH2380)								●	●					●											
KENT (RIVER) (FH2471)	●							●	●													●		●	
LAZY (RIVER) (FH2641)								●	●					●											
LICKLE (RIVER) (FH2714)								●	●					●											
LONSDALE COUNTRY PARK (FH2997)			●				●							●		●			●		●		●		
LOWESWATER LAKE (FH3096)				●		●		●	●			●							●	3		●		●	
LUNE (RIVER) (FH3107)	●	●						●	●													●		●	●
LUNE (RIVER) (FH3109)								●	●																
LUNE (RIVER) (FH3108)								●	●													●			
OAKBANK LAKES (FH3560)	●	●	●	●				●	●					●		●	●		●	3	●		●		
RAWTHEY (RIVER) (FH3897)								●	●																
RAWTHEY (RIVER) (FH3899)								●	●													●			
SOUTH TYNE (RIVER) (FH4340)								●																	
SPRINT (RIVER) (FH4378)	●							●	●													●		●	
TEWITFIELDS TROUT FISHERY (FH4752)			●					●	●									●			●		●		
TRANQUIL OTTER (FH4904)								●	●																
TWISS (RIVER) (FH5006)								●	●													●			
ULVERSTON CANAL (FH5043)			●																						
WATENDLATH TROUT FISHERY (FH5169)		●		●				●	●																
WITHERSLACK HALL TARN (FH5443)													●												
DERBYSHIRE																									
ALLESTREE LAKE (FH0078)		●														●		●	●	2	●				
ALVASTON LAKE (FH0089)		●														●		●	●	2	●				
BEEHIVE FARM WOODLANDS LAKES (FH0371)																			●						
CARSINGTON WATER (FH0854)								●	●																
CATTON PARK LAKE (FH0875)	●		●	●													●		●	2			●		
COPPICE LAKE (FH1112)																			●						
DERWENT VALLEY FISHERY (FH1361)																			●						
DONKHILL FISHERIES (FH1404)	●	●			●			●	●										●	2			●		
ERRWOOD RESERVOIR (FH1616)								●	●																
FOREMARK TROUT FISHERY (FH1764)								●	●																
HARLESTHORPE DAM (FH2107)			●																●			●	●		
HIGHAM FARM COARSE FISHING (FH2211)			●																						
LADYBOWER RESERVOIR (FH2549)								●	●																
MARKEATON LAKE (FH3183)		●														●		●	●	2	●				
MELBOURNE POOL (FH3243)		●	●													●		●	●		●				
MONSAL DALE FISHERY (FH3352)	●	●		●				●	●																
POSSY LODGE PONDS (FH3832)			●											●		●			●		●		●		
PRESS MANOR (FH3840)																							●		
RINGWOOD LAKE (FH3956)		●	●										●	●		●	●	●	●						
SUTTON BROOK (FH4562)	●			●				●	●																
TRENT AND MERSEY CANAL (FH4940)	●	●	●	●		●				●	●	●		●		●	●	●	●	2	●	●	●	●	
WINGERWORTH LIDO (FH5416)						●										●						●			
YEAVELEY ESTATE TROUT FISHERY (FH5560)	●			●				●	●										●	6					
DEVON																									
ABBROOK POND (FH0012)		●	●											●		●			●		●				
ALDER LAKE (FH0059)	●		●	●								●		●		●		●	●			●			
ANGLERS ELDORADO (FH0106)			●										●	●		●			●				●		
ANGLERS PARADISE (FH0108)			●										●						●		●		●		
ANGLERS SHANGRILA (FH0109)			●											●		●		●					●		
ASHCOMBE FISHERY (FH0159)			●				●											●	●						
BAKERS FARM (FH0254)																			●	2					

FISHING ALLOWANCES

England (by County)

Fishing Allowances UK & Irish Fisheries

	Bank Fishing Only	Barbed Hooks	Boilies	Catch & Release	Kill All Fish Caught	Dead Bait	Live Bait	Dry Fly	Wet Fly	Electric Bait Boats	Sonar Boats	Fixed Weights Allowed	Floater Fish	Floating Bait	Floating Rings - Game	Ground Baiting	Hair Rigs	Keep Nets	More than one rod	Number of Rods Allowed	Particle Baits	Spinners	Unhooking Mats essential	Wading	Worms Only
BELLBROOK VALLEY (FH0377)								●	●																
BICKERTON FARM FISHERY (FH0406)																			●						
BLUE LAKE (FH0509)			●																						
CAMEL (RIVER) (FH0811)		●					●	●	●													●			
CAMEL (RIVER) (FH0810)		●						●	●			●										●		●	
CLAWFORD FISHERIES (FH0985)			●					●	●					●		●			●		●		●		
COOMBE FISHERIES (FH1106)	●		●	●		●	●					●		●		●	●	●	●	2	●		●	●	
COOMBE WATER FISHERY (FH1110)			●	●		●	●							●				●	●	2					
CREEDY LAKES (FH1176)	●		●	●		●	●			●	●		●	●		●	●		●	3	●		●		
CULM (RIVER) (FH1218)		●	●															●	●		●	●			
DEER PARK COUNTRY HOTEL (FH1324)								●	●																
DORES POND - RACKERHAYES (FH1413)			●																	2			●		
DRAKELANDS GAME FISHERY (FH1435)								●	●																
EGGESFORD WATERS (FH1551)								●	●										●						
EXE (RIVER) (FH1643)	●		●	●									●				●					●			●
EXE (RIVER) (FH1640)		●						●	●													●		●	
EXE (RIVER) (FH1639)		●	●															●	●		●	●			
EXEMOOR FARM (FH1646)																			●						
EXETER SHIP CANAL (FH1648)		●	●											●		●		●	●		●	●			
FENECK POND (FH1695)		●	●															●	●		●	●			
FISHPONDS HOUSE (FH1736)	●			●								●		●			●		●	2	●		●		
FOSFELLE COUNTRY HOUSE HOTEL (FH1774)			●				●	●	●				●					●	●			●			
FOUR PONDS (FH1781)			●																						
HARTSMOOR FISHERIES (FH2121)	●		●	●						●				●		●	●	●		2	●		●		
HATCHLAND TROUT FISHERY (FH2129)								●	●							●			●						
HOGSBROOK LAKES (FH2246)																			●				●		
HOME FARM FISHERY (FH2280)	●			●										●			●		●	2					
INDIO POND (FH2365)	●		●	●	●	●				●	●		●	●			●		●	2	●	●	●	●	●
ISLAND POND - RACKERHAYES (FH2391)			●																●				●		
KINGSMEAD CENTRE (FH2515)																●		●							
LEGGE FARM COARSE FISHERY (FH2688)																			●						
LUCCOMBES PONDS (FH3101)			●	●												●		●	●	2	●				
MILEMEAD FISHERIES (FH3274)	●		●	●									●	●		●	●		●	2	●				
MILL LEAT TROUT FISHERY (FH3291)		●						●	●																
MILL PARK COARSE FISHING LAKE (FH3297)																		●	●						
MILLHAYES (FH3313)							●							●		●		●	●				●		
MILTON FARM PONDS (FH3319)																			●						
NEW BARN ANGLING CENTRE (FH3461)																●	●		●	2			●		
NEWCOURT PONDS (FH3482)																		●	●						
NEWHOUSE FISHERY (FH3486)		●						●	●										●						
OAKTREE FISHERY (FH3568)			●															●	●				●		
OLDBOROUGH FISHING RETREAT (FH3604)	●			●						●			●	●			●		●	2	●	●	●		●
OTTER (RIVER) (FH3630)	●			●	●			●	●															●	
OTTER FALLS FISHERY (FH3631)	●			●		●		●	●																
PADBROOK PARK (FH3681)							●												●				●		
RIVERTON HOUSE AND LAKES (FH3970)	●		●	●						●				●		●	●	●	●	3	●	●	●		
SALMONHUTCH COARSE FISHERY (FH4087)			●				●											●	●				●		
SAMPFORD PEVERAL PONDS (FH4090)		●	●															●	●		●	●			
SIMPSON VALLEY FISHERY (FH4274)																			●						
SLAPTON LEY (FH4294)			●				●	●	●									●				●			
SOUTH VIEW FARM FISHERY (FH4344)																			●				●		
STEVENSTONE LAKES (FH4452)							●							●				●	●				●		
STILL WATERS TROUT FISHERY (FH4456)								●	●																
SUMMERLEAZE POND (FH4554)		●	●	●															●	2				●	
SUNRIDGE FISHERY (FH4557)		●	●	●		●	●			●	●							●					●		
TAMAR (RIVER) (FH4642)																								●	
TAMAR LAKE (LOWER) (FH4644)	●																								
TAVISTOCK TROUT FISHERY (FH4670)	●				●			●	●										●	2					
TAW FISHING CLUB (FH4674)								●	●																
TINNEY WATERS (FH4855)							●							●					●				●		
TORRIDGE (RIVER) (FH4885)																			●						
TORRIDGE (RIVER) (FH4883)		●						●	●													●		●	
TOWN PARKS COARSE FISHERY (FH4893)	●		●	●				●	●					●		●	●	●	●	3	●		●		
TRAGO MILLS (FH4903)																			●						
TRENCHFORD RESERVOIR (FH4915)																						●			
UPHAM FARM PONDS (FH5050)	●	●	●		●									●					●		●		●		
UPPER YEALM FISHERY (FH5061)		●						●	●													●			
UPTON WARREN LAKE (FH5062)														●		●		●	●		●		●		

FISHING ALLOWANCES

England (by County)

Fishing Allowances UK & Irish Fisheries

Fishery	Bank Fishing Only	Barbed Hooks	Boilies	Catch & Release	Kill All Fish Caught	Dead Bait	Live Bait	Dry Fly	Wet Fly	Electric Bait Boats	Sonar Boats	Fixed Weights Allowed	Floater Fish	Floating Bait	Floating Rings - Game	Ground Baiting	Hair Rigs	Keep Nets	More than one rod	Number of Rods Allowed	Particle Baits	Spinners	Unhooking Mats essential	Wading	Worms Only
VALLEY SPRINGS TROUT FISHERY (FH5088)	●		●					●	●			●		●			●				●		●		
WAPPERWELL POND (FH5146)																●									
WATERCRESS FARM TROUT FISHERY (FH5174)								●	●																
WEST PITT FARM FISHERY (FH5264)																		●	●		●				
WILLOWFIELD LAKE COTTAGES (FH5393)			●	●										●			●		●	2	●		●		
WISCOMBE FISHERY (FH5433)	●	●			●		●	●	●			●		●			●	●				●			
WISTLANDPOUND RESERVOIR (FH5436)								●	●																
WOODACOTT ARMS (FH5464)																			●						
DORSET																									
AMHERST LODGE FISHERY (FH0101)								●	●																
AVON TYRRELL LAKES (FH0230)	●	●	●	●		●						●		●		●	●		●	2	●		●		
CHRISTCHURCH LOWER STOUR (FH0948)			●																						
DORSET FROME (FH1417)	●	●		●		●										●		●							
FLOWERS FARM TROUT LAKES (FH1750)		●			●			●	●										●	2					
HAMPSHIRE AVON (RIVER) (FH2087)																			●						
HARROW POND (FH2111)														●											
HERMITAGE LAKES (FH2189)	●		●		●	●		●	●					●						2	●				
HYDE LAKE (FH2353)																			●						
KINGCOMBE COARSE FARM (FH2492)	●		●	●				●	●			●		●		●	●	●	●		●		●		
KINGCOMBE LAKE (FH2493)	●			●								●		●		●	●	●	●	2	●				
LUCKFIELD LAKE FISHERY (FH3102)													●	●											
PALLINGTON LAKES (FH3687)	●		●	●										●			●		●	3			●		
RADIPOLE LAKE (FH3875)			●																●						
ROYALTY FISHERY (FH4049)		●	●				●	●	●									●	●		●				
STOUR (DORSET) (RIVER) (FH4488)							●																		
STOUR (DORSET) (RIVER) (FH4485)						●										●						●			
STOUR (DORSET) (RIVER) (FH4489)	●	●		●		●		●	●			●				●		●	●	2		●			
STOUR (DORSET) (RIVER) (FH4479)						●	●							●											
STOUR (DORSET) (RIVER) (FH4478)																		●							
STOUR (DORSET) (RIVER) (FH4490)						●	●											●							
STOUR (RIVER) (FH4493)		●														●		●	●						
TODBER MANOR (FH4862)			●											●		●	●	●	●	2	●				
WALLYS LAKE (FH5124)			●											●		●			●				●		
WESSEX TROUT LAKES (FH5254)	●				●			●	●																
WHITEMOOR LAKE (FH5351)																●									
WHITESHEET TROUT FISHERY (FH5353)								●	●																
WINKTON FISHERY (FH5418)		●	●				●						●					●	●		●				
ESSEX																									
ALBYNS LAKE (FH0053)																●		●	●						
ARDLEIGH RESERVOIR (FH0130)	●	●	●			●						●		●		●	●	●		2	●	●			
ARMIGERS FARM (FH0138)			●															●	●	2					
ASHELDHAM FISHERY (FH0160)			●															●	●	2		●			
BARLEYLANDS RESERVOIR (FH0310)			●															●	●	2					
BEDFORDS PARK LAKE (FH0365)																			●						
BERWICK PONDS (FH0393)																●			●						
BIRDS GREEN (FH0428)																			●	2					
BLACKMORE WOOD (FH0452)		●	●										●	●		●		●	●			●	●		
BLACKWATER (RIVER) (FH0477)		●	●															●	●	2		●			
BLASFORD HILL FISHERIES (FH0492)			●										●			●							●		
BLUNTS AND CANTS MERES (FH0516)		●	●													●		●	●		●		●		
BORDEAUX PIT (FH0545)			●											●				●			●		●		
BOREHAM FISHERY (FH0548)		●	●				●									●		●	●		●				
BOREHAM MERES (FH0549)		●	●				●									●			●		●	●	●		
BOVINGTON MERE 1 (FH0569)			●													●	●	●	●	3	●				
BOVINGTON MERE 2 (FH0570)			●													●	●	●	●	3	●				
BRAXTED HALL ESTATE (FH0605)		●	●				●						●					●	●		●	●	●		
BRICKHOUSE FARM FISHERIES (FH0621)								●	●									●							
BROAD GREEN AND TUFNELL MERE (FH0663)		●	●															●	●		●		●		
BROOKHALL FISHERY (FH0682)			●													●			●	2	●				
BULPHAN PARK FISHERIES (FH0730)													●						●						
BURROWS FARM (FH0754)			●										●												
CARP FARM FRYERNING FISHERIES (FH0845)			●				●	●	●	●	●		●	●		●		●	●		●	●	●		
CHASE FISHERY (FH0907)			●				●									●		●	●				●		
CHELMER & BLACKWATER (FH0913)		●	●					●	●									●	●		●	●			
CHELMER (RIVER) (FH0910)		●	●				●											●	●		●	●			
CHELMER (RIVER) (FH0911)		●	●				●						●					●	●			●			
CHIGBOROUGH (FH0940)		●	●				●			●	●		●	●		●		●	●		●				
CHIGBOROUGH FISHERIES (FH0941)	●	●	●	●	●	●		●	●								●		●	3			●		

FISHING ALLOWANCES

England (by County)

Fishing Allowances UK & Irish Fisheries

FISHING ALLOWANCES

England (by County)

Fishery	Bank Fishing Only	Barbed Hooks	Boilies	Catch & Release	Kill All Fish Caught	Dead Bait	Live Bait	Dry Fly	Wet Fly	Electric Bait Boats	Sonar Boats	Fixed Weights Allowed	Floater Fish	Floating Bait	Floating Rings - Game	Ground Baiting	Hair Rigs	Keep Nets	More than one rod	Number of Rods Allowed	Particle Baits	Spinners	Unhooking Mats essential	Wading	Worms Only
CHURCHWOOD FISHERIES (FH0957)																			●						
CLAVERHAMBURY LAKE (FH0982)			●																●		●				
CONNAUGHT WATER (FH1087)			●																●		●				
CROW GREEN FISHERY (FH1197)			●																●		●		●		
CROWN NETHERHALL (FH1201)			●										●						●				●		
DODDS FARM (FH1389)		●	●											●				●				●	●		
DONYLANDS LAKES (FH1406)		●	●				●			●			●					●	●		●	●	●		
EWSONS WATER (FH1638)			●															●	●	2					
FAIRLOP EAST LAKE (FH1653)																			●						
FENNES FISHERIES (FH1697)			●				●									●		●	●						
FISHERS GREEN (FH1731)		●	●				●						●	●		●		●	●		●				
GARNISH HALL (FH1837)			●														●			1			●		
GLOUCESTER PARK LAKE (FH1900)	●	●	●	●		●								●		●	●	●	●	3	●				
GREAT MYLES LAKE (FH1984)																			●						
GREEN OAKS TROUT FISHERY (FH2003)																			●	2					
HANNINGFIELD TROUT FISHERY (FH2101)		●						●	●																
HARWOOD HALL LAKE (FH2125)			●													●	●	●	●	2			●		
HOCKLEY LAKES (FH2239)																			●						
HOLYFIELD FISHERY (FH2278)			●															●	●	2			●		
HOOKS MARSH (FH2289)		●	●				●						●	●		●		●	●		●	●			
HOUCHINS RESERVOIRS (FH2315)			●													●	●	●	●	3	●				
JACKLETTS FARM (FH2405)			●											●		●		●	●	2		●			
JIMMYS LAKE (FH2411)																			●						
JOHNS LAKE FISHERIES (FH2414)	●		●	●												●	●		●	2			●		●
KENNEL LANE (FH2434)		●	●															●					●		
LAKE MEADOWS (FH2562)	●	●	●	●		●								●		●	●	●	●	4	●		●		
LAYER PIT (FH2639)																●		●	●	2	●				
LEE FLOOD RELIEF CHANNEL (FH2661)																			●	2					
LITTLE BRAXTED FARM ESTATE (FH2742)		●	●													●		●	●		●		●		
LITTLE EASTON FISHERIES (FH2750)			●							●															
LITTLE EASTON MANOR (FH2751)	●		●	●		●						●		●		●	●	●		2		●	●		
MAYBRAND FISHERY (FH3214)																●									
MILL BARN FISHERY (FH3279)			●	●		●	●	●	●			●		●		●	●		●	4	●	●	●	●	●
MILLENNIUM LAKES (FH3309)																			●						
MOATHOUSE LAKE (FH3330)		●	●															●					●		
NAZEING MEADS (FH3431)		●	●				●						●	●		●		●	●	3			●		
NEWLAND HALL CARP FISHERY (FH3487)							●	●	●				●						●	2	●	●	●		
NORTHLANDS PARK (FH3546)		●	●	●		●	●							●		●	●	●	●	4	●	●			
NUPERS FARM (FH3555)																			●	2			●		
OLIVERS LAKE (FH3608)	●		●	●												●	●	●	●	3	●				
PANT (RIVER) (FH3690)		●	●															●	●	2		●			
PANT (RIVER) (FH3689)		●	●															●	●						
PAR (FH3695)			●																						
PARSONAGE FARM (FH3712)			●																			●			
PEA LANE FISHERY (FH3722)			●														●		●	2			●		
PICKS COTTAGE CARP LAKES (FH3768)			●																						
PIPPS HILL FISHERIES (FH3788)																			●						
PRESTONS LAKE (FH3842)			●													●	●		●	3	●				
RAPHAELS PARK (FH3888)																			●						
RAYNE LODGE FARM (FH3903)																			●						
RECTORY FARM POND (FH3906)			●															●	●	2		●			
ROCHFORD RESERVOIR (FH3981)																			●						
ROCKELLS FARM (FH3983)							●											●	●						
RODING (RIVER) (FH3991)		●																●	●			●			
RODING (RIVER) (FH3993)		●																●	●			●			
RODING (RIVER) (FH3992)		●																●	●			●			
RODING VALLEY LAKE (FH3994)																			●						
SHALFORD RESERVOIRS (FH4204)			●											●											
SLOUGH HOUSE LAKE (FH4301)	●		●											●		●	●		●	2			●		
SOUTHMINSTER FISHERIES (FH4352)			●															●	●			●			
STANFORD-LE-HOPE (FH4418)		●	●				●			●	●		●	●		●		●	●		●	●			
STRAITS MILL (FH4518)			●															●	●			●			
VALENCE MOAT (FH5085)																				1			●		
WAKE VALLEY POND (FH5114)			●																●		●		●		
WARREN (FH5150)			●																●						
WHARF POOL (FH5295)		●	●				●			●	●		●	●		●		●	●		●	●	●		
WICK MERE (FH5363)		●	●				●											●	●		●	●	●		
WID (RIVER) (FH5366)		●	●				●						●					●				●			

Fishing Allowances UK & Irish Fisheries

	Bank Fishing Only	Barbed Hooks	Boilies	Catch & Release	Kill All Fish Caught	Dead Bait	Live Bait	Dry Fly	Wet Fly	Electric Bait Boats	Sonar Boats	Fixed Weights Allowed	Floater Fish	Floating Bait	Floating Rings - Game	Ground Baiting	Hair Rigs	Keep Nets	More than one rod	Number of Rods Allowed	Particle Baits	Spinners	Unhooking Mats essential	Wading	Worms Only
WILLOWS (FH5395)		●	●													●		●	●				●		
FIFE																									
WEY (RIVER) (FH5289)		●	●				●			●	●		●	●		●		●	●		●	●			
GLOUCESTERSHIRE																									
ADLESTROP LAKE (FH0027)	●		●	●		●								●			●	●	●	2	●		●		
AVON (RIVER) (FH0205)																			●						
BOURTON-ON-THE-WATER PIT NO1 (FH0568)	●	●	●	●		●						●		●		●	●	●				●	●		
BROOK FARM TROUT FISHERY (FH0677)	●				●			●	●																
BUSHYLEAZE TROUT FISHERY (FH0770)		●						●	●																
COKES PIT (FH1056)	●		●	●		●				●		●		●		●	●	●	●	3	●	●	●		
COLN (RIVER) (FH1066)								●																	
COTSWOLD HOBURNE (FH1131)		●	●				●							●		●			●		●		●		
DONNINGTON TROUT FISHERY (FH1405)								●	●																
GLOUCESTER CANAL (FH1898)																●									
HAM POOL (FH2078)			●																						
HILL VIEW LAKES (FH2223)													●	●									●		
HILLVIEW FISHERY (FH2228)																			●						
ISIS NO 1 LAKE 19 (FH2386)		●	●				●	●	●	●	●		●	●		●		●	●		●	●	●		
KEYNES COUNTRY PARK (FH2475)	●		●	●		●				●		●		●		●	●	●	●	3	●	●	●		
KEYNES PARK TOP LAKE (FH2476)			●										●	●		●		●	●		●		●		
LAKE NUMBER ONE (LAKE19) (FH2565)		●	●				●	●	●	●			●					●	●		●	●			
LECHLADE TROUT FISHERY (FH2656)		●						●	●																
LEMINGTON LAKES (FH2696)																			●						
LIGHTMOOR POOL (FH2719)																		●	●						
MARIONS POOL (FH3181)														●				●	●				●		
MEADOWCLIFFE POOL (FH3226)	●			●								●		●			●	●	●		●				
MILESTONE FISHERY (FH3275)			●													●			●	2	●		●		
NEIGH BRIDGE LAKE (FH3437)			●										●	●		●		●	●		●		●		
NORTON FRUIT FARM (FH3548)							●	●	●	●	●								●				●		
PLUMP HILL POOL (FH3806)														●					●						
RED LION FISHERY (FH3910)			●				●											●	●			●			
SEVERN (RIVER) (FH4147)																		●							
STAUNTON COURT LAKES (FH4441)	●		●									●	●	●			●	●	●	2	●		●		
STEAM MILLS LAKE (FH4444)														●		●		●	●				●		
WATERLOO SCREENS (FH5179)														●				●	●				●		
WATERSMEET LAKES (FH5186)																		●							
WHELFORD POOLS COARSE FISHERY (FH5319)	●		●	●		●				●	●			●		●	●		●	2	●	●	●		
WITCOMBE WATERS (FH5437)								●	●																
HAMPSHIRE																									
ABBOTTS WORTHY (FH0011)								●										●							
ANTON LAKE (FH0118)																			●						
AVON RIVER FISHERIES (FH0228)		●					●	●	●										●						
BASINGSTOKE CANAL (FH0342)																●									
BILCOMBES POND (FH0415)			●														●		●				●		●
BROADLANDS LAKES (FH0664)			●				●	●	●				●						●			●	●		
BROADLANDS MAIN LAKE (FH0665)			●			●	●												●	2					
CHIPHALL LAKE TROUT FISHERY (FH0943)								●	●																
COOKS POND (FH1100)	●	●		●								●				●	●	●	●	2					
DARK LANE PONDS (FH1274)																●	●	●	●	2			●		
DEVER SPRINGS TROUT FISHERY (FH1362)								●	●																
EAST MOORS LAKE (FH1511)																			●	2			●		
FRIMLEY LAKES (FH1802)	●	●	●				●			●	●		●	●		●	●	●	●	4		●	●		
GOLD VALLEY LAKES (FH1909)			●														●								
GOLDEN POND FISHERY (FH1912)																●			●				●		
GREENRIDGE FARM LAKES (FH2009)	●			●			●					●		●		●	●	●	●	2	●		●		
HAMPSHIRE AVON (RIVER) (FH2089)			●																●						
HAMPSHIRE AVON (RIVER) (FH2092)	●			●																				●	
HATCHET POND (FH2128)			●																●		●	●	●		
HOLBURY LAKES (FH2247)	●	●			●			●	●																
HOLLYBUSH LANE LAKES (FH2262)			●															●	●		●	●			
HURST POND (FH2346)		●	●				●						●	●		●		●	●	2	●		●		
ITCHEN (RIVER) (FH2397)								●																	
JANESMOOR POND (FH2406)			●																●		●	●	●		
KIMBRIDGE (FH2488)								●										●							
LAKE FARM (FH2556)														●									●		
LAKESIDE (FH2581)																●									
LAKESIDE COUNTRY PARK (FH2589)		●	●													●		●	●		●		●		
LEOMINSTEAD TROUT FISHERY (FH2703)	●	●			●			●	●																

Fishing Allowances UK & Irish Fisheries

Fishery	Bank Fishing Only	Barbed Hooks	Boilies	Catch & Release	Kill All Fish Caught	Dead Bait	Live Bait	Dry Fly	Wet Fly	Electric Bait Boats	Sonar Boats	Fixed Weights Allowed	Floater Fish	Floating Bait	Floating Rings - Game	Ground Baiting	Hair Rigs	Keep Nets	More than one rod	Number of Rods Allowed	Particle Baits	Spinners	Unhooking Mats essential	Wading	Worms Only
LONGBRIDGE LAKES (FH2987)																			●						
MEON SPRINGS FLY FISHERY (FH3255)		●						●	●									●	●				●		
MILL POND LAKE (FH3300)			●											●		●		●	●		●		●		
MOORHEN FARM TROUT LAKE (FH3361)								●	●																
MOORS VALLEY COUNTRY PARK (FH3366)																			●						
MOPLEY POND (FH3367)	●		●														●		●	2			●		
NETHER WALLOP (FH3452)								●	●																
NEW FOREST WATER PARK (FH3464)	●		●	●		●								●		●	●		●	2	●	●	●		
NORTHFIELD LAKES (FH3544)		●	●													●		●	●	3		●	●		
NUTRABAITS YATELEY COMPLEX (FH3556)			●				●						●	●		●			●		●		●		
NUTRABAITS YATELEY SOUTH LAKE (FH3557)																			●				●		
ORCHARD LAKES (FH3616)																			●						
PARSONAGE (RIVER) TEST (FH3711)	●			●				●																	
PETERSFIELD HEATH LAKE (FH3757)																							●		
RIVER FARM (FH3964)		●						●	●																
ROCKBOURNE TROUT FISHERY (FH3982)								●	●																
ROCKFORD LAKE (FH3984)			●																●				●		
ROOKSBURY MILL (FH4007)		●						●	●																
SOMERLEY LAKES (FH4322)			●				●						●					●	●		●	●			
SWAY LAKES (FH4605)			●																●				●		
TEST (RIVER) (FH4745)								●										●	●						
WHINWHISTLE COARSE FISHERY (FH5324)																●			●	3					
WILLOW PARK (FH5387)			●													●			●	2					
WINTERSHILL TROUT LAKE (FH5430)		●						●	●																
WOODINGTON FISHERY (FH5476)								●	●																
WOODMILL SALMON FISHERY (FH5488)								●	●				●									●	●		
HEREFORDSHIRE																									
CARADOC FISHERY (FH0836)																			●						
DOCKLOW POOLS (FH1386)	●		●							●				●			●		●	3			●		
DRUMMOND DUB (FH1450)		●	●										●					●	●		●		●		
HAYCASTLE WATER (FH2150)	●	●				●		●	●					●		●		●				●		●	
INGESTONE FISHERY (FH2366)																			●						
KINGFISHER TROUT LAKE (FH2502)	●	●		●	●			●	●											1					
MARSH HOUSE FARM (FH3192)																		●	●		●		●		
MILLPOND (FH3314)	●													●			●	●	●	3	●		●		
MOCCAS FISHERY (FH3333)							●												●		●		●		
MUNDERFIELD HAROLD (FH3402)																		●	●						
PIXLEY POOL (FH3797)			●										●			●	●	●							
REDMIRE POOL (FH3921)			●														●		●		●		●		
WYE (RIVER) (FH5530)								●	●													●			
HERTFORDSHIRE																									
ADMIRALS WALK LAKE (FH0029)		●	●				●						●	●		●		●	●	2			●		
ALDENHAM RESERVOIR (FH0058)			●					●	●							●			●	2	●	●	●		
AMWELL LAKES (FH0104)		●	●				●			●	●		●	●		●		●	●		●	●	●		
BATCHWORTH LAKE (FH0346)																			●	4					
BIERTON FISHING LAKES (FH0410)	●		●	●						●	●	●		●		●	●		●	2	●	●			
BOWMANS LAKES (FH0574)	●	●	●	●		●	●	●	●	●	●		●	●		●	●	●	●	3	●	●	●	●	
BOWYERS WATER (FH0576)		●	●				●						●			●		●	●	3	●				
BROAD COLNEY LAKES (FH0662)		●																				●			
CARTHAGENA FISHERY (FH0855)	●	●	●			●								●		●	●	●	●	2	●				
CROXLEY HALL TROUT FISHERY (FH1203)								●	●																
DOBBS WEIR FISHERY (FH1381)		●	●				●						●	●		●		●	●	2			●		
GAYWOODS (FH1845)																			●						
GRAND UNION CANAL (FH1944)		●	●											●		●		●	●		●		●		
GRAND UNION CANAL (FH1947)		●	●											●		●		●	●		●		●		
HOLWELL HYDE LAKE (FH2275)																		●							
HOOK LAKE (FH2288)		●	●				●			●	●		●	●		●			●		●	●	●		
INNS LAKE (FH2371)																			●						
KINGS WEIR FISHERY (FH2509)																			●						
LEA (RIVER) (FH2645)																			●	2					
LEE NAVIGATION (FH2662)		●	●				●	●	●				●					●	●		●	●			
LOWBELL LANE (FH3069)		●																●			●				
MERCHANT TAYLORS SCL LAKES (FH3257)																			●						
NORTH MET PIT (FH3532)	●		●	●												●	●					●			
OAKFIELD FISHERY (FH3561)	●		●											●			●		●	2	●				
OLD MILL AND MEADOWS (FH3594)		●	●				●						●	●		●		●	●	2	●	●	●		
PIXIES MERE (FH3796)													●	●		●			●		●	●	●		
RYEMEADS (FH4076)		●	●				●			●	●		●	●		●		●	●		●	●			

FISHING ALLOWANCES

England (by County)

Fishing Allowances UK & Irish Fisheries

	Bank Fishing Only	Barbed Hooks	Boilies	Catch & Release	Kill All Fish Caught	Dead Bait	Live Bait	Dry Fly	Wet Fly	Electric Bait Boats	Sonar Boats	Fixed Weights Allowed	Floater Fish	Floating Bait	Floating Rings - Game	Ground Baiting	Hair Rigs	Keep Nets	More than one rod	Number of Rods Allowed	Particle Baits	Spinners	Unhooking Mats essential	Wading	Worms Only
SLIPE LANE PITS (FH4299)		●	●				●						●	●		●		●	●	2		●			
STANSTEAD ABBOTTS (FH4423)		●	●				●						●	●		●		●	●	4	●	●			
TRING RESERVOIRS (FH4957)	●					●	●					●		●		●	●		●	2	●	●			
WORMLEBURY (FH5505)																			●						
HUMBERSIDE																									
AIRE AND CALDER CANAL (FH0047)	●	●		●		●						●		●			●		●	2	●	●			
BEVERLEY CANAL (FH0400)																●									
BIG HOLE PIT (FH0411)	●	●	●	●								●		●		●	●	●	●	3	●	●			
BILLABONG PARK (FH0416)																			●						
BLUE LAGOON (FH0505)		●	●				●						●					●	●		●	●			
BRANDESBURTON (FH0600)		●	●				●			●			●					●	●		●	●			
BRICKYARD POND (FH0626)		●	●				●			●			●					●	●		●	●			
BURTON CONSTABLE COUNTRY PARK (FH0759)			●	●		●						●				●	●		●	2	●	●	●		
DACRE LAKESIDE PARK (FH1244)																			●						
EMMOTLAND PONDS (FH1587)	●	●	●	●		●				●				●		●	●	●	●	3	●				
FAR GRANGE PARK (FH1663)	●			●				●	●			●		●		●	●		●	2	●		●		
FISHPONDS FARM AND FISHERY (FH1735)										●									●				●		
HALSHAM POND (FH2075)							●												●						
HULL (RIVER) (FH2332)						●										●									
MOTORWAY POND (FH3382)		●	●				●			●			●						●		●	●			
NODDLE HILL LAKE (FH3513)	●			●								●		●		●	●	●	●	2					
STAR CARR TROUT FARM (FH4427)				●		●	●	●	●			●		●		●	●	●			●	●			
THORPE HALL (FH4822)																			●						
TILARY LAKE (FH4841)		●	●				●			●			●					●	●	3	●	●			
WILLITOFT FISH FARM (FH5376)	●			●																					
WOODALLS POND (FH5465)																			●						
ISLE OF WIGHT																									
GUNVILLE LAKE (FH2038)			●											●		●		●	●		●		●		
ISLAND FISH FARM/MEADOW LAKES (FH2390)	●		●	●			●	●	●					●			●			2	●				
MERSTONE FISHERIES (FH3258)			●							●	●		●	●		●			●		●		●		
MORTON FARM (FH3373)			●																●				●		
KENT																									
ALDERS LAKES (FH0064)																●		●	●	3					
BALLAST PIT (FH0259)		●	●											●		●		●	●	2			●		
BARDEN LAKE (FH0304)			●																●	2					
BARTLEY MILL FISHERY (FH0336)																			●						
BEWL WATER (FH0403)		●			●			●	●															●	
BIRCHDEN FARM FISHERY (FH0426)			●																●		●				
BLUE LAGOON LAKE (FH0507)			●			●											●		●	2		●	●		
BOUGH BEECH RESERVOIR (FH0564)		●	●				●	●	●	●			●					●	●		●	●	●		
BYWATER LAKE (FH0785)								●	●	●			●	●		●		●	●		●				
CACKLE HILL LAKES (FH0787)																			●						
CAPSTONE FARM COUNTRY PARK (FH0834)																●			●	2					
CHEQUERTREE FISHERY (FH0914)				●				●	●										●				●		
CHILHAM LAKE (FH0942)			●														●		●			●	●		●
CONNINGBROOK (FH1088)			●			●											●		●			●	●		
COTTINGTON LAKES (FH1137)			●				●	●	●									●	●				●		
DARENT (RIVER) (FH1272)		●						●	●																
DARENTH FISHING COMPLEX (FH1273)		●	●				●	●	●				●						●		●	●			
DUNDALE LAKE (FH1474)			●										●	●					●						
EDEN (RIVER) (FH1542)		●												●		●		●	●		●				
FRANT LAKES (FH1798)	●		●	●		●								●		●	●			2	●		●		●
HANDLE LAKE (FH2100)			●			●											●		●			●	●		
HARTLEY LANDS FARM (FH2118)																●									
HAWKHURST FISH FARM (FH2142)	●		●	●		●	●									●	●	●	●	2	●		●		●
HAYES TROUT FISHERY (FH2153)								●	●																
HAYSDEN COUNTRY PARK (FH2160)		●	●				●						●					●	●			●			
HOOKSTEAD LAKE (FH2290)																		●	●						
LARKFIELD LAKES (FH2625)		●	●				●			●	●		●	●		●		●	●		●	●	●		
LITTLE CANSIRON FISHING LAKES (FH2745)	●		●	●								●		●		●	●		●	2			●		
LONGFIELD LAKE (FH2988)		●	●													●		●	●				●		
MATCH LAKE (FH3208)																	●								●
MEDWAY (RIVER) (FH3233)			●														●					●			●
MEDWAY (RIVER) (FH3238)		●	●				●						●					●	●			●			
MEDWAY (RIVER) (FH3239)		●	●				●											●	●			●			
MEDWAY (RIVER) (FH3236)		●														●		●	●						
MEDWAY (RIVER) (FH3232)						●	●									●						●			●
MID KENT FISHERIES (FH3263)		●	●				●	●					●					●	●			●	●		

FISHING ALLOWANCES

England (by County)

Fishing Allowances UK & Irish Fisheries

Fishery	Bank Fishing Only	Barbed Hooks	Boilies	Catch & Release	Kill All Fish Caught	Dead Bait	Live Bait	Dry Fly	Wet Fly	Electric Bait Boats	Sonar Boats	Fixed Weights Allowed	Floater Fish	Floating Bait	Floating Rings - Game	Ground Baiting	Hair Rigs	Keep Nets	More than one rod	Number of Rods Allowed	Particle Baits	Spinners	Unhooking Mats essential	Wading	Worms Only
MILL POOL (FH3301)			●			●											●		●	2		●	●		
MILTON PAN LAKE (FH3323)																				3					
MONK LAKE FISHERIES (FH3342)			●										●						●				●		
NACCOLT LAKE (FH3408)			●			●											●		●			●	●		
NOOK & CRANNY LAKE (FH3514)			●			●											●		●	2		●	●		
REED LAKE (FH3923)			●			●											●		●	2		●	●		
ROOKERY LAKE (FH4004)	●	●	●	●									●			●	●		●				●		
ROYAL MILITARY CANAL (FH4046)			●														●					●			●
SILVER SPRINGS FISHERY (FH4270)																			●						
SINGLETON LAKE (FH4276)																●		●	●						
ST CLERE LAKE (FH4383)			●			●											●		●				●		
STOUR (RIVER) (FH4499)																	●								●
STOUR LAKE (FH4506)			●														●		●				●		●
STOWTING TROUT LAKE (FH4514)								●	●																
SURRENDEN LAKES (FH4558)																●			●						
SUTTON AT HONE LAKE TWO (FH4559)		●	●				●			●	●		●	●		●		●	●		●	●	●		
SUTTON AT HONE LAKES 1 & 3 (FH4560)		●	●				●			●	●		●	●		●		●	●		●	●			
SWAN LAKE (FH4591)			●			●											●		●			●	●		
TEISE (RIVER) (FH4720)	●		●	●		●								●		●	●		●	3			●		●
TENTERDEN TROUT WATERS (FH4738)	●			●				●	●																
TONFORD LAKE (FH4871)			●			●											●		●			●	●		
TRIANGLE LAKE (FH4952)			●			●											●		●	2		●	●		
WIDEHURST FARM (FH5367)			●				●												●		●		●		
WINGHAM FISHERY (FH5417)																				4					
WOOD POOL (FH5461)			●			●											●		●	2		●	●		
LANCASHIRE																									
BALL GROVE LAKE (FH0258)	●	●	●	●						●	●	●		●		●	●	●	●	2	●		●		
BANK HOUSE FLY FISHERY (FH0286)	●	●		●				●	●																
BARNSFOLD WATERS (FH0318)								●	●																
BRADFORD RESERVOIR (FH0587)			●																						
BRADSHAW HALL FISHERIES (FH0591)																●			●		●		●		
CALDER (RIVER) (FH0792)								●	●																
CLIVIGER FISH PONDS (FH1012)	●	●	●	●				●	●			●		●		●	●	●	●	2	●				
COLNE WATER (FH1075)								●	●													●			
COPTHORNE COARSE FISHERIES (FH1115)																		●			●				
CROFT FISHERIES (FH1182)																		●	●						
DEAN CLOUGH RESERVOIR (FH1287)								●	●																
DEEP PIT (FH1323)																●									
DIXON GREEN RESERVOIR (FH1380)		●												●		●		●	●		●	●			
DOFFCOCKER LODGE (FH1392)		●	●					●	●				●	●		●		●	●		●	●	●		
DRAKESHEAD FLY FISHERY (FH1436)								●	●																
ERIC FISHWICK NATURE RESERVE (FH1608)								●	●										●						
FOULRIDGE RESERVOIR (FH1778)	●		●	●		●				●	●	●		●		●	●	●	●	2	●	●		●	
HIGHER HALL FLASH (FH2215)																●					●				
HODDER (RIVER) (FH2241)								●	●																
HOLDEN WOOD RESERVOIR (FH2250)	●			●																			●		
JUMBLES RESERVOIR (FH2418)											●		●	●				●	●		●		●		
KNIGHT BOTTOMS LAKE (FH2534)																			●				●		
LITTLE DALE HALL (FH2747)	●	●	●	●								●		●			●	●	●	2			●		
LONGTON BRICKCROFT (FH2996)																			●						
LOVECLOUGH TROUT FISHERY (FH3065)				●				●	●		●			●				●							
LOWER RIVINGTON RESERVOIR (FH3091)																		●	●						
LUNE (RIVER) (FH3112)				●	●			●	●													●			●
OGDEN RESERVOIR (FH3577)	●			●				●	●																
ORRELL WATER PARK (FH3625)	●		●	●		●						●		●		●	●		●	2			●		
PARSONAGE RESERVOIR (FH3713)	●																								
PORTSMOUTH RESERVIOR (FH3831)	●	●		●		●						●		●		●	●	●			●	●		●	
RIBBLE (RIVER) (FH3943)								●	●																
ROUGHLEE TROUT FISHERY (FH4034)				●				●	●																
ST MICHAELS WYRESIDE FISHERY (FH4394)			●										●	●				●	●		●		●		
STOCKS FLY FISHERY (FH4463)		●						●	●																
THURSLAND HILL FARM (FH4838)	●			●			●							●					●	3			●		
TWIN LAKES TROUT FISHERY (FH5004)				●				●	●						●										
WALVERDEN RESERVOIR (FH5137)	●	●	●	●						●	●	●		●		●	●	●			●		●		
WENNING (RIVER) (FH5242)								●	●																
WENNING (RIVER) (FH5243)								●	●															●	
WITHNELL RESERVOIRS (FH5445)		●	●											●		●		●	●		●	●	●		
WOODFOLD FARM FISHERIES (FH5473)																		●	●						

FISHING ALLOWANCES

England (by County)

Fishing Allowances UK & Irish Fisheries

	Bank Fishing Only	Barbed Hooks	Boilies	Catch & Release	Kill All Fish Caught	Dead Bait	Live Bait	Dry Fly	Wet Fly	Electric Bait Boats	Sonar Boats	Fixed Weights Allowed	Floater Fish	Floating Bait	Floating Rings - Game	Ground Baiting	Hair Rigs	Keep Nets	More than one rod	Number of Rods Allowed	Particle Baits	Spinners	Unhooking Mats essential	Wading	Worms Only
WYRESIDE LAKES (FH5550)			●					●	●				●				●		●	3		●	●		
LEICESTERSHIRE																									
BROOME FISHERIES (FH0692)		●	●											●		●		●	●		●				
C J FISHERIES (FH0786)														●				●							
EYEBROOK TROUT FISHERY (FH1649)								●	●																
FRISBY LAKES (FH1803)	●	●				●								●		●		●	●	2		●			
HALL FARM (FH2066)	●			●										●			●	●	●	2	●		●		
HOLLY FARM FISHERY (FH2261)																		●							
LAKESIDE FISHING (FH2593)													●	●											
LYNCHGATE LANE FISHERY (FH3119)			●													●		●	●	2					
MALLORY PARK FISHERIES (FH3152)			●													●							●		
MANOR FARM (FH3161)		●	●											●		●		●	●		●				
MANOR FARM POOLS (FH3165)																			●	2					
MILL FARM FISHERY (FH3280)			●															●	●		●		●		
NANPANTAN RESERVOIR (FH3417)			●																●		●	●	●		
THORNTON RESERVOIR (FH4820)								●	●																
WATERMEAD PARK LAKES (FH5180)	●	●	●	●		●	●					●		●		●	●	●	●	2	●	●			
WATERY GATE FISHERY (FH5187)																●		●							
WHETSTONE GORSE (FH5320)																●			●	2					
WILLOWS FARM FISHING (FH5399)			●							●			●					●	●		●	●			
LINCOLNSHIRE																									
BOULTHAM PARK LAKE (FH0565)		●	●															●	●			●			
BRICKYARD FISHERY (FH0623)	●		●											●		●		●	●	2					
DAIWA GULL POOL (FH1247)	●	●	●	●		●	●			●		●	●	●		●	●		●	4	●	●	●		
DENNIS RAINWATER LAKE (FH1331)																			●						
GOLTHO LAKE (FH1917)	●	●		●										●			●	●	●	2	●	●			
HARTSHOLME PARK LAKE (FH2119)		●	●															●	●			●			
HAVERHOLME PARK (FH2137)																●		●							
HILL VIEW LAKES (FH2224)				●						●	●	●		●			●		●	2					
HOBHOLE DRAIN (FH2238)						●																●			
HOLLAND PARK (FH2255)								●	●									●	●						
KEAL COATES FISHERY (FH2422)			●											●			●		●	2					
LAKE HELEN (FH2558)	●		●									●		●			●	●	●	4	●		●		
LAKE ROSS FISHERY (FH2572)																		●	●	2			●		
LAKESIDE LEISURE PARK (FH2594)			●							●								●	●				●		
LOBBY FIELD PONDS (FH2834)			●											●					●		●				
MILL HILL LAKES (FH3285)																		●							
MILL ROAD LAKES (FH3304)																		●	●						
MOON LAKE (FH3356)																			●	2					
OAKHILL LEISURE (FH3563)	●		●	●						●						●	●		●	3	●		●		
OASIS LAKES (FH3570)	●		●	●						●	●	●		●		●	●	●	●	3	●		●		
OHAM LAKES (FH3583)	●		●									●		●		●	●	●	●	3	●				
PEACOCK LAKE (FH3723)			●													●		●	●	2					
ROACH FARM PARK (FH3972)																		●							
ROSSWAYS WATER (FH4021)			●											●		●		●	●	2	●		●		
SHANDY KEV FISHERIES (FH4207)														●					●				●		
SKEGNESS WATER LEISURE PARK (FH4285)																							●		
STARMERS PIT (FH4433)		●	●															●	●			●			
STICKNEY BRICKPONDS (FH4455)			●			●								●		●									
SUDBROOK POND (FH4533)																			●						
SWAN LAKE (FH4592)			●													●	●	●	●	2					
SYCAMORE FISHING LAKES (FH4618)	●		●	●										●			●	●	●	3			●		
TATTERSHALL LEISURE PARK (FH4663)	●	●	●	●		●				●	●	●		●		●	●	●	●		●	●	●	●	
THORPE LE VALE FISHERY (FH4823)								●	●																
TILL (RIVER) (FH4846)		●	●							●								●	●			●			
TILL (RIVER) (FH4847)		●	●							●								●	●			●			
TOFT NEWTON TROUT FISHERY (FH4864)				●				●	●		●														
TRENT (RIVER) (FH4921)		●	●					●	●	●			●					●	●			●			
TRENT (RIVER) (FH4920)		●	●										●					●	●		●	●			
TRENT (RIVER) (FH4919)		●	●					●	●	●			●					●	●			●			
UPPER WITHAM (RIVER) (FH5060)		●	●				●			●								●	●			●			
VICKERS POND (FH5097)	●			●		●								●			●	●	●			●	●		
WELLAND (RIVER) (FH5233)							●									●									
WEST FEN DRAIN (FH5259)	●	●				●								●		●		●			●				
WHISBY GARDEN CENTRE (FH5329)																●		●							
WHITE HOUSE PREDATOR LAKE (FH5336)						●													●	2		●			
WHITE SWAN ANGLING CLUB (FH5342)		●	●										●					●	●		●	●			
WILLOW BANK FISHERY (FH5377)		●	●				●			●	●		●	●		●		●	●		●	●	●		

Fishing Allowances UK & Irish Fisheries

	Bank Fishing Only	Barbed Hooks	Boilies	Catch & Release	Kill All Fish Caught	Dead Bait	Live Bait	Dry Fly	Wet Fly	Electric Bait Boats	Sonar Boats	Fixed Weights Allowed	Floater Fish	Floating Bait	Floating Rings - Game	Ground Baiting	Hair Rigs	Keep Nets	More than one rod	Number of Rods Allowed	Particle Baits	Spinners	Unhooking Mats essential	Wading	Worms Only
WILLOW LAKES (FH5384)			●										●	●				●	●		●		●		
WOODLAND WATERS (FH5482)																			●						
LINCOLNSHIRE (NORTH)																									
BARTON BROADS LAKE (FH0337)	●															●							●		
HOE HILL POND (FH2245)		●	●													●		●					●		
KINGFISHER LODGE (FH2501)	●	●	●									●		●			●		●	3	●	●			
PASTURE HOUSE FISHERY (FH3716)		●														●		●							
STADDLETHORPE POND (FH4398)																●							●		
TILEYARD LANE (FH4844)		●														●		●					●		
LONDON (GREATER)																									
ASHMERE FISHERIES (FH0167)								●	●																
BEDFONT LAKE (FH0363)		●	●				●							●		●		●	●		●		●		
BOXERS LAKE (FH0577)	●			●										●			●				●		●		
BROOMWOOD LAKE (FH0696)	●	●	●	●												●	●		●	2	●	●	●		●
CARGILL LAKE (FH0841)	●	●	●	●		●	●							●		●	●	●	●		●	●	●	●	●
CLAPHAM COMMON POND (FH0973)																							●		
COPPER MILLSTREAM (FH1111)		●	●				●						●					●	●		●	●	●		
COWLEY LAKE (FH1152)																			●						
GRAND UNION CANAL (FH1956)		●														●		●	●	2					
HALLIFORD MERE LAKES (FH2071)		●		●				●	●						●										
HAMPSTEAD HEATH (FH2094)			●																						
HAREFIELD CARP LAKE (FH2105)		●	●											●		●			●	3	●		●		
HIGH MAYNARD RESERVOIR (FH2207)		●	●				●	●	●				●					●	●		●	●	●		
HIGHAMS PARK LAKE (FH2213)	●		●	●		●	●					●		●		●	●		●	2	●	●	●	●	
HOLLOW PONDS (FH2259)	●		●	●		●	●					●		●		●	●		●	2	●	●	●	●	
HORSEMILL STREAM (FH2306)																			●	2					
LITTLE BRITAIN LAKE (FH2743)		●	●				●						●					●	●		●	●			
LIZARD LAKES (FH2766)			●				●						●	●		●			●		●		●		
LOCKWOOD RESERVOIR (FH2974)		●	●				●	●	●				●					●	●		●	●	●		
LOW MAYNARD RESERVOIR (FH3067)		●	●				●						●					●	●		●	●			
NORTH TROY LAKE & COLNE (FH3536)			●				●						●	●		●			●		●		●		
OSTERLEY PARK MIDDLE LAKE (FH3629)			●																●						
PERCH POND (FH3751)			●					●	●				●						●		●		●		
REGENTS CANAL (FH3928)		●	●				●							●		●		●	●		●				
RODNEY MEADOW (FH3995)																			●						
SHEEPWALK LAKE (FH4218)			●				●	●	●				●					●	●		●	●	●		
SHEPPERTON LAKE (FH4230)		●	●			●	●			●	●		●	●		●		●	●		●	●	●		
STOCKLEY ROAD LAKES (FH4461)		●	●				●							●		●		●	●	2	●	●	●		
SYON PARK FISHERY (FH4621)	●	●			●			●	●																
THORNEY POOL (FH4816)		●	●				●							●		●		●	●		●		●		
VALE OF HEATH POND (FH5083)			●																						
WALTHAMSTOW (NO 2 & NO 3) (FH5131)		●	●				●						●					●	●		●	●	●		
WALTHAMSTOW (EAST WARWICK) (FH5129)								●	●																
WALTHAMSTOW (NO 4 TROUT) (FH5132)		●						●	●													●			
WALTHAMSTOW (WEST WARWICK) (FH5134)		●	●				●						●					●	●		●	●	●		
WALTHAMSTOW RESERVOIR (NO 1) (FH5130)			●				●						●					●	●		●	●	●		
WALTHAMSTOW RESERVOIR (NO 5) (FH5133)								●	●																
WANSTEAD PARK LAKES (FH5145)																			●	2					
WOOLWICH DOCKYARD (FH5501)				●		●								●		●			●	2	●		●		●
WRAYSBURY ONE (FH5513)		●	●				●			●	●		●	●		●		●	●	4	●	●	●		
WRAYSBURY TWO (FH5514)		●	●				●			●	●		●	●		●		●	●		●	●	●		
MANCHESTER (GREATER)																									
ALEXANDRA PARK (FH0072)			●																						
BLACKLEACH RESERVOIR (FH0451)		●																●	●		●	●			
BOGGART HOLE CLOUGH (FH0524)																●									
BRIDGEWATER CANAL (FH0638)						●										●						●			
CARCUS WATERS (FH0838)																							●		
CLEGG HALL LAKES (FH1001)																●			●						
CROFT HEAD FISHERY (FH1183)	●	●	●	●						●		●	●	●		●	●	●	●	2	●	●			
ELTON RESERVOIR (FH1574)																●									
GEIGYS WATER (FH1847)	●	●	●			●	●			●				●		●	●	●	●	2	●	●	●		
GORSE PIT RESERVOIR (FH1922)		●																●	●		●	●			
GROVE LODGE (FH2031)		●	●							●			●					●	●		●	●			
HOLLINGWORTH LAKE (FH2258)	●	●	●	●						●						●		●	●			●	●		
HUDDERSFIELD NARROW CANAL (FH2328)			●													●		●	●		●				
LEEDS TO LIVERPOOL CANAL (FH2677)																●									
LOWER TOWN HOUSE FISHERY (FH3095)	●	●	●	●						●		●	●	●		●	●	●	●	2	●	●			
PENNINE TROUT FISHERY (FH3737)								●	●																

FISHING ALLOWANCES

England (by County)

Fishing Allowances UK & Irish Fisheries

Fishery	Bank Fishing Only	Barbed Hooks	Boilies	Catch & Release	Kill All Fish Caught	Dead Bait	Live Bait	Dry Fly	Wet Fly	Electric Bait Boats	Sonar Boats	Fixed Weights Allowed	Floater Fish	Floating Bait	Floating Rings - Game	Ground Baiting	Hair Rigs	Keep Nets	More than one rod	Number of Rods Allowed	Particle Baits	Spinners	Unhooking Mats essential	Wading	Worms Only
PENNINGTON FLASH (FH3738)																●									
PIETHORNE RESERVOIR (FH3771)		●						●	●																
REDDISH VALE MILL PONDS (FH3913)			●																●	2					
RHODES LODGE (FH3936)	●	●	●	●		●	●			●				●		●	●		●	2	●	●	●		
ROCHDALE CANAL (FH3977)		●	●							●			●					●	●		●	●			
ROYAL GEORGE MILL COMPLEX (FH4044)			●							●						●		●	●		●		●		
STAKEHILL LODGES (FH4411)	●		●	●		●	●							●			●			2	●	●			
TWINE VALLEY TROUT FISHERY (FH5005)			●				●	●	●							●		●			●		●		
WHITELEY KNOWL RESERVOIR (FH5349)	●	●		●				●	●			●				●	●	●				●			
WHITTLE BROOK RESERVOIR (FH5358)		●											●	●		●		●	●		●	●			
MERSEYSIDE																									
CALDERSTONES PARK LAKE (FH0799)			●											●		●	●		●	2					
MILL HOUSE FISHERY (FH3287)																			●	2					
PRINCES PARK LAKE (FH3846)													●	●											
WOODHOUSE FISH FARM (FH5475)								●	●																
MIDLANDS (WEST)																									
ALVECHURCH FISHERIES (FH0090)																		●	●						
ASTBURY FALLS FISH FARM (FH0175)																●									
BLYTHE (RIVER) (FH0517)			●									●	●	●		●	●	●	●	2			●		
BLYTHE WATERS (FH0518)																		●	●						
CANNOCK EXTENSION CANAL (FH0822)																●		●			●				
CHURCH POOL (FH0956)			●																●		●		●		
CUTTLE MILL CARP FISHERY (FH1232)			●																●				●		
DAYHOUSE FARM (FH1282)			●													●	●	●		2	●				
FOXHILLS FISHERY (FH1791)			●	●										●					●	2					●
HEATHFIELD POOL (FH2175)																			●	2					
KINGSBURY WATER PARK (FH2510)																				2					
KINGSNORDLEY (FH2517)																			●						
LAVENDER HALL (FH2632)			●													●			●	2					
MEADOWLANDS (FH3227)																●									
PACKINGTON SOMERS FISHERY (FH3679)			●									●	●	●		●	●	●	●	2			●		
PACKINGTON TROUT FISHERY (FH3680)								●	●																
PATSHULL PARK (FH3717)							●	●	●							●		●	●				●		
PENNS HALL LAKE (FH3740)	●		●										●	●			●		●	3	●		●		
SHUSTOKE FLY FISHERS (FH4262)		●		●				●	●																
SWAN POOL (FH4595)																●		●	●	2					
WASSELL GROVE FISHERIES (FH5167)			●																●	2					
NORFOLK																									
ABBEY WATERS (FH0004)												●						●		1					
ABBOTS HALL (FH0007)								●																	
BARFORD LAKES FISHERY (FH0305)	●			●								●								1					
BARNINGHAM HALL LAKE (FH0317)	●	●	●	●		●						●		●			●	●	●	2		●	●		●
BAWBURGH LAKES (FH0348)			●										●			●	●		●	3	●				
BILNEY LAKES (FH0424)	●		●									●		●			●	●	●	2	●		●		
BLICKLING PARK LAKE (FH0500)																●			●						
BOOTON CLAY PIT (FH0543)		●	●				●						●	●				●	●		●	●	●		
BRIDGE FARM FISHERIES (FH0629)																							●		
BRIDGE INN FISHERY (FH0631)	●	●	●	●		●	●	●	●		●			●		●	●			2	●	●	●	●	
BURE (RIVER) (FH0736)	●	●	●	●		●	●			●	●	●		●		●	●	●			●	●	●	●	●
BURE VALLEY LAKES (FH0737)		●	●	●	●			●	●				●	●		●	●		●		●		●		
CATCH 22 FISHERY (FH0872)		●	●										●						●		●		●		
COLTON LAKE (FH1078)												●						●		1					
DENTS OF HILGAY (FH1333)			●																						
DISS MERE (FH1376)		●	●										●					●				●	●		
FELBRIGG HALL LAKE (FH1681)																	●		●	2					
FELTHORPE LAKE (FH1690)																							●		
FRITTON LAKE (FH1804)		●	●	●		●				●	●	●		●		●	●		●		●	●	●		●
GATTON WATER CARAVAN SITE (FH1843)	●			●		●								●		●		●					●		
GIMINGHAM LAKES (FH1858)																			●						
GLEN MERE (FH1882)													●												
GREAT MELTON FISHERY (FH1983)	●	●	●	●		●						●	●	●		●	●	●	●	2		●	●	●	●
GUNTON PARK LAKE (FH2037)																			●						
HALL FARM LAKES (FH2068)			●																●				●		
HAVERINGLAND HALL PARK (FH2138)			●										●	●		●		●	●	2	●				
HEVINGHAM LAKES (FH2197)	●		●	●		●						●		●			●		●	2					
HINDERCLAY LAKES (FH2233)																			●						
KINGFISHER LAKES (FH2500)			●														●		●	2					
LAKESIDE CARAVAN PARK (FH2587)																			●						

FISHING ALLOWANCES

England (by County)

Fishing Allowances UK & Irish Fisheries

	Bank Fishing Only	Barbed Hooks	Boilies	Catch & Release	Kill All Fish Caught	Dead Bait	Live Bait	Dry Fly	Wet Fly	Electric Bait Boats	Sonar Boats	Fixed Weights Allowed	Floater Fish	Floating Bait	Floating Rings - Game	Ground Baiting	Hair Rigs	Keep Nets	More than one rod	Number of Rods Allowed	Particle Baits	Spinners	Unhooking Mats essential	Wading	Worms Only
LENWADE COMMON LAKES (FH2700)			●				●			●			●	●		●		●	●		●	●	●		
LITTLE DUNHAM CARP LAKES (FH2749)																			●						
MILL FARM FISHERY (FH3282)		●	●	●		●						●	●	●		●	●	●	●			●	●	●	●
NARBOROUGH TROUT FARM (FH3424)		●						●	●												●		●		
NATURES HAVEN LAKES (FH3429)	●		●	●									●			●	●		●	2	●				
PARK LIME PIT (FH3700)	●						●						●	●				●					●		
PENTNEY LAKES (FH3742)																●									
RACKHEATH SPRINGS (FH3872)	●	●	●	●		●						●	●	●		●	●	●	●	2		●	●		●
RAILWAY LAKE (FH3877)			●							●			●					●	●		●	●			
RAILWAY LAKE (FH3878)												●				●		●		1	●				
REEPHAM FISHERY (FH3924)							●							●					●				●		
RINGLAND PITS (FH3953)		●	●				●			●	●		●	●		●		●	●		●	●			
RUSTON REACHES (FH4066)	●			●		●	●					●		●			●					●	●		
SCOULTON MERE (FH4119)			●	●												●	●	●	●	2	●	●			
SHALLOW BROOK LAKES (FH4205)																			●	2					
SWANTON MORLEY FISHERY (FH4602)	●	●		●		●		●	●					●		●	●	●	●	2	●	●			
TASWOOD LAKES (FH4662)																			●						
TAVERHAM (FH4668)																			●						
TAVERHAM MILLS FISHERY (FH4669)	●	●	●	●		●		●	●					●		●	●	●		2		●	●		
UNIVERSITY BROAD (FH5048)			●														●		●	3					
UPPER BURE (STREAM) (FH5052)		●	●	●	●			●	●				●	●		●	●		●		●		●		
WALNUT FARM FISHERIES (FH5125)	●			●								●		●		●	●	●	●	2	●		●		
WENSUM (RIVER) (FH5249)		●	●					●	●				●					●	●		●	●			
WENSUM (RIVER) (FH5247)	●	●		●		●		●	●					●		●	●	●	●	2	●	●			
WENSUM (RIVER) (FH5245)	●	●	●	●		●	●	●	●		●			●		●	●		●	2	●	●	●	●	
WEYBREAD FISHERY (FH5293)								●	●				●	●		●			●		●		●		
WILLOWCROFT FISHERY (FH5392)																●		●	●						
WILLSMORE WATER (FH5403)			●							●			●					●	●		●				
WOODLAKES FISHERY (FH5477)			●				●									●			●				●		
WOODRISING WATER MEADOWS (FH5489)			●														●		●	2	●		●		
YARE (RIVER) (FH5557)																●		●							
NORTHAMPTONSHIRE																									
BODDINGTON RESERVOIR (FH0521)																●					●		●		
CANONS ASHBY LAKES (FH0824)																●		●	●				●		
CHESTER FARM LAKE (FH0929)																			●						
CRESCENT LAKE (FH1179)																●		●			●				
DAVENTRY COUNTRY PARK (FH1281)			●							●						●		●	●			●	●		
DUSTON RESERVOIR (FH1486)			●															●	●		●		●		
ELINOR TROUT FISHERY (FH1562)								●	●																
FOXHOLES FISHERIES (FH1792)	●		●	●										●		●			●		●		●		
GRAND UNION CANAL (FH1959)		●	●				●	●	●				●					●	●		●	●			
GREEN FARM LAKES (FH2000)			●													●		●	●		●		●		
HEYFORD FISHERY (FH2200)																●		●			●				
HOLLOWELL RESERVOIR (FH2260)			●																						
ISE (RIVER) (FH2384)		●	●					●	●				●	●		●		●	●		●	●	●		
ISLIP NATURE LAKE (FH2396)		●	●											●		●		●	●		●		●		
LITTLE IRCHESTER COMPLEX (FH2754)			●															●	●				●		
LYNN POOL FISHERY (FH3125)																●		●							
MENAGERIE POND (FH3253)		●	●										●	●					●				●		
NENE (RIVER) (FH3447)		●	●			●		●	●		●	●		●		●	●	●			●	●	●	●	
NENE (RIVER) (FH3448)		●																●	●						
NORTHAMPTON JUNCTION CANAL (FH3542)		●																●	●						
OXFORD CANAL (FH3667)		●																●	●						
RAVENSTHORPE TROUT FISHERY (FH3895)								●	●																
RINGSTEAD GRANGE (FH3954)		●		●				●	●	●															
SILVER LAKE (FH4269)																		●	●						
ST JAMES SMALL PARK LAKE (FH4389)			●													●		●	●				●		
THORPE WATERVILLE LAKE (FH4827)		●	●					●	●					●		●		●	●		●	●	●		
THRAPSTON LAKES (FH4829)		●	●					●	●				●	●		●		●	●		●	●	●		
WEYBREAD GRAVEL PITS (FH5294)			●														●		●						
WOOTTON BROOK LAKE (FH5503)			●															●	●				●		
NORTHUMBERLAND																									
ALN (RIVER) (FH0085)	●	●		●				●	●													●		●	
COQUET (RIVER) (FH1116)	●					●		●	●													●		●	
HORTON GRANGE LAKE (FH2312)		●												●		●		●	●		●				
IRTHING (RIVER) (FH2381)		●						●	●													●			
LINNEL WOOD LAKE (FH2737)		●					●	●	●																
SOUTH TYNE (RIVER) (FH4341)		●						●	●													●			

Fishing Allowances UK & Irish Fisheries

Fishery	Bank Fishing Only	Barbed Hooks	Boilies	Catch & Release	Kill All Fish Caught	Dead Bait	Live Bait	Dry Fly	Wet Fly	Electric Bait Boats	Sonar Boats	Fixed Weights Allowed	Floater Fish	Floating Bait	Floating Rings - Game	Ground Baiting	Hair Rigs	Keep Nets	More than one rod	Number of Rods Allowed	Particle Baits	Spinners	Unhooking Mats essential	Wading	Worms Only
TWEED (RIVER) (FH4990)		●					●	●	●									●							
WANSBECK (RIVER) (FH5139)	●	●		●		●	●	●	●			●		●			●				●	●		●	
WHITEADDER (RIVER) (FH5345)	●	●		●				●	●															●	
WREIGH (RIVER) (FH5516)	●					●		●	●													●		●	
NOTTINGHAMSHIRE																									
COLWICK COUNTRY PARK (FH1080)		●	●	●		●		●	●			●		●		●	●	●	●		●	●			
DOLAR POND (FH1396)		●																●	●						
FLEET (RIVER) (FH1745)		●	●							●	●		●	●		●		●	●		●	●	●		
GRANTHAM CANAL (FH1975)	●	●	●	●								●				●		●		2				●	
HALLCROFT FISHERIES (FH2070)																			●						
LAKESIDE FISHERY (FH2592)	●		●	●	●			●		●				●	●		●						●		
LANGOLD LAKES (FH2616)		●		●		●										●	●	●				●	●	●	
MAUN (RIVER) (FH3209)	●											●		●		●	●	●	●	2	●		●		
NOTTINGHAM CASTLE MARINA (FH3553)	●	●		●								●				●		●	●	2					
OWDY LANE TROUT FISHERY (FH3660)								●	●																
PINDERS PONDS (FH3776)		●																●							
SAPPHIRE LAKES (FH4104)	●		●	●						●	●	●	●	●		●	●	●	●	3	●		●		
SHERWOOD FOREST FISHERY (FH4234)	●											●		●		●	●	●	●	2	●		●		
SMEATONS LAKES (FH4304)			●							●				●		●		●	●		●	●	●		
TRENT (RIVER) (FH4929)		●																●	●						
TRENT (RIVER) (FH4928)	●	●	●	●		●	●					●		●		●	●	●		3	●	●		●	
TRENT (RIVER) (FH4924)	●	●		●												●		●	●	2				●	
TRENT (RIVER) (FH4927)		●		●		●		●	●			●												●	
TRENT (RIVER) (FH4933)		●																●							
TRENT (RIVER) (FH4934)		●	●															●			●				
OXFORDSHIRE																									
BARNES TROUT LAKES (FH0316)	●		●	●		●		●	●										●	2		●			
BEIRTON LAKES (FH0373)																			●						
BUTLERS HILL FARM (FH0775)			●																●		●				
CHAD LAKES (FH0890)	●		●	●								●		●			●		●	2			●		●
CHRISTCHURCH LAKE (FH0947)			●													●		●	●	4	●		●		
CLATTERCOTE RESERVOIR (FH0979)			●																●						
CLEARWATER FISH FARM (FH0997)	●	●	●	●	●	●	●	●	●	●	●	●		●		●	●				●	●			●
COLLEGE FARM FISHING (FH1063)																●		●							
CORNBURY PARK FISHERY (FH1120)								●	●																
DARLOW LAKE (FH1275)	●	●		●				●	●																
FARMOOR 1 RESERVOIR (FH1675)	●	●		●				●	●																
FARMOOR TROUT FISHERY (FH1676)								●	●																
GAUNTS LAKE (FH1844)	●	●	●	●								●		●		●	●		●	3	●	●	●		
HARDWICK LAKE AND SMITHS POOL (FH2104)	●	●	●	●		●	●					●		●		●	●		●	3	●	●	●		
HEYFORD LAKES (FH2201)	●		●	●		●						●				●	●	●			●	●	●		●
HORSE AND GROOM INN (FH2303)	●		●	●									●	●		●	●		●	3	●				●
HUNTS CORNER (FH2342)	●	●	●	●		●	●					●		●		●	●		●	3	●	●	●		
LINCH HILL FISHERY (FH2725)		●	●							●								●	●	3	●	●	●		
LOCKINGE TROUT FISHERY (FH2972)								●	●										●						
MANOR FARM LAKE (FH3162)	●	●	●	●		●	●					●		●		●	●		●	3	●	●	●		
MILTON POOLS FARM (FH3326)			●							●				●		●			●		●		●		
NELL BRIDGE FISHERY (FH3439)																			●	2			●		
ORCHID LAKES (FH3618)	●		●							●				●		●	●				●		●		
OXLEASE LAKE (FH3678)	●	●	●	●								●		●		●	●		●	3	●	●	●		
SALFORD TROUT LAKES (FH4083)	●				●			●	●																
ST JOHNS POOL (FH4391)	●	●	●	●		●	●					●		●		●	●		●	3	●	●	●		
UNITY LAKE (FH5047)	●	●	●	●								●		●		●	●		●	3	●	●	●		
WINDRUSH (RIVER) (FH5411)		●																●			●				
WINDRUSH (RIVER) (FH5413)	●	●		●													●				●		●	●	
YEOMANS LAKE (FH5565)	●	●	●	●								●		●		●	●		●	3	●	●	●		
RUTLAND																									
SWEETHEDGES FARM FISHERY (FH4607)	●			●								●		●			●		●	2					
SHROPSHIRE																									
ACTON BURNELL (FH0025)			●																●				●		
APLEY POOLS (FH0121)																●									
AQUALATE MERE (FH0124)		●												●		●		●	●		●		●		
BAYLIS POOLS (FH0351)			●																						
BEECHES POOL (FH0367)																●			●	2					
BIRCH GROVE (FH0425)	●	●	●	●									●				●		●	4	●		●		
BLAKEMERE (FH0490)																			●						
BOLDINGS POOLS (FH0530)	●			●				●	●					●			●			2					
COUND TROUT FISHERY (FH1140)		●						●	●																

FISHING ALLOWANCES

England (by County)

Fishing Allowances UK & Irish Fisheries

	Bank Fishing Only	Barbed Hooks	Boilies	Catch & Release	Kill All Fish Caught	Dead Bait	Live Bait	Dry Fly	Wet Fly	Electric Bait Boats	Sonar Boats	Fixed Weights Allowed	Floater Fish	Floating Bait	Floating Rings - Game	Ground Baiting	Hair Rigs	Keep Nets	More than one rod	Number of Rods Allowed	Particle Baits	Spinners	Unhooking Mats essential	Wading	Worms Only
DEARNFORD HALL TROUT FISHERY (FH1291)				●				●	●						●					1				●	
DELBURY HALL TROUT FISHERY (FH1326)	●			●				●	●																
ELLERDINE LAKES (FH1566)	●	●		●	●			●	●			●										●			●
HOLMER LAKE (FH2269)																●			●		●				
ISLE LAKE (FH2395)			●																●						
LOWER HILL FARM (FH3081)																			●	2					
MEESE (RIVER) (FH3240)		●												●		●		●	●		●		●		
MIDDLE POOL (FH3267)			●																●			●			
ONNY (RIVER) (FH3613)		●		●				●	●															●	
RIVER (TERN) (FH3963)								●	●													●			
SEVERN (RIVER) (FH4178)																						●			
SEVERN (RIVER) (FH4172)								●	●													●			
SEVERN (RIVER) (FH4182)		●					●							●		●		●	●		●		●		
SEVERN (RIVER) (FH4177)								●	●													●			
SEVERN (RIVER) (FH4176)																						●			
SEVERN (RIVER) (FH4168)						●								●								●			
SEVERN (RIVER) (FH4175)																						●			
TEME (RIVER) (FH4722)	●	●	●			●		●	●		●	●		●			●	●	●	2	●	●		●	
TEME (RIVER) (FH4723)	●	●	●			●		●	●		●	●		●			●	●	●	2	●	●		●	
TERN (RIVER) (FH4740)								●	●																
TOWNSEND FISHERY (FH4894)														●		●		●	●		●		●		
VOWNOG FISH LAKE (FH5101)								●	●																
VYRNWY (RIVER) (FH5109)								●	●													●		●	
WALCOT WEST LAKE (FH5117)	●	●	●			●					●	●		●			●	●			●	●		●	
WOODCOTE HALL (FH5470)			●										●					●			●				
SOMERSET																									
AVALON FISHERIES (FH0186)	●		●							●	●					●	●	●	●	3	●		●		
BARLE (RIVER) (FH0309)		●						●	●																
BARROW RESERVOIRS (FH0329)	●	●		●				●	●																
BLAGDON LAKE (FH0487)		●		●				●	●																
BRISTOL AVON (FH0649)	●	●	●	●		●		●	●	●	●	●		●		●	●	●	●	3	●	●		●	
BRISTOL AVON (FH0648)	●	●	●	●		●		●	●	●	●	●		●		●	●	●	●	3	●	●		●	
BRISTOL AVON (FH0647)	●	●	●	●		●		●	●	●	●	●		●		●	●	●	●	3	●	●		●	
BULLOCKS FARM FISHING LAKES (FH0728)																		●	●		●		●		
CAMELEY TROUT LAKES (FH0812)								●	●																
CHEDDAR RESERVOIR (FH0909)			●							●			●					●	●		●	●	●		
CHEW VALLEY LAKE (FH0936)		●		●				●	●															●	
COOMBE LAKE (FH1107)	●			●		●						●		●		●	●	●	●	2					
DANDYS & KNIGHTINGALE LAKES (FH1254)		●														●		●	●						
DURLEIGH RESERVOIR (FH1484)			●																						
EMBORUGH LAKE (FH1583)		●	●										●			●	●	●	●	2	●		●		●
EMERALD POOL FISHERY (FH1585)	●		●	●									●			●	●	●	●		●		●		
EXE VALLEY FISHERY (FH1645)								●	●																
FOLLY FOOT FARM (FH1755)			●													●	●		●	3	●				
FOLLYFOOT FARM (FH1757)			●										●	●		●	●	●	●		●				●
GODNEY MOOR PONDS (FH1906)																			●						
HAWKRIDGE RESERVOIR (FH2144)								●	●																
HORSESHOE LAKE (FH2308)			●										●					●	●			●			
HUNSTRETE LAKE COMPLEX (FH2338)																●		●							
KENN (RIVER) (FH2433)		●	●															●	●		●	●			
LANDS END FARM (FH2607)													●	●		●		●	●		●		●		
LANGFORD LAKES (FH2612)							●												●				●		
LITTON RESERVOIR (FH2765)		●		●				●	●																
OLD MILL FISHERY (FH3595)																					●				
OTTERHEAD LAKES (FH3632)								●	●																
OXENLEAZE FARM FISHERY (FH3666)			●																●						
PARRETT (RIVER) (FH3708)	●					●										●		●	●	2					
PAULTON LAKES (FH3718)																							●		
PAWLETT PONDS (FH3719)		●	●				●	●	●				●					●	●		●	●			
PLANTATIONS LAKES (FH3798)																			●						
QUANTOCK FISHERIES (FH3862)	●							●	●						●										
ST ALGARS FARM LAKE (FH4381)	●				●			●	●															●	
STONE YARD FISHERY (FH4470)			●													●		●	●	2	●				
THORNEY LAKES (FH4815)	●			●		●	●							●					●	2		●			
VIADUCT FISHERY (FH5095)	●			●						●	●			●			●	●	●	2	●				
WELLINGTON BASIN (FH5240)							●							●		●									
WOOLBRIDGE MANOR (FH5499)								●	●													●			

FISHING ALLOWANCES

England (by County)

Fishing Allowances UK & Irish Fisheries

	Bank Fishing Only	Barbed Hooks	Boilies	Catch & Release	Kill All Fish Caught	Dead Bait	Live Bait	Dry Fly	Wet Fly	Electric Bait Boats	Sonar Boats	Fixed Weights Allowed	Floater Fish	Floating Bait	Floating Rings - Game	Ground Baiting	Hair Rigs	Keep Nets	More than one rod	Number of Rods Allowed	Particle Baits	Spinners	Unhooking Mats essential	Wading	Worms Only
STAFFORDSHIRE																									
ALBRIGHTON MOAT PROJECT (FH0051)				●		●																			
ASHLEY POOLS (FH0165)			●														●	●	●	2					
BADEN HALL FISHERY (FH0245)	●			●						●		●		●		●	●	●	●	2	●		●	●	
BASFORD COARSE FISHERY (FH0340)																			●	2					
BIDDULPH GRANGE (FH0409)			●																●	2					
BLACK LAKE (FH0443)			●														●	●	●	2					
BLACKWOOD POOL (FH0483)	●	●	●	●										●		●	●	●	●	3	●	●	●	●	●
BROWNING CUDMORE FISHERY (FH0702)			●							●						●		●	●		●	●	●		
CHURNET (RIVER) (FH0961)	●			●				●	●																
CONSALL NATURE PARK (FH1091)																		●	●	2					
DEEP HAYES COUNTRY PARK (FH1322)																			●	2					
DILHORNE HALL POOLS (FH1367)			●														●	●	●	2					
DOVE (RIVER) (FH1428)		●												●		●		●	●		●		●		
DOVE (RIVER) (FH1427)		●												●		●		●	●		●		●		
ELLENHALL NINE POOLS (FH1564)		●	●											●		●		●	●		●		●		
FISHERWICK LAKES (FH1732)			●					●	●				●	●		●		●	●		●		●		
GAILEY TROUT AND PIKE FISHERY (FH1828)				●		●	●	●	●		●				●									●	
HAMPS (RIVER) (FH2081)								●	●													●		●	
HAMSTALL FISHERY (FH2097)		●						●	●				●	●							●		●		
HANCHURCH FISHERIES (FH2099)								●	●					●				●	●		●		●		
HERONBROOK FISHERY (FH2191)			●											●		●			●						
HIMLEY HALL AND PARK LAKE (FH2230)			●																●						
HORSEBRIDGE POOL (FH2304)		●												●		●		●	●		●				
IZAAK WALTON FISHERY (FH2404)	●			●								●				●	●	●	●	2					
KNYPERSLEY RESERVOIR (FH2544)			●														●		●	2					
LOYNTON TROUT FISHERIES (FH3100)		●						●																	
PILLATON POOLS (FH3772)	●			●												●			●	2					
PINE POOL (FH3778)																			●						
POOL HOUSE FARM (FH3820)	●													●			●	●	●	2					
SIDEWAY OVERFLOW (FH4265)			●														●	●	●	2					
SMITHPOOL LAKE (FH4307)			●														●	●	●	2					
SOW (RIVER) (FH4355)		●					●							●		●		●	●		●		●		
STAFFORD AND WORCESTER CANAL (FH4400)	●	●	●	●		●		●	●	●	●			●			●	●	●	2	●	●		●	●
SWAN PIT POOL (FH4594)														●					●				●		
SWARBORN (RIVER) (FH4603)																					●	●			
TAME (RIVER) (FH4647)																						●			
TITTESWORTH RESERVOIR (FH4858)								●	●																
TRENT (RIVER) (FH4935)																						●			
TRENT (RIVER) (FH4936)																					●	●			
TRENT AND MERSEY CANAL (FH4945)																		●	●	2					
WILLOWS POOLS (FH5401)			●														●								
SUFFOLK																									
ALTON WATER RESERVOIR (FH0088)	●	●	●	●		●						●		●		●	●	●	●	2	●	●	●		
BARHAM B PIT (FH0307)	●		●	●													●		●	3					
BREAKAWAY PIT (FH0609)			●				●			●			●					●	●		●	●			
BROOME PITS (FH0693)	●	●		●		●										●		●	●	2			●		
CAMELOT LAKE (FH0813)																			●						
CLICKETTS HILL AND PLANTATION (FH1005)		●	●				●						●					●	●		●	●	●		
CLUB PIT (FH1028)	●	●		●		●												●	●	2			●		
CROSS GREEN FLY FISHERY (FH1192)								●	●																
FLOOD PARK (FH1749)																			●						
GIPPING (RIVER) (FH1860)																			●						
HOMERSFIELD LAKE (FH2284)			●														●		●						
LARK (RIVER) (FH2624)		●	●					●	●	●			●					●	●		●	●			
LARKWOOD TROUT FISHERY (FH2626)	●			●				●	●																
LAYZELLS FARM (FH2640)		●	●				●			●			●					●	●		●	●	●		
LITTLE BEVILLS ESTATE (FH2740)		●	●				●						●					●	●		●	●	●		
LITTLE OUSE (RIVER) (FH2758)		●					●						●						●		●	●	●		
LOAM POND (FH2833)			●										●				●								
MARSH FARM LAKES (FH3191)	●			●										●					●	3			●		●
MELDUM WASHLANDS (FLOODPARK) (FH3247)		●	●										●					●	●		●		●		
NEEDHAM LAKE (FH3435)						●										●		●	●				●		
NORTH MEADOWS (FH3531)		●	●				●						●					●	●		●	●	●		
SINKS PIT (FH4277)	●		●	●									●				●		●	2					
STOUR (RIVER) (FH4501)		●	●				●						●					●	●		●	●	●		
STOUR (RIVER) (FH4500)		●	●															●	●	2		●			
STOW (RIVER) (FH4511)		●	●				●						●					●	●		●	●	●		

FISHING ALLOWANCES

England (by County)

Fishing Allowances UK & Irish Fisheries

	Bank Fishing Only	Barbed Hooks	Boilies	Catch & Release	Kill All Fish Caught	Dead Bait	Live Bait	Dry Fly	Wet Fly	Electric Bait Boats	Sonar Boats	Fixed Weights Allowed	Floater Fish	Floating Bait	Floating Rings - Game	Ground Baiting	Hair Rigs	Keep Nets	More than one rod	Number of Rods Allowed	Particle Baits	Spinners	Unhooking Mats essential	Wading	Worms Only
STOW (RIVER) (FH4509)		●	●				●						●					●	●		●	●	●		
STOW (RIVER) (FH4510)		●	●				●						●					●	●		●	●	●		
STOW (RIVER) (FH4508)		●	●				●			●			●					●	●		●	●	●		
STOW (RIVER) (FH4512)		●	●				●			●			●					●	●		●	●	●		
THET (RIVER) (FH4809)																●		●							
WAVENEY (RIVER) (FH5191)	●	●		●		●										●		●				●	●		
WAVENEY VALLEY LAKES (FH5192)																			●				●		
WICKHAM MARKET RESERVOIRS (FH5365)			●					●	●				●					●	●		●	●	●		
WRIGHTS FARM (FH5517)		●	●				●			●			●					●	●		●	●	●		
SURREY																									
ALBURY ESTATE FISHERIES (FH0052)	●	●			●			●	●																
BEAVER FARM FISHERY (FH0359)			●				●						●						●				●		
BURY HILL FISHERIES (FH0764)			●	●		●	●							●		●	●		●	2		●	●		●
BUSBRIDGE LAKE (FH0765)			●										●			●	●	●	●	2					
BUSHEY PARK (FH0769)	●		●	●													●		●	2			●		
CHERTSEY (FH0916)		●	●				●			●	●		●	●		●		●	●		●	●			
CROSSWATER MILL FISHERY (FH1194)	●			●				●	●										●	3					
ENTON LAKES TROUT FISHERY (FH1596)								●	●																
FISHERIES THE (FH1729)																							●		
FRENSHAM TROUT FISHERY (FH1800)	●			●				●	●										●	3					
HENFOLD LAKES FISHERY (FH2182)																			●				●		
HOME PARK (FH2282)	●		●	●													●		●	2			●		
JOHNSONS LAKE (FH2415)	●		●	●									●			●	●	●	●		●	●			●
KINGFISHER FISHERY (FH2495)								●	●					●		●			●				●		
ONE ISLAND POND (FH3612)			●																						
PAINSHILL PARK LAKE (FH3685)	●		●			●	●							●		●	●	●	●	2	●	●	●		
PAPERCOURT FISHERY (FH3694)		●	●				●			●	●		●	●		●		●	●		●	●	●		
RUSHMOOR LAKES (FH4063)	●		●			●	●							●		●	●	●			●				
TWYNERSH FISHING COMPLEX (FH5012)	●		●			●	●							●		●	●		●	4	●	●	●		
WEY (RIVER) (FH5290)	●	●			●			●	●																
WHITEVANE POND (FH5354)	●	●	●							●				●		●	●		●	2	●		●		
WILLINGHURST COARSE FISHERY (FH5373)			●					●	●					●		●		●	●				●		
WILLINGHURST TROUT FISHERY (FH5374)			●					●	●					●		●		●	●				●		
WYPHURST AND HYHURST LAKES (FH5547)																							●		
SUSSEX (EAST)																									
ARLINGTON TROUT FISHERY (FH0137)		●			●			●	●																
BALLS GREEN LAKES (FH0272)	●			●																			●		
BARCOMBE RESERVOIR (FH0303)					●			●	●																
BELFREY COARSE FISHERY (FH0375)			●											●					●				●		
BEVERN STREAM (FH0401)			●				●	●	●				●					●	●		●	●	●		
BRICK FARM LAKE (FH0620)	●	●			●			●	●																
BROOMHAM FISHERY (FH0695)			●																						
BUXTED OAST FISHERY (FH0780)	●			●						●	●	●		●		●	●		●		●		●		
CLIVE VALE RESERVOIRS (FH1010)													●			●									
DARWELL WATER (FH1279)								●	●																
FRAMFIELD PARK FISHERIES (FH1797)																		●	●						
HOLTS LAKES (FH2274)			●										●					●	●		●	●	●		
HONEYS GREEN COARSE FISHERY (FH2286)							●												●				●		
HORAM MANOR FISHERY (FH2294)	●		●	●		●		●	●	●	●			●		●	●		●	2	●	●			●
IDEN WOOD FISHERY (FH2358)																			●				●		
MICHELHAM PRIORY MOAT (FH3260)			●				●			●	●		●	●		●			●	3	●	●	●		
MOOR HALL POOL (FH3357)			●										●						●				●		
OLD MILL (FH3593)							●	●	●									●	●			●			
OLIVES FARM FISHERY (FH3609)								●																	
OUSE (RIVER) (FH3645)			●				●	●	●				●	●		●		●	●		●	●			
PENNY BRIDGE (FH3741)			●										●					●	●		●		●		
PIPPINGFORD PARK ESTATE LAKES (FH3786)	●		●	●		●						●		●			●		●	4	●	●	●		
POWDERMILL (FH3838)		●			●			●	●															●	
ROSEBANK FARM FISHERY (FH4012)			●										●						●		●				
RYE NOOK FISHERY (FH4075)	●		●	●										●		●	●	●	●	4	●		●		●
SCALAND WOOD (FH4110)			●										●					●	●				●		
SHARNFOLD FARM FISHERY (FH4210)																			●						
SOUTHBOURNE LAKE (FH4349)			●					●	●	●									●		●	●	●		
SPRING WOOD FISHERY AND FARM (FH4372)		●	●					●	●				●					●	●		●				
SWANBOROUGH LAKES (FH4597)			●																●				●		
TANYARD FISHERIES (FH4654)	●		●			●	●	●		●				●		●	●		●	4		●	●		
WEIR WOOD FISHERY (FH5227)			●			●		●	●								●		●						
WYLANDS CENTRE (FH5545)			●				●						●	●		●		●	●		●		●		

FISHING ALLOWANCES

England (by County)

Fishing Allowances UK & Irish Fisheries

Fishery	Bank Fishing Only	Barbed Hooks	Boilies	Catch & Release	Kill All Fish Caught	Dead Bait	Live Bait	Dry Fly	Wet Fly	Electric Bait Boats	Sonar Boats	Fixed Weights Allowed	Floater Fish	Floating Bait	Floating Rings - Game	Ground Baiting	Hair Rigs	Keep Nets	More than one rod	Number of Rods Allowed	Particle Baits	Spinners	Unhooking Mats essential	Wading	Worms Only
YEW TREE TROUT FISHERY (FH5570)		●						●	●																
SUSSEX (WEST)																									
ALDERWOOD PONDS (FH0066)	●		●	●		●								●		●	●	●	●	2	●		●		
ARDINGLY RESERVOIR (FH0129)		●	●			●	●			●	●	●	●			●	●	●	●	4	●	●	●	●	
ARUN (RIVER) (FH0152)	●	●	●			●	●									●		●				●			
BLACKWOOL TROUT FISHERY (FH0484)	●	●			●			●	●																
BORDE HILL GARDEN LAKES (FH0544)													●	●		●			●		●		●		
CHALK SPRINGS TROUT FISHERY (FH0891)		●						●	●																
DUNCANS POND (FH1472)			●										●	●		●	●				●				
DUNCTON MILL (FH1473)								●	●																
FURNACE LAKES (FH1821)	●	●	●							●				●		●	●		●	2	●		●		
HAMBROOK TROUT FISHERY (FH2080)								●	●																
LAYBROOK LAKES (FH2638)														●		●									
MILL FARM FISHERY (FH3283)																			●	3					
NEW POND (FH3475)	●	●	●	●								●				●	●	●	●	2					
NEWELLS FISHERIES (FH3483)	●	●	●			●	●							●			●		●	3		●	●		
PASSIES PONDS (FH3715)														●		●		●	●	2	●		●		
ROTHER (RIVER) (FH4028)	●	●		●		●	●	●	●			●		●		●	●	●	●	2		●			
ROTHERFIELD POND (FH4030)	●	●	●									●		●		●	●	●	●	2					
SPARKS FARM FISHERY (FH4358)	●		●	●								●		●		●	●	●	●	2	●	●			
STUBPOND FISHERIES (FH4531)														●		●									
WINTONS FISHERY (FH5432)	●	●	●	●		●											●		●				●		
TYNE AND WEAR																									
BOLAM LAKE COUNTRY PARK (FH0528)	●	●		●		●						●					●		●	2	●			●	
DISSINGTON POND (FH1377)																							●		
LEAZES PARK LAKE (FH2655)			●							●								●	●				●		
MILKHOPE POND (FH3276)														●				●	●		●				
MOUNT PLEASANT LAKE (FH3387)																●									
RED BARNS POND (FH3908)													●	●		●		●							
SWEETHOPE LOUGHS (FH4608)	●			●				●	●						●									●	
THROCKLEY REIGH (FH4833)								●																	
WHITTLE DENE TROUT FISHERY (FH5360)								●	●																
WARWICKSHIRE																									
ADAMS POOL (FH0026)	●		●	●		●	●							●			●		●	3			●		
ASHBY CANAL (FH0157)																●									
BLACK HILL POOLS (FH0441)																		●							
BOSWORTH & FRIEZELAND (FH0561)														●		●		●	●						
CHESTERTON MILL (FH0934)								●	●																
DRAYCOTE WATER (FH1438)		●						●	●																
KINGSTON POOLS (FH2518)							●							●				●	●						
MAKIN FISHERIES (FH3150)			●											●		●					●				
NAPTON RESERVOIR (FH3421)																		●							
OXFORD CANAL (FH3677)	●	●		●								●		●		●	●	●			●				
RIDDINGS FISHERY (FH3949)			●											●				●	●		●		●		
TUNNEL BARN FARM (FH4972)														●		●			●		●		●		
WEST HILLBOROUGH (FH5261)		●	●										●					●			●	●			
WESTON LAWN FISHERIES (FH5285)	●		●	●							●			●		●	●	●	●	2	●	●	●		
WILTSHIRE																									
AVON (BRISTOL) (RIVER) (FH0195)		●	●				●	●	●	●			●					●	●		●	●			
AVON (RIVER) (FH0216)														●		●		●	●						
AVON (RIVER) (FH0218)		●						●	●				●	●		●		●	●		●		●		
AVON (RIVER) (FH0220)		●														●		●	●						
AVON ANGLING CLUB (FH0226)		●	●											●		●		●	●		●		●		
AVON SPRINGS FISHERY (FH0229)	●	●			●			●	●									●							
BLACKLAND LAKES (FH0450)	●		●										●				●		●	2			●		●
BRISTOL AVON (FH0651)																●									
BRISTOL AVON (FH0650)	●	●	●	●		●		●	●	●	●	●		●		●	●	●	●	3	●	●		●	
COATE WATER COUNTRY PARK (FH1046)			●																						
CUCKOOS REST (FH1211)																●		●							
IVY HOUSE FARM (FH2403)																●			●						
KENNET AND AVON CANAL (FH2465)		●	●															●	●		●	●			
LANGFORD FISHERIES (FH2611)								●	●																
LONGLEAT LAKES (FH2992)			●																●				●		
LOWER MOOR FISHERY (FH3090)		●	●					●	●							●	●	●	●	2	●				
NADDER (RIVER) (FH3409)		●														●		●	●						
PETERS FINGER LAKES (FH3756)		●														●		●	●						
PLAUMS PIT (FH3802)			●										●					●	●		●	●			
ROOD ASHTON LAKE (FH4002)													●						●		●				

FISHING ALLOWANCES

England (by County)

Fishing Allowances UK & Irish Fisheries

	Bank Fishing Only	Barbed Hooks	Boilies	Catch & Release	Kill All Fish Caught	Dead Bait	Live Bait	Dry Fly	Wet Fly	Electric Bait Boats	Sonar Boats	Fixed Weights Allowed	Floater Fish	Floating Bait	Floating Rings - Game	Ground Baiting	Hair Rigs	Keep Nets	More than one rod	Number of Rods Allowed	Particle Baits	Spinners	Unhooking Mats essential	Wading	Worms Only
SABRE AND SWORDS LAKES (FH4079)																●									
SHAFTESBURY LAKE (FH4200)																		●	●			●			
SILVERLANDS LAKE (FH4272)			●	●		●	●							●		●		●	●	3		●	●		
STEEPLE LANGFORD LAKES (FH4447)		●														●		●	●						
SUTTON VENY ESTATE (FH4566)								●	●																
THAMES (RIVER) (FH4805)		●	●				●	●	●	●			●					●	●		●	●			
WOODLAND PARK (FH5480)			●	●			●												●	2				●	
WYATTS LAKE (FH5523)																			●						
WORCESTERSHIRE																									
ABBOTS SALFORD PARK (FH0009)	●			●		●								●				●							
ARROW VALLEY LAKE (FH0141)			●													●		●	●	2	●				
BRANSFORD GAME FISHERY (FH0601)								●	●																
BROCKAMIN POOLS (FH0667)																●		●							
CAPTAINS POOL (FH0835)	●	●	●	●		●	●						●	●		●	●	●	●	2	●	●	●		
FURNACE MILL FISHERY (FH1822)																		●							
HUXLEYS HAMPTON FERRY FISHERY (FH2352)	●	●	●	●		●	●					●		●		●	●	●			●	●		●	
LEIGH SINTON FISHING LAKES (FH2692)																		●	●						
LENCHES LAKES (FH2697)		●						●	●																
LENCHFORD (FH2698)	●	●	●	●		●	●							●		●	●	●		2	●	●		●	
MAVER LARFORD (FH3210)			●																●	3					
MOORLANDS FARM (FH3363)	●																		●						
RED BECK LAKE (FH3909)	●		●	●										●		●			●	2	●				
SEVERN (RIVER) (FH4186)								●	●							●		●							
SHATTERFORD FISHERY (FH4212)			●					●	●				●	●					●				●		
SILLIGROVE FISHERY (FH4267)	●			●				●	●																
SION FARM FISHERIES (FH4279)			●																●						
SNUFF MILL POOL (FH4314)		●	●															●	●				●		
TEME (RIVER) (FH4732)		●	●					●	●									●	●			●			
TEME (RIVER) (FH4725)	●																●				●	●			●
TEME (RIVER) (FH4724)		●						●	●																
TRIMPLEY RESERVOIR (FH4956)								●	●																
UNWICKS FARM FISHERY (FH5049)																●		●	●	2					
WARWICKSHIRE & AVON (FH5154)	●	●		●		●	●												●	2		●			
WARWICKSHIRE AVON (FH5159)	●	●		●		●	●					●		●		●				2	●	●			
WARWICKSHIRE AVON (FH5158)																	●								
WHARTONS PARK COARSE FISHING (FH5314)																			●						
WILLOW FARM (FH5380)																		●							
WILLOW MARSH (FH5386)	●											●					●		●	2					
WINDMILL LAKE (FH5409)																●		●							
WITLEY POOLS (FH5449)		●	●				●						●					●	●			●	●		
WOODROW FISH POND (FH5490)								●	●					●				●	●		●				
WREXHAM																									
EMRAL BROOK (FH1588)																	●				●	●			
WYCH BROOK (FH5524)																	●					●			
YORKSHIRE (NORTH)																									
BIRKDALE FISHERY (FH0430)																			●						
BOLTON ABBEY FISHERIES (FH0539)								●	●																
BRAFFERTON COARSE FISHERY (FH0593)	●		●	●								●		●		●	●	●	●	2	●				
BROKEN BREA FISHERY (FH0674)																●		●	●	2					
BROOKLANDS (FH0683)			●				●			●				●		●			●				●		
CARP VALE (FH0846)	●		●	●						●		●		●		●	●				●				
CAWOOD HOLIDAY PARK (FH0877)		●	●																						
CHAPMANS POND (FH0897)																			●						
COD BECK (FH1049)		●					●	●	●					●		●		●	●		●				
CRABTREE ANGLING LAKE (FH1155)		●						●										●							
DERWENT (RIVER) (FH1357)								●	●													●			
EGTON ESTATE BEAT (FH1555)								●	●										●						
ELLERTON PARK (FH1568)			●	●		●	●			●	●	●		●		●	●	●	●	2	●	●			
ELVINGTON LAKE (FH1575)																		●	●	3					
FAIRVIEW LAKE (FH1656)			●			●							●	●		●	●	●	●	3	●	●	●		
FLETCHERS POND (FH1747)																			●						
HAZELHEAD LAKE (FH2165)								●	●										●	4					
HESSAY POND (FH2196)								●	●																
HOLLINGWOOD FISHERY (FH2257)														●									●		
KILNSEY PARK AND TROUT FARM (FH2487)	●	●		●				●	●																
KINGSLEY CARP LAKE (FH2513)	●			●								●		●		●	●	●			●				
LAKEHOUSE LAKE (FH2576)																						●			
LAKESIDE LODGES (FH2595)	●	●	●	●		●				●				●		●	●	●	●	3	●	●	●		

FISHING ALLOWANCES

England (by County)

Fishing Allowances UK & Irish Fisheries

	Bank Fishing Only	Barbed Hooks	Boilies	Catch & Release	Kill All Fish Caught	Dead Bait	Live Bait	Dry Fly	Wet Fly	Electric Bait Boats	Sonar Boats	Fixed Weights Allowed	Floater Fish	Floating Bait	Floating Rings - Game	Ground Baiting	Hair Rigs	Keep Nets	More than one rod	Number of Rods Allowed	Particle Baits	Spinners	Unhooking Mats essential	Wading	Worms Only
LEIGHTON RESERVOIR (FH2693)								●	●																
LOW OSGOODBY LAKE (FH3068)								●	●																
MARSTON WYSE TROUT FARM (FH3197)								●	●																
MUNBY POND (FH3401)		●																							
NEWHAY DAY TICKET LAKE (FH3484)										●									●						
NEWHAY SPECIMEN LAKE (FH3485)			●							●									●				●		
NIDD (RIVER) (FH3503)		●	●					●	●							●		●	●		●				
NIDD (RIVER) (FH3507)		●	●					●	●							●		●	●		●		●		
NIDD (RIVER) (FH3506)		●	●					●	●							●		●	●		●		●		
NIDD (RIVER) (FH3505)						●																●			
OAKS FISHERY (FH3565)																●		●	●	2					
ORCHARD FARM PONDS (FH3615)																●									
OUSE (RIVER) (FH3651)		●	●					●	●							●		●	●		●		●		
PARKLANDS (FH3703)	●			●								●		●		●	●	●	●	2	●				●
PICKERING PARK FISHING LAKE (FH3766)	●		●	●		●				●		●		●		●	●	●			●				
POTTERY LAKE (FH3834)	●		●	●		●	●			●	●			●		●	●	●	●	2	●	●	●		
RAKER LAKES (FH3884)	●		●	●				●	●					●	●		●	●	●	2	●		●		
RASKELF LAKE (FH3889)			●																						
SCARBOROUGH MERE (FH4113)																			●						
SELBY 3 LAKES (FH4129)	●		●	●										●			●	●	●	3			●	●	
SELBY CANAL (FH4133)		●					●									●		●	●						
SELLEY BRIDGE LAKE (FH4134)																●									
SEMERWATER (FH4137)																			●						
STONEBRIDGE LAKES (FH4471)	●			●				●	●										●	2					
SWALE (RIVER) (FH4578)			●											●		●			●						
SWALE (RIVER) (FH4574)																						●			
SWALE (RIVER) (FH4573)		●	●					●	●							●		●	●		●				
SWALE (RIVER) (FH4569)			●	●		●	●					●		●			●		●	2	●	●		●	
SWALE (RIVER) (FH4567)		●	●	●		●	●					●		●		●	●	●			●	●		●	
TANFIELD LAKE (FH4651)	●	●		●				●	●																
URE (RIVER) (FH5072)		●	●					●	●							●		●	●		●		●		
WASHBURN VALLEY (FH5164)								●	●																
WATERMEADOWS FISHERY (FH5181)								●	●									●	●						
WELHAM LAKE (FH5231)														●					●						
WEST HADDLESEY LAKE (FH5260)	●			●														●	●	2					
WESTERLY LAKE (FH5271)			●															●	●						
WHARFE (RIVER) (FH5302)		●		●				●	●													●		●	●
WHARFE (RIVER) (FH5298)								●	●																
WOODLAND LAKES (FH5479)	●											●		●		●	●		●	2	●				
YORKSHIRE (SOUTH)																									
ARKSEY STATION POND (FH0135)																			●	2					
BRICKYARD PONDS (FH0628)	●	●	●	●		●	●									●	●		●		●	●	●		●
CHESTERFIELD CANAL (FH0931)		●	●											●		●		●					●		
DAM FLASK RESERVOIR (FH1251)						●													●	4			●		
HOWBROOK RESERVOIR (FH2318)			●										●			●	●		●	3	●	●			
KJS FISHERIES (FH2532)																●									
MORE HALL RESERVOIR (FH3368)								●	●																
NEWBIGGIN POND (FH3478)			●													●	●		●	2	●	●			
SALLY WALSHES DAM (FH4084)			●										●			●	●	●	●	2					
SCOUT DYKE RESERVOIR (FH4121)		●					●	●	●												●	●			
SHIREOAKS PARK (FH4243)			●																●						
SLIVER FISHERY (FH4300)		●	●					●	●	●			●	●		●		●	●		●	●	●		
STANBOROUGH FISHERIES (FH4414)	●			●							●	●					●		●	3	●	●	●	●	●
THRYBERGH COUNTRY PARK (FH4835)								●	●																
TINKERS PONDS (FH4854)		●														●		●							
TYRAM HALL (FH5035)																●									
WESTWOOD COUNTRY PARK (FH5288)			●													●	●		●	3	●	●			
WHARNCLIFFE FLY FISHERY (FH5313)								●	●																
WORSBOROUGH RESERVOIR (FH5506)		●														●		●		1	●				
WORSBROUGH RESERVOIR (FH5508)																●									
YORKSHIRE (WEST)																									
ACKTON POND (FH0020)																		●							
AIRE (RIVER) (FH0043)		●		●		●	●	●	●			●		●		●	●	●			●	●		●	
AIRE AND CALDER CANAL (FH0048)	●			●												●	●	●							
BOTTOMS DAM (FH0562)			●				●									●		●	●	2	●		●		
CALDER (RIVER) (FH0794)		●	●					●	●	●			●					●	●		●	●			
COLNE (RIVER) (FH1074)		●					●	●	●				●	●		●		●			●		●		
COPPICE POND (FH1113)																			●						

FISHING ALLOWANCES

England (by County)

Fishing Allowances UK & Irish Fisheries

Fishery	Bank Fishing Only	Barbed Hooks	Boilies	Catch & Release	Kill All Fish Caught	Dead Bait	Live Bait	Dry Fly	Wet Fly	Electric Bait Boats	Sonar Boats	Fixed Weights Allowed	Floater Fish	Floating Bait	Floating Rings - Game	Ground Baiting	Hair Rigs	Keep Nets	More than one rod	Number of Rods Allowed	Particle Baits	Spinners	Unhooking Mats essential	Wading	Worms Only
DYEHOUSE POND (FH1493)		●																●			●				
HILL TOP RESERVOIR (FH2222)			●				●						●	●		●		●	●	2	●		●		
HOLME (RIVER) (FH2263)								●	●														●		
HOLME MILL DAM (SQUARE DAM) (FH2267)			●				●						●	●		●		●			●		●		
HORBURY LAGOON (FH2295)			●																						
KNOTFORD LAGOON (FH2542)			●																						
LEEDS AND LIVERPOOL CANAL (FH2671)	●	●				●	●					●		●		●	●	●			●	●			●
LEEDS TO LIVERPOOL CANAL (FH2682)		●																●			●				
LOWTHER LAKE (FH3099)		●				●						●		●		●	●	●	●	2	●	●		●	
NARROW CANAL (FH3426)			●				●						●	●		●		●			●		●		
NARROW CANAL (FH3425)			●				●						●	●		●		●			●		●		
NEW MILL DAM (FH3474)		●	●	●								●		●		●	●	●	●	2	●				
NOSTELL PRIORY LAKE (FH3551)		●	●										●					●	●		●	●	●		
OAKS SCAR RESERVOIR (FH3566)			●				●						●	●		●		●			●		●		
PUGNEYS COUNTRY PARK (FH3855)								●	●					●		●			●				●		
PUSH DAM (FH3860)			●				●						●	●		●		●			●		●		
RAYGILL FISHERY (FH3902)			●	●		●		●	●	●	●	●		●	●		●		●	2	●		●		
ROCHDALE CANAL (FH3979)		●	●							●			●					●	●		●	●			
ROWLEY DAM (FH4040)			●				●						●	●		●		●			●		●		
STAVELEY LAKES (FH4443)	●	●	●	●		●	●	●	●			●		●				●			●		●		●
SWILLINGTON PARK (FH4609)			●				●			●	●			●		●			●				●		
TONG PARK DAM (FH4872)	●			●				●	●																●
TP WOODS POND (FH4902)			●				●									●		●			●				
WALSDEN PRINTING CO LODGES (FH5128)	●		●	●				●	●			●		●		●	●	●	●	2	●	●			
WHARFE (RIVER) (FH5311)	●		●	●		●		●	●			●		●		●	●	●			●	●		●	
WHARFE (RIVER) (FH5304)																●	●				●	●			●
WHARFE (RIVER) (FH5310)			●	●		●		●	●			●		●		●	●	●			●	●		●	
WINTERSETT RESERVOIR (FH5428)																●									
WORKSHOP POND (FH5504)			●													●	●								

FISHING ALLOWANCES

England (by County)

Fishing Allowances UK & Irish Fisheries

	Bank Fishing Only	Barbed Hooks	Boilies	Catch & Release	Kill All Fish Caught	Dead Bait	Live Bait	Dry Fly	Wet Fly	Electric Bait Boats	Sonar Boats	Fixed Weights Allowed	Floater Fish	Floating Bait	Floating Rings - Game	Ground Baiting	Hair Rigs	Keep Nets	More than one rod	Number of Rods Allowed	Particle Baits	Spinners	Unhooking Mats essential	Wading	Worms Only
IRELAND																									
COUNTY CARLOW																									
BURREN (RIVER) (FH0752)								●	●																
DOUGLAS (RIVER) (FH1419)								●	●																
GREESE (RIVER) (FH2010)								●	●																
LERR (RIVER) (FH2705)								●	●																
COUNTY CAVAN																									
LOUGH RAMOR (FH3053)		●	●					●	●	●			●	●		●		●	●		●	●	●		
COUNTY CORK																									
BANDON (RIVER) (FH0283)								●	●																
BANDON (RIVER) (FH0282)								●	●																
CAREYSVILLE (FH0840)	●	●			●			●	●													●		●	
DERRYVEGALL LAKE (FH1341)								●	●													●			●
DERRYVEGALL LAKE (FH1342)								●	●													●			
DRIMINIDY LAKE (FH1444)								●	●													●			
GARRANES LAKE (FH1838)								●	●													●			●
LOUGH ADERRA (FH2999)									●													●			●
LOUGH AVAUL (LOWER) (FH3006)				●				●	●													●			●
LOUGH AVAUL (UPPER) (FH3007)				●				●	●													●			●
LOUGH BOFINNE (FH3013)				●				●	●													●			●
MANCH HOUSE FISHERY (FH3154)		●						●	●																
SCHULL RESERVOIR (FH4117)				●				●	●													●			●
SHEPPERTON LAKES (FH4231)				●				●	●													●			
COUNTY DONEGAL																									
ASSAROE LAKE (FH0174)							●	●	●									●	●			●			
CLOGHAN LODGE ESTATE FISHERY (FH1016)	●	●					●	●	●			●							●	2		●		●	●
FINN (RIVER) (FH1715)	●	●					●	●	●			●							●	2		●		●	●
ROSSES FISHERY (FH4017)				●				●	●															●	
COUNTY GALWAY																									
DOOHULLA (FH1408)								●	●																
LOUGH COOLIN (FH3019)		●						●	●													●			
LOUGH CORRIB (FH3021)		●						●	●					●		●		●	●		●				
LOUGH MASK (FH3041)		●						●	●													●			
COUNTY KERRY																									
LOUGH BARFINNIHY (FH3010)								●	●													●			●
LOUGH CAUM (FH3016)								●	●													●			●
LOUGH FADDA (FH3030)								●	●													●			●
LOUGH NAKIRKA (FH3045)								●	●													●			●
COUNTY KILDARE																									
GRAND CANAL (BARROW TRACK) (FH1942)								●																	
GREESE (RIVER) (FH2012)							●	●	●									●	●			●			
COUNTY KILKENNY																									
NORE (RIVER) (FH3521)								●	●																
NORE (RIVER) (FH3518)		●						●	●				●					●				●			
COUNTY LAOIS																									
BARROW (RIVER) (FH0327)		●					●											●				●			
BARROW (UPPER) (RIVER) (FH0328)								●																	
GRANSTOWN LAKE (FH1972)				●																2			●		
COUNTY LEITRIM																									
LOUGH ALLEN (FH3001)				●					●																
LOUGH MELVIN (FH3043)									●																
COUNTY LIMERICK																									
CASTLECONNELL SALMON FISHERY (FH0867)		●						●	●													●			
COUNTY LOUTH																									
BALLYMASCANLON (RIVER) (FH0277)		●						●	●													●			
CASTLETON (RIVER) (FH0871)		●						●	●													●			
FANE (RIVER) (FH1661)		●						●	●													●			
COUNTY MAYO																									
CLOONGEE FISHERY (FH1021)				●	●			●	●															●	●
GLORE (RIVER) (FH1896)									●																
LOUGH CARRA (FH3014)								●	●																
LOUGH CORRIB (UPPER) (FH3022)								●	●																
MOUNT FALCON SALMON FISHERY (FH3385)		●					●		●													●			
MOY FISHERY (FH3394)		●						●	●																
MULLAGHANOE (RIVER) (FH3400)								●	●																
OWENGARVE (RIVER) (FH3661)								●	●																
POLLAGH (RIVER) (FH3811)								●	●																

FISHING ALLOWANCES

Ireland (by County)

Fishing Allowances UK & Irish Fisheries

	Bank Fishing Only	Barbed Hooks	Boilies	Catch & Release	Kill All Fish Caught	Dead Bait	Live Bait	Dry Fly	Wet Fly	Electric Bait Boats	Sonar Boats	Fixed Weights Allowed	Floater Fish	Floating Bait	Floating Rings - Game	Ground Baiting	Hair Rigs	Keep Nets	More than one rod	Number of Rods Allowed	Particle Baits	Spinners	Unhooking Mats essential	Wading	Worms Only
COUNTY MEATH																									
BOYNE (RIVER) (FH0583)								●																	
COUNTY OFFALY																									
EDENDERRY OFFALY EIRE (FH1544)		●	●															●	●						
GRAND CANAL (FH1940)				●								●		●		●		●	●	2					
COUNTY ROSCOMMON																									
LOUGH ARROW (FH3003)								●	●													●			
LOUGH GARA (FH3032)				●															●	2					
LUNG RIVER (FH3113)				●															●	2					
COUNTY SLIGO																									
LOUGH BO (FH3012)								●	●																
COUNTY TIPPERARY																									
ARA (RIVER) (FH0125)								●	●													●			
CLONANAU FLY FISHING CENTRE (FH1018)								●	●																
SUIR (RIVER) (FH4536)								●	●																
SUIR (RIVER) (FH4544)								●	●																
COUNTY WATERFORD																									
BALLYSHUNNOCK (FH0279)								●	●																
BLACKWATER LODGE (FH0481)							●	●	●													●			
KNOCKDERRY (FH2540)								●	●																

Fishing Allowances UK & Irish Fisheries

	Bank Fishing Only	Barbed Hooks	Boilies	Catch & Release	Kill All Fish Caught	Dead Bait	Live Bait	Dry Fly	Wet Fly	Electric Bait Boats	Sonar Boats	Fixed Weights Allowed	Floater Fish	Floating Bait	Floating Rings - Game	Ground Baiting	Hair Rigs	Keep Nets	More than one rod	Number of Rods Allowed	Particle Baits	Spinners	Unhooking Mats essential	Wading	Worms Only
NORTHERN IRELAND																									
COUNTY ANTRIM																									
BUSH (RIVER) (FH0767)		●						●	●													●			
CAREY (RIVER) (FH0839)								●	●																
CLADY (RIVER) (FH0968)								●	●																
CLOGHWATER (RIVER) (FH1017)								●	●													●			
CLOUGH (RIVER) (FH1022)								●	●																
CRUMLIN (RIVER) (FH1204)								●	●																
DALL (RIVER) (FH1249)								●	●																
DUN (RIVER) (FH1470)								●	●																
GLENARM (RIVER) (FH1884)								●	●													●			
GLENARRIFF (RIVER) (FH1885)								●	●																
GLENSHESK (RIVER) (FH1895)								●	●																
INVER (RIVER) (FH2373)								●	●																
KELLSWATER (RIVER) (FH2427)								●	●													●			
MAINE (RIVER) (FH3144)								●	●																
MAINE (RIVER) (FH3145)								●	●																
MAINE (RIVER) (FH3146)								●	●																
MAINE (RIVER) (FH3142)								●	●										●						
MARGEY (RIVER) (FH3179)								●	●																
MCCAMMANS LAKE (FH3219)								●	●																
SIX MILE WATER (FH4283)								●	●													●			
SIX MILE WATER (FH4284)								●	●													●			
SPRINGWATER MEADOW (FH4376)								●	●																
STRAID FISHERY (FH4516)		●						●	●																
TILDARG FISHERY (FH4842)								●	●																
WOODFORD FISHERY (FH5474)		●					●	●	●																
COUNTY ARMAGH																									
BANN (UPPER) (RIVER) (FH0296)								●	●																
BLACKWATER (RIVER) (FH0456)								●	●																
CALLAN (RIVER) (FH0802)								●	●																
LAGAN (RIVER) (FH2551)								●	●																
LOUGHGALL COARSE FISHERY (FH3056)	●	●	●	●		●						●		●		●	●	●	●	2	●				
LOWRYS LAKE (FH3097)	●							●	●															●	
SEAGAHAN RESERVOIR DAM (FH4125)								●	●															●	
SHAWS LAKE (FH4214)								●	●																
SHAWS LAKE (FH4215)	●			●				●	●															●	
TULLNAWOOD LAKE (FH4966)	●			●	●			●	●															●	
TULLYNAWOOD RESERVOIR (FH4969)								●	●																
COUNTY DOWN																									
BALLYLOUGH (FH0275)								●	●																
BANN (UPPER) (RIVER) (FH0298)								●	●																
BANN (UPPER) (RIVER) (FH0297)								●	●																
BANN (UPPER) AND TRIBUTARIES (FH0299)								●	●																
CLANRYE (RIVER) (FH0972)	●	●	●	●	●	●	●	●	●			●		●	●		●	●			●	●		●	●
CLEGGAN (RIVER) (FH1002)								●	●																
CULLY (RIVER) (FH1216)								●	●																
FANE (RIVER) (FH1660)								●	●																
FORKHILL (RIVER) (FH1768)								●	●																
INLER (RIVER) (FH2368)								●	●																
KILKEEL (RIVER) (FH2481)								●	●																
LAGAN (RIVER) (FH2552)								●	●																
LOUGH CASHEL (FH3015)								●	●																
LOUGH COWEY FISHERY (FH3023)								●	●																
LOUGH GLASSDRUMMAN (FH3033)								●	●																
LOUGH KILTYBAINE (FH3039)								●	●																
LOUGH MULLAGHABAN (FH3044)								●	●																
MCCOURTS LAKE (FH3220)								●	●							●									
MILL LODGE FISHERY (FH3293)	●		●	●												●	●		●	2	●		●		
MONEYCARRAGH (RIVER) (FH3341)								●	●																
RINGDUFFERIN ESTUARY (FH3951)	●	●			●			●	●									●							
WHITEWATER (RIVER) (FH5355)								●	●																
WRITES LOUGH (FH5518)								●	●																
COUNTY FERMANAGH																									
BALLINAMALLARD (RIVER) (FH0263)								●	●																
COLEBROOKE (RIVER) (FH1059)								●	●																
COOLYERMER LOUGH FISHERY (FH1103)		●		●				●	●	●	●				●			●	●	2					
ERNE (RIVER) (FH1614)		●					●	●	●									●	●		●	●			

Fishing Allowances UK & Irish Fisheries

	Bank Fishing Only	Barbed Hooks	Boilies	Catch & Release	Kill All Fish Caught	Dead Bait	Live Bait	Dry Fly	Wet Fly	Electric Bait Boats	Sonar Boats	Fixed Weights Allowed	Floater Fish	Floating Bait	Floating Rings - Game	Ground Baiting	Hair Rigs	Keep Nets	More than one rod	Number of Rods Allowed	Particle Baits	Spinners	Unhooking Mats essential	Wading	Worms Only
LOUGH MELVIN (FH3042)	●	●		●			●	●	●		●	●							●	2		●		●	●
TEMPO (RIVER) (FH4736)								●	●																
COUNTY LONDONDERRY																									
AGIVEY (RIVER) (FH0039)								●	●																
BANN (LOWER) (RIVER) (FH0292)								●	●																
CREGGAN RESERVOIRS (FH1178)								●	●																
FAUGHAN (RIVER) (FH1679)		●					●	●	●													●			●
FAUGHAN (RIVER) (FH1678)					●			●	●													●			●
MACOSQUIN (RIVER) (FH3133)								●	●																
MOORBROOK LODGE (FH3359)	●	●		●				●	●										●	2			●	●	
MOYOLA (RIVER) (FH3395)				●				●	●			●		●			●		●	10		●		●	●
COUNTY TYRONE																									
ALTMORE FISHERIES (FH0086)								●	●																
ANNAGINNY STILL WATER FISHERY (FH0112)	●	●	●	●		●		●	●	●		●		●		●	●	●	●	2	●	●	●		●
BALLINDERRY (RIVER) (FH0266)								●	●																
BALLINDERRY (RIVER) (FH0267)								●	●																
BALLINDERRY (RIVER) (FH0268)								●	●																
BLACKWATER (RIVER) (FH0467)								●	●																
BRANTRY LOUGH (FH0602)								●	●																
BURN DENNETT (RIVER) (FH0747)								●	●																
CAMOWEN (RIVER) (FH0815)	●	●				●	●	●	●			●			●	●						●		●	
DERG (RIVER) (FH1339)								●	●																
DERG (RIVER) (FH1337)								●	●																
DRUMRAGH (RIVER) (FH1453)	●	●				●	●	●	●			●			●	●						●		●	
DUNGANNON PARK FISHERY (FH1475)		●						●	●																
FINN (RIVER) (FH1716)		●	●				●	●	●			●							●			●		●	
FINN (RIVER) (FH1717)								●	●																
FOYLE (RIVER) (FH1794)								●	●																
GLENELLY (RIVER) (FH1888)								●	●																
LOUGH FEA (FH3031)								●	●																
MOURNE (RIVER) (FH3390)								●	●																
MOURNE (RIVER) (FH3389)								●	●																
MOURNE (RIVER) (FH3388)								●	●																
OWENKILLEW (RIVER) (FH3662)	●	●				●	●	●	●			●			●	●						●		●	
OWENKILLEW (RIVER) (FH3663)								●	●																
PARK LAKE TROUT FISHERY (FH3699)								●	●																
STRULE (RIVER) (FH4530)	●	●				●	●	●	●			●			●	●						●		●	
TORRENT (RIVER) (FH4882)								●	●																
TULLYLAGAN (RIVER) (FH4968)								●	●																
WHITE LOUGH (FH5340)								●	●													●			●

Fishing Allowances UK & Irish Fisheries

	Bank Fishing Only	Barbed Hooks	Boilies	Catch & Release	Kill All Fish Caught	Dead Bait	Live Bait	Dry Fly	Wet Fly	Electric Bait Boats	Sonar Boats	Fixed Weights Allowed	Floater Fish	Floating Bait	Floating Rings - Game	Ground Baiting	Hair Rigs	Keep Nets	More than one rod	Number of Rods Allowed	Particle Baits	Spinners	Unhooking Mats essential	Wading	Worms Only
SCOTLAND																									
ABERDEENSHIRE																									
BOGNIE & MOUNTBLAIRY FISHING (FH0525)								●	●													●			
LOCH INSCH FISHERY (FH2894)	●	●		●				●	●										●	2					
MILL OF ELRICK FISHERY (FH3296)	●	●			●	●		●	●													●			●
WAULKMILL FISHERIES (FH5190)								●	●																
YTHAN FISHERY (FH5575)								●	●																
YTHAN VALLEY FISHERY (FH5576)								●	●																
ANGUS																									
DEAN (RIVER) (FH1285)								●	●																
ISLA (RIVER) (FH2387)								●	●																
KINGENNIE FISHINGS (FH2494)	●	●		●	●		●	●	●			●		●			●					●			●
MILL OF CRIGGIE TROUT FISHERY (FH3295)								●	●																
PIPERDAM (FH3784)		●						●	●																
ARGYLL AND BUTE																									
DUNOON RESERVOIR (FH1478)								●	●																
FRUIN (RIVER) (FH1817)								●	●																
INVERAWE FISHERIES (FH2374)		●						●	●										●						
LOCH AVICH (FH2847)		●				●		●	●													●		●	
LOCH AWE (FH2848)		●				●		●	●													●		●	
LOCH FAD (FH2879)		●			●			●	●			●					●					●		●	
LOCH QUIEN (FH2936)		●		●				●	●						●									●	
MILL HOUSE FISHERIES (FH3286)		●					●	●	●																
RUEL (RIVER) (FH4053)								●	●																
AYRSHIRE (NORTH)																									
CAMPHILL RESERVOIR (FH0816)								●	●																
MIDDLETON FISHERY (FH3268)		●						●	●																
PORT-NA-LOCHAN (FH3829)	●	●		●				●	●			●		●			●				●				
AYRSHIRE (SOUTH)																									
CRAITH RESERVOIR (FH1162)		●					●	●	●	●												●	●		
DOON (RIVER) (FH1410)	●	●						●	●													●		●	
SPRINGWATER FISHERY (FH4374)	●		●	●		●	●	●	●			●		●	●		●	●			●	●	●		●
STINCHAR (RIVER) (FH4457)								●	●																
DUMFRIES AND GALLOWAY																									
ANNAN (RIVER) (FH0113)		●		●				●	●			●										●		●	
BROOM FISHERIES (FH0689)	●			●	●			●	●										●	2		●			
BUITTLE RESERVOIR (FH0723)	●			●	●			●	●																
CLATTERINGSHAWS LOCH (FH0980)	●	●				●					●								●	2		●			
CRAIGHLAW (FH1159)	●	●	●	●		●	●					●		●		●	●	●	●	2	●	●			
DORMONT LAKE COARSE FISHERY (FH1415)			●											●		●		●	●		●		●		
ESK (RIVER) (FH1620)								●	●													●		●	●
GALLOWAY FOREST PARK (FH1829)		●	●					●	●	●				●				●	●			●			
HODDOM WATER (FH2244)		●						●	●													●			
KELHEAD WATER (FH2425)		●					●	●	●									●	●		●	●			
KEN (RIVER) (FH2429)		●						●	●									●	●						
KINMOUNT LAKE (FH2520)		●																	●						
KIRKWOOD WATER (FH2527)		●						●	●													●			
KIRRIEREOCH LOCH (FH2528)		●					●	●	●																
KNOCKQUASSEN RESERVOIR (FH2541)	●	●						●	●															●	
LOCH ROAN (FH2939)								●	●										●	2					
LOCH WHINYEON (FH2958)	●	●						●	●															●	
LOCHENBRECK LOCH (FH2964)	●	●						●	●															●	
MORTON POND (FH3376)																			●						
NEW ABBEY DOW (FH3460)	●	●		●	●			●	●															●	
NITH (RIVER) (FH3512)		●						●	●										●			●			
PURDOMSTONE RESERVOIR (FH3857)		●						●	●																
SLATEHOUSE LOCH (FH4295)								●	●										●						
STARBURN LOCH (FH4430)								●	●										●						
TORHOUSEKIE AND KIRWAUGH (FH4879)		●							●																
URR (RIVER) (FH5076)	●			●				●	●													●		●	●
FIFE																									
CRAIGLUSCAR RESERVOIR (FH1160)								●	●																
LOCH FITTY TROUT FISHERY (FH2883)		●			●	●		●	●			●		●	●	●	●	●			●	●		●	●
NEWTON FARM FISHERY (FH3494)		●						●	●										●						
RAITH LAKE FISHERY (FH3882)		●		●				●	●						●			●							
GLASGOW (CITY OF)																									
NEILSTON TROUT FISHERY (FH3438)		●						●	●																
HIGHLAND																									

FISHING ALLOWANCES

Scotland (by County)

Fishing Allowances UK & Irish Fisheries

	Bank Fishing Only	Barbed Hooks	Boilies	Catch & Release	Kill All Fish Caught	Dead Bait	Live Bait	Dry Fly	Wet Fly	Electric Bait Boats	Sonar Boats	Fixed Weights Allowed	Floater Fish	Floating Bait	Floating Rings - Game	Ground Baiting	Hair Rigs	Keep Nets	More than one rod	Number of Rods Allowed	Particle Baits	Spinners	Unhooking Mats essential	Wading	Worms Only
CONON (RIVER) (FH1089)	●	●	●			●	●	●	●			●		●		●					●	●		●	
GARRY UPPER (RIVER) (FH1839)								●	●																
GLASS (RIVER) (FH1873)		●						●	●																
GLENCOE LOCHAN (FH1886)		●				●	●	●	●			●		●			●				●	●			
LOCH BORRALAN (FH2858)								●	●													●			
LOCH GARRY (FH2885)								●	●																
LOCH INCH LAGGAN (FH2893)								●	●																
LOCH INSH (FH2895)	●	●		●		●		●	●													●		●	
LOCH POULARY (FH2935)								●	●																
LOCH QUOICH (FH2937)								●	●																
LOCH TOFTINGALL (FH2953)								●	●																
LOCH USSIE (FH2954)	●	●	●			●	●	●	●			●		●		●					●	●		●	
LOCH WATTEN (FH2957)								●	●																
NESS (RIVER) (FH3450)	●	●		●	●			●	●													●		●	●
SCOURIE HOTEL (FH4120)								●	●																
SPEY (RIVER) (FH4363)								●	●																
SPEY (RIVER) (FH4364)		●		●		●		●	●													●		●	
ST JOHNS LOCH (FH4390)								●	●																
STONEYFIELD LOCH (FH4475)		●						●	●																
STRATHMANAIRD LOCHS (FH4520)		●						●	●																
TARVIE LOCHS FISHERY (FH4661)		●	●	●			●	●	●													●			
INVERCLYDE																									
ARDGOWAN TROUT FISHERY (FH0128)		●		●				●	●			●		●	●							●		●	
LOCH THOM (FH2952)								●	●																
PINEWOOD TROUT FISHERY (FH3780)		●					●	●	●																
LANARKSHIRE (NORTH)																									
CLYDE (RIVER) (FH1039)		●					●	●	●													●			
HILLEND LOCH (FH2226)	●	●	●		●	●	●	●	●	●		●		●			●				●	●	●	●	●
LILY LOCH (FH2722)		●					●	●	●				●								●	●	●		
MONKLAND CANAL (FH3344)	●			●		●						●		●		●	●	●			●	●			
LANARKSHIRE (SOUTH)																									
TINTO TROUT FISHERIES (FH4856)	●			●				●	●															●	
LOTHIAN (EAST)																									
MARKLE FISHERIES (FH3186)		●	●				●	●	●				●					●	●				●		
TYNE (RIVER) (FH5018)								●	●																
LOTHIAN (MID)																									
LOGANLEA TROUT FISHERY (FH2980)								●	●										●						
LOTHIAN (WEST)																									
ALLANDALE TARN (FH0076)							●	●	●																
HOPETOUN FISHERY (FH2291)		●	●					●	●				●					●					●		
LINLITHGOW LOCH (FH2736)		●		●	●			●	●															●	
PARKLEY FISHERY (FH3705)		●						●	●																
SELM MUIR FISHERY (FH4135)		●						●	●																
MORAY																									
BROOM OF MOY (FH0690)									●																
GLEN OF ROTHES TROUT FISHERY (FH1883)	●			●			●	●	●			●													●
PERTH AND KINROSS																									
ABERFELDY ASSOCIATION BEAT (FH0014)																			●						
BALLECHIN BEAT (FH0260)																			●						
BOLFRACKS BEAT (FH0533)								●	●										●						
BRAAN (RIVER) (FH0584)	●	●						●	●															●	
CASTLE BEAT (FH0859)								●	●										●						
CLOCHFOLDICH BEAT (FH1013)								●	●										●						
CUILALUINN BEAT (FH1213)								●	●																
DERCULICH BEAT (FH1335)								●	●										●						
EASTERTYRE BEAT (FH1524)																			●						
FARLEYER BEAT (FH1666)								●	●										●						
GLENFARG FISHERY (FH1889)		●					●	●	●														●		
HEATHERYFORD FISHERY (FH2174)								●	●																
KENMORE BEAT (FH2431)																			●						
LOCH BHAC (FH2857)								●	●																
LOCH EIGHEACH (FH2876)	●	●						●	●															●	
LOCH TAY (FH2950)								●	●																
LOWER ABERUTHVEN FISHINGS (FH3070)	●							●	●													●		●	
LOWER FARLEYER BEAT (FH3078)																			●						
MONTAGUE RESERVOIR (FH3353)	●	●			●			●	●																
ORCHILL LOCH TROUT FISHERY (FH3619)		●						●	●										●						
PITCASTLE BEAT (FH3790)								●	●										●						

Fishing Allowances UK & Irish Fisheries

	Bank Fishing Only	Barbed Hooks	Boilies	Catch & Release	Kill All Fish Caught	Dead Bait	Live Bait	Dry Fly	Wet Fly	Electric Bait Boats	Sonar Boats	Fixed Weights Allowed	Floater Fish	Floating Bait	Floating Rings - Game	Ground Baiting	Hair Rigs	Keep Nets	More than one rod	Number of Rods Allowed	Particle Baits	Spinners	Unhooking Mats essential	Wading	Worms Only
PITLOCHRY BOATING STATION (FH3792)		●					●	●	●									●				●			
SANDYKNOWES FISHING (FH4099)								●	●																
SEAMAW LOCH (FH4126)	●	●			●			●	●																
SKETEWAN BEAT (FH4290)																			●						
TAY (RIVER) (FH4678)	●	●						●	●															●	
TOMBUIE BEAT (FH4868)								●	●										●						
TULLYPOWRIE BEAT (FH4970)																			●						
UPPER BORLICK BEAT (FH5051)																			●						
RENFREWSHIRE																									
CARN LOCH (FH0844)		●						●	●																
CLACHAIG (LOCH) (FH0967)		●						●	●																
COILLE BHAR (LOCH) (FH1055)		●						●	●																
GLEAN LOCH (FH1875)		●						●	●																
HOWWOOD TROUT FISHERY (FH2321)		●		●				●	●			●		●	●				●						●
LEIPEIG (LOCH) (FH2694)		●						●	●																
LOCH BARNLUASGAN (FH2853)		●						●	●																
LOCH DHU (FH2870)		●						●	●																
LOCH-AN-ADD (FH2961)		●						●	●																
LOCH-NA-BRIC (FH2967)		●						●	●																
LOCH-NA-FAOILINN (FH2968)		●						●	●																
MAICH WATERS (FH3140)	●	●		●		●		●	●			●		●			●		●	2				●	●
NEW LOCH (FH3471)		●						●	●																
SCOTTISH BORDERS																									
ACREKNOWE RESERVOIR (FH0024)		●						●	●																
AKERMOOR LOCH (FH0049)							●	●	●					●											
ALEMOOR RESERVOIR (FH0070)		●						●	●				●												
BUCCLEUCH ESTATES (FH0715)								●	●										●						
CLERKLAND FLY FISHERY (FH1003)								●	●																
ETTRICK AND YARROW (RIVER) (FH1632)								●	●										●						
HELLMOOR LOCH (FH2178)		●					●	●	●																
MACBIEHILL ESTATE (FH3127)				●				●	●						●										
ST MARYS LOCH (FH4393)								●	●																
TEVIOT (RIVER) (FH4751)		●						●	●																
TEVIOT (RIVER) (FH4750)								●	●										●						
TWEED (RIVER) (FH4999)								●	●																
WATCH RESERVOIR (FH5168)		●						●	●																
WULLIESTRUTHER LOCH (FH5522)		●					●	●	●																
STIRLING																									
AUCHESSON BEAT (FH0184)																			●						
BARNCROFT (FH0315)																			●						
BORELAND (FH0550)								●	●										●						
DOCHART (RIVER) (FH1382)		●					●	●	●													●			
DOCHART (RIVER) (FH1383)																			●						
DOCHART (RIVER) (FH1385)		●						●	●							●									
ENDRICK (RIVER) (FH1592)								●	●																
KILLEARN HOUSE FISHERY (FH2482)		●						●	●																
KILLIN BREADALBANE AC WATERS (FH2483)		●					●	●	●													●			
KINNEL (FH2521)							●	●	●	●			●	●							●	●			
LAKE OF MENTEITH FISHERIES (FH2566)								●	●																
LOCH VOIL (FH2956)		●		●			●		●													●		●	
LOCHAN NA LARAIG (FH2960)		●					●	●	●													●			
LOCHAY (RIVER) (FH2963)		●					●	●	●													●			
NORTH THIRD TROUT FISHERY (FH3534)		●						●	●																
PORTNELLAN (FH3830)								●	●													●			
SUIE (FH4534)								●	●										●						
SWANSWATER FISHERY (FH4600)					●			●	●																
WESTERN ISLES																									
CEANN-AN-ORA FISHERY (FH0878)		●					●	●	●										●			●			
LACASDALE LOCHS (FH2548)		●						●	●										●						
OBBE FISHINGS (FH3571)									●																
SOVAL ESTATE (FH4353)								●	●																
YORKSHIRE (SOUTH)																									
BANK END COARSE FISHERIES (FH0285)			●													●		●	●	2					
HAYFIELD LAKES (FH2155)																					●		●		
LINDHOLME FISHERIES (1) (FH2729)	●	●	●	●							●	●	●	●		●	●	●	●	2	●				
LINDHOLME FISHERIES (2) (FH2730)	●	●	●	●							●	●	●	●		●	●	●	●	2	●				
LINDHOLME FISHERIES (3) (FH2731)	●			●				●	●			●							●	2					
LINDHOLME FISHERIES 4) (FH2732)	●	●	●	●							●	●	●	●		●	●	●	●	2	●				

FISHING ALLOWANCES

Scotland (by County)

Fishing Allowances UK & Irish Fisheries

FISHING ALLOWANCES

Wales (by County)

	Bank Fishing Only	Barbed Hooks	Boilies	Catch & Release	Kill All Fish Caught	Dead Bait	Live Bait	Dry Fly	Wet Fly	Electric Bait Boats	Sonar Boats	Fixed Weights Allowed	Floater Fish	Floating Bait	Floating Rings - Game	Ground Baiting	Hair Rigs	Keep Nets	More than one rod	Number of Rods Allowed	Particle Baits	Spinners	Unhooking Mats essential	Wading	Worms Only
BLAENAU GWENT																									
BUTE TOWN RESERVOIR (FH0773)																●									
BRIDGEND																									
LLYNFI (RIVER) (FH2826)								●																	
CARMARTHENSHIRE																									
COTHI (RIVER) (FH1130)								●	●													●			
COWIN (RIVER) (FH1151)							●	●	●																
CYNIN (RIVER) (FH1241)							●	●	●																
DOLGWM MILL FISHERY (FH1397)								●																	
GLAS-LLYN FISHERY (FH1870)																			●						
LLYN CARFAN (FH2798)	●			●								●		●			●	●		2	●			●	
PANT Y BEDW FISHING LAKES (FH3693)								●	●																
PEWI FACH (RIVER) (FH3763)							●	●	●																
SPRINGWATER LAKES (FH4375)			●					●	●					●		●			●				●		
TAF (RIVER) (FH4628)							●	●	●																
TEIFI (RIVER) (FH4705)		●					●	●	●													●			
WHITE HOUSE MILL (FH5335)	●				●			●	●																●
CEREDIGION																									
CELLAN FISHERY (FH0885)								●	●																
CWMMACKWITH FISHERY (FH1238)								●																	
FRON FARM FISHERY (FH1814)	●		●		●			●	●					●			●	●							
LLANARTH FISHERY (FH2768)	●			●								●		●		●	●	●	●	2	●				
NANT Y MOCH RESERVOIR (FH3418)								●	●																
NINE OAKS (FH3509)								●	●					●					●		●		●		
TEIFI (RIVER) (FH4708)		●						●	●																
TEIFI (RIVER) (FH4711)								●	●																
TEIFI (RIVER) (FH4712)								●	●																
YSTWYTH (RIVER) (FH5574)								●	●													●			
CONWY																									
CONWY VALLEY FISHERIES (FH1099)	●	●		●										●		●					●				
GILER ARMS LAKE (FH1855)	●		●	●								●		●			●			2	●	●	●		
LLYN ALED (FH2791)	●			●		●		●	●			●		●			●				●	●		●	●
TYDDYN MAWR TROUT FARM (FH5015)		●					●	●	●									●							
DENBIGHSHIRE																									
ABBEY FISHERY (FH0002)								●	●							●		●							
ALWEN RESERVOIR (FH0093)	●				●			●	●													●		●	●
CEIRIOG (RIVER) (FH0882)																			●						
CEIRW STREAM (FH0884)		●						●	●				●									●			
DEE (RIVER) (FH1307)								●	●																
DEE (RIVER) (FH1311)		●						●	●				●									●			
DOLWEN AND PLAS UCHAF (FH1398)	●	●			●			●	●			●					●					●		●	●
FELIN-Y-GORS FISHERIES (FH1683)								●	●																
LLYN ALWEN (FH2792)		●						●	●				●									●			
LLYN BRENIG (FH2795)		●			●			●	●															●	
FLINTSHIRE																									
BUCKLEY TRAP POOL (FH0718)	●		●			●							●	●		●	●		●		●	●	●		
CLAWDD OFFAS DYKE (FH0984)																		●							
FOREST HILL TROUT FARM (FH1766)								●	●																
GWERYD LAKES FISHING (FH2047)																●		●	●						
GYRN CASTLE FISHERY (FH2056)																							●		
PADESWOOD POOL (FH3684)			●											●		●			●				●		
SARN MILL FISHERIES (FH4106)			●				●	●	●							●		●			●		●		
SEVEN SPRINGS FISHERIES (FH4143)							●	●	●																
WAL GOCH FLY (FH5115)								●	●																
WHEELER (RIVER) (FH5317)								●	●																
GLAMORGAN (VALE OF)																									
PONTSTICILL RESERVOIR (FH3817)																							●		
TAFF BARGOED (FH4633)								●	●					●				●							
GWYNEDD																									
AFON LLYFNI (RIVER) (FH0037)		●			●	●		●	●													●		●	
AFON SEIONT (RIVER) (FH0038)		●			●	●		●	●													●		●	
CREGENNAN LAKES (FH1177)				●				●	●																
CWM SILYN LAKE (FH1235)		●			●	●		●	●													●		●	
DEE (RIVER) (FH1314)		●	●				●	●	●									●			●	●			
DWYFACH (RIVER) (FH1488)								●	●																
DWYTHWCH LAKE (FH1492)		●			●	●		●	●													●		●	
DYSYNNI (RIVER) (FH1496)	●			●				●	●															●	
DYWARCHEN RESERVOIR (FH1498)		●			●	●		●	●													●		●	

Fishing Allowances UK & Irish Fisheries

	Bank Fishing Only	Barbed Hooks	Boilies	Catch & Release	Kill All Fish Caught	Dead Bait	Live Bait	Dry Fly	Wet Fly	Electric Bait Boats	Sonar Boats	Fixed Weights Allowed	Floater Fish	Floating Bait	Floating Rings - Game	Ground Baiting	Hair Rigs	Keep Nets	More than one rod	Number of Rods Allowed	Particle Baits	Spinners	Unhooking Mats essential	Wading	Worms Only
EDEN (RIVER) (FH1538)								●	●					●		●									
ERCH (RIVER) (FH1605)	●			●				●	●			●										●		●	●
FFESTINIOG FISHERY (FH1702)		●					●	●	●													●			
GLAN MORFA MAWR FISHERY (FH1868)		●					●	●	●				●									●			
GWYRFAI (RIVER) (FH2055)		●			●	●		●	●													●		●	
LLYN CWELLYN RESERVOIR (FH2804)		●			●	●													●			●		●	
LLYN CWMYSTRADLLYN (FH2805)	●			●				●	●			●										●		●	●
LLYN CYNWCH LAKE (FH2807)		●						●	●													●			
LLYN DDU (BLACK LAKE) (FH2808)								●	●																
LLYN PADARN (FH2821)		●			●	●		●	●													●		●	
LLYN TEGID (BALA LAKE) (FH2823)		●	●				●											●	●			●			
MAWDDACH (RIVER) (FH3212)								●	●																
MAWDDACH AND WNION (RIVERS) (FH3213)		●						●	●													●			
NANTLLE LAKE (FH3419)		●			●	●		●	●													●		●	
RHYDHIR (RIVER) (FH3939)	●			●				●	●			●										●		●	●
TALYLLYN LAKE (FH4640)		●		●				●	●										●	2				●	
TANYGRISIAU RESERVOIR (FH4656)																						●			
TRAWFFYNYDD RESERVOIR (FH4905)								●	●					●		●		●							
TRYWERYN (RIVER) (FH4962)		●	●				●	●	●									●			●	●			
WNION (RIVER) (FH5452)								●	●																
ISLE OF ANGLESEY																									
BREAKWATER PARK (FH0610)	●	●	●	●						●		●		●		●	●	●		1	●				
CEFNI RESERVOIR (FH0881)								●	●																
LLYN DEWI (FH2809)	●	●	●	●						●		●		●		●	●	●		1	●				
LLYN NANT ANOG (FH2817)	●	●	●	●						●		●		●		●	●	●		1	●				
LLYN TACAN (FH2822)	●	●	●	●						●		●		●		●	●	●		1	●				
MONMOUTHSHIRE																									
CWMCELYN POND (FH1237)		●	●							●			●	●		●		●			●		●		
FAIROAK FISHERY (FH1655)	●			●	●			●	●																
MONNOW (RIVER) (FH3351)		●	●					●	●												●	●			
RAVENSNEST FISHERY (FH3894)								●	●										●						
NEATH PORT TALBOT																									
HEPSTE (STREAM) (FH2188)		●					●	●	●																
NEATH (RIVER) (FH3434)		●					●	●	●													●			
NEWPORT																									
DEE (RIVER) (FH1298)								●	●										●						
WENTWOOD RESERVOIR (FH5251)								●	●																
YNYS-Y-FRO RESERVOIR (FH5571)					●			●	●																
NORFOLK																									
DEE (RIVER) (FH1315)								●	●													●			
PEMBROKESHIRE																									
EASTERN CLEDDAU (RIVER) (FH1521)																						●		●	●
EASTERN CLEDDAU (RIVER) (FH1520)				●				●	●			●		●		●	●				●	●	●	●	
HAYSCASTLE TROUT FISHERY (FH2159)								●	●																
IAN HEAPS PREMIER FISHERIES (FH2356)				●				●	●			●		●		●	●				●	●	●	●	
LLYS Y FRAN RESERVOIR (FH2829)					●			●	●																●
LUDCHURCH LAKE (FH3103)			●				●	●	●	●	●		●	●		●			●		●	●	●		
ROADSIDE FARM (FH3974)							●							●		●			●				●		
ROSEBUSH RESERVOIR (FH4013)		●						●	●															●	
WEST ATHESTON COARSE FISHERY (FH5256)			●											●				●	●						
POWYS																									
CAER BERIS MANOR HOTEL (FH0789)		●						●	●				●	●		●			●		●		●		
CLYNWEDOG RESERVOIR (FH1041)								●	●																
DEE (RIVER) (FH1316)								●	●																
DULAS (RIVER) (FH1469)								●	●																
DULAS (RIVER) (FH1467)								●	●																
GWYDDIOR LAKE (FH2053)								●	●															●	
IRFON (RIVER) (FH2377)								●	●																
ITHON (RIVER) (FH2400)	●	●	●		●	●	●	●	●			●		●	●	●	●	●			●			●	
LLANGORSE LAKE (FH2773)			●				●						●	●		●		●	●		●	●			
LLYN ALARCH (FH2789)		●						●	●																
LLYN-COCH HWYAD (FH2825)		●		●																				●	
RIVERSIDE CARAVAN PARK (FH3968)																			●						
SEVERN (RIVER) (FH4158)								●	●													●			
SEVERN (RIVER) (FH4154)								●	●																
SEVERN (RIVER) (FH4155)								●	●													●			
SEVERN (RIVER) (FH4153)								●	●																
SHROPSHIRE UNION CANAL (FH4252)																	●				●	●			

Fishing Allowances UK & Irish Fisheries

	Bank Fishing Only	Barbed Hooks	Boilies	Catch & Release	Kill All Fish Caught	Dead Bait	Live Bait	Dry Fly	Wet Fly	Electric Bait Boats	Sonar Boats	Fixed Weights Allowed	Floater Fish	Floating Bait	Floating Rings - Game	Ground Baiting	Hair Rigs	Keep Nets	More than one rod	Number of Rods Allowed	Particle Baits	Spinners	Unhooking Mats essential	Wading	Worms Only
USK RESERVOIR (FH5080)		●	●				●	●	●	●	●		●	●		●		●	●		●	●	●		
VYRNWY (RIVER) (FH5102)								●	●													●		●	
VYRNWY (RIVER) (FH5107)								●	●																
WESTLAKE FISHERY (FH5282)	●		●	●				●	●			●		●		●	●	●	●	2	●				
WYE (RIVER) (FH5538)								●	●																
WYE (RIVER) (FH5541)		●						●	●									●							
RHONDDA CYNON TAFF																									
LLYN ALAW (FH2790)		●			●			●	●			●			●							●		●	●
SEVEN OAKS FISHERY (FH4141)	●			●	●			●	●					●		●					●				
SWANSEA																									
FENDROD LAKE (FH1694)	●	●	●													●	●	●	●	2	●		●		
GOWERTON COARSE FISHERY (FH1929)	●			●		●	●					●		●		●	●	●	●	2					
LOWER LLIW (FH3087)								●	●																
MAES GWYN FISHERY (FH3136)	●		●	●	●	●		●	●			●		●			●		●	2	●		●		
WHITE SPRINGS LAKES (FH5341)			●					●	●	●				●		●		●	●		●	●	●		
TORFAEN																									
CWMBRAN BOATING LAKE (FH1236)		●	●															●	●		●				
WREXHAM																									
ALYN (RIVER) (FH0095)								●	●																
ALYN (RIVER) (FH0096)		●						●	●																
DEE (RIVER) (FH1318)								●	●													●			
DEE (RIVER) (FH1320)								●	●													●			
DEE (RIVER) (FH1301)																		●					●		
LLANDEGLA TROUT FISHERY (FH2770)	●	●		●				●	●			●										●			●
LLYN CYFYNWY (FH2806)								●	●																
TREE TOPS FLY FISHERY (FH4910)	●			●				●	●																

Day Ticket Prices (Adult)

SECTION 8

This section allows you to search for Day Ticket Prices for Adults to help you to make the right choice.

e.g under £5

Once you have located a Fishery you can either look up further details in Section 1 or use the other sections to find what else the Fishery may have to offer.

UNDER £1

SUFFOLK

ALDEBY HALL FARM PITS (FH0057) **£0.50**
BARSHAM DRAIN (FH0334) **£0.50**

YORKSHIRE (WEST)

ROYDS HALL DAM (FH4050) **£0.70**

UNDER £3

BEDFORDSHIRE

GREAT OUSE (RIVER) (FH1986) **£2.00**
PRIORY COUNTRY PARK (FH3848) **£2.50**

BERKSHIRE

FARLEYMOOR LAKE (FH1667) **£2.50**
LODDON (RIVER) (FH2977) **£2.50**
SAVERNAKE POND (FH4108) **£2.00**
THAMES (RIVER) (FH4769) **£2.50**
WELLINGTON COUNTRY PARK (FH5241) **£2.60**

BRISTOL

AVON (BRISTOL) (RIVER) (FH0191) **£1.50**
AVON (BRISTOL) (RIVER) (FH0192) **£2.00**
AVON (RIVER) (FH0202) **£2.00**
BRISTOL DOCKS (FH0655) **£2.50**

BUCKINGHAMSHIRE

OUSE (RIVER) (FH3641) **£2.50**

CAMBRIDGESHIRE

COTTERSTOCK RIVER (FH1136) **£2.00**
GODMANCHESTER (RIVER) (FH1905) **£1.00**
GREAT OUSE (RIVER) (FH1993) **£2.00**
GREAT OUSE (RIVER) (FH1990) **£2.00**
GUNWADE LAKE (FH2039) **£2.00**
HINCHINGBROOKE COUNTRY PARK (FH2232) **£2.00**
HUNDRED FOOT (RIVER) (FH2336) **£2.00**
HUNTINGDON (RIVER) (FH2340) **£2.00**
LITTLE PAXTON FISHERY (FH2759) **£2.00**
NENE (RIVER) (FH3441) **£2.00**
OLD NENE (RIVER) (FH3597) **£2.00**
OUNDLE (RIVER) (FH3637) **£2.00**
PAXTON LAKE (FH3720) **£1.00**
STEW POND (FH4453) **£2.00**

CHESHIRE

ASTBURY MERE (FH0176) **£2.50**
BOTTOMS RESERVOIR (FH0563) **£2.00**
BRERTON QUARRY (FH0617) **£2.00**
BRIDGEWATER CANAL (FH0635) **£2.00**
KNIGHTS POOL (FH2536) **£1.50**
LYMM DAM (FH3115) **£2.50**
RUNCORN PARK LAKE (FH4057) **£2.00**
SANKEY ST HELENS CANAL (FH4101) **£2.50**
WEAVER (RIVER) (FH5217) **£2.00**
WEAVER (RIVER) (FH5219) **£2.00**

CLEVELAND

CHARLTONS PONDS (FH0905) **£1.00**
HART RESERVOIR (FH2112) **£2.00**
HEMLINGTON LAKE (FH2179) **£2.20**
LOCKE PARK (FH2971) **£1.20**
ROSSMERE PARK LAKE (FH4020) **£2.00**

CORNWALL

PORT ELLIOT LAKE (FH3824) **£2.00**
TRENESTRALL LAKE (FH4916) **£2.00**

COUNTY DURHAM

FIGHTING COCKS RESERVOIR (FH1706) **£2.00**
GREENCROFT POND (FH2006) **£2.00**
HURWORTH BURN RESERVOIR (FH2348) **£2.00**
WEAR (RIVER) (FH5198) **£1.25**
WELLFIELD POND (FH5238) **£1.50**

CUMBRIA

BASSENTHWAITE LAKE (FH0344) **£2.00**
BORROWDALE FISHERIES (FH0553) **£2.50**
EAST VIEW FISHERY (FH1515) **£2.00**
KILLINGTON RESERVOIR (FH2485) **£2.00**
LOUGHRIGG TARN (FH3060) **£1.00**
WINSTER (RIVER) (FH5422) **£1.50**

DERBYSHIRE

ALLESTREE LAKE (FH0078) **£2.70**
ALVASTON LAKE (FH0089) **£2.70**
DERWENT (RIVER) (FH1346) **£2.00**
MARKEATON LAKE (FH3183) **£2.70**
RINGWOOD LAKE (FH3956) **£2.10**
SOAR (RIVER) (FH4315) **£2.00**
WINGERWORTH LIDO (FH5416) **£2.00**

DEVON

BERRYNARBOR MILL POND (FH0392) **£1.00**
DARRACOTT RESERVOIR (FH1276) **£2.50**
EASTCOTT FARM AND LODGES (FH1518) **£2.50**
GRAND WESTERN CANAL (FH1968) **£2.50**
MELBURY RESERVOIR (FH3244) **£2.20**
STAR BARTON PONDS (FH4426) **£2.00**
STOUR FARM FISHERY (FH4505) **£2.00**

DORSET

BERKELEY FARM (FH0391) **£2.00**
KNAPP HILL FARM LAKES (FH2533) **£1.00**
THAMES (RIVER) (FH4783) **£2.00**

ESSEX

BEDFORDS PARK LAKE (FH0365) **£2.00**
CENTRAL PARK LAKE (FH0887) **£2.00**
MAYSBROOK LAKES (FH3217) **£2.00**
PIPPS HILL FISHERIES (FH3788) **£2.00**
ROCHFORD RESERVOIR (FH3981) **£2.00**
WANSTEAD AND WOODFORD PONDS (FH5144) **£2.00**

GLOUCESTERSHIRE

GLOUCESTER AND SHARPNESS CANAL (FH1897) **£2.50**
GLOUCESTER CANAL (FH1898) **£2.50**
GLOUCESTER CANAL (FH1899) **£2.50**

HAMPSHIRE

BASINGSTOKE CANAL (FH0341) **£2.00**
BASINGSTOKE CANAL (FH0342) **£2.50**
LAKESIDE COUNTRY PARK (FH2589) **£2.00**

HEREFORDSHIRE

HERRIOTS POOL (FH2194) **£1.00**

HERTFORDSHIRE

DOBBS WEIR FISHERY (FH1381) **£2.80**
FEILDES WEIR (FH1680) **£2.50**
KINGS WEIR FISHERY (FH2509) **£2.00**
LEA (RIVER) (FH2645) **£2.90**
LEA NAVIGATION (FH2647) **£2.50**
LEE NAVIGATION (FH2664) **£2.50**
LEE NAVIGATION (FH2666) **£2.50**
LEE NAVIGATION (FH2667) **£2.50**
LEE NAVIGATION (FH2669) **£2.50**
LEE NAVIGATION (FH2663) **£2.50**
LEE NAVIGATION (FH2662) **£2.50**
LEE NAVIGATION (FH2668) **£2.50**
LEE NAVIGATION (FH2665) **£2.50**
OLD MILL AND MEADOWS (FH3594) **£2.90**

HUMBERSIDE

AIRE AND CALDER CANAL (FH0047) **£2.50**
BEVERLEY BECK (FH0399) **£2.50**
BURSTWICK SKI LAKE (FH0758) **£2.00**
DACRE LAKESIDE PARK (FH1244) **£2.00**
FARM PONDS (FH1670) **£2.00**
HALSHAM POND (FH2075) **£2.50**
LANGHOLME FISHERIES (FH2614) **£2.00**
MARKET WEIGHTON CANAL (FH3184) **£2.00**
REDFERNS POND (FH3917) **£2.50**
WOODALLS POND (FH5465) **£2.00**

ISLE OF WIGHT

GILLEES POND (FH1856) **£2.00**

KENT

SHORNE COUNTRY PARK LAKES (FH4246) **£2.50**

LANCASHIRE

ANGLEZARKE RESERVOIR (FH0110) **£1.00**
ASHTON CANAL (FH0170) **£1.00**
CROMPTON LODGE (FH1185) **£1.75**
DEEP PIT (FH1323) **£2.00**
DIXON GREEN RESERVOIR (FH1380) **£2.00**
FORSTERS LODGES (FH1770) **£2.00**
HIGHER HALL FLASH (FH2215) **£2.50**
HODDLESDEN RESERVOIR (FH2243) **£2.50**
LEEDS TO LIVERPOOL CANAL (FH2676) **£2.00**
LEEDS TO LIVERPOOL CANAL (FH2673) **£2.00**
POLLYS FLASH (FH3812) **£1.50**
STARMOUNT LODGES (FH4434) **£2.00**
UPPER RIVINGTON RESERVOIR (FH5057) **£2.50**
WAYOH RESERVOIR (FH5193) **£1.50**
WIDOWS FLASH (FH5368) **£2.50**

LEICESTERSHIRE

WATERY GATE FISHERY (FH5187) **£2.00**

LINCOLNSHIRE

BOULTHAM PARK LAKE (FH0565) **£2.00**
DENNIS RAINWATER LAKE (FH1331) **£2.00**
GOLTHO LAKE (FH1917) **£2.00**
GROOBYS PIT (FH2028) **£2.00**
HARTSHOLME PARK LAKE (FH2119) **£2.00**
SHANDY KEV FISHERIES (FH4207) **£2.00**
STARMERS PIT (FH4433) **£2.00**
TILL (RIVER) (FH4846) **£2.00**
TILL (RIVER) (FH4847) **£2.00**
TRENT (RIVER) (FH4919) **£2.00**
TRENT (RIVER) (FH4921) **£2.00**
TRENT (RIVER) (FH4920) **£2.50**
UPPER WITHAM (RIVER) (FH5060) **£2.00**
WARPING DRAIN (FH5149) **£2.00**

WHARFE (RIVER) (FH5296) £2.00
WINTERS LAKE (FH5427) £2.50

LINCOLNSHIRE (NORTH)

KINGFISHER LODGE (FH2501) £2.50
OLD ANCHOLME (RIVER) (FH3584) £2.00
ORCHARD POND (FH3617) £1.50

LONDON (GREATER)

ALEXANDRA PALACE LAKE (FH0071) £2.00
EAST WARWICK (FH1516) £2.50
LEA NAVIGATION (FH2648) £2.50
LEA NAVIGATION (FH2649) £2.50
LEE NAVIGATION (FH2670) £2.50
NORWOOD LAKE (FH3550) £2.00
OLD LEE (RIVER) (FH3591) £2.50
PERCH POND (FH3751) £2.50
REGENTS CANAL (FH3928) £2.00
REGENTS CANAL (FH3925) £2.50
REGENTS CANAL (FH3926) £2.50
SAVAY LAKE (FH4107) £2.00
WANSTEAD PARK LAKES (FH5145) £2.50

MANCHESTER (GREATER)

ALEXANDRA PARK (FH0072) £1.50
BLACKLEACH RESERVOIR (FH0451) £2.00
BOGGART HOLE CLOUGH (FH0524) £2.50
BRIDGEWATER CANAL (FH0638) £2.00
CHORLTON WATER PARK (FH0946) £2.50
CLIFTON MARINA (FH1008) £2.00
GORSE PIT RESERVOIR (FH1922) £2.00
GORTON (UPPER) RESERVOIR (FH1925) £2.00
HEATON PARK (FH2176) £2.00
HUDDERSFIELD NARROW CANAL (FH2328) £2.00
KING GEORGE V POOL (FH2489) £2.50
MYRTLE ROAD LODGES (FH3406) £2.00
PAINSWICK PARK LAKE (FH3686) £2.50
PENNINGTON FLASH (FH3738) £2.00
PLATT FIELDS (FH3800) £2.00
STAMFORD PARK LAKES (FH4413) £2.00
SWAN LODGE (FH4593) £2.50
WHITTLE BROOK RESERVOIR (FH5358) £2.00

MERSEYSIDE

CARR LANE POOL (FH0847) £2.00
LEEDS TO LIVERPOOL (FH2672) £2.00

MIDLANDS (WEST)

BULL FISHERY (FH0724) £1.00
CANNOCK EXTENSION CANAL (FH0822) £1.50
EDGBASTON RESERVOIR (FH1545) £2.30
KINGSBURY WATER PARK (FH2510) £1.70
RUSHALL CANAL (FH4059) £1.00
RUSHALL CANAL (FH4060) £1.75
RYTON POOLS COUNTRY PARK (FH4077) £1.50
SOHO LOOP CANAL (FH4321) £2.00
STAFFORD TO WORCESTER CANAL (FH4404) £2.00
SUTTON PARK (FH4564) £2.50
SWAN POOL (FH4595) £2.20
TAME VALLEY CANAL (FH4648) £1.00

NORFOLK

COSTESSEY PITS (FH1125) £2.00
HARDLEY MARSHES (FH2102) £1.00
HILGAY (RIVER) (FH2221) £2.50

NOTTINGHAMSHIRE

A1 PITS (FH0001) £2.00
DOLAR POND (FH1396) £2.50
FLEET (RIVER) (FH1745) £2.50
GRANTHAM CANAL (FH1974) £2.00
GRANTHAM CANAL (FH1975) £2.00
HOLME PIERPOINT (FH2268) £2.50
LANGOLD LAKES (FH2616) £2.80
PINDERS PONDS (FH3776) £2.00
TRENT (RIVER) (FH4926) £2.50
TRENT (RIVER) (FH4924) £2.50
TRENT (RIVER) (FH4929) £2.50
TRENT (RIVER) (FH4933) £2.50
TRENT (RIVER) (FH4934) £2.50

OXFORDSHIRE

CHERWELL (RIVER) (FH0921) £2.50
CHERWELL (RIVER) (FH0922) £2.50
CHERWELL (RIVER) (FH0923) £2.00
CHERWELL (RIVER) (FH0919) £2.00
CLEARWATER FISH FARM (FH0997) £1.50
OXFORD CANAL (FH3670) £2.00
OXFORD CANAL (FH3671) £2.50
THAME (RIVER) (FH4759) £2.00
THAMES (RIVER) (FH4800) £2.00

SHROPSHIRE

SEVERN (RIVER) (FH4180) £2.00
SEVERN (RIVER) (FH4167) £2.50
SEVERN (RIVER) (FH4173) £2.50

SOMERSET

APEX LAKE (FH0120) £2.50
AVON (RIVER) (FH0212) £2.00
BROWNES POND (FH0699) £2.00
BRUE (RIVER) (FH0707) £2.50
FROME (RIVER) (FH1810) £2.00
HUNSTRETE LAKE COMPLEX (FH2338) £2.50
ISLE (RIVER) (FH2393) £2.50
KENN (RIVER) (FH2433) £2.50
KENN (RIVER) (FH2432) £2.50
KENNET AND AVON CANAL (FH2456) £2.00
KENNET AND AVON CANAL (FH2457) £2.00
MARSTON LAKE (FH3195) £2.00
NEWTOWN LAKE (FH3499) £2.50
PARRETT (RIVER) (FH3707) £2.50
PAWLETT PONDS (FH3719) £2.00
TAUNTON ROAD PONDS (FH4666) £2.00
YEO (RIVER) (FH5563) £2.50
YEO (RIVER) (FH5564) £2.00

STAFFORDSHIRE

BORROWPIT LAKE (FH0554) £1.50
RUDYARD LAKE (FH4052) £1.50
SHROPSHIRE UNION CANAL (FH4259) £2.00
SHROPSHIRE UNION CANAL (FH4256) £2.50
STAFFORD AND WORCESTER CANAL (FH4400) £2.50
STAFFORD TO WORCESTER CANAL (FH4405) £2.50
TRENT AND MERSEY CANAL (FH4941) £1.50

SUFFOLK

ALTON WATER RESERVOIR (FH0088) £2.50
BLUE WATERS (FH0511) £2.00
BROOME PITS (FH0693) £2.50

SURREY

KINGFISHER FISHERY (FH2495) £2.00
WAGGONERS WELLS (FH5112) £1.50
WEY (RIVER) (FH5291) £2.50
WEY NAVIGATION (RIVER) (FH5292) £2.50

WILLINGHURST COARSE FISHERY (FH5373) £2.00
WILLINGHURST TROUT FISHERY (FH5374) £2.00

SUSSEX (WEST)

ADUR (RIVER) (FH0032) £2.50
ARUN (RIVER) (FH0146) £2.00
WESTERN ROTHER (RIVER) (FH5275) £2.50

TYNE AND WEAR

FELLGATE FISHERIES (FH1685) £2.00
KILLINGWORTH LAKE (FH2486) £2.50
LEAZES PARK LAKE (FH2655) £2.00
MARDEN QUARRY (FH3178) £2.00
MOUNT PLEASANT LAKE (FH3387) £2.00
STARGATE PONDS (FH4432) £2.00
WEAR (RIVER) (FH5212) £2.00
WILLOWS (THE) (FH5397) £2.00

WARWICKSHIRE

AVON (RIVER) (FH0213) £2.50
AVON (RIVER) (FH0215) £2.50
BLACK HILL POOLS (FH0441) £2.00
GRAND UNION CANAL (FH1966) £1.50
KINGSTON POOLS (FH2518) £1.00
NORTH OXFORD CANAL (FH3533) £2.00
OXFORD CANAL (FH3677) £1.50
OXFORD CANAL (FH3676) £2.00
PARK FARM (FH3697) £2.00
WARWICKSHIRE AVON (FH5157) £2.50

WILTSHIRE

AVON (BRISTOL) (RIVER) (FH0197) £2.00
AVON (BRISTOL) (RIVER) (FH0200) £2.00
AVON (RIVER) (FH0222) £2.50
KENNET AND AVON CANAL (FH2462) £2.00
SHAFTESBURY LAKE (FH4200) £2.00

WORCESTERSHIRE

DROITWICH CANAL (FH1446) £1.50
SEVERN (RIVER) (FH4186) £2.50
SEVERN (RIVER) (FH4195) £2.00
UPTON WARREN LAKE (FH5063) £2.00

YORKSHIRE (NORTH)

BACON FACTORY POND (FH0243) £2.00
BARLOW COMMON NATURE RESERVE (FH0311) £2.50
DERWENT (RIVER) (FH1356) £1.50
NIDD (RIVER) (FH3504) £1.00
OAK MERE FISHERY (FH3558) £2.00
OUSE (RIVER) (FH3653) £1.50
RUSWARP (RIVER) (FH4067) £2.00
RYE AND SEVEN (RIVERS) (FH4074) £2.50
SELBY CANAL (FH4130) £2.00
SELBY CANAL (FH4131) £2.00
SELBY CANAL (FH4132) £2.50
SHIELD TROUT FISHERY (FH4236) £2.00
SWALE (RIVER) (FH4572) £2.00
SWALE (RIVER) (FH4583) £2.50
ULLESKELF (RIVER) (FH5040) £1.50
URE (RIVER) (FH5073) £2.00
WEST HADDLESEY LAKE (FH5260) £2.00

YORKSHIRE (SOUTH)

BRAMPTON CANAL (FH0598) £2.50
BULL HOLE (FH0725) £1.50

CHESTERFIELD CANAL (FH0931) £1.25
CUMWELL LANE (FH1222) £2.50
CUSWORTH HALL LAKE (FH1228) £1.50
DAM FLASK RESERVOIR (FH1251) £2.80
DEARNE (RIVER) (FH1289) £2.00
DELVES FISH PONDS (FH1329) £2.00
DELVES LAKES (FH1330) £2.50
DON (RIVER) (FH1400) £2.00
DON (RIVER) (FH1401) £2.00
DON (RIVER) (FH1399) £2.50
ELSECAR RESERVOIR (FH1572) £2.00
HOWBROOK RESERVOIR (FH2318) £2.50
IDLE (RIVER) (FH2359) £2.00
IDLE (RIVER) (FH2360) £2.00
LONG POND (FH2983) £1.50
MILTON PONDS (FH3325) £2.00
NEW JUNCTION CANAL (FH3470) £2.00
NEW JUNCTION CANAL (FH3468) £2.50
NEWBIGGIN POND (FH3478) £2.00
SHEFFIELD CANAL (FH4223) £1.50
SOUTH YORKSHIRE NAVIGATION CANAL (FH4348) £1.00
SOUTH YORKSHIRE NAVIGATION CANAL (FH4347) £2.00
SOUTHFIELD RESERVOIRS (FH4350) £2.00
STAINFORTH AND KEADBY CANAL (FH4409) £2.00
STAINFORTH AND KEADBY CANAL (FH4410) £2.00
STAINFORTH AND KEADBY CANAL (FH4408) £2.10
THORNE NORTH POND (FH4814) £1.00
TINKERS PONDS (FH4854) £2.50
UNDERBANK RESERVOIR (FH5044) £2.60
WESTWOOD COUNTRY PARK (FH5288) £2.50
WORSBOROUGH RESERVOIR (FH5506) £2.50
WORSBROUGH CANAL (FH5507) £2.50
WORSBROUGH RESERVOIR (FH5508) £2.50

YORKSHIRE (WEST)

AIRE (RIVER) (FH0044) £2.00
AIRE (RIVER) (FH0045) £2.00
AIRE (RIVER) (FH0043) £2.00
BROOKFOOT LAKE (FH0681) £2.50
CALDER AND HEBBLE CANAL (FH0797) £2.00
HORNSEA MERE (FH2301) £2.00
LEEDS AND LIVERPOOL CANAL (FH2671) £2.00
LEEDS TO LIVERPOOL CANAL (FH2682) £2.00
OUSE (RIVER) (FH3657) £2.00
PUGNEYS COUNTRY PARK (FH3855) £1.50
ROUNDHAY PARK LAKES (FH4037) £2.00
WHARFE (RIVER) (FH5305) £2.00
WHARFE (RIVER) (FH5306) £2.00
WHARFE (RIVER) (FH5307) £2.00
WHARFE (RIVER) (FH5303) £2.00
WHARFE (RIVER) (FH5311) £2.00

UNDER £5

BEDFORDSHIRE

LEDBURN ROAD (FH2659) £4.00
SOUTH LAGOON (FH4333) £4.00

BERKSHIRE

ALBERT BRIDGE (FH0050) £3.00
KENNET AND AVON CANAL (FH2449) £3.00
LONGMOOR LAKE (FH2994) £4.00
MILL POND (FH3298) £3.00
MOATLANDS POOL (FH3331) £3.00
ROMNEY ISLAND AND MEADOW (FH4001) £3.00
SEACOURT (STREAM) (FH4124) £3.00
SOUTH FIELD PARK (FH4329) £3.00
SOUTH HILL PARK LAKE (FH4331) £3.00
THAMES (RIVER) (FH4764) £3.50
THAMES (RIVER) (FH4760) £3.00
WHITE SWAN LAKE (FH5343) £4.00

BRISTOL

BITTERWELL LAKE (FH0438) £3.00
TANHOUSE FARM LAKE (FH4652) £3.00

BUCKINGHAMSHIRE

COSGROVE LEISURE PARK (FH1122) £3.00
GALLOWS POOL (FH1830) £3.00
GREAT LINFORD LAKES (FH1982) £4.00
KINGFISHER GOLF CLUB (FH2496) £4.00
LODGE LAKES (FH2978) £4.00
LOUGHTON LODGE LAKE (FH3063) £4.00
OUSE (RIVER) (FH3640) £3.00
TEARDROP LAKES (FH4680) £3.00
THAMES (RIVER) (FH4779) £3.00
THAMES (RIVER) (FH4781) £3.00

CAMBRIDGESHIRE

BARNWELL COUNTRY PARK (FH0320) £4.00
BLOCK FEN COMPLEX (FH0503) £3.00
BURWELL LODE (FH0763) £3.00
CAM (RIVER) (FH0805) £3.00
CHAWSTON LAKES (FH0908) £3.00
FERRY MEADOWS (FH1701) £3.00
FIELDS END WATER (FH1704) £4.00
GREAT OUSE (RIVER) (FH1991) £3.00
GREAT OUSE (RIVER) (FH1992) £3.00
GREAT OUSE (RIVER) (FH1994) £4.00
GREAT OUSE (RIVER) (FH1995) £3.00
GREAT OUSE (RIVER) (FH1996) £3.00
HOLME FEN FISHING (FH2264) £4.00
KINGFISHER LAKE (FH2497) £3.00
LARK (RIVER) (FH2622) £3.00
MEPAL PIT (FH3256) £4.00
MIDDLE LEVEL DRAIN (FH3266) £3.00
NENE (RIVER) (FH3440) £3.00
NENE (RIVER) (FH3445) £3.00
NENE (RIVER) (FH3446) £3.00
NENE NORTH BANK (RIVER) (FH3449) £3.00
OFFORD CLUNY (FH3574) £3.00
OFFORD WEIRPOOL (FH3575) £3.00
OLD WEST (RIVER) (FH3602) £4.00
RANDALLS LAKE (FH3887) £3.50
RAVELEY DRAIN (FH3893) £3.00
ROSWELL PITS (FH4022) £3.00
SAND MARTIN LAKE (FH4091) £3.00
SPORTSMANS PIT (FH4366) £3.00
ST IVES COMPLEX (FH4387) £4.00
SWAN LAKE (FH4589) £3.00
TURKS HEAD LAKE (FH4977) £4.00
TWENTY FOOT DRAIN (FH5003) £3.00
WELDON RESERVOIR (FH5228) £3.00
WHITTLESEY DYKE/ BEVILLS LEAM (FH5361) £3.00
WILDEN RESERVOIR (FH5370) £3.00
WILLOW CREEK (FH5378) £3.00
WOOD POOL (FH5459) £3.00
WOOLPACK FISHERY (FH5500) £4.00

CHESHIRE

BLUNDELLS FARM FISHERY (FH0514) £3.50
BREAM HOLE (FH0611) £3.00
BRERETON HEATH COUNTRY PARK (FH0616) £3.00
BROOKSIDE FISHERIES (FH0686) £4.50
DOODLESPOOL FARM LAKE (FH1407) £4.00
GRIMESDITCH MILL POOL (FH2020) £3.00
GRIMSDITCH MILL POOL (FH2023) £3.00
HOLMSTON HALL FISHERY (FH2270) £4.00
LLOYDS MEADOW FISHERIES (FH2784) £4.00
MORETON MERE FISHERY (FH3370) £4.00
RODE POOL (FH3989) £3.00
SALE WATER PARK (FH4081) £3.50
SHAKERLEY MERE (FH4202) £3.00
TATTON MERE (FH4664) £4.00
TEGGSNOSE RESERVOIR (FH4700) £3.00
WINTERLEY POOL FISHERY (FH5426) £3.00

CLEVELAND

HARTBURN BRICK PIT (FH2113) £3.00
WHITEHOUSE CARAVAN PARK LAKE (FH5348) £4.00

CORNWALL

AMALWHIDDEN FARM (FH0099) £3.50
ARGAL RESERVOIR (FH0134) £4.50
BADHAM FARM LAKE (FH0246) £4.00
BILLS POOL (FH0423) £4.00
BOSCATHNOE RESERVOIR (FH0556) £4.00
BUDE CANAL (FH0721) £3.00
BUSSOW RESERVOIR (FH0772) £3.50
CHOONE FARM (FH0945) £3.50
COLLEGE RESERVOIR (FH1064) £4.50
EAST ROSE FARM (FH1513) £4.00
ELMFIELD FARM COARSE FISHERY (FH1570) £4.00
FERNDALE (FH1699) £3.50
GLENLEIGH FARM FISHERY (FH1892) £4.50
GOONHAVERN COARSE FISHING LAKE (FH1920) £3.00
HIDDEN VALLEY (FH2203) £4.00
LAKEVIEW COUNTRY CLUB (FH2598) £4.50
LANGARTH POOLS (FH2610) £4.00
MEADOWSIDE COARSE FISHERY (FH3228) £3.50
MIDDLE BOSWIN FARM (FH3264) £4.00
NEETS VALLEY PARK (FH3436) £3.50
OAKSIDE FISHERY (FH3567) £3.50
PORTH RESERVOIR (FH3825) £4.50
PRINCE PARK (FH3845) £3.50
ROSE PARK FISHERY (FH4011) £4.00
ROSEWATER LAKE (FH4014) £4.00
SHARKEYS PIT (FH4209) £4.00
ST ERTH FISHERY (FH4385) £4.50
ST GERMANS LAKE (FH4386) £3.00

ST LEONARDS FISHING LAKE (FH4392) **£3.50**
STOWFORD GRANGE FISHERIES (FH4513) **£4.50**
TAMAR LAKE (UPPER) (FH4645) **£4.00**
TIN DENE FISHERY (FH4850) **£3.00**
TORY FARM LAKE (FH4887) **£4.00**
TREBELLAN PARK LAKES (FH4907) **£3.50**
TRETHIGGEY FARM POND (FH4949) **£3.00**
WOONSMITH LAKE (FH5502) **£4.00**

COUNTY DURHAM

FIELDSONS POND (FH1705) **£3.00**
FINCHALE ABBEY FARM (FH1709) **£4.00**
MIDDLETON WATER PARK (FH3269) **£3.50**
SHAFTOS LAKE (FH4201) **£4.00**

CUMBRIA

ATKINSONS TARN COARSE FISHERY (FH0181) **£3.00**
BANKS POND (FH0289) **£3.00**
BIGLAND HALL LAKE (FH0414) **£4.00**
BLELHAM TARN (FH0495) **£4.00**
BRATHAY (RIVER) (FH0604) **£4.00**
BUTTERMERE LAKE (FH0777) **£3.00**
CLEABARROW TARN (FH0996) **£3.00**
CRUMMOCK WATER LAKE (FH1206) **£3.00**
ELLERBECK FARM AND FISHERY (FH1565) **£4.00**
GRASMERE COARSE FISHERY (FH1976) **£4.00**
HAWESWATER RESERVOIR (FH2140) **£3.50**
HAYESWATER RESERVOIR (FH2154) **£4.00**
HOLEHIRD TARN (FH2251) **£4.00**
LAKE WINDERMERE (FH2574) **£4.00**
LONSDALE COUNTRY PARK (FH2997) **£4.50**
LOWESWATER LAKE (FH3096) **£3.00**
MOSS ECCLES TARN (FH3378) **£4.00**
RATHER HEATH TARN (FH3891) **£4.00**
RYDAL WATER (FH4071) **£4.00**
SCHOOL KNOTT TARN (FH4115) **£3.50**
ULVERSTON CANAL (FH5043) **£3.00**
WINSTER (RIVER) (FH5423) **£3.00**
WITHERSLACK HALL TARN (FH5443) **£3.00**

DERBYSHIRE

BARLOW FISHERIES (FH0312) **£4.00**
BUTTERLEY RESERVOIR (FH0776) **£3.00**
CODNOR PARK RESERVOIR (FH1051) **£3.00**
COMBS RESERVOIR (FH1081) **£3.50**
COPPICE LAKE (FH1112) **£3.00**
DERWENT VALLEY FISHERY (FH1361) **£4.00**
PRESS MANOR (FH3840) **£4.00**

DEVON

ABBROOK POND (FH0012) **£3.00**
ALDER LAKE (FH0059) **£3.00**
ANGLERS ELDORADO (FH0106) **£4.00**
ASHCOMBE FISHERY (FH0159) **£4.50**
AXE (RIVER) (FH0234) **£3.00**
BAKERS FARM (FH0254) **£3.00**
BICKERTON FARM FISHERY (FH0406) **£3.50**
CADOVER BRIDGE PITS (FH0788) **£3.00**
CHARLECOMBE (FH0902) **£4.00**
CLOVELLY LAKES (FH1024) **£3.00**
COOMBE FARM FISHPONDS (FH1105) **£3.00**
COOMBE FISHERIES (FH1106) **£4.00**
CREEDY (RIVER) (FH1174) **£3.00**
CULM (RIVER) (FH1217) **£3.00**
CULM (RIVER) (FH1218) **£3.00**
DUNSLEY FARM (FH1481) **£3.00**
EDDISON POND (FH1532) **£4.00**
EXE (RIVER) (FH1639) **£3.00**
EXE (RIVER) (FH1643) **£3.50**
EXEMOOR FARM (FH1646) **£3.00**
EXETER CANAL (FH1647) **£3.00**
EXETER SHIP CANAL (FH1648) **£3.00**
FENECK POND (FH1695) **£3.00**
FINLAKE PONDS (FH1713) **£3.00**
FOUR PONDS (FH1781) **£4.00**
GRAND WESTERN CANAL (FH1967) **£4.00**
HATCHLAND TROUT FISHERY (FH2129) **£4.00**
HOGSBROOK LAKES (FH2246) **£3.50**
HOLLIES TROUT FARM AND FISHERY (FH2256) **£3.00**
HOME FARM FISHERY (FH2280) **£4.50**
JENNETTS RESERVOIR (FH2409) **£4.00**
LEGGE FARM COARSE FISHERY (FH2688) **£4.50**
LITTLE ALLERS COARSE FISHERY (FH2739) **£4.00**
LITTLE WEACH (FH2763) **£4.00**
LOWER HALLACOMBE FISHERY (FH3080) **£4.00**
LOWER SLADE RESERVOIR (FH3094) **£4.50**
LYN (RIVER) (FH3118) **£3.00**
MILL PARK COARSE FISHING LAKE (FH3297) **£3.50**
MILLHAYES (FH3313) **£4.00**
MILTON FARM PONDS (FH3319) **£3.00**
NEWCOURT PONDS (FH3482) **£3.00**
NEWTON ABBOT SPRING PONDS (FH3493) **£4.00**
OAKTREE FISHERY (FH3568) **£4.00**
OLDBOROUGH FISHING RETREAT (FH3604) **£4.00**
PADBROOK PARK (FH3681) **£4.00**
PICFRESH (FH3765) **£3.50**
POUND POND FARM (FH3836) **£3.00**
ROCOMBE PONDS (FH3986) **£4.00**
RUB - A - DUB POND (FH4051) **£3.00**
SAMPFORD PEVERAL PONDS (FH4090) **£3.00**
SAWMILLS LAKE (FH4109) **£4.00**
SIMPSON VALLEY FISHERY (FH4274) **£4.00**
SLADE RESERVOIRS (FH4292) **£4.00**
SOUTH HAY FARM (FH4330) **£3.00**
SPIRES LAKES (FH4365) **£4.50**
SQUABMOOR RESERVOIR (FH4379) **£3.50**
STEVENSTONE LAKES (FH4452) **£3.00**
SUMMERLEAZE POND (FH4554) **£3.00**
SUNRIDGE FISHERY (FH4557) **£4.00**
TRAGO MILLS (FH4903) **£3.00**
TRENCHFORD RESERVOIR (FH4915) **£4.50**
UPTON WARREN LAKE (FH5062) **£3.50**
WAPPERWELL POND (FH5146) **£4.00**
WATERSMEET AND GLENTHORNE FISHERIES (FH5185) **£3.00**
WEST PITT FARM FISHERY (FH5264) **£3.50**
WISCOMBE FISHERY (FH5433) **£3.50**

DORSET

BLASHFORD LAKES (FH0493) **£4.50**
CULVERS FARM FISHERIES (FH1220) **£4.00**
HERMITAGE LAKES (FH2189) **£4.00**
HILLVIEW FARM LAKE (FH2227) **£4.00**
KINGCOMBE COARSE FARM (FH2492) **£4.00**
LYONS GATE CARAVAN PARK (FH3126) **£4.00**
MAPPOWDER COURT (FH3174) **£4.00**
RADIPOLE LAKE (FH3875) **£3.60**
REVELS FISHERY (FH3932) **£4.00**
STOUR (DORSET) (RIVER) (FH4487) **£3.00**
STOUR (DORSET) (RIVER) (FH4486) **£3.00**
STOUR (RIVER) (FH4492) **£3.00**
UPPER STOUR (RIVER) (FH5059) **£4.00**
WOOD FARM CARAVAN PARK (FH5458) **£3.30**

ESSEX

ALBYNS LAKE (FH0053) **£3.00**
BERWICK PONDS (FH0393) **£3.50**
BLACKWATER (RIVER) (FH0475) **£3.00**
BLACKWATER (RIVER) (FH0473) **£3.00**
CHASE FISHERY (FH0907) **£3.00**
CHELMER (RIVER) (FH0910) **£3.00**
CHELMER AND BLACKWATER NAVIGATION CANAL (FH0913) **£3.00**
CHIGBOROUGH (FH0940) **£4.00**
CONNAUGHT WATER (FH1087) **£3.00**
GLOUCESTER PARK LAKE (FH1900) **£4.00**
HAINAULT FOREST COUNTRY PARK (FH2063) **£4.00**
HARWOOD HALL LAKE (FH2125) **£3.00**
HOOKS MARSH (FH2289) **£4.00**
LAKE MEADOWS (FH2562) **£3.00**
NORTHLANDS PARK (FH3546) **£3.00**
PAR (FH3695) **£3.00**
RAPHAELS PARK (FH3888) **£3.00**
RODING VALLEY LAKE (FH3994) **£3.00**
STAMBRIDGE STARR FISHERIES (FH4412) **£3.00**
WAKE VALLEY POND (FH5114) **£3.00**
WARREN (FH5150) **£4.00**

GLOUCESTERSHIRE

ADLESTROP LAKE (FH0027) **£4.00**
AVON (RIVER) (FH0205) **£3.00**
BOURTON ON THE WATER GRAVEL PIT NO1 (FH0568) **£4.00**
BURLEY FIELDS LAKE (FH0744) **£4.00**
CANNOP PONDS (FH0823) **£3.50**
COKES PIT (FH1056) **£4.00**
HIGHNAM COURT LAKE (FH2219) **£4.00**
KEYNES COUNTRY PARK (FH2475) **£4.00**
KEYNES PARK TOP LAKE (FH2476) **£4.00**
LIGHTMOOR POOL (FH2719) **£3.00**
LYDNEY BOATING LAKE (FH3114) **£3.00**
MARIONS POOL (FH3181) **£3.00**

MEADOWCLIFFE POOL (FH3226) £4.00
MILL LAKE (NO 44) (FH3289) £4.00
MYTHE POOL (FH3407) £3.00
NEIGH BRIDGE LAKE (FH3437) £4.00
PLUMP HILL POOL (FH3806) £3.00
RED LION FISHERY (FH3910) £4.00
SEVERN (RIVER) (FH4147) £3.00
SEVERN (RIVER) (FH4146) £3.00
STAUNTON COURT LAKES (FH4441) £4.00
STEAM MILLS LAKE (FH4444) £3.00
STONE END FARM LAKES (FH4467) £3.50
THAMES (RIVER) (FH4785) £3.00
WATERLOO SCREENS (FH5179) £3.00
WICK WATER (FH5364) £4.00

HAMPSHIRE

ANTON LAKE (FH0118) £4.00
CHARLTON PITS (FH0904) £3.00
CROOKED WILLOWS (FH1188) £4.00
FOXCOTTE LAKE (FH1789) £4.00
MOORS VALLEY COUNTRY PARK (FH3366) £3.00
ORCHARD LAKES (FH3616) £4.00
QUEENS ROAD POND (FH3867) £3.00
RIVER FARM (FH3964) £3.50
STEPSTONES LAKES (FH4451) £4.00

HEREFORDSHIRE

CHURCH POOL (FH0955) £3.00
COURT FARM (FH1143) £3.00
HUNDRED POOL (FH2337) £3.00
MARSH HOUSE FARM (FH3192) £3.50
MUNDERFIELD HAROLD (FH3402) £4.00
PRIDEWOOD LAKE (FH3844) £4.00
RED BANK POOLS (FH3907) £4.00
ROTHERWAS LONG POOL (FH4031) £3.00
WYE (RIVER) (FH5533) £3.00
WYE (RIVER) (FH5535) £3.50
WYE (RIVER) (FH5536) £4.00

HERTFORDSHIRE

AYLESBURY ARM CANAL (FH0236) £3.00
BATCHWORTH LAKE (FH0346) £3.50
BROOKFIELD LAKE (FH0680) £3.00
FAIRLANDS VALLEY PARK (FH1652) £4.00
GRAND UNION CANAL (FH1949) £3.00
GRAND UNION CANAL (FH1945) £3.00
GRAND UNION CANAL (FH1944) £3.00
GRAND UNION CANAL (FH1947) £3.00
GRAND UNION CANAL (FH1948) £3.00
GRAND UNION CANAL (FH1951) £3.00
GRAND UNION CANAL (FH1946) £3.00
GRAND UNION CANAL (FH1950) £3.00
HATFIELD FOREST LAKE (FH2131) £3.50
LEA (RIVER) (FH2644) £3.00
RYEMEADS (FH4076) £4.00
STANBOROUGH LAKE (FH4415) £3.00
STARTOPS RESERVOIR (FH4435) £3.50
THAME (RIVER) (FH4755) £3.00
TRING RESERVOIRS (FH4957) £4.00
WILSTONE RESERVOIR (FH5404) £4.00

HUMBERSIDE

BEVERLEY CANAL (FH0400) £3.50
BILLABONG WATER SPORTS AND CARAVAN PARK (FH0416) £3.00
BURTON CONSTABLE COUNTRY PARK (FH0759) £4.00
DRIFFIELD CANAL (FH1442) £3.00
EMMOTLAND PONDS (FH1587) £3.00
FISHPONDS FARM AND FISHERY (FH1734) £3.00
FISHPONDS FARM AND FISHERY (FH1735) £3.00
GOWDALL LAKES (FH1928) £4.00
HOLME LAKE FISHERY (FH2266) £4.00
LAKEMINSTER PARK (FH2577) £3.00
LAMBWATH LAKES (FH2600) £3.00
LEVEN CANAL (FH2709) £3.50
LEVEN PARK LAKE (FH2711) £3.50
NEST (FH3451) £4.00
NODDLE HILL LAKE (FH3513) £3.00
OAKLANDS WATER (FH3564) £3.00
STAR CARR TROUT FARM (FH4427) £3.50
THORPE HALL (FH4822) £3.00
WILLITOFT FISH FARM (FH5376) £3.00
WILLOW SPRINGS (FH5390) £3.00

ISLE OF WIGHT

NETTLECOMBE FARMS (FH3457) £3.00
SOMERTON RESERVOIR (FH4325) £4.00

KENT

BROOKLANDS LAKE (FH0684) £3.00
BYWATER LAKE (FH0785) £3.50
CHIDDINGSTONE CASTLE LAKE (FH0939) £3.50
HAYSDEN COUNTRY PARK (FH2160) £3.00
LONGFORD LAKE (FH2989) £3.00
MEDWAY (RIVER) (FH3231) £3.00
MEDWAY (RIVER) (FH3238) £3.00
MEDWAY (RIVER) (FH3239) £3.00
RUXLEY PITS (FH4069) £4.00
SINGLETON LAKE (FH4276) £3.00
SURRENDEN LAKES (FH4558) £4.00

LANCASHIRE

BALL GROVE LAKE (FH0258) £3.00
BANNISTER HALL FARM (FH0300) £3.00
BRYAN HEY RESERVOIR (FH0711) £3.00
CHURCH GARDEN (FH0952) £4.00
CLIVIGER FISH PONDS (FH1012) £3.00
COTTAGE GREEN GARDEN CENTRE (FH1133) £3.00
CROFT FISHERIES (FH1182) £3.00
FOULRIDGE RESERVOIR (FH1778) £3.50
GREENHALGH LODGE FISHERY (FH2007) £4.00
INCE MOSS FISHERIES (FH2363) £3.00
LANCASTER CANAL (FH2604) £3.00
LANCASTER HOUSE (FH2605) £3.00
LATHOM FISHERIES (FH2627) £3.00
LEISURE LAKES (FH2695) £3.20
LITTLE DALE HALL COARSE FISHERY (FH2747) £3.00
MARTIN HALL FARM (FH3200) £3.00
ORRELL WATER PARK (FH3625) £3.60
PINE LODGE FISHERIES (FH3777) £3.50
RIBBLE (RIVER) (FH3946) £3.00
STANLEY PARK LAKE (FH4420) £4.00
SWANTLEY LAKE (FH4601) £3.00
WALVERDEN RESERVOIR (FH5137) £3.00
WYRESIDE LAKES FISHERY AND LODGINGS (FH5550) £4.50

LEICESTERSHIRE

C J FISHERIES (FH0786) £4.00
HOLLY FARM FISHERY (FH2261) £4.00
MILL FARM FISHERY (FH3280) £4.00
MONNOW (RIVER) (FH3350) £3.00
NANPANTAN RESERVOIR (FH3417) £3.00
PROCTORS PLEASURE PARK (FH3851) £3.00

LINCOLNSHIRE

ASHBY PARK FISHERIES (FH0158) £3.80
BELVOIR CASTLE (FH0383) £4.50
BRICKYARD FISHERY (FH0623) £4.00
DENTON RESERVOIR (FH1332) £3.00
FISH POND FARM (FH1725) £3.00
GRANGE FARM LEISURE (FH1969) £3.00
GRIMSTHORPE LAKE (FH2024) £4.70
HATTON TROUT LAKE (FH2134) £3.00
HAVERHOLME PARK (FH2137) £4.00
HILL VIEW LAKES (FH2224) £4.00
HOLLAND PARK (FH2255) £3.00
KEAL COATES FISHERY (FH2422) £4.00
LAKESIDE (FH2582) £3.00
LAKESIDE LEISURE PARK (FH2594) £3.50
LOBBY FIELD PONDS (FH2834) £3.50
MARRIS LAKES (FH3190) £3.50
MOON LAKE (FH3356) £4.00
OLSTEN FISHERY (FH3610) £3.50
PEACOCK LAKE (FH3723) £3.50
REVESBY RESERVOIR (FH3933) £3.00
ROSSWAYS WATER (FH4021) £3.00
SKEGNESS WATER LEISURE PARK (FH4285) £3.50
STEEPING (RIVER) (FH4446) £4.00
STICKNEY BRICKPONDS (FH4455) £3.00
SUDBROOK POND (FH4533) £3.50
SWAN LAKE (FH4592) £3.00
SYCAMORE FISHING LAKES (FH4618) £4.00
TATTERSHALL LEISURE PARK (FH4663) £4.00
VICKERS POND (FH5097) £4.00
WATERSIDE LEISURE PARK (FH5184) £3.00
WHISBY GARDEN CENTRE (FH5329) £4.00
WILLOW LAKES (FH5384) £4.00
WOODLAND WATERS (FH5482) £4.50
WOODLANDS FISHERY (FH5483) £3.50

LINCOLNSHIRE (NORTH)

BARTON BROADS LAKE (FH0337) £4.50
HOE HILL POND (FH2245) £3.00
STADDLETHORPE POND (FH4398) £4.50
WESTFIELD LAKES (FH5277) £3.00

LONDON (GREATER)

BOXERS LAKE (FH0577) £3.00
COWLEY LAKE (FH1152) £3.00
CUTTING LAKE (FH1231) £3.00

- GRAND UNION CANAL (FH1954) £3.00
- GRAND UNION CANAL (FH1955) £3.00
- GRAND UNION CANAL (FH1956) £4.00
- HIGHAMS PARK LAKE (FH2213) £4.00
- HOLLOW PONDS (FH2259) £4.00
- LITTLE BRITAIN LAKE (FH2743) £3.00
- MULGROVE POND (FH3399) £4.00
- POTOMAC POND (FH3833) £3.50
- REGENTS CANAL (FH3927) £3.00
- TRENT COUNTRY PARK LAKES (FH4946) £3.00
- TRENT PARK LAKES (FH4947) £3.10
- WEST RESERVOIR (FH5265) £4.00
- WOOLWICH DOCKYARD (FH5501) £3.00

MANCHESTER (GREATER)

- CROFT HEAD FISHERY (FH1183) £3.00
- DOWRY AND NEW YEARS BRIDGE RESERVOIR (FH1433) £3.00
- ELTON RESERVOIR (FH1574) £3.50
- GROVE LODGE (FH2031) £3.00
- HOLLINGWORTH LAKE COUNTRY PARK (FH2258) £3.00
- KING WILLIAM IV RESERVOIR (FH2491) £3.00
- LOWER TOWN HOUSE FISHERY (FH3095) £3.00
- PILSWORTH FISHERY COMPLEX (FH3773) £4.00
- REDDISH VALE MILL PONDS (FH3913) £3.00
- RHODES LODGE (FH3936) £3.00
- ROMAN LAKE LEISURE PARK (FH4000) £3.75
- SALFORD QUAYS (FH4082) £3.50

MERSEYSIDE

- MORETON MERE (FH3369) £3.00

MIDLANDS (WEST)

- ALVECHURCH FISHERIES (FH0090) £3.50
- COOMBE ABBEY LAKE (FH1104) £3.50
- COOMBE POOL (FH1109) £3.50
- DAYHOUSE FARM (FH1282) £4.00
- EARLSWOOD LAKES (FH1503) £3.00
- HEATHFIELD POOL (FH2175) £3.20
- KINGSNORDLEY (FH2517) £3.00
- PATSHULL PARK (FH3717) £4.00
- POOL HALL (FH3819) £4.00
- POOLE HALL FARM (FH3821) £4.00
- ROYAL BRITISH LEGION POOLS (FH4043) £3.00
- SOMERS FISHERY (FH4323) £3.00
- WALCOT EAST LAKE (FH5116) £3.00
- WASSELL GROVE FISHERIES (FH5167) £4.00

NORFOLK

- BLICKLING PARK LAKE (FH0500) £4.00
- BOOTON CLAY PIT (FH0543) £3.00
- GATTON WATER CARAVAN SITE (FH1843) £3.50
- GIMINGHAM LAKES (FH1858) £3.00
- GLEN MERE (FH1882) £3.50
- GREAT OUSE (RIVER) (FH1997) £3.00
- GREAT OUSE (RIVER) (FH1998) £3.00
- GUNTON PARK LAKE (FH2037) £3.50
- HALL FARM LAKES (FH2068) £3.00
- HAVERINGLAND HALL PARK (FH2138) £3.50
- HEVINGHAM LAKES (FH2197) £3.00
- HINDERCLAY LAKES (FH2233) £4.50
- LAKESIDE CARAVAN PARK (FH2587) £3.00
- LITTLE DUNHAM CARP LAKES (FH2749) £3.50
- LITTLE OUSE (RIVER) (FH2757) £3.00
- MARTHAM PITS (FH3199) £3.00
- MEADOW LAKE (FH3223) £4.50
- MIDDLE HARLING LAKE (FH3265) £4.00
- PECK MEADOW POND (FH3730) £4.00
- RELIEF CHANNEL (FH3929) £3.00
- RINGLAND LAKES (FH3952) £3.00
- RINGLAND PITS (FH3953) £3.00
- SCOULTON MERE (FH4119) £3.00
- SOVEREIGN LAKES (FH4354) £3.00
- TAVERHAM (FH4668) £3.00
- TEN MILE BANK (FH4737) £3.50
- WALNUT FARM FISHERIES (FH5125) £4.00
- WISSEY (RIVER) (FH5435) £3.50
- WOODRISING WATER MEADOWS (FH5489) £3.50
- YARE (RIVER) (FH5557) £3.00

NORTHAMPTONSHIRE

- DAVENTRY COUNTRY PARK (FH1281) £3.30
- GRAND UNION CANAL (FH1958) £3.00
- GRAND UNION CANAL (FH1959) £3.00
- ISE (RIVER) (FH2384) £3.00
- ISLIP NATURE LAKE (FH2396) £3.00
- NENE (RIVER) (FH3447) £3.00
- NENE (RIVER) (FH3448) £3.00
- NORTHAMPTON JUNCTION CANAL (FH3542) £3.00
- OXFORD CANAL (FH3667) £3.00
- THORPE WATERVILLE LAKE (FH4827) £3.00
- THRAPSTON LAKES (FH4829) £3.00
- WOOTTON BROOK LAKE (FH5503) £3.00

NORTHUMBERLAND

- NORTH TYNE (RIVER) (FH3539) £4.80

NOTTINGHAMSHIRE

- CLUMBER LAKE (FH1030) £4.00
- COLWICK COUNTRY PARK (FH1080) £3.50
- HALLCROFT FISHERIES (FH2070) £4.00
- LAKESIDE FISHERY (FH2592) £4.00
- MAUN (RIVER) (FH3209) £4.00
- SAPPHIRE LAKES (FH4104) £4.00
- SHERWOOD FOREST FARM PARK FISHERY (FH4234) £4.00
- SMEATONS LAKES (FH4304) £4.00
- TRENT (RIVER) (FH4923) £3.50
- TRENT (RIVER) (FH4930) £3.00
- TRENT (RIVER) (FH4932) £3.00

OXFORDSHIRE

- BUSCOT LOCK (FH0766) £3.00
- BUTLERS HILL FARM (FH0775) £4.00
- CHERWELL (RIVER) (FH0920) £3.00
- CHERWELL (RIVER) (FH0924) £3.00
- CHEYNEY MANOR FISHERY (FH0937) £3.00
- COLLEGE FARM FISHING (FH1063) £4.00
- GLEBE COURT LAKE (FH1877) £3.00
- GRAND UNION CANAL (FH1960) £3.00
- GRAND UNION CANAL (FH1961) £3.00
- HORSE AND GROOM LAKES (FH2303) £3.00
- LINCH HILL FISHERY (FH2725) £3.00
- MANOR HOUSE (FH3166) £3.00
- MILTON POOLS FARM (FH3326) £4.25
- OXFORD CANAL (FH3668) £3.50
- OXFORD CANAL (FH3669) £3.00
- OXFORD CANAL (FH3672) £3.00
- OXFORD CANAL (FH3673) £3.00
- OXFORD CANAL (FH3674) £3.00
- PIMLICO FARM LAKES (FH3775) £4.00
- RUSHEY WEIR (FH4062) £3.00
- THAMES (RIVER) (FH4797) £3.50
- THAMES (RIVER) (FH4798) £3.00
- THAMES (RIVER) (FH4790) £3.50
- THAMES (RIVER) (FH4802) £3.50
- THAMES (RIVER) (FH4803) £3.00
- THAMES (RIVER) (FH4795) £3.00
- THAMES (RIVER) (FH4794) £4.00
- THAMES (RIVER) (FH4801) £3.00
- THAMES (RIVER) (FH4793) £3.00

SHROPSHIRE

- APLEY POOLS (FH0121) £3.00
- BAYLIS POOLS (FH0351) £4.00
- BEECHES POOL (FH0367) £3.00
- BLUE POOL (FH0510) £3.00
- BOLDINGS POOLS (FH0530) £4.00
- COLEMERE COUNTRY PARK (FH1061) £3.00
- HINKSHAY POOLS (FH2235) £4.00
- LOWER HILL FARM (FH3081) £4.00
- MIDDLE POOL (FH3267) £3.00
- MILLRIDE FISHERY (FH3317) £3.00
- MONKHALL FISHERIES (FH3343) £4.50
- SEVERN (RIVER) (FH4181) £3.00
- SEVERN (RIVER) (FH4168) £3.00
- SEVERN (RIVER) (FH4166) £3.00
- SPRING LEE (FH4369) £4.00
- STIRCHLEY POOLS (FH4458) £4.00
- TANAT (RIVER) (FH4650) £4.00
- TOWNSEND FISHERY (FH4894) £3.00
- WALCOT WEST LAKE (FH5117) £3.50

SOMERSET

- AVALON FISHERIES (FH0186) £4.00
- AVON (BRISTOL) (RIVER) (FH0193) £4.00
- BRISTOL AVON (FH0647) £4.00
- BRISTOL AVON (FH0648) £4.00
- BRISTOL AVON (FH0649) £4.00
- CHARD RESERVOIR (FH0899) £3.00
- COOMBE LAKE (FH1107) £3.00
- DUNWEAR LAKES (FH1482) £3.50
- DURLEIGH RESERVOIR (FH1484) £4.50
- EDNEYS FISHERIES (FH1548) £4.00
- EMERALD POOL FISHERY (FH1585) £4.00
- FROME (RIVER) (FH1811) £3.50
- GODNEY MOOR PONDS (FH1906) £4.00
- HIGHLANDS DAIRY LAKE (FH2218) £3.00
- HORSESHOE LAKE (FH2308) £4.50
- HOWLEY STREET POND (FH2320) £3.50
- HUNTSPILL (RIVER) (FH2343) £3.00
- ISLE (RIVER) (FH2394) £4.00
- KING SEDGEMOOR DRAIN (FH2490) £3.00
- LANGFORD LAKES (FH2612) £3.00

- LOWER LOVELYNCH FISHERIES (FH3089) **£4.00**
- MELLS PIT (FH3250) **£4.00**
- NEWTON PARK (FH3497) **£3.00**
- PARRETT (RIVER) (FH3710) **£3.00**
- PARRETT (RIVER) (FH3708) **£3.00**
- STATHE DRAIN (FH4438) **£4.00**
- SUMMERHAYES (FH4553) **£4.00**
- TAUNTON AND BRIDGWATER CANAL (FH4665) **£3.00**
- TAUNTON TO BRIDGWATER CANAL (FH4667) **£3.00**
- THURLEYBEARE POND (FH4836) **£3.00**
- TONE (RIVER) (FH4869) **£4.00**
- TUCKING MILL (FH4963) **£4.50**
- WELLINGTON BASIN (FH5240) **£3.00**
- WITHAM FRIARY LAKE (FH5441) **£3.50**
- WYCH LODGE LAKE (FH5526) **£3.00**

STAFFORDSHIRE

- BASFORD COARSE FISHERY (FH0340) **£3.50**
- DRAYTON BRIDGE (FH1439) **£3.00**
- HANCHURCH FISHERIES (FH2099) **£4.00**
- HIMLEY HALL AND PARK LAKE (FH2230) **£4.00**
- HOLDEN LANE POOL (FH2249) **£3.00**
- IZAAK WALTON FISHERY (FH2404) **£4.00**
- PINE POOL (FH3778) **£3.30**
- SOUTH POPLARS (FH4337) **£4.00**
- STAFFORD AND WORCESTER CANAL (FH4401) **£3.00**
- SWAN PIT POOL (FH4594) **£4.00**

SUFFOLK

- BREAKAWAY PIT (FH0609) **£3.00**
- BRIDGE FARM RESERVOIRS (FH0630) **£3.00**
- CAMELOT LAKE (FH0813) **£4.50**
- HIGHFIELD FISHERY (FH2216) **£4.00**
- NEEDHAM LAKE (FH3435) **£3.50**
- NORTH MEADOWS (FH3531) **£4.00**
- STOUR (RIVER) (FH4501) **£4.00**
- STOW (RIVER) (FH4508) **£4.00**
- STOW (RIVER) (FH4509) **£4.00**
- STOW (RIVER) (FH4510) **£4.00**
- STOW (RIVER) (FH4511) **£4.00**
- THET (RIVER) (FH4809) **£4.00**
- WICKHAM MARKET RESERVOIRS (FH5365) **£3.00**
- WRIGHTS FARM (FH5517) **£4.00**

SURREY

- BOLDERMERE (FH0529) **£4.00**
- BRITTENS POND (FH0658) **£4.00**
- LAKESIDE (FH2586) **£3.00**

SUSSEX (EAST)

- BELFREY COARSE FISHERY (FH0375) **£3.50**
- CUCKMERE (RIVER) (FH1209) **£3.00**
- DECOY LAKE (FH1296) **£4.00**
- HORAM MANOR FISHERY (FH2294) **£3.00**
- ROSEBANK FARM FISHERY (FH4012) **£3.00**
- SCALAND WOOD (FH4110) **£4.00**
- WISHING TREE RESERVOIR (FH5434) **£4.00**

SUSSEX (WEST)

- ADUR (RIVER) (FH0031) **£4.00**
- PASSIES PONDS (FH3715) **£4.00**
- ROTHER (RIVER) (FH4028) **£3.50**
- WESTERN ROTHER (FH5274) **£3.00**

TYNE AND WEAR

- BOLAM LAKE COUNTRY PARK (FH0528) **£4.00**
- SILKSWORTH SPORTS COMPLEX (FH4266) **£3.00**
- STEPHENSON LAKE (FH4450) **£3.00**

WARWICKSHIRE

- BANKS (THE) (FH0288) **£4.00**
- BISHOPS BOWL LAKES (FH0435) **£3.00**
- LANNYS LAGOON (FH2620) **£3.00**
- MILL POOL (FH3302) **£4.00**
- MONKS POOL (FH3347) **£3.50**
- OAKHAM FARM POOLS (FH3562) **£4.00**
- TUNNEL BARN FARM (FH4972) **£3.00**
- WARWICKSHIRE AVON (FH5155) **£3.00**
- WEST HILLBOROUGH (FH5261) **£3.00**

WILTSHIRE

- AVON (BRISTOL) (RIVER) (FH0196) **£3.50**
- AVON (BRISTOL) (RIVER) (FH0199) **£4.00**
- AVON (BRISTOL) (RIVER) (FH0201) **£4.00**
- AVON (BRISTOL) (RIVER) (FH0194) **£4.00**
- AVON (RIVER) (FH0216) **£3.50**
- AVON (RIVER) (FH0218) **£3.50**
- BRISTOL AVON (FH0653) **£4.00**
- BURBROOKS RESERVOIR (FH0733) **£4.00**
- CLIVEY PONDS (FH1011) **£3.00**
- COATE WATER COUNTRY PARK (FH1046) **£3.50**
- CUCKOOS REST (FH1211) **£3.50**
- HUNTERS MOON (FH2339) **£4.00**
- KENNET AND AVON CANAL (FH2460) **£3.00**
- KENNET AND AVON CANAL (FH2465) **£3.00**
- KENNET AND AVON CANAL (FH2459) **£3.00**
- KENNET AND AVON CANAL (FH2461) **£3.00**
- KENNET AND AVON CANAL (FH2463) **£3.00**
- LIDEN LAGOON (FH2717) **£3.00**
- MANOR BROOK LAKE (FH3160) **£3.00**
- PEARMOOR LAKE (FH3726) **£3.00**
- PEATMOOR LAGOON (FH3728) **£3.00**
- PEMBROKE POND (FH3733) **£3.50**
- PLAUMS PIT (FH3802) **£3.50**
- PURTON LAKE (FH3859) **£3.00**
- SABRE AND SWORDS LAKES (FH4079) **£4.00**
- SOUTHLEIGH LAKE (FH4351) **£4.00**
- TURNERS PADDOCK LAKE (FH4981) **£4.00**
- WHITE HORSE INN LAKE (FH5334) **£4.00**
- WOODLAND PARK (FH5480) **£4.50**
- WYATTS LAKE (FH5523) **£4.00**

WORCESTERSHIRE

- ARROW VALLEY LAKE (FH0141) **£4.20**
- BIRMINGHAM TO WORCESTER CANAL (FH0434) **£3.00**
- BRAKE MILL POOL (FH0596) **£3.50**
- BROAD ACRES LAKE (FH0661) **£4.00**
- BROCKAMIN POOLS (FH0667) **£3.50**
- CASTLE GREEN POOLS (FH0860) **£4.00**
- ELMBRIDGE LAKES (FH1569) **£4.50**
- EVESBATCH FISHERIES (FH1635) **£3.50**
- FURNACE MILL FISHERY (FH1822) **£4.00**
- HAYE FARM FISHERY (FH2152) **£3.00**
- HURCOTT POOL (FH2344) **£3.00**
- HUXLEYS HAMPTON FERRY FISHERIES (FH2352) **£3.00**
- LEDWYCHE BROOK (FH2660) **£3.00**
- LEIGH SINTON FISHING LAKES (FH2692) **£4.50**
- LOWER BROADHEATH POOLS (FH3074) **£3.50**
- SALWARPE (RIVER) (FH4089) **£3.00**
- SEVERN (RIVER) (FH4184) **£3.00**
- SEVERN (RIVER) (FH4185) **£3.00**
- SEVERN (RIVER) (FH4190) **£3.00**
- SEVERN (RIVER) (FH4188) **£3.50**
- SEVERN (RIVER) (FH4189) **£4.00**
- SEVERN (RIVER) (FH4194) **£4.00**
- SHATTERFORD FISHERY AND WILDLIFE SANCTUARY (FH4212) **£4.50**
- SILLIGROVE FISHERY (FH4267) **£4.50**
- SION FARM FISHERIES (FH4279) **£3.00**
- SNUFF MILL POOL (FH4314) **£3.00**
- STAFFORD TO WORCESTER CANAL (FH4406) **£3.00**
- TEME (RIVER) (FH4732) **£3.00**
- TEME (RIVER) (FH4731) **£3.00**
- TEME (RIVER) (FH4726) **£3.00**
- TEME (RIVER) (FH4728) **£3.00**
- TOP BARN ANGLING CENTRE (FH4875) **£4.00**
- TWYFORD FARM POOL (FH5009) **£3.00**
- UCKINGHALL POOL (FH5038) **£3.00**
- UNWICKS FARM FISHERY (FH5049) **£4.00**
- WARWICKSHIRE & AVON (FH5154) **£3.00**
- WARWICKSHIRE AVON (FH5158) **£4.00**
- WARWICKSHIRE AVON (FH5161) **£3.00**
- WASH POOL (FH5163) **£3.00**
- WHARFE INN POOL (FH5312) **£4.00**
- WHARTONS PARK COARSE FISHING (FH5314) **£3.50**
- WILLOW FARM (FH5380) **£3.50**
- WILLOW MARSH (FH5386) **£4.00**
- WINDMILL LAKE (FH5409) **£4.00**
- WITLEY FISHERY (FH5448) **£3.00**
- WITLEY POOLS (FH5449) **£3.00**
- WOOD POOL (FH5462) **£4.00**
- WOODROW FISH POND (FH5490) **£4.00**
- WOODSTON MANOR POOLS (FH5496) **£4.00**

YORKSHIRE (NORTH)

- BIRKDALE FISHERY (FH0430) **£3.00**
- CASTLE HOWARD GREAT LAKE (FH0861) **£3.00**
- CATTERICK LAKES (FH0874) **£4.00**
- CAWOOD HOLIDAY PARK (FH0877) **£4.00**
- CLIFTON MOOR LAKE (FH1009) **£3.00**
- COD BECK (FH1049) **£4.00**
- CUNDALL LODGE FISHERY (FH1223) **£3.00**
- DANBY (RIVER) (FH1253) **£3.00**
- ELLERTON PARK (FH1568) **£3.50**
- ELVINGTON LAKE (FH1575) **£4.00**
- ESK (RIVER) (FH1625) **£3.00**
- FAIRVIEW LAKE (FH1656) **£3.00**
- FOGGLESKYTE WATERS (FH1753) **£3.00**
- HESSAY POND (FH2196) **£3.00**
- HIGH MOOR FARM PARK (FH2208) **£4.00**
- HOLLINGWOOD FISHERY (FH2257) **£4.00**
- HOXNE FARM PONDS (FH2322) **£3.00**
- LAKEHOUSE LAKE (FH2576) **£3.00**
- LINGCROFT FARM POND (FH2735) **£3.00**
- MARSTON WYSE TROUT FARM (FH3197) **£4.00**

MOULTON LANE POND (FH3384) £4.00
MUNBY POND (FH3401) £3.50
NEWBY HALL FISHERIES (FH3481) £4.00
NEWHAY DAY TICKET LAKE (FH3484) £4.00
NIDD (RIVER) (FH3501) £3.00
NIDD (RIVER) (FH3502) £3.00
ORCHARD FARM PONDS (FH3615) £4.00
PICKERING PARK FISHING LAKE (FH3766) £3.00
PROSPECT FARM POND (FH3852) £3.00
RACECOURSE LAKE (FH3871) £4.00
RIPON RACECOURSE LAKE (FH3959) £4.00
RIVER VIEW COTTAGE (FH3966) £3.00
ROGERS POND (FH3997) £4.00
SCARBOROUGH MERE (FH4113) £4.00
SELBY CANAL (FH4133) £3.00
SEMERWATER (FH4137) £3.50
STONEY LANE PONDS (FH4473) £4.00
SWALE (RIVER) (FH4571) £3.00
SWALE (RIVER) (FH4574) £3.00
SWALE (RIVER) (FH4582) £3.00
SWALE (RIVER) (FH4567) £3.00
SWALE (RIVER) (FH4569) £3.00
SWALE (RIVER) (FH4576) £3.00
SWALE (RIVER) (FH4577) £3.00
THORNTON BRIDGE (FH4819) £3.00
URE (RIVER) (FH5069) £3.50
URE (RIVER) (FH5070) £3.00
WHARFE (RIVER) (FH5300) £3.00
YORKSHIRE OUSE (FH5572) £3.00

YORKSHIRE (SOUTH)

ARKSEY STATION POND (FH0135) £4.00
BRICKYARD PONDS (FH0628) £3.50
FLEETS DAM (FH1746) £4.00
HARTHILL RESERVIORS (FH2115) £3.00
HAVEN (FH2136) £3.50
KJS FISHERIES (FH2532) £3.00
NEW JUNCTION CANAL (FH3469) £3.00
PEBLEY RESERVOIR (FH3729) £3.00
RAILWAY POND (FH3880) £3.00
SHIREOAKS PARK (FH4243) £4.00
STANBOROUGH FISHERIES (FH4414) £4.00
STRAIGHT MILE FISHERY (FH4517) £4.00
TRIANGS FISHERY (FH4953) £4.00
ULLEY RESERVOIR (FH5041) £3.15
WILLOW GARTH FISHERY (FH5381) £3.00
WILLOWGARTH LAKE (FH5394) £3.50

YORKSHIRE (WEST)

ACKTON POND (FH0020) £3.00
BOTTOMS DAM (FH0562) £3.50
FLANSHAW DAM (FH1742) £3.00
HILL TOP RESERVOIR (FH2222) £3.50
MILLRACE (FH3316) £4.00
NARROW CANAL (FH3427) £3.00
NARROW CANAL (FH3425) £3.50
NARROW CANAL (FH3426) £3.50
NOSTELL PRIORY LAKE (FH3551) £4.00
OAKS SCAR RESERVOIR (FH3566) £3.50
PINFOLD DAMS (FH3781) £3.00
PONTEFRACT PARK LAKE (FH3816) £3.00
ROCHDALE CANAL (FH3979) £3.00
ROWLEY DAM (FH4040) £3.50
SPARTH RESERVOIR (FH4360) £3.50
T P POND DAM (FH4624) £3.00
TP WOODS POND (FH4902) £3.50
WALSDEN PRINTING CO LODGES (FH5128) £3.00
YEADON TARN (FH5559) £3.00

UNDER £10

BEDFORDSHIRE

ARLESEY LAKE (FH0136) £5.00
BRIARWOOD FISHERY (FH0619) £5.00
MANOR FARM LEISURE (FH3163) £6.00
TINGRITH COARSE FISHERY (FH4851) £6.50
WATER END FISHERY (FH5170) £5.00

BERKSHIRE

ASHRIDGE MANOR (FH0169) £5.00
BENS LAKE (FH0385) £5.00
BISHOPS GREEN FARM LAKE (FH0436) £5.00
BURGHFIELD BLUE POOL (FH0740) £6.00
BURGHFIELD MATCH LAKE (FH0742) £6.00
CHURCH FARM (FH0950) £5.00
FROBURY FARM SPORTING CLUB (FH1805) £5.00
HOLME GRANGE (FH2265) £6.00
JINGLES FARM (FH2412) £5.00
KENNET (RIVER) (FH2448) £8.00
KENNET (RIVER) (FH2438) £9.00
KENNET AND AVON CANAL (FH2450) £5.00
LONGMOOR FARM FISHING LAKE (FH2993) £6.00
MATCH AND BLUE POOLS (FH3207) £6.00
OLD MILL (FH3592) £8.00
ROYAL BERKSHIRE FISHERY (FH4042) £6.00
SWAN VALLEY (FH4596) £5.00
TRI-LAKES (FH4954) £7.50

BRISTOL

BAGWOOD LAKE (FH0249) £5.00
SEVINGTON LAKES FISHERY (FH4199) £5.00

BUCKINGHAMSHIRE

ALDERS FARM TROUT FISHERY (FH0062) £7.00
DOVECOTE LAKE FISHERY (FH1430) £6.00
GILBRATAR LAKE (FH1854) £5.00
OUSE (RIVER) (FH3642) £6.00
TINGRITH LAKES (FH4852) £6.50

CAMBRIDGESHIRE

BARNWELL PIT (FH0321) £5.00
BLUEBELL LAKE (FH0513) £5.00
DECOY LAKE (FH1295) £5.00
EARITH FISHERY (FH1501) £6.00
EAST DELPH LAKES (FH1507) £5.00
ELDERNELL LAKE (FH1559) £5.00
FENLAND FISHERIES (FH1696) £6.00
GERARDS CARP LAKE (FH1849) £5.00
HIGH FLYER LAKE (FH2206) £5.00
KINGSLAND RESERVOIRS (FH2512) £5.00
LILY PARK LAKES (FH2723) £5.00
MAGPIE LAKE (FH3139) £5.00
NORTHEY PARK FISHERY (FH3543) £5.00
OLD WEST (RIVER) (FH3601) £5.00
OVER MAIN DRAIN (FH3659) £5.00
PISCES CARAVAN PARK AND FISHERY (FH3789) £5.00
SIBSON FISHERIES (FH4264) £6.00
STRETHAM LAKE (FH4524) £5.00
VIRGINIA LAKE (FH5100) £5.00
WHITE HOUSE TROUT FARM (FH5337) £6.50
WILLOW LAKE (FH5382) £5.00

CHESHIRE

APPLETON RESERVOIR (FH0123) £5.00
BORDER FISHERIES (FH0546) £5.00
BROOKSIDE LAKES (FH0687) £5.00
BURTON MERE FISHERIES (FH0761) £6.00
CAPESTHORNE HALL STOCK POND (FH0831) £6.00
CHESHIRE FISHING (FH0925) £5.00
DANE RIVERSIDE FISHERY (FH1267) £5.00
EGERTON LAKE (FH1550) £5.00
GORSTY HALL (FH1923) £5.00
GOWY FISHERY (FH1932) £5.00
HAMPTON SPRINGS (FH2096) £5.00
HARTHILL (FH2114) £5.00
LAMALOAD RESERVOIR (FH2599) £8.00
MARTON HEATH COARSE POOL (FH3202) £6.00
MEADOW FISHERY (FH3222) £7.50
MEADOW VIEW FISHERY (FH3225) £5.00
MILTON GREEN (FH3320) £5.00
MOULDSWORTH MERE (FH3383) £5.00
PARTRIDGE LAKES (FH3714) £5.00
TURNERS POOL (FH4982) £5.00
WALKERWOOD RESERVOIR (FH5119) £5.00
WALL POOL LODGE (FH5121) £5.00
WESTLOW MERE (FH5283) £7.00
WINSFORD FLASH (FH5421) £5.00

CLEVELAND

PRIORY COTTAGE LAKE (FH3847) £6.00
SHOTTON COLLIERY LAKE (FH4248) £5.00

CORNWALL

BOLINGEY LAKE (FH0534) £5.00
BRAGGS WOOD TROUT FISHERY (FH0594) £5.00
BUSH LAKES FARM (FH0768) £5.00
COLLIFORD LAKE (FH1065) £7.00
DRIFT RESERVOIR (FH1443) £7.00
DUTSON WATER (FH1487) £5.00
ELECTRICITY POOL (FH1560) £6.00
GWINEAR POOLS COARSE FISHERY (FH2049) £5.00
MELLONWATTS MILL (FH3249) £5.00
MILLBROOK COARSE FISHERY (FH3305) £5.00
NANCE LAKES (FH3414) £5.00
RETALLACK WATERS (FH3931) £5.00
SHILLAMILL LAKES COUNTRY PARK (FH4238) £8.00
SIBLYBACK LAKE (FH4263) £7.00
TAMAR (RIVER) (FH4641) £5.00

COUNTY DURHAM

AYCLIFFE LAKE (FH0235) £5.00
BEAUMONT FISHERIES (FH0358) £6.00
FLYLANDS POND (FH1752) £5.00
LANGSDALE LAKE (FH2617) £5.00
MAINSFORTH POND (FH3149) £5.00
SHOTTON POND (FH4249) £5.00
WEAR (RIVER) (FH5199) £5.00

CUMBRIA

BARN LAKE (FH0313) £8.00

BESSY BECK TROUT FARM (FH0394) **£5.00**
CARLETON HILL (FH0842) **£5.00**
DERWENT (RIVER) (FH1345) **£5.00**
DOE (RIVER) (FH1390) **£5.00**
DRUNKEN DUCK TARN FISHERY (FH1454) **£5.00**
GHYLL HEAD TROUT FISHERY (FH1851) **£8.50**
GRETA (RIVER) (FH2016) **£5.00**
KENT (RIVER) (FH2472) **£5.00**
OAKBANK LAKES (FH3560) **£6.00**
SANDFORD ARMS (FH4094) **£8.00**
SKELSMERGH LAKE (FH4288) **£5.00**
TEWITFIELDS TROUT FISHERY (FH4752) **£6.00**
TRANQUIL OTTER (FH4904) **£7.50**
TWISS (RIVER) (FH5006) **£5.00**
TYNE (RIVER) (FH5017) **£5.00**
WHINS POND (FH5323) **£5.00**

DERBYSHIRE

BEEHIVE FARM WOODLANDS LAKES (FH0371) **£5.00**
CATTON PARK LAKE (FH0875) **£5.00**
ERRWOOD RESERVOIR (FH1616) **£9.00**
FOREMARK TROUT FISHERY (FH1764) **£6.00**
HARLESTHORPE DAM (FH2107) **£5.00**
HIGHAM FARM COARSE FISHING (FH2211) **£5.00**
MELBOURNE POOL (FH3243) **£5.00**
POSSY LODGE PONDS (FH3832) **£5.00**
SWARKESTONE GRAVEL PITS (FH4604) **£5.00**

DEVON

BELLBROOK VALLEY TROUT FISHERY (FH0377) **£5.50**
BILLINGSMOOR FARM (FH0422) **£5.00**
BLUE LAKE (FH0509) **£8.00**
BURRATOR RESERVOIR (FH0751) **£7.00**
CLAWFORD VINEYARD AND FISHERIES (FH0985) **£5.00**
COOMBE WATER FISHERY (FH1110) **£5.00**
CREEDY (RIVER) (FH1175) **£5.00**
CREEDY LAKES (FH1176) **£5.00**
FERNWORTHY RESERVOIR (FH1700) **£7.00**
FISHPONDS HOUSE (FH1736) **£6.00**
FOSFELLE COUNTRY HOUSE HOTEL (FH1774) **£5.00**
GREENACRE TROUT LAKES (FH2004) **£8.50**
HARTSMOOR FISHERIES (FH2121) **£5.00**
LITTLE COMFORT FARM (FH2746) **£5.00**
LUCCOMBES PONDS (FH3101) **£5.00**
MILEMEAD FISHERIES (FH3274) **£5.00**
MILL LEAT TROUT FISHERY (FH3291) **£5.00**
NEW BARN ANGLING CENTRE (FH3461) **£5.00**
RIVERTON HOUSE AND LAKES (FH3970) **£5.00**
SHOBROOKE PARK (FH4244) **£6.00**
SLAPTON LEY NATIONAL NATURE RESERVE (FH4294) **£7.00**
SOUTH VIEW FARM FISHERY (FH4344) **£5.00**
TAMAR LAKE (LOWER) (FH4644) **£5.00**
TAW (RIVER) (FH4673) **£8.00**
TOWN PARKS COARSE FISHERY (FH4893) **£5.00**
UPHAM FARM PONDS (FH5050) **£5.00**

VALLEY SPRINGS TROUT FISHERY (FH5088) **£7.00**
WISTLANDPOUND RESERVOIR (FH5436) **£7.00**
WOODACOTT ARMS (FH5464) **£5.00**
YEO (RIVER) (FH5562) **£8.00**

DORSET

AVON TYRRELL LAKES (FH0230) **£5.00**
CHRISTCHURCH LOWER STOUR (FH0948) **£5.00**
CLUB LAKE (FH1027) **£5.00**
CRANBOURNE FRUIT FARM (FH1163) **£6.00**
FROME (RIVER) (FH1809) **£5.00**
GOLD OAK FISH FARM (FH1908) **£7.00**
HAMPSHIRE AVON (RIVER) (FH2083) **£5.00**
HAMPSHIRE AVON (RIVER) (FH2086) **£5.00**
HAMPSHIRE AVON (RIVER) (FH2087) **£8.00**
LUCKFIELD LAKE FISHERY (FH3102) **£6.00**
MARTINS FARM (FH3201) **£6.00**
MUDEFORD WOOD LAKE (FH3397) **£5.00**
PALLINGTON LAKES (FH3687) **£7.00**
PIDDLE (RIVER) (FH3770) **£5.00**
ROYALTY FISHERY (FH4049) **£8.00**
SOPLEY FARM (FH4327) **£5.00**
STOUR (DORSET) (RIVER) (FH4478) **£7.50**
STOUR (DORSET) (RIVER) (FH4488) **£7.50**
STOUR (DORSET) (RIVER) (FH4483) **£5.00**
STOUR (RIVER) (FH4494) **£5.00**
THROOP FISHERIES (FH4834) **£7.50**
TODBER MANOR (FH4862) **£5.00**
WALLYS LAKE (FH5124) **£5.00**
WHIRLWIND LAKE (FH5328) **£6.50**
WHITEMOOR LAKE (FH5351) **£5.00**
WINKTON FISHERY (FH5418) **£5.00**

ESSEX

BIRDS GREEN (FH0428) **£7.00**
BLASFORD HILL FISHERIES (FH0492) **£5.00**
BRICKHOUSE FARM FISHERIES (FH0621) **£5.00**
BROOKHALL FISHERY (FH0682) **£6.00**
BURROWS FARM (FH0754) **£8.00**
CHIGBOROUGH FISHERIES (FH0941) **£6.00**
CLAVERHAMBURY LAKE (FH0982) **£7.00**
COBBLERS MEAD LAKE (FH1048) **£5.00**
CROW GREEN FISHERY (FH1197) **£6.50**
CROWN NETHERHALL (FH1201) **£5.00**
FAIRLOP EAST LAKE (FH1653) **£5.00**
FAIRLOP WATERS (FH1654) **£5.00**
FENNES FISHERIES (FH1697) **£6.00**
GOSFIELD LAKE RESORT (FH1926) **£5.00**
GREAT MYLES LAKE (FH1984) **£5.00**
HOCKLEY LAKES (FH2239) **£6.00**
HOLYFIELD FISHERY (FH2278) **£6.00**
HOME FARM FISHERY (FH2281) **£6.00**
JOHNS LAKE FISHERIES (FH2414) **£7.00**
LEA (RIVER) (FH2642) **£7.00**
LITTLE EASTON MANOR (FH2751) **£6.00**
MAGIC LAKE (FH3138) **£7.00**

MAYBRAND FISHERY (FH3214) **£6.00**
MILLENNIUM LAKES (FH3309) **£6.00**
NEWLAND HALL CARP FISHERY (FH3487) **£7.00**
NUPERS FARM (FH3555) **£7.00**
PEA LANE FISHERY (FH3722) **£5.00**
PICKS COTTAGE CARP LAKES (FH3768) **£5.00**
RAYNE LODGE FARM (FH3903) **£6.00**
ROCKELLS FARM (FH3983) **£5.00**
SLOUGH HOUSE LAKE (FH4301) **£6.00**
VALENCE MOAT (FH5085) **£5.00**

GLOUCESTERSHIRE

CLAYDON PARK FISHERY (FH0992) **£5.00**
COURT FARM (FH1142) **£5.00**
HILL VIEW LAKES (FH2223) **£5.00**
HILLVIEW FISHERY (FH2228) **£5.00**
HORSESHOE LAKE (FH2307) **£6.00**
LEMINGTON LAKES (FH2696) **£6.00**
MILESTONE FISHERY (FH3275) **£5.00**
NETHERWOOD LAKE (FH3456) **£5.00**
NORTON FRUIT FARM (FH3548) **£5.00**
STANBOROUGH POOL (FH4416) **£5.00**
WATERSMEET LAKES (FH5186) **£5.00**
WHELFORD POOLS COARSE FISHERY (FH5319) **£7.00**

HAMPSHIRE

BEECHES BROOK FISHERY (FH0366) **£5.00**
BROADLANDS LAKES (FH0664) **£6.00**
BROADLANDS MAIN LAKE (FH0665) **£6.00**
CARRON ROW FARM PONDS (FH0852) **£8.00**
DARK LANE PONDS (FH1274) **£5.50**
EAST MOORS LAKE (FH1511) **£5.00**
FIRGROVE LAKES (FH1722) **£5.00**
GOLDEN POND FISHERY (FH1912) **£5.50**
GREENRIDGE FARM LAKES (FH2009) **£6.00**
HAMPSHIRE AVON (FH2082) **£6.00**
HAMPSHIRE AVON (RIVER) (FH2088) **£8.00**
HAMPSHIRE AVON (RIVER) (FH2090) **£7.50**
HATCHET POND (FH2128) **£5.00**
HIGHTOWN LAKE (FH2220) **£7.50**
HOLLYBUSH LANE LAKES (FH2262) **£5.00**
HORDLE LAKES (FH2296) **£6.00**
HURST POND (FH2346) **£5.00**
LAKE FARM (FH2556) **£6.00**
LAKESIDE (FH2581) **£5.00**
LAKESIDE (FH2580) **£5.00**
LEOMINSTEAD MILL POND (FH2702) **£6.00**
LONGBRIDGE LAKES (FH2987) **£6.00**
MBK LEISURE BARRONS POND (FH3218) **£6.00**
MILL POND LAKE (FH3300) **£6.00**
MOPLEY POND (FH3367) **£6.50**
NEW FOREST WATER PARK (FH3464) **£5.00**
NORTHFIELD LAKES (FH3544) **£7.50**
NUTRABAITS YATELEY SOUTH LAKE (FH3557) **£6.00**
PERIL LAKE (FH3752) **£5.00**
PETERSFIELD HEATH LAKE (FH3757) **£5.00**

ROTHERWICK AND NIGHTINGALE LAKES (FH4032) £5.00
SWAY LAKES (FH4605) £5.00
TITCHFIELD ABBEY GOLF AND COARSE FISHING LAKES (FH4857) £6.50
TURF CROFT FARM (FH4975) £6.00
WHINWHISTLE COARSE FISHERY (FH5324) £5.00
WHITEWATER (RIVER) (FH5356) £5.00
WILLOW PARK (FH5387) £9.00

HEREFORDSHIRE

BIDDLESTONE LAKE (FH0408) £5.00
DOCKLOW POOLS (FH1386) £5.00
DRUMMOND DUB (FH1450) £6.00
LILY AND WILLOW POOLS (FH2721) £5.00
MILLPOND (FH3314) £5.00
MOCCAS FISHERY (FH3333) £6.00
PIXLEY POOL (FH3797) £7.00
RUSSELLS END RESERVOIR (FH4065) £5.00

HERTFORDSHIRE

ALDENHAM RESERVOIR (FH0058) £5.00
BOWMANS LAKES (FH0574) £5.00
GAYWOODS (FH1845) £6.00
HOLWELL HYDE LAKE (FH2275) £5.00
OAKFIELD FISHERY (FH3561) £5.00
PIXIES MERE (FH3796) £5.00
WOODLAND FARM (FH5478) £7.00

HUMBERSIDE

FAR GRANGE CARAVAN AND COUNTRY PARK (FH1663) £5.00

ISLE OF WIGHT

GUNVILLE LAKE (FH2038) £6.00
ISLAND FISH FARM AND MEADOW LAKES (FH2390) £5.00
MERSTONE FISHERIES (FH3258) £6.00
MORTON FARM (FH3373) £5.00
ROOKLEY COUNTRY PARK (FH4006) £5.00

KENT

BARDEN LAKE (FH0304) £6.00
BARTLEY MILL FISHERY (FH0336) £5.00
BIRCHDEN FARM FISHERY (FH0426) £6.00
CACKLE HILL LAKES (FH0787) £6.00
CAPSTONE FARM COUNTRY PARK (FH0834) £6.80
CHEQUERTREE TROUT AND COARSE FISHERY (FH0914) £7.00
CHILHAM LAKE (FH0942) £5.00
COTTINGTON LAKES TROUT AND COARSE FISHERY (FH1137) £6.00
DARENTH FISHING COMPLEX (FH1273) £6.00
FRANT LAKES (FH1798) £7.00
HARTLEY LANDS FARM (FH2118) £7.00
HAWKHURST FISH FARM (FH2142) £7.50
HOOKSTEAD LAKE (FH2290) £5.00
LAVENDER FARM (FH2631) £7.00
LITTLE CANSIRON FISHING LAKES (FH2745) £7.00
LONGSHAW FARM FISHING LAKES (FH2995) £5.00
MEDWAY (RIVER) (FH3235) £5.00
MID KENT FISHERIES (FH3263) £5.00
MONK LAKE FISHERIES (FH3342) £7.00

MOTE PARK FISHERY (FH3381) £5.00
ROUKES DRIFT FARM (FH4035) £5.00
SCARLETTS LAKE (FH4114) £5.50
SILVER SPRINGS FISHERY (FH4270) £5.00
TEISE (RIVER) (FH4720) £7.00
WIDEHURST FARM (FH5367) £6.00

LANCASHIRE

BARNSFOLD WATERS (FH0318) £7.00
BRADSHAW HALL FISHERIES (FH0591) £5.00
CONDER VALLEY FLY FISHERY (FH1084) £5.00
COPTHORNE COARSE FISHERIES (FH1115) £6.00
DINGLE RESERVOIR (FH1373) £7.00
DRAKESHEAD FLY FISHERY (FH1436) £8.50
EDISFORD AND BRUNGERLEY PARK (FH1546) £8.00
ERIC FISHWICK NATURE RESERVE (FH1608) £6.00
FIR TREE LODGE (FH1721) £5.00
KNIGHT BOTTOMS LAKE (FH2534) £5.00
MITCHELLS HOUSE RESERVOIR (FH3329) £8.00
RED ROCKS FISHERY (FH3911) £5.00
STOCKS FLY FISHERY (FH4463) £6.50
THURSLAND HILL FARM (FH4838) £5.00
TURBARY HOUSE NURSARY (FH4974) £5.00
UPPER RODDLESWORTH RESERVOIR (FH5058) £7.00
WENNING (RIVER) (FH5244) £6.00

LEICESTERSHIRE

EYEBROOK TROUT FISHERY (FH1649) £9.00
LAKESIDE FISHING (FH2593) £5.50
LYNCHGATE LANE FISHERY (FH3119) £5.00
MANOR FARM POOLS (FH3165) £5.00
THORNTON RESERVOIR (FH4820) £7.00
WHETSTONE GORSE (FH5320) £5.00

LINCOLNSHIRE

BURGHLEY PARK LAKE (FH0743) £5.00
LAKE HELEN (FH2558) £5.00
LAKE ROSS FISHERY (FH2572) £6.00
OAKHILL LEISURE (FH3563) £6.00
OASIS LAKES (FH3570) £5.00
OHAM LAKES (FH3583) £5.00
THORPE LE VALE FISHERY (FH4823) £7.00
TOFT NEWTON TROUT FISHERY (FH4864) £7.50
WHITE HOUSE PREDATOR LAKE (FH5336) £7.50

LONDON (GREATER)

BEDFONT LAKE (FH0363) £5.50
BIRCHMERE (FH0427) £5.00
COPPER MILLSTREAM (FH1111) £6.00
HIGH MAYNARD RESERVOIR (FH2207) £6.00
LIZARD LAKES (FH2766) £6.00
LOW MAYNARD RESERVOIR (FH3067) £6.00
NEW CUT (FH3463) £5.00
SHEEPWALK LAKE (FH4218) £5.00
STUDIO AND BROADWATER (FH4532) £5.00
SYON PARK FISHERY (FH4621) £7.00

WALTHAMSTOW RESERVOIR (EAST WARWICK) (FH5129) £6.00
WALTHAMSTOW RESERVOIR (NO 1) (FH5130) £6.00
WALTHAMSTOW RESERVOIR (NO 2 AND NO 3) (FH5131) £6.00
WILLOWSIDE CARP LAKE (FH5402) £5.00

MANCHESTER (GREATER)

CLEGG HALL LAKES (FH1001) £5.00
FISHERMANS RETREAT (FH1730) £6.00
PENNINE TROUT FISHERY (FH3737) £7.50
TWINE VALLEY TROUT FISHERY (FH5005) £6.00

MERSEYSIDE

MILL HOUSE FISHERY (FH3287) £5.00
WOODHOUSE FISH FARM (FH5475) £7.00

MIDLANDS (WEST)

BLYTHE (RIVER) (FH0517) £5.00
BLYTHE WATERS (FH0518) £5.00
CUTTLE MILL CARP FISHERY (FH1232) £5.50
FOXHILLS FISHERY (FH1791) £5.00
GREY MILL FARM (FH2017) £5.00
HOPSFORD HALL FISHERY (FH2292) £5.00
LAVENDER HALL (FH2632) £5.00
MEADOWLANDS (FH3227) £5.00
PACKINGTON SOMERS FISHERY (FH3679) £5.00
PENNS HALL LAKE (FH3740) £5.00

NORFOLK

BARFORD LAKES FISHERY (FH0305) £6.00
BARTLES LODGE (FH0335) £5.00
BILNEY LAKES (FH0424) £5.00
BRIDGE FARM FISHERIES (FH0629) £5.00
BRIDGE INN FISHERY (FH0631) £5.00
BUCKENHAM PITS (FH0717) £5.00
BURE VALLEY LAKES (FH0737) £5.00
CHARITY LAKES (FH0901) £5.00
COBBLEACRES LAKES (FH1047) £6.00
DENTS OF HILGAY (FH1333) £5.00
FELBRIGG HALL LAKE (FH1681) £5.00
FELTHORPE LAKE (FH1690) £5.00
FRITTON LAKE (FH1804) £5.30
KINGFISHER LAKES (FH2500) £5.00
LAKESIDE (FH2583) £5.00
LENWADE COMMON LAKES (FH2700) £5.00
LOCH NEATON (FH2922) £5.00
MILL FARM FISHERY (FH3281) £5.00
NARBOROUGH TROUT FARM (FH3424) £5.00
NATURES HAVEN LAKES (FH3429) £5.00
PENTNEY LAKES (FH3742) £5.00
RAILWAY LAKE (FH3877) £5.00
REEPHAM FISHERY (FH3924) £5.00
RUSTON REACHES (FH4066) £5.00
SHALLOW BROOK LAKES (FH4205) £5.00
SWANGEY LAKES (FH4598) £6.00
SWANTON MORLEY FISHERY (FH4602) £5.00
TASWOOD LAKES FISH FARM AND FISHERY (FH4662) £5.00
TAVERHAM MILLS FISHERY (FH4669) £6.00
UPPER BURE (STREAM) (FH5052) £5.00
WENSUM (RIVER) (FH5247) £5.00

WENSUM (RIVER) (FH5246) £5.00
WENSUM (RIVER) (FH5249) £5.00
WENSUM (RIVER) (FH5245) £5.00
WEYBREAD FISHERY (FH5293) £5.00
WHINBURGH TROUT LAKE (FH5321) £7.50
WILLOWCROFT FISHERY (FH5392) £5.00
WILLSMORE WATER (FH5403) £5.00
WOODLAKES FISHERY (FH5477) £5.00

NORTHAMPTONSHIRE

BODDINGTON RESERVOIR (FH0521) £5.00
CANONS ASHBY LAKES (FH0824) £6.00
CASTLE ASHBY LAKES (FH0858) £5.00
CRESCENT LAKE (FH1179) £5.00
DRAYTON RESERVOIR (FH1441) £6.00
DUSTON RESERVOIR (FH1486) £6.00
FOXHOLES FISHERIES (FH1792) £5.00
GREEN FARM LAKES (FH2000) £5.00
HEYFORD FISHERY (FH2200) £6.00
HOLLOWELL RESERVOIR (FH2260) £6.00
LYNN POOL FISHERY (FH3125) £5.00
SILVER LAKE (FH4269) £6.00
ST JAMES SMALL PARK LAKE (FH4389) £6.00
SYWELL RESERVOIR (FH4623) £5.00

NORTHUMBERLAND

COQUET (RIVER) (FH1116) £6.00
KIELDER WATER (FH2477) £8.00
NORTH TYNE (RIVER) (FH3538) £5.00
TYNE (RIVER) (FH5019) £5.00
WREIGH (RIVER) (FH5516) £6.00

NOTTINGHAMSHIRE

L-LAKE FISHERY (FH2767) £5.00

OXFORDSHIRE

BARNES TROUT LAKES (FH0316) £6.00
CHAD LAKES (FH0890) £5.00
CHRISTCHURCH LAKE (FH0947) £5.00
CLATTERCOTE RESERVOIR (FH0979) £5.00
GOLDFISH BOWL (THE) (FH1915) £5.00
HEYFORD LAKES (FH2201) £5.00
MANOR LAKE (FH3169) £5.00
NELL BRIDGE FISHERY (FH3439) £5.00
ORCHID LAKES (FH3618) £6.00
ROLFS LAKE (FH3998) £5.00
STATES LAGOON (FH4436) £5.00
SWISS FARM LAKE (FH4614) £5.00
THAMES (RIVER) (FH4799) £5.00
WINDRUSH (RIVER) (FH5410) £5.00

RUTLAND

SWEETHEDGES FARM FISHERY (FH4607) £6.00

SHROPSHIRE

COUND TROUT FISHERY (FH1140) £8.00
VOWNOG FISH LAKE (FH5101) £6.00

SOMERSET

BULLOCKS FARM FISHING LAKES (FH0728) £5.00
CHEDDAR RESERVOIR (FH0909) £5.00
EXE VALLEY FISHERY (FH1645) £5.50
FOLLY FOOT FARM (FH1755) £5.00
FOLLYFOOT FARM (FH1757) £5.00
LAKESIDE (FH2584) £5.00
LANDS END FARM (FH2607) £5.00
MINERS PONDS (FH3327) £5.00
OTTERHEAD LAKES (FH3632) £5.00
OXENLEAZE FARM CARAVANS AND COARSE FISHERY (FH3666) £5.00
PAULTON LAKES (FH3718) £5.00
PLANTATIONS LAKES (FH3798) £5.00
SEDGES (FH4128) £5.00
STONE YARD FISHERY (FH4470) £5.00
THORNEY LAKES (FH4815) £5.00
VIADUCT FISHERY (FH5095) £5.00

STAFFORDSHIRE

ALBRIGHTON MOAT PROJECT (FH0051) £6.00
BADEN HALL FISHERY (FH0245) £5.00
BROWNING CUDMORE FISHERY (FH0702) £6.00
FISHERWICK LAKES (FH1732) £5.00
HAMSTALL FISHERY (FH2097) £5.00
HERONBROOK FISHERY (FH2191) £5.00
MADELEY POOL (FH3134) £5.00
PILLATON POOLS (FH3772) £6.00
POOL HOUSE FARM (FH3820) £5.50
TITTESWORTH RESERVOIR (FH4858) £8.00
WILLOWS POOLS (FH5401) £5.00

SUFFOLK

CROSS DROVE (FH1191) £5.00
HOLTON PIT (FH2273) £5.00
MARSH FARM LAKES (FH3191) £5.00
MILLERS LAKE (FH3310) £5.00
SINKS PIT (FH4277) £5.00
WAVENEY VALLEY LAKES (FH5192) £7.00

SURREY

BEAVER FARM FISHERY (FH0359) £7.00
BURY HILL FISHERIES (FH0764) £9.00
EPSOM STEW POND (FH1604) £5.00
FURZE FARM (FH1824) £7.00
GOLDSWORTH WATER PARK (FH1916) £5.50
HENFOLD LAKES FISHERY (FH2182) £8.00
MOLE (RIVER) (FH3338) £5.00
RUSHMOOR LAKES (FH4063) £6.00
SHAWFIELDS LAKES (FH4213) £5.00
TWYNERSH FISHING COMPLEX (FH5012) £5.00

SUSSEX (EAST)

ALEXANDRA PARK WATERS (FH0074) £5.00
BEVERN STREAM (FH0401) £5.00
BRICK FARM LAKE (FH0620) £5.00
BUXTED OAST FISHERY (FH0780) £6.00
CLAREMONT LAKE (FH0976) £5.00
CLIVE VALE RESERVOIRS (FH1010) £5.00
CUCKMERE (RIVER) (FH1210) £5.00
FALKENVIL FISHERY (FH1658) £6.00
FRAMFIELD PARK FISHERIES (FH1797) £6.00
FURNACE BROOK FISHERY (FH1820) £5.00
HONEYS GREEN COARSE FISHERY (FH2286) £5.00
IDEN WOOD FISHERY (FH2358) £6.00
LEABRIDGE FARM (FH2650) £5.00
MOOR HALL POOL (FH3357) £5.00
OLD IRON (RIVER) (FH3587) £5.00
OUSE (RIVER) (FH3645) £5.00
PEVENSEY HAVEN (FH3762) £5.00
RYE NOOK FISHERY (FH4075) £5.00
SHARNFOLD FARM FISHERY (FH4210) £5.00
SOUTHBOURNE LAKE (FH4349) £5.00
SPRING WOOD FISHERY AND FARM (FH4372) £6.00
ST IVES FARM (FH4388) £5.00
SWANBOROUGH LAKES (FH4597) £8.00
TANYARD FISHERIES (FH4654) £7.00
WALLERS HAVEN (FH5122) £5.00
WEIR WOOD FISHERY (FH5227) £7.00
WYLANDS INTERNATIONAL ANGLING CENTRE (FH5545) £7.00

SUSSEX (WEST)

ADUR (RIVER) (FH0033) £5.00
ALDERWOOD PONDS (FH0066) £5.00
ARDINGLY RESERVOIR (FH0129) £8.00
ARUN (RIVER) (FH0150) £5.00
ARUN (RIVER) (FH0151) £5.00
BALCOMBE LAKE (FH0256) £7.00
BORDE HILL GARDEN LAKES (FH0544) £8.00
FURNACE LAKES (FH1821) £8.00
LAYBROOK LAKES (FH2638) £5.00
MILL FARM FISHERY (FH3283) £7.50
ROTHERFIELD POND (FH4030) £5.00
SPARKS FARM FISHERY (FH4358) £6.00
STUBPOND FISHERIES (FH4531) £6.00
VALE BRIDGE LAKE (FH5081) £7.00
WATTLEHURST FARM TROUT LAKES (FH5188) £5.00

WARWICKSHIRE

BOSWORTH WATER TRUST AND FRIEZELAND POOLS (FH0561) £5.00
BRAMCOTE MAINS FISHERY (FH0597) £5.00
CLIFTON LAKES FISHERY (FH1006) £5.00
DRAYCOTE WATER (FH1438) £9.50
HAWKESBURY FISHERY (FH2141) £5.00
MAKIN FISHERIES (FH3150) £5.00
NAPTON RESERVOIR (FH3421) £5.00
RIDDINGS FISHERY (FH3949) £5.00
WESTON LAWN FISHERIES (FH5285) £5.00

WILTSHIRE

AVON (RIVER) (FH0217) £5.00
BLACKLAND LAKES HOLIDAY AND LEISURE CENTRE (FH0450) £7.00
ERLESTOKE LAKE (FH1612) £7.00
IVY HOUSE FARM (FH2403) £5.00
LONGLEAT LAKES (FH2992) £6.00
LOWER MOOR FISHERY (FH3090) £5.00
NADDER (RIVER) (FH3410) £5.00
ROOD ASHTON LAKE (FH4002) £6.00
SHEAR WATER (FH4216) £6.00
SILVERLANDS LAKE (FH4272) £5.00
WALDENS FARM FISHERY (FH5118) £6.00
WITHERINGTON FARM FISHING (FH5442) £5.00
WROUGHTON RESERVOIR (FH5519) £5.00

WYTHERINGTON FARM (FH5552) £5.00

WORCESTERSHIRE

ABBOTS SALFORD PARK (FH0009) £7.00
ERICS POOL (FH1609) £5.50
FOREST FARM (FH1765) £5.00
MAVER LARFORD (FH3210) £5.00
MOORLANDS FARM (FH3363) £5.00
SHAKESPEARE MOORLANDS FARM (FH4203) £5.00
WOODLAND VIEW (FH5481) £5.00

YORKSHIRE (NORTH)

BRAFFERTON COARSE FISHERY (FH0593) £6.00
BRICKYARD FARM LAKE (FH0622) £5.00
BROKEN BREA FISHERY (FH0674) £5.00
BROOKLANDS (FH0683) £5.00
CARP VALE (FH0846) £6.00
CLAY PIT (FH0988) £5.00
CORNHILL PONDS (FH1121) £5.00
DERWENT (RIVER) (FH1355) £8.00
FLETCHERS POND (FH1747) £5.00
GRAFTON MERE (FH1936) £6.00
KINGSLEY CARP LAKE (FH2513) £5.50
LAKESIDE FISHERIES (FH2591) £6.00
LANGTON POND (FH2618) £5.00
NIDD (RIVER) (FH3500) £8.00
OAKS FISHERY (FH3565) £6.00
OAKTREE LEISURE (FH3569) £5.00
PARKLANDS (FH3703) £5.00
POOL BRIDGE FARM LAKES (FH3818) £5.00
POTTERY LAKE (FH3834) £5.00
RAKER LAKES (FH3884) £5.00
SELBY 3 LAKES (FH4129) £5.00
SELLEY BRIDGE LAKE (FH4134) £5.00
SHIELD FISHERY (FH4235) £5.00
SKIRFARE (RIVER) (FH4291) £7.00
SWALE (RIVER) (FH4585) £5.00
SWALE (RIVER) (FH4570) £5.00
SWALE (RIVER) (FH4578) £5.00
THORPE PERROW QUARRY (FH4825) £5.00
THREE LAKES (FH4830) £5.00
TOLLERTON FISHING PONDS (FH4867) £5.00
URE (RIVER) (FH5071) £8.00
WATERMEADOWS FISHERY (FH5181) £5.00
WELHAM LAKE (FH5231) £8.00
WESTERLY LAKE (FH5271) £5.00
WHINNYGILL RESERVOIR (FH5322) £5.00
WOODLAND LAKES (FH5479) £6.00
Y2K LAKE (FH5553) £5.00

YORKSHIRE (SOUTH)

FINA HAYFIELD LAKES (FH1708) £5.00
MICKS PLACE (FH3262) £5.00
MORE HALL RESERVOIR (FH3368) £9.00
PRESTON INNOVATIONS SILVER FISHERY (FH3841) £5.00
SALLY WALSHES DAM (FH4084) £5.00
SCOUT DYKE RESERVOIR (FH4121) £7.00
SLIVER FISHERY (FH4300) £5.00
THRYBERGH COUNTRY PARK (FH4835) £8.00
TYRAM HALL (FH5035) £5.00

YORKSHIRE (WEST)

BILLING DAM (FH0419) £7.00
DOE PARK RESERVOIR (FH1391) £5.00
RAYGILL FISHERY (FH3902) £6.00
SPRING VALLEY WATERS (FH4371) £6.00
TONG PARK DAM (FH4872) £5.00
WHARFE (RIVER) (FH5308) £6.50
WINTERSETT RESERVOIR (FH5428) £6.00

UNDER £20

BEDFORDSHIRE

LAKESIDE TROUT AND COARSE FISHERY (FH2597) £12.50
LITTLE HEATH FARM TROUT FISHERY (FH2753) £15.00

BERKSHIRE

BARTON COURT FISHERY (FH0338) £12.00
PANG VALLEY TROUT LAKE (FH3688) £15.00
PONDWOOD CARP LAKES (FH3814) £10.00

BUCKINGHAMSHIRE

LATIMER PARK FLY FISHERY (FH2628) £14.00
VICARAGE SPINNEY TROUT FISHERY (FH5096) £12.50

CAMBRIDGESHIRE

DICKERSONS PIT (FH1366) £10.00
GRAFHAM WATER (FH1934) £16.00
NORTH BANK TROUT FISHERY (FH3526) £11.00

CHESHIRE

CLAY LANE FISHERY (FH0987) £18.00
DANEBRIDGE FISHERIES (FH1268) £14.00
LAKEMORE COUNTRY PARK (FH2578) £10.00
RIDGEGATE RESERVOIR (FH3950) £12.00
WALKERWOOD TROUT FISHERY (FH5120) £15.00

CLEVELAND

LOCKWOOD BECK RESERVOIR (FH2973) £12.00
SCALING DAM (FH4111) £11.00

CORNWALL

BUTTERWELL (FH0779) £15.00
FENWICK TROUT FISHERY (FH1698) £18.00
FOWEY (RIVER) (FH1783) £10.00
FOWEY (RIVER) (FH1787) £15.00
FOWEY (RIVER) (FH1785) £15.00
FOWEY (RIVER) (FH1782) £10.00
FOWEY (RIVER) (FH1784) £10.00
FOWEY (RIVER) (FH1786) £10.00
GWARNICK MILL TROUT FISHERY (FH2040) £10.00
INNY (RIVER) (FH2372) £15.00
LAKE PENRYN (FH2568) £12.00
LYNHER (RIVER) (FH3124) £15.00
ORVIS INNIS COUNTRY CLUB AND FLY FISHERY (FH3626) £10.00
SEATON (RIVER) (FH4127) £15.00
STITHIANS RESERVOIR (FH4459) £10.00
TREE MEADOW TROUT FISHERY (FH4909) £15.00
WEST LOOE (RIVER) (FH5263) £12.50
WHITEACRES COUNTRY PARK (FH5344) £10.00

COUNTY DURHAM

BEAMISH LAKE FLY FISHERY (FH0356) £15.00
BURNHOPE FISHERY (FH0749) £10.00
DERWENT RESERVOIR (FH1360) £13.00
JUBILEE LAKES (FH2417) £11.00
WEAR (RIVER) (FH5210) £15.00
WITTON CASTLE LAKES (FH5451) £18.00

CUMBRIA

ANNAS (RIVER) (FH0115) £12.00
ANNAS STREAM (FH0116) £15.00
BAYSTONE BANK RESERVIOR (FH0352) £12.00
BLENCARN LAKE (FH0496) £16.00
CLOUGH (RIVER) (FH1023) £10.00
CROSSFIELD FISHERY (FH1193) £10.00
DEE (RIVER) (FH1305) £10.00
DEVOKE WATER (FH1363) £15.00
DUBBS TROUT FISHERY (FH1458) £10.00
EDEN (RIVER) (FH1533) £15.00
ESK (RIVER) (FH1618) £12.00
ESTHWAITE WATER (FH1630) £16.00
HIGH NEWTON RESERVOIR (FH2209) £10.00
IRT (RIVER) (FH2380) £12.00
KENT (RIVER) (FH2471) £12.00
KNOTT END TARN (FH2543) £12.00
LAZY (RIVER) (FH2641) £12.00
LICKLE (RIVER) (FH2714) £12.00
LOUGHSIDE FISHERY (FH3062) £11.00
LOW GILL (FH3066) £10.00
LUNE (RIVER) (FH3108) £10.00
NEW HILLS TROUT FARM FISHERY (FH3465) £12.00
RAWTHEY (RIVER) (FH3898) £10.00
RAWTHEY (RIVER) (FH3899) £10.00
SPRINT (RIVER) (FH4378) £12.00

DERBYSHIRE

ALTON MANOR FARM (FH0087) £13.00
ARNFIELD RESERVOIR (FH0140) £12.00
CARSINGTON WATER (FH0854) £12.00
LADYBOWER RESERVOIR (FH2549) £10.90
SYDNOPE FISHERIES (FH4619) £10.00
YEAVELEY ESTATE TROUT FISHERY (FH5560) £17.00

DEVON

ANGLERS PARADISE (FH0108) £13.00
BLAKEWELL FISHERIES (FH0491) £12.00
CAMEL (RIVER) (FH0810) £15.00
CAMEL (RIVER) (FH0811) £15.00
DRAKELANDS GAME FISHERY (FH1435) £11.00
EGGESFORD COUNTRY HOTEL WATERS (FH1551) £10.00
HARTLAND FOREST FISHERY GOLF CLUB (FH2116) £10.00
KENNICK RESERVOIR (FH2469) £13.00
NEWHOUSE FISHERY (FH3486) £11.00
PLYM (RIVER) (FH3807) £10.00
ROADFORD RESERVOIR (FH3973) £13.50
SOMERSWOOD LAKE (FH4324) £16.00
STAFFORD MOOR FISHERY (FH4402) £13.00
STILL WATERS TROUT FISHERY (FH4456) £10.00
TAMAR (RIVER) (FH4643) £16.00
TAVISTOCK TROUT FISHERY (FH4670) £16.50
TAVY (RIVER) (FH4671) £10.00
TEIGN (RIVER) (FH4719) £17.00
TORRIDGE (RIVER) (FH4883) £15.00
UPPER YEALM FISHERY (FH5061) £10.00

DORSET

AMHERST LODGE FISHERY (FH0101) £15.00

FLOWERS FARM TROUT LAKES (FH1750) **£19.00**
FROME (RIVER) (FH1808) **£17.00**
WHITESHEET TROUT FISHERY (FH5353) **£15.00**

ESSEX

BLUNTS AND CANTS MERES (FH0516) **£10.00**
BULPHAN PARK FISHERIES (FH0730) **£10.00**
CHURCHWOOD FISHERIES (FH0957) **£10.00**
CLAVERING TROUT LAKE (FH0983) **£12.00**
GREEN OAKS TROUT FISHERY (FH2003) **£15.00**
HANNINGFIELD TROUT FISHERY (FH2101) **£11.00**
JIMMYS LAKE (FH2411) **£10.00**
WILLOWS (FH5395) **£10.00**

GLOUCESTERSHIRE

CHURN POOL TROUT FISHERY (FH0959) **£12.00**
COTSWOLD WATER PARK (FH1132) **£10.00**
DONNINGTON TROUT FISHERY (FH1405) **£10.00**
GREAT BURROWS TROUT FISHERY (FH1981) **£12.00**
STROUDWATER CANAL (FH4528) **£10.00**

HAMPSHIRE

AWBRIDGE DANES LAKE (FH0231) **£10.00**
BARONS PONDS (NEW SITE) (FH0322) **£10.00**
FIVE OAKS TROUT LAKE (FH1739) **£16.00**
GOLD VALLEY LAKES (FH1909) **£10.00**
JOHN OGAUNTS FISHERY (FH2413) **£18.00**
MOORHEN FARM TROUT LAKE (FH3361) **£15.00**
SPRINGLAKES (FH4373) **£10.00**
WOODMILL SALMON FISHERY (FH5488) **£17.00**

HEREFORDSHIRE

MARLIAS (RIVER) (FH3189) **£10.00**

HERTFORDSHIRE

BIERTON FISHING LAKES (FH0410) **£10.00**
CROXLEY HALL TROUT FISHERY (FH1203) **£15.00**
RIB VALLEY FISHING LAKE (FH3942) **£11.00**

KENT

BEWL WATER (FH0403) **£14.30**
HAYES TROUT FISHERY (FH2153) **£18.00**
STOUTING LAKE (FH4507) **£13.00**
STOWTING TROUT LAKE (FH4514) **£13.00**

LANCASHIRE

BOLTON CANAL (FH0540) **£18.00**
DEAN CLOUGH RESERVOIR (FH1287) **£10.00**
DUDDON (RIVER) (FH1460) **£12.00**
EARNSDALE RESERVOIR (FH1504) **£10.00**
ENTWHISTLES RESERVOIR (FH1597) **£16.00**
HOLDEN WOOD RESERVOIR (FH2250) **£14.50**
LANESHAW RESERVOIR (FH2609) **£12.00**
OGDEN RESERVOIR (FH3577) **£14.50**
ROUGHLEE TROUT FISHERY (FH4034) **£10.00**
ST MICHAELS WYRESIDE FISHERY (FH4394) **£10.50**

LEICESTERSHIRE

RUTLAND WATER (FH4068) **£10.00**
STEMBOROUGH MILL TROUT FARM (FH4449) **£12.00**

LINCOLNSHIRE

SYSTON PARK TROUT LAKE (FH4622) **£15.50**
WILLOW BANK FISHERY (FH5377) **£15.00**

LONDON (GREATER)

LOCKWOOD RESERVOIR (FH2974) **£10.00**
WALTHAMSTOW RESERVOIR (WEST WARWICK) (FH5134) **£10.00**

MANCHESTER (GREATER)

BLACK BECK (RIVER) (FH0439) **£12.00**

MIDLANDS (WEST)

SHUSTOKE FLY FISHERS (FH4262) **£12.00**

NORFOLK

CATCH 22 FISHERY (FH0872) **£10.00**
NORFOLK AND SUFFOLK FLY FISHERIES LAKE (FH3524) **£15.00**

NORTHAMPTONSHIRE

ELINOR TROUT FISHERY (FH1562) **£13.50**
RAVENSTHORPE TROUT FISHERY (FH3895) **£10.00**

NORTHUMBERLAND

ALN (RIVER) (FH0085) **£15.00**
HADRIAN LODGE (FH2061) **£10.00**
LINNEL WOOD LAKE (FH2737) **£15.00**
WANSBECK (RIVER) (FH5139) **£10.00**
WHITEADDER (RIVER) (FH5345) **£10.00**
WHITTLE DEAN RESERVOIR (FH5359) **£16.00**

NOTTINGHAMSHIRE

OWDY LANE TROUT FISHERY (FH3660) **£10.00**

OXFORDSHIRE

BEIRTON LAKES (FH0373) **£10.00**
DORCHESTER LAGOON (FH1412) **£15.00**
FARMOOR TROUT FISHERY (FH1676) **£13.00**
HEART OF ENGLAND FISHERY (FH2171) **£12.50**

SHROPSHIRE

DELBURY HALL TROUT FISHERY (FH1326) **£18.00**
ELLERDINE LAKES (FH1566) **£10.00**

SOMERSET

BARLE (RIVER) (FH0309) **£15.00**
BARROW RESERVOIRS (FH0329) **£10.50**
BLAGDON LAKE (FH0487) **£15.00**
CAMELEY TROUT LAKES (FH0812) **£18.00**
CHEW VALLEY LAKE (FH0936) **£13.00**
CLATWORTHY RESERVOIR (FH0981) **£12.00**
HAWKRIDGE RESERVOIR (FH2144) **£12.00**
QUANTOCK FISHERIES (FH3862) **£17.00**
SUTTON BINGHAM RESERVOIR (FH4561) **£12.00**

SUFFOLK

CROSS GREEN FLY FISHERY (FH1192) **£15.00**
LARKWOOD TROUT FISHERY (FH2626) **£15.00**
WILLOW LAKES TROUT FISHERY (FH5385) **£15.00**

SURREY

WHITEVANE POND (FH5354) **£10.00**

SUSSEX (EAST)

BORINGWHEEL TROUT FISHERY (FH0551) **£15.00**
DARWELL WATER (FH1279) **£13.50**
MICHELHAM PRIORY MOAT (FH3260) **£12.50**
POWDERMILL (GREAT SANDERS) WATER (FH3838) **£15.00**
YEW TREE TROUT FISHERY (FH5570) **£11.50**

SUSSEX (WEST)

CHALK SPRINGS TROUT FISHERY (FH0891) **£18.50**
MENARDS LAKE (FH3254) **£10.00**
NEWELLS SPECIMEN CARP AND COARSE FISHERIES (FH3483) **£15.00**

TYNE AND WEAR

REDE (RIVER) (FH3915) **£10.00**
SWEETHOPE LOUGHS (FH4608) **£10.00**
WHITTLE DENE TROUT FISHERY (FH5360) **£16.00**

WARWICKSHIRE

ADAMS POOL (FH0026) **£12.00**
ARDENCOTE MANOR HOTEL AND COUNTRY CLUB (FH0127) **£16.00**
HEATHCOTE LAKE (FH2173) **£14.00**

WILTSHIRE

LANGFORD FISHERIES (FH2611) **£19.00**
MILL FARM TROUT LAKES (FH3284) **£16.00**

WORCESTERSHIRE

BRANSFORD GAME FISHERY (FH0601) **£10.00**
TEME (RIVER) (FH4724) **£10.00**

YORKSHIRE (NORTH)

BOLTON ABBEY FISHERIES (FH0539) **£15.00**
CRABTREE ANGLING LAKE (FH1155) **£12.00**
HAZELHEAD LAKE (FH2165) **£14.00**
KIPLIN TROUT FISHERY (FH2523) **£15.00**
LEIGHTON RESERVOIR (FH2693) **£13.00**
LOW OSGOODBY LAKE (FH3068) **£10.00**
NEWHAY SPECIMEN LAKE (FH3485) **£10.00**
TANFIELD LAKE (FH4651) **£10.00**
WASHBURN VALLEY (FEWSTON AND SWINSTY) (FH5164) **£10.00**
WHARFE (RIVER) (FH5298) **£10.00**
WHARFE (RIVER) (FH5299) **£18.00**
WYKEHAM LAKES (FH5544) **£10.00**

YORKSHIRE (SOUTH)

HORSESHOE LAKE TROUT FISHERY (FH2309) **£10.50**

£20 AND ABOVE

BERKSHIRE

FELIX FARM TROUT FISHERY (FH1684) **£25.00**
NEWBURY TROUT LAKES (FH3480) **£25.00**
SHEEPHOUSE FARM TROUT FISHERY (FH4217) **£26.00**

BUCKINGHAMSHIRE

CHURCH HILL FISHERY (FH0953) **£26.00**

CHESHIRE

KAZAKO PONDS (FH2421) **£20.00**

CUMBRIA

- LIDDEL WATER (FH2715) £20.00

DERBYSHIRE

- MONSAL DALE FISHERY (FH3352) £25.00

DEVON

- DEER PARK COUNTRY HOTEL (FH1324) £30.00
- EXE (RIVER) (FH1642) £25.00
- EXE (RIVER) (FH1640) £40.00
- INDIO POND (FH2365) £25.00
- MOLE (RIVER) (FH3337) £25.00
- OTTER (RIVER) (FH3630) £30.00
- OTTER FALLS FISHERY (FH3631) £20.00
- TAMAR (RIVER) (FH4642) £20.00
- TAR (RIVER) (FH4658) £25.00
- TEIGN (FH4716) £25.00
- TORRIDGE (RIVER) (FH4885) £40.00
- WATERCRESS FARM TROUT FISHERY (FH5174) £20.50
- YEO (RIVER) (FH5561) £25.00

DORSET

- LAWRENCES FARM (FH2636) £23.00
- PIDDLE (RIVER) (FH3769) £26.00
- WESSEX FLY FISHING TROUT LAKES (FH5254) £26.00

GLOUCESTERSHIRE

- BROOK FARM TROUT FISHERY (FH0677) £45.00
- BUSHYLEAZE TROUT FISHERY (FH0770) £25.00
- COLN (RIVER) (FH1066) £20.00
- LECHLADE TROUT FISHERY (FH2656) £37.00
- WITCOMBE WATERS (FH5437) £25.00

HAMPSHIRE

- ABBOTTS WORTHY (FH0011) £390.00
- ANTON (RIVER) (FH0117) £36.00
- CHIPHALL LAKE TROUT FISHERY (FH0943) £28.50
- DEVER SPRINGS TROUT FISHERY (FH1362) £30.00
- HOLBURY LAKES (FH2247) £31.00
- ITCHEN (RIVER) (FH2397) £175.00
- KIMBRIDGE (FH2488) £390.00
- LEOMINSTEAD TROUT FISHERY (FH2703) £23.00
- MEON SPRINGS FLY FISHERY (FH3255) £22.00
- NETHER WALLOP FLY FISHING SCHOOL (FH3452) £20.00
- ROCKBOURNE TROUT FISHERY (FH3982) £32.00
- ROOKSBURY MILL TROUT FISHERIES (FH4007) £28.00
- TEST (RIVER) (FH4745) £75.00
- VALE FARM FISHERY (FH5082) £28.00

HEREFORDSHIRE

- CARADOC FISHERY (FH0836) £50.00
- INGESTONE FISHERY (FH2366) £20.00

HUMBERSIDE

- BRANDES BURTON 3 AND 4 (FH0599) £23.00

KENT

- BRITTON COURT FARM (FH0659) £20.00
- TENTERDEN TROUT WATERS (FH4738) £24.00

LANCASHIRE

- BANK HOUSE FLY FISHERY (FH0286) £21.00
- LOVECLOUGH TROUT FISHERY (FH3065) £20.00
- TWIN LAKES TROUT FISHERY (FH5004) £20.00

NORTHUMBERLAND

- GILSLAND LAKE (FH1857) £20.00
- IRTHING (RIVER) (FH2381) £20.00
- SOUTH TYNE (RIVER) (FH4341) £20.00
- TWEED (RIVER) (FH4989) £25.00
- TWEED (RIVER) (FH4992) £25.00
- TWEED (RIVER) (FH4993) £25.00
- TWEED (RIVER) (FH4991) £25.00
- TYNE (RIVER) (FH5027) £35.00

OXFORDSHIRE

- BLADON LAKE (FH0486) £25.00
- CORNBURY PARK FISHERY (FH1120) £25.00
- FARINGDON LAKE (FH1664) £25.00
- SALFORD TROUT LAKES (FH4083) £20.00

SHROPSHIRE

- DEARNFORD HALL TROUT FISHERY (FH1291) £20.00

SOMERSET

- WOOLBRIDGE MANOR (FH5499) £25.00

STAFFORDSHIRE

- GAILEY TROUT AND PIKE FISHERY (FH1828) £20.00
- LOYNTON TROUT FISHERIES (FH3100) £25.00

SURREY

- CROSSWATER MILL FISHERY (FH1194) £30.00
- ENTON LAKES TROUT FISHERY (FH1596) £25.00
- FRENSHAM TROUT FISHERY (FH1800) £30.00
- POWDER MILLS FISHERY (FH3837) £25.00
- WESTON FISHERY (FH5284) £21.00

SUSSEX (EAST)

- LAKEDOWN TROUT FISHERY (FH2575) £29.50

SUSSEX (WEST)

- BLACKWOOL TROUT FISHERY (FH0484) £45.00
- DUNCTON MILL (FH1473) £26.00
- HAMBROOK TROUT FISHERY (FH2080) £25.00
- WINTONS FISHERY (FH5432) £20.00

WARWICKSHIRE

- CHESTERTON MILL POOL TROUT FISHERY (FH0934) £20.00

WILTSHIRE

- AVON SPRINGS FISHERY (FH0229) £33.00
- SUTTON VENY ESTATE (FH4566) £50.00

WORCESTERSHIRE

- LENCHES LAKES (FH2697) £28.00

YORKSHIRE (NORTH)

- BELLFLASK TROUT FISHERY (FH0379) £20.00
- EGTON ESTATE BEAT (FH1555) £20.00

UNDER £3

COUNTY LAOIS

- **ERKINA (RIVER)** (FH1611) **£2.00**

COUNTY SLIGO

- **LOUGH AUGH** (FH3005) **£1.00**

UNDER £5

COUNTY MAYO

- **CLOONGEE FISHERY** (FH1021) **£3.00**

COUNTY TIPPERARY

- **ARA (RIVER)** (FH0125) **£3.00**
- **NORE (RIVER)** (FH3523) **£4.00**
- **WHITE HORSE (RIVER)** (FH5332) **£4.00**

UNDER £10

COUNTY CORK

- **DERRYVEGALL LAKE** (FH1342) **£6.00**
- **DRIMINIDY LAKE** (FH1444) **£6.00**
- **GARRANES LAKE** (FH1838) **£6.00**
- **GLENGARIFF (RIVER)** (FH1890) **£5.00**
- **LOUGH ADERRA** (FH2999) **£6.00**
- **LOUGH AVAUL (LOWER)** (FH3006) **£6.00**
- **LOUGH AVAUL (UPPER)** (FH3007) **£6.00**
- **LOUGH BOFINNE** (FH3013) **£6.00**
- **SCHULL RESERVOIR** (FH4117) **£6.00**
- **SHEPPERTON LAKES** (FH4231) **£6.00**

COUNTY DONEGAL

- **ASSAROE LAKE** (FH0174) **£5.00**
- **ROSSES FISHERY** (FH4017) **£5.00**

COUNTY GALWAY

- **DOOHULLA** (FH1408) **£5.00**

COUNTY KERRY

- **LOUGH BARFINNIHY** (FH3010) **£6.00**
- **LOUGH CAUM** (FH3016) **£6.00**
- **LOUGH FADDA** (FH3030) **£6.00**
- **LOUGH NAKIRKA** (FH3045) **£6.00**

COUNTY LEITRIM

- **LOUGH MELVIN** (FH3043) **£5.00**

COUNTY LOUTH

- **BALLYMASCANLON (RIVER)** (FH0277) **£5.00**
- **BARNATTIN RESERVOIR** (FH0314) **£6.00**
- **CASTLETON (RIVER)** (FH0871) **£5.00**
- **FANE (RIVER)** (FH1661) **£5.00**
- **KILLINEER RESERVOIR** (FH2484) **£6.00**

COUNTY TIPPERARY

- **SUIR (RIVER)** (FH4542) **£5.00**
- **SUIR (RIVER)** (FH4536) **£5.00**
- **SUIR (RIVER)** (FH4549) **£5.00**
- **SUIR (RIVER)** (FH4544) **£5.00**

COUNTY WATERFORD

- **BLACKWATER (RIVER)** (FH0471) **£5.00**

UNDER £20

COUNTY CLARE

- **LICKEEN LAKE** (FH2713) **£10.00**

COUNTY CORK

- **BANDON (RIVER)** (FH0282) **£15.00**
- **BLACKWATER (RIVER)** (FH0465) **£12.00**
- **CORK LOUGH** (FH1119) **£10.00**
- **ILEN (RIVER)** (FH2362) **£15.00**

COUNTY DONEGAL

- **CLOGHAN LODGE ESTATE FISHERY** (FH1016) **£10.00**
- **FINN (RIVER)** (FH1715) **£10.00**
- **GLENMORE FISHERY** (FH1893) **£10.00**

COUNTY GALWAY

- **ERRIFF FISHERY** (FH1615) **£10.00**

COUNTY LIMERICK

- **CASTLECONNELL SALMON FISHERY** (FH0867) **£10.00**

COUNTY MAYO

- **MOY FISHERY** (FH3394) **£10.00**

COUNTY MEATH

- **BOYNE (RIVER)** (FH0582) **£10.00**

COUNTY TIPPERARY

- **CLONANAU FLY FISHING CENTRE** (FH1018) **£15.00**

COUNTY WESTMEATH

- **BALLINAFID LAKE** (FH0261) **£10.00**
- **DOOLIN POND** (FH1409) **£10.00**
- **GALMOYLESTOWN LAKE** (FH1831) **£10.00**

£20 AND ABOVE

COUNTY CORK

- **BLACKWATER (RIVER)** (FH0459) **£35.00**
- **BLACKWATER SALMON FISHERY** (FH0482) **£50.00**
- **CAREYSVILLE** (FH0840) **£65.00**

COUNTY KERRY

- **KERRYFISHERIES** (FH2474) **£20.00**

COUNTY MAYO

- **MOUNT FALCON SALMON FISHERY** (FH3385) **£20.00**

COUNTY MEATH

- **RATHBEGGAN LAKES** (FH3890) **£20.00**

COUNTY ROSCOMMON

- **LOUGH ARROW** (FH3003) **£25.00**

COUNTY WATERFORD

- **BLACKWATER LODGE HOTEL AND FISHERY** (FH0481) **£35.00**

UNDER £3

COUNTY DOWN

BALLY GRANGE FISHERY (FH0273) £1.00

COUNTY TYRONE

MOURNE (RIVER) (FH3389) £2.00

UNDER £5

COUNTY ANTRIM

BRAID (RIVER) (FH0595) £4.00
CLOGHWATER (RIVER) (FH1017) £3.00
CLOUGH (RIVER) (FH1022) £3.00
CRUMLIN (RIVER) (FH1204) £3.00
DALL (RIVER) (FH1249) £4.00
DUN (RIVER) (FH1470) £4.00
GLENARRIFF (RIVER) (FH1885) £4.00
KELLSWATER (RIVER) (FH2427) £3.00
MAINE (RIVER) (FH3145) £3.00
MAINE (RIVER) (FH3146) £4.00
SIX MILE WATER (FH4283) £3.00

COUNTY ARMAGH

BANN (UPPER) (RIVER) (FH0296) £3.50
LOUGHGALL COARSE FISHERY (FH3056) £3.00

COUNTY DOWN

BANN (UPPER) (RIVER) (FH0297) £4.00
LAGAN (RIVER) (FH2552) £4.00

COUNTY FERMANAGH

BALLINAMALLARD (RIVER) (FH0263) £3.00
KNOCKBRACKEN TROUT LAKES (FH2539) £3.50

COUNTY TYRONE

BALLINDERRY (RIVER) (FH0267) £3.00
TULLYLAGAN (RIVER) (FH4968) £3.00

UNDER £10

COUNTY ANTRIM

CAREY (RIVER) (FH0839) £7.00
CLADY (RIVER) (FH0968) £5.00
GLENSHESK (RIVER) (FH1895) £7.00
INVER (RIVER) (FH2373) £5.00
MAINE (RIVER) (FH3143) £5.00
MAINE (RIVER) (FH3144) £5.00
MARGEY (RIVER) (FH3179) £7.00
MCCAMMANS LAKE (FH3219) £5.00
SIX MILE WATER (FH4284) £5.00
SPRINGWATER MEADOW (FH4376) £6.00
TURNAGROVE FISHERY (FH4980) £7.00
WOODFORD FISHERY (FH5474) £7.00

COUNTY ARMAGH

BLACKWATER (RIVER) (FH0456) £8.00
CALLAN (RIVER) (FH0802) £8.00
LAGAN (RIVER) (FH2551) £6.00
LOWRYS LAKE (FH3097) £8.00
SEAGAHAN RESERVOIR DAM (FH4125) £8.00
SHAWS LAKE (FH4214) £8.00
SHAWS LAKE (FH4215) £8.00
TULLNAWOOD LAKE (FH4966) £8.00
TULLYNAWOOD RESERVOIR (FH4969) £8.00

COUNTY DOWN

BANN (UPPER) (RIVER) (FH0298) £7.00
BANN (UPPER) AND TRIBUTARIES (FH0299) £5.00
INLER (RIVER) (FH2368) £5.00
MILL LODGE FISHERY (FH3293) £5.00
SHIMNA (RIVER) (FH4240) £9.00

COUNTY FERMANAGH

COLEBROOKE (RIVER) (FH1059) £5.00
LOUGH MELVIN (FH3042) £7.00
MILL LOUGH BELLANALECK (FH3294) £7.00
TEMPO (RIVER) (FH4736) £5.00

COUNTY LONDONDERRY

AGIVEY (RIVER) (FH0039) £5.00
CREGGAN RESERVOIRS (FH1178) £8.00
MACOSQUIN (RIVER) (FH3133) £5.00
ROE (RIVER) (FH3996) £5.00
TURNAFACE TROUT FISHERY (FH4979) £8.00

COUNTY TYRONE

BALLINDERRY (RIVER) (FH0266) £5.00
BALLINDERRY (RIVER) (FH0269) £5.00
BALLINDERRY (RIVER) (FH0268) £6.00
BURN DENNETT (RIVER) (FH0747) £5.00
DUNGANNON PARK FISHERY (FH1475) £7.00
LOUGH FEA (FH3031) £7.50
TORRENT (RIVER) (FH4882) £5.00

UNDER £20

COUNTY ANTRIM

STRAID FISHERY (FH4516) £10.00

COUNTY DOWN

BALLYLOUGH (FH0275) £10.00
CLANRYE (RIVER) (FH0972) £10.00
CLEGGAN (RIVER) (FH1002) £10.00
CULLY (RIVER) (FH1216) £10.00
FANE (RIVER) (FH1660) £10.00
FORKHILL (RIVER) (FH1768) £10.00
KILKEEL (RIVER) (FH2481) £10.00
LOUGH CASHEL (FH3015) £10.00
LOUGH GLASSDRUMMAN (FH3033) £10.00
LOUGH KILTYBAINE (FH3039) £10.00
LOUGH MULLAGHABAN (FH3044) £10.00
MCCOURTS LAKE (FH3220) £10.00
RINGDUFFERIN ESTUARY (FH3951) £12.00
WHITEWATER (RIVER) (FH5355) £10.00
WRITES LOUGH (FH5518) £10.00

COUNTY FERMANAGH

COOLYERMER LOUGH FISHERY (FH1103) £10.00
ERNE (RIVER) (FH1614) £10.00
LOWER LOUGH ERNE (FH3088) £11.00

COUNTY LONDONDERRY

BANN (LOWER) (RIVER) (FH0292) £15.00
FAUGHAN (RIVER) (FH1678) £10.00
FAUGHAN (RIVER) (FH1679) £15.00
MOYOLA (RIVER) (FH3395) £10.00
PADDY MCNAMARAS LAKE (FH3683) £10.00

COUNTY TYRONE

BLACKWATER (RIVER) (FH0467) £10.00
DERG (RIVER) (FH1337) £15.00
DERG (RIVER) (FH1339) £10.00
GLENELLY (RIVER) (FH1888) £10.00
OWENKILLEW (RIVER) (FH3663) £10.00

£20 AND ABOVE

COUNTY ANTRIM

GLENARM (RIVER) (FH1884) £35.00
MAINE (RIVER) (FH3142) £20.00

COUNTY TYRONE

FINN (RIVER) (FH1716) £20.00

UNDER £3

ANGUS
- DEAN (RIVER) (FH1285) £2.00
- ISLA (RIVER) (FH2387) £2.00

DUMFRIES AND GALLOWAY
- BLADNOCH (RIVER) (FH0485) £2.00
- CLATTERINGSHAWS LOCH (FH0980) £2.00
- KEN (RIVER) (FH2429) £2.00

HIGHLAND
- ST JOHNS LOCH (FH4390) £2.00

INVERCLYDE
- LOCH THOM (FH2952) £2.00

LOTHIAN (WEST)
- UNION CANAL (FH5046) £1.00

PERTH AND KINROSS
- ALMOND (RIVER) (FH0083) £2.00
- ALMOND (RIVER) (FH0084) £1.00
- AMULREE BEAT (FH0103) £1.00
- BALLECHIN BEAT (FH0260) £2.00
- CASTLE MENZIES BEAT (FH0863) £1.50
- LOCH FREUCHIE (FH2884) £1.00
- LOWER FARLEYER BEAT (FH3078) £1.50
- LOWER SCONE BEAT (FH3093) £1.00
- RUMBLING BRIDGE (FH4055) £1.00

SCOTTISH BORDERS
- WEST WATER RESERVOIR (FH5269) £1.00

STIRLING
- LOCH VOIL (FH2956) £2.50

YORKSHIRE (SOUTH)
- TORNE (RIVER) (FH4881) £2.00

UNDER £5

ARGYLL AND BUTE
- LOCH AVICH (FH2847) £4.00
- LOCH AWE (FH2848) £4.00

AYRSHIRE (NORTH)
- SKELMORLIE FISHERIES (FH4287) £3.50

DUMFRIES AND GALLOWAY
- COWANS FARM (FH1149) £4.00
- CRAIGHLAW (FH1159) £4.00
- DORMONT LAKE COARSE FISHERY (FH1415) £4.00
- GALLOWAY FOREST PARK (FH1829) £3.00
- KELHEAD WATER (FH2425) £4.00
- LOCH BARNBARROCH (FH2852) £4.00
- LOCH KEN (FH2898) £3.00
- NEW ABBEY DOW (FH3460) £3.00
- NEWTON LOCHAN (FH3495) £3.00
- TONGUE OF BOMBIE LOCHAN (FH4873) £3.50

GLASGOW (CITY OF)
- CLYDE (RIVER) (FH1037) £3.00

HIGHLAND
- LOCH GARRY (FH2885) £3.00
- LOCH INCH LAGGAN (FH2893) £3.00
- LOCH POULARY (FH2935) £3.00
- LOCH QUOICH (FH2937) £3.00

LANARKSHIRE (SOUTH)
- LANARK LOCH (FH2602) £3.50

LOTHIAN (EAST)
- TYNE (RIVER) (FH5018) £4.00

PERTH AND KINROSS
- BRAAN (RIVER) (FH0584) £4.00
- LOCH EIGHEACH (FH2876) £3.00
- NEWTON OF LOGIERAIT BEAT (FH3496) £3.00
- PITLOCHRY BOATING STATION AND LOCHSIDE CAFÉ (FH3792) £3.00
- TAY (RIVER) (FH4678) £4.00
- TROCHRY BEAT (FH4958) £4.00
- UPPER BORLICK BEAT (FH5051) £3.00
- UPPER KINNAIRD BEAT (FH5054) £3.00

STIRLING
- BARNCROFT (FH0315) £4.00
- DOCHART (RIVER) (FH1385) £4.00
- KINNEL (FH2521) £4.00

YORKSHIRE (SOUTH)
- BANK END COARSE FISHERIES (FH0285) £4.00
- LINDHOLME LEISURE LAKES FISHERIES (1) (FH2729) £4.00
- LINDHOLME LEISURE LAKES FISHERIES (2) (FH2730) £4.00
- LINDHOLME LEISURE LAKES FISHERIES (4) (FH2732) £4.00

UNDER £10

ABERDEENSHIRE
- MILL OF ELRICK FISHERY (FH3296) £5.00
- TULLICH FISHERY (FH4965) £5.00

ANGUS
- KINGENNIE FISHINGS (FH2494) £6.00

ARGYLL AND BUTE
- CUR (RIVER) (FH1224) £7.00
- FINNART (RIVER) (FH1718) £6.00
- LOCH TARSAN (FH2948) £7.00
- MASSAN (RIVER) (FH3205) £7.00
- MILL HOUSE FISHERIES (FH3286) £5.00

AYRSHIRE (EAST)
- COWANS LAW TROUT FISHERY (FH1150) £8.00

AYRSHIRE (SOUTH)
- CRAITH RESERVOIR (FH1162) £7.00
- LOCH MAYBERRY (FH2911) £5.00

DUMFRIES AND GALLOWAY
- ANNAN (RIVER) (FH0114) £8.00
- EARLSTOUN LOCH (FH1502) £5.00
- NITH (RIVER) (FH3512) £9.40
- PURDOMSTONE RESERVOIR (FH3857) £8.00

FALKIRK
- LOCH EARN (FH2875) £6.00
- LOCH VENACHAR (FH2955) £7.00

FIFE
- NEWTON FARM FISHERY (FH3494) £6.75

GLASGOW (CITY OF)
- NEILSTON TROUT FISHERY (FH3438) £7.50

HIGHLAND
- CONON (RIVER) (FH1089) £6.00
- GLENCOE LOCHAN (FH1886) £5.00
- LOCH INSH (FH2895) £6.50
- LOCH TOFTINGALL (FH2953) £5.00
- LOCH USSIE (FH2954) £6.00
- SCOURIE HOTEL (FH4120) £5.00
- SPEY (RIVER) (FH4364) £6.50
- STONEYFIELD LOCH TROUT FISHERY (FH4475) £7.00
- STRATHMANAIRD LOCHS (FH4520) £6.00

LANARKSHIRE (NORTH)
- CLYDE (RIVER) (FH1039) £5.00
- HILLEND LOCH (FH2226) £5.00
- LILY LOCH (FH2722) £5.00

LANARKSHIRE (SOUTH)
- AVON (RIVER) (FH0207) £5.00
- FRUID RESERVOIR (FH1816) £6.00
- TALLA RESERVOIR (FH4635) £5.00

LOTHIAN (EAST)
- MARKLE FISHERIES (FH3186) £9.00

PERTH AND KINROSS
- ABERFELDY ASSOCIATION BEAT (FH0014) £5.00
- CLOCHFOLDICH BEAT (FH1013) £5.00
- CUILALUINN BEAT (FH1213) £5.00
- DERCULICH BEAT (FH1335) £5.00
- FARLEYER BEAT (FH1666) £5.00
- FINDYNATE BEAT (FH1710) £5.00
- HAUGH OF GRANDTULLY BEAT (FH2135) £5.00
- LOGIERAIT BEAT (FH2981) £5.00
- PITCASTLE BEAT (FH3790) £5.00
- PITNACREE BEAT (FH3793) £5.00
- SKETEWAN BEAT (FH4290) £5.00
- WEEM BEAT (FH5226) £5.00

SCOTTISH BORDERS
- ACREKNOWE RESERVOIR (FH0024) £7.00
- AKERMOOR LOCH (FH0049) £7.00
- HELLMOOR LOCH (FH2178) £7.00
- KAILZIE GARDENS FISHERY (FH2419) £8.00
- LIDDLE (RIVER) (FH2716) £7.00
- MEGGET RESERVOIR (FH3241) £6.00
- ST MARYS LOCH (FH4393) £5.00
- TEVIOT (RIVER) (FH4751) £7.00
- TWEED (RIVER) (FH4999) £8.00
- WULLIESTRUTHER LOCH (FH5522) £7.00

STIRLING
- BORELAND (FH0550) £5.00
- CRAIGNAVIE (FH1161) £5.00
- DOCHART (RIVER) (FH1382) £5.00
- DOCHART (RIVER) (FH1384) £5.00
- FINLARIG (FH1714) £5.00
- KILLIN BREADALBANE ANGLING CLUB WATERS (FH2483) £5.00
- LESKINE (FH2706) £8.00
- LOCHAN NA LARAIG (FH2960) £5.00
- LOCHAY (RIVER) (FH2963) £5.00
- PORTNELLAN (FH3830) £5.00

WESTERN ISLES
- CEANN-AN-ORA FISHERY (FH0878) £8.00

YORKSHIRE (SOUTH)
- HAYFIELD LAKES (FH2155) £5.00

UNDER £20

ABERDEENSHIRE
- BOGNIE AND MOUNTBLAIRY FISHING (FH0525) £13.00

ANGUS
- PIPERDAM GOLF AND COUNTRY PARK (FH3784) £16.00

ARGYLL AND BUTE
- CLYDE ESTUARY (FH1040) £15.00
- DUNOON RESERVOIR (FH1478) £11.00
- FRUIN (RIVER) (FH1817) £15.00
- LOCH FAD (FH2879) £14.00
- LOCH LOSKIN (THE LOCHAN) (FH2905) £10.00
- RUEL (RIVER) (FH4053) £12.00

AYRSHIRE (NORTH)
- MIDDLETON FISHERY (FH3268) £13.50
- PORT-NA-LOCHAN (FH3829) £18.50

AYRSHIRE (SOUTH)
- DOON (RIVER) (FH1410) £15.00
- LOCH DORNAL (FH2872) £12.00

SPRINGWATER FISHERY (FH4374) £12.00

CLACKMANNANSHIRE

EASTER BALADO TROUT FISHERY (KINROSS) (FH1519) £16.00

DUMFRIES AND GALLOWAY

ANNAN (RIVER) (FH0113) £10.00
BUITTLE RESERVOIR (FH0723) £14.00
DINDINNIE RESERVOIR (FH1371) £15.00
DUNSKEY LOCHS (FH1480) £15.00
ESK (RIVER) (FH1619) £12.00
FYNTALLOCH LOCH (FH1826) £10.00
HODDOM WATER (FH2244) £10.00
JERICHO LOCHS (FH2410) £10.00
KINMOUNT LAKE (FH2520) £15.00
KIRKCHRIST (FH2526) £10.00
KIRRIEREOCH LOCH (FH2528) £10.00
KNOCKQUASSEN RESERVOIR (FH2541) £10.00
LABRAX FISHING (FH2547) £15.00
LOCH WHINYEON (FH2958) £12.00
LOCHENBRECK LOCH (FH2964) £12.00
MAINS OF PENNINGHAM FISHERY (FH3148) £12.00
MORTON POND (FH3376) £10.00
NAHINE LOCH (FH3411) £10.00
OCHILTREE LOCH (FH3573) £10.00
SLATEHOUSE LOCH (FH4295) £12.00
URR (RIVER) (FH5076) £16.00
WEE GLEN AMOUR LOCH (FH5223) £10.00

FALKIRK

CENTRAL SCOTLAND TROUT FISHERY (FH0889) £12.50

FIFE

CRAIGLUSCAR RESERVOIR (FH1160) £11.00
LOCH FITTY TROUT FISHERY (FH2883) £16.00
RAITH LAKE FISHERY (FH3882) £12.00

HIGHLAND

GLASS (RIVER) (FH1873) £10.00
NAIRN (RIVER) (FH3412) £13.00
NESS (RIVER) (FH3450) £10.00
TARVIE LOCHS FISHERY (FH4661) £15.00

INVERCLYDE

ARDGOWAN TROUT FISHERY (FH0128) £15.00
PINEWOOD TROUT FISHERY (FH3780) £15.00

LOTHIAN (MID)

LOGANLEA TROUT FISHERY (FH2980) £18.00

LOTHIAN (WEST)

ALLANDALE TARN (FH0076) £14.00
HOPETOUN FISHERY (FH2291) £10.00
PARKLEY FISHERY (FH3705) £16.00

MORAY

BROOM OF MOY (FH0690) £10.00

PERTH AND KINROSS

BOLFRACKS BEAT (FH0533) £15.00
CASTLE BEAT (FH0859) £15.00
HEATHERYFORD FISHERY (FH2174) £18.00
KENMORE BEAT (FH2431) £15.00
LOCH LEVEN FISHERIES (FH2902) £15.00
LOWER ABERUTHVEN FISHINGS (FH3070) £15.00
MONTAGUE RESERVOIR (FH3353) £10.00
SANDYKNOWES FISHING (FH4099) £10.00
SEAMAW LOCH (FH4126) £10.00

RENFREWSHIRE

HOWWOOD TROUT FISHERY (FH2321) £16.00

SCOTTISH BORDERS

CLERKLAND FLY FISHERY (FH1003) £10.00
COLDINGHAM LOCH (FH1057) £11.00
HEADSHAW FISHERY (FH2166) £12.00
LINDEAN RESERVOIR (FH2727) £15.00
WATCH RESERVOIR (FH5168) £13.00

STIRLING

ENDRICK (RIVER) (FH1592) £15.00
KILLEARN HOUSE FISHERY (FH2482) £10.00
LAKE OF MENTEITH FISHERIES (FH2566) £15.00
LOCH LOMOND (FH2904) £15.00
NORTH THIRD TROUT FISHERY (FH3534) £15.00

£20 AND ABOVE

ABERDEENSHIRE

LOCH INSCH FISHERY (FH2894) £20.00
YTHAN VALLEY FISHERY (FH5576) £22.00

ARGYLL AND BUTE

INVERAWE FISHERIES (FH2374) £20.50

DUMFRIES AND GALLOWAY

ESK (RIVER) (FH1621) £26.00
ESK (RIVER) (FH1620) £20.00
LOCH ROAN (FH2939) £25.00
LOWER LIDDLE (RIVER) (FH3086) £20.00
MORTON LOCH (FH3375) £40.00
STARBURN LOCH (FH4430) £30.00
TORHOUSEKIE AND KIRWAUGH (FH4879) £25.00

HIGHLAND

LOCH RUITH A PHUILL (FH2941) £22.00
LOCH TARVIE (FH2949) £22.00
SPEY (RIVER) (FH4363) £30.00
TWEED (RIVER) (FH4987) £25.00

PERTH AND KINROSS

ORCHILL LOCH TROUT FISHERY (FH3619) £20.00

SCOTTISH BORDERS

BUCCLEUCH ESTATES (FH0715) £40.00
ETTRICK AND YARROW (RIVER) (FH1632) £20.00
MACBIEHILL ESTATE (FH3127) £45.00
TEVIOT (RIVER) (FH4750) £20.00
TWEED (RIVER) (FH4995) £25.00
TWEED (RIVER) (FH4998) £25.00
TWEED (RIVER) (FH5002) £25.00
TWEED (RIVER) (FH5001) £25.00
TWEED (RIVER) (FH4997) £25.00
TWEED (RIVER) (FH4994) £25.00
TWEED (RIVER) (FH4996) £25.00

STIRLING

LOCH TAY HIGHLAND LODGES (FH2951) £25.00

WESTERN ISLES

LACASDALE LOCHS (FH2548) £30.00
OBBE FISHINGS (FH3571) £25.00

UNDER £3

BLAENAU GWENT
- BUTE TOWN RESERVOIR (FH0773) **£2.80**

CEREDIGION
- FRON FARM FISHERY (FH1814) **£2.50**

GLAMORGAN (VALE OF)
- PENTWYN RESERVOIR (FH3745) **£2.50**
- PENYWERN PONDS (FH3750) **£2.50**

GWYNEDD
- LLYN TEGID (BALA LAKE) (FH2823) **£2.50**

POWYS
- LLANGORSE LAKE (FH2773) **£2.50**
- SEVERN (RIVER) (FH4157) **£1.00**
- VYRNWY (RIVER) (FH5106) **£2.00**

WREXHAM
- TAN LLAN (FH4649) **£2.00**

UNDER £5

CAERPHILLY
- OGILVIE LAKE (FH3578) **£3.00**
- RIVERSIDE TROUT FISHERY (FH3969) **£4.00**

CEREDIGION
- GLWYDWERN TROUT FISHERY (FH1902) **£4.00**

CONWY
- LLYN ALED (FH2791) **£3.50**

FLINTSHIRE
- BUCKLEY TRAP POOL (FH0718) **£4.00**
- CLAWDD OFFAS DYKE (FH0984) **£4.00**
- SARN MILL FISHERIES (FH4106) **£4.00**

GWYNEDD
- LLIW (RIVER) (FH2781) **£3.00**

ISLE OF ANGLESEY
- BREAKWATER PARK (FH0610) **£4.00**
- LLYN DEWI (FH2809) **£4.00**
- LLYN NANT ANOG (FH2817) **£4.00**
- LLYN TACAN (FH2822) **£4.00**

MONMOUTHSHIRE
- CWMCELYN POND (FH1237) **£3.00**
- FIVE TREES (FH1740) **£3.50**
- OLWAY BROOK (FH3611) **£4.00**
- TREFALDU FISHERY (FH4911) **£4.50**

NEATH PORT TALBOT
- GLYNCORRWG PONDS FISHERY (FH1903) **£4.00**

NEWPORT
- LLISWERRY POND (FH2780) **£3.00**
- WOODSTOCK POOL (FH5495) **£3.50**

PEMBROKESHIRE
- ROADSIDE FARM (FH3974) **£4.00**
- WEST ATHESTON COARSE FISHERY (FH5256) **£4.00**

POWYS
- CLAERWEN RESERVOIR (FH0970) **£4.50**
- FACHWEN POOL (FH1651) **£4.00**
- RIVERSIDE CARAVAN PARK (FH3968) **£3.50**
- WESTLAKE FISHERY (FH5282) **£3.00**
- WYE (RIVER) (FH5540) **£3.00**

SWANSEA
- FENDROD LAKE (FH1694) **£3.10**
- GOWERTON COARSE FISHERY (FH1929) **£3.00**
- WHITE SPRINGS LAKES (FH5341) **£4.00**

TORFAEN
- BEACONS RESERVOIRS (FH0354) **£4.50**
- CWMBRAN BOATING LAKE (FH1236) **£3.00**
- LLYWD (RIVER) (FH2831) **£4.00**

WREXHAM
- DEE ABBEY FISHERIES (FH1321) **£4.00**

UNDER £10

BLAENAU GWENT
- HAYRICK LAKES (FH2158) **£7.00**

CAERPHILLY
- SIRHOWY (RIVER) (FH4281) **£7.00**

CARDIFF
- TAFF (RIVER) (FH4630) **£8.00**
- TAFF (RIVER) (FH4631) **£8.00**

CARMARTHENSHIRE
- GLAS-LLYN FISHERY (FH1870) **£5.00**
- LLYN CARFAN (FH2798) **£5.00**
- LOUGHOR (RIVER) (FH3058) **£5.00**
- LOUGHOR VALLEY FISHERY (FH3059) **£5.00**
- SPRINGWATER LAKES (FH4375) **£5.00**
- TAF (RIVER) (FH4627) **£8.00**
- TAF (RIVER) (FH4629) **£6.00**
- TEIFI (RIVER) (FH4704) **£8.50**
- TEIFI (RIVER) (FH4705) **£8.50**

CEREDIGION
- CWM RHEIDOL FISHERY (FH1234) **£6.00**
- LLANARTH FISHERY (FH2768) **£5.00**
- NINE OAKS (FH3509) **£5.00**
- TEGLAN LAKE (FH4701) **£5.00**
- TEIFI (RIVER) (FH4710) **£6.00**
- TEIFY POOLS FISHERY (FH4715) **£6.00**

CONWY
- CONWY VALLEY FISHERIES (FH1099) **£6.00**
- GILER ARMS LAKE (FH1855) **£5.00**
- TAN-Y-MYNYDD TROUT LAKES (FH4657) **£6.00**
- TYDDYN MAWR TROUT FARM (FH5015) **£6.00**

DENBIGHSHIRE
- ALWEN (RIVER) (FH0092) **£8.50**
- CEIRIOG (RIVER) (FH0882) **£7.00**
- DEE (RIVER) (FH1308) **£6.00**
- DEE (RIVER) (FH1309) **£8.00**
- FELIN-Y-GORS FISHERIES (FH1683) **£6.00**

FLINTSHIRE
- GWERYD LAKES FISHING (FH2047) **£5.00**
- SEVEN SPRINGS TROUT FARM AND FISHERIES (FH4143) **£7.50**

GLAMORGAN (VALE OF)
- HAZELCOURT PONDS (FH2164) **£5.00**
- LLYWN-ON RESERVOIR (FH2832) **£8.00**
- TAFF BARGOED (FH4633) **£6.00**

GWYNEDD
- AFON LLYFNI (RIVER) (FH0037) **£8.00**
- DEE (RIVER) (FH1314) **£7.50**
- DWYRYD (RIVER) (FH1491) **£7.00**
- DYSYNNI (RIVER) (FH1496) **£5.00**
- EDEN (RIVER) (FH1538) **£9.00**
- ERCH (RIVER) (FH1605) **£9.00**
- FFESTINIOG FISHERY (FH1702) **£7.00**
- LLYN BUGEILYN (FH2797) **£8.00**
- RHYDHIR (RIVER) (FH3939) **£9.00**
- TRAWFFYNYDD RESERVOIR (FH4905) **£9.00**
- TRYWERYN (RIVER) (FH4962) **£7.50**

ISLE OF ANGLESEY
- LLYN CORON (FH2801) **£8.00**
- LLYN Y GORS (FH2824) **£9.00**
- TY HEN LAKE (FH5013) **£5.00**

MONMOUTHSHIRE
- USK (RIVER) (FH5077) **£8.00**

NEATH PORT TALBOT
- NEATH (RIVER) (FH3432) **£8.00**

PEMBROKESHIRE
- EASTERN CLEDDAU (RIVER) (FH1521) **£6.00**
- HOLGAN TROUT FARM FISHERY (FH2252) **£5.00**
- IAN HEAPS PREMIER FISHERIES AND SCHOOL OF ANGLING (FH2356) **£5.00**
- LUDCHURCH LAKE (FH3103) **£5.00**
- ROSEBUSH RESERVOIR (FH4013) **£6.50**
- WESTERN CLEDDAU (RIVER) (FH5273) **£8.00**

POWYS
- CANTEF RESERVOIR (FH0826) **£9.00**
- CLYNWEDOG RESERVOIR (FH1041) **£8.00**
- CLYWEDOG (RIVER) (FH1043) **£8.00**
- DULAS (RIVER) (FH1468) **£8.00**
- ELAN (RIVER) (FH1557) **£5.00**
- ELAN VALLEY RESERVOIR (FH1558) **£7.50**
- GWYDDIOR LAKE (FH2053) **£8.00**
- IRFON (RIVER) (FH2375) **£5.00**
- LLYN CLYWEDOG (FH2800) **£8.00**
- LLYN-COCH HWYAD (FH2825) **£8.00**
- MAERDY BROOK (FH3135) **£6.00**
- SEVERN (RIVER) (FH4153) **£8.00**
- TWYMYN (RIVER) (FH5011) **£6.00**
- USK RESERVOIR (FH5080) **£8.50**
- WYE (RIVER) (FH5541) **£9.00**
- WYE (RIVER) (FH5538) **£7.00**
- WYE (RIVER) (FH5542) **£5.00**

RHONDDA CYNON TAFF
- CMPRAC (RIVER) (FH1045) **£8.00**
- ELY (RIVER) (FH1579) **£5.00**

SWANSEA
- LOWER LLIW (FH3087) **£9.00**

TORFAEN
- LISVANE RESERVOIR (FH2738) **£9.50**
- LLANISHEN RESERVOIR (FH2774) **£9.50**
- LLYN ON RESERVOIR (FH2820) **£9.50**

WREXHAM
- ALYN (RIVER) (FH0095) **£6.00**
- DEE (RIVER) (FH1300) **£5.00**
- DEE (RIVER) (FH1302) **£8.00**

UNDER £20

BLAENAU GWENT
- SIRHOWY (RIVER) (FH4280) **£11.00**

CAERPHILLY
- EBBW (RIVER) (FH1528) **£11.00**

CARMARTHENSHIRE
- COTHI (RIVER) (FH1128) **£10.00**
- COWIN (RIVER) (FH1151) **£10.00**
- CYNIN (RIVER) (FH1241) **£10.00**
- GARNFFRWD FISHERY (FH1836) **£10.00**
- PANT Y BEDW FISHING LAKES (FH3693) **£10.00**
- PEWI FACH (RIVER) (FH3763) **£10.00**

TAF (RIVER) (FH4628) **£10.00**
TEIFI (RIVER) (FH4703) **£15.00**
TOWI (RIVER) (FH4891) **£15.00**
TOWY (RIVER) (FH4899) **£10.00**
TOWY (RIVER) (FH4900) **£10.00**
TOWY (RIVER) (FH4898) **£10.00**

CEREDIGION

AERON (RIVER) (FH0035) **£11.00**
GEORGE BORROW HOTEL (FH1848) **£10.00**
LAKE BLAENMELINDWR (FH2554) **£10.00**
LAKE CRAIGYPISTYLL (FH2555) **£10.00**
LAKE FRONGOCH (FH2557) **£10.00**
LAKE LLYGAD (FH2561) **£10.00**
LAKE PENDHAM (FH2567) **£10.00**
LAKE RHEIDOL (FH2569) **£10.00**
LAKE RHOSGOCH (FH2570) **£10.00**
LAKE RHOSRHYDD (FH2571) **£10.00**
LLWYNDURIS MANSION FISHERY (FH2787) **£10.00**
RHEIDOL (RIVER) (FH3935) **£10.00**
TEIFI (RIVER (FH4702) **£17.00**
YSTWYTH (RIVER) (FH5574) **£12.00**

CONWY

CONWY (RIVER) (FH1094) **£18.00**
CONWY (RIVER) (FH1097) **£15.00**
GRAIGLWYD SPRINGS FISHERY (FH1937) **£11.00**
LLYN CRAFNANT FISHERIES (FH2803) **£12.00**

DENBIGHSHIRE

ABBEY FISHERY (FH0002) **£14.00**
BRENIG RESERVOIR (FH0614) **£10.50**
CLWYD (RIVER) (FH1034) **£10.00**
DRAGONFLY FISHERIES (FH1434) **£14.00**
LLYN BRENIG (FH2795) **£12.50**

FLINTSHIRE

GYRN CASTLE FISHERY (FH2056) **£15.00**

GLAMORGAN (VALE OF)

MELLTE (STREAM) (FH3251) **£10.00**

GWYNEDD

AFON SEIONT (RIVER) (FH0038) **£15.00**
CREGENNAN LAKES (FH1177) **£15.00**
CWM SILYN LAKE (FH1235) **£15.00**
DWYFACH (RIVER) (FH1488) **£10.00**
DWYTHWCH LAKE (FH1492) **£15.00**
DYWARCHEN RESERVOIR (FH1498) **£15.00**
GLAN MORFA MAWR FISHERY (FH1868) **£11.00**
GLASLYN (RIVER) (FH1871) **£10.00**
GWYRFAI (RIVER) (FH2055) **£15.00**
LERI (RIVER) (FH2704) **£10.00**
LLYN CWELLYN RESERVOIR (FH2804) **£15.00**
LLYN CYNWCH LAKE (FH2807) **£14.00**
LLYN GADAIR (FH2812) **£14.00**
LLYN NANTLLE (FH2818) **£14.00**
LLYN PADARN (FH2821) **£15.00**
MAWDDACH AND WNION (RIVERS) (FH3213) **£14.00**
NANTLLE LAKE (FH3419) **£15.00**
OGWEN (RIVER) (FH3582) **£10.00**
TALYLLYN LAKE (FH4640) **£15.00**

ISLE OF ANGLESEY

CEFNI RESERVOIR (FH0881) **£12.00**
LLYN ALAN (FH2788) **£12.00**

MONMOUTHSHIRE

FAIROAK FISHERY (FH1655) **£10.00**
RAVENSNEST FISHERY (FH3894) **£10.00**

NEATH PORT TALBOT

ABERNANT FARM FISHERY (FH0015) **£16.50**
DULAIS (RIVER) (FH1466) **£10.00**
EGLWYS NUNYDD RESERVOIR (FH1553) **£10.00**
HEPSTE (STREAM) (FH2188) **£10.00**
NEATH (RIVER) (FH3434) **£10.00**

NEWPORT

WENTWOOD RESERVOIR (FH5251) **£12.00**
YNYS-Y-FRO RESERVOIR (FH5571) **£12.00**

PEMBROKESHIRE

HAYCASTLE TROUT FISHERY (FH2149) **£10.00**
LLYS Y FRAN RESERVOIR AND COUNTRY PARK (FH2829) **£12.00**
WESTERN CLEDDAU (RIVER) (FH5272) **£10.00**
YET-Y-GORS FISHERY (FH5566) **£10.00**

POWYS

DYFI (RIVER) (FH1494) **£10.00**
IRFON (RIVER) (FH2377) **£10.00**
IRFON (RIVER) (FH2376) **£15.00**
LLNGWYN FISHERY (FH2782) **£10.00**
LLYN ALARCH (FH2789) **£16.00**
LLYNGWYN LAKE (FH2828) **£12.50**
USK (RIVER) (FH5079) **£15.50**

RHONDDA CYNON TAFF

LLYN ALAW (FH2790) **£12.00**
SEVEN OAKS FISHERY (FH4141) **£12.00**

SWANSEA

MAES GWYN FISHERY (FH3136) **£10.00**
SHIMANO FELINDRE TROUT FISHERY (FH4239) **£19.50**
TAWE (RIVER) (FH4675) **£15.00**
TAWE (RIVER) (FH4676) **£16.00**

WREXHAM

BODIDRIS GAME FISHERY (FH0522) **£16.00**
DEE (RIVER) (FH1303) **£15.00**
LLANDEGLA TROUT FISHERY (FH2770) **£16.00**
LLYN CYFYNWY SPORT TROUT FISHERY (FH2806) **£12.00**
PENYCAE LOWER RESERVOIR (FH3748) **£11.00**
PENYCAE UPPER RESERVOIR (FH3749) **£11.00**
TREE TOPS FLY FISHERY (FH4910) **£18.00**
TY MAWR RESERVOIR (FH5014) **£12.50**

£20 AND ABOVE

CARMARTHENSHIRE

BRO TYWI FISHERIES (FH0660) **£20.00**
GWENDRAETH FACH (RIVER) (FH2045) **£20.00**
GWILI (RIVER) (FH2048) **£20.00**
TOWY (RIVER) (FH4897) **£20.00**
TOWY (RIVER) (FH4895) **£20.00**

CEREDIGION

TEIFI (RIVER) (FH4706) **£20.00**
TROED-Y-BRYN FISHERY (FH4959) **£20.00**

POWYS

GLUDY LAKE (FH1901) **£180.00**

Day Ticket Prices (Junior)

SECTION 9

This section allows you to search for Day Ticket Prices for Juniors to help you to make the right choice.

e.g under £1

Once you have located a Fishery you can either look up further details in Section 1 or use the other sections to find what else the Fishery may have to offer.

Angling Times Fishooked Directory

UNDER £1

BEDFORDSHIRE
- PRIORY COUNTRY PARK (FH3848) £0.50

CLEVELAND
- CHARLTONS PONDS (FH0905) £0.75
- LOCKE PARK (FH2971) £0.75

COUNTY DURHAM
- WELLFIELD POND (FH5238) £0.75

HUMBERSIDE
- BEVERLEY BECK (FH0399) £0.50

LANCASHIRE
- BIRKACRE LODGES (FH0429) £0.30
- BRYN FLASH (FH0712) £0.30
- DEEP PIT (FH1323) £0.30
- FAN LODGE (FH1659) £0.30
- FORSTERS LODGES (FH1770) £0.30
- HEAPEY NO 1 (FH2167) £0.30
- HEAPEY NO 2 (FH2168) £0.30
- HORROCKS FLASH (FH2302) £0.30
- HOUGHTONS LODGE (FH2317) £0.30
- INCE PARK LAKE (FH2364) £0.30
- LEEDS TO LIVERPOOL CANAL (FH2674) £0.30
- MELLINGS NO 1 (FH3248) £0.30
- RUFFORD CANAL (FH4054) £0.30
- SCOT LANE PONDS (FH4118) £0.30
- SQUARE LODGE (FH4380) £0.30
- WAYOH RESERVOIR (FH5193) £0.50
- WORTHINGTON NO 1 (FH5510) £0.30
- WORTHINGTON NO 2 (FH5511) £0.30
- WORTHINGTON NO 3 (FH5512) £0.30

LINCOLNSHIRE
- TRENT (RIVER) (FH4920) £0.50

MANCHESTER (GREATER)
- ALEXANDRA PARK (FH0072) £0.75
- SALFORD QUAYS (FH4082) £0.50

MIDLANDS (WEST)
- RUSHALL CANAL (FH4060) £0.75
- TAME VALLEY CANAL (FH4648) £0.50

NORTHAMPTONSHIRE
- GRAND UNION CANAL (FH1958) £0.50

SOMERSET
- WELLINGTON BASIN (FH5240) £0.50

YORKSHIRE (SOUTH)
- SHEFFIELD CANAL (FH4223) £0.75

YORKSHIRE (WEST)
- WHARFE (RIVER) (FH5311) £0.50

UNDER £3

BEDFORDSHIRE
- LEDBURN ROAD (FH2659) £2.00

BERKSHIRE
- ALBERT BRIDGE (FH0050) £1.50
- BENS LAKE (FH0385) £2.50
- FARLEYMOOR LAKE (FH1667) £1.00
- LONGMOOR LAKE (FH2994) £2.50
- MILL POND (FH3298) £1.50
- ROMNEY ISLAND AND MEADOW (FH4001) £1.50
- SOUTH FIELD PARK (FH4329) £1.50
- SOUTH HILL PARK LAKE (FH4331) £1.50
- SWAN VALLEY (FH4596) £2.00
- WHITE SWAN LAKE (FH5343) £2.50

BRISTOL
- BRISTOL DOCKS (FH0655) £1.00
- SEVINGTON LAKES FISHERY (FH4199) £2.50
- TANHOUSE FARM LAKE (FH4652) £2.00

BUCKINGHAMSHIRE
- COSGROVE LEISURE PARK (FH1122) £1.50
- OUSE (RIVER) (FH3641) £2.50
- TYRINGHAM ESTATE (FH5037) £2.00

CAMBRIDGESHIRE
- BARNWELL COUNTRY PARK (FH0320) £2.00
- CHAWSTON LAKES (FH0908) £1.50
- FERRY MEADOWS (FH1701) £1.50
- GREAT OUSE (RIVER) (FH1994) £2.00
- GREAT OUSE (RIVER) (FH1996) £1.00
- GREAT OUSE (RIVER) (FH1995) £1.50
- HINCHINGBROOKE COUNTRY PARK (FH2232) £1.00
- KINGFISHER LAKE (FH2497) £2.50
- KINGSLAND RESERVOIRS (FH2512) £2.50
- MAGPIE LAKE (FH3139) £2.00
- MEPAL PIT (FH3256) £2.00
- NENE (RIVER) (FH3440) £1.00
- NENE (RIVER) (FH3441) £1.00
- NENE (RIVER) (FH3445) £1.50
- NENE (RIVER) (FH3446) £2.50
- NENE NORTH BANK (RIVER) (FH3449) £1.50
- OFFORD WEIRPOOL (FH3575) £1.00
- OLD WEST (RIVER) (FH3602) £2.00
- SAND MARTIN LAKE (FH4091) £2.50
- SWAN LAKE (FH4589) £2.50
- TWENTY FOOT DRAIN (FH5003) £1.00
- WELDON RESERVOIR (FH5228) £1.50
- WHITTLESEY DYKE/ BEVILLS LEAM (FH5361) £1.00
- WILLOW CREEK (FH5378) £2.50
- WOOD POOL (FH5459) £2.50

CHESHIRE
- BOTTOMS RESERVOIR (FH0563) £1.00
- BREAM HOLE (FH0611) £1.50
- BRIDGEWATER CANAL (FH0635) £1.00
- CHESHIRE FISHING (FH0925) £2.50
- GOWY FISHERY (FH1932) £2.00
- GRIMESDITCH MILL POOL (FH2020) £1.50
- KNIGHTS POOL (FH2536) £1.00
- LLOYDS MEADOW FISHERIES (FH2784) £2.50
- SALE WATER PARK (FH4081) £1.20
- TATTON MERE (FH4664) £2.00
- WINSFORD FLASH (FH5421) £1.50

CLEVELAND
- HEMLINGTON LAKE (FH2179) £1.60

CORNWALL
- AMALWHIDDEN FARM (FH0099) £2.00
- BILLS POOL (FH0423) £2.50
- BUDE CANAL (FH0721) £1.50
- COLLEGE RESERVOIR (FH1064) £2.00
- EAST ROSE FARM (FH1513) £2.75
- FERNDALE (FH1699) £2.50
- GOONHAVERN COARSE FISHING LAKE (FH1920) £2.00
- MEADOWSIDE COARSE FISHERY (FH3228) £2.50
- NEETS VALLEY PARK (FH3436) £1.75
- OAKSIDE FISHERY (FH3567) £2.50
- ST ERTH FISHERY (FH4385) £2.50
- STOWFORD GRANGE FISHERIES (FH4513) £2.50
- TIN DENE FISHERY (FH4850) £2.00
- TRETHIGGEY FARM POND (FH4949) £1.50
- WOONSMITH LAKE (FH5502) £2.50

COUNTY DURHAM
- AYCLIFFE LAKE (FH0235) £2.50
- FINCHALE ABBEY FARM (FH1709) £2.00
- MAINSFORTH POND (FH3149) £2.00
- MIDDLETON WATER PARK (FH3269) £2.00

CUMBRIA
- ANNAS (RIVER) (FH0115) £2.00
- ATKINSONS TARN COARSE FISHERY (FH0181) £1.50
- BANKS POND (FH0289) £2.00
- BAYSTONE BANK RESERVIOR (FH0352) £2.00
- BESSY BECK TROUT FARM (FH0394) £1.50
- BIGLAND HALL LAKE (FH0414) £2.00
- BLELHAM TARN (FH0495) £2.00
- BRATHAY (RIVER) (FH0604) £2.00
- BUTTERMERE LAKE (FH0777) £1.50
- CLEABARROW TARN (FH0996) £2.00
- CRUMMOCK WATER LAKE (FH1206) £1.50
- EAST VIEW FISHERY (FH1515) £1.50
- ESK (RIVER) (FH1618) £2.00
- GRASMERE COARSE FISHERY (FH1976) £2.00
- HAWESWATER RESERVOIR (FH2140) £2.00
- HAYESWATER RESERVOIR (FH2154) £2.00
- HOLEHIRD TARN (FH2251) £2.00
- IRT (RIVER) (FH2380) £2.00
- LAKE WINDERMERE (FH2574) £2.00
- LAZY (RIVER) (FH2641) £2.00
- LICKLE (RIVER) (FH2714) £2.00
- LOWESWATER LAKE (FH3096) £1.50
- MOSS ECCLES TARN (FH3378) £2.00
- RATHER HEATH TARN (FH3891) £2.00
- RYDAL WATER (FH4071) £2.00
- SCHOOL KNOTT TARN (FH4115) £2.00
- TEWITFIELDS TROUT FISHERY (FH4752) £2.00
- ULVERSTON CANAL (FH5043) £1.50
- WINSTER (RIVER) (FH5423) £2.00
- WITHERSLACK HALL TARN (FH5443) £2.00

DERBYSHIRE
- ALLESTREE LAKE (FH0078) £1.45
- ALVASTON LAKE (FH0089) £1.45
- CODNOR PARK RESERVOIR (FH1051) £1.50
- COMBS RESERVOIR (FH1081) £2.00
- COPPICE LAKE (FH1112) £2.50
- MARKEATON LAKE (FH3183) £1.45
- PRESS MANOR (FH3840) £2.50
- RINGWOOD LAKE (FH3956) £1.60

DEVON
- ABBROOK POND (FH0012) £1.25
- BICKERTON FARM FISHERY (FH0406) £2.50

CHARLECOMBE (FH0902) £2.00
COOMBE WATER FISHERY (FH1110) £2.50
CREEDY (RIVER) (FH1174) £1.25
CULM (RIVER) (FH1217) £1.25
CULM (RIVER) (FH1218) £1.25
DARRACOTT RESERVOIR (FH1276) £1.50
EDDISON POND (FH1532) £2.00
EXE (RIVER) (FH1639) £1.25
EXE (RIVER) (FH1643) £1.25
EXEMOOR FARM (FH1646) £1.50
EXETER CANAL (FH1647) £1.25
EXETER SHIP CANAL (FH1648) £1.25
FENECK POND (FH1695) £1.25
GRAND WESTERN CANAL (FH1967) £2.50
HATCHLAND TROUT FISHERY (FH2129) £2.00
HOGSBROOK LAKES (FH2246) £2.50
HOME FARM FISHERY (FH2280) £2.50
LITTLE ALLERS COARSE FISHERY (FH2739) £2.50
LITTLE WEACH (FH2763) £2.00
MELBURY RESERVOIR (FH3244) £1.50
MILL PARK COARSE FISHING LAKE (FH3297) £2.00
MILLHAYES (FH3313) £2.50
MILTON FARM PONDS (FH3319) £2.00
NEWCOURT PONDS (FH3482) £2.00
NEWHOUSE FISHERY (FH3486) £1.80
NEWTON ABBOT SPRING PONDS (FH3493) £2.00
PADBROOK PARK (FH3681) £2.00
PICFRESH (FH3765) £2.50
POUND POND FARM (FH3836) £1.50
ROCOMBE PONDS (FH3986) £2.00
SAMPFORD PEVERAL PONDS (FH4090) £1.25
SIMPSON VALLEY FISHERY (FH4274) £2.00
SPIRES LAKES (FH4365) £2.50
SUMMERLEAZE POND (FH4554) £1.50
UPTON WARREN LAKE (FH5062) £2.50

DORSET

AVON TYRRELL LAKES (FH0230) £2.50
HERMITAGE LAKES (FH2189) £2.50
KINGCOMBE COARSE FARM (FH2492) £1.50
RADIPOLE LAKE (FH3875) £1.60
REVELS FISHERY (FH3932) £2.50
STOUR (DORSET) (RIVER) (FH4486) £1.00
STOUR (RIVER) (FH4492) £2.00
WALLYS LAKE (FH5124) £2.50

ESSEX

ALBYNS LAKE (FH0053) £1.50
CHASE FISHERY (FH0907) £1.50
CHELMER (RIVER) (FH0910) £1.50
CHELMER AND BLACKWATER NAVIGATION CANAL (FH0913) £1.50
CHIGBOROUGH (FH0940) £2.00
GLOUCESTER PARK LAKE (FH1900) £2.00
HAINAULT FOREST COUNTRY PARK (FH2063) £2.00
HARWOOD HALL LAKE (FH2125) £2.00
HOOKS MARSH (FH2289) £2.00
LAKE MEADOWS (FH2562) £2.00
MAYSBROOK LAKES (FH3217) £1.00
NORTHLANDS PARK (FH3546) £2.00
RAPHAELS PARK (FH3888) £1.50
ROCHFORD RESERVOIR (FH3981) £1.00
RODING VALLEY LAKE (FH3994) £1.50
WAKE VALLEY POND (FH5114) £1.50
WARREN (FH5150) £1.50

GLOUCESTERSHIRE

CANNOP PONDS (FH0823) £2.00
CLAYDON PARK FISHERY (FH0992) £1.50
COKES PIT (FH1056) £1.50
GLOUCESTER AND SHARPNESS CANAL (FH1897) £1.25
GLOUCESTER CANAL (FH1899) £1.25
KEYNES COUNTRY PARK (FH2475) £1.50
KEYNES PARK TOP LAKE (FH2476) £1.50
LIGHTMOOR POOL (FH2719) £1.50
MARIONS POOL (FH3181) £1.50
MEADOWCLIFFE POOL (FH3226) £2.00
MILL LAKE (NO 44) (FH3289) £2.00
NEIGH BRIDGE LAKE (FH3437) £1.50
PLUMP HILL POOL (FH3806) £1.50
SEVERN (RIVER) (FH4147) £2.00
STEAM MILLS LAKE (FH4444) £1.50
WATERLOO SCREENS (FH5179) £1.50

HAMPSHIRE

CROOKED WILLOWS (FH1188) £2.00
HATCHET POND (FH2128) £2.50
HOLLYBUSH LANE LAKES (FH2262) £2.50
LAKESIDE COUNTRY PARK (FH2589) £2.50
MOORS VALLEY COUNTRY PARK (FH3366) £2.00
QUEENS ROAD POND (FH3867) £1.50

HEREFORDSHIRE

COURT FARM (FH1143) £2.00
MARSH HOUSE FARM (FH3192) £2.50
PRIDEWOOD LAKE (FH3844) £1.00

HERTFORDSHIRE

AYLESBURY ARM CANAL (FH0236) £1.50
DOBBS WEIR FISHERY (FH1381) £1.80
FAIRLANDS VALLEY PARK (FH1652) £2.00
FEILDES WEIR (FH1680) £1.25
GRAND UNION CANAL (FH1949) £1.50
GRAND UNION CANAL (FH1945) £1.50
GRAND UNION CANAL (FH1944) £1.50
GRAND UNION CANAL (FH1947) £1.50
GRAND UNION CANAL (FH1948) £1.50
GRAND UNION CANAL (FH1951) £1.50
LEA (RIVER) (FH2645) £1.90
LEE NAVIGATION (FH2664) £1.25
LEE NAVIGATION (FH2667) £1.25
LEE NAVIGATION (FH2669) £1.25
LEE NAVIGATION (FH2663) £1.25
LEE NAVIGATION (FH2662) £1.25
LEE NAVIGATION (FH2668) £1.25
LEE NAVIGATION (FH2665) £1.25
OLD MILL AND MEADOWS (FH3594) £1.90
RYEMEADS (FH4076) £2.00
STANBOROUGH LAKE (FH4415) £1.50
STARTOPS RESERVOIR (FH4435) £2.50
THAME (RIVER) (FH4755) £1.50
WILSTONE RESERVOIR (FH5404) £2.50

HUMBERSIDE

BURSTWICK SKI LAKE (FH0758) £1.00
BURTON CONSTABLE COUNTRY PARK (FH0759) £2.50
DACRE LAKESIDE PARK (FH1244) £1.00
DRIFFIELD CANAL (FH1442) £1.50
FARM PONDS (FH1670) £1.50
HALSHAM POND (FH2075) £2.50
LEVEN CANAL (FH2709) £1.50
NODDLE HILL LAKE (FH3513) £1.50
REDFERNS POND (FH3917) £1.50
WILLITOFT FISH FARM (FH5376) £2.00

ISLE OF WIGHT

ISLAND FISH FARM AND MEADOW LAKES (FH2390) £2.50
SOMERTON RESERVOIR (FH4325) £1.50

KENT

BROOKLANDS LAKE (FH0684) £1.50
CHILHAM LAKE (FH0942) £2.50
HAYSDEN COUNTRY PARK (FH2160) £1.00
MEDWAY (RIVER) (FH3231) £1.00
MEDWAY (RIVER) (FH3238) £1.00
MEDWAY (RIVER) (FH3239) £1.00
MID KENT FISHERIES (FH3263) £2.50
MOTE PARK FISHERY (FH3381) £2.50
SHORNE COUNTRY PARK LAKES (FH4246) £1.50

LANCASHIRE

BALL GROVE LAKE (FH0258) £1.60
BRYAN HEY RESERVOIR (FH0711) £1.00
CHURCH GARDEN (FH0952) £2.00
CLIVIGER FISH PONDS (FH1012) £1.50
COTTAGE GREEN GARDEN CENTRE (FH1133) £2.00
CROFT FISHERIES (FH1182) £2.00
DIXON GREEN RESERVOIR (FH1380) £1.00
DUDDON (RIVER) (FH1460) £2.00
FOULRIDGE RESERVOIR (FH1778) £2.25
INCE MOSS FISHERIES (FH2363) £1.00
LANCASTER HOUSE (FH2605) £2.00
LATHOM FISHERIES (FH2627) £2.00
LEISURE LAKES (FH2695) £2.20
MARTIN HALL FARM (FH3200) £1.00
ORRELL WATER PARK (FH3625) £2.40
POLLYS FLASH (FH3812) £1.00
RED ROCKS FISHERY (FH3911) £1.00
STANLEY PARK LAKE (FH4420) £2.00
UPPER RIVINGTON RESERVOIR (FH5057) £1.50
WALVERDEN RESERVOIR (FH5137) £1.00

LEICESTERSHIRE

LAKESIDE FISHING (FH2593) £2.50
MILL FARM FISHERY (FH3280) £2.50
NANPANTAN RESERVOIR (FH3417) £1.50
PROCTORS PLEASURE PARK (FH3851) £2.00

LINCOLNSHIRE

BOULTHAM PARK LAKE (FH0565) £2.00
GRANGE FARM LEISURE (FH1969) £1.50
HARTSHOLME PARK LAKE (FH2119) £2.00
HOLLAND PARK (FH2255) £1.50
KEAL COATES FISHERY (FH2422) £2.50
LOBBY FIELD PONDS (FH2834) £2.50
REVESBY RESERVOIR (FH3933) £2.00
ROSSWAYS WATER (FH4021) £2.50
SHANDY KEV FISHERIES (FH4207) £2.00
SKEGNESS WATER LEISURE PARK (FH4285) £2.00
STARMERS PIT (FH4433) £2.00
STICKNEY BRICKPONDS (FH4455) £1.50
TILL (RIVER) (FH4846) £2.00
TILL (RIVER) (FH4847) £2.00
TRENT (RIVER) (FH4919) £2.00
TRENT (RIVER) (FH4921) £2.00
UPPER WITHAM (RIVER) (FH5060) £2.00
WARPING DRAIN (FH5149) £1.00
WINTERS LAKE (FH5427) £1.50

LINCOLNSHIRE (NORTH)

KINGFISHER LODGE (FH2501) £1.50

LONDON (GREATER)

ALEXANDRA PALACE LAKE (FH0071) £1.00
BIRCHMERE (FH0427) £2.50
BOXERS LAKE (FH0577) £1.50
GRAND UNION CANAL (FH1954) £1.50
GRAND UNION CANAL (FH1956) £2.00
HIGHAMS PARK LAKE (FH2213) £2.00
HOLLOW PONDS (FH2259) £2.00
LEA NAVIGATION (FH2648) £1.25
LEE NAVIGATION (FH2670) £1.25
LITTLE BRITAIN LAKE (FH2743) £2.00
MULGROVE POND (FH3399) £2.50
NORWOOD LAKE (FH3550) £1.50
OLD LEE (RIVER) (FH3591) £1.25
PERCH POND (FH3751) £1.00
REGENTS CANAL (FH3928) £1.00
REGENTS CANAL (FH3925) £1.50
REGENTS CANAL (FH3926) £1.50
REGENTS CANAL (FH3927) £1.50
TRENT COUNTRY PARK LAKES (FH4946) £1.50
TRENT PARK LAKES (FH4947) £1.55
WANSTEAD PARK LAKES (FH5145) £1.00
WOOLWICH DOCKYARD (FH5501) £1.00

MANCHESTER (GREATER)

BLACK BECK (RIVER) (FH0439) £2.00
BLACKLEACH RESERVOIR (FH0451) £1.00
BOGGART HOLE CLOUGH (FH0524) £1.25
BRIDGEWATER CANAL (FH0638) £1.00
CHORLTON WATER PARK (FH0946) £1.25
CLIFTON MARINA (FH1008) £1.00
CROFT HEAD FISHERY (FH1183) £1.50
DOWRY AND NEW YEARS BRIDGE RESERVOIR (FH1433) £1.50
GORSE PIT RESERVOIR (FH1922) £1.00
GORTON (UPPER) RESERVOIR (FH1925) £1.00
GROVE LODGE (FH2031) £1.50
HEATON PARK (FH2176) £1.00
HOLLINGWORTH LAKE COUNTRY PARK (FH2258) £1.50
HUDDERSFIELD NARROW CANAL (FH2328) £2.00
KING GEORGE V POOL (FH2489) £1.10
LOWER TOWN HOUSE FISHERY (FH3095) £1.50
PAINSWICK PARK LAKE (FH3686) £1.00
PLATT FIELDS (FH3800) £1.00
REDDISH VALE MILL PONDS (FH3913) £1.50
RHODES LODGE (FH3936) £1.50
SWAN LODGE (FH4593) £1.50
WHITTLE BROOK RESERVOIR (FH5358) £1.00

MERSEYSIDE

MORETON MERE (FH3369) £1.50

MIDLANDS (WEST)

ALVECHURCH FISHERIES (FH0090) £2.50
BLYTHE WATERS (FH0518) £2.00
COOMBE POOL (FH1109) £2.00
DAYHOUSE FARM (FH1282) £2.50
EARLSWOOD LAKES (FH1503) £2.00
HEATHFIELD POOL (FH2175) £1.50
KINGSBURY WATER PARK (FH2510) £1.20
SUTTON PARK (FH4564) £1.50

NORFOLK

BLICKLING PARK LAKE (FH0500) £2.00
BOOTON CLAY PIT (FH0543) £1.00
BURE VALLEY LAKES (FH0737) £2.50
COSTESSEY PITS (FH1125) £1.00
GUNTON PARK LAKE (FH2037) £1.50
LENWADE COMMON LAKES (FH2700) £2.00
LOCH NEATON (FH2922) £2.00
NATURES HAVEN LAKES (FH3429) £2.00
PECK MEADOW POND (FH3730) £2.00
RINGLAND PITS (FH3953) £1.50
SOVEREIGN LAKES (FH4354) £2.00
SWANTON MORLEY FISHERY (FH4602) £2.50
TAVERHAM (FH4668) £1.50
UPPER BURE (STREAM) (FH5052) £2.50
WENSUM (RIVER) (FH5247) £2.50
WOODRISING WATER MEADOWS (FH5489) £2.50

NORTHAMPTONSHIRE

CRESCENT LAKE (FH1179) £2.50
DAVENTRY COUNTRY PARK (FH1281) £1.70
GRAND UNION CANAL (FH1959) £1.00
GREEN FARM LAKES (FH2000) £2.50
HEYFORD FISHERY (FH2200) £2.00
ISE (RIVER) (FH2384) £1.50
ISLIP NATURE LAKE (FH2396) £1.50
NENE (RIVER) (FH3447) £2.00
NENE (RIVER) (FH3448) £1.50
NORTHAMPTON JUNCTION CANAL (FH3542) £1.50
OXFORD CANAL (FH3667) £1.50
THORPE WATERVILLE LAKE (FH4827) £1.50
THRAPSTON LAKES (FH4829) £1.50
WOOTTON BROOK LAKE (FH5503) £1.50

NORTHUMBERLAND

NORTH TYNE (RIVER) (FH3539) £2.40
TYNE (RIVER) (FH5019) £2.60

NOTTINGHAMSHIRE

COLWICK COUNTRY PARK (FH1080) £1.80
GRANTHAM CANAL (FH1974) £1.00
LAKESIDE FISHERY (FH2592) £2.00
LANGOLD LAKES (FH2616) £1.80
PINDERS PONDS (FH3776) £1.00
SMEATONS LAKES (FH4304) £2.00

OXFORDSHIRE

BUTLERS HILL FARM (FH0775) £2.00
COLLEGE FARM FISHING (FH1063) £2.50
GRAND UNION CANAL (FH1960) £1.50
GRAND UNION CANAL (FH1961) £1.50
LINCH HILL FISHERY (FH2725) £1.50
MILTON POOLS FARM (FH3326) £2.50
NELL BRIDGE FISHERY (FH3439) £2.50
OXFORD CANAL (FH3670) £1.00
OXFORD CANAL (FH3672) £1.50
PIMLICO FARM LAKES (FH3775) £1.00
RUSHEY WEIR (FH4062) £1.50
THAMES (RIVER) (FH4798) £1.50

SHROPSHIRE

APLEY POOLS (FH0121) £1.50
BAYLIS POOLS (FH0351) £2.00
BLUE POOL (FH0510) £1.50
COLEMERE COUNTRY PARK (FH1061) £1.00
MILLRIDE FISHERY (FH3317) £2.00

SOMERSET

AVALON FISHERIES (FH0186) £2.50
BRISTOL AVON (FH0647) £2.00
BRISTOL AVON (FH0648) £2.00
BRISTOL AVON (FH0649) £2.00
COOMBE LAKE (FH1107) £1.50
EDNEYS FISHERIES (FH1548) £2.50
FOLLY FOOT FARM (FH1755) £2.50
FROME (RIVER) (FH1811) £1.50
HORSESHOE LAKE (FH2308) £2.50
ISLE (RIVER) (FH2393) £1.00
KENN (RIVER) (FH2433) £2.50
LANGFORD LAKES (FH2612) £2.50
LOWER LOVELYNCH FISHERIES (FH3089) £2.50
PARRETT (RIVER) (FH3708) £1.50
PARRETT (RIVER) (FH3707) £1.00
PAWLETT PONDS (FH3719) £2.00
STATHE DRAIN (FH4438) £2.00
STONE YARD FISHERY (FH4470) £2.50
TONE (RIVER) (FH4869) £2.00
WYCH LODGE LAKE (FH5526) £2.00

STAFFORDSHIRE

HIMLEY HALL AND PARK LAKE (FH2230) £1.80
STAFFORD AND WORCESTER CANAL (FH4400) £1.50

SUFFOLK

ALTON WATER RESERVOIR (FH0088) £1.25
BREAKAWAY PIT (FH0609) £2.50
BROOME PITS (FH0693) £2.00
HIGHFIELD FISHERY (FH2216) £2.50
NORTH MEADOWS (FH3531) £2.00
STOUR (RIVER) (FH4501) £2.00
STOW (RIVER) (FH4508) £2.00
STOW (RIVER) (FH4509) £2.00
STOW (RIVER) (FH4510) £2.00
STOW (RIVER) (FH4511) £2.00

THET (RIVER) (FH4809) **£2.00**
WRIGHTS FARM (FH5517) **£2.00**

SURREY

SHAWFIELDS LAKES (FH4213) **£2.50**
WEY (RIVER) (FH5291) **£1.00**
WEY NAVIGATION (RIVER) (FH5292) **£1.00**
WILLINGHURST COARSE FISHERY (FH5373) **£2.00**
WILLINGHURST TROUT FISHERY (FH5374) **£2.00**

SUSSEX (EAST)

BELFREY COARSE FISHERY (FH0375) **£2.50**
BEVERN STREAM (FH0401) **£2.50**
HONEYS GREEN COARSE FISHERY (FH2286) **£2.00**
HORAM MANOR FISHERY (FH2294) **£2.00**
OLD IRON (RIVER) (FH3587) **£2.50**
OUSE (RIVER) (FH3645) **£2.50**
ROSEBANK FARM FISHERY (FH4012) **£2.00**
SCALAND WOOD (FH4110) **£2.00**

SUSSEX (WEST)

ADUR (RIVER) (FH0031) **£2.50**
PASSIES PONDS (FH3715) **£2.00**

TYNE AND WEAR

BOLAM LAKE COUNTRY PARK (FH0528) **£1.50**
LEAZES PARK LAKE (FH2655) **£2.00**
MOUNT PLEASANT LAKE (FH3387) **£1.00**
STEPHENSON LAKE (FH4450) **£1.50**
WILLOWS (THE) (FH5397) **£1.00**

WARWICKSHIRE

BISHOPS BOWL LAKES (FH0435) **£2.00**
BLACK HILL POOLS (FH0441) **£1.00**
CLIFTON LAKES FISHERY (FH1006) **£2.50**
HAWKESBURY FISHERY (FH2141) **£2.50**
KINGSTON POOLS (FH2518) **£2.00**
MONKS POOL (FH3347) **£2.50**
NAPTON RESERVOIR (FH3421) **£2.50**
NORTH OXFORD CANAL (FH3533) **£1.00**
OXFORD CANAL (FH3677) **£1.00**
WARWICKSHIRE AVON (FH5157) **£1.50**

WILTSHIRE

AVON (BRISTOL) (RIVER) (FH0199) **£2.00**
AVON (BRISTOL) (RIVER) (FH0201) **£2.00**
AVON (BRISTOL) (RIVER) (FH0194) **£2.00**
BRISTOL AVON (FH0653) **£2.00**
BURBROOKS RESERVOIR (FH0733) **£2.00**
CLIVEY PONDS (FH1011) **£2.00**
COATE WATER COUNTRY PARK (FH1046) **£2.50**
CUCKOOS REST (FH1211) **£2.50**
KENNET AND AVON CANAL (FH2460) **£1.50**
KENNET AND AVON CANAL (FH2465) **£1.50**
KENNET AND AVON CANAL (FH2461) **£2.00**
KENNET AND AVON CANAL (FH2463) **£2.00**
PEATMOOR LAGOON (FH3728) **£1.50**
PLAUMS PIT (FH3802) **£1.50**
SABRE AND SWORDS LAKES (FH4079) **£2.00**
WHITE HORSE INN LAKE (FH5334) **£2.00**

WORCESTERSHIRE

ARROW VALLEY LAKE (FH0141) **£2.10**
BRAKE MILL POOL (FH0596) **£2.50**
BROCKAMIN POOLS (FH0667) **£2.50**
EVESBATCH FISHERIES (FH1635) **£2.50**
HAYE FARM FISHERY (FH2152) **£2.00**
SION FARM FISHERIES (FH4279) **£2.00**
TWYFORD FARM POOL (FH5009) **£2.00**
WARWICKSHIRE & AVON (FH5154) **£1.50**
WARWICKSHIRE AVON (FH5158) **£2.00**
WHARFE INN POOL (FH5312) **£2.00**
WHARTONS PARK COARSE FISHING (FH5314) **£2.50**
WINDMILL LAKE (FH5409) **£2.00**
WITLEY FISHERY (FH5448) **£1.00**
WOODROW FISH POND (FH5490) **£2.00**

YORKSHIRE (NORTH)

BARLOW COMMON NATURE RESERVE (FH0311) **£2.50**
CASTLE HOWARD GREAT LAKE (FH0861) **£1.50**
CAWOOD HOLIDAY PARK (FH0877) **£2.50**
COD BECK (FH1049) **£2.00**
ELLERTON PARK (FH1568) **£2.50**
FOGGLESKYTE WATERS (FH1753) **£2.00**
HESSAY POND (FH2196) **£1.50**
HOLLINGWOOD FISHERY (FH2257) **£2.50**
HOXNE FARM PONDS (FH2322) **£2.00**
LANGTON POND (FH2618) **£2.50**
NEWBY HALL FISHERIES (FH3481) **£2.00**
PICKERING PARK FISHING LAKE (FH3766) **£1.50**
PROSPECT FARM POND (FH3852) **£2.00**
RACECOURSE LAKE (FH3871) **£2.00**
RIPON RACECOURSE LAKE (FH3959) **£2.00**
RUSWARP (RIVER) (FH4067) **£1.00**
SCARBOROUGH MERE (FH4113) **£2.00**
SELBY CANAL (FH4132) **£1.00**
SWALE (RIVER) (FH4569) **£1.50**
SWALE (RIVER) (FH4567) **£2.00**
THORNTON BRIDGE (FH4819) **£2.00**
THORPE PERROW QUARRY (FH4825) **£2.50**
TOLLERTON FISHING PONDS (FH4867) **£2.50**
WEST HADDLESEY LAKE (FH5260) **£2.00**

YORKSHIRE (SOUTH)

BRAMPTON CANAL (FH0598) **£1.25**
CHESTERFIELD CANAL (FH0931) **£1.25**
CUSWORTH HALL LAKE (FH1228) **£1.00**
DAM FLASK RESERVOIR (FH1251) **£2.00**
DELVES FISH PONDS (FH1329) **£1.00**
DON (RIVER) (FH1400) **£1.00**
DON (RIVER) (FH1401) **£1.00**
HARTHILL RESERVIORS (FH2115) **£1.50**
IDLE (RIVER) (FH2359) **£1.00**
IDLE (RIVER) (FH2360) **£1.00**
NEW JUNCTION CANAL (FH3470) **£1.00**
PEBLEY RESERVOIR (FH3729) **£1.00**
RAILWAY POND (FH3880) **£2.00**
SALLY WALSHES DAM (FH4084) **£1.25**
SOUTH YORKSHIRE NAVIGATION CANAL (FH4347) **£1.00**
SOUTHFIELD RESERVOIRS (FH4350) **£1.00**
STAINFORTH AND KEADBY CANAL (FH4409) **£1.00**
STAINFORTH AND KEADBY CANAL (FH4410) **£1.00**
STAINFORTH AND KEADBY CANAL (FH4408) **£1.20**
TINKERS PONDS (FH4854) **£1.25**
ULLEY RESERVOIR (FH5041) **£1.50**
WORSBOROUGH RESERVOIR (FH5506) **£1.25**
WORSBROUGH CANAL (FH5507) **£1.75**
WORSBROUGH RESERVOIR (FH5508) **£1.25**

YORKSHIRE (WEST)

ACKTON POND (FH0020) **£1.50**
AIRE (RIVER) (FH0043) **£1.00**
FLANSHAW DAM (FH1742) **£1.50**
HORNSEA MERE (FH2301) **£1.00**
LEEDS AND LIVERPOOL CANAL (FH2671) **£1.00**
PUGNEYS COUNTRY PARK (FH3855) **£1.00**
ROCHDALE CANAL (FH3979) **£1.50**
ROUNDHAY PARK LAKES (FH4037) **£1.00**
TONG PARK DAM (FH4872) **£2.50**
WALSDEN PRINTING CO LODGES (FH5128) **£1.50**
WHARFE (RIVER) (FH5305) **£1.00**
WHARFE (RIVER) (FH5306) **£1.00**
WHARFE (RIVER) (FH5307) **£1.00**
YEADON TARN (FH5559) **£1.50**

UNDER £5

BEDFORDSHIRE

MANOR FARM LEISURE (FH3163) **£4.50**
TINGRITH COARSE FISHERY (FH4851) **£4.00**

BERKSHIRE

FROBURY FARM SPORTING CLUB (FH1805) **£3.00**
HOLME GRANGE (FH2265) **£4.00**
KENNET AND AVON CANAL (FH2450) **£3.00**
LONGMOOR FARM FISHING LAKE (FH2993) **£4.50**

BRISTOL

BITTERWELL LAKE (FH0438) **£3.00**

BUCKINGHAMSHIRE

DOVECOTE LAKE FISHERY (FH1430) **£3.00**
GILBRATAR LAKE (FH1854) **£3.00**
GREAT OUSE (RIVER) (FH1987) **£4.50**
TINGRITH LAKES (FH4852) **£4.00**

CAMBRIDGESHIRE

DECOY LAKE (FH1295) **£3.00**
FENLAND FISHERIES (FH1696) **£4.50**
GERARDS CARP LAKE (FH1849) **£3.00**
GREAT OUSE (RIVER) (FH1991) **£3.00**
HIGH FLYER LAKE (FH2206) **£3.00**
NORTHEY PARK FISHERY (FH3543) **£3.00**
SIBSON FISHERIES (FH4264) **£4.00**
WILLOW LAKE (FH5382) **£3.00**

CHESHIRE

BLUNDELLS FARM FISHERY (FH0514) **£3.50**

BORDER FISHERIES (FH0546) £3.50
BROOKSIDE LAKES (FH0687) £3.50
CAPESTHORNE HALL STOCK POND (FH0831) £4.00
EGERTON LAKE (FH1550) £3.50
HAMPTON SPRINGS (FH2096) £3.00
MARTON HEATH COARSE POOL (FH3202) £3.00
MEADOW VIEW FISHERY (FH3225) £3.00
MILTON GREEN (FH3320) £3.00
MORETON MERE FISHERY (FH3370) £3.00
PARTRIDGE LAKES (FH3714) £4.00
WALL POOL LODGE (FH5121) £3.00
WESTLOW MERE (FH5283) £4.00

CORNWALL

ARGAL RESERVOIR (FH0134) £3.50
BOLINGEY LAKE (FH0534) £3.50
BUSSOW RESERVOIR (FH0772) £3.00
ELECTRICITY POOL (FH1560) £3.00
ELMFIELD FARM COARSE FISHERY (FH1570) £3.00
GLENLEIGH FARM FISHERY (FH1892) £3.50
GWINEAR POOLS COARSE FISHERY (FH2049) £3.00
HIDDEN VALLEY (FH2203) £3.00
LAKEVIEW COUNTRY CLUB (FH2598) £3.00
LANGARTH POOLS (FH2610) £3.00
MIDDLE BOSWIN FARM (FH3264) £3.00
PORTH RESERVOIR (FH3825) £3.50
RETALLACK WATERS (FH3931) £4.00
ROSEWATER LAKE (FH4014) £3.00
SHARKEYS PIT (FH4209) £3.00
TAMAR LAKE (UPPER) (FH4645) £3.25

COUNTY DURHAM

LANGSDALE LAKE (FH2617) £3.00

CUMBRIA

CARLETON HILL (FH0842) £4.00
ELLERBECK FARM AND FISHERY (FH1565) £4.00
KENT (RIVER) (FH2472) £3.00
LONSDALE COUNTRY PARK (FH2997) £3.00
OAKBANK LAKES (FH3560) £4.00
TRANQUIL OTTER (FH4904) £3.75
WHINS POND (FH5323) £3.50

DERBYSHIRE

BARLOW FISHERIES (FH0312) £3.00
CATTON PARK LAKE (FH0875) £3.00
HARLESTHORPE DAM (FH2107) £4.00
POSSY LODGE PONDS (FH3832) £4.00

DEVON

ALDER LAKE (FH0059) £3.00
ANGLERS ELDORADO (FH0106) £3.00
ASHCOMBE FISHERY (FH0159) £3.75
COOMBE FISHERIES (FH1106) £4.00
FISHPONDS HOUSE (FH1736) £3.00
GREENACRE TROUT LAKES (FH2004) £3.00
HARTSMOOR FISHERIES (FH2121) £3.00
JENNETTS RESERVOIR (FH2409) £3.25
LEGGE FARM COARSE FISHERY (FH2688) £3.00
LOWER HALLACOMBE FISHERY (FH3080) £3.00
LOWER SLADE RESERVOIR (FH3094) £3.50
LUCCOMBES PONDS (FH3101) £3.00
MILEMEAD FISHERIES (FH3274) £4.00
NEW BARN ANGLING CENTRE (FH3461) £3.00
OAKTREE FISHERY (FH3568) £3.00
OLDBOROUGH FISHING RETREAT (FH3604) £3.00
RIVERTON HOUSE AND LAKES (FH3970) £3.00
SHOBROOKE PARK (FH4244) £3.00
SOUTH VIEW FARM FISHERY (FH4344) £4.00
STEVENSTONE LAKES (FH4452) £3.00
SUNRIDGE FISHERY (FH4557) £3.00
TAVISTOCK TROUT FISHERY (FH4670) £3.52
TOWN PARKS COARSE FISHERY (FH4893) £4.00
TRENCHFORD RESERVOIR (FH4915) £3.50
UPHAM FARM PONDS (FH5050) £4.00
WEST PITT FARM FISHERY (FH5264) £3.50
WOODACOTT ARMS (FH5464) £3.00

DORSET

BLASHFORD LAKES (FH0493) £3.00
CHRISTCHURCH LOWER STOUR (FH0948) £3.00
CRANBOURNE FRUIT FARM (FH1163) £3.00
CULVERS FARM FISHERIES (FH1220) £3.00
MARTINS FARM (FH3201) £3.50
PALLINGTON LAKES (FH3687) £3.50
SOPLEY FARM (FH4327) £3.00
STOUR (DORSET) (RIVER) (FH4483) £3.00
TODBER MANOR (FH4862) £4.00
WHIRLWIND LAKE (FH5328) £4.00
WHITEMOOR LAKE (FH5351) £3.00

ESSEX

BLASFORD HILL FISHERIES (FH0492) £3.00
BROOKHALL FISHERY (FH0682) £3.00
CROWN NETHERHALL (FH1201) £4.00
FAIRLOP EAST LAKE (FH1653) £3.00
FAIRLOP WATERS (FH1654) £3.50
FENNES FISHERIES (FH1697) £4.00
GOSFIELD LAKE RESORT (FH1926) £3.00
MAGIC LAKE (FH3138) £4.00
MAYBRAND FISHERY (FH3214) £4.00
RAYNE LODGE FARM (FH3903) £4.00
SLOUGH HOUSE LAKE (FH4301) £4.00

GLOUCESTERSHIRE

ADLESTROP LAKE (FH0027) £4.00
BOURTON ON THE WATER GRAVEL PIT NO1 (FH0568) £4.00
HILL VIEW LAKES (FH2223) £4.00
MILESTONE FISHERY (FH3275) £3.00
RED LION FISHERY (FH3910) £3.00
STANBOROUGH POOL (FH4416) £4.00
STAUNTON COURT LAKES (FH4441) £4.00
WATERSMEET LAKES (FH5186) £3.00
WHELFORD POOLS COARSE FISHERY (FH5319) £4.00

HAMPSHIRE

BROADLANDS LAKES (FH0664) £4.00
DARK LANE PONDS (FH1274) £4.00
GOLDEN POND FISHERY (FH1912) £3.50
GREENRIDGE FARM LAKES (FH2009) £3.00
HAMPSHIRE AVON (FH2082) £3.00
HORDLE LAKES (FH2296) £3.00
HURST POND (FH2346) £3.50
LAKE FARM (FH2556) £3.00
LAKESIDE (FH2580) £3.50
LEOMINSTEAD MILL POND (FH2702) £3.00
MBK LEISURE BARRONS POND (FH3218) £4.00
MILL POND LAKE (FH3300) £3.00
SWAY LAKES (FH4605) £3.50

HEREFORDSHIRE

BIDDLESTONE LAKE (FH0408) £4.00
DOCKLOW POOLS (FH1386) £4.00
LILY AND WILLOW POOLS (FH2721) £3.00
MOCCAS FISHERY (FH3333) £3.00
MUNDERFIELD HAROLD (FH3402) £3.00
RUSSELLS END RESERVOIR (FH4065) £4.00

HERTFORDSHIRE

ALDENHAM RESERVOIR (FH0058) £3.00
BOWMANS LAKES (FH0574) £4.00
GAYWOODS (FH1845) £4.00
HOLWELL HYDE LAKE (FH2275) £3.50
OAKFIELD FISHERY (FH3561) £3.00
PIXIES MERE (FH3796) £4.00
TRING RESERVOIRS (FH4957) £3.00

HUMBERSIDE

FAR GRANGE CARAVAN AND COUNTRY PARK (FH1663) £3.00
STAR CARR TROUT FARM (FH4427) £3.50

KENT

BEWL WATER (FH0403) £4.00
BIRCHDEN FARM FISHERY (FH0426) £4.00
CACKLE HILL LAKES (FH0787) £4.00
CAPSTONE FARM COUNTRY PARK (FH0834) £3.70
COTTINGTON LAKES TROUT AND COARSE FISHERY (FH1137) £3.00
DARENTH FISHING COMPLEX (FH1273) £3.00
HARTLEY LANDS FARM (FH2118) £3.50
HOOKSTEAD LAKE (FH2290) £3.00
LAVENDER FARM (FH2631) £4.00
MEDWAY (RIVER) (FH3235) £3.00
MONK LAKE FISHERIES (FH3342) £4.00
SILVER SPRINGS FISHERY (FH4270) £4.00
SINGLETON LAKE (FH4276) £3.00
WIDEHURST FARM (FH5367) £3.00

LANCASHIRE

BRADSHAW HALL FISHERIES (FH0591) £3.00
COPTHORNE COARSE FISHERIES (FH1115) £4.00

- EDISFORD AND BRUNGERLEY PARK (FH1546) £4.00
- FIR TREE LODGE (FH1721) £3.00
- LITTLE DALE HALL COARSE FISHERY (FH2747) £3.00
- TURBARY HOUSE NURSARY (FH4974) £3.00

LEICESTERSHIRE

- C J FISHERIES (FH0786) £3.00
- LYNCHGATE LANE FISHERY (FH3119) £3.00
- WHETSTONE GORSE (FH5320) £3.00

LINCOLNSHIRE

- BELVOIR CASTLE (FH0383) £3.50
- BRICKYARD FISHERY (FH0623) £3.00
- HILL VIEW LAKES (FH2224) £3.50
- LAKE HELEN (FH2558) £3.00
- OASIS LAKES (FH3570) £3.00
- OHAM LAKES (FH3583) £3.00
- SYCAMORE FISHING LAKES (FH4618) £3.50
- VICKERS POND (FH5097) £4.00
- WILLOW LAKES (FH5384) £3.00

LINCOLNSHIRE (NORTH)

- BARTON BROADS LAKE (FH0337) £3.50
- STADDLETHORPE POND (FH4398) £3.50

LONDON (GREATER)

- COPPER MILLSTREAM (FH1111) £4.00
- HIGH MAYNARD RESERVOIR (FH2207) £4.00
- LIZARD LAKES (FH2766) £3.00
- LOW MAYNARD RESERVOIR (FH3067) £4.00
- STUDIO AND BROADWATER (FH4532) £3.00
- WALTHAMSTOW RESERVOIR (EAST WARWICK) (FH5129) £4.00
- WALTHAMSTOW RESERVOIR (NO 1) (FH5130) £4.00
- WALTHAMSTOW RESERVOIR (NO 2 AND NO 3) (FH5131) £4.00
- WILLOWSIDE CARP LAKE (FH5402) £4.00

MANCHESTER (GREATER)

- FARM LODGE (FH1669) £4.00
- PILSWORTH FISHERY COMPLEX (FH3773) £3.00

MIDLANDS (WEST)

- BLYTHE (RIVER) (FH0517) £4.00
- FOXHILLS FISHERY (FH1791) £4.00
- HOPSFORD HALL FISHERY (FH2292) £3.50
- MEADOWLANDS (FH3227) £3.50
- PACKINGTON SOMERS FISHERY (FH3679) £4.00
- PATSHULL PARK (FH3717) £3.00
- POOL HALL (FH3819) £3.00
- POOLE HALL FARM (FH3821) £3.00
- WASSELL GROVE FISHERIES (FH5167) £3.00

NORFOLK

- BARFORD LAKES FISHERY (FH0305) £4.50
- BILNEY LAKES (FH0424) £3.00
- BRIDGE INN FISHERY (FH0631) £3.00
- CUT OFF CHANNEL (FH1229) £3.50
- DENTS OF HILGAY (FH1333) £3.00
- FELTHORPE LAKE (FH1690) £3.50
- FRITTON LAKE (FH1804) £3.80
- GREAT OUSE RELIEF CHANNEL (FH1999) £3.52
- HINDERCLAY LAKES (FH2233) £3.50
- LITTLE OUSE (RIVER) (FH2757) £3.50
- MILL FARM FISHERY (FH3281) £3.00
- NARBOROUGH TROUT FARM (FH3424) £4.50
- PENTNEY LAKES (FH3742) £4.00
- REEPHAM FISHERY (FH3924) £3.50
- TASWOOD LAKES FISH FARM AND FISHERY (FH4662) £3.00
- TAVERHAM MILLS FISHERY (FH4669) £3.00
- TEN MILE BANK (FH4737) £3.50
- WALNUT FARM FISHERIES (FH5125) £4.00
- WENSUM (RIVER) (FH5245) £3.00
- WEYBREAD FISHERY (FH5293) £3.50
- WISSEY (RIVER) (FH5435) £3.50
- WOODLAKES FISHERY (FH5477) £3.00

NORTHAMPTONSHIRE

- BODDINGTON RESERVOIR (FH0521) £3.00
- CANONS ASHBY LAKES (FH0824) £3.00
- DRAYTON RESERVOIR (FH1441) £3.00
- DUSTON RESERVOIR (FH1486) £3.00
- SILVER LAKE (FH4269) £3.00
- ST JAMES SMALL PARK LAKE (FH4389) £3.00

NORTHUMBERLAND

- COQUET (RIVER) (FH1116) £3.00
- WREIGH (RIVER) (FH5516) £3.00

NOTTINGHAMSHIRE

- HALLCROFT FISHERIES (FH2070) £3.00
- MAUN (RIVER) (FH3209) £3.00
- SAPPHIRE LAKES (FH4104) £3.00
- SHERWOOD FOREST FARM PARK FISHERY (FH4234) £3.00

OXFORDSHIRE

- BARNES TROUT LAKES (FH0316) £3.00
- CHAD LAKES (FH0890) £3.00
- CLATTERCOTE RESERVOIR (FH0979) £3.00
- WINDRUSH (RIVER) (FH5410) £3.00

RUTLAND

- SWEETHEDGES FARM FISHERY (FH4607) £3.00

SHROPSHIRE

- BOLDINGS POOLS (FH0530) £3.00

SOMERSET

- BULLOCKS FARM FISHING LAKES (FH0728) £3.00
- CHEDDAR RESERVOIR (FH0909) £3.00
- DURLEIGH RESERVOIR (FH1484) £3.00
- EMERALD POOL FISHERY (FH1585) £3.00
- EXE VALLEY FISHERY (FH1645) £3.00
- PLANTATIONS LAKES (FH3798) £3.00
- SEDGES (FH4128) £4.00
- SUMMERHAYES (FH4553) £3.00
- THORNEY LAKES (FH4815) £3.00
- TUCKING MILL (FH4963) £3.00
- VIADUCT FISHERY (FH5095) £4.00

STAFFORDSHIRE

- BADEN HALL FISHERY (FH0245) £3.50
- BROWNING CUDMORE FISHERY (FH0702) £4.00
- FISHERWICK LAKES (FH1732) £4.00
- HAMSTALL FISHERY (FH2097) £4.00
- HANCHURCH FISHERIES (FH2099) £4.00
- HERONBROOK FISHERY (FH2191) £4.00
- IZAAK WALTON FISHERY (FH2404) £3.00
- PILLATON POOLS (FH3772) £4.00

SUFFOLK

- CROSS DROVE (FH1191) £4.00
- MARSH FARM LAKES (FH3191) £4.00

SURREY

- BEAVER FARM FISHERY (FH0359) £3.50
- EPSOM STEW POND (FH1604) £3.00
- GOLDSWORTH WATER PARK (FH1916) £3.00
- HENFOLD LAKES FISHERY (FH2182) £4.50
- KINGFISHER FISHERY (FH2495) £3.00
- MOLE (RIVER) (FH3338) £3.00
- RUSHMOOR LAKES (FH4063) £3.50
- TWYNERSH FISHING COMPLEX (FH5012) £4.00

SUSSEX (EAST)

- FRAMFIELD PARK FISHERIES (FH1797) £4.00
- FURNACE BROOK FISHERY (FH1820) £3.00
- IDEN WOOD FISHERY (FH2358) £4.00
- SPRING WOOD FISHERY AND FARM (FH4372) £3.00

SUSSEX (WEST)

- ADUR (RIVER) (FH0033) £3.00
- ALDERWOOD PONDS (FH0066) £3.00
- ARDINGLY RESERVOIR (FH0129) £4.00
- ARUN (RIVER) (FH0151) £3.00
- ROTHER (RIVER) (FH4028) £3.50
- STUBPOND FISHERIES (FH4531) £3.00

WARWICKSHIRE

- BANKS (THE) (FH0288) £3.00
- OAKHAM FARM POOLS (FH3562) £3.00
- RIDDINGS FISHERY (FH3949) £3.00
- TUNNEL BARN FARM (FH4972) £3.00
- WESTON LAWN FISHERIES (FH5285) £3.00

WILTSHIRE

- AVON (RIVER) (FH0218) £3.50
- ERLESTOKE LAKE (FH1612) £3.00
- IVY HOUSE FARM (FH2403) £3.00
- LONGLEAT LAKES (FH2992) £3.00
- SHEAR WATER (FH4216) £3.00
- WALDENS FARM FISHERY (FH5118) £4.00
- WITHERINGTON FARM FISHING (FH5442) £3.00
- WOODLAND PARK (FH5480) £3.00
- WYTHERINGTON FARM (FH5552) £3.00

WORCESTERSHIRE

- ABBOTS SALFORD PARK (FH0009) £3.50
- BROAD ACRES LAKE (FH0661) £3.00
- CASTLE GREEN POOLS (FH0860) £3.00
- ELMBRIDGE LAKES (FH1569) £3.00
- FURNACE MILL FISHERY (FH1822) £3.50
- LEIGH SINTON FISHING LAKES (FH2692) £3.50
- MAVER LARFORD (FH3210) £4.00
- SILLIGROVE FISHERY (FH4267) £4.00
- WILLOW FARM (FH5380) £3.00
- WILLOW MARSH (FH5386) £3.00

- WOODLAND VIEW (FH5481) **£3.00**
- WOODSTON MANOR POOLS (FH5496) **£3.00**

YORKSHIRE (NORTH)

- BRAFFERTON COARSE FISHERY (FH0593) **£3.00**
- BROKEN BREA FISHERY (FH0674) **£3.00**
- BROOKLANDS (FH0683) **£3.50**
- CARP VALE (FH0846) **£4.00**
- CORNHILL PONDS (FH1121) **£3.00**
- CRABTREE ANGLING LAKE (FH1155) **£4.00**
- KINGSLEY CARP LAKE (FH2513) **£4.00**
- MOULTON LANE POND (FH3384) **£3.00**
- MUNBY POND (FH3401) **£3.50**
- NEWHAY DAY TICKET LAKE (FH3484) **£4.00**
- OAKS FISHERY (FH3565) **£4.00**
- OAKTREE LEISURE (FH3569) **£3.00**
- PARKLANDS (FH3703) **£3.50**
- POTTERY LAKE (FH3834) **£3.00**
- RAKER LAKES (FH3884) **£4.00**
- SHIELD FISHERY (FH4235) **£3.00**
- STONEY LANE PONDS (FH4473) **£3.00**
- WESTERLY LAKE (FH5271) **£3.00**
- WOODLAND LAKES (FH5479) **£4.00**
- Y2K LAKE (FH5553) **£4.00**

YORKSHIRE (SOUTH)

- FINA HAYFIELD LAKES (FH1708) **£3.50**
- MICKS PLACE (FH3262) **£3.00**
- PRESTON INNOVATIONS SILVER FISHERY (FH3841) **£3.00**
- SCOUT DYKE RESERVOIR (FH4121) **£3.00**
- SLIVER FISHERY (FH4300) **£3.00**
- STANBOROUGH FISHERIES (FH4414) **£3.00**
- STRAIGHT MILE FISHERY (FH4517) **£3.00**

YORKSHIRE (WEST)

- BOTTOMS DAM (FH0562) **£3.50**
- MILLRACE (FH3316) **£3.00**
- NOSTELL PRIORY LAKE (FH3551) **£3.00**
- OAKS SCAR RESERVOIR (FH3566) **£3.50**
- ROWLEY DAM (FH4040) **£3.50**
- SPARTH RESERVOIR (FH4360) **£3.50**
- TP WOODS POND (FH4902) **£3.50**

UNDER £10

BERKSHIRE

- BURGHFIELD BLUE POOL (FH0740) **£6.00**
- KENNET (RIVER) (FH2438) **£6.00**
- TRI-LAKES (FH4954) **£8.00**

BUCKINGHAMSHIRE

- ALDERS FARM TROUT FISHERY (FH0062) **£5.00**
- FARLOWS LAKE (FH1668) **£5.00**
- OUSE (RIVER) (FH3642) **£5.00**

CHESHIRE

- MEADOW FISHERY (FH3222) **£5.00**

CLEVELAND

- PRIORY COTTAGE LAKE (FH3847) **£5.00**

CORNWALL

- DUTSON WATER (FH1487) **£5.00**
- FOWEY (RIVER) (FH1787) **£7.50**
- FOWEY (RIVER) (FH1785) **£7.50**
- GWARNICK MILL TROUT FISHERY (FH2040) **£5.00**
- INNY (RIVER) (FH2372) **£7.50**
- LYNHER (RIVER) (FH3124) **£7.50**
- ORVIS INNIS COUNTRY CLUB AND FLY FISHERY (FH3626) **£5.00**
- SEATON (RIVER) (FH4127) **£7.50**
- TAMAR (RIVER) (FH4641) **£5.00**
- WEST LOOE (RIVER) (FH5263) **£7.50**
- WHITEACRES COUNTRY PARK (FH5344) **£6.00**

CUMBRIA

- DOE (RIVER) (FH1390) **£5.00**
- ESTHWAITE WATER (FH1630) **£8.00**
- GRETA (RIVER) (FH2016) **£5.00**
- TWISS (RIVER) (FH5006) **£5.00**

DERBYSHIRE

- CARSINGTON WATER (FH0854) **£7.50**
- FOREMARK TROUT FISHERY (FH1764) **£9.00**
- LADYBOWER RESERVOIR (FH2549) **£6.90**
- MELBOURNE POOL (FH3243) **£5.00**

DEVON

- BELLBROOK VALLEY TROUT FISHERY (FH0377) **£5.50**
- CAMEL (RIVER) (FH0810) **£7.50**
- CLAWFORD VINEYARD AND FISHERIES (FH0985) **£5.00**
- CREEDY LAKES (FH1176) **£5.00**
- HARTLAND FOREST FISHERY GOLF CLUB (FH2116) **£5.00**
- VALLEY SPRINGS TROUT FISHERY (FH5088) **£7.00**

DORSET

- GOLD OAK FISH FARM (FH1908) **£5.00**
- HAMPSHIRE AVON (RIVER) (FH2087) **£5.00**
- ROYALTY FISHERY (FH4049) **£5.00**
- STOUR (DORSET) (RIVER) (FH4488) **£5.00**
- THROOP FISHERIES (FH4834) **£5.00**
- WINKTON FISHERY (FH5418) **£5.00**

ESSEX

- BULPHAN PARK FISHERIES (FH0730) **£5.00**
- CHIGBOROUGH FISHERIES (FH0941) **£5.00**
- CLAVERHAMBURY LAKE (FH0982) **£6.00**
- HOLYFIELD FISHERY (FH2278) **£5.00**
- LITTLE EASTON MANOR (FH2751) **£6.00**
- NEWLAND HALL CARP FISHERY (FH3487) **£5.00**
- NUPERS FARM (FH3555) **£5.00**

GLOUCESTERSHIRE

- LEMINGTON LAKES (FH2696) **£5.00**

HAMPSHIRE

- CARRON ROW FARM PONDS (FH0852) **£6.00**
- HAMPSHIRE AVON (RIVER) (FH2090) **£5.00**
- HIGHTOWN LAKE (FH2220) **£5.00**
- MOORHEN FARM TROUT LAKE (FH3361) **£9.00**
- NEW FOREST WATER PARK (FH3464) **£5.00**

HEREFORDSHIRE

- DRUMMOND DUB (FH1450) **£6.00**
- MARLIAS (RIVER) (FH3189) **£5.00**

HERTFORDSHIRE

- BIERTON FISHING LAKES (FH0410) **£5.00**

HUMBERSIDE

- BRANDES BURTON 3 AND 4 (FH0599) **£7.00**

ISLE OF WIGHT

- MORTON FARM (FH3373) **£5.00**

KENT

- FRANT LAKES (FH1798) **£5.00**
- HAWKHURST FISH FARM (FH2142) **£5.00**
- HAYES TROUT FISHERY (FH2153) **£9.00**
- LITTLE CANSIRON FISHING LAKES (FH2745) **£5.00**
- ROUKES DRIFT FARM (FH4035) **£5.00**
- TEISE (RIVER) (FH4720) **£5.00**

LANCASHIRE

- BOLTON CANAL (FH0540) **£6.50**
- DRAKESHEAD FLY FISHERY (FH1436) **£8.50**
- HOLDEN WOOD RESERVOIR (FH2250) **£7.25**
- OGDEN RESERVOIR (FH3577) **£7.25**
- THURSLAND HILL FARM (FH4838) **£5.00**
- UPPER RODDLESWORTH RESERVOIR (FH5058) **£6.00**

LEICESTERSHIRE

- EYEBROOK TROUT FISHERY (FH1649) **£6.50**
- THORNTON RESERVOIR (FH4820) **£6.00**

LINCOLNSHIRE

- LAKE ROSS FISHERY (FH2572) **£6.00**

LONDON (GREATER)

- SHEEPWALK LAKE (FH4218) **£5.00**

NORFOLK

- CATCH 22 FISHERY (FH0872) **£5.00**
- RAILWAY LAKE (FH3877) **£5.00**
- RUSTON REACHES (FH4066) **£5.00**
- WENSUM (RIVER) (FH5249) **£5.00**
- WILLSMORE WATER (FH5403) **£5.00**

NORTHAMPTONSHIRE

- ELINOR TROUT FISHERY (FH1562) **£8.00**
- FOXHOLES FISHERIES (FH1792) **£5.00**

NORTHUMBERLAND

- KIELDER WATER (FH2477) **£6.00**

OXFORDSHIRE

- HEYFORD LAKES (FH2201) **£5.00**

SHROPSHIRE

- COUND TROUT FISHERY (FH1140) **£6.00**
- DEARNFORD HALL TROUT FISHERY (FH1291) **£6.00**

SOMERSET

- BARROW RESERVOIRS (FH0329) **£6.00**
- BLAGDON LAKE (FH0487) **£7.50**
- CHEW VALLEY LAKE (FH0936) **£6.50**
- OTTERHEAD LAKES (FH3632) **£5.00**
- PAULTON LAKES (FH3718) **£5.00**

STAFFORDSHIRE

- POOL HOUSE FARM (FH3820) **£5.50**
- TITTESWORTH RESERVOIR (FH4858) **£8.00**

SURREY

- BURY HILL FISHERIES (FH0764) **£6.00**
- FURZE FARM (FH1824) **£5.00**

SUSSEX (EAST)

- BUXTED OAST FISHERY (FH0780) **£5.00**
- DARWELL WATER (FH1279) **£8.50**
- MOOR HALL POOL (FH3357) **£5.00**
- SOUTHBOURNE LAKE (FH4349) **£5.00**

SWANBOROUGH LAKES (FH4597) **£6.00**
TANYARD FISHERIES (FH4654) **£7.00**

SUSSEX (WEST)

BORDE HILL GARDEN LAKES (FH0544) **£5.00**
FURNACE LAKES (FH1821) **£5.00**
MILL FARM FISHERY (FH3283) **£5.00**
ROTHERFIELD POND (FH4030) **£5.00**
SPARKS FARM FISHERY (FH4358) **£5.00**

TYNE AND WEAR

SWEETHOPE LOUGHS (FH4608) **£6.00**

WARWICKSHIRE

MAKIN FISHERIES (FH3150) **£5.00**

WILTSHIRE

ROOD ASHTON LAKE (FH4002) **£6.00**
SILVERLANDS LAKE (FH4272) **£5.00**

WORCESTERSHIRE

LENCHES LAKES (FH2697) **£5.00**
MOORLANDS FARM (FH3363) **£5.00**
SHAKESPEARE MOORLANDS FARM (FH4203) **£5.00**

YORKSHIRE (NORTH)

BOLTON ABBEY FISHERIES (FH0539) **£5.00**
LEIGHTON RESERVOIR (FH2693) **£9.00**
SELBY 3 LAKES (FH4129) **£5.00**
TANFIELD LAKE (FH4651) **£5.00**

YORKSHIRE (SOUTH)

THRYBERGH COUNTRY PARK (FH4835) **£6.00**

YORKSHIRE (WEST)

SPRING VALLEY WATERS (FH4371) **£5.00**

UNDER £20

BERKSHIRE

FELIX FARM TROUT FISHERY (FH1684) **£13.00**
PONDWOOD CARP LAKES (FH3814) **£10.00**

CHESHIRE

WALKERWOOD TROUT FISHERY (FH5120) **£10.00**

CORNWALL

BUTTERWELL (FH0779) **£15.00**
FOWEY (RIVER) (FH1782) **£10.00**
TREE MEADOW TROUT FISHERY (FH4909) **£14.00**

COUNTY DURHAM

DERWENT RESERVOIR (FH1360) **£11.00**
WITTON CASTLE LAKES (FH5451) **£18.00**

CUMBRIA

DUBBS TROUT FISHERY (FH1458) **£10.00**
GHYLL HEAD TROUT FISHERY (FH1851) **£10.00**
HIGH NEWTON RESERVOIR (FH2209) **£10.00**
KENT (RIVER) (FH2471) **£12.00**
SPRINT (RIVER) (FH4378) **£12.00**

DERBYSHIRE

YEAVELEY ESTATE TROUT FISHERY (FH5560) **£17.00**

DEVON

DEER PARK COUNTRY HOTEL (FH1324) **£10.00**
EGGESFORD COUNTRY HOTEL WATERS (FH1551) **£10.00**
OTTER FALLS FISHERY (FH3631) **£12.00**
TORRIDGE (RIVER) (FH4883) **£15.00**

ESSEX

BLUNTS AND CANTS MERES (FH0516) **£10.00**

GLOUCESTERSHIRE

BUSHYLEAZE TROUT FISHERY (FH0770) **£12.50**
LECHLADE TROUT FISHERY (FH2656) **£18.50**

HAMPSHIRE

ROOKSBURY MILL TROUT FISHERIES (FH4007) **£14.00**
WOODMILL SALMON FISHERY (FH5488) **£17.00**

KENT

STOWTING TROUT LAKE (FH4514) **£11.00**
TENTERDEN TROUT WATERS (FH4738) **£12.00**

LANCASHIRE

BANK HOUSE FLY FISHERY (FH0286) **£11.00**
STOCKS FLY FISHERY (FH4463) **£11.00**

NORTHUMBERLAND

IRTHING (RIVER) (FH2381) **£10.00**
SOUTH TYNE (RIVER) (FH4341) **£10.00**
WANSBECK (RIVER) (FH5139) **£10.00**
WHITEADDER (RIVER) (FH5345) **£10.00**

OXFORDSHIRE

FARMOOR TROUT FISHERY (FH1676) **£10.00**
SALFORD TROUT LAKES (FH4083) **£14.00**

SOMERSET

CAMELEY TROUT LAKES (FH0812) **£10.00**
CLATWORTHY RESERVOIR (FH0981) **£10.00**
HAWKRIDGE RESERVOIR (FH2144) **£10.00**
QUANTOCK FISHERIES (FH3862) **£15.00**
SUTTON BINGHAM RESERVOIR (FH4561) **£10.00**

SUFFOLK

LARKWOOD TROUT FISHERY (FH2626) **£10.00**

SUSSEX (EAST)

POWDERMILL (GREAT SANDERS) WATER (FH3838) **£10.00**

SUSSEX (WEST)

CHALK SPRINGS TROUT FISHERY (FH0891) **£15.75**
NEWELLS SPECIMEN CARP AND COARSE FISHERIES (FH3483) **£10.00**

WARWICKSHIRE

ADAMS POOL (FH0026) **£12.00**

WILTSHIRE

LANGFORD FISHERIES (FH2611) **£19.00**

YORKSHIRE (NORTH)

NEWHAY SPECIMEN LAKE (FH3485) **£10.00**

£20 AND ABOVE

DERBYSHIRE

MONSAL DALE FISHERY (FH3352) **£25.00**

DEVON

EXE (RIVER) (FH1640) **£40.00**

HAMPSHIRE

HOLBURY LAKES (FH2247) **£29.00**
NETHER WALLOP FLY FISHING SCHOOL (FH3452) **£20.00**

LANCASHIRE

LOVECLOUGH TROUT FISHERY (FH3065) **£20.00**
TWIN LAKES TROUT FISHERY (FH5004) **£20.00**

NORTHUMBERLAND

TYNE (RIVER) (FH5027) **£25.00**

SURREY

CROSSWATER MILL FISHERY (FH1194) **£25.00**
ENTON LAKES TROUT FISHERY (FH1596) **£25.00**
FRENSHAM TROUT FISHERY (FH1800) **£25.00**

WILTSHIRE

AVON SPRINGS FISHERY (FH0229) **£20.00**

UNDER £3

COUNTY CORK

- GLENGARIFF (RIVER) (FH1890) **£2.00**

COUNTY DONEGAL

- ASSAROE LAKE (FH0174) **£1.00**

COUNTY TIPPERARY

- NORE (RIVER) (FH3523) **£1.00**
- WHITE HORSE (RIVER) (FH5332) **£1.00**

UNDER £10

COUNTY CORK

- DERRYVEGALL LAKE (FH1342) **£6.00**
- ILEN (RIVER) (FH2362) **£7.50**

COUNTY KERRY

- LOUGH BARFINNIHY (FH3010) **£6.00**
- LOUGH NAKIRKA (FH3045) **£6.00**

COUNTY MEATH

- BOYNE (RIVER) (FH0582) **£5.00**

UNDER £20

COUNTY DONEGAL

- CLOGHAN LODGE ESTATE FISHERY (FH1016) **£10.00**
- FINN (RIVER) (FH1715) **£10.00**

UNDER £3

COUNTY ANTRIM

- CLOGHWATER (RIVER) (FH1017) **£2.00**

COUNTY ARMAGH

- BANN (UPPER) (RIVER) (FH0296) **£1.50**

COUNTY DOWN

- BANN (UPPER) (RIVER) (FH0297) **£2.00**
- INLER (RIVER) (FH2368) **£2.00**
- LAGAN (RIVER) (FH2552) **£1.00**

UNDER £5

COUNTY ARMAGH

- LOUGHGALL COARSE FISHERY (FH3056) **£3.00**

UNDER £10

COUNTY ANTRIM

- SPRINGWATER MEADOW (FH4376) **£6.00**
- STRAID FISHERY (FH4516) **£6.00**

COUNTY ARMAGH

- LOWRYS LAKE (FH3097) **£8.00**
- SEAGAHAN RESERVOIR DAM (FH4125) **£8.00**
- SHAWS LAKE (FH4215) **£8.00**
- TULLNAWOOD LAKE (FH4966) **£8.00**

COUNTY DOWN

- RINGDUFFERIN ESTUARY (FH3951) **£5.00**

COUNTY FERMANAGH

- COOLYERMER LOUGH FISHERY (FH1103) **£5.00**

COUNTY LONDONDERRY

- CREGGAN RESERVOIRS (FH1178) **£5.00**
- FAUGHAN (RIVER) (FH1678) **£5.00**

COUNTY TYRONE

- DUNGANNON PARK FISHERY (FH1475) **£6.50**
- FINN (RIVER) (FH1716) **£5.00**

UNDER £20

COUNTY DOWN

- CLANRYE (RIVER) (FH0972) **£10.00**
- MCCOURTS LAKE (FH3220) **£10.00**

COUNTY LONDONDERRY

- FAUGHAN (RIVER) (FH1679) **£10.00**

UNDER £1

PERTH AND KINROSS

- ALMOND (RIVER) (FH0084) £0.50
- LOWER SCONE BEAT (FH3093) £0.50

UNDER £3

ANGUS

- DEAN (RIVER) (FH1285) £1.00
- ISLA (RIVER) (FH2387) £1.00

ARGYLL AND BUTE

- CLYDE ESTUARY (FH1040) £2.50
- FRUIN (RIVER) (FH1817) £2.50
- LOCH AVICH (FH2847) £2.00
- LOCH AWE (FH2848) £2.00
- MILL HOUSE FISHERIES (FH3286) £1.00

AYRSHIRE (SOUTH)

- LOCH MAYBERRY (FH2911) £2.50

DUMFRIES AND GALLOWAY

- CLATTERINGSHAWS LOCH (FH0980) £1.00
- CRAIGHLAW (FH1159) £2.00
- DORMONT LAKE COARSE FISHERY (FH1415) £2.00
- EARLSTOUN LOCH (FH1502) £2.50
- GALLOWAY FOREST PARK (FH1829) £1.50
- KEN (RIVER) (FH2429) £1.00
- NEW ABBEY DOW (FH3460) £2.00
- TONGUE OF BOMBIE LOCHAN (FH4873) £2.00

HIGHLAND

- GLENCOE LOCHAN (FH1886) £2.50

INVERCLYDE

- LOCH THOM (FH2952) £2.00

PERTH AND KINROSS

- ABERFELDY ASSOCIATION BEAT (FH0014) £2.50
- ALMOND (RIVER) (FH0083) £1.00
- AMULREE BEAT (FH0103) £1.00
- BRAAN (RIVER) (FH0584) £2.00
- CLOCHFOLDICH BEAT (FH1013) £2.50
- DERCULICH BEAT (FH1335) £2.50
- FINDYNATE BEAT (FH1710) £2.50
- LOCH EIGHEACH (FH2876) £1.50
- LOCH FREUCHIE (FH2884) £1.00
- NEWTON OF LOGIERAIT BEAT (FH3496) £1.00
- PITCASTLE BEAT (FH3790) £2.50
- RUMBLING BRIDGE (FH4055) £1.00
- TAY (RIVER) (FH4678) £2.00
- TROCHRY BEAT (FH4958) £2.00
- UPPER BORLICK BEAT (FH5051) £1.50
- UPPER KINNAIRD BEAT (FH5054) £1.00
- WEEM BEAT (FH5226) £2.50

SCOTTISH BORDERS

- ST MARYS LOCH (FH4393) £2.50

STIRLING

- BORELAND (FH0550) £2.50
- CRAIGNAVIE (FH1161) £2.50
- DOCHART (RIVER) (FH1382) £2.50
- DOCHART (RIVER) (FH1384) £2.50
- ENDRICK (RIVER) (FH1592) £2.50
- FINLARIG (FH1714) £2.50
- KILLIN BREADALBANE ANGLING CLUB WATERS (FH2483) £2.50
- LOCH LOMOND (FH2904) £2.50
- LOCHAN NA LARAIG (FH2960) £2.50
- LOCHAY (RIVER) (FH2963) £2.50

YORKSHIRE (SOUTH)

- TORNE (RIVER) (FH4881) £1.00

UNDER £5

ABERDEENSHIRE

- MILL OF ELRICK FISHERY (FH3296) £3.00

ARGYLL AND BUTE

- FINNART (RIVER) (FH1718) £3.00

HIGHLAND

- LOCH GARRY (FH2885) £3.00
- LOCH INCH LAGGAN (FH2893) £3.00
- LOCH POULARY (FH2935) £3.00
- LOCH QUOICH (FH2937) £3.00
- STRATHMANAIRD LOCHS (FH4520) £3.00

LANARKSHIRE (NORTH)

- LILY LOCH (FH2722) £3.00

SCOTTISH BORDERS

- TWEED (RIVER) (FH4999) £4.00

STIRLING

- LESKINE (FH2706) £4.00
- PORTNELLAN (FH3830) £3.00

WESTERN ISLES

- CEANN-AN-ORA FISHERY (FH0878) £4.00

YORKSHIRE (SOUTH)

- BANK END COARSE FISHERIES (FH0285) £3.00
- HAYFIELD LAKES (FH2155) £3.50
- LINDHOLME LEISURE LAKES FISHERIES (1) (FH2729) £3.00
- LINDHOLME LEISURE LAKES FISHERIES (2) (FH2730) £3.00
- LINDHOLME LEISURE LAKES FISHERIES (4) (FH2732) £3.00

UNDER £10

ABERDEENSHIRE

- LOCH INSCH FISHERY (FH2894) £7.00

ANGUS

- KINGENNIE FISHINGS (FH2494) £6.00

ARGYLL AND BUTE

- DUNOON RESERVOIR (FH1478) £5.50
- LOCH FAD (FH2879) £6.00

AYRSHIRE (SOUTH)

- CRAITH RESERVOIR (FH1162) £5.00
- LOCH DORNAL (FH2872) £6.00

DUMFRIES AND GALLOWAY

- BUITTLE RESERVOIR (FH0723) £7.00
- DINDINNIE RESERVOIR (FH1371) £7.50
- FYNTALLOCH LOCH (FH1826) £5.00
- KIRRIEREOCH LOCH (FH2528) £5.00
- KNOCKQUASSEN RESERVOIR (FH2541) £5.00
- LOCH WHINYEON (FH2958) £5.00
- LOCHENBRECK LOCH (FH2964) £5.00
- NAHINE LOCH (FH3411) £5.00
- OCHILTREE LOCH (FH3573) £5.00
- URR (RIVER) (FH5076) £8.00
- WEE GLEN AMOUR LOCH (FH5223) £5.00

FIFE

- CRAIGLUSCAR RESERVOIR (FH1160) £5.00
- NEWTON FARM FISHERY (FH3494) £7.00

GLASGOW (CITY OF)

- NEILSTON TROUT FISHERY (FH3438) £7.50

HIGHLAND

- LOCH INSH (FH2895) £6.50
- NAIRN (RIVER) (FH3412) £6.50
- NESS (RIVER) (FH3450) £5.00
- SPEY (RIVER) (FH4364) £6.50

LANARKSHIRE (NORTH)

- HILLEND LOCH (FH2226) £5.00

LANARKSHIRE (SOUTH)

- AVON (RIVER) (FH0207) £5.00

LOTHIAN (EAST)

- MARKLE FISHERIES (FH3186) £5.00

LOTHIAN (WEST)

- ALLANDALE TARN (FH0076) £9.00

PERTH AND KINROSS

- HEATHERYFORD FISHERY (FH2174) £8.00
- SANDYKNOWES FISHING (FH4099) £8.00

RENFREWSHIRE

- HOWWOOD TROUT FISHERY (FH2321) £7.00

SCOTTISH BORDERS

- ACREKNOWE RESERVOIR (FH0024) £7.00
- AKERMOOR LOCH (FH0049) £7.00
- HELLMOOR LOCH (FH2178) £7.00
- WATCH RESERVOIR (FH5168) £8.00
- WULLIESTRUTHER LOCH (FH5522) £7.00

UNDER £20

ABERDEENSHIRE

- YTHAN VALLEY FISHERY (FH5576) £10.00

ARGYLL AND BUTE

- INVERAWE FISHERIES (FH2374) £13.50

AYRSHIRE (NORTH)

- MIDDLETON FISHERY (FH3268) £13.50

AYRSHIRE (SOUTH)

- SPRINGWATER FISHERY (FH4374) £12.00

DUMFRIES AND GALLOWAY

- ANNAN (RIVER) (FH0113) £10.00
- TORHOUSEKIE AND KIRWAUGH (FH4879) £15.00

FIFE

- RAITH LAKE FISHERY (FH3882) £12.00

INVERCLYDE

- ARDGOWAN TROUT FISHERY (FH0128) £12.00

LOTHIAN (MID)

- LOGANLEA TROUT FISHERY (FH2980) £10.00

LOTHIAN (WEST)

- PARKLEY FISHERY (FH3705) £12.00

PERTH AND KINROSS

- LOWER ABERUTHVEN FISHINGS (FH3070) £10.00
- ORCHILL LOCH TROUT FISHERY (FH3619) £12.00

WESTERN ISLES

- LACASDALE LOCHS (FH2548) £15.00

UNDER £3

CAERPHILLY

- OGILVIE LAKE (FH3578) £2.00

CARMARTHENSHIRE

- COWIN (RIVER) (FH1151) £1.00
- CYNIN (RIVER) (FH1241) £1.00
- PEWI FACH (RIVER) (FH3763) £1.00
- TAF (RIVER) (FH4628) £1.00
- TAF (RIVER) (FH4627) £2.00

FLINTSHIRE

- BUCKLEY TRAP POOL (FH0718) £2.00
- CLAWDD OFFAS DYKE (FH0984) £2.00

GLAMORGAN (VALE OF)

- PENYWERN PONDS (FH3750) £1.30

ISLE OF ANGLESEY

- BREAKWATER PARK (FH0610) £2.00
- LLYN DEWI (FH2809) £2.00
- LLYN NANT ANOG (FH2817) £2.00
- LLYN TACAN (FH2822) £2.00

MONMOUTHSHIRE

- CWMCELYN POND (FH1237) £1.50
- FIVE TREES (FH1740) £2.50

PEMBROKESHIRE

- WEST ATHESTON COARSE FISHERY (FH5256) £2.00

POWYS

- LLYN-COCH HWYAD (FH2825) £2.00
- TWYMYN (RIVER) (FH5011) £2.00

SWANSEA

- FENDROD LAKE (FH1694) £2.20

TORFAEN

- CWMBRAN BOATING LAKE (FH1236) £1.75

WREXHAM

- TAN LLAN (FH4649) £1.00

UNDER £5

CAERPHILLY

- RIVERSIDE TROUT FISHERY (FH3969) £3.50

CARDIFF

- TAFF (RIVER) (FH4631) £4.00

CARMARTHENSHIRE

- GLAS-LLYN FISHERY (FH1870) £3.50
- LLYN CARFAN (FH2798) £3.00
- LOUGHOR VALLEY FISHERY (FH3059) £4.50
- SPRINGWATER LAKES (FH4375) £3.00

CEREDIGION

- LLANARTH FISHERY (FH2768) £3.00
- NINE OAKS (FH3509) £3.00

CONWY

- CONWY VALLEY FISHERIES (FH1099) £4.00
- GILER ARMS LAKE (FH1855) £3.00
- LLYN ALED (FH2791) £3.00

GWYNEDD

- AFON LLYFNI (RIVER) (FH0037) £4.00
- EDEN (RIVER) (FH1538) £4.00
- FFESTINIOG FISHERY (FH1702) £3.00
- TRAWFFYNYDD RESERVOIR (FH4905) £4.00

PEMBROKESHIRE

- LLYS Y FRAN RESERVOIR AND COUNTRY PARK (FH2829) £4.50
- LUDCHURCH LAKE (FH3103) £3.00
- ROADSIDE FARM (FH3974) £3.00

POWYS

- CLYNWEDOG RESERVOIR (FH1041) £4.00
- DULAS (RIVER) (FH1468) £4.00
- ELAN (RIVER) (FH1557) £3.00
- GWYDDIOR LAKE (FH2053) £4.00
- SEVERN (RIVER) (FH4153) £4.00
- WESTLAKE FISHERY (FH5282) £3.00
- WYE (RIVER) (FH5542) £3.00

RHONDDA CYNON TAFF

- LLYN ALAW (FH2790) £4.50

SWANSEA

- GOWERTON COARSE FISHERY (FH1929) £3.00
- WHITE SPRINGS LAKES (FH5341) £4.00

UNDER £10

CARMARTHENSHIRE

- TEIFI (RIVER) (FH4705) £8.50
- TOWY (RIVER) (FH4900) £5.00
- TOWY (RIVER) (FH4895) £5.50
- TOWY (RIVER) (FH4898) £5.00

CEREDIGION

- YSTWYTH (RIVER) (FH5574) £6.00

CONWY

- LLYN CRAFNANT FISHERIES (FH2803) £6.00
- TYDDYN MAWR TROUT FARM (FH5015) £6.00

DENBIGHSHIRE

- ALWEN (RIVER) (FH0092) £7.50
- DEE (RIVER) (FH1309) £8.00
- LLYN BRENIG (FH2795) £5.00

FLINTSHIRE

- GYRN CASTLE FISHERY (FH2056) £7.00

GLAMORGAN (VALE OF)

- MELLTE (STREAM) (FH3251) £5.00
- TAFF BARGOED (FH4633) £6.00

GWYNEDD

- AFON SEIONT (RIVER) (FH0038) £7.00
- CREGENNAN LAKES (FH1177) £8.00
- CWM SILYN LAKE (FH1235) £7.00
- DWYTHWCH LAKE (FH1492) £7.00
- DYWARCHEN RESERVOIR (FH1498) £7.00
- ERCH (RIVER) (FH1605) £6.00
- GWYRFAI (RIVER) (FH2055) £7.00
- LLYN CWELLYN RESERVOIR (FH2804) £7.00
- LLYN PADARN (FH2821) £7.00
- NANTLLE LAKE (FH3419) £7.00
- OGWEN (RIVER) (FH3582) £5.00
- RHYDHIR (RIVER) (FH3939) £6.00

NEATH PORT TALBOT

- EGLWYS NUNYDD RESERVOIR (FH1553) £5.00
- HEPSTE (STREAM) (FH2188) £5.00
- NEATH (RIVER) (FH3434) £5.00

NEWPORT

- YNYS-Y-FRO RESERVOIR (FH5571) £8.50

PEMBROKESHIRE

- IAN HEAPS PREMIER FISHERIES AND SCHOOL OF ANGLING (FH2356) £5.00
- ROSEBUSH RESERVOIR (FH4013) £6.50

POWYS

- LLYN ALARCH (FH2789) £8.00
- WYE (RIVER) (FH5538) £5.00

SWANSEA

- TAWE (RIVER) (FH4675) £7.00

TORFAEN

- LISVANE RESERVOIR (FH2738) £9.50
- LLANISHEN RESERVOIR (FH2774) £9.50
- LLYN ON RESERVOIR (FH2820) £6.50

WREXHAM

- LLANDEGLA TROUT FISHERY (FH2770) £8.00

UNDER £20

CEREDIGION

- RHEIDOL (RIVER) (FH3935) £10.00

GWYNEDD

- LLYN CYNWCH LAKE (FH2807) £14.00
- MAWDDACH AND WNION (RIVERS) (FH3213) £14.00
- TALYLLYN LAKE (FH4640) £10.00

ISLE OF ANGLESEY

- LLYN ALAN (FH2788) £10.50

SWANSEA

- SHIMANO FELINDRE TROUT FISHERY (FH4239) £17.50
- TAWE (RIVER) (FH4676) £13.00

Free Fishing Available

SECTION 10

This section allows you to search for Fisheries which can offer Free Fishing. This is also indicated in Section 1 with a £Fr symbol.

Once you have located a Fishery you can either look up further details in Section 1 or use the other sections to find what else the Fishery may have to offer.

ENGLAND

BEDFORDSHIRE
- MANOR FARM LEISURE (FH3163)

BERKSHIRE
- ASHRIDGE MANOR (FH0169)
- LODDON (RIVER) (FH2977)
- THAMES (RIVER) (FH4761)

BRISTOL
- AVON (BRISTOL) (RIVER) (FH0191)

BUCKINGHAMSHIRE
- BLACK PARK (FH0447)
- COMMON POND (FH1083)
- THAMES (RIVER) (FH4778)

CAMBRIDGESHIRE
- BARNWELL COUNTRY PARK (FH0320)
- CAM (RIVER) (FH0807)
- FIELDS END WATER (FH1704)
- GREAT OUSE (RIVER) (FH1990)
- HATTON PARK POND (FH2133)
- OUNDLE (RIVER) (FH3637)
- PISCES CARAVAN PARK AND FISHERY (FH3789)
- SILVER STREET MILL (FH4271)

CHESHIRE
- BOUNDARY WATER PARK (FH0566)
- BRIDGEWATER CANAL (FH0634)
- GOWY FISHERY (FH1932)
- TAX MERE (FH4677)

CLEVELAND
- HUTTON RUDBY PONDS (FH2351)

CORNWALL
- FORDA HOLIDAY LODGES (FH1761)
- FOWEY (RIVER) (FH1783)
- GWARNICK MILL TROUT FISHERY (FH2040)
- MILLBROOK COARSE FISHERY (FH3305)
- TREVELLA CARAVAN AND CAMPING PARK (FH4950)

COUNTY DURHAM
- TEES (RIVER) (FH4693)
- TEES (RIVER) (FH4692)
- TEES (RIVER) (FH4691)
- TEES (RIVER) (FH4686)
- TEES (RIVER) (FH4685)
- TRIMDON POND (FH4955)
- WEAR (RIVER) (FH5208)

CUMBRIA
- AIRA BECK (FH0041)
- BLENHEIM LODGE HOTEL (FH0498)
- CODALE TARN (FH1050)
- EASEDALE TARN (FH1505)
- HAWESWATER (FH2139)
- KENT (RIVER) (FH2471)
- LONSDALE COUNTRY PARK (FH2997)
- SPRINT (RIVER) (FH4378)
- THIRLMERE (FH4810)
- ULLSWATER LAKE (FH5042)

DERBYSHIRE
- BARLOW FISHERIES (FH0312)
- DERWENT (RIVER) (FH1346)
- TRENT (RIVER) (FH4917)

DEVON
- AVON DAM (FH0227)
- LUCCOMBES PONDS (FH3101)
- MELDON RESERVOIR (FH3246)
- STAFFORD MOOR FISHERY (FH4402)
- VENFORD RESERVOIR (FH5091)
- WILLOWFIELD LAKE COTTAGES (FH5393)
- WISCOMBE FISHERY (FH5433)

DORSET
- FROME (RIVER) (FH1809)
- HAMWORTHY LAKE (FH2098)
- NEW MEADOWS LAKE (FH3473)
- PALLINGTON LAKES (FH3687)
- STOUR (DORSET) (RIVER) (FH4481)
- STOUR (RIVER) (FH4491)

ESSEX
- GLOUCESTER PARK LAKE (FH1900)
- WANSTEAD AND WOODFORD PONDS (FH5144)
- WARREN (FH5150)

FIFE
- EMBER (RIVER) (FH1580)

HAMPSHIRE
- HAMPSHIRE AVON (RIVER) (FH2092)
- JANESMOOR POND (FH2406)

HEREFORDSHIRE
- GOLDEN VALLEY (FH1914)
- HERRIOTS POOL (FH2194)

HERTFORDSHIRE
- GADE (RIVER) (FH1827)

HUMBERSIDE
- DERWENT (RIVER) (FH1351)
- ESK (RIVER) (FH1622)
- HULL (RIVER) (FH2330)
- HULL (RIVER) (FH2331)
- HULL (RIVER) (FH2332)

KENT
- BEWL WATER (FH0403)
- EAST FARLEIGH (FH1509)
- MEDWAY (RIVER) (FH3230)
- MEDWAY (RIVER) (FH3232)

LANCASHIRE
- BANK HOUSE FLY FISHERY (FH0286)
- GRIZEDALE LEA RESERVOIR (FH2026)
- JUMBLES RESERVOIR (FH2418)
- STANLEY PARK LAKE (FH4420)

LEICESTERSHIRE
- SOAR (RIVER) (FH4319)

LINCOLNSHIRE
- HOBHOLE DRAIN (FH2238)
- TRENT (RIVER) (FH4922)
- WELLAND (RIVER) (FH5233)
- WEST FEN DRAIN (FH5259)
- WILLOW BANK FISHERY (FH5377)
- WITHAM (RIVER) (FH5439)

LONDON (GREATER)
- ALEXANDRA PARK LAKE (FH0073)
- ASHVALE FISHERIES (FH0172)
- CLAPHAM COMMON POND (FH0973)
- HAMPSTEAD HEATH (FH2094)
- HEATH VALE POND (FH2172)
- HIGHGATE PONDS (FH2217)
- TEDDINGTON LOCK (FH4682)
- THAMES (RIVER) (FH4789)
- VALE OF HEATH POND (FH5083)

MANCHESTER (GREATER)
- CRIME LAKE (FH1180)
- LANKYS MILL POND (FH2619)
- STONEY PIT RESERVOIR (FH4474)
- TANNERS DAM (FH4653)

MERSEYSIDE
- GREENBANK PARK LAKE (FH2005)
- PRINCES PARK LAKE (FH3846)
- STANLEY PARK LAKE (FH4421)
- WALTON HALL PARK (FH5135)

MIDLANDS (WEST)
- GREY MILL FARM (FH2017)
- KINGSBURY WATER PARK (FH2510)
- PATSHULL PARK (FH3717)
- SEVERN (RIVER) (FH4149)

NORFOLK
- ACLE (RIVER) (FH0022)
- BRIDGE INN FISHERY (FH0631)
- BURE (RIVER) (FH0735)
- CANTLEY (RIVER) (FH0827)
- DRAYTON GREEN (RIVER) (FH1440)
- HAVERINGLAND HALL PARK (FH2138)
- HORNING (RIVER) (FH2299)
- RUSTON REACHES (FH4066)
- STOKESBY (RIVER) (FH4465)
- SWANTON MORLEY FISHERY (FH4602)
- TAVERHAM MILLS FISHERY (FH4669)
- WENSUM (RIVER) (FH5246)
- WENSUM (RIVER) (FH5250)
- WENSUM (RIVER) (FH5247)
- YARE (RIVER) (FH5556)

NORTHUMBERLAND
- NORTH TYNE (RIVER) (FH3539)
- TWEED (RIVER) (FH4990)
- TYNE (RIVER) (FH5022)

SHROPSHIRE
- SEVERN (RIVER) (FH4169)
- SEVERN (RIVER) (FH4170)
- TERN (RIVER) (FH4741)
- TERN FISHERIES (FH4743)
- VOWNOG FISH LAKE (FH5101)

SOMERSET
- HUNTSPILL (RIVER) (FH2343)
- TUCKING MILL (FH4963)

STAFFORDSHIRE
- SMITH POOL (FH4305)

SUFFOLK
- ALDE (RIVER) (FH0056)
- BECCLES QUAY (FH0360)
- HOMERSFIELD (RIVER) (FH2283)
- OULTON BROAD (FH3634)

SURREY
- ONE ISLAND POND (FH3612)
- PAINSHILL PARK LAKE (FH3685)
- SEVEN ISLANDS (FH4140)
- THAMES (RIVER) (FH4804)
- WHIPLEY MANOR (FH5325)

SUSSEX (EAST)
- CLIVE VALE RESERVOIRS (FH1010)

SUSSEX (WEST)
- BOLEBROOK CASTLE (FH0531)
- PILTDOWN POND (FH3774)
- STUBPOND FISHERIES (FH4531)

TYNE AND WEAR
- TEES (RIVER) (FH4699)
- WHITTLE DENE TROUT FISHERY (FH5360)

WARWICKSHIRE
- AVON (RIVER) (FH0214)
- AVON (RIVER) (FH0213)

WORCESTERSHIRE
- HUXLEYS HAMPTON FERRY FISHERIES (FH2352)
- SEVERN (RIVER) (FH4188)
- SEVERN (RIVER) (FH4191)
- SEVERN (RIVER) (FH4192)
- SEVERN (RIVER) (FH4195)

YORKSHIRE (NORTH)
- BLEA TARN (FH0494)
- CHAPMANS POND (FH0897)
- CORNHILL PONDS (FH1121)
- DERWENT (RIVER) (FH1359)
- ESK (RIVER) (FH1626)
- ESK (RIVER) (FH1623)
- ESK (RIVER) (FH1624)
- FOSS (RIVER) (FH1775)

- LOW OSGOODBY LAKE (FH3068)
- OUSE (RIVER) (FH3654)

YORKSHIRE (SOUTH)

- CROOKES VALLEY PARK LAKE (FH1189)
- DEARNE VALLEY PARK LAKE (FH1290)
- DON (RIVER) (FH1402)
- IDLE (RIVER) (FH2360)
- IDLE (RIVER) (FH2361)

IRELAND

COUNTY CORK

- BALLINCOLLIG RESERVOIR (FH0265)
- CAHA (RIVER) (FH0791)
- CHAPEL LAKE (FH0894)
- CURRAGHALICKEY LAKE (FH1225)
- LOUGH ATARRIFF (FH3004)
- LOUGH BALLYNACARRIGA (FH3009)
- LOUGH COOLKEELURE (FH3020)
- LOUGH CULLENAGH (FH3024)

COUNTY GALWAY

- LOUGH CORRIB (FH3021)

COUNTY KILDARE

- GRAND CANAL (FH1939)
- GRAND CANAL (FH1938)
- GRAND CANAL (BARROW TRACK) (FH1942)

COUNTY KILKENNY

- BALLINAKILL LAKE (FH0262)

COUNTY LAOIS

- GRANSTOWN LAKE (FH1972)

COUNTY TIPPERARY

- LINGAUN (RIVER) (FH2734)

NORTHERN IRELAND

COUNTY ANTRIM

- CAREY (RIVER) (FH0839)
- GLENSHESK (RIVER) (FH1895)
- MARGEY (RIVER) (FH3179)

COUNTY TYRONE

- BALLYGAWLEY (RIVER) (FH0274)
- OONA RIVER (FH3614)

SCOTLAND

ANGUS

- CLATIO LOCH (FH0978)

DUMFRIES AND GALLOWAY

- ANNAN (RIVER) (FH0113)

EDINBURGH (CITY OF)

- DUDDINGSTON LOCH (FH1459)

FIFE

- KINGHORN LOCH (FH2503)

GLASGOW (CITY OF)

- BALGRAVE RESERVOIR (FH0257)
- FORTH AND CLYDE CANAL (FH1772)

HIGHLAND

- SCOURIE HOTEL (FH4120)

PERTH AND KINROSS

- LOCH EIGHEACH (FH2876)
- LOCH LEVEN FISHERIES (FH2902)

STIRLING

- AUCHESSON BEAT (FH0184)
- DOCHART (RIVER) (FH1383)
- KINNEL (FH2521)
- LOCH TAY HIGHLAND LODGES (FH2951)
- LOCH VOIL (FH2956)
- LOCHAY (RIVER) (FH2962)

WALES

BRIDGEND

- GARW (RIVER) (FH1841)
- OGMORE (RIVER) (FH3580)

CEREDIGION

- RHEIDOL (RIVER) (FH3935)

CONWY

- CONWY VALLEY FISHERIES (FH1099)

DENBIGHSHIRE

- DEE (RIVER) (FH1310)

GWYNEDD

- MAWDDACH (RIVER) (FH3212)

POWYS

- CAER BERIS MANOR HOTEL (FH0789)
- DOL LLYS FARM (FH1394)
- LLANGORSE LAKE (FH2773)
- NEW INN (FH3467)

RHONDDA CYNON TAFF

- LLYN ALAW (FH2790)

WREXHAM

- ARGAE LAKE (FH0133)

Fish Species Available

SECTION 11

This section allows you to see what species are present within a particular fishery, so that you know where to fish for your chosen quarry, coarse or game.

e.g Fisheries containing Carp

Once you have located a Fishery you can either look up further details in Section 1 or use the other sections to find what else the Fishery may have to offer.

Fish Species Available at UK & Irish Fisheries

ENGLAND

BEDFORDSHIRE

Fishery	Barbel	Bleak	Bream	Carp Blue	Carp Common	Carp Crucian	Carp Ghost	Carp Grass	Carp Koi	Carp Leather	Carp Mirror	Carp Silver	Carp Wild	Catfish	Catfish Albino	Catfish American Bullhead	Catfish Black Bullhead	Charr	Chub	Dace	Eel
ARLESEY LAKE (FH0136)			●		●						●			●							●
BECKERINGS RESERVOIR (FH0361)			●		●						●										
BRIARWOOD FISHERY (FH0619)			●		●						●										
BROGBOROUGH NO.1 PIT (FH0672)			●		●						●										
BROOM (FH0688)					●						●										
CLAYDON LAKE (FH0990)			●		●						●			●							
ELSTOW PITS (FH1573)			●		●						●										●
FELMERSHAM GRAVEL PITS (FH1688)					●						●										
GREAT OUSE (RIVER) (FH1985)	●																		●	●	
GREAT OUSE (RIVER) (FH1986)	●																				
HAROLD FISHERY (FH2109)	●				●						●			●					●	●	
HENLOW GRANGE (FH2185)					●						●										
HOUGHTON REGIS QUARRY (FH2316)			●		●						●										
IVEL (RIVER) (FH2401)																			●	●	
IVEL (RIVER) (FH2402)			●		●						●			●					●	●	
JONES PIT (FH2416)			●		●						●			●	●						
LEDBURN ROAD (FH2659)			●		●						●			●							
LITTLE HEATH FARM (FH2753)																					
MANOR FARM LEISURE (FH3163)	●		●		●		●				●								●		
MARSTON PITS (FH3196)			●		●						●								●		
OUSE (RIVER) (FH3639)			●																●	●	
OUSE (RIVER) (FH3638)	●	●	●																●	●	
PRIORY COUNTRY PARK (FH3848)	●	●	●		●	●				●	●			●					●	●	●
RACKLEY HILLS PIT (FH3873)						●								●							
RADWELL COMPLEX (FH3876)					●						●										
SOUTH LAGOON (FH4333)			●		●						●										
STANFORD PIT (FH4417)					●						●										
TIDDENFOOT PIT (FH4840)					●									●							
TINGRITH COARSE FISHERY (FH4851)					●	●	●				●								●		
TINGRITH MANOR LAKE (FH4853)														●							
VAUXHALL PIT (FH5090)					●						●			●							

Fishery	Flounder	Goldfish	Grayling	Grilse	Gudgeon	Gwyniad	Minnow	Orfe	Orfe Blue	Orfe Golden	Perch	Pike	Roach	Rudd	Ruffe	Salmon	Steelhead	Sturgeon	Tench	Tench Golden	Trount American Brook	Trout Blue	Trout Brook	Trout Brown	Trout Golden	Trout Lake	Ttrout Rainbow	Trout Sea	Trout Tiger	Trout Wild	Vendace	Zander
ARLESEY LAKE (FH0136)											●	●	●						●													
BECKERINGS RESERVOIR (FH0361)																																
BRIARWOOD FISHERY (FH0619)											●	●	●	●					●													
BROGBOROUGH NO.1 PIT (FH0672)												●																				
BROOM (FH0688)																																
CLAYDON LAKE (FH0990)												●	●	●																		●
ELSTOW PITS (FH1573)											●		●	●					●													
FELMERSHAM GRAVEL PITS (FH1688)																																
GREAT OUSE (RIVER) (FH1985)													●																			
GREAT OUSE (RIVER) (FH1986)																																
HAROLD FISHERY (FH2109)												●	●																			
HENLOW GRANGE (FH2185)																																
HOUGHTON REGIS QUARRY (FH2316)												●	●						●													
IVEL (RIVER) (FH2401)													●																			
IVEL (RIVER) (FH2402)											●	●	●																			
JONES PIT (FH2416)											●	●	●	●					●													
LEDBURN ROAD (FH2659)											●		●	●					●													
LITTLE HEATH FARM (FH2753)																								●			●					
MANOR FARM LEISURE (FH3163)					●		●				●	●	●	●					●					●			●					
MARSTON PITS (FH3196)											●	●							●													
OUSE (RIVER) (FH3639)											●		●						●													
OUSE (RIVER) (FH3638)					●						●	●	●						●													
PRIORY COUNTRY PARK (FH3848)					●						●	●	●	●	●				●													●
RACKLEY HILLS PIT (FH3873)																																
RADWELL COMPLEX (FH3876)																																
SOUTH LAGOON (FH4333)											●	●	●	●					●													●
STANFORD PIT (FH4417)																																
TIDDENFOOT PIT (FH4840)											●	●	●																			
TINGRITH COARSE FISHERY (FH4851)													●	●					●													
TINGRITH MANOR LAKE (FH4853)											●	●		●																		
VAUXHALL PIT (FH5090)											●	●	●						●													

Fish Species Available at UK & Irish Fisheries

	Barbel	Bleak	Bream	Carp Blue	Carp Common	Carp Crucian	Carp Ghost	Carp Grass	Carp Koi	Carp Leather	Carp Mirror	Carp Silver	Carp Wild	Catfish	Catfish Albino	Catfish American Bullhead	Catfish Black Bullhead	Charr	Chub	Dace	Eel	Flounder	Goldfish	Grayling	Grilse	Gudgeon	Gwyniad	Minnow	Orfe	Orfe Blue	Orfe Golden	Perch	Pike	Roach	Rudd	Ruffe	Salmon	Steelhead	Sturgeon	Tench	Tench Golden	Trount American Brook	Trout Blue	Trout Brook	Trout Brown	Trout Golden	Trout Lake	Ttrout Rainbow	Trout Sea	Trout Tiger	Trout Wild	Vendace	Zander
WATER END FISHERY (FH5170)			●			●													●	●									●					●	●					●													
WILLINGTON LAKE (FH5375)					●						●																																										
WITHY POOL (FH5446)					●						●			●																																							
WOBURN SANDS (FH5455)			●		●						●			●																			●	●	●					●													
BERKSHIRE																																																					
ALBERT BRIDGE (FH0050)			●																●																																		
ALDERMASTON (FH0061)					●						●																																										
AMERDEN POOL (FH0100)			●		●						●																					●	●	●	●					●													
ASHRIDGE MANOR (FH0169)					●				●		●			●																																							
BARTON COURT FISHERY (FH0338)			●																●	●				●		●		●				●	●	●											●								
BENS LAKE (FH0385)			●		●						●															●								●	●					●													
BISHOPS GREEN FARM LAKE (FH0436)			●		●	●					●															●								●						●													
BRAY LOCK (FH0607)			●		●														●	●	●					●						●	●	●			●								●								
BURGHFIELD (FH0739)	●		●		●						●								●		●			●								●	●	●						●													
BURGHFIELD BLUE POOL (FH0740)			●		●						●																					●		●						●													
BURGHFIELD CANAL (FH0741)			●																●													●	●							●													
BURGHFIELD MATCH LAKE (FH0742)					●	●					●								●													●			●					●													
CHURCH FARM (FH0950)			●		●														●													●	●	●	●					●													
COTTAGE LANE (FH1134)			●		●						●																								●					●													
COURT FARM (FH1141)					●						●																							●	●					●													
DINTON PASTURES COUNTRY PARK (FH1375)	●		●								●								●		●											●	●	●						●								●					
EAST TOWNEY (FH1514)			●		●						●								●	●												●	●	●						●													
ENGLEFIELD LAGOON (FH1594)			●		●						●																					●	●	●						●													
FARLEYMOOR LAKE (FH1667)					●						●																					●	●	●						●													
FARNHAM FLINT (FH1677)			●		●						●																					●	●	●						●													
FELIX FARM TROUT FISHERY (FH1684)																																													●			●					
FROBURY FARM SPORTING CLUB (FH1805)					●	●		●			●																					●			●					●								●					
FROXFIELD A AND B (FH1815)			●		●						●								●													●	●	●						●													
HAMBRIDGE LANE (FH2079)			●		●	●					●																					●								●													
HOLME GRANGE (FH2265)					●						●								●															●						●													
HOLYBROOK (FH2277)	●		●																●	●												●	●	●																			
JINGLES FARM (FH2412)					●						●																		●						●					●													
KENNET (RIVER) (FH2441)	●		●																●	●													●	●																			
KENNET (RIVER) (FH2435)	●																		●													●		●																			

Fish Species Available at UK & Irish Fisheries

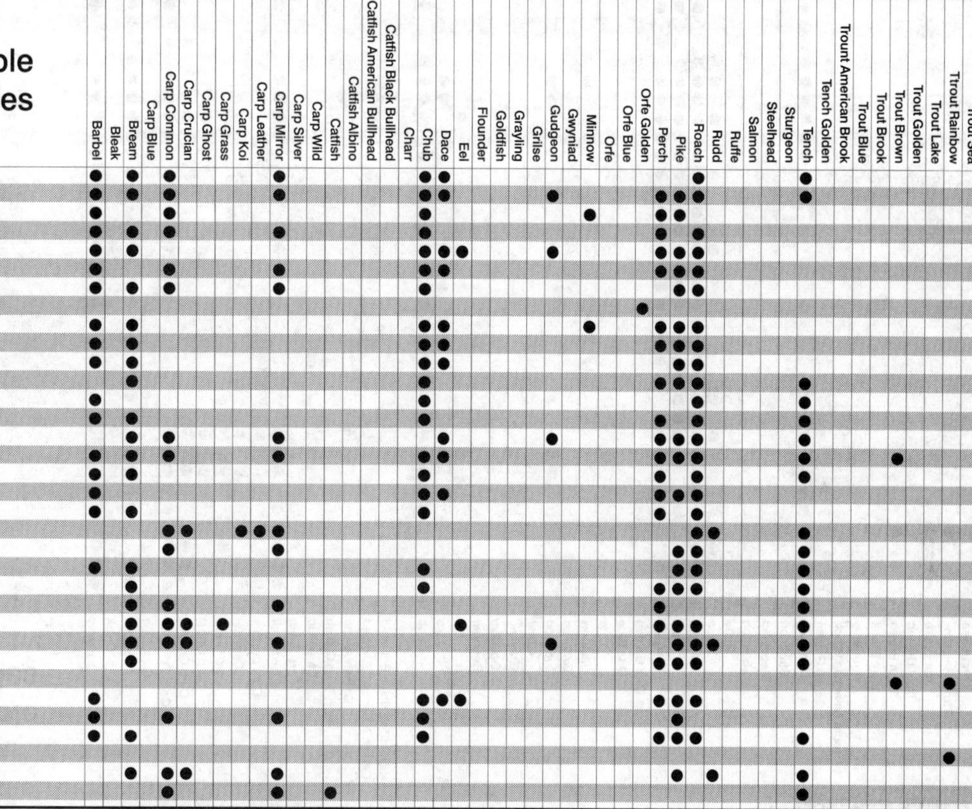

Fishery	Barbel	Bleak	Bream	Carp Blue	Carp Common	Carp Crucian	Carp Ghost	Carp Grass	Carp Koi	Carp Leather	Carp Mirror	Carp Silver	Carp Wild	Catfish	Catfish Albino	Catfish American Bullhead	Catfish Black Bullhead	Charr	Chub	Dace	Eel	Flounder	Goldfish	Grayling	Grilse	Gudgeon	Gwyniad
KENNET (RIVER) (FH2442)	●		●		●						●								●	●							
KENNET (RIVER) (FH2437)	●		●		●						●								●	●						●	
KENNET (RIVER) (FH2438)	●				●														●								
KENNET (RIVER) (FH2440)	●		●		●						●								●								
KENNET (RIVER) (FH2436)	●		●																●	●	●					●	
KENNET (RIVER) (FH2448)	●				●						●								●	●							
KENNET (RIVER) (FH2444)	●		●		●						●								●								
KENNET (RIVER) (FH2439)																											
KENNET (RIVER) (FH2445)	●		●																●	●							
KENNET (RIVER) (FH2443)	●		●																●	●							
KENNET (RIVER) (FH2446)	●		●																●	●							
KENNET AND AVON CANAL (FH2455)			●																●								
KENNET AND AVON CANAL (FH2451)	●																		●								
KENNET AND AVON CANAL (FH2452)	●		●																●								
KENNET AND AVON CANAL (FH2449)			●		●						●									●						●	
KENNET AND AVON CANAL (FH2450)	●		●		●						●								●	●							
KENNET AND AVON CANAL (FH2454)	●		●																●								
KENNET AND ENTORNE (RIVERS) (FH2468)	●																		●	●							
LODDON (RIVER) (FH2977)	●		●																●								
LONGMOOR FARM FISHING LAKE (FH2993)					●	●			●	●	●																
LONGMOOR LAKE (FH2994)					●						●																
LOWER BENYONS (FH3073)	●		●																●								
MAPLEDURHAM A AND B (FH3172)			●																●								
MATCH AND BLUE POOLS (FH3207)			●		●						●																
MILL LANE (FH3290)			●		●	●		●													●						
MILL POND (FH3298)			●		●	●					●															●	
MOATLANDS POOL (FH3331)			●																								
NEWBURY TROUT LAKES (FH3480)																											
OLD MILL (FH3592)	●																		●	●	●						
PADWORTH MILL (FH2447)	●				●						●								●								
PADWORTH ROTA (FH2453)	●		●																●								
PANG VALLEY TROUT LAKE (FH3688)																											
PINGEWOOD LAGOON (FH3783)			●		●	●					●																
PONDWOOD CARP LAKES (FH3814)					●						●			●													

Fishery	Minnow	Orfe	Orfe Blue	Orfe Golden	Perch	Pike	Roach	Rudd	Ruffe	Salmon	Steelhead	Sturgeon	Tench	Tench Golden	Trount American Brook	Trout Blue	Trout Brook	Trout Brown	Trout Golden	Trout Lake	Ttrout Rainbow	Trout Sea	Trout Tiger	Trout Wild	Vendace	Zander
KENNET (RIVER) (FH2442)							●						●													
KENNET (RIVER) (FH2437)					●	●	●						●													
KENNET (RIVER) (FH2438)	●				●	●																				
KENNET (RIVER) (FH2440)					●		●																			
KENNET (RIVER) (FH2436)					●	●	●																			
KENNET (RIVER) (FH2448)					●	●	●																			
KENNET (RIVER) (FH2444)						●	●																			
KENNET (RIVER) (FH2439)				●																						
KENNET (RIVER) (FH2445)	●				●	●	●																			
KENNET (RIVER) (FH2443)					●	●	●																			
KENNET (RIVER) (FH2446)						●	●																			
KENNET AND AVON CANAL (FH2455)					●	●	●						●													
KENNET AND AVON CANAL (FH2451)							●						●													
KENNET AND AVON CANAL (FH2452)					●		●						●													
KENNET AND AVON CANAL (FH2449)					●	●	●						●													
KENNET AND AVON CANAL (FH2450)					●	●	●						●					●								
KENNET AND AVON CANAL (FH2454)					●		●						●													
KENNET AND ENTORNE (RIVERS) (FH2468)					●	●	●																			
LODDON (RIVER) (FH2977)					●		●																			
LONGMOOR FARM FISHING LAKE (FH2993)							●	●					●													
LONGMOOR LAKE (FH2994)						●	●						●													
LOWER BENYONS (FH3073)						●	●						●													
MAPLEDURHAM A AND B (FH3172)					●	●	●						●													
MATCH AND BLUE POOLS (FH3207)					●								●													
MILL LANE (FH3290)					●	●	●						●													
MILL POND (FH3298)						●	●	●					●													
MOATLANDS POOL (FH3331)					●	●	●						●													
NEWBURY TROUT LAKES (FH3480)																		●			●					
OLD MILL (FH3592)					●	●	●																			
PADWORTH MILL (FH2447)						●																				
PADWORTH ROTA (FH2453)					●	●	●						●													
PANG VALLEY TROUT LAKE (FH3688)																					●					
PINGEWOOD LAGOON (FH3783)						●		●					●													
PONDWOOD CARP LAKES (FH3814)													●													

Fish Species Available at UK & Irish Fisheries

Fishery	Barbel	Bleak	Bream	Carp Blue	Carp Common	Carp Crucian	Carp Ghost	Carp Grass	Carp Koi	Carp Leather	Carp Mirror	Carp Silver	Carp Wild	Catfish	Catfish Albino	Catfish American Bullhead	Catfish Black Bullhead	Charr	Chub	Dace	Eel	Flounder	Goldfish	Grayling	Grilse	Gudgeon	Gwyniad	Minnow	Orfe	Orfe Blue	Orfe Golden	Perch	Pike	Roach	Rudd	Ruffe	Salmon	Steelhead	Sturgeon	Tench	Tench Golden	Trount American Brook	Trout Blue	Trout Brook	Trout Brown	Trout Golden	Trout Lake	Ttrout Rainbow	Trout Sea	Trout Tiger	Trout Wild	Vendace	Zander
PURLEY (FH3858)			●																●													●	●	●						●													
ROMNEY ISLAND AND MEADOW (FH4001)	●		●		●						●								●																		●																
ROYAL BERKSHIRE FISHERY (FH4042)	●		●		●	●					●								●													●		●						●													
SAVERNAKE POND (FH4108)					●	●		●			●																							●	●																		
SHEEPHOUSE FARM TROUT FISHERY (FH4217)																																													●			●					
SONNING EYE (FH4326)	●		●		●						●								●													●	●	●						●													
SOUTH FIELD PARK (FH4329)			●		●	●																										●		●						●													
SOUTH HILL PARK LAKE (FH4331)			●		●	●	●		●		●								●							●						●		●	●					●													
ST PATRICKS (FH4395)	●		●		●						●								●	●	●					●						●		●																			
SWAN VALLEY (FH4596)					●		●		●	●	●								●	●												●	●	●	●					●													
THAMES (RIVER) (FH4764)			●																●													●	●																				
THAMES (RIVER) (FH4761)			●																●														●	●																			
THAMES (RIVER) (FH4771)			●																●													●	●	●																			
THAMES (RIVER) (FH4776)	●																		●													●	●	●																			
THAMES (RIVER) (FH4766)			●																●													●	●																				
THAMES (RIVER) (FH4772)			●																●	●												●		●																			
THAMES (RIVER) (FH4763)	●		●																●													●	●	●						●													
THAMES (RIVER) (FH4760)	●		●																●	●	●											●	●	●																			
THAMES (RIVER) (FH4768)	●																		●													●	●	●																			
THAMES (RIVER) (FH4769)	●	●	●		●						●									●						●							●	●	●																		
THAMES (RIVER) (FH4773)	●																		●													●	●	●																			
THAMES (RIVER) (FH4774)	●																		●													●	●	●																			
THAMES (RIVER) (FH4770)			●																															●																			
THEALE (FH4806)			●																													●	●	●	●					●													
THEALE CANAL (FH4807)	●		●																●													●	●	●						●													
THEALE LAGOON (FH4808)			●		●						●																					●	●							●													
TRI-LAKES (FH4954)			●		●	●	●				●										●											●	●	●	●					●													
TWYFORD BBONT (FH5008)	●		●		●						●								●	●						●						●	●	●						●													
TWYFORD WATERS (FH5010)	●		●		●						●								●	●						●		●				●	●	●	●					●													
UFTON CANAL (FH5039)			●																●														●	●						●													
WASING WOODS (FH5165)					●	●					●																													●													
WELLINGTON COUNTRY PARK (FH5241)			●																														●							●													
WHITE SWAN LAKE (FH5343)	●		●		●						●								●													●	●	●						●													
WYLIES LAKE (FH5546)			●																													●			●					●													

Fish Species Available at UK & Irish Fisheries

Fishery	Barbel	Bleak	Bream	Carp Blue	Carp Common	Carp Crucian	Carp Ghost	Carp Grass	Carp Koi	Carp Leather	Carp Mirror	Carp Silver	Carp Wild	Catfish	Catfish Albino	Catfish American Bullhead	Catfish Black Bullhead	Charr	Chub	Dace	Eel	Flounder	Goldfish	Grayling	Grilse	Gudgeon	Gwyniad	Minnow	Orfe	Orfe Blue	Orfe Golden	Perch	Pike	Roach	Rudd	Ruffe	Salmon	Steelhead	Sturgeon	Tench	Tench Golden	Trount American Brook	Trout Blue	Trout Brook	Trout Brown	Trout Golden	Trout Lake	Ttrout Rainbow	Trout Sea	Trout Tiger	Trout Wild	Vendace	Zander
BRISTOL																																																					
AVON (BRISTOL) (RIVER) (FH0192)			●																●		●													●																			
AVON (BRISTOL) (RIVER) (FH0191)			●		●						●								●	●	●											●		●						●													
AVON (RIVER) (FH0202)																			●	●	●											●		●																			
BAGWOOD LAKE (FH0249)					●						●																																										
BITTERWELL LAKE (FH0438)			●		●	●					●										●											●		●	●					●													
BRISTOL AVON (FH0646)	●		●								●								●	●												●		●																			
BRISTOL DOCKS (FH0655)			●		●						●										●											●	●																				
FISHPONDS LIDO (FH1737)											●																							●	●																		
FROME (RIVER) (FH1807)			●		●						●								●													●	●																				
HENLEAZE LAKE (FH2184)					●	●					●																					●	●	●						●													
SEVINGTON LAKES FISHERY (FH4199)					●	●					●																													●													
WEST COUNTRY WATER PARK (FH5257)					●						●																																										
BUCKINGHAMSHIRE																																																					
ALDERS FARM TROUT FISHERY (FH0062)					●						●																								●										●		●	●					
BACKWATER (FH0242)			●		●	●					●																					●		●	●					●													
BEDFORD BOATING LAKE (FH0364)					●						●																																										
BILLET LANE (FH0417)			●																●													●		●	●					●													
BLACK PARK (FH0447)			●		●						●																						●																				
BOURTON FISHERIES (FH0567)			●																●	●												●	●	●																			
CALVES LANE LAKE (FH0804)																																●	●	●						●													
CHESS (RIVER) (FH0927)																								●																													
CHESS (RIVER) (FH0928)																																													●			●					
CHURCH HILL FISHERY (FH0953)																																													●		●	●					
CLAYDON LAKE (FH0991)			●											●																																							●
COLNBROOK WEST (FH1068)			●		●						●																						●	●	●					●													
COLNEBROOK (RIVER) (FH1076)	●		●																●	●	●					●		●				●	●	●						●													
COMMON POND (FH1083)					●						●																							●						●													
CRAYFISH POOL (FH1171)					●						●																																										
DOVECOTE LAKE FISHERY (FH1430)	●	●	●		●	●		●			●								●	●						●						●	●	●		●			●	●													
FARLOWS LAKE (FH1668)			●		●	●					●																					●	●	●	●					●													
FURZTON LAKE (FH1825)																																●			●					●													
GALLOWS POOL (FH1830)			●			●													●	●						●						●		●	●					●					●								
GILBRATAR LAKE (FH1854)					●						●								●	●												●		●						●													

Fish Species Available at UK & Irish Fisheries

Species	GREAT LINFORD LAKES (FH1982)	GREAT OUSE (RIVER) (FH1988)	GREAT OUSE (RIVER) (FH1987)	HARROLD ODELL COUNTRY PARK (FH2110)	HILL WOOD POND (FH2225)	HORTON BOAT POOL (FH2310)	HORTON CHURCH LAKE (FH2311)	HYDE LANE LAKES (FH2354)	KEMPSTONE HARDWICK (FH2428)	KINGFISHER GOLF CLUB (FH2496)	KINGSMEAD 1 (FH2514)	KINGSMEAD ISLAND LAKE (FH2516)	LATIMER PARK FLY FISHERY (FH2628)	LODGE LAKES (FH2978)	LOUGHTON LODGE LAKE (FH3063)	MAYFIELDS LAKE (FH3216)	NEWPORT PAGNELL GRAVEL PITS (FH3490)	OLD SLADE LANE LAKE (FH3599)	ORLITTS LAKES (FH3622)	OUSE (RIVER) (FH3642)	OUSE (RIVER) (FH3640)	SHELSWELL LAKE (FH4228)	SILVERWING LAKE (FH4273)	SNOWBERRY (FH4313)	SPADE OAK LAKE (FH4357)	TEARDROP LAKES (FH4680)	THAME (RIVER) (FH4753)	THAMES (RIVER) (FH4777)	THAMES (RIVER) (FH4780)	THAMES (RIVER) (FH4781)	THAMES (RIVER) (FH4782)	TINGRITH LAKES (FH4852)	TYRINGHAM ESTATE (FH5037)	VICARAGE SPINNEY FISHERY (FH5096)
Zander																								●										
Vendace																																		
Trout Wild																																		
Trout Tiger																																		
Trout Sea																																		
Ttrout Rainbow													●																					●
Trout Lake																																		
Trout Golden																																		
Trout Brown		●											●							●														●
Trout Brook																																		
Trout Blue																																		
Trount American Brook																																		
Tench Golden																																		
Tench	●		●	●	●	●	●		●	●	●			●	●	●	●	●	●	●		●	●	●	●	●						●	●	
Sturgeon						●																												
Steelhead																																		
Salmon																																		
Ruffe																				●														
Rudd				●	●									●		●		●		●					●							●		
Roach		●	●	●					●	●	●	●		●	●	●	●	●		●		●	●	●	●	●	●	●	●	●	●	●	●	
Pike		●	●	●			●		●	●	●	●				●	●	●	●	●		●	●		●			●	●	●	●	●	●	
Perch	●	●	●	●		●			●	●	●	●		●		●	●	●	●	●		●	●		●		●	●	●	●	●	●	●	
Orfe Golden							●																											
Orfe Blue																																		
Orfe																																●		
Minnow																				●			●											
Gwyniad																																		
Gudgeon																				●			●					●	●	●	●	●		
Grilse																																		
Grayling																																		
Goldfish																																		
Flounder																																		
Eel						●					●									●			●							●				
Dace		●																●		●			●					●	●	●	●			
Chub	●	●	●															●		●			●			●	●	●	●	●	●	●	●	
Charr																																		
Catfish Black Bullhead																																		
Catfish American Bullhead																																		
Catfish Albino																																		
Catfish	●					●		●								●										●								
Carp Wild																																		
Carp Silver																																		
Carp Mirror	●		●			●	●	●		●	●	●		●		●	●	●	●		●		●	●	●	●			●	●	●	●		
Carp Leather														●																		●		
Carp Koi	●																																	
Carp Grass						●	●				●																							
Carp Ghost																																●		
Carp Crucian					●									●	●									●								●		
Carp Common	●		●			●	●	●		●	●	●		●		●	●	●	●	●	●		●	●	●	●			●	●	●	●		
Carp Blue																																		
Bream	●	●	●	●	●	●	●		●	●	●	●		●	●	●	●	●	●	●	●		●	●	●	●		●	●	●	●	●	●	
Bleak																		●		●					●									
Barbel		●																		●	●		●					●		●			●	

Fish Species Available at UK & Irish Fisheries

	Barbel	Bleak	Bream	Carp Blue	Carp Common	Carp Crucian	Carp Ghost	Carp Grass	Carp Koi	Carp Leather	Carp Mirror	Carp Silver	Carp Wild	Catfish	Catfish Albino	Catfish American Bullhead	Catfish Black Bullhead	Charr	Chub	Dace	Eel	Flounder	Goldfish	Grayling	Grilse	Gudgeon	Gwyniad	Minnow	Orfe	Orfe Blue	Orfe Golden	Perch	Pike	Roach	Rudd	Ruffe	Salmon	Steelhead	Sturgeon	Tench	Tench Golden	Trount American Brook	Trout Blue	Trout Brook	Trout Brown	Trout Golden	Trout Lake	Ttrout Rainbow	Trout Sea	Trout Tiger	Trout Wild	Vendace	Zander
WATTS POOL (FH5189)	●		●		●						●								●	●	●					●		●				●	●	●						●													
WESTFIELD FARM (FH5276)			●		●	●					●								●	●			●									●	●	●						●													
WESTHORPE PARK LAKE (FH5281)					●						●																					●	●	●	●					●													
WESTON TERVELL RESERVOIR (FH5286)					●						●																																										
WOLVERTON LAKES (FH5456)						●																										●		●						●													
CAMBRIDGESHIRE																																																					
BARNWELL COUNTRY PARK (FH0320)		●	●		●	●					●								●	●	●					●						●	●	●	●					●													
BARNWELL PIT (FH0321)			●			●								●							●					●						●		●	●					●													
BARWAY LAKE (FH0339)						●						●																						●						●													
BLOCK FEN COMPLEX (FH0503)			●		●						●																							●	●																		
BLUEBELL LAKE (FH0513)		●	●		●	●	●	●	●	●	●			●					●	●	●			●		●		●	●			●	●	●	●	●				●													
BRACKHILL LAKE (FH0586)			●		●						●																					●		●	●					●													
BURNSIDE LAKE (FH0750)			●		●						●								●													●	●	●	●																		
BURWELL LODE (FH0763)			●																													●	●	●	●					●													
CAM (RIVER) (FH0807)			●								●								●	●	●											●	●	●	●					●													
CAM (RIVER) (FH0805)		●	●																●	●	●											●	●	●	●	●				●													
CHAWSTON LAKES (FH0908)			●		●						●								●														●	●																			
CLEARWATERS COARSE FISHERY (FH0999)					●						●																													●													
COTTERSTOCK RIVER (FH1136)			●																●	●												●	●	●						●													
DECOY LAKE (FH1295)					●						●																																										
DICKERSONS PIT (FH1366)					●						●																						●		●					●													
EARITH FISHERY (FH1501)					●						●								●													●	●	●	●					●							●						
EAST DELPH LAKES (FH1507)			●		●						●																							●	●					●													
ELDERNELL LAKE (FH1559)			●		●						●																							●	●					●													
FEN DRAYTON COMPLEX (FH1692)					●						●																																										●
FEN DRAYTON LAKE (FH1693)					●						●																																										
FENLAND FISHERIES (FH1696)	●		●		●	●		●			●																							●	●					●													
FERRY MEADOWS (FH1701)		●	●		●						●								●	●	●					●						●	●	●	●					●													●
FIELDS END WATER (FH1704)					●						●																					●		●						●													
GERARDS CARP LAKE (FH1849)					●						●																																										
GODMANCHESTER (RIVER) (FH1905)			●		●						●								●															●																			
GRAFHAM WATER (FH1934)																																													●			●					
GREAT OUSE (RIVER) (FH1991)		●	●		●															●	●					●						●	●	●	●	●				●									●				●
GREAT OUSE (RIVER) (FH1992)			●																		●											●	●	●																			●

Fish Species Available at UK & Irish Fisheries

Fishery	Barbel	Bleak	Bream	Carp Blue	Carp Common	Carp Crucian	Carp Ghost	Carp Grass	Carp Koi	Carp Leather	Carp Mirror	Carp Silver	Carp Wild	Catfish	Catfish Albino	Catfish American Bullhead	Catfish Black Bullhead	Charr
GREAT OUSE (RIVER) (FH1994)			●															
GREAT OUSE (RIVER) (FH1993)		●	●															
GREAT OUSE (RIVER) (FH1996)	●	●	●		●	●		●			●			●				
GREAT OUSE (RIVER) (FH1995)			●		●						●							
GUNWADE LAKE (FH2039)			●															
HATTON PARK POND (FH2133)					●						●							
HIGH FLYER LAKE (FH2206)					●	●					●							
HINCHINGBROOKE COUNTRY PARK (FH2232)			●		●						●							
HOLME FEN FISHING (FH2264)			●		●	●					●							
HUNTINGDON (RIVER) (FH2340)			●															
KINGSLAND RESERVOIRS (FH2512)					●	●	●				●							
LARK (RIVER) (FH2622)			●															
LEES BROOK (FH2685)			●		●						●							
LILY PARK LAKES (FH2723)			●		●						●							
LITTLE PAXTON FISHERY (FH2759)					●						●							
LONG REACH (FH2984)					●						●							
MAGPIE LAKE (FH3139)			●		●													
MEPAL PIT (FH3256)					●						●							
MIDDLE LEVEL DRAIN (FH3266)			●															
MILTON COUNTRY PARK (FH3318)					●					●	●							
MILTON PITS (FH3324)					●						●							
NENE (RIVER) (FH3440)			●		●						●							
NENE (RIVER) (FH3441)		●	●		●						●							
NENE (RIVER) (FH3442)																		
NENE (RIVER) (FH3446)											●							
NENE (RIVER) (FH3444)			●															
NENE NORTH BANK (RIVER) (FH3449)		●	●		●						●							
NORTH BANK TROUT FISHERY (FH3526)																		
NORTH HOUSE LAKE (FH3529)			●		●	●					●							
NORTHEY PARK FISHERY (FH3543)	●		●		●						●			●				
OFFORD CLUNY (FH3574)	●		●		●						●			●				
OFFORD WEIRPOOL (FH3575)			●		●						●							
OLD NENE (RIVER) (FH3597)			●															
OLD WEST (RIVER) (FH3601)			●															

Fishery	Chub	Dace	Eel	Flounder	Goldfish	Grayling	Grilse	Gudgeon	Gwyniad	Minnow	Orfe	Orfe Blue	Orfe Golden	Perch	Pike	Roach	Rudd	Ruffe
GREAT OUSE (RIVER) (FH1994)	●														●			
GREAT OUSE (RIVER) (FH1993)	●	●	●											●	●	●		
GREAT OUSE (RIVER) (FH1996)	●	●	●					●						●	●	●	●	●
GREAT OUSE (RIVER) (FH1995)	●														●	●		
GUNWADE LAKE (FH2039)														●		●		
HATTON PARK POND (FH2133)																	●	
HIGH FLYER LAKE (FH2206)																●	●	
HINCHINGBROOKE COUNTRY PARK (FH2232)	●		●											●	●	●		
HOLME FEN FISHING (FH2264)																●	●	
HUNTINGDON (RIVER) (FH2340)	●															●		
KINGSLAND RESERVOIRS (FH2512)					●											●	●	
LARK (RIVER) (FH2622)			●											●	●	●		
LEES BROOK (FH2685)	●	●						●						●		●		
LILY PARK LAKES (FH2723)															●		●	
LITTLE PAXTON FISHERY (FH2759)																		
LONG REACH (FH2984)																		
MAGPIE LAKE (FH3139)											●			●		●	●	
MEPAL PIT (FH3256)															●	●	●	
MIDDLE LEVEL DRAIN (FH3266)														●	●	●	●	
MILTON COUNTRY PARK (FH3318)			●											●	●	●	●	
MILTON PITS (FH3324)																		
NENE (RIVER) (FH3440)	●		●					●						●	●	●		
NENE (RIVER) (FH3441)	●	●	●					●						●	●	●		●
NENE (RIVER) (FH3442)	●															●		
NENE (RIVER) (FH3446)	●		●			●										●		
NENE (RIVER) (FH3444)																●		
NENE NORTH BANK (RIVER) (FH3449)	●		●					●						●	●	●	●	
NORTH BANK TROUT FISHERY (FH3526)																		
NORTH HOUSE LAKE (FH3529)																	●	
NORTHEY PARK FISHERY (FH3543)	●															●	●	
OFFORD CLUNY (FH3574)	●															●		
OFFORD WEIRPOOL (FH3575)	●														●	●		
OLD NENE (RIVER) (FH3597)														●	●	●		
OLD WEST (RIVER) (FH3601)			●											●			●	

Fishery	Salmon	Steelhead	Sturgeon	Tench	Tench Golden	Trount American Brook	Trout Blue	Trout Brook	Trout Brown	Trout Golden	Trout Lake	Ttrout Rainbow	Trout Sea	Trout Tiger	Trout Wild	Vendace	Zander
GREAT OUSE (RIVER) (FH1994)				●													
GREAT OUSE (RIVER) (FH1993)				●													●
GREAT OUSE (RIVER) (FH1996)				●					●								●
GREAT OUSE (RIVER) (FH1995)																	
GUNWADE LAKE (FH2039)																	●
HATTON PARK POND (FH2133)				●													
HIGH FLYER LAKE (FH2206)																	
HINCHINGBROOKE COUNTRY PARK (FH2232)				●													
HOLME FEN FISHING (FH2264)				●													
HUNTINGDON (RIVER) (FH2340)				●													
KINGSLAND RESERVOIRS (FH2512)				●													
LARK (RIVER) (FH2622)				●													●
LEES BROOK (FH2685)																	
LILY PARK LAKES (FH2723)				●													
LITTLE PAXTON FISHERY (FH2759)																	
LONG REACH (FH2984)																	
MAGPIE LAKE (FH3139)																	
MEPAL PIT (FH3256)				●													●
MIDDLE LEVEL DRAIN (FH3266)				●													●
MILTON COUNTRY PARK (FH3318)				●													
MILTON PITS (FH3324)																	
NENE (RIVER) (FH3440)				●													
NENE (RIVER) (FH3441)				●													
NENE (RIVER) (FH3442)																	
NENE (RIVER) (FH3446)				●													
NENE (RIVER) (FH3444)																	
NENE NORTH BANK (RIVER) (FH3449)				●													●
NORTH BANK TROUT FISHERY (FH3526)									●			●					
NORTH HOUSE LAKE (FH3529)				●													
NORTHEY PARK FISHERY (FH3543)				●													
OFFORD CLUNY (FH3574)				●													
OFFORD WEIRPOOL (FH3575)																	
OLD NENE (RIVER) (FH3597)				●													●
OLD WEST (RIVER) (FH3601)																	

Fish Species Available at UK & Irish Fisheries

	Barbel	Bleak	Bream	Carp Blue	Carp Common	Carp Crucian	Carp Ghost	Carp Grass	Carp Koi	Carp Leather	Carp Mirror	Carp Silver	Carp Wild	Catfish	Catfish Albino	Catfish American Bullhead	Catfish Black Bullhead	Charr	Chub	Dace	Eel	Flounder	Goldfish	Grayling	Grilse	Gudgeon	Gwyniad	Minnow	Orfe	Orfe Blue	Orfe Golden	Perch	Pike	Roach	Rudd	Ruffe	Salmon	Steelhead	Sturgeon	Tench	Tench Golden	Trount American Brook	Trout Blue	Trout Brook	Trout Brown	Trout Golden	Trout Lake	Ttrout Rainbow	Trout Sea	Trout Tiger	Trout Wild	Vendace	Zander
OUNDLE (RIVER) (FH3637)			●		●						●									●														●						●													
OVER MAIN DRAIN (FH3659)																																●	●		●					●													
PAXTON LAKE (FH3720)			●		●						●								●															●						●													
PERIO MILL (FH3753)																																													●								
PISCES FISHERY (FH3789)			●		●	●					●										●											●	●	●	●					●													
RANDALLS LAKE (FH3887)			●		●	●					●								●		●												●	●	●					●													●
RAVELEY DRAIN (FH3893)			●																														●	●						●													●
REDLANDS PITS (FH3920)																																			●					●													
ROSWELL PITS (FH4022)			●		●						●																					●	●	●	●					●													●
SIBSON FISHERIES (FH4264)					●						●								●													●	●	●	●					●													
SILVER STREET MILL (FH4271)					●						●								●	●														●																			
SOHAM BY-PASS LAKE (FH4320)					●	●					●																								●																		
SPORTSMANS PIT (FH4366)					●						●																					●	●	●	●					●													
ST IVES COMPLEX (FH4387)	●		●		●						●								●	●						●						●	●	●	●					●													
STEW POND (FH4453)					●						●																																										
STRETHAM LAKE (FH4524)			●		●																●											●	●	●	●					●													●
TURKS HEAD LAKE (FH4977)			●		●	●					●										●													●	●					●													
VIRGINIA LAKE (FH5100)	●		●		●	●	●				●								●		●					●						●		●	●					●													
WELDON RESERVOIR (FH5228)			●		●						●								●														●	●																			
WERRINGTON LAKE (FH5253)					●						●			●																				●						●													
WHITE HOUSE TROUT FARM (FH5337)					●						●																																		●			●					
WILDEN RESERVOIR (FH5370)			●		●						●								●															●						●													
WILLOW LAKE (FH5382)					●																																																
WIMBLINGTON MERE (FH5406)			●		●	●					●																							●						●													
WOBURN CLOSE LAKE (FH5454)					●						●																																										
WOOLPACK FISHERY (FH5500)			●		●						●																						●		●					●													
YARWELL MILL LAKE (FH5558)					●						●																																										
CHESHIRE																																																					
ACKERS PIT (FH0019)			●		●						●																					●	●	●						●													
ANTROBUS LAKES (FH0119)	●		●		●	●		●			●								●	●												●		●	●					●													
APPLETON RESERVOIR (FH0123)																																													●								
ASHLEY (RIVER) (FH0163)																				●													●	●											●								
ASHLEY POOL (FH0164)						●																										●		●	●																		
ASTBURY MERE (FH0176)			●		●						●																					●	●																				

Fish Species Available at UK & Irish Fisheries

Fishery	Barbel	Bleak	Bream	Carp Blue	Carp Common	Carp Crucian	Carp Ghost	Carp Grass	Carp Koi	Carp Leather	Carp Mirror	Carp Silver	Carp Wild	Catfish	Catfish Albino	Catfish American Bullhead	Catfish Black Bullhead	Charr	Chub	Dace	Eel	Flounder	Goldfish	Grayling	Grilse	Gudgeon	Gwyniad	Minnow	Orfe	Orfe Blue	Orfe Golden	Perch	Pike	Roach	Rudd	Ruffe	Salmon	Steelhead	Sturgeon	Tench	Tench Golden	Trount American Brook	Trout Blue	Trout Brook	Trout Brown	Trout Golden	Trout Lake	Ttrout Rainbow	Trout Sea	Trout Tiger	Trout Wild	Vendace	Zander
ASTLE POOL (FH0177)			●		●	●					●																						●	●						●													
BADDILEY RESERVOIR (FH0244)																																													●			●					
BELMONT POOL (FH0381)			●		●	●																				●								●	●																		
BENTLEY TROUT POOL (FH0390)																																													●								
BETLEY MERE (FH0396)			●		●					●	●																					●	●	●						●													
BILLINGE GREEN (FH0420)			●		●						●																					●		●						●													
BLACK LAKE (FH0442)																										●						●		●	●																		
BLAKEMERE (FH0489)			●		●						●																					●	●	●						●													
BLUNDELLS FARM FISHERY (FH0514)	●		●		●	●	●			●	●								●										●			●		●	●					●													
BOLESWORTH CASTLE (FH0532)			●		●	●					●		●								●													●	●					●													
BORDER FISHERIES (FH0546)			●		●	●	●				●								●													●			●					●													
BOSLEY RESERVOIR (FH0557)			●		●						●																						●	●																			
BOTTOMS RESERVOIR (FH0563)																																●		●											●								
BOUNDARY WATER PARK (FH0566)			●		●	●					●																					●	●	●	●																		
BREAM HOLE (FH0611)			●		●						●										●					●								●		●																	
BRERETON HEATH COUNTRY PARK (FH0616)			●		●						●																						●	●																			
BRERTON QUARRY (FH0617)	●																		●	●																																	
BRIDGEWATER CANAL (FH0634)			●																													●	●	●	●					●													
BRIDGEWATER CANAL (FH0636)			●		●						●																							●																			
BRIDGEWATER CANAL (FH0635)			●		●						●																						●							●													
BRIGHOUSE POOL (FH0643)			●			●																										●		●	●																		
BROOK BANK POOL (FH0676)			●		●	●					●															●									●					●													
BROOKSIDE FISHERIES (FH0686)					●						●																							●														●					
BROOKSIDE LAKES (FH0687)			●		●	●	●	●			●															●						●		●	●					●													
BROWNLEES POND (FH0703)					●	●																										●		●	●					●													
BUDWORTH MERE (FH0722)			●		●						●																					●	●	●	●					●													
BULLS POOL (FH0729)					●						●																																										
BURTON MERE FISHERIES (FH0761)			●		●	●					●			●				●			●											●		●	●					●													
BYLEY FISHERIES (FH0783)			●		●	●	●				●								●							●			●			●		●						●													
CANAL PIT (FH0819)					●						●																																										
CAPESTHORNE HALL STOCK POND (FH0831)					●	●					●																							●						●													
CAPESTHORNE MAIN POOL (FH0832)			●		●						●																					●		●	●					●													
CAPESTHORNE TOP POOL (FH0833)			●		●	●					●																					●	●	●						●													
CATCHPENNY POOL (FH0873)																																													●			●					

Fish Species Available at UK & Irish Fisheries

Fishery	Barbel	Bleak	Bream	Carp Blue	Carp Common	Carp Crucian	Carp Ghost	Carp Grass	Carp Koi	Carp Leather	Carp Mirror	Carp Silver	Carp Wild	Catfish	Catfish Albino	Catfish American Bullhead	Catfish Black Bullhead	Charr
CHESHIRE FISHING (FH0925)	●		●		●						●							
CICELY MILL POOL (FH0965)					●						●							
CRABMILL FLASH (FH1154)					●						●							
CRABTREE MOSS FARM POOL (FH1156)						●							●					
DANE (RIVER) (FH1255)	●				●						●							
DANE (RIVER) (FH1257)																		
DANE (RIVER) (FH1262)																		
DANE (RIVER) (FH1265)																		
DANE (RIVER) (FH1256)	●																	
DANE (RIVER) (FH1266)	●																	
DANE (RIVER) (FH1260)	●				●						●							
DANE (RIVER) (FH1258)	●																	
DANE (RIVER) (FH1259)																		
DANE (RIVER) (FH1264)	●																	
DANE RIVERSIDE FISHERY (FH1267)	●		●		●													
DANEBRIDGE FISHERIES (FH1268)																		
DEAN (RIVER) (FH1286)																		
DOODLESPOOL FARM LAKE (FH1407)			●		●						●							
DOVEMERE, SANDMERE & WOODLANDS (FH1431)					●						●							
DUKES POOL (FH1465)					●													
EGERTON LAKE (FH1550)					●	●					●							
FANSHAWE LANE POOL (FH1662)					●						●							
FINGERPOST POOL (FH1711)						●												
FLUSHING MEADOWS FISHERY (FH1751)					●						●							
FOUNDERS POOL (FH1779)			●			●												
FRIARS POOL (FH1801)			●		●	●												
GODWINS POOL (FH1907)					●						●							
GORSTY HALL (FH1923)			●								●							
GOWY (RIVER) (FH1930)																		
GOWY (RIVER) (FH1931)																		
GOWY FISHERY (FH1932)			●															
GREAT BUDWORTH MERE LAKE (FH1980)			●															
GREY MIST MERE (FH2018)					●						●							
GRIMESDITCH MILL POOL (FH2020)			●		●			●			●			●				

Fishery	Chub	Dace	Eel	Flounder	Goldfish	Grayling	Grilse	Gudgeon	Gwyniad	Minnow	Orfe	Orfe Blue	Orfe Golden	Perch	Pike	Roach	Rudd	Ruffe
CHESHIRE FISHING (FH0925)	●												●	●		●	●	
CICELY MILL POOL (FH0965)																		
CRABMILL FLASH (FH1154)																		
CRABTREE MOSS FARM POOL (FH1156)														●		●	●	
DANE (RIVER) (FH1255)	●	●						●		●				●	●	●		
DANE (RIVER) (FH1257)																		
DANE (RIVER) (FH1262)																		
DANE (RIVER) (FH1265)																		
DANE (RIVER) (FH1256)	●	●				●								●		●		
DANE (RIVER) (FH1266)	●	●						●										
DANE (RIVER) (FH1260)	●	●												●	●	●		
DANE (RIVER) (FH1258)	●	●						●								●		
DANE (RIVER) (FH1259)	●	●												●				
DANE (RIVER) (FH1264)	●	●						●								●		
DANE RIVERSIDE FISHERY (FH1267)	●															●		
DANEBRIDGE FISHERIES (FH1268)																		
DEAN (RIVER) (FH1286)	●	●				●										●		
DOODLESPOOL FARM LAKE (FH1407)														●		●		
DOVEMERE, SANDMERE & WOODLANDS (FH1431)																		
DUKES POOL (FH1465)																		
EGERTON LAKE (FH1550)																●	●	
FANSHAWE LANE POOL (FH1662)																		
FINGERPOST POOL (FH1711)																	●	
FLUSHING MEADOWS FISHERY (FH1751)																●	●	
FOUNDERS POOL (FH1779)														●		●	●	
FRIARS POOL (FH1801)																●		
GODWINS POOL (FH1907)																		
GORSTY HALL (FH1923)	●													●		●		
GOWY (RIVER) (FH1930)	●	●	●			●		●							●	●	●	
GOWY (RIVER) (FH1931)						●												
GOWY FISHERY (FH1932)	●	●	●	●		●		●		●					●	●		
GREAT BUDWORTH MERE LAKE (FH1980)															●			
GREY MIST MERE (FH2018)																		
GRIMESDITCH MILL POOL (FH2020)											●		●	●		●	●	

Fishery	Salmon	Steelhead	Sturgeon	Tench	Tench Golden	Trount American Brook	Trout Blue	Trout Brook	Trout Brown	Trout Golden	Trout Lake	Ttrout Rainbow	Trout Sea	Trout Tiger	Trout Wild	Vendace	Zander
CHESHIRE FISHING (FH0925)				●													
CICELY MILL POOL (FH0965)																	
CRABMILL FLASH (FH1154)																	
CRABTREE MOSS FARM POOL (FH1156)																	
DANE (RIVER) (FH1255)																	
DANE (RIVER) (FH1257)									●			●					
DANE (RIVER) (FH1262)									●			●					
DANE (RIVER) (FH1265)									●								
DANE (RIVER) (FH1256)																	
DANE (RIVER) (FH1266)																	
DANE (RIVER) (FH1260)																	
DANE (RIVER) (FH1258)																	
DANE (RIVER) (FH1259)																	
DANE (RIVER) (FH1264)																	
DANE RIVERSIDE FISHERY (FH1267)																	
DANEBRIDGE FISHERIES (FH1268)									●			●					
DEAN (RIVER) (FH1286)																	
DOODLESPOOL FARM LAKE (FH1407)				●													
DOVEMERE, SANDMERE & WOODLANDS (FH1431)																	
DUKES POOL (FH1465)																	
EGERTON LAKE (FH1550)				●													
FANSHAWE LANE POOL (FH1662)																	
FINGERPOST POOL (FH1711)																	
FLUSHING MEADOWS FISHERY (FH1751)				●													
FOUNDERS POOL (FH1779)																	
FRIARS POOL (FH1801)																	
GODWINS POOL (FH1907)				●													
GORSTY HALL (FH1923)				●													
GOWY (RIVER) (FH1930)																	
GOWY (RIVER) (FH1931)									●								
GOWY FISHERY (FH1932)									●			●					
GREAT BUDWORTH MERE LAKE (FH1980)																	
GREY MIST MERE (FH2018)																	
GRIMESDITCH MILL POOL (FH2020)																	

Fish Species Available at UK & Irish Fisheries

	Barbel	Bleak	Bream	Carp Blue	Carp Common	Carp Crucian	Carp Ghost	Carp Grass	Carp Koi	Carp Leather	Carp Mirror	Carp Silver	Carp Wild	Catfish	Catfish Albino	Catfish American Bullhead	Catfish Black Bullhead
GRIMSDITCH MILL POOL (FH2023)			●		●						●			●			
HACK GREEN LAKE (FH2057)			●		●						●						
HAMPTON SPRINGS (FH2096)	●		●		●	●					●						
HARTHILL (FH2114)			●		●						●						
HAYDAN FISHERY (FH2151)					●						●						
HOLMSTON HALL FISHERY (FH2270)			●		●	●					●						
HORSECOPPICE RESERVOIR (FH2305)																	
HUDDERSFIELD NARROW CANAL (FH2326)	●		●		●						●						
JARMAN FARM POOL (FH2407)					●						●						
KAZAKO PONDS (FH2421)																	
KNIGHTS POOL (FH2536)			●		●	●					●						
LAKEMORE COUNTRY PARK (FH2578)					●						●			●			
LAMALOAD RESERVOIR (FH2599)																	
LITTLE BUDWORTH (FH2744)			●		●						●						
LITTLE MILL (FH2755)			●		●	●					●						
LITTLE REEDS MERE (FH2760)			●		●	●					●						
LLOYDS MEADOW FISHERIES (FH2784)			●		●	●	●				●						
LONGBARN POOL (FH2985)			●		●												
LYMM DAM (FH3115)			●		●						●			●			
LYMM VALE (FH3116)	●		●								●			●			
MACCLESFIELD CANAL (FH3128)			●								●						
MANOR POOL (FH3171)					●						●						
MARBURY MERE (FH3175)			●		●						●						
MARTON HEATH COARSE POOL (FH3202)					●	●					●						
MARTON HEATH TROUT POOLS (FH3203)																	
MARY ANN POND (FH3204)						●											
MEADOW FISHERY (FH3222)																	
MEADOW VIEW FISHERY (FH3225)			●			●	●	●			●						
MILL LODGE (FH3292)					●						●						
MILTON GREEN (FH3320)			●		●	●	●										
MOBBERLEY POOL (FH3332)					●						●						
MONKS MOAT (FH3345)			●		●	●											
MOOR POOL (FH3358)			●		●	●					●						
MOORE QUARRY (FH3360)			●		●	●		●			●						

	Charr	Chub	Dace	Eel	Flounder	Goldfish	Grayling	Grilse	Gudgeon	Gwyniad	Minnow	Orfe	Orfe Blue	Orfe Golden	Perch	Pike	Roach	Rudd	Ruffe	Salmon	Steelhead	Sturgeon	Tench
GRIMSDITCH MILL POOL (FH2023)															●		●	●					
HACK GREEN LAKE (FH2057)																	●						●
HAMPTON SPRINGS (FH2096)															●		●	●					●
HARTHILL (FH2114)									●						●			●					●
HAYDAN FISHERY (FH2151)																							
HOLMSTON HALL FISHERY (FH2270)		●															●	●					●
HORSECOPPICE RESERVOIR (FH2305)																							
HUDDERSFIELD NARROW CANAL (FH2326)		●							●						●	●	●						●
JARMAN FARM POOL (FH2407)																							
KAZAKO PONDS (FH2421)													●										
KNIGHTS POOL (FH2536)									●						●		●	●					●
LAKEMORE COUNTRY PARK (FH2578)		●															●	●					
LAMALOAD RESERVOIR (FH2599)																							
LITTLE BUDWORTH (FH2744)															●		●						●
LITTLE MILL (FH2755)															●		●						●
LITTLE REEDS MERE (FH2760)									●			●			●		●	●					●
LLOYDS MEADOW FISHERIES (FH2784)		●							●						●		●	●					●
LONGBARN POOL (FH2985)															●	●	●	●					
LYMM DAM (FH3115)																●	●						
LYMM VALE (FH3116)		●										●		●				●					●
MACCLESFIELD CANAL (FH3128)									●						●		●	●					●
MANOR POOL (FH3171)															●		●						
MARBURY MERE (FH3175)				●											●	●	●	●					●
MARTON HEATH COARSE POOL (FH3202)															●		●	●					●
MARTON HEATH TROUT POOLS (FH3203)																							
MARY ANN POND (FH3204)															●		●	●					●
MEADOW FISHERY (FH3222)																							
MEADOW VIEW FISHERY (FH3225)		●							●					●	●		●						●
MILL LODGE (FH3292)																							
MILTON GREEN (FH3320)		●													●		●						●
MOBBERLEY POOL (FH3332)																							
MONKS MOAT (FH3345)																	●						
MOOR POOL (FH3358)															●		●	●					
MOORE QUARRY (FH3360)		●							●						●	●	●						●

	Tench Golden	Trount American Brook	Trout Blue	Trout Brook	Trout Brown	Trout Golden	Trout Lake	Ttrout Rainbow	Trout Sea	Trout Tiger	Trout Wild	Vendace	Zander
GRIMSDITCH MILL POOL (FH2023)													
HACK GREEN LAKE (FH2057)													
HAMPTON SPRINGS (FH2096)													
HARTHILL (FH2114)													
HAYDAN FISHERY (FH2151)													
HOLMSTON HALL FISHERY (FH2270)													
HORSECOPPICE RESERVOIR (FH2305)					●								
HUDDERSFIELD NARROW CANAL (FH2326)													
JARMAN FARM POOL (FH2407)													
KAZAKO PONDS (FH2421)					●								
KNIGHTS POOL (FH2536)													
LAKEMORE COUNTRY PARK (FH2578)													
LAMALOAD RESERVOIR (FH2599)								●			●		
LITTLE BUDWORTH (FH2744)													
LITTLE MILL (FH2755)													
LITTLE REEDS MERE (FH2760)													
LLOYDS MEADOW FISHERIES (FH2784)													
LONGBARN POOL (FH2985)													
LYMM DAM (FH3115)													
LYMM VALE (FH3116)	●												
MACCLESFIELD CANAL (FH3128)													
MANOR POOL (FH3171)													
MARBURY MERE (FH3175)													
MARTON HEATH COARSE POOL (FH3202)													
MARTON HEATH TROUT POOLS (FH3203)					●			●					
MARY ANN POND (FH3204)													
MEADOW FISHERY (FH3222)					●			●					
MEADOW VIEW FISHERY (FH3225)													
MILL LODGE (FH3292)													
MILTON GREEN (FH3320)													
MOBBERLEY POOL (FH3332)													
MONKS MOAT (FH3345)													
MOOR POOL (FH3358)													
MOORE QUARRY (FH3360)													

Fish Species Available at UK & Irish Fisheries

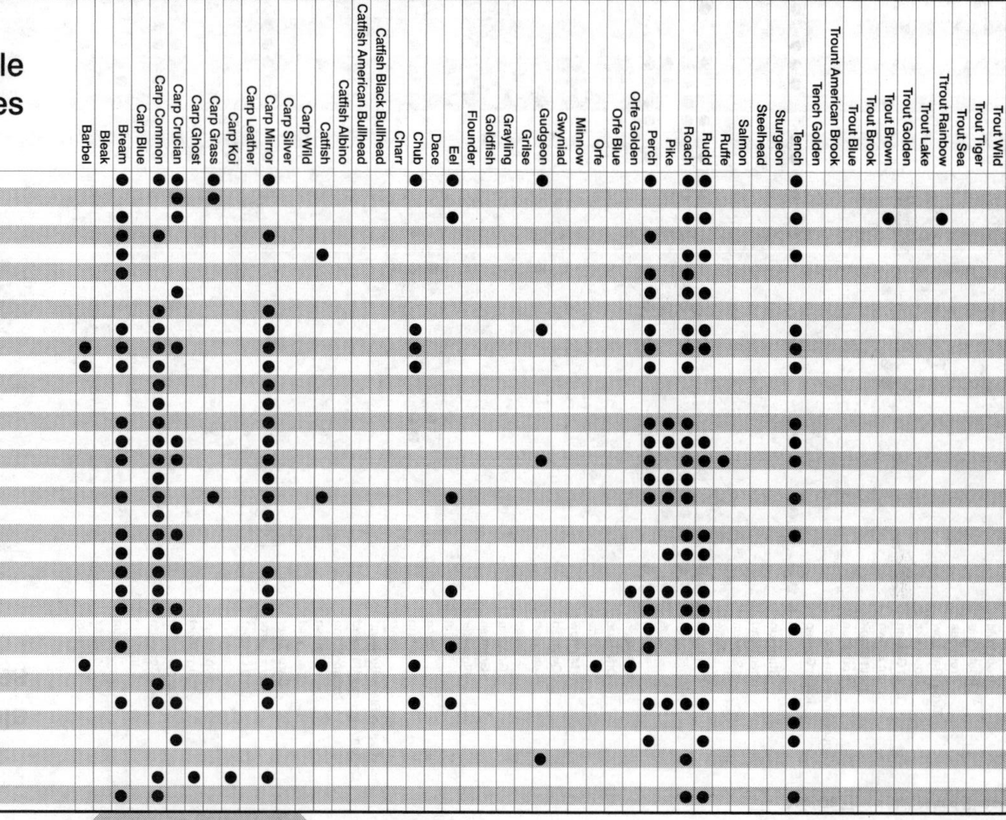

	Barbel	Bleak	Bream	Carp Blue	Carp Common	Carp Crucian	Carp Ghost	Carp Grass	Carp Koi	Carp Leather	Carp Mirror	Carp Silver	Carp Wild	Catfish	Catfish Albino	Catfish American Bullhead	Catfish Black Bullhead	Charr	Chub	Dace	Eel	Flounder	Goldfish	Grayling	Grilse	Gudgeon	Gwyniad	Minnow	Orfe	Orfe Blue	Orfe Golden	Perch	Pike	Roach	Rudd	Ruffe	Salmon	Steelhead	Sturgeon	Tench	Tench Golden	Trount American Brook	Trout Blue	Trout Brook	Trout Brown	Trout Golden	Trout Lake	Ttrout Rainbow	Trout Sea	Trout Tiger	Trout Wild	Vendace	Zander
MORETON MERE FISHERY (FH3370)			●		●	●		●			●								●		●					●						●		●	●					●													
MOSS POOLS (FH3379)						●		●																																													
MOULDSWORTH MERE (FH3383)			●			●															●													●	●					●					●			●					
NEW BRIDGE POOL (FH3462)			●		●						●																					●																					
NEW POOL (FH3476)			●											●																				●	●					●													
NORBURY POOL (FH3515)			●																													●		●																			
OAK POOL (FH3559)						●																										●		●	●																		
OCEAN POOL (FH3572)					●						●																																										
OLDHAMS WATER (FH3607)			●		●						●								●							●						●		●	●					●													
PARK POOL (FH3701)	●		●		●	●					●								●													●		●	●					●													
PARTRIDGE LAKES (FH3714)	●		●		●						●								●													●		●						●													
PETTY POOL (FH3761)					●						●																																										
PLEX FLASH (FH3804)					●						●																																										
REDESMERE (FH3916)			●		●						●																					●	●	●						●													
RODE POOL (FH3989)			●		●	●					●																					●	●	●	●					●													
ROSSMERE (FH4019)			●		●	●					●															●						●		●	●	●				●													
RUNCORN PARK LAKE (FH4057)					●						●																					●	●	●																			
SALE WATER PARK (FH4081)			●		●			●			●			●							●											●	●	●						●													
SAND MERE LAKE (FH4092)					●						●																																										
SANDYBANK POOL (FH4098)			●		●	●																												●	●					●													
SANKEY ST HELENS CANAL (FH4100)			●		●																												●	●	●																		
SANKEY ST HELENS CANAL (FH4101)			●		●						●																																										
SANKEY ST HELENS CANAL (LAC) (FH4102)			●		●						●										●										●	●	●	●	●																		
SHAKERLEY MERE (FH4202)			●		●	●					●																					●		●	●																		
SHELLOW FARM POOLS (FH4226)						●																										●		●	●					●													
SHIPBROOK FLASH (FH4241)			●																		●											●																					
SPRING POOL (FH4370)	●					●								●					●										●		●				●																		
SPRINGWOOD POOL (FH4377)					●						●																																										
STATHAM POOL (FH4437)			●		●	●					●								●		●											●	●	●	●					●													
STOCKPOND (FH4462)																																								●													
STRETTON WATER (FH4525)						●																										●			●					●													
SUTTON RESERVOIR (FH4565)																										●								●																			
SWANLEY (FH4599)					●		●		●		●																																										
TABLEY MERE (FH4625)			●		●																													●	●					●													

Fish Species Available at UK & Irish Fisheries

	Barbel	Bleak	Bream	Carp Blue	Carp Common	Carp Crucian	Carp Ghost	Carp Grass	Carp Koi	Carp Leather	Carp Mirror	Carp Silver	Carp Wild	Catfish	Catfish Albino	Catfish American Bullhead	Catfish Black Bullhead	Charr	Chub	Dace	Eel	Flounder	Goldfish	Grayling	Grilse	Gudgeon	Gwyniad	Minnow	Orfe	Orfe Blue	Orfe Golden	Perch	Pike	Roach	Rudd	Ruffe	Salmon	Steelhead	Sturgeon	Tench	Tench Golden	Trount American Brook	Trout Blue	Trout Brook	Trout Brown	Trout Golden	Trout Lake	Ttrout Rainbow	Trout Sea	Trout Tiger	Trout Wild	Vendace	Zander
TABLEY MOAT (FH4626)			●		●																											●	●	●	●					●													
TATTON MERE (FH4664)					●						●																					●	●	●	●					●													
TAX MERE (FH4677)			●		●	●					●																					●		●	●					●													
TEGGSNOSE RESERVOIR (FH4700)					●						●																																										
TETTON LAKE (FH4749)			●		●						●																							●						●													
THORNEYCROFT LAKES (FH4817)			●		●						●																						●	●						●													
TOFT POOL (FH4865)			●		●						●																					●	●	●																			
TOP FARM POOL (FH4876)					●	●					●												●						●			●		●	●																		
TOWN PARK LANE (FH4892)			●																							●						●	●	●						●													
TURNERS POOL (FH4982)					●					●	●								●													●			●					●													
VALE ROYAL LOCKS (FH5084)			●		●	●					●								●	●	●											●	●	●						●													
VILLAGE POOL (FH5098)					●						●																																										
WALKERWOOD RESERVOIR (FH5119)																																													●								
WALKERWOOD TROUT FISHERY (FH5120)																																													●			●					
WALL POOL LODGE (FH5121)	●		●		●	●					●								●													●		●	●					●													
WEAVER (RIVER) (FH5220)			●																																																		
WEAVER (RIVER) (FH5214)			●			●					●																					●	●	●																			
WEAVER (RIVER) (FH5216)																			●	●														●											●								
WEAVER (RIVER) (FH5217)																			●	●				●		●						●		●																			
WEAVER (RIVER) (FH5219)			●		●						●																							●						●													
WEAVER (RIVER) (FH5215)			●		●														●													●	●	●						●													
WESTLOW MERE (FH5283)																																													●			●					
WHIRLEY MERE (FH5326)					●	●					●																						●	●	●					●													
WHIRLEY POOL (FH5327)																																			●					●								●					
WHITEGATE POND (FH5347)			●		●	●	●		●		●								●		●					●						●		●	●					●													
WHITLEY POOL (FH5357)					●	●																	●																	●													
WILLOW POOL (FH5388)					●																											●		●	●																		
WINCHAM BROOK (FH5407)																				●				●		●						●		●											●								
WINSFORD FLASH (FH5421)			●		●						●																					●	●	●						●													
WINTERLEY POOL FISHERY (FH5426)			●		●	●					●			●							●											●	●	●	●					●													
WOOD POOL (FH5460)	●		●		●	●					●								●													●		●	●					●													
WOODLANDS LAKE (FH5484)					●						●																																										
WOODSIDE POOL (FH5493)						●		●																											●					●													

Fish Species Available at UK & Irish Fisheries

	Barbel	Bleak	Bream	Carp Blue	Carp Common	Carp Crucian	Carp Ghost	Carp Grass	Carp Koi	Carp Leather	Carp Mirror	Carp Silver	Carp Wild	Catfish	Catfish Albino	Catfish American Bullhead	Catfish Black Bullhead	Charr	Chub	Dace	Eel	Flounder	Goldfish	Grayling	Grilse	Gudgeon	Gwyniad	Minnow	Orfe	Orfe Blue	Orfe Golden	Perch	Pike	Roach	Rudd	Ruffe	Salmon	Steelhead	Sturgeon	Tench	Tench Golden	Trount American Brook	Trout Blue	Trout Brook	Trout Brown	Trout Golden	Trout Lake	Ttrout Rainbow	Trout Sea	Trout Tiger	Trout Wild	Vendace	Zander
CLEVELAND																																																					
ASCOTT PONDS (FH0154)					●						●																							●	●																		
CHARLTONS PONDS (FH0905)			●		●	●					●										●		●									●		●	●					●													
HART RESERVOIR (FH2112)			●		●						●															●						●	●	●																			
HARTBURN BRICK PIT (FH2113)			●			●																												●						●													
HARTLEPOOL RESERVOIR (FH2117)					●						●																																										
HEMLINGTON LAKE (FH2179)			●		●	●					●																							●																			
HUTTON RUDBY PONDS (FH2351)			●			●																										●		●	●					●													
ISLAND WATERS (FH2392)						●					●								●																●					●													
LOCH KENNY (FH2899)			●		●	●					●																					●		●						●													
LOCKE PARK (FH2971)			●		●	●					●																					●		●																			
NEW MARSKE RESERVOIR (FH3472)			●		●						●																																										
PRIORY COTTAGE LAKE (FH3847)			●		●						●																					●		●																			
ROSSMERE PARK LAKE (FH4020)			●		●						●																					●		●						●													
SCALING DAM (FH4111)																																																●					
SHOTTON COLLIERY LAKE (FH4248)			●		●	●																												●						●													
TILERY LAKE (FH4843)			●		●						●										●											●		●						●													
WHITEHOUSE CARAVAN PARK LAKE (FH5348)			●		●		●				●																								●																		
CORNWALL																																																					
AMALWHIDDEN FARM (FH0099)					●						●																					●								●													
ARGAL RESERVOIR (FH0134)			●		●						●										●											●	●	●						●													
AVALLON HOLIDAY PARK (FH0185)			●		●						●																							●						●													
BADHAM FARM LAKE (FH0246)					●						●																							●	●					●													
BAKE FISHING LAKES (FH0253)			●		●	●	●				●										●					●								●	●					●					●			●					
BILLS POOL (FH0423)			●		●	●					●										●					●			●			●		●	●					●													
BOLINGEY LAKE (FH0534)					●						●																					●		●	●					●													
BOSCATHNOE RESERVOIR (FH0556)			●		●	●					●										●					●								●	●					●													
BRAGGS WOOD TROUT FISHERY (FH0594)																																													●			●					
BUDE CANAL (FH0721)			●		●						●									●	●					●						●		●																			
BUSH LAKES FARM (FH0768)			●		●	●					●										●											●		●	●					●					●								
BUSSOW RESERVOIR (FH0772)			●		●						●										●											●		●	●					●													
BUTTERWELL (FH0779)																																					●												●				
CAMEL (RIVER) (FH0808)																																					●								●				●				
CHOONE FARM (FH0945)					●						●																					●			●					●													

Fish Species Available at UK & Irish Fisheries

Fishery	Barbel	Bleak	Bream	Carp Blue	Carp Common	Carp Crucian	Carp Ghost	Carp Grass	Carp Koi	Carp Leather	Carp Mirror	Carp Silver	Carp Wild	Catfish	Catfish Albino	Catfish American Bullhead	Catfish Black Bullhead	Charr	Chub	Dace	Eel	Flounder	Goldfish	Grayling	Grilse	Gudgeon	Gwyniad
CHYRAISE LODGE HOTEL (FH0964)			●																								
COLLEGE RESERVOIR (FH1064)			●		●						●										●						
COLLIFORD LAKE (FH1065)																											
CONSTANTINE BROOK (FH1092)																											
CRAFTHOLE LAKE (FH1157)					●						●																
CROWDY RESERVOIR (FH1199)																											
DRIFT RESERVOIR (FH1443)																											
DUTSON WATER (FH1487)			●		●	●					●										●			●			
EAST ROSE FARM (FH1513)			●		●	●					●																
ELECTRICITY POOL (FH1560)					●				●		●										●						
ELMFIELD FARM COARSE FISHERY (FH1570)			●		●						●																
EMFIELD COARSE FISHERY (FH1586)			●		●				●		●																
FENWICK TROUT FISHERY (FH1698)																											
FERNDALE (FH1699)			●		●	●					●										●						
FORDA HOLIDAY LODGES (FH1761)			●		●						●																
FOWEY (RIVER) (FH1786)																											
FOWEY (RIVER) (FH1787)																											
FOWEY (RIVER) (FH1788)																											
FOWEY (RIVER) (FH1782)																											
FOWEY (RIVER) (FH1785)																											
FOWEY (RIVER) (FH1784)																											
GLENLEIGH FARM FISHERY (FH1892)					●		●		●	●	●										●					●	
GOONHAVERN LAKE (FH1920)	●		●		●	●	●	●			●								●								
GWARNICK MILL TROUT FISHERY (FH2040)																											
GWINEAR POOLS COARSE FISHERY (FH2049)			●		●						●										●					●	
GWINNEAR POOLS (FH2050)			●		●						●																
HAYLE CAUSEWAY (FH2156)																											
HIDDEN VALLEY (FH2203)			●		●	●	●				●																
INNY (RIVER) (FH2372)																											
LAKE PENRYN (FH2568)																											
LAKEVIEW COUNTRY CLUB (FH2598)			●		●	●	●		●	●	●								●	●	●					●	
LANGARTH POOLS (FH2610)	●		●		●	●	●		●	●	●								●		●					●	
LYNHER (RIVER) (FH3124)																											
MEADOWSIDE COARSE FISHERY (FH3228)	●		●		●	●	●	●			●										●					●	

Fishery	Minnow	Orfe	Orfe Blue	Orfe Golden	Perch	Pike	Roach	Rudd	Ruffe	Salmon	Steelhead	Sturgeon	Tench	Tench Golden	Trount American Brook	Trout Blue	Trout Brook	Trout Brown	Trout Golden	Trout Lake	Ttrout Rainbow	Trout Sea	Trout Tiger	Trout Wild	Vendace	Zander
CHYRAISE LODGE HOTEL (FH0964)							●						●													
COLLEGE RESERVOIR (FH1064)					●	●	●	●					●													
COLLIFORD LAKE (FH1065)																		●								
CONSTANTINE BROOK (FH1092)																		●								
CRAFTHOLE LAKE (FH1157)													●													
CROWDY RESERVOIR (FH1199)																		●			●					
DRIFT RESERVOIR (FH1443)																		●		●	●					
DUTSON WATER (FH1487)					●			●					●													
EAST ROSE FARM (FH1513)							●	●					●													
ELECTRICITY POOL (FH1560)		●			●			●					●													
ELMFIELD FARM COARSE FISHERY (FH1570)		●			●		●						●													
EMFIELD COARSE FISHERY (FH1586)		●			●		●						●													
FENWICK TROUT FISHERY (FH1698)										●								●			●	●				
FERNDALE (FH1699)		●					●	●					●													
FORDA HOLIDAY LODGES (FH1761)								●					●													
FOWEY (RIVER) (FH1786)										●								●			●	●				
FOWEY (RIVER) (FH1787)										●												●				
FOWEY (RIVER) (FH1788)										●												●				
FOWEY (RIVER) (FH1782)										●								●				●				
FOWEY (RIVER) (FH1785)										●												●				
FOWEY (RIVER) (FH1784)										●								●				●				
GLENLEIGH FARM FISHERY (FH1892)					●		●	●					●													
GOONHAVERN LAKE (FH1920)					●		●	●					●													
GWARNICK MILL TROUT FISHERY (FH2040)																		●			●					
GWINEAR POOLS COARSE FISHERY (FH2049)					●		●	●																		
GWINNEAR POOLS (FH2050)					●		●	●					●													
HAYLE CAUSEWAY (FH2156)																		●								
HIDDEN VALLEY (FH2203)							●	●					●													
INNY (RIVER) (FH2372)										●												●				
LAKE PENRYN (FH2568)																					●					
LAKEVIEW COUNTRY CLUB (FH2598)	●				●		●	●					●													
LANGARTH POOLS (FH2610)	●				●		●	●	●				●				●	●								
LYNHER (RIVER) (FH3124)										●												●				
MEADOWSIDE COARSE FISHERY (FH3228)					●		●	●					●													

Fish Species Available at UK & Irish Fisheries

Fishery	Barbel	Bleak	Bream	Carp Blue	Carp Common	Carp Crucian	Carp Ghost	Carp Grass	Carp Koi	Carp Leather	Carp Mirror	Carp Silver	Carp Wild	Catfish	Catfish Albino	Catfish American Bullhead	Catfish Black Bullhead	Charr	Chub	Dace	Eel	Flounder	Goldfish	Grayling	Grilse	Gudgeon	Gwyniad
MELANHYL LAKE (FH3242)																											
MELLONWATTS MILL (FH3249)						●																					
MIDDLE BOSWIN FARM (FH3264)			●		●	●					●										●						
MILLBROOK COARSE FISHERY (FH3305)			●		●	●	●	●		●	●										●						
MILLPOOL FISHERIES (FH3315)			●		●						●																
MILTON MOUNT LAKE (FH3322)					●						●															●	
NANCE LAKES (FH3414)			●		●						●																
NEETS VALLEY PARK (FH3436)					●						●																
OAKSIDE FISHERY (FH3567)			●		●	●					●										●						
ORVIS INNIS FLY FISHERY (FH3626)																											
POLCOVERACK FARM (FH3810)					●	●					●																
PORT ELLIOT LAKE (FH3824)			●		●						●										●						
PORTH RESERVOIR (FH3825)			●		●						●										●						
PRINCE PARK (FH3845)			●		●	●					●																
RETALLACK WATERS (FH3931)	●		●		●		●			●	●								●		●					●	
ROSE PARK FISHERY (FH4011)																											
ROSEWATER LAKE (FH4014)	●		●		●	●	●		●		●										●						
ROWFANT HOUSE FISHERY (FH4039)					●																						
SEATON (RIVER) (FH4127)																											
SHARKEYS PIT (FH4209)					●	●	●				●															●	
SHILLAMILL LAKES COUNTRY PARK (FH4238)					●	●				●	●																
SIBLYBACK LAKE (FH4263)																											
ST BENETS ABBEY (RIVER) (FH4382)			●																								
ST ERTH FISHERY (FH4385)			●		●	●					●								●								
ST GERMANS LAKE (FH4386)			●		●						●																
ST LEONARDS FISHING LAKE (FH4392)			●		●						●																
ST TINNEY FARM HOLIDAYS (FH4397)			●		●						●																
STITHIANS RESERVOIR (FH4459)																											
STOWFORD GRANGE FISHERIES (FH4513)			●		●						●										●					●	
TAMAR (RIVER) (FH4641)																				●				●			
TAMAR LAKE (UPPER) (FH4645)			●		●						●										●						
TEMPLE TROUT FISHERY (FH4735)																					●						
TIN DENE FISHERY (FH4850)					●	●					●										●					●	
TORY FARM LAKE (FH4887)					●						●		●														

Fishery	Minnow	Orfe	Orfe Blue	Orfe Golden	Perch	Pike	Roach	Rudd	Ruffe	Salmon	Steelhead	Sturgeon	Tench	Tench Golden	Trount American Brook	Trout Blue	Trout Brook	Trout Brown	Trout Golden	Trout Lake	Ttrout Rainbow	Trout Sea	Trout Tiger	Trout Wild	Vendace	Zander
MELANHYL LAKE (FH3242)																		●			●					
MELLONWATTS MILL (FH3249)							●	●					●													
MIDDLE BOSWIN FARM (FH3264)					●		●	●					●													
MILLBROOK COARSE FISHERY (FH3305)					●		●	●					●													
MILLPOOL FISHERIES (FH3315)							●						●													
MILTON MOUNT LAKE (FH3322)					●			●					●													
NANCE LAKES (FH3414)							●																			
NEETS VALLEY PARK (FH3436)								●					●													
OAKSIDE FISHERY (FH3567)					●		●	●					●													
ORVIS INNIS FLY FISHERY (FH3626)																					●					
POLCOVERACK FARM (FH3810)					●								●													
PORT ELLIOT LAKE (FH3824)					●		●	●					●													
PORTH RESERVOIR (FH3825)					●		●	●					●					●								
PRINCE PARK (FH3845)							●	●					●													
RETALLACK WATERS (FH3931)		●		●	●	●	●	●					●													
ROSE PARK FISHERY (FH4011)																		●			●					
ROSEWATER LAKE (FH4014)		●					●	●					●													
ROWFANT HOUSE FISHERY (FH4039)																										
SEATON (RIVER) (FH4127)																						●				
SHARKEYS PIT (FH4209)					●		●	●					●													
SHILLAMILL LAKES COUNTRY PARK (FH4238)		●			●		●	●					●													
SIBLYBACK LAKE (FH4263)																					●					
ST BENETS ABBEY (RIVER) (FH4382)							●																			
ST ERTH FISHERY (FH4385)					●		●						●													
ST GERMANS LAKE (FH4386)					●		●	●					●													
ST LEONARDS FISHING LAKE (FH4392)					●								●													
ST TINNEY FARM HOLIDAYS (FH4397)					●		●	●					●					●								
STITHIANS RESERVOIR (FH4459)																		●			●					
STOWFORD GRANGE FISHERIES (FH4513)				●	●		●	●					●													
TAMAR (RIVER) (FH4641)										●								●				●				
TAMAR LAKE (UPPER) (FH4645)					●		●	●					●													
TEMPLE TROUT FISHERY (FH4735)																		●	●		●					
TIN DENE FISHERY (FH4850)	●				●		●	●					●													
TORY FARM LAKE (FH4887)								●																		

Fish Species Available at UK & Irish Fisheries

Fishery	Barbel	Bleak	Bream	Carp Blue	Carp Common	Carp Crucian	Carp Ghost	Carp Grass	Carp Koi	Carp Leather	Carp Mirror	Carp Silver	Carp Wild	Catfish	Catfish Albino	Catfish American Bullhead	Catfish Black Bullhead	Charr	Chub	Dace	Eel	Flounder	Goldfish	Grayling	Grilse	Gudgeon	Gwyniad	Minnow	Orfe	Orfe Blue	Orfe Golden	Perch	Pike	Roach	Rudd	Ruffe	Salmon	Steelhead	Sturgeon	Tench	Tench Golden	Trount American Brook	Trout Blue	Trout Brook	Trout Brown	Trout Golden	Trout Lake	Ttrout Rainbow	Trout Sea	Trout Tiger	Trout Wild	Vendace	Zander
TREBELLAN PARK LAKES (FH4907)					●						●																							●	●					●													
TREDIDON BARTON LAKE (FH4908)			●		●		●				●																							●	●					●													
TREE MEADOW TROUT FISHERY (FH4909)																																													●			●					
TRENESTRALL LAKE (FH4916)					●						●																							●						●													
TRETHIGGEY FARM POND (FH4949)			●		●						●																							●	●					●													
TREVELLA PARK (FH4950)			●		●						●																							●	●					●													
WATERFRONT FISHING LAKE (FH5176)					●						●										●													●	●										●								
WEST LOOE (RIVER) (FH5262)																																					●												●				
WEST LOOE (RIVER) (FH5263)																																																	●				
WHEAL GREY (FH5315)					●	●					●																					●		●	●																		
WHEAL RASHLEIGH PITS (FH5316)			●		●						●																					●								●													
WHITEACRES COUNTRY PARK (FH5344)			●		●						●			●																				●						●													
WOODLAY HOLIDAY LAKES (FH5486)					●						●																							●	●					●													
WOONSMITH LAKE (FH5502)			●		●						●										●					●						●		●	●					●													
COUNTY DURHAM																																																					
AYCLIFFE LAKE (FH0235)			●		●	●					●								●		●					●				●		●		●						●	●												
BEAUMONT FISHERIES (FH0358)	●		●		●	●	●			●	●								●							●			●			●		●	●					●													
BLACKTON RESERVOIR (FH0455)																																													●			●					
BRASSIDE POND (FH0603)			●		●	●					●															●						●	●	●	●					●													
BROWNEY (RIVER) (FH0700)																																					●								●				●				
BURNHOPE FISHERY (FH0749)																																																●					
BYERS GREEN (FH0782)																			●					●																					●								
COW GREEN FISHERY (FH1148)																																													●								
DERWENT RESERVOIR (FH1360)																																													●			●					
EDMONDSLEY POND (FH1547)			●		●	●					●															●						●		●						●													
FIELDSONS POND (FH1705)			●		●	●					●																					●		●	●					●													
FIGHTING COCKS RESERVOIR (FH1706)			●		●						●																					●		●																			
FLYLANDS POND (FH1752)			●		●						●																							●						●													
GRASSHOLME RESERVOIR (FH1977)																																																●					
GREENCROFT POND (FH2006)					●	●					●								●																					●													
HALNEBY LAKE (FH2074)			●		●						●																							●						●													
HURWORTH BURN RESERVOIR (FH2348)																																●		●											●								
HURY RESERVOIR (FH2349)																																																●					
JUBILEE LAKES (FH2417)																																													●			●					

Fish Species Available at UK & Irish Fisheries

	Barbel	Bleak	Bream	Carp Blue	Carp Common	Carp Crucian	Carp Ghost	Carp Grass	Carp Koi	Carp Leather	Carp Mirror	Carp Silver	Carp Wild	Catfish	Catfish Albino	Catfish American Bullhead	Catfish Black Bullhead	Charr	Chub	Dace	Eel	Flounder	Goldfish	Grayling	Grilse	Gudgeon	Gwyniad	Minnow	Orfe	Orfe Blue	Orfe Golden	Perch	Pike	Roach	Rudd	Ruffe	Salmon	Steelhead	Sturgeon	Tench	Tench Golden	Trount American Brook	Trout Blue	Trout Brook	Trout Brown	Trout Golden	Trout Lake	Ttrout Rainbow	Trout Sea	Trout Tiger	Trout Wild	Vendace	Zander
KELLOW LAW POND (FH2426)					●	●					●																					●			●																		
KNITSLEY MILL TROUT FISHERIES (FH2538)																																																●					
LANGSDALE LAKE (FH2617)			●		●	●					●																					●		●	●					●													
MAINSFORTH POND (FH3149)																																●		●						●													
MIDDLETON WATER PARK (FH3269)					●						●																					●		●						●													
SELSET RESERVOIR (FH4136)																																																●					
SHAFTOS LAKE (FH4201)																			●													●		●	●																		
SHOTTON POND (FH4249)			●		●	●					●															●						●		●	●					●													
TEES (RIVER) (FH4696)																																					●								●								
TEES (RIVER) (FH4697)																			●		●			●				●				●					●								●				●		●		
TEES (RIVER) (FH4685)																																					●								●								
TEES (RIVER) (FH4688)																																					●								●								
TEES (RIVER) (FH4686)																																					●								●								
TEES (RIVER) (FH4692)	●																		●																																		
TEES (RIVER) (FH4691)																																					●								●								
TEES (RIVER) (FH4694)																																					●								●								
TEES (RIVER) (FH4693)																																					●								●								
TEES (RIVER) (FH4684)	●																		●	●	●			●		●						●		●											●								
TEES (RIVER) (FH4690)																			●	●									●					●			●								●								
TEES (RIVER) (FH4689)																																					●								●								
TEES (RIVER) (FH4695)																			●	●	●			●								●		●											●								
TEES (RIVER) (FH4687)																																					●								●				●				
TRIMDON POND (FH4955)			●		●	●					●								●							●						●		●						●													
TUNSTALL RESERVOIR (FH4973)																																													●			●					
TURNSIDE POOL (FH4983)					●						●																					●		●																			
TURSDALE POND (FH4984)			●							●	●																						●																				
TURSDALE POND (LANGLEY PARK) (FH4985)			●		●						●			●												●								●	●					●													
WADSWORTH FISHERY (FH5111)					●						●																					●																					
WASKERLEY RESERVOIR (FH5166)																																													●			●					
WEAR (RIVER) (FH5205)	●																		●	●				●													●								●				●				
WEAR (RIVER) (FH5206)																																					●								●				●				
WEAR (RIVER) (FH5211)	●																		●	●				●		●						●		●															●				
WEAR (RIVER) (FH5201)	●																		●	●												●	●	●																			
WEAR (RIVER) (FH5198)	●																		●	●	●													●			●								●								

Fish Species Available at UK & Irish Fisheries

Fishery	Barbel	Bleak	Bream	Carp Blue	Carp Common	Carp Crucian	Carp Ghost	Carp Grass	Carp Koi	Carp Leather	Carp Mirror	Carp Silver	Carp Wild	Catfish	Catfish Albino
WEAR (RIVER) (FH5207)															
WEAR (RIVER) (FH5210)															
WEAR (RIVER) (FH5208)															
WEAR (RIVER) (FH5200)	●														
WEAR (RIVER) (FH5209)	●														
WELLFIELD POND (FH5238)			●		●	●					●				
WITTON CASTLE LAKES (FH5451)															
CUMBRIA															
AIRA BECK (FH0041)															
ANNAS STREAM (FH0116)															
ATKINSONS TARN COARSE FISHERY (FH0181)			●		●						●				
BANKS POND (FH0289)					●						●				
BARN LAKE (FH0313)					●						●				
BASSENTHWAITE LAKE (FH0344)															
BESSY BECK TROUT FARM (FH0394)															
BIGLAND HALL LAKE (FH0414)			●		●						●				
BLELHAM TARN (FH0495)															
BLENCARN LAKE (FH0496)															
BORROWDALE FISHERIES (FH0553)															
BORWICK LAKE (FH0555)					●						●				
BRATHAY (RIVER) (FH0604)															
BRAYTON POND (FH0608)					●	●					●				
BRIGHAM (RIVER) (FH0641)															
BUTTERMERE LAKE (FH0777)															
CARLETON HILL (FH0842)			●		●						●				
CLEABARROW TARN (FH0996)			●		●						●				
CLOUGH (RIVER) (FH1023)															
CODALE TARN (FH1050)															
COGRA MOSS (FH1054)															
CROSSFIELD FISHERY (FH1193)															
CRUMMOCK WATER LAKE (FH1206)															
DEE (RIVER) (FH1306)															
DEE (RIVER) (FH1305)															
DERWENT (RIVER) (FH1344)															

Fishery	Catfish American Bullhead	Catfish Black Bullhead	Charr	Chub	Dace	Eel	Flounder	Goldfish	Grayling	Grilse	Gudgeon	Gwyniad	Minnow	Orfe	Orfe Blue	Orfe Golden	Perch	Pike	Roach	Rudd	Ruffe
WEAR (RIVER) (FH5207)																					
WEAR (RIVER) (FH5210)																					
WEAR (RIVER) (FH5208)				●	●												●		●		
WEAR (RIVER) (FH5200)				●	●						●						●		●		
WEAR (RIVER) (FH5209)				●		●			●				●				●				
WELLFIELD POND (FH5238)											●						●		●	●	
WITTON CASTLE LAKES (FH5451)																					
CUMBRIA																					
AIRA BECK (FH0041)																					
ANNAS STREAM (FH0116)																					
ATKINSONS TARN COARSE FISHERY (FH0181)																					
BANKS POND (FH0289)				●		●					●						●		●		
BARN LAKE (FH0313)																					
BASSENTHWAITE LAKE (FH0344)						●							●				●	●	●		●
BESSY BECK TROUT FARM (FH0394)						●															
BIGLAND HALL LAKE (FH0414)						●											●	●	●	●	
BLELHAM TARN (FH0495)						●											●	●	●		
BLENCARN LAKE (FH0496)																					
BORROWDALE FISHERIES (FH0553)																					
BORWICK LAKE (FH0555)																					
BRATHAY (RIVER) (FH0604)																					
BRAYTON POND (FH0608)																					
BRIGHAM (RIVER) (FH0641)																					
BUTTERMERE LAKE (FH0777)			●			●							●				●	●			
CARLETON HILL (FH0842)				●													●		●		
CLEABARROW TARN (FH0996)						●					●								●	●	
CLOUGH (RIVER) (FH1023)																					
CODALE TARN (FH1050)																	●				
COGRA MOSS (FH1054)																					
CROSSFIELD FISHERY (FH1193)									●												
CRUMMOCK WATER LAKE (FH1206)			●			●							●				●	●			
DEE (RIVER) (FH1306)																					
DEE (RIVER) (FH1305)																					
DERWENT (RIVER) (FH1344)																					

Fishery	Salmon	Steelhead	Sturgeon	Tench	Tench Golden	Trount American Brook	Trout Blue	Trout Brook	Trout Brown	Trout Golden	Trout Lake	Ttrout Rainbow	Trout Sea	Trout Tiger	Trout Wild	Vendace	Zander
WEAR (RIVER) (FH5207)	●								●								
WEAR (RIVER) (FH5210)	●								●								
WEAR (RIVER) (FH5208)																	
WEAR (RIVER) (FH5200)																	
WEAR (RIVER) (FH5209)	●								●				●		●		
WELLFIELD POND (FH5238)				●													
WITTON CASTLE LAKES (FH5451)												●					
CUMBRIA																	
AIRA BECK (FH0041)	●								●								
ANNAS STREAM (FH0116)	●								●								
ATKINSONS TARN COARSE FISHERY (FH0181)									●			●					
BANKS POND (FH0289)				●													
BARN LAKE (FH0313)																	
BASSENTHWAITE LAKE (FH0344)	●								●				●			●	
BESSY BECK TROUT FARM (FH0394)									●	●		●					
BIGLAND HALL LAKE (FH0414)				●													
BLELHAM TARN (FH0495)									●								
BLENCARN LAKE (FH0496)									●			●					
BORROWDALE FISHERIES (FH0553)												●					
BORWICK LAKE (FH0555)																	
BRATHAY (RIVER) (FH0604)	●								●			●					
BRAYTON POND (FH0608)																	
BRIGHAM (RIVER) (FH0641)	●								●								
BUTTERMERE LAKE (FH0777)	●								●				●				
CARLETON HILL (FH0842)				●													
CLEABARROW TARN (FH0996)				●													
CLOUGH (RIVER) (FH1023)	●								●				●				
CODALE TARN (FH1050)									●								
COGRA MOSS (FH1054)									●			●					
CROSSFIELD FISHERY (FH1193)	●								●								
CRUMMOCK WATER LAKE (FH1206)	●								●				●				
DEE (RIVER) (FH1306)	●								●				●				
DEE (RIVER) (FH1305)	●								●				●				
DERWENT (RIVER) (FH1344)	●								●				●				

Fish Species Available at UK & Irish Fisheries

Fishery	Barbel	Bleak	Bream	Carp Blue	Carp Common	Carp Crucian	Carp Ghost	Carp Grass	Carp Koi	Carp Leather	Carp Mirror	Carp Silver	Carp Wild	Catfish	Catfish Albino	Catfish American Bullhead	Catfish Black Bullhead	Charr	Chub	Dace	Eel	Flounder	Goldfish	Grayling	Grilse	Gudgeon	Gwyniad	Minnow	Orfe	Orfe Blue	Orfe Golden	Perch	Pike	Roach	Rudd	Ruffe	Salmon	Steelhead	Sturgeon	Tench	Tench Golden	Trount American Brook	Trout Blue	Trout Brook	Trout Brown	Trout Golden	Trout Lake	Ttrout Rainbow	Trout Sea	Trout Tiger	Trout Wild	Vendace	Zander
DERWENT (RIVER) (FH1345)																																					●								●								
DEVOKE WATER (FH1363)																																													●								
DOE (RIVER) (FH1390)																																					●								●				●				
DRUNKEN DUCK TARN FISHERY (FH1454)																																													●			●					
DUBBS TROUT FISHERY (FH1458)																																																●					
EAMONT (RIVER) (FH1500)																																					●								●								
EASEDALE TARN (FH1505)																																●													●								
EAST VIEW FISHERY (FH1515)			●		●	●															●					●						●	●	●						●													
EDEN (RIVER) (FH1535)																																													●								
EDEN (RIVER) (FH1533)																																					●																
EDEN (RIVER) (FH1537)																																					●																
EDEN (RIVER) (FH1536)																			●					●																					●								
EDEN VALLEY TROUT LAKE (FH1543)																																													●			●					
ELLEN (RIVER) (FH1563)																																					●								●				●				
ELLERBECK FARM AND FISHERY (FH1565)			●		●	●			●		●								●		●							●				●		●	●					●					●								
ENNERDALE LAKE FISHERY (FH1595)																		●																													●						
ESK (RIVER) (FH1617)																																					●								●				●				
ESTHWAITE WATER (FH1630)																					●					●		●				●	●	●	●		●			●					●			●	●				
FISHER TARN (FH1727)																																													●								
GHYLL HEAD TROUT FISHERY (FH1851)																																													●			●					
GRASMERE COARSE FISHERY (FH1976)																					●											●	●	●											●								
GRETA (RIVER) (FH2016)																																					●								●				●				
GRIZEDALE BECK (FH2025)																																													●								
HARLOCK RESERVOIR (FH2108)																																													●								
HAWESWATER (FH2139)																																●													●								
HAWESWATER RESERVOIR (FH2140)																																													●			●					
HAYESWATER RESERVOIR (FH2154)																																													●			●					
HIGH ARNSIDE TARN (FH2204)																																													●			●					
HIGH NEWTON RESERVOIR (FH2209)																																													●			●					
HOLEHIRD TARN (FH2251)			●		●	●					●								●		●					●						●		●	●					●													
KENT (RIVER) (FH2471)																					●							●				●	●				●								●			●	●		●		
KENT (RIVER) (FH2472)																																					●								●				●				
KENTMERE FISHERY (FH2473)																																													●			●					
KILLINGTON RESERVOIR (FH2485)																																●	●												●								

Fish Species Available at UK & Irish Fisheries

Fishery	Barbel	Bleak	Bream	Carp Blue	Carp Common	Carp Crucian	Carp Ghost	Carp Grass	Carp Koi	Carp Leather	Carp Mirror	Carp Silver	Carp Wild	Catfish	Catfish Albino	Catfish American Bullhead	Catfish Black Bullhead	Charr	Chub	Dace	Eel	Flounder	Goldfish	Grayling	Grilse	Gudgeon	Gwyniad	Minnow	Orfe	Orfe Blue	Orfe Golden	Perch	Pike	Roach	Rudd	Ruffe	Salmon	Steelhead	Sturgeon	Tench	Tench Golden	Trount American Brook	Trout Blue	Trout Brook	Trout Brown	Trout Golden	Trout Lake	Ttrout Rainbow	Trout Sea	Trout Tiger	Trout Wild	Vendace	Zander
KIRKBY THORE (RIVER) (FH2525)																								●													●								●								
KNOTT END TARN (FH2543)																																													●								
LAKE WINDERMERE (FH2574)			●		●						●							●	●		●											●	●				●								●				●				
LIDDEL WATER (FH2715)																																					●												●				
LITTLE MUSGRAVE (FH2756)																																													●			●					
LONSDALE COUNTRY PARK (FH2997)					●		●	●			●																					●	●	●						●													
LOUGHRIGG TARN (FH3060)																					●											●	●	●																			
LOW GILL (FH3066)																																					●								●								
LOWESWATER LAKE (FH3096)																					●							●				●	●												●				●				
LOWTHER (RIVER) (FH3098)																																													●								
LUNE (RIVER) (FH3109)																																					●								●				●				
LUNE (RIVER) (FH3107)																																					●								●				●				
LUNE (RIVER) (FH3108)																																					●								●				●				
MEADLEY RESERVOIR (FH3221)																																													●			●					
MOCKERKIN TARN (FH3334)					●						●																																										
MOSS ECCLES TARN (FH3378)																																													●								
NETHERBY ESTATE (FH3453)																																					●																
NEW HILLS TROUT FARM FISHERY (FH3465)																																													●			●					
OAKBANK LAKES (FH3560)					●					●	●								●	●								●				●		●	●					●					●								
PENNINIGTON RESERVOIR (FH3739)																																													●								
PRYHEAD FISHERY (FH3853)																																																●					
RATHER HEATH TARN (FH3891)			●		●	●					●															●						●		●	●					●													
RAWTHEY (RIVER) (FH3898)																																					●								●								
RAWTHEY (RIVER) (FH3899)																																					●								●				●				
RAWTHEY (RIVER) (FH3897)																																					●								●				●				
ROANHEAD FISHERIES (FH3975)					●						●										●													●	●																		
RYDAL WATER (FH4071)																					●											●		●	●	●									●								
SANDFORD ARMS (FH4094)																																					●								●								
SCHOOL KNOTT TARN (FH4115)																																													●			●					
SHARPLEY WATERS (FH4211)																																													●								
SKELSMERGH LAKE (FH4288)																																●								●													
SOUTH TYNE (RIVER) (FH4340)																																					●								●				●				
SPRINT (RIVER) (FH4378)																					●							●				●	●				●								●			●	●		●		
TEWITFIELDS TROUT FISHERY (FH4752)					●	●					●															●								●						●								●					

Fish Species Available at UK & Irish Fisheries

	Barbel	Bleak	Bream	Carp Blue	Carp Common	Carp Crucian	Carp Ghost	Carp Grass	Carp Koi	Carp Leather	Carp Mirror	Carp Silver	Carp Wild	Catfish	Catfish Albino	Catfish American Bullhead	Catfish Black Bullhead	Charr	Chub	Dace	Eel	Flounder	Goldfish	Grayling	Grilse	Gudgeon	Gwyniad	Minnow	Orfe	Orfe Blue	Orfe Golden	Perch	Pike	Roach	Rudd	Ruffe	Salmon	Steelhead	Sturgeon	Tench	Tench Golden	Trount American Brook	Trout Blue	Trout Brook	Trout Brown	Trout Golden	Trout Lake	Ttrout Rainbow	Trout Sea	Trout Tiger	Trout Wild	Vendace	Zander
THIRLMERE (FH4810)																					●							●				●	●												●								
TRANQUIL OTTER (FH4904)																																																●					
TWISS (RIVER) (FH5006)																																					●								●				●				
TYNE (RIVER) (FH5017)																																					●								●				●				
ULLSWATER LAKE (FH5042)																																													●								
ULVERSTON CANAL (FH5043)			●		●						●								●		●							●				●	●	●	●					●													
WATENDLATH TROUT FISHERY (FH5169)																																													●	●		●					
WHINS POND (FH5323)			●		●	●					●								●		●					●						●		●	●					●								●					
WINSTER (RIVER) (FH5422)																					●																								●				●				
WINSTER (RIVER) (FH5423)			●																		●											●	●	●	●					●					●								
WITHERSLACK HALL TARN (FH5443)																					●											●	●	●																			
YEW TREE TARN (FH5569)																																													●			●					
DERBYSHIRE																																																					
ALDAMORE POOL (FH0054)					●						●																																										
ALLESTREE LAKE (FH0078)			●		●						●								●														●	●	●																		
ALVASTON LAKE (FH0089)			●		●						●																							●	●					●													
ARNFIELD RESERVOIR (FH0140)																																													●			●					
ASHGROVE LAKE (FH0162)			●		●						●								●													●		●	●					●													
BARLOW FISHERIES (FH0312)			●		●		●	●			●								●										●			●		●	●					●													
BEEHIVE FARM WOODLANDS LAKES (FH0371)			●		●						●															●						●		●	●					●													
BELPER POND (FH0382)					●						●																																										
BUTTERLEY RESERVOIR (FH0776)			●		●	●					●																					●	●	●						●													
CARSINGTON WATER (FH0854)																																		●	●										●								
CATTON PARK LAKE (FH0875)	●		●		●	●	●			●	●								●	●						●		●				●	●	●	●					●													
CHAPEL WHEEL DAM (FH0896)					●						●																																										
CODNOR PARK RESERVOIR (FH1051)			●		●						●																					●	●	●						●													
COMBS RESERVOIR (FH1081)			●		●						●																						●	●																			
CONDOR PARK RESERVOIR (FH1085)			●		●																																																
COPPICE LAKE (FH1112)			●		●						●								●													●		●	●					●													
COTE LODGE RESERVOIR (FH1126)																																													●								
DERBYSHIRE TROUT FISHERY (FH1334)																																													●			●					
DERWENT (RIVER) (FH1347)			●																●																																		
DERWENT (RIVER) (FH1349)	●																		●	●													●	●																			
DERWENT VALLEY FISHERY (FH1361)					●						●								●																					●													

Fish Species Available at UK & Irish Fisheries

Fishery	Barbel	Bleak	Bream	Carp Blue	Carp Common	Carp Crucian	Carp Ghost	Carp Grass	Carp Koi	Carp Leather	Carp Mirror	Carp Silver	Carp Wild	Catfish	Catfish Albino	Catfish American Bullhead	Catfish Black Bullhead	Charr	Chub	Dace	Eel	Flounder	Goldfish	Grayling	Grilse
DONKHILL FISHERIES (FH1404)																									
DOVE (RIVER) (FH1422)	●																		●	●				●	
DOVE (RIVER) (FH1423)																								●	
ERRWOOD RESERVOIR (FH1616)																									
FOREMARK TROUT FISHERY (FH1764)																									
FOXTON DAM (FH1793)					●						●														
HARLESTHORPE DAM (FH2107)			●		●	●					●								●						
HENMORE (RIVER) (FH2186)																								●	
HIGHAM FARM COARSE FISHING (FH2211)			●		●						●								●						
KEGWORTH DEEP LOCK (FH2424)																			●						
LADYBOWER RESERVOIR (FH2549)																									
LOCHO PARK LAKE (FH2970)					●						●														
MAPPERLEY RESERVOIR (FH3173)					●						●														
MARKEATON LAKE (FH3183)			●		●						●														
MELBOURNE POOL (FH3243)			●		●						●										●				
MONSAL DALE FISHERY (FH3352)																									
MOSS BROOK (FH3377)																									
POSSY LODGE PONDS (FH3832)						●	●				●														
PRESS MANOR (FH3840)					●		●				●														
RINGWOOD LAKE (FH3956)			●		●	●					●														
SOAR (RIVER) (FH4315)			●		●						●								●						
SUTTON BROOK (FH4562)	●																		●	●				●	
SWARKESTONE GRAVEL PITS (FH4604)			●		●						●														
SYDNOPE FISHERIES (FH4619)																									
TRENT (RIVER) (FH4917)																			●					●	
TRENT (RIVER) (FH4918)	●		●		●						●								●						
TRENT AND MERSEY CANAL (FH4940)					●						●								●						
WINGERWORTH LIDO (FH5416)					●																				
WYE (RIVER) (FH5528)																									
WYE (RIVER) (FH5529)																									
YEAVELEY ESTATE TROUT FISHERY (FH5560)																									
DEVON																									
ABBROOK POND (FH0012)			●		●						●														
ALDER LAKE (FH0059)			●		●																●				

Fishery	Gudgeon	Gwyniad	Minnow	Orfe	Orfe Blue	Orfe Golden	Perch	Pike	Roach	Rudd	Ruffe	Salmon	Steelhead	Sturgeon	Tench	Tench Golden	Trount American Brook	Trout Blue	Trout Brook	Trout Brown	Trout Golden	Trout Lake	Ttrout Rainbow	Trout Sea	Trout Tiger	Trout Wild	Vendace	Zander
DONKHILL FISHERIES (FH1404)																			●		●		●					
DOVE (RIVER) (FH1422)																				●								
DOVE (RIVER) (FH1423)																				●			●					
ERRWOOD RESERVOIR (FH1616)																				●			●					
FOREMARK TROUT FISHERY (FH1764)																				●			●					
FOXTON DAM (FH1793)							●	●	●						●													
HARLESTHORPE DAM (FH2107)	●					●	●	●	●		●				●													
HENMORE (RIVER) (FH2186)																				●			●					
HIGHAM FARM COARSE FISHING (FH2211)									●						●													
KEGWORTH DEEP LOCK (FH2424)									●																			
LADYBOWER RESERVOIR (FH2549)																				●			●					
LOCHO PARK LAKE (FH2970)									●						●													
MAPPERLEY RESERVOIR (FH3173)																												
MARKEATON LAKE (FH3183)								●	●	●																		
MELBOURNE POOL (FH3243)								●							●													
MONSAL DALE FISHERY (FH3352)																			●	●			●			●		
MOSS BROOK (FH3377)																				●								
POSSY LODGE PONDS (FH3832)									●	●					●													
PRESS MANOR (FH3840)																												
RINGWOOD LAKE (FH3956)							●		●	●					●													
SOAR (RIVER) (FH4315)	●						●		●																			
SUTTON BROOK (FH4562)																				●								
SWARKESTONE GRAVEL PITS (FH4604)							●	●	●						●													
SYDNOPE FISHERIES (FH4619)																				●			●					
TRENT (RIVER) (FH4917)																				●								
TRENT (RIVER) (FH4918)							●	●	●						●													
TRENT AND MERSEY CANAL (FH4940)	●						●		●																			
WINGERWORTH LIDO (FH5416)							●	●	●						●													
WYE (RIVER) (FH5528)												●																
WYE (RIVER) (FH5529)																				●								
YEAVELEY ESTATE TROUT FISHERY (FH5560)																				●			●					
DEVON																												
ABBROOK POND (FH0012)									●						●													
ALDER LAKE (FH0059)							●		●						●					●						●		

Fish Species Available at UK & Irish Fisheries

Fishery	Barbel	Bleak	Bream	Carp Blue	Carp Common	Carp Crucian	Carp Ghost	Carp Grass	Carp Koi	Carp Leather	Carp Mirror	Carp Silver	Carp Wild	Catfish	Catfish Albino	Catfish American Bullhead	Catfish Black Bullhead
ANGLERS ELDORADO (FH0106)					●			●	●		●			●			
ANGLERS PARADISE (FH0108)					●			●			●			●		●	
ANGLERS SHANGRILA (FH0109)					●			●			●						
ASHCOMBE FISHERY (FH0159)			●		●		●				●						
AVETON GIFFORD STREAM (FH0188)																	
AVON (RIVER) (FH0203)																	
AVON DAM (FH0227)																	
AXE (RIVER) (FH0234)																	
AXE (RIVER) (FH0233)																	
BAKERS FARM (FH0254)					●						●						
BELLBROOK VALLEY (FH0377)																	
BERRYNARBOR MILL POND (FH0392)			●		●						●						
BICKERTON FARM FISHERY (FH0406)			●		●						●						
BILLINGSMOOR FARM (FH0422)					●						●						
BLAKEWELL FISHERIES (FH0491)																	
BLUE LAKE (FH0509)					●						●						
BULWORTHY FISHERY (FH0731)					●						●						
CADOVER BRIDGE PITS (FH0788)			●		●	●					●						
CAMEL (RIVER) (FH0811)																	
CAMEL (RIVER) (FH0810)																	
CHARLECOMBE (FH0902)			●		●						●						
CLAWFORD FISHERIES (FH0985)			●		●	●	●				●						
CLOVELLY LAKES (FH1024)			●		●						●						
COFTON PARK FARM (FH1052)			●														
COOMBE FARM FISHPONDS (FH1105)			●		●						●						
COOMBE FISHERIES (FH1106)			●		●		●			●	●						
COOMBE WATER FISHERY (FH1110)			●		●	●					●						
CREEDY (RIVER) (FH1174)																	
CREEDY (RIVER) (FH1175)																	
CREEDY LAKES (FH1176)					●	●	●		●		●						
CULM (RIVER) (FH1218)					●						●						
CULM (RIVER) (FH1217)																	
DARRACOTT RESERVOIR (FH1276)			●		●						●						
DEER PARK COUNTRY HOTEL (FH1324)					●						●						

Fishery	Charr	Chub	Dace	Eel	Flounder	Goldfish	Grayling	Grilse	Gudgeon	Gwyniad	Minnow	Orfe	Orfe Blue	Orfe Golden	Perch	Pike	Roach	Rudd
ANGLERS ELDORADO (FH0106)				●										●				●
ANGLERS PARADISE (FH0108)				●										●				●
ANGLERS SHANGRILA (FH0109)														●				●
ASHCOMBE FISHERY (FH0159)				●													●	
AVETON GIFFORD STREAM (FH0188)																		
AVON (RIVER) (FH0203)																		
AVON DAM (FH0227)																		
AXE (RIVER) (FH0234)																		
AXE (RIVER) (FH0233)																		
BAKERS FARM (FH0254)																	●	●
BELLBROOK VALLEY (FH0377)																		
BERRYNARBOR MILL POND (FH0392)															●		●	
BICKERTON FARM FISHERY (FH0406)				●											●		●	●
BILLINGSMOOR FARM (FH0422)															●		●	●
BLAKEWELL FISHERIES (FH0491)																		
BLUE LAKE (FH0509)																		●
BULWORTHY FISHERY (FH0731)																		
CADOVER BRIDGE PITS (FH0788)																	●	●
CAMEL (RIVER) (FH0811)																		
CAMEL (RIVER) (FH0810)																		
CHARLECOMBE (FH0902)																		●
CLAWFORD FISHERIES (FH0985)		●															●	
CLOVELLY LAKES (FH1024)												●					●	●
COFTON PARK FARM (FH1052)																	●	
COOMBE FARM FISHPONDS (FH1105)																		●
COOMBE FISHERIES (FH1106)				●													●	●
COOMBE WATER FISHERY (FH1110)																	●	
CREEDY (RIVER) (FH1174)		●					●										●	
CREEDY (RIVER) (FH1175)																		
CREEDY LAKES (FH1176)				●														
CULM (RIVER) (FH1218)		●	●				●									●	●	
CULM (RIVER) (FH1217)		●	●				●									●	●	
DARRACOTT RESERVOIR (FH1276)															●		●	●
DEER PARK COUNTRY HOTEL (FH1324)																		

Fishery	Ruffe	Salmon	Steelhead	Sturgeon	Tench	Tench Golden	Trount American Brook	Trout Blue	Trout Brook	Trout Brown	Trout Golden	Trout Lake	Ttrout Rainbow	Trout Sea	Trout Tiger	Trout Wild	Vendace	Zander
ANGLERS ELDORADO (FH0106)					●													
ANGLERS PARADISE (FH0108)					●	●												
ANGLERS SHANGRILA (FH0109)					●													
ASHCOMBE FISHERY (FH0159)					●													
AVETON GIFFORD STREAM (FH0188)		●								●								
AVON (RIVER) (FH0203)		●								●								
AVON DAM (FH0227)										●								
AXE (RIVER) (FH0234)										●								
AXE (RIVER) (FH0233)		●								●								
BAKERS FARM (FH0254)					●													
BELLBROOK VALLEY (FH0377)								●		●	●		●					
BERRYNARBOR MILL POND (FH0392)																		
BICKERTON FARM FISHERY (FH0406)					●													
BILLINGSMOOR FARM (FH0422)					●													
BLAKEWELL FISHERIES (FH0491)										●			●					
BLUE LAKE (FH0509)																		
BULWORTHY FISHERY (FH0731)													●					
CADOVER BRIDGE PITS (FH0788)					●													
CAMEL (RIVER) (FH0811)		●								●				●				
CAMEL (RIVER) (FH0810)		●								●				●				
CHARLECOMBE (FH0902)					●													
CLAWFORD FISHERIES (FH0985)					●								●					
CLOVELLY LAKES (FH1024)					●													
COFTON PARK FARM (FH1052)					●													
COOMBE FARM FISHPONDS (FH1105)					●													
COOMBE FISHERIES (FH1106)					●				●									
COOMBE WATER FISHERY (FH1110)					●													
CREEDY (RIVER) (FH1174)										●								
CREEDY (RIVER) (FH1175)		●								●				●				
CREEDY LAKES (FH1176)					●													
CULM (RIVER) (FH1218)										●								
CULM (RIVER) (FH1217)										●								
DARRACOTT RESERVOIR (FH1276)																		
DEER PARK COUNTRY HOTEL (FH1324)										●								

Fish Species Available at UK & Irish Fisheries

Fishery	Barbel	Bleak	Bream	Carp Blue	Carp Common	Carp Crucian	Carp Ghost	Carp Grass	Carp Koi	Carp Leather	Carp Mirror	Carp Silver	Carp Wild	Catfish	Catfish Albino	Catfish American Bullhead	Catfish Black Bullhead	Charr	Chub	Dace	Eel	Flounder	Goldfish	Grayling	Grilse	Gudgeon	Gwyniad	Minnow	Orfe	Orfe Blue	Orfe Golden	Perch	Pike	Roach	Rudd	Ruffe	Salmon	Steelhead	Sturgeon	Tench	Tench Golden	Trount American Brook	Trout Blue	Trout Brook	Trout Brown	Trout Golden	Trout Lake	Ttrout Rainbow	Trout Sea	Trout Tiger	Trout Wild	Vendace	Zander
DORES POND - RACKERHAYES (FH1413)					●					●	●																																										
DRAKELANDS GAME FISHERY (FH1435)																																													●			●					
DUNSLEY FARM (FH1481)					●						●																							●	●					●													
EASTCOTT FARM AND LODGES (FH1518)					●						●																																										
EDDISON POND (FH1532)					●						●										●											●		●						●													
EGGESFORD WATERS (FH1551)																																					●								●				●				
EXE (RIVER) (FH1642)																																					●								●				●				
EXE (RIVER) (FH1640)																								●													●								●			●					
EXE (RIVER) (FH1639)					●						●								●					●								●		●																			
EXE (RIVER) (FH1643)			●		●						●								●													●	●	●																			
EXEMOOR FARM (FH1646)					●	●					●																		●					●	●					●													
EXETER CANAL (FH1647)			●		●						●										●											●	●	●	●					●													
EXETER SHIP CANAL (FH1648)					●						●																						●																				
FENECK POND (FH1695)			●																															●						●													
FERNWORTHY RESERVOIR (FH1700)																																													●								
FINLAKE PONDS (FH1713)			●			●																												●	●					●													
FISHPONDS HOUSE (FH1736)					●	●	●				●																		●					●	●					●													
FOSFELLE COUNTRY HOUSE HOTEL (FH1774)			●		●						●																							●	●													●					
FOUR PONDS (FH1781)			●		●																											●		●	●					●													
GRAND WESTERN CANAL (FH1968)			●		●						●										●											●	●	●	●					●													
GRAND WESTERN CANAL (FH1967)			●								●										●											●	●	●						●													
HARTLAND FOREST FISHERY (FH2116)					●						●																								●					●													
HARTSMOOR FISHERIES (FH2121)	●		●		●	●	●	●	●	●	●								●		●					●			●			●		●	●					●													
HATCHLAND TROUT FISHERY (FH2129)			●		●						●															●								●	●					●					●			●					
HOGSBROOK LAKES (FH2246)			●		●	●					●															●						●		●	●					●													
HOLLIES TROUT FISHERY (FH2256)																																													●								
HOME FARM FISHERY (FH2280)					●		●		●		●																							●	●					●													
INDIO POND (FH2365)					●	●	●		●	●	●										●											●			●					●	●							●					
ISLAND POND - RACKERHAYES (FH2391)			●		●						●																							●						●													
JENNETTS RESERVOIR (FH2409)			●		●						●										●											●		●	●					●													
KENNICK RESERVOIR (FH2469)																																															●					
KINGSMEAD CENTRE (FH2515)			●		●		●				●								●												●	●		●						●													
LEGGE FARM COARSE FISHERY (FH2688)			●		●	●	●	●			●																					●		●	●					●													
LEWORTHY FARM (FH2712)					●						●																																										

Fish Species Available at UK & Irish Fisheries

Fishery	Barbel	Bleak	Bream	Carp Blue	Carp Common	Carp Crucian	Carp Ghost	Carp Grass	Carp Koi	Carp Leather	Carp Mirror	Carp Silver	Carp Wild	Catfish	Catfish Albino	Catfish American Bullhead	Catfish Black Bullhead	Charr	Chub	Dace	Eel	Flounder	Goldfish	Grayling	Grilse	Gudgeon	Gwyniad	Minnow	Orfe	Orfe Blue	Orfe Golden	Perch	Pike	Roach	Rudd	Ruffe	Salmon	Steelhead	Sturgeon	Tench	Tench Golden	Trount American Brook	Trout Blue	Trout Brook	Trout Brown	Trout Golden	Trout Lake	Ttrout Rainbow	Trout Sea	Trout Tiger	Trout Wild	Vendace	Zander
LITTLE ALLERS COARSE FISHERY (FH2739)			●		●		●				●																							●	●					●													
LITTLE COMFORT FARM (FH2746)			●		●						●																								●										●								
LITTLE WEACH (FH2763)			●		●		●		●		●												●											●	●					●													
LODDISWELL STREAM (FH2975)																																					●								●								
LONGLANDS FARM (FH2991)					●						●																																										
LOWER HALLACOMBE FISHERY (FH3080)					●	●			●		●																					●		●	●					●													
LOWER SLADE RESERVOIR (FH3094)			●		●						●															●						●		●	●					●													
LUCCOMBES PONDS (FH3101)			●		●	●	●		●	●	●																		●					●	●					●													
LYN (RIVER) (FH3118)																																					●								●								
MELBURY RESERVOIR (FH3244)			●		●						●																					●		●	●																		
MELDON RESERVOIR (FH3246)																																													●			●					
MILEMEAD FISHERIES (FH3274)			●		●	●	●		●	●	●										●					●								●	●					●	●												
MILL (FH3277)					●						●																					●			●					●													
MILL LEAT TROUT FISHERY (FH3291)																																																●					
MILL PARK COARSE FISHING LAKE (FH3297)			●		●	●					●																				●	●		●	●					●													
MILLHAYES (FH3313)					●						●																							●	●					●													
MILTON FARM PONDS (FH3319)			●		●	●					●																							●						●													
MOLE (RIVER) (FH3337)																																					●								●				●				
NEW BARN ANGLING CENTRE (FH3461)			●		●		●				●										●											●		●	●					●													
NEWCOURT PONDS (FH3482)			●		●						●																		●					●						●													
NEWHOUSE FISHERY (FH3486)																																													●			●					
NEWTON ABBOT SPRING PONDS (FH3493)			●		●						●																							●																			
OAKTREE FISHERY (FH3568)			●		●	●					●			●																		●		●	●																		
OLD MILL RESERVOIR (FH3596)			●		●						●										●													●	●					●													
OLDBOROUGH FISHING RETREAT (FH3604)					●					●	●										●											●		●	●					●													
OTTER (RIVER) (FH3630)																																													●								
OTTER FALLS FISHERY (FH3631)			●		●																											●		●	●					●								●					
PADBROOK PARK (FH3681)					●						●																																										
PICFRESH (FH3765)			●		●						●																							●	●					●													
PLYM (RIVER) (FH3807)																																					●												●		●		
POUND POND FARM (FH3836)					●						●																					●			●					●													
PYEWELL FARM (FH3861)					●						●																													●													
RIVERTON HOUSE AND LAKES (FH3970)			●		●	●	●		●		●															●						●		●	●					●													
ROADFORD RESERVOIR (FH3973)																																													●								

Fish Species Available at UK & Irish Fisheries

Fishery	Barbel	Bleak	Bream	Carp Blue	Carp Common	Carp Crucian	Carp Ghost	Carp Grass	Carp Koi	Carp Leather	Carp Mirror	Carp Silver	Carp Wild	Catfish
ROCOMBE PONDS (FH3986)			●		●		●				●			
RUB - A - DUB POND (FH4051)					●						●			
SALMONHUTCH COARSE FISHERY (FH4087)					●						●			
SAMPFORD PEVERAL PONDS (FH4090)					●						●			
SAWMILLS LAKE (FH4109)			●		●						●			●
SHOBROOKE PARK (FH4244)					●						●			
SIMPSON VALLEY FISHERY (FH4274)					●	●	●				●			
SLADE RESERVOIRS (FH4292)			●		●						●			
SLAPTON LEY (FH4294)														
SOUTH HAY FARM (FH4330)					●									
SOUTH REED LAKE (FH4338)					●						●			
SOUTH VIEW FARM FISHERY (FH4344)			●		●	●	●				●			
SPIRES LAKES (FH4365)			●		●	●	●				●			
SQUABMOOR RESERVOIR (FH4379)			●		●						●			
STAFFORD MOOR FISHERY (FH4402)														
STAR BARTON PONDS (FH4426)					●						●			
STEVENSTONE LAKES (FH4452)					●						●			
STILL WATERS TROUT FISHERY (FH4456)														
STONE FARM QUARRY (FH4469)			●		●						●			
STOUR FARM FISHERY (FH4505)					●						●			
SUMMERLEAZE POND (FH4554)					●	●					●			
SUNRIDGE FISHERY (FH4557)					●						●			
SWIMBRIDGE POOL (FH4610)			●		●						●			
TAMAR (RIVER) (FH4643)														
TAMAR (RIVER) (FH4642)														
TAMAR LAKE (LOWER) (FH4644)														
TAR (RIVER) (FH4658)														
TAVISTOCK TROUT FISHERY (FH4670)														
TAVY (RIVER) (FH4671)														
TAW FISHING CLUB (FH4674)														
TEIGN (FH4716)														
TEIGN (RIVER) (FH4719)														
TINNEY WATERS (FH4855)			●		●			●			●			
TORRIDGE (RIVER) (FH4883)														

Fishery	Catfish Albino	Catfish American Bullhead	Catfish Black Bullhead	Charr	Chub	Dace	Eel	Flounder	Goldfish	Grayling	Grilse	Gudgeon	Gwyniad	Minnow	Orfe	Orfe Blue	Orfe Golden
ROCOMBE PONDS (FH3986)															●		
RUB - A - DUB POND (FH4051)																	
SALMONHUTCH COARSE FISHERY (FH4087)																	
SAMPFORD PEVERAL PONDS (FH4090)																	
SAWMILLS LAKE (FH4109)																	
SHOBROOKE PARK (FH4244)																	
SIMPSON VALLEY FISHERY (FH4274)					●							●					
SLADE RESERVOIRS (FH4292)																	
SLAPTON LEY (FH4294)							●										
SOUTH HAY FARM (FH4330)															●		
SOUTH REED LAKE (FH4338)																	
SOUTH VIEW FARM FISHERY (FH4344)												●		●			
SPIRES LAKES (FH4365)															●		
SQUABMOOR RESERVOIR (FH4379)																	
STAFFORD MOOR FISHERY (FH4402)																	
STAR BARTON PONDS (FH4426)																	
STEVENSTONE LAKES (FH4452)																	
STILL WATERS TROUT FISHERY (FH4456)																	
STONE FARM QUARRY (FH4469)																	
STOUR FARM FISHERY (FH4505)																	
SUMMERLEAZE POND (FH4554)																	
SUNRIDGE FISHERY (FH4557)							●										
SWIMBRIDGE POOL (FH4610)																	
TAMAR (RIVER) (FH4643)																	
TAMAR (RIVER) (FH4642)																	
TAMAR LAKE (LOWER) (FH4644)																	
TAR (RIVER) (FH4658)																	
TAVISTOCK TROUT FISHERY (FH4670)																	
TAVY (RIVER) (FH4671)																	
TAW FISHING CLUB (FH4674)																	
TEIGN (FH4716)																	
TEIGN (RIVER) (FH4719)																	
TINNEY WATERS (FH4855)																	
TORRIDGE (RIVER) (FH4883)																	

Fishery	Perch	Pike	Roach	Rudd	Ruffe	Salmon	Steelhead	Sturgeon	Tench	Tench Golden	Trount American Brook	Trout Blue	Trout Brook	Trout Brown	Trout Golden	Trout Lake	Ttrout Rainbow	Trout Sea	Trout Tiger	Trout Wild	Vendace	Zander
ROCOMBE PONDS (FH3986)	●		●	●					●													
RUB - A - DUB POND (FH4051)	●		●						●													
SALMONHUTCH COARSE FISHERY (FH4087)				●					●													
SAMPFORD PEVERAL PONDS (FH4090)																						
SAWMILLS LAKE (FH4109)	●		●						●													
SHOBROOKE PARK (FH4244)			●						●													
SIMPSON VALLEY FISHERY (FH4274)			●	●					●													
SLADE RESERVOIRS (FH4292)	●		●						●													
SLAPTON LEY (FH4294)	●	●	●	●																		
SOUTH HAY FARM (FH4330)				●					●					●								
SOUTH REED LAKE (FH4338)																						
SOUTH VIEW FARM FISHERY (FH4344)	●		●	●					●													
SPIRES LAKES (FH4365)	●		●	●					●													
SQUABMOOR RESERVOIR (FH4379)			●	●					●													
STAFFORD MOOR FISHERY (FH4402)																	●					
STAR BARTON PONDS (FH4426)									●													
STEVENSTONE LAKES (FH4452)				●					●													
STILL WATERS TROUT FISHERY (FH4456)						●								●			●	●				
STONE FARM QUARRY (FH4469)			●	●					●													
STOUR FARM FISHERY (FH4505)																						
SUMMERLEAZE POND (FH4554)	●		●																			
SUNRIDGE FISHERY (FH4557)																						
SWIMBRIDGE POOL (FH4610)	●			●					●													
TAMAR (RIVER) (FH4643)						●								●								
TAMAR (RIVER) (FH4642)						●								●				●				
TAMAR LAKE (LOWER) (FH4644)														●			●					
TAR (RIVER) (FH4658)						●								●				●				
TAVISTOCK TROUT FISHERY (FH4670)														●			●					
TAVY (RIVER) (FH4671)						●												●		●		
TAW FISHING CLUB (FH4674)						●								●				●				
TEIGN (FH4716)						●								●				●				
TEIGN (RIVER) (FH4719)						●								●				●				
TINNEY WATERS (FH4855)	●			●					●													
TORRIDGE (RIVER) (FH4883)						●								●				●				

Fish Species Available at UK & Irish Fisheries

Fishery	Barbel	Bleak	Bream	Carp Blue	Carp Common	Carp Crucian	Carp Ghost	Carp Grass	Carp Koi	Carp Leather	Carp Mirror	Carp Silver	Carp Wild	Catfish	Catfish Albino	Catfish American Bullhead	Catfish Black Bullhead	Charr	Chub	Dace	Eel	Flounder	Goldfish	Grayling	Grilse	Gudgeon	Gwyniad	Minnow	Orfe	Orfe Blue	Orfe Golden	Perch	Pike	Roach	Rudd	Ruffe	Salmon	Steelhead	Sturgeon	Tench	Tench Golden	Trount American Brook	Trout Blue	Trout Brook	Trout Brown	Trout Golden	Trout Lake	Ttrout Rainbow	Trout Sea	Trout Tiger	Trout Wild	Vendace	Zander
TORRIDGE (RIVER) (FH4885)																								●													●								●								
TOWN PARKS COARSE FISHERY (FH4893)			●		●	●	●		●	●	●								●	●	●					●					●	●		●	●					●													
TRAGO MILLS (FH4903)			●		●						●																													●													
TRENCHFORD RESERVOIR (FH4915)																																●	●	●																			
UPHAM FARM PONDS (FH5050)					●			●			●										●																			●													
UPPER YEALM FISHERY (FH5061)																																													●				●				
UPTON WARREN LAKE (FH5062)			●		●	●					●								●	●						●						●		●	●					●													
VALLEY SPRINGS TROUT FISHERY (FH5088)					●	●	●		●	●	●			●							●													●	●					●				●	●		●	●					
VALLEY VIEW FISHERY (FH5089)					●						●																																										
VENFORD RESERVOIR (FH5091)																																													●			●					
VENN POOL (FH5093)			●		●						●																					●			●					●													
WAPPERWELL POND (FH5146)			●			●																												●	●					●													
WATERCRESS FARM TROUT FISHERY (FH5174)																																													●		●	●					
WEST PITT FARM FISHERY (FH5264)	●		●		●	●					●								●													●		●	●					●													
WEST VIEW POND (FH5267)																																		●	●																		
WILLOWFIELD LAKE COTTAGES (FH5393)					●	●					●																							●						●													
WISCOMBE FISHERY (FH5433)			●		●																																			●								●					
WISTLANDPOUND RESERVOIR (FH5436)																																													●								
WOODACOTT ARMS (FH5464)			●		●						●																					●		●	●					●													
YEO (RIVER) (FH5561)																																					●								●				●				
YEO (RIVER) (FH5562)																																													●								
DORSET																																																					
AMHERST LODGE FISHERY (FH0101)																																													●			●					
AVON (RIVER) (FH0204)	●		●		●						●								●	●												●	●	●			●								●								
AVON TYRRELL LAKES (FH0230)					●	●					●										●											●		●	●					●													
BERKELEY FARM (FH0391)																					●														●					●													
BLASHFORD LAKES (FH0493)			●		●						●								●														●	●						●													
CHRISTCHURCH LOWER STOUR (FH0948)	●		●		●						●								●	●	●					●						●	●	●			●												●				
CLUB LAKE (FH1027)					●	●					●			●																				●	●					●													
CRANBOURNE FRUIT FARM (FH1163)			●		●	●					●												●									●		●						●													
CROW POOL (FH1198)					●						●								●	●												●	●	●	●					●													
CULVERS FARM FISHERIES (FH1220)			●		●						●																							●						●													
DORSET FROME (FH1417)																				●				●										●																			
FLOWERS FARM TROUT LAKES (FH1750)																																													●			●					

Fish Species Available at UK & Irish Fisheries

	Barbel	Bleak	Bream	Carp Blue	Carp Common	Carp Crucian	Carp Ghost	Carp Grass	Carp Koi	Carp Leather	Carp Mirror	Carp Silver	Carp Wild	Catfish	Catfish Albino	Catfish American Bullhead	Catfish Black Bullhead	Charr	Chub	Dace	Eel	Flounder	Goldfish	Grayling	Grilse	Gudgeon	Gwyniad	Minnow	Orfe	Orfe Blue	Orfe Golden	Perch	Pike	Roach	Rudd	Ruffe	Salmon	Steelhead	Sturgeon	Tench	Tench Golden	Trount American Brook	Trout Blue	Trout Brook	Trout Brown	Trout Golden	Trout Lake	Ttrout Rainbow	Trout Sea	Trout Tiger	Trout Wild	Vendace	Zander
FROME (RIVER) (FH1809)											●									●				●									●	●															●				
GOLD OAK FISH FARM (FH1908)			●		●	●					●								●													●		●						●	●												
GOLDEN SPRINGS LAKES (FH1913)					●						●																							●						●					●								
HAMPSHIRE AVON (RIVER) (FH2087)	●		●		●						●								●																					●													
HAMPSHIRE AVON (RIVER) (FH2083)	●																		●	●	●												●	●																			
HAMPSHIRE AVON (RIVER) (FH2085)	●																		●	●													●	●																			
HAMPSHIRE AVON (RIVER) (FH2084)	●																		●	●													●	●																			
HAMPSHIRE AVON (RIVER) (FH2086)	●		●		●						●								●	●						●						●	●	●																			
HAMWORTHY LAKE (FH2098)					●						●										●											●	●	●	●					●													
HARROW POND (FH2111)					●						●																						●	●						●													
HERMITAGE LAKES (FH2189)					●					●	●																																		●			●					
HILLVIEW FARM LAKE (FH2227)					●	●					●																					●								●													
HOLT WOOD PONDS (FH2272)					●	●					●																							●	●					●													
HYDE LAKE (FH2353)					●	●																												●	●					●													
KINGCOMBE COARSE FARM (FH2492)			●		●	●	●	●	●		●								●							●			●			●		●	●					●													
KINGCOMBE LAKE (FH2493)			●		●	●				●	●																							●																			
KNAPP HILL FARM LAKES (FH2533)					●						●																							●	●					●													
LAWRENCES FARM (FH2636)																																													●								
LUCKFIELD LAKE FISHERY (FH3102)					●			●	●		●										●													●						●	●												
LYONS GATE CARAVAN PARK (FH3126)			●		●	●	●		●		●												●											●	●				●	●													
MAPPOWDER COURT (FH3174)			●		●	●					●																					●		●	●					●													
MARTINS FARM (FH3201)					●	●					●										●											●		●						●													
MUDEFORD WOOD LAKE (FH3397)					●	●					●																					●		●	●					●													
NEW MEADOWS LAKE (FH3473)			●		●		●				●																							●						●													
PALLINGTON LAKES (FH3687)			●		●					●	●								●		●			●				●				●		●	●					●													
PIDDLE (RIVER) (FH3770)					●						●									●												●	●	●																			
PIDDLE (RIVER) (FH3769)																																													●								
RADIPOLE LAKE (FH3875)					●						●									●	●												●	●	●																		
RAWLSBURY WATERS (FH3896)																																													●								
REVEL'S FISHERY (FH3932)			●		●	●	●	●		●	●			●					●												●	●	●	●	●					●													
ROYALTY FISHERY (FH4049)	●		●		●						●								●	●	●							●				●	●	●			●			●									●				
SHERBORNE LAKE (FH4233)			●																																					●													
SOPLEY FARM (FH4327)			●		●						●																							●	●																		
STOUR (DORSET) (RIVER) (FH4490)	●				●														●	●												●	●	●																			

Fish Species Available at UK & Irish Fisheries

Fishery	Barbel	Bleak	Bream	Carp Blue	Carp Common	Carp Crucian	Carp Ghost	Carp Grass	Carp Koi	Carp Leather	Carp Mirror	Carp Silver	Carp Wild	Catfish	Catfish Albino	Catfish American Bullhead	Catfish Black Bullhead	Charr	Chub	Dace	Eel	Flounder	Goldfish	Grayling	Grilse	Gudgeon	Gwyniad	Minnow	Orfe	Orfe Blue	Orfe Golden	Perch	Pike	Roach	Rudd	Ruffe	Salmon	Steelhead	Sturgeon	Tench	Tench Golden	Trount American Brook	Trout Blue	Trout Brook	Trout Brown	Trout Golden	Trout Lake	Ttrout Rainbow	Trout Sea	Trout Tiger	Trout Wild	Vendace	Zander
STOUR (DORSET) (RIVER) (FH4477)			●		●						●								●	●												●	●	●						●													
STOUR (DORSET) (RIVER) (FH4478)	●		●		●						●								●	●	●	●											●	●																			
STOUR (DORSET) (RIVER) (FH4479)																			●														●	●																			
STOUR (DORSET) (RIVER) (FH4485)			●		●														●	●	●					●						●	●	●						●													
STOUR (DORSET) (RIVER) (FH4489)			●																●	●	●					●		●				●	●	●																			
STOUR (DORSET) (RIVER) (FH4488)	●		●		●														●	●	●											●	●	●																			
STOUR (DORSET) (RIVER) (FH4486)			●		●						●								●	●												●	●	●	●					●													
STOUR (DORSET) (RIVER) (FH4481)	●		●		●						●								●		●											●	●	●																			
STOUR (DORSET) (RIVER) (FH4483)	●		●		●						●								●	●													●	●															●				
STOUR (DORSET) (RIVER) (FH4476)			●																															●																			
STOUR (DORSET) (RIVER) (FH4487)			●																													●	●	●																			
STOUR (DORSET) (RIVER) (FH4480)	●		●		●						●								●	●	●					●		●					●	●																			
STOUR (DORSET) (RIVER) (FH4484)	●																																																				
STOUR (DORSET) (RIVER) (FH4482)	●		●		●						●								●	●	●												●	●															●				
STOUR (RIVER) (FH4493)			●		●						●								●	●													●	●																			
STOUR (RIVER) (FH4491)	●		●																●	●	●											●	●	●																			
STOUR (RIVER) (FH4494)			●		●						●								●	●												●	●	●						●													
STOUR (RIVER) (FH4492)			●		●						●								●														●	●						●													
THAMES (RIVER) (FH4783)		●	●		●	●					●									●						●						●	●	●	●																		
THROOP FISHERIES (FH4834)	●		●		●						●								●	●	●	●										●	●	●						●													
TODBER MANOR (FH4862)	●		●		●						●								●							●						●		●						●													
UPPER STOUR (RIVER) (FH5059)			●																●	●						●						●	●	●																			
WALLYS LAKE (FH5124)			●		●	●					●										●													●	●					●													
WARMWELL HOLIDAY PARK (FH5148)					●						●																																										
WATERMILL LAKE (FH5182)																																																●					
WESSEX TROUT LAKES (FH5254)																																																●					
WHIRLWIND LAKE (FH5328)					●	●					●								●															●						●													
WHITEMOOR LAKE (FH5351)	●		●		●	●					●								●													●		●	●					●													
WHITESHEET TROUT FISHERY (FH5353)																																													●			●					
WINKTON FISHERY (FH5418)	●		●		●						●								●		●			●		●		●				●	●	●			●												●				
WOOD FARM CARAVAN PARK (FH5458)					●	●	●				●																					●		●	●					●													
ESSEX																																																					
ALBYNS LAKE (FH0053)			●		●	●					●								●													●	●	●	●					●													
ARDLEIGH RESERVOIR (FH0130)			●		●	●	●		●		●										●					●						●	●	●	●					●													

Fish Species Available at UK & Irish Fisheries

Fishery	Barbel	Bleak	Bream	Carp Blue	Carp Common	Carp Crucian	Carp Ghost	Carp Grass	Carp Koi	Carp Leather	Carp Mirror	Carp Silver	Carp Wild	Catfish	Catfish Albino	Catfish American Bullhead	Catfish Black Bullhead	Charr	Chub	Dace	Eel	Flounder	Goldfish	Grayling	Grilse	Gudgeon
ARENA LAKE (FH0132)					●						●															
ARMIGERS FARM (FH0138)					●	●					●															
ASHELDHAM FISHERY (FH0160)					●	●					●			●							●					
AVELEY LAKES (FH0187)					●						●															
BARLEYLANDS RESERVOIR (FH0310)			●		●	●					●															
BEDFORDS PARK LAKE (FH0365)			●		●						●															
BERWICK PONDS (FH0393)			●		●	●	●				●			●							●					
BIRDS GREEN (FH0428)			●		●	●					●								●							
BLACKMORE WOOD (FH0452)			●		●	●					●								●		●					●
BLACKWATER (RIVER) (FH0474)																			●	●						
BLACKWATER (RIVER) (FH0475)			●		●						●								●							
BLACKWATER (RIVER) (FH0476)			●		●						●									●						●
BLACKWATER (RIVER) (FH0477)			●		●														●	●	●					●
BLASFORD HILL FISHERIES (FH0492)			●		●	●					●								●	●	●					●
BLUNTS AND CANTS MERES (FH0516)					●	●					●										●					
BOG GROVE (FH0523)					●						●															
BORDEAUX PIT (FH0545)					●	●					●															
BOREHAM FISHERY (FH0548)			●		●						●															
BOREHAM MERES (FH0549)			●		●	●					●										●					
BOVINGTON MERE 1 (FH0569)			●		●						●															
BOVINGTON MERE 2 (FH0570)			●		●						●															
BRAXTED HALL ESTATE (FH0605)			●		●	●		●			●										●					
BRICKHOUSE FARM FISHERIES (FH0621)			●		●	●					●								●		●					
BROAD GREEN AND TUFNELL MERE (FH0663)			●		●	●					●										●					●
BROOKHALL FISHERY (FH0682)			●		●	●					●															
BULPHAN PARK FISHERIES (FH0730)			●		●				●		●															
BURROWS FARM (FH0754)			●		●						●															
CANTS MERE (FH0830)					●						●															
CARP FARM FRYERNING FISHERIES (FH0845)			●		●	●		●			●			●												
CENTRAL PARK LAKE (FH0887)					●						●															
CHASE FISHERY (FH0907)			●		●	●					●															
CHELMER & BLACKWATER (FH0913)			●		●	●					●								●	●	●					●
CHELMER (RIVER) (FH0910)	●		●		●						●								●	●	●					●
CHELMER (RIVER) (FH0911)			●		●						●								●	●	●					●

Fishery	Gwyniad	Minnow	Orfe	Orfe Blue	Orfe Golden	Perch	Pike	Roach	Rudd	Ruffe	Salmon	Steelhead	Sturgeon	Tench	Tench Golden	Trount American Brook	Trout Blue	Trout Brook	Trout Brown	Trout Golden	Trout Lake	Ttrout Rainbow	Trout Sea	Trout Tiger	Trout Wild	Vendace	Zander
ARENA LAKE (FH0132)								●						●													
ARMIGERS FARM (FH0138)								●	●					●													
ASHELDHAM FISHERY (FH0160)						●		●	●																		
AVELEY LAKES (FH0187)																											
BARLEYLANDS RESERVOIR (FH0310)								●	●					●													
BEDFORDS PARK LAKE (FH0365)						●	●	●	●					●													
BERWICK PONDS (FH0393)						●	●	●						●													
BIRDS GREEN (FH0428)			●					●						●													
BLACKMORE WOOD (FH0452)						●	●	●	●					●													
BLACKWATER (RIVER) (FH0474)						●		●	●																		
BLACKWATER (RIVER) (FH0475)																											
BLACKWATER (RIVER) (FH0476)						●	●	●	●					●													
BLACKWATER (RIVER) (FH0477)								●																			
BLASFORD HILL FISHERIES (FH0492)						●	●	●	●					●													
BLUNTS AND CANTS MERES (FH0516)								●	●					●													
BOG GROVE (FH0523)																											
BORDEAUX PIT (FH0545)								●																			
BOREHAM FISHERY (FH0548)							●	●	●					●													
BOREHAM MERES (FH0549)						●	●	●	●					●													
BOVINGTON MERE 1 (FH0569)						●	●	●																			
BOVINGTON MERE 2 (FH0570)							●	●	●					●													
BRAXTED HALL ESTATE (FH0605)						●	●	●	●					●													
BRICKHOUSE FARM FISHERIES (FH0621)						●		●	●					●					●			●					
BROAD GREEN AND TUFNELL MERE (FH0663)						●		●	●					●													
BROOKHALL FISHERY (FH0682)						●		●	●					●													
BULPHAN PARK FISHERIES (FH0730)						●		●						●													
BURROWS FARM (FH0754)						●		●																			
CANTS MERE (FH0830)																											
CARP FARM FRYERNING FISHERIES (FH0845)						●	●	●	●	●				●					●		●	●					
CENTRAL PARK LAKE (FH0887)								●	●					●													
CHASE FISHERY (FH0907)						●	●	●						●													
CHELMER & BLACKWATER (FH0913)		●				●	●	●	●	●				●													
CHELMER (RIVER) (FH0910)		●				●	●	●	●	●				●													
CHELMER (RIVER) (FH0911)						●	●	●	●	●				●													

Fish Species Available at UK & Irish Fisheries

Fishery	Barbel	Bleak	Bream	Carp Blue	Carp Common	Carp Crucian	Carp Ghost	Carp Grass	Carp Koi	Carp Leather	Carp Mirror	Carp Silver	Carp Wild	Catfish	Catfish Albino	Catfish American Bullhead	Catfish Black Bullhead	Charr	Chub	Dace	Eel	Flounder	Goldfish	Grayling	Grilse	Gudgeon	Gwyniad	Minnow	Orfe	Orfe Blue	Orfe Golden	Perch	Pike	Roach	Rudd	Ruffe	Salmon	Steelhead	Sturgeon	Tench	Tench Golden	Trount American Brook	Trout Blue	Trout Brook	Trout Brown	Trout Golden	Trout Lake	Ttrout Rainbow	Trout Sea	Trout Tiger	Trout Wild	Vendace	Zander
CHIGBOROUGH (FH0940)			●		●	●					●										●											●		●	●					●													
CHIGBOROUGH FISHERIES (FH0941)			●		●	●					●			●							●											●		●	●					●					●			●					
CHURCH LAKE (FH0954)																															●																						
CHURCHWOOD FISHERIES (FH0957)					●						●			●																		●		●						●													
CLAVERHAMBURY LAKE (FH0982)					●						●			●																				●	●					●													
COBBLERS MEAD LAKE (FH1048)			●		●	●								●							●											●		●	●					●													
COLNE (RIVER) (FH1069)			●																●	●												●	●	●																			
CONNAUGHT WATER (FH1087)			●		●						●															●						●	●	●						●													
CROW GREEN FISHERY (FH1197)					●						●					●																							●														
CROWN NETHERHALL (FH1201)			●		●						●			●																		●	●							●													
DANBURY COUNTRY PARK (FH1252)			●																													●		●	●					●													
DODDS FARM (FH1389)					●	●					●								●		●					●						●		●	●					●													
DOGGETTS FARM FISHERY (FH1393)											●																							●						●													
DONYLANDS LAKES (FH1406)					●						●			●							●											●	●	●	●					●													
EWSONS WATER (FH1638)			●		●	●					●																							●																			
FAIRLOP EAST LAKE (FH1653)			●		●						●																							●	●					●													
FAIRLOP WATERS (FH1654)			●		●	●					●										●					●						●		●	●					●													
FENNES FISHERIES (FH1697)			●		●						●																					●		●						●													
FISHERS GREEN (FH1731)	●		●		●						●								●		●											●	●	●						●													
GARNISH HALL (FH1837)					●	●					●															●								●	●																		
GLOUCESTER PARK LAKE (FH1900)	●		●		●	●		●		●	●								●		●					●						●	●	●	●					●													●
GOSFIELD LAKE RESORT (FH1926)			●		●	●					●																	●				●	●	●	●					●													
GRANGE WATER (FH1971)					●						●																																										
GREAT MYLES LAKE (FH1984)			●		●						●																					●		●						●													
HAINAULT FOREST COUNTRY PARK (FH2063)						●					●																					●	●	●						●													
HANNINGFIELD TROUT FISHERY (FH2101)																																													●			●					
HARWOOD HALL LAKE (FH2125)			●		●	●					●								●							●						●	●	●						●													
HOCKLEY LAKES (FH2239)			●		●	●					●																					●		●						●													
HOLYFIELD FISHERY (FH2278)					●	●		●			●																					●			●																		
HOME FARM FISHERY (FH2281)					●						●																					●		●						●													
HOOKS MARSH (FH2289)			●		●						●																					●	●	●						●													
HOUCHINS RESERVOIRS (FH2315)			●		●						●			●					●		●											●								●													
JACKLETTS FARM (FH2405)			●		●	●					●																					●		●	●					●													
JIMMYS LAKE (FH2411)					●						●			●																																							

Fish Species Available at UK & Irish Fisheries

Fishery	Barbel	Bleak	Bream	Carp Blue	Carp Common	Carp Crucian	Carp Ghost	Carp Grass	Carp Koi	Carp Leather	Carp Mirror	Carp Silver	Carp Wild	Catfish	Catfish Albino	Catfish American Bullhead	Catfish Black Bullhead	Charr	Chub	Dace	Eel	Flounder	Goldfish	Grayling	Grilse	Gudgeon	Gwyniad	Minnow	Orfe	Orfe Blue	Orfe Golden	Perch	Pike	Roach	Rudd	Ruffe	Salmon	Steelhead	Sturgeon	Tench	Tench Golden	Trount American Brook	Trout Blue	Trout Brook	Trout Brown	Trout Golden	Trout Lake	Ttrout Rainbow	Trout Sea	Trout Tiger	Trout Wild	Vendace	Zander
JOHNS LAKE FISHERIES (FH2414)			●		●	●					●																					●		●	●					●													
KENNEL LANE (FH2434)			●		●	●					●								●		●					●						●		●	●					●													
KNIGHTS PIT (FH2535)			●		●						●																						●							●													
LAKE MEADOWS (FH2562)			●		●	●					●						●				●					●						●	●	●	●					●													
LAUNDRY LAKE (FH2630)					●						●																								●					●													
LAYER PIT (FH2639)			●		●						●																					●	●	●	●					●													
LEA (RIVER) (FH2642)	●																		●	●																																	
LEE FLOOD RELIEF CHANNEL (FH2661)	●		●		●						●								●																					●													
LITTLE BRAXTED FARM ESTATE (FH2742)			●		●						●										●											●		●						●													
LITTLE EASTON FISHERIES (FH2750)			●		●	●					●																							●	●					●													
LITTLE EASTON MANOR (FH2751)					●	●				●	●															●						●	●	●	●					●													
MAGIC LAKE (FH3138)	●		●		●		●				●								●													●		●						●													
MANNINGTREE RIVER POOLS (FH3159)			●		●						●																						●	●	●					●													
MARCONIS PIT (FH3177)					●	●					●																																										
MAYBRAND FISHERY (FH3214)			●		●	●			●		●								●				●											●	●					●													
MAYSBROOK LAKES (FH3217)			●		●						●																					●		●						●													
MILL BARN FISHERY (FH3279)			●		●	●	●	●	●	●	●								●	●						●		●	●			●		●		●				●													
MILLENNIUM LAKES (FH3309)			●		●	●	●				●								●													●		●	●					●													
MOATHOUSE LAKE (FH3330)			●		●	●					●										●					●						●		●	●					●													
NAZEING MEADS (FH3431)			●		●						●								●		●											●	●	●						●													
NEWLAND HALL CARP FISHERY (FH3487)			●		●	●					●																					●		●	●					●													
NORTHLANDS PARK (FH3546)			●		●	●					●								●		●											●	●	●	●					●													
NUPERS FARM (FH3555)			●		●		●				●								●							●						●		●	●					●													
OLIVERS LAKE (FH3608)	●		●		●	●					●								●		●										●	●		●	●					●													
PANT (RIVER) (FH3689)			●								●								●	●						●								●											●			●					
PANT (RIVER) (FH3690)			●																●	●						●						●		●																			
PAR (FH3695)					●						●																													●													
PARSONAGE FARM (FH3712)			●			●					●																					●		●	●					●													
PEA LANE FISHERY (FH3722)			●		●	●			●		●																							●	●					●													
PICKS COTTAGE CARP LAKES (FH3768)			●		●	●					●																		●			●	●	●	●					●	●												
PIPPS HILL FISHERIES (FH3788)					●						●																																										
PRESTONS LAKE (FH3842)			●		●						●								●		●					●						●	●	●	●					●													
PRIORY PARK LAKES (FH3849)					●						●																																									
RAPHAELS PARK (FH3888)			●		●	●					●																					●		●						●													

Fish Species Available at UK & Irish Fisheries

Fishery	Barbel	Bleak	Bream	Carp Blue	Carp Common	Carp Crucian	Carp Ghost	Carp Grass	Carp Koi	Carp Leather	Carp Mirror	Carp Silver	Carp Wild	Catfish	Catfish Albino	Catfish American Bullhead	Catfish Black Bullhead	Charr	Chub	Dace	Eel	Flounder	Goldfish	Grayling	Grilse	Gudgeon	Gwyniad	Minnow	Orfe	Orfe Blue	Orfe Golden	Perch	Pike	Roach	Rudd	Ruffe	Salmon	Steelhead	Sturgeon	Tench	Tench Golden	Trount American Brook	Trout Blue	Trout Brook	Trout Brown	Trout Golden	Trout Lake	Ttrout Rainbow	Trout Sea	Trout Tiger	Trout Wild	Vendace	Zander
RAYNE LODGE FARM (FH3903)			●		●	●					●															●			●					●						●													
RECTORY FARM POND (FH3906)			●		●	●					●																					●	●	●	●																		
ROCHFORD RESERVOIR (FH3981)			●		●	●					●																					●		●						●													
ROCKELLS FARM (FH3983)					●	●					●								●															●	●					●													
RODING (RIVER) (FH3993)			●								●								●	●						●						●	●	●						●													
RODING (RIVER) (FH3990)			●		●						●								●														●	●						●													
RODING (RIVER) (FH3992)																			●	●												●	●	●																			
RODING (RIVER) (FH3991)																			●	●						●						●	●	●																			
RODING VALLEY LAKE (FH3994)			●		●	●					●								●														●	●						●													
SHALFORD RESERVOIRS (FH4204)					●	●					●								●															●	●					●													
SHOEBURY PARK (FH4245)					●						●																							●						●													
SILVER END PIT (FH4268)			●		●						●										●												●																				
SLOUGH HOUSE LAKE (FH4301)			●		●		●				●			●							●											●		●	●																		
SOUTHMINSTER FISHERIES (FH4352)			●		●	●					●															●						●		●	●	●																	
SPARROWS POND (FH4359)					●						●																													●													
STANFORD-LE-HOPE (FH4418)			●		●	●					●										●											●	●	●	●					●													
STAR LANE (FH4428)					●						●																						●	●						●													
STOUR (RIVER) (FH4495)			●		●						●									●												●	●	●						●													
STOUR (SUFFOLK) (RIVER) (FH4502)	●				●						●								●	●												●	●	●																			
STRAITS MILL (FH4518)			●		●	●					●								●	●	●											●	●	●	●					●													
THORNDON PARK LAKE (FH4813)			●		●						●																						●	●						●													
VALENCE MOAT (FH5085)					●	●					●										●					●								●	●					●													
WAKE VALLEY POND (FH5114)					●						●																					●	●	●	●					●													
WANSTEAD AND WOODFORD PONDS (FH5144)					●						●																						●	●																			
WARREN (FH5150)			●		●	●					●										●					●						●	●	●	●					●													
WEALD COUNTRY PARK (FH5194)			●		●						●															●						●	●	●	●					●													
WHARF POOL (FH5295)			●		●						●																					●		●	●					●													
WICK MERE (FH5363)			●		●						●										●											●	●	●	●					●													
WID (RIVER) (FH5366)			●																●	●	●					●		●				●	●	●	●	●				●													
WILLOWS (FH5395)			●		●						●								●	●	●					●		●				●		●	●					●													
WILLOWS LAKE (FH5400)											●																																									
FIFE																																																					
EMBER (RIVER) (FH1580)	●				●						●								●																																		
WEY (RIVER) (FH5289)	●		●																●		●											●	●	●																			

Fish Species Available at UK & Irish Fisheries

Fishery	Barbel	Bleak	Bream	Carp Blue	Carp Common	Carp Crucian	Carp Ghost	Carp Grass	Carp Koi	Carp Leather	Carp Mirror	Carp Silver	Carp Wild	Catfish	Catfish Albino	Catfish American Bullhead	Catfish Black Bullhead	Charr	Chub	Dace	Eel	Flounder	Goldfish	Grayling	Grilse	Gudgeon	Gwyniad
GLOUCESTERSHIRE																											
ADLESTROP LAKE (FH0027)					●	●	●			●	●								●		●						
APPERLEY POOLS (FH0122)			●		●						●								●								
ASHTON KEYNES POOL (FH0171)			●		●						●									●							
AVON (RIVER) (FH0205)			●		●						●								●								
BRADLEYS PIT (FH0589)			●		●						●								●								
BREDONS HARDWICK (FH0612)			●		●						●																
BROOK FARM TROUT FISHERY (FH0677)																											
BURLEY FIELDS LAKE (FH0744)	●		●		●						●									●							
BUSHYLEAZE TROUT FISHERY (FH0770)																											
CANNOP PONDS (FH0823)			●		●	●					●																
CHURN POOL TROUT FISHERY (FH0959)																											
CLAYDON PARK FISHERY (FH0992)			●		●						●																
COKES PIT (FH1056)			●		●						●																
COLN (RIVER) (FH1067)																											
COLN (RIVER) (FH1066)																								●			
COTSWOLD HOBURNE (FH1131)			●																								
COTSWOLD WATER PARK (FH1132)			●		●						●																
COURT FARM (FH1142)					●			●			●								●								
DONNINGTON TROUT FISHERY (FH1405)																											
FARMHOUSE LAKE (THE) (FH1672)			●		●						●																
GARDNERS POOL (FH1835)			●		●	●	●				●								●		●						
GLOUCESTER & SHARPNESS (FH1897)	●		●		●						●								●		●						
GLOUCESTER CANAL (FH1899)			●																●		●						
GLOUCESTER CANAL (FH1898)		●	●																●		●					●	
HAM POOL (FH2078)			●		●	●					●																
HIGHNAM COURT LAKE (FH2219)			●		●						●																
HILL VIEW LAKES (FH2223)			●		●	●	●				●															●	
HILLVIEW FISHERY (FH2228)			●		●	●		●			●								●								
HORSESHOE LAKE (FH2307)			●		●	●					●																
HUNTLEY CARP POOLS (FH2341)					●						●										●						
ISIS NO 1 LAKE 19 (FH2386)					●						●																
KEYNES COUNTRY PARK (FH2475)			●		●						●								●								
KEYNES PARK TOP LAKE (FH2476)			●								●																

Fishery	Minnow	Orfe	Orfe Blue	Orfe Golden	Perch	Pike	Roach	Rudd	Ruffe	Salmon	Steelhead	Sturgeon	Tench	Tench Golden	Trount American Brook	Trout Blue	Trout Brook	Trout Brown	Trout Golden	Trout Lake	Ttrout Rainbow	Trout Sea	Trout Tiger	Trout Wild	Vendace	Zander
GLOUCESTERSHIRE																										
ADLESTROP LAKE (FH0027)	●				●	●	●						●													
APPERLEY POOLS (FH0122)					●		●																			
ASHTON KEYNES POOL (FH0171)					●	●	●						●													
AVON (RIVER) (FH0205)					●	●																				
BRADLEYS PIT (FH0589)						●	●						●													
BREDONS HARDWICK (FH0612)					●		●	●					●													
BROOK FARM TROUT FISHERY (FH0677)																		●			●					
BURLEY FIELDS LAKE (FH0744)					●		●	●					●													
BUSHYLEAZE TROUT FISHERY (FH0770)																		●			●					
CANNOP PONDS (FH0823)					●	●	●						●													
CHURN POOL TROUT FISHERY (FH0959)																		●			●					
CLAYDON PARK FISHERY (FH0992)					●	●	●						●													
COKES PIT (FH1056)					●	●	●	●					●													
COLN (RIVER) (FH1067)																					●					
COLN (RIVER) (FH1066)																		●								
COTSWOLD HOBURNE (FH1131)					●		●	●					●													
COTSWOLD WATER PARK (FH1132)					●	●	●						●													
COURT FARM (FH1142)					●			●										●								
DONNINGTON TROUT FISHERY (FH1405)																		●			●					
FARMHOUSE LAKE (THE) (FH1672)							●						●													
GARDNERS POOL (FH1835)					●		●	●					●													
GLOUCESTER & SHARPNESS (FH1897)					●		●																			●
GLOUCESTER CANAL (FH1899)					●		●																			●
GLOUCESTER CANAL (FH1898)					●	●	●		●																	●
HAM POOL (FH2078)						●	●	●					●													
HIGHNAM COURT LAKE (FH2219)							●	●					●													
HILL VIEW LAKES (FH2223)		●			●		●						●													
HILLVIEW FISHERY (FH2228)		●					●	●					●													
HORSESHOE LAKE (FH2307)					●		●	●					●													
HUNTLEY CARP POOLS (FH2341)							●	●					●					●								
ISIS NO 1 LAKE 19 (FH2386)					●	●	●	●					●													
KEYNES COUNTRY PARK (FH2475)					●	●	●	●					●													
KEYNES PARK TOP LAKE (FH2476)					●	●	●						●													

Fish Species Available at UK & Irish Fisheries

	Barbel	Bleak	Bream	Carp Blue	Carp Common	Carp Crucian	Carp Ghost	Carp Grass	Carp Koi	Carp Leather	Carp Mirror	Carp Silver	Carp Wild	Catfish	Catfish Albino	Catfish American Bullhead	Catfish Black Bullhead	Charr	Chub	Dace	Eel	Flounder	Goldfish	Grayling	Grilse	Gudgeon	Gwyniad	Minnow	Orfe	Orfe Blue	Orfe Golden	Perch	Pike	Roach	Rudd	Ruffe	Salmon	Steelhead	Sturgeon	Tench	Tench Golden	Trount American Brook	Trout Blue	Trout Brook	Trout Brown	Trout Golden	Trout Lake	Ttrout Rainbow	Trout Sea	Trout Tiger	Trout Wild	Vendace	Zander
LAKE NUMBER ONE (LAKE19) (FH2565)			●		●	●					●										●											●	●	●	●					●								●					
LECHLADE TROUT FISHERY (FH2656)																																	●												●			●					
LEMINGTON LAKES (FH2696)			●		●														●	●												●		●	●					●													
LIGHTMOOR POOL (FH2719)			●		●	●					●															●						●		●	●					●													
LYDNEY BOATING LAKE (FH3114)	●		●		●						●										●													●	●					●													
MARIONS POOL (FH3181)											●																													●													
MEADOWCLIFFE POOL (FH3226)			●		●	●				●	●										●											●		●	●					●													
MILESTONE FISHERY (FH3275)			●		●						●																					●	●		●					●					●								
MILL AVON (FH3278)					●						●																																										
MILL LAKE (NO 44) (FH3289)			●		●						●								●													●								●													
MORETON PITS (FH3371)			●		●						●																					●	●	●						●													
MYTHE POOL (FH3407)			●		●						●															●						●		●																			
NEIGH BRIDGE LAKE (FH3437)											●																					●	●	●						●													
NETHERWOOD LAKE (FH3456)					●						●																					●		●						●													
NORTON FRUIT FARM (FH3548)			●		●						●																		●			●		●	●					●													
PLUMP HILL POOL (FH3806)	●										●								●																																		
RAINBOW LAKES (FH3881)																																																●					
RED LION FISHERY (FH3910)	●	●	●		●						●								●	●	●					●						●	●	●	●																		●
SANTHILL FISHERY (FH4103)																																													●			●					
SEVERN (RIVER) (FH4145)																																																					●
SEVERN (RIVER) (FH4147)	●		●		●						●								●	●												●	●	●																			●
SEVERN (RIVER) (FH4146)	●		●																●	●	●											●	●		●																		
SEVERN ON THE HAM (FH4198)			●																															●																			
STANBOROUGH POOL (FH4416)			●		●	●					●								●													●		●	●					●													
STAUNTON COURT LAKES (FH4441)			●		●	●	●			●	●								●							●			●			●		●	●					●													
STEAM MILLS LAKE (FH4444)			●		●	●					●								●													●		●	●					●													
STONE END FARM LAKES (FH4467)			●		●						●																						●	●						●													
STROUDWATER CANAL (FH4528)			●		●						●																					●	●	●						●													
THAMES (RIVER) (FH4784)			●																●	●												●		●																			
THAMES (RIVER) (FH4785)	●	●	●																●							●						●	●	●																			
WATERLEY BROOK (FH5178)																																													●								
WATERLOO SCREENS (FH5179)					●						●								●															●	●					●													
WATERSMEET LAKES (FH5186)			●		●						●																						●	●	●					●													
WHELFORD POOLS COARSE FISHERY (FH5319)			●		●			●		●	●																					●	●	●						●													

www.fishooked.com

FISH SPECIES AVAILABLE

England (by County)

Fish Species Available at UK & Irish Fisheries

Fishery	Barbel	Bleak	Bream	Carp Blue	Carp Common	Carp Crucian	Carp Ghost	Carp Grass	Carp Koi	Carp Leather	Carp Mirror	Carp Silver	Carp Wild	Catfish	Catfish Albino	Catfish American Bullhead	Catfish Black Bullhead	Charr	Chub	Dace	Eel	Flounder	Goldfish	Grayling	Grilse	Gudgeon	Gwyniad	Minnow	Orfe	Orfe Blue	Orfe Golden	Perch	Pike	Roach	Rudd	Ruffe	Salmon	Steelhead	Sturgeon	Tench	Tench Golden	Trount American Brook	Trout Blue	Trout Brook	Trout Brown	Trout Golden	Trout Lake	Ttrout Rainbow	Trout Sea	Trout Tiger	Trout Wild	Vendace	Zander
WICK WATER (FH5364)			●		●	●					●			●																		●	●	●	●					●													
WITCOMBE WATERS (FH5437)																																													●		●	●					
HAMPSHIRE																																																					
ANTON (RIVER) (FH0117)																																													●			●					
ANTON LAKE (FH0118)			●		●						●																					●	●	●						●													
AVINGTON TROUT FISHERIES (FH0190)																																										●						●					
AVON (RIVER) (FH0206)	●																																																				
AVON RIVER FISHERIES (FH0228)	●		●		●	●					●								●	●	●			●		●		●				●	●	●	●		●			●					●			●	●				
AWBRIDGE DANES LAKE (FH0231)			●		●						●										●					●						●		●	●					●													
BARONS PONDS (NEW SITE) (FH0322)					●	●					●															●									●					●													
BASINGSTOKE CANAL (FH0342)			●		●						●																					●		●						●													
BASINGSTOKE CANAL (FH0341)					●						●																																										
BICKERLEY MILLSTREAM (FH0404)	●																		●	●	●			●		●						●	●	●																			
BILCOMBES POND (FH0415)					●						●																																										
BROADLANDS LAKES (FH0664)			●		●			●			●								●	●	●			●								●	●	●	●					●					●								
BROADLANDS MAIN LAKE (FH0665)			●		●		●	●		●	●																							●																			
CARRON ROW FARM PONDS (FH0852)					●						●																								●					●													
CHARLTON PITS (FH0904)					●						●									●												●		●	●					●													
CHIPHALL LAKE TROUT FISHERY (FH0943)																																													●		●	●					
COOKS POND (FH1100)						●															●		●									●		●	●					●													
CROOKED WILLOWS (FH1188)			●		●	●					●								●													●		●						●													
CUTT MILL (FH1230)							●																																														
DARK LANE PONDS (FH1274)			●		●	●	●	●			●								●							●						●		●	●					●													
DEVER SPRINGS TROUT FISHERY (FH1362)																																													●			●					
EAST MOORS LAKE (FH1511)					●		●			●	●								●		●											●	●	●						●													
FIRGROVE LAKES (FH1722)			●		●	●																										●		●	●					●													
FOXCOTTE LAKE (FH1789)			●		●						●																					●	●	●						●													
FRIMLEY LAKES (FH1802)			●		●	●					●										●											●	●	●	●					●													
FUNTLEY POND (FH1819)			●		●						●																					●		●	●					●													
GOLD VALLEY LAKES (FH1909)			●		●	●	●				●										●		●									●		●						●													
GOLDEN POND FISHERY (FH1912)					●	●	●				●								●	●	●					●						●		●	●					●													
GREENRIDGE FARM LAKES (FH2009)			●		●	●	●	●	●		●									●									●					●	●					●													
HAMPSHIRE AVON (FH2082)	●		●		●						●								●	●				●		●						●	●	●			●																
HAMPSHIRE AVON (RIVER) (FH2091)	●		●		●						●								●	●	●												●	●																			

Fish Species Available at UK & Irish Fisheries

Fishery	Barbel	Bleak	Bream	Carp Blue	Carp Common	Carp Crucian	Carp Ghost	Carp Grass	Carp Koi	Carp Leather	Carp Mirror	Carp Silver	Carp Wild	Catfish	Catfish Albino	Catfish American Bullhead	Catfish Black Bullhead	Charr	Chub
HAMPSHIRE AVON (RIVER) (FH2090)	●		●		●						●								●
HAMPSHIRE AVON (RIVER) (FH2088)	●				●						●								●
HAMPSHIRE AVON (RIVER) (FH2092)	●		●		●														●
HAMPSHIRE AVON (RIVER) (FH2089)	●				●						●								●
HATCHET POND (FH2128)			●		●						●								
HIGHTOWN LAKE (FH2220)			●		●						●								●
HILSEA MOATS (FH2229)			●		●	●					●								
HMS DRYAD LAKE (FH2236)					●						●								
HOLBURY LAKES (FH2247)																			
HOLBURY MANOR POND (FH2248)					●						●								
HOLLYBUSH LANE LAKES (FH2262)			●		●						●								
HORDLE LAKES (FH2296)			●		●	●					●								
HUCKLESBROOK LAKE (FH2324)						●					●								
HURST POND (FH2346)					●	●					●								
IBSLEY POOLS (FH2357)			●		●	●					●								
ITCHEN (RIVER) (FH2398)																			
ITCHEN (RIVER) (FH2397)																			
ITCHEN NAVIGATION (FH2399)																			
JANESMOOR POND (FH2406)											●								
KINGFISHER LAKE (A) (FH2499)					●						●								●
LAKE FARM (FH2556)					●						●								
LAKESIDE (FH2580)			●		●						●								
LAKESIDE (FH2581)			●		●	●													
LAKESIDE COUNTRY PARK (FH2589)			●		●						●								
LEOMINSTEAD MILL POND (FH2702)			●		●						●								
LEOMINSTEAD TROUT FISHERY (FH2703)																			
LONGBRIDGE LAKES (FH2987)			●			●	●	●			●								●
LOWER ITCHEN FISHERY (FH3084)																			
LYNDHURST LAKE (FH3121)					●														
MBK LEISURE BARRONS POND (FH3218)					●						●								
MEON SPRINGS FLY FISHERY (FH3255)																			
MILL POND LAKE (FH3300)			●		●						●								
MOORHEN FARM TROUT LAKE (FH3361)																			
MOORS VALLEY COUNTRY PARK (FH3366)																			

Fishery	Dace	Eel	Flounder	Goldfish	Grayling	Grilse	Gudgeon	Gwyniad	Minnow	Orfe	Orfe Blue	Orfe Golden	Perch	Pike	Roach	Rudd	Ruffe	Salmon	Steelhead
HAMPSHIRE AVON (RIVER) (FH2090)	●	●			●		●						●	●	●				
HAMPSHIRE AVON (RIVER) (FH2088)														●	●				
HAMPSHIRE AVON (RIVER) (FH2092)	●	●			●		●		●					●	●			●	
HAMPSHIRE AVON (RIVER) (FH2089)	●				●									●	●				
HATCHET POND (FH2128)		●											●	●	●				
HIGHTOWN LAKE (FH2220)		●												●	●				
HILSEA MOATS (FH2229)													●		●	●			
HMS DRYAD LAKE (FH2236)																			
HOLBURY LAKES (FH2247)																			
HOLBURY MANOR POND (FH2248)														●	●				
HOLLYBUSH LANE LAKES (FH2262)		●											●	●	●	●			
HORDLE LAKES (FH2296)													●		●	●			
HUCKLESBROOK LAKE (FH2324)													●		●				
HURST POND (FH2346)		●											●		●	●			
IBSLEY POOLS (FH2357)													●	●	●				
ITCHEN (RIVER) (FH2398)																			
ITCHEN (RIVER) (FH2397)					●														
ITCHEN NAVIGATION (FH2399)					●														
JANESMOOR POND (FH2406)															●	●			
KINGFISHER LAKE (A) (FH2499)													●		●				
LAKE FARM (FH2556)		●																	
LAKESIDE (FH2580)		●												●	●				
LAKESIDE (FH2581)													●	●	●				
LAKESIDE COUNTRY PARK (FH2589)		●												●	●				
LEOMINSTEAD MILL POND (FH2702)														●	●	●			
LEOMINSTEAD TROUT FISHERY (FH2703)																			
LONGBRIDGE LAKES (FH2987)		●											●		●	●			
LOWER ITCHEN FISHERY (FH3084)																		●	
LYNDHURST LAKE (FH3121)													●		●	●			
MBK LEISURE BARRONS POND (FH3218)															●				
MEON SPRINGS FLY FISHERY (FH3255)																			
MILL POND LAKE (FH3300)														●	●				
MOORHEN FARM TROUT LAKE (FH3361)																			
MOORS VALLEY COUNTRY PARK (FH3366)	●	●											●	●	●	●			

Fishery	Sturgeon	Tench	Tench Golden	Trount American Brook	Trout Blue	Trout Brook	Trout Brown	Trout Golden	Trout Lake	Ttrout Rainbow	Trout Sea	Trout Tiger	Trout Wild	Vendace	Zander
HAMPSHIRE AVON (RIVER) (FH2090)							●								
HAMPSHIRE AVON (RIVER) (FH2088)															
HAMPSHIRE AVON (RIVER) (FH2092)		●					●			●	●				
HAMPSHIRE AVON (RIVER) (FH2089)															
HATCHET POND (FH2128)		●													
HIGHTOWN LAKE (FH2220)		●													
HILSEA MOATS (FH2229)		●													
HMS DRYAD LAKE (FH2236)															
HOLBURY LAKES (FH2247)					●		●			●			●		
HOLBURY MANOR POND (FH2248)		●													
HOLLYBUSH LANE LAKES (FH2262)		●													
HORDLE LAKES (FH2296)		●													
HUCKLESBROOK LAKE (FH2324)		●													
HURST POND (FH2346)		●													
IBSLEY POOLS (FH2357)		●													
ITCHEN (RIVER) (FH2398)							●								
ITCHEN (RIVER) (FH2397)							●								
ITCHEN NAVIGATION (FH2399)															
JANESMOOR POND (FH2406)		●													
KINGFISHER LAKE (A) (FH2499)		●													
LAKE FARM (FH2556)		●													
LAKESIDE (FH2580)		●													
LAKESIDE (FH2581)		●													
LAKESIDE COUNTRY PARK (FH2589)		●													
LEOMINSTEAD MILL POND (FH2702)		●													
LEOMINSTEAD TROUT FISHERY (FH2703)						●	●			●		●			
LONGBRIDGE LAKES (FH2987)		●													
LOWER ITCHEN FISHERY (FH3084)							●								
LYNDHURST LAKE (FH3121)		●													
MBK LEISURE BARRONS POND (FH3218)															
MEON SPRINGS FLY FISHERY (FH3255)							●			●					
MILL POND LAKE (FH3300)		●													
MOORHEN FARM TROUT LAKE (FH3361)										●					
MOORS VALLEY COUNTRY PARK (FH3366)		●													

Fish Species Available at UK & Irish Fisheries

	Barbel	Bleak	Bream	Carp Blue	Carp Common	Carp Crucian	Carp Ghost	Carp Grass	Carp Koi	Carp Leather	Carp Mirror	Carp Silver	Carp Wild	Catfish	Catfish Albino	Catfish American Bullhead	Catfish Black Bullhead	Charr	Chub	Dace	Eel	Flounder	Goldfish	Grayling	Grilse	Gudgeon	Gwyniad	Minnow	Orfe	Orfe Blue	Orfe Golden	Perch	Pike	Roach	Rudd	Ruffe	Salmon	Steelhead	Sturgeon	Tench	Tench Golden	Trount American Brook	Trout Blue	Trout Brook	Trout Brown	Trout Golden	Trout Lake	Ttrout Rainbow	Trout Sea	Trout Tiger	Trout Wild	Vendace	Zander
MOPLEY POND (FH3367)					●		●			●	●																																										
NETHER WALLOP (FH3452)																																													●			●					
NEW FOREST WATER PARK (FH3464)					●						●																					●	●	●	●					●													
NORTHFIELD LAKES (FH3544)			●		●						●								●		●												●	●	●					●													
NUTRABAITS YATELEY COMPLEX (FH3556)			●		●	●				●	●			●					●	●	●											●	●	●	●					●													
NUTRABAITS YATELEY SOUTH LAKE (FH3557)					●						●																													●													
ORCHARD LAKES (FH3616)			●		●	●					●															●						●		●	●					●													
PARSONAGE (RIVER) TEST (FH3711)																								●																					●			●					
PERIL LAKE (FH3752)			●		●	●					●								●	●	●											●		●	●					●													
PETERSFIELD HEATH LAKE (FH3757)			●		●						●																					●	●	●	●																		
QUEENS ROAD POND (FH3867)					●						●																							●	●					●													
RIVER FARM (FH3964)																																													●			●					
ROCKBOURNE TROUT FISHERY (FH3982)																																													●			●					
ROCKFORD LAKE (FH3984)			●		●	●					●																					●		●	●					●													
ROOKSBURY MILL (FH4007)																																													●			●					
ROTHERWICK & NIGHTINGALE (FH4032)			●			●					●																					●		●						●													
SOMERLEY LAKES (FH4322)			●		●	●					●																					●	●	●	●					●													
SPRINGLAKES (FH4373)			●		●						●																							●	●					●													
STEPSTONES LAKES (FH4451)					●						●										●													●	●					●													
STONEHAM LAKES (FH4472)			●		●	●					●										●											●	●	●	●					●													
STOUR (RIVER) (FH4496)					●						●								●	●				●								●	●	●						●					●								
SWAY LAKES (FH4605)					●			●			●																					●		●						●													
TEST (RIVER) (FH4745)																								●							●																	●	●				
TEST (RIVER) (FH4744)																																													●								
TITCHFIELD ABBEY LAKES (FH4857)			●		●	●					●								●													●		●	●					●													
TOPACRE LAKE (FH4878)					●						●																																										
TURF CROFT FARM (FH4975)			●		●		●				●																							●	●					●													
VALE FARM FISHERY (FH5082)																																													●			●					
WAINSFORD RESERVOIR (FH5113)					●						●																					●			●																		
WEDGEHILL PONDS (FH5222)					●	●					●																								●					●													
WHINWHISTLE COARSE FISHERY (FH5324)			●		●	●					●								●	●	●										●	●	●	●	●					●													
WHITEWATER (RIVER) (FH5356)	●																		●	●						●						●	●	●											●								
WILLOW PARK (FH5387)			●		●	●				●	●																					●	●	●	●					●													
WINTERSHILL TROUT LAKE (FH5430)																																															●						

Fish Species Available at UK & Irish Fisheries

Fishery	Barbel	Bleak	Bream	Carp Blue	Carp Common	Carp Crucian	Carp Ghost	Carp Grass	Carp Koi	Carp Leather	Carp Mirror	Carp Silver	Carp Wild	Catfish	Catfish Albino	Catfish American Bullhead	Catfish Black Bullhead	Charr
WOODINGTON FISHERY (FH5476)																		
WOODMILL SALMON FISHERY (FH5488)		●			●						●							
HEREFORDSHIRE																		
ASHPERTON MOAT (FH0168)					●						●							
BETULA WATERS (FH0397)					●						●							
BIDDLESTONE LAKE (FH0408)			●		●						●							
CASTLEMORTON (FH0868)			●		●													
CHURCH POOL (FH0955)					●						●							
COURT FARM (FH1143)					●						●							
DOCKLOW POOLS (FH1386)	●		●		●	●	●	●	●	●	●			●				
DRUMMOND DUB (FH1450)			●		●	●					●							
EASTNOR CASTLE (FH1525)			●		●						●							
EVESBATCH TOP LAKE (FH1636)					●													
GOLDEN VALLEY (FH1914)			●		●	●					●							
HAYCASTLE WATER (FH2150)	●																	
HERRIOTS POOL (FH2194)					●	●					●							
HUNDRED POOL (FH2337)			●		●						●							
KINGFISHER TROUT LAKE (FH2502)																		
LILY AND WILLOW POOLS (FH2721)			●								●							
LLYNFI (RIVER) (FH2827)																		
MARLIAS (RIVER) (FH3189)																		
MARSH HOUSE FARM (FH3192)			●		●						●							
MILLPOND (FH3314)			●		●	●	●	●		●	●							
MOCCAS FISHERY (FH3333)	●																	
MONNOW (RIVER) (FH3349)																		
MUNDERFIELD HAROLD (FH3402)			●		●						●							
PIXLEY POOL (FH3797)					●	●					●							
PRIDEWOOD LAKE (FH3844)			●		●	●					●							
RED BANK POOLS (FH3907)					●						●							
REDMIRE POOL (FH3921)					●						●							
ROTHERWAS LONG POOL (FH4031)					●						●							
ROYAL OAK POOL (FH4047)					●						●							
RUSSELLS END RESERVOIR (FH4065)					●						●							
WYE (RIVER) (FH5530)	●	●									●							

Fishery	Chub	Dace	Eel	Flounder	Goldfish	Grayling	Grilse	Gudgeon	Gwyniad	Minnow	Orfe	Orfe Blue	Orfe Golden	Perch	Pike	Roach	Rudd	Ruffe	Salmon
WOODINGTON FISHERY (FH5476)																			
WOODMILL SALMON FISHERY (FH5488)	●	●	●			●		●		●				●	●	●	●	●	●
HEREFORDSHIRE																			
ASHPERTON MOAT (FH0168)																●			
BETULA WATERS (FH0397)																			
BIDDLESTONE LAKE (FH0408)																●			
CASTLEMORTON (FH0868)																			
CHURCH POOL (FH0955)																			
COURT FARM (FH1143)																			
DOCKLOW POOLS (FH1386)	●	●	●					●						●		●	●	●	
DRUMMOND DUB (FH1450)			●													●			
EASTNOR CASTLE (FH1525)																●	●		
EVESBATCH TOP LAKE (FH1636)																●			
GOLDEN VALLEY (FH1914)														●		●			
HAYCASTLE WATER (FH2150)	●	●	●			●		●		●				●	●				
HERRIOTS POOL (FH2194)																●			
HUNDRED POOL (FH2337)														●		●	●		
KINGFISHER TROUT LAKE (FH2502)																			
LILY AND WILLOW POOLS (FH2721)																●	●		
LLYNFI (RIVER) (FH2827)						●													
MARLIAS (RIVER) (FH3189)																			●
MARSH HOUSE FARM (FH3192)																●	●		
MILLPOND (FH3314)								●			●			●		●	●		
MOCCAS FISHERY (FH3333)	●	●													●				●
MONNOW (RIVER) (FH3349)																			●
MUNDERFIELD HAROLD (FH3402)																●	●		
PIXLEY POOL (FH3797)																			
PRIDEWOOD LAKE (FH3844)			●											●	●				
RED BANK POOLS (FH3907)																			
REDMIRE POOL (FH3921)																			
ROTHERWAS LONG POOL (FH4031)																			
ROYAL OAK POOL (FH4047)																			
RUSSELLS END RESERVOIR (FH4065)			●													●	●		
WYE (RIVER) (FH5530)	●	●	●												●	●			●

Fishery	Steelhead	Sturgeon	Tench	Tench Golden	Trount American Brook	Trout Blue	Trout Brook	Trout Brown	Trout Golden	Trout Lake	Ttrout Rainbow	Trout Sea	Trout Tiger	Trout Wild	Vendace	Zander
WOODINGTON FISHERY (FH5476)								●			●	●		●		
WOODMILL SALMON FISHERY (FH5488)			●					●								
HEREFORDSHIRE																
ASHPERTON MOAT (FH0168)																
BETULA WATERS (FH0397)																
BIDDLESTONE LAKE (FH0408)			●													
CASTLEMORTON (FH0868)																
CHURCH POOL (FH0955)																
COURT FARM (FH1143)																
DOCKLOW POOLS (FH1386)			●													
DRUMMOND DUB (FH1450)																
EASTNOR CASTLE (FH1525)			●													
EVESBATCH TOP LAKE (FH1636)																
GOLDEN VALLEY (FH1914)																
HAYCASTLE WATER (FH2150)							●	●				●				
HERRIOTS POOL (FH2194)																
HUNDRED POOL (FH2337)			●													
KINGFISHER TROUT LAKE (FH2502)								●	●		●					
LILY AND WILLOW POOLS (FH2721)			●													
LLYNFI (RIVER) (FH2827)								●								
MARLIAS (RIVER) (FH3189)								●								
MARSH HOUSE FARM (FH3192)			●													
MILLPOND (FH3314)			●													
MOCCAS FISHERY (FH3333)								●								
MONNOW (RIVER) (FH3349)								●								
MUNDERFIELD HAROLD (FH3402)			●													
PIXLEY POOL (FH3797)			●													
PRIDEWOOD LAKE (FH3844)			●													
RED BANK POOLS (FH3907)																
REDMIRE POOL (FH3921)																
ROTHERWAS LONG POOL (FH4031)																
ROYAL OAK POOL (FH4047)																
RUSSELLS END RESERVOIR (FH4065)			●													
WYE (RIVER) (FH5530)																

Fish Species Available at UK & Irish Fisheries

Species	WYE (RIVER) (FH5535)	WYE (RIVER) (FH5533)	WYE (RIVER) (FH5534)	WYE (RIVER) (FH5531)	WYE (RIVER) (FH5536)	HERTFORDSHIRE	ADMIRALS WALK LAKE (FH0029)	ALDENHAM RESERVOIR (FH0058)	AMWELL LAKES (FH0104)	AYLESBURY ARM CANAL (FH0237)	AYLESBURY ARM CANAL (FH0236)	BATCHWORTH LAKE (FH0346)	BIERTON FISHING LAKES (FH0410)	BLUE LAGOON (FH0504)	BOWMANS LAKES (FH0574)	BOWYERS WATER (FH0576)	BROAD COLNEY LAKES (FH0662)	BROOKFIELD LAKE (FH0680)	BROXBOURNE (FH0705)	CARTHAGENA FISHERY (FH0855)	CHESHUNT SOUTH RESERVOIR (FH0926)	COLNE (RIVER) (FH1071)	COLNEY HEATH LAKE (FH1077)	CROXLEY HALL TROUT FISHERY (FH1203)	DOBBS WEIR FISHERY (FH1381)	DURRANTS LAKE (FH1485)	FAIRLANDS VALLEY PARK (FH1652)	FEILDES WEIR (FH1680)	GADE (RIVER) (FH1827)	GAYWOODS (FH1845)	GRAND UNION CANAL (FH1947)	GRAND UNION CANAL (FH1949)	GRAND UNION CANAL (FH1950)	GRAND UNION CANAL (FH1948)
Zander																																		
Vendace																																		
Trout Wild																																		
Trout Tiger																																		
Trout Sea																																		
Ttrout Rainbow								●																●										
Trout Lake								●																										
Trout Golden																																		
Trout Brown		●	●	●				●																●										
Trout Brook																																		
Trout Blue																																		
Trount American Brook																																		
Tench Golden																																		
Tench		●					●	●	●		●	●	●	●	●	●	●	●	●	●			●	●	●	●	●			●				
Sturgeon																																		
Steelhead																																		
Salmon		●	●	●																														
Ruffe															●					●														
Rudd								●			●		●	●	●	●				●						●	●			●				
Roach	●	●			●		●	●	●		●	●	●	●	●		●		●	●	●	●			●	●	●	●	●	●	●	●	●	●
Pike	●	●			●		●	●	●					●	●	●	●		●	●			●	●	●	●		●	●					
Perch		●			●			●	●		●	●	●	●	●		●	●	●	●		●			●				●	●	●	●		●
Orfe Golden																																		
Orfe Blue																																		
Orfe																																		
Minnow																				●														
Gwyniad																																		
Gudgeon		●									●		●		●					●											●	●		●
Grilse																																		
Grayling															●																			
Goldfish																																		
Flounder																																		
Eel								●					●		●				●	●					●									
Dace					●										●					●									●					
Chub	●	●			●			●	●				●	●	●					●		●			●			●		●				
Charr																																		
Catfish Black Bullhead																																		
Catfish American Bullhead																																		
Catfish Albino																																		
Catfish								●							●																			
Carp Wild																																		
Carp Silver																																		
Carp Mirror		●			●		●	●	●	●	●	●	●		●	●	●	●	●	●	●		●	●	●		●		●	●			●	●
Carp Leather													●			●				●														
Carp Koi													●																					
Carp Grass								●					●		●															●				
Carp Ghost													●																					
Carp Crucian								●	●				●		●		●		●											●				
Carp Common		●			●		●	●	●	●	●	●	●		●	●	●	●	●	●	●	●	●	●	●		●		●	●			●	●
Carp Blue																																		
Bream		●					●	●	●			●		●	●	●	●	●		●		●	●		●	●		●			●	●	●	
Bleak																				●														
Barbel	●	●			●															●		●			●			●						

Fish Species Available at UK & Irish Fisheries

Species	GRAND UNION CANAL (FH1946)	GRAND UNION CANAL (FH1945)	GRAND UNION CANAL (FH1944)	GRAND UNION CANAL (FH1951)	HATFIELD BROADWATER (FH2130)	HATFIELD FOREST LAKE (FH2131)	HOLWELL HYDE LAKE (FH2275)	HOOK LAKE (FH2288)	INNS LAKE (FH2371)	KINGS WEIR FISHERY (FH2509)	LEA (RIVER) (FH2646)	LEA (RIVER) (FH2643)	LEA (RIVER) (FH2645)	LEA (RIVER) (FH2644)	LEA NAVIGATION (FH2647)	LEE NAVIGATION (FH2665)	LEE NAVIGATION (FH2668)	LEE NAVIGATION (FH2669)	LEE NAVIGATION (FH2664)	LEE NAVIGATION (FH2667)	LEE NAVIGATION (FH2662)	LEE NAVIGATION (FH2666)	LOWBELL LANE (FH3069)	MARSWORTH RESERVOIR (FH3198)	MERCHANT TAYLORS SCL LAKES (FH3257)	NEW RIVER (FH3477)	NORTH MET PIT (FH3532)	OAKFIELD FISHERY (FH3561)	OLD LEE (RIVER) (FH3590)	OLD LEE (RIVER) (FH3589)	OLD MILL AND MEADOWS (FH3594)	OLDFIELD (FH3605)	OUGHTON (RIVER) (FH3633)	PAYNES LANE PIT (FH3721)
Zander																																		
Vendace																																		
Trout Wild																																		
Trout Tiger																																		
Trout Sea																																		
Ttrout Rainbow																					●								●					
Trout Lake																																		
Trout Golden																																		
Trout Brown																					●	●				●			●	●			●	
Trout Brook																																		
Trout Blue																																		
Trount American Brook																																		
Tench Golden																																		
Tench		●			●	●	●	●	●	●		●	●				●	●		●	●		●		●		●	●			●	●		
Sturgeon																																		
Steelhead																																		
Salmon																																		
Ruffe																					●							●						
Rudd		●				●	●	●	●												●							●				●		
Roach	●	●		●	●	●	●	●	●	●		●		●	●	●	●	●		●	●		●			●		●	●	●	●	●		●
Pike	●					●	●	●	●	●		●	●			●	●	●	●	●	●		●		●	●	●				●			●
Perch	●	●		●			●	●	●	●		●				●	●	●		●	●					●		●	●	●	●	●		●
Orfe Golden																																		
Orfe Blue																																		
Orfe																																		
Minnow																					●													
Gwyniad																																		
Gudgeon				●													●				●		●											
Grilse																																		
Grayling																																		
Goldfish																												●						
Flounder																																		
Eel										●							●				●													
Dace										●		●								●	●													
Chub	●	●								●		●	●	●	●	●				●	●		●			●			●		●		●	
Charr																																		
Catfish Black Bullhead																																		
Catfish American Bullhead																																		
Catfish Albino																																		
Catfish																								●										
Carp Wild																																		
Carp Silver																																		
Carp Mirror	●		●		●	●	●	●	●	●			●	●				●	●	●	●		●		●		●	●			●			
Carp Leather																												●						
Carp Koi																												●						
Carp Grass																																		
Carp Ghost																												●						
Carp Crucian							●														●						●	●						
Carp Common	●	●	●	●	●	●	●	●	●	●			●	●				●	●	●	●		●		●	●	●	●			●			●
Carp Blue																																		
Bream		●		●	●		●		●	●		●	●	●		●	●	●	●	●	●		●		●	●	●	●	●	●		●		●
Bleak																					●													
Barbel										●	●		●	●							●	●				●								

Fish Species Available at UK & Irish Fisheries

Fishery	Barbel	Bleak	Bream	Carp Blue	Carp Common	Carp Crucian	Carp Ghost	Carp Grass	Carp Koi	Carp Leather	Carp Mirror	Carp Silver	Carp Wild	Catfish	Catfish Albino	Catfish American Bullhead	Catfish Black Bullhead	Charr	Chub	Dace	Eel	Flounder	Goldfish	Grayling	Grilse	Gudgeon	Gwyniad	Minnow	Orfe	Orfe Blue	Orfe Golden	Perch	Pike	Roach	Rudd	Ruffe	Salmon	Steelhead	Sturgeon	Tench	Tench Golden	Trount American Brook	Trout Blue	Trout Brook	Trout Brown	Trout Golden	Trout Lake	Ttrout Rainbow	Trout Sea	Trout Tiger	Trout Wild	Vendace	Zander
PIXIES MERE (FH3796)		●		●		●				●								●												●	●	●	●					●													
RIB VALLEY FISHING LAKE (FH3942)																																																	●					
RISLIP LAKE (FH3962)		●		●																										●		●	●					●													
RYEMEADS (FH4076)		●																		●												●	●	●	●					●													
SHEPHERDS WAY (FH4229)		●		●	●					●																				●		●																				
SLIPE LANE PITS (FH4299)		●		●	●					●			●																		●	●	●	●					●													
STANBOROUGH LAKE (FH4415)		●		●						●			●																					●	●					●													
STANSTEAD ABBOTTS (FH4423)	●		●		●						●								●												●	●	●						●													
STARTOPS RESERVOIR (FH4435)		●		●						●																				●	●	●						●													
THAME (RIVER) (FH4756)		●																		●	●						●						●		●																					
THAME (RIVER) (FH4755)		●																		●	●													●	●																					
THAME (RIVER) (FH4754)	●		●																		●	●						●						●	●	●																					
TRING RESERVOIRS (FH4957)		●		●						●			●																		●	●	●	●	●				●													
WESTBROOK MERE (FH5270)		●		●						●																				●	●	●	●					●													
WESTONS LAKE (FH5287)		●		●	●					●																								●					●													
WILSTONE RESERVOIR (FH5404)		●		●	●					●			●													●						●	●	●	●					●													
WOODLAND FARM (FH5478)		●		●	●																					●									●	●																					
WORMLEBURY (FH5505)		●		●						●			●																		●	●		●																					
HUMBERSIDE																																																					
AIRE AND CALDER CANAL (FH0047)	●	●	●		●						●								●	●	●					●							●	●	●	●	●				●							●					
BEVERLEY BECK (FH0399)		●																		●															●						●													
BEVERLEY CANAL (FH0400)		●			●															●												●	●	●						●													
BIG HOLE PIT (FH0411)		●		●	●	●			●	●																				●		●	●					●													
BILLABONG PARK (FH0416)		●		●						●																				●	●	●											●								
BLUE LAGOON (FH0505)		●																				●										●	●		●																					
BRANDES BURTON 3 AND 4 (FH0599)		●		●	●	●				●										●										●	●	●	●					●													
BRANDESBURTON (FH0600)		●		●						●										●										●	●	●	●					●													
BRICKYARD POND (FH0626)		●		●						●										●										●	●	●	●					●													
BURSHILL A POND (FH0757)		●		●						●								●															●	●				●													
BURSTWICK SKI LAKE (FH0758)		●		●	●	●				●																				●		●	●					●													
BURTON CONSTABLE COUNTRY PARK (FH0759)		●		●						●										●										●	●	●	●					●													
DACRE LAKESIDE PARK (FH1244)											●															●						●	●	●						●													
DERWENT (RIVER) (FH1350)	●																			●	●	●					●						●	●	●																					
DERWENT (RIVER) (FH1351)		●																				●						●						●	●	●																					

Fish Species Available at UK & Irish Fisheries

Fishery	Barbel	Bleak	Bream	Carp Blue	Carp Common	Carp Crucian	Carp Ghost	Carp Grass	Carp Koi	Carp Leather	Carp Mirror	Carp Silver	Carp Wild	Catfish	Catfish Albino	Catfish American Bullhead	Catfish Black Bullhead	Char
DRIFFIELD CANAL (FH1442)			●		●						●							
EMMOTLAND PONDS (FH1587)			●		●	●	●			●	●							
ESK (RIVER) (FH1622)																		
FAR GRANGE PARK (FH1663)			●		●	●	●				●							
FARM PONDS (FH1670)			●		●						●							
FISH TRADES POND (FH1726)			●		●						●							
FISHPONDS FARM AND FISHERY (FH1734)					●	●												
FISHPONDS FARM AND FISHERY (FH1735)			●			●					●							
FOSSEHILL LAKES (FH1776)			●		●						●							
GOWDALL LAKES (FH1928)			●		●	●					●							
HALSHAM POND (FH2075)			●		●						●							
HOLME LAKE FISHERY (FH2266)			●		●						●							
HULL (RIVER) (FH2332)			●															
HULL (RIVER) (FH2331)			●															
LAKEMINSTER PARK (FH2577)			●		●	●					●							
LAMBWATH LAKES (FH2600)			●		●	●		●			●							
LANGHOLME FISHERIES (FH2614)			●		●						●							
LEVEN CANAL (FH2710)																		
LEVEN CANAL (FH2709)			●		●						●							
LEVEN PARK LAKE (FH2711)	●		●		●	●	●		●		●							
MARKET WEIGHTON CANAL (FH3184)			●															
MOTORWAY POND (FH3382)			●		●	●					●			●				
NEST (FH3451)					●	●		●			●			●				
NODDLE HILL LAKE (FH3513)			●															
NORTH THORESBY FISHERIES (FH3535)					●						●							
OAKLANDS WATER (FH3564)			●		●						●							
REDFERNS POND (FH3917)			●		●						●							
RUSH LYVARS LAKE (FH4058)			●		●			●			●							
STAR CARR TROUT FARM (FH4427)			●		●	●		●	●	●	●							
TETNEY LOCK ANGLING CLUB (FH4747)			●		●						●							
THORPE HALL (FH4822)			●		●						●							
TILARY LAKE (FH4841)			●		●						●							
URE (RIVER) (FH5065)																		
WANSFORD TROUT LAKE (FH5143)																		

Fishery	Chub	Dace	Eel	Flounder	Goldfish	Grayling	Grilse	Gudgeon	Gwyniad	Minnow	Orfe	Orfe Blue	Orfe Golden	Perch	Pike	Roach	Rudd
DRIFFIELD CANAL (FH1442)	●					●								●	●	●	●
EMMOTLAND PONDS (FH1587)			●											●	●	●	
ESK (RIVER) (FH1622)																	
FAR GRANGE PARK (FH1663)	●		●					●			●			●		●	●
FARM PONDS (FH1670)														●	●	●	●
FISH TRADES POND (FH1726)														●	●	●	
FISHPONDS FARM AND FISHERY (FH1734)																●	●
FISHPONDS FARM AND FISHERY (FH1735)														●		●	●
FOSSEHILL LAKES (FH1776)																	
GOWDALL LAKES (FH1928)														●		●	●
HALSHAM POND (FH2075)														●			●
HOLME LAKE FISHERY (FH2266)														●			●
HULL (RIVER) (FH2332)	●	●	●											●	●	●	
HULL (RIVER) (FH2331)	●	●	●											●	●	●	
LAKEMINSTER PARK (FH2577)	●													●		●	●
LAMBWATH LAKES (FH2600)	●										●		●	●		●	●
LANGHOLME FISHERIES (FH2614)			●											●	●	●	
LEVEN CANAL (FH2710)																	
LEVEN CANAL (FH2709)			●											●	●	●	●
LEVEN PARK LAKE (FH2711)	●							●			●			●		●	●
MARKET WEIGHTON CANAL (FH3184)	●	●	●											●	●	●	
MOTORWAY POND (FH3382)			●											●	●	●	●
NEST (FH3451)														●		●	●
NODDLE HILL LAKE (FH3513)														●		●	●
NORTH THORESBY FISHERIES (FH3535)																	
OAKLANDS WATER (FH3564)													●			●	
REDFERNS POND (FH3917)	●							●						●		●	
RUSH LYVARS LAKE (FH4058)														●			
STAR CARR TROUT FARM (FH4427)														●	●	●	●
TETNEY LOCK ANGLING CLUB (FH4747)																●	●
THORPE HALL (FH4822)	●															●	
TILARY LAKE (FH4841)			●											●	●	●	
URE (RIVER) (FH5065)	●													●		●	
WANSFORD TROUT LAKE (FH5143)																	

Fishery	Ruffe	Salmon	Steelhead	Sturgeon	Tench	Tench Golden	Trount American Brook	Trout Blue	Trout Brook	Trout Brown	Trout Golden	Trout Lake	Ttrout Rainbow	Trout Sea	Trout Tiger	Trout Wild	Vendace	Zander
DRIFFIELD CANAL (FH1442)					●								●					
EMMOTLAND PONDS (FH1587)					●													
ESK (RIVER) (FH1622)		●												●				
FAR GRANGE PARK (FH1663)					●													
FARM PONDS (FH1670)					●													
FISH TRADES POND (FH1726)					●					●								
FISHPONDS FARM AND FISHERY (FH1734)					●													
FISHPONDS FARM AND FISHERY (FH1735)					●													
FOSSEHILL LAKES (FH1776)					●													
GOWDALL LAKES (FH1928)					●													
HALSHAM POND (FH2075)					●													
HOLME LAKE FISHERY (FH2266)																		
HULL (RIVER) (FH2332)																		
HULL (RIVER) (FH2331)																		
LAKEMINSTER PARK (FH2577)					●													
LAMBWATH LAKES (FH2600)					●													
LANGHOLME FISHERIES (FH2614)					●													
LEVEN CANAL (FH2710)					●													
LEVEN CANAL (FH2709)					●													
LEVEN PARK LAKE (FH2711)					●													
MARKET WEIGHTON CANAL (FH3184)					●													
MOTORWAY POND (FH3382)					●													
NEST (FH3451)					●													
NODDLE HILL LAKE (FH3513)					●													
NORTH THORESBY FISHERIES (FH3535)										●								
OAKLANDS WATER (FH3564)					●													
REDFERNS POND (FH3917)					●													
RUSH LYVARS LAKE (FH4058)					●													
STAR CARR TROUT FARM (FH4427)					●					●	●		●					
TETNEY LOCK ANGLING CLUB (FH4747)					●													
THORPE HALL (FH4822)					●													
TILARY LAKE (FH4841)																		
URE (RIVER) (FH5065)																		
WANSFORD TROUT LAKE (FH5143)										●			●					

Fish Species Available at UK & Irish Fisheries

	Barbel	Bleak	Bream	Carp Blue	Carp Common	Carp Crucian	Carp Ghost	Carp Grass	Carp Koi	Carp Leather	Carp Mirror	Carp Silver	Carp Wild	Catfish	Catfish Albino	Catfish American Bullhead	Catfish Black Bullhead	Charr	Chub	Dace	Eel	Flounder	Goldfish	Grayling	Grilse	Gudgeon	Gwyniad	Minnow	Orfe	Orfe Blue	Orfe Golden	Perch	Pike	Roach	Rudd	Ruffe	Salmon	Steelhead	Sturgeon	Tench	Tench Golden	Trount American Brook	Trout Blue	Trout Brook	Trout Brown	Trout Golden	Trout Lake	Ttrout Rainbow	Trout Sea	Trout Tiger	Trout Wild	Vendace	Zander
WILLITOFT FISH FARM (FH5376)			●		●	●	●		●		●								●		●								●					●	●					●													
WILLOW SPRINGS (FH5390)	●				●	●					●															●								●	●					●													
WOODALLS POND (FH5465)			●		●						●																							●						●													
ISLE OF WIGHT																																																					
GUNVILLE LAKE (FH2038)			●		●						●																						●	●	●					●													
HALE MANOR LAKES (FH2064)					●						●																																										
ISLAND FISH FARM/MEADOW LAKES (FH2390)					●						●																							●	●								●					●					
MERSTONE FISHERIES (FH3258)			●		●						●																					●		●						●													
MORTON FARM (FH3373)					●	●	●				●										●											●		●	●					●													
NETTLECOMBE FARMS (FH3457)					●						●																					●		●																			
ROOKLEY COUNTRY PARK (FH4006)					●						●																					●		●	●					●													
SOMERTON RESERVOIR (FH4325)					●						●																					●		●	●																		
YAR (A) (RIVER) (FH5554)					●						●									●	●					●						●		●																			
YAR (RIVER) (FH5555)			●		●						●									●	●					●						●		●	●					●													
KENT																																																					
ALDERS LAKES (FH0064)		●	●		●		●				●		●						●	●												●	●	●	●					●													
BALLAST PIT (FH0259)			●								●																						●	●	●					●													
BARDEN LAKE (FH0304)			●		●		●				●										●					●						●	●	●	●					●													
BARTLEY MILL FISHERY (FH0336)					●						●																								●					●													
BEWL WATER (FH0403)																																													●			●					
BIRCHDEN FARM FISHERY (FH0426)			●		●	●					●															●						●		●	●					●													
BLUE LAGOON LAKE (FH0507)			●		●						●								●													●	●	●	●					●													
BOUGH BEECH RESERVOIR (FH0564)			●		●	●					●								●													●	●	●						●					●			●					
BRITTON COURT FARM (FH0659)																																																●					
BROOKLANDS LAKE (FH0684)			●		●						●																													●													
BURNHAM RESERVOIR (FH0748)			●		●						●								●															●																			
BYSINGWOOD (FH0784)			●		●						●										●																			●													
BYWATER LAKE (FH0785)			●		●	●	●				●																					●		●	●					●													
CACKLE HILL LAKES (FH0787)			●		●		●				●			●					●													●		●	●					●	●												
CAPSTONE FARM COUNTRY PARK (FH0834)			●		●						●																						●	●	●																		
CHALYBEATE SPRINGS (FH0892)																																																●					
CHEQUERTREE FISHERY (FH0914)					●						●																					●	●		●					●					●			●					
CHIDDINGSTONE CASTLE LAKE (FH0939)			●		●						●															●						●		●	●																		
CHILHAM LAKE (FH0942)			●		●	●		●			●			●					●													●	●	●	●					●													

Fish Species Available at UK & Irish Fisheries

Fishery	Barbel	Bleak	Bream	Carp Blue	Carp Common	Carp Crucian	Carp Ghost	Carp Grass	Carp Koi	Carp Leather	Carp Mirror	Carp Silver	Carp Wild	Catfish	Catfish Albino	Catfish American Bullhead	Catfish Black Bullhead	Charr
CHIPSTEAD LAKES (FH0944)			●		●						●							
CONNINGBROOK (FH1088)					●						●							
COTTINGTON LAKES (FH1137)			●		●	●		●			●							
COTTON FARM FISHERY (FH1138)			●		●						●							
CRAYFORD (RIVER) (FH1172)			●		●						●							
DANSON PARK LAKE (FH1270)					●	●					●							
DARENT (RIVER) (FH1272)																		
DARENT (RIVER) (FH1271)			●		●						●							
DARENTH FISHING COMPLEX (FH1273)	●		●		●	●				●	●			●				
DUNDALE LAKE (FH1474)					●						●							
EDEN (RIVER) (FH1540)																		
EDEN (RIVER) (FH1542)			●															
EDEN (RIVER) (FH1539)	●				●						●							
EDEN (RIVER) (FH1541)			●		●						●							
EUREKA (FH1633)					●						●							
FORDCOMBE (FH1762)	●				●						●							
FRANT LAKES (FH1798)	●	●	●		●	●	●	●	●	●	●			●				
GRANGE POOL (FH1970)					●						●							
HANDLE LAKE (FH2100)			●		●						●							
HARTLEY LANDS FARM (FH2118)					●						●							
HAWKHURST FISH FARM (FH2142)	●			●	●	●		●			●			●				
HAYES TROUT FISHERY (FH2153)																		
HAYSDEN COUNTRY PARK (FH2160)	●	●	●		●	●					●							
HERONSVIEW FISHERIES (FH2193)					●						●							
HEXDEN CHANNEL (FH2198)			●		●						●							
HOO LAKES (FH2287)			●		●						●							
HOOKSTEAD LAKE (FH2290)					●						●							
LARKFIELD LAKES (FH2625)			●		●						●							
LAVENDER FARM (FH2631)						●					●							
LITTLE CANSIRON FISHING LAKES (FH2745)					●	●	●	●	●	●	●							
LONGFIELD LAKE (FH2988)			●								●							
LONGFORD LAKE (FH2989)			●		●						●							
LONGSHAW FARM FISHING LAKES (FH2995)			●		●						●							
MATCH LAKE (FH3208)			●		●						●							

Fishery	Chub	Dace	Eel	Flounder	Goldfish	Grayling	Grilse	Gudgeon	Gwyniad	Minnow	Orfe	Orfe Blue	Orfe Golden	Perch	Pike	Roach	Rudd	Ruffe
CHIPSTEAD LAKES (FH0944)																●	●	
CONNINGBROOK (FH1088)															●	●		
COTTINGTON LAKES (FH1137)	●		●											●	●	●	●	
COTTON FARM FISHERY (FH1138)															●	●		
CRAYFORD (RIVER) (FH1172)														●	●	●	●	
DANSON PARK LAKE (FH1270)								●						●		●		
DARENT (RIVER) (FH1272)																		
DARENT (RIVER) (FH1271)														●		●		
DARENTH FISHING COMPLEX (FH1273)	●	●	●											●	●	●	●	
DUNDALE LAKE (FH1474)														●		●		
EDEN (RIVER) (FH1540)	●															●		
EDEN (RIVER) (FH1542)	●															●		
EDEN (RIVER) (FH1539)	●	●														●		
EDEN (RIVER) (FH1541)	●	●						●						●	●	●		
EUREKA (FH1633)														●		●	●	
FORDCOMBE (FH1762)																		
FRANT LAKES (FH1798)	●	●	●		●			●			●			●		●	●	
GRANGE POOL (FH1970)														●				
HANDLE LAKE (FH2100)														●	●	●		
HARTLEY LANDS FARM (FH2118)	●													●		●		
HAWKHURST FISH FARM (FH2142)	●		●											●	●	●	●	
HAYES TROUT FISHERY (FH2153)																		
HAYSDEN COUNTRY PARK (FH2160)	●	●	●					●		●				●	●	●	●	●
HERONSVIEW FISHERIES (FH2193)																		
HEXDEN CHANNEL (FH2198)															●			
HOO LAKES (FH2287)														●		●	●	
HOOKSTEAD LAKE (FH2290)	●													●		●	●	
LARKFIELD LAKES (FH2625)			●												●	●		
LAVENDER FARM (FH2631)			●										●				●	
LITTLE CANSIRON FISHING LAKES (FH2745)											●			●		●	●	
LONGFIELD LAKE (FH2988)														●	●	●	●	
LONGFORD LAKE (FH2989)			●											●	●	●	●	
LONGSHAW FARM FISHING LAKES (FH2995)														●				
MATCH LAKE (FH3208)	●													●		●	●	

Fishery	Salmon	Steelhead	Sturgeon	Tench	Tench Golden	Trount American Brook	Trout Blue	Trout Brook	Trout Brown	Trout Golden	Trout Lake	Ttrout Rainbow	Trout Sea	Trout Tiger	Trout Wild	Vendace	Zander
CHIPSTEAD LAKES (FH0944)				●													
CONNINGBROOK (FH1088)																	
COTTINGTON LAKES (FH1137)				●					●			●					
COTTON FARM FISHERY (FH1138)																	
CRAYFORD (RIVER) (FH1172)				●													
DANSON PARK LAKE (FH1270)																	
DARENT (RIVER) (FH1272)									●								
DARENT (RIVER) (FH1271)																	
DARENTH FISHING COMPLEX (FH1273)				●													
DUNDALE LAKE (FH1474)				●													
EDEN (RIVER) (FH1540)																	
EDEN (RIVER) (FH1542)																	
EDEN (RIVER) (FH1539)																	
EDEN (RIVER) (FH1541)				●													
EUREKA (FH1633)				●													
FORDCOMBE (FH1762)																	
FRANT LAKES (FH1798)				●													
GRANGE POOL (FH1970)																	
HANDLE LAKE (FH2100)				●													
HARTLEY LANDS FARM (FH2118)				●													
HAWKHURST FISH FARM (FH2142)			●	●													
HAYES TROUT FISHERY (FH2153)												●					
HAYSDEN COUNTRY PARK (FH2160)				●													
HERONSVIEW FISHERIES (FH2193)																	
HEXDEN CHANNEL (FH2198)				●													
HOO LAKES (FH2287)				●													
HOOKSTEAD LAKE (FH2290)				●													
LARKFIELD LAKES (FH2625)				●													
LAVENDER FARM (FH2631)				●													
LITTLE CANSIRON FISHING LAKES (FH2745)				●				●	●						●		
LONGFIELD LAKE (FH2988)																	
LONGFORD LAKE (FH2989)				●													
LONGSHAW FARM FISHING LAKES (FH2995)				●													
MATCH LAKE (FH3208)																	

Fish Species Available at UK & Irish Fisheries

Fishery	Barbel	Bleak	Bream	Carp Blue	Carp Common	Carp Crucian	Carp Ghost	Carp Grass	Carp Koi	Carp Leather	Carp Mirror	Carp Silver	Carp Wild	Catfish	Catfish Albino	Catfish American Bullhead	Catfish Black Bullhead	Charr	Chub	Dace	Eel	Flounder	Goldfish	Grayling	Grilse	Gudgeon
MEDWAY (RIVER) (FH3231)			●		●						●								●							●
MEDWAY (RIVER) (FH3233)			●		●						●										●					
MEDWAY (RIVER) (FH3235)		●	●		●														●	●	●					●
MEDWAY (RIVER) (FH3237)		●	●		●														●	●	●					●
MEDWAY (RIVER) (FH3236)			●																●							
MEDWAY (RIVER) (FH3232)			●								●								●	●						
MEDWAY (RIVER) (FH3238)		●	●		●						●								●	●	●					●
MEDWAY (RIVER) (FH3230)		●	●		●														●	●						
MEDWAY (RIVER) (FH3234)	●		●																●							
MEDWAY (RIVER) (FH3239)		●	●		●						●								●	●						●
MID KENT FISHERIES (FH3263)		●	●		●	●		●			●			●					●	●	●			●		●
MILL POOL (FH3301)			●		●						●															
MILTON PAN LAKE (FH3323)			●		●						●															
MONK LAKE FISHERIES (FH3342)	●	●	●		●	●	●	●		●	●								●	●	●					
MOTE PARK FISHERY (FH3381)			●		●						●															
MOUSEHOLE LAKE (FH3392)																										
NACCOLT LAKE (FH3408)					●						●															
NOOK & CRANNY LAKE (FH3514)			●		●						●															
PIPPINS FARM LAKE (FH3787)																										
PITTLANDS LAKES (FH3795)																										
REED LAKE (FH3923)			●		●	●					●															
ROOKERY LAKE (FH4004)			●								●			●												
ROTHER (RIVER) (FH4025)			●		●						●															
ROTHER (RIVER) (FH4026)																			●							
ROUKES DRIFT FARM (FH4035)			●		●	●					●								●		●					●
ROYAL MILITARY CANAL (FH4046)			●		●						●										●					
RUXLEY PITS (FH4069)					●						●															
SCARLETTS LAKE (FH4114)					●			●											●	●						
SILVER SPRINGS FISHERY (FH4270)					●						●															
SINGLETON LAKE (FH4276)			●		●						●										●					
SPRING HILL TROUT WATERS (FH4368)																										
ST CLERE LAKE (FH4383)					●						●															
STOUR (RIVER) (FH4498)	●		●																●							
STOUR (RIVER) (FH4499)	●		●																●	●						

Fishery	Gwyniad	Minnow	Orfe	Orfe Blue	Orfe Golden	Perch	Pike	Roach	Rudd	Ruffe	Salmon	Steelhead	Sturgeon	Tench	Tench Golden	Trount American Brook	Trout Blue	Trout Brook	Trout Brown	Trout Golden	Trout Lake	Ttrout Rainbow	Trout Sea	Trout Tiger	Trout Wild	Vendace	Zander
MEDWAY (RIVER) (FH3231)						●	●	●	●					●													
MEDWAY (RIVER) (FH3233)		●				●	●	●																			
MEDWAY (RIVER) (FH3235)		●				●	●	●	●	●				●													
MEDWAY (RIVER) (FH3237)		●				●	●	●	●	●				●													
MEDWAY (RIVER) (FH3236)						●	●	●																			
MEDWAY (RIVER) (FH3232)						●	●	●																			
MEDWAY (RIVER) (FH3238)		●				●	●	●	●					●													
MEDWAY (RIVER) (FH3230)						●	●	●																			
MEDWAY (RIVER) (FH3234)						●	●	●																			
MEDWAY (RIVER) (FH3239)		●				●	●	●						●													
MID KENT FISHERIES (FH3263)		●				●	●	●	●	●			●	●					●				●				
MILL POOL (FH3301)								●	●					●													
MILTON PAN LAKE (FH3323)						●	●	●						●													
MONK LAKE FISHERIES (FH3342)					●	●	●	●	●					●	●												
MOTE PARK FISHERY (FH3381)								●						●													
MOUSEHOLE LAKE (FH3392)																			●								
NACCOLT LAKE (FH3408)						●		●	●					●													
NOOK & CRANNY LAKE (FH3514)						●	●	●						●													
PIPPINS FARM LAKE (FH3787)								●	●					●													
PITTLANDS LAKES (FH3795)						●																					
REED LAKE (FH3923)						●	●	●	●					●													
ROOKERY LAKE (FH4004)						●	●	●						●													
ROTHER (RIVER) (FH4025)							●							●													
ROTHER (RIVER) (FH4026)																											
ROUKES DRIFT FARM (FH4035)						●		●	●					●													
ROYAL MILITARY CANAL (FH4046)						●		●		●				●													
RUXLEY PITS (FH4069)																											
SCARLETTS LAKE (FH4114)						●		●	●					●													
SILVER SPRINGS FISHERY (FH4270)						●		●	●					●													
SINGLETON LAKE (FH4276)						●	●							●													
SPRING HILL TROUT WATERS (FH4368)																			●			●					
ST CLERE LAKE (FH4383)																											
STOUR (RIVER) (FH4498)							●	●																			
STOUR (RIVER) (FH4499)								●																			

Fish Species Available at UK & Irish Fisheries

Fishery	Barbel	Bleak	Bream	Carp Blue	Carp Common	Carp Crucian	Carp Ghost	Carp Grass	Carp Koi	Carp Leather	Carp Mirror	Carp Silver	Carp Wild	Catfish	Catfish Albino	Catfish American Bullhead	Catfish Black Bullhead	Charr	Chub	Dace	Eel	Flounder	Goldfish	Grayling	Grilse	Gudgeon
STOUR LAKE (FH4506)					●						●															
STOUTING LAKE (FH4507)																										
STOWTING TROUT LAKE (FH4514)																										
SURRENDEN LAKES (FH4558)	●		●		●	●					●								●							
SUTTON AT HONE LAKE TWO (FH4559)			●		●						●										●					
SUTTON AT HONE LAKES 1 & 3 (FH4560)			●		●	●					●										●					
SWAN LAKE (FH4591)					●						●															
TEISE (RIVER) (FH4720)	●	●	●		●	●	●	●	●	●	●								●	●	●					●
TENTERDEN TROUT WATERS (FH4738)																										
TONFORD LAKE (FH4871)			●		●						●															
TRIANGLE LAKE (FH4952)			●		●														●							
WIDEHURST FARM (FH5367)					●	●					●															
WINGHAM FISHERY (FH5417)			●		●						●										●					
WOOD POOL (FH5461)			●		●						●															
LANCASHIRE																										
ABBEY LAKES (FH0003)						●																				
ASHTON CANAL (FH0170)			●																							
BALL GROVE LAKE (FH0258)			●		●	●					●										●					●
BANK HOUSE FLY FISHERY (FH0286)																										
BANNISTER HALL FARM (FH0300)			●		●	●					●															●
BARNSFOLD WATERS (FH0318)																										
BARRETTS FARM FISHERY (FH0324)			●		●	●					●															●
BARROWFORD RESERVOIR (FH0330)																										●
BENTHAM STREAM (FH0388)																										
BIRKACRE LODGES (FH0429)			●																							
BOLTON CANAL (FH0540)			●		●	●					●										●					
BRADFORD RESERVOIR (FH0587)			●		●						●															●
BRADSHAW HALL FISHERIES (FH0591)			●		●	●	●	●			●								●							
BRIARCROFT FISHERY (FH0618)			●		●						●															●
BRINSCALL LODGE (FH0645)			●		●						●															
BROWNHILL RESERVOIR (FH0701)																										
BRYAN HEY RESERVOIR (FH0711)			●		●	●					●															●
BRYN FLASH (FH0712)			●		●						●															
BURSCOUGH BRICKWORKS LAKE (FH0756)			●		●						●								●							

Fishery	Gwyniad	Minnow	Orfe	Orfe Blue	Orfe Golden	Perch	Pike	Roach	Rudd	Ruffe	Salmon	Steelhead	Sturgeon	Tench	Tench Golden	Trount American Brook	Trout Blue	Trout Brook	Trout Brown	Trout Golden	Trout Lake	Ttrout Rainbow	Trout Sea	Trout Tiger	Trout Wild	Vendace	Zander
STOUR LAKE (FH4506)						●	●	●	●					●													
STOUTING LAKE (FH4507)											●								●			●					
STOWTING TROUT LAKE (FH4514)																			●			●					
SURRENDEN LAKES (FH4558)						●		●	●					●													
SUTTON AT HONE LAKE TWO (FH4559)						●	●	●						●													
SUTTON AT HONE LAKES 1 & 3 (FH4560)						●	●	●	●					●													
SWAN LAKE (FH4591)						●	●																				
TEISE (RIVER) (FH4720)		●	●				●	●	●					●					●						●		
TENTERDEN TROUT WATERS (FH4738)																			●			●					
TONFORD LAKE (FH4871)						●		●	●					●													
TRIANGLE LAKE (FH4952)						●	●	●	●					●													
WIDEHURST FARM (FH5367)														●													
WINGHAM FISHERY (FH5417)						●		●	●					●													
WOOD POOL (FH5461)						●		●	●					●													
LANCASHIRE																											
ABBEY LAKES (FH0003)							●	●						●													
ASHTON CANAL (FH0170)							●	●																			
BALL GROVE LAKE (FH0258)						●		●	●					●					●								
BANK HOUSE FLY FISHERY (FH0286)																			●			●		●			
BANNISTER HALL FARM (FH0300)						●		●	●					●													
BARNSFOLD WATERS (FH0318)																			●			●					
BARRETTS FARM FISHERY (FH0324)						●		●						●													
BARROWFORD RESERVOIR (FH0330)								●																			
BENTHAM STREAM (FH0388)																			●								
BIRKACRE LODGES (FH0429)						●	●	●	●					●													
BOLTON CANAL (FH0540)						●	●	●	●					●													
BRADFORD RESERVOIR (FH0587)						●	●	●						●													
BRADSHAW HALL FISHERIES (FH0591)						●		●						●													
BRIARCROFT FISHERY (FH0618)						●		●						●													
BRINSCALL LODGE (FH0645)						●	●	●																			
BROWNHILL RESERVOIR (FH0701)																			●								
BRYAN HEY RESERVOIR (FH0711)						●	●	●						●													
BRYN FLASH (FH0712)								●						●													
BURSCOUGH BRICKWORKS LAKE (FH0756)						●		●	●					●													

Fish Species Available at UK & Irish Fisheries

Fishery	Barbel	Bleak	Bream	Carp Blue	Carp Common	Carp Crucian	Carp Ghost	Carp Grass	Carp Koi	Carp Leather	Carp Mirror	Carp Silver	Carp Wild	Catfish	Catfish Albino	Catfish American Bullhead	Catfish Black Bullhead	Charr	Chub	Dace	Eel	Flounder	Goldfish	Grayling	Grilse	Gudgeon	Gwyniad
CALDER (RIVER) (FH0792)																										
CALDER (RIVER) (FH0793)																		●	●						●	
CHARITY FARM FISHERY (FH0900)		●		●						●								●									
CHURCH GARDEN (FH0952)		●		●						●																	
CLAYLANDS CARAVAN SITE (FH0994)		●		●	●					●																	
CLEVELEY BRIDGE FISHERY (FH1004)	●		●		●	●		●			●								●							●	
CLIVIGER FISH PONDS (FH1012)	●		●		●	●	●		●	●	●								●							●	
COLDWELL (LOWER) RESERVOIR (FH1058)																										
COLNE WATER (FH1075)																										
COPTHORNE COARSE FISHERIES (FH1115)		●		●	●					●								●									
COTTAGE GREEN GARDEN CENTRE (FH1133)		●		●						●																	
CROFT FISHERIES (FH1182)	●		●		●		●				●															●	
CROMPTON LODGE (FH1185)		●																●									
CUERDEN VALLEY LAKE (FH1212)		●		●						●															●	
DEAN CLOUGH RESERVOIR (FH1287)																										
DEEP PIT (FH1323)		●		●	●					●																	
DERWENT (RIVER) (FH1352)		●																	●	●					●	
DILWORTH (UPPER) RESERVOIR (FH1368)																										
DIXON GREEN RESERVOIR (FH1380)		●		●	●					●								●		●					●	
DOFFCOCKER LODGE (FH1392)		●		●						●																	
DOUGLAS (RIVER) (FH1420)																		●	●							
DRAKESHEAD FLY FISHERY (FH1436)																										
DUNSCAR SHORE LODGE (FH1479)		●			●														●						
EARNSDALE RESERVOIR (FH1504)																										
ERIC FISHWICK NATURE RESERVE (FH1608)	●		●		●	●		●			●								●		●					●	
FAN LODGE (FH1659)		●		●						●																	
FARINGTON LODGES (FH1665)		●		●						●																	
FIR TREE LODGE (FH1721)	●				●	●					●								●		●						
FORSTERS LODGES (FH1770)																				●						
FOULRIDGE RESERVOIR (FH1778)		●		●						●										●						
FOUNDRY LODGE (FH1780)		●																								
GLEAVES RESERVOIR (FH1876)		●			●																						
GREAT BIRCH WOOD PONDS (FH1979)		●		●	●					●																	
GREEN LANE PONDS (FH2002)		●		●	●					●															●	

Fishery	Minnow	Orfe	Orfe Blue	Orfe Golden	Perch	Pike	Roach	Rudd	Ruffe	Salmon	Steelhead	Sturgeon	Tench	Tench Golden	Trount American Brook	Trout Blue	Trout Brook	Trout Brown	Trout Golden	Trout Lake	Ttrout Rainbow	Trout Sea	Trout Tiger	Trout Wild	Vendace	Zander
CALDER (RIVER) (FH0792)											●								●				●				
CALDER (RIVER) (FH0793)							●														●					
CHARITY FARM FISHERY (FH0900)					●		●						●														
CHURCH GARDEN (FH0952)																									
CLAYLANDS CARAVAN SITE (FH0994)					●		●						●														
CLEVELEY BRIDGE FISHERY (FH1004)					●		●	●					●														
CLIVIGER FISH PONDS (FH1012)		●		●	●		●	●					●	●				●	●									
COLDWELL (LOWER) RESERVOIR (FH1058)																			●							
COLNE WATER (FH1075)																			●							
COPTHORNE COARSE FISHERIES (FH1115)				●	●		●	●					●														
COTTAGE GREEN GARDEN CENTRE (FH1133)														●														
CROFT FISHERIES (FH1182)					●		●						●														
CROMPTON LODGE (FH1185)					●	●							●														
CUERDEN VALLEY LAKE (FH1212)					●	●	●						●														
DEAN CLOUGH RESERVOIR (FH1287)																			●			●					
DEEP PIT (FH1323)					●		●						●														
DERWENT (RIVER) (FH1352)					●		●																			
DILWORTH (UPPER) RESERVOIR (FH1368)																			●							
DIXON GREEN RESERVOIR (FH1380)					●	●	●	●					●														
DOFFCOCKER LODGE (FH1392)						●	●																				
DOUGLAS (RIVER) (FH1420)					●		●																			
DRAKESHEAD FLY FISHERY (FH1436)																							●					
DUNSCAR SHORE LODGE (FH1479)					●	●	●						●														
EARNSDALE RESERVOIR (FH1504)																			●			●					
ERIC FISHWICK NATURE RESERVE (FH1608)	●				●		●	●					●								●					
FAN LODGE (FH1659)					●	●	●						●														
FARINGTON LODGES (FH1665)						●							●														
FIR TREE LODGE (FH1721)			●	●	●		●	●					●														
FORSTERS LODGES (FH1770)					●		●						●														
FOULRIDGE RESERVOIR (FH1778)					●	●	●						●														
FOUNDRY LODGE (FH1780)					●	●	●						●														
GLEAVES RESERVOIR (FH1876)					●	●	●						●					●							
GREAT BIRCH WOOD PONDS (FH1979)							●						●														
GREEN LANE PONDS (FH2002)					●		●						●														

Fish Species Available at UK & Irish Fisheries

Fishery	Barbel	Bleak	Bream	Carp Blue	Carp Common	Carp Crucian	Carp Ghost	Carp Grass	Carp Koi	Carp Leather	Carp Mirror	Carp Silver	Carp Wild	Catfish	Catfish Albino	Catfish American Bullhead	Catfish Black Bullhead	Charr	Chub	Dace	Eel	Flounder	Goldfish	Grayling	Grilse	Gudgeon	Gwyniad	Minnow	Orfe	Orfe Blue	Orfe Golden	Perch	Pike	Roach	Rudd	Ruffe	Salmon	Steelhead	Sturgeon	Tench	Tench Golden	Trount American Brook	Trout Blue	Trout Brook	Trout Brown	Trout Golden	Trout Lake	Ttrout Rainbow	Trout Sea	Trout Tiger	Trout Wild	Vendace	Zander
GREENHALGH LODGE FISHERY (FH2007)					●						●																																										
GRIMSARGH RESERVOIR (FH2021)			●		●						●																						●	●						●					●								
GRIZEDALE LEA RESERVOIR (FH2026)																																																●					
HEAPEY NO 1 (FH2167)			●		●						●								●													●		●						●													
HEAPEY NO 2 (FH2168)			●		●						●																					●		●																			
HEAPEY NO 3 (FH2169)			●		●						●								●													●		●						●													
HEAPEY NO 6 (FH2170)			●																●													●	●	●						●													
HESKIN OLD FARM FISHERY (FH2195)			●		●						●																					●		●	●					●													
HIGHER HALL FLASH (FH2215)			●		●	●					●																						●	●	●					●													
HODDER (RIVER) (FH2241)																																					●								●				●				
HODDLESDEN LAKE (FH2242)																																													●								
HODDLESDEN RESERVOIR (FH2243)			●		●						●																					●		●						●													
HOLDEN WOOD RESERVOIR (FH2250)																																												●	●	●			●				
HORROCKS FLASH (FH2302)			●																													●		●						●													
HOUGHTONS LODGE (FH2317)			●		●						●																					●		●						●													
HUDSONS FARM (FH2329)			●		●						●																													●													
HULTON PARK LAKE (FH2334)					●						●																					●		●						●													
INCE MOSS FISHERIES (FH2363)			●		●	●					●								●													●		●						●													
INCE PARK LAKE (FH2364)			●																													●		●						●													
ISLAND DAM (FH2389)			●		●						●																						●	●						●													
KNIGHT BOTTOMS LAKE (FH2534)					●						●								●													●		●	●					●													
LANCASTER CANAL (FH2604)																																●	●	●																			
LANCASTER CANAL (FH2603)			●		●						●										●					●						●	●	●						●													
LANCASTER HOUSE (FH2605)					●	●					●								●							●								●						●													
LANCASTER HOUSE FARM FISHERY (FH2606)			●			●																										●		●						●													
LANESHAW RESERVOIR (FH2609)																																●		●											●			●					
LATHOM FISHERIES (FH2627)	●				●						●								●													●		●						●													
LEEDS TO LIVERPOOL CANAL (FH2674)			●		●						●																					●		●						●													
LEEDS TO LIVERPOOL CANAL (FH2673)			●																													●	●	●																			
LEEDS TO LIVERPOOL CANAL (FH2676)			●																															●																			
LEISURE LAKES (FH2695)			●		●						●										●					●						●	●	●						●													
LITTLE DALE HALL (FH2747)			●		●	●		●		●	●			●																		●		●	●					●													
LONGTON BRICKCROFT (FH2996)			●		●	●					●										●											●	●	●	●					●													
LOVECLOUGH TROUT FISHERY (FH3065)			●																																										●			●					

Fish Species Available at UK & Irish Fisheries

Fishery	Barbel	Bleak	Bream	Carp Blue	Carp Common	Carp Crucian	Carp Ghost	Carp Grass	Carp Koi	Carp Leather	Carp Mirror	Carp Silver	Carp Wild	Catfish	Catfish Albino	Catfish American Bullhead	Catfish Black Bullhead	Charr
LOWER COLDWELL RESERVOIR (FH3076)																		
LOWER HOUSE LODGE (FH3083)			●		●						●							
LOWER RIVINGTON RESERVOIR (FH3091)			●															
LOWER RODDLESWORTH RESERVOIR (FH3092)																		
LUNE (RIVER) (FH3112)																		
LUNE (RIVER) (FH3111)																		
LYNDHURST FARM LAKE (FH3120)			●		●						●			●				
MANOR HOUSE FISHERY (FH3167)			●		●	●					●							
MARTIN HALL FARM (FH3200)			●		●	●												
MELCHES POND (FH3245)					●						●							
MELLINGS NO 1 (FH3248)																		
MITCHELLS HOUSE RESERVOIR (FH3329)																		
OGDEN RESERVOIR (FH3577)																		
ORRELL WATER PARK (FH3625)			●		●		●				●							
PARSONAGE RESERVOIR (FH3713)			●		●						●							
PENDLE WATER (FH3735)																		
PINE LODGE FISHERIES (FH3777)			●		●			●			●							
POLLYS FLASH (FH3812)			●		●						●							
PORTSMOUTH RESERVIOR (FH3831)			●		●						●							
RED ROCKS FISHERY (FH3911)			●		●	●					●							
RIBBLE (RIVER) (FH3946)	●																	
RIBBLE (RIVER) (FH3943)																		
RIBBLE (RIVER) (FH3945)																		
RIBBLE (RIVER) (FH3944)	●																	
RISHTON RESERVOIR (FH3960)			●		●						●							
ROUGHLEE TROUT FISHERY (FH4034)																		
ROWLEY PARK LAKE (FH4041)			●		●						●							
RUFFORD CANAL (FH4054)			●															
RUMWORTH LODGE RESERVOIR (FH4056)			●		●						●							
RUSHYVARS LAKES (FH4064)					●						●							
SCOT LANE PONDS (FH4118)			●			●												
SHRUGGS WOOD FISHERY (FH4261)			●		●	●					●							
SPADE MILL RESERVOIR NO.2 (FH4356)																		
SQUARE LODGE (FH4380)					●	●					●							

Fishery	Chub	Dace	Eel	Flounder	Goldfish	Grayling	Grilse	Gudgeon	Gwyniad	Minnow	Orfe	Orfe Blue	Orfe Golden	Perch	Pike	Roach	Rudd	Ruffe
LOWER COLDWELL RESERVOIR (FH3076)																		
LOWER HOUSE LODGE (FH3083)														●	●	●		●
LOWER RIVINGTON RESERVOIR (FH3091)														●	●	●		
LOWER RODDLESWORTH RESERVOIR (FH3092)															●			
LUNE (RIVER) (FH3112)										●								
LUNE (RIVER) (FH3111)																		
LYNDHURST FARM LAKE (FH3120)														●		●	●	
MANOR HOUSE FISHERY (FH3167)														●		●	●	
MARTIN HALL FARM (FH3200)																●	●	
MELCHES POND (FH3245)																		
MELLINGS NO 1 (FH3248)														●		●		
MITCHELLS HOUSE RESERVOIR (FH3329)																		
OGDEN RESERVOIR (FH3577)																		
ORRELL WATER PARK (FH3625)	●		●					●						●		●	●	
PARSONAGE RESERVOIR (FH3713)														●		●	●	
PENDLE WATER (FH3735)	●													●		●		
PINE LODGE FISHERIES (FH3777)														●		●		
POLLYS FLASH (FH3812)	●							●						●		●		
PORTSMOUTH RESERVIOR (FH3831)	●													●		●	●	
RED ROCKS FISHERY (FH3911)														●		●	●	
RIBBLE (RIVER) (FH3946)	●																	
RIBBLE (RIVER) (FH3943)																		
RIBBLE (RIVER) (FH3945)																		
RIBBLE (RIVER) (FH3944)	●	●														●		
RISHTON RESERVOIR (FH3960)	●							●								●		
ROUGHLEE TROUT FISHERY (FH4034)																		
ROWLEY PARK LAKE (FH4041)			●					●						●	●	●	●	
RUFFORD CANAL (FH4054)			●											●	●	●		
RUMWORTH LODGE RESERVOIR (FH4056)														●	●	●		
RUSHYVARS LAKES (FH4064)																	●	
SCOT LANE PONDS (FH4118)	●													●		●		
SHRUGGS WOOD FISHERY (FH4261)														●		●		
SPADE MILL RESERVOIR NO.2 (FH4356)																		
SQUARE LODGE (FH4380)														●		●		

Fishery	Salmon	Steelhead	Sturgeon	Tench	Tench Golden	Trount American Brook	Trout Blue	Trout Brook	Trout Brown	Trout Golden	Trout Lake	Ttrout Rainbow	Trout Sea	Trout Tiger	Trout Wild	Vendace	Zander
LOWER COLDWELL RESERVOIR (FH3076)									●								
LOWER HOUSE LODGE (FH3083)																	
LOWER RIVINGTON RESERVOIR (FH3091)				●													
LOWER RODDLESWORTH RESERVOIR (FH3092)																	
LUNE (RIVER) (FH3112)	●								●			●	●				
LUNE (RIVER) (FH3111)	●												●				
LYNDHURST FARM LAKE (FH3120)				●													
MANOR HOUSE FISHERY (FH3167)				●													
MARTIN HALL FARM (FH3200)				●													
MELCHES POND (FH3245)																	
MELLINGS NO 1 (FH3248)				●													
MITCHELLS HOUSE RESERVOIR (FH3329)												●					
OGDEN RESERVOIR (FH3577)								●	●	●		●					
ORRELL WATER PARK (FH3625)				●													
PARSONAGE RESERVOIR (FH3713)				●													
PENDLE WATER (FH3735)									●								
PINE LODGE FISHERIES (FH3777)				●													
POLLYS FLASH (FH3812)				●													
PORTSMOUTH RESERVIOR (FH3831)				●													
RED ROCKS FISHERY (FH3911)				●													
RIBBLE (RIVER) (FH3946)	●								●								
RIBBLE (RIVER) (FH3943)	●								●				●				
RIBBLE (RIVER) (FH3945)	●								●								
RIBBLE (RIVER) (FH3944)																	
RISHTON RESERVOIR (FH3960)				●													
ROUGHLEE TROUT FISHERY (FH4034)									●	●		●			●		
ROWLEY PARK LAKE (FH4041)				●													
RUFFORD CANAL (FH4054)																	
RUMWORTH LODGE RESERVOIR (FH4056)				●													
RUSHYVARS LAKES (FH4064)				●					●								
SCOT LANE PONDS (FH4118)				●													
SHRUGGS WOOD FISHERY (FH4261)				●													
SPADE MILL RESERVOIR NO.2 (FH4356)									●			●					
SQUARE LODGE (FH4380)				●													

Fish Species Available at UK & Irish Fisheries

	Barbel	Bleak	Bream	Carp Blue	Carp Common	Carp Crucian	Carp Ghost	Carp Grass	Carp Koi	Carp Leather	Carp Mirror	Carp Silver	Carp Wild	Catfish	Catfish Albino	Catfish American Bullhead	Catfish Black Bullhead	Charr	Chub	Dace	Eel	Flounder	Goldfish	Grayling	Grilse	Gudgeon	Gwyniad
ST MICHAELS WYRESIDE FISHERY (FH4394)			●		●	●					●			●					●	●						●	
STANLEY PARK LAKE (FH4420)			●		●						●																
STANWORTH RESERVOIR (FH4425)			●		●						●																
STARMOUNT LODGES (FH4434)					●						●								●							●	
STOCKS FLY FISHERY (FH4463)																											
SWANTLEY LAKE (FH4601)					●	●					●																
SWINDEN RESERVOIR (FH4611)																											
TEMPLE SPRINGS (FH4734)					●						●																
THURSLAND HILL FARM (FH4838)					●	●					●																
TURBARY HOUSE NURSARY (FH4974)			●		●	●					●																
TURTON & ENTWISTLE RESERVOIR (FH4986)																											
TWIN LAKES TROUT FISHERY (FH5004)																											
WALVERDEN RESERVOIR (FH5137)			●		●						●								●								
WENNING (RIVER) (FH5243)																											
WENNING (RIVER) (FH5242)																											
WHITEMOOR RESERVOIR (FH5352)																										●	
WIDOWS FLASH (FH5368)					●																						
WITHNELL RESERVOIRS (FH5445)			●		●						●																
WOODFOLD FARM FISHERIES (FH5473)			●		●	●					●								●								
WORTHINGTON NO 1 (FH5510)	●																										
WORTHINGTON NO 2 (FH5511)	●		●																								
WORTHINGTON NO 3 (FH5512)	●																										
WRYE (RIVER) (FH5521)																			●		●						
WYRE (RIVER) (FH5549)																			●								
WYRESIDE LAKES (FH5550)			●		●						●								●								
LEICESTERSHIRE																											
BAXTERS GARDEN FARM LAKE (FH0349)					●																						
BROOME FISHERIES (FH0692)					●						●																
C J FISHERIES (FH0786)			●		●	●					●																
CHARNWOOD WATER (FH0906)					●																						
EYEBROOK TROUT FISHERY (FH1649)																											
FRISBY LAKES (FH1803)			●		●		●				●																
GROBY FISHING LAKES (FH2027)			●		●																						
HALL FARM (FH2066)			●		●	●	●			●	●																

	Minnow	Orfe	Orfe Blue	Orfe Golden	Perch	Pike	Roach	Rudd	Ruffe	Salmon	Steelhead	Sturgeon	Tench	Tench Golden	Trount American Brook	Trout Blue	Trout Brook	Trout Brown	Trout Golden	Trout Lake	Ttrout Rainbow	Trout Sea	Trout Tiger	Trout Wild	Vendace	Zander
ST MICHAELS WYRESIDE FISHERY (FH4394)					●		●	●					●													
STANLEY PARK LAKE (FH4420)																										
STANWORTH RESERVOIR (FH4425)					●		●	●					●													
STARMOUNT LODGES (FH4434)					●		●	●																		
STOCKS FLY FISHERY (FH4463)																		●			●					
SWANTLEY LAKE (FH4601)							●	●					●													
SWINDEN RESERVOIR (FH4611)																		●								
TEMPLE SPRINGS (FH4734)							●	●					●													
THURSLAND HILL FARM (FH4838)					●		●	●					●													
TURBARY HOUSE NURSARY (FH4974)					●								●													
TURTON & ENTWISTLE RESERVOIR (FH4986)																					●					
TWIN LAKES TROUT FISHERY (FH5004)																		●			●					
WALVERDEN RESERVOIR (FH5137)					●		●						●													
WENNING (RIVER) (FH5243)										●											●	●				
WENNING (RIVER) (FH5242)										●								●				●				
WHITEMOOR RESERVOIR (FH5352)							●																			
WIDOWS FLASH (FH5368)																										
WITHNELL RESERVOIRS (FH5445)							●						●													
WOODFOLD FARM FISHERIES (FH5473)					●		●	●					●													
WORTHINGTON NO 1 (FH5510)					●		●																			
WORTHINGTON NO 2 (FH5511)					●		●																			
WORTHINGTON NO 3 (FH5512)					●		●																			
WRYE (RIVER) (FH5521)							●																			
WYRE (RIVER) (FH5549)							●			●												●				
WYRESIDE LAKES (FH5550)					●	●		●					●					●			●					
LEICESTERSHIRE																										
BAXTERS GARDEN FARM LAKE (FH0349)							●																			
BROOME FISHERIES (FH0692)																										
C J FISHERIES (FH0786)							●	●					●													
CHARNWOOD WATER (FH0906)						●																				
EYEBROOK TROUT FISHERY (FH1649)																		●			●					
FRISBY LAKES (FH1803)					●	●	●	●					●													
GROBY FISHING LAKES (FH2027)					●								●													
HALL FARM (FH2066)					●		●	●																		

Fish Species Available at UK & Irish Fisheries

Fishery	Barbel	Bleak	Bream	Carp Blue	Carp Common	Carp Crucian	Carp Ghost	Carp Grass	Carp Koi	Carp Leather	Carp Mirror	Carp Silver	Carp Wild	Catfish	Catfish Albino	Catfish American Bullhead	Catfish Black Bullhead	Charr	Chub	Dace	Eel
HALL FARM FISHING (FH2067)					●																
HOLLY FARM FISHERY (FH2261)			●		●						●										
LAKESIDE FISHING (FH2593)			●		●	●					●								●		
LEICESTER GRAND UNION CANAL (FH2690)																					
LOUGHBOROUGH SOAR CANAL (FH3055)																					
LYNCHGATE LANE FISHERY (FH3119)			●		●	●					●										
MALLORY PARK FISHERIES (FH3152)					●						●										
MANOR FARM (FH3161)			●																		
MANOR FARM POOLS (FH3165)			●		●						●										
MILL FARM FISHERY (FH3280)			●		●	●	●				●								●		
MONNOW (RIVER) (FH3350)																					
NANPANTAN RESERVOIR (FH3417)			●		●						●								●		
PARKLANDS FISHERY (FH3704)					●																
PEATLING POOLS (1-6) (FH3727)					●																
PROCTORS PLEASURE PARK (FH3851)			●		●	●					●										
RUTLAND WATER (FH4068)																					
SHELL FRESH LAKE (FH4225)					●																
SNIBSON COLLIERY CARP LAKE (FH4311)					●																
SOAR (RIVER) (FH4316)																			●		
STEMBOROUGH MILL TROUT FARM (FH4449)																					
SWITHLAND RESERVOIR (FH4616)			●																		
THORNTON RESERVOIR (FH4820)																					
WATERMEAD PARK LAKES (FH5180)			●		●	●				●	●										
WATERY GATE FISHERY (FH5187)			●		●						●										
WHETSTONE GORSE (FH5320)			●		●	●	●				●								●		
WILLOWS FARM FISHING (FH5399)			●		●	●					●								●	●	
WREAKE (RIVER) (FH5515)																			●		
LINCOLNSHIRE																					
ASHBY PARK FISHERIES (FH0158)			●		●						●								●		●
BELVOIR CASTLE (FH0383)			●																		
BOULTHAM PARK LAKE (FH0565)			●		●						●								●		●
BRICKYARD FISHERY (FH0623)			●		●						●										●
BRICKYARD POND (FH0627)					●						●										
BURGHLEY PARK LAKE (FH0743)			●																		

Fishery	Flounder	Goldfish	Grayling	Grilse	Gudgeon	Gwyniad	Minnow	Orfe	Orfe Blue	Orfe Golden	Perch	Pike	Roach	Rudd	Ruffe	Salmon	Steelhead	Sturgeon	Tench	Tench Golden	Trount American Brook	Trout Blue	Trout Brook	Trout Brown	Trout Golden	Trout Lake	Ttrout Rainbow	Trout Sea	Trout Tiger	Trout Wild	Vendace	Zander
HALL FARM FISHING (FH2067)													●																			
HOLLY FARM FISHERY (FH2261)											●		●	●					●	●												
LAKESIDE FISHING (FH2593)					●						●		●						●													
LEICESTER GRAND UNION CANAL (FH2690)											●		●																			
LOUGHBOROUGH SOAR CANAL (FH3055)					●								●																			
LYNCHGATE LANE FISHERY (FH3119)											●	●	●	●					●													
MALLORY PARK FISHERIES (FH3152)																																
MANOR FARM (FH3161)																																
MANOR FARM POOLS (FH3165)											●		●	●																		
MILL FARM FISHERY (FH3280)								●			●		●	●					●													
MONNOW (RIVER) (FH3350)																●								●								
NANPANTAN RESERVOIR (FH3417)											●	●	●						●													
PARKLANDS FISHERY (FH3704)													●																			
PEATLING POOLS (1-6) (FH3727)													●																			
PROCTORS PLEASURE PARK (FH3851)												●							●													
RUTLAND WATER (FH4068)												●												●			●					
SHELL FRESH LAKE (FH4225)													●																			
SNIBSON COLLIERY CARP LAKE (FH4311)													●						●													
SOAR (RIVER) (FH4316)													●																			
STEMBOROUGH MILL TROUT FARM (FH4449)																											●					
SWITHLAND RESERVOIR (FH4616)																																
THORNTON RESERVOIR (FH4820)																											●					
WATERMEAD PARK LAKES (FH5180)					●						●	●	●	●					●													●
WATERY GATE FISHERY (FH5187)													●						●													
WHETSTONE GORSE (FH5320)											●		●	●					●													
WILLOWS FARM FISHING (FH5399)					●						●	●	●	●					●													●
WREAKE (RIVER) (FH5515)													●																			
LINCOLNSHIRE																																
ASHBY PARK FISHERIES (FH0158)											●		●	●					●													
BELVOIR CASTLE (FH0383)												●																				
BOULTHAM PARK LAKE (FH0565)					●						●	●	●		●				●													
BRICKYARD FISHERY (FH0623)											●		●	●					●													
BRICKYARD POND (FH0627)																																
BURGHLEY PARK LAKE (FH0743)														●					●					●								

Fish Species Available at UK & Irish Fisheries

Fishery	Barbel	Bleak	Bream	Carp Blue	Carp Common	Carp Crucian	Carp Ghost	Carp Grass	Carp Koi	Carp Leather	Carp Mirror	Carp Silver	Carp Wild	Catfish	Catfish Albino	Catfish American Bullhead	Catfish Black Bullhead	Charr	Chub	Dace	Eel	Flounder	Goldfish	Grayling	Grilse	Gudgeon	Gwyniad
CHARLES STREET POND (FH0903)						●																					
DAIWA GULL POOL (FH1247)					●		●	●	●	●	●			●													
DENNIS RAINWATER LAKE (FH1331)					●						●																
DENTON RESERVOIR (FH1332)					●						●																
GOLTHO LAKE (FH1917)			●		●	●	●				●								●	●	●					●	
GRANGE FARM LEISURE (FH1969)			●		●	●	●				●								●							●	
GROOBYS PIT (FH2028)			●		●						●																
HARTSHOLME PARK LAKE (FH2119)			●		●						●										●					●	
HATTON TROUT LAKE (FH2134)			●		●		●	●	●	●	●								●		●						
HAVERHOLME PARK (FH2137)	●		●		●						●								●								
HERONS MEAD (FH2192)																											
HILL VIEW LAKES (FH2224)			●		●	●	●				●																
HOBHOLE DRAIN (FH2238)		●	●		●																						
HOLLAND PARK (FH2255)			●		●	●		●		●	●										●						
KEAL COATES FISHERY (FH2422)					●						●																
KINPTON RESERVOIR (FH2522)			●																								
LAKE HELEN (FH2558)			●		●	●	●		●	●	●								●	●	●					●	
LAKE ROSS FISHERY (FH2572)	●				●						●								●								
LAKESIDE (FH2582)			●		●			●			●								●								
LAKESIDE LEISURE PARK (FH2594)			●		●	●		●			●			●					●		●					●	
LOBBY FIELD PONDS (FH2834)					●						●																
MARRIS LAKES (FH3190)			●		●						●																
MILL HILL LAKES (FH3285)	●		●			●													●								
MILL ROAD LAKES (FH3304)	●		●		●	●					●								●								
MOON LAKE (FH3356)	●		●		●	●					●								●								
OAKHILL LEISURE (FH3563)					●						●																
OASIS LAKES (FH3570)	●		●		●	●	●	●	●	●	●			●					●	●	●					●	
OHAM LAKES (FH3583)	●	●	●		●	●	●	●	●	●	●			●					●	●	●					●	
PEACOCK LAKE (FH3723)			●		●						●										●						
REVESBY RESERVOIR (FH3933)			●																		●						
ROACH FARM PARK (FH3972)					●						●								●								
ROSSWAYS WATER (FH4021)			●		●	●					●										●						
SHANDY KEV FISHERIES (FH4207)					●						●																
SKEGNESS WATER LEISURE PARK (FH4285)			●		●						●																

Fishery	Minnow	Orfe	Orfe Blue	Orfe Golden	Perch	Pike	Roach	Rudd	Ruffe	Salmon	Steelhead	Sturgeon	Tench	Tench Golden	Trount American Brook	Trout Blue	Trout Brook	Trout Brown	Trout Golden	Trout Lake	Ttrout Rainbow	Trout Sea	Trout Tiger	Trout Wild	Vendace	Zander
CHARLES STREET POND (FH0903)													●													
DAIWA GULL POOL (FH1247)																										
DENNIS RAINWATER LAKE (FH1331)								●					●													
DENTON RESERVOIR (FH1332)																										
GOLTHO LAKE (FH1917)					●		●	●					●													
GRANGE FARM LEISURE (FH1969)					●		●	●					●													
GROOBYS PIT (FH2028)					●		●						●													
HARTSHOLME PARK LAKE (FH2119)					●	●	●		●				●													
HATTON TROUT LAKE (FH2134)							●	●					●													
HAVERHOLME PARK (FH2137)							●	●					●													
HERONS MEAD (FH2192)							●	●																		
HILL VIEW LAKES (FH2224)		●			●		●	●					●													
HOBHOLE DRAIN (FH2238)					●	●	●		●				●													
HOLLAND PARK (FH2255)					●		●	●					●								●					
KEAL COATES FISHERY (FH2422)													●													
KINPTON RESERVOIR (FH2522)							●																			
LAKE HELEN (FH2558)		●			●		●	●	●				●													
LAKE ROSS FISHERY (FH2572)							●	●					●													
LAKESIDE (FH2582)		●			●		●	●					●													
LAKESIDE LEISURE PARK (FH2594)					●		●	●	●				●													
LOBBY FIELD PONDS (FH2834)					●		●	●					●													
MARRIS LAKES (FH3190)							●	●					●													
MILL HILL LAKES (FH3285)							●	●					●													
MILL ROAD LAKES (FH3304)				●	●		●	●					●													
MOON LAKE (FH3356)							●	●					●													
OAKHILL LEISURE (FH3563)							●	●					●													
OASIS LAKES (FH3570)		●			●		●	●	●				●								●					
OHAM LAKES (FH3583)		●			●		●	●	●				●													
PEACOCK LAKE (FH3723)					●		●	●					●													
REVESBY RESERVOIR (FH3933)					●	●	●						●													
ROACH FARM PARK (FH3972)							●	●					●													
ROSSWAYS WATER (FH4021)		●			●		●	●					●													
SHANDY KEV FISHERIES (FH4207)							●	●																		
SKEGNESS WATER LEISURE PARK (FH4285)		●			●		●						●													

Fish Species Available at UK & Irish Fisheries

Fishery	Barbel	Bleak	Bream	Carp Blue	Carp Common	Carp Crucian	Carp Ghost	Carp Grass	Carp Koi	Carp Leather	Carp Mirror	Carp Silver	Carp Wild	Catfish	Catfish Albino	Catfish American Bullhead	Catfish Black Bullhead	Charr	Chub	Dace	Eel	Flounder	Goldfish	Grayling	Grilse	Gudgeon	Gwyniad	Minnow	Orfe	Orfe Blue	Orfe Golden	Perch	Pike	Roach	Rudd	Ruffe	Salmon	Steelhead	Sturgeon	Tench	Tench Golden	Trount American Brook	Trout Blue	Trout Brook	Trout Brown	Trout Golden	Trout Lake	Ttrout Rainbow	Trout Sea	Trout Tiger	Trout Wild	Vendace	Zander
ST EAU FISHING SYNDICATE (FH4384)																																													●								
STARMERS PIT (FH4433)			●		●						●								●		●											●	●	●		●				●													
STEEPING (RIVER) (FH4446)			●																													●		●																			
STICKNEY BRICKPONDS (FH4455)			●		●																												●	●						●													
SUDBROOK POND (FH4533)			●		●						●																		●			●		●						●													
SWAN LAKE (FH4592)	●				●	●					●										●													●	●					●													
SYCAMORE FISHING LAKES (FH4618)					●	●	●		●	●	●										●										●	●		●	●					●													
SYSTON PARK TROUT LAKE (FH4622)																																													●			●					
TATTERSHALL LEISURE PARK (FH4663)			●		●						●																					●	●	●	●					●													
THORPE LE VALE FISHERY (FH4823)																																													●			●					
TILL (RIVER) (FH4846)			●																●	●	●					●						●	●	●		●				●													
TILL (RIVER) (FH4847)			●																●	●	●					●						●	●	●		●				●													
TOFT NEWTON TROUT FISHERY (FH4864)																																					●							●	●	●		●					
TRENT (RIVER) (FH4920)	●	●	●		●						●								●	●	●					●						●	●	●		●																	
TRENT (RIVER) (FH4919)	●		●		●						●								●	●	●					●						●	●	●		●				●													
TRENT (RIVER) (FH4921)	●		●		●						●								●	●	●					●						●	●	●		●				●													
TRENT (RIVER) (FH4922)																																					●								●								
UPPER WITHAM (RIVER) (FH5060)	●		●		●						●								●	●	●					●						●	●	●		●				●													
VICKERS POND (FH5097)			●		●	●		●		●	●										●											●	●	●	●					●													
WARPING DRAIN (FH5149)			●																●		●					●						●	●	●						●													
WARREN POND (FH5152)			●		●						●																					●			●					●													
WATERSIDE LEISURE PARK (FH5184)			●		●			●			●																		●			●		●	●					●													
WELLAND (RIVER) (FH5232)			●																															●																			
WELLAND (RIVER) (FH5233)																																		●																			
WEST FEN DRAIN (FH5259)		●	●																	●	●					●		●				●	●	●	●	●				●													
WHARFE (RIVER) (FH5296)	●		●																●	●				●								●		●																			
WHISBY GARDEN CENTRE (FH5329)			●		●	●					●								●															●	●					●													
WHITE HOUSE PREDATOR LAKE (FH5336)														●							●											●	●																				●
WILLOW BANK FISHERY (FH5377)			●		●						●			●					●														●	●	●					●													
WILLOW LAKES (FH5384)					●	●					●																							●	●					●													
WINTERS LAKE (FH5427)			●																															●						●													
WITHAM (RIVER) (FH5439)																			●															●																			
WITHAM (RIVER) (FH5438)			●																●	●												●	●	●						●													
WOODLAND WATERS (FH5482)			●		●						●								●		●											●	●	●	●					●													

Fish Species Available at UK & Irish Fisheries

	Barbel	Bleak	Bream	Carp Blue	Carp Common	Carp Crucian	Carp Ghost	Carp Grass	Carp Koi	Carp Leather	Carp Mirror	Carp Silver	Carp Wild	Catfish	Catfish Albino	Catfish American Bullhead	Catfish Black Bullhead	Charr	Chub	Dace	Eel	Flounder	Goldfish	Grayling	Grilse	Gudgeon	Gwyniad	Minnow	Orfe	Orfe Blue	Orfe Golden	Perch	Pike	Roach	Rudd	Ruffe	Salmon	Steelhead	Sturgeon	Tench	Tench Golden	Trount American Brook	Trout Blue	Trout Brook	Trout Brown	Trout Golden	Trout Lake	Ttrout Rainbow	Trout Sea	Trout Tiger	Trout Wild	Vendace	Zander
WOODLANDS FISHERY (FH5483)					●						●																							●						●													
WOODLANDS LAKE (FH5485)					●																																			●													
LINCOLNSHIRE (NORTH)																																																					
BARTON BROADS LAKE (FH0337)	●		●		●	●	●			●	●			●					●		●					●			●			●	●	●	●	●				●													
HOE HILL POND (FH2245)			●																●		●											●		●	●					●													
KINGFISHER LODGE (FH2501)			●		●	●	●			●	●								●	●												●		●	●					●													
MARSHLANDS (FH3194)	●		●																																					●													
OLD ANCHOLME (RIVER) (FH3584)			●																													●	●	●						●													
ORCHARD POND (FH3617)					●	●					●								●													●																					
PASTURE HOUSE FISHERY (FH3716)	●		●		●	●					●								●														●	●	●																		
PELICAN POND (FH3732)			●																		●												●	●						●													
STADDLETHORPE POND (FH4398)	●		●		●	●	●			●	●								●		●					●			●			●	●	●	●					●													
TILEYARD LANE (FH4844)			●		●	●					●																						●	●						●													
WESTFIELD LAKES (FH5277)			●		●						●																						●	●						●													
LONDON (GREATER)																																																					
ALEXANDRA PALACE LAKE (FH0071)			●		●						●																					●	●	●						●													
ALEXANDRA PARK LAKE (FH0073)			●		●						●																							●	●					●													
ASHMERE FISHERIES (FH0167)																																																●					
BEDFONT LAKE (FH0363)			●		●	●					●																					●	●	●	●					●													
BIRCHMERE (FH0427)			●		●						●										●											●	●	●	●					●													
BOXERS LAKE (FH0577)					●	●	●			●	●										●					●						●		●	●					●													
BROOMWOOD LAKE (FH0696)			●		●						●								●													●	●	●	●					●													
CARGILL LAKE (FH0841)			●		●						●																													●													
CLAPHAM COMMON POND (FH0973)			●		●						●										●											●		●						●													
COLNE (RIVER) (FH1073)	●		●																●	●														●																			
COLNE (RIVER) (FH1072)	●	●	●		●														●	●						●						●	●	●	●					●													
COPPER MILLSTREAM (FH1111)	●		●		●						●								●	●				●								●	●	●																			
COWLEY LAKE (FH1152)			●		●	●		●			●										●					●						●	●	●	●					●													
CUTTING LAKE (FH1231)			●		●						●																							●						●													
EAST WARWICK (FH1516)			●		●						●																					●		●						●													
ENFIELD LOCK (FH1593)			●																														●	●						●													
FLAKE STREAM (FH1741)	●																		●	●												●		●																			
FORTY HALL LAKE (FH1773)			●																													●		●	●					●													
GRAND UNION CANAL (FH1955)			●																●													●	●	●																			

Fish Species Available at UK & Irish Fisheries

	Barbel	Bleak	Bream	Carp Blue	Carp Common	Carp Crucian	Carp Ghost	Carp Grass	Carp Koi	Carp Leather	Carp Mirror	Carp Silver	Carp Wild	Catfish	Catfish Albino	Catfish American Bullhead	Catfish Black Bullhead	Charr	Chub	Dace	Eel	Flounder	Goldfish	Grayling	Grilse	Gudgeon	Gwyniad	Minnow	Orfe	Orfe Blue	Orfe Golden	Perch	Pike	Roach	Rudd	Ruffe	Salmon	Steelhead	Sturgeon	Tench	Tench Golden	Trount American Brook	Trout Blue	Trout Brook	Trout Brown	Trout Golden	Trout Lake	Ttrout Rainbow	Trout Sea	Trout Tiger	Trout Wild	Vendace	Zander
GRAND UNION CANAL (FH1952)			●		●						●																					●		●																			
GRAND UNION CANAL (FH1954)	●		●		●						●								●	●						●						●	●	●						●													
GRAND UNION CANAL (FH1956)			●		●																●					●						●	●	●	●					●													
GRAND UNION CANAL (FH1953)			●	●																												●		●																			
GREENHAMS (FH2008)			●		●						●																					●		●						●													
HALLIFORD MERE LAKES (FH2071)																																													●			●					
HAMPSTEAD HEATH (FH2094)			●		●						●								●														●	●						●													
HAREFIELD CARP LAKE (FH2105)			●		●						●																					●	●	●																			
HEATH VALE POND (FH2172)			●		●						●																						●	●	●																		
HIGH MAYNARD RESERVOIR (FH2207)			●		●						●																					●								●													
HIGHAMS PARK LAKE (FH2213)					●	●				●	●										●					●						●	●		●					●													
HIGHGATE PONDS (FH2217)			●		●	●					●																					●	●	●	●					●													
HOLLOW PONDS (FH2259)			●		●						●										●					●						●	●	●						●													
HORSEMILL STREAM (FH2306)	●		●		●						●								●														●	●						●													
KINGFISHER LAKE (FH2498)			●		●						●																						●	●																			
KNIGHTSCOTE PONDS (FH2537)					●						●																					●		●	●					●													
KORDA LAKE (FH2545)					●						●																																									
LEA NAVIGATION (FH2648)		●	●		●						●								●		●					●						●	●	●																			
LEA NAVIGATION (FH2649)		●	●		●	●					●								●							●						●	●	●																			
LITTLE BRITAIN LAKE (FH2743)					●	●					●																					●	●	●						●													
LIZARD LAKES (FH2766)			●		●	●	●				●								●		●											●		●						●													
LOCKWOOD RESERVOIR (FH2974)			●								●																							●																		
LOW MAYNARD RESERVOIR (FH3067)			●		●						●																					●	●	●						●													
MULGROVE POND (FH3399)					●			●			●															●						●		●	●					●													
NEW CUT (FH3463)			●		●						●								●															●																		
NORTH TROY LAKE & COLNE (FH3536)	●		●		●						●																					●	●							●													
NORWOOD LAKE (FH3550)			●		●						●																					●		●																			
OLD LEE (RIVER) (FH3591)	●		●																●	●						●						●	●	●						●													
OSTERLEY PARK MIDDLE LAKE (FH3629)			●		●	●					●																						●	●	●					●													
PERCH POND (FH3751)			●		●						●										●											●	●	●						●													
PONDERS END (FH3813)			●																															●																		
POTOMAC POND (FH3833)					●						●																					●	●	●	●																		
REGENTS CANAL (FH3926)			●		●						●										●											●	●	●	●					●													
REGENTS CANAL (FH3928)					●						●																																									

Fish Species Available at UK & Irish Fisheries

Fishery	Barbel	Bleak	Bream	Carp Blue	Carp Common	Carp Crucian	Carp Ghost	Carp Grass	Carp Koi	Carp Leather	Carp Mirror	Carp Silver	Carp Wild	Catfish	Catfish Albino	Catfish American Bullhead	Catfish Black Bullhead	Charr	Chub	Dace	Eel
REGENTS CANAL (FH3927)			●								●										●
REGENTS CANAL (FH3925)			●		●						●										●
RODNEY MEADOW (FH3995)			●		●						●										●
SAVAY LAKE (FH4107)			●		●						●										
SHEEPWALK LAKE (FH4218)			●		●						●										●
SHEPPERTON LAKE (FH4230)			●		●						●										●
SOUTH NORWOOD LAKE (FH4335)					●						●										
STOCKLEY ROAD LAKES (FH4461)			●		●						●										
STUDIO AND BROADWATER (FH4532)			●																		
SYON PARK FISHERY (FH4621)																					
TEDDINGTON LOCK (FH4682)			●		●						●								●	●	
THAMES (RIVER) (FH4786)			●																		
THAMES (RIVER) (FH4789)			●		●						●										
THORNEY POOL (FH4816)			●		●	●					●										
TRENT COUNTRY PARK LAKES (FH4946)					●						●										
TRENT PARK LAKES (FH4947)					●																
VALE OF HEATH POND (FH5083)			●		●						●										●
WALTHAMSTOW (NO 2 & NO 3) (FH5131)			●		●						●										
WALTHAMSTOW (EAST WARWICK) (FH5129)											●										
WALTHAMSTOW (NO 4 TROUT) (FH5132)											●										
WALTHAMSTOW (WEST WARWICK) (FH5134)			●		●						●										
WALTHAMSTOW RESERVOIR (NO 1) (FH5130)			●		●						●										
WALTHAMSTOW RESERVOIR (NO 5) (FH5133)											●										
WANDSWORTH COMMON POND (FH5138)			●		●						●										
WANSTEAD PARK LAKES (FH5145)			●		●																
WEST RESERVOIR (FH5265)	●				●		●				●										
WEST WARWICK (FH5268)					●						●										
WILLOWSIDE CARP LAKE (FH5402)			●		●	●	●				●										
WOOLWICH DOCKYARD (FH5501)			●		●	●	●		●		●			●					●		●
WRAYSBURY ONE (FH5513)			●		●						●										●
WRAYSBURY TWO (FH5514)			●		●						●										●
MANCHESTER (GREATER)																					
ALEXANDRA PARK (FH0072)			●		●																
ASHENHURST LAKES (FH0161)					●			●			●										

Fishery	Flounder	Goldfish	Grayling	Grilse	Gudgeon	Gwyniad	Minnow	Orfe	Orfe Blue	Orfe Golden	Perch	Pike	Roach	Rudd	Ruffe	Salmon	Steelhead	Sturgeon	Tench	Tench Golden	Trount American Brook	Trout Blue	Trout Brook	Trout Brown	Trout Golden	Trout Lake	Ttrout Rainbow	Trout Sea	Trout Tiger	Trout Wild	Vendace	Zander
REGENTS CANAL (FH3927)											●	●	●	●					●													
REGENTS CANAL (FH3925)											●	●	●	●					●													
RODNEY MEADOW (FH3995)											●	●	●						●													
SAVAY LAKE (FH4107)											●	●	●						●													
SHEEPWALK LAKE (FH4218)											●	●	●						●													
SHEPPERTON LAKE (FH4230)											●	●	●						●													
SOUTH NORWOOD LAKE (FH4335)											●	●		●					●													
STOCKLEY ROAD LAKES (FH4461)											●	●	●	●					●													
STUDIO AND BROADWATER (FH4532)											●	●	●						●													
SYON PARK FISHERY (FH4621)																								●			●					
TEDDINGTON LOCK (FH4682)											●		●																			
THAMES (RIVER) (FH4786)													●																			
THAMES (RIVER) (FH4789)											●		●																			
THORNEY POOL (FH4816)											●	●	●	●					●													
TRENT COUNTRY PARK LAKES (FH4946)											●	●	●						●													
TRENT PARK LAKES (FH4947)											●		●	●					●													
VALE OF HEATH POND (FH5083)											●	●	●						●													
WALTHAMSTOW (NO 2 & NO 3) (FH5131)													●						●													
WALTHAMSTOW (EAST WARWICK) (FH5129)																								●			●					
WALTHAMSTOW (NO 4 TROUT) (FH5132)																								●			●					
WALTHAMSTOW (WEST WARWICK) (FH5134)													●						●								●					
WALTHAMSTOW RESERVOIR (NO 1) (FH5130)											●		●						●													
WALTHAMSTOW RESERVOIR (NO 5) (FH5133)																								●			●					
WANDSWORTH COMMON POND (FH5138)												●	●	●																		
WANSTEAD PARK LAKES (FH5145)											●	●	●	●					●													
WEST RESERVOIR (FH5265)								●			●	●	●						●													
WEST WARWICK (FH5268)																																
WILLOWSIDE CARP LAKE (FH5402)														●																		
WOOLWICH DOCKYARD (FH5501)											●	●	●	●					●													
WRAYSBURY ONE (FH5513)											●	●	●						●													
WRAYSBURY TWO (FH5514)											●	●	●						●													
MANCHESTER (GREATER)																																
ALEXANDRA PARK (FH0072)											●		●						●													
ASHENHURST LAKES (FH0161)													●																			

Fish Species Available at UK & Irish Fisheries

	Barbel	Bleak	Bream	Carp Blue	Carp Common	Carp Crucian	Carp Ghost	Carp Grass	Carp Koi	Carp Leather	Carp Mirror	Carp Silver	Carp Wild	Catfish	Catfish Albino	Catfish American Bullhead	Catfish Black Bullhead	Charr	Chub	Dace	Eel	Flounder	Goldfish	Grayling	Grilse	Gudgeon	Gwyniad	Minnow	Orfe	Orfe Blue	Orfe Golden	Perch	Pike	Roach	Rudd	Ruffe	Salmon	Steelhead	Sturgeon	Tench	Tench Golden	Trount American Brook	Trout Blue	Trout Brook	Trout Brown	Trout Golden	Trout Lake	Ttrout Rainbow	Trout Sea	Trout Tiger	Trout Wild	Vendace	Zander
BLACKLEACH RESERVOIR (FH0451)			●		●	●					●																					●	●	●						●													
BOGGART HOLE CLOUGH (FH0524)			●		●	●					●										●											●								●													
BOWKER LAKES (FH0572)					●						●																					●		●						●													
BRIDGEWATER CANAL (FH0639)			●		●						●																					●		●																			
BRIDGEWATER CANAL (FH0638)			●		●																											●	●	●						●													
CARCUS WATERS (FH0838)			●		●						●																					●	●	●						●													
CHORLTON WATER PARK (FH0946)			●		●						●																					●	●	●						●													
CLEGG HALL LAKES (FH1001)			●		●	●					●															●						●		●	●					●					●			●					
CLIFTON MARINA (FH1008)			●		●	●					●																					●	●	●						●													
CRIME LAKE (FH1180)						●																										●		●																			
CROFT HEAD FISHERY (FH1183)			●		●						●																					●		●	●					●													
CROMPTONS WATER (FH1186)			●		●						●																					●		●						●													
DAVENPORT (FH1280)					●						●																																										
DEBDALE RESERVOIRS (FH1292)					●						●																						●																				
DINGLE LODGE (FH1372)			●		●						●																					●		●						●													
DOUBLEWOODS (FH1418)	●					●													●															●	●					●													
DOWRY & NEW YEARS BRIDGE (FH1433)					●	●	●		●		●																				●	●		●						●					●						●		
ELTON RESERVOIR (FH1574)			●																															●																			
FARM LODGE (FH1669)					●						●																					●		●																			
FIR TREE FLASH (FH1720)			●		●	●					●																					●	●	●	●					●													
GEIGYS WATER (FH1847)			●		●	●				●	●										●					●						●	●	●	●	●				●													
GORSE PIT RESERVOIR (FH1922)			●			●					●															●						●	●	●	●					●													
GROVE LODGE (FH2031)			●		●	●					●								●							●						●		●	●	●				●													
HEATON PARK (FH2176)			●		●						●																						●	●						●													
HOLLINGWORTH LAKE (FH2258)			●		●						●																					●	●	●	●	●				●													
HUDDERSFIELD NARROW CANAL (FH2328)	●		●		●						●								●	●						●						●	●	●	●					●													
IRWELL (RIVER) (FH2383)			●		●						●																					●		●																			
KING GEORGE V POOL (FH2489)			●		●		●				●															●						●								●													
KING WILLIAM IV RESERVOIR (FH2491)			●		●						●																					●		●	●					●													
LANKYS MILL POND (FH2619)			●		●						●																							●																			
LEEDS TO LIVERPOOL CANAL (FH2677)			●		●						●																					●		●						●													
LEEKES WATER (FH2683)			●			●																				●						●		●						●													
LOWER TOWN HOUSE FISHERY (FH3095)			●		●						●																					●		●	●					●													
MYRTLE ROAD LODGES (FH3406)			●		●						●																					●		●						●													

Fish Species Available at UK & Irish Fisheries

	Barbel	Bleak	Bream	Carp Blue	Carp Common	Carp Crucian	Carp Ghost	Carp Grass	Carp Koi	Carp Leather	Carp Mirror	Carp Silver	Carp Wild	Catfish	Catfish Albino	Catfish American Bullhead	Catfish Black Bullhead	Charr	Chub	Dace	Eel	Flounder	Goldfish	Grayling	Grilse	Gudgeon	Gwyniad	Minnow	Orfe	Orfe Blue	Orfe Golden	Perch	Pike	Roach	Rudd	Ruffe	Salmon	Steelhead	Sturgeon	Tench	Tench Golden	Trount American Brook	Trout Blue	Trout Brook	Trout Brown	Trout Golden	Trout Lake	Ttrout Rainbow	Trout Sea	Trout Tiger	Trout Wild	Vendace	Zander
NEW HOUSE FARM POOL (FH3466)			●		●						●																					●	●	●						●													
PAINSWICK PARK LAKE (FH3686)			●		●	●					●																					●		●						●													
PENNINE TROUT FISHERY (FH3737)																																													●	●		●					
PENNINGTON FLASH (FH3738)			●		●						●																					●		●																			
PIETHORNE RESERVOIR (FH3771)																																●													●			●					
PILSWORTH FISHERY COMPLEX (FH3773)	●		●		●	●					●								●							●			●			●	●	●	●	●				●	●												
PLATT FIELDS (FH3800)					●					●	●																		●			●		●		●				●													
POYNTON POOL (FH3839)			●		●	●					●																						●	●																		
REDDISH VALE MILL PONDS (FH3913)			●		●	●		●			●																					●	●	●						●													
RHODES LODGE (FH3936)			●		●						●																					●	●	●						●													
ROCHDALE CANAL (FH3977)			●		●	●					●								●																																		
ROMAN LAKE LEISURE PARK (FH4000)			●		●						●																					●	●	●						●													
ROYAL GEORGE MILL COMPLEX (FH4044)			●		●						●								●	●						●						●	●	●						●													
SALFORD QUAYS (FH4082)			●		●						●																					●		●																			
STAKEHILL LODGES (FH4411)			●		●	●				●	●															●			●			●		●	●	●				●													
STAMFORD PARK LAKES (FH4413)			●		●	●					●																					●	●							●													
STONEY PIT RESERVOIR (FH4474)			●		●						●															●						●								●													
SWAN LODGE (FH4593)			●		●						●																							●						●													
TAME (RIVER) (FH4646)			●		●						●								●	●						●						●	●	●						●					●								
TANNERS DAM (FH4653)			●		●						●								●							●						●		●	●					●													
TWINE VALLEY TROUT FISHERY (FH5005)			●		●	●					●								●							●						●		●	●					●					●			●					
WESTGATE POOL (FH5278)					●						●																								●					●													
WHITELEY KNOWL RESERVOIR (FH5349)																																●												●	●								
WHITTLE BROOK RESERVOIR (FH5358)			●		●	●					●															●						●		●	●					●													
WOODBANK PARK POOL (FH5466)			●		●						●																					●	●	●						●													
MERSEYSIDE																																																					
BIRKENHEAD LOWER PARK LAKE (FH0431)			●		●	●					●																						●	●	●					●													
CALDERSTONES PARK LAKE (FH0799)					●						●																					●		●						●													
CARR LANE POOL (FH0847)			●		●						●																					●		●						●													
CARR MILL DAM (FH0848)			●		●						●																							●						●													
EVE A LYN FARM (FH1634)					●	●					●								●	●														●	●					●													
GREENBANK PARK LAKE (FH2005)					●	●					●																					●	●							●													
LEEDS TO LIVERPOOL (FH2672)			●		●						●																							●	●					●													
LEEDS TO LIVERPOOL CANAL (FH2678)			●		●						●																					●		●						●													

Fish Species Available at UK & Irish Fisheries

Fishery	Barbel	Bleak	Bream	Carp Blue	Carp Common	Carp Crucian	Carp Ghost	Carp Grass	Carp Koi	Carp Leather	Carp Mirror	Carp Silver	Carp Wild	Catfish	Catfish Albino	Catfish American Bullhead	Catfish Black Bullhead	Charr	Chub	Dace	Eel	Flounder	Goldfish	Grayling	Grilse	Gudgeon	Gwyniad	Minnow	Orfe	Orfe Blue	Orfe Golden	Perch	Pike	Roach	Rudd	Ruffe	Salmon	Steelhead	Sturgeon	Tench	Tench Golden	Trount American Brook	Trout Blue	Trout Brook	Trout Brown	Trout Golden	Trout Lake	Ttrout Rainbow	Trout Sea	Trout Tiger	Trout Wild	Vendace	Zander
LEEDS TO LIVERPOOL CANAL (FH2679)					●						●										●											●		●						●													
LOWER LAKE (FH3085)			●		●	●					●																						●	●	●					●													
MILL HOUSE FISHERY (FH3287)			●		●																								●					●	●					●													
MORETON MERE (FH3369)			●		●	●					●																						●	●	●					●													
NEWSHAM PARK (FH3492)					●						●																													●													
PRINCES PARK LAKE (FH3846)			●		●	●					●																					●		●	●					●													
STANLEY PARK LAKE (FH4421)						●																												●						●													
WALTON HALL PARK (FH5135)			●																													●	●																				
WOODHOUSE FISH FARM (FH5475)																																													●			●					
MIDLANDS (WEST)																																																					
ALVECHURCH FISHERIES (FH0090)	●		●		●	●	●	●			●								●		●					●			●			●		●	●					●													
ASTBURY FALLS FISH FARM (FH0175)			●		●	●					●								●															●	●				●	●								●					
AVON (RIVER) (FH0209)			●																														●																			
AVON (RIVER) (FH0208)																			●															●																			
BLYTHE (RIVER) (FH0517)			●		●	●	●			●	●								●	●	●					●		●				●	●	●	●					●													
BLYTHE WATERS (FH0518)	●		●		●	●					●															●			●			●		●	●	●				●													
BULL FISHERY (FH0724)					●						●																					●		●						●													
CANNOCK EXTENSION CANAL (FH0822)			●		●						●																					●		●						●													
CHURCH POOL (FH0956)					●						●																																									
COOMBE ABBEY LAKE (FH1104)			●																														●	●																			●
COOMBE POOL (FH1109)			●		●						●										●												●	●						●													●
CUTTLE MILL CARP FISHERY (FH1232)			●		●	●					●										●					●						●		●	●					●													
DARTMOUTH PARK (FH1278)			●		●																																																
DAYHOUSE FARM (FH1282)			●		●						●																							●	●					●													
EARLSWOOD LAKES (FH1503)			●																															●																			
EDGBASTON RESERVOIR (FH1545)			●		●																													●						●													
FOXHILLS FISHERY (FH1791)			●		●	●					●													●		●		●				●		●	●					●													
GRAND UNION CANAL (FH1957)			●																													●		●																			
HEATHFIELD POOL (FH2175)			●		●						●																							●	●					●													
HOPSFORD HALL FISHERY (FH2292)			●		●		●				●																																										
KINGSBURY WATER PARK (FH2510)					●						●																						●							●													
KINGSHURST LAKE (FH2511)					●																													●																			
KINGSNORDLEY (FH2517)	●		●		●						●								●							●						●		●	●					●													
LAVENDER HALL (FH2632)			●		●		●				●																					●		●	●					●													

Fish Species Available at UK & Irish Fisheries

Fishery	Barbel	Bleak	Bream	Carp Blue	Carp Common	Carp Crucian	Carp Ghost	Carp Grass	Carp Koi	Carp Leather	Carp Mirror	Carp Silver	Carp Wild	Catfish	Catfish Albino	Catfish American Bullhead	Catfish Black Bullhead	Charr	Chub	Dace	Eel	Flounder	Goldfish	Grayling	Grilse	Gudgeon	Gwyniad	Minnow	Orfe	Orfe Blue	Orfe Golden	Perch	Pike	Roach	Rudd	Ruffe	Salmon	Steelhead	Sturgeon	Tench	Tench Golden	Trount American Brook	Trout Blue	Trout Brook	Trout Brown	Trout Golden	Trout Lake	Ttrout Rainbow	Trout Sea	Trout Tiger	Trout Wild	Vendace	Zander
MEADOWLANDS (FH3227)	●		●		●	●	●	●			●								●											●	●	●		●	●					●													
PACKINGTON SOMERS FISHERY (FH3679)			●		●	●	●			●	●								●	●	●					●		●				●	●	●	●					●													
PACKINGTON TROUT FISHERY (FH3680)																																													●			●					
PATSHULL PARK (FH3717)			●		●						●										●					●						●	●	●	●					●					●			●					
PENNS HALL LAKE (FH3740)			●		●						●																							●						●													
POOL HALL (FH3819)			●		●						●			●																		●		●	●					●					●			●					
POOLE HALL FARM (FH3821)					●	●					●										●											●	●	●						●													
ROYAL BRITISH LEGION POOLS (FH4043)					●																													●																			
RUSHALL CANAL (FH4060)																																		●						●													
RUSHALL CANAL (FH4059)			●		●						●																					●		●						●													
RYTON POOLS COUNTRY PARK (FH4077)			●																														●	●																			
SEVERN (RIVER) (FH4149)	●																		●	●														●																			
SEVERN (RIVER) (FH4150)	●																		●																																		
SEVERN (RIVER) (FH4148)	●																		●																																		
SHUSTOKE FLY FISHERS (FH4262)																																													●			●					
SNEYD POOL (FH4310)					●																																			●													
SOHO LOOP CANAL (FH4321)																																		●																			
SOMERS FISHERY (FH4323)			●		●						●																					●	●	●	●					●													
STAFFORD TO WORCESTER CANAL (FH4403)																										●								●																			
STAFFORD TO WORCESTER CANAL (FH4404)			●								●								●							●						●		●						●													
SUTTON PARK (FH4564)			●		●						●																						●	●																			
SWAN POOL (FH4595)			●		●	●					●								●													●	●	●	●					●													
TAME VALLEY CANAL (FH4648)			●																													●	●	●						●													
TIDBURY GREEN GOLF CLUB (FH4839)			●		●																																																
WALCOT EAST LAKE (FH5116)			●		●						●										●					●						●		●						●													
WALSALL ARBORETUM (FH5127)					●																																			●													
WASSELL GROVE FISHERIES (FH5167)			●		●	●					●								●													●		●	●					●													
NORFOLK																																																					
ABBEY WATERS (FH0004)					●						●																							●	●					●													
ABBOTS HALL (FH0007)																																													●								
ACLE (RIVER) (FH0022)			●																													●	●	●																			
BARFORD LAKES FISHERY (FH0305)	●		●		●	●	●				●								●												●	●		●	●					●													
BARNINGHAM HALL LAKE (FH0317)			●		●		●			●	●								●		●			●		●		●				●	●	●	●	●				●													
BARTLES LODGE (FH0335)			●		●	●	●		●		●																					●		●						●													

Fish Species Available at UK & Irish Fisheries

Species	BAWBURGH LAKES (FH0348)	BILNEY LAKES (FH0424)	BLICKLING PARK LAKE (FH0500)	BOOTON CLAY PIT (FH0543)	BRIDGE FARM FISHERIES (FH0629)	BRIDGE INN FISHERY (FH0631)	BUCKENHAM PITS (FH0717)	BURE (RIVER) (FH0735)	BURE (RIVER) (FH0734)	BURE (RIVER) (FH0736)	BURE VALLEY LAKES (FH0737)	CANTLEY (RIVER) (FH0827)	CATCH 22 FISHERY (FH0872)	CHARITY LAKES (FH0901)	COBBLEACRES LAKES (FH1047)	COLTON LAKE (FH1078)	COSTESSEY PITS (FH1125)	CUT OFF CHANNEL (FH1229)	DENTS OF HILGAY (FH1333)	DISS MERE (FH1376)	DOVE BROOK (FH1429)	DRAYTON GREEN (RIVER) (FH1440)	FELBRIGG HALL LAKE (FH1681)	FELTHORPE LAKE (FH1690)	FRITTON LAKE (FH1804)	GATTON WATER CARAVAN SITE (FH1843)	GIMINGHAM LAKES (FH1858)	GLEN MERE (FH1882)	GREAT MELTON FISHERY (FH1983)	GREAT OUSE (RIVER) (FH1997)	GREAT OUSE (RIVER) (FH1998)	GREAT OUSE RELIEF CHANNEL (FH1999)	GUNTON PARK LAKE (FH2037)	HADDISCOE PIT (FH2058)
Zander																														●	●	●		
Vendace																																		
Trout Wild																																		
Trout Tiger																																		
Trout Sea																																		
Ttrout Rainbow						●					●																							
Trout Lake																																		
Trout Golden																																		
Trout Brown						●			●		●																							
Trout Brook																																		
Trout Blue																																		
Trount American Brook																																		
Tench Golden																																		
Tench	●	●	●	●	●	●	●			●	●		●	●			●	●	●	●			●		●	●	●			●	●		●	●
Sturgeon																																		
Steelhead																																		
Salmon																																		
Ruffe										●																								
Rudd	●	●		●	●	●				●	●		●			●			●	●			●		●	●	●	●	●			●		●
Roach	●	●	●	●	●	●	●			●	●	●	●			●	●	●	●	●		●			●	●	●	●	●	●	●	●	●	●
Pike	●		●	●		●	●	●		●	●		●				●	●				●			●					●	●	●	●	
Perch	●	●	●	●		●	●			●	●	●					●	●	●						●	●	●		●	●	●	●		●
Orfe Golden					●																													
Orfe Blue																																		
Orfe		●																																
Minnow						●				●																								
Gwyniad																																		
Gudgeon		●				●				●									●								●		●					
Grilse																																		
Grayling						●																												
Goldfish						●																												
Flounder																																		
Eel	●	●				●				●	●									●					●				●			●		●
Dace						●				●											●	●												
Chub		●						●		●							●		●			●							●					
Charr																																		
Catfish Black Bullhead																																		
Catfish American Bullhead																																		
Catfish Albino																																		
Catfish																																		
Carp Wild																			●															
Carp Silver																																		
Carp Mirror	●	●		●	●	●	●				●		●	●	●	●	●		●	●			●	●	●		●	●	●				●	●
Carp Leather		●				●					●																		●					
Carp Koi		●				●					●								●															
Carp Grass		●																																
Carp Ghost		●									●								●										●					
Carp Crucian	●	●		●		●													●	●					●	●	●	●					●	●
Carp Common	●	●		●	●	●	●				●		●	●	●	●	●		●	●			●	●	●	●	●	●	●				●	●
Carp Blue																																		
Bream	●	●	●	●		●	●			●		●	●	●			●	●	●			●			●	●	●	●		●	●	●	●	●
Bleak																																		
Barbel		●																	●															

Fish Species Available at UK & Irish Fisheries

Fishery	Barbel	Bleak	Bream	Carp Blue	Carp Common	Carp Crucian	Carp Ghost	Carp Grass	Carp Koi	Carp Leather	Carp Mirror	Carp Silver	Carp Wild	Catfish	Catfish Albino	Catfish American Bullhead	Catfish Black Bullhead	Charr	Chub	Dace	Eel	Flounder	Goldfish	Grayling	Grilse	Gudgeon	Gwyniad	Minnow	Orfe	Orfe Blue	Orfe Golden	Perch	Pike	Roach	Rudd	Ruffe	Salmon	Steelhead	Sturgeon	Tench	Tench Golden	Trount American Brook	Trout Blue	Trout Brook	Trout Brown	Trout Golden	Trout Lake	Ttrout Rainbow	Trout Sea	Trout Tiger	Trout Wild	Vendace	Zander
HALL FARM LAKES (FH2068)			●		●						●																					●		●	●					●													
HAVERINGLAND HALL PARK (FH2138)			●																		●											●	●	●	●					●													
HEVINGHAM LAKES (FH2197)			●		●	●				●	●								●		●					●								●	●					●													
HINDERCLAY LAKES (FH2233)			●		●		●				●										●								●			●		●	●					●													
HINGHAM FISHMERE (FH2234)					●					●	●																																									
HORNING (RIVER) (FH2299)			●																													●	●	●	●					●													
KINGFISHER LAKES (FH2500)					●						●																							●	●					●													
LAKESIDE (FH2583)			●		●						●																					●		●						●													
LAKESIDE CARAVAN PARK (FH2587)			●		●						●																					●		●	●					●													
LENWADE COMMON LAKES (FH2700)			●		●						●								●													●	●	●						●													
LITTLE DUNHAM CARP LAKES (FH2749)					●						●																							●	●					●													
LITTLE OUSE (RIVER) (FH2757)			●																	●	●											●	●	●						●													
LOCH NEATON (FH2922)			●		●						●																					●		●	●					●													
MANOR LAKE (FH3168)					●	●					●																					●			●					●													
MARTHAM PITS (FH3199)			●		●	●					●										●											●	●		●					●													
MEADOW LAKE (FH3223)			●		●						●								●							●						●		●						●													
MIDDLE HARLING LAKE (FH3265)			●		●	●					●																							●						●													
MILL FARM FISHERY (FH3281)			●		●	●	●				●								●													●		●						●													
MILL FARM FISHERY (FH3282)			●		●	●	●		●	●									●	●	●												●	●	●	●				●													
NAR (RIVER) (FH3422)																																					●								●								
NAR STREAM (FH3423)																																													●								
NARBOROUGH TROUT FARM (FH3424)			●		●						●								●	●						●		●				●		●	●					●								●					
NATURES HAVEN LAKES (FH3429)			●		●	●			●		●																					●		●	●					●													
NORFOLK & SUFFOLK FLY FISHERY (FH3524)																																													●			●					
PARK LIME PIT (FH3700)			●		●																							●				●	●	●						●													
PECK MEADOW POND (FH3730)					●	●					●										●											●		●	●																		
PENTNEY LAKES (FH3742)			●		●	●		●			●			●																		●	●	●	●					●													
RAILWAY LAKE (FH3878)			●																●															●	●					●													
RAILWAY LAKE (FH3877)			●		●	●					●										●											●		●	●					●													
REEPHAM FISHERY (FH3924)					●					●	●																													●													
RELIEF CHANNEL (FH3929)			●		●						●																						●	●						●													●
RINGLAND LAKES (FH3952)			●		●	●					●																					●	●							●													
RINGLAND PITS (FH3953)			●		●	●					●								●														●	●						●													
RUSTON REACHES (FH4066)			●		●	●	●				●										●											●	●	●	●					●													

Fish Species Available at UK & Irish Fisheries

Fishery	Barbel	Bleak	Bream	Carp Blue	Carp Common	Carp Crucian	Carp Ghost	Carp Grass	Carp Koi	Carp Leather	Carp Mirror	Carp Silver	Carp Wild	Catfish	Catfish Albino	Catfish American Bullhead	Catfish Black Bullhead	Charr	Chub	Dace	Eel	Flounder	Goldfish	Grayling	Grilse	Gudgeon	Gwyniad	Minnow	Orfe	Orfe Blue	Orfe Golden	Perch	Pike	Roach	Rudd	Ruffe	Salmon	Steelhead	Sturgeon	Tench	Tench Golden	Trount American Brook	Trout Blue	Trout Brook	Trout Brown	Trout Golden	Trout Lake	Ttrout Rainbow	Trout Sea	Trout Tiger	Trout Wild	Vendace	Zander
SCOULTON MERE (FH4119)					●						●																					●	●	●	●					●													
SHALLOW BROOK LAKES (FH4205)			●			●																												●						●													
SOVEREIGN LAKES (FH4354)			●		●						●										●											●	●	●						●													
STOKESBY (RIVER) (FH4465)			●																													●	●	●																			
SWANGEY LAKES (FH4598)			●		●	●					●			●																		●	●	●	●					●													
SWANTON MORLEY FISHERY (FH4602)			●		●	●				●	●								●	●	●											●	●	●	●					●													
TASWOOD LAKES (FH4662)			●		●	●	●	●			●																				●	●		●	●					●													
TAVERHAM (FH4668)			●		●	●					●								●	●												●	●	●						●													
TAVERHAM MILLS FISHERY (FH4669)	●		●		●					●	●			●					●	●	●			●		●		●				●	●	●	●					●					●								
TEN MILE BANK (FH4737)			●																														●	●						●													
THURNE MOUTH (RIVER) (FH4837)			●																		●											●	●	●																			
TOTTENHILL PIT (FH4888)			●		●	●					●																						●	●	●																		
UNIVERSITY BROAD (FH5048)			●		●						●																					●	●	●	●					●													
UPPER BURE (STREAM) (FH5052)																																													●								
WALNUT FARM FISHERIES (FH5125)			●		●	●	●		●	●	●								●		●		●			●			●		●	●		●	●					●													
WENSUM (RIVER) (FH5249)																				●	●					●						●		●											●								
WENSUM (RIVER) (FH5250)			●		●						●								●													●								●													
WENSUM (RIVER) (FH5246)																				●	●					●						●		●											●								
WENSUM (RIVER) (FH5245)	●					●			●	●									●	●	●			●		●		●				●			●										●			●			●		
WENSUM (RIVER) (FH5247)			●		●	●				●	●								●	●	●											●	●	●	●					●													
WEYBREAD FISHERY (FH5293)			●		●	●	●	●	●		●								●										●			●		●	●					●													
WHINBURGH TROUT LAKE (FH5321)																																													●			●					
WILLOWCROFT FISHERY (FH5392)			●		●		●	●			●			●																		●	●	●	●					●													
WILLSMORE WATER (FH5403)			●		●	●					●										●											●		●	●					●													
WISSEY (RIVER) (FH5435)			●																●	●												●	●	●						●													
WOODLAKES FISHERY (FH5477)			●		●						●										●											●	●	●	●					●													
WOODRISING WATER MEADOWS (FH5489)					●						●																							●	●					●													
WROXHAM BROAD (FH5520)			●																													●	●	●	●					●													
YARE (RIVER) (FH5557)			●		●						●									●	●	●										●	●	●																			
YARE (RIVER) (FH5556)																																●	●																				
NORTHAMPTONSHIRE																																																					
BARKERS LAKE (FH0308)			●		●						●																																										
BILLING AQUADROME (FH0418)											●																																										
BLUNHAM PITS (FH0515)					●						●																					●	●	●	●					●													

Fish Species Available at UK & Irish Fisheries

Fishery	Barbel	Bleak	Bream	Carp Blue	Carp Common	Carp Crucian	Carp Ghost	Carp Grass	Carp Koi	Carp Leather	Carp Mirror	Carp Silver	Carp Wild	Catfish	Catfish Albino	Catfish American Bullhead	Catfish Black Bullhead	Charr	Chub	Dace	Eel	Flounder	Goldfish	Grayling	Grilse	Gudgeon
BODDINGTON RESERVOIR (FH0521)					●	●					●															
CANONS ASHBY LAKES (FH0824)	●		●		●	●					●								●							
CASTLE ASHBY LAKES (FH0858)					●						●															
CHESTER FARM LAKE (FH0929)			●		●					●	●															
CRESCENT LAKE (FH1179)					●	●					●															
DAVENTRY COUNTRY PARK (FH1281)			●																		●					
DRAYTON RESERVOIR (FH1441)					●						●															
DUSTON RESERVOIR (FH1486)			●		●						●								●							
ELINOR TROUT FISHERY (FH1562)					●						●								●		●					
FLECKNOE FARM FISHERIES (FH1744)					●																					
FOXHOLES FISHERIES (FH1792)			●		●	●	●			●	●			●					●							
GRAND UNION CANAL (FH1959)					●						●								●		●					●
GRAND UNION CANAL (FH1958)																										
GREEN FARM LAKES (FH2000)					●	●					●															
HEYFORD FISHERY (FH2200)	●		●		●	●		●			●								●							●
HOLLOWELL RESERVOIR (FH2260)			●		●						●															
ISE (RIVER) (FH2384)					●						●								●	●						
ISLIP NATURE LAKE (FH2396)	●	●	●		●	●					●								●		●					●
LITTLE IRCHESTER COMPLEX (FH2754)			●		●	●					●															
LYNN POOL FISHERY (FH3125)			●		●		●				●															
MENAGERIE POND (FH3253)					●						●															
NASEBY RESERVOIR (FH3428)					●						●															
NENE (RIVER) (FH3447)	●	●	●		●						●								●	●	●					●
NENE (RIVER) (FH3448)			●		●						●								●	●	●					●
NORTHAMPTON JUNCTION CANAL (FH3542)			●		●						●															●
OXFORD CANAL (FH3667)			●		●						●															●
RAVENSTHORPE TROUT FISHERY (FH3895)																										
RINGSTEAD GRANGE (FH3954)																										
SILVER LAKE (FH4269)			●		●	●					●								●							
SOUTH VIEW FARM CARP FISHERY (FH4343)					●	●					●															
ST JAMES SMALL PARK LAKE (FH4389)			●		●	●					●								●							
SULBY RESERVOIR (FH4551)					●						●															
SYWELL RESERVOIR (FH4623)					●						●															
THORPE WATERVILLE LAKE (FH4827)	●	●	●		●	●					●								●	●	●					●

Fishery	Gwyniad	Minnow	Orfe	Orfe Blue	Orfe Golden	Perch	Pike	Roach	Rudd	Ruffe	Salmon	Steelhead	Sturgeon	Tench	Tench Golden	Trount American Brook	Trout Blue	Trout Brook	Trout Brown	Trout Golden	Trout Lake	Ttrout Rainbow	Trout Sea	Trout Tiger	Trout Wild	Vendace	Zander
BODDINGTON RESERVOIR (FH0521)						●		●						●													
CANONS ASHBY LAKES (FH0824)						●		●	●					●													
CASTLE ASHBY LAKES (FH0858)																											
CHESTER FARM LAKE (FH0929)							●							●													
CRESCENT LAKE (FH1179)								●	●					●													
DAVENTRY COUNTRY PARK (FH1281)						●	●	●	●	●				●													
DRAYTON RESERVOIR (FH1441)							●	●						●													
DUSTON RESERVOIR (FH1486)						●		●						●													
ELINOR TROUT FISHERY (FH1562)							●	●						●					●			●					
FLECKNOE FARM FISHERIES (FH1744)																											
FOXHOLES FISHERIES (FH1792)						●		●						●													
GRAND UNION CANAL (FH1959)						●		●	●	●				●													
GRAND UNION CANAL (FH1958)						●		●						●													
GREEN FARM LAKES (FH2000)																											
HEYFORD FISHERY (FH2200)						●		●	●	●				●													
HOLLOWELL RESERVOIR (FH2260)						●	●							●													
ISE (RIVER) (FH2384)						●		●						●													
ISLIP NATURE LAKE (FH2396)		●				●	●	●	●	●				●													
LITTLE IRCHESTER COMPLEX (FH2754)						●		●	●					●													
LYNN POOL FISHERY (FH3125)								●	●					●													
MENAGERIE POND (FH3253)																											
NASEBY RESERVOIR (FH3428)									●					●													
NENE (RIVER) (FH3447)		●				●	●	●	●					●								●					
NENE (RIVER) (FH3448)						●	●	●	●					●					●								
NORTHAMPTON JUNCTION CANAL (FH3542)						●	●	●	●					●													
OXFORD CANAL (FH3667)						●		●						●													
RAVENSTHORPE TROUT FISHERY (FH3895)																			●			●					
RINGSTEAD GRANGE (FH3954)											●								●			●					
SILVER LAKE (FH4269)						●		●	●					●													
SOUTH VIEW FARM CARP FISHERY (FH4343)								●						●													
ST JAMES SMALL PARK LAKE (FH4389)						●	●	●	●					●													
SULBY RESERVOIR (FH4551)																											
SYWELL RESERVOIR (FH4623)						●	●	●						●													
THORPE WATERVILLE LAKE (FH4827)		●				●	●	●	●	●				●													

Fish Species Available at UK & Irish Fisheries

	Barbel	Bleak	Bream	Carp Blue	Carp Common	Carp Crucian	Carp Ghost	Carp Grass	Carp Koi	Carp Leather	Carp Mirror	Carp Silver	Carp Wild	Catfish	Catfish Albino	Catfish American Bullhead	Catfish Black Bullhead	Charr	Chub	Dace	Eel	Flounder	Goldfish	Grayling	Grilse	Gudgeon	Gwyniad	Minnow	Orfe	Orfe Blue	Orfe Golden	Perch	Pike	Roach	Rudd	Ruffe	Salmon	Steelhead	Sturgeon	Tench	Tench Golden	Trount American Brook	Trout Blue	Trout Brook	Trout Brown	Trout Golden	Trout Lake	Ttrout Rainbow	Trout Sea	Trout Tiger	Trout Wild	Vendace	Zander
THRAPSTON (RIVER) (FH4828)																				●												●		●																			
THRAPSTON LAKES (FH4829)	●	●	●		●	●					●								●	●	●					●		●				●	●	●	●	●				●													
WELFORD RESERVOIR (FH5230)			●		●						●																					●	●	●						●													
WEYBREAD GRAVEL PITS (FH5294)			●		●						●																					●	●	●						●													
WOOTTON BROOK LAKE (FH5503)			●		●	●					●								●	●												●	●	●	●					●													
NORTHUMBERLAND																																																					
ALN (RIVER) (FH0085)																																					●								●				●		●		
COQUET (RIVER) (FH1116)																					●							●									●								●				●		●		
COQUET (RIVER) (FH1117)																																					●								●				●				
FELTON FENCE FARM PONDS (FH1691)			●		●						●																					●		●	●					●													
FONTBURN RESERVOIR (FH1758)																																										●			●			●					
GILSLAND LAKE (FH1857)																																													●								
HADRIAN LODGE (FH2061)																																													●			●					
HORTON GRANGE LAKE (FH2312)			●																															●	●																		
IRTHING (RIVER) (FH2381)																				●	●							●					●				●								●				●				
KIELDER WATER (FH2477)																																													●			●					
LANGLEY DAM FISHERIES (FH2615)																																																●					
LEET (RIVER) (FH2686)																																													●								
LINNEL WOOD LAKE (FH2737)																																																●					
NORTH TYNE (RIVER) (FH3538)																				●																	●								●				●				
NORTH TYNE (RIVER) (FH3537)																																					●								●				●				
NORTH TYNE (RIVER) (FH3541)																																					●								●				●				
NORTH TYNE (RIVER) (FH3540)																																					●								●				●				
NORTH TYNE (RIVER) (FH3539)																				●																	●								●				●				
QUEEN ELIZABETH II COUNTRY PK (FH3864)			●																														●	●	●																		
REDE (RIVER) (FH3914)																					●																								●				●				
SOUTH TYNE (RIVER) (FH4341)																				●																																	
THORNBROUGH LAKE (FH4811)			●		●						●															●						●								●													
TWEED (RIVER) (FH4988)																								●										●											●								
TWEED (RIVER) (FH4990)																					●			●		●		●				●		●											●								
TWEED (RIVER) (FH4991)																																					●												●				
TWEED (RIVER) (FH4989)																																					●												●				
TWEED (RIVER) (FH4993)																																					●												●				
TWEED (RIVER) (FH4992)																																					●												●				

Fish Species Available at UK & Irish Fisheries

	Barbel	Bleak	Bream	Carp Blue	Carp Common	Carp Crucian	Carp Ghost	Carp Grass	Carp Koi	Carp Leather	Carp Mirror	Carp Silver	Carp Wild	Catfish	Catfish Albino	Catfish American Bullhead	Catfish Black Bullhead	Charr	Chub	Dace	Eel	Flounder	Goldfish	Grayling	Grilse	Gudgeon	Gwyniad	Minnow	Orfe	Orfe Blue	Orfe Golden	Perch	Pike	Roach	Rudd	Ruffe	Salmon	Steelhead	Sturgeon	Tench	Tench Golden	Trount American Brook	Trout Blue	Trout Brook	Trout Brown	Trout Golden	Trout Lake	Ttrout Rainbow	Trout Sea	Trout Tiger	Trout Wild	Vendace	Zander
TYNE (RIVER) (FH5027)																			●	●						●								●			●								●								
TYNE (RIVER) (FH5024)																			●	●												●					●																
TYNE (RIVER) (FH5020)																																					●																
TYNE (RIVER) (FH5019)																																					●																
TYNE (RIVER) (FH5025)																			●	●	●					●		●						●											●								
TYNE (RIVER) (FH5028)																																													●								
WANSBECK (RIVER) (FH5140)																					●																								●				●				
WANSBECK (RIVER) (FH5139)																												●					●				●							●	●			●			●		
WANSBECK STREAM (FH5141)																																													●								
WHITEADDER (RIVER) (FH5345)																																					●								●				●				
WHITTLE DEAN RESERVOIR (FH5359)																																																●					
WILLIES WELL (FH5372)					●	●					●																					●		●	●					●													
WREIGH (RIVER) (FH5516)																				●	●																●								●				●		●		
NOTTINGHAMSHIRE																																																					
A1 PITS (FH0001)	●		●		●						●								●		●											●	●	●						●													
ATTENBOROUGH GRAVEL PITS (FH0182)			●																															●																			
CHESTERFIELD CANAL (FH0930)																			●															●																			
CLUMBER LAKE (FH1030)			●		●						●										●											●	●	●						●													
COLWICK COUNTRY PARK (FH1080)	●	●	●		●	●					●								●	●	●					●						●	●	●		●				●					●			●					●
CRANFLEET CANAL (FH1165)																																●		●																			
DANESHILL LAKES (FH1269)					●																												●																				
DOLAR POND (FH1396)	●	●	●		●						●							●		●	●					●		●				●	●	●						●													
EREWASH CANAL (FH1607)			●																															●																			
FLEET (RIVER) (FH1745)	●	●	●		●						●								●	●	●					●						●	●	●		●																	
GRANTHAM CANAL (FH1974)					●						●																					●		●						●													
GRANTHAM CANAL (FH1973)																																		●						●													
GRANTHAM CANAL (FH1975)			●		●	●				●	●										●					●		●				●	●	●	●					●													
HALLCROFT FISHERIES (FH2070)			●		●	●					●								●		●					●						●		●	●					●													
HOLME PIERPOINT (FH2268)	●	●	●		●						●								●	●	●					●		●				●	●	●						●													
IRONMONGERS POND (FH2379)																																		●						●													
KINGS MILL RESERVOIR (FH2507)					●																													●																			
LAKESIDE FARM (FH2590)																			●					●								●		●											●								
LAKESIDE FISHERY (FH2592)			●		●	●	●	●		●	●								●							●		●	●			●		●	●					●					●		●	●					
LANGOLD LAKES (FH2616)			●		●					●	●								●													●	●	●						●													

Fish Species Available at UK & Irish Fisheries

Fishery	Barbel	Bleak	Bream	Carp Blue	Carp Common	Carp Crucian	Carp Ghost	Carp Grass	Carp Koi	Carp Leather	Carp Mirror	Carp Silver	Carp Wild	Catfish	Catfish Albino	Catfish American Bullhead	Catfish Black Bullhead	Charr
L-LAKE FISHERY (FH2767)			●		●						●							
MAUN (RIVER) (FH3209)			●		●	●	●											
NOTTINGHAM CANAL (FH3552)			●															
NOTTINGHAM CASTLE MARINA (FH3553)		●	●		●	●				●	●							
OWDY LANE TROUT FISHERY (FH3660)																		
PINDERS PONDS (FH3776)																		
SANDHILL LAKE (FH4096)			●															
SAPPHIRE LAKES (FH4104)			●		●	●				●	●							
SHERWOOD FOREST FISHERY (FH4234)			●		●	●	●		●	●	●							
SMEATONS LAKES (FH4304)	●	●	●		●	●		●			●							
TRENT (RIVER) (FH4923)	●																	
TRENT (RIVER) (FH4930)			●															
TRENT (RIVER) (FH4933)	●		●		●						●							
TRENT (RIVER) (FH4929)	●	●	●		●						●							
TRENT (RIVER) (FH4927)																		
TRENT (RIVER) (FH4926)	●	●	●		●						●							
TRENT (RIVER) (FH4925)			●															
TRENT (RIVER) (FH4924)	●	●	●		●	●												
TRENT (RIVER) (FH4931)																		
TRENT (RIVER) (FH4928)	●	●	●		●	●					●							
TRENT (RIVER) (FH4934)	●	●	●		●						●							
TRENT (RIVER) (FH4932)	●																	
WHARFE (RIVER) (FH5297)	●																	
WINFIELD LAGOON (FH5415)																		
WITHAM (RIVER) (FH5440)			●															
WOODEND QUARRY POND (FH5472)					●													
WOODSETTS QUARRY POND (FH5492)			●		●													
OXFORDSHIRE																		
BARNES TROUT LAKES (FH0316)			●		●					●	●							
BEIRTON LAKES (FH0373)			●		●	●					●							
BLADON LAKE (FH0486)			●															
BLENHEIM LAKE (FH0497)			●															
BUSCOT LOCK (FH0766)	●		●															
BUTLERS HILL FARM (FH0775)			●		●			●			●							

Fishery	Chub	Dace	Eel	Flounder	Goldfish	Grayling	Grilse	Gudgeon	Gwyniad	Minnow	Orfe	Orfe Blue	Orfe Golden	Perch	Pike	Roach	Rudd	Ruffe
L-LAKE FISHERY (FH2767)															●			
MAUN (RIVER) (FH3209)	●																●	
NOTTINGHAM CANAL (FH3552)																●		
NOTTINGHAM CASTLE MARINA (FH3553)	●	●	●					●		●				●	●	●	●	
OWDY LANE TROUT FISHERY (FH3660)																		
PINDERS PONDS (FH3776)																		
SANDHILL LAKE (FH4096)																●		
SAPPHIRE LAKES (FH4104)	●													●	●	●		
SHERWOOD FOREST FISHERY (FH4234)	●	●	●					●			●			●		●	●	
SMEATONS LAKES (FH4304)	●		●					●						●	●	●	●	
TRENT (RIVER) (FH4923)	●															●		
TRENT (RIVER) (FH4930)	●														●	●		
TRENT (RIVER) (FH4933)	●		●					●						●	●	●		
TRENT (RIVER) (FH4929)	●	●	●					●		●				●	●	●		
TRENT (RIVER) (FH4927)																		
TRENT (RIVER) (FH4926)	●	●	●					●						●	●	●		●
TRENT (RIVER) (FH4925)	●	●													●	●		
TRENT (RIVER) (FH4924)	●	●	●					●		●				●	●	●	●	●
TRENT (RIVER) (FH4931)	●															●		
TRENT (RIVER) (FH4928)	●		●					●						●	●	●	●	●
TRENT (RIVER) (FH4934)	●	●						●						●		●	●	●
TRENT (RIVER) (FH4932)	●														●			
WHARFE (RIVER) (FH5297)	●	●	●			●				●								
WINFIELD LAGOON (FH5415)														●		●		
WITHAM (RIVER) (FH5440)	●	●				●										●		
WOODEND QUARRY POND (FH5472)																●		
WOODSETTS QUARRY POND (FH5492)																		
OXFORDSHIRE																		
BARNES TROUT LAKES (FH0316)	●													●	●	●	●	
BEIRTON LAKES (FH0373)	●							●						●		●	●	
BLADON LAKE (FH0486)														●	●	●		
BLENHEIM LAKE (FH0497)														●	●	●		
BUSCOT LOCK (FH0766)	●													●	●	●		
BUTLERS HILL FARM (FH0775)	●															●	●	

Fishery	Salmon	Steelhead	Sturgeon	Tench	Tench Golden	Trount American Brook	Trout Blue	Trout Brook	Trout Brown	Trout Golden	Trout Lake	Ttrout Rainbow	Trout Sea	Trout Tiger	Trout Wild	Vendace	Zander
L-LAKE FISHERY (FH2767)				●													
MAUN (RIVER) (FH3209)				●													
NOTTINGHAM CANAL (FH3552)																	
NOTTINGHAM CASTLE MARINA (FH3553)																	
OWDY LANE TROUT FISHERY (FH3660)									●			●					
PINDERS PONDS (FH3776)				●													
SANDHILL LAKE (FH4096)																	
SAPPHIRE LAKES (FH4104)				●													
SHERWOOD FOREST FISHERY (FH4234)				●													
SMEATONS LAKES (FH4304)				●													
TRENT (RIVER) (FH4923)																	
TRENT (RIVER) (FH4930)																	
TRENT (RIVER) (FH4933)																	
TRENT (RIVER) (FH4929)				●													
TRENT (RIVER) (FH4927)									●			●					
TRENT (RIVER) (FH4926)																	
TRENT (RIVER) (FH4925)																	
TRENT (RIVER) (FH4924)																	
TRENT (RIVER) (FH4931)																	
TRENT (RIVER) (FH4928)				●													
TRENT (RIVER) (FH4934)				●													
TRENT (RIVER) (FH4932)																	
WHARFE (RIVER) (FH5297)									●								
WINFIELD LAGOON (FH5415)																	
WITHAM (RIVER) (FH5440)																	
WOODEND QUARRY POND (FH5472)																	
WOODSETTS QUARRY POND (FH5492)																	
OXFORDSHIRE																	
BARNES TROUT LAKES (FH0316)				●					●			●					
BEIRTON LAKES (FH0373)				●													
BLADON LAKE (FH0486)				●													
BLENHEIM LAKE (FH0497)				●													
BUSCOT LOCK (FH0766)																	
BUTLERS HILL FARM (FH0775)				●													

Fish Species Available at UK & Irish Fisheries

Fishery	Barbel	Bleak	Bream	Carp Blue	Carp Common	Carp Crucian	Carp Ghost	Carp Grass	Carp Koi	Carp Leather	Carp Mirror	Carp Silver	Carp Wild	Catfish	Catfish Albino	Catfish American Bullhead	Catfish Black Bullhead	Charr	Chub	Dace	Eel	Flounder	Goldfish	Grayling	Grilse	Gudgeon
CHAD LAKES (FH0890)			●		●	●					●								●		●					●
CHERWELL (RIVER) (FH0922)			●																●	●						
CHERWELL (RIVER) (FH0918)			●																●							
CHERWELL (RIVER) (FH0921)	●		●																●	●						
CHERWELL (RIVER) (FH0923)	●		●																●	●				●		
CHERWELL (RIVER) (FH0919)			●		●						●								●	●						
CHERWELL (RIVER) (FH0917)	●																		●							
CHERWELL (RIVER) (FH0924)																										
CHRISTCHURCH LAKE (FH0947)			●		●						●			●												
CLATTERCOTE RESERVOIR (FH0979)			●		●	●					●								●							
CLEARWATER FISH FARM (FH0997)					●																					
COLLEGE FARM FISHING (FH1063)			●		●	●					●								●							●
CORNBURY PARK FISHERY (FH1120)																										
DARLOW LAKE (FH1275)																										
DORCHESTER LAGOON (FH1412)					●						●															
FARINGDON LAKE (FH1664)			●																							
FARMOOR 1 RESERVOIR (FH1675)																										
FARMOOR TROUT FISHERY (FH1676)																										
GAUNTS LAKE (FH1844)					●						●															
GLEBE COURT LAKE (FH1877)			●		●	●					●								●							●
GOLDFISH BOWL (THE) (FH1915)					●						●												●			
GRAND UNION CANAL (FH1961)			●		●						●															
GRAND UNION CANAL (FH1960)			●		●						●								●							●
HARDWICK LAKE AND SMITHS POOL (FH2104)			●		●						●								●							
HEART OF ENGLAND FISHERY (FH2171)																										
HEYFORD LAKES (FH2201)			●		●					●	●								●		●					
HORSE AND GROOM INN (FH2303)			●		●	●				●	●								●							
HUNTS CORNER (FH2342)					●						●															
LINCH HILL FISHERY (FH2725)			●		●						●			●					●		●					
LOCKINGE TROUT FISHERY (FH2972)																										
MANOR FARM LAKE (FH3162)			●		●						●															
MANOR HOUSE (FH3166)					●						●															
MANOR LAKE (FH3169)			●		●						●															
MILLETS FARM TROUT FISHERY (FH3311)																										

Fishery	Gwyniad	Minnow	Orfe	Orfe Blue	Orfe Golden	Perch	Pike	Roach	Rudd	Ruffe	Salmon	Steelhead	Sturgeon	Tench	Tench Golden	Trount American Brook	Trout Blue	Trout Brook	Trout Brown	Trout Golden	Trout Lake	Ttrout Rainbow	Trout Sea	Trout Tiger	Trout Wild	Vendace	Zander
CHAD LAKES (FH0890)						●		●						●													
CHERWELL (RIVER) (FH0922)						●	●	●																			
CHERWELL (RIVER) (FH0918)								●																			
CHERWELL (RIVER) (FH0921)						●	●	●																			
CHERWELL (RIVER) (FH0923)						●	●	●						●													
CHERWELL (RIVER) (FH0919)						●	●	●						●													
CHERWELL (RIVER) (FH0917)								●																			
CHERWELL (RIVER) (FH0924)								●	●					●													
CHRISTCHURCH LAKE (FH0947)						●	●	●	●					●													
CLATTERCOTE RESERVOIR (FH0979)						●		●						●													
CLEARWATER FISH FARM (FH0997)																			●			●					
COLLEGE FARM FISHING (FH1063)								●	●					●													
CORNBURY PARK FISHERY (FH1120)																			●			●					
DARLOW LAKE (FH1275)																			●			●					
DORCHESTER LAGOON (FH1412)																											
FARINGDON LAKE (FH1664)						●	●	●						●													
FARMOOR 1 RESERVOIR (FH1675)																			●			●					
FARMOOR TROUT FISHERY (FH1676)																			●			●					
GAUNTS LAKE (FH1844)																											
GLEBE COURT LAKE (FH1877)						●		●						●								●					
GOLDFISH BOWL (THE) (FH1915)						●		●														●					
GRAND UNION CANAL (FH1961)						●		●	●					●													
GRAND UNION CANAL (FH1960)						●		●	●																		
HARDWICK LAKE AND SMITHS POOL (FH2104)						●		●	●					●													
HEART OF ENGLAND FISHERY (FH2171)																			●			●					
HEYFORD LAKES (FH2201)						●	●	●	●					●													
HORSE AND GROOM INN (FH2303)						●		●	●					●													
HUNTS CORNER (FH2342)																											
LINCH HILL FISHERY (FH2725)						●	●	●	●					●													
LOCKINGE TROUT FISHERY (FH2972)																			●			●					
MANOR FARM LAKE (FH3162)							●							●													
MANOR HOUSE (FH3166)								●	●					●													
MANOR LAKE (FH3169)						●	●							●													
MILLETS FARM TROUT FISHERY (FH3311)																			●			●					

Fish Species Available at UK & Irish Fisheries

	Barbel	Bleak	Bream	Carp Blue	Carp Common	Carp Crucian	Carp Ghost	Carp Grass	Carp Koi	Carp Leather	Carp Mirror	Carp Silver	Carp Wild	Catfish	Catfish Albino	Catfish American Bullhead	Catfish Black Bullhead	Charr	Chub	Dace	Eel	Flounder	Goldfish	Grayling	Grilse	Gudgeon
MILTON POOLS FARM (FH3326)					●						●															
NELL BRIDGE FISHERY (FH3439)			●		●		●				●								●							
ORCHID LAKES (FH3618)					●						●			●												
OXFORD CANAL (FH3669)			●																●							
OXFORD CANAL (FH3670)					●						●								●							
OXFORD CANAL (FH3672)			●																●	●						
OXFORD CANAL (FH3673)			●																●							
OXFORD CANAL (FH3668)					●						●								●							●
OXFORD CANAL (FH3671)					●						●								●	●						●
OXLEASE LAKE (FH3678)					●						●								●							
PIMLICO FARM LAKES (FH3775)					●	●					●															
ROLFS LAKE (FH3998)			●		●														●							●
RUSHEY WEIR (FH4062)	●		●																●	●						●
SALFORD TROUT LAKES (FH4083)																										
SEVERALLS FARM A AND B (FH4144)	●		●		●						●								●							
ST JOHNS POOL (FH4391)			●		●						●			●												
STATES LAGOON (FH4436)	●		●		●	●					●								●		●					
SWISS FARM LAKE (FH4614)					●						●															
THAME (RIVER) (FH4757)	●	●	●																●	●						●
THAME (RIVER) (FH4759)		●	●		●	●					●									●						●
THAMES (RIVER) (FH4799)	●		●		●						●								●	●						
THAMES (RIVER) (FH4794)	●	●	●																●	●						
THAMES (RIVER) (FH4792)	●																		●							
THAMES (RIVER) (FH4795)	●		●		●						●								●	●						
THAMES (RIVER) (FH4791)	●																		●							
THAMES (RIVER) (FH4797)			●																●							
THAMES (RIVER) (FH4801)	●																		●							
THAMES (RIVER) (FH4793)																			●							
THAMES (RIVER) (FH4790)			●																●							
THAMES (RIVER) (FH4798)	●		●																●	●						●
THAMES (RIVER) (FH4802)			●																●							
UNITY LAKE (FH5047)					●		●				●															
WINDRUSH (RIVER) (FH5410)																			●	●				●		●
WINDRUSH (RIVER) (FH5412)																			●	●				●		●

	Gwyniad	Minnow	Orfe	Orfe Blue	Orfe Golden	Perch	Pike	Roach	Rudd	Ruffe	Salmon	Steelhead	Sturgeon	Tench	Tench Golden	Trount American Brook	Trout Blue	Trout Brook	Trout Brown	Trout Golden	Trout Lake	Ttrout Rainbow	Trout Sea	Trout Tiger	Trout Wild	Vendace	Zander
MILTON POOLS FARM (FH3326)						●	●	●	●					●													
NELL BRIDGE FISHERY (FH3439)						●	●	●	●					●													
ORCHID LAKES (FH3618)						●		●	●					●													
OXFORD CANAL (FH3669)																											
OXFORD CANAL (FH3670)						●		●																			
OXFORD CANAL (FH3672)						●		●																			
OXFORD CANAL (FH3673)								●																			
OXFORD CANAL (FH3668)						●																					
OXFORD CANAL (FH3671)						●		●																			
OXLEASE LAKE (FH3678)						●	●							●													
PIMLICO FARM LAKES (FH3775)						●		●	●					●													
ROLFS LAKE (FH3998)								●						●													
RUSHEY WEIR (FH4062)						●	●																				
SALFORD TROUT LAKES (FH4083)																			●			●					
SEVERALLS FARM A AND B (FH4144)							●	●																			
ST JOHNS POOL (FH4391)							●							●													
STATES LAGOON (FH4436)						●	●	●	●					●													
SWISS FARM LAKE (FH4614)								●						●													
THAME (RIVER) (FH4757)						●	●	●						●													
THAME (RIVER) (FH4759)						●	●	●	●																		
THAMES (RIVER) (FH4799)						●		●																			
THAMES (RIVER) (FH4794)						●	●	●																			
THAMES (RIVER) (FH4792)						●	●	●						●													
THAMES (RIVER) (FH4795)							●	●	●					●													
THAMES (RIVER) (FH4791)						●	●	●																			
THAMES (RIVER) (FH4797)						●	●																				
THAMES (RIVER) (FH4801)						●	●	●																			
THAMES (RIVER) (FH4793)																											
THAMES (RIVER) (FH4790)						●	●																				
THAMES (RIVER) (FH4798)						●	●	●																			
THAMES (RIVER) (FH4802)						●	●																				
UNITY LAKE (FH5047)														●													
WINDRUSH (RIVER) (FH5410)						●	●	●											●								
WINDRUSH (RIVER) (FH5412)						●	●	●											●								

Fish Species Available at UK & Irish Fisheries

Fishery	Barbel	Bleak	Bream	Carp Blue	Carp Common	Carp Crucian	Carp Ghost	Carp Grass	Carp Koi	Carp Leather	Carp Mirror	Carp Silver	Carp Wild	Catfish	Catfish Albino	Catfish American Bullhead	Catfish Black Bullhead	Charr	Chub	Dace	Eel	Flounder	Goldfish	Grayling	Grilse	Gudgeon	Gwyniad	Minnow	Orfe	Orfe Blue	Orfe Golden	Perch	Pike	Roach	Rudd	Ruffe	Salmon	Steelhead	Sturgeon	Tench	Tench Golden	Trount American Brook	Trout Blue	Trout Brook	Trout Brown	Trout Golden	Trout Lake	Ttrout Rainbow	Trout Sea	Trout Tiger	Trout Wild	Vendace	Zander
WINDRUSH (RIVER) (FH5411)																			●	●												●		●																			
WINDRUSH (RIVER) (FH5413)	●																		●	●												●	●	●											●								
YEOMANS LAKE (FH5565)					●						●																																										
RUTLAND																																																					
SWEETHEDGES FARM FISHERY (FH4607)			●		●						●								●													●		●						●													
WELLAND (RIVER) (FH5236)																			●	●												●		●																			
WELLAND (RIVER) (FH5235)			●																●	●												●		●																			
SHROPSHIRE																																																					
ACTON BURNELL (FH0025)					●						●																																										
APLEY POOLS (FH0121)					●	●					●															●						●		●	●					●													
AQUALATE MERE (FH0124)			●		●						●																						●	●						●													
BACHE POOL (FH0240)					●						●																					●		●	●					●													
BAYLIS POOLS (FH0351)			●		●	●	●	●			●			●																		●		●						●													
BEECHES POOL (FH0367)			●		●	●					●																							●						●													
BENTHALL LAKE (FH0387)					●																													●																			
BIRCH GROVE (FH0425)			●		●					●	●										●													●						●													
BIRMINGHAM TO WORCESTER CANAL (FH0432)											●																							●																			
BLUE POOL (FH0510)					●						●																						●	●																			
BOLDINGS POOLS (FH0530)	●		●		●	●	●		●	●	●								●							●			●			●		●	●					●					●			●					
COLEMERE COUNTRY PARK (FH1061)			●		●						●										●											●	●	●						●													
COUND TROUT FISHERY (FH1140)																																										●			●			●					
CROSEMERE (FH1190)			●		●						●																					●	●	●						●													
DEARNFORD HALL TROUT FISHERY (FH1291)																																												●	●	●		●					
DELBURY HALL TROUT FISHERY (FH1326)																																													●			●					
ELLERDINE LAKES (FH1566)			●		●	●					●										●							●				●		●	●					●					●	●		●					
FOLLY FARM POOL (FH1754)					●						●										●																																
HINKSHAY POOLS (FH2235)			●		●						●															●						●	●	●	●																		
HORESHAY POOL (FH2297)			●																																					●													
ISLE LAKE (FH2395)					●						●																																										
LAKE VYRNWY (FH2573)																																													●			●					
LITTLE DAWLEY POOLS (FH2748)			●		●						●																							●																			
LOWER HILL FARM (FH3081)					●						●															●						●		●	●					●													
MIDDLE POOL (FH3267)			●		●	●					●																					●	●	●						●													
MILLRIDE FISHERY (FH3317)			●		●	●					●															●						●		●						●								●					

Fish Species Available at UK & Irish Fisheries

	Barbel	Bleak	Bream	Carp Blue	Carp Common	Carp Crucian	Carp Ghost	Carp Grass	Carp Koi	Carp Leather	Carp Mirror	Carp Silver	Carp Wild	Catfish	Catfish Albino	Catfish American Bullhead	Catfish Black Bullhead	Charr	Chub	Dace	Eel	Flounder	Goldfish	Grayling	Grilse	Gudgeon
MONKHALL FISHERIES (FH3343)					●	●			●		●								●							
NEWPORT CANAL (FH3489)																										
ONNY (RIVER) (FH3613)																										
OSS MERE (FH3628)			●		●						●															
PERRY (RIVER) (FH3755)																			●							
PERRY (RIVER) (FH3754)																			●	●						
RIVER (TERN) (FH3963)	●																		●	●						
SEVERN (RIVER) (FH4167)	●		●		●						●								●	●				●		
SEVERN (RIVER) (FH4180)	●		●																●	●						
SEVERN (RIVER) (FH4179)	●																		●	●	●					
SEVERN (RIVER) (FH4163)	●																		●							
SEVERN (RIVER) (FH4170)	●																		●							
SEVERN (RIVER) (FH4165)																			●							
SEVERN (RIVER) (FH4166)	●																		●	●						●
SEVERN (RIVER) (FH4176)	●		●																●	●	●					
SEVERN (RIVER) (FH4168)	●		●																●	●						
SEVERN (RIVER) (FH4181)	●																		●	●	●					●
SEVERN (RIVER) (FH4175)	●																		●	●	●					●
SEVERN (RIVER) (FH4164)	●																		●							
SEVERN (RIVER) (FH4162)	●																		●	●	●					●
SEVERN (RIVER) (FH4177)	●																		●	●						
SEVERN (RIVER) (FH4178)	●																		●	●						
SEVERN (RIVER) (FH4169)	●																		●							
SEVERN (RIVER) (FH4173)	●																		●	●						
SEVERN (RIVER) (FH4174)	●		●		●						●								●	●						●
SEVERN (RIVER) (FH4182)	●		●																●							
SEVERN (RIVER) (FH4171)	●																		●							
SEVERN (RIVER) (FH4172)	●		●																●	●	●					●
SHROPSHIRE UNION CANAL (FH4253)			●																							
SPRING LEE (FH4369)			●		●	●					●															
STIRCHLEY POOLS (FH4458)			●		●						●															●
SWEENEYCLIFFE HOUSE FISHERY (FH4606)	●		●																●	●						
TANAT (RIVER) (FH4650)																								●		
TELFORD TOWN PARK (FH4721)					●																					

	Gwyniad	Minnow	Orfe	Orfe Blue	Orfe Golden	Perch	Pike	Roach	Rudd	Ruffe	Salmon	Steelhead	Sturgeon	Tench	Tench Golden	Trount American Brook	Trout Blue	Trout Brook	Trout Brown	Trout Golden	Trout Lake	Ttrout Rainbow	Trout Sea	Trout Tiger	Trout Wild	Vendace	Zander
MONKHALL FISHERIES (FH3343)						●		●	●					●													
NEWPORT CANAL (FH3489)								●						●													
ONNY (RIVER) (FH3613)																			●						●		
OSS MERE (FH3628)						●	●	●						●													
PERRY (RIVER) (FH3755)							●																				
PERRY (RIVER) (FH3754)							●	●																			
RIVER (TERN) (FH3963)						●	●	●											●			●					
SEVERN (RIVER) (FH4167)						●	●	●						●					●								
SEVERN (RIVER) (FH4180)							●	●						●													
SEVERN (RIVER) (FH4179)						●	●				●																
SEVERN (RIVER) (FH4163)																											
SEVERN (RIVER) (FH4170)																											
SEVERN (RIVER) (FH4165)								●																			
SEVERN (RIVER) (FH4166)								●																			
SEVERN (RIVER) (FH4176)							●	●																			
SEVERN (RIVER) (FH4168)							●	●																			
SEVERN (RIVER) (FH4181)		●					●	●																			
SEVERN (RIVER) (FH4175)						●	●	●																			
SEVERN (RIVER) (FH4164)																											
SEVERN (RIVER) (FH4162)		●				●	●	●	●		●								●			●					
SEVERN (RIVER) (FH4177)						●	●	●			●								●								
SEVERN (RIVER) (FH4178)						●	●	●																			
SEVERN (RIVER) (FH4169)																											
SEVERN (RIVER) (FH4173)								●																			
SEVERN (RIVER) (FH4174)						●	●	●			●			●					●								
SEVERN (RIVER) (FH4182)																											
SEVERN (RIVER) (FH4171)							●																				
SEVERN (RIVER) (FH4172)							●	●			●																
SHROPSHIRE UNION CANAL (FH4253)								●																			
SPRING LEE (FH4369)			●		●			●	●					●													
STIRCHLEY POOLS (FH4458)						●	●	●	●																		
SWEENEYCLIFFE HOUSE FISHERY (FH4606)						●	●	●																			
TANAT (RIVER) (FH4650)																						●					
TELFORD TOWN PARK (FH4721)								●																			

Fish Species Available at UK & Irish Fisheries

	Barbel	Bleak	Bream	Carp Blue	Carp Common	Carp Crucian	Carp Ghost	Carp Grass	Carp Koi	Carp Leather	Carp Mirror	Carp Silver	Carp Wild	Catfish	Catfish Albino	Catfish American Bullhead	Catfish Black Bullhead	Charr	Chub	Dace	Eel	Flounder	Goldfish	Grayling	Grilse	Gudgeon	Gwyniad	Minnow	Orfe	Orfe Blue	Orfe Golden	Perch	Pike	Roach	Rudd	Ruffe	Salmon	Steelhead	Sturgeon	Tench	Tench Golden	Trount American Brook	Trout Blue	Trout Brook	Trout Brown	Trout Golden	Trout Lake	Ttrout Rainbow	Trout Sea	Trout Tiger	Trout Wild	Vendace	Zander
TEME (RIVER) (FH4723)																			●	●																																	
TEME (RIVER) (FH4722)																			●	●																																	
TERN (RIVER) (FH4740)																			●																										●			●					
TERN (RIVER) (FH4742)																			●															●																			
TERN (RIVER) (FH4741)																			●	●																									●								
TERN (RIVER) (FH4739)																																													●			●					
TERN FISHERIES (FH4743)																																													●								
TOWNSEND FISHERY (FH4894)			●											●					●													●								●													
VOWNOG FISH LAKE (FH5101)																																													●			●					
VYRNWY (RIVER) (FH5109)	●	●																	●	●				●		●							●			●	●																
WALCOT WEST LAKE (FH5117)			●		●	●					●										●											●	●	●	●					●													
WHITEMERE (FH5350)			●		●						●																					●	●	●						●													
WITHY POOL (FH5447)														●																																							
WOODCOTE HALL (FH5470)			●		●	●					●																							●	●					●													
WYRLEY ESSINGTON CANAL (FH5551)																																		●						●													
SOMERSET																																																					
APEX LAKE (FH0120)			●		●						●																					●	●	●						●													
AVALON FISHERIES (FH0186)			●		●		●			●	●										●					●						●	●	●	●					●													
AVON (BRISTOL) (RIVER) (FH0193)			●		●						●								●															●	●																		
AVON (RIVER) (FH0212)	●																																																				
AVON (RIVER) (FH0210)	●																																												●								
BARLE (RIVER) (FH0309)																																					●								●								
BARROW RESERVOIRS (FH0329)																																													●			●					
BASON BRIDGE (FH0343)					●						●								●													●	●	●						●													
BLAGDON LAKE (FH0487)																																													●			●					
BRISTOL AVON (FH0647)	●	●	●		●		●			●	●								●	●	●			●		●						●	●	●	●					●					●			●					
BRISTOL AVON (FH0649)	●	●	●		●		●			●	●								●	●	●			●		●						●	●	●	●					●					●			●					
BRISTOL AVON (FH0648)	●	●	●		●		●			●	●								●	●	●			●		●						●	●	●	●					●					●			●					
BROWNES POND (FH0699)			●		●						●																					●		●						●													
BULLOCKS FARM FISHING LAKES (FH0728)			●		●	●		●			●								●															●	●					●													
CAMELEY TROUT LAKES (FH0812)																																													●								
CHARD RESERVOIR (FH0899)			●		●						●										●											●		●						●													
CHEDDAR RESERVOIR (FH0909)																					●											●	●	●						●													
CHEW VALLEY LAKE (FH0936)																																													●			●					

Fish Species Available at UK & Irish Fisheries

	Barbel	Bleak	Bream	Carp Blue	Carp Common	Carp Crucian	Carp Ghost	Carp Grass	Carp Koi	Carp Leather	Carp Mirror	Carp Silver	Carp Wild	Catfish	Catfish Albino	Catfish American Bullhead	Catfish Black Bullhead	Charr	Chub	Dace	Eel
CLATWORTHY RESERVOIR (FH0981)																					
COMBWICH PONDS (FH1082)					●						●										
COOMBE LAKE (FH1107)			●		●	●					●								●		●
DANDYS & KNIGHTINGALE LAKES (FH1254)			●		●						●								●	●	
DUNWEAR LAKES (FH1482)			●		●						●										●
DURLEIGH RESERVOIR (FH1484)			●		●						●										
EDNEYS FISHERIES (FH1548)					●		●			●	●										
EMBOROUGH POOL (FH1582)					●	●					●										
EMBORUGH LAKE (FH1583)					●						●										
EMERALD POOL FISHERY (FH1585)	●		●		●	●					●								●	●	●
EXE VALLEY FISHERY (FH1645)																					
FOLLY FOOT FARM (FH1755)					●	●	●		●		●										
FOLLYFOOT FARM (FH1757)					●		●		●		●										●
FROME (RIVER) (FH1811)			●																●	●	
FROME (RIVER) (FH1810)			●																●		
GLASTONBURY (FH1874)			●																●		
GODNEY MOOR PONDS (FH1906)			●		●	●					●										●
HAWKRIDGE RESERVOIR (FH2144)																					
HIGHLANDS DAIRY LAKE (FH2218)					●						●										
HORNER WATER (FH2298)																					
HORSESHOE LAKE (FH2308)			●		●						●										●
HOWLEY STREET POND (FH2320)			●				●				●										
HUNSTRETE LAKE COMPLEX (FH2338)			●		●	●					●										●
HUNTSPILL (RIVER) (FH2343)			●																		●
HUTON POND (FH2350)			●		●						●										
ISLE (RIVER) (FH2393)			●		●						●									●	
ISLE (RIVER) (FH2394)			●																		
KENN (RIVER) (FH2433)			●		●						●										●
KENNET AND AVON CANAL (FH2456)			●		●						●										
KENNET AND AVON CANAL (FH2457)			●								●								●		
KING SEDGEMOOR DRAIN (FH2490)			●		●						●										●
LAKESIDE (FH2584)			●		●	●					●										
LANDS END FARM (FH2607)	●		●		●			●			●								●		
LANDS END FISHERIES (FH2608)			●		●						●										

	Flounder	Goldfish	Grayling	Grilse	Gudgeon	Gwyniad	Minnow	Orfe	Orfe Blue	Orfe Golden	Perch	Pike	Roach	Rudd	Ruffe	Salmon	Steelhead	Sturgeon	Tench	Tench Golden	Trount American Brook	Trout Blue	Trout Brook	Trout Brown	Trout Golden	Trout Lake	Ttrout Rainbow	Trout Sea	Trout Tiger	Trout Wild	Vendace	Zander
CLATWORTHY RESERVOIR (FH0981)																								●			●					
COMBWICH PONDS (FH1082)											●		●						●													
COOMBE LAKE (FH1107)					●		●				●	●	●	●	●				●													
DANDYS & KNIGHTINGALE LAKES (FH1254)												●	●																			
DUNWEAR LAKES (FH1482)											●		●	●					●													
DURLEIGH RESERVOIR (FH1484)												●	●						●													
EDNEYS FISHERIES (FH1548)											●		●	●					●													
EMBOROUGH POOL (FH1582)													●						●													
EMBORUGH LAKE (FH1583)											●		●						●													
EMERALD POOL FISHERY (FH1585)					●					●	●		●	●	●			●	●													
EXE VALLEY FISHERY (FH1645)																											●					
FOLLY FOOT FARM (FH1755)										●																						
FOLLYFOOT FARM (FH1757)																																
FROME (RIVER) (FH1811)												●	●						●													
FROME (RIVER) (FH1810)													●																			
GLASTONBURY (FH1874)													●																			
GODNEY MOOR PONDS (FH1906)												●		●					●													
HAWKRIDGE RESERVOIR (FH2144)																								●			●					
HIGHLANDS DAIRY LAKE (FH2218)											●		●	●																		
HORNER WATER (FH2298)																								●								
HORSESHOE LAKE (FH2308)											●		●	●					●													
HOWLEY STREET POND (FH2320)											●		●																			
HUNSTRETE LAKE COMPLEX (FH2338)											●	●	●						●													
HUNTSPILL (RIVER) (FH2343)													●																			
HUTON POND (FH2350)													●	●					●													
ISLE (RIVER) (FH2393)												●		●					●													
ISLE (RIVER) (FH2394)											●	●																				
KENN (RIVER) (FH2433)											●	●	●	●					●													
KENNET AND AVON CANAL (FH2456)											●		●						●													
KENNET AND AVON CANAL (FH2457)											●		●						●													
KING SEDGEMOOR DRAIN (FH2490)					●						●	●	●	●					●													
LAKESIDE (FH2584)													●						●													
LANDS END FARM (FH2607)								●			●		●	●					●													
LANDS END FISHERIES (FH2608)											●		●																			

Fish Species Available at UK & Irish Fisheries

Fishery	Barbel	Bleak	Bream	Carp Blue	Carp Common	Carp Crucian	Carp Ghost	Carp Grass	Carp Koi	Carp Leather	Carp Mirror	Carp Silver	Carp Wild	Catfish	Catfish Albino	Catfish American Bullhead	Catfish Black Bullhead	Charr
LITTON RESERVOIR (FH2765)																		
LOWER LOVELYNCH FISHERIES (FH3089)					●						●							
MARK (RIVER) (FH3182)					●						●							
MARSTON LAKE (FH3195)					●						●							
MELLS PIT (FH3250)					●						●							
MINERS PONDS (FH3327)			●		●						●							
NEWTON PARK (FH3497)					●						●							
NEWTOWN LAKE (FH3499)			●		●						●							
OLD MILL FISHERY (FH3595)	●		●		●	●					●							
OTTERHEAD LAKES (FH3632)																		
OXENLEAZE FARM FISHERY (FH3666)			●		●	●					●							
PARRET (RIVER) (FH3706)																		
PARRETT (RIVER) (FH3709)			●		●						●							
PARRETT (RIVER) (FH3708)			●		●						●							
PARRETT (RIVER) (FH3710)			●		●						●							
PARRETT (RIVER) (FH3707)					●						●							
PAULTON LAKES (FH3718)								●			●							
PAWLETT PONDS (FH3719)			●		●	●		●			●							
PLANTATIONS LAKES (FH3798)	●				●	●					●							
QUANTOCK FISHERIES (FH3862)																		
SCREECH OWL PONDS (FH4123)					●						●							
SEDGES (FH4128)			●		●						●							
ST ALGARS FARM LAKE (FH4381)																		
STATHE DRAIN (FH4438)			●								●							
STONE YARD FISHERY (FH4470)					●						●							
SUMMERHAYES (FH4553)			●		●	●					●							
SUTTON BINGHAM RESERVOIR (FH4561)																		
TAUNTON AND BRIDGWATER CANAL (FH4665)			●															
TAUNTON ROAD PONDS (FH4666)			●		●						●							
TAUNTON TO BRIDGWATER CANAL (FH4667)			●															
THORNEY LAKES (FH4815)			●		●	●					●							
THURLEYBEARE POND (FH4836)			●		●						●							
TONE (RIVER) (FH4869)			●		●						●							
VIADUCT FISHERY (FH5095)			●		●	●	●				●							

Fishery	Chub	Dace	Eel	Flounder	Goldfish	Grayling	Grilse	Gudgeon	Gwyniad	Minnow	Orfe	Orfe Blue	Orfe Golden	Perch	Pike	Roach	Rudd	Ruffe	Salmon	Steelhead	Sturgeon	Tench	Tench Golden	Trount American Brook	Trout Blue	Trout Brook	Trout Brown	Trout Golden	Trout Lake	Ttrout Rainbow	Trout Sea	Trout Tiger	Trout Wild	Vendace	Zander
LITTON RESERVOIR (FH2765)																											●			●					
LOWER LOVELYNCH FISHERIES (FH3089)														●			●					●													
MARK (RIVER) (FH3182)	●													●	●	●						●													
MARSTON LAKE (FH3195)															●	●						●													
MELLS PIT (FH3250)																●	●																		
MINERS PONDS (FH3327)														●		●						●													
NEWTON PARK (FH3497)	●													●	●	●																			
NEWTOWN LAKE (FH3499)																						●													
OLD MILL FISHERY (FH3595)	●	●	●					●						●		●	●				●	●					●								
OTTERHEAD LAKES (FH3632)																											●			●					
OXENLEAZE FARM FISHERY (FH3666)																●	●					●													
PARRET (RIVER) (FH3706)		●														●											●								
PARRETT (RIVER) (FH3709)														●	●	●		●																	
PARRETT (RIVER) (FH3708)	●	●	●					●						●	●	●	●	●				●													
PARRETT (RIVER) (FH3710)	●		●											●	●	●						●													
PARRETT (RIVER) (FH3707)																																			
PAULTON LAKES (FH3718)	●															●						●													
PAWLETT PONDS (FH3719)			●											●		●	●					●													
PLANTATIONS LAKES (FH3798)	●															●																			
QUANTOCK FISHERIES (FH3862)																											●			●		●			
SCREECH OWL PONDS (FH4123)														●	●	●						●													
SEDGES (FH4128)			●											●		●	●					●													
ST ALGARS FARM LAKE (FH4381)																														●					
STATHE DRAIN (FH4438)			●											●	●	●	●					●													
STONE YARD FISHERY (FH4470)					●																	●													
SUMMERHAYES (FH4553)														●		●	●					●													
SUTTON BINGHAM RESERVOIR (FH4561)																											●			●					
TAUNTON AND BRIDGWATER CANAL (FH4665)														●		●	●					●													
TAUNTON ROAD PONDS (FH4666)																						●													
TAUNTON TO BRIDGWATER CANAL (FH4667)														●	●	●	●					●													
THORNEY LAKES (FH4815)	●	●	●					●		●				●		●	●					●													
THURLEYBEARE POND (FH4836)														●								●													
TONE (RIVER) (FH4869)			●											●	●	●																			
VIADUCT FISHERY (FH5095)			●											●		●	●					●													

Fish Species Available at UK & Irish Fisheries

	Barbel	Bleak	Bream	Carp Blue	Carp Common	Carp Crucian	Carp Ghost	Carp Grass	Carp Koi	Carp Leather	Carp Mirror	Carp Silver	Carp Wild	Catfish	Catfish Albino	Catfish American Bullhead	Catfish Black Bullhead	Charr	Chub	Dace	Eel	Flounder	Goldfish	Grayling	Grilse	Gudgeon	Gwyniad	Minnow	Orfe	Orfe Blue	Orfe Golden	Perch	Pike	Roach	Rudd	Ruffe	Salmon	Steelhead	Sturgeon	Tench	Tench Golden	Trount American Brook	Trout Blue	Trout Brook	Trout Brown	Trout Golden	Trout Lake	Ttrout Rainbow	Trout Sea	Trout Tiger	Trout Wild	Vendace	Zander
WELLINGTON BASIN (FH5240)			●		●																											●		●	●																		
WESTHAY LAKE (FH5280)					●						●																													●													
WITHAM FRIARY LAKE (FH5441)					●						●															●						●		●						●													
WOODBOROUGH PARK LAKE (FH5467)					●						●																					●		●						●													
WOOLBRIDGE MANOR (FH5499)																																					●																
WYCH LODGE LAKE (FH5526)			●		●						●																					●			●					●													
YEO (RIVER) (FH5564)					●						●									●						●								●						●													
YEO (RIVER) (FH5563)																										●								●											●								
STAFFORDSHIRE																																																					
ALBRIGHTON MOAT PROJECT (FH0051)					●	●					●																							●	●																		
ANKER (RIVER) (FH0111)			●																	●																																	
ASHLEY POOLS (FH0165)			●		●						●								●													●		●						●													
BADEN HALL FISHERY (FH0245)	●		●		●					●	●								●		●					●						●		●						●													
BASFORD COARSE FISHERY (FH0340)			●		●						●																					●		●	●					●													
BIDDULPH GRANGE (FH0409)			●		●						●																					●		●	●					●													
BLACK LAKE (FH0443)						●																											●	●																			
BLACKSHAW FARM LAKES (FH0454)			●		●						●																							●						●													
BLACKWOOD POOL (FH0483)			●		●	●				●	●															●						●		●	●					●													
BLITHE (RIVER) (FH0501)																			●																										●								
BLITHFIELD RESERVOIR (FH0502)																																	●												●								
BORROWPIT LAKE (FH0554)			●		●						●															●						●		●						●													
BROWNING CUDMORE FISHERY (FH0702)	●		●		●	●					●								●													●	●	●	●					●													
CHURNET (RIVER) (FH0962)																																													●			●					
CHURNET (RIVER) (FH0963)																			●	●																									●								
CHURNET (RIVER) (FH0961)																			●					●																					●								
CONSALL NATURE PARK (FH1091)					●						●			●																		●		●	●					●													
COVENTRY CANAL (FH1145)																																●		●																			
COVENTRY CANAL (FH1144)																																●		●																			
DEEP HAYES COUNTRY PARK (FH1322)					●						●																					●	●	●	●					●													
DILHORNE HALL POOLS (FH1367)			●		●					●	●																													●													
DOVE (RIVER) (FH1427)	●																		●	●				●																													
DOVE (RIVER) (FH1426)	●		●																●	●				●								●	●	●																			
DOVE (RIVER) (FH1425)																								●																					●								
DOVE (RIVER) (FH1428)	●																		●	●				●																													

Fish Species Available at UK & Irish Fisheries

Fishery	Barbel	Bleak	Bream	Carp Blue	Carp Common	Carp Crucian	Carp Ghost	Carp Grass	Carp Koi	Carp Leather	Carp Mirror	Carp Silver	Carp Wild	Catfish	Catfish Albino	Catfish American Bullhead	Catfish Black Bullhead	Charr
DRAYTON BRIDGE (FH1439)					●						●							
ELLENHALL NINE POOLS (FH1564)					●						●							
FISHERWICK LAKES (FH1732)	●		●		●	●		●			●							
GAILEY TROUT AND PIKE FISHERY (FH1828)					●						●							
HAMPS (RIVER) (FH2081)																		
HAMSTALL FISHERY (FH2097)			●		●						●							
HANCHURCH FISHERIES (FH2099)			●		●	●					●							
HEDNESFORD ROAD LAKE (FH2177)			●		●	●					●							
HERONBROOK FISHERY (FH2191)			●		●						●							
HIMLEY HALL AND PARK LAKE (FH2230)			●		●	●		●			●							
HOLDEN LANE POOL (FH2249)			●		●						●							
HORNS (FH2300)			●		●	●					●							
IZAAK WALTON FISHERY (FH2404)		●	●		●	●	●			●	●			●				
KNYPERSLEY RESERVOIR (FH2544)			●		●						●							
LITTLETONS AND MIDDLE POOL (FH2764)			●		●						●							
LOYNTON TROUT FISHERIES (FH3100)																		
MADELEY POOL (FH3134)			●		●						●							
MIDLAND GAME FISHERIES (FH3272)					●													
PARKES HALL (FH3702)					●													
PILLATON POOLS (FH3772)			●		●	●					●							
PINE POOL (FH3778)			●		●						●							
POOL HOUSE FARM (FH3820)			●		●	●					●							
RUDYARD LAKE (FH4052)			●															
SHROPSHIRE UNION CANAL (FH4256)																		
SHROPSHIRE UNION CANAL (FH4254)			●															
SHROPSHIRE UNION CANAL (FH4257)			●															
SHROPSHIRE UNION CANAL (FH4260)			●		●						●							
SHROPSHIRE UNION CANAL (FH4255)																		
SHROPSHIRE UNION CANAL (FH4259)			●															
SIDEWAY OVERFLOW (FH4265)			●		●						●							
SMITH POOL (FH4305)					●													
SMITHPOOL LAKE (FH4307)			●		●						●							
SOUTH POPLARS (FH4337)			●		●	●	●				●							
SOW (RIVER) (FH4355)			●															

Fishery	Chub	Dace	Eel	Flounder	Goldfish	Grayling	Grilse	Gudgeon	Gwyniad	Minnow	Orfe	Orfe Blue	Orfe Golden	Perch	Pike	Roach	Rudd
DRAYTON BRIDGE (FH1439)														●			
ELLENHALL NINE POOLS (FH1564)																	
FISHERWICK LAKES (FH1732)	●	●	●					●						●	●	●	●
GAILEY TROUT AND PIKE FISHERY (FH1828)															●		
HAMPS (RIVER) (FH2081)																	
HAMSTALL FISHERY (FH2097)	●													●		●	●
HANCHURCH FISHERIES (FH2099)	●							●						●		●	●
HEDNESFORD ROAD LAKE (FH2177)								●						●	●	●	
HERONBROOK FISHERY (FH2191)	●													●		●	
HIMLEY HALL AND PARK LAKE (FH2230)														●	●	●	
HOLDEN LANE POOL (FH2249)	●													●	●	●	
HORNS (FH2300)														●	●	●	●
IZAAK WALTON FISHERY (FH2404)	●	●	●					●		●	●			●	●	●	●
KNYPERSLEY RESERVOIR (FH2544)														●	●	●	
LITTLETONS AND MIDDLE POOL (FH2764)														●		●	
LOYNTON TROUT FISHERIES (FH3100)																	
MADELEY POOL (FH3134)								●						●		●	●
MIDLAND GAME FISHERIES (FH3272)																●	
PARKES HALL (FH3702)																●	
PILLATON POOLS (FH3772)			●											●		●	●
PINE POOL (FH3778)															●		
POOL HOUSE FARM (FH3820)	●							●						●		●	●
RUDYARD LAKE (FH4052)														●	●	●	
SHROPSHIRE UNION CANAL (FH4256)								●						●		●	
SHROPSHIRE UNION CANAL (FH4254)																●	
SHROPSHIRE UNION CANAL (FH4257)																●	
SHROPSHIRE UNION CANAL (FH4260)	●							●						●		●	
SHROPSHIRE UNION CANAL (FH4255)								●								●	
SHROPSHIRE UNION CANAL (FH4259)	●							●						●		●	
SIDEWAY OVERFLOW (FH4265)																●	●
SMITH POOL (FH4305)																●	
SMITHPOOL LAKE (FH4307)																●	
SOUTH POPLARS (FH4337)											●					●	●
SOW (RIVER) (FH4355)																	

Fishery	Ruffe	Salmon	Steelhead	Sturgeon	Tench	Tench Golden	Trount American Brook	Trout Blue	Trout Brook	Trout Brown	Trout Golden	Trout Lake	Ttrout Rainbow	Trout Sea	Trout Tiger	Trout Wild	Vendace	Zander
DRAYTON BRIDGE (FH1439)																		●
ELLENHALL NINE POOLS (FH1564)																		
FISHERWICK LAKES (FH1732)					●					●			●					
GAILEY TROUT AND PIKE FISHERY (FH1828)							●			●	●	●	●		●			
HAMPS (RIVER) (FH2081)										●								
HAMSTALL FISHERY (FH2097)					●													
HANCHURCH FISHERIES (FH2099)					●					●			●					
HEDNESFORD ROAD LAKE (FH2177)					●													
HERONBROOK FISHERY (FH2191)																		
HIMLEY HALL AND PARK LAKE (FH2230)					●													
HOLDEN LANE POOL (FH2249)					●													
HORNS (FH2300)					●													
IZAAK WALTON FISHERY (FH2404)					●				●	●								
KNYPERSLEY RESERVOIR (FH2544)																		
LITTLETONS AND MIDDLE POOL (FH2764)					●													
LOYNTON TROUT FISHERIES (FH3100)										●			●					
MADELEY POOL (FH3134)					●													
MIDLAND GAME FISHERIES (FH3272)																		
PARKES HALL (FH3702)																		
PILLATON POOLS (FH3772)					●													
PINE POOL (FH3778)																		
POOL HOUSE FARM (FH3820)					●													
RUDYARD LAKE (FH4052)																		
SHROPSHIRE UNION CANAL (FH4256)																		
SHROPSHIRE UNION CANAL (FH4254)																		
SHROPSHIRE UNION CANAL (FH4257)																		
SHROPSHIRE UNION CANAL (FH4260)																		
SHROPSHIRE UNION CANAL (FH4255)																		
SHROPSHIRE UNION CANAL (FH4259)																		
SIDEWAY OVERFLOW (FH4265)																		
SMITH POOL (FH4305)																		
SMITHPOOL LAKE (FH4307)																		
SOUTH POPLARS (FH4337)					●													
SOW (RIVER) (FH4355)																		

Fish Species Available at UK & Irish Fisheries

Fishery	Barbel	Bleak	Bream	Carp Blue	Carp Common	Carp Crucian	Carp Ghost	Carp Grass	Carp Koi	Carp Leather	Carp Mirror	Carp Silver	Carp Wild	Catfish	Catfish Albino	Catfish American Bullhead	Catfish Black Bullhead	Charr	Chub	Dace	Eel	Flounder	Goldfish	Grayling	Grilse	Gudgeon	Gwyniad	Minnow	Orfe	Orfe Blue	Orfe Golden	Perch	Pike	Roach	Rudd	Ruffe	Salmon	Steelhead	Sturgeon	Tench	Tench Golden	Trount American Brook	Trout Blue	Trout Brook	Trout Brown	Trout Golden	Trout Lake	Ttrout Rainbow	Trout Sea	Trout Tiger	Trout Wild	Vendace	Zander
STAFFORD AND WORCESTER CANAL (FH4401)			●																															●																							
STAFFORD AND WORCESTER CANAL (FH4400)			●		●						●								●						●						●	●	●		●																				
STAFFORD AND WORCESTER CANAL (FH4399)																									●								●																						
STAFFORD TO WORCESTER CANAL (FH4405)					●						●																●						●		●																					
STANLEY RESERVOIR (FH4422)			●																												●	●	●																						
SWAN PIT POOL (FH4594)			●		●						●								●															●	●					●													
SWARBORN (RIVER) (FH4603)																				●																																			
TAME (RIVER) (FH4647)																				●																																			
TITTESWORTH RESERVOIR (FH4858)																																														●			●						
TRENT (RIVER) (FH4937)																																					●								●									
TRENT (RIVER) (FH4935)	●																				●	●						●									●																						
TRENT (RIVER) (FH4936)	●		●																		●	●												●		●																						
TRENT AND MERSEY CANAL (FH4945)			●		●						●																				●	●	●	●																				
TRENT AND MERSEY CANAL (FH4941)			●		●						●								●						●						●		●		●																				
TRENTHAM GARDENS (FH4948)			●		●																																																	
WADE LAKE (FH5110)			●		●						●																				●	●		●					●													
WILLOWS POOLS (FH5401)			●		●						●																				●		●						●													
SUFFOLK																																																						
ALDE (RIVER) (FH0056)																					●																																		
ALDEBY HALL FARM PITS (FH0057)					●						●																							●						●													
ALDERSONS LAKES (FH0065)			●		●						●																							●						●													
ALTON WATER RESERVOIR (FH0088)			●																			●												●	●	●		●				●													
BARHAM A PIT (FH0306)			●		●						●																				●	●	●	●					●													
BARHAM B PIT (FH0307)			●		●						●																				●	●	●						●													
BECCLES QUAY (FH0360)			●																													●	●																					
BLUE WATERS (FH0511)			●																													●																							
BREAKAWAY PIT (FH0609)			●		●						●																				●	●	●						●													
BRIDGE FARM RESERVOIRS (FH0630)			●																			●											●	●	●	●					●													
BROOME PITS (FH0693)			●		●	●				●									●	●					●					●	●	●	●					●													
BUNGAY (RIVER) (FH0732)			●																	●														●	●	●						●													
CAMELOT LAKE (FH0813)			●		●	●	●				●			●					●		●												●		●						●													
CAUSEWAY LAKES (FH0876)			●		●						●								●		●												●	●	●						●													
CHESTERFORD FISHERIES (FH0933)					●						●																				●	●	●						●					●							
CLARE PARK LAKE (FH0975)			●		●						●																					●						●													

Fish Species Available at UK & Irish Fisheries

Fishery	Barbel	Bleak	Bream	Carp Blue	Carp Common	Carp Crucian	Carp Ghost	Carp Grass	Carp Koi	Carp Leather	Carp Mirror	Carp Silver	Carp Wild	Catfish	Catfish Albino	Catfish American Bullhead	Catfish Black Bullhead	Charr	Chub	Dace	Eel	Flounder	Goldfish	Grayling	Grilse	Gudgeon	Gwyniad	Minnow	Orfe	Orfe Blue	Orfe Golden	Perch	Pike	Roach	Rudd	Ruffe	Salmon	Steelhead	Sturgeon	Tench	Tench Golden	Trount American Brook	Trout Blue	Trout Brook	Trout Brown	Trout Golden	Trout Lake	Ttrout Rainbow	Trout Sea	Trout Tiger	Trout Wild	Vendace	Zander
CLICKETTS HILL AND PLANTATION (FH1005)	●		●																●	●												●	●	●						●													●
CLUB PIT (FH1028)			●		●	●					●																					●		●	●					●													
CROSS DROVE (FH1191)			●		●	●					●																					●		●	●					●													
CROSS GREEN FLY FISHERY (FH1192)											●																																		●			●					
DEBEN (RIVER) (FH1293)																																●	●	●						●													
DITCHINGHAM PIT (FH1379)			●		●						●																					●	●	●	●					●													
FLIXTON DECOY (FH1748)			●																													●			●					●													
FLOOD PARK (FH1749)			●		●	●					●															●			●			●		●	●					●													
GIPPING (RIVER) (FH1861)																			●													●	●	●	●																		
GIPPING (RIVER) (FH1865)					●						●																					●	●	●	●																		
GIPPING (RIVER) (FH1860)																			●													●	●	●	●																		
GIPPING (RIVER) (FH1863)																			●		●											●	●	●																			
GIPPING (RIVER) (FH1864)					●						●								●													●	●	●	●																		
GIPPING (RIVER) (FH1862)																			●													●	●	●	●																		
HATCHERY HOUSE TROUT LAKES (FH2127)																																																●					
HIGHFIELD FISHERY (FH2216)			●		●	●					●								●							●						●		●	●					●													
HOLTON PIT (FH2273)			●		●	●					●																							●	●					●													
HOMERSFIELD (RIVER) (FH2283)																				●												●	●	●						●													
HOMERSFIELD LAKE (FH2284)					●						●			●																		●		●	●																		
LARK (RIVER) (FH2624)		●	●		●						●								●	●	●					●						●	●	●	●	●				●					●								
LARK (RIVER) (FH2623)			●		●						●								●	●	●					●						●	●	●	●					●					●								
LARKWOOD TROUT FISHERY (FH2626)																																													●			●					
LAYZELLS FARM (FH2640)			●		●						●								●	●	●											●	●	●						●													●
LITTLE BEVILLS ESTATE (FH2740)			●																●	●	●											●	●	●						●													●
LITTLE OUSE (RIVER) (FH2758)						●														●																																	
LOAM POND (FH2833)			●		●						●																					●		●						●													
MARSH FARM LAKES (FH3191)			●		●	●	●			●	●																					●		●	●					●													
MELDUM WASHLANDS (FLOODPARK) (FH3247)			●		●	●					●															●						●		●	●					●													
MILLERS LAKE (FH3310)						●																																															
NEEDHAM LAKE (FH3435)			●		●						●																					●	●	●	●					●													
NORTH MEADOWS (FH3531)			●		●						●								●	●						●							●	●						●													●
OULTON BROAD (FH3634)			●																		●												●	●																			
OULTON DYKE (FH3635)			●																		●											●		●																			
REYDON LAKES (FH3934)					●						●																							●	●					●													

www.fishooked.com

FISH SPECIES AVAILABLE

England (by County)

Fish Species Available at UK & Irish Fisheries

Fishery	Barbel	Bleak	Bream	Carp Blue	Carp Common	Carp Crucian	Carp Ghost	Carp Grass	Carp Koi	Carp Leather	Carp Mirror	Carp Silver	Carp Wild	Catfish	Catfish Albino	Catfish American Bullhead	Catfish Black Bullhead	Charr	Chub	Dace	Eel	Flounder	Goldfish	Grayling	Grilse	Gudgeon	Gwyniad	Minnow	Orfe	Orfe Blue	Orfe Golden	Perch	Pike	Roach	Rudd	Ruffe	Salmon	Steelhead	Sturgeon	Tench	Tench Golden	Trount American Brook	Trout Blue	Trout Brook	Trout Brown	Trout Golden	Trout Lake	Ttrout Rainbow	Trout Sea	Trout Tiger	Trout Wild	Vendace	Zander
SINKS PIT (FH4277)					●	●					●																					●		●						●													
STANTONS FARM RESERVOIR (FH4424)			●		●						●																					●		●	●					●													
STARFIELD PIT (FH4431)			●			●					●																							●						●													
STOUR (RIVER) (FH4500)	●		●																●	●	●					●						●	●	●						●													
STOUR (RIVER) (FH4501)			●		●						●								●	●												●	●	●						●													●
STOW (RIVER) (FH4511)	●		●		●						●								●	●												●	●	●						●													
STOW (RIVER) (FH4509)			●		●						●								●	●						●						●	●	●						●													●
STOW (RIVER) (FH4508)			●		●						●								●	●	●					●						●	●	●						●													●
STOW (RIVER) (FH4510)			●		●						●								●	●	●											●	●	●						●													●
STOW (RIVER) (FH4512)			●		●						●								●	●						●						●	●	●						●													●
SWALE PIT (FH4588)			●		●						●																																										
THET (RIVER) (FH4809)																				●													●	●																			
WAVENEY (RIVER) (FH5191)			●																●	●												●	●	●	●					●													
WAVENEY VALLEY LAKES (FH5192)			●		●	●					●										●											●	●	●	●					●													
WEST STOW COUNTRY PARK (FH5266)					●						●																													●													
WICKHAM MARKET RESERVOIRS (FH5365)			●																		●											●	●	●	●					●													
WILLOW LAKES TROUT FISHERY (FH5385)																																													●			●					
WRIGHTS FARM (FH5517)	●		●		●						●								●	●	●					●						●	●	●		●				●													●
WYE (RIVER) (FH5543)																																				●																
YEW TREE FISHERIES (FH5567)					●						●			●																																						
SURREY																																																					
ALBURY ESTATE FISHERIES (FH0052)																																													●			●					
ALDERBROOK LAKE (FH0060)					●						●																							●																			
ALFORD ROAD FISHERIES (FH0075)			●		●						●																							●	●					●													
BADSHOT LEA (FH0247)			●		●						●			●																				●						●													
BEAVER FARM FISHERY (FH0359)	●		●		●	●	●	●			●			●					●	●	●					●						●	●	●	●				●	●													
BOLDERMERE (FH0529)			●		●						●																					●	●	●						●													●
BRITTENS POND (FH0658)					●	●	●				●																					●		●	●					●													
BROADWATER LAKE (FH0666)						●																																															
BURY HILL FISHERIES (FH0764)			●		●	●	●				●								●													●	●	●	●	●				●													●
BUSBRIDGE LAKE (FH0765)			●		●	●					●																					●	●	●	●					●													
BUSHEY PARK (FH0769)					●																●											●	●	●						●													
CHERTSEY (FH0916)			●		●						●								●	●	●					●						●	●	●						●													
CROSSWATER MILL FISHERY (FH1194)																																													●			●		●			

Fish Species Available at UK & Irish Fisheries

Fishery	Barbel	Bleak	Bream	Carp Blue	Carp Common	Carp Crucian	Carp Ghost	Carp Grass	Carp Koi	Carp Leather	Carp Mirror	Carp Silver	Carp Wild	Catfish	Catfish Albino	Catfish American Bullhead	Catfish Black Bullhead	Charr	Chub	Dace	Eel	Flounder	Goldfish	Grayling	Grilse	Gudgeon	Gwyniad	Minnow	Orfe	Orfe Blue	Orfe Golden	Perch	Pike	Roach	Rudd	Ruffe	Salmon	Steelhead	Sturgeon	Tench	Tench Golden	Trount American Brook	Trout Blue	Trout Brook	Trout Brown	Trout Golden	Trout Lake	Ttrout Rainbow	Trout Sea	Trout Tiger	Trout Wild	Vendace	Zander
DEE (RIVER) (FH1317)																																					●								●								
EAST WHIPLEY RESERVOIR (FH1517)											●															●						●		●	●																		
ENTON LAKES TROUT FISHERY (FH1596)																																																●					
EPSOM STEW POND (FH1604)			●		●		●				●																					●	●	●						●													
FRENSHAM TROUT FISHERY (FH1800)																																													●			●		●			
FURZE FARM (FH1824)			●		●																					●						●		●	●					●													
GATTON MANOR LAKES (FH1842)			●		●						●																						●		●					●													
GOLDSWORTH WATER PARK (FH1916)			●		●						●																					●	●	●	●					●													
HENFOLD LAKES FISHERY (FH2182)					●	●	●				●								●							●						●		●	●					●	●												
HOME PARK (FH2282)					●																●											●	●	●						●													
JOHNSONS LAKE (FH2415)					●	●					●																					●		●	●					●													
KINGFISHER FISHERY (FH2495)			●		●	●					●								●													●		●	●					●					●			●					
LAKESIDE (FH2586)					●						●																					●		●																			
LONG COPSE PONDS (FH2982)					●	●					●																					●		●	●					●													
MANOR POND (FH3170)			●		●	●					●																					●	●	●	●					●													
MILL POND (FH3299)			●																														●	●	●					●													
MOLE (RIVER) (FH3338)			●																●	●	●					●						●	●	●						●													
MOLE (RIVER) (FH3339)	●																		●	●																																	
NAVIES HOLE (FH3430)			●		●	●					●																					●		●	●					●													
ONE ISLAND POND (FH3612)					●						●																					●	●	●	●					●													
PAINSHILL PARK LAKE (FH3685)		●	●		●		●			●	●								●	●	●					●		●				●	●	●	●	●				●													
PAPERCOURT FISHERY (FH3694)			●		●						●										●											●	●	●						●													
PUDDENHOLE POND (FH3854)			●		●						●																							●						●													
RUSHMOOR LAKES (FH4063)			●		●	●	●	●	●	●	●			●					●	●						●		●	●			●			●					●					●								
SEVEN ISLANDS (FH4140)					●						●																					●	●	●	●					●													
SHAWFIELDS LAKES (FH4213)					●	●					●																					●		●						●													
ST PATRICKS LANE CARP LAKES (FH4396)					●						●																																										
STOCKBRIDGE POND (FH4460)						●																												●						●													
THAMES (RIVER) (FH4804)			●																														●																				
THORPE PARK WATERSKI LAKE (FH4824)			●								●																						●							●													
TWYNERSH FISHING COMPLEX (FH5012)			●		●		●	●			●								●	●	●					●						●	●	●	●					●													
WAGGONERS WELLS (FH5112)					●						●																					●		●						●					●								
WEY (RIVER) (FH5290)																																													●			●					
WEY (RIVER) (FH5291)			●																●		●					●						●	●	●						●													

Fish Species Available at UK & Irish Fisheries

	Barbel	Bleak	Bream	Carp Blue	Carp Common	Carp Crucian	Carp Ghost	Carp Grass	Carp Koi	Carp Leather	Carp Mirror	Carp Silver	Carp Wild	Catfish	Catfish Albino	Catfish American Bullhead	Catfish Black Bullhead	Charr	Chub	Dace	Eel	Flounder	Goldfish	Grayling	Grilse	Gudgeon	Gwyniad	Minnow	Orfe	Orfe Blue	Orfe Golden	Perch	Pike	Roach	Rudd	Ruffe	Salmon	Steelhead	Sturgeon	Tench	Tench Golden	Trount American Brook	Trout Blue	Trout Brook	Trout Brown	Trout Golden	Trout Lake	Ttrout Rainbow	Trout Sea	Trout Tiger	Trout Wild	Vendace	Zander
WEY NAVIGATION (RIVER) (FH5292)	●				●						●								●	●	●					●						●	●	●						●													
WHIPLEY MANOR (FH5325)			●		●				●		●			●					●	●												●		●	●					●													
WHITEVANE POND (FH5354)			●		●	●	●			●	●																					●		●	●					●													
WILLINGHURST COARSE FISHERY (FH5373)					●						●																																										
WILLINGHURST TROUT FISHERY (FH5374)																																													●								
WYPHURST AND HYHURST LAKES (FH5547)			●		●						●																					●		●						●													
SUSSEX (EAST)																																																					
ALEXANDRA PARK WATERS (FH0074)			●		●					●	●																						●	●	●					●													
ARLINGTON TROUT FISHERY (FH0137)																																																●					
BALLS GREEN LAKES (FH0272)					●		●				●																					●		●	●					●													
BARCOMBE RESERVOIR (FH0303)																																																●					
BELFREY COARSE FISHERY (FH0375)					●						●								●															●						●													
BEVERN STREAM (FH0401)	●		●		●			●			●							●		●	●											●	●	●	●					●					●				●				
BORINGWHEEL TROUT FISHERY (FH0551)																																																●					
BRICK FARM LAKE (FH0620)																																													●			●					
BROOMHAM FISHERY (FH0695)						●																										●		●	●					●													
BUXTED OAST FISHERY (FH0780)					●	●					●																							●						●													
BUXTED PARK FISHERY (FH0781)					●						●								●													●		●	●					●													
CLAREMONT LAKE (FH0976)					●						●																					●	●	●																			
CLIVE VALE RESERVOIRS (FH1010)					●						●								●													●		●	●					●													
COGHURST HALL (FH1053)			●		●						●																					●		●	●					●													
COLIN GODMANS TROUTING (FH1062)																																													●			●					
CUCKMERE (RIVER) (FH1209)			●																														●							●													
DARWELL WATER (FH1279)																																	●												●			●					
DECOY LAKE (FH1296)					●						●																								●																		
FALKENVIL FISHERY (FH1658)					●						●								●															●						●	●												
FRAMFIELD PARK FISHERIES (FH1797)			●		●	●		●			●			●							●											●		●	●					●													
FURNACE BROOK FISHERY (FH1820)			●		●			●			●																					●		●	●					●					●								
HOLTS LAKES (FH2274)	●					●					●								●		●					●						●		●	●					●													
HONEYS GREEN COARSE FISHERY (FH2286)	●				●	●					●															●						●		●	●					●													
HORAM MANOR FISHERY (FH2294)			●		●	●				●	●									●	●					●		●				●		●	●					●					●						●		
IDEN WOOD FISHERY (FH2358)			●		●						●										●					●						●		●	●					●													
ISFIELD (RIVER) (FH2385)																																													●								
LAKEDOWN TROUT FISHERY (FH2575)																																													●			●					

Fish Species Available at UK & Irish Fisheries

Fishery	Barbel	Bleak	Bream	Carp Blue	Carp Common	Carp Crucian	Carp Ghost	Carp Grass	Carp Koi	Carp Leather	Carp Mirror	Carp Silver	Carp Wild
LEABRIDGE FARM (FH2650)					●								
MICHELHAM PRIORY MOAT (FH3260)			●		●						●		●
MOOR HALL POOL (FH3357)					●						●		
OLD IRON (RIVER) (FH3587)					●						●		
OLD MILL (FH3593)	●		●		●	●		●			●		
OLIVES FARM FISHERY (FH3609)			●		●						●		
OUSE (RIVER) (FH3645)	●		●		●			●			●		
PENNY BRIDGE (FH3741)			●			●							
PETT POOLS (FH3759)			●		●						●		
PIPPINGFORD PARK ESTATE LAKES (FH3786)			●		●	●				●	●		
POWDERMILL (FH3838)													
ROSEBANK FARM FISHERY (FH4012)			●		●	●					●		
ROTHER (RIVER) (FH4027)													
RYE NOOK FISHERY (FH4075)			●		●						●		
SCALAND WOOD (FH4110)					●	●					●		
SHARNFOLD FARM FISHERY (FH4210)	●		●										
SOUTHBOURNE LAKE (FH4349)			●		●						●		
SPRING WOOD FISHERY AND FARM (FH4372)			●		●	●		●			●		
ST IVES FARM (FH4388)			●		●	●							
SWANBOROUGH LAKES (FH4597)			●		●	●	●	●			●		
TANYARD FISHERIES (FH4654)	●		●		●	●	●	●	●	●	●		
VINEHALL SCHOOL LAKE (FH5099)					●						●		
WALLERS HAVEN (FH5123)			●										
WEIR WOOD FISHERY (FH5227)			●		●						●		
WISHING TREE RESERVOIR (FH5434)					●						●		
WOODMANCOTE PLACE FISHERY (FH5487)					●								
WYLANDS CENTRE (FH5545)	●				●	●		●			●		
YEW TREE TROUT FISHERY (FH5570)													
SUSSEX (WEST)													
ADUR (RIVER) (FH0034)					●						●		
ADUR (RIVER) (FH0032)			●		●						●		
ADUR (RIVER) (FH0031)			●		●						●		
ADUR (RIVER) (FH0033)			●										
ADUR (RIVER) (FH0030)					●						●		

Fishery	Catfish	Catfish Albino	Catfish American Bullhead	Catfish Black Bullhead	Charr	Chub	Dace	Eel	Flounder	Goldfish	Grayling	Grilse	Gudgeon	Gwyniad	Minnow	Orfe	Orfe Blue	Orfe Golden
LEABRIDGE FARM (FH2650)																		
MICHELHAM PRIORY MOAT (FH3260)						●		●										
MOOR HALL POOL (FH3357)								●										
OLD IRON (RIVER) (FH3587)																		
OLD MILL (FH3593)						●	●	●					●		●			
OLIVES FARM FISHERY (FH3609)								●										
OUSE (RIVER) (FH3645)						●	●	●					●		●			
PENNY BRIDGE (FH3741)																		
PETT POOLS (FH3759)								●										
PIPPINGFORD PARK ESTATE LAKES (FH3786)						●		●								●		
POWDERMILL (FH3838)																		
ROSEBANK FARM FISHERY (FH4012)								●					●					
ROTHER (RIVER) (FH4027)						●	●											
RYE NOOK FISHERY (FH4075)	●						●											
SCALAND WOOD (FH4110)																		
SHARNFOLD FARM FISHERY (FH4210)						●												
SOUTHBOURNE LAKE (FH4349)								●										
SPRING WOOD FISHERY AND FARM (FH4372)																		
ST IVES FARM (FH4388)						●												
SWANBOROUGH LAKES (FH4597)						●							●			●		
TANYARD FISHERIES (FH4654)	●					●		●					●			●		
VINEHALL SCHOOL LAKE (FH5099)																		
WALLERS HAVEN (FH5123)																		
WEIR WOOD FISHERY (FH5227)								●										
WISHING TREE RESERVOIR (FH5434)																		
WOODMANCOTE PLACE FISHERY (FH5487)																		
WYLANDS CENTRE (FH5545)	●					●		●										
YEW TREE TROUT FISHERY (FH5570)																		
SUSSEX (WEST)																		
ADUR (RIVER) (FH0034)																		
ADUR (RIVER) (FH0032)						●							●					
ADUR (RIVER) (FH0031)						●	●											
ADUR (RIVER) (FH0033)						●		●										
ADUR (RIVER) (FH0030)								●										

Fishery	Perch	Pike	Roach	Rudd	Ruffe	Salmon	Steelhead	Sturgeon	Tench	Tench Golden	Trount American Brook	Trout Blue	Trout Brook	Trout Brown	Trout Golden	Trout Lake	Ttrout Rainbow	Trout Sea	Trout Tiger	Trout Wild	Vendace	Zander
LEABRIDGE FARM (FH2650)																						
MICHELHAM PRIORY MOAT (FH3260)	●	●	●	●					●													
MOOR HALL POOL (FH3357)	●		●	●					●													
OLD IRON (RIVER) (FH3587)				●					●													
OLD MILL (FH3593)	●	●	●	●					●					●			●	●				
OLIVES FARM FISHERY (FH3609)	●	●	●	●					●													
OUSE (RIVER) (FH3645)	●	●	●	●					●					●				●				
PENNY BRIDGE (FH3741)	●		●	●					●													
PETT POOLS (FH3759)	●		●	●					●													
PIPPINGFORD PARK ESTATE LAKES (FH3786)	●	●	●						●													
POWDERMILL (FH3838)														●			●			●		
ROSEBANK FARM FISHERY (FH4012)			●	●					●													
ROTHER (RIVER) (FH4027)														●								
RYE NOOK FISHERY (FH4075)	●		●	●					●					●								
SCALAND WOOD (FH4110)	●		●						●													
SHARNFOLD FARM FISHERY (FH4210)	●		●	●					●													
SOUTHBOURNE LAKE (FH4349)	●	●	●	●					●													
SPRING WOOD FISHERY AND FARM (FH4372)	●		●	●					●					●			●					
ST IVES FARM (FH4388)	●			●					●													
SWANBOROUGH LAKES (FH4597)			●	●					●													
TANYARD FISHERIES (FH4654)	●	●	●	●	●				●													
VINEHALL SCHOOL LAKE (FH5099)				●					●													
WALLERS HAVEN (FH5123)	●	●	●						●													
WEIR WOOD FISHERY (FH5227)		●	●	●										●								
WISHING TREE RESERVOIR (FH5434)	●		●						●													
WOODMANCOTE PLACE FISHERY (FH5487)																						
WYLANDS CENTRE (FH5545)	●		●	●					●													
YEW TREE TROUT FISHERY (FH5570)														●			●					
SUSSEX (WEST)																						
ADUR (RIVER) (FH0034)			●						●					●								
ADUR (RIVER) (FH0032)	●	●	●	●					●													
ADUR (RIVER) (FH0031)		●	●															●				
ADUR (RIVER) (FH0033)	●	●	●																			
ADUR (RIVER) (FH0030)	●	●												●				●				

Fish Species Available at UK & Irish Fisheries

Fishery	Barbel	Bleak	Bream	Carp Blue	Carp Common	Carp Crucian	Carp Ghost	Carp Grass	Carp Koi	Carp Leather	Carp Mirror	Carp Silver	Carp Wild	Catfish	Catfish Albino	Catfish American Bullhead	Catfish Black Bullhead	Charr
ALDERWOOD PONDS (FH0066)					●	●	●		●	●	●							
ARDINGLY RESERVOIR (FH0129)			●		●						●							
ARUN (RIVER) (FH0150)			●															
ARUN (RIVER) (FH0152)	●	●	●		●													
ARUN (RIVER) (FH0153)			●		●						●							
ARUN (RIVER) (FH0149)																		
ARUN (RIVER) (FH0148)		●	●															
ARUN (RIVER) (FH0144)			●		●						●							
ARUN (RIVER) (FH0151)			●		●						●							
ARUN (RIVER) (FH0146)			●															
BALCOMBE LAKE (FH0256)			●		●						●							
BLACKWOOL TROUT FISHERY (FH0484)																		
BOLEBROOK CASTLE (FH0531)					●			●			●							
BORDE HILL GARDEN LAKES (FH0544)					●						●							
CASTLE TROUT POND (FH0865)																		
CHALK SPRINGS TROUT FISHERY (FH0891)																		
DAYLANDS FARM (FH1283)					●						●							
DUNCANS POND (FH1472)					●						●							
DUNCTON MILL (FH1473)																		
FURNACE LAKES (FH1821)			●		●	●	●			●	●			●				
HAMBROOK TROUT FISHERY (FH2080)																		
HAYWARDS HEATH RIVER (FH2161)																		
HAZELCOPSE LAKES (FH2163)																		
HURSTON LANE (FH2347)					●	●					●							
LAYBROOK LAKES (FH2638)					●						●							
LECONFIELD ESTATE (FH2658)																		
MENARDS LAKE (FH3254)					●						●							
MILL FARM FISHERY (FH3283)			●		●	●	●				●							
NEW POND (FH3475)			●		●	●					●							
NEWELLS FISHERIES (FH3483)					●	●	●			●	●							
PASSIES PONDS (FH3715)	●		●		●	●					●							
PILTDOWN POND (FH3774)					●						●							
ROTHER (RIVER) (FH4028)	●	●	●		●						●							
ROTHER (RIVER) (FH4029)																		

Fishery	Chub	Dace	Eel	Flounder	Goldfish	Grayling	Grilse	Gudgeon	Gwyniad	Minnow	Orfe	Orfe Blue	Orfe Golden	Perch	Pike	Roach	Rudd
ALDERWOOD PONDS (FH0066)								●			●			●		●	●
ARDINGLY RESERVOIR (FH0129)			●					●						●	●	●	●
ARUN (RIVER) (FH0150)	●	●	●											●	●	●	●
ARUN (RIVER) (FH0152)	●	●	●					●								●	
ARUN (RIVER) (FH0153)	●		●											●	●	●	
ARUN (RIVER) (FH0149)	●	●												●	●		
ARUN (RIVER) (FH0148)	●	●						●						●	●	●	
ARUN (RIVER) (FH0144)	●		●											●	●	●	
ARUN (RIVER) (FH0151)	●	●	●					●						●	●	●	●
ARUN (RIVER) (FH0146)		●														●	
BALCOMBE LAKE (FH0256)														●	●	●	●
BLACKWOOL TROUT FISHERY (FH0484)																	
BOLEBROOK CASTLE (FH0531)																	
BORDE HILL GARDEN LAKES (FH0544)	●													●		●	●
CASTLE TROUT POND (FH0865)																	
CHALK SPRINGS TROUT FISHERY (FH0891)																	
DAYLANDS FARM (FH1283)	●																●
DUNCANS POND (FH1472)								●								●	●
DUNCTON MILL (FH1473)																	
FURNACE LAKES (FH1821)			●					●						●	●	●	●
HAMBROOK TROUT FISHERY (FH2080)																	
HAYWARDS HEATH RIVER (FH2161)																	
HAZELCOPSE LAKES (FH2163)																	
HURSTON LANE (FH2347)																	
LAYBROOK LAKES (FH2638)																●	
LECONFIELD ESTATE (FH2658)	●	●												●	●	●	
MENARDS LAKE (FH3254)																	
MILL FARM FISHERY (FH3283)								●						●		●	
NEW POND (FH3475)			●					●						●		●	●
NEWELLS FISHERIES (FH3483)			●											●	●	●	●
PASSIES PONDS (FH3715)	●		●	●										●		●	●
PILTDOWN POND (FH3774)																	
ROTHER (RIVER) (FH4028)	●	●	●			●		●		●				●	●	●	●
ROTHER (RIVER) (FH4029)		●	●			●		●							●	●	

Fishery	Ruffe	Salmon	Steelhead	Sturgeon	Tench	Tench Golden	Trount American Brook	Trout Blue	Trout Brook	Trout Brown	Trout Golden	Trout Lake	Ttrout Rainbow	Trout Sea	Trout Tiger	Trout Wild	Vendace	Zander
ALDERWOOD PONDS (FH0066)					●													
ARDINGLY RESERVOIR (FH0129)					●													
ARUN (RIVER) (FH0150)																		
ARUN (RIVER) (FH0152)														●				
ARUN (RIVER) (FH0153)																		
ARUN (RIVER) (FH0149)										●				●				
ARUN (RIVER) (FH0148)														●				
ARUN (RIVER) (FH0144)																		
ARUN (RIVER) (FH0151)																		
ARUN (RIVER) (FH0146)																		
BALCOMBE LAKE (FH0256)					●													
BLACKWOOL TROUT FISHERY (FH0484)									●	●	●	●	●					
BOLEBROOK CASTLE (FH0531)																		
BORDE HILL GARDEN LAKES (FH0544)					●													
CASTLE TROUT POND (FH0865)										●								
CHALK SPRINGS TROUT FISHERY (FH0891)								●		●			●		●			
DAYLANDS FARM (FH1283)																		
DUNCANS POND (FH1472)					●													
DUNCTON MILL (FH1473)										●			●		●			
FURNACE LAKES (FH1821)					●													
HAMBROOK TROUT FISHERY (FH2080)										●			●					
HAYWARDS HEATH RIVER (FH2161)										●								
HAZELCOPSE LAKES (FH2163)		●											●					
HURSTON LANE (FH2347)					●													
LAYBROOK LAKES (FH2638)					●													
LECONFIELD ESTATE (FH2658)										●				●				
MENARDS LAKE (FH3254)																		
MILL FARM FISHERY (FH3283)					●													
NEW POND (FH3475)					●													
NEWELLS FISHERIES (FH3483)					●													
PASSIES PONDS (FH3715)					●													
PILTDOWN POND (FH3774)																		
ROTHER (RIVER) (FH4028)					●					●			●					
ROTHER (RIVER) (FH4029)										●								

Fish Species Available at UK & Irish Fisheries

Species	ROTHERFIELD POND (FH4030)	SPARKS FARM FISHERY (FH4358)	STUBPOND FISHERIES (FH4531)	TILGATE LAKES (FH4845)	VALE BRIDGE LAKE (FH5081)	WATTLEHURST FARM TROUT LAKES (FH5188)	WESTERN ROTHER (FH5274)	WESTERN ROTHER (RIVER) (FH5275)	WILDERNESS LAKE (FH5371)	WINTONS FISHERY (FH5432)	TYNE AND WEAR	BIG WATERS (FH0412)	BOLAM LAKE COUNTRY PARK (FH0528)	DERWENT (RIVER) (FH1353)	DISSINGTON POND (FH1377)	FELLGATE FISHERIES (FH1685)	FELLGATE PONDS (FH1686)	KILLINGWORTH LAKE (FH2486)	LEAZES PARK LAKE (FH2655)	LEVEN (RIVER) (FH2708)	LITTLE BIG WATER (FH2741)	MAIN TYNE (FH3141)	MARDEN QUARRY (FH3178)	MILKHOPE POND (FH3276)	MOUNT PLEASANT LAKE (FH3387)	RED BARNS POND (FH3908)	REDE (RIVER) (FH3915)	SILKSWORTH SPORTS COMPLEX (FH4266)	STARGATE PONDS (FH4432)	STEPHENSON LAKE (FH4450)	SWEETHOPE LOUGHS (FH4608)	TEES (RIVER) (FH4699)	TEES (RIVER) (FH4698)	THROCKLEY REIGH (FH4833)
Zander																																		
Vendace																																		
Trout Wild																															●			
Trout Tiger																																		
Trout Sea								●												●		●												
Ttrout Rainbow						●								●																	●			
Trout Lake																															●			
Trout Golden																																		
Trout Brown								●						●													●				●		●	
Trout Brook																																		
Trout Blue																																		
Trount American Brook																																		
Tench Golden																																		
Tench	●		●	●	●		●					●			●	●			●		●			●	●	●		●	●	●				
Sturgeon																																		
Steelhead																																		
Salmon																						●											●	
Ruffe																																		
Rudd	●	●	●	●	●		●		●				●		●				●				●		●			●	●	●				●
Roach	●	●	●	●	●		●	●	●				●			●		●	●				●		●			●	●	●		●		●
Pike				●			●	●					●					●													●	●		
Perch	●		●	●	●		●	●					●		●	●		●	●				●		●	●		●		●		●		●
Orfe Golden																																		
Orfe Blue																																		
Orfe																								●	●									
Minnow																																		
Gwyniad																																		
Gudgeon									●										●				●		●									
Grilse																																		
Grayling																																		
Goldfish																										●								
Flounder																																		
Eel	●						●					●							●		●													●
Dace							●	●								●									●							●		
Chub			●					●																	●	●				●		●		
Charr																																		
Catfish Black Bullhead																																		
Catfish American Bullhead																																		
Catfish Albino																																		
Catfish										●																								
Carp Wild																																		
Carp Silver																																		
Carp Mirror	●	●	●	●			●		●	●		●			●	●	●		●		●		●	●	●	●		●	●	●				
Carp Leather																●																		
Carp Koi										●																								
Carp Grass																																		
Carp Ghost			●												●																			
Carp Crucian	●	●	●		●										●			●	●					●		●								●
Carp Common	●	●	●	●	●		●		●	●		●			●	●	●		●		●		●	●	●	●		●	●	●				
Carp Blue																																		
Bream	●		●	●	●		●					●			●				●		●		●		●			●		●		●		
Bleak																																		
Barbel			●																															

Fish Species Available at UK & Irish Fisheries

	Barbel	Bleak	Bream	Carp Blue	Carp Common	Carp Crucian	Carp Ghost	Carp Grass	Carp Koi	Carp Leather	Carp Mirror	Carp Silver	Carp Wild	Catfish	Catfish Albino	Catfish American Bullhead	Catfish Black Bullhead	Charr	Chub	Dace	Eel	Flounder	Goldfish	Grayling	Grilse	Gudgeon	Gwyniad	Minnow	Orfe	Orfe Blue	Orfe Golden	Perch	Pike	Roach	Rudd	Ruffe	Salmon	Steelhead	Sturgeon	Tench	Tench Golden	Trount American Brook	Trout Blue	Trout Brook	Trout Brown	Trout Golden	Trout Lake	Ttrout Rainbow	Trout Sea	Trout Tiger	Trout Wild	Vendace	Zander
TYNE (RIVER) (FH5031)																				●														●																			
WEAR (RIVER) (FH5212)	●		●																●	●	●					●						●	●	●			●								●								
WHITTLE DENE TROUT FISHERY (FH5360)																																													●			●					
WILLOWS (THE) (FH5397)			●		●	●					●										●												●	●						●													
WARWICKSHIRE																																																					
ADAMS POOL (FH0026)					●	●					●			●												●						●		●						●													
ARDENCOTE (FH0127)																																																●		●			
ASHBY CANAL (FH0156)			●																															●																			
ASHBY CANAL (FH0157)			●																●													●		●																			
AVON (RIVER) (FH0215)	●		●		●						●								●	●	●					●						●		●																			
AVON (RIVER) (FH0214)																			●															●																			
AVON (RIVER) (FH0213)	●																																																				
BANKS (THE) (FH0288)	●				●	●					●								●													●		●						●													
BISHOPS BOWL LAKES (FH0435)	●				●		●				●								●										●				●	●	●					●													
BLACK HILL POOLS (FH0441)					●						●																							●	●																		
BOSWORTH & FRIEZELAND (FH0561)			●		●						●								●													●																					
BOSWORTH PARK LAKE (FH0560)																																●								●													
BRAMCOTE MAINS FISHERY (FH0597)					●						●																							●	●																		
CHESTERTON MILL (FH0934)																																																●					
CLIFTON LAKES FISHERY (FH1006)	●		●		●	●	●				●								●		●											●	●	●						●													
COVENTRY CANAL (FH1146)																																●		●																			
DRAYCOTE WATER (FH1438)																																													●			●					
GRAND UNION CANAL (FH1964)			●																															●																			
GRAND UNION CANAL (FH1963)											●																							●																			
GRAND UNION CANAL (FH1966)			●		●						●															●						●	●	●						●													
GRAND UNION CANAL (FH1962)			●																															●																			
GRAND UNION CANAL (FH1965)			●																															●																			
HAWKESBURY FISHERY (FH2141)			●		●	●	●				●																					●		●						●													
HEATHCOTE LAKE (FH2173)																																													●			●					
HIGH CLAYS FARM (FH2205)					●																													●																			
KINGSTON POOLS (FH2518)			●		●						●																																										
LANNYS LAGOON (FH2620)			●		●	●	●				●																					●		●	●					●													
LEAM (RIVER) (FH2653)																																●		●																			
LEAM (RIVER) (FH2654)																																●		●																			

Fish Species Available at UK & Irish Fisheries

	Barbel	Bleak	Bream	Carp Blue	Carp Common	Carp Crucian	Carp Ghost	Carp Grass	Carp Koi	Carp Leather	Carp Mirror	Carp Silver	Carp Wild	Catfish	Catfish Albino	Catfish American Bullhead	Catfish Black Bullhead	Charr	Chub	Dace	Eel	Flounder	Goldfish	Grayling	Grilse	Gudgeon	Gwyniad	Minnow	Orfe	Orfe Blue	Orfe Golden	Perch	Pike	Roach	Rudd	Ruffe	Salmon	Steelhead	Sturgeon	Tench	Tench Golden	Trount American Brook	Trout Blue	Trout Brook	Trout Brown	Trout Golden	Trout Lake	Ttrout Rainbow	Trout Sea	Trout Tiger	Trout Wild	Vendace	Zander
MAKIN FISHERIES (FH3150)	●		●		●		●				●								●							●								●						●													
MILL POOL (FH3302)	●		●		●	●					●			●					●							●						●		●						●													
MONKS POOL (FH3347)			●		●	●	●				●												●			●						●		●						●													
NAPTON RESERVOIR (FH3421)			●		●	●					●																					●	●	●						●													
NORTH OXFORD CANAL (FH3533)			●																													●		●																			
OAKHAM FARM POOLS (FH3562)			●		●						●																							●						●													
OXFORD CANAL (FH3676)			●		●						●										●					●						●		●																			
OXFORD CANAL (FH3677)			●		●																					●		●				●	●	●		●				●													●
PARK FARM (FH3697)			●																		●											●	●	●						●													
RIDDINGS FISHERY (FH3949)			●		●	●					●								●										●					●	●					●													
SHEEPY MAGNA LAKE (FH4219)					●																																			●													
SNITTERFIELD FRUIT FARM (FH4312)			●		●	●					●								●	●						●						●		●	●					●													
SOUTH STRATFORD CANAL (FH4339)											●																							●																			
STOUR (WARWICKSHIRE) (FH4504)																			●		●					●						●	●	●																			
TUNNEL BARN FARM (FH4972)	●		●		●	●					●								●													●		●	●					●													
WARWICKSHIRE AVON (FH5155)	●		●																●							●						●	●	●																			
WARWICKSHIRE AVON (FH5157)	●		●																●	●						●						●	●	●																			
WEST HILLBOROUGH (FH5261)	●	●	●		●						●								●	●	●					●		●				●	●	●	●	●				●													●
WESTON LAWN FISHERIES (FH5285)			●		●	●					●			●																		●		●					●	●													
WILTSHIRE																																																					
AVON (BRISTOL) (RIVER) (FH0195)	●	●	●		●						●								●		●											●	●	●						●					●								
AVON (BRISTOL) (RIVER) (FH0200)	●		●		●						●								●	●	●			●								●	●	●						●													
AVON (BRISTOL) (RIVER) (FH0201)			●																●	●	●					●						●		●						●													
AVON (BRISTOL) (RIVER) (FH0196)	●		●		●						●								●													●	●	●						●													
AVON (BRISTOL) (RIVER) (FH0197)	●	●	●		●						●								●	●	●					●						●	●	●						●													
AVON (BRISTOL) (RIVER) (FH0198)	●	●																	●	●						●						●	●	●																			
AVON (BRISTOL) (RIVER) (FH0194)	●		●																●	●	●					●						●	●	●						●													
AVON (BRISTOL) (RIVER) (FH0199)	●		●																●															●																			
AVON (RIVER) (FH0216)	●		●																													●	●							●													
AVON (RIVER) (FH0219)																			●	●				●										●											●								
AVON (RIVER) (FH0218)	●		●		●						●								●													●	●	●																			
AVON (RIVER) (FH0217)			●		●						●																					●		●																			
AVON (RIVER) (FH0222)					●						●																																										
AVON (RIVER) (FH0221)																								●																					●								

Fish Species Available at UK & Irish Fisheries

Fishery	Barbel	Bleak	Bream	Carp Blue	Carp Common	Carp Crucian	Carp Ghost	Carp Grass	Carp Koi	Carp Leather	Carp Mirror	Carp Silver	Carp Wild	Catfish	Catfish Albino	Catfish American Bullhead	Catfish Black Bullhead
AVON (RIVER) (FH0220)			●		●						●						
AVON ANGLING CLUB (FH0226)	●		●														
AVON SPRINGS FISHERY (FH0229)																	
BLACKLAND LAKES (FH0450)					●						●						
BOWOOD LAKE (FH0575)					●						●						
BRISTOL AVON (FH0650)	●	●	●		●		●			●	●						
BRISTOL AVON (FH0651)	●		●														
BRISTOL AVON (FH0653)	●		●														
BURBROOKS RESERVOIR (FH0733)			●		●	●					●						
BURTON HILL LAKE (FH0760)					●						●						
CLIVEY PONDS (FH1011)			●		●	●					●						
COATE WATER COUNTRY PARK (FH1046)			●		●						●						
CUCKOOS REST (FH1211)			●		●												
DORKHAM STORMWATER (FH1414)																	
ERLESTOKE LAKE (FH1612)					●						●						
HIGH PENN (FH2210)			●		●						●						
HUNTERS MOON (FH2339)					●						●						
IVY HOUSE FARM (FH2403)			●		●	●	●	●			●						
KENNET AND AVON CANAL (FH2465)			●		●	●					●						
KENNET AND AVON CANAL (FH2462)			●														
KENNET AND AVON CANAL (FH2461)			●		●						●						
KENNET AND AVON CANAL (FH2464)			●														
KENNET AND AVON CANAL (FH2459)			●		●						●						
KENNET AND AVON CANAL (FH2463)			●														
KENNET AND AVON CANAL (FH2467)					●						●						
KENNET AND AVON CANAL (FH2460)			●														
LANGFORD FISHERIES (FH2611)																	
LAWNS (THE) (FH2635)																	
LIDEN LAGOON (FH2717)			●		●						●						
LONGLEAT LAKES (FH2992)			●		●	●					●						
LOWER MOOR FISHERY (FH3090)					●						●						
MANOR BROOK LAKE (FH3160)			●		●						●						
MILL FARM TROUT LAKES (FH3284)																	
NADDER (RIVER) (FH3410)					●						●						

Fishery	Charr	Chub	Dace	Eel	Flounder	Goldfish	Grayling	Grilse	Gudgeon	Gwyniad	Minnow	Orfe	Orfe Blue	Orfe Golden	Perch	Pike	Roach	Rudd	Ruffe	Salmon	Steelhead	Sturgeon	Tench
AVON (RIVER) (FH0220)		●	●													●	●						
AVON ANGLING CLUB (FH0226)		●													●	●	●						
AVON SPRINGS FISHERY (FH0229)							●																
BLACKLAND LAKES (FH0450)															●		●						●
BOWOOD LAKE (FH0575)															●	●	●						●
BRISTOL AVON (FH0650)		●	●	●			●		●						●	●	●	●					●
BRISTOL AVON (FH0651)		●	●													●	●						●
BRISTOL AVON (FH0653)		●																					
BURBROOKS RESERVOIR (FH0733)		●							●						●								●
BURTON HILL LAKE (FH0760)																	●						●
CLIVEY PONDS (FH1011)									●						●		●	●					
COATE WATER COUNTRY PARK (FH1046)															●	●	●						●
CUCKOOS REST (FH1211)		●													●		●	●					●
DORKHAM STORMWATER (FH1414)															●		●						●
ERLESTOKE LAKE (FH1612)																							
HIGH PENN (FH2210)									●						●		●	●					●
HUNTERS MOON (FH2339)																							
IVY HOUSE FARM (FH2403)		●							●						●		●	●					●
KENNET AND AVON CANAL (FH2465)				●											●	●	●	●					●
KENNET AND AVON CANAL (FH2462)									●						●		●						
KENNET AND AVON CANAL (FH2461)															●	●	●						●
KENNET AND AVON CANAL (FH2464)															●		●						●
KENNET AND AVON CANAL (FH2459)									●						●	●	●						●
KENNET AND AVON CANAL (FH2463)									●								●						●
KENNET AND AVON CANAL (FH2467)															●	●							●
KENNET AND AVON CANAL (FH2460)															●		●						●
LANGFORD FISHERIES (FH2611)							●																
LAWNS (THE) (FH2635)															●		●						●
LIDEN LAGOON (FH2717)		●													●	●	●	●					●
LONGLEAT LAKES (FH2992)									●						●		●	●					●
LOWER MOOR FISHERY (FH3090)															●	●		●					●
MANOR BROOK LAKE (FH3160)															●	●	●						●
MILL FARM TROUT LAKES (FH3284)																							
NADDER (RIVER) (FH3410)		●							●						●	●	●						

Fishery	Tench Golden	Trount American Brook	Trout Blue	Trout Brook	Trout Brown	Trout Golden	Trout Lake	Ttrout Rainbow	Trout Sea	Trout Tiger	Trout Wild	Vendace	Zander
AVON (RIVER) (FH0220)													
AVON ANGLING CLUB (FH0226)													
AVON SPRINGS FISHERY (FH0229)					●		●	●					
BLACKLAND LAKES (FH0450)													
BOWOOD LAKE (FH0575)													
BRISTOL AVON (FH0650)					●			●					
BRISTOL AVON (FH0651)													
BRISTOL AVON (FH0653)													
BURBROOKS RESERVOIR (FH0733)													
BURTON HILL LAKE (FH0760)													
CLIVEY PONDS (FH1011)													
COATE WATER COUNTRY PARK (FH1046)													
CUCKOOS REST (FH1211)													
DORKHAM STORMWATER (FH1414)													
ERLESTOKE LAKE (FH1612)													
HIGH PENN (FH2210)													
HUNTERS MOON (FH2339)													
IVY HOUSE FARM (FH2403)													
KENNET AND AVON CANAL (FH2465)													
KENNET AND AVON CANAL (FH2462)													
KENNET AND AVON CANAL (FH2461)													
KENNET AND AVON CANAL (FH2464)													
KENNET AND AVON CANAL (FH2459)													
KENNET AND AVON CANAL (FH2463)													
KENNET AND AVON CANAL (FH2467)													
KENNET AND AVON CANAL (FH2460)													
LANGFORD FISHERIES (FH2611)					●			●					
LAWNS (THE) (FH2635)													
LIDEN LAGOON (FH2717)													
LONGLEAT LAKES (FH2992)													
LOWER MOOR FISHERY (FH3090)					●								
MANOR BROOK LAKE (FH3160)					●								
MILL FARM TROUT LAKES (FH3284)								●					
NADDER (RIVER) (FH3410)					●								

Fish Species Available at UK & Irish Fisheries

	Barbel	Bleak	Bream	Carp Blue	Carp Common	Carp Crucian	Carp Ghost	Carp Grass	Carp Koi	Carp Leather	Carp Mirror	Carp Silver	Carp Wild	Catfish	Catfish Albino	Catfish American Bullhead	Catfish Black Bullhead	Charr	Chub	Dace	Eel	Flounder	Goldfish	Grayling	Grilse	Gudgeon	Gwyniad	Minnow	Orfe	Orfe Blue	Orfe Golden	Perch	Pike	Roach	Rudd	Ruffe	Salmon	Steelhead	Sturgeon	Tench	Tench Golden	Trount American Brook	Trout Blue	Trout Brook	Trout Brown	Trout Golden	Trout Lake	Ttrout Rainbow	Trout Sea	Trout Tiger	Trout Wild	Vendace	Zander
OLD WARDOUR (FH3600)																																		●						●													
PEATMOOR LAGOON (FH3728)			●		●						●								●	●						●						●	●	●	●					●													
PEMBROKE POND (FH3733)					●						●								●													●		●	●					●													
PETERS FINGER LAKES (FH3756)			●		●						●								●	●													●	●																			
PLAUMS PIT (FH3802)			●		●	●					●								●	●						●						●	●	●	●					●													
PURTON LAKE (FH3859)			●		●						●																					●	●	●						●													
RAY (RIVER) (FH3900)			●																●	●						●						●	●	●																			
RODBOURNE LAGOON (FH3988)			●		●						●								●							●								●	●					●													
ROOD ASHTON LAKE (FH4002)					●						●																							●						●													
SABRE AND SWORDS LAKES (FH4079)			●		●	●					●										●											●		●						●													
SHAFTESBURY LAKE (FH4200)			●								●										●					●						●	●	●						●													
SHEAR WATER (FH4216)			●		●						●																					●		●	●					●													
SILVERLANDS LAKE (FH4272)			●		●	●					●										●					●						●	●	●						●													
SOUTHLEIGH LAKE (FH4351)			●		●						●																							●						●													
STEEPLE LANGFORD LAKES (FH4447)			●		●						●								●	●													●	●																			
SUTTON VENY ESTATE (FH4566)																								●																					●								
THAMES (RIVER) (FH4805)	●		●																●	●	●											●	●	●						●													
TOCKENHAM RESERVOIR (FH4861)			●		●	●	●				●																					●		●	●					●													
TURNERS PADDOCK LAKE (FH4981)			●																															●						●													
WALDENS FARM FISHERY (FH5118)	●		●		●	●	●				●								●										●			●	●	●	●					●													
WHITE HORSE INN LAKE (FH5334)					●						●																						●	●						●													
WITHERINGTON FARM FISHING (FH5442)			●		●						●								●													●		●	●					●													
WOODLAND PARK (FH5480)					●						●																					●		●																			
WROUGHTON RESERVOIR (FH5519)			●		●						●									●												●	●	●	●					●													
WYATTS LAKE (FH5523)					●						●																																									
WYTHERINGTON FARM (FH5552)			●		●						●																													●													
ZEALS TROUT FISHERY (FH5577)																																																●					
WORCESTERSHIRE																																																					
ABBOTS SALFORD PARK (FH0009)	●		●		●						●																					●	●	●																			
ACR FISHERIES (FH0023)					●						●																																									
ANCHOR MEADOWS FISHERY (FH0105)	●																		●																																	
ARROW VALLEY LAKE (FH0141)			●		●	●					●																							●	●					●													
ASTWOOD FISHERY (FH0178)			●		●						●																																									
AVON (RIVER) (FH0225)			●																●														●																			

Fish Species Available at UK & Irish Fisheries

Fishery	Barbel	Bleak	Bream	Carp Blue	Carp Common	Carp Crucian	Carp Ghost	Carp Grass	Carp Koi	Carp Leather	Carp Mirror	Carp Silver	Carp Wild	Catfish	Catfish Albino	Catfish American Bullhead	Catfish Black Bullhead	Charr	Chub	Dace	Eel	Flounder	Goldfish	Grayling	Grilse	Gudgeon
AVON (RIVER) (FH0224)																										
AVON (RIVER) (FH0223)	●		●		●						●															
BANKES POOL (FH0287)					●						●															
BENNETTS POOL (FH0384)					●																					
BIRMINGHAM TO WORCESTER CANAL (FH0433)																			●							
BIRMINGHAM TO WORCESTER CANAL (FH0434)			●		●						●								●							●
BRAKE MILL POOL (FH0596)					●		●				●															
BRANSFORD GAME FISHERY (FH0601)																										
BROAD ACRES LAKE (FH0661)			●		●						●															●
BROCKAMIN POOLS (FH0667)			●		●	●	●				●															
BROCKHILL FARM TROUT POOLS (FH0669)																										
CAPTAINS POOL (FH0835)					●	●					●										●					
CASTLE GREEN POOLS (FH0860)			●		●						●								●							
DEXTER POOL (FH1364)					●																					
DOWLES BROOK (FH1432)																			●	●				●		
DROITWICH CANAL (FH1446)			●			●															●					
ELMBRIDGE LAKES (FH1569)			●		●						●															
ERICS POOL (FH1609)			●		●		●		●		●															
EVESBATCH FISHERIES (FH1635)			●		●	●					●										●					
FOREST FARM (FH1765)			●		●	●					●								●							●
FURNACE MILL FISHERY (FH1822)			●		●	●					●								●							●
GROVE FARM (FH2029)					●																					
HARVEY POOL (FH2122)					●																					
HARVINGTON MANOR FISHERY (FH2123)	●																		●							
HAYE FARM FISHERY (FH2152)			●		●						●															
HOLT FLEET POOL (FH2271)			●		●																					
HURCOTT POOL (FH2344)			●																							
HUXLEYS HAMPTON FERRY FISHERY (FH2352)	●	●	●		●	●													●	●	●					●
LEDWYCHE BROOK (FH2660)	●																		●					●		
LEIGH SINTON FISHING LAKES (FH2692)			●		●	●	●	●			●								●							
LENCHES LAKES (FH2697)																										
LENCHFORD (FH2698)	●	●	●		●						●								●	●	●					●
LODGE PARK LAKE (FH2979)					●						●															
LOWER BROADHEATH POOLS (FH3074)	●		●		●	●					●								●							

Fishery	Gwyniad	Minnow	Orfe	Orfe Blue	Orfe Golden	Perch	Pike	Roach	Rudd	Ruffe	Salmon	Steelhead	Sturgeon	Tench	Tench Golden	Trount American Brook	Trout Blue	Trout Brook	Trout Brown	Trout Golden	Trout Lake	Ttrout Rainbow	Trout Sea	Trout Tiger	Trout Wild	Vendace	Zander
AVON (RIVER) (FH0224)						●		●																			
AVON (RIVER) (FH0223)						●		●																			
BANKES POOL (FH0287)																											
BENNETTS POOL (FH0384)								●																			
BIRMINGHAM TO WORCESTER CANAL (FH0433)								●																			
BIRMINGHAM TO WORCESTER CANAL (FH0434)						●		●		●																	
BRAKE MILL POOL (FH0596)								●																			
BRANSFORD GAME FISHERY (FH0601)																			●			●					
BROAD ACRES LAKE (FH0661)						●		●						●													
BROCKAMIN POOLS (FH0667)						●		●	●					●													
BROCKHILL FARM TROUT POOLS (FH0669)																			●			●					
CAPTAINS POOL (FH0835)						●		●						●													
CASTLE GREEN POOLS (FH0860)								●						●													
DEXTER POOL (FH1364)								●																			
DOWLES BROOK (FH1432)							●				●								●								
DROITWICH CANAL (FH1446)						●		●						●													
ELMBRIDGE LAKES (FH1569)								●						●													
ERICS POOL (FH1609)							●	●																			
EVESBATCH FISHERIES (FH1635)						●		●	●					●													
FOREST FARM (FH1765)						●		●	●					●													
FURNACE MILL FISHERY (FH1822)						●		●	●					●													
GROVE FARM (FH2029)								●																			
HARVEY POOL (FH2122)								●																			
HARVINGTON MANOR FISHERY (FH2123)																											
HAYE FARM FISHERY (FH2152)								●	●					●													
HOLT FLEET POOL (FH2271)																											
HURCOTT POOL (FH2344)								●						●													
HUXLEYS HAMPTON FERRY FISHERY (FH2352)		●				●	●	●	●	●				●				●	●						●		●
LEDWYCHE BROOK (FH2660)							●				●								●								
LEIGH SINTON FISHING LAKES (FH2692)						●		●	●					●													
LENCHES LAKES (FH2697)																						●					
LENCHFORD (FH2698)		●				●	●	●		●	●																●
LODGE PARK LAKE (FH2979)																											
LOWER BROADHEATH POOLS (FH3074)								●	●					●													

Fish Species Available at UK & Irish Fisheries

Fishery	Barbel	Bleak	Bream	Carp Blue	Carp Common	Carp Crucian	Carp Ghost	Carp Grass	Carp Koi	Carp Leather	Carp Mirror	Carp Silver	Carp Wild	Catfish	Catfish Albino	Catfish American Bullhead	Catfish Black Bullhead	Charr	Chub	Dace	Eel	Flounder	Goldfish	Grayling	Grilse	Gudgeon	Gwyniad	Minnow	Orfe	Orfe Blue	Orfe Golden	Perch	Pike	Roach	Rudd	Ruffe	Salmon	Steelhead	Sturgeon	Tench	Tench Golden	Trount American Brook	Trout Blue	Trout Brook	Trout Brown	Trout Golden	Trout Lake	Ttrout Rainbow	Trout Sea	Trout Tiger	Trout Wild	Vendace	Zander
MASTERS (THE) (FH3206)																																																●					
MAVER LARFORD (FH3210)			●		●						●																					●	●	●	●					●													
MILL POOL (FH3303)					●																													●																			
MOORLANDS FARM (FH3363)			●		●	●	●				●								●							●						●		●	●					●													
MOORS POOL (FH3365)			●		●						●																					●		●																			
POOLE HALL FISHERY (FH3822)					●																					●								●						●					●			●					
RED BECK LAKE (FH3909)					●					●	●																																										
SALWARPE (RIVER) (FH4089)																			●															●																			
SEVERN (RIVER) (FH4194)	●		●																●		●											●		●																			
SEVERN (RIVER) (FH4183)																																●		●			●																
SEVERN (RIVER) (FH4186)	●	●	●		●	●					●								●	●	●					●						●	●	●		●	●								●			●					
SEVERN (RIVER) (FH4192)																			●															●																			
SEVERN (RIVER) (FH4195)	●		●																●	●												●	●	●																			●
SEVERN (RIVER) (FH4191)	●		●																●													●		●																			●
SEVERN (RIVER) (FH4193)	●																		●																																		
SEVERN (RIVER) (FH4188)	●	●	●																●		●											●	●	●																			●
SEVERN (RIVER) (FH4197)			●								●																																										
SEVERN (RIVER) (FH4196)	●		●																																																		
SEVERN (RIVER) (FH4189)	●		●		●						●								●	●												●	●	●																			
SEVERN (RIVER) (FH4185)	●																		●		●											●	●	●																			
SEVERN (RIVER) (FH4190)	●																		●	●												●		●																			
SEVERN (RIVER) (FH4187)	●																		●																																		
SEVERN (RIVER) (FH4184)	●	●	●																●	●	●					●						●	●	●																			
SHAKESPEARE MOORLANDS FARM (FH4203)			●		●	●					●								●				●			●						●		●	●																		
SHATTERFORD FISHERY (FH4212)	●		●		●	●		●			●			●																		●		●						●								●					
SILLIGROVE FISHERY (FH4267)			●		●	●	●	●			●								●													●		●	●					●			●		●		●	●					
SINDON MILL FARM (FH4275)																																																●					
SION FARM FISHERIES (FH4279)			●		●	●					●																					●		●	●					●													
SNUFF MILL POOL (FH4314)			●		●	●					●								●	●	●					●						●		●	●	●				●													
STAFFORD TO WORCESTER CANAL (FH4406)					●						●								●	●	●					●						●		●																			
STAINFORTH AND KEADBY CANAL (FH4407)			●																															●																			
STANKLIN POOL (FH4419)					●						●																																										
STELLA LAKE (FH4448)					●																																			●													
STEWARDS POOL (FH4454)					●									●																																							

Fish Species Available at UK & Irish Fisheries

Fishery	Barbel	Bleak	Bream	Carp Blue	Carp Common	Carp Crucian	Carp Ghost	Carp Grass	Carp Koi	Carp Leather	Carp Mirror	Carp Silver	Carp Wild	Catfish	Catfish Albino	Catfish American Bullhead	Catfish Black Bullhead	Charr	Chub	Dace	Eel	Flounder	Goldfish	Grayling	Grilse	Gudgeon	Gwyniad	Minnow	Orfe	Orfe Blue	Orfe Golden	Perch	Pike	Roach	Rudd	Ruffe	Salmon	Steelhead	Sturgeon	Tench	Tench Golden	Trount American Brook	Trout Blue	Trout Brook	Trout Brown	Trout Golden	Trout Lake	Ttrout Rainbow	Trout Sea	Trout Tiger	Trout Wild	Vendace	Zander
TEME (RIVER) (FH4729)	●																							●																													
TEME (RIVER) (FH4733)	●																																																				
TEME (RIVER) (FH4728)	●		●																●	●	●											●	●	●			●								●								
TEME (RIVER) (FH4730)	●																																																				
TEME (RIVER) (FH4726)	●																		●	●				●								●	●	●																			
TEME (RIVER) (FH4724)	●		●																●	●	●			●		●		●				●	●				●								●								
TEME (RIVER) (FH4732)	●		●																●	●	●			●		●		●				●	●	●		●	●								●			●					
TEME (RIVER) (FH4725)	●																		●	●														●																			
TEME (RIVER) (FH4727)	●																		●																																		
TEME (RIVER) (FH4731)	●																		●	●												●					●								●								
TOP BARN ANGLING CENTRE (FH4875)	●		●		●	●					●								●													●		●	●					●													
TRIMPLEY RESERVOIR (FH4956)																																													●								
TWYFORD FARM POOL (FH5009)			●		●	●					●								●							●						●		●						●													
UCKINGHALL POOL (FH5038)			●		●			●			●										●											●	●	●	●					●													
UNWICKS FARM FISHERY (FH5049)			●		●	●																												●	●					●													
UPTON WARREN LAKE (FH5063)			●		●						●									●	●											●		●	●																		
WARWICKSHIRE & AVON (FH5154)	●	●	●		●	●													●	●	●					●		●				●	●	●	●	●				●													●
WARWICKSHIRE AVON (FH5159)	●	●	●			●													●	●	●					●		●				●	●	●	●	●				●													●
WARWICKSHIRE AVON (FH5158)	●		●		●						●								●													●	●	●						●													
WARWICKSHIRE AVON (FH5161)	●		●																●	●												●	●	●																			●
WASH POOL (FH5163)			●		●	●					●																							●						●													
WELFIELD POOLS (FH5229)			●		●						●								●															●						●													
WHARFE INN POOL (FH5312)	●		●		●						●								●															●																			
WHARTONS PARK COARSE FISHING (FH5314)			●		●						●								●		●					●								●						●													
WILDEN POOL (FH5369)					●						●																																										
WILLOW FARM (FH5380)			●		●	●					●																							●	●					●													
WILLOW MARSH (FH5386)			●		●						●															●						●		●	●					●													
WINDMILL LAKE (FH5409)			●		●	●					●								●													●		●	●					●													
WINTERFOLD PARK FISHERIES (FH5425)					●																													●																			
WITLEY FISHERY (FH5448)					●	●	●				●																							●	●																		
WITLEY POOLS (FH5449)			●		●	●					●								●	●						●			●			●	●	●	●	●				●													
WOOD POOL (FH5462)			●		●	●					●																					●		●						●													
WOODLAND VIEW (FH5481)	●		●		●	●	●				●								●							●			●			●		●	●					●													
WOODROW FISH POND (FH5490)					●	●					●								●																●					●													

Fish Species Available at UK & Irish Fisheries

Fishery	Barbel	Bleak	Bream	Carp Blue	Carp Common	Carp Crucian	Carp Ghost	Carp Grass	Carp Koi	Carp Leather	Carp Mirror	Carp Silver	Carp Wild	Catfish	Catfish Albino	Catfish American Bullhead	Catfish Black Bullhead	Charr	Chub	Dace	Eel	Flounder	Goldfish	Grayling	Grilse	Gudgeon	Gwyniad	Minnow	Orfe	Orfe Blue	Orfe Golden	Perch	Pike	Roach	Rudd	Ruffe	Salmon	Steelhead	Sturgeon	Tench	Tench Golden	Trount American Brook	Trout Blue	Trout Brook	Trout Brown	Trout Golden	Trout Lake	Ttrout Rainbow	Trout Sea	Trout Tiger	Trout Wild	Vendace	Zander
WOODSTON MANOR POOLS (FH5496)			●		●						●																							●	●																			
WREXHAM																																																					
CLYWEDOG (RIVER) (FH1044)	●																		●	●												●		●																			
DEE (RIVER) (FH1319)																			●	●				●									●																				
EMRAL BROOK (FH1588)																			●	●	●					●																											
WYCH BROOK (FH5524)																			●	●	●																																
YORKSHIRE (NORTH)																																																					
BACON FACTORY POND (FH0243)			●		●						●																					●		●						●													
BAIN (RIVER) (FH0252)			●																													●		●																			
BARLOW COMMON NATURE RESERVE (FH0311)			●		●						●																					●		●	●					●													
BEDALE BECK (FH0362)																			●	●	●			●										●																			
BELLFLASK TROUT FISHERY (FH0379)																																													●			●					
BIRKDALE FISHERY (FH0430)			●		●						●																							●						●													
BLEA TARN (FH0494)																																●													●								
BOLTON ABBEY FISHERIES (FH0539)																								●																					●								
BRAFFERTON COARSE FISHERY (FH0593)			●		●	●				●	●								●										●					●	●					●													
BRICKYARD FARM LAKE (FH0622)			●		●	●	●				●								●							●						●		●	●					●													
BRICKYARD FISHERY (FH0624)			●																●							●									●																		
BROKEN BREA FISHERY (FH0674)			●		●	●					●								●							●						●		●						●	●												
BROOKLANDS (FH0683)			●		●						●																							●						●													
CARP VALE (FH0846)			●		●	●	●			●	●			●					●		●					●			●			●		●	●	●				●								●					
CASTLE HOWARD GREAT LAKE (FH0861)			●																		●												●	●	●					●													
CATTERICK LAKES (FH0874)			●		●						●								●													●		●																			
CAWOOD HOLIDAY PARK (FH0877)			●		●						●								●		●											●	●	●	●					●													
CHAPMANS POND (FH0897)			●		●						●										●											●	●	●						●													
CLAY PIT (FH0988)			●		●	●					●								●													●		●	●					●													
CLIFTON MOOR LAKE (FH1009)			●		●	●					●								●		●											●		●						●													
COD BECK (FH1049)	●																		●	●	●			●									●												●								
CORNHILL PONDS (FH1121)			●		●	●	●	●			●																		●						●					●													
CRABTREE ANGLING LAKE (FH1155)																																													●		●	●					
CUNDALL LODGE FISHERY (FH1223)	●		●																●														●	●																			
DANBY (RIVER) (FH1253)																								●													●								●								
DERWENT (RIVER) (FH1356)			●																●		●					●							●	●																			
DERWENT (RIVER) (FH1357)																		●		●													●	●																			

Fish Species Available at UK & Irish Fisheries

	Barbel	Bleak	Bream	Carp Blue	Carp Common	Carp Crucian	Carp Ghost	Carp Grass	Carp Koi	Carp Leather	Carp Mirror	Carp Silver	Carp Wild	Catfish	Catfish Albino	Catfish American Bullhead	Catfish Black Bullhead	Charr
DERWENT (RIVER) (FH1354)	●																	
DERWENT (RIVER) (FH1358)			●															
EAST COTTINGWITH WATERS (FH1506)																		
EGTON BRIDGE (RIVER) (FH1554)																		
EGTON ESTATE BEAT (FH1555)																		
ELLERTON LANDING (FH1567)			●															
ELLERTON PARK (FH1568)	●		●		●						●							
ELVINGTON LAKE (FH1575)	●		●		●	●	●	●		●	●			●				
ESK (RIVER) (FH1624)																		
ESK (RIVER) (FH1623)																		
ESK (RIVER) (FH1626)																		
ESK (RIVER) (FH1625)																		
ESK (RIVER) (FH1627)																		
FAIRVIEW LAKE (FH1656)					●	●					●							
FARMIRE TROUT FISHERY (FH1674)																		
FLETCHERS POND (FH1747)			●		●	●	●				●							
FOGGLESKYTE WATERS (FH1753)			●		●						●							
FOSS (RIVER) (FH1775)			●															
GLAISDALE (RIVER) (FH1867)																		
GRAFTON MERE (FH1936)			●		●	●					●			●				
HAZEL HALL FARM FISHING (FH2162)																		
HAZELHEAD LAKE (FH2165)																		
HIGH MOOR FARM PARK (FH2208)			●		●						●							
HOLLINGWOOD FISHERY (FH2257)					●						●							
HOXNE FARM PONDS (FH2322)			●		●						●							
KILBURN POND (FH2479)			●			●												
KILNSEY PARK AND TROUT FARM (FH2487)																		
KINGSLEY CARP LAKE (FH2513)			●		●	●	●			●	●			●				
KIPLIN TROUT FISHERY (FH2523)																		
LAKEHOUSE LAKE (FH2576)			●															
LAKESIDE LODGES (FH2595)			●		●		●			●	●							
LANGTON POND (FH2618)			●		●						●							
LAVER (RIVER) (FH2633)																		
LEEMING (RIVER) (FH2684)																		

	Chub	Dace	Eel	Flounder	Goldfish	Grayling	Grilse	Gudgeon	Gwyniad	Minnow	Orfe	Orfe Blue	Orfe Golden	Perch	Pike	Roach	Rudd	Ruffe
DERWENT (RIVER) (FH1354)	●	●	●					●						●	●	●		
DERWENT (RIVER) (FH1358)	●	●	●											●	●	●		
EAST COTTINGWITH WATERS (FH1506)	●														●			
EGTON BRIDGE (RIVER) (FH1554)																		
EGTON ESTATE BEAT (FH1555)																		
ELLERTON LANDING (FH1567)	●	●	●											●	●	●		
ELLERTON PARK (FH1568)														●	●	●		
ELVINGTON LAKE (FH1575)	●		●					●		●				●		●	●	●
ESK (RIVER) (FH1624)																		
ESK (RIVER) (FH1623)																		
ESK (RIVER) (FH1626)																		
ESK (RIVER) (FH1625)						●												
ESK (RIVER) (FH1627)																		
FAIRVIEW LAKE (FH1656)			●											●	●	●	●	
FARMIRE TROUT FISHERY (FH1674)																		
FLETCHERS POND (FH1747)								●			●		●	●		●		
FOGGLESKYTE WATERS (FH1753)																●		
FOSS (RIVER) (FH1775)															●	●		
GLAISDALE (RIVER) (FH1867)																		
GRAFTON MERE (FH1936)	●													●		●	●	
HAZEL HALL FARM FISHING (FH2162)																		
HAZELHEAD LAKE (FH2165)																		
HIGH MOOR FARM PARK (FH2208)																●		
HOLLINGWOOD FISHERY (FH2257)																		
HOXNE FARM PONDS (FH2322)												●	●	●		●	●	
KILBURN POND (FH2479)														●		●	●	
KILNSEY PARK AND TROUT FARM (FH2487)																		
KINGSLEY CARP LAKE (FH2513)	●		●								●			●		●	●	
KIPLIN TROUT FISHERY (FH2523)																		
LAKEHOUSE LAKE (FH2576)	●														●	●		
LAKESIDE LODGES (FH2595)			●											●	●	●	●	
LANGTON POND (FH2618)		●												●	●	●		
LAVER (RIVER) (FH2633)						●												
LEEMING (RIVER) (FH2684)																		

	Salmon	Steelhead	Sturgeon	Tench	Tench Golden	Trount American Brook	Trout Blue	Trout Brook	Trout Brown	Trout Golden	Trout Lake	Ttrout Rainbow	Trout Sea	Trout Tiger	Trout Wild	Vendace	Zander
DERWENT (RIVER) (FH1354)																	
DERWENT (RIVER) (FH1358)																	
EAST COTTINGWITH WATERS (FH1506)																	
EGTON BRIDGE (RIVER) (FH1554)	●								●								
EGTON ESTATE BEAT (FH1555)	●												●				
ELLERTON LANDING (FH1567)																	
ELLERTON PARK (FH1568)				●													
ELVINGTON LAKE (FH1575)				●					●			●					
ESK (RIVER) (FH1624)	●												●				
ESK (RIVER) (FH1623)	●												●				
ESK (RIVER) (FH1626)	●												●				
ESK (RIVER) (FH1625)	●								●								
ESK (RIVER) (FH1627)									●								
FAIRVIEW LAKE (FH1656)				●													
FARMIRE TROUT FISHERY (FH1674)									●								
FLETCHERS POND (FH1747)				●													
FOGGLESKYTE WATERS (FH1753)				●													
FOSS (RIVER) (FH1775)																	
GLAISDALE (RIVER) (FH1867)	●								●								
GRAFTON MERE (FH1936)				●													
HAZEL HALL FARM FISHING (FH2162)									●								
HAZELHEAD LAKE (FH2165)									●								
HIGH MOOR FARM PARK (FH2208)				●													
HOLLINGWOOD FISHERY (FH2257)																	
HOXNE FARM PONDS (FH2322)				●													
KILBURN POND (FH2479)																	
KILNSEY PARK AND TROUT FARM (FH2487)									●			●					
KINGSLEY CARP LAKE (FH2513)				●													
KIPLIN TROUT FISHERY (FH2523)									●			●					
LAKEHOUSE LAKE (FH2576)				●													
LAKESIDE LODGES (FH2595)				●													
LANGTON POND (FH2618)				●													
LAVER (RIVER) (FH2633)									●								
LEEMING (RIVER) (FH2684)									●								

Fish Species Available at UK & Irish Fisheries

Fishery	Barbel	Bleak	Bream	Carp Blue	Carp Common	Carp Crucian	Carp Ghost	Carp Grass	Carp Koi	Carp Leather	Carp Mirror	Carp Silver	Carp Wild	Catfish	Catfish Albino	Catfish American Bullhead	Catfish Black Bullhead	Charr	Chub	Dace	Eel	Flounder	Goldfish	Grayling	Grilse	Gudgeon	Gwyniad	Minnow	Orfe	Orfe Blue	Orfe Golden	Perch	Pike	Roach	Rudd	Ruffe	Salmon	Steelhead	Sturgeon	Tench	Tench Golden	Trount American Brook	Trout Blue	Trout Brook	Trout Brown	Trout Golden	Trout Lake	Ttrout Rainbow	Trout Sea	Trout Tiger	Trout Wild	Vendace	Zander
LEIGHTON RESERVOIR (FH2693)																																													●			●					
LINGCROFT FARM POND (FH2735)			●		●						●								●															●						●													
LOW OSGOODBY LAKE (FH3068)																																																●					
MARSTON WYSE TROUT FARM (FH3197)																																													●			●					
MILBY CUT (FH3273)																			●													●	●	●																			
MOORLANDS FARM PONDS (FH3364)			●		●						●																					●		●																			
MOULTON LANE POND (FH3384)			●		●						●																					●		●	●					●													
MUNBY POND (FH3401)			●		●	●					●																					●		●						●													
NEWBY HALL FISHERIES (FH3481)																																													●								
NEWHAY DAY TICKET LAKE (FH3484)	●		●		●	●		●			●								●							●						●		●	●					●													
NEWHAY SPECIMEN LAKE (FH3485)					●			●			●																													●													
NEWTON RIVER (FH3498)	●																																●																				
NIDD (RIVER) (FH3504)	●		●																●	●	●					●						●	●	●																			
NIDD (RIVER) (FH3507)	●		●		●						●								●	●				●								●		●																			
NIDD (RIVER) (FH3500)																								●																					●								
NIDD (RIVER) (FH3503)	●																		●					●								●	●												●								
NIDD (RIVER) (FH3502)	●		●																●	●												●	●	●																			
NIDD (RIVER) (FH3505)	●																		●													●	●	●																			
NIDD (RIVER) (FH3501)	●																		●																																		
NIDD (RIVER) (FH3506)	●																		●					●								●	●																				
NIDD BRIDGE (FH3508)																								●																					●								
NORTHINGALES FISHERY (FH3545)			●																	●						●						●		●						●													
OAK MERE FISHERY (FH3558)			●		●	●					●																								●					●													
OAKS FISHERY (FH3565)			●		●			●			●															●					●	●		●	●					●													
OAKTREE LEISURE (FH3569)			●		●			●			●																													●													
ORCHARD FARM PONDS (FH3615)					●						●								●															●	●					●													
OUSE (RIVER) (FH3648)																																		●																			
OUSE (RIVER) (FH3651)			●																															●																			
OUSE (RIVER) (FH3653)	●		●		●						●																						●	●																			
OUSE (RIVER) (FH3654)			●																	●												●	●	●																			
OUSE (RIVER) (FH3647)																								●																					●								
PARKLANDS (FH3703)			●		●	●	●				●			●					●	●	●					●						●		●	●					●													
PICKERING PARK FISHING LAKE (FH3766)			●		●	●	●				●										●											●	●	●	●					●													
PICKERING TROUT LAKE (FH3767)																																													●								

Fish Species Available at UK & Irish Fisheries

Fishery	Barbel	Bleak	Bream	Carp Blue	Carp Common	Carp Crucian	Carp Ghost	Carp Grass	Carp Koi	Carp Leather	Carp Mirror	Carp Silver	Carp Wild	Catfish	Catfish Albino	Catfish American Bullhead	Catfish Black Bullhead	Charr	Chub	Dace	Eel	Flounder	Goldfish	Grayling	Grilse	Gudgeon	Gwyniad	Minnow	Orfe	Orfe Blue	Orfe Golden	Perch	Pike	Roach	Rudd	Ruffe	Salmon	Steelhead	Sturgeon	Tench	Tench Golden	Trount American Brook	Trout Blue	Trout Brook	Trout Brown	Trout Golden	Trout Lake	Ttrout Rainbow	Trout Sea	Trout Tiger	Trout Wild	Vendace	Zander
POCKLINGTON CANAL (FH3809)			●																													●	●	●																				
POOL BRIDGE FARM LAKES (FH3818)					●																																																
POPPLETON (RIVER) (FH3823)	●																																●																				
POTTERY LAKE (FH3834)	●		●		●	●	●				●								●		●					●						●	●	●	●					●													
PROSPECT FARM POND (FH3852)			●		●						●																					●		●						●													
QUEEN MARYS POND (FH3865)			●		●						●																					●	●	●	●					●													
RACECOURSE LAKE (FH3871)			●		●						●																					●		●	●					●													
RAKER LAKES (FH3884)					●	●	●		●	●	●								●	●									●			●		●	●					●					●			●					
RASKELF LAKE (FH3889)			●		●						●								●		●											●		●	●					●													
RICCAL (RIVER) (FH3947)																																												●								
RIPLEY CASTLE (FH3957)			●		●						●																					●			●					●													
RIPON CANAL (FH3958)			●		●						●								●													●		●																			
RIPON RACECOURSE LAKE (FH3959)					●						●								●													●	●	●						●													
RIVER VIEW COTTAGE (FH3966)	●																			●				●								●	●	●											●			●					
ROGERS POND (FH3997)			●		●	●					●								●							●														●													
RUSWARP (RIVER) (FH4067)																					●			●													●								●								
RYE (RIVER) (FH4073)																			●	●	●			●								●	●	●		●									●								
RYE AND SEVEN (RIVERS) (FH4074)																			●	●				●									●	●											●								
SCAR HOUSE RESERVOIR (FH4112)																																													●								
SCARBOROUGH MERE (FH4113)			●		●						●																						●	●						●													
SELBY 3 LAKES (FH4129)		●	●		●	●	●	●	●	●	●								●					●		●		●	●			●		●	●	●				●													
SELBY CANAL (FH4132)			●		●						●								●		●											●	●	●						●													
SELBY CANAL (FH4131)		●	●		●						●								●															●	●																		
SELBY CANAL (FH4130)																																●	●	●																		
SELBY CANAL (FH4133)			●																●							●						●		●						●													
SELLEY BRIDGE LAKE (FH4134)			●		●	●					●										●											●		●	●					●													
SEMERWATER (FH4137)																																												●								
SHIELD FISHERY (FH4235)			●		●						●																							●													●					
SHIELD TROUT FISHERY (FH4236)																																															●					
SINNINGTON (RIVER) (FH4278)																								●																					●			●					
SKELL (RIVER) (FH4286)																								●																					●								
SLEIGHTS (RIVER) (FH4298)																					●			●													●								●								
STONEBRIDGE LAKES (FH4471)																																													●	●		●					
STONEY LANE PONDS (FH4473)					●	●					●								●															●	●					●													

Fish Species Available at UK & Irish Fisheries

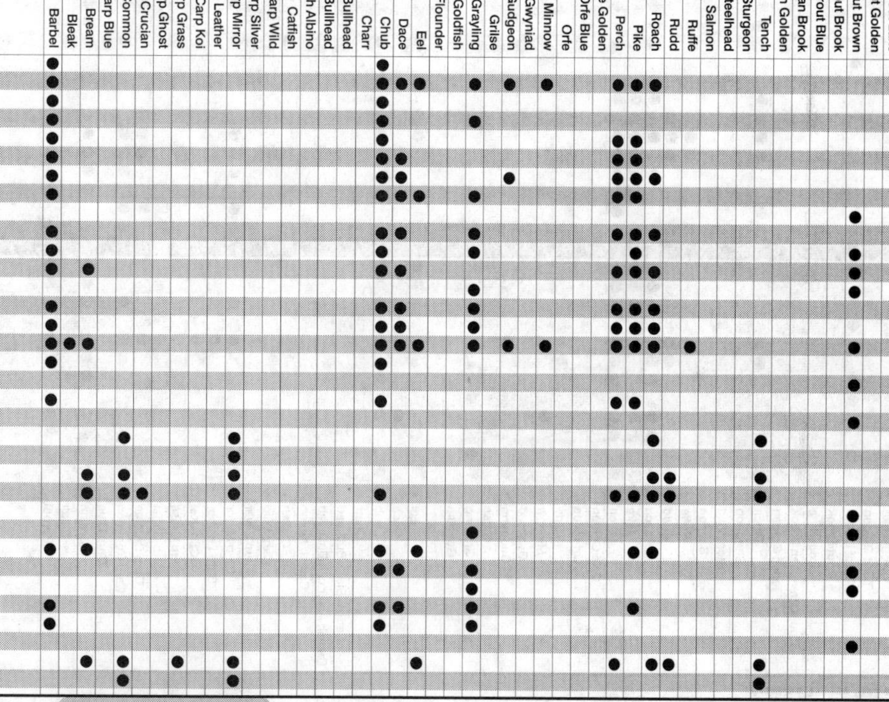

Fishery	Barbel	Bleak	Bream	Carp Blue	Carp Common	Carp Crucian	Carp Ghost	Carp Grass	Carp Koi	Carp Leather	Carp Mirror	Carp Silver	Carp Wild	Catfish	Catfish Albino	Catfish American Bullhead	Catfish Black Bullhead	Charr	Chub	Dace	Eel	Flounder	Goldfish	Grayling	Grilse	Gudgeon	Gwyniad	Minnow	Orfe	Orfe Blue	Orfe Golden	Perch	Pike	Roach	Rudd	Ruffe	Salmon	Steelhead	Sturgeon	Tench	Tench Golden	Trount American Brook	Trout Blue	Trout Brook	Trout Brown	Trout Golden	Trout Lake	Ttrout Rainbow	Trout Sea	Trout Tiger	Trout Wild	Vendace	Zander
SWALE (RIVER) (FH4573)	●																		●																																			
SWALE (RIVER) (FH4567)	●																		●	●	●			●		●		●				●	●	●																				
SWALE (RIVER) (FH4579)	●																		●																																			
SWALE (RIVER) (FH4584)	●																		●					●																														
SWALE (RIVER) (FH4586)	●																		●													●	●																						
SWALE (RIVER) (FH4574)	●																		●	●												●	●																						
SWALE (RIVER) (FH4572)	●																		●	●						●						●	●	●																					
SWALE (RIVER) (FH4576)	●																		●	●	●			●								●	●																						
SWALE (RIVER) (FH4587)																																												●								
SWALE (RIVER) (FH4575)	●																		●	●				●								●	●	●																					
SWALE (RIVER) (FH4585)	●																		●					●									●												●								
SWALE (RIVER) (FH4578)	●		●																●	●											●	●	●										●								
SWALE (RIVER) (FH4570)																								●																					●								
SWALE (RIVER) (FH4582)	●																		●	●				●								●	●	●																					
SWALE (RIVER) (FH4571)	●																		●	●				●								●	●	●																					
SWALE (RIVER) (FH4569)	●	●	●																●	●	●			●		●		●				●	●	●		●										●								
SWALE (RIVER) (FH4583)	●																		●																																			
TANFIELD LAKE (FH4651)																																												●			●						
THORNTON BRIDGE (FH4819)	●																		●													●	●																						
THORNTON STEWARD RESERVOIR (FH4821)																																												●			●						
THORPE PERROW QUARRY (FH4825)					●						●																									●						●														
THORPE UNDERWOOD (FH4826)											●																																										
THREE LAKES (FH4830)			●		●						●																									●	●					●														
TOLLERTON FISHING PONDS (FH4867)			●		●	●						●								●													●	●	●	●					●														
TROUT POND BARN (FH4961)																																												●			●						
URE (RIVER AND TRIBUTARIES) (FH5064)																								●																					●								
URE (RIVER) (FH5070)	●		●																	●		●														●	●																					
URE (RIVER) (FH5069)																			●	●				●																					●								
URE (RIVER) (FH5067)																								●																					●								
URE (RIVER) (FH5073)	●																		●	●				●									●																					
URE (RIVER) (FH5072)	●																		●					●																														
WASHBURN VALLEY (FH5164)																																												●								
WATERMEADOWS FISHERY (FH5181)			●		●			●			●										●										●		●	●					●								●				
WELHAM LAKE (FH5231)					●						●																												●														

Fish Species Available at UK & Irish Fisheries

Fishery	Barbel	Bleak	Bream	Carp Blue	Carp Common	Carp Crucian	Carp Ghost	Carp Grass	Carp Koi	Carp Leather	Carp Mirror	Carp Silver	Carp Wild	Catfish	Catfish Albino	Catfish American Bullhead	Catfish Black Bullhead	Charr	Chub	Dace	Eel	Flounder	Goldfish	Grayling	Grilse	Gudgeon	Gwyniad	Minnow	Orfe	Orfe Blue	Orfe Golden	Perch	Pike	Roach	Rudd	Ruffe	Salmon	Steelhead	Sturgeon	Tench	Tench Golden	Trount American Brook	Trout Blue	Trout Brook	Trout Brown	Trout Golden	Trout Lake	Ttrout Rainbow	Trout Sea	Trout Tiger	Trout Wild	Vendace	Zander
WEST HADDLESEY LAKE (FH5260)			●																●		●											●	●	●						●													
WESTERLY LAKE (FH5271)			●		●	●		●			●								●							●						●		●	●					●													
WHARFE (RIVER) (FH5298)																								●																					●								
WHARFE (RIVER) (FH5301)	●		●																●	●	●											●	●	●																			
WHARFE (RIVER) (FH5300)	●		●																●	●								●				●	●	●																			
WHARFE (RIVER) (FH5302)																								●																					●			●					
WHINNYGILL RESERVOIR (FH5322)			●																●													●		●											●			●					
WILLOWS (FH5396)			●		●						●																		●			●		●	●					●													
WOODLAND LAKES (FH5479)	●		●		●	●	●	●	●	●	●								●							●			●			●		●	●					●													
WYKEHAM LAKES (FH5544)																																													●			●					
Y2K LAKE (FH5553)			●		●						●								●														●	●														●					
YORKSHIRE OUSE (FH5572)	●		●																●		●					●						●	●	●																			
YORKSHIRE OUSE (FH5573)	●		●																●		●											●	●	●																			
YORKSHIRE (SOUTH)																																																					
ARKSEY STATION POND (FH0135)	●		●		●						●																					●		●	●					●													
ASKERN LAKE (FH0173)					●	●					●																					●								●													
ATHERSLEY MEMORIAL LAKE (FH0179)			●																													●		●																			
BARNSLEY CANAL (FH0319)			●		●						●																					●		●																			
BRAMPTON CANAL (FH0598)			●		●	●					●															●						●	●	●	●	●				●													
BRICKYARD PONDS (FH0628)			●		●	●					●								●		●											●	●	●	●	●				●													
BULL HOLE (FH0725)			●			●															●											●	●	●	●					●													
CAMPSALL COUNTRY PARK (FH0818)																																●	●	●						●													
CHESTERFIELD CANAL (FH0931)			●		●						●								●		●											●		●																			
CHESTERFIELD CANAL (FH0932)																																													●								
CROOKES VALLEY PARK LAKE (FH1189)			●		●						●			●					●		●											●		●																			
CUMWELL LANE (FH1222)			●																															●						●													
CUSWORTH HALL LAKE (FH1228)			●		●	●					●																					●		●						●													
DAM FLASK RESERVOIR (FH1251)			●																●	●												●	●	●						●													
DEARNE (RIVER) (FH1289)	●																		●	●						●								●																			
DEARNE VALLEY PARK LAKE (FH1290)			●		●						●																					●		●																			
DELVES FISH PONDS (FH1329)			●		●						●																					●		●						●													
DELVES LAKES (FH1330)			●		●						●																							●						●													
DON (RIVER) (FH1399)																																●		●																			
DON (RIVER) (FH1400)			●																●	●						●						●		●																			

Fish Species Available at UK & Irish Fisheries

Fishery	Barbel	Bleak	Bream	Carp Blue	Carp Common	Carp Crucian	Carp Ghost	Carp Grass	Carp Koi	Carp Leather	Carp Mirror	Carp Silver	Carp Wild	Catfish	Catfish Albino	Catfish American Bullhead	Catfish Black Bullhead	Charr	Chub	Dace	Eel	Flounder	Goldfish	Grayling	Grilse	Gudgeon	Gwyniad	Minnow	Orfe	Orfe Blue	Orfe Golden	Perch	Pike	Roach	Rudd	Ruffe	Salmon	Steelhead	Sturgeon	Tench	Tench Golden	Trount American Brook	Trout Blue	Trout Brook	Trout Brown	Trout Golden	Trout Lake	Ttrout Rainbow	Trout Sea	Trout Tiger	Trout Wild	Vendace	Zander
DON (RIVER) (FH1401)	●		●																●	●						●						●		●																			
DON (RIVER) (FH1402)			●		●						●								●															●																			
ELSECAR CANAL (FH1571)																																●	●	●						●													
ELSECAR RESERVOIR (FH1572)			●																													●	●	●						●													
FINA HAYFIELD LAKES (FH1708)					●						●																							●																			
FITZWILLIAM CANAL (FH1738)			●		●						●																					●	●	●						●													
FLEETS DAM (FH1746)			●		●						●																							●						●													
HARTHILL RESERVIORS (FH2115)			●		●						●										●											●	●	●	●	●				●													
HAVEN (FH2136)					●																								●					●	●					●													
HORSESHOE LAKE TROUT FISHERY (FH2309)																																													●			●					
HOWBROOK RESERVOIR (FH2318)			●		●	●					●																					●		●						●													
IDLE (RIVER) (FH2360)			●		●						●								●	●													●	●																			
IDLE (RIVER) (FH2359)			●		●						●								●	●						●							●	●																			
IDLE (RIVER) (FH2361)			●																●															●																			
KIVETON HALL (FH2531)	●										●								●															●																			
KJS FISHERIES (FH2532)			●		●	●			●		●																		●			●		●	●					●													
LONG POND (FH2983)			●		●						●																					●	●	●						●													
MICKS PLACE (FH3262)			●		●				●		●								●										●			●		●	●					●													
MILTON PONDS (FH3325)			●		●						●								●		●											●		●	●					●													
MISSION LINEBANK PONDS (FH3328)					●																												●	●						●													
MORE HALL RESERVOIR (FH3368)																																													●			●					
NANCY POND (FH3415)			●		●						●																					●		●						●													
NETHERWOOD COUNTRY PARK (FH3455)			●																													●		●	●																		
NEW JUNCTION CANAL (FH3470)			●		●						●								●							●						●		●						●													
NEW JUNCTION CANAL (FH3468)																																		●																			
NEW JUNCTION CANAL (FH3469)																																●		●																			
NEWBIGGIN POND (FH3478)			●		●	●					●								●													●		●						●													
PEBLEY RESERVOIR (FH3729)			●		●						●																						●	●						●													
PRESTON INNOVATIONS (SILVER) (FH3841)	●		●																●												●	●	●	●	●					●	●												
RAILWAY POND (FH3880)			●		●	●					●																					●	●	●	●					●													
ROSSINGTON BRICK POND (FH4018)					●						●																					●		●	●					●													
S YORKS NAVIGATION CANAL (FH4347)			●																●													●		●						●													
S YORKS NAVIGATION CANAL (FH4348)			●																●							●						●		●																			
S YORKS NAVIGATION CANAL (FH4346)																																		●																			

Fish Species Available at UK & Irish Fisheries

	Barbel	Bleak	Bream	Carp Blue	Carp Common	Carp Crucian	Carp Ghost	Carp Grass	Carp Koi	Carp Leather	Carp Mirror	Carp Silver	Carp Wild	Catfish	Catfish Albino	Catfish American Bullhead	Catfish Black Bullhead	Charr	Chub	Dace	Eel	Flounder	Goldfish	Grayling	Grilse	Gudgeon	Gwyniad	Minnow	Orfe	Orfe Blue	Orfe Golden	Perch	Pike	Roach	Rudd	Ruffe	Salmon	Steelhead	Sturgeon	Tench	Tench Golden	Trount American Brook	Trout Blue	Trout Brook	Trout Brown	Trout Golden	Trout Lake	Ttrout Rainbow	Trout Sea	Trout Tiger	Trout Wild	Vendace	Zander
SALLY WALSHES DAM (FH4084)			●		●	●					●			●																		●		●						●													
SANDERSONS POND (FH4093)					●						●																					●		●																			
SCOUT DYKE RESERVOIR (FH4121)																																															●						
SHEFFIELD & S YORKS NAVIGATION (FH4221)																																●		●																			
SHEFFIELD & S YORKS NAVIGATION (FH4220)			●																													●		●																			
SHEFFIELD CANAL (FH4222)			●		●						●								●		●											●		●	●					●													
SHEFFIELD CANAL (FH4223)					●						●								●		●					●						●		●	●					●													
SHIREOAKS PARK (FH4243)			●		●	●		●			●								●													●		●						●													
SLIVER FISHERY (FH4300)			●																													●	●	●	●					●													
SMITHIES RESERVOIR (FH4306)			●		●						●																					●		●						●													
SOUTHFIELD RESERVOIRS (FH4350)			●																													●		●																			
STAINFORTH AND KEADBY CANAL (FH4409)			●		●						●								●		●					●						●		●						●													
STAINFORTH AND KEADBY CANAL (FH4410)			●		●						●								●		●					●						●	●	●						●													
STAINFORTH AND KEADBY CANAL (FH4408)			●		●						●								●		●					●						●	●	●						●													
STANBOROUGH FISHERIES (FH4414)			●		●						●								●													●	●	●	●					●													
STRAIGHT MILE FISHERY (FH4517)	●				●						●								●															●																			
THORNE NORTH POND (FH4814)			●		●						●								●													●		●						●													
THRYBERGH COUNTRY PARK (FH4835)																																●	●												●			●					
TINKERS PONDS (FH4854)			●		●	●					●																					●		●	●					●													
TOLL BAR POND (FH4866)			●			●													●													●	●	●	●					●													
TORNE (RIVER) (FH4880)			●																																					●													
TRENT (RIVER) (FH4938)		●																																																			
TRIANGS FISHERY (FH4953)			●		●						●																		●				●	●						●													
TYRAM HALL (FH5035)			●		●						●																						●	●																			
ULLEY RESERVOIR (FH5041)			●		●						●								●													●	●	●						●													
UNDERBANK RESERVOIR (FH5044)			●																●	●												●	●	●																			
WESTWOOD COUNTRY PARK (FH5288)			●		●						●								●													●		●						●													
WILLOW GARTH FISHERY (FH5381)			●		●	●	●				●								●										●			●		●	●					●													
WILLOWGARTH LAKE (FH5394)			●		●	●					●								●															●	●					●													
WORSBOROUGH RESERVOIR (FH5506)			●		●	●					●																					●		●						●													
WORSBROUGH CANAL (FH5507)			●		●	●													●							●						●		●	●					●													
WORSBROUGH RESERVOIR (FH5508)			●																													●		●																			
YORKSHIRE (WEST)																																																					
ACKTON POND (FH0020)			●		●																													●	●					●													

Fish Species Available at UK & Irish Fisheries

Fishery	Barbel	Bleak	Bream	Carp Blue	Carp Common	Carp Crucian	Carp Ghost	Carp Grass	Carp Koi	Carp Leather	Carp Mirror	Carp Silver	Carp Wild	Catfish	Catfish Albino	Catfish American Bullhead	Catfish Black Bullhead	Charr	Chub	Dace	Eel	Flounder	Goldfish	Grayling	Grilse	Gudgeon	Gwyniad	Minnow	Orfe	Orfe Blue	Orfe Golden	Perch	Pike	Roach	Rudd	Ruffe	Salmon	Steelhead	Sturgeon	Tench	Tench Golden	Trount American Brook	Trout Blue	Trout Brook	Trout Brown	Trout Golden	Trout Lake	Ttrout Rainbow	Trout Sea	Trout Tiger	Trout Wild	Vendace	Zander
AIRE (RIVER) (FH0045)			●																●	●				●								●	●	●											●								
AIRE (RIVER) (FH0044)																			●					●																					●								
AIRE (RIVER) (FH0043)	●		●																●	●				●		●		●				●	●	●	●	●				●					●								
AIRE AND CALDER CANAL (FH0048)			●		●						●								●							●						●		●																			
BOSTON SPA (FH0559)	●		●																●					●									●												●								
BOTTOMS DAM (FH0562)			●																													●		●											●								
BRIGHOUSE (FH0642)																																		●																			
BROOKFOOT LAKE (FH0681)			●		●						●																						●	●	●					●													
CALDER (RIVER) (FH0796)			●																●	●						●								●											●			●					
CALDER (RIVER) (FH0794)																			●														●	●											●								
CALDER AND HEBBLE CANAL (FH0797)			●		●						●																						●	●						●													
CALDER AND HEBBLE CANAL (FH0798)			●		●						●								●													●		●						●													
CLAYTON WOOD PONDS (FH0995)					●						●										●											●		●						●													
CLEARWATER LAKE (FH0998)			●		●						●																					●		●						●													
COLNE (RIVER) (FH1074)																																													●								
COPPICE POND (FH1113)			●		●	●					●																					●		●						●													
DYEHOUSE POND (FH1493)			●		●	●					●								●													●		●	●					●													
HILL TOP RESERVOIR (FH2222)			●		●						●																					●	●	●																			
HOLME (RIVER) (FH2263)																								●																					●						●		
HOLME MILL DAM (SQUARE DAM) (FH2267)			●		●						●																					●		●						●													
HOPTON WATERS (FH2293)			●		●						●								●										●			●		●	●					●													
HORBURY LAGOON (FH2295)			●		●						●																					●		●						●													
HORNSEA MERE (FH2301)			●		●						●																					●	●	●	●					●													
HUDDERSFIELD BROAD CANAL (FH2325)			●		●						●								●													●	●	●						●													
KIPPAX POND (FH2524)			●		●						●								●													●								●													
KNOTFORD LAGOON (FH2542)	●		●		●						●																					●		●						●													
LEEDS AND LIVERPOOL CANAL (FH2671)			●		●	●	●			●	●								●							●						●	●	●	●	●				●					●								
LEEDS TO LIVERPOOL CANAL (FH2681)			●		●						●																					●		●																			
LEEDS TO LIVERPOOL CANAL (FH2682)							●												●													●		●	●					●													
LONGBOTTOMS DAM (FH2986)			●		●						●																					●		●						●													
LOWTHER LAKE (FH3099)			●																●		●					●						●		●						●													
MILLRACE (FH3316)			●		●	●					●								●							●			●			●		●	●					●													
NARROW CANAL (FH3425)			●																●							●						●		●																			
NARROW CANAL (FH3426)					●						●																																										

Fish Species Available at UK & Irish Fisheries

Fishery	Barbel	Bleak	Bream	Carp Blue	Carp Common	Carp Crucian	Carp Ghost	Carp Grass	Carp Koi	Carp Leather	Carp Mirror	Carp Silver	Carp Wild	Catfish	Catfish Albino	Catfish American Bullhead	Catfish Black Bullhead	Charr	Chub	Dace	Eel	Flounder	Goldfish	Grayling	Grilse	Gudgeon
NARROW CANAL (FH3427)			●		●						●															
NEW MILL DAM (FH3474)			●		●	●	●	●	●	●	●								●							●
NOSTELL PRIORY LAKE (FH3551)			●		●						●										●					
OAKS SCAR RESERVOIR (FH3566)																										
OUSE (RIVER) (FH3657)	●		●																●					●		
PINFOLD DAMS (FH3781)																										
PONTEFRACT PARK LAKE (FH3816)			●		●						●															
PUGNEYS COUNTRY PARK (FH3855)			●		●						●															
PUSH DAM (FH3860)			●		●						●															
RAYGILL FISHERY (FH3902)			●		●	●	●			●	●								●							●
ROBERTS POND (FH3976)			●		●						●								●							
ROCHDALE CANAL (FH3979)			●		●	●					●								●	●						●
ROCHDALE CANAL (FH3980)			●		●						●								●							
ROUNDHAY PARK LAKES (FH4037)			●		●						●															
ROWLEY DAM (FH4040)			●		●						●															
ROYDS HALL DAM (FH4050)			●																							
SPARTH RESERVOIR (FH4360)			●																							
SPRING VALLEY WATERS (FH4371)					●	●	●		●		●															
STAVELEY LAKES (FH4443)			●		●	●	●	●	●	●	●								●							
SWILLINGTON PARK (FH4609)			●		●						●															
SWINSTY & FEWSTON (FH4612)																										
T P POND DAM (FH4624)			●		●						●															
THORNHILL POND (FH4818)			●		●						●															●
TONG PARK DAM (FH4872)																										
WALSDEN PRINTING CO LODGES (FH5128)			●		●						●								●							
WHARFE (RIVER) (FH5307)	●																		●	●						
WHARFE (RIVER) (FH5305)	●																		●	●						
WHARFE (RIVER) (FH5303)	●		●																●	●				●		
WHARFE (RIVER) (FH5304)	●																		●					●		
WHARFE (RIVER) (FH5309)																										
WHARFE (RIVER) (FH5306)	●		●																●	●				●		●
WHARFE (RIVER) (FH5308)																			●					●		
WHARFE (RIVER) (FH5311)	●		●																●	●	●			●		●
WHARFE (RIVER) (FH5310)																			●	●				●		

Fishery	Gwyniad	Minnow	Orfe	Orfe Blue	Orfe Golden	Perch	Pike	Roach	Rudd	Ruffe	Salmon	Steelhead	Sturgeon	Tench	Tench Golden	Trount American Brook	Trout Blue	Trout Brook	Trout Brown	Trout Golden	Trout Lake	Ttrout Rainbow	Trout Sea	Trout Tiger	Trout Wild	Vendace	Zander
NARROW CANAL (FH3427)						●		●																			
NEW MILL DAM (FH3474)						●		●	●	●				●				●	●			●					
NOSTELL PRIORY LAKE (FH3551)						●	●	●						●													
OAKS SCAR RESERVOIR (FH3566)						●																					
OUSE (RIVER) (FH3657)							●												●								
PINFOLD DAMS (FH3781)						●																					
PONTEFRACT PARK LAKE (FH3816)						●	●	●																			
PUGNEYS COUNTRY PARK (FH3855)							●	●																			
PUSH DAM (FH3860)						●		●						●													
RAYGILL FISHERY (FH3902)						●	●	●	●		●			●				●	●			●					
ROBERTS POND (FH3976)						●	●	●																			
ROCHDALE CANAL (FH3979)						●	●	●	●	●				●					●			●					
ROCHDALE CANAL (FH3980)						●	●	●																			
ROUNDHAY PARK LAKES (FH4037)						●		●																			
ROWLEY DAM (FH4040)																											
ROYDS HALL DAM (FH4050)								●																			
SPARTH RESERVOIR (FH4360)						●	●	●																			
SPRING VALLEY WATERS (FH4371)			●					●						●													
STAVELEY LAKES (FH4443)						●	●	●						●													
SWILLINGTON PARK (FH4609)						●		●																			
SWINSTY & FEWSTON (FH4612)																			●								
T P POND DAM (FH4624)						●		●						●													
THORNHILL POND (FH4818)								●						●													
TONG PARK DAM (FH4872)																			●			●					
WALSDEN PRINTING CO LODGES (FH5128)						●		●						●													
WHARFE (RIVER) (FH5307)						●	●	●																			
WHARFE (RIVER) (FH5305)						●	●	●																			
WHARFE (RIVER) (FH5303)						●	●	●																			
WHARFE (RIVER) (FH5304)						●	●	●																			
WHARFE (RIVER) (FH5309)								●	●										●								
WHARFE (RIVER) (FH5306)						●	●	●																			
WHARFE (RIVER) (FH5308)																			●								
WHARFE (RIVER) (FH5311)		●				●	●	●		●									●								
WHARFE (RIVER) (FH5310)						●		●																			

AnglersNet co.uk

The online magazine for all anglers

Free Competitions
Reviews, Hints & Tips
Junior Net
Gallery
Anglers Net Members Club

Fishing Forums
Articles
Tackle Auctions
Readers Net
Press Releases

What AnglersNet say about Fishooked

"The Fishooked online database is a great asset to the Internet. It must take a phenomenal amount of time and commitment to angling to keep such a quality product up to date."

"I don't need to search the internet now for fishery details. Fishooked have done all the work for me!"

Elton Murphy - Editor, AnglersNet.co.uk

AnglersNet have awarded www.fishooked.com the prestigious AN Golden Fish Award

www.anglersnet.co.uk

Are you a member?

fishooked

Help Line

Please do not hesitate in contacting us:

- If you have had a good specimen, match or pleasure catch, you could be in for a prize!
- If you have any queries regarding details listed within the Fishooked directory.
- If you would like your fishery or angling related business to be included in the Fishooked directory.
- If you are looking for details on a water not currently listed within the Fishooked directory, we will endeavour to find all the information you require.
- If you are experiencing difficulties in using the Fishooked directory.
- If you have any comments or suggestions regarding the Fishooked directory.

TEL - 0870 742 0042

FAX - 0870 744 0903

Email: julian@hccpublishing.co.uk

HCC Publishing Ltd, Meaford Power Station, Stone, Staffordshire, ST15 0UU.

Order
Direct
08707
420042
fishooked
The UK & Irish Fisheries Directory
ON CD
& WEB
Over 2,300 Photos
of UK & Irish Fisheries
On the Web:
www.fishooked.com

Fish Species Available at UK & Irish Fisheries

Fishery	Barbel	Bleak	Bream	Carp Blue	Carp Common	Carp Crucian	Carp Ghost	Carp Grass	Carp Koi	Carp Leather	Carp Mirror	Carp Silver	Carp Wild	Catfish	Catfish Albino	Catfish American Bullhead	Catfish Black Bullhead	Charr	Chub	Dace	Eel
WINTERSETT RESERVOIR (FH5428)			●		●						●										
WORKSHOP POND (FH5504)					●																
YEADON TARN (FH5559)			●		●	●					●										

Fishery	Flounder	Goldfish	Grayling	Grilse	Gudgeon	Gwyniad	Minnow	Orfe	Orfe Blue	Orfe Golden	Perch	Pike	Roach	Rudd	Ruffe	Salmon	Steelhead	Sturgeon	Tench	Tench Golden	Trount American Brook	Trout Blue	Trout Brook	Trout Brown	Trout Golden	Trout Lake	Ttrout Rainbow	Trout Sea	Trout Tiger	Trout Wild	Vendace	Zander
WINTERSETT RESERVOIR (FH5428)												●	●																			
WORKSHOP POND (FH5504)											●	●	●						●													
YEADON TARN (FH5559)					●						●		●						●													

Fish Species Available at UK & Irish Fisheries

	Barbel	Bleak	Bream	Carp Blue	Carp Common	Carp Crucian	Carp Ghost	Carp Grass	Carp Koi	Carp Leather	Carp Mirror	Carp Silver	Carp Wild	Catfish	Catfish Albino	Catfish American Bullhead	Catfish Black Bullhead	Charr	Chub	Dace	Eel	Flounder	Goldfish	Grayling	Grilse	Gudgeon	Gwyniad
IRELAND																											
COUNTY CARLOW																											
BARROW (RIVER) (FH0325)			●																								
BURREN (RIVER) (FH0752)			●																								
DOUGLAS (RIVER) (FH1419)			●																								
GREESE (RIVER) (FH2010)			●																								
LERR (RIVER) (FH2705)			●																								
COUNTY CAVAN																											
ARDAN GRANGE ANGLING (FH0126)			●																								
BAILIEBORO LAKES (FH0251)			●																								
LOUGH RAMOR (FH3053)			●																								
COUNTY CLARE																											
AILLBRACK LOUGH (FH0040)																											
ALLARD FISHERIES (FH0077)			●																		●						
DROMORE AND BALLYLINE (FH1449)																											
LICKEEN LAKE (FH2713)																											
COUNTY CORK																											
BALLINCOLLIG RESERVOIR (FH0265)					●						●																
BANDON (RIVER) (FH0282)																											
BANDON (RIVER) (FH0283)																											
BANDON (RIVER) (FH0281)																											
BANDON (RIVER) (FH0284)																											
BLACKWATER (RIVER) (FH0459)																											
BLACKWATER (RIVER) (FH0463)																											
BLACKWATER (RIVER) (FH0465)																											
BLACKWATER (RIVER) (FH0457)																				●							
BLACKWATER (RIVER) (FH0460)																				●						●	
BLACKWATER (RIVER) (FH0464)																											
BLACKWATER SALMON FISHERY (FH0482)																											
CAHA (RIVER) (FH0791)																											
CAREYSVILLE (FH0840)																											
CORK LOUGH (FH1119)					●						●										●						
DERRYVEGALL LAKE (FH1341)																											

	Minnow	Orfe	Orfe Blue	Orfe Golden	Perch	Pike	Roach	Rudd	Ruffe	Salmon	Steelhead	Sturgeon	Tench	Tench Golden	Trount American Brook	Trout Blue	Trout Brook	Trout Brown	Trout Golden	Trout Lake	Ttrout Rainbow	Trout Sea	Trout Tiger	Trout Wild	Vendace	Zander
IRELAND																										
COUNTY CARLOW																										
BARROW (RIVER) (FH0325)						●																				
BURREN (RIVER) (FH0752)						●		●										●								
DOUGLAS (RIVER) (FH1419)						●	●											●								
GREESE (RIVER) (FH2010)						●	●											●								
LERR (RIVER) (FH2705)						●		●										●								
COUNTY CAVAN																										
ARDAN GRANGE ANGLING (FH0126)					●	●	●																			
BAILIEBORO LAKES (FH0251)					●	●	●	●					●													
LOUGH RAMOR (FH3053)					●	●																				
COUNTY CLARE																										
AILLBRACK LOUGH (FH0040)																		●								
ALLARD FISHERIES (FH0077)					●	●	●			●			●							●						
DROMORE AND BALLYLINE (FH1449)																		●								
LICKEEN LAKE (FH2713)																		●			●					
COUNTY CORK																										
BALLINCOLLIG RESERVOIR (FH0265)													●													
BANDON (RIVER) (FH0282)										●								●								
BANDON (RIVER) (FH0283)										●								●								
BANDON (RIVER) (FH0281)										●								●								
BANDON (RIVER) (FH0284)										●								●								
BLACKWATER (RIVER) (FH0459)										●																
BLACKWATER (RIVER) (FH0463)										●																
BLACKWATER (RIVER) (FH0465)										●								●								
BLACKWATER (RIVER) (FH0457)							●																			
BLACKWATER (RIVER) (FH0460)					●	●	●			●								●								
BLACKWATER (RIVER) (FH0464)										●																
BLACKWATER SALMON FISHERY (FH0482)										●																
CAHA (RIVER) (FH0791)																		●								
CAREYSVILLE (FH0840)										●																
CORK LOUGH (FH1119)					●			●					●													
DERRYVEGALL LAKE (FH1341)																		●								

Fish Species Available at UK & Irish Fisheries

Fishery	Barbel	Bleak	Bream	Carp Blue	Carp Common	Carp Crucian	Carp Ghost	Carp Grass	Carp Koi	Carp Leather	Carp Mirror	Carp Silver	Carp Wild	Catfish	Catfish Albino	Catfish American Bullhead	Catfish Black Bullhead	Charr	Chub	Dace	Eel	Flounder	Goldfish	Grayling	Grilse	Gudgeon	Gwyniad
DERRYVEGALL LAKE (FH1342)																											
DRIMINIDY LAKE (FH1444)																											
FINISK (RIVER) (FH1712)																											
GARRANES LAKE (FH1838)																					●						
GLENGARIFF (RIVER) (FH1890)																											
ILEN (RIVER) (FH2362)																											
INNISCARRA LAKE (FH2370)			●																								
LOUGH ADERRA (FH2999)																											
LOUGH AVAUL (LOWER) (FH3006)																					●						
LOUGH AVAUL (UPPER) (FH3007)																					●						
LOUGH BOFINNE (FH3013)																					●						
LOUGH NEASKIN (FH3050)																											
MANCH HOUSE FISHERY (FH3154)																											
MUNSTER BLACKWATER (RIVER) (FH3403)																											
OWENSHED (RIVER) (FH3665)																											
SCHULL RESERVOIR (FH4117)																					●						
SHEPPERTON LAKES (FH4231)																					●						
COUNTY DONEGAL																											
ASSAROE LAKE (FH0174)			●																		●						
CLOGHAN LODGE ESTATE FISHERY (FH1016)																		●			●						
FINN (RIVER) (FH1715)																											
GLENMORE FISHERY (FH1893)																											
LOUGH BEAGH (FH3011)																											
ROSSES FISHERY (FH4017)																					●						
COUNTY GALWAY																											
ACLAUREEN (LOUGH) (FH0021)			●																		●						
BALLINDOOLY LOUGH AND POND (FH0270)																											
BALLYNAHINCH CASTLE FISHERY (FH0278)																											
CASTLEREAGH LOUGHS (FH0869)			●																		●						
CLARE LOUGH (FH0974)			●																		●						
CLOONDROON LAKE (FH1020)			●																								
COSTELLO AND FERMOYLE FISHERY (FH1124)																											
DOOHULLA (FH1408)																											
ERRIFF FISHERY (FH1615)																											

Fishery	Minnow	Orfe	Orfe Blue	Orfe Golden	Perch	Pike	Roach	Rudd	Ruffe	Salmon	Steelhead	Sturgeon	Tench	Tench Golden	Trount American Brook	Trout Blue	Trout Brook	Trout Brown	Trout Golden	Trout Lake	Ttrout Rainbow	Trout Sea	Trout Tiger	Trout Wild	Vendace	Zander
DERRYVEGALL LAKE (FH1342)																		●								
DRIMINIDY LAKE (FH1444)																		●			●					
FINISK (RIVER) (FH1712)																		●								
GARRANES LAKE (FH1838)								●										●			●					
GLENGARIFF (RIVER) (FH1890)										●								●				●				
ILEN (RIVER) (FH2362)										●												●				
INNISCARRA LAKE (FH2370)								●																		
LOUGH ADERRA (FH2999)								●										●			●					
LOUGH AVAUL (LOWER) (FH3006)								●										●			●					
LOUGH AVAUL (UPPER) (FH3007)								●										●			●					
LOUGH BOFINNE (FH3013)					●	●		●													●					
LOUGH NEASKIN (FH3050)																		●								
MANCH HOUSE FISHERY (FH3154)										●								●								
MUNSTER BLACKWATER (RIVER) (FH3403)										●																
OWENSHED (RIVER) (FH3665)																		●								
SCHULL RESERVOIR (FH4117)								●										●			●					
SHEPPERTON LAKES (FH4231)						●		●										●			●					
COUNTY DONEGAL																										
ASSAROE LAKE (FH0174)					●	●	●			●								●		●		●				
CLOGHAN LODGE ESTATE FISHERY (FH1016)						●				●								●		●		●		●		
FINN (RIVER) (FH1715)						●				●																
GLENMORE FISHERY (FH1893)										●												●				
LOUGH BEAGH (FH3011)										●								●			●					
ROSSES FISHERY (FH4017)										●								●			●	●		●		
COUNTY GALWAY																										
ACLAUREEN (LOUGH) (FH0021)					●	●	●	●					●													
BALLINDOOLY LOUGH AND POND (FH0270)					●	●		●					●													
BALLYNAHINCH CASTLE FISHERY (FH0278)										●																
CASTLEREAGH LOUGHS (FH0869)					●	●	●																			
CLARE LOUGH (FH0974)					●	●																				
CLOONDROON LAKE (FH1020)					●	●	●																			
COSTELLO AND FERMOYLE FISHERY (FH1124)										●								●			●	●				
DOOHULLA (FH1408)										●								●				●				
ERRIFF FISHERY (FH1615)										●												●				

Fish Species Available at UK & Irish Fisheries

	Barbel	Bleak	Bream	Carp Blue	Carp Common	Carp Crucian	Carp Ghost	Carp Grass	Carp Koi	Carp Leather	Carp Mirror	Carp Silver	Carp Wild	Catfish	Catfish Albino	Catfish American Bullhead	Catfish Black Bullhead	Charr	Chub	Dace	Eel	Flounder	Goldfish	Grayling	Grilse	Gudgeon	Gwyniad	Minnow	Orfe	Orfe Blue	Orfe Golden	Perch	Pike	Roach	Rudd	Ruffe	Salmon	Steelhead	Sturgeon	Tench	Tench Golden	Trount American Brook	Trout Blue	Trout Brook	Trout Brown	Trout Golden	Trout Lake	Ttrout Rainbow	Trout Sea	Trout Tiger	Trout Wild	Vendace	Zander
KYLEMORE HOUSE FISHERY (FH2546)																																					●																
LOUGH ACEELAGH (FH2998)			●																													●	●	●	●					●													
LOUGH ARORAM (FH3002)			●																		●												●		●					●													
LOUGH BALLYLUIRKE (FH3008)			●																													●	●	●	●					●													
LOUGH CORRIB (FH3021)			●																													●	●	●			●								●								
LOUGH DOWN (FH3025)			●																													●	●		●																		
LOUGH DOWNBEG (FH3026)			●																													●	●	●																			
LOUGH HEMUSHMACONRY (FH3034)			●																		●												●	●	●					●													
LOUGH MASK (FH3041)																					●											●	●	●			●								●								
LOUGH PARKYFLAHERTY (FH3051)			●																		●											●	●	●	●																		
LOUGH POLLALHY (FH3052)			●																		●											●	●		●																		
MAYFIELD LAKE (FH3215)			●																		●											●	●																				
NANANNAGH (LOUGH) (FH3413)			●																		●											●	●																				
NANEVIN (LOUGH) (FH3416)																					●											●	●	●	●																		
ROSS LAKE (FH4016)			●																		●											●	●	●	●					●													
SUMMERVILLE LOUGH (FH4555)																																●	●		●					●													
COUNTY KERRY																																																					
KERRYFISHERIES (FH2474)																																					●								●				●				
LAKE HOUSE HOTEL (FH2560)																																					●								●				●				
LAKES OF KILLARNEY (FH2579)																					●											●					●			●					●		●		●				
LOUGH BARFINNIHY (FH3010)																																													●								
LOUGH CAUM (FH3016)																																													●			●					
LOUGH FADDA (FH3030)																					●														●										●			●					
LOUGH NAKIRKA (FH3045)																					●														●										●								
COUNTY KILDARE																																																					
BARROW (RIVER) (FH0326)																																													●								
BOHERBAUN (RIVER) (FH0526)																																													●								
GRAND CANAL (FH1938)			●																														●		●					●													
GRAND CANAL (FH1939)			●																														●		●					●													
GRAND CANAL (BARROW TRACK) (FH1942)			●																													●	●		●					●													
GREESE (RIVER) (FH2011)			●																														●		●										●								
GREESE (RIVER) (FH2012)																																													●								
STRADBALLY (RIVER) (FH4515)																																													●								

Fish Species Available at UK & Irish Fisheries

	Barbel	Bleak	Bream	Carp Blue	Carp Common	Carp Crucian	Carp Ghost	Carp Grass	Carp Koi	Carp Leather	Carp Mirror	Carp Silver	Carp Wild	Catfish	Catfish Albino	Catfish American Bullhead	Catfish Black Bullhead	Charr	Chub	Dace	Eel	Flounder	Goldfish	Grayling	Grilse	Gudgeon	Gwyniad	Minnow	Orfe	Orfe Blue	Orfe Golden	Perch	Pike	Roach	Rudd	Ruffe	Salmon	Steelhead	Sturgeon	Tench	Tench Golden	Trount American Brook	Trout Blue	Trout Brook	Trout Brown	Trout Golden	Trout Lake	Ttrout Rainbow	Trout Sea	Trout Tiger	Trout Wild	Vendace	Zander
COUNTY KILKENNY																																																					
BALLINAKILL LAKE (FH0262)																																●	●		●					●													
DININ (RIVER) (FH1374)																																					●								●								
NORE (RIVER) (FH3520)																																					●								●								
NORE (RIVER) (FH3521)																																					●								●								
NORE (RIVER) (FH3517)																																					●								●								
NORE (RIVER) (FH3518)																				●	●							●				●					●								●				●				
COUNTY LAOIS																																																					
BARROW (RIVER) (FH0327)																					●					●		●				●	●	●			●								●								
BARROW (UPPER) (RIVER) (FH0328)																																													●								
ERKINA (RIVER) (FH1611)																																													●								
FIGILE (RIVER) (FH1707)																																													●								
GRANSTOWN LAKE (FH1972)																					●											●	●	●	●					●													
COUNTY LEITRIM																																																					
LOUGH ALLEN (FH3001)			●																		●											●	●	●	●										●		●						
LOUGH MELVIN (FH3043)																																					●								●		●						
SHANNON (UPPER) (RIVER) (FH4208)			●																		●												●	●	●										●								
COUNTY LIMERICK																																																					
CASTLECONNELL SALMON FISHERY (FH0867)																																					●																
COUNTY LOUTH																																																					
BALLYMASCANLON (RIVER) (FH0277)																																					●								●				●				
BARNATTIN RESERVOIR (FH0314)																																													●			●					
BOYNE (RIVER) (FH0580)																																					●												●				
CASTLETON (RIVER) (FH0871)																																					●								●				●				
FANE (RIVER) (FH1661)																																					●								●				●				
KILLINEER RESERVOIR (FH2484)																																													●			●					
COUNTY MAYO																																																					
BROHLY (LOUGH) (FH0673)																																													●			●					
BURRISHOOLE FISHERY (FH0753)																																					●																
CALLOW LAKES (FH0803)																																													●								
CASTLEBAR LAKES (FH0866)																																													●								
CLOONGEE FISHERY (FH1021)																					●											●	●				●								●				●				
GLORE (RIVER) (FH1896)																																													●								
LOUGH CARRA (FH3014)																																													●								

Fish Species Available at UK & Irish Fisheries

Fishery	Barbel	Bleak	Bream	Carp Blue	Carp Common	Carp Crucian	Carp Ghost	Carp Grass	Carp Koi	Carp Leather	Carp Mirror	Carp Silver	Carp Wild	Catfish	Catfish Albino	Catfish American Bullhead	Catfish Black Bullhead	Charr	Chub	Dace	Eel	Flounder	Goldfish	Grayling	Grilse	Gudgeon	Gwyniad	Minnow	Orfe	Orfe Blue	Orfe Golden	Perch	Pike	Roach	Rudd	Ruffe	Salmon	Steelhead	Sturgeon	Tench	Tench Golden	Trount American Brook	Trout Blue	Trout Brook	Trout Brown	Trout Golden	Trout Lake	Ttrout Rainbow	Trout Sea	Trout Tiger	Trout Wild	Vendace	Zander
LOUGH CORRIB (UPPER) (FH3022)																					●												●	●			●							●	●		●				●		
LOUGHS COY CULLIN (FH3061)																																					●								●								
MOUNT FALCON SALMON FISHERY (FH3385)																																					●																
MOY (RIVER) (FH3393)																																					●																
MOY FISHERY (FH3394)																																					●												●				
MUCK (LOUGH) (FH3396)																																													●								
MULLAGHANOE (RIVER) (FH3400)																																													●								
OWENGARVE (RIVER) (FH3661)																																													●								
POLLAGH (RIVER) (FH3811)																																													●								
TALT (LOUGH) (FH4637)																																													●								
COUNTY MEATH																																																					
BOYNE (RIVER) (FH0582)																																					●								●								
BOYNE (RIVER) (FH0583)																																													●								
RATHBEGGAN LAKES (FH3890)																																																●					
COUNTY OFFALY																																																					
EDENDERRY OFFALY EIRE (FH1544)			●								●										●					●						●		●	●					●													
GRAND CANAL (FH1940)			●		●						●															●						●		●	●					●													
COUNTY ROSCOMMON																																																					
BOYLE (RIVER) (FH0579)			●																		●											●		●	●										●								
LOUGH ARROW (FH3003)																					●							●				●	●												●								
LOUGH GARA (FH3032)																					●							●				●	●	●	●					●				●	●								
LOUGH KEY (FH3037)			●																		●											●		●	●										●								
LOUGH NASOOL (FH3047)																																																●					
LUNG RIVER (FH3113)																					●							●				●	●	●	●					●				●	●								
COUNTY SLIGO																																																					
LAKE NA LEIBE (FH2564)																																																●					
LOUGH BO (FH3012)																																													●								
LOUGH KEY (FH3038)																																●													●								
COUNTY TIPPERARY																																																					
ARA (RIVER) (FH0125)																																													●								
CLODIAGH (RIVER) (FH1014)																																					●								●								
CLONANAU FLY FISHING CENTRE (FH1018)																																					●								●		●	●					
COUMSHINGAUN LOUGH (FH1139)																																					●								●								
CROTTYS LOUGH (FH1196)																																					●								●								

Fish Species Available at UK & Irish Fisheries

	Barbel	Bleak	Bream	Carp Blue	Carp Common	Carp Crucian	Carp Ghost	Carp Grass	Carp Koi	Carp Leather	Carp Mirror	Carp Silver	Carp Wild	Catfish	Catfish Albino	Catfish American Bullhead	Catfish Black Bullhead	Charr	Chub	Dace	Eel	Flounder	Goldfish	Grayling	Grilse	Gudgeon	Gwyniad	Minnow	Orfe	Orfe Blue	Orfe Golden	Perch	Pike	Roach	Rudd	Ruffe	Salmon	Steelhead	Sturgeon	Tench	Tench Golden	Trount American Brook	Trout Blue	Trout Brook	Trout Brown	Trout Golden	Trout Lake	Ttrout Rainbow	Trout Sea	Trout Tiger	Trout Wild	Vendace	Zander
DUAG ANNER STREAM (FH1456)																																													●								
LINGAUN (RIVER) (FH2734)																																													●								
NIRE STREAM (FH3511)																																													●								
NORE (RIVER) (FH3523)																																	●				●			●					●								
SUIR (RIVER) (FH4536)																																													●								
SUIR (RIVER) (FH4538)																																					●								●								
SUIR (RIVER) (FH4539)																																					●								●								
SUIR (RIVER) (FH4540)																																					●								●								
SUIR (RIVER) (FH4548)																																													●								
SUIR (RIVER) (FH4549)																																					●								●								
SUIR VALLEY FISHERY (FH4550)																																					●								●								
WHITE HORSE (RIVER) (FH5332)																																	●				●			●					●		●	●	●				
COUNTY WATERFORD																																																					
BALLYSHUNNOCK (FH0279)																																													●			●					
BLACKWATER (RIVER) (FH0468)																																													●								
BLACKWATER (RIVER) (FH0469)																																													●								
BLACKWATER (RIVER) (FH0471)																				●														●			●								●								
BLACKWATER LODGE (FH0481)			●																●	●	●													●			●								●				●				
KNOCKDERRY (FH2540)																																													●			●					
COUNTY WESTMEATH																																																					
BALLINAFID LAKE (FH0261)			●		●						●																													●													
DOOLIN POND (FH1409)					●						●																																										
GALMOYLESTOWN LAKE (FH1831)					●						●																																		●								
LOUGH ENNEL FISHERY (FH3028)																																													●								

Fish Species Available at UK & Irish Fisheries

	Barbel	Bleak	Bream	Carp Blue	Carp Common	Carp Crucian	Carp Ghost	Carp Grass	Carp Koi	Carp Leather	Carp Mirror	Carp Silver	Carp Wild	Catfish	Catfish Albino	Catfish American Bullhead	Catfish Black Bullhead	Charr	Chub	Dace	Eel	Flounder	Goldfish	Grayling	Grilse	Gudgeon	Gwyniad	Minnow	Orfe	Orfe Blue	Orfe Golden	Perch	Pike	Roach	Rudd	Ruffe	Salmon	Steelhead	Sturgeon	Tench	Tench Golden	Trount American Brook	Trout Blue	Trout Brook	Trout Brown	Trout Golden	Trout Lake	Ttrout Rainbow	Trout Sea	Trout Tiger	Trout Wild	Vendace	Zander
NORTHERN IRELAND																																																					
COUNTY ANTRIM																																																					
BANN (LOWER) (RIVER) (FH0291)			●																													●	●	●																			
BANN (LWR) NAVIGATIONAL CANAL (FH0293)			●																		●											●	●	●																			
BANN (LWR) NAVIGATIONAL CANAL (FH0294)			●																		●											●	●	●																			
BANN (LWR) NAVIGATIONAL CANAL (FH0295)			●																		●											●	●	●																			
BRAID (RIVER) (FH0595)																																					●								●								
BUSH (RIVER) (FH0767)																																					●								●				●				
CAREY (RIVER) (FH0839)																																					●								●				●				
CLADY (RIVER) (FH0968)																																					●								●								
CLOGHWATER (RIVER) (FH1017)																																					●								●								
CLOUGH (RIVER) (FH1022)																																					●								●								
CRUMLIN (RIVER) (FH1204)																																					●								●								
DALL (RIVER) (FH1249)																																					●												●				
DUN (RIVER) (FH1470)																																					●												●				
GLENARM (RIVER) (FH1884)																																					●								●				●				
GLENARRIFF (RIVER) (FH1885)																																					●												●				
GLENSHESK (RIVER) (FH1895)																																					●								●				●				
INVER (RIVER) (FH2373)																																					●								●				●				
KELLSWATER (RIVER) (FH2427)																																					●								●								
LAGAN (RIVER) (FH2550)			●																							●						●	●	●	●																		
LOWER BANN (RIVER) (FH3071)			●																													●	●	●																			
MAINE (RIVER) (FH3144)																																					●								●								
MAINE (RIVER) (FH3146)																																					●								●								
MAINE (RIVER) (FH3142)																																					●								●								
MAINE (RIVER) (FH3145)																																					●								●								
MARGEY (RIVER) (FH3179)																																					●								●				●				
MCCAMMANS LAKE (FH3219)																																					●								●				●				
SIX MILE WATER (FH4284)																																					●								●								
SIX MILE WATER (FH4283)																																					●								●								
SPRINGWATER MEADOW (FH4376)																																																●					
STRAID FISHERY (FH4516)																																																●					
WOODFORD FISHERY (FH5474)																																																●					

Fish Species Available at UK & Irish Fisheries

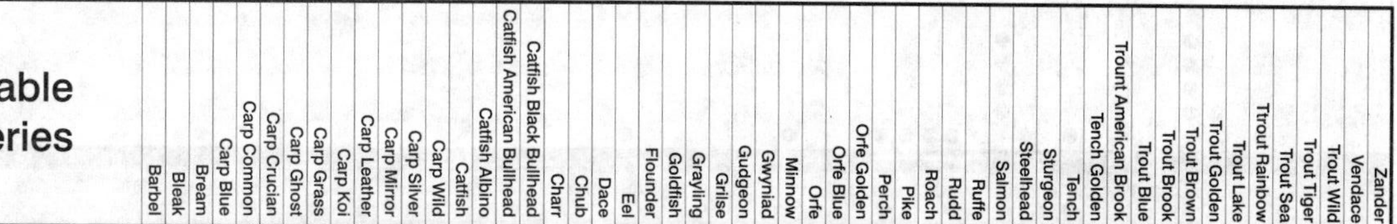

Fishery	Barbel	Bleak	Bream	Carp Blue	Carp Common	Carp Crucian	Carp Ghost	Carp Grass	Carp Koi	Carp Leather	Carp Mirror	Carp Silver	Carp Wild	Catfish	Catfish Albino	Catfish American Bullhead	Catfish Black Bullhead	Charr	Chub	Dace	Eel	Flounder	Goldfish	Grayling	Grilse	Gudgeon	Gwyniad	Minnow	Orfe	Orfe Blue	Orfe Golden	Perch	Pike	Roach	Rudd	Ruffe	Salmon	Steelhead	Sturgeon	Tench	Tench Golden	Trount American Brook	Trout Blue	Trout Brook	Trout Brown	Trout Golden	Trout Lake	Ttrout Rainbow	Trout Sea	Trout Tiger	Trout Wild	Vendace	Zander
COUNTY ARMAGH																																																					
BANN (UPPER) (RIVER) (FH0296)																																					●								●								
BLACKWATER (RIVER) (FH0456)																																					●								●			●					
CALLAN (RIVER) (FH0802)																																					●								●			●					
LAGAN (RIVER) (FH2551)																																													●								
LOUGHGALL COARSE FISHERY (FH3056)																					●											●	●	●	●					●													
LOWRYS LAKE (FH3097)																																													●			●					
SEAGAHAN RESERVOIR DAM (FH4125)																																													●			●					
SHAWS LAKE (FH4214)																																					●								●			●					
SHAWS LAKE (FH4215)																																●													●			●					
TULLNAWOOD LAKE (FH4966)																																	●	●											●			●					
TULLYNAWOOD RESERVOIR (FH4969)																																					●								●			●					
COUNTY DOWN																																																					
BALLY GRANGE FISHERY (FH0273)																																																●					
BALLYLOUGH (FH0275)																																													●			●					
BANN (UPPER) (RIVER) (FH0297)																																					●								●								
BANN (UPPER) (RIVER) (FH0298)																																					●								●								
BANN (UPPER) AND TRIBUTARIES (FH0299)																																					●								●								
CLANRYE (RIVER) (FH0972)																					●												●				●							●	●				●		●		
CLEGGAN (RIVER) (FH1002)																																					●												●				
CULLY (RIVER) (FH1216)																																					●												●				
FANE (RIVER) (FH1660)																																					●								●			●	●				
FORKHILL (RIVER) (FH1768)																																					●								●			●	●				
INLER (RIVER) (FH2368)																																													●				●				
KILKEEL (RIVER) (FH2481)																																					●								●				●				
LAGAN (RIVER) (FH2552)																																													●								
LOUGH CASHEL (FH3015)																																					●								●			●	●				
LOUGH GLASSDRUMMAN (FH3033)																																					●								●			●	●				
LOUGH KILTYBAINE (FH3039)																																					●								●			●	●				
MCCOURTS LAKE (FH3220)																																													●			●					
MILL LODGE FISHERY (FH3293)					●						●																																										
MONEYCARRAGH (RIVER) (FH3341)																																					●												●				
OWENREAGH (RIVER) (FH3664)																																													●				●				
RINGDUFFERIN ESTUARY (FH3951)																																																●					

Fish Species Available at UK & Irish Fisheries

Fishery	Barbel	Bleak	Bream	Carp Blue	Carp Common	Carp Crucian	Carp Ghost	Carp Grass	Carp Koi	Carp Leather	Carp Mirror	Carp Silver	Carp Wild	Catfish	Catfish Albino	Catfish American Bullhead	Catfish Black Bullhead	Charr	Chub	Dace	Eel	Flounder	Goldfish	Grayling	Grilse	Gudgeon	Gwyniad	Minnow	Orfe	Orfe Blue	Orfe Golden	Perch	Pike	Roach	Rudd	Ruffe	Salmon	Steelhead	Sturgeon	Tench	Tench Golden	Trount American Brook	Trout Blue	Trout Brook	Trout Brown	Trout Golden	Trout Lake	Ttrout Rainbow	Trout Sea	Trout Tiger	Trout Wild	Vendace	Zander
SHIMNA (RIVER) (FH4240)																																					●								●				●				
WHITEWATER (RIVER) (FH5355)																																					●								●				●				
WRITES LOUGH (FH5518)																																													●			●					
COUNTY FERMANAGH																																																					
BALLINAMALLARD (RIVER) (FH0263)																																													●		●						
COLEBROOKE (RIVER) (FH1059)																																													●		●						
COLEBROOKE PARK (FH1060)																																																●					
COOLYERMER LOUGH FISHERY (FH1103)																																						●							●			●					
ERNE (RIVER) (FH1614)			●																		●											●	●	●			●								●		●		●				
KNOCKBRACKEN TROUT LAKES (FH2539)																																																●					
LOUGH MELVIN (FH3042)																					●														●		●								●		●		●		●		
LOWER LOUGH ERNE (FH3088)																																													●								
MILL LOUGH BELLANALECK (FH3294)																																													●			●					
TEMPO (RIVER) (FH4736)																																													●		●						
COUNTY LONDONDERRY																																																					
AGIVEY (RIVER) (FH0039)																																					●								●								
BANN (LOWER) (RIVER) (FH0292)																																													●								
CREGGAN RESERVOIRS (FH1178)																																			●													●					
FAUGHAN (RIVER) (FH1678)																																					●								●				●				
FAUGHAN (RIVER) (FH1679)																					●																●								●				●				
LOWER BANN (RIVER) (FH3072)			●																		●											●	●	●																			
MACOSQUIN (RIVER) (FH3133)																																													●								
MOORBROOK LODGE (FH3359)																																													●			●					
MOYOLA (RIVER) (FH3395)			●																		●												●	●	●		●							●	●				●				
PADDY MCNAMARAS LAKE (FH3683)					●						●																					●			●					●													
TURNAFACE TROUT FISHERY (FH4979)																																																●					
COUNTY TYRONE																																																					
ANNAGINNY STILL WATER FISHERY (FH0112)			●																		●							●				●	●	●	●			●		●								●					
BALLINDERRY (RIVER) (FH0269)																																					●								●								
BALLINDERRY (RIVER) (FH0268)																																					●								●								
BALLINDERRY (RIVER) (FH0267)																																					●								●								
BALLINDERRY (RIVER) (FH0266)																																					●								●								
BALLYGAWLEY (RIVER) (FH0274)																																													●								
BARONSCOURT LAKES (FH0323)																																	●																				

Fish Species Available at UK & Irish Fisheries

Fishery	Barbel	Bleak	Bream	Carp Blue	Carp Common	Carp Crucian	Carp Ghost	Carp Grass	Carp Koi	Carp Leather	Carp Mirror	Carp Silver	Carp Wild	Catfish	Catfish Albino	Catfish American Bullhead	Catfish Black Bullhead	Charr	Chub	Dace	Eel	Flounder	Goldfish	Grayling	Grilse	Gudgeon	Gwyniad	Minnow	Orfe	Orfe Blue	Orfe Golden	Perch	Pike	Roach	Rudd	Ruffe	Salmon	Steelhead	Sturgeon	Tench	Tench Golden	Trount American Brook	Trout Blue	Trout Brook	Trout Brown	Trout Golden	Trout Lake	Ttrout Rainbow	Trout Sea	Trout Tiger	Trout Wild	Vendace	Zander
BLACKWATER (RIVER) (FH0467)																																					●								●								
BRANTRY LOUGH (FH0602)																																													●								
BURN DENNETT (RIVER) (FH0747)																																					●								●				●				
CAMOWEN (RIVER) (FH0815)																					●												●				●								●				●		●		
CARRICK LOUGH (FH0849)			●																													●	●	●																			
CRANS LOUGH (FH1167)																																●	●	●																			
DERG (RIVER) (FH1339)																																					●								●				●				
DERG (RIVER) (FH1337)																																					●								●				●				
DRUMRAGH (RIVER) (FH1453)																					●												●	●			●								●				●		●		
DUNGANNON PARK FISHERY (FH1475)																																																●					
FAIRY WATER (FH1657)																																		●																			
FINN (RIVER) (FH1716)																																		●			●								●				●		●		
FINN (RIVER) (FH1717)																																					●												●				
FOYLE (RIVER) (FH1794)																																					●												●				
GLENELLY (RIVER) (FH1888)																																					●								●				●				
GREEVE LOUGH (FH2013)			●																													●	●																				
LOUGH FEA (FH3031)																																													●			●					
LOUGH MACRONAN (FH3040)			●																													●	●	●																			
LOUGHMORE (FH3057)																																													●								
MOURNE (RIVER) (FH3388)																																					●								●				●				
MOURNE (RIVER) (FH3390)																																													●								
MOURNE (RIVER) (FH3389)																																					●								●				●				
OONA RIVER (FH3614)																																													●								
OWENKILLEW (RIVER) (FH3662)																					●												●	●			●								●				●		●		
OWENKILLEW (RIVER) (FH3663)																																					●								●				●				
QUIET WATERS (FH3868)			●																													●	●																				
ROUGHAN LOUGH (FH4033)																																●	●	●																			
ROUND LAKE (FH4036)																																●	●	●	●																		
STRULE (RIVER) (FH4530)																					●												●	●			●								●				●		●		
STRULE (RIVER) (FH4529)																					●													●																			
TORRENT (RIVER) (FH4882)																																													●								
TULLYGIVEN LOUGH (FH4967)			●																		●											●	●							●													
TULLYLAGAN (RIVER) (FH4968)																																													●								
WHITE LOUGH (FH5340)																																																●					

Fish Species Available at UK & Irish Fisheries

	Barbel	Bleak	Bream	Carp Blue	Carp Common	Carp Crucian	Carp Ghost	Carp Grass	Carp Koi	Carp Leather	Carp Mirror	Carp Silver	Carp Wild	Catfish	Catfish Albino	Catfish American Bullhead	Catfish Black Bullhead	Charr	Chub	Dace	Eel	Flounder	Goldfish	Grayling	Grilse	Gudgeon	Gwyniad	Minnow	Orfe	Orfe Blue	Orfe Golden	Perch	Pike	Roach	Rudd	Ruffe	Salmon	Steelhead	Sturgeon	Tench	Tench Golden	Trount American Brook	Trout Blue	Trout Brook	Trout Brown	Trout Golden	Trout Lake	Ttrout Rainbow	Trout Sea	Trout Tiger	Trout Wild	Vendace	Zander
SCOTLAND																																																					
ABERDEENSHIRE																																																					
BOGNIE & MOUNTBLAIRY FISHING (FH0525)																																					●								●				●				
LOCH INSCH FISHERY (FH2894)																																						●						●	●	●		●		●			
MILL OF ELRICK FISHERY (FH3296)																					●																								●			●					
TULLICH FISHERY (FH4965)																																																●					
YTHAN VALLEY FISHERY (FH5576)																																					●							●	●			●					
ANGUS																																																					
CLATIO LOCH (FH0978)			●																													●		●																			
GLEN ESK CARAVAN PARK (FH1880)					●						●																										●								●								
KINGENNIE FISHINGS (FH2494)																																											●	●	●	●		●					
MILL OF CRIGGIE TROUT FISHERY (FH3295)																																													●			●					
PIPERDAM (FH3784)																																													●			●					
ARGYLL AND BUTE																																																					
CLYDE ESTUARY (FH1040)																																					●												●				
CUR (RIVER) (FH1224)																																					●												●				
DUNOON RESERVOIR (FH1478)																																																●					
FINNART (RIVER) (FH1718)																																					●												●				
FRUIN (RIVER) (FH1817)																																					●												●				
INVERAWE FISHERIES (FH2374)																																													●			●					
LOCH AVICH (FH2847)																																													●								
LOCH AWE (FH2848)																		●			●							●				●	●	●			●								●			●	●				
LOCH FAD (FH2879)																																													●			●					
LOCH LOSKIN (THE LOCHAN) (FH2905)																																													●				●				
LOCH QUIEN (FH2936)																																													●								
LOCH TARSAN (FH2948)																																													●								
MASSAN (RIVER) (FH3205)																																					●												●				
MILL HOUSE FISHERIES (FH3286)																																													●			●					
AYRSHIRE (EAST)																																																					
COWANS LAW TROUT FISHERY (FH1150)																																																●					
AYRSHIRE (NORTH)																																																					
CAMPHILL RESERVOIR (FH0816)																																													●								
GOOSELOAN POND (FH1921)					●						●																																										

Fish Species Available at UK & Irish Fisheries

	Barbel	Bleak	Bream	Carp Blue	Carp Common	Carp Crucian	Carp Ghost	Carp Grass	Carp Koi	Carp Leather	Carp Mirror	Carp Silver	Carp Wild	Catfish	Catfish Albino	Catfish American Bullhead	Catfish Black Bullhead	Charr	Chub	Dace	Eel	Flounder	Goldfish	Grayling	Grilse	Gudgeon	Gwyniad	Minnow	Orfe	Orfe Blue	Orfe Golden	Perch	Pike	Roach	Rudd	Ruffe	Salmon	Steelhead	Sturgeon	Tench	Tench Golden	Trount American Brook	Trout Blue	Trout Brook	Trout Brown	Trout Golden	Trout Lake	Ttrout Rainbow	Trout Sea	Trout Tiger	Trout Wild	Vendace	Zander
MIDDLETON FISHERY (FH3268)																																													●			●					
PORT-NA-LOCHAN (FH3829)																					●																							●	●	●		●			●		
SKELMORLIE FISHERIES (FH4287)																																																●					
AYRSHIRE (SOUTH)																																																					
CRAITH RESERVOIR (FH1162)																																																●					
DOON (RIVER) (FH1410)																																					●								●				●				
LOCH DORNAL (FH2872)																																													●			●					
LOCH MAYBERRY (FH2911)																																	●																				
SPRINGWATER FISHERY (FH4374)			●		●	●	●				●																							●	●			●							●	●		●					
STINCHAR (RIVER) (FH4457)																																					●																
DUMFRIES AND GALLOWAY																																																					
ANNAN (RIVER) (FH0113)																								●													●								●				●				
ANNAN (RIVER) (FH0114)																			●																																		
BARSCOBE LOCH (FH0333)																																													●								
BLADNOCH (RIVER) (FH0485)																																	●				●																
BROOM FISHERIES (FH0689)			●		●	●					●																					●		●									●		●	●		●		●			
BUITTLE RESERVOIR (FH0723)																																													●	●		●			●		
CLATTERINGSHAWS LOCH (FH0980)																																●	●												●								
COWANS FARM (FH1149)			●		●						●																							●	●					●													
CRAIGHLAW (FH1159)			●			●	●				●																					●	●	●	●					●											●		
CREE (RIVER) (FH1173)																																					●								●				●				
CULSCADDEN FARM POND (FH1219)			●		●	●					●																					●		●	●					●													
DALBEATTIE RESERVOIR (FH1248)																																													●	●		●			●		
DORMONT LAKE COARSE FISHERY (FH1415)					●						●																							●						●													
DUNSKEY LOCHS (FH1480)																																													●			●					
EARLSTOUN LOCH (FH1502)																																													●								
ESK (RIVER) (FH1619)																																					●								●				●				
FYNTALLOCH LOCH (FH1826)																																													●			●					
GALLOWAY FOREST PARK (FH1829)																					●											●	●	●	●		●			●					●								
GLENDARROCH LOCH (FH1887)			●		●						●																					●		●	●					●													
HODDOM WATER (FH2244)																			●																		●								●				●				
JERICHO LOCHS (FH2410)																																													●			●					
KELHEAD WATER (FH2425)			●		●						●								●		●					●						●	●	●	●					●								●					
KINMOUNT LAKE (FH2520)																																	●																				

Fish Species Available at UK & Irish Fisheries

Fishery	Barbel	Bleak	Bream	Carp Blue	Carp Common	Carp Crucian	Carp Ghost	Carp Grass	Carp Koi	Carp Leather	Carp Mirror	Carp Silver	Carp Wild	Catfish	Catfish Albino	Catfish American Bullhead	Catfish Black Bullhead	Charr	Chub	Dace	Eel	Flounder	Goldfish	Grayling	Grilse	Gudgeon	Gwyniad
KIRKCHRIST (FH2526)																											
KIRKWOOD WATER (FH2527)																			●					●			
KIRRIEREOCH LOCH (FH2528)																											
KIRTLE WATER STREAM (FH2529)																											
KNOCKQUASSEN RESERVOIR (FH2541)																											
LABRAX FISHING (FH2547)																											
LOCH BARNBARROCH (FH2852)			●		●						●																
LOCH HERON (FH2890)			●		●						●																
LOCH KEN (FH2898)																											
LOCH MONREITH (FH2915)																											
LOCH ROAN (FH2939)																											
LOCH RONALD (FH2940)																											
LOCH WHINYEON (FH2958)																											
LOCH WHITEFIELD (FH2959)																											
LOCHENBRECK LOCH (FH2964)																											
MAINS OF PENNINGHAM FISHERY (FH3148)																											
MOFFAT FISHERIES (FH3336)																								●			
MORTON LOCH (FH3375)																											
MORTON POND (FH3376)					●						●										●						
NAHINE LOCH (FH3411)																											
NEW ABBEY DOW (FH3460)																					●						
NEWTON LOCHAN (FH3495)			●		●						●																
NITH (RIVER) (FH3512)																								●	●		
OCHILTREE LOCH (FH3573)																											
PURDOMSTONE RESERVOIR (FH3857)																											
SARK STREAM (FH4105)																											
SLATEHOUSE LOCH (FH4295)																											
STARBURN LOCH (FH4430)																											
TONGUE OF BOMBIE LOCHAN (FH4873)			●																								
TORHOUSEKIE AND KIRWAUGH (FH4879)																											
URR (RIVER) (FH5076)																					●						
WEE GLEN AMOUR LOCH (FH5223)																											
WHITE LOCH OF MYRTON (FH5339)																											

Fishery	Minnow	Orfe	Orfe Blue	Orfe Golden	Perch	Pike	Roach	Rudd	Ruffe	Salmon	Steelhead	Sturgeon	Tench	Tench Golden	Trount American Brook	Trout Blue	Trout Brook	Trout Brown	Trout Golden	Trout Lake	Ttrout Rainbow	Trout Sea	Trout Tiger	Trout Wild	Vendace	Zander
KIRKCHRIST (FH2526)																		●			●					
KIRKWOOD WATER (FH2527)										●								●				●				
KIRRIEREOCH LOCH (FH2528)																		●			●					
KIRTLE WATER STREAM (FH2529)																		●								
KNOCKQUASSEN RESERVOIR (FH2541)																		●								
LABRAX FISHING (FH2547)																					●					
LOCH BARNBARROCH (FH2852)					●		●	●					●													
LOCH HERON (FH2890)					●	●	●	●					●													
LOCH KEN (FH2898)						●	●																			
LOCH MONREITH (FH2915)						●	●	●																		
LOCH ROAN (FH2939)																		●			●					
LOCH RONALD (FH2940)						●	●														●					
LOCH WHINYEON (FH2958)																		●								
LOCH WHITEFIELD (FH2959)					●																					
LOCHENBRECK LOCH (FH2964)																					●					
MAINS OF PENNINGHAM FISHERY (FH3148)																		●			●					
MOFFAT FISHERIES (FH3336)										●								●								
MORTON LOCH (FH3375)													●					●			●					
MORTON POND (FH3376)					●								●													
NAHINE LOCH (FH3411)																		●			●					
NEW ABBEY DOW (FH3460)										●							●	●				●				
NEWTON LOCHAN (FH3495)						●	●						●													
NITH (RIVER) (FH3512)										●								●				●				
OCHILTREE LOCH (FH3573)																		●			●					
PURDOMSTONE RESERVOIR (FH3857)																		●								
SARK STREAM (FH4105)																		●								
SLATEHOUSE LOCH (FH4295)																		●			●					
STARBURN LOCH (FH4430)																		●			●					
TONGUE OF BOMBIE LOCHAN (FH4873)					●		●	●					●													
TORHOUSEKIE AND KIRWAUGH (FH4879)																		●			●					
URR (RIVER) (FH5076)	●									●								●				●		●		
WEE GLEN AMOUR LOCH (FH5223)																		●			●					
WHITE LOCH OF MYRTON (FH5339)						●	●	●																		

Fish Species Available at UK & Irish Fisheries

	Barbel	Bleak	Bream	Carp Blue	Carp Common	Carp Crucian	Carp Ghost	Carp Grass	Carp Koi	Carp Leather	Carp Mirror	Carp Silver	Carp Wild	Catfish	Catfish Albino	Catfish American Bullhead	Catfish Black Bullhead	Charr	Chub	Dace	Eel	Flounder	Goldfish	Grayling	Grilse	Gudgeon	Gwyniad	Minnow	Orfe	Orfe Blue	Orfe Golden	Perch	Pike	Roach	Rudd	Ruffe	Salmon	Steelhead	Sturgeon	Tench	Tench Golden	Trount American Brook	Trout Blue	Trout Brook	Trout Brown	Trout Golden	Trout Lake	Ttrout Rainbow	Trout Sea	Trout Tiger	Trout Wild	Vendace	Zander
EDINBURGH (CITY OF)																																																					
DUDDINGSTON LOCH (FH1459)			●		●						●																					●		●																			
THREIPMUIR RESERVOIRS (FH4832)																																													●			●					
FALKIRK																																																					
C.SCOTLAND TROUT FISHERY (FH0889)																																													●			●					
LOCH EARN (FH2875)																		●																											●			●					
LOCH FINLAS (FH2882)																																													●								
LOCH VENACHAR (FH2955)																																													●								
FIFE																																																					
CRAIGLUSCAR RESERVOIR (FH1160)																																													●			●					
KINGHORN LOCH (FH2503)					●						●																							●																			
LOCH FITTY TROUT FISHERY (FH2883)					●						●																						●	●	●			●							●		●	●					
NEWTON FARM FISHERY (FH3494)																																													●			●					
RAITH LAKE FISHERY (FH3882)																					●							●				●	●											●	●	●	●	●					
GLASGOW (CITY OF)																																																					
CLYDE (RIVER) (FH1037)																								●																					●								
CULCREUCH CASTLE POND (FH1214)					●						●																																										
FORTH AND CLYDE CANAL (FH1772)					●						●																					●	●																				
NEILSTON TROUT FISHERY (FH3438)																					●							●				●	●	●											●		●	●					
HIGHLAND																																																					
CONON (RIVER) (FH1089)																					●											●	●												●			●					
GARRY UPPER (RIVER) (FH1839)																																					●								●								
GLASS (RIVER) (FH1872)																																					●								●								
GLASS (RIVER) (FH1873)																																					●										●						
GLENCOE LOCHAN (FH1886)																																																●					
HOSPITAL LOCHAN (FH2314)																																																●					
LOCH ARKAIG (FH2843)																		●																																			
LOCH ASSYNT (FH2846)																																													●								
LOCH BORRALAN (FH2858)																		●																											●								
LOCH GARRY (FH2885)																																													●								
LOCH INCH LAGGAN (FH2893)																		●																											●								
LOCH INSH (FH2895)																		●			●												●				●								●				●		●		
LOCH MEIG (FH2913)																																													●								
LOCH POULARY (FH2935)																																													●								

Fish Species Available at UK & Irish Fisheries

Fishery	Barbel	Bleak	Bream	Carp Blue	Carp Common	Carp Crucian	Carp Ghost	Carp Grass	Carp Koi	Carp Leather	Carp Mirror	Carp Silver	Carp Wild	Catfish	Catfish Albino	Catfish American Bullhead	Catfish Black Bullhead	Charr	Chub	Dace	Eel	Flounder	Goldfish	Grayling	Grilse	Gudgeon
LOCH QUOICH (FH2937)																										
LOCH TOFTINGALL (FH2953)																										
LOCH USSIE (FH2954)																					●					
LOCH WATTEN (FH2957)																										
NAIRN (RIVER) (FH3412)																										
NESS (RIVER) (FH3450)																										
SCOURIE HOTEL (FH4120)																										
SPEY (RIVER) (FH4364)																		●			●					
SPEY (RIVER) (FH4363)																										
ST JOHNS LOCH (FH4390)																										
STONEYFIELD LOCH (FH4475)																										
TARVIE LOCHS FISHERY (FH4661)																										
TWEED (RIVER) (FH4987)																										
INVERCLYDE																										
ARDGOWAN TROUT FISHERY (FH0128)																										
GRYFFE (RIVER) (FH2032)																								●		
LOCH THOM (FH2952)																										
PINEWOOD TROUT FISHERY (FH3780)																										
LANARKSHIRE (NORTH)																										
CLYDE (RIVER) (FH1039)	●		●																●	●	●			●		●
HILLEND LOCH (FH2226)																										
LILY LOCH (FH2722)																										
MONKLAND CANAL (FH3344)			●		●						●									●						●
LANARKSHIRE (SOUTH)																										
AVON (RIVER) (FH0207)																								●		
FRUID RESERVOIR (FH1816)																										
LANARK LOCH (FH2602)					●																●					
TINTO TROUT FISHERIES (FH4856)																										
LOTHIAN (EAST)																										
MALTINGS FISHERY (FH3153)																										
MARKLE FISHERIES (FH3186)					●	●					●										●					
TYNE (RIVER) (FH5018)																										
WHITEADDER RESERVOIR (FH5346)																										

Fishery	Gwyniad	Minnow	Orfe	Orfe Blue	Orfe Golden	Perch	Pike	Roach	Rudd	Ruffe	Salmon	Steelhead	Sturgeon	Tench	Tench Golden	Trount American Brook	Trout Blue	Trout Brook	Trout Brown	Trout Golden	Trout Lake	Ttrout Rainbow	Trout Sea	Trout Tiger	Trout Wild	Vendace	Zander
LOCH QUOICH (FH2937)																			●								
LOCH TOFTINGALL (FH2953)											●								●				●				
LOCH USSIE (FH2954)						●	●																				
LOCH WATTEN (FH2957)											●								●				●				
NAIRN (RIVER) (FH3412)											●												●				
NESS (RIVER) (FH3450)											●								●				●		●		
SCOURIE HOTEL (FH4120)											●								●				●				
SPEY (RIVER) (FH4364)							●				●								●				●		●		
SPEY (RIVER) (FH4363)											●												●				
ST JOHNS LOCH (FH4390)																			●								
STONEYFIELD LOCH (FH4475)																						●					
TARVIE LOCHS FISHERY (FH4661)																			●			●					
TWEED (RIVER) (FH4987)											●												●				
INVERCLYDE																											
ARDGOWAN TROUT FISHERY (FH0128)																		●	●			●		●	●		
GRYFFE (RIVER) (FH2032)																			●								
LOCH THOM (FH2952)																			●								
PINEWOOD TROUT FISHERY (FH3780)																						●					
LANARKSHIRE (NORTH)																											
CLYDE (RIVER) (FH1039)		●				●	●	●			●								●				●				
HILLEND LOCH (FH2226)						●	●										●		●			●			●		
LILY LOCH (FH2722)		●				●	●												●			●					
MONKLAND CANAL (FH3344)						●	●	●	●					●													
LANARKSHIRE (SOUTH)																											
AVON (RIVER) (FH0207)																			●								
FRUID RESERVOIR (FH1816)																			●								
LANARK LOCH (FH2602)						●		●	●					●													
TINTO TROUT FISHERIES (FH4856)																			●			●			●		
LOTHIAN (EAST)																											
MALTINGS FISHERY (FH3153)																			●								
MARKLE FISHERIES (FH3186)									●					●					●			●					
TYNE (RIVER) (FH5018)											●								●				●				
WHITEADDER RESERVOIR (FH5346)																			●								

Fish Species Available at UK & Irish Fisheries

Fishery	Barbel	Bleak	Bream	Carp Blue	Carp Common	Carp Crucian	Carp Ghost	Carp Grass	Carp Koi	Carp Leather	Carp Mirror	Carp Silver	Carp Wild	Catfish	Catfish Albino	Catfish American Bullhead	Catfish Black Bullhead	Charr	Chub	Dace	Eel	Flounder	Goldfish	Grayling	Grilse	Gudgeon	Gwyniad	Minnow	Orfe	Orfe Blue	Orfe Golden	Perch	Pike	Roach	Rudd	Ruffe	Salmon	Steelhead	Sturgeon	Tench	Tench Golden	Trount American Brook	Trout Blue	Trout Brook	Trout Brown	Trout Golden	Trout Lake	Ttrout Rainbow	Trout Sea	Trout Tiger	Trout Wild	Vendace	Zander
LOTHIAN (MID)																																																					
LOGANLEA TROUT FISHERY (FH2980)																												●																	●			●					
PORTMORE LOCH (FH3828)																																													●								
LOTHIAN (WEST)																																																					
ALLANDALE TARN (FH0076)																																											●		●	●		●					
ALMOND (RIVER) (FH0082)																																					●								●				●				
HOPETOUN FISHERY (FH2291)					●						●										●											●		●						●					●			●					
LINLITHGOW LOCH (FH2736)																																													●			●					
PARKLEY FISHERY (FH3705)																																													●								
SELM MUIR FISHERY (FH4135)																																													●			●					
UNION CANAL (FH5046)			●																													●	●	●	●					●													
MORAY																																																					
BROOM OF MOY (FH0690)																																					●												●				
GLEN OF ROTHES TROUT FISHERY (FH1883)																																												●	●			●			●		
PERTH AND KINROSS																																																					
ABERFELDY ASSOCIATION BEAT (FH0014)																																					●								●								
ALMOND (RIVER) (FH0084)																																													●								
AMULREE BEAT (FH0103)																																					●								●								
BOLFRACKS BEAT (FH0533)																																													●								
BRAAN (RIVER) (FH0584)																																													●								
CASTLE BEAT (FH0859)																																	●				●								●								
CASTLE MENZIES BEAT (FH0863)																																					●								●								
CLOCHFOLDICH BEAT (FH1013)																								●													●								●								
COSHIEVILLE FARM (FH1123)																																					●								●								
CUILALUINN BEAT (FH1213)																																					●								●								
DERCULICH BEAT (FH1335)																																					●								●								
EASTERTYRE BEAT (FH1524)																																																●					
FARLEYER BEAT (FH1666)																																					●																
FINDYNATE BEAT (FH1710)																								●													●											●					
GLENFARG FISHERY (FH1889)																																						●							●			●					
HEATHERYFORD FISHERY (FH2174)																																													●			●					
KENMORE BEAT (FH2431)																																					●								●								
LOCH BHAC (FH2857)																																													●								
LOCH EIGHEACH (FH2876)																																	●												●								

Fish Species Available at UK & Irish Fisheries

	Barbel	Bleak	Bream	Carp Blue	Carp Common	Carp Crucian	Carp Ghost	Carp Grass	Carp Koi	Carp Leather	Carp Mirror	Carp Silver	Carp Wild	Catfish	Catfish Albino	Catfish American Bullhead	Catfish Black Bullhead	Charr	Chub	Dace	Eel	Flounder	Goldfish	Grayling	Grilse	Gudgeon	Gwyniad	Minnow	Orfe	Orfe Blue	Orfe Golden	Perch	Pike	Roach	Rudd	Ruffe	Salmon	Steelhead	Sturgeon	Tench	Tench Golden	Trount American Brook	Trout Blue	Trout Brook	Trout Brown	Trout Golden	Trout Lake	Ttrout Rainbow	Trout Sea	Trout Tiger	Trout Wild	Vendace	Zander
LOCH LEVEN FISHERIES (FH2902)																																													●			●					
LOCH RANNOCH (FH2938)																																	●												●								
LOCH TAY (FH2950)																		●														●	●				●								●			●	●		●		
LOWER ABERUTHVEN FISHINGS (FH3070)																								●													●								●			●	●				
LOWER FARLEYER BEAT (FH3078)																																													●								
MAINS OF MURTHLY (FH3147)																																					●								●								
MONTAGUE RESERVOIR (FH3353)																																																●					
ORCHILL LOCH TROUT FISHERY (FH3619)																																													●								
PITCASTLE BEAT (FH3790)																								●													●								●								
PITLOCHRY BOATING STATION (FH3792)																					●			●								●	●				●								●				●				
RUMBLING BRIDGE (FH4055)																																					●								●								
SANDYKNOWES FISHING (FH4099)																																													●			●					
SEAMAW LOCH (FH4126)																																																●					
TAY (RIVER) (FH4678)																								●																					●								
TOMBUIE BEAT (FH4868)																								●													●								●								
TROCHRY BEAT (FH4958)																																					●								●								
TULLYPOWRIE BEAT (FH4970)																																																●					
UPPER BORLICK BEAT (FH5051)																								●													●								●								
WEEM BEAT (FH5226)																																					●								●								
RENFREWSHIRE																																																					
HOWWOOD TROUT FISHERY (FH2321)																										●						●						●					●	●	●	●		●			●		
MAICH WATERS (FH3140)																																						●							●	●		●			●		
SCOTTISH BORDERS																																																					
ACREKNOWE RESERVOIR (FH0024)																																																●					
AKERMOOR LOCH (FH0049)																																													●								
ALEMOOR RESERVOIR (FH0070)																																	●																				
BAILEY (RIVER) (FH0250)																																					●								●								
BUCCLEUCH ESTATES (FH0715)																																													●								
CLERKLAND FLY FISHERY (FH1003)																																													●			●					
COLDINGHAM LOCH (FH1057)																																											●		●			●					
ETTERICK (RIVER) (FH1631)																																													●								
ETTRICK AND YARROW (RIVER) (FH1632)																																					●																
HEADSHAW FISHERY (FH2166)																																													●			●					
HELLMOOR LOCH (FH2178)																																													●								

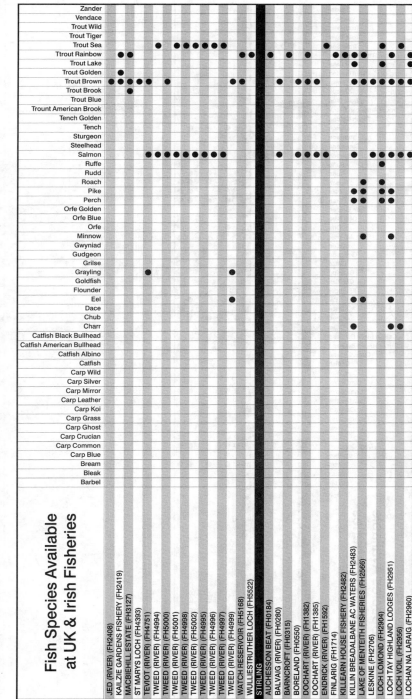

Fish Species Available at UK & Irish Fisheries

	Barbel	Bleak	Bream	Carp Blue	Carp Common	Carp Crucian	Carp Ghost	Carp Grass	Carp Koi	Carp Leather	Carp Mirror	Carp Silver	Carp Wild	Catfish	Catfish Albino	Catfish American Bullhead	Catfish Black Bullhead	Charr	Chub	Dace	Eel	Flounder	Goldfish	Grayling	Grilse	Gudgeon	Gwyniad	Minnow	Orfe	Orfe Blue	Orfe Golden	Perch	Pike	Roach	Rudd	Ruffe	Salmon	Steelhead	Sturgeon	Tench	Tench Golden	Trount American Brook	Trout Blue	Trout Brook	Trout Brown	Trout Golden	Trout Lake	Ttrout Rainbow	Trout Sea	Trout Tiger	Trout Wild	Vendace	Zander
JED (RIVER) (FH2408)																																													●								
KAILZIE GARDENS FISHERY (FH2419)																																													●	●		●					
MACBIEHILL ESTATE (FH3127)																																												●	●			●					
ST MARYS LOCH (FH4393)																																													●								
TEVIOT (RIVER) (FH4751)																								●													●								●								
TWEED (RIVER) (FH4994)																																					●												●				
TWEED (RIVER) (FH5000)																																					●								●								
TWEED (RIVER) (FH5001)																																					●												●				
TWEED (RIVER) (FH4998)																																					●												●				
TWEED (RIVER) (FH5002)																																					●												●				
TWEED (RIVER) (FH4995)																																					●												●				
TWEED (RIVER) (FH4996)																																					●												●				
TWEED (RIVER) (FH4997)																																					●												●				
TWEED (RIVER) (FH4999)																					●			●																					●								
WATCH RESERVOIR (FH5168)																																													●			●					
WULLIESTRUTHER LOCH (FH5522)																																																●					
STIRLING																																																					
AUCHESSON BEAT (FH0184)																																																●					
BALVAIG (RIVER) (FH0280)																																					●								●								
BARNCROFT (FH0315)																																																●					
BORELAND (FH0550)																																					●								●								
DOCHART (RIVER) (FH1382)																																					●								●			●					
DOCHART (RIVER) (FH1385)																																					●								●								
ENDRICK (RIVER) (FH1592)																																					●												●				
FINLARIG (FH1714)																																																●					
KILLEARN HOUSE FISHERY (FH2482)																																																●					
KILLIN BREADALBANE AC WATERS (FH2483)																		●			●											●	●				●								●		●	●					
LAKE OF MENTEITH FISHERIES (FH2566)																					●							●				●	●	●											●			●					
LESKINE (FH2706)																																					●								●								
LOCH LOMOND (FH2904)																																●	●	●		●	●								●		●		●				
LOCH TAY HIGHLAND LODGES (FH2951)																		●			●							●				●	●				●								●			●					
LOCH VOIL (FH2956)																		●																			●								●				●				
LOCHAN NA LARAIG (FH2960)																																					●								●		●	●					
NORTH THIRD TROUT FISHERY (FH3534)																																													●			●					

Fish Species Available at UK & Irish Fisheries

	Barbel	Bleak	Bream	Carp Blue	Carp Common	Carp Crucian	Carp Ghost	Carp Grass	Carp Koi	Carp Leather	Carp Mirror	Carp Silver	Carp Wild	Catfish	Catfish Albino	Catfish American Bullhead	Catfish Black Bullhead	Charr	Chub	Dace	Eel	Flounder	Goldfish	Grayling	Grilse	Gudgeon	Gwyniad
PORTNELLAN (FH3830)																											
SWANSWATER FISHERY (FH4600)																											
WESTERN ISLES																											
CEANN-AN-ORA FISHERY (FH0878)																											
GRIMERSTA LODGE (FH2019)																											
LACASDALE LOCHS (FH2548)																											
OBBE FISHINGS (FH3571)																											
SOVAL ESTATE (FH4353)																											
YORKSHIRE (SOUTH)																											
BANK END COARSE FISHERIES (FH0285)			●		●	●					●								●								
HAYFIELD LAKES (FH2155)	●		●	●	●						●																
LINDHOLME FISHERIES (1) (FH2729)					●						●																
LINDHOLME FISHERIES (2) (FH2730)			●																●								
LINDHOLME FISHERIES (3) (FH2731)																											
LINDHOLME FISHERIES 4) (FH2732)			●		●						●								●		●						
TORNE (RIVER) (FH4881)			●		●						●									●							

	Minnow	Orfe	Orfe Blue	Orfe Golden	Perch	Pike	Roach	Rudd	Ruffe	Salmon	Steelhead	Sturgeon	Tench	Tench Golden	Trount American Brook	Trout Blue	Trout Brook	Trout Brown	Trout Golden	Trout Lake	Ttrout Rainbow	Trout Sea	Trout Tiger	Trout Wild	Vendace	Zander
PORTNELLAN (FH3830)					●					●								●								
SWANSWATER FISHERY (FH4600)											●						●	●	●		●					
WESTERN ISLES																										
CEANN-AN-ORA FISHERY (FH0878)										●								●				●				
GRIMERSTA LODGE (FH2019)										●								●				●				
LACASDALE LOCHS (FH2548)										●								●				●				
OBBE FISHINGS (FH3571)										●								●				●				
SOVAL ESTATE (FH4353)										●								●								
YORKSHIRE (SOUTH)																										
BANK END COARSE FISHERIES (FH0285)							●	●					●													
HAYFIELD LAKES (FH2155)		●			●								●													
LINDHOLME FISHERIES (1) (FH2729)																										
LINDHOLME FISHERIES (2) (FH2730)					●		●	●					●													
LINDHOLME FISHERIES (3) (FH2731)																		●			●					
LINDHOLME FISHERIES 4) (FH2732)					●	●	●	●					●													
TORNE (RIVER) (FH4881)					●	●	●																			

Fish Species Available at UK & Irish Fisheries

	Barbel	Bleak	Bream	Carp Blue	Carp Common	Carp Crucian	Carp Ghost	Carp Grass	Carp Koi	Carp Leather	Carp Mirror	Carp Silver	Carp Wild	Catfish	Catfish Albino	Catfish American Bullhead	Catfish Black Bullhead	Charr	Chub	Dace	Eel	Flounder	Goldfish	Grayling	Grilse	Gudgeon	Gwyniad	Minnow	Orfe	Orfe Blue	Orfe Golden	Perch	Pike	Roach	Rudd	Ruffe	Salmon	Steelhead	Sturgeon	Tench	Tench Golden	Trount American Brook	Trout Blue	Trout Brook	Trout Brown	Trout Golden	Trout Lake	Ttrout Rainbow	Trout Sea	Trout Tiger	Trout Wild	Vendace	Zander
WALES																																																					
BLAENAU GWENT																																																					
BLUE LAKE (FH0508)					●						●								●							●						●		●						●													
BOAT POND (FH0519)					●	●					●									●												●		●																			
BUTE TOWN RESERVOIR (FH0773)			●		●																					●						●		●						●													
HAYRICK LAKES (FH2158)																																											●					●		●			
LYMOOR POOL 1 AND 2 (FH3117)																																●		●						●													
MACHINE POND (FH3132)					●						●								●							●						●	●	●						●													
SIRHOWY (RIVER) (FH4280)																																													●								
BRIDGEND																																																					
GARW (RIVER) (FH1841)																																					●																
LLYNFI (RIVER) (FH2826)																				●																	●								●								
OGMORE (RIVER) (FH3579)																																					●								●				●				
OGMORE (RIVER) (FH3580)																																					●								●								
CAERPHILLY																																																					
EBBW (RIVER) (FH1528)																																													●								
OGILVIE LAKE (FH3578)			●		●						●																							●						●													
RIVERSIDE TROUT FISHERY (FH3969)			●		●		●			●	●																							●	●					●					●			●					
SIRHOWY (RIVER) (FH4281)																																					●								●								
CARDIFF																																																					
CEFN MABLEY (FH0879)			●		●																																			●													
EAST DOCK (FH1508)			●		●						●																													●													
TAFF (RIVER) (FH4631)																								●													●								●								
TAFF (RIVER) (FH4630)																																					●								●								
CARMARTHENSHIRE																																																					
COTHI (RIVER) (FH1130)																																					●												●				
COTHI (RIVER) (FH1127)																																					●								●				●				
COTHI (RIVER) (FH1128)																																					●								●								
COWIN (RIVER) (FH1151)																																					●												●				
CYNIN (RIVER) (FH1241)																																					●												●				
DOL WATTS FISHERY (FH1395)																																					●																
DUAD (RIVER) (FH1455)																																					●								●								
GARNFFRWD FISHERY (FH1836)																																													●			●					

Fish Species Available at UK & Irish Fisheries

Fishery	Barbel	Bleak	Bream	Carp Blue	Carp Common	Carp Crucian	Carp Ghost	Carp Grass	Carp Koi	Carp Leather	Carp Mirror	Carp Silver	Carp Wild	Catfish	Catfish Albino	Catfish American Bullhead	Catfish Black Bullhead	Charr	Chub	Dace	Eel	Flounder	Goldfish	Grayling	Grilse	Gudgeon	Gwyniad	Minnow	Orfe	Orfe Blue	Orfe Golden	Perch	Pike	Roach	Rudd	Ruffe	Salmon	Steelhead	Sturgeon	Tench	Tench Golden	Trount American Brook	Trout Blue	Trout Brook	Trout Brown	Trout Golden	Trout Lake	Ttrout Rainbow	Trout Sea	Trout Tiger	Trout Wild	Vendace	Zander
GLAS-LLYN FISHERY (FH1870)					●						●																							●	●					●					●								
GWENDRAETH FACH (RIVER) (FH2044)																																					●								●								
GWENDRAETH FACH (RIVER) (FH2045)																																					●								●								
GWENDRAETH FACH (RIVER) (FH2043)																																													●								
GWILI (RIVER) (FH2048)																																					●								●								
HENDY FISHERY (FH2181)																																					●								●								
LLYN CARFAN (FH2798)					●	●		●	●	●	●																							●	●					●													
LOUGHOR (RIVER) (FH3058)																																					●								●								
LOUGHOR VALLEY FISHERY (FH3059)																																																●					
PANT Y BEDW FISHING LAKES (FH3693)																																													●			●					
PEWI FACH (RIVER) (FH3763)																																					●												●				
RHYDFACH FISHERY (FH3938)																																					●								●								
SPRINGWATER LAKES (FH4375)			●		●	●					●										●													●	●					●					●			●					
TAF (RIVER) (FH4629)																																					●								●								
TAF (RIVER) (FH4628)																																					●												●				
TAF (RIVER) (FH4627)																																					●								●								
TAN-Y-COED FISHERY (FH4655)																																																●					
TEIFI (RIVER) (FH4704)																																					●								●								
TEIFI (RIVER) (FH4705)																																					●								●				●				
TEIFI (RIVER) (FH4703)																																					●								●								
TOWI (RIVER) (FH4891)																																					●								●				●				
TOWY (RIVER) (FH4899)																																					●								●								
TOWY (RIVER) (FH4897)																																					●								●								
TOWY (RIVER) (FH4898)																																					●								●								
TOWY (RIVER) (FH4900)																																					●								●								
TOWY (RIVER) (FH4895)																																					●								●								
TOWY (RIVER) (FH4896)																																					●								●								
WHITE HOUSE MILL (FH5335)																																													●	●		●					
CEREDIGION																																																					
ARTRO (RIVER) (FH0143)																																					●								●								
CWM RHEIDOL FISHERY (FH1234)																																													●			●					
CYCH (RIVER) (FH1240)																																					●								●								
FRON FARM FISHERY (FH1814)					●		●		●	●	●																		●			●		●						●				●	●			●			●		
LLANARTH FISHERY (FH2768)					●		●			●	●									●									●																								

Fish Species Available at UK & Irish Fisheries

	Barbel	Bleak	Bream	Carp Blue	Carp Common	Carp Crucian	Carp Ghost	Carp Grass	Carp Koi	Carp Leather	Carp Mirror	Carp Silver	Carp Wild	Catfish	Catfish Albino	Catfish American Bullhead	Catfish Black Bullhead	Charr
LLWYNDURIS MANSION FISHERY (FH2787)																		
NEUADDLAS COUNTRY GUEST HOUSE (FH3458)																		
NINE OAKS (FH3509)											●							
RHEIDOL (RIVER) (FH3935)																		
RHYDLEWIS TROUT FISHERY (FH3940)																		
TALYBONT RESERVOIR (FH4638)																		
TEGLAN LAKE (FH4701)					●													
TEIFI (RIVER (FH4702)																		
TEIFI (RIVER) (FH4707)																		
TEIFI (RIVER) (FH4706)																		
TEIFI (RIVER) (FH4710)																		
TEIFI (RIVER) (FH4711)																		
TEIFI (RIVER) (FH4708)																		
TEIFI (RIVER) (FH4712)																		
TEIFY POOLS FISHERY (FH4715)																		
YSTWYTH (RIVER) (FH5574)																		
CONWY																		
ALED (RIVER) (FH0069)																		
CLWYD (RIVER) (FH1032)																		
CONWY (RIVER) (FH1096)																		
CONWY (RIVER) (FH1093)																		
CONWY (RIVER) (FH1097)																		
CONWY (RIVER) (FH1095)																		
CONWY (RIVER) (FH1094)																		
CONWY VALLEY FISHERIES (FH1099)			●		●	●	●	●	●		●							
ELWY (RIVER) (FH1576)																		
ELWY (RIVER) (FH1577)																		
GILER ARMS LAKE (FH1855)			●		●						●							
LLEDR (RIVER) (FH2777)																		
LLYN ALED (FH2791)																		
LLYN CRAFNANT FISHERIES (FH2803)																		
LLYN NANT-Y-CERRIG (FH2819)			●		●						●							
TAN-Y-MYNYDD TROUT LAKES (FH4657)																		
TREFANT POOL (FH4912)			●		●						●							

	Chub	Dace	Eel	Flounder	Goldfish	Grayling	Grilse	Gudgeon	Gwyniad	Minnow	Orfe	Orfe Blue	Orfe Golden	Perch	Pike	Roach	Rudd	Ruffe
LLWYNDURIS MANSION FISHERY (FH2787)																		
NEUADDLAS COUNTRY GUEST HOUSE (FH3458)															●			
NINE OAKS (FH3509)																●		
RHEIDOL (RIVER) (FH3935)																		
RHYDLEWIS TROUT FISHERY (FH3940)																		
TALYBONT RESERVOIR (FH4638)																		
TEGLAN LAKE (FH4701)																		
TEIFI (RIVER (FH4702)																		
TEIFI (RIVER) (FH4707)																		
TEIFI (RIVER) (FH4706)																		
TEIFI (RIVER) (FH4710)																		
TEIFI (RIVER) (FH4711)																		
TEIFI (RIVER) (FH4708)																		
TEIFI (RIVER) (FH4712)															●			
TEIFY POOLS FISHERY (FH4715)																		
YSTWYTH (RIVER) (FH5574)																		
CONWY																		
ALED (RIVER) (FH0069)																		
CLWYD (RIVER) (FH1032)																		
CONWY (RIVER) (FH1096)																		
CONWY (RIVER) (FH1093)																		
CONWY (RIVER) (FH1097)																		
CONWY (RIVER) (FH1095)																		
CONWY (RIVER) (FH1094)																		
CONWY VALLEY FISHERIES (FH1099)			●								●					●	●	
ELWY (RIVER) (FH1576)																		
ELWY (RIVER) (FH1577)																		
GILER ARMS LAKE (FH1855)			●											●		●		
LLEDR (RIVER) (FH2777)																		
LLYN ALED (FH2791)														●	●	●		
LLYN CRAFNANT FISHERIES (FH2803)																		
LLYN NANT-Y-CERRIG (FH2819)														●				
TAN-Y-MYNYDD TROUT LAKES (FH4657)																		
TREFANT POOL (FH4912)														●				

	Salmon	Steelhead	Sturgeon	Tench	Tench Golden	Trount American Brook	Trout Blue	Trout Brook	Trout Brown	Trout Golden	Trout Lake	Ttrout Rainbow	Trout Sea	Trout Tiger	Trout Wild	Vendace	Zander
LLWYNDURIS MANSION FISHERY (FH2787)	●												●				
NEUADDLAS COUNTRY GUEST HOUSE (FH3458)									●			●					
NINE OAKS (FH3509)				●													
RHEIDOL (RIVER) (FH3935)	●								●								
RHYDLEWIS TROUT FISHERY (FH3940)												●					
TALYBONT RESERVOIR (FH4638)									●								
TEGLAN LAKE (FH4701)																	
TEIFI (RIVER (FH4702)	●								●								
TEIFI (RIVER) (FH4707)	●								●			●	●				
TEIFI (RIVER) (FH4706)	●								●								
TEIFI (RIVER) (FH4710)	●								●								
TEIFI (RIVER) (FH4711)	●												●				
TEIFI (RIVER) (FH4708)	●								●				●				
TEIFI (RIVER) (FH4712)													●				
TEIFY POOLS FISHERY (FH4715)									●								
YSTWYTH (RIVER) (FH5574)	●								●				●				
CONWY																	
ALED (RIVER) (FH0069)	●								●								
CLWYD (RIVER) (FH1032)	●								●								
CONWY (RIVER) (FH1096)	●								●								
CONWY (RIVER) (FH1093)	●								●				●				
CONWY (RIVER) (FH1097)	●								●								
CONWY (RIVER) (FH1095)	●								●								
CONWY (RIVER) (FH1094)	●								●				●				
CONWY VALLEY FISHERIES (FH1099)				●													
ELWY (RIVER) (FH1576)	●								●								
ELWY (RIVER) (FH1577)	●								●								
GILER ARMS LAKE (FH1855)				●													
LLEDR (RIVER) (FH2777)	●								●								
LLYN ALED (FH2791)									●								
LLYN CRAFNANT FISHERIES (FH2803)												●					
LLYN NANT-Y-CERRIG (FH2819)				●													
TAN-Y-MYNYDD TROUT LAKES (FH4657)												●					
TREFANT POOL (FH4912)				●													

Fish Species Available at UK & Irish Fisheries

Fishery	Barbel	Bleak	Bream	Carp Blue	Carp Common	Carp Crucian	Carp Ghost	Carp Grass	Carp Koi	Carp Leather	Carp Mirror	Carp Silver	Carp Wild	Catfish	Catfish Albino	Catfish American Bullhead	Catfish Black Bullhead	Charr	Chub	Dace	Eel	Flounder	Goldfish	Grayling	Grilse	Gudgeon	Gwyniad	Minnow	Orfe	Orfe Blue	Orfe Golden	Perch	Pike	Roach	Rudd	Ruffe	Salmon	Steelhead	Sturgeon	Tench	Tench Golden	Trount American Brook	Trout Blue	Trout Brook	Trout Brown	Trout Golden	Trout Lake	Ttrout Rainbow	Trout Sea	Trout Tiger	Trout Wild	Vendace	Zander
TYDDYN MAWR TROUT FARM (FH5015)																																																●					
DENBIGHSHIRE																																																					
ABBEY FISHERY (FH0002)																																													●								
ALWEN (RIVER) (FH0092)																																													●								
ALWEN RESERVOIR (FH0093)																																●													●			●					
CEIRIOG (RIVER) (FH0882)																								●																					●			●					
CEIRIOG (RIVER) (FH0883)																																													●								
CEIRW STREAM (FH0884)																								●									●				●								●				●				
CLWYD (RIVER) (FH1034)																																					●								●								
CLWYD (RIVER) (FH1033)																																					●								●								
CLYWEDOG (RIVER) (FH1042)																																					●								●								
DEE (RIVER) (FH1309)			●																●	●	●			●		●		●				●	●	●		●	●								●			●	●		●		
DEE (RIVER) (FH1310)																																													●								
DEE (RIVER) (FH1311)																								●									●				●								●				●				
DEE (RIVER) (FH1307)																								●													●								●								
DOLWEN AND PLAS UCHAF (FH1398)																																													●			●					
DRAGONFLY FISHERIES (FH1434)																																										●			●			●					
ELWY (RIVER) (FH1578)																																					●								●								
GWYDDELWERN POOL (FH2052)					●						●																													●													
LLYN ALWEN (FH2792)																								●									●				●								●				●				
LLYN BRENIG (FH2795)																																													●			●		●			
MONKS POOL (FH3346)			●		●						●								●													●	●	●						●													
PANT GLAS RESERVOIR (FH3691)																																													●			●					
FLINTSHIRE																																																					
ALLTAMI CLAY PITS (FH0081)			●		●						●																							●						●													
ALYN (RIVER) (FH0097)																								●													●								●								
ALYN (RIVER) (FH0098)																																													●								
BUCKLEY TRAP POOL (FH0718)			●		●	●					●																					●		●	●					●													
CLAWDD OFFAS DYKE (FH0984)			●		●	●	●				●																					●		●	●					●													
CLWYD (RIVER) (FH1035)																																					●								●								
DEE (RIVER) (FH1312)																																					●								●								
FOREST HILL TROUT FARM (FH1766)																																													●			●					
GWERYD LAKES FISHING (FH2047)			●		●	●					●																					●		●	●					●													
GYRN CASTLE FISHERY (FH2056)					●	●	●				●																								●					●													

Fish Species Available at UK & Irish Fisheries

Fishery	Barbel	Bleak	Bream	Carp Blue	Carp Common	Carp Crucian	Carp Ghost	Carp Grass	Carp Koi	Carp Leather	Carp Mirror	Carp Silver	Carp Wild	Catfish	Catfish Albino	Catfish American Bullhead	Catfish Black Bullhead	Charr	Chub	Dace	Eel	Flounder	Goldfish	Grayling	Grilse	Gudgeon
NANT-Y-GAIN FISHERY (FH3420)																										
PADESWOOD POOL (FH3684)					●						●															
SARN MILL FISHERIES (FH4106)					●	●					●															
SEVEN SPRINGS FISHERIES (FH4143)																										
SWAN LAKE (FH4590)					●						●															
WAL GOCH FLY (FH5115)																										
WHEELER (RIVER) (FH5317)																										
GLAMORGAN (VALE OF)																										
HAZELCOURT PONDS (FH2164)							●		●		●										●					
MELLTE (STREAM) (FH3251)																										
PENTWYN RESERVOIR (FH3745)			●		●						●															
PENYWERN PONDS (FH3750)			●		●						●															●
PONTSTICILL RESERVOIR (FH3817)			●		●						●								●							
TAFF (RIVER) (FH4632)																										
TAFF BARGOED (FH4633)																										
GWYNEDD																										
AFON LLYFNI (RIVER) (FH0037)																										
AFON SEIONT (RIVER) (FH0038)																		●			●					
BONTNEWYDD FISHERY (FH0542)																										
BRON EIFION FISHERIES (FH0675)																										
CLWYD (RIVER) (FH1036)																										
CONWY (RIVER) (FH1098)																					●					
CREGENNAN LAKES (FH1177)																										
CWM SILYN LAKE (FH1235)																										
DEE (RIVER) (FH1314)																		●		●	●			●		
DEE (RIVER) (FH1313)																								●		
DUGOED (RIVER) (FH1462)																					●					
DWYRYD (RIVER) (FH1490)																										
DYSYNNI (RIVER) (FH1497)																										
DYSYNNI (RIVER) (FH1496)																										
DYWARCHEN RESERVOIR (FH1498)																										
EDEN (RIVER) (FH1538)																										
ERCH (RIVER) (FH1605)																										
FFESTINIOG FISHERY (FH1702)																										

Fishery	Gwyniad	Minnow	Orfe	Orfe Blue	Orfe Golden	Perch	Pike	Roach	Rudd	Ruffe	Salmon	Steelhead	Sturgeon	Tench	Tench Golden	Trount American Brook	Trout Blue	Trout Brook	Trout Brown	Trout Golden	Trout Lake	Ttrout Rainbow	Trout Sea	Trout Tiger	Trout Wild	Vendace	Zander
NANT-Y-GAIN FISHERY (FH3420)																			●			●					
PADESWOOD POOL (FH3684)																											
SARN MILL FISHERIES (FH4106)								●	●					●					●			●					
SEVEN SPRINGS FISHERIES (FH4143)																			●			●					
SWAN LAKE (FH4590)								●						●													
WAL GOCH FLY (FH5115)																			●			●					
WHEELER (RIVER) (FH5317)											●								●								
GLAMORGAN (VALE OF)																											
HAZELCOURT PONDS (FH2164)									●					●													
MELLTE (STREAM) (FH3251)											●								●								
PENTWYN RESERVOIR (FH3745)						●	●	●																			
PENYWERN PONDS (FH3750)						●		●						●													
PONTSTICILL RESERVOIR (FH3817)						●	●	●	●					●					●								
TAFF (RIVER) (FH4632)											●								●								
TAFF BARGOED (FH4633)																			●			●					
GWYNEDD																											
AFON LLYFNI (RIVER) (FH0037)											●								●				●				
AFON SEIONT (RIVER) (FH0038)		●									●								●		●	●	●				
BONTNEWYDD FISHERY (FH0542)											●								●								
BRON EIFION FISHERIES (FH0675)																			●								
CLWYD (RIVER) (FH1036)											●								●								
CONWY (RIVER) (FH1098)											●												●				
CREGENNAN LAKES (FH1177)																			●			●					
CWM SILYN LAKE (FH1235)																			●								
DEE (RIVER) (FH1314)		●				●	●	●	●		●								●		●						
DEE (RIVER) (FH1313)											●								●								
DUGOED (RIVER) (FH1462)											●								●				●				
DWYRYD (RIVER) (FH1490)											●								●								
DYSYNNI (RIVER) (FH1497)											●								●								
DYSYNNI (RIVER) (FH1496)											●								●				●				
DYWARCHEN RESERVOIR (FH1498)																						●					
EDEN (RIVER) (FH1538)											●								●								
ERCH (RIVER) (FH1605)											●								●				●		●		
FFESTINIOG FISHERY (FH1702)																			●								

Fish Species Available at UK & Irish Fisheries

Fishery	Barbel	Bleak	Bream	Carp Blue	Carp Common	Carp Crucian	Carp Ghost	Carp Grass	Carp Koi	Carp Leather	Carp Mirror	Carp Silver	Carp Wild	Catfish	Catfish Albino	Catfish American Bullhead	Catfish Black Bullhead	Charr	Chub	Dace	Eel	Flounder	Goldfish	Grayling	Grilse	Gudgeon	Gwyniad	Minnow	Orfe	Orfe Blue	Orfe Golden	Perch	Pike	Roach	Rudd	Ruffe	Salmon	Steelhead	Sturgeon	Tench	Tench Golden	Trount American Brook	Trout Blue	Trout Brook	Trout Brown	Trout Golden	Trout Lake	Ttrout Rainbow	Trout Sea	Trout Tiger	Trout Wild	Vendace	Zander
GLAN MORFA MAWR FISHERY (FH1868)																					●																												●					
GWYNEDD (RIVER) (FH2054)																																					●												●				
GWYRFAI (RIVER) (FH2055)																																					●												●				
LERI (RIVER) (FH2704)																																					●								●								
LLIW (RIVER) (FH2781)																																					●								●								
LLYN BUGEILYN (FH2797)																																					●								●								
LLYN CWELLYN RESERVOIR (FH2804)																																													●								
LLYN CWMYSTRADLLYN (FH2805)																					●																								●			●			●		
LLYN CYNWCH LAKE (FH2807)																																					●								●								
LLYN DDU (BLACK LAKE) (FH2808)																																																	●		●		
LLYN DINAS (FH2810)																																					●																
LLYN GLAN MOFA MAWR (FH2813)																																																●					
LLYN PADARN (FH2821)																		●																										●				●				
LLYN TEGID (BALA LAKE) (FH2823)																					●					●	●	●				●	●	●			●								●								
MAWDDACH (RIVER) (FH3211)																																					●												●				
MAWDDACH (RIVER) (FH3212)																																					●												●				
MAWDDACH AND WNION (RIVERS) (FH3213)																																					●								●				●				
NANTLLE LAKE (FH3419)																																					●								●				●				
OGWEN (RIVER) (FH3582)																																					●								●								
PORTH WATERS FISHERY (FH3826)																																					●								●								
RHYDHIR (RIVER) (FH3939)																																					●								●				●		●		
TALYLLYN LAKE (FH4640)																																					●								●				●				
TANYGRISIAU RESERVOIR (FH4656)																																													●			●					
TRAWFFYNYDD RESERVOIR (FH4905)								●																								●			●										●			●					
TRYWERYN (RIVER) (FH4962)																																													●		●						
WNION (RIVER) (FH5453)																																					●												●				
WNION (RIVER) (FH5452)																																					●												●				
ISLE OF ANGLESEY																																																					
BREAKWATER PARK (FH0610)					●	●	●				●										●											●		●	●																			
CEFNI RESERVOIR (FH0881)																																													●			●					
LLYN ALAN (FH2788)																																													●			●					
LLYN BRYNTIRION (FH2796)					●						●																					●																					
LLYN DEWI (FH2809)			●		●	●					●										●											●		●	●					●													
LLYN LLWYDIARTH FAWR (FH2815)																																			●										●								

Fish Species Available at UK & Irish Fisheries

Species	LLYN NANT ANOG (FH2817)	LLYN TACAN (FH2822)	LLYN Y GORS (FH2824)	PARC NEWYDD TROUT FISHERY (FH3696)	PLAS-Y-NANT TROUT FISHERY (FH3799)	TY HEN LAKE (FH5013)	TYDDYN SARGENT (FH5016)
Zander							
Vendace							
Trout Wild							
Trout Tiger							
Trout Sea							
Ttrout Rainbow				●	●		
Trout Lake							
Trout Golden							
Trout Brown				●	●		
Trout Brook							
Trout Blue							
Trount American Brook					●		
Tench Golden							
Tench	●	●	●			●	●
Sturgeon							
Steelhead							
Salmon							
Ruffe							
Rudd	●	●	●			●	●
Roach	●	●	●			●	●
Pike			●				
Perch	●	●	●				
Orfe Golden							
Orfe Blue							
Orfe							
Minnow							
Gwyniad							
Gudgeon							
Grilse							
Grayling							
Goldfish							
Flounder							
Eel	●	●	●				
Dace							
Chub							
Charr							
Catfish Black Bullhead							
Catfish American Bullhead							
Catfish Albino							
Catfish			●				
Carp Wild							
Carp Silver							
Carp Mirror	●		●			●	●
Carp Leather							
Carp Koi							
Carp Grass							
Carp Ghost			●				●
Carp Crucian	●		●			●	●
Carp Common	●		●			●	●
Carp Blue							
Bream	●	●	●				●
Bleak							
Barbel							

MONMOUTHSHIRE

Species	CWMCELYN POND (FH1237)	FAIROAK FISHERY (FH1655)	FIVE TREES (FH1740)	MONNOW (RIVER) (FH3351)	OLWAY BROOK (FH3611)	TREFALDU FISHERY (FH4911)	TROTHY (RIVER) (FH4960)	USK (RIVER) (FH5078)	USK (RIVER) (FH5077)	WYE (RIVER) (FH5537)
Zander										
Vendace										
Trout Wild										
Trout Tiger										
Trout Sea										
Ttrout Rainbow		●								
Trout Lake										
Trout Golden										
Trout Brown		●		●	●		●	●	●	●
Trout Brook										
Trout Blue										
Trount American Brook										
Tench Golden										
Tench	●			●		●				
Sturgeon										
Steelhead										
Salmon					●		●	●		●
Ruffe										
Rudd						●				
Roach	●					●				
Pike										●
Perch	●									
Orfe Golden										
Orfe Blue										
Orfe										
Minnow										
Gwyniad										
Gudgeon	●			●						
Grilse										
Grayling				●						
Goldfish										
Flounder										
Eel				●						
Dace	●			●						●
Chub	●			●						●
Charr										
Catfish Black Bullhead										
Catfish American Bullhead										
Catfish Albino										
Catfish										
Carp Wild										
Carp Silver										
Carp Mirror	●		●	●		●				
Carp Leather										
Carp Koi										
Carp Grass						●				
Carp Ghost										
Carp Crucian	●					●				
Carp Common	●		●	●		●				
Carp Blue										
Bream						●				
Bleak				●						
Barbel										

NEATH PORT TALBOT

Species	AFAN STREAM (FH0036)	DULAIS (RIVER) (FH1466)	GLYNCORRWG PONDS FISHERY (FH1903)	HEPSTE (STREAM) (FH2188)	NEATH (RIVER) (FH3434)	NEATH (RIVER) (FH3433)	NEATH (RIVER) (FH3432)
Zander							
Vendace							
Trout Wild							
Trout Tiger							
Trout Sea					●	●	
Ttrout Rainbow			●				
Trout Lake							
Trout Golden							
Trout Brown	●	●		●	●	●	●
Trout Brook							
Trout Blue							
Trount American Brook							
Tench Golden							
Tench							
Sturgeon							
Steelhead							
Salmon	●	●		●	●	●	●
Ruffe							
Rudd							
Roach							
Pike							
Perch							
Orfe Golden							
Orfe Blue							
Orfe							
Minnow							
Gwyniad							
Gudgeon							
Grilse							
Grayling							
Goldfish							
Flounder							
Eel							
Dace							
Chub							
Charr							
Catfish Black Bullhead							
Catfish American Bullhead							
Catfish Albino							
Catfish							
Carp Wild							
Carp Silver							
Carp Mirror							
Carp Leather							
Carp Koi							
Carp Grass							
Carp Ghost							
Carp Crucian							
Carp Common							
Carp Blue							
Bream							
Bleak							
Barbel							

NEWPORT

Species	DEE (RIVER) (FH1298)	LLISWERRY POND (FH2780)	MONMOUTHSHIRE & BRECON CANAL (FH3348)	SHROPSHIRE UNION CANAL (FH4250)	WENTWOOD RESERVOIR (FH5251)	WOODSTOCK POOL (FH5495)	YNYS-Y-FRO RESERVOIR (FH5571)
Zander							
Vendace							
Trout Wild							
Trout Tiger							
Trout Sea							
Ttrout Rainbow					●		●
Trout Lake							
Trout Golden							
Trout Brown	●				●		●
Trout Brook							
Trout Blue							
Trount American Brook							
Tench Golden							
Tench		●				●	
Sturgeon							
Steelhead							
Salmon	●						
Ruffe							
Rudd		●				●	
Roach		●		●		●	
Pike							
Perch						●	
Orfe Golden							
Orfe Blue							
Orfe							
Minnow							
Gwyniad							
Gudgeon							
Grilse							
Grayling							
Goldfish							
Flounder							
Eel							
Dace							
Chub							
Charr							
Catfish Black Bullhead							
Catfish American Bullhead							
Catfish Albino							
Catfish							
Carp Wild							
Carp Silver							
Carp Mirror		●		●		●	
Carp Leather							
Carp Koi							
Carp Grass							
Carp Ghost							
Carp Crucian			●				
Carp Common		●				●	
Carp Blue							
Bream		●				●	
Bleak							
Barbel							

Fish Species Available at UK & Irish Fisheries

Fishery	Barbel	Bleak	Bream	Carp Blue	Carp Common	Carp Crucian	Carp Ghost	Carp Grass	Carp Koi	Carp Leather	Carp Mirror	Carp Silver	Carp Wild	Catfish	Catfish Albino	Catfish American Bullhead	Catfish Black Bullhead	Charr	Chub	Dace	Eel	Flounder	Goldfish	Grayling	Grilse	Gudgeon	Gwyniad	Minnow	Orfe	Orfe Blue	Orfe Golden	Perch	Pike	Roach	Rudd	Ruffe	Salmon	Steelhead	Sturgeon	Tench	Tench Golden	Trount American Brook	Trout Blue	Trout Brook	Trout Brown	Trout Golden	Trout Lake	Ttrout Rainbow	Trout Sea	Trout Tiger	Trout Wild	Vendace	Zander
NORFOLK																																																					
DEE (RIVER) (FH1315)	●																		●	●				●									●	●			●								●				●				
PEMBROKESHIRE																																																					
EASTERN CLEDDAU (RIVER) (FH1522)																																					●								●								
EASTERN CLEDDAU (RIVER) (FH1521)																																					●								●				●		●		
EASTERN CLEDDAU (RIVER) (FH1520)																																					●							●	●			●	●		●		
EWENNY (RIVER) (FH1637)																																					●																
HAYCASTLE TROUT FISHERY (FH2149)																																																●					
HAYSCASTLE TROUT FISHERY (FH2159)																																													●								
HOLGAN TROUT FARM FISHERY (FH2252)						●																															●			●													
IAN HEAPS PREMIER FISHERIES (FH2356)			●		●	●	●		●	●	●								●		●					●		●	●		●			●	●					●													
LLYS Y FRAN RESERVOIR (FH2829)																																													●			●					
LUDCHURCH LAKE (FH3103)					●						●																					●			●					●													
ROADSIDE FARM (FH3974)			●		●	●					●																							●																			
ROSEBUSH RESERVOIR (FH4013)																																													●								
WEST ATHESTON COARSE FISHERY (FH5256)	●		●		●	●		●			●																					●		●	●					●													
WESTERN CLEDDAU (RIVER) (FH5272)																																					●								●								
WESTERN CLEDDAU (RIVER) (FH5273)																																					●								●								
YET-Y-GORS FISHERY (FH5566)																																											●					●					
POWYS																																																					
BOATSIDE FARM (FH0520)																																					●								●								
CAER BERIS MANOR HOTEL (FH0789)	●																		●					●													●								●								
CLYNWEDOG RESERVOIR (FH1041)																																													●			●					
CLYWEDOG (RIVER) (FH1043)																																													●			●					
DEE (RIVER) (FH1316)																								●													●								●								
DOL LLYS FARM (FH1394)																																													●								
DULAS (RIVER) (FH1469)																																					●												●				
DULAS (RIVER) (FH1468)																																													●			●					
DULAS (RIVER) (FH1467)																																					●												●				
DYFI (RIVER) (FH1494)																																					●												●				
ELAN (RIVER) (FH1557)																			●					●																					●								
ERCH (RIVER) (FH1606)																																													●								
FACHWEN POOL (FH1651)			●		●						●																							●						●													
GWYDDIOR LAKE (FH2053)																																													●								

Fish Species Available at UK & Irish Fisheries

	Barbel	Bleak	Bream	Carp Blue	Carp Common	Carp Crucian	Carp Ghost	Carp Grass	Carp Koi	Carp Leather	Carp Mirror	Carp Silver	Carp Wild	Catfish	Catfish Albino	Catfish American Bullhead	Catfish Black Bullhead	Charr	Chub	Dace	Eel	Flounder	Goldfish	Grayling	Grilse	Gudgeon	Gwyniad	Minnow	Orfe	Orfe Blue	Orfe Golden	Perch	Pike	Roach	Rudd	Ruffe	Salmon	Steelhead	Sturgeon	Tench	Tench Golden	Trount American Brook	Trout Blue	Trout Brook	Trout Brown	Trout Golden	Trout Lake	Ttrout Rainbow	Trout Sea	Trout Tiger	Trout Wild	Vendace	Zander
IRFON (RIVER) (FH2376)																																					●								●								
IRFON (RIVER) (FH2375)																																					●								●								
IRFON (RIVER) (FH2378)	●																		●		●			●				●					●				●								●								
IRFON (RIVER) (FH2377)																								●																					●								
ITHON (RIVER) (FH2400)																			●	●	●			●				●									●								●								
LLANDRINIO WEST LAKE (FH2771)					●																													●											●			●					
LLANGORSE LAKE (FH2773)			●																		●											●	●	●																			
LLYN ALARCH (FH2789)																																													●			●					
LLYN CLYWEDOG (FH2800)																																													●			●					
LLYN-COCH HWYAD (FH2825)																																													●						●		
LLYNGWYN LAKE (FH2828)																																													●			●					
MONTGOMERY CANAL (FH3355)																			●					●																													
MULE (RIVER) (FH3398)																																													●								
NEW INN (FH3467)																																													●								
RIVERSIDE CARAVAN PARK (FH3968)																			●																										●								
SEVERN (RIVER) (FH4159)	●																		●	●																	●								●								
SEVERN (RIVER) (FH4155)	●																		●	●				●		●		●				●	●	●			●								●								
SEVERN (RIVER) (FH4154)	●																		●	●				●								●	●	●			●								●								
SEVERN (RIVER) (FH4158)	●																		●	●	●											●	●	●			●								●								
SEVERN (RIVER) (FH4160)																																													●								
SEVERN (RIVER) (FH4151)	●																		●	●																	●								●								
SEVERN (RIVER) (FH4153)																																													●			●					
SEVERN (RIVER) (FH4156)																			●					●																					●								
SEVERN (RIVER) (FH4161)																			●					●													●								●								
SEVERN (RIVER) (FH4152)																			●	●																	●								●								
SHROPSHIRE UNION CANAL (FH4252)					●						●								●		●											●	●	●	●					●													
TWYMYN (RIVER) (FH5011)																																					●								●				●				
USK (RIVER) (FH5079)																																					●								●								
VYRNWY (RIVER) (FH5104)																																					●								●								
VYRNWY (RIVER) (FH5105)																																													●								
VYRNWY (RIVER) (FH5107)																																					●								●								
VYRNWY (RIVER) (FH5108)	●																		●																																		
VYRNWY (RIVER) (FH5102)																			●	●				●									●	●											●								
VYRNWY (RIVER) (FH5103)	●																		●	●												●		●			●								●								

Fish Species Available at UK & Irish Fisheries

	Barbel	Bleak	Bream	Carp Blue	Carp Common	Carp Crucian	Carp Ghost	Carp Grass	Carp Koi	Carp Leather	Carp Mirror	Carp Silver	Carp Wild	Catfish	Catfish Albino	Catfish American Bullhead	Catfish Black Bullhead	Charr	Chub	Dace	Eel	Flounder	Goldfish	Grayling	Grilse	Gudgeon	Gwyniad	Minnow	Orfe	Orfe Blue	Orfe Golden	Perch	Pike	Roach	Rudd	Ruffe	Salmon	Steelhead	Sturgeon	Tench	Tench Golden	Trount American Brook	Trout Blue	Trout Brook	Trout Brown	Trout Golden	Trout Lake	Ttrout Rainbow	Trout Sea	Trout Tiger	Trout Wild	Vendace	Zander
WESTLAKE FISHERY (FH5282)					●	●	●			●	●								●													●		●	●										●	●			●				
WYE (RIVER) (FH5538)																								●													●								●							
WYE (RIVER) (FH5541)	●																		●	●	●			●				●				●				●									●							
WYE (RIVER) (FH5540)																																				●								●							
WYE (RIVER) (FH5542)																								●																					●							
RHONDDA CYNON TAFF																																																					
CMPRAC (RIVER) (FH1045)																																													●			●					
ELY (RIVER) (FH1579)																																				●								●							
LLYN ALAW (FH2790)																				●													●											●			●			●		
RHONDDA (RIVER) (FH3937)																																													●			●					
SEVEN OAKS FISHERY (FH4141)			●		●	●	●			●	●																									●	●					●			●		●		●	●		●			
TRI NANT TROUT FARM (FH4951)																																																●					
SWANSEA																																																					
FENDROD LAKE (FH1694)			●		●	●			●	●	●									●	●							●	●			●		●	●					●													
GOWERTON COARSE FISHERY (FH1929)			●		●	●					●								●	●						●					●	●		●	●					●													
MAES GWYN FISHERY (FH3136)					●		●		●	●	●			●																																	●					
SHIMANO FELINDRE (FH4239)																																													●			●					
TAWE (RIVER) (FH4675)																																				●								●							
WHITE SPRINGS LAKES (FH5341)			●		●	●	●	●		●	●											●					●						●	●	●	●	●					●					●			●				
TORFAEN																																																					
BEACONS RESERVOIRS (FH0354)																																													●			●					
CWMBRAN BOATING LAKE (FH1236)			●		●						●								●		●					●					●		●		●						●													
LISVANE RESERVOIR (FH2738)																																													●			●					
LLANDEGFEDD RESERVOIR (FH2769)																																	●																					
LLANISHEN RESERVOIR (FH2774)																																													●			●					
LLYN ON RESERVOIR (FH2820)																																													●			●					
LLYWD (RIVER) (FH2831)																																				●								●							
MORGANS POND (FH3372)					●						●																																									
WREXHAM																																																					
ALYN (RIVER) (FH0095)																																													●							
ALYN (RIVER) (FH0094)																																													●							
ALYN (RIVER) (FH0096)																																													●							
ARGAE LAKE (FH0133)					●						●								●											●		●																				
DEE (RIVER) (FH1302)																																													●							

Fish Species Available at UK & Irish Fisheries

Fishery	Barbel	Bleak	Bream	Carp Blue	Carp Common	Carp Crucian	Carp Ghost	Carp Grass	Carp Koi	Carp Leather	Carp Mirror	Carp Silver	Carp Wild	Catfish	Catfish Albino	Catfish American Bullhead	Catfish Black Bullhead	Charr
DEE (RIVER) (FH1320)																		
DEE (RIVER) (FH1318)																		
DEE (RIVER) (FH1301)																		
DEE (RIVER) (FH1300)																		
DEE (RIVER) (FH1304)																		
DEE (RIVER) (FH1303)																		
DEE (RIVER) (FH1299)																		
DEE ABBEY FISHERIES (FH1321)																		
FLASH (FH1743)					●						●							
LLANDEGLA TROUT FISHERY (FH2770)																		
LLAY RESERVOIR (FH2776)					●						●							
PENYCAE LOWER RESERVOIR (FH3748)																		
PENYCAE UPPER RESERVOIR (FH3749)																		
PONKY POOL (FH3815)			●		●						●							
TAN LLAN (FH4649)			●			●	●											
TREE TOPS FLY FISHERY (FH4910)																		
TRENCH FISHERIES (FH4913)					●	●					●							
TY MAWR RESERVOIR (FH5014)																		
WORTHENBURY BROOK (FH5509)																		

Fishery	Chub	Dace	Eel	Flounder	Goldfish	Grayling	Grilse	Gudgeon	Gwyniad	Minnow	Orfe	Orfe Blue	Orfe Golden	Perch	Pike	Roach	Rudd	Ruffe
DEE (RIVER) (FH1320)	●	●													●	●		
DEE (RIVER) (FH1318)	●	●	●												●			
DEE (RIVER) (FH1301)						●												
DEE (RIVER) (FH1300)																		
DEE (RIVER) (FH1304)																		
DEE (RIVER) (FH1303)																		
DEE (RIVER) (FH1299)																		
DEE ABBEY FISHERIES (FH1321)						●												
FLASH (FH1743)															●		●	
LLANDEGLA TROUT FISHERY (FH2770)																		
LLAY RESERVOIR (FH2776)														●	●		●	
PENYCAE LOWER RESERVOIR (FH3748)																		
PENYCAE UPPER RESERVOIR (FH3749)																		
PONKY POOL (FH3815)																●		
TAN LLAN (FH4649)											●			●		●	●	
TREE TOPS FLY FISHERY (FH4910)																		
TRENCH FISHERIES (FH4913)		●															●	
TY MAWR RESERVOIR (FH5014)																		
WORTHENBURY BROOK (FH5509)						●												

Fishery	Salmon	Steelhead	Sturgeon	Tench	Tench Golden	Trount American Brook	Trout Blue	Trout Brook	Trout Brown	Trout Golden	Trout Lake	Ttrout Rainbow	Trout Sea	Trout Tiger	Trout Wild	Vendace	Zander
DEE (RIVER) (FH1320)	●								●				●				
DEE (RIVER) (FH1318)	●								●				●				
DEE (RIVER) (FH1301)	●								●								
DEE (RIVER) (FH1300)	●								●								
DEE (RIVER) (FH1304)	●								●								
DEE (RIVER) (FH1303)	●								●								
DEE (RIVER) (FH1299)	●								●								
DEE ABBEY FISHERIES (FH1321)									●			●					
FLASH (FH1743)				●													
LLANDEGLA TROUT FISHERY (FH2770)						●			●			●					
LLAY RESERVOIR (FH2776)				●													
PENYCAE LOWER RESERVOIR (FH3748)									●			●					
PENYCAE UPPER RESERVOIR (FH3749)									●			●					
PONKY POOL (FH3815)				●													
TAN LLAN (FH4649)				●													
TREE TOPS FLY FISHERY (FH4910)												●					
TRENCH FISHERIES (FH4913)				●													
TY MAWR RESERVOIR (FH5014)									●			●					
WORTHENBURY BROOK (FH5509)	●								●								

by Species by Specimen Weights

SECTION 12

This section allows you to search for specimen weights of species known to have been caught at Fisheries.

e.g Find a 60lb Mirror Carp?

Once you have located a Fishery you can either look up further details in Section 1 or use the other sections to find what else the Fishery may have to offer.

Angling Times Fishooked Directory

BARBEL

19lbs 2ozs
- OUSE (RIVER) (FH3642)

19lbs 1ozs
- GREAT OUSE (RIVER) (FH1986)

16lbs 14ozs
- GREAT OUSE (RIVER) (FH1988)

16lbs 6ozs
- TAVERHAM MILLS FISHERY (FH4669)

16lbs 5ozs
- MAKIN FISHERIES (FH3150)

16lbs 4ozs
- AVON RIVER FISHERIES (FH0228)
- FORDCOMBE (FH1762)

16lbs 2ozs
- MEDWAY (RIVER) (FH3234)

14lbs 15ozs
- BRISTOL AVON (FH0647)
- BRISTOL AVON (FH0648)
- BRISTOL AVON (FH0649)
- BRISTOL AVON (FH0650)

14lbs 14ozs
- AVON (RIVER) (FH0218)

14lbs 11ozs
- HAMPSHIRE AVON (FH2082)

14lbs 8ozs
- HAMPSHIRE AVON (RIVER) (FH2088)

14lbs 6ozs
- AVON (RIVER) (FH0212)
- HAMPSHIRE AVON (RIVER) (FH2091)
- THAMES (RIVER) (FH4795)
- WARWICKSHIRE AVON (FH5158)

14lbs 5ozs
- SEVERN (RIVER) (FH4186)

14lbs 2ozs
- KENNET (RIVER) (FH2438)
- SEVERN (RIVER) (FH4167)
- THROOP FISHERIES (FH4834)

13lbs 12ozs
- LEA (RIVER) (FH2646)
- TYRINGHAM ESTATE (FH5037)

13lbs 8ozs
- BURGHFIELD (FH0739)
- MOCCAS FISHERY (FH3333)
- SEVERN (RIVER) (FH4189)
- SEVERN (RIVER) (FH4194)
- WINKTON FISHERY (FH5418)

13lbs 6ozs
- KINGSNORDLEY (FH2517)

13lbs 5ozs
- ROYALTY FISHERY (FH4049)

13lbs 1ozs
- AVON (BRISTOL) (RIVER) (FH0197)
- AVON (BRISTOL) (RIVER) (FH0200)
- ST PATRICKS (FH4395)

12lbs 14ozs
- FISHERS GREEN (FH1731)

12lbs 12ozs
- DINTON PASTURES COUNTRY PARK (FH1375)

12lbs 10ozs
- FLEET (RIVER) (FH1745)
- HAMPSHIRE AVON (RIVER) (FH2090)

12lbs 8ozs
- BRISTOL AVON (FH0653)
- COLWICK COUNTRY PARK (FH1080)
- HAYSDEN COUNTRY PARK (FH2160)
- KENNET (RIVER) (FH2445)

12lbs 0ozs
- MEADOWLANDS (FH3227)

11lbs 15ozs
- AVON (BRISTOL) (RIVER) (FH0195)

11lbs 8ozs
- RED LION FISHERY (FH3910)
- WARWICKSHIRE AVON (FH5161)

11lbs 6ozs
- FRANT LAKES (FH1798)
- SWALE (RIVER) (FH4569)
- SWALE (RIVER) (FH4576)

11lbs 4ozs
- CAER BERIS MANOR HOTEL (FH0789)

11lbs 2ozs
- HAMPSHIRE AVON (RIVER) (FH2087)

10lbs 4ozs
- TWYFORD BBONT (FH5008)

10lbs 0ozs
- MARSHLANDS (FH3194)
- SEVERN (RIVER) (FH4172)
- SEVERN (RIVER) (FH4176)
- TEME (RIVER) (FH4725)

9lbs 14ozs
- THAMES (RIVER) (FH4805)

9lbs 12ozs
- CARTHAGENA FISHERY (FH0855)
- MONK LAKE FISHERIES (FH3342)

9lbs 10ozs
- CATTON PARK LAKE (FH0875)
- DOVECOTE LAKE FISHERY (FH1430)

9lbs 8ozs
- COLNE (RIVER) (FH1072)
- KENNET (RIVER) (FH2440)
- LYMM VALE (FH3116)

9lbs 0ozs
- LEA (RIVER) (FH2644)
- TRENT (RIVER) (FH4936)
- WHITEWATER (RIVER) (FH5356)
- WOODLAND LAKES (FH5479)

8lbs 13ozs
- AVON (RIVER) (FH0215)

8lbs 8ozs
- STOW (RIVER) (FH4511)
- WEY NAVIGATION (RIVER) (FH5292)

8lbs 2ozs
- NIDD (RIVER) (FH3501)

8lbs 0ozs
- LEA (RIVER) (FH2645)
- WYE (RIVER) (FH5530)

7lbs 8ozs
- SWALE (RIVER) (FH4585)
- TEME (RIVER) (FH4728)

6lbs 10ozs
- STANSTEAD ABBOTTS (FH4423)

6lbs 8ozs
- BISHOPS BOWL LAKES (FH0435)
- WEY (RIVER) (FH5289)

6lbs 0ozs
- DANE (RIVER) (FH1266)
- LATHOM FISHERIES (FH2627)

BREAM

18lbs 15ozs
- BAWBURGH LAKES (FH0348)

16lbs 12ozs
- SWITHLAND RESERVOIR (FH4616)

14lbs 12ozs
- LINCH HILL FISHERY (FH2725)
- WHITE SWAN LAKE (FH5343)

14lbs 10ozs
- LOCKWOOD RESERVOIR (FH2974)

14lbs 8ozs
- RYEMEADS (FH4076)

13lbs 10ozs
- WOOLPACK FISHERY (FH5500)

13lbs 8ozs
- BROADLANDS LAKES (FH0664)
- CHIDDINGSTONE CASTLE LAKE (FH0939)
- HAREFIELD CARP LAKE (FH2105)
- LOW MAYNARD RESERVOIR (FH3067)

12lbs 13ozs
- LAYZELLS FARM (FH2640)

12lbs 10ozs
- BLUEBELL LAKE (FH0513)
- PONTSTICILL RESERVOIR (FH3817)

12lbs 9ozs
- SWANGEY LAKES (FH4598)

12lbs 8ozs
- NORTH TROY LAKE AND COLNE (RIVER) (FH3536)

11lbs 11ozs
- FRIMLEY LAKES (FH1802)

11lbs 8ozs
- CLAWFORD VINEYARD AND FISHERIES (FH0985)
- NEWHAY DAY TICKET LAKE (FH3484)
- ROSSWAYS WATER (FH4021)
- WOODLAND WATERS (FH5482)

10lbs 12ozs
- HANCHURCH FISHERIES (FH2099)
- LIZARD LAKES (FH2766)
- NORTH MET PIT (FH3532)

10lbs 11ozs
- FISHERS GREEN (FH1731)

10lbs 8ozs
- DARENTH FISHING COMPLEX (FH1273)
- ELLERTON PARK (FH1568)
- SOVEREIGN LAKES (FH4354)
- SWILLINGTON PARK (FH4609)
- WICKHAM MARKET RESERVOIRS (FH5365)

9lbs 15ozs
- THORPE PARK WATERSKI LAKE (FH4824)

9lbs 14ozs
- AVON RIVER FISHERIES (FH0228)

9lbs 12ozs
- ASHBY PARK FISHERIES (FH0158)
- UPTON WARREN LAKE (FH5062)

9lbs 10ozs
- GOLD VALLEY LAKES (FH1909)
- STANFORD-LE-HOPE (FH4418)

9lbs 9ozs
- STOW (RIVER) (FH4510)

9lbs 8ozs
- GREAT OUSE (RIVER) (FH1996)
- ST MICHAELS WYRESIDE FISHERY (FH4394)
- STONE END FARM LAKES (FH4467)
- WHITE SPRINGS LAKES (FH5341)

8lbs 15ozs

- PALLINGTON LAKES (FH3687)

8lbs 12ozs

- AMWELL LAKES (FH0104)
- AVON (RIVER) (FH0220)
- DANDYS LAKE AND KNIGHTINGALE LAKE (FH1254)
- KENN (RIVER) (FH2433)
- PETERS FINGER LAKES (FH3756)
- STEEPLE LANGFORD LAKES (FH4447)
- STOUR (RIVER) (FH4493)
- TANYARD FISHERIES (FH4654)

8lbs 9ozs

- BOUGH BEECH RESERVOIR (FH0564)

8lbs 8ozs

- AVON (RIVER) (FH0218)
- BUCKLEY TRAP POOL (FH0718)
- CARTHAGENA FISHERY (FH0855)
- FOULRIDGE RESERVOIR (FH1778)
- FRANT LAKES (FH1798)
- HUNSTRETE LAKE COMPLEX (FH2338)
- MILLRACE (FH3316)
- NORTHEY PARK FISHERY (FH3543)
- OUSE (RIVER) (FH3651)
- WRIGHTS FARM (FH5517)

7lbs 15ozs

- LAKE NUMBER ONE (LAKE19) (FH2565)
- STOUR (RIVER) (FH4501)

7lbs 14ozs

- SWALE (RIVER) (FH4569)

7lbs 12ozs

- CHAWSTON LAKES (FH0908)
- GREAT OUSE (RIVER) (FH1991)
- GREAT OUSE (RIVER) (FH1995)
- MONK LAKE FISHERIES (FH3342)
- RINGLAND PITS (FH3953)
- TAVERHAM (FH4668)
- TYRINGHAM ESTATE (FH5037)
- WALL POOL LODGE (FH5121)
- WELDON RESERVOIR (FH5228)

7lbs 11ozs

- NORTH MEADOWS (FH3531)
- WOODLAND LAKES (FH5479)

7lbs 9ozs

- MOTE PARK FISHERY (FH3381)

7lbs 8ozs

- ARDLEIGH RESERVOIR (FH0130)
- BRADSHAW HALL FISHERIES (FH0591)
- CHAD LAKES (FH0890)
- CONNAUGHT WATER (FH1087)
- COOMBE LAKE (FH1107)
- CUTTLE MILL CARP FISHERY (FH1232)
- DIXON GREEN RESERVOIR (FH1380)
- DURLEIGH RESERVOIR (FH1484)
- FACHWEN POOL (FH1651)
- FOXCOTTE LAKE (FH1789)
- MANOR FARM (FH3161)
- MAPLEDURHAM A AND B (FH3172)
- MORETON MERE FISHERY (FH3370)
- OUSE (RIVER) (FH3640)
- PURLEY (FH3858)
- RUSHEY WEIR (FH4062)
- THAMES (RIVER) (FH4798)
- THAMES (RIVER) (FH4763)

6lbs 15ozs

- THAMES (RIVER) (FH4805)

6lbs 12ozs

- MEDWAY (RIVER) (FH3238)
- WILLSMORE WATER (FH5403)

6lbs 11ozs

- BILNEY LAKES (FH0424)

6lbs 10ozs

- LAKE HELEN (FH2558)

6lbs 8ozs

- AVON (BRISTOL) (RIVER) (FH0197)
- COOMBE WATER FISHERY (FH1110)
- CROSS DROVE (FH1191)
- EDEN (RIVER) (FH1542)
- OUSE (RIVER) (FH3639)
- TATTERSHALL LEISURE PARK (FH4663)
- WITHNELL RESERVOIRS (FH5445)

CARP COMMON

56lbs 2ozs

- BLUEBELL LAKE (FH0513)

52lbs 2ozs

- GREENRIDGE FARM LAKES (FH2009)

51lbs 6ozs

- ACTON BURNELL (FH0025)

51lbs 4ozs

- HAWKHURST FISH FARM (FH2142)

46lbs 8ozs

- DONYLANDS LAKES (FH1406)

45lbs 12ozs

- DARENTH FISHING COMPLEX (FH1273)

44lbs 0ozs

- REDMIRE POOL (FH3921)

43lbs 10ozs

- HAREFIELD CARP LAKE (FH2105)

42lbs 12ozs

- SALLY WALSHES DAM (FH4084)

42lbs 0ozs

- WITHY POOL (FH5446)

41lbs 8ozs

- BURGHFIELD (FH0739)

41lbs 0ozs

- NAZEING MEADS (FH3431)
- SONNING EYE (FH4326)

40lbs 0ozs

- HOMERSFIELD LAKE (FH2284)

39lbs 12ozs

- CRAYFISH POOL (FH1171)

39lbs 2ozs

- FISHERS GREEN (FH1731)

39lbs 1ozs

- TAVERHAM MILLS FISHERY (FH4669)

38lbs 12ozs

- REDESMERE (FH3916)

38lbs 10ozs

- ALEXANDRA PARK WATERS (FH0074)

38lbs 0ozs

- MILTON PAN LAKE (FH3323)
- WINGHAM FISHERY (FH5417)

37lbs 13ozs

- AMWELL LAKES (FH0104)

37lbs 12ozs

- TWYFORD BBONT (FH5008)

37lbs 8ozs

- CROWN NETHERHALL (FH1201)

37lbs 2ozs

- ALDERS LAKES (FH0064)

36lbs 8ozs

- PAPERCOURT FISHERY (FH3694)
- WOOLPACK FISHERY (FH5500)

36lbs 6ozs

- SHEPPERTON LAKE (FH4230)

36lbs 4ozs

- MILTON POOLS FARM (FH3326)

36lbs 0ozs

- ALDENHAM RESERVOIR (FH0058)
- PATSHULL PARK (FH3717)

35lbs 14ozs

- DORCHESTER LAGOON (FH1412)

35lbs 11ozs

- CUTTLE MILL CARP FISHERY (FH1232)

35lbs 10ozs

- WRAYSBURY TWO (FH5514)

35lbs 0ozs

- CHRISTCHURCH LAKE (FH0947)
- OAKHILL LEISURE (FH3563)

34lbs 14ozs

- LAKESIDE FISHERY (FH2592)
- RINGLAND PITS (FH3953)

34lbs 10ozs

- ARGAL RESERVOIR (FH0134)

34lbs 9ozs

- FURNACE LAKES (FH1821)
- TAVERHAM (FH4668)

34lbs 8ozs

- HAYSDEN COUNTRY PARK (FH2160)

34lbs 4ozs

- LAKESIDE LEISURE PARK (FH2594)

34lbs 0ozs

- PONTSTICILL RESERVOIR (FH3817)
- YEOMANS LAKE (FH5565)

33lbs 12ozs

- WHITE SWAN LAKE (FH5343)

33lbs 8ozs

- HARTSMOOR FISHERIES (FH2121)
- TWYNERSH FISHING COMPLEX (FH5012)

33lbs 0ozs

- NEWHAY SPECIMEN LAKE (FH3485)

32lbs 12ozs

- CLIFTON MARINA (FH1008)

32lbs 8ozs

- AVELEY LAKES (FH0187)
- CROXLEY HALL TROUT FISHERY (FH1203)

32lbs 4ozs

- PERCH POND (FH3751)

32lbs 2ozs

- MEDWAY (RIVER) (FH3238)

32lbs 1ozs

- HANCHURCH FISHERIES (FH2099)

32lbs 0ozs

- FRIMLEY LAKES (FH1802)
- GIMINGHAM LAKES (FH1858)
- HEYFORD LAKES (FH2201)
- ISLAND POND - RACKERHAYES (FH2391)

31lbs 14ozs

- WINTONS FISHERY (FH5432)

31lbs 8ozs

- ELMBRIDGE LAKES (FH1569)
- WOODLAND WATERS (FH5482)

31lbs 7ozs

- WESTON LAWN FISHERIES (FH5285)

31lbs 4ozs

- MAYFIELDS LAKE (FH3216)

30lbs 12ozs

- LONGMOOR LAKE (FH2994)

30lbs 10ozs

- CHIGBOROUGH FISHERIES (FH0941)

30lbs 8ozs

- ST JAMES SMALL PARK LAKE (FH4389)

30lbs 7ozs

- FURNACE MILL FISHERY (FH1822)

30lbs 4ozs

- CATCH 22 FISHERY (FH0872)
- LINCH HILL FISHERY (FH2725)

30lbs 2ozs

- OASIS LAKES (FH3570)

30lbs 0ozs

- BAWBURGH LAKES (FH0348)
- BLUE LAGOON LAKE (FH0507)
- BUSBRIDGE LAKE (FH0765)
- EXE (RIVER) (FH1643)
- LYNN POOL FISHERY (FH3125)
- ROCKFORD LAKE (FH3984)
- RYE NOOK FISHERY (FH4075)
- TRI-LAKES (FH4954)
- WILLOW PARK (FH5387)
- WOODRISING WATER MEADOWS (FH5489)
- YEW TREE FISHERIES (FH5567)

CARP CRUCIAN

5lbs 4ozs

- STANFORD-LE-HOPE (FH4418)

5lbs 2ozs

- CLAWFORD VINEYARD AND FISHERIES (FH0985)

4lbs 11ozs

- BROADWATER LAKE (FH0666)
- BURY HILL FISHERIES (FH0764)

4lbs 10ozs

- ALDENHAM RESERVOIR (FH0058)
- CUTTLE MILL CARP FISHERY (FH1232)
- GOLD VALLEY LAKES (FH1909)
- WASING WOODS (FH5165)

4lbs 9ozs

- NUTRABAITS YATELEY COMPLEX (FH3556)

4lbs 8ozs

- ALVECHURCH FISHERIES (FH0090)
- LIGHTMOOR POOL (FH2719)
- RACKLEY HILLS PIT (FH3873)
- WYLANDS INTERNATIONAL ANGLING CENTRE (FH5545)

4lbs 4ozs

- NEWHAY DAY TICKET LAKE (FH3484)

4lbs 2ozs

- BLACKMORE WOOD (FH0452)
- FRIMLEY LAKES (FH1802)

4lbs 1ozs

- BROWNING CUDMORE FISHERY (FH0702)
- NORTH MET PIT (FH3532)

4lbs 0ozs

- FAIRVIEW LAKE (FH1656)

3lbs 14ozs

- WESTFIELD FARM (FH5276)
- WOODFOLD FARM FISHERIES (FH5473)

3lbs 12ozs

- BEAVER FARM FISHERY (FH0359)
- INDIO POND (FH2365)
- TRI-LAKES (FH4954)

3lbs 11ozs

- WEYBREAD FISHERY (FH5293)

3lbs 10ozs

- CHIGBOROUGH FISHERIES (FH0941)
- CLIFTON MARINA (FH1008)

3lbs 9ozs

- HENFOLD LAKES FISHERY (FH2182)

3lbs 8ozs

- ARROW VALLEY LAKE (FH0141)
- AYCLIFFE LAKE (FH0235)
- BARTON BROADS LAKE (FH0337)
- CLUB LAKE (FH1027)
- FLETCHERS POND (FH1747)
- GOLD OAK FISH FARM (FH1908)
- HAWKESBURY FISHERY (FH2141)
- HURST POND (FH2346)
- JOHNSONS LAKE (FH2415)
- LIZARD LAKES (FH2766)
- MEADOWLANDS (FH3227)
- POOL HOUSE FARM (FH3820)
- PROCTORS PLEASURE PARK (FH3851)
- SHOTTON COLLIERY LAKE (FH4248)
- SURRENDEN LAKES (FH4558)
- TASWOOD LAKES FISH FARM AND FISHERY (FH4662)
- THORNEY POOL (FH4816)

3lbs 6ozs

- FISHPONDS FARM AND FISHERY (FH1735)

3lbs 4ozs

- DOCKLOW POOLS (FH1386)
- EVESBATCH FISHERIES (FH1635)
- FENDROD LAKE (FH1694)
- LAKE HELEN (FH2558)
- RINGLAND LAKES (FH3952)
- RINGLAND PITS (FH3953)
- TAVERHAM (FH4668)

3lbs 3ozs

- AVON TYRRELL LAKES (FH0230)

3lbs 2ozs

- BOOTON CLAY PIT (FH0543)
- DISS MERE (FH1376)
- RAKER LAKES (FH3884)
- TINGRITH LAKES (FH4852)
- WIDEHURST FARM (FH5367)
- WILLSMORE WATER (FH5403)

3lbs 0ozs

- BROOKHALL FISHERY (FH0682)
- CAPESTHORNE TOP POOL (FH0833)
- GIMINGHAM LAKES (FH1858)

2lbs 15ozs

- LAKE NUMBER ONE (LAKE19) (FH2565)

2lbs 14ozs

- BORDEAUX PIT (FH0545)

2lbs 12ozs

- CANONS ASHBY LAKES (FH0824)
- ROCKFORD LAKE (FH3984)
- TILEYARD LANE (FH4844)

2lbs 10ozs

- CLATTERCOTE RESERVOIR (FH0979)
- MILL ROAD LAKES (FH3304)

2lbs 9ozs

- FURNACE MILL FISHERY (FH1822)

2lbs 8ozs

- BLUNDELLS FARM FISHERY (FH0514)
- COPPICE POND (FH1113)
- DOUBLEWOODS (FH1418)
- HUCKLESBROOK LAKE (FH2324)
- LAKESIDE FISHING (FH2593)
- LAKESIDE LEISURE PARK (FH2594)
- MARTINS FARM (FH3201)
- MILL POND (FH3298)
- MOATHOUSE LAKE (FH3330)
- MUDEFORD WOOD LAKE (FH3397)
- OHAM LAKES (FH3583)
- RIDDINGS FISHERY (FH3949)
- RINGWOOD LAKE (FH3956)
- ROTHERFIELD POND (FH4030)
- SHAKERLEY MERE (FH4202)
- SUTTON AT HONE LAKES ONE AND THREE (FH4560)
- SYCAMORE FISHING LAKES (FH4618)
- TOTTENHILL PIT (FH4888)
- VALE ROYAL LOCKS (FH5084)

2lbs 7ozs

- BILNEY LAKES (FH0424)
- WILLOW LAKES (FH5384)

2lbs 6ozs

- HANCHURCH FISHERIES (FH2099)
- SILVER LAKE (FH4269)

2lbs 5ozs

- LONGBRIDGE LAKES (FH2987)
- NEW POND (FH3475)

2lbs 4ozs

- GOLDEN POND FISHERY (FH1912)

2lbs 3ozs

- RAILWAY LAKE (FH3877)

2lbs 2ozs

- PACKINGTON SOMERS FISHERY (FH3679)
- SHERWOOD FOREST FARM PARK FISHERY (FH4234)

2lbs 1ozs

- DIXON GREEN RESERVOIR (FH1380)
- KENNET AND AVON CANAL (FH2465)
- MORETON MERE FISHERY (FH3370)
- SPIRES LAKES (FH4365)

2lbs 0ozs

- BRICKYARD PONDS (FH0628)
- EMERALD POOL FISHERY (FH1585)
- HUNSTRETE LAKE COMPLEX (FH2338)
- SHAWFIELDS LAKES (FH4213)
- SINKS PIT (FH4277)
- WILLOWS (THE) (FH5397)

CARP GHOST

26lbs 10ozs

- SWAN VALLEY (FH4596)

25lbs 4ozs

- LONSDALE COUNTRY PARK (FH2997)

25lbs 2ozs

- UNITY LAKE (FH5047)

25lbs 0ozs

- FOLLY FOOT FARM (FH1755)

24lbs 12ozs

- VIADUCT FISHERY (FH5095)

23lbs 15ozs

- CUTT MILL (FH1230)

23lbs 5ozs

- BEAVER FARM FISHERY (FH0359)

22lbs 8ozs

- LONGBRIDGE LAKES (FH2987)

22lbs 0ozs

ALDERS LAKES (FH0064)
TRI-LAKES (FH4954)

19lbs 8ozs

TINGRITH LAKES (FH4852)

18lbs 0ozs

NEW BARN ANGLING CENTRE (FH3461)

15lbs 8ozs

FLETCHERS POND (FH1747)

15lbs 7ozs

BILNEY LAKES (FH0424)

15lbs 0ozs

WOODLAND LAKES (FH5479)

CARP GRASS

33lbs 12ozs

HORTON CHURCH LAKE (FH2311)

26lbs 6ozs

TANYARD FISHERIES (FH4654)

25lbs 12ozs

DOCKLOW POOLS (FH1386)

25lbs 0ozs

BEAVER FARM FISHERY (FH0359)

24lbs 0ozs

CHILHAM LAKE (FH0942)

23lbs 12ozs

GLOUCESTER PARK LAKE (FH1900)

23lbs 4ozs

MEADOWLANDS (FH3227)

22lbs 12ozs

SPRING WOOD FISHERY AND FARM (FH4372)

22lbs 11ozs

SWAY LAKES (FH4605)

21lbs 11ozs

HIMLEY HALL AND PARK LAKE (FH2230)

21lbs 6ozs

CARP FARM FRYERNING FISHERIES (FH0845)

20lbs 3ozs

LLYN CARFAN (FH2798)

20lbs 0ozs

OAKS FISHERY (FH3565)

18lbs 8ozs

NEWHAY SPECIMEN LAKE (FH3485)

17lbs 14ozs

BROADLANDS LAKES (FH0664)

17lbs 10ozs

TWYNERSH FISHING COMPLEX (FH5012)

CARP KOI

33lbs 12ozs

GREAT LINFORD LAKES (FH1982)

18lbs 9ozs

FENDROD LAKE (FH1694)

18lbs 4ozs

CREEDY LAKES (FH1176)

18lbs 0ozs

FOLLY FOOT FARM (FH1755)

14lbs 4ozs

SOUTH HILL PARK LAKE (FH4331)

12lbs 8ozs

TANYARD FISHERIES (FH4654)

12lbs 6ozs

PEA LANE FISHERY (FH3722)

CARP LEATHER

49lbs 12ozs

DARENTH FISHING COMPLEX (FH1273)

35lbs 0ozs

HEYFORD LAKES (FH2201)

32lbs 8ozs

WHITE SPRINGS LAKES (FH5341)

31lbs 4ozs

BURE VALLEY LAKES (FH0737)

30lbs 2ozs

BADEN HALL FISHERY (FH0245)

CARP MIRROR

61lbs 2ozs

CONNINGBROOK (FH1088)

56lbs 6ozs

WRAYSBURY ONE (FH5513)

56lbs 2ozs

MID KENT FISHERIES (FH3263)

52lbs 0ozs

SONNING EYE (FH4326)

51lbs 0ozs

REDMIRE POOL (FH3921)

50lbs 8ozs

DARENTH FISHING COMPLEX (FH1273)

50lbs 0ozs

HOMERSFIELD LAKE (FH2284)

49lbs 12ozs

ST IVES COMPLEX (FH4387)

48lbs 8ozs

ACTON BURNELL (FH0025)

47lbs 8ozs

NUTRABAITS YATELEY COMPLEX (FH3556)

47lbs 0ozs

CHRISTCHURCH LAKE (FH0947)
KINGFISHER LAKES (FH2500)

46lbs 8ozs

ELSTOW PITS (FH1573)
HAWKHURST FISH FARM (FH2142)

45lbs 11ozs

DINTON PASTURES COUNTRY PARK (FH1375)

45lbs 2ozs

WHITE SWAN LAKE (FH5343)

44lbs 12ozs

COLNBROOK WEST (FH1068)

44lbs 8ozs

HAYSDEN COUNTRY PARK (FH2160)
WITHY POOL (FH5446)

42lbs 8ozs

MOTORWAY POND (FH3382)
WINTONS FISHERY (FH5432)

40lbs 13ozs

LINCH HILL FISHERY (FH2725)

40lbs 8ozs

WHITEVANE POND (FH5354)

40lbs 2ozs

MANOR FARM LAKE (FH3162)

40lbs 0ozs

MILTON PAN LAKE (FH3323)
NAZEING MEADS (FH3431)
RYE NOOK FISHERY (FH4075)

39lbs 14ozs

HIGHTOWN LAKE (FH2220)

39lbs 12ozs

HEYFORD LAKES (FH2201)

39lbs 8ozs

LIZARD LAKES (FH2766)

39lbs 4ozs

WYRESIDE LAKES FISHERY AND LODGINGS (FH5550)

39lbs 2ozs

CUTTLE MILL CARP FISHERY (FH1232)

38lbs 13ozs

CHAD LAKES (FH0890)

38lbs 8ozs

ORCHID LAKES (FH3618)

37lbs 12ozs

PACKINGTON SOMERS FISHERY (FH3679)

37lbs 10ozs

KINGSMEAD 1 (FH2514)

37lbs 8ozs

SALLY WALSHES DAM (FH4084)
WILLOW BANK FISHERY (FH5377)

37lbs 6ozs

REDESMERE (FH3916)

37lbs 2ozs

THREE LAKES (FH4830)

37lbs 0ozs

LAYER PIT (FH2639)

36lbs 6ozs

BAWBURGH LAKES (FH0348)
FARLOWS LAKE (FH1668)

36lbs 4ozs

BOWYERS WATER (FH0576)
HORSESHOE LAKE (FH2307)

36lbs 3ozs

BRICKYARD POND (FH0626)

36lbs 0ozs

ARGAL RESERVOIR (FH0134)
HEYFORD FISHERY (FH2200)
ISLAND POND - RACKERHAYES (FH2391)
PONTSTICILL RESERVOIR (FH3817)
ROYAL BERKSHIRE FISHERY (FH4042)
TILARY LAKE (FH4841)

35lbs 12ozs

LITTLE IRCHESTER COMPLEX (FH2754)

35lbs 8ozs

EARITH FISHERY (FH1501)

35lbs 7ozs

LITTLE EASTON MANOR (FH2751)

35lbs 4ozs

BROADLANDS LAKES (FH0664)
EMMOTLAND PONDS (FH1587)

35lbs 2ozs

WEST STOW COUNTRY PARK (FH5266)

35lbs 0ozs

CATTERICK LAKES (FH0874)
GIMINGHAM LAKES (FH1858)
PRESTONS LAKE (FH3842)
SELBY 3 LAKES (FH4129)
STOUR LAKE (FH4506)
YEW TREE FISHERIES (FH5567)

34lbs 14ozs

COTTINGTON LAKES TROUT AND COARSE FISHERY (FH1137)
LAKESIDE FISHERY (FH2592)

34lbs 10ozs
SWAN LAKE (FH4591)
34lbs 8ozs
SAPPHIRE LAKES (FH4104)
TYRAM HALL (FH5035)
34lbs 7ozs
TWYNERSH FISHING COMPLEX (FH5012)
34lbs 5ozs
WHELFORD POOLS COARSE FISHERY (FH5319)
34lbs 4ozs
NENE (RIVER) (FH3446)
34lbs 0ozs
KEAL COATES FISHERY (FH2422)
33lbs 8ozs
STANSTEAD ABBOTTS (FH4423)
WADSWORTH FISHERY (FH5111)
33lbs 6ozs
CROWN NETHERHALL (FH1201)
33lbs 2ozs
GREAT LINFORD LAKES (FH1982)
33lbs 0ozs
ALDENHAM RESERVOIR (FH0058)
NEWHAY SPECIMEN LAKE (FH3485)
32lbs 10ozs
NEW FOREST WATER PARK (FH3464)
RODNEY MEADOW (FH3995)
32lbs 8ozs
BURE VALLEY LAKES (FH0737)
LAKE NUMBER ONE (LAKE19) (FH2565)
SLIPE LANE PITS (FH4299)
32lbs 4ozs
HARTSMOOR FISHERIES (FH2121)
LONGLEAT LAKES (FH2992)
SHEEPWALK LAKE (FH4218)
32lbs 3ozs
PISCES CARAVAN PARK AND FISHERY (FH3789)
32lbs 0ozs
BIRCHMERE (FH0427)
HARDWICK LAKE AND SMITHS POOL (FH2104)
31lbs 8ozs
ANGLERS PARADISE (FH0108)
GYRN CASTLE FISHERY (FH2056)
31lbs 7ozs
WESTON LAWN FISHERIES (FH5285)
31lbs 5ozs
LAKESIDE LODGES (FH2595)
31lbs 4ozs
HOOK LAKE (FH2288)
MANOR FARM LEISURE (FH3163)
SWAN VALLEY (FH4596)
31lbs 2ozs
WOODLAND WATERS (FH5482)
31lbs 0ozs
WINSFORD FLASH (FH5421)
30lbs 30ozs
SPIRES LAKES (FH4365)
30lbs 12ozs
HIGHAM FARM COARSE FISHING (FH2211)
PALLINGTON LAKES (FH3687)
30lbs 10ozs
CHIGBOROUGH FISHERIES (FH0941)
KORDA LAKE (FH2545)

30lbs 8ozs
ALDERS LAKES (FH0064)
BURY HILL FISHERIES (FH0764)
30lbs 5ozs
RACECOURSE LAKE (FH3871)
RIPON RACECOURSE LAKE (FH3959)
30lbs 4ozs
LONSDALE COUNTRY PARK (FH2997)
MENARDS LAKE (FH3254)
WILLOW PARK (FH5387)
30lbs 2ozs
ROSSWAYS WATER (FH4021)
30lbs 0ozs
ALLESTREE LAKE (FH0078)
BADEN HALL FISHERY (FH0245)
BLUE LAGOON LAKE (FH0507)
BUSBRIDGE LAKE (FH0765)
EXE (RIVER) (FH1643)
FERRY MEADOWS (FH1701)
HOLLY FARM FISHERY (FH2261)
HOLLYBUSH LANE LAKES (FH2262)
JOHNS LAKE FISHERIES (FH2414)
JOHNSONS LAKE (FH2415)
LYNN POOL FISHERY (FH3125)
MILL POOL (FH3301)
NACCOLT LAKE (FH3408)
NOOK & CRANNY LAKE (FH3514)
PARTRIDGE LAKES (FH3714)
PATSHULL PARK (FH3717)
ROCKFORD LAKE (FH3984)
ROYAL MILITARY CANAL (FH4046)
SCOULTON MERE (FH4119)
TILGATE LAKES (FH4845)
TRI-LAKES (FH4954)
WEYBREAD GRAVEL PITS (FH5294)
WINGHAM FISHERY (FH5417)
YEOMANS LAKE (FH5565)

CARP WILD

10lbs 8ozs
TORY FARM LAKE (FH4887)

CATFISH

86lbs 8ozs
WILLOW BANK FISHERY (FH5377)
65lbs 0ozs
WINTONS FISHERY (FH5432)
62lbs 0ozs
WITHY POOL (FH5446)
61lbs 11ozs
DARENTH FISHING COMPLEX (FH1273)
60lbs 0ozs
YEW TREE FISHERIES (FH5567)
50lbs 0ozs
HOMERSFIELD LAKE (FH2284)
48lbs 11ozs
MARSWORTH RESERVOIR (FH3198)
48lbs 8ozs
JIMMYS LAKE (FH2411)
48lbs 5ozs
TRING RESERVOIRS (FH4957)
47lbs 12ozs
BLUEBELL LAKE (FH0513)
39lbs 0ozs
HOUCHINS RESERVOIRS (FH2315)
37lbs 8ozs
SWANGEY LAKES (FH4598)
35lbs 4ozs
JONES PIT (FH2416)

35lbs 0ozs
BEAVER FARM FISHERY (FH0359)
34lbs 4ozs
CLAVERHAMBURY LAKE (FH0982)
33lbs 0ozs
ST JOHNS POOL (FH4391)
32lbs 8ozs
WHITEACRES COUNTRY PARK (FH5344)
32lbs 4ozs
RACKLEY HILLS PIT (FH3873)
32lbs 0ozs
CHRISTCHURCH LAKE (FH0947)
31lbs 10ozs
CROWN NETHERHALL (FH1201)
31lbs 8ozs
ORCHID LAKES (FH3618)
31lbs 0ozs
BADSHOT LEA (FH0247)
30lbs 8ozs
MID KENT FISHERIES (FH3263)
30lbs 3ozs
TOWNSEND FISHERY (FH4894)
30lbs 0ozs
CHILHAM LAKE (FH0942)

CHARR

9lbs 8ozs
LOCH ARKAIG (FH2843)
LOCH INCH LAGGAN (FH2893)
5lbs 3ozs
LOCH EARN (FH2875)

CHUB

10lbs 8ozs
ANNAN (RIVER) (FH0114)
KIRKWOOD WATER (FH2527)
8lbs 14ozs
WISSEY (RIVER) (FH5435)
8lbs 12ozs
MOLE (RIVER) (FH3338)
8lbs 10ozs
TEES (RIVER) (FH4684)
TEES (RIVER) (FH4692)
8lbs 8ozs
ROTHER (RIVER) (FH4026)
8lbs 4ozs
AVON (RIVER) (FH0225)
AVON RIVER FISHERIES (FH0228)
7lbs 15ozs
GREAT OUSE (RIVER) (FH1994)
STOUR (DORSET) (RIVER) (FH4486)
7lbs 11ozs
KENNET (RIVER) (FH2438)
TOWNSEND FISHERY (FH4894)
7lbs 10ozs
AVON (BRISTOL) (RIVER) (FH0191)
AVON (RIVER) (FH0218)
MEADOWLANDS (FH3227)
7lbs 7ozs
FISHERS GREEN (FH1731)
7lbs 6ozs
HAMPSHIRE AVON (RIVER) (FH2084)
ISLIP NATURE LAKE (FH2396)
THRAPSTON LAKES (FH4829)
7lbs 3ozs
THROOP FISHERIES (FH4834)

7lbs 2ozs

- LODDON (RIVER) (FH2977)
- MAKIN FISHERIES (FH3150)
- SMEATONS LAKES (FH4304)
- WALSDEN PRINTING CO LODGES (FH5128)

7lbs 0ozs

- OXLEASE LAKE (FH3678)

6lbs 15ozs

- SWALE (RIVER) (FH4572)

6lbs 14ozs

- BURGHFIELD (FH0739)

6lbs 13ozs

- HOE HILL POND (FH2245)

6lbs 12ozs

- CARTHAGENA FISHERY (FH0855)
- HAMPSHIRE AVON (FH2082)
- LENWADE COMMON LAKES (FH2700)
- LYMM VALE (FH3116)

6lbs 11ozs

- SWALE (RIVER) (FH4569)
- SWALE (RIVER) (FH4576)

6lbs 10ozs

- STOW (RIVER) (FH4509)

6lbs 9ozs

- FURNACE MILL FISHERY (FH1822)
- OUSE (RIVER) (FH3642)
- PASSIES PONDS (FH3715)
- TAVERHAM MILLS FISHERY (FH4669)

6lbs 8ozs

- BLACKWATER (RIVER) (FH0477)
- BURGHFIELD MATCH LAKE (FH0742)
- KENNET (RIVER) (FH2446)
- KINGFISHER LODGE (FH2501)
- MOCCAS FISHERY (FH3333)
- MONK LAKE FISHERIES (FH3342)
- NEWHAY DAY TICKET LAKE (FH3484)
- OUSE (RIVER) (FH3645)
- STOW (RIVER) (FH4511)
- SWALE (RIVER) (FH4586)
- UPPER WITHAM (RIVER) (FH5060)

6lbs 7ozs

- DOVECOTE LAKE FISHERY (FH1430)
- LEA (RIVER) (FH2642)
- MARSTON PITS (FH3196)
- SEVERN (RIVER) (FH4167)
- STOW (RIVER) (FH4510)

6lbs 5ozs

- BRISTOL AVON (FH0647)
- BRISTOL AVON (FH0648)
- BRISTOL AVON (FH0649)
- BRISTOL AVON (FH0650)
- GREAT OUSE (RIVER) (FH1985)
- HANCHURCH FISHERIES (FH2099)

6lbs 4ozs

- HEYFORD LAKES (FH2201)
- MEDWAY (RIVER) (FH3239)
- ST PATRICKS (FH4395)
- STOW (RIVER) (FH4508)

6lbs 3ozs

- AVON (RIVER) (FH0220)
- DANDYS LAKE AND KNIGHTINGALE LAKE (FH1254)
- PETERS FINGER LAKES (FH3756)
- STEEPLE LANGFORD LAKES (FH4447)
- STOUR (RIVER) (FH4493)

6lbs 2ozs

- CHAWSTON LAKES (FH0908)
- CLICKETTS HILL AND PLANTATION (FH1005)
- DAM FLASK RESERVOIR (FH1251)
- EDEN (RIVER) (FH1542)
- GREAT OUSE (RIVER) (FH1995)
- LINCH HILL FISHERY (FH2725)
- RYEMEADS (FH4076)
- WELDON RESERVOIR (FH5228)
- WEST HILLBOROUGH (FH5261)
- WEY (RIVER) (FH5289)

6lbs 1ozs

- WARWICKSHIRE AVON (FH5158)

6lbs 0ozs

- EXE (RIVER) (FH1643)
- FIR TREE LODGE (FH1721)
- HARDWICK LAKE AND SMITHS POOL (FH2104)
- STOUR (RIVER) (FH4498)
- STOUR (RIVER) (FH4499)
- SUTTON BROOK (FH4562)

5lbs 15ozs

- AVON (BRISTOL) (RIVER) (FH0195)
- HAYSDEN COUNTRY PARK (FH2160)

5lbs 14ozs

- BROADLANDS LAKES (FH0664)

5lbs 13ozs

- ALDENHAM RESERVOIR (FH0058)
- NORTH MEADOWS (FH3531)

5lbs 12ozs

- MEDWAY (RIVER) (FH3238)
- NEWTON PARK (FH3497)
- TINGRITH LAKES (FH4852)
- TRENT (RIVER) (FH4934)

5lbs 10ozs

- DARENTH FISHING COMPLEX (FH1273)
- MEDWAY (RIVER) (FH3236)
- PACKINGTON SOMERS FISHERY (FH3679)
- PAINSHILL PARK LAKE (FH3685)
- TYRINGHAM ESTATE (FH5037)

5lbs 9ozs

- BLASFORD HILL FISHERIES (FH0492)

5lbs 8ozs

- BOURTON FISHERIES (FH0567)
- CLIFTON LAKES FISHERY (FH1006)
- KENNET (RIVER) (FH2435)
- KENNET (RIVER) (FH2443)
- KENNET (RIVER) (FH2445)
- LARK (RIVER) (FH2624)
- MID KENT FISHERIES (FH3263)
- MONNOW (RIVER) (FH3351)
- RUSHEY WEIR (FH4062)
- SEVERN (RIVER) (FH4188)
- STAINFORTH AND KEADBY CANAL (FH4409)
- THAMES (RIVER) (FH4798)
- THAMES (RIVER) (FH4792)
- TUNNEL BARN FARM (FH4972)
- WEAR (RIVER) (FH5205)

5lbs 7ozs

- FAR GRANGE CARAVAN AND COUNTRY PARK (FH1663)
- IVEL (RIVER) (FH2402)

5lbs 6ozs

- BROOMWOOD LAKE (FH0696)
- MANOR FARM LEISURE (FH3163)

5lbs 4ozs

- DANE (RIVER) (FH1255)
- DOBBS WEIR FISHERY (FH1381)
- ERIC FISHWICK NATURE RESERVE (FH1608)
- MORETON MERE FISHERY (FH3370)
- STOW (RIVER) (FH4512)

5lbs 3ozs

- FLEET (RIVER) (FH1745)
- WRIGHTS FARM (FH5517)

5lbs 2ozs

- BILNEY LAKES (FH0424)
- HERONBROOK FISHERY (FH2191)
- WITHAM (RIVER) (FH5438)

5lbs 1ozs

- STAFFORD AND WORCESTER CANAL (FH4400)
- WATERLOO SCREENS (FH5179)

5lbs 0ozs

- GIPPING (RIVER) (FH1863)
- HIGHTOWN LAKE (FH2220)
- LEA (RIVER) (FH2645)
- ROYAL BERKSHIRE FISHERY (FH4042)
- RUSHMOOR LAKES (FH4063)
- SEVERN (RIVER) (FH4176)
- SEVERN (RIVER) (FH4154)
- TRIANGLE LAKE (FH4952)
- WHITEWATER (RIVER) (FH5356)
- WYE (RIVER) (FH5530)

4lbs 15ozs

- THAMES (RIVER) (FH4805)

4lbs 14ozs

- BRICKHOUSE FARM FISHERIES (FH0621)

4lbs 12ozs

- BROWNING CUDMORE FISHERY (FH0702)
- LAKEMORE COUNTRY PARK (FH2578)

4lbs 9ozs

- COTTINGTON LAKES TROUT AND COARSE FISHERY (FH1137)
- WEAR (RIVER) (FH5198)

4lbs 8ozs

- AYCLIFFE LAKE (FH0235)
- BOUGH BEECH RESERVOIR (FH0564)
- CHAD LAKES (FH0890)
- DUSTON RESERVOIR (FH1486)
- LITTLE BEVILLS ESTATE (FH2740)
- MEDWAY (RIVER) (FH3231)
- OUSE (RIVER) (FH3639)
- POOL HOUSE FARM (FH3820)
- PURLEY (FH3858)
- SEVERN (RIVER) (FH4147)
- STANSTEAD ABBOTTS (FH4423)
- STAUNTON COURT LAKES (FH4441)
- TWYFORD BBONT (FH5008)
- WESTERLY LAKE (FH5271)
- WEY (RIVER) (FH5291)

4lbs 6ozs

- COD BECK (FH1049)
- WINDRUSH (RIVER) (FH5410)

4lbs 3ozs

- PALLINGTON LAKES (FH3687)

4lbs 2ozs

- CLAWFORD VINEYARD AND FISHERIES (FH0985)
- RIDDINGS FISHERY (FH3949)

4lbs 0ozs

- BARFORD LAKES FISHERY (FH0305)
- DANE (RIVER) (FH1266)
- KIPPAX POND (FH2524)
- SEVERN (RIVER) (FH4172)
- WESTWOOD COUNTRY PARK (FH5288)
- WHINWHISTLE COARSE FISHERY (FH5324)
- WINDMILL LAKE (FH5409)

EEL

8lbs 12ozs

- BURGHFIELD (FH0739)
- DARENTH FISHING COMPLEX (FH1273)

8lbs 10ozs
- AVON RIVER FISHERIES (FH0228)
- HUNSTRETE LAKE COMPLEX (FH2338)

8lbs 8ozs
- BITTERWELL LAKE (FH0438)
- UPPER WITHAM (RIVER) (FH5060)

8lbs 4ozs
- TEES (RIVER) (FH4684)

8lbs 2ozs
- BROADLANDS LAKES (FH0664)
- DOCKLOW POOLS (FH1386)

8lbs 0ozs
- HIGHTOWN LAKE (FH2220)

7lbs 13ozs
- ARLESEY LAKE (FH0136)

7lbs 8ozs
- LAKESIDE LEISURE PARK (FH2594)
- WRAYSBURY ONE (FH5513)

7lbs 4ozs
- BURE VALLEY LAKES (FH0737)
- EVESBATCH FISHERIES (FH1635)

7lbs 1oz
- BLUEBELL LAKE (FH0513)
- ESTHWAITE WATER (FH1630)

7lbs 0ozs
- FAIRVIEW LAKE (FH1656)
- SEDGES (FH4128)
- WHITE HOUSE PREDATOR LAKE (FH5336)

6lbs 12ozs
- TANYARD FISHERIES (FH4654)

6lbs 10ozs
- DISS MERE (FH1376)

6lbs 8ozs
- CAMELOT LAKE (FH0813)
- LAKE FARM (FH2556)

6lbs 7ozs
- LARKFIELD LAKES (FH2625)
- PAPERCOURT FISHERY (FH3694)

6lbs 4ozs
- MID KENT FISHERIES (FH3263)

6lbs 0ozs
- BIRCHMERE (FH0427)
- NEW BARN ANGLING CENTRE (FH3461)
- SWAN LAKE (FH4592)

5lbs 15ozs
- VIRGINIA LAKE (FH5100)

5lbs 12ozs
- ASHBY PARK FISHERIES (FH0158)

5lbs 10ozs
- ELECTRICITY POOL (FH1560)
- FRIMLEY LAKES (FH1802)
- OLDBOROUGH FISHING RETREAT (FH3604)

5lbs 8ozs
- AYCLIFFE LAKE (FH0235)
- COOMBE POOL (FH1109)
- HAZELCOURT PONDS (FH2164)
- KINGSMEAD 1 (FH2514)
- PAINSHILL PARK LAKE (FH3685)
- WINTERLEY POOL FISHERY (FH5426)

5lbs 7ozs
- PACKINGTON SOMERS FISHERY (FH3679)

5lbs 6ozs
- WYLANDS INTERNATIONAL ANGLING CENTRE (FH5545)

5lbs 4ozs
- HOPETOUN FISHERY (FH2291)
- MORTON FARM (FH3373)

5lbs 3ozs
- DONYLANDS LAKES (FH1406)
- NOSTELL PRIORY LAKE (FH3551)
- NUTRABAITS YATELEY COMPLEX (FH3556)

5lbs 0ozs
- FOLLYFOOT FARM (FH1757)
- HOLLYBUSH LANE LAKES (FH2262)
- SHIPBROOK FLASH (FH4241)
- TILARY LAKE (FH4841)
- TRI-LAKES (FH4954)

GOLDFISH

3lbs 8ozs
- LYONS GATE CARAVAN PARK (FH3126)
- RED BARNS POND (FH3908)

GRAYLING

4lbs 4ozs
- ITCHEN NAVIGATION (FH2399)

4lbs 3ozs
- DORSET FROME (FH1417)

3lbs 14ozs
- DRIFFIELD CANAL (FH1442)

3lbs 8ozs
- NITH (RIVER) (FH3512)

3lbs 4ozs
- DEE (RIVER) (FH1309)
- IRFON (RIVER) (FH2378)
- WYE (RIVER) (FH5541)

3lbs 2ozs
- BARTON COURT FISHERY (FH0338)
- CAER BERIS MANOR HOTEL (FH0789)

3lbs 1oz
- COD BECK (FH1049)

2lbs 12ozs
- TEES (RIVER) (FH4697)
- WEAR (RIVER) (FH5209)

2lbs 11ozs
- BROADLANDS LAKES (FH0664)
- SWALE (RIVER) (FH4569)

2lbs 10ozs
- TEVIOT (RIVER) (FH4751)

2lbs 8ozs
- MONNOW (RIVER) (FH3351)
- PARSONAGE (RIVER) TEST (FH3711)
- TWEED (RIVER) (FH4990)
- WEAR (RIVER) (FH5211)
- WINKTON FISHERY (FH5418)

2lbs 4ozs
- LANGFORD FISHERIES (FH2611)
- MID KENT FISHERIES (FH3263)

2lbs 2ozs
- BOLTON ABBEY FISHERIES (FH0539)

2lbs 0ozs
- DOVE (RIVER) (FH1423)
- HENMORE (RIVER) (FH2186)

ORFE

7lbs 3ozs
- RIDDINGS FISHERY (FH3949)

6lbs 13ozs
- BILNEY LAKES (FH0424)

5lbs 8ozs
- WILLITOFT FISH FARM (FH5376)

ORFE BLUE

5lbs 0ozs
- FIR TREE LODGE (FH1721)

ORFE GOLDEN

8lbs 5ozs
- LYMM VALE (FH3116)

7lbs 8ozs
- HORTON CHURCH LAKE (FH2311)

7lbs 7ozs
- CHURCH LAKE (FH0954)

7lbs 6ozs
- ANGLERS PARADISE (FH0108)

5lbs 8ozs
- ANGLERS SHANGRILA (FH0109)
- FOLLY FOOT FARM (FH1755)
- LAVENDER FARM (FH2631)

5lbs 0ozs
- FIR TREE LODGE (FH1721)

4lbs 8ozs
- FLETCHERS POND (FH1747)

4lbs 3ozs
- KENNET (RIVER) (FH2439)
- TEST (RIVER) (FH4745)

PERCH

5lbs 8ozs
- OLD NENE (RIVER) (FH3597)

4lbs 15ozs
- ALDENHAM RESERVOIR (FH0058)

4lbs 14ozs
- PAINSHILL PARK LAKE (FH3685)

4lbs 13ozs
- PALLINGTON LAKES (FH3687)

4lbs 12ozs
- BLUEBELL LAKE (FH0513)
- FRANT LAKES (FH1798)
- TITCHFIELD ABBEY GOLF AND COARSE FISHING LAKES (FH4857)

4lbs 11ozs
- BROWNING CUDMORE FISHERY (FH0702)

4lbs 9ozs
- BARTON COURT FISHERY (FH0338)

4lbs 8ozs
- BUSH LAKES FARM (FH0768)
- CHEDDAR RESERVOIR (FH0909)
- DOWRY AND NEW YEARS BRIDGE RESERVOIR (FH1433)
- HAYSDEN COUNTRY PARK (FH2160)
- IDEN WOOD FISHERY (FH2358)
- MILL FARM FISHERY (FH3283)
- OXLEASE LAKE (FH3678)
- PARK LIME PIT (FH3700)
- PAWLETT PONDS (FH3719)
- TANYARD FISHERIES (FH4654)

3lbs 15ozs
- LONSDALE COUNTRY PARK (FH2997)
- PORTSMOUTH RESERVIOR (FH3831)

3lbs 14ozs
- BILNEY LAKES (FH0424)
- KENNET AND ENTORNE (RIVERS) (FH2468)

3lbs 13ozs
- AVON (RIVER) (FH0218)

3lbs 12ozs
- ALEXANDRA PARK (FH0072)
- BURGHFIELD MATCH LAKE (FH0742)

- ERIC FISHWICK NATURE RESERVE (FH1608)
- LODDON (RIVER) (FH2977)
- MONK LAKE FISHERIES (FH3342)
- NOSTELL PRIORY LAKE (FH3551)
- ROYAL BERKSHIRE FISHERY (FH4042)
- SOUTHMINSTER FISHERIES (FH4352)
- TAX MERE (FH4677)
- WELLFIELD POND (FH5238)
- WHITE SWAN LAKE (FH5343)
- WITHERINGTON FARM FISHING (FH5442)

3lbs 11ozs

- BROADLANDS LAKES (FH0664)
- CLATTERCOTE RESERVOIR (FH0979)
- STOW (RIVER) (FH4510)
- SWALE (RIVER) (FH4569)

3lbs 10ozs

- ARDINGLY RESERVOIR (FH0129)
- BRISTOL AVON (FH0647)
- BRISTOL AVON (FH0648)
- BRISTOL AVON (FH0649)
- BRISTOL AVON (FH0650)
- DACRE LAKESIDE PARK (FH1244)
- FRIMLEY LAKES (FH1802)
- GOLTHO LAKE (FH1917)
- LAKE MEADOWS (FH2562)
- LITTLE DALE HALL COARSE FISHERY (FH2747)
- SLIVER FISHERY (FH4300)
- STAFFORD AND WORCESTER CANAL (FH4400)
- STUBPOND FISHERIES (FH4531)

3lbs 9ozs

- BURGHFIELD (FH0739)
- LOUGHGALL COARSE FISHERY (FH3056)
- MORETON MERE FISHERY (FH3370)

3lbs 8ozs

- ALDERS LAKES (FH0064)
- ALDERWOOD PONDS (FH0066)
- ALVECHURCH FISHERIES (FH0090)
- AVON (BRISTOL) (RIVER) (FH0195)
- BILLS POOL (FH0423)
- BLUNDELLS FARM FISHERY (FH0514)
- BORDER FISHERIES (FH0546)
- BOUGH BEECH RESERVOIR (FH0564)
- BULL HOLE (FH0725)
- BURTON CONSTABLE COUNTRY PARK (FH0759)
- CAM (RIVER) (FH0807)
- CAMELOT LAKE (FH0813)
- CHERWELL (RIVER) (FH0921)
- CHIGBOROUGH FISHERIES (FH0941)
- CROWN NETHERHALL (FH1201)
- FISHPONDS FARM AND FISHERY (FH1735)
- FURNACE LAKES (FH1821)
- GOLD VALLEY LAKES (FH1909)
- GREAT OUSE (RIVER) (FH1996)
- GREAT OUSE (RIVER) (FH1988)
- HIMLEY HALL AND PARK LAKE (FH2230)
- HORAM MANOR FISHERY (FH2294)
- JOHNSONS LAKE (FH2415)
- KINGSMEAD 1 (FH2514)
- KINGSMEAD ISLAND LAKE (FH2516)
- LITTLE EASTON MANOR (FH2751)
- LIZARD LAKES (FH2766)
- LOW MAYNARD RESERVOIR (FH3067)
- MEADOW LAKE (FH3223)
- MILL LAKE (NO 44) (FH3289)
- MILL POOL (FH3302)
- MILTON MOUNT LAKE (FH3322)
- POOL HALL (FH3819)
- REGENTS CANAL (FH3925)
- REGENTS CANAL (FH3926)
- ROCKFORD LAKE (FH3984)
- RODING (RIVER) (FH3991)
- SOUTH VIEW FARM FISHERY (FH4344)
- SUDBROOK POND (FH4533)
- SWALE (RIVER) (FH4576)
- TUNNEL BARN FARM (FH4972)
- WHARFE (RIVER) (FH5306)

2lbs 15ozs

- MEDWAY (RIVER) (FH3238)

2lbs 14ozs

- AMWELL LAKES (FH0104)
- CANONS ASHBY LAKES (FH0824)
- PACKINGTON SOMERS FISHERY (FH3679)
- STOW (RIVER) (FH4512)

2lbs 13ozs

- CUCKOOS REST (FH1211)

2lbs 12ozs

- BEDFONT LAKE (FH0363)
- HORTON BOAT POOL (FH2310)
- LINDHOLME LEISURE LAKES FISHERIES (4) (FH2732)
- PLAUMS PIT (FH3802)
- RIVERTON HOUSE AND LAKES (FH3970)
- STOW (RIVER) (FH4508)
- TIN DENE FISHERY (FH4850)
- WEST RESERVOIR (FH5265)
- WRIGHTS FARM (FH5517)

2lbs 11ozs

- CLICKETTS HILL AND PLANTATION (FH1005)
- WRAYSBURY ONE (FH5513)

2lbs 10ozs

- ISE (RIVER) (FH2384)
- STANSTEAD ABBOTTS (FH4423)
- THEALE (FH4806)

2lbs 9ozs

- BAWBURGH LAKES (FH0348)
- DONYLANDS LAKES (FH1406)
- STOUR (RIVER) (FH4501)

2lbs 8ozs

- AVON (BRISTOL) (RIVER) (FH0198)
- BEEHIVE FARM WOODLANDS LAKES (FH0371)
- BLASFORD HILL FISHERIES (FH0492)
- BLYTHE WATERS (FH0518)
- BOOTON CLAY PIT (FH0543)
- BOSWORTH WATER TRUST AND FRIEZELAND POOLS (FH0561)
- BRANDES BURTON 3 AND 4 (FH0599)
- BRITTENS POND (FH0658)
- BRYAN HEY RESERVOIR (FH0711)
- BUCKLEY TRAP POOL (FH0718)
- CLAWDD OFFAS DYKE (FH0984)
- CLIVIGER FISH PONDS (FH1012)
- CLOONGEE FISHERY (FH1021)
- DYEHOUSE POND (FH1493)
- EAST TOWNEY (FH1514)
- GALLOWAY FOREST PARK (FH1829)
- GOLD OAK FISH FARM (FH1908)
- GRAND UNION CANAL (FH1959)
- HINDERCLAY LAKES (FH2233)
- HUCKLESBROOK LAKE (FH2324)
- HUNSTRETE LAKE COMPLEX (FH2338)
- INDIO POND (FH2365)
- KENNET AND AVON CANAL (FH2465)
- LANDS END FARM (FH2607)
- LOCH KENNY (FH2899)
- LYNCHGATE LANE FISHERY (FH3119)
- MARSH FARM LAKES (FH3191)
- MEADOW VIEW FISHERY (FH3225)
- MOLE (RIVER) (FH3338)
- OAKSIDE FISHERY (FH3567)
- OLIVES FARM FISHERY (FH3609)
- PAPERCOURT FISHERY (FH3694)
- POOL HOUSE FARM (FH3820)
- PORTNELLAN (FH3830)
- RAPHAELS PARK (FH3888)
- SHAKESPEARE MOORLANDS FARM (FH4203)
- SHARNFOLD FARM FISHERY (FH4210)
- SHEFFIELD CANAL (FH4223)
- SILVER LAKE (FH4269)
- SILVER SPRINGS FISHERY (FH4270)
- SINGLETON LAKE (FH4276)
- SMEATONS LAKES (FH4304)
- STANBOROUGH POOL (FH4416)
- STATES LAGOON (FH4436)
- STATHAM POOL (FH4437)
- STEAM MILLS LAKE (FH4444)
- SWAY LAKES (FH4605)
- TASWOOD LAKES FISH FARM AND FISHERY (FH4662)
- TEME (RIVER) (FH4731)
- THURLEYBEARE POND (FH4836)
- TYRINGHAM ESTATE (FH5037)
- UNIVERSITY BROAD (FH5048)
- WARWICKSHIRE AVON (FH5155)
- WINKTON FISHERY (FH5418)
- WINTERLEY POOL FISHERY (FH5426)
- WOOD FARM CARAVAN PARK (FH5458)
- WOONSMITH LAKE (FH5502)

PIKE

47lbs 11ozs

- LOCH LOMOND (FH2904)

46lbs 13ozs

- LLANDEGFEDD RESERVOIR (FH2769)

44lbs 14ozs

- ARDLEIGH RESERVOIR (FH0130)

44lbs 2ozs

- BARNES TROUT LAKES (FH0316)

42lbs 8ozs

- ROYALTY FISHERY (FH4049)

41lbs 12ozs

- BLUEBELL LAKE (FH0513)
- BOUGH BEECH RESERVOIR (FH0564)

40lbs 8ozs

- LOUGH ARROW (FH3003)

39lbs 4ozs

- BROADLANDS LAKES (FH0664)

38lbs 10ozs

- PISCES CARAVAN PARK AND FISHERY (FH3789)

38lbs 8ozs

- HARTHILL RESERVIORS (FH2115)
- MARKEATON LAKE (FH3183)

37lbs 8ozs

- HAMPSHIRE AVON (RIVER) (FH2091)

37lbs 6ozs

- ESTHWAITE WATER (FH1630)

36lbs 0ozs

- ALDERS LAKES (FH0064)
- MILTON PAN LAKE (FH3323)

35lbs 12ozs

- PACKINGTON SOMERS FISHERY (FH3679)

35lbs 8ozs

- TRING RESERVOIRS (FH4957)

35lbs 0ozs
- WEYBREAD GRAVEL PITS (FH5294)
- WHITE HOUSE PREDATOR LAKE (FH5336)

34lbs 13ozs
- PAPERCOURT FISHERY (FH3694)

34lbs 5ozs
- HEYFORD LAKES (FH2201)

34lbs 2ozs
- SWANGEY LAKES (FH4598)

33lbs 8ozs
- AVON (RIVER) (FH0218)
- BLITHFIELD RESERVOIR (FH0502)
- NEWELLS SPECIMEN CARP AND COARSE FISHERIES (FH3483)
- UPPER WITHAM (RIVER) (FH5060)

33lbs 7ozs
- HILLEND LOCH (FH2226)

33lbs 6ozs
- PATSHULL PARK (FH3717)

32lbs 8ozs
- LINDHOLME LEISURE LAKES FISHERIES (4) (FH2732)

32lbs 6ozs
- LOUGH GARA (FH3032)
- LUNG RIVER (FH3113)

32lbs 4ozs
- MILTON POOLS FARM (FH3326)

32lbs 0ozs
- BOSLEY RESERVOIR (FH0557)
- HARWOOD HALL LAKE (FH2125)
- SWAN LAKE (FH4591)
- WEIR WOOD FISHERY (FH5227)

31lbs 10ozs
- FRIMLEY LAKES (FH1802)

31lbs 8ozs
- WRAYSBURY ONE (FH5513)

31lbs 6ozs
- MEDWAY (RIVER) (FH3238)

31lbs 2ozs
- FRISBY LAKES (FH1803)

30lbs 12ozs
- DARENTH FISHING COMPLEX (FH1273)

30lbs 8ozs
- BARTON COURT FISHERY (FH0338)

30lbs 7ozs
- SUTTON AT HONE LAKES ONE AND THREE (FH4560)

30lbs 6ozs
- CLIFTON MARINA (FH1008)

30lbs 4ozs
- TANYARD FISHERIES (FH4654)

30lbs 2ozs
- NUTRABAITS YATELEY COMPLEX (FH3556)

30lbs 0ozs
- ARGAL RESERVOIR (FH0134)
- BAWBURGH LAKES (FH0348)
- BLUE LAGOON LAKE (FH0507)
- CONNINGBROOK (FH1088)
- HIGHTOWN LAKE (FH2220)
- LOWER MOOR FISHERY (FH3090)
- NOOK & CRANNY LAKE (FH3514)
- PRESTONS LAKE (FH3842)

ROACH

5lbs 12ozs
- TATTON MERE (FH4664)

4lbs 3ozs
- STOUR (DORSET) (RIVER) (FH4482)

4lbs 2ozs
- THURNE MOUTH (RIVER) (FH4837)

3lbs 14ozs
- KENN (RIVER) (FH2433)

3lbs 13ozs
- CHRISTCHURCH LAKE (FH0947)

3lbs 10ozs
- DOWRY AND NEW YEARS BRIDGE RESERVOIR (FH1433)
- HAMPSHIRE AVON (RIVER) (FH2084)
- HAMPSHIRE AVON (RIVER) (FH2091)
- HORNSEA MERE (FH2301)
- LINCH HILL FISHERY (FH2725)
- THAMES (RIVER) (FH4795)
- WINKTON FISHERY (FH5418)

3lbs 9ozs
- BROADLANDS LAKES (FH0664)

3lbs 8ozs
- BROWNING CUDMORE FISHERY (FH0702)
- MID KENT FISHERIES (FH3263)
- PAWLETT PONDS (FH3719)
- WARREN (FH5150)
- WEYBREAD FISHERY (FH5293)

3lbs 7ozs
- BURE VALLEY LAKES (FH0737)
- HAMPSHIRE AVON (RIVER) (FH2088)
- LOCKWOOD RESERVOIR (FH2974)
- SLADE RESERVOIRS (FH4292)

3lbs 6ozs
- ALDENHAM RESERVOIR (FH0058)
- AVON (RIVER) (FH0220)
- BARTON COURT FISHERY (FH0338)
- DANDYS LAKE AND KNIGHTINGALE LAKE (FH1254)
- DARENTH FISHING COMPLEX (FH1273)
- FIR TREE LODGE (FH1721)
- LLYN CARFAN (FH2798)
- LOW MAYNARD RESERVOIR (FH3067)
- PETERS FINGER LAKES (FH3756)
- STEEPLE LANGFORD LAKES (FH4447)
- STOUR (RIVER) (FH4493)
- WRAYSBURY ONE (FH5513)

3lbs 5ozs
- NUTRABAITS YATELEY COMPLEX (FH3556)
- TRING RESERVOIRS (FH4957)

3lbs 4ozs
- AVON RIVER FISHERIES (FH0228)
- HOPETOUN FISHERY (FH2291)
- HULL (RIVER) (FH2332)
- LARK (RIVER) (FH2624)
- NAZEING MEADS (FH3431)
- ORCHID LAKES (FH3618)
- OSS MERE (FH3628)
- SHIREOAKS PARK (FH4243)

3lbs 3ozs
- HADDISCOE PIT (FH2058)
- JONES PIT (FH2416)
- MEADOWLANDS (FH3227)
- SEVERN (RIVER) (FH4186)

3lbs 2ozs
- ALDERWOOD PONDS (FH0066)
- AVON (BRISTOL) (RIVER) (FH0195)
- AVON (RIVER) (FH0218)
- BILNEY LAKES (FH0424)
- BURGHFIELD (FH0739)
- MAKIN FISHERIES (FH3150)

3lbs 1ozs
- DOCKLOW POOLS (FH1386)
- FENDROD LAKE (FH1694)
- FROME (RIVER) (FH1809)
- GLOUCESTER PARK LAKE (FH1900)
- HEYFORD LAKES (FH2201)
- ISE (RIVER) (FH2384)
- LAKE HELEN (FH2558)
- SWAY LAKES (FH4605)
- VIRGINIA LAKE (FH5100)

3lbs 0ozs
- FAIRVIEW LAKE (FH1656)
- HOMERSFIELD LAKE (FH2284)
- JOHNSONS LAKE (FH2415)
- MEDWAY (RIVER) (FH3233)
- MILTON PAN LAKE (FH3323)
- NOOK & CRANNY LAKE (FH3514)
- TILARY LAKE (FH4841)

2lbs 15ozs
- BOOTON CLAY PIT (FH0543)
- ST MICHAELS WYRESIDE FISHERY (FH4394)
- STONE END FARM LAKES (FH4467)

2lbs 14ozs
- KEYNES COUNTRY PARK (FH2475)
- KEYNES PARK TOP LAKE (FH2476)
- WOODFOLD FARM FISHERIES (FH5473)

2lbs 13ozs
- ARENA LAKE (FH0132)
- AVON (BRISTOL) (RIVER) (FH0191)
- BOUGH BEECH RESERVOIR (FH0564)
- FRIMLEY LAKES (FH1802)

2lbs 12ozs
- DINTON PASTURES COUNTRY PARK (FH1375)
- FARLOWS LAKE (FH1668)
- HURST POND (FH2346)
- LARKFIELD LAKES (FH2625)
- LONSDALE COUNTRY PARK (FH2997)
- MEDWAY (RIVER) (FH3238)
- MONK LAKE FISHERIES (FH3342)
- NEWHAY DAY TICKET LAKE (FH3484)
- NOSTELL PRIORY LAKE (FH3551)
- RODING (RIVER) (FH3993)
- THAMES (RIVER) (FH4805)
- VICKERS POND (FH5097)
- WEST HILLBOROUGH (FH5261)

2lbs 11ozs
- FURNACE MILL FISHERY (FH1822)
- NORTH MEADOWS (FH3531)
- STOUR (DORSET) (RIVER) (FH4481)

2lbs 10ozs
- CARTHAGENA FISHERY (FH0855)
- EDENDERRY OFFALY EIRE (FH1544)
- PALLINGTON LAKES (FH3687)
- RAKER LAKES (FH3884)
- TWYNERSH FISHING COMPLEX (FH5012)
- WHELFORD POOLS COARSE FISHERY (FH5319)

2lbs 9ozs
- BREAKAWAY PIT (FH0609)
- COTTINGTON LAKES TROUT AND COARSE FISHERY (FH1137)
- LAKESIDE LEISURE PARK (FH2594)
- LAYZELLS FARM (FH2640)
- STOW (RIVER) (FH4512)
- SWALE (RIVER) (FH4569)

2lbs 8ozs

- AIRE (RIVER) (FH0045)
- ALEXANDRA PARK (FH0072)
- AQUALATE MERE (FH0124)
- AVON (BRISTOL) (RIVER) (FH0198)
- BARLEYLANDS RESERVOIR (FH0310)
- BISHOPS BOWL LAKES (FH0435)
- BLACKWATER (RIVER) (FH0477)
- BROOKSIDE FISHERIES (FH0686)
- BROOME PITS (FH0693)
- BULL HOLE (FH0725)
- CHAWSTON LAKES (FH0908)
- CHEDDAR RESERVOIR (FH0909)
- CHERTSEY (FH0916)
- CHERWELL (RIVER) (FH0921)
- CHIGBOROUGH (FH0940)
- CHRISTCHURCH LOWER STOUR (FH0948)
- CLAWFORD VINEYARD AND FISHERIES (FH0985)
- DACRE LAKESIDE PARK (FH1244)
- DOVECOTE LAKE FISHERY (FH1430)
- FINLAKE PONDS (FH1713)
- FRAMFIELD PARK FISHERIES (FH1797)
- FURZE FARM (FH1824)
- GOLDEN POND FISHERY (FH1912)
- GRANSTOWN LAKE (FH1972)
- GREAT OUSE (RIVER) (FH1995)
- GREAT OUSE (RIVER) (FH1996)
- GWERYD LAKES FISHING (FH2047)
- HAWKESBURY FISHERY (FH2141)
- HAWKHURST FISH FARM (FH2142)
- HAYE FARM FISHERY (FH2152)
- HORAM MANOR FISHERY (FH2294)
- HUNSTRETE LAKE COMPLEX (FH2338)
- IVEL (RIVER) (FH2402)
- JACKLETTS FARM (FH2405)
- KENNET (RIVER) (FH2445)
- KINGFISHER LODGE (FH2501)
- LAKESIDE LODGES (FH2595)
- LENWADE COMMON LAKES (FH2700)
- LEOMINSTEAD MILL POND (FH2702)
- LIZARD LAKES (FH2766)
- LODDON (RIVER) (FH2977)
- LONGMOOR LAKE (FH2994)
- MIDDLE BOSWIN FARM (FH3264)
- MIDDLE POOL (FH3267)
- MOATHOUSE LAKE (FH3330)
- NEST (FH3451)
- OASIS LAKES (FH3570)
- OHAM LAKES (FH3583)
- OUSE (RIVER) (FH3645)
- PANT (RIVER) (FH3690)
- PASSIES PONDS (FH3715)
- POOL HALL (FH3819)
- REVELS FISHERY (FH3932)
- RODING (RIVER) (FH3991)
- RODING VALLEY LAKE (FH3994)
- ROYAL BERKSHIRE FISHERY (FH4042)
- RUSSELLS END RESERVOIR (FH4065)
- SAPPHIRE LAKES (FH4104)
- SHEPPERTON LAKE (FH4230)
- SOUTH VIEW FARM FISHERY (FH4344)
- STAUNTON COURT LAKES (FH4441)
- STOUR (DORSET) (RIVER) (FH4477)
- STOUR (RIVER) (FH4500)
- STRAITS MILL (FH4518)
- SURRENDEN LAKES (FH4558)
- SWEETHEDGES FARM FISHERY (FH4607)
- TANYARD FISHERIES (FH4654)
- THORNEY LAKES (FH4815)
- THROOP FISHERIES (FH4834)
- TILERY LAKE (FH4843)
- TIN DENE FISHERY (FH4850)
- TRIMDON POND (FH4955)
- TWYFORD FARM POOL (FH5009)
- WALDENS FARM FISHERY (FH5118)
- WALL POOL LODGE (FH5121)
- WELDON RESERVOIR (FH5228)
- WILLOWS FARM FISHING (FH5399)
- WORSBROUGH RESERVOIR (FH5508)
- WYLANDS INTERNATIONAL ANGLING CENTRE (FH5545)

2lbs 7ozs

- ALTON WATER RESERVOIR (FH0088)
- MILL ROAD LAKES (FH3304)
- STANFORD-LE-HOPE (FH4418)
- STOW (RIVER) (FH4510)
- THET (RIVER) (FH4809)
- TWINE VALLEY TROUT FISHERY (FH5005)
- WILLOW LAKES (FH5384)

2lbs 6ozs

- BALLAST PIT (FH0259)
- BOURTON FISHERIES (FH0567)
- CHIGBOROUGH FISHERIES (FH0941)
- EMMOTLAND PONDS (FH1587)
- HOOK LAKE (FH2288)
- MILL POND LAKE (FH3300)
- PIXIES MERE (FH3796)
- TINGRITH LAKES (FH4852)
- WALTHAMSTOW RESERVOIR (NO 1) (FH5130)
- WALTHAMSTOW RESERVOIR (NO 2 AND NO 3) (FH5131)
- WHITE SWAN LAKE (FH5343)

2lbs 5ozs

- BLACKLEACH RESERVOIR (FH0451)
- GOLD VALLEY LAKES (FH1909)
- HANCHURCH FISHERIES (FH2099)
- LANDS END FARM (FH2607)
- OLD MILL AND MEADOWS (FH3594)
- PISCES CARAVAN PARK AND FISHERY (FH3789)
- SHATTERFORD FISHERY AND WILDLIFE SANCTUARY (FH4212)
- TAVERHAM (FH4668)

2lbs 4ozs

- BADEN HALL FISHERY (FH0245)
- BORDEAUX PIT (FH0545)
- CANONS ASHBY LAKES (FH0824)
- CLAVERHAMBURY LAKE (FH0982)
- FISHERS GREEN (FH1731)
- FISHPONDS FARM AND FISHERY (FH1735)
- MEDWAY (RIVER) (FH3239)
- MILEMEAD FISHERIES (FH3274)
- NENE (RIVER) (FH3447)
- PAPERCOURT FISHERY (FH3694)
- SHARKEYS PIT (FH4209)
- SMEATONS LAKES (FH4304)
- THEALE (FH4806)
- VIADUCT FISHERY (FH5095)
- WENSUM (RIVER) (FH5249)

2lbs 3ozs

- FAR GRANGE CARAVAN AND COUNTRY PARK (FH1663)
- FENNES FISHERIES (FH1697)
- KINGSLEY CARP LAKE (FH2513)

2lbs 2ozs

- BRASSIDE POND (FH0603)
- CUTTLE MILL CARP FISHERY (FH1232)
- EDEN (RIVER) (FH1542)
- ERIC FISHWICK NATURE RESERVE (FH1608)
- HOE HILL POND (FH2245)
- LAKE NUMBER ONE (LAKE19) (FH2565)
- NORTHLANDS PARK (FH3546)
- SPRING WOOD FISHERY AND FARM (FH4372)
- WITLEY FISHERY (FH5448)

2lbs 1ozs

- HENFOLD LAKES FISHERY (FH2182)
- MEDWAY (RIVER) (FH3236)
- PACKINGTON SOMERS FISHERY (FH3679)
- TILEYARD LANE (FH4844)
- TWYFORD BBONT (FH5008)

2lbs 0ozs

- ALDERS LAKES (FH0064)
- ARROW VALLEY LAKE (FH0141)
- BARFORD LAKES FISHERY (FH0305)
- BORROWPIT LAKE (FH0554)
- CANNOCK EXTENSION CANAL (FH0822)
- COWANS FARM (FH1149)
- EAST MOORS LAKE (FH1511)
- FERRY MEADOWS (FH1701)
- FLYLANDS POND (FH1752)
- GIPPING (RIVER) (FH1863)
- HANDLE LAKE (FH2100)
- HARDWICK LAKE AND SMITHS POOL (FH2104)
- HILL VIEW LAKES (FH2224)
- LATHOM FISHERIES (FH2627)
- MARBURY MERE (FH3175)
- NACCOLT LAKE (FH3408)
- NEEDHAM LAKE (FH3435)
- NEW BARN ANGLING CENTRE (FH3461)
- OLD MILL RESERVOIR (FH3596)
- ROSSMERE (FH4019)
- ROYAL MILITARY CANAL (FH4046)
- RYE NOOK FISHERY (FH4075)
- SEVERN (RIVER) (FH4172)
- SHEAR WATER (FH4216)
- STICKNEY BRICKPONDS (FH4455)
- STOUR LAKE (FH4506)
- TILGATE LAKES (FH4845)
- TRIANGLE LAKE (FH4952)
- TRI-LAKES (FH4954)
- WHINWHISTLE COARSE FISHERY (FH5324)
- WILLOWS POOLS (FH5401)
- WINSFORD FLASH (FH5421)

RUDD

4lbs 8ozs

- ELSTOW PITS (FH1573)
- JINGLES FARM (FH2412)

4lbs 5ozs

- WOOLPACK FISHERY (FH5500)

4lbs 1ozs

- GRANSTOWN LAKE (FH1972)

3lbs 13ozs

- THAMES (RIVER) (FH4795)

3lbs 12ozs

- TAUNTON AND BRIDGWATER CANAL (FH4665)
- WHITE SPRINGS LAKES (FH5341)

3lbs 11ozs

- PISCES CARAVAN PARK AND FISHERY (FH3789)

3lbs 10ozs

- HORSESHOE LAKE (FH2307)

3lbs 8ozs

- BLUNTS AND CANTS MERES (FH0516)
- PINGEWOOD LAGOON (FH3783)
- STRAITS MILL (FH4518)

3lbs 6ozs

- FENDROD LAKE (FH1694)

3lbs 4ozs
- HARTSMOOR FISHERIES (FH2121)
- TAVERHAM MILLS FISHERY (FH4669)

3lbs 3ozs
- EDENDERRY OFFALY EIRE (FH1544)
- MEADOWLANDS (FH3227)

3lbs 2ozs
- OLDBOROUGH FISHING RETREAT (FH3604)
- WOODFOLD FARM FISHERIES (FH5473)

3lbs 1ozs
- LAKE NUMBER ONE (LAKE19) (FH2565)

3lbs 0ozs
- FIR TREE LODGE (FH1721)
- NACCOLT LAKE (FH3408)
- RYE NOOK FISHERY (FH4075)

2lbs 14ozs
- BILNEY LAKES (FH0424)
- TATTERSHALL LEISURE PARK (FH4663)

2lbs 12ozs
- ROSWELL PITS (FH4022)
- SYCAMORE FISHING LAKES (FH4618)
- TANYARD FISHERIES (FH4654)

2lbs 10ozs
- LINCH HILL FISHERY (FH2725)
- MILTON COUNTRY PARK (FH3318)
- NUTRABAITS YATELEY COMPLEX (FH3556)

2lbs 9ozs
- AVALON FISHERIES (FH0186)
- BROADLANDS LAKES (FH0664)
- ERIC FISHWICK NATURE RESERVE (FH1608)

2lbs 8ozs
- BOOTON CLAY PIT (FH0543)
- BOUNDARY WATER PARK (FH0566)
- CATCH 22 FISHERY (FH0872)
- COTTINGTON LAKES TROUT AND COARSE FISHERY (FH1137)
- ELECTRICITY POOL (FH1560)
- GRANGE FARM LEISURE (FH1969)
- HAYE FARM FISHERY (FH2152)
- HORAM MANOR FISHERY (FH2294)
- ISIS NO 1 LAKE 19 (FH2386)
- LEMINGTON LAKES (FH2696)
- MIDDLE BOSWIN FARM (FH3264)
- MOULDSWORTH MERE (FH3383)
- NEWELLS SPECIMEN CARP AND COARSE FISHERIES (FH3483)
- REVELS FISHERY (FH3932)
- ROSEWATER LAKE (FH4014)
- SCARLETTS LAKE (FH4114)
- SOUTHMINSTER FISHERIES (FH4352)
- STANFORD-LE-HOPE (FH4418)
- TAX MERE (FH4677)
- TINNEY WATERS (FH4855)
- WALDENS FARM FISHERY (FH5118)

2lbs 6ozs
- PASSIES PONDS (FH3715)

2lbs 4ozs
- ARDINGLY RESERVOIR (FH0129)
- BURE VALLEY LAKES (FH0737)
- CAM (RIVER) (FH0807)
- LONGFIELD LAKE (FH2988)
- PETT POOLS (FH3759)
- SOUTH VIEW FARM FISHERY (FH4344)
- STAUNTON COURT LAKES (FH4441)
- STOCKLEY ROAD LAKES (FH4461)
- THEALE (FH4806)
- WALL POOL LODGE (FH5121)

2lbs 3ozs
- DOCKLOW POOLS (FH1386)
- FURNACE MILL FISHERY (FH1822)

2lbs 2ozs
- BALLAST PIT (FH0259)
- JONES PIT (FH2416)

2lbs 1ozs
- TRING RESERVOIRS (FH4957)
- WILLOW LAKES (FH5384)

2lbs 0ozs
- ASHLEY POOL (FH0164)
- CHRISTCHURCH LAKE (FH0947)
- COWANS FARM (FH1149)
- HARDWICK LAKE AND SMITHS POOL (FH2104)
- JOHNSONS LAKE (FH2415)
- LOCH BARNBARROCH (FH2852)
- NEW BARN ANGLING CENTRE (FH3461)
- PARSONAGE FARM (FH3712)
- STOUR LAKE (FH4506)
- STRETHAM LAKE (FH4524)
- TILGATE LAKES (FH4845)
- TRIANGLE LAKE (FH4952)
- TRI-LAKES (FH4954)
- WHINWHISTLE COARSE FISHERY (FH5324)
- WINGHAM FISHERY (FH5417)
- WOODSTON MANOR POOLS (FH5496)

SALMON

59lbs 8ozs
- WYE (RIVER) (FH5528)

49lbs 8ozs
- ROYALTY FISHERY (FH4049)

43lbs 8ozs
- LOWER ITCHEN FISHERY (FH3084)

38lbs 8ozs
- IRFON (RIVER) (FH2378)
- WYE (RIVER) (FH5541)

37lbs 3ozs
- FINN (RIVER) (FH1716)

36lbs 4ozs
- AVON RIVER FISHERIES (FH0228)

32lbs 8ozs
- TEIFI (RIVER) (FH4708)

28lbs 8ozs
- CLOONGEE FISHERY (FH1021)

27lbs 8ozs
- PITLOCHRY BOATING STATION AND LOCHSIDE CAFÉ (FH3792)

23lbs 12ozs
- LOUGH CORRIB (FH3021)

23lbs 8ozs
- CAMOWEN (RIVER) (FH0815)

23lbs 3ozs
- LOCH INSH (FH2895)

22lbs 8ozs
- TEES (RIVER) (FH4697)
- WEAR (RIVER) (FH5209)

21lbs 10ozs
- TWYMYN (RIVER) (FH5011)

21lbs 8ozs
- ILEN (RIVER) (FH2362)

21lbs 4ozs
- FINN (RIVER) (FH1715)

20lbs 6ozs
- TOFT NEWTON TROUT FISHERY (FH4864)

20lbs 0ozs
- WYE (RIVER) (FH5530)

STURGEON

18lbs 8ozs
- DOVECOTE LAKE FISHERY (FH1430)

TENCH

14lbs 3ozs
- WRAYSBURY ONE (FH5513)

13lbs 7ozs
- LARKFIELD LAKES (FH2625)

13lbs 5ozs
- TRING RESERVOIRS (FH4957)

13lbs 3ozs
- MID KENT FISHERIES (FH3263)

12lbs 9ozs
- WILSTONE RESERVOIR (FH5404)

12lbs 5ozs
- AVON (BRISTOL) (RIVER) (FH0201)

12lbs 4ozs
- BLUEBELL LAKE (FH0513)
- BOUGH BEECH RESERVOIR (FH0564)

12lbs 3ozs
- PALLINGTON LAKES (FH3687)

12lbs 2ozs
- TATTON MERE (FH4664)

12lbs 0ozs
- ALDERS LAKES (FH0064)
- BETLEY MERE (FH0396)

11lbs 8ozs
- BROWNING CUDMORE FISHERY (FH0702)
- HORTON CHURCH LAKE (FH2311)
- L-LAKE FISHERY (FH2767)
- WITHNELL RESERVOIRS (FH5445)

11lbs 6ozs
- LIZARD LAKES (FH2766)

11lbs 5ozs
- BAWBURGH LAKES (FH0348)

11lbs 4ozs
- STANSTEAD ABBOTTS (FH4423)
- TINGRITH LAKES (FH4852)

11lbs 3ozs
- GIMINGHAM LAKES (FH1858)
- HEYFORD LAKES (FH2201)

11lbs 2ozs
- PAPERCOURT FISHERY (FH3694)
- WHITE SWAN LAKE (FH5343)

11lbs 1ozs
- WEYBREAD FISHERY (FH5293)

11lbs 0ozs
- CHRISTCHURCH LAKE (FH0947)
- FIR TREE LODGE (FH1721)
- MILTON PAN LAKE (FH3323)
- NOOK & CRANNY LAKE (FH3514)
- PARTRIDGE LAKES (FH3714)

10lbs 12ozs
- NAZEING MEADS (FH3431)

10lbs 8ozs
- DARENTH FISHING COMPLEX (FH1273)
- FISHERWICK LAKES (FH1732)
- FRIMLEY LAKES (FH1802)
- LONSDALE COUNTRY PARK (FH2997)

10lbs 7ozs
- SHEEPWALK LAKE (FH4218)

10lbs 6ozs
- FISHERS GREEN (FH1731)
- LONGMOOR LAKE (FH2994)
- SUTTON AT HONE LAKE TWO (FH4559)

10lbs 5ozs
- BRADSHAW HALL FISHERIES (FH0591)
- CLIFTON MARINA (FH1008)
- COTTINGTON LAKES TROUT AND COARSE FISHERY (FH1137)
- PACKINGTON SOMERS FISHERY (FH3679)

10lbs 4ozs
- ALDENHAM RESERVOIR (FH0058)
- CROXLEY HALL TROUT FISHERY (FH1203)
- WOOLPACK FISHERY (FH5500)

10lbs 2ozs
- BURY HILL FISHERIES (FH0764)
- HOOKS MARSH (FH2289)
- LINCH HILL FISHERY (FH2725)
- LOW MAYNARD RESERVOIR (FH3067)
- SWAN POOL (FH4595)
- TAVERHAM MILLS FISHERY (FH4669)
- WHELFORD POOLS COARSE FISHERY (FH5319)

10lbs 0ozs
- BLUE LAGOON LAKE (FH0507)
- BROOMWOOD LAKE (FH0696)
- HANDLE LAKE (FH2100)
- JOHNSONS LAKE (FH2415)
- LOWTHER LAKE (FH3099)
- MANOR FARM LAKE (FH3162)
- ST JOHNS POOL (FH4391)
- TRIANGLE LAKE (FH4952)
- WILLOW BANK FISHERY (FH5377)

9lbs 14ozs
- CHEDDAR RESERVOIR (FH0909)
- GREAT LINFORD LAKES (FH1982)

9lbs 12ozs
- CROWN NETHERHALL (FH1201)
- ELINOR TROUT FISHERY (FH1562)
- HAYSDEN COUNTRY PARK (FH2160)
- RINGLAND PITS (FH3953)
- TAVERHAM (FH4668)

9lbs 11ozs
- WALL POOL LODGE (FH5121)

9lbs 10ozs
- RYEMEADS (FH4076)
- THORPE PARK WATERSKI LAKE (FH4824)

9lbs 8ozs
- ARKSEY STATION POND (FH0135)
- MILL FARM FISHERY (FH3283)
- ORCHID LAKES (FH3618)
- TWYNERSH FISHING COMPLEX (FH5012)
- WOODLAND WATERS (FH5482)

9lbs 7ozs
- RIDDINGS FISHERY (FH3949)

9lbs 6ozs
- CHIGBOROUGH FISHERIES (FH0941)
- COLNBROOK WEST (FH1068)
- THRAPSTON LAKES (FH4829)
- WALL POOL LODGE (FH5121)

9lbs 4ozs
- HATCHET POND (FH2128)
- HIMLEY HALL AND PARK LAKE (FH2230)
- RYE NOOK FISHERY (FH4075)
- STANFORD-LE-HOPE (FH4418)
- WINGHAM FISHERY (FH5417)

9lbs 3ozs
- DONYLANDS LAKES (FH1406)
- LONG POND (FH2983)

9lbs 2ozs
- BALLAST PIT (FH0259)
- DOVECOTE LAKE FISHERY (FH1430)
- JONES PIT (FH2416)

9lbs 1ozs
- DISS MERE (FH1376)
- MILL ROAD LAKES (FH3304)
- SYWELL RESERVOIR (FH4623)

9lbs 0ozs
- CANNOCK EXTENSION CANAL (FH0822)
- HUNSTRETE LAKE COMPLEX (FH2338)
- NEEDHAM LAKE (FH3435)
- UNITY LAKE (FH5047)

8lbs 14ozs
- HORSESHOE LAKE (FH2307)
- NORTH MET PIT (FH3532)

8lbs 12ozs
- CHERTSEY (FH0916)
- TWYFORD BBONT (FH5008)

8lbs 10ozs
- BRISTOL AVON (FH0647)
- BRISTOL AVON (FH0648)
- BRISTOL AVON (FH0649)
- BRISTOL AVON (FH0650)

8lbs 8ozs
- A1 PITS (FH0001)
- COLLEGE RESERVOIR (FH1064)
- ERIC FISHWICK NATURE RESERVE (FH1608)
- EXETER CANAL (FH1647)
- FARLOWS LAKE (FH1668)
- FRAMFIELD PARK FISHERIES (FH1797)
- HAWKHURST FISH FARM (FH2142)
- HOOKSTEAD LAKE (FH2290)
- LAKE NUMBER ONE (LAKE19) (FH2565)
- LANGHOLME FISHERIES (FH2614)
- LYMM VALE (FH3116)
- NUPERS FARM (FH3555)
- OXLEASE LAKE (FH3678)
- SCARLETTS LAKE (FH4114)
- STRAITS MILL (FH4518)
- SWANGEY LAKES (FH4598)
- SWEETHEDGES FARM FISHERY (FH4607)
- UPHAM FARM PONDS (FH5050)

8lbs 6ozs
- POTTERY LAKE (FH3834)

8lbs 5ozs
- BURGHFIELD (FH0739)

8lbs 4ozs
- BADEN HALL FISHERY (FH0245)
- BLENHEIM LAKE (FH0497)
- KINGSMEAD 1 (FH2514)
- MONK LAKE FISHERIES (FH3342)
- PRIORY COUNTRY PARK (FH3848)
- TOWNSEND FISHERY (FH4894)

8lbs 3ozs
- COOMBE LAKE (FH1107)
- HOE HILL POND (FH2245)
- WESTFIELD FARM (FH5276)

8lbs 2ozs
- BLUNDELLS FARM FISHERY (FH0514)
- CATCH 22 FISHERY (FH0872)
- GRANSTOWN LAKE (FH1972)
- INDIO POND (FH2365)
- ISLAND POND - RACKERHAYES (FH2391)
- KENN (RIVER) (FH2433)

8lbs 1ozs
- FENNES FISHERIES (FH1697)
- MAYFIELDS LAKE (FH3216)
- MILL POND LAKE (FH3300)
- STOCKLEY ROAD LAKES (FH4461)

8lbs 0ozs
- BARHAM A PIT (FH0306)
- BOVINGTON MERE 2 (FH0570)
- CROSS DROVE (FH1191)
- FAIRVIEW LAKE (FH1656)
- HOLLYBUSH LANE LAKES (FH2262)
- LYNN POOL FISHERY (FH3125)
- MARBURY MERE (FH3175)
- MEADOWLANDS (FH3227)
- NACCOLT LAKE (FH3408)
- PEACOCK LAKE (FH3723)
- ROYAL MILITARY CANAL (FH4046)
- STRETHAM LAKE (FH4524)
- TILGATE LAKES (FH4845)
- TRI-LAKES (FH4954)
- UNIVERSITY BROAD (FH5048)
- WADE LAKE (FH5110)
- WHISBY GARDEN CENTRE (FH5329)

7lbs 14ozs
- LINDHOLME LEISURE LAKES FISHERIES (4) (FH2732)
- MILTON POOLS FARM (FH3326)

7lbs 13ozs
- EDENDERRY OFFALY EIRE (FH1544)

7lbs 12ozs
- AVALON FISHERIES (FH0186)
- BROADLANDS LAKES (FH0664)
- FRISBY LAKES (FH1803)
- LUCCOMBES PONDS (FH3101)

7lbs 10ozs
- CARP VALE (FH0846)
- LONGMOOR FARM FISHING LAKE (FH2993)
- MORTON FARM (FH3373)
- OSTERLEY PARK MIDDLE LAKE (FH3629)

7lbs 9ozs
- BILNEY LAKES (FH0424)

7lbs 8ozs
- ARENA LAKE (FH0132)
- ARLESEY LAKE (FH0136)
- AWBRIDGE DANES LAKE (FH0231)
- BEAVER FARM FISHERY (FH0359)
- COTTAGE GREEN GARDEN CENTRE (FH1133)
- EAST MOORS LAKE (FH1511)
- GRAND WESTERN CANAL (FH1967)
- HURST POND (FH2346)
- PARSONAGE FARM (FH3712)
- PARSONAGE RESERVOIR (FH3713)
- SCOULTON MERE (FH4119)
- SILVER SPRINGS FISHERY (FH4270)
- STICKNEY BRICKPONDS (FH4455)
- SUTTON AT HONE LAKES ONE AND THREE (FH4560)
- SWAY LAKES (FH4605)
- WEAVER (RIVER) (FH5215)

7lbs 7ozs
- ANGLERS PARADISE (FH0108)
- STOUR (RIVER) (FH4501)

7lbs 6ozs
- LONGFORD LAKE (FH2989)
- TASWOOD LAKES FISH FARM AND FISHERY (FH4662)

7lbs 5ozs
- ISLIP NATURE LAKE (FH2396)

PAINSHILL PARK LAKE (FH3685)
THEALE (FH4806)

7lbs 4ozs

GODNEY MOOR PONDS (FH1906)
OLDBOROUGH FISHING RETREAT (FH3604)
STOW (RIVER) (FH4512)
SYCAMORE FISHING LAKES (FH4618)
ULVERSTON CANAL (FH5043)

7lbs 3ozs

NENE (RIVER) (FH3447)
PAR (FH3695)

7lbs 2ozs

MILL FARM FISHERY (FH3281)
ROSSWAYS WATER (FH4021)
WASING WOODS (FH5165)

7lbs 1ozs

DOCKLOW POOLS (FH1386)
LAKE HELEN (FH2558)
MORETON MERE FISHERY (FH3370)
OAKFIELD FISHERY (FH3561)

7lbs 0ozs

BARHAM B PIT (FH0307)
BIRCHMERE (FH0427)
BROOKHALL FISHERY (FH0682)
BUSBRIDGE LAKE (FH0765)
CHESHIRE FISHING (FH0925)
EMBORUGH LAKE (FH1583)
HEATHFIELD POOL (FH2175)
HIGHTOWN LAKE (FH2220)
KEAL COATES FISHERY (FH2422)
LATHOM FISHERIES (FH2627)
MILL POOL (FH3301)
NEW BARN ANGLING CENTRE (FH3461)
SEDGES (FH4128)
SWAN LAKE (FH4592)
WOODRISING WATER MEADOWS (FH5489)

6lbs 12ozs

HARTSMOOR FISHERIES (FH2121)
STOW (RIVER) (FH4508)

6lbs 11ozs

CLAVERHAMBURY LAKE (FH0982)
WRIGHTS FARM (FH5517)

6lbs 10ozs

ALVECHURCH FISHERIES (FH0090)
GREAT OUSE (RIVER) (FH1994)

6lbs 9ozs

STOW (RIVER) (FH4510)

6lbs 8ozs

BRAFFERTON COARSE FISHERY (FH0593)
BURGHFIELD BLUE POOL (FH0740)
CLIVIGER FISH PONDS (FH1012)
FENDROD LAKE (FH1694)
HAMWORTHY LAKE (FH2098)
KELHEAD WATER (FH2425)
LOUGHGALL COARSE FISHERY (FH3056)
MARTHAM PITS (FH3199)
MATCH AND BLUE POOLS (FH3207)
MILL POOL (FH3302)
OUSE (RIVER) (FH3645)
TATTERSHALL LEISURE PARK (FH4663)
THAMES (RIVER) (FH4805)
VICKERS POND (FH5097)
WASH POOL (FH5163)
WOODACOTT ARMS (FH5464)
WOODLAY HOLIDAY LAKES (FH5486)
WYLANDS INTERNATIONAL ANGLING CENTRE (FH5545)

6lbs 7ozs

CLUB PIT (FH1028)

6lbs 6ozs

THORNEY LAKES (FH4815)

6lbs 4ozs

FISHPONDS HOUSE (FH1736)
ROUKES DRIFT FARM (FH4035)
SWAN VALLEY (FH4596)
WALNUT FARM FISHERIES (FH5125)

6lbs 3ozs

HANCHURCH FISHERIES (FH2099)

6lbs 2ozs

DIXON GREEN RESERVOIR (FH1380)
MEDWAY (RIVER) (FH3239)
TYRINGHAM ESTATE (FH5037)
WILLOW LAKES (FH5384)

6lbs 1ozs

WEST HADDLESEY LAKE (FH5260)

6lbs 0ozs

BAKERS FARM (FH0254)
BARFORD LAKES FISHERY (FH0305)
BORROWPIT LAKE (FH0554)
HADDISCOE PIT (FH2058)
HARDWICK LAKE AND SMITHS POOL (FH2104)
HOLLY FARM FISHERY (FH2261)
HOO LAKES (FH2287)
HORSE AND GROOM LAKES (FH2303)
LEA (RIVER) (FH2645)
LOAM POND (FH2833)
MOON LAKE (FH3356)
OAKS FISHERY (FH3565)
PEA LANE FISHERY (FH3722)
PRESTONS LAKE (FH3842)
SHEAR WATER (FH4216)
WALLYS LAKE (FH5124)
WEYBREAD GRAVEL PITS (FH5294)
WILLOWS (THE) (FH5397)
WILLOWS POOLS (FH5401)
WINSFORD FLASH (FH5421)
WOODLAND LAKES (FH5479)

TENCH GOLDEN

6lbs 3ozs

LYMM VALE (FH3116)

6lbs 2ozs

FALKENVIL FISHERY (FH1658)

TROUT AMERICAN BROOK

35lbs 3ozs

GAILEY TROUT AND PIKE FISHERY (FH1828)

8lbs 3ozs

FONTBURN RESERVOIR (FH1758)

5lbs 14ozs

AVINGTON TROUT FISHERIES (FH0190)

TROUT BLUE

11lbs 12ozs

KINGENNIE FISHINGS (FH2494)

10lbs 8ozs

HOLBURY LAKES (FH2247)

8lbs 13ozs

BELLBROOK VALLEY TROUT FISHERY (FH0377)

4lbs 8ozs

HOWWOOD TROUT FISHERY (FH2321)

3lbs 2ozs

ALLANDALE TARN (FH0076)

TROUT BROOK

5lbs 2ozs

HOWWOOD TROUT FISHERY (FH2321)

4lbs 11ozs

YTHAN VALLEY FISHERY (FH5576)

4lbs 10ozs

LEOMINSTEAD TROUT FISHERY (FH2703)

4lbs 8ozs

SWANSWATER FISHERY (FH4600)

3lbs 15ozs

ARDGOWAN TROUT FISHERY (FH0128)

3lbs 11ozs

PORT-NA-LOCHAN (FH3829)

3lbs 1ozs

TOFT NEWTON TROUT FISHERY (FH4864)

TROUT BROWN

36lbs 14ozs

DEVER SPRINGS TROUT FISHERY (FH1362)

30lbs 8ozs

LOCH AWE (FH2848)

21lbs 4ozs

STONEBRIDGE LAKES (FH4471)

21lbs 3ozs

LOCH EARN (FH2875)

21lbs 2ozs

SHIMANO FELINDRE TROUT FISHERY (FH4239)

19lbs 12ozs

GRAFHAM WATER (FH1934)

19lbs 10ozs

LOCH AVICH (FH2847)

19lbs 8ozs

FRENSHAM TROUT FISHERY (FH1800)
LOCH QUOICH (FH2937)
LOYNTON TROUT FISHERIES (FH3100)

18lbs 13ozs

WENTWOOD RESERVOIR (FH5251)

17lbs 6ozs

DUNCTON MILL (FH1473)

17lbs 4ozs

AVON SPRINGS FISHERY (FH0229)

16lbs 8ozs

WILLINGHURST TROUT FISHERY (FH5374)

16lbs 6ozs

TEMPLE TROUT FISHERY (FH4735)

16lbs 5ozs

RAYGILL FISHERY (FH3902)

15lbs 12ozs

KINGENNIE FISHINGS (FH2494)

15lbs 8ozs

LECHLADE TROUT FISHERY (FH2656)
PENNINE TROUT FISHERY (FH3737)

15lbs 4ozs

CLYDE (RIVER) (FH1039)

14lbs 11ozs

CHIGBOROUGH FISHERIES (FH0941)

14lbs 9ozs
- COUND TROUT FISHERY (FH1140)

14lbs 3ozs
- NEWBURY TROUT LAKES (FH3480)

14lbs 2ozs
- FISHERWICK LAKES (FH1732)

13lbs 12ozs
- SWANSWATER FISHERY (FH4600)

13lbs 10ozs
- DEARNFORD HALL TROUT FISHERY (FH1291)

13lbs 8ozs
- ALLANDALE TARN (FH0076)
- KIPLIN TROUT FISHERY (FH2523)

13lbs 7ozs
- CHALK SPRINGS TROUT FISHERY (FH0891)

13lbs 6ozs
- SPRING WOOD FISHERY AND FARM (FH4372)

13lbs 5ozs
- LOWER MOOR FISHERY (FH3090)

13lbs 4ozs
- QUANTOCK FISHERIES (FH3862)

13lbs 3ozs
- CHEW VALLEY LAKE (FH0936)

13lbs 2ozs
- PARKLEY FISHERY (FH3705)

12lbs 12ozs
- HALLIFORD MERE LAKES (FH2071)

12lbs 8ozs
- DARWELL WATER (FH1279)
- OWDY LANE TROUT FISHERY (FH3660)
- ROOKSBURY MILL TROUT FISHERIES (FH4007)
- SELM MUIR FISHERY (FH4135)

12lbs 7ozs
- BEWL WATER (FH0403)
- CAMELEY TROUT LAKES (FH0812)
- CLYNWEDOG RESERVOIR (FH1041)
- DULAS (RIVER) (FH1468)

12lbs 6ozs
- DRAKELANDS GAME FISHERY (FH1435)

12lbs 5ozs
- GAILEY TROUT AND PIKE FISHERY (FH1828)
- RAVENSTHORPE TROUT FISHERY (FH3895)

11lbs 12ozs
- WATENDLATH TROUT FISHERY (FH5169)

11lbs 11ozs
- DRAYCOTE WATER (FH1438)

11lbs 7ozs
- LADYBOWER RESERVOIR (FH2549)

11lbs 4ozs
- EYEBROOK TROUT FISHERY (FH1649)

10lbs 12ozs
- ESTHWAITE WATER (FH1630)
- GARRY UPPER (RIVER) (FH1839)
- STOCKS FLY FISHERY (FH4463)

10lbs 8ozs
- HOWWOOD TROUT FISHERY (FH2321)
- TENTERDEN TROUT WATERS (FH4738)
- WHITE HOUSE MILL (FH5335)
- WHITE SPRINGS LAKES (FH5341)

10lbs 5ozs
- WALTHAMSTOW RESERVOIR (NO 4 TROUT) (FH5132)

10lbs 4ozs
- BLAGDON LAKE (FH0487)
- CROXLEY HALL TROUT FISHERY (FH1203)
- MONNOW (RIVER) (FH3351)

10lbs 3ozs
- BANK HOUSE FLY FISHERY (FH0286)

10lbs 2ozs
- FRON FARM FISHERY (FH1814)
- MARTON HEATH TROUT POOLS (FH3203)

TROUT GOLDEN

22lbs 10ozs
- STONEBRIDGE LAKES (FH4471)

14lbs 8ozs
- PENNINE TROUT FISHERY (FH3737)

14lbs 2ozs
- BELLBROOK VALLEY TROUT FISHERY (FH0377)

9lbs 8ozs
- LOCH INSCH FISHERY (FH2894)

6lbs 8ozs
- SWANSWATER FISHERY (FH4600)

5lbs 11ozs
- ALLANDALE TARN (FH0076)

5lbs 5ozs
- ROUGHLEE TROUT FISHERY (FH4034)

4lbs 9ozs
- HOWWOOD TROUT FISHERY (FH2321)

4lbs 3ozs
- PORT-NA-LOCHAN (FH3829)

4lbs 2ozs
- TOFT NEWTON TROUT FISHERY (FH4864)

TROUT LAKE

29lbs 12ozs
- SEVEN OAKS FISHERY (FH4141)

16lbs 8ozs
- LOCH LOMOND (FH2904)

14lbs 14ozs
- LAKESIDE FISHERY (FH2592)

12lbs 3ozs
- ERNE (RIVER) (FH1614)

11lbs 6ozs
- SCOUT DYKE RESERVOIR (FH4121)

10lbs 7ozs
- AVON SPRINGS FISHERY (FH0229)

10lbs 4ozs
- WINTERSHILL TROUT LAKE (FH5430)

TROUT RAINBOW

36lbs 15ozs
- DEVER SPRINGS TROUT FISHERY (FH1362)

30lbs 12ozs
- TAVISTOCK TROUT FISHERY (FH4670)

29lbs 12ozs
- SHIMANO FELINDRE TROUT FISHERY (FH4239)

29lbs 7ozs
- PENNINE TROUT FISHERY (FH3737)

28lbs 7ozs
- STONEBRIDGE LAKES (FH4471)

27lbs 8ozs
- LOYNTON TROUT FISHERIES (FH3100)

25lbs 4ozs
- MOORHEN FARM TROUT LAKE (FH3361)

25lbs 3ozs
- MAES GWYN FISHERY (FH3136)

24lbs 8ozs
- JUBILEE LAKES (FH2417)
- SPRING WOOD FISHERY AND FARM (FH4372)

24lbs 1ozs
- HANNINGFIELD TROUT FISHERY (FH2101)

23lbs 8ozs
- NARBOROUGH TROUT FARM (FH3424)
- SELM MUIR FISHERY (FH4135)

23lbs 5ozs
- LOCH INSCH FISHERY (FH2894)

23lbs 4ozs
- BELLBROOK VALLEY TROUT FISHERY (FH0377)
- DEARNFORD HALL TROUT FISHERY (FH1291)
- FONTBURN RESERVOIR (FH1758)

23lbs 1ozs
- CLERKLAND FLY FISHERY (FH1003)

22lbs 16ozs
- WESTLOW MERE (FH5283)

22lbs 12ozs
- LECHLADE TROUT FISHERY (FH2656)

22lbs 9ozs
- GAILEY TROUT AND PIKE FISHERY (FH1828)
- NEWBURY TROUT LAKES (FH3480)

22lbs 8ozs
- HOWWOOD TROUT FISHERY (FH2321)
- KINGENNIE FISHINGS (FH2494)
- PINEWOOD TROUT FISHERY (FH3780)

22lbs 4ozs
- COUND TROUT FISHERY (FH1140)
- HOPETOUN FISHERY (FH2291)

22lbs 3ozs
- OTTER FALLS FISHERY (FH3631)

22lbs 2ozs
- SPRINGWATER FISHERY (FH4374)

21lbs 9ozs
- RAYGILL FISHERY (FH3902)

21lbs 8ozs
- BLACKWOOL TROUT FISHERY (FH0484)
- BROOK FARM TROUT FISHERY (FH0677)
- FRENSHAM TROUT FISHERY (FH1800)

21lbs 3ozs
- LLANDEGLA TROUT FISHERY (FH2770)

20lbs 8ozs

HAZELCOPSE LAKES (FH2163)

20lbs 7ozs

AVINGTON TROUT FISHERIES (FH0190)

20lbs 6ozs

MIDDLETON FISHERY (FH3268)

19lbs 13ozs

NORTH THIRD TROUT FISHERY (FH3534)

19lbs 12ozs

CHIGBOROUGH FISHERIES (FH0941)

19lbs 8ozs

INVERAWE FISHERIES (FH2374)

19lbs 6ozs

WHITE SPRINGS LAKES (FH5341)

19lbs 4ozs

JERICHO LOCHS (FH2410)
LANGFORD FISHERIES (FH2611)

19lbs 2ozs

LEOMINSTEAD TROUT FISHERY (FH2703)
LOCH FAD (FH2879)

19lbs 1ozs

NEWHOUSE FISHERY (FH3486)

18lbs 12ozs

ALBURY ESTATE FISHERIES (FH0052)

18lbs 10ozs

WITTON CASTLE LAKES (FH5451)
YET-Y-GORS FISHERY (FH5566)

18lbs 8ozs

CLAWFORD VINEYARD AND FISHERIES (FH0985)
ORVIS INNIS COUNTRY CLUB AND FLY FISHERY (FH3626)

18lbs 6ozs

BRANSFORD GAME FISHERY (FH0601)

18lbs 4ozs

ALLANDALE TARN (FH0076)
LEIGHTON RESERVOIR (FH2693)

17lbs 12ozs

PACKINGTON TROUT FISHERY (FH3680)
WOODFORD FISHERY (FH5474)

17lbs 8ozs

QUANTOCK FISHERIES (FH3862)

17lbs 4ozs

CROXLEY HALL TROUT FISHERY (FH1203)
FARMOOR TROUT FISHERY (FH1676)
LADYBOWER RESERVOIR (FH2549)
STRAID FISHERY (FH4516)
WATCH RESERVOIR (FH5168)

17lbs 2ozs

CHURCH HILL FISHERY (FH0953)

16lbs 14ozs

SWANSWATER FISHERY (FH4600)

16lbs 11ozs

GLEN OF ROTHES TROUT FISHERY (FH1883)

16lbs 10ozs

CLATWORTHY RESERVOIR (FH0981)
DANEBRIDGE FISHERIES (FH1268)

16lbs 8ozs

PIPERDAM GOLF AND COUNTRY PARK (FH3784)
SANDYKNOWES FISHING (FH4099)
SKELMORLIE FISHERIES (FH4287)
TREE TOPS FLY FISHERY (FH4910)

16lbs 7ozs

TWIN LAKES TROUT FISHERY (FH5004)
WYKEHAM LAKES (FH5544)

16lbs 5ozs

MARKLE FISHERIES (FH3186)

16lbs 4ozs

KINGFISHER TROUT LAKE (FH2502)
PANT Y BEDW FISHING LAKES (FH3693)

16lbs 3ozs

BLAGDON LAKE (FH0487)
ESTHWAITE WATER (FH1630)
HANCHURCH FISHERIES (FH2099)
TRAWFFYNYDD RESERVOIR (FH4905)

16lbs 2ozs

FISHERWICK LAKES (FH1732)
MEADOW FISHERY (FH3222)

15lbs 12ozs

ROOKSBURY MILL TROUT FISHERIES (FH4007)

15lbs 10ozs

WHITE HOUSE MILL (FH5335)

15lbs 9ozs

NORTH BANK TROUT FISHERY (FH3526)
WATERCRESS FARM TROUT FISHERY (FH5174)

15lbs 7ozs

BEWL WATER (FH0403)

15lbs 6ozs

WENTWOOD RESERVOIR (FH5251)

15lbs 4ozs

BARNSFOLD WATERS (FH0318)

15lbs 3ozs

FAIROAK FISHERY (FH1655)

15lbs 2ozs

TEWITFIELDS TROUT FISHERY (FH4752)

15lbs 1ozs

HEADSHAW FISHERY (FH2166)

TROUT SEA

25lbs 6ozs

TEST (RIVER) (FH4745)

22lbs 8ozs

LOCH LOMOND (FH2904)

20lbs 2ozs

ESK (RIVER) (FH1626)

17lbs 10ozs

TWYMYN (RIVER) (FH5011)

16lbs 4ozs

TEIFI (RIVER) (FH4708)

14lbs 8ozs

FOWEY (RIVER) (FH1784)

14lbs 2ozs

TEES (RIVER) (FH4697)
WEAR (RIVER) (FH5209)

13lbs 8ozs

OBBE FISHINGS (FH3571)

13lbs 6ozs

FOWEY (RIVER) (FH1786)

12lbs 4ozs

NEATH (RIVER) (FH3434)

11lbs 8ozs

ERCH (RIVER) (FH1605)
TAW FISHING CLUB (FH4674)

10lbs 8ozs

CLOONGEE FISHERY (FH1021)

10lbs 1ozs

EGGESFORD COUNTRY HOTEL WATERS (FH1551)

TROUT TIGER

14lbs 2ozs

CHALK SPRINGS TROUT FISHERY (FH0891)

7lbs 0ozs

LLYN BRENIG (FH2795)

5lbs 11ozs

ARDGOWAN TROUT FISHERY (FH0128)

3lbs 8ozs

GAILEY TROUT AND PIKE FISHERY (FH1828)

TROUT WILD

7lbs 4ozs

CAMOWEN (RIVER) (FH0815)

ZANDER

19lbs 6ozs

FEN DRAYTON COMPLEX (FH1692)

19lbs 4ozs

COOMBE POOL (FH1109)

18lbs 10ozs

SEVERN (RIVER) (FH4145)

18lbs 6ozs

ROSWELL PITS (FH4022)

17lbs 3ozs

COOMBE ABBEY LAKE (FH1104)

16lbs 3ozs

BURY HILL FISHERIES (FH0764)

11lbs 11ozs

STOW (RIVER) (FH4512)
STOW (RIVER) (FH4508)

10lbs 3ozs

STOUR (RIVER) (FH4501)

Useful Addresses - Tackle Shops

SECTION 13

This section contains useful contact details for tackle shops suppliers, manufacturers and consultants.

Listed by Country by County.

Angling Times Fishooked Directory

ENGLAND

BEDFORDSHIRE

ANDY'S ANGLING CENTRE, 19 High Street, Shefford, BEDFORDSHIRE, SG17 5DD **England**
Mr A Davis (Proprietor)
(T) 01462 850061.

BLEAK HALL SPORTS, 1 High Street, Kempston, Bedford, BEDFORDSHIRE, MK42 7BT **England**
Mr M Jolley (Director)
(T) 01234 852530.

CHESNUT POOL FISHERIES, Chestnut Pool Fishery, Church Street, Langford, Biggleswade, BEDFORDSHIRE, SG18 9QT **England**
Mr P Wilson (Proprietor)
(T) 01462 701865.

CHESTNUT POOL FISHERY, Chestnut Pool, Off Church Street, Biggleswade, BEDFORDSHIRE, SG18 0JS **England**
Mrs J Wilfon (Partner)
(T) 01462 712758.

CHILTERN BAIT, Pike Farm, London Road, Houghton Conquest, Bedford, BEDFORDSHIRE, MK45 3LR **England**
(T) 01234 740356.

COUNTRY SPORTS, Barkers Lane, Bedford, BEDFORDSHIRE, MK41 9DJ **England**
Mr S Charkley (Proprietor)
(T) 01234 272082.

DELKIM LTD, P O Box 270, Bedford, BEDFORDSHIRE, MK43 7DZ **England**
Mr L Romang (Manager)
(T) 01234 721116.

DIXON BROS, 95 Tavistock Street, Bedford, BEDFORDSHIRE, MK40 2RR **England**
Mr C Ellis (Proprietor)
(T) 01234 267145.

FIRST LINE TACKLE, Unit 2, Bullpond Lane, Dunstable, BEDFORDSHIRE, LU6 3AH **England**
Mr J Brown (Director)
(T) 01582 608085.

LESLIES OF LUTON, 89-93 Park Street, Luton, BEDFORDSHIRE, LU1 3HG **England**
Mr D Sayce (Partner)
(T) 01582 453542.

LUTON ANGLING CENTRE, 68 Calverton Road, Luton, BEDFORDSHIRE, LU3 2SZ **England**
Mr G High (Partner)
(T) 01582 594359.

PEDDERS, 110 Victoria Street, Dunstable, BEDFORDSHIRE, LU6 3BA **England**
Mr C Bird (Proprietor)
(T) 01582 668643.

SPORTSMANS LODGE, 3-5 Howard Street, Bedford, BEDFORDSHIRE, MK40 3HS **England**
Mr Rob Pickering (Manager)
(T) 01234 269724.

TERMINAL TACKLE, 4 Friday Street, Leighton Buzzard, BEDFORDSHIRE, LU7 7AN **England**
Mr David Allan (Partner)
(T) 01525 370779.

THOMPSON TACKLE, 2b Hitchin Road, Arlesey, BEDFORDSHIRE, SG15 6RP **England**
Mr R Thompson (Proprietor)
(T) 01462 835269.

WORLD SPORT FISHING, Staploe Road, Wyboston, Bedford, BEDFORDSHIRE, MK44 3AT **England**
Mr R Shade (Director)
(T) 01480 403293.

ZEBCO SPORTS UK, 11-13 Scott Road, Luton, BEDFORDSHIRE, LU3 3BF **England**
Mr D Byrne (General Manager)
(T) 01582 492200.

BERKSHIRE

CROWNMEAD ANGLING CENTRE, 10 Crown Mead, Bath Road, Thatcham, BERKSHIRE, RG18 3JW **England**
Mr F Peacock (Proprietor)
(T) 01635 863092.

FARLOWS SPORTFISH LTD, Haywards Farm, Station Road, Theale, Reading, BERKSHIRE, RG7 4AS **England**
Mr Chris Ryan (Manager)
(T) 0118-930 3860.

FIELD & STREAM, 109 Bartholomew Street, Newbury, BERKSHIRE, RG14 5DT **England**
Mr R Benjamin (Proprietor)
(T) 01635 43186.

FRANK J WALLACE, 97 Silchester Road, Reading, BERKSHIRE, RG30 3EJ **England**
Mr F J Wallace (Proprietor)
(T) 0118-950 2585.

FRANK J WALLACE, 97 Southcote Road, Reading, BERKSHIRE, RG30 2AA **England**
Mr F J Wallace (Proprietor)
(T) 01189 502585.

KINGS OF MAIDENHEAD, 18 Ray Street, Maidenhead, BERKSHIRE, SL6 8PW **England**
(T) 01628 629283.

M D PRODUCTS, 64 St. Peters Avenue, Caversham, Reading, BERKSHIRE, RG4 7DH **England**
Mr M Dize (Proprietor)
(T) 0118-948 3332.

MAIDENHEAD BAIT & TACKLE, 11-13 Station Parade, Station Hill, Cookham, Maidenhead, BERKSHIRE, SL6 9BR **England**
Mr M Hutt (Manager)
(T) 01628 530500.

R & R TACKLE, 74 High Street, Sandhurst, BERKSHIRE, GU47 8ED **England**
(T) 01252 870007.

READING ANGLING CENTRE, 69 Northumberland Avenue, Reading, BERKSHIRE, RG2 7PS **England**
Mr A Tibble (Partner)
(T) 0118-987 2216.

ROXTON SPORTING LTD, 10-11 Bridge Street, Hungerford, BERKSHIRE, RG17 0EH **England**
(T) 01488 684943.

STOW'S ANGLING SHOP, 8 Upton Lea Parade, Wexham Road, Slough, BERKSHIRE, SL2 5JU **England**
Mr C Harrison (Manager)
(T) 01753 521612.

TADLEY ANGLING, Padworth Common, Padworth Road, Padworth Common, Reading, BERKSHIRE, RG7 4QG **England**
(T) 0118-970 1533.

THAMES VALLEY ANGLING, 258 Kentwood Hill, Tilehurst, Reading, BERKSHIRE, RG31 6DR **England**
(T) 0118-942 8249.

THATCHAM ANGLING CENTRE, Unit 4 154 Sagecroft Road, Thatcham, BERKSHIRE, RG18 3BQ **England**
Mr C Shepherd (Proprietor)
(T) 01635 871450.

WINDSOR ANGLING CENTRE, 153 St Leonards Road, Windsor, BERKSHIRE, SL4 3DW **England**
Mr Malcolm Hicks (Proprietor)
(T) 01753 867210.

BUCKINGHAMSHIRE

ANGLERS ALL, 13 St Marys Avenue, Bletchley, Milton Keynes, BUCKINGHAMSHIRE, MK3 5DT **England**
(T) 01908 371167.

AYLESBURY ANGLING CENTRE, Duck Farm Court, Station Way, Aylesbury, BUCKINGHAMSHIRE, HP20 2SQ **England**
Mr J C Hookway (Proprietor)
(T) 01296 437555.

BOYER LEISURE, Ford Lane, Iver, BUCKINGHAMSHIRE, SL0 9LL **England**
Mr G Davis (Manager)
(T) 01753 630302.

GREAT LINFORD TACKLE, Wolverton Road, Great Linford, Milton Keynes, BUCKINGHAMSHIRE, MK14 5AH **England**
Mr T Hodges (Proprietor)
(T) 01908 237233.

MILTON KEYNES ANGLING CENTRE, 4 St. Giles House, 21 Victoria Road, Bletchley, Milton Keynes, BUCKINGHAMSHIRE, MK2 2NG **England**
(T) 01908 374400.

SEAHAWK SUPPLIES, 4 Castle Street, Buckingham, BUCKINGHAMSHIRE, MK18 1BS **England**
Mr Chris Hawkins (Proprietor)
(T) 01280 817807.

SPORTSMANS LODGE, 26 Church Street, Wolverton, Milton Keynes, BUCKINGHAMSHIRE, MK12 5JN **England**
Mr Michael Bubhulder (Manager)
(T) 01908 313158.

STONEY ANGLING CENTRE, 53 Wolverton Road, Stony Stratford, Milton Keynes, BUCKINGHAMSHIRE, MK11 1ED **England**
Mr J Wood (Proprietor)
(T) 01908 569088.

CAMBRIDGESHIRE

ACE ANGLING CENTRE, 175 St. Neots Road, Hardwick, Cambridge, CAMBRIDGESHIRE, CB3 7QJ **England**
Mrs V Graves (Partner)
(T) 01954 212674.

ARBURY ANGLING CENTRE, 48 Arbury Court, Cambridge, CAMBRIDGESHIRE, CB4 2JQ **England**
Mr J Belshore (Proprietor)
(T) 01223 300216.

BAITSTREAM LTD, 1 Farmersfield, Oxney Road, Peterborough, CAMBRIDGESHIRE, PE1 5YZ **England**
Mr Martin Lockland (Director)
(T) 01733 345091.

BENWICK SPORTS, 29 Main Street, Little Downham, Ely, CAMBRIDGESHIRE, CB6 2ST **England**
Mr A Crane (Proprietor)
(T) 01353 698936.

BOUNDARY TACKLEBOX, 64 High Street, Market Deeping, Peterborough, CAMBRIDGESHIRE, PE6 8EB **England**
Mr S R Bowler (Proprietor)
(T) 01778 349203.

BRUCE & WALKER LTD, High Street, Upwood, Ramsey, Huntingdon, CAMBRIDGESHIRE, PE26 2QE **England**
Mr K Walker (Managing Director)
(T) 01487 813764.

BRYAN LAKEY, 12 Hill Street, Wisbech, CAMBRIDGESHIRE, PE13 1BA **England**
Mr B Lakey (Proprietor)
(T) 01945 585278.

BRYAN LAKEY, 12 Hill Street, Leverington, Wisbech, CAMBRIDGESHIRE, PE13 5AB **England**
Mr B Lakey (Proprietor)
(T) 01945 585278.

COLEBYS, 15 Granby Street, Littleport, Ely, CAMBRIDGESHIRE, CB6 1NE **England**
Mrs Irene Day (Partner)
(T) 01353 860419.

CONTINENTAL POLE TACKLE LTD, 29 Primrose Hill, Doddington, March, CAMBRIDGESHIRE, PE15 0SU **England**
Mr R Sladden (Director)
(T) 01354 741330.

COOPER & SON, 12 Milton Road, Cambridge, CAMBRIDGESHIRE, CB4 1JY **England**
Mr S Cooper (Proprietor)
(T) 01223 365987.

CRAFTY CATCHER PRODUCTS, 28 The Cotes, Soham, Ely, CAMBRIDGESHIRE, CB7 5EP **England**
Mr R Sherwood (Proprietor)
(T) 01353 723097.

EMNETH ANGLING, 21 Gaultree Square, Emneth, Wisbech, CAMBRIDGESHIRE, PE14 8DA **England**
Mr K Melnyk (Partner)
(T) 01945 589920.

F WADE & SON, 247 High Street, Peterborough, CAMBRIDGESHIRE, PE2 9EH **England**
Mr Ken Wade (Partner)
(T) 01733 565159.

FARRINGTON, 2-4 Ferry Lane, Cambridge, CAMBRIDGESHIRE, CB4 1NT **England**
Mr F Farrington (Proprietor)
(T) 01223 461361.

FULLING MILL LTD, Towermead Business Centre, High Street, Peterborough, CAMBRIDGESHIRE, PE2 9DY **England**
Mr Tim Hunt (General Manager)
(T) 01733 341413.

J A C D A LTD, 12 Saville Rd Industrial Estate, Peterborough, CAMBRIDGESHIRE, PE3 7PR **England**
Mr J Lowenthal (Director)
(T) 01733 765207.

KELLY'S, 18 High Street, Huntingdon, CAMBRIDGESHIRE, PE18 6TE **England**
Mr T Kelly (Proprietor)
(T) 01480 450363.

MARCH ANGLING CENTRE, 88a High Street, March, CAMBRIDGESHIRE, PE15 9LQ **England**
Mrs S Gill (Proprietor)
(T) 01354 658747.

MILL VIEW, 3 Nene Parade, March, CAMBRIDGESHIRE, PE15 8TD **England**
Mr M Spies (Proprietor)
(T) 01354 656150.

OUSE VALLEY SPECIALIST ANGLING, 25-31 Huntingdon Street, St. Neots, CAMBRIDGESHIRE, PE19 1BG **England**
Mr D L Barker (Proprietor)
(T) 01480 386088.

P.D'S FISHING TACKLE, 721 Lincoln Road, Peterborough, CAMBRIDGESHIRE, PE1 3HD **England**
(T) 01733 344899.

RAY NIMMO ENTERPRISES, Chettisham Business Pk, Lynn Road, Chettisham, Ely, CAMBRIDGESHIRE, CB6 1RY **England**
Mr R Nimmo (Proprietor)
(T) 01353 666342.

SHELTONS OF PETERBOROUGH LTD, 67 South Street, Stanground, Peterborough, CAMBRIDGESHIRE, PE2 8EX **England**
M. Charles Dean Shelton (Director)
(T) 01733 565287.

SOHAM PETS & LEISURE, 27 High Street, Soham, Ely, CAMBRIDGESHIRE, CB7 5HA **England**
Mrs G Swain (Partner)
(T) 01353 720454.

ST IVES ANGLING CENTRE, 8 Crown Street, St. Ives, CAMBRIDGESHIRE, PE27 5EB **England**
Mr T Jones (Partner)
(T) 01480 301903.

ST NEOTS ANGLING CENTRE, 39a New Street, St. Neots, CAMBRIDGESHIRE, PE19 1AJ **England**
Mr M Richardson (Proprietor)
(T) 01480 356330.

STANJAY, 7 Old Ct Hall, Godmanchester, Huntingdon, CAMBRIDGESHIRE, PE29 2HS **England**
Mr S J Binge (Proprietor)
(T) 01480 453303.

WATERSIDE ANGLING WHOLESALE SUPPLIES, Coldhams Road, Cambridge, CAMBRIDGESHIRE, CB1 3EW **England**
(T) 01223 411713.

WEBBS, 196 Newark Avenue, Peterborough, CAMBRIDGESHIRE, PE1 4NP **England**
Mrs S C Parker (Proprietor)
(T) 01733 566466.

CARMARTHENSHIRE

BLAENPLWYF FISHING & ANGLING, Blaenplwyf, Aberystwyth, CARMARTHENSHIRE, SY23 4DH **England**
(T) 01970 612499.

CHESHIRE

A D BRADBURY, 16 The Square, Halebarns, Altrincham, CHESHIRE, WA15 8ST **England**
Mr Phil Curzons (Proprietor)
(T) 01619 802836.

A6 ANGLING, 141 Wellington Rd North, Stockport, CHESHIRE, SK4 2PF **England**
Mr Steve Cooke (Proprietor)
(T) 0161-432 6136.

ANDICO ANGLING DIRECT LTD, P O Box 40, Crewe, CHESHIRE, CW1 5FE **England**
M. Nicholas Martin Dunn (Joint Director)
(T) 01270 252750.

AQUA PRODUCTS, 18 Frances Street, Crewe, CHESHIRE, CW2 6HF **England**
Mr C Manifold (Proprietor)
(T) 01270 580006.

AQUA PRODUCTS, London Road, Stapeley, Nantwich, CHESHIRE, CW5 7LH **England**
Mr Chris Manifold (Proprietor)
(T) 01270 629999.

BARLOWS, 47 Bond Street, Macclesfield, CHESHIRE, SK11 6QS **England**
Mr Adam Barlow (Proprietor)
(T) 01625 619935.

CHESHIRE ANGLING, 279a Thelwell Lane, Warrington, CHESHIRE, WA4 1NF **England**
(T) 01925 637397.

COMPLETE ANGLER, 104 Gainsborough Road, Warrington, CHESHIRE, WA4 6BN **England**
Mr W Stubbs (Partner)
(T) 01925 656441.

CONTACT PETS, 9 The Parade, Blacon, Chester, CHESHIRE, CH1 5HN **England**
Mr D Clark (Proprietor)
(T) 01244 377442.

CROW WOOD PETS, 202 Warrington Road, Widnes, CHESHIRE, WA8 0AX **England**
Mr I Nicholson (Proprietor)
(T) 0151-495 1702.

DAVE'S OF MIDDLEWICH, Lewin Street, Middlewich, CHESHIRE, CW10 9BG **England**
Mr D W Costello (Proprietor)
(T) 01606 833853.

DYSONS, 72 Manchester Road, Altrincham, CHESHIRE, WA14 4PJ **England**
Mr C R Dyson (Proprietor)
(T) 0161-941 3558.

EDGELEY SPORTS & FISHING, 145 Castle Street, Stockport, CHESHIRE, SK3 9AR **England**
Mr B Pearce (Director)
(T) 0161-480 2511.

GIBSON DAVID, 13 Pepper Row, Chester, CHESHIRE, CH1 1EA **England**
(T) 01244 316132.

HALTON ANGLING, Deacon Road, Widnes, CHESHIRE, WA8 6EG **England**
Mr E Morgan (Proprietor)
(T) 0151-495 2223.

HAZEL GROVE ANGLING CENTRE, 2 Fiveways Parade, Hazel Grove, Stockport, CHESHIRE, SK7 6DG **England**
Mr Mike Ashton (Proprietor)
(T) 01625 858643.

HOOLE ANGLING CENTRE LTD, 140 Tarvin Road, Chester, CHESHIRE, CH3 5EE **England**
Mrs J Millard (Proprietor)
(T) 01244 345069.

J & A TACKLE, 87 Victoria Street, Crewe, CHESHIRE, CW1 2JH **England**
(T) 01270 253891.

J & R ANGLING CENTRE, 43 Victoria Road, Widnes, CHESHIRE, WA8 7RP **England**
Mr R Kinsella (Proprietor)
(T) 0151-420 0940.

JIM SHAW, 72 Evelyn Street, Warrington, CHESHIRE, WA5 1BD **England**
Mr Jim Shaw (Proprietor)
(T) 01925 659090.

JONES FISHING TACKLE, 39 Vernon Road, Chester, CHESHIRE, CH1 4JT **England**
Mr I D Jones (Proprietor)
(T) 01244 390596.

MIKES FISHING & BIKES, 35 Queens Avenue, Widnes, CHESHIRE, WA8 8HR **England**
Mr M O'connor (Proprietor)
(T) 01514 205390.

MOHMAR, Bait Farm, Hack Green, Baddington, Nantwich, CHESHIRE, CW5 8AL **England**
Mr E W Marsh (Partner)
(T) 01270 627419.

NEPTUNE PRODUCTS, 16 Gainsborough Road, Crewe, CHESHIRE, CW2 7PH **England**
Mr D Williams (Proprietor)
(T) 01270 650744.

NORMANS OF WOODLEY, 3 Woodley Precinct, Woodley, Stockport, CHESHIRE, SK6 1RJ **England**
Mrs C Durkin (Manageress)
(T) 0161-494 5422.

PURE FISHING UK LTD, Unit 5, Aston Way, Middlewich, CHESHIRE, CW10 0HS **England**
Mr G Thomas (Managing Director)
(T) 01606 836921.

STALYBRIDGE ANGLING SUPPLIES, 33 Grosvenor Street, Stalybridge, CHESHIRE, SK15 2JN **England**
(T) 0161-338 2539.

STAPELEY ANGLING CENTRE, 92 London Road, Stapeley, Nantwich, CHESHIRE, CW5 7LH **England**
Mrs B Davis (Proprietor)
(T) 01270 611500.

STOCKPORT FLY FISHING SUPPLIES, 11 Shaw Road, Stockport, CHESHIRE, SK4 4AG **England**
(T) 0161-431 7474.

STU'S TACKLE & PETS, 29 Heath Street, Golborne, Warrington, CHESHIRE, WA3 3BN **England**
(T) 01942 721400.

TENERIFE HOLIDAYS & TACKLE SHOP, 28 Christleton Road, Chester, CHESHIRE, CH3 5UG **England**
Mr Chris Weller (Proprietor)
(T) 01244 323081.

TENSION PRODUCTS UK, 82-84 Station Road, Northwich, CHESHIRE, CW9 5RB **England**
Mr R Scott (Proprietor)
(T) 01606 330916.

TERRYS FISHING TACKLE SHOP, 47 Lawton Street, Congleton, CHESHIRE, CW12 1RU **England**
(T) 01260 273770.

TREVOR ALLEN, 16 Altrincham Road, Wilmslow, CHESHIRE, SK9 5ND **England**
Mr T Allen (Proprietor)
(T) 01625 528831.

WEAVERSIDE ANGLING CENTRE, 1a Wharton Road, Winsford, CHESHIRE, CW7 3AA **England**
Mr F W Churchill (Proprietor)
(T) 01606 861572.

WESTON POINT ANGLING CENTRE, 98A Russell Road, Runcorn, CHESHIRE, WA7 4DW **England**
Mr J Stringer (Proprietor)
(T) 01928 578200.

CLEVELAND

A E DORRELL, 49 Kings Road, North Ormesby, Middlesbrough, CLEVELAND, TS3 6NH **England**
(T) 01642 246274.

ANGLERS CHOICE, 53 Clive Road, Middlesbrough, CLEVELAND, TS5 6BH **England**
Mr Steve Bland (Proprietor)
(T) 01642 899288.

ANGLERS SERVICES, 27 Park Road, Hartlepool, CLEVELAND, TS24 7PW **England**
Mr P Arrowsmith (Proprietor)
(T) 01429 274844.

CARP CRAZY, 4 Three Tuns Wynd, High Street, Stokesley, Middlesbrough, CLEVELAND, TS9 5DQ **England**
Mr M Pitchers (Proprietor)
(T) 01642 714141.

CLEVELAND ANGLING CENTRE, 22a Westbury Street, Thornaby, Stockton-on-Tees, CLEVELAND, TS17 6PG **England**
Mr P Rambow (Proprietor)
(T) 01642 677000.

FLYNN FISHING TACKLE, Care Of Dickens, Portrack Lane, Stockton-on-Tees, CLEVELAND, TS18 2DB **England**
Mr F Flynn (Partner)
(T) 01642 617775.

FLYNN FISHING TACKLE, Care Of Dickens, Portrack Lane, Stockton-on-Tees, CLEVELAND, TS18 2PQ **England**
Mr F Flynn (Partner)
(T) 01642 617775.

FLYNNS FISHING TACKLE & COUNTRY WEAR, 12 Varo Ter, Stockton-on-Tees, CLEVELAND, TS18 1JY **England**
Mr F Flynn (Partner)
(T) 01642 676473.

FRIARAGE, 39 Northgate, Hartlepool, CLEVELAND, TS24 0JX **England**
Mr T Foster (Proprietor)
(T) 01429 273145.

JOHN F GENT LTD, 161 York Road, Hartlepool, CLEVELAND, TS26 9EQ **England**
Mr John Gent (Managing Director)
(T) 01429 272585.

KEITHS SPORTS, 31 Milton Street, Saltburn-by-the-Sea, CLEVELAND, TS12 1DN **England**
(T) 01287 624296.

REDCAR ANGLING CENTRE, 159 High Street, Redcar, CLEVELAND, TS10 3AN **England**
Mr D Turnbull (Proprietor)
(T) 01642 474006.

TACKLE BOX, 46 Station Road, Billingham, CLEVELAND, TS23 1AB **England**
Mr P Boswell (Proprietor)
(T) 01642 532034.

CORNWALL

AMMODYTES CO LTD, Penbeagle Industrial Estate, St. Ives, CORNWALL, TR26 2JH **England**
Susan Gilbert (Joint Director)
(T) 01736 797086.

ATLANTIC ANGLING CENTRE, 9B Cliff Road, Newquay, CORNWALL, TR7 2NE **England**
Mr R Martin (Proprietor)
(T) 01637 850777.

ATLANTIC FISHING TACKLE, 36 Wendron Street, Helston, CORNWALL, TR13 8PS **England**
Mr Stuart Athay (Proprietor)
(T) 01326 561640.

ATLANTIC SUPPLIES, Barkla Shop, St. Agnes, CORNWALL, TR5 0XN **England**
Mrs A Shine (Proprietor)
(T) 01872 552332.

BAIT BUNKER, 5 Polmorla Road, Wadebridge, CORNWALL, PL27 7NB **England**
Mr M K Watts (Proprietor)
(T) 01208 816403.

BAIT SHOP, 70 Fore Street, Newquay, CORNWALL, TR7 1EY **England**
Mrs S M Nash (Proprietor)
(T) 01637 873869.

BANDOLIER ENGINEERING, 6 Annear Road, Penryn, CORNWALL, TR10 9ER **England**
Mr A Clynick (Director)
(T) 01326 376866.

BATARA STAR FISHING TRIPS, Rock, Wadebridge, CORNWALL, PL27 6LD **England**
Mr W R Burt (Proprietor)
(T) 01208 863975.

BRITISH FLY REELS LTD, Tregoniggie Industrial Estate, Falmouth, CORNWALL, TR11 4RS **England**
Mr J Gall (Director)
(T) 01326 372441.

BUDE ANGLING SUPPLIES, 6 Queen Street, Bude, CORNWALL, EX23 8BB **England**
(T) 01288 353396.

CITY ANGLING CENTRE, Peoples Palace, Pydar Street, Truro, CORNWALL, TR1 2AZ **England**
Mr Peter Bottono (Proprietor)
(T) 01872 275340.

COUNTY ANGLER, 39 Cross Street, Camborne, CORNWALL, TR14 8ES **England**
Mrs K Stacey (Partner)
(T) 01209 718490.

END TACKLE, 24 Fore Street, St. Blazey, Par, CORNWALL, PL24 2NJ **England**
Mr T Hodgkiss (Proprietor)
(T) 01726 814007.

JACK BRAY & SON, The Quay, East Looe, Looe, CORNWALL, PL13 1AL **England**
(T) 01503 262504.

JIMS DISCOUNT TACKLE, 56 Fore Street, Redruth, CORNWALL, TR15 2AQ **England**
Mr J Smyth (Proprietor)
(T) 01209 313994.

LAKEVIEW TACKLE SHOP & FISHING LAKES, Old Coach Road, Lanivet, Bodmin, CORNWALL, PL30 5HB **England**
Mr L P Pearce (Proprietor)
(T) 01208 831079.

LOSTWITHIEL ANGLING CENTRE, 22 Queen Street, Lostwithiel, CORNWALL, PL22 0AD **England**
Mr S Clementson (Proprietor)
(T) 01208 873392.

LYNHER LEADS, Wolsdon Lodge, Antony, Torpoint, CORNWALL, PL11 3AD **England**
Mr D Livick (Proprietor)
(T) 01752 813141.

M L SUPPLIES, 9c Tregoniggie Industrial Estate, Falmouth, CORNWALL, TR11 4SN **England**
(T) 01326 374748.

MATRIX MARKETING CORPORATION LTD, Gwel Avon Business Pk, 1 Gilston Road, Saltash, CORNWALL, PL12 6TW **England**
Mr Martin Beer (Managing Director)
(T) 01752 841140.

MEVAGISSEY SHARK & ANGLING CENTRE, West Wharf, Mevagissey, St. Austell, CORNWALL, PL26 6UJ **England**
Mr D Bowman (Partner)
(T) 01726 843430.

NEWQUAY FISHING & SHOOTING CENTRE, 12-14 Fore Street, Newquay, CORNWALL, TR7 1LN **England**
Mr P Rawling (Proprietor)
(T) 01637 874139.

NEWTOWN ANGLING CENTRE, Newtown, Germoe, Penzance, CORNWALL, TR20 9AE **England**
Mr C Bird (Proprietor)
(T) 01736 763721.

PADSTOW ANGLING CENTRE, 1-3 South Quay, Padstow, CORNWALL, PL28 8BL **England**
Mr E Schlisske (Proprietor)
(T) 01841 532762.

PORTHLEVEN ANGLING CENTRE, Mount Pleasant Road, Porthleven, Helston, CORNWALL, TR13 9JS **England**
Mr Stuart Athay (Proprietor)
(T) 01326 561885.

QUAY SHOP, 18 Quay Street, Penzance, CORNWALL, TR18 4BD **England**
(T) 01736 363397.

RED-GILL FISHING LURES, 40 Kiln Close, Mevagissey, St. Austell, CORNWALL, PL26 6TP **England**
Mr Stuart Ingram (Partner)
(T) 01726 843214.

ROGERS TACKLE SHOP, Higher Bore Street, Bodmin, CORNWALL, PL31 1JZ **England**
Mr Roger Lashbrook (Proprietor)
(T) 01208 78006.

SPENCER-CARTER LTD, Tregoniggie Industrial Estate, Falmouth, CORNWALL, TR11 4SN **England**
Mr Stephen Carter (Joint Director)
(T) 01326 373423.

TACKLE BOX, 1 Swanpool Street, Falmouth, CORNWALL, TR11 3HU **England**
Mr P Dodgson (Proprietor)
(T) 01326 315849.

TREYARNON ANGLING CENTRE, Treyarnon Bay Hotel, Treyarnon Bay, Padstow, CORNWALL, PL28 8JN **England**
(T) 01841 521157.

W M HOSKING, Tidewatch, Peverell Ter, Porthleven, Helston, CORNWALL, TR13 9DX **England**
Mrs J Hosking (Partner)
(T) 01326 561505.

W S B TACKLE, Blowing House Hill, St. Austell, CORNWALL, PL25 5AH **England**
Mr R Crowle (Proprietor)
(T) 01726 75681.

WATERFRONT FISHING & SHOOTING, Lower Wharf Centre, The Wharf, Bude, CORNWALL, EX23 8LG **England**
Mr S P Brett (Manager)
(T) 01288 359606.

WEIGHTS & BAITS, 10 Globe Yard, St. Austell, CORNWALL, PL25 5JH **England**
Mr N Parish (Proprietor)
(T) 01726 72866.

WEST CORNWALL ANGLING, 1 Alexandra Road, Penzance, CORNWALL, TR18 4LY **England**
Mr Stuart Athay (Proprietor)
(T) 01736 362363.

WSB TACKLE, Bugle Generating Station, Roche Road, Bugle, St. Austell, CORNWALL, PL26 8PP **England**
Mrs N Crowle (Partner)
(T) 01726 852662.

COUNTY DURHAM

A M H ANGLING, 30 Front Street, Annfield Plain, Stanley, COUNTY DURHAM, DH9 8HY **England**
Mrs M Hodegson (Proprietor)
(T) 01207 281673.

ANGLERS SERVICES (HARTLEPOOL) LTD, 45 Claypath, Durham, COUNTY DURHAM, DH1 1QS **England**
Mr Peter Arrowsmith (Proprietor)
(T) 01913 847584.

AYCLIFFE ANGLING & OUTDOOR CENTRE, 8 Neville Parade, Newton Aycliffe, COUNTY DURHAM, DL5 5DH **England**
(T) 01325 320500.

BAIT BOX, 5 North Terrace, Seaham, COUNTY DURHAM, SR7 7EU **England**
Mr P Pomfrett (Manager)
(T) 0191-581 9585.

C L S ANGLING, 21 North Burns, Chester le Street, COUNTY DURHAM, DH3 3TF **England**
Mr I Macklie (Proprietor)
(T) 0191-388 2154.

COAST ROAD FISHING TACKLE, 3 Sunderland Road, Horden, Peterlee, COUNTY DURHAM, SR8 4QJ **England**
Mrs Elaine Wilks (Proprietor)
(T) 0191-518 0742.

DARLINGTON ANGLING CENTRE, 341 North Road, Darlington, COUNTY DURHAM, DL1 3BL **England**
Mr Peter Ranbow (Proprietor)
(T) 01325 481818.

DELTAFLASH, 40 Broom Road, Ferryhill, COUNTY DURHAM, DL17 8AF **England**
Mrs M Pennock (Partner)
(T) 01740 652360.

EASTBOURNE FISHING TACKLE, 1 Belgrave Street, Darlington, COUNTY DURHAM, DL1 4AN **England**
Mr K Ragettli (Proprietor)
(T) 01325 355156.

EASTBOURNE FISHING TACKLE, 123 Neasham Road, Darlington, COUNTY DURHAM, DL1 4BE **England**
(T) 01325 355156.

IAN D MARTIN, 45 Sandriggs, Darlington, COUNTY DURHAM, DL3 0TY **England**
Mr Ian Martin (Proprietor)
(T) 01325 286463.

LEES, 73 High Street, Willington, Crook, COUNTY DURHAM, DL15 0PF **England**
Mrs J Lee (Proprietor)
(T) 01388 747571.

QUALI-TYE, 11 Station Road, Consett, COUNTY DURHAM, DH8 5RL **England**
(T) 01207 508010.

REID FISHING TACKLE & SPORTS, 33 Hope Street, Crook, COUNTY DURHAM, DL15 9HU **England**
Mr Roy Reid (Proprietor)
(T) 01388 763867.

RIGS, 72 Church Street, Seaham, COUNTY DURHAM, SR7 7HE **England**
Mr G Mcghee (Proprietor)
(T) 0191-581 7915.

SWEENEY TODDS, 8 Bucktons Yard, Darlington, COUNTY DURHAM, DL3 7QL **England**
Mr A J Armitstead (Proprietor)
(T) 01325 480209.

TURNERS FISHING TACKLE, 25 Front Street, Sacriston, Durham, COUNTY DURHAM, DH7 6JS **England**
Mr J H Turner (Proprietor)
(T) 0191-371 1804.

W P ADAMS, 42 Duke Street, Darlington, COUNTY DURHAM, DL3 7AJ **England**
(T) 01325 468069.

CUMBRIA

B WARWICK, Market Place, Brampton, CUMBRIA, CA8 1NW **England**
Mr B Warwick (Proprietor)
(T) 016977 2361.

BOOMERS BASIT & TACKLE, Kings Mews, 19 King Street, Ulverston, CUMBRIA, LA12 7DZ **England**
Mr P S Walsh (Proprietor)
(T) 01229 580261.

CARLSONS, 64-66 Kirkland, Kendal, CUMBRIA, LA9 5AP **England**
Mrs Vera Carlson (Proprietor)
(T) 01539 724867.

COMPLEAT ANGLER, 4 King Street, Whitehaven, CUMBRIA, CA28 7LA **England**
Mr P Johnstone (Proprietor)
(T) 01946 695322.

CUMBRIA ANGLING CENTRE, 5 Tangiers Buildings, George Street, Whitehaven, CUMBRIA, CA28 7EY **England**
Mr J M Sterland (Proprietor)
(T) 01946 693233.

CUMBRIA ROD & GUN, 72 Main Street, Egremont, CUMBRIA, CA22 2DB **England**
Ms S Watson (Proprietor)
(T) 01946 821127.

EDDIE'S, 70 Shaddongate, Carlisle, CUMBRIA, CA2 5UG **England**
Mr H Harris (Manager)
(T) 01228 810744.

GO FISHING, Robinson Place, Bowness-on-Windermere, Windermere, CUMBRIA, LA23 3DQ **England**
Mrs S Wren (Proprietor)
(T) 015394 47086.

GRAHAMS GUN & TACKLE, 9-15 South William Street, Workington, CUMBRIA, CA14 2ED **England**
Mr R Graham (Proprietor)
(T) 01900 605093.

HOOLS FISHING TACKLE, 185 Rawlinson Street, Barrow-in-Furness, CUMBRIA, LA14 1ED **England**
Mr Stanley Hool (Proprietor)
(T) 01229 430425.

J NORRIS, 21 Victoria Road, Penrith, CUMBRIA, CA11 8HP **England**
Mr J Norris (Proprietor)
(T) 01768 864211.

MCHARDY'S FISHING TACKLE SPECIALISTS, South Henry Street, Carlisle, CUMBRIA, CA1 1SF **England**
Mr John Park (Partner)
(T) 01228 523988.

MURRAYS FISHING TACKLE, 16 Fisher Street, Carlisle, CUMBRIA, CA3 8RN **England**
Mr Andrew Murray (Proprietor)
(T) 01228 523816.

R HADWIN, The Boulevard, Windermere Road, Grange-over-Sands, CUMBRIA, LA11 6EG **England**
Mr R Hadwin (Proprietor)
(T) 015395 32854.

RODS 'N' SODS, The Gill, Ulverston, CUMBRIA, LA12 7BJ **England**
Mr A J Dickson (Proprietor)
(T) 01229 582367.

TACKLEBASE, 96 Main Street, Haverigg, Millom, CUMBRIA, LA18 4EY **England**
Mr Gerald Lowrey (Proprietor)
(T) 01229 772338.

DERBYSHIRE

ALFRETON ANGLING CENTRE, 11 Park Street, Alfreton, DERBYSHIRE, DE55 7JE **England**
Mr J Spencer (Proprietor)
(T) 01773 832611.

ANGLERS CORNER, 344 Osmaston Road, Derby, DERBYSHIRE, DE24 8AF **England**
Mr Terry Ollerenshaw (Proprietor)
(T) 01332 343870.

ANGLING CENTRE DERBY, 27-33 Nightingale Road, Derby, DERBYSHIRE, DE24 8BG **England**
Mr T Johnson (Advertising Manager)
(T) 01332 380605.

ARTISAN ANGLING, 141 London Road, Derby, DERBYSHIRE, DE1 2QN **England**
Mr K Priestley (Proprietor)
(T) 01332 340981.

ARUNDEL AQUATICS & ANGLING SUPPLIES, 56 Arundel Street, Glossop, DERBYSHIRE, SK13 7AB **England**
Mr A S Turner (Manager)
(T) 01457 866727.

BACCHUS & RHONE, 127-129 High Street, Woodville, Swadlincote, DERBYSHIRE, DE11 7DU **England**
Mr R Harvey (Manager)
(T) 01283 216870.

BAKEWELL FLY FISHING, 3a Hebden Court, Matlock Street, Bakewell, DERBYSHIRE, DE45 1EE **England**
Mr P Arfield (Manager)
(T) 01629 813531.

BELPER TACKLE, 37 Bridge Street, Belper, DERBYSHIRE, DE56 1AY **England**
Mr R Bacon (Proprietor)
(T) 01773 822525.

BUXTON AQUATIC CENTRE, 4 Fairfield Road, Buxton, DERBYSHIRE, SK17 7DW **England**
(T) 01298 22729.

CHESTERFIELD ANGLING CENTRE, 34 Chester Street, Chesterfield, DERBYSHIRE, S40 1DW **England**
Mr N C Sibbring (Proprietor)
(T) 01246 208710.

CLAY CROSS ANGLING, 51 High Street, Clay Cross, Chesterfield, DERBYSHIRE, S45 9DX **England**
Mr M Jakes (Proprietor)
(T) 01246 861888.

CORNER TACKLE, 1 Bolsover Road, Shuttlewood, Chesterfield, DERBYSHIRE, S44 6QX **England**
Mr A Evil (Proprietor)
(T) 01246 823177.

DERWENT TACKLE, 2A Station Road, Borrowash, Derby, DERBYSHIRE, DE72 3LG **England**
Mr J Houghton (Proprietor)
(T) 01332 662379.

FOSTERS OF ASHBOURNE LTD, 45 Church Street, Ashbourne, DERBYSHIRE, DE6 1AJ **England**
Mr Robert Stone (Proprietor)
(T) 01335 343135.

GRESTY S N, Reaps Farm, Torside, Glossop, DERBYSHIRE, SK13 1JF **England**
(T) 01457 854623.

LATHKILL TACKLE, Unity Complex, Dale Road North, Darley Dale, Matlock, DERBYSHIRE, DE4 2HX **England**
Mrs M White (Proprietor)
(T) 01629 735101.

LEEGEM ANGLING CENTRE, 81 Sheffield Road, Chesterfield, DERBYSHIRE, S41 7LT **England**
Mr Phillip Wright (Proprietor)
(T) 01246 559480.

MADDEN CLIFF, 5 Church Street, Staveley, Chesterfield, DERBYSHIRE, S43 3TL **England**
Mr C Madden (Proprietor)
(T) 01246 472410.

MATCH WINNER, 46 Eckington Road, Coal Aston, Dronfield, DERBYSHIRE, S18 3AT **England**
Mr A Flint (Proprietor)
(T) 01246 290928.

MIDDY TACKLE INTERNATIONAL LTD, Thorpes Road, Heanor Gate Industrial Estate, Heanor, DERBYSHIRE, DE75 7GY **England**
Mr D Middleton (Director)
(T) 01773 533533.

NATHAN'S OF DERBY, 9-19 Edgware Road, Derby, DERBYSHIRE, DE22 4EW **England**
Mr N Hughes (Proprietor)
(T) 01332 523630.

NATHANS TACKLE, 1 Ward Street, Derby, DERBYSHIRE, DE22 3RY **England**
Mr J Hughes (Proprietor)
(T) 01332 366200.

ROD & LINE TACKLE, 17 Nottingham Road, Ripley, DERBYSHIRE, DE5 3DJ **England**
Mr D Spencer (Proprietor)
(T) 01773 749545.

SHORELINK, Wholesale, 3 Bridle Lane, Lower Hartshay, Ripley, DERBYSHIRE, DE5 3RQ **England**
(T) 01773 512035.

STEVE WOOLLEY, Belle Vue Road, Ashbourne, DERBYSHIRE, DE6 1AT **England**
Mr Steve Woolley (Proprietor)
(T) 01335 300095.

TACKLE BOX, 323 Somercotes Hill, Somercotes, Alfreton, DERBYSHIRE, DE55 4JX **England**
Mr T Marriott (Proprietor)
(T) 01773 602985.

TAYLORS TACKLE & TROPHIES, 136 Cotmanhay Road, Ilkeston, DERBYSHIRE, DE7 8NZ **England**
Mr P Taylor (Partner)
(T) 0115-930 1610.

TOUCHSTONE LTD, 55 Hollincross Lane, Glossop, DERBYSHIRE, SK13 8JQ **England**
Mr P Richards (Proprietor)
(T) 01457 861202.

TRADITIONAL ANGLING PRODUCTS, Flat, 21A Market Street, Castle Donington, Derby, DERBYSHIRE, DE74 2JB **England**
Mr S Middleton (Proprietor)
(T) 01332 855000.

DEVON

ALL ANGLES, Exeter Hill, Cullompton, DEVON, EX15 1DJ **England**
(T) 01884 33332.

BRAILEYS FIELD SPORTS, Market Street, Exeter, DEVON, EX1 1DW **England**
Mr H Austin (Manager)
(T) 01392 210066.

BRIXHAM BAIT & TACKLE, 10 The Quay, Brixham, DEVON, TQ5 8AW **England**
Mr G Dryer (Partner)
(T) 01803 853390.

CAEN FISHING SUPPLIES, 4 West Cross, Caen Street, Braunton, DEVON, EX33 1AQ **England**
Mr A Foster (Partner)
(T) 01271 812375.

CLIVE'S TACKLE & BAIT, 182 Exeter Street, Plymouth, DEVON, PL4 0NQ **England**
Mr Clive Way (Proprietor)
(T) 01752 228940.

COVE-CLARK, 45-47 Torbay Road, Paignton, DEVON, TQ4 6AA **England**
(T) 01803 559214.

D K SPORTS, 88 Vauxhall Street, Plymouth, DEVON, PL4 0EX **England**
Mr Simon Kingdom (Partner)
(T) 01752 662361.

D KIDDY, 28 Barton Road, Torquay, DEVON, TQ1 4DP **England**
Mr D Kiddy (Partner)
(T) 01803 293999.

DELTA TACKLE LTD, 3 Willow Court, St Modwen Road, Plymouth, DEVON, PL6 8LQ **England**
Mrs E A Mcconnell (Director)
(T) 01752 672126.

DEVON ANGLING CENTRE, Orchard Meadow, Orchard Way, Chillington, Kingsbridge, DEVON, TQ7 2LB **England**
Mr M Barnet (Manager)
(T) 01548 580888.

EUROPEAN NET DESIGN LTD, 6 Rea Barn Road, Brixham, DEVON, TQ5 9DU **England**
Mr S Simons (Managing Director)
(T) 01803 854007.

EXE VALLEY ANGLING, 19 Westexe South, Tiverton, DEVON, EX16 5DQ **England**
Mr John Smallwood (Proprietor)
(T) 01884 242275.

EXETER ANGLING CENTRE, Smythen Street, Exeter, DEVON, EX1 1BN **England**
Mr K Salisbury (Proprietor)
(T) 01392 436404.

FISHTEK, Unit 3d Betton Way, Moretonhampstead, Newton Abbot, DEVON, TQ13 8NA **England**
Mr Ben Kibel (Director)
(T) 01647 441020.

H TURRALL & CO, Northbrook, Dolton, Winkleigh, DEVON, EX19 8QJ **England**
Mrs S Ursell (General Manager)
(T) 01805 804352.

HOOK LINE & SINKER FISHING TACKLE, The Harbour, Axmouth, Seaton, DEVON, EX12 4AA **England**
Mr J Bolaam (Proprietor)
(T) 01297 23380.

J BLACK, Ferndale, Lapford, Crediton, DEVON, EX17 6QT **England**
Mr J Black (Proprietor)
(T) 01363 83655.

JACKMANS SPORTS & TACKLE SHOP, 1b Northumberland Place, Teignmouth, DEVON, TQ14 8DD **England**
Mr Chris Jackman (Proprietor)
(T) 01626 779508.

JOHNSTON'S GIFTS, 40 The Strand, Exmouth, DEVON, EX8 1AH **England**
Ms M Johnston (Proprietor)
(T) 01395 278090.

KINGFISHER, 22 Castle Street, Barnstaple, DEVON, EX31 1DR **England**
Mr G Tyzack (Proprietor)
(T) 01271 344919.

MERC, The Rap Store, Northfields Industrial Estate, Brixham, DEVON, TQ5 8UA **England**
Mr M Eden (Partner)
(T) 01803 850450.

MIKE CORNISH, Unit 4 Miglo Industrial Estate, Yalberton Road, Paignton, DEVON, TQ4 7QW **England**
Mr M Cornish (Proprietor)
(T) 01803 664196.

NORMARK SPORT LTD, Pottery Road, Bovey Tracey, Newton Abbot, DEVON, TQ13 9DS **England**
Mr John Mitchell (Managing Director)
(T) 01626 832889.

ORVIS CO INC, 22 Cathedral Yard, Exeter, DEVON, EX1 1HB **England**
Mr A Roberts (Manager)
(T) 01392 272599.

OSBORNE & CRAGG, 37 Breton Side, Plymouth, DEVON, PL4 0BB **England**
Mr S Osborne (Partner)
(T) 01752 223141.

PORTZIC POTS, Unit 2 Butlands Industrial Estate, Causeway Cross, Ipplepen, Newton Abbot, DEVON, TQ12 5TB **England**
(T) 01803 812700.

QUAY STORES, 23 Victoria Parade, Torquay, DEVON, TQ1 2BD **England**
(T) 01803 292080.

ROY'S TACKLE & BAIT, 134 Albert Road, Plymouth, DEVON, PL2 1AQ **England**
Mr Roy Hoskins (Proprietor)
(T) 01752 606300.

S W TACKLE DEVELOPMENTS, 76 Winner Street, Paignton, DEVON, TQ3 3BH **England**
Mr Phil Hyde (Proprietor)
(T) 01803 553660.

SEAFIELD & EMIEL TRAWLERS, Northfields Industrial Estate, Brixham, DEVON, TQ5 8UA **England**
Mr G Perks (Director)
(T) 01803 854545.

SNOWBEE (UK) LTD, Drakes Court, Langage Business Park, Plymouth, DEVON, PL7 5JY **England**
Mr Russell Weston B.Sc. (Managing Director)
(T) 01752 334933.

SPORT 'N' FISH, 16 Fairfax Place, Dartmouth, DEVON, TQ6 9AB **England**
Mrs E W Weeks (Proprietor)
(T) 01803 833509.

STEVE'S TACKLE BOX, 1A Berachah Road, Torquay, DEVON, TQ1 3AX **England**
Mr Steve Davey (Proprietor)
(T) 01803 299946.

SUMMERLANDS TACKLE, Golf Links Road, Westward Ho, Bideford, DEVON, EX39 1LH **England**
(T) 01237 471291.

TACKLE & BAIT, Billacombe Road, Plymouth, DEVON, PL9 7HP **England**
Mr Mark Horton (Proprietor)
(T) 01752 484233.

TACKLE & BAIT SHOP, 93 Victoria Road, Plymouth, DEVON, PL5 1RX **England**
Mr M Horton (Proprietor)
(T) 01752 484233.

TACKLE DIRECT, 15 Church Street, Ilfracombe, DEVON, EX34 8HB **England**
(T) 01271 862363.

TACKLE TRADERS, 2 Wharf Road, Newton Abbot, DEVON, TQ12 2DA **England**
Mr M Palmer (Proprietor)
(T) 01626 331613.

TIGHT LINES, 44 Winner Street, Paignton, DEVON, TQ3 3BQ **England**
Mr S White (Proprietor)
(T) 01803 401004.

TORBAY ANGLING, 7 Dartmouth Road, Paignton, DEVON, TQ4 5AA **England**
Mr A Pearce (Manager)
(T) 01803 552496.

TURNERS TACKLE, Fore Street, Holsworthy, DEVON, EX22 6EB **England**
Mr A Turner (Proprietor)
(T) 01409 259300.

VARIETY SPORTS, 23 Broad Street, Ilfracombe, DEVON, EX34 9EE **England**
Mr J Fennell (Proprietor)
(T) 01271 862039.

DORSET

A C ANGLING, 4 Victoria Road, Poole, DORSET, BH12 3BB **England**
Mr S J Andrews (Proprietor)
(T) 01202 734451.

ANGLER'S TACKLE STORE, 64 Park Street, Weymouth, DORSET, DT4 7DE **England**
Mr I Harrington (Proprietor)
(T) 01305 782624.

BOURNEMOUTH FISHING LODGE, 904 Wimborne Road, Bournemouth, DORSET, BH9 2DW **England**
Mr Iver Brittain (Manager)
(T) 01202 514345.

CASTAWAYS FISHING TACKLE, 78 Ashley Road, Poole, DORSET, BH14 9BN **England**
Mr Tim Simpson (Proprietor)
(T) 01202 739202.

CHRISTCHURCH ANGLING CENTRE, 7 Castle Parade, Bournemouth, DORSET, BH7 6SH **England**
Mr R Edwards (Proprietor)
(T) 01202 480520.

COASTAL, Unit 61, St. Michaels Trading Estate, Bridport, DORSET, DT6 3RR **England**
Mr R C Barr (Proprietor)
(T) 01308 427885.

DAVIS FISHING TACKLE, 75 Bargates, Christchurch, DORSET, BH23 1QE **England**
Mrs C Pepler (Partner)
(T) 01202 485169.

DENNING, 114 Portland Road, Weymouth, DORSET, DT4 9AD **England**
Mr D Abrams (Partner)
(T) 01305 783145.

DORCHESTER ANGLING CENTRE, 1 Nappers Court, Dorchester, DORSET, DT1 1TW **England**
(T) 01305 261261.

FUTURE ANGLING, 499 Christchurch Road, Bournemouth, DORSET, BH1 4AE **England**
Mr W Thompson (Proprietor)
(T) 01202 303402.

ISLAND POTS, Unit 15c Southwell Business Park, Southwell Business Park, Portland, DORSET, DT5 2JS **England**
Mr D Lane (Proprietor)
(T) 01305 822232.

MICK'S, Colwell Shopping Centre, School Street, Weymouth, DORSET, DT4 8NJ **England**
Mr M Willimas (Proprietor)
(T) 01305 839595.

POOLE SEA ANGLING CENTRE, 5 High Street, Poole, DORSET, BH15 1AB **England**
(T) 01202 676597.

PRO TACKLE, 258 Barrack Road, Christchurch, DORSET, BH23 2BJ **England**
Mrs J Croft (Partner)
(T) 01202 484518.

PURBECK ANGLING, 28 South Street, Wareham, DORSET, BH20 4LU **England**
Mr B Watts (Proprietor)
(T) 01929 550770.

QUALITY FISHING PLUGS, 7a Castle Parade, Bournemouth, DORSET, BH7 6SH **England**
Mr Ron Edwards (Proprietor)
(T) 01202 470709.

R N G CANDY, Manor Farm, Todber, Sturminster Newton, DORSET, DT10 1JB **England**
Mr J Candy (Partner)
(T) 01258 820384.

REELS & DEALS, 61B St. Thomas Street, Weymouth, DORSET, DT4 8EQ **England**
Mr B Axford (Proprietor)
(T) 01305 787848.

REVELS FISHERY & TACKLE SHOP, Cosmore, Dorchester, DORSET, DT2 7TW **England**
Mrs V Fricker (Proprietor)
(T) 01300 345301.

SEA FISHING, The Quay, Poole, DORSET, BH15 1HJ **England**
Mr R Watton (Proprietor)
(T) 01202 679666.

SPECIALIST ANGLING SUPPLIES, 1 Athelstan Road, Dorchester, DORSET, DT1 1NR **England**
Mr John Aplin (Proprietor)
(T) 01305 266500.

STALBRIDGE ANGLING, High Street, Stalbridge, Sturminster Newton, DORSET, DT10 2LJ **England**
Mrs D Chant (Partner)
(T) 01963 362291.

SWANAGE ANGLING CENTRE, 6 High Street, Swanage, DORSET, BH19 2NT **England**
Mr C Payne (Manager)
(T) 01929 424989.

TACKLE BOX, 18 Marine Parade, The Cobb, Lyme Regis, DORSET, DT7 3JF **England**
(T) 01297 443373.

TACKLE SHOP, 9A, West Bay, Bridport, DORSET, DT6 4EN **England**
Mr H L Rathbone (Partner)
(T) 01308 423475.

TM FISHING TACKLE, Unit 4/Greyhound Square, Market Place, Blandford Forum, DORSET, DT11 7EB **England**
Mr John Candy (Proprietor)
(T) 01258 459404.

WESSEX ANGLING CENTRE, 321 Wimborne Road, Poole, DORSET, BH15 3DH **England**
Mr Simon Barber (Proprietor)
(T) 01202 668244.

WESSEX FLY FISHING, Lawrences Farm, Southover, Tolpuddle, Dorchester, DORSET, DT2 7HF **England**
Mrs M E Slocock (Proprietor)
(T) 01305 848460.

WEST BAY WATER SPORTS, 10a West Bay, West Bay, Bridport, DORSET, DT6 4EL **England**
Mr S Marley (Proprietor)
(T) 01308 421800.

WEYMOUTH ANGLING CENTRE, 24 Trinity Road, Weymouth, DORSET, DT4 8TJ **England**
Mr A Selby (Manager)
(T) 01305 777771.

YESTERDAY TACKLE & BOOKS, 42 Clingan Road, Bournemouth, DORSET, BH6 5PZ **England**
Mr D Dobbyn (Proprietor)
(T) 01202 476586.

YYS INTERNATIONAL UK LTD, 174c Shelbourne Road, Bournemouth, DORSET, BH8 8RA **England**
Mr M Debear (Director)
(T) 01202 777711.

YYS INTERNATIONAL UK LTD, Unit 6 YYS Business Pk, 147A Rosemary Road, Poole, DORSET, BH12 3HE **England**
Mr M Debear (Managing Director)
(T) 01202 777740.

ESSEX

A1 ANGLING, 176 High Road, Woodford Green, ESSEX, IG8 9EF **England**
(T) 0208-504 4848.

ALEXANDRA ANGLING CENTRE, 21 Alexandra Street, Southend-on-Sea, ESSEX, SS1 1BX **England**
Mr T Knott (Proprietor)
(T) 01702 437066.

AVENUE ANGLING LTD, 22a Woodford Avenue, Ilford, ESSEX, IG2 6XG **England**
Mr A Francis (Proprietor)
(T) 0208-550 7815.

B & T ANGLING, 3 Grange Road, Romford, ESSEX, RM3 7DU **England**
Mr B Bray (Partner)
(T) 01708 370033.

BAIT & TACKLE CENTRE, 258 Southchurch Road, Southend-on-Sea, ESSEX, SS1 2NP **England**
Mr R Power (Proprietor)
(T) 01702 617764.

BASILDON ANGLING CENTRE, 402 Whitmore Way, Basildon, ESSEX, SS14 2HB **England**
(T) 01268 520144.

BEVAN CARP TACKLE, 3 Havengore, Chelmsford, ESSEX, CM1 6JP **England**
Mr S Bevan (Proprietor)
(T) 01245 266833.

BIG JOHN DISCOUNT ANGLING CENTRE, 6 Kibcaps, Basildon, ESSEX, SS16 5SA **England**
Mr J Pearce (Proprietor)
(T) 01268 415958.

BILLERICAY ANGLING 2000, 15 Radford Way, Billericay, ESSEX, CM12 0AA **England**
Mr S Daniels (Proprietor)
(T) 01277 622865.

BILLS TACKLE, 95-97 High Street, Braintree, ESSEX, CM7 1JS **England**
Mr William Langton (Proprietor)
(T) 01376 552767.

BLUEWATER ANGLING, 139 East Street, Southend-on-Sea, ESSEX, SS2 5EB **England**
Mr (T) 01702 460610.

BOWLERS ANGLING, 2-3 Cinema Parade, Whalebone La South, Dagenham, ESSEX, RM8 1AA **England**
Mr K Bowler (Proprietor)
(T) 0208-592 3273.

BRENTWOOD ANGLING, 118 Warley Hill, Warley, Brentwood, ESSEX, CM14 5HB **England**
Mr W Dunthorne (Proprietor)
(T) 01277 200985.

BRENTWOOD ANGLING, 16 Broomfield Road, Chelmsford, ESSEX, CM1 1SN **England**
Mr N Amos (Manager)
(T) 01245 357689.

BRIAN DEAN, 43 Pallister Road, Clacton-on-Sea, ESSEX, CO15 1PG **England**
Mr P Thatcher (Partner)
(T) 01255 425992.

BROMAGES LTD, 666 Green Lane, Ilford, ESSEX, IG3 9RX **England**
Mr M Woodly (Partner)
(T) 0208-590 3521.

BUDGET GUNS & TACKLE, Commerce Way, Colchester, ESSEX, CO2 8HH **England**
Mr R C Nash (Proprietor)
(T) 01206 795333.

CANVEY ANGLING CENTRE, 132 Furtherwick Road, Canvey Island, ESSEX, SS8 7AL **England**
Mr George Baker (Proprietor)
(T) 01268 691542.

CARP UNLIMITED, 16 Peartree Business Centre, Peartree Road, Stanway, Colchester, ESSEX, CO3 5JN **England**
Mr P Tew (Proprietor)
(T) 01206 760775.

CHERRYTREE TACKLE, 109 Rainham Road, Rainham, ESSEX, RM13 7QX **England**
Mr S Edmunds (Partner)
(T) 01708 520869.

CHUBB LEISURE LTD, Driberg Way, Braintree, ESSEX, CM7 1NB **England**
(T) 01376 331609.

COLCHESTER BAIT & TACKLE, 243a Harwich Road, Colchester, ESSEX, CO4 3DQ **England**
Mr Douglas Titshall (Proprietor)
(T) 01206 860649.

COUNTY ANGLING, 19 Suttons Lane, Hornchurch, ESSEX, RM12 6RD **England**
Mr S O'rourke (Partner)
(T) 01708 477834.

E & J TACKLE, 16 Church Street, Witham, ESSEX, CM8 2JL **England**
Mr Kim Crisell (Proprietor)
(T) 01376 512255.

EAST ESSEX ANGLING CENTRE, 48 The Street, Maldon, ESSEX, CM9 4NB **England**
Mr A Tavener (Proprietor)
(T) 01621 840414.

EMSON & SON, 88 High Street, Earls Colne, Colchester, ESSEX, CO6 2QX **England**
Mr P Emson (Proprietor)
(T) 01787 223413.

ESSEX ANGLING, 5 Broadway Parade, Hornchurch, ESSEX, RM12 4RS **England**
Mr M Woodrow (Manager)
(T) 01708 438220.

ESSEX ANGLING CENTRE, 109 Leigh Road, Leigh-on-Sea, ESSEX, SS9 1JH **England**
Mr P G Marshall (Proprietor)
(T) 01702 711231.

ESSEX BAIT SERVICES LTD, 12 Rose Way, Rochford, ESSEX, SS4 1LY **England**
Mr D Poxon (Managing Director)
(T) 01702 530750.

ESSEX BAIT SERVICES LTD, 4 The Vanguards, Vanguard Way, Shoeburyness, Southend-on-Sea, ESSEX, SS3 9QJ **England**
Mr David Poxon (Proprietor)
(T) 01702 299720.

FOX INTERNATIONAL LTD, 56-58 Fowler Road, Hainault Industrial Estate, Ilford, ESSEX, IG6 3UT **England**
M. Clifford Royston Fox (Managing Director)
(T) 0208-501 0921.

FUTURE ANGLING PRODUCTS, 56-58 Peregrine Road, Ilford, ESSEX, IG6 3SZ **England**
Mr K Stack (Proprietor)
(T) 0208-559 8116.

G B S COLMIC, Unit 5 Mudlands Industrial Estate, Manor Way, Rainham, ESSEX, RM13 8RH **England**
Mr G Blanks (Director)
(T) 01708 630921.

GORESBROOK FISHING TACKLE, 6 Chequers Parade, Ripple Road, Dagenham, ESSEX, RM9 6RT **England**
Mr S Potter (Proprietor)
(T) 0208-517 5335.

HALFWAY KOI CO, 78 Cadogan Avenue, West Horndon, Brentwood, ESSEX, CM13 3TX **England**
(T) 01277 810870.

HALLS TACKLE, 44 Highbridge Street, Waltham Abbey, ESSEX, EN9 1BS **England**
Mr P Hall (Proprietor)
(T) 01992 711932.

HARLOW ANGLING CENTRE, 5/Long House, Bush Fair, Harlow, ESSEX, CM18 6NR **England**
Mr Anthony Fenson (Proprietor)
(T) 01279 444249.

HOOK LINE & SINKER FISHING TACKLE LTD, 15-17 Kents Hill Road, Benfleet, ESSEX, SS7 5PN **England**
Mr Paul Griffiths (Proprietor)
(T) 01268 792573.

HORNCHURCH ANGLING CENTRE, 226 Hornchurch Road, Hornchurch, ESSEX, RM11 1QJ **England**
Mr F Breedon (Proprietor)
(T) 01708 620608.

J J METCALFE, 15 Newgate Street, Walton on the Naze, ESSEX, CO14 8DT **England**
Mr R Holgate (Proprietor)
(T) 01255 675680.

J R C PRODUCTS LTD, 9-11 Bowlers Croft, Cranes Farm Road, Basildon, ESSEX, SS14 3DU **England**
Ms Lisa Edgar (Manager)
(T) 01268 273423.

JETTY ANGLERS, 47 Eastern Esplanade, Southend-on-Sea, ESSEX, SS1 2ES **England**
Mr R Wilkes (Partner)
(T) 01702 611826.

JP TACKLE, 159 High Street, Maldon, ESSEX, CM9 5BS **England**
Mr J Penn (Proprietor)
(T) 01621 854588.

K D RADCLIFFE LTD, 150 High Street, Colchester, ESSEX, CO1 1PG **England**
Mr R B Radcliffe (Proprietor)
(T) 01206 572758.

KESWALL WOODFORD LTD, 618 Chigwell Road, Woodford Green, ESSEX, IG8 8AA **England**
Mrs J Chapman (Manageress)
(T) 0208-504 1929.

KINGFISHER AQUACULTURE FISH FARM CONSULTANCY DESIGN & SUPPL, Owls Hall, Blackmore End, Braintree, ESSEX, CM7 4DF **England**
Mrs S Richardson (Partner)
(T) 01371 850360.

LEN'S TACKLE, 31 Spa Road, Hockley, ESSEX, SS5 4AZ **England**
Mr L J Mason (Proprietor)
(T) 01702 206085.

LOUGHTON BAIT BOX, 68-70 The Broadway, Loughton, ESSEX, IG10 3SY **England**
Mr L Lee-Lezone (Partner)
(T) 0208-502 3011.

M C CARP TACKLE, Runwell Road, Runwell, Wickford, ESSEX, SS11 7PS **England**
Mr M Chant (Proprietor)
(T) 01268 575600.

MYTHS & TALES, 1717 London Road, Leigh-on-Sea, ESSEX, SS9 2SW **England**
(T) 01702 480591.

OCKENDON BAIT & TACKLE, 9 Broxburn Parade, South Ockendon, ESSEX, RM15 5QZ **England**
Mr Dave Taffs (Proprietor)
(T) 01708 856455.

PAULS ANGLING, 26 The Stow, Harlow, ESSEX, CM20 3AN **England**
Mrs H Higginson (Director)
(T) 01279 431436.

PENGE ANGLING, Arterial Road, Rayleigh, ESSEX, SS6 7TR **England**
Mr D Potter (Manager)
(T) 01268 772331.

PHILLIPS ANGLING, Unit 17 Milgraves Industrial Estate, Lower Dunton Road, Bulphan, Upminster, ESSEX, RM14 3TD **England**
Mr P Hippel (Proprietor)
(T) 01268 542919.

PREDATOR BAITS LTD, Cornsland, Hall Lane, Upminster, ESSEX, RM14 1TX **England**
Mr Brian Knight (Partner)
(T) 01708 371780.

PRESTIGE ENGINEERING UK, Unit 10 Capstan Centre, Thurrock Parkway, Tilbury, ESSEX, RM18 7HH **England**
Mr Alan Silver (Managing Director)
(T) 01375 850851.

PRO MASTER ANGLING CENTRE LTD, 6 Fullwell Parade/Fulwell Avenue, Clayhall, Ilford, ESSEX, IG5 0RF **England**
Mr G Huth (Managing Director)
(T) 0208-551 4033.

ROCHFORD TACKLE, 51 West Street, Rochford, ESSEX, SS4 1BE **England**
Mr M Crissall (Manager)
(T) 01702 544226.

RODS N REELS, 17 Grover Walk, Corringham, Stanford-le-Hope, ESSEX, SS17 7LP **England**
Mr M Blinkhorne (Proprietor)
(T) 01375 642113.

ROMFORD ANGLING CENTRE, 120 North Street, Romford, ESSEX, RM1 1DL **England**
Mr M Woodley (Partner)
(T) 01708 751600.

S & J SUPPLIES, 27 Prittle Close, Benfleet, ESSEX, SS7 3YR **England**
Mr J Stewart (Proprietor)
(T) 01702 555458.

SNAGS, 28a Military Road, Colchester, ESSEX, CO1 2AJ **England**
Mr M Birdbeer (Proprietor)
(T) 01206 576629.

SOUTH EAST AQUATICS KOI, Hillcrest Farm, Stock Road, Stock, Ingatestone, ESSEX, CM4 9QZ **England**
Mr H Roberts (Proprietor)
(T) 01277 840598.

SOUTHEND ANGLING CENTRE, 5-6 Pier Approach, Southend-on-Sea, ESSEX, SS1 2EH **England**
Mr J R Coase (Proprietor)
(T) 01702 603303.

SPECIALIST TACKLE MAIL ORDER, Mail Order Only, 93 Chase Cross Road, Romford, ESSEX, RM5 3RP **England**
Mr P Jones (Manager)
(T) 01708 752277.

STANFORD TACKLE CENTRE, 12 Wharf Road, Stanford-le-Hope, ESSEX, SS17 0DH **England**
Mr B Moore (Proprietor)
(T) 01375 676739.

STARMER BAIT LTD, Unit 4, Kings Road, Canvey Island, ESSEX, SS8 0QY **England**
Mr G Starmer (Director)
(T) 01268 690300.

T N T TACKLE, Southend Farm, Southend Lane, Waltham Abbey, ESSEX, EN9 3SE **England**
Mr C Nicolaou (Proprietor)
(T) 01992 719496.

TACKLE & GO, 88 Ravenscourt Drive, Basildon, ESSEX, SS16 4HX **England**
Miss V Taylor (Proprietor)
(T) 01268 527788.

TACKLE UP, 100 Pier Avenue, Clacton-on-Sea, ESSEX, CO15 1NJ **England**
Mr P Brown (Proprietor)
(T) 01255 221863.

TRENT TACKLE, 48-48A Trent Road, Chelmsford, ESSEX, CM1 2LQ **England**
Mr D Scales (Proprietor)
(T) 01245 355521.

TRENT TACKLE, The Causeway, Halstead, ESSEX, CO9 1ET **England**
Mr K Fewell (Manager)
(T) 01787 475423.

WICKFORD ANGLING CENTRE, 1a London Road, Wickford, ESSEX, SS12 0AH **England**
Mr C Bird (Manager)
(T) 01268 768857.

FLINTSHIRE

ALANS FISHING TACKLE, 31 High Street, Holywell, FLINTSHIRE, CH8 7TE **England**
Mr Aj Illman (Proprietor)
(T) 01745 561798.

DEESIDE FISHING TACKLE, 28 Chester Road East, Shotton, Deeside, FLINTSHIRE, CH5 1QA **England**
Mr C Hett (Proprietor)
(T) 01244 813674.

LIONELS TACKLE SHOP, Ash Grove, Pentre Lane, Buckley, FLINTSHIRE, CH7 3PA **England**
Mr L Evison (Proprietor)
(T) 01244 543191.

PEN-Y-FFRITH FLY FISHING CENTRE, Pen Y Ffrith, Llandegla Road, Llanarmon-yn-Ial, Mold, FLINTSHIRE, CH7 4QX **England**
Mrs Wendy Minshull (Proprietor)
(T) 01824 780501.

GLOUCESTERSHIRE

ACTI SPORTS, 61 High Street, Cinderford, GLOUCESTERSHIRE, GL14 2SU **England**
Mr N P Phelps (Proprietor)
(T) 01594 822461.

ALLSPORTS FISHING TACKLE SUPPLIERS, 126-128 Eastgate Street, Gloucester, GLOUCESTERSHIRE, GL1 1QT **England**
Mr R A Meadows (Proprietor)
(T) 01452 522756.

CHELTENHAM ANGLING CENTRE, 442 High Street, Cheltenham, GLOUCESTERSHIRE, GL50 3JA **England**
Mr P Maizonnier (Proprietor)
(T) 01242 582270.

FISHERMANS CREEL, 256 Barton Street, Gloucester, GLOUCESTERSHIRE, GL1 4JR **England**
Mr Paul Matthews (Proprietor)
(T) 01452 301504.

GLOUCESTER ANGLING CENTRE, 47 Bristol Road, Gloucester, GLOUCESTERSHIRE, GL1 5SA **England**
Mr D Caldwell (Proprietor)
(T) 01452 520074.

GLOUCESTER ROD & GUN ROOM, 67 Alvin Street, Gloucester, GLOUCESTERSHIRE, GL1 3EH **England**
Mr Peter Wilkins (Proprietor)
(T) 01452 410444.

HILLCOURT WORM FARM, Frogmarsh, Corse Lawn, Gloucester, GLOUCESTERSHIRE, GL19 4PW **England**
Mrs Nicola Cole (Proprietor)
(T) 01452 840690.

LOBBYS TACKLE, 58a High Street, Stonehouse, GLOUCESTERSHIRE, GL10 2NA **England**
Mr D M Gardiner (Partner)
(T) 01453 791417.

LOBBYS TACKLE TOO, 14 George Street, Stroud, GLOUCESTERSHIRE, GL5 3DY **England**
Mr R J Carter (Manager)
(T) 01453 753511.

MAC'S TACKLE, Unit 3 The Industrial Estate, Station Road, Bourton-on-the-Water, Cheltenham, GLOUCESTERSHIRE, GL54 2EP **England**
Mrs C M Mckenzie (Proprietor)
(T) 01451 822207.

MASTERLINE (INTERNATIONAL) LTD, Cotteswold Road, Tewkesbury, GLOUCESTERSHIRE, GL20 5DJ **England**
Mr P R Tallents (Managing Director)
(T) 01684 299000.

STAUNTON ANGLING CENTRE, Unit 11 Staunton Court Business Park, Ledbury Road, Staunton, Gloucester, GLOUCESTERSHIRE, GL19 3QS **England**
Ms G Fedte (Proprietor)
(T) 01452 840048.

TACKLE SHOP, 31 Barton Street, Tewkesbury, GLOUCESTERSHIRE, GL20 5PR **England**
Mrs R Danter (Proprietor)
(T) 01684 293234.

TREDWORTH FISHING TACKLE, 78 High Street, Gloucester, GLOUCESTERSHIRE, GL1 4SR **England**
Mrs P Pryce (Partner)
(T) 01452 523009.

HAMPSHIRE

A & K, 59 Brockhurst Road, Gosport, HAMPSHIRE, PO12 3AP **England**
Mr A G Marshall (Proprietor)
(T) 02392 428736.

ALLAN'S MARINE, 143 Twyford Avenue, Portsmouth, HAMPSHIRE, PO2 8HU **England**
(T) 02392671833.

AVON ANGLING CENTRE, 31 West Street, Ringwood, HAMPSHIRE, BH24 1DY **England**
Mr Andy Brown (Partner)
(T) 01425 461038.

BARRIE WELHAM, Rownhams House, Rownhams, Southampton, HAMPSHIRE, SO16 8LS **England**
Mr Barrie Welham (Chairman)
(T) 02380 740000.

BBC TACKLE, 3 Elmfield Court, Liphook Road, Lindford, Bordon, HAMPSHIRE, GU35 0QA **England**
Mr T Barnett (Proprietor)
(T) 01420 472573.

BENNETTS OF HAVANT, 10 Park Rd South, Havant, HAMPSHIRE, PO9 1HB **England**
Mr C Bennett (Proprietor)
(T) 02392 450700.

BIOPLANCTON SA, Oak House, Hawkley, Liss, HAMPSHIRE, GU33 6NF **England**
Mrs C H Stewart (Managing Director)
(T) 01730 827737.

CHALLIS TACKLE, 60 Mylen Road, Andover, HAMPSHIRE, SP10 3HA **England**
(T) 01264 361103.

CREEL, 36 Station Road, Aldershot, HAMPSHIRE, GU11 1HT **England**
(T) 01252 320871.

D & P MERRITT, 337 Copnor Road, Portsmouth, HAMPSHIRE, PO3 5EQ **England**
Mr D Merritt (Partner)
(T) 02392 642200.

DAVE ADAMS, 24 Laburnum Grove, Hayling Island, HAMPSHIRE, PO11 9DR **England**
Mr D Adams (Proprietor)
(T) 02392 464256.

DAVE'S TACKLE, 1 The Precinct, South Street, Gosport, HAMPSHIRE, PO12 1HA **England**
Mr D W F Ellis (Proprietor)
(T) 02392 529107.

GAME ON FISHING TACKLE LTD, Lyndhurst Road, Beaulieu, Brockenhurst, HAMPSHIRE, SO42 7YE **England**
Mr R Thompson (Partner)
(T) 01590 612608.

GOSPORT FISHING TACKLE, 27 Brockhurst Road, Gosport, HAMPSHIRE, PO12 3AJ **England**
(T) 02392 584068.

HAMPSHIRE TACKLE, 342 High Street, Aldershot, HAMPSHIRE, GU12 4LU **England**
Mr Richard Burley (Proprietor)
(T) 01252 318937.

HANSFORDS, 3 High Street, Fareham, HAMPSHIRE, PO16 7AN **England**
Mr A Poyngeestre (Proprietor)
(T) 01329 282010.

HOME STORES, 68 High Road, Southampton, HAMPSHIRE, SO16 2HZ **England**
Mr C Watts (Proprietor)
(T) 02380 551974.

IAN GOLDS TACKLE DEVELOPMENTS LTD, 4 Scratchface Lane, Havant, HAMPSHIRE, PO9 3NG **England**
Mr I Golds (Managing Director)
(T) 02392 486922.

J R WALLACE, 362b Spring Road, Southampton, HAMPSHIRE, SO19 2PB **England**
Mrs J Wallace (Proprietor)
(T) 02380 421919.

LONI'S ANGLING CENTRE, 119-123 Old Milton Road, New Milton, HAMPSHIRE, BH25 6DP **England**
Mr P Lonnigan (Proprietor)
(T) 01425 616323.

M B K LEISURES, Marken, Shortheath Common, Oakhanger, Bordon, HAMPSHIRE, GU35 9JS **England**
(T) 01420 474969.

MAPPAM LTD, 325 Market Street, Eastleigh, HAMPSHIRE, SO50 5QE **England**
Mr P Colier (Managing Director)
(T) 02380 343661.

NIX ANGLING SUPPLIES, 60 Whetstone Road, Farnborough, HAMPSHIRE, GU14 9SU **England**
Mrs N Carter (Proprietor)
(T) 01252 512550.

NIX ANGLING SUPPLIES, White House Farm, Hook Road, Winchfield, Hook, HAMPSHIRE, RG27 8BZ **England**
Mrs N Carter (Proprietor)
(T) 01256 767532.

NOEL'S FISHING TACKLE, 314 Fernhill Road, Farnborough, HAMPSHIRE, GU14 9EE **England**
(T) 01276 32488.

ORVIS SHOP, Bridge House, High Street, Stockbridge, HAMPSHIRE, SO20 6HB **England**
Mr Tim Reader (Manager)
(T) 01264 810017.

OWENS USED TACKLE, 147 Ash Hill Road, Ash, Aldershot, HAMPSHIRE, GU12 5DW **England**
Mr S Owen (Proprietor)
(T) 01252 333202.

PAIGE'S FISHING TACKLE, 36 Station Road, Hayling Island, HAMPSHIRE, PO11 0EQ **England**
(T) 02392 463500.

PET & TACKLE EMPORIUM, 4 Market Place, Romsey, HAMPSHIRE, SO51 8NB **England**
Mr H Hampton (Proprietor)
(T) 01794 512103.

PETERSFIELD ANGLING CENTRE, 34 Dragon Street, Petersfield, HAMPSHIRE, GU31 4JJ **England**
Mr P Archer (Proprietor)
(T) 01730 266999.

POINGDESTRE'S ANGLING CENTRE, 1-5 Cannon Street, Southampton, HAMPSHIRE, SO15 5PQ **England**
Mr J Poingdestre (Proprietor)
(T) 02380 510077.

R D S TACKLE, 26 Elm Grove, Southsea, HAMPSHIRE, PO5 1JG **England**
Mr L Szabados (Proprietor)
(T) 02392 812478.

REEL CARE, 100 Kendal Avenue, Southampton, HAMPSHIRE, SO16 9LY **England**
Mr W Skip (Partner)
(T) 02380 777232.

RINGWOOD TACKLE, 5 The Bridges, Ringwood, HAMPSHIRE, BH24 1EA **England**
Mr R Middleton (Manager)
(T) 01425 475155.

ROBJENTS, Halfway House, High Street, Stockbridge, HAMPSHIRE, SO20 6EX **England**
Mr A Colebrook-Robjents (Proprietor)
(T) 01264 810829.

ROD BOX, London Road, Kings Worthy, Winchester, HAMPSHIRE, SO23 7QN **England**
Mr J I Hey (Proprietor)
(T) 01962 883600.

RODS 'N' REELS OF FARLINGTON, 418 Havant Road, Farlington, Portsmouth, HAMPSHIRE, PO6 1NF **England**
Mr Bob Clarke (Proprietor)
(T) 02392 789090.

ROGATE BAIT, Pear Tree Buildings, Rogate, Petersfield, HAMPSHIRE, GU31 5BP **England**
Mr Eric Best (Proprietor)
(T) 01730 818448.

ROVERS FISHING TACKLE, 178a West Street, Fareham, HAMPSHIRE, PO16 0EQ **England**
Mr P Roberts (Proprietor)
(T) 01329 220354.

SAMMY'S FISHING TACKLE & BAITS, Cabin Boat Yard, Bursledon, Southampton, HAMPSHIRE, SO31 8AW **England**
Mr P C Birch (Proprietor)
(T) 02380 406378.

SOUTH COAST TACKLE, 179 High Street, Lee-on-the-Solent, HAMPSHIRE, PO13 9BX **England**
Mr Alan Noble (Proprietor)
(T) 02392 550209.

ST DENYS SEABAIT & TACKLE, 1a St Denys Road, Southampton, HAMPSHIRE, SO17 2GN **England**
Mr S Masterman (Proprietor)
(T) 02380 672773.

TIGHT-LINES ANGLING CENTRE, 1A Rumbridge Street, Totton, Southampton, HAMPSHIRE, SO40 9DQ **England**
Mr B Hogben (Proprietor)
(T) 02380 863068.

TWO GUYS LTD, 27a Burnaby Close, Basingstoke, HAMPSHIRE, RG22 6UJ **England**
Mr Max Pentlow (Proprietor)
(T) 01256 464981.

WITLOCK PRODUCTS, Unit 7 Laundry Lane, Milford on Sea, Lymington, HAMPSHIRE, SO41 0WJ **England**
Mr Fred Witlock (Proprietor)
(T) 01590 643528.

YATELEY ANGLING CENTRE, 12-16 Reading Road, Yateley, HAMPSHIRE, GU46 7UN **England**
Mr J Lockwood (Proprietor)
(T) 01252 861955.

HEREFORDSHIRE

BODENHAM WORMS, The Forge, Bodenham, Hereford, HEREFORDSHIRE, HR1 3JZ **England**
Mr A J Timmer (Partner)
(T) 01568 797144.

DOCKLOW ANGLING CENTRE, West End Farm, Docklow, Leominster, HEREFORDSHIRE, HR6 0RU **England**
Mr Simon Bozward (Partner)
(T) 01568 760544.

GO FISHING WITH DAVE, 46 West Street, Leominster, HEREFORDSHIRE, HR6 8ES **England**
(T) 01568 616047.

HATTON'S FISHING TACKLE, 64 St. Owen Street, Hereford, HEREFORDSHIRE, HR1 2PU **England**
Mr P Stallard (Proprietor)
(T) 01432 272317.

INTERNATIONAL FLY, 15 Copse Cross Street, Ross-on-Wye, HEREFORDSHIRE, HR9 5PD **England**
Mr Mike Dawes (Proprietor)
(T) 01989 762244.

LEDBURY TACKLE CENTRE, 3 The Southend, Ledbury, HEREFORDSHIRE, HR8 2EY **England**
(T) 01531 632768.

RAGS, Appledore, Bridstow, Ross-on-Wye, HEREFORDSHIRE, HR9 6AJ **England**
Mr G Haynes (Proprietor)
(T) 01989 565216.

SPORTFISH, Winforton, Winforton, Hereford, HEREFORDSHIRE, HR3 6SP **England**
Mr P Parkinson (Partner)
(T) 01544 327111.

WOODY'S ANGLING CENTRE, 67 White Cross Road, Hereford, HEREFORDSHIRE, HR4 0DQ **England**
Mr P Woodward (Proprietor)
(T) 01432 344644.

WOODY'S ANGLING CENTRE, 67 Whitecross Road, Hereford, HEREFORDSHIRE, HR4 9HG **England**
Mr P Woodward (Proprietor)
(T) 01432 344644.

WYE FLIES LTD, 70, Hentland, Ross-on-Wye, HEREFORDSHIRE, HR9 6LP **England**
Mrs R Wilson (Managing Director)
(T) 01989 730517.

HERTFORDSHIRE

BAIT BOX, 255 High Street, Waltham Cross, HERTFORDSHIRE, EN8 7BE **England**
Mr F R Dennis (Partner)
(T) 01992 622987.

BAIT CO THE LTD, The Paddock, Great Munden, Ware, HERTFORDSHIRE, SG11 1HP **England**
Mr David Wiles (Director)
(T) 01920 438338.

CHILTERN TACKLE, 33 Western Road, Tring, HERTFORDSHIRE, HP23 4BQ **England**
Mr C Green (Proprietor)
(T) 01442 825257.

COLNE VALLEY ANGLING CENTRE, 165a Uxbridge Road, Rickmansworth, HERTFORDSHIRE, WD3 7DW **England**
Mr J Marsh (Manager)
(T) 01923 774977.

HOWES & DRAGE, 16 The Wynd, Letchworth, HERTFORDSHIRE, SG6 3EL **England**
Mr Alan Howes (Partner)
(T) 01462 674861.

JOHNSON ROSS TACKLE, 3 Amwell Street, Hoddesdon, HERTFORDSHIRE, EN11 8TP **England**
Mrs F Johnson (Partner)
(T) 01992 462044.

MALCOLM'S FISHING TACKLE, 22 London Road, Hemel Hempstead, HERTFORDSHIRE, HP3 9SB **England**
Mr D Gulzar (Proprietor)
(T) 01442 255748.

MELBOURN ANGLING CENTRE, 58b High Street, Melbourn, Royston, HERTFORDSHIRE, SG8 6AB **England**
Mr B K Whybrow (Proprietor)
(T) 01763 262291.

NORTH HERTS ANGLING CENTRE, 25 London Road, Baldock, HERTFORDSHIRE, SG7 6NB **England**
Mr S Birak (Proprietor)
(T) 01462 896336.

OAKWOOD ANGLING, Hall Grove, Welwyn Garden City, HERTFORDSHIRE, AL7 4PH **England**
Mr P Tilbury (Manager)
(T) 01707 334462.

OLD HATFIELD ANGLING CENTRE, 3 The Broadway, Hatfield, HERTFORDSHIRE, AL9 5BG **England**
Mr Chris Brown (Proprietor)
(T) 01707 271247.

OLD TOWN ANGLING CENTRE, 75 High Street, Hemel Hempstead, HERTFORDSHIRE, HP1 3AF **England**
Mr K Roth (Proprietor)
(T) 01442 252373.

OXHEY ANGLING CENTRE, 28 Pinner Road, Watford, HERTFORDSHIRE, WD1 4ED **England**
Mr D Drew (Proprietor)
(T) 01923 226849.

OXHEY ANGLING CENTRE, 28 Pinner Road, Watford, HERTFORDSHIRE, WD19 4ED **England**
Mr D Drew (Proprietor)
(T) 01923 226849.

POPLETTS TACKLE, 12 The Hyde, Stevenage, HERTFORDSHIRE, SG2 9SE **England**
Mr S Poplett (Proprietor)
(T) 01438 352415.

PRO ANGLING, 78 Ware Road, Hertford, HERTFORDSHIRE, SG13 7HN **England**
Miss Julia Arnold (Manager)
(T) 01992 505852.

PRO ANGLING, 20a Baldock Street, Ware, HERTFORDSHIRE, SG12 9DZ **England**
Mr Peter Arnold (Proprietor)
(T) 01920 464003.

QUEENSWAY ANGLING, 52 Queensway, Hemel Hempstead, HERTFORDSHIRE, HP2 5HA **England**
Mrs W D Sage (Senior Partner)
(T) 01442 254723.

R CHAPMAN & CO, 10 Bowling Road, Ware, HERTFORDSHIRE, SG12 7EE **England**
Mr B Chapman (Partner)
(T) 01920 462658.

SIMPSONS OF TURNFORD, Nunsbury Drive, Broxbourne, HERTFORDSHIRE, EN10 6AQ **England**
Mr Jack Simpson (Managing Director)
(T) 01992 468799.

STORT ANGLING, 40a Hockerill Street, Bishop's Stortford, HERTFORDSHIRE, CM23 2DW **England**
Mr F Wadham (Proprietor)
(T) 01279 657061.

TACKLE CARRIER, 155-157 St. Albans Road, Watford, HERTFORDSHIRE, WD2 5BD **England**
Mr R Foulger (Proprietor)
(T) 01923 232393.

TACKLE TRADER, 65 The Brow, Watford, HERTFORDSHIRE, WD2 7ES **England**
Mr Harry Wells (Proprietor)
(T) 01923 672224.

TACKLE TRADER, 65 The Brow, Watford, HERTFORDSHIRE, WD25 7ES **England**
Mr Harry Wells (Proprietor)
(T) 01923 672224.

VERULAM ANGLING CENTRE, 159 Hatfield Road, St. Albans, HERTFORDSHIRE, AL1 4LB **England**
(T) 01727 762676.

VIC GIBSON, 112 Cappell Lane, Stanstead Abbotts, Ware, HERTFORDSHIRE, SG12 8BY **England**
Mr V Gibson (Proprietor)
(T) 01920 870775.

HUMBERSIDE (NORTH)

A & D TACKLE, 50 New Bridge Road, Hull, HUMBERSIDE (NORTH), HU9 2RE **England**
Mr A Thompson (Proprietor)
(T) 01482 227171.

ANGLER'S CORNER, 831 Hessle Road, Hull, HUMBERSIDE (NORTH), HU4 6QF **England**
Mr D Elm (Proprietor)
(T) 01482 507350.

COMPLEAT ANGLER, 58 Chanterlands Avenue, Hull, HUMBERSIDE (NORTH), HU5 3TT **England**
Mr K Wiles (Proprietor)
(T) 01482 346842.

EAST COAST FISHING TACKLE, 1b Willow Drive, Hornsea, HUMBERSIDE (NORTH), HU18 1DA **England**
Mr Keith Lanning (Proprietor)
(T) 01964 535064.

EVERETTS ANGLING & OUTDOOR WORLD, 316-318 Beverley Road, Hull, HUMBERSIDE (NORTH), HU5 1BA **England**
(T) 01482 440766.

EVERETTS ANGLING & OUTDOOR WORLD, 691 Holderness Road, Hull, HUMBERSIDE (NORTH), HU8 9AN **England**
Mr Mark Everett (Proprietor)
(T) 01482 374201.

FIELD SPORTS CENTRE, 22 West Street, Bridlington, HUMBERSIDE (NORTH), YO15 3DX **England**
Mr M Clulow (Proprietor)
(T) 01262 671770.

FISHING BASKET, 470 Beverley Road, Hull, HUMBERSIDE (NORTH), HU5 1NE **England**
Mr D Boasman (Partner)
(T) 01482 445284.

FISHING SHOP, 293 Ings Road, Hull, HUMBERSIDE (NORTH), HU8 0NB **England**
Mr D Laws (Proprietor)
(T) 01482 781926.

FISHING TACKLE DIRECT, 25 Westfield Avenue, Goole, HUMBERSIDE (NORTH), DN14 6JY **England**
Mr D Johnson (Manager)
(T) 01405 767614.

HEDON ANGLING CENTRE, 1c George Street, Hedon, Hull, HUMBERSIDE (NORTH), HU12 8JH **England**
Mr J Osgerby (Proprietor)
(T) 01482 891479.

LINFORDS FISHING TACKLE, 12 Hilderthorpe Road, Bridlington, HUMBERSIDE (NORTH), YO15 3BB **England**
Mr S Whittaker (Proprietor)
(T) 01262 678045.

MALLARD ANGLING SUPPLIES, 5 Harbour Road, Bridlington, HUMBERSIDE (NORTH), YO15 2NR **England**
Mr D P Brookfield (Proprietor)
(T) 01262 673103.

MATCHMAN, 794 Beverley Road, Hull, HUMBERSIDE (NORTH), HU6 7EY **England**
Mr D Havler (Proprietor)
(T) 01482 853193.

R S TACKLE & GUNS, Unit 1 Carlisle Street, Goole, HUMBERSIDE (NORTH), DN14 5DS **England**
Mr J R Smith (Proprietor)
(T) 01405 720292.

TOP SPORTS, 118 Queen Street, Withernsea, HUMBERSIDE (NORTH), HU19 2HB **England**
Mr Steve Fisher (Proprietor)
(T) 01964 612340.

ULTIMATE BAITS, Unit 46, 254-260 Wincolmlee, Hull, HUMBERSIDE (NORTH), HU2 0PZ **England**
Mr S Devine (Partner)
(T) 01482 581599.

HUMBERSIDE (SOUTH)

BAIT BOX, Gilbey Road, Grimsby, HUMBERSIDE (SOUTH), DN31 2SJ **England**
Mrs Vickey Bird (Partner)
(T) 01472 348404.

BAITLINE INTERNATIONAL, The Barn/New Road, Grimsby Road, Laceby, Grimsby, HUMBERSIDE (SOUTH), DN37 7DA **England**
(T) 01472 278570.

CHAPMAN'S TACKLE, 23 Beechway, Scunthorpe, HUMBERSIDE (SOUTH), DN16 2HF **England**
Mrs J Wilkinson (Proprietor)
(T) 01724 277618.

CLEETHORPES ANGLING CENTRE, 291 Brereton Avenue, Cleethorpes, HUMBERSIDE (SOUTH), DN35 7QX **England**
Mr R Tarvet (Proprietor)
(T) 01472 602002.

CLEETHORPES TIGHT LINES, 51 Cambridge Street, Cleethorpes, HUMBERSIDE (SOUTH), DN35 8HD **England**
(T) 01472 322206.

COUNTRY LINES, 4 Alexandria Terrace, Bridge Street, Brigg, HUMBERSIDE (SOUTH), DN20 8NW **England**
(T) 01652 651650.

DAVE'S USED & NEW TACKLE, 78 Durban Road, Grimsby, HUMBERSIDE (SOUTH), DN32 8BA **England**
Mr David Moore (Proprietor)
(T) 01472 313260.

F W LIGHTWOODS, 172 Cleethorpe Road, Grimsby, HUMBERSIDE (SOUTH), DN31 3HW **England**
Mr P Gray (Proprietor)
(T) 01472 343536.

FISH POND, 297 Heneage Road, Grimsby, HUMBERSIDE (SOUTH), DN32 9NP **England**
Mr Carl Frist (Proprietor)
(T) 01472 362101.

FRED'S FISHING TACKLE, 413 Weelsby Street, Grimsby, HUMBERSIDE (SOUTH), DN32 8BJ **England**
Mr F Butler (Proprietor)
(T) 01472 352922.

H A C PRODUCTS, 63-67 Pasture Street, Grimsby, HUMBERSIDE (SOUTH), DN32 9AB **England**
Mr B Ilsley (Proprietor)
(T) 01472 250400.

HUMBERSIDE BAIT, Twigmore Grange, Brigg Road, Messingham, Scunthorpe, HUMBERSIDE (SOUTH), DN17 3QP **England**
(T) 01652 658386.

HUMBERSIDE TACKLE EXCHANGE, 95 Mary Street, Scunthorpe, HUMBERSIDE (SOUTH), DN15 6LB **England**
Mr R Anderson (Proprietor)
(T) 01724 856668.

KINGFISHER TACKLE SHOP, 102 High Street, Barton-upon-Humber, HUMBERSIDE (SOUTH), DN18 5PU **England**
Mr A Kirby (Manager)
(T) 01652 636868.

KINGFISHER TACKLE SHOP, 37 Fleetgate, Barton-upon-Humber, HUMBERSIDE (SOUTH), DN18 5QA **England**
Mr A Kirby (Manager)
(T) 01652 636868.

PASTURE HOUSE FISHERY, Pasture House, Pasture Road North, Barton-upon-Humber, HUMBERSIDE (SOUTH), DN18 5RB **England**
Mrs G Card (Partner)
(T) 01652 635119.

R A HATFIELD, 125 Rowland Road, Scunthorpe, HUMBERSIDE (SOUTH), DN16 1TQ **England**
Mr R A Hatfield (Proprietor)
(T) 01724 861786.

RENCO, King Edward Street, Grimsby, HUMBERSIDE (SOUTH), DN31 3LA **England**
Mr J Yorgenson (Proprietor)
(T) 01472 241289.

SCUNTHORPE FISHING TACKLE CENTRE, 9 Laneham Street, Scunthorpe, HUMBERSIDE (SOUTH), DN15 6LJ **England**
(T) 01724 849815.

SPARKS BROS, 43a Cromwell Avenue, Grimsby, HUMBERSIDE (SOUTH), DN31 2DR **England**
Mr R G Wright (Proprietor)
(T) 01472 342613.

W HEATHFIELD & SON, Marshlands, Chapelfield Road, Goxhill, Barrow-upon-Humber, HUMBERSIDE (SOUTH), DN19 7NG **England**
Mr W Heathfield (Proprietor)
(T) 01469 531209.

ISLE OF MAN

ROLAND WESTCOTT TACKLE CO, Ballaquayle Road, Douglas, ISLE OF MAN, IM2 5DF **England**
Mrs D Madigan (Proprietor)
(T) 01624 629599.

ISLE OF WIGHT

3 HIGH, 81 High Street, Sandown, ISLE OF WIGHT, PO36 8AQ **England**
Mr R Ward (Proprietor)
(T) 01983 404014.

CASTAWAYS, 23 Clarendon Road, Shanklin, ISLE OF WIGHT, PO37 6DP **England**
Mr John Milford (Partner)
(T) 01983 868100.

SCOTTIES, 22 Fitzroy Street, Sandown, ISLE OF WIGHT, PO36 8HZ **England**
Mr Paul Jackson (Manager)
(T) 01983 404555.

SCREAMING REEL, 55 St Johns Road, Ryde, ISLE OF WIGHT, PO33 2RW **England**
Mr D Chappell (Proprietor)
(T) 01983 568745.

SPORTS & MODEL SHOPS, 9 Union Street, Ryde, ISLE OF WIGHT, PO33 2DU **England**
Mrs J Ballander (Manageress)
(T) 01983 563836.

STUARTS BAIT & TACKLE SUPPLIES, 7a Clarence Road, East Cowes, ISLE OF WIGHT, PO32 6EP **England**
Mr J Benham (Proprietor)
(T) 01983 280985.

TACKLE BOX, Broadway, Totland Bay, ISLE OF WIGHT, PO39 0BX **England**
Mr David Bryan (Proprietor)
(T) 01983 752260.

KENT

A & I FISHING TACKLE, 33 High Street, Green Street Green, Orpington, KENT, BR6 6BG **England**
Mr Tony Thistleton (Manager)
(T) 01689 862302.

ANGLERS DEN, 10 Franklin Road, Gillingham, KENT, ME7 4DF **England**
Mr E Scott (Proprietor)
(T) 01634 852180.

ANGLERS REST, 42 Park View Road, Welling, KENT, DA16 1RT **England**
Mr J L Frost (Proprietor)
(T) 0208-303 3155.

ANGLING JOURNALIST & CONSULTANT, 3 Broomfield Road, Folkestone, KENT, CT19 4DJ **England**
Mr A Yates (Proprietor)
(T) 01303 278877.

AQUATIC CONSULTANCY SERVICE, 5 Hill Rise, Dartford, KENT, DA2 7HX **England**
(T) 01474 709669.

AQUATIC CONSULTANCY SERVICE, 9 Charlton Lane, West Farleigh, Maidstone, KENT, ME15 0NX **England**
Miss B Brewster (Proprietor)
(T) 01622 815255.

ASHFORD TACKLE SHOP, 115 Ellingham Ind Centre, Ellingham Way, Ashford, KENT, TN23 6LZ **England**
Mr Paul Harrison (Manager)
(T) 01233 630914.

ASHFORD TACKLE SHOP, 3b Stanhope Square, Ashford, KENT, TN23 5SH **England**
Mr Paul Harris (Manager)
(T) 01233 630914.

ASHFORD TACKLE SHOP, 52 St Marys Road, Faversham, KENT, ME13 8EH **England**
Mr C Dyson (Partner)
(T) 01795 530160.

ASHFORD TACKLE SHOP, 26 Shakespeare Road, Sittingbourne, KENT, ME10 3AB **England**
Mr Mark Coker (Manager)
(T) 01795 426011.

B W BRADLEY, Unit 2/Hoo Farm, 147 Monkton Road, Minster, Ramsgate, KENT, CT12 4JB **England**
Mr B Reed (Partner)
(T) 01843 825486.

BAIT SHOP, 71 Central Parade, Herne Bay, KENT, CT6 5JQ **England**
Mr A Ingle (Manager)
(T) 01227 742942.

BIGGIN HILL ANGLING CENTRE, 216-218 Main Road, Biggin Hill, Westerham, KENT, TN16 3BD **England**
Mr Peter James (Proprietor)
(T) 01959 570265.

BILLS BAIT & TACKLE, 121 Snargate Street, Dover, KENT, CT17 9DA **England**
Mr William Solley (Proprietor)
(T) 01304 204542.

BOB MORRIS, PO Box 126, South Darenth, Dartford, KENT, DA4 9BD **England**
Mr B Morris (Proprietor)
(T) 01322 866015.

BOB MORRIS TACKLE, 1 Lincolnshire Terrace, Lane End, Dartford, KENT, DA2 7JP **England**
Mr Bob Morris (Proprietor)
(T) 01322 278519.

BRADLEY BAIT, Unit 4 Kestner Industrial Estate, King Edward Road, Greenhithe, KENT, DA9 9BT **England**
(T) 01322 370387.

BRAZILS OF DOVER, 162 Snargate Street, Dover, KENT, CT17 9BZ **England**
Mr K J Brazil (Proprietor)
(T) 01304 201457.

CHANNEL ANGLING, Beach Street, Deal, KENT, CT14 6HZ **England**
Mr S Allmark (Proprietor)
(T) 01304 373104.

CHANNEL ANGLING, 158-160 Snargate Street, Dover, KENT, CT17 9BZ **England**
Mr R Skelton (Proprietor)
(T) 01304 203742.

CHARLIES BAIT TACKLE & PET SUPPLIES, 10 Hedge Place Road, Greenhithe, KENT, DA9 9JZ **England**
Mrs C Rayner (Proprietor)
(T) 01322 381187.

D ROLFE, Hookstead, Steeds Lane, Kingsnorth, Ashford, KENT, TN26 1NH **England**
Mr D Rolfe (Proprietor)
(T) 01233 635022.

DANSON ANGLING, 159 Blendon Road, Bexley, KENT, DA5 1BT **England**
Mr T Ford (Partner)
(T) 0208-298 9090.

DARTFORD ANGLING CENTRE, 84 Lowfield Street, Dartford, KENT, DA1 1HS **England**
Mr G Hough (Proprietor)
(T) 01322 228532.

DENS TACKLE, 73 Dymchurch Road, Hythe, KENT, CT21 6JN **England**
Mr D Malpass (Proprietor)
(T) 01303 267053.

DOLPHIN ANGLING CENTRE, 5 Queen Street, Gravesend, KENT, DA12 2EQ **England**
Mr G Heast (Proprietor)
(T) 01474 355440.

DOLPHIN ANGLING CENTRE, 8 Queen Street, Gravesend, KENT, DA12 2EE **England**
Mr G East (Proprietor)
(T) 01474 325943.

DOWNHAM TACKLE, 443 Bromley Road, Bromley, KENT, BR1 4PH **England**
(T) 0500 300286.

FISHERMAN'S CORNER, 6 Kent Place, Ramsgate, KENT, CT11 8LT **England**
Mr B T A Sales (Proprietor)
(T) 01843 582174.

FOC'SLE FISHING TACKLE STORES, 33 Beach Street, Deal, KENT, CT14 6HY **England**
Mr Peter Young (Proprietor)
(T) 01304 374013.

FOLKESTONE ANGLING, 12 Tontine Street, Folkestone, KENT, CT20 1JU **England**
Mr P Owne (Proprietor)
(T) 01303 253881.

FRIENDLY FISHERMAN, 25 Camden Road, Tunbridge Wells, KENT, TN1 2PS **England**
Mr Andrew Lush (Proprietor)
(T) 01892 528677.

HARBOUR TACKLE, 10 Beach Street, Folkestone, KENT, CT20 1QW **England**
Mr P Tanner (Proprietor)
(T) 01303 220763.

HOBBIES, 146 Snargate Street, Dover, KENT, CT17 9BZ **England**
Mr F Davies (Partner)
(T) 01304 242346.

HOOK LINE & SINKA, 12 High Street, Chatham, KENT, ME4 4EP **England**
Mr Roger Sulley (Proprietor)
(T) 01634 880770.

JOHN ROBERTS, Preston Road, Manston, Ramsgate, KENT, CT12 5BA **England**
Mr J Roberts (Proprietor)
(T) 01843 824005.

JOHN'S, 26 Dover Road, Walmer, Deal, KENT, CT14 7JW **England**
Mr J Kehoe (Proprietor)
(T) 01304 389859.

KENT PARTICLES, 10 Halfway Street, Sidcup, KENT, DA15 8LL **England**
Mr A Pocock (Manager)
(T) 0208-309 6113.

KENT SEA BAITS & RIGS, 135 Midfield Way, Orpington, KENT, BR5 2QW **England**
Mr D Parrot (Employee)
(T) 0208-302 2632.

KINGFISHERIES, 34 King Street, Margate, KENT, CT9 1DA **England**
Mr R J Holloway (Proprietor)
(T) 01843 223866.

KINGSRIGHT FISHING TACKLE, 6-8 Mereworth Road, Tunbridge Wells, KENT, TN4 9PL **England**
Mr S T King (Proprietor)
(T) 01892 516778.

MAIDSTONE ANGLING CENTRE, 15 Perryfield Street, Maidstone, KENT, ME14 2SY **England**
Mr Rob Earl (Managing Director)
(T) 01622 677326.

MARK II ANGLING, 24-26 Crayford High Street, Dartford, KENT, DA1 4HG **England**
Mr M J Barnet (Proprietor)
(T) 01322 554545.

MARSH TACKLE, 6 High Street, Dymchurch, Romney Marsh, KENT, TN29 0NG **England**
Mr D Hughes (Proprietor)
(T) 01303 873020.

MEDWAY BAIT & TACKLE, 64b St. Johns Road, Gillingham, KENT, ME7 5NB **England**
Mr M Carter (Proprietor)
(T) 01634 856948.

MEDWAY TACKLE, 103 Shipbourne Road, Tonbridge, KENT, TN10 3EJ **England**
Mr D Roberts (Proprietor)
(T) 01732 360690.

MEDWAY TACKLE SUPPLIES, 374 Canterbury Street, Gillingham, KENT, ME7 5JU **England**
Mrs C Cullen (Proprietor)
(T) 01634 570740.

MICK'S TACKLE, 1 Thirlestane, Dymchurch Road, Hythe, KENT, CT21 6LB **England**
Mr M Sullivan (Proprietor)
(T) 01303 266334.

MID KENT TACKLE CO, 146 Milton Street, Maidstone, KENT, ME16 8LL **England**
Mr M G Muddle (Proprietor)
(T) 01622 200274.

N & S TACKLE, 94 Hunter Avenue, Willesborough, Ashford, KENT, TN24 0HG **England**
Mr John Bridgeland (Proprietor)
(T) 01233 661770.

NICKS TACKLE EXCHANGE, 10 Knightrider Street, Maidstone, KENT, ME15 6LP **England**
Mr N Puncher (Proprietor)
(T) 01622 673899.

ORIGINAL VIDEO, 27 Porchester Cl, Hartley, Longfield, KENT, DA3 7DQ **England**
Mr T Smith (Director)
(T) 01474 708707.

PENGE ANGLING, 309-311 Beckenham Road, Beckenham, KENT, BR3 4RL **England**
Mr Mike Davies (Partner)
(T) 0208-659 7202.

POINT TACKLE SHOP, Dungeness Road, Dungeness, Romney Marsh, KENT, TN29 9ND **England**
(T) 01797 320049.

PREMIERE BAITS, Unit 8 3 Wilton Road, Ramsgate, KENT, CT12 5HG **England**
Mr T Smitherman (Proprietor)
(T) 01843 583595.

ROD & LINE, 38c Marion Cresent, Orpington, KENT, BR5 2DD **England**
(T) 01689 874060.

RON EDWARDS, 50-52 High Street, Herne Bay, KENT, CT6 5LH **England**
Mr R Cannon (Proprietor)
(T) 01227 372517.

SANDWICH BAIT & TACKLE, 13 The Chain, Sandwich, KENT, CT13 9BJ **England**
(T) 01304 613752.

SANDWICH BAIT & TACKLE, Dover Road, Sandwich, KENT, CT13 0DG **England**
Mr Bryan Bayliss (Proprietor)
(T) 01304 613752.

SEA ANGLING CENTRE, West Street, Queenborough, KENT, ME11 5AD **England**
Mr S Standen (Proprietor)
(T) 01795 660594.

SEAGULL FISHING TACKLE, 4 The Parade, Greatstone, New Romney, KENT, TN28 8NP **England**
Mrs P Hills (Director)
(T) 01797 366837.

SEAKING LTD, 50 St. Mildreds Road, Westgate-on-Sea, KENT, CT8 8RF **England**
Mrs L Agnew (Partner)
(T) 01843 834373.

SOLAR TACKLE, P O Box 22, Orpington, KENT, BR6 7XF **England**
Mr M Lock (Proprietor)
(T) 01689 874654.

SPECIALIZED ANGLING CENTRE, 3 Holborough Road, Snodland, KENT, ME6 5NL **England**
Mr C Reynolds (Proprietor)
(T) 01634 243112.

STROOD ANGLING FISHING TRIPS, 167c High Street, Rochester, KENT, ME2 4PH **England**
(T) 01634 721300.

SUNDRIDGE TACKLE LTD, Vicarage Lane, Hoo, Rochester, KENT, ME3 9LW **England**
Mr J Carroll (Managing Director)
(T) 01634 253487.

TACKLE & GUN, 3 East Well, High Street, Tenterden, KENT, TN30 6AH **England**
Mr G Parry (Proprietor)
(T) 01580 764851.

TACKLE BOX, Watling Street, Dartford, KENT, DA2 6EG **England**
Mr Kevin Peet (Partner)
(T) 01322 292400.

TACKLE STORE, 40 Windmill Street, Gravesend, KENT, DA12 1BA **England**
Mr J White (Proprietor)
(T) 01474 334802.

TIGHT LINE FISHING TACKLE, Unit 8a Spectrum Business Centre, Anthonys Way, Rochester, KENT, ME2 4NP **England**
Mr T Franks (Proprietor)
(T) 01634 724666.

TIGHT LINES BAIT & TACKLE LTD, 98 Tankerton Road, Whitstable, KENT, CT5 2AH **England**
Mr M Satchell (Director)
(T) 01227 281677.

TONBRIDGE ROD & LINES, 17a Priory Road, Tonbridge, KENT, TN9 2AQ **England**
Mr P Barlett (Manager)
(T) 01732 352450.

TRACE ACE TACKLE LTD, P O Box 236, Chatham, KENT, ME4 6LF **England**
Mr L Short (Proprietor)
(T) 01634 720720.

UNITY TACKLE, 88 Unity Street, Sittingbourne, KENT, ME10 1HX **England**
Mr Steve Langley (Proprietor)
(T) 01795 423912.

ZZIPLEX LTD, Units 1-2, Mountfield Road, New Romney, KENT, TN28 8LH **England**
Mrs B Carroll (Director)
(T) 01797 366602.

LANCASHIRE

ADDISONS, 48 High Street, Lees, Oldham, LANCASHIRE, OL4 5AQ **England**
Mr K Addison (Proprietor)
(T) 01616 241308.

ANGLERS ALL, The Old Forge, 6 Raglan Street, Colne, LANCASHIRE, BB8 0ET **England**
Mr Denis Holstead (Proprietor)
(T) 01282 860515.

ANGLERS DEN, 19 Blackburn Road, Darwen, LANCASHIRE, BB3 1EJ **England**
Mr H Rothwell (Proprietor)
(T) 01254 706713.

ANGLERS WORLD, 183 Preston Old Road, Blackpool, LANCASHIRE, FY3 9SF **England**
Mr B Barks (Proprietor)
(T) 01253 764505.

AQUACULTURE ENGINEERING, Unit 31 Spotland Bridge Mill, Mellor Street, Rochdale, LANCASHIRE, OL11 5BT **England**
Mr R Snedden (Partner)
(T) 01706 715550.

ASHTON SUPPLIES, 41 Garden Street, Audenshaw, Manchester, LANCASHIRE, M34 5DD **England**
Mr S Cooke (Proprietor)
(T) 0161-337 9777.

ASHTON TACKLE EXCHANGE, 66 Penny Meadow, Ashton-under-Lyne, LANCASHIRE, OL6 6EL **England**
Mr T Stevens (Proprietor)
(T) 0161-339 6319.

ATHERTON TACKLE SHOP, 136 Market Street, Atherton, Manchester, LANCASHIRE, M46 0DX **England**
Mr Steven Hop (Proprietor)
(T) 01942 876163.

BLACKPOOL ANGLING CENTRE, 326 Church Street, Blackpool, LANCASHIRE, FY1 3QH **England**
Mr F Porter (Manager)
(T) 01253 290961.

BOBS TACKLE SHOP, 35 Beach Road, Thornton-Cleveleys, LANCASHIRE, FY5 1EG **England**
Mr D Fisher (Proprietor)
(T) 01253 860616.

BOLTON ANGLING CENTRE, 185 St. Helens Road, Bolton, LANCASHIRE, BL3 3PS **England**
Mr M Thompson (Proprietor)
(T) 01204 658989.

BOYCES, 44 Manchester Road, Nelson, LANCASHIRE, BB9 7HB **England**
Mr W Pawson (Proprietor)
(T) 01282 614412.

BRILO BOX CO, Unit 20, Clayton Street, Nelson, LANCASHIRE, BB9 7PH **England**
Mr B Hill (Proprietor)
(T) 01282 613374.

BURSCOUGH ANGLING SUPPLIES, 2 Lords Gate Lane, Burscough, Ormskirk, LANCASHIRE, L40 7ST **England**
Mr R Wright (Proprietor)
(T) 01704 896252.

BURSCOUGH ANGLING SUPPLIES, Unit B4 Platts Lane, Burscough, Ormskirk, LANCASHIRE, L40 7TE **England**
Mr R Wright (Proprietor)
(T) 01704 896252.

C E HOWARTH, 128 Watson Road, Blackpool, LANCASHIRE, FY4 2BP **England**
Mrs C Howarth (Proprietor)
(T) 01253 344016.

CARTER TED & SONS, 87 Church Street, Preston, LANCASHIRE, PR1 3BS **England**
(T) 01772 253476.

CHARLTON & BAGNALL LTD, 3-5 Damside Street, Lancaster, LANCASHIRE, LA1 1PD **England**
Miss F Davis (Manager)
(T) 01524 63043.

CHORLEY ANGLERS, 12 Gillibrand Street, Chorley, LANCASHIRE, PR7 2EJ **England**
Mr John Walsh (Proprietor)
(T) 01257 263513.

CHORLEY TACKLE & GUN CENTRE, 240 Pall Mall, Chorley, LANCASHIRE, PR7 2LH **England**
Mr A Wilson (Proprietor)
(T) 01257 274508.

CHRIS WEBB, 52 St. Annes Road, Blackpool, LANCASHIRE, FY4 2AS **England**
Mr Chris Webb (Proprietor)
(T) 01253 470004.

CLEVELEYS OUTDOOR CENTRE, St. Georges Lane, Thornton-Cleveleys, LANCASHIRE, FY5 3LT **England**
Mr K Bates (Proprietor)
(T) 01253 821521.

COUNTRY WAYS, 2 Bankside Lane, Bacup, LANCASHIRE, OL13 8HG **England**
Mrs A Mccarthy (Proprietor)
(T) 01706 872498.

CROW HILL ANGLING SUPPLIES, 57 Crowhill Road, Ashton-under-Lyne, LANCASHIRE, OL7 9HD **England**
Mr G Hampson (Proprietor)
(T) 0161-331 9388.

CROWN TACKLE & BAIT, 4a Chorley New Road, Horwich, Bolton, LANCASHIRE, BL6 7QH **England**
Mr B Jones (Manager)
(T) 01204 668223.

DAVID YATES, 31 Malvern Avenue, Preston, LANCASHIRE, PR1 4PL **England**
(T) 01772 250204.

DIAMOND BRAND, Unit 1 31 Cecil Street, Bolton, LANCASHIRE, BL2 1AL **England**
Mr C Diamond (Proprietor)
(T) 01204 370771.

DONS FISHING TACKLE, 8 Mill Street, Coppull, Chorley, LANCASHIRE, PR7 5AZ **England**
Mr D Astley (Proprietor)
(T) 01257 794040.

DREAM ANGLING TACKLE & BAIT CENTRE, 63 Preston Road, Standish, Wigan, LANCASHIRE, WN6 0JH **England**
Mr R Green (Proprietor)
(T) 01257 472707.

DS OF ROCHDALE LTD, Leisure House, Royle Road, Rochdale, LANCASHIRE, OL11 3ES **England**
Mrs Doreen Farkas (Partner)
(T) 01706 868677.

ECCLES ANGLING, 404 Liverpool Road, Eccles, Manchester, LANCASHIRE, M30 7HA **England**
Mr P Banks (Proprietor)
(T) 0161-787 7052.

ELTON TACKLE, 47 Church Street West, Radcliffe, Manchester, LANCASHIRE, M26 2SP **England**
Mr B J Gregory (Proprietor)
(T) 0161-724 5425.

FISHERMANS WAY, 45 Walmersley Road, Bury, LANCASHIRE, BL9 5AE **England**
Mr D Chadwick (Proprietor)
(T) 0161-761 1359.

FISHING ETC, 4 New Market Street, Clitheroe, LANCASHIRE, BB7 2JW **England**
Mr K Hawkin (Proprietor)
(T) 01200 428070.

FISHING TACKLE SHOP, 41 Lower Green, Poulton-le-Fylde, LANCASHIRE, FY6 7EJ **England**
Mr M Gibbons (Proprietor)
(T) 01253 885684.

FRESHWATER ANGLING SUPPLIERS, 415 Chorley Road, Swinton, Manchester, LANCASHIRE, M27 9UQ **England**
(T) 0161-793 6805.

FYLDE COAST TACKLE, 100 Buchanan Street, Blackpool, LANCASHIRE, FY1 3BP **England**
Mr H Varley (Proprietor)
(T) 01253 627228.

G & L FISHING SUPPLIES, 105 Waterloo Road, Blackpool, LANCASHIRE, FY4 2AB **England**
Mr G Dronfield (Proprietor)
(T) 01253 298714.

G B CARP PRODUCTS, Unit 6/Whiteside Buildings, Back St. Annes Rd West, Lytham St. Annes, LANCASHIRE, FY8 1RD **England**
Mr C Banks (Proprietor)
(T) 01253 720686.

GEOFF DONE, 12-14 Southworth Street, Blackburn, LANCASHIRE, BB2 3PD **England**
Mr G Done (Proprietor)
(T) 01254 698161.

GEORGE'S FISHING TACKLE, 15 Frog Lane, Wigan, LANCASHIRE, WN6 7DE **England**
Mr G Lane (Proprietor)
(T) 01942 241932.

GERRY'S OF MORECAMBE, 5-7 Parliament Street, Morecambe, LANCASHIRE, LA3 1RQ **England**
Mr Darren Breen (Manager)
(T) 01524 422146.

GILDER'S FISHING TACKLE, 718 Oldham Road, Failsworth, Manchester, LANCASHIRE, M35 9FD **England**
Mr G Lees (Partner)
(T) 0161-681 2538.

H & C GLASSBROOK, 359 Ainsworth Road, Radcliffe, Manchester, LANCASHIRE, M26 4HA **England**
Mr Colin Glassbrook (Partner)
(T) 0161-723 3088.

HARRY'S TACKLE, 213 Old Road, Ashton-in-Makerfield, Wigan, LANCASHIRE, WN4 9QP **England**
Mr Harry Simm (Proprietor)
(T) 01942 728532.

HIGHFIELD ANGLING SUPPLIES, 36 Highfield Road, Farnworth, Bolton, LANCASHIRE, BL4 0AD **England**
(T) 01204 572219.

HI-TECH HANDLING PRODUCTS, Unit 5 Alpha Court, Windmill Lane Industrial Estate, Denton, Manchester, LANCASHIRE, M34 3RB **England**
(T) 0161-320 8972.

HOOK & LINE FISHING TACKLE, 375 Victoria Avenue, Manchester, LANCASHIRE, M9 8WQ **England**
Mr John Jeffrey (Proprietor)
(T) 0161-720 6577.

HOOK LINE & SINKER, 31 Garswood Street, Ashton-in-Makerfield, Wigan, LANCASHIRE, WN4 9AF **England**
Mr Paul Hudson (Proprietor)
(T) 01942 276690.

HYDBURN ANGLING & DARTS CENTRE, 71 Abbey Street, Accrington, LANCASHIRE, BB5 1EH **England**
Mr G Griffiths (Proprietor)
(T) 01254 397612.

JACKSON'S FISHING TACKLE, 27 Albion Street, Earby, Barnoldswick, LANCASHIRE, BB18 6QA **England**
Mr M J Jackson (Proprietor)
(T) 01282 843333.

JED, 307 Station Road, Bamber Bridge, Preston, LANCASHIRE, PR5 6ED **England**
Mr Jed Dimmock (Proprietor)
(T) 01772 498361.

JOHN BURTON & CO (ANGLING) LTD, Rough Hey Road, Grimsargh, Preston, LANCASHIRE, PR2 5AD **England**
Mr J Burton (Director)
(T) 01772 797070.

KRYSTON ADVANCED ANGLING, Trade Only/Bolton Enterprise Centre, Washington Street, Bolton, LANCASHIRE, BL3 5EY **England**
Mr David Chilton (Managing Director)
(T) 01204 364283.

L P QUINN, Turf Nest Farm/Moss Lane, Astley, Tyldesley, Manchester, LANCASHIRE, M29 7LN **England**
Mr P Rawson (Manager)
(T) 01942 671683.

LAKE VIEW TACKLE, 38 Lodge Road, Orrell, Wigan, LANCASHIRE, WN5 7AT **England**
Mrs E Saunders (Proprietor)
(T) 01695 625634.

LAKESIDE DESIGNS, Unit 21, Guinness Road, Trafford Park, Manchester, LANCASHIRE, M17 1SD **England**
Mr G Delaney (Director)
(T) 0161-877 6750.

LEATHERBARROWS, 196-198 Church Road, Urmston, Manchester, LANCASHIRE, M41 9DX **England**
Mr C V Leatherbarrow (Director)
(T) 0161-748 0959.

LEIGH ANGLING CENTRE, 261 Twist Lane, Leigh, LANCASHIRE, WN7 4EH **England**
Mr G Smith (Partner)
(T) 01942 670890.

LEIGH TACKLE & BAIT, 30 Warrington Road, Leigh, LANCASHIRE, WN7 3EB **England**
Mr T L Roberts (Manager)
(T) 01942 604125.

LEONARDS ANGLING, 5 Whalley Road, Clayton le Moors, Accrington, LANCASHIRE, BB5 5EE **England**
Mr J Leonard (Proprietor)
(T) 01254 231148.

LORYAN, Unit 11 Chanters Industrial Estate, Atherton, Manchester, LANCASHIRE, M46 9BE **England**
Mr J H Holt (Proprietor)
(T) 01942 889295.

LOSTOCK TACKLE BOX, 16 Watkin Lane, Lostock Hall, Preston, LANCASHIRE, PR5 5RD **England**
Mr B Whitlock (Proprietor)
(T) 01772 626585.

M S JACKSON, 33 Moor Lane, Preston, LANCASHIRE, PR1 7AT **England**
Mr M S Jackson (Proprietor)
(T) 01772 558670.

MACK'S FISHING TACKLE, 33a Parliament Street, Burnley, LANCASHIRE, BB11 3JU **England**
(T) 01282 427386.

MANCHESTER BAIT SERVICE, 227 Eccles New Road, Salford, LANCASHIRE, M5 2QG **England**
Mr R Stiner (Proprietor)
(T) 0161-737 1133.

MCBRIDE'S, 143 Acregate Lane, Preston, LANCASHIRE, PR1 5QQ **England**
(T) 01772 796320.

MIDDLETON ANGLING CENTRE, 79 Long Street, Middleton, Manchester, LANCASHIRE, M24 6UN **England**
Mr Alan Wash (Manager)
(T) 0161-655 3402.

MORECAMBE ANGLING CENTRE, Old Grand Garage, Thornton Road, Morecambe, LANCASHIRE, LA4 5PB **England**
Mr H Parker (Proprietor)
(T) 01524 832332.

MR DISCOUNT FISHING TACKLE, 3 Anchorsholme Lane East, Thornton-Cleveleys, LANCASHIRE, FY5 3QL **England**
Mr C Lawson (Proprietor)
(T) 01253 828800.

N B ANGLE SPORT LTD, Holmefield Works, Garstang Road, Preston, LANCASHIRE, PR1 1PP **England**
Ms Sylvia Butler (Sole Director)
(T) 01253 790804.

N B ANGLE SPORT LTD, Holmefield Works, Garstang Road, Preston, LANCASHIRE, PR1 1QW **England**
Ms Sylvia Butler (Sole Director)
(T) 01253 790804.

NEW TACKLE FACTORY, 36 Davyhulme Road East, Stretford, Manchester, LANCASHIRE, M32 0DW **England**
Mr M North (Proprietor)
(T) 01618 652646.

NEW TACKLE FACTORY, 854 Chester Road, Stretford, Manchester, LANCASHIRE, M32 0QJ **England**
Mr F Madaf (Proprietor)
(T) 0161-865 2646.

NICHOLLS & SON, 92 Chatsworth Road, Morecambe, LANCASHIRE, LA3 1BL **England**
Mr M Nicholls (Proprietor)
(T) 01524 831818.

NORTH WEST ANGLING CENTRE, Chapel Street, Hindley, Wigan, LANCASHIRE, WN2 3AD **England**
Mr B Powell (Manager)
(T) 01942 255993.

NORTH WESTERN BLANKS LTD, Grimshaw Lane, Middleton, Manchester, LANCASHIRE, M24 2AA **England**
Mr J Cox (Managing Director)
(T) 0161-653 3500.

OLDHAM ANGLING CENTRE, 159 Oldham Road, Springhead, Oldham, LANCASHIRE, OL4 4QJ **England**
(T) 0161-624 7711.

OPENSHAW BAIT CENTRE, 1365 Ashton Old Road, Manchester, LANCASHIRE, M11 1JT **England**
Mr A Boardman (Proprietor)
(T) 0161-370 1826.

PEARSONS FISHING TACKLE, 137 Lee Lane, Horwich, Bolton, LANCASHIRE, BL6 7AG **England**
Mr Terry Pearson (Proprietor)
(T) 01204 692938.

PENDLEBURY (UK) LTD, Bacup Road, Todmorden, LANCASHIRE, OL14 7JU **England**
Mr J Pendlebury (Proprietor)
(T) 01706 877323.

PENDLEBURY ANGLING SUPPLIES, 700 Bolton Road, Swinton, Manchester, LANCASHIRE, M27 6EL **England**
Mr E Filipek (Proprietor)
(T) 0161-794 6171.

PETER KELSALL, Chathill Farm, Lancaster Road, Out Rawcliffe, Preston, LANCASHIRE, PR3 6BP **England**
(T) 01253 790357.

PLATT BRIDGE ANGLING CENTRE, 68 Warrington Road, Platt Bridge, Wigan, LANCASHIRE, WN2 5JA **England**
Mr P Aspinall (Proprietor)
(T) 01942 865540.

R MILLINGTON, 32 Steeley Lane, Chorley, LANCASHIRE, PR6 0RD **England**
Mrs E Millington (Proprietor)
(T) 01257 272392.

ROCHDALE ANGLING CENTRE, 161 Yorkshire Street, Rochdale, LANCASHIRE, OL12 0DR **England**
Mr S J Edwards (Proprietor)
(T) 01706 527604.

ROE LEE TACKLE BOX, 336 Whalley New Road, Blackburn, LANCASHIRE, BB1 9SL **England**
Mr N Speak (Proprietor)
(T) 01254 676977.

ROXY ANGLING SUPPLIES, 171 Queens Road, Ashton-under-Lyne, LANCASHIRE, OL6 8EW **England**
Mr J Williams (Proprietor)
(T) 0161-330 7714.

SAM'S PLAICE, 35A-35C North Albert Street, Fleetwood, LANCASHIRE, FY7 6AJ **England**
Mr S Johnstone (Proprietor)
(T) 01253 870848.

SAVICK HARDWEAR & FISHING TACKLE, 14 Birkdale Drive, Ashton-on-Ribble, Preston, LANCASHIRE, PR2 1UL **England**
Mrs S Hodson (Proprietor)
(T) 01772 463827.

SHEDDINGS ANGLING SUPPLIES, 301 Ripponden Road, Oldham, LANCASHIRE, OL1 4JJ **England**
(T) 0161-345 2761.

SHORROCK'S BROS, 210-212 Albert Road, Farnworth, Bolton, LANCASHIRE, BL4 9JB **England**
Mr G Shorrock (Partner)
(T) 01204 571386.

SPINTEC, 107-109 Johnston Street, Blackburn, LANCASHIRE, BB2 1HY **England**
Mrs S Ellison (Partner)
(T) 01254 55871.

STOCKS FLY FISHERY, Bank House, Lancaster Road, Caton, Lancaster, LANCASHIRE, LA2 9HX **England**
Mrs J Dobson (Manager)
(T) 01524 770412.

STONES QUALITY FISHING TACKLE, 13 Golden Hill Lane, Leyland, Preston, LANCASHIRE, PR5 2NP **England**
(T) 01772 421953.

SWINTON ANGLING CENTRE, 57 Worsley Road, Swinton, Manchester, LANCASHIRE, M27 5NE **England**
Mr E Battersby (Partner)
(T) 0161-794 2784.

T M ANGLING, 73 Liverpool Old Road, Walmer Bridge, Preston, LANCASHIRE, PR4 5QE **England**
Mr M S Reynolds (Proprietor)
(T) 01772 612941.

TIGHT LINES, 164 Milnrow Road, Shaw, Oldham, LANCASHIRE, OL2 8AY **England**
Mr J Platt (Manager)
(T) 01706 881459.

TONGE MOOR ANGLING SUPPLIES, 143 Tonge Moor Road, Bolton, LANCASHIRE, BL2 2HR **England**
(T) 01204 363370.

TRAFFORD ANGLING SUPPLIES, 34 Moss Road, Stretford, Manchester, LANCASHIRE, M32 0AY **England**
Mr Brian Wade (Proprietor)
(T) 0161-864 1211.

TRI-CAST COMPOSITE TUBES LTD, Watson Works, Duke Street, Rochdale, LANCASHIRE, OL12 0LT **England**
Mr R Harris (Director)
(T) 01706 861807.

WAYAHEAD TACKLE LTD, Off Back Market Street, Hindley, Wigan, LANCASHIRE, WN2 3AD **England**
Mr J Roberts (Managing Director)
(T) 01942 525868.

WHELLEY ANGLING, 160 Whelley, Wigan, LANCASHIRE, WN1 3UE **England**
Mr A Mayren (Proprietor)
(T) 01942 496806.

WIGAN ANGLING CENTRE, 15 Orrell Road, Orrell, Wigan, LANCASHIRE, WN5 8EY **England**
(T) 01942 226427.

WORSLEY ANGLING CENTRE, 40 Worsley Road North, Worsley, Manchester, LANCASHIRE, M28 3GW **England**
Mr J Buckley (Proprietor)
(T) 0161-799 9248.

LEICESTERSHIRE

A M R COUNTRY CLOTHING, 20 The Green, Ashby-de-la-Zouch, LEICESTERSHIRE, LE65 1JU **England**
Mrs Ann Camp (Proprietor)
(T) 01530 415074.

ALL SEASONS ANGLING, 8 Dunton Street, Wigston, LEICESTERSHIRE, LE18 4PU **England**
Mr N Berry (Proprietor)
(T) 0116-278 2440.

ANGLING MAN, 228 Melton Road, Leicester, LEICESTERSHIRE, LE4 7PG **England**
(T) 0116-266 5579.

BAIT BOX, 19 Nelson Street, Market Harborough, LEICESTERSHIRE, LE16 9AX **England**
Mr M Freer (Proprietor)
(T) 01858 462355.

BENNETTS ANGLING STORES LTD, 9 Market Place, Mountsorrel, Loughborough, LEICESTERSHIRE, LE12 7BA **England**
Mrs L Bennett (Director)
(T) 0116-230 2818.

BERRY FISHING TACKLE, 38 Countesthorpe Road, Wigston, LEICESTERSHIRE, LE18 4PF **England**
(T) 0116-277 4050.

BIRSTALL ANGLING CENTRE, 291A Birstall Road, Birstall, Leicester, LEICESTERSHIRE, LE4 4DJ **England**
Mr I Nicholas (Proprietor)
(T) 0116-267 2758.

BRAIDED INTERNATIONAL LINES LTD, Albion Road, Sileby, Loughborough, LEICESTERSHIRE, LE12 7RA **England**
Mr David Hurst (Proprietor)
(T) 01509 813702.

BRITISH WORM BREEDERS, Potters Kiln, Stanton Lane, Croft, Leicester, LEICESTERSHIRE, LE9 3JQ **England**
Mr M E Clarke (Proprietor)
(T) 01455 282072.

D F BONE, Angling Corner, 3 Denton Street, Leicester, LEICESTERSHIRE, LE3 6DD **England**
(T) 01162 557934.

F A HOLLOWAY, Malt Mill Bank, Barwell, Leicester, LEICESTERSHIRE, LE9 8GS **England**
(T) 01455 842078.

GONE FISHING, 5 Hill Street, Hinckley, LEICESTERSHIRE, LE10 1DS **England**
Mrs J B Hackett (Partner)
(T) 01455 617313.

IBSTOCK GUN & TACKLE, 61-63 Chapel Street, Ibstock, LEICESTERSHIRE, LE67 6HF **England**
Mr D Storer (Partner)
(T) 01530 260901.

J C TOWNSEND LTD, 394 Humberstone Road, Leicester, LEICESTERSHIRE, LE5 0SA **England**
Mr Michael Harrison (Joint Director)
(T) 0116-276 6393.

JAYS TACKLE & GUN, 68-70 Belvoir Road, Coalville, LEICESTERSHIRE, LE67 3PP **England**
Mr J Storer (Manager)
(T) 01530 832410.

KOBRA PRODUCTS, Unit 1, 52b Oakley Road, Leicester, LEICESTERSHIRE, LE5 3NH **England**
Mr J Wagstaffe (Managing Director)
(T) 0116-221 1995.

MATCH CATCH, 14 The Green, Syston, Leicester, LEICESTERSHIRE, LE7 1HQ **England**
Mrs Helen Sutton (Proprietor)
(T) 0116-260 0850.

OADBY ANGLING, 89 London Road, Oadby, Leicester, LEICESTERSHIRE, LE2 5DN **England**
Mr P Wootton (Proprietor)
(T) 0116-271 0789.

P J BAITS, 155 Cavendish Road, Leicester, LEICESTERSHIRE, LE2 7PJ **England**
Mr P Jordan (Proprietor)
(T) 0116-283 7007.

REUBEN HEATON LTD, Unit 10, Sunnyside Park Industrial Estate, Wheatfield Way, Hinkley, LEICESTERSHIRE, LE10 1PJ **England**
Mr Andrew Race (Manager)
(T) 01455 230241.

RICHARDS FIELD & SPORT, 37 Bridge Road, Coalville, LEICESTERSHIRE, LE67 3PW **England**
Mr E J Richards (Proprietor)
(T) 01530 815730.

RIGS & THINGS, 52b Oakley Road, Leicester, LEICESTERSHIRE, LE5 3NH **England**
Mr J Wagstaff (Proprietor)
(T) 0116-276 1323.

RODS & REELS, 6 Chapel Street, Barwell, Leicester, LEICESTERSHIRE, LE9 8DD **England**
Mr J Novak (Proprietor)
(T) 01455 842450.

RODS & REELS, 6 Chapel Street, Earl Shilton, Leicester, LEICESTERSHIRE, LE9 7LQ **England**
Mr J Novak (Proprietor)
(T) 01455 842450.

RODS & REELS, 22 Mill Street, Oakham, LEICESTERSHIRE, LE15 6EA **England**
Mrs J Hearth (Partner)
(T) 01572 755950.

SOAR VALLEY TACKLE, 7 Woodbrook Road, Loughborough, LEICESTERSHIRE, LE11 3QB **England**
Mr Rodney Hubbard (Proprietor)
(T) 01509 231817.

SPORTMANS LODGE, 39 Tudor Road, Leicester, LEICESTERSHIRE, LE3 5JF **England**
Mr C Wilson (Proprietor)
(T) 0116-253 7714.

TONY HORTON, 98 Wolvey Road, Hinckley, LEICESTERSHIRE, LE10 2JJ **England**
Mr T Horton (Proprietor)
(T) 01455 632269.

LINCOLNSHIRE

ABBEYFAME LTD, Priory Road, Ruskington, Sleaford, LINCOLNSHIRE, NG34 9DJ **England**
Ms P Mccutcheon (Proprietor)
(T) 01526 834444.

ALLENS TACKLE BOX, 13A Foundry Road, Stamford, LINCOLNSHIRE, PE9 2PY **England**
Mrs E Allen (Partner)
(T) 01780 754541.

ANGLIA BAIT CO, Horncastle Road, Roughton Moor, Woodhall Spa, LINCOLNSHIRE, LN10 6UX **England**
Mr L Chapman (Proprietor)
(T) 01526 352802.

BOSTON ANGLING CENTRE, 11 Horncastle Road, Boston, LINCOLNSHIRE, PE21 9BN **England**
Mr Brian Bolverson (Proprietor)
(T) 01205 353436.

BOUNDARY PET STORES, 6 Bunkers Hill, Lincoln, LINCOLNSHIRE, LN2 4QP **England**
Mrs P A Brown (Partner)
(T) 01522 520772.

CASTALINE, 18-20 Upgate, Louth, LINCOLNSHIRE, LN11 9ET **England**
Mr P Collings (Partner)
(T) 01507 602149.

CASTAWAY TACKLE ANGLING CENTRE, Unit 8b Chieftain Way, Tritton Road Trading Estate, Lincoln, LINCOLNSHIRE, LN6 7RY **England**
Ms A Would (Partner)
(T) 01522 567090.

CHANGE COARSE LTD, Unit 5-7 Wetherby Cresent, Lincoln, LINCOLNSHIRE, LN6 8SY **England**
(T) 01522 690031.

CHAPEL TACKLE SHOP, Vine Hotel, South Road, Chapel St. Leonards, Skegness, LINCOLNSHIRE, PE24 5TH **England**
(T) 01754 871657.

DAVES PEG, Corner Shop, 1 London Road, Sleaford, LINCOLNSHIRE, NG34 7LF **England**
Mr D Woolerton (Proprietor)
(T) 01529 415896.

F B T, Newbridge Hill, Louth, LINCOLNSHIRE, LN11 0JT **England**
(T) 01507 601774.

GEDS FENLAND TACKLE, 49 Hallgate, Holbeach, Spalding, LINCOLNSHIRE, PE12 7JA **England**
Mr G Cavanagh (Proprietor)
(T) 01406 422020.

GEMINI TACKLE CO LTD, Gemini Works, Mill Lane, Caistor, Market Rasen, LINCOLNSHIRE, LN7 6UA **England**
Mr Chris Caton (Managing Director)
(T) 01472 852966.

GLENSIDE DISCOUNT TACKLE, 152 Station Road, Surfleet, Spalding, LINCOLNSHIRE, PE11 4DG **England**
Mr C Gerrems (Proprietor)
(T) 01775 680401.

HOOKED, 44 High Street, Boston, LINCOLNSHIRE, PE21 8SP **England**
(T) 01205 355655.

K W STORR, 37-38 High Street, Wainfleet, Skegness, LINCOLNSHIRE, PE24 4BJ **England**
Mr Keith Storr (Manager)
(T) 01754 880378.

L M D FARMS, Blyton Airfield, Kirton Road, Blyton, Gainsborough, LINCOLNSHIRE, DN21 3LB **England**
Mr M Hardwick (Partner)
(T) 01427 628059.

LAKESIDE LEISURE, Trunch Lane, Chapel St. Leonards, Skegness, LINCOLNSHIRE, PE24 5TU **England**
Ms Nancy Willmott (Joint Director)
(T) 01754 872631.

MABLETHORPE ANGLING, 2A-2B Tennyson Road, Mablethorpe, LINCOLNSHIRE, LN12 1HQ **England**
Mr A Hurst (Proprietor)
(T) 01507 478444.

OHAM LAKE, Main Road, Maltby le Marsh, Alford, LINCOLNSHIRE, LN13 0JP **England**
Mr C Beckenham (Proprietor)
(T) 01507 450623.

PALMERS, 11 High Street, Skegness, LINCOLNSHIRE, PE25 3NY **England**
Mr R Dent (Proprietor)
(T) 01754 764404.

PETER TAYLOR, South Cottage, Church Lane, Algarkirk, Boston, LINCOLNSHIRE, PE20 2HH **England**
Mr Peter Taylor (Proprietor)
(T) 01205 460072.

PETS & PLANTS, Clifton House, High Street, Mablethorpe, LINCOLNSHIRE, LN12 1AU **England**
Mrs J A Gurin (Proprietor)
(T) 01507 473104.

PINTAIL PRODUCTS LTD, Langrick Road, Hubberts Bridge, Boston, LINCOLNSHIRE, PE20 3SG **England**
Mrs V Van-Wijk (Director)
(T) 01205 290448.

RIVERSIDE TACKLE, 1 Dogdyke Bank, Tattershall Bridge, Lincoln, LINCOLNSHIRE, LN4 4JQ **England**
Mrs Valerie Thornley (Proprietor)
(T) 01526 344660.

ROD HUTCHINSON, Station Road, Legbourne, Louth, LINCOLNSHIRE, LN11 8LL **England**
Mr R E Hutchinson (Proprietor)
(T) 01507 609069.

RUTLAND FISHING, Unit 3 7 St Pauls Street, Stamford, LINCOLNSHIRE, PE9 2BE **England**
Mr S Illsley (Partner)
(T) 01780 482901.

SKEGNESS FISHING TACKLE, 155 Roman Bank, Skegness, LINCOLNSHIRE, PE25 1RY **England**
Mrs V Pain (Partner)
(T) 01754 611172.

SOUTH END ANGLING, 447 High Street, Lincoln, LINCOLNSHIRE, LN5 8HZ **England**
Mr T Mccarthy (Director)
(T) 01522 823003.

SPORT FLIES, 5786, Boothby Pagnell, Grantham, LINCOLNSHIRE, NG33 4DN **England**
Mrs A Sorsberg (Proprietor)
(T) 01476 585859.

TACKLE SHOP, Bridge Road, Gainsborough, LINCOLNSHIRE, DN21 1JS **England**
Mr Neville Fickling (Proprietor)
(T) 01427 613002.

TIDSWELLS, New Bungalow, Burr Lane, Spalding, LINCOLNSHIRE, PE12 6AZ **England**
Mrs I Tidswell (Proprietor)
(T) 01775 723640.

TIGHTLINE SERVICES, 55 Croft Street, Lincoln, LINCOLNSHIRE, LN2 5AZ **England**
Mr R A Bullivant (Proprietor)
(T) 01522 523834.

VANGUARD FISHING TACKLE, Midland Buildings, Skegness Road, Ingoldmells, Skegness, LINCOLNSHIRE, PE25 1JW **England**
(T) 01754 874950.

VANGUARD TACKLE, 25 Wide Bargate, Boston, LINCOLNSHIRE, PE21 6SR **England**
Mr C Payne (Partner)
(T) 01205 369994.

WOODLAND WATERS LTD, Willoughby Road, Ancaster, Grantham, LINCOLNSHIRE, NG32 3RT **England**
Mr M Curridean (Proprietor)
(T) 01400 230888.

LONDON (GREATER)

ACTON ANGLING CENTRE, 185 Old Oak Road, London, LONDON (GREATER), W3 7HH **England**
Mr J Males (Proprietor)
(T) 020 87433381.

AIKEN LTD, Order Line, 139 Kirkdale, London, LONDON (GREATER), SE26 4QW **England**
Mr W Aiken (Proprietor)
(T) 020 82919999.

ANCHOR TACKLE LTD, 67 Albert Road, London, LONDON (GREATER), SE25 4JD **England**
Mr R Keightley (Managing Director)
(T) 0208-656 6716.

AQUACULTURE TRADING LTD, 15 Alderville Road, London, LONDON (GREATER), SW6 3RL **England**
Mr Ivar Warrer-Hansen (Director)
(T) 0207-731 2885.

ASHPOLES OF ISLINGTON, 15 Green Lanes, London, LONDON (GREATER), N16 9BS **England**
Mr Julian Ashpole (Partner)
(T) 0207-226 6575.

BROWNS FISHING TACKLE LTD, 682 Romford Road, London, LONDON (GREATER), E12 5AJ **England**
Mr I G Douglas (Proprietor)
(T) 0208-478 0389.

D & A TACKLE, 242-244 Woodhouse Road, London, LONDON (GREATER), N12 0RU **England**
Mr A Channon (Partner)
(T) 0208-368 8799.

DELLS, 213 St. Johns Hill, London, LONDON (GREATER), SW11 1TH **England**
Mr S Down (Proprietor)
(T) 0207-207 1489.

DELLS TACKLE SHACK, 350 Garratt Lane, London, LONDON (GREATER), SW18 4ES **England**
Mr S Down (Proprietor)
(T) 0208-874 4683.

DON'S OF EDMONTON, 239 Fore Street, London, LONDON (GREATER), N18 2TZ **England**
Mr Don Neish (Proprietor)
(T) 0208-807 5219.

E17 ANGLING, 123 Fulbourne Road, London, LONDON (GREATER), E17 4HA **England**
Mr M Scanlen (Proprietor)
(T) 0208-527 1135.

FARLOW'S OF PALL MALL, 5 Pall Mall, London, LONDON (GREATER), SW1Y 5NP **England**
Mr N Armstead (General Manager)
(T) 0207-839 2423.

FINELINE, 299 Mitcham Road, London, LONDON (GREATER), SW17 9JQ **England**
Mr J Barefield (Proprietor)
(T) 0208-672 1699.

FISHERMANS FRIENDS, 194-196 Jamaica Road, London, LONDON (GREATER), SE16 4RT **England**
Mr G Andrews (Proprietor)
(T) 0207-237 7702.

FRAMES, 202 The Broadway, London, LONDON (GREATER), NW9 7EE **England**
Mr D Frame (Proprietor)
(T) 0208-202 0264.

GERRYS OF WIMBLEDON, 170-176 The Broadway, London, LONDON (GREATER), SW19 1RX **England**
Mr S Heath (Manager)
(T) 0208-540 6773.

HACKNEY ANGLING CENTRE, 28 Broadway Market, London, LONDON (GREATER), E8 4QJ **England**
Mr A Hume (Proprietor)
(T) 0207-275 0059.

HOUSE OF HARDY LTD, 61 Pall Mall, London, LONDON (GREATER), SW1Y 5JA **England**
Mr N Armstead (General Manager)
(T) 0207-839 5515.

J & B'S FISHING TACKLE, 594 Hertford Road, London, LONDON (GREATER), N9 8AH **England**
Mr Jason Venis (Partner)
(T) 0208-805 6050.

KEANES, 65 Bloomfield Road, London, LONDON (GREATER), SE18 7JJ **England**
Mr M French (Proprietor)
(T) 0208-854 1731.

K-PRO ELITE TACKLE LTD, Unit 4 Lennon Edward Business Centre, Borwick Avenue, London, LONDON (GREATER), E17 6RA **England**
(T) 0208-509 9666.

LEA BRIDGE ANGLING CENTRE, 512 Lea Bridge Road, London, LONDON (GREATER), E10 7DT **England**
Mr Mick Miller (Proprietor)
(T) 0208-558 5718.

LEE ANGLING CENTRE, 286 Lee High Road, London, LONDON (GREATER), SE13 5PJ **England**
Mr G Fletcher (Proprietor)
(T) 0208-297 2191.

NORWOOD ANGLING, 100 Portland Road, London, LONDON (GREATER), SE25 4PJ **England**
Mr M Bates (Proprietor)
(T) 0208-656 3050.

OAKWOOD ANGLING, 29 Reservoir Road, London, LONDON (GREATER), N14 4BB **England**
(T) 0208-882 6821.

ORVIS CO INC, 36 Dover Street, London, LONDON (GREATER), W1S 4NS **England**
Mr C Knight (Manager)
(T) 0207-499 7496.

ORVIS CO INC, 36 Dover Street, London, LONDON (GREATER), W1X 3RB **England**
Mr C Knight (Manager)
(T) 020 74997496.

PENGE ANGLING, 5 Tudor Parade/Well Hall Road, Eltham, London, LONDON (GREATER), SE9 6SX **England**
(T) 020 88592901.

RON SUMMERS, 509 Abbey Road, London, LONDON (GREATER), SE2 9HA **England**
Mr R Summers (Proprietor)
(T) 0208-310 2750.

RONS, 465 Upper Richmond Road West, London, LONDON (GREATER), SW14 7PU **England**
Mr R Chenery (Proprietor)
(T) 0208-876 4897.

SHARPE'S OF ABERDEEN, 67 York Street, London, LONDON (GREATER), W1H 1PQ **England**
Mr M Oreilly (Manager)
(T) 0207-258 1233.

SHARPS FISHING TACKLE, 162 Malden Road, London, LONDON (GREATER), NW5 4BS **England**
Mr Bob Sharp (Proprietor)
(T) 0207-485 1759.

SPORT FISH AT PALL MALL, 13 Pall Mall, London, LONDON (GREATER), SW1Y 5LU **England**
Mr P Parkinson (Managing Director)
(T) 0207-839 9008.

STATE & COUNTRY SPORTS EQUIPMENT LTD, 276 St. Pauls Road, London, LONDON (GREATER), N1 2LH **England**
Mr B W Cross (Manager)
(T) 0207-226 3445.

SWIFTY'S, 44-46 Wilcox Road, London, LONDON (GREATER), SW8 2UX **England**
Mr S Lemar (Manager)
(T) 0207-627 5907.

TACKLE & BAIT, 36 Nunhead Green, London, LONDON (GREATER), SE15 3QF **England**
Mrs C Jacobs (Proprietor)
(T) 0207-635 9905.

TOTTENHAM ANGLING CENTRE, 80a White Hart Lane, London, LONDON (GREATER), N17 8HP **England**
Mr Tony Clark (Manager)
(T) 0208-801 0062.

MERSEYSIDE

ANFIELD TACKLE, 119 Oakfield Road, Walton, Liverpool, MERSEYSIDE, L4 0UE **England**
Mr N Noone (Proprietor)
(T) 0151-260 8223.

BANDIT BAITS, 37 Nutgrove Road, St. Helens, MERSEYSIDE, WA9 5PJ **England**
Ms Wendy Doubleday (Partner)
(T) 01744 817424.

CATCH 22, Birkdale Trading Estate, 174 Liverpool Road, Southport, MERSEYSIDE, PR8 4PZ **England**
Mr John Summerville (Proprietor)
(T) 01704 568450.

FISHERMAN TACKLE & BAIT, 179 Laird Street, Birkenhead, MERSEYSIDE, CH41 0AA **England**
Mr D P Stanton (Proprietor)
(T) 0151-653 4070.

FISHERMAN TACKLE & BAIT, 179 Laird Street, Birkenhead, MERSEYSIDE, CH41 8EN **England**
Mr D P Stanton (Proprietor)
(T) 01516 534070.

FISHERMANS COVE ANGLING CENTRE, 60 Milton Road, Ellesmere Port, MERSEYSIDE, CH65 5DD **England**
Mr Darrel Evans (Proprietor)
(T) 0151-356 9030.

GARRY BONNER, 119 Duke Street, Birkenhead, MERSEYSIDE, CH41 8BN **England**
Mr G Bonner (Proprietor)
(T) 01516 520606.

GARY BONNER, 87 Hoylake Road, Wirral, MERSEYSIDE, CH46 9PY **England**
Mr G Bonner (Proprietor)
(T) 0151-677 8092.

GEORGE'S TACKLE, 196 Islands Brow, St. Helens, MERSEYSIDE, WA11 9PG **England**
Mr Ray Birchall (Manager)
(T) 01744 732527.

HARRISON RODS, Unit 201 Summers Road, Brunswick Business Park, Liverpool, MERSEYSIDE, L3 4BL **England**
Dr S Harrison (Proprietor)
(T) 0151-709 6096.

J E ROBINSON & SON, 71 Sussex Road, Southport, MERSEYSIDE, PR9 0SP **England**
Mr J E Robinson (Partner)
(T) 01704 534136.

JOHNS BAIT & TACKLE, 75-77 Poulton Road, Wallasey, MERSEYSIDE, CH44 9DE **England**
Mr J Crane (Proprietor)
(T) 0151-639 1069.

JOHNSONS ANGLING CENTRE, 469 Rice Lane, Liverpool, MERSEYSIDE, L9 8AP **England**
Mr A Johnson (Proprietor)
(T) 0151-525 5574.

KEN WATSON, 283 Poulton Road, Wallasey, MERSEYSIDE, CH44 4BT **England**
(T) 0151-638 4505.

MAGHULL ANGLING CENTRE, 160-162a Liverpool Road, Lydiate, Liverpool, MERSEYSIDE, L31 2ND **England**
Mr Ian Bruce (Proprietor)
(T) 0151-531 8619.

MAGHULL ANGLING CENTRE, 162-162A Liverpool Rd North, Liverpool, MERSEYSIDE, L31 2HP **England**
Mr I Bruce (Proprietor)
(T) 0151-531 8614.

PRESCOT ANGLING CENTRE, 18-20 St. Helens Road, Prescot, MERSEYSIDE, L34 6HR **England**
Mrs K Dunn (Proprietor)
(T) 0151-426 5011.

RAYS TACKLE, 22 Childwall Lane, Bowring Park, Liverpool, MERSEYSIDE, L14 6TX **England**
Mr R Minger (Proprietor)
(T) 0151-489 6103.

ROD 'N' REEL, 27-29 Enfield Road, Ellesmere Port, MERSEYSIDE, CH65 8DA **England**
Mr A Dean (Proprietor)
(T) 0151-356 0687.

SHARPE FISHING TACKLE, 23 Rawson Road, Liverpool, MERSEYSIDE, L21 1BS **England**
(T) 0151-928 2626.

STAR ANGLING, 101 Duke Street, St. Helens, MERSEYSIDE, WA10 2JG **England**
Mr I Reynolds (Proprietor)
(T) 01744 738605.

TACKLE SHED, St Helens Home & Garden Centre, Jubits Lane, Sutton Manor, St. Helens, MERSEYSIDE, WA9 4RT **England**
Mrs S Peet (Proprietor)
(T) 01744 810805.

TIGHTLINES TACKLE CENTRE, 2 Hampton Road, Southport, MERSEYSIDE, PR8 6SS **England**
Mr R Anderson (Manager)
(T) 01704 541014.

WIRRAL ANGLING CENTRE, 207 Church Road, Birkenhead, MERSEYSIDE, CH42 0LD **England**
Ms Joyce Cooke (Proprietor)
(T) 0151-644 7554.

MIDDLESEX

ANGLERS CORNER, 52 Browning Road, Enfield, MIDDLESEX, EN2 0EN **England**
Mr Ken Mathews (Partner)
(T) 020 83421300.

ARBITRATOR ROD CO, 18 Uxbridge Road, Feltham, MIDDLESEX, TW13 5EE **England**
Mr T Parker (Proprietor)
(T) 0208-894 9022.

ASHFORD ANGLING CENTRE, 357 Staines Road West, Ashford, MIDDLESEX, TW15 1RP **England**
Mr M Jennings (Partner)
(T) 01784 240013.

DAVIES ANGLING, 47-49 Church Street, Staines, MIDDLESEX, TW18 4EN **England**
Mr B Davies (Proprietor)
(T) 01784 461832.

EDWARDS THE ANGLERS STORE, 491 Hertford Road, Enfield, MIDDLESEX, EN3 5XH **England**
Mr D Parrott (Partner)
(T) 020 84432224.

EXCHANGE TACKLE, 53 Fairfield Road, West Drayton, MIDDLESEX, UB7 8EZ **England**
Mr D J Rentle (Proprietor)
(T) 01895 442424.

FISHERMANS CABIN, 795 Field End Road, Ruislip, MIDDLESEX, HA4 0QL **England**
Mr Steve Brown (Proprietor)
(T) 0208-248 8100.

GUNS & TACKLE, 81 High Street, Whitton, Twickenham, MIDDLESEX, TW2 7LD **England**
Mr T Turner (Partner)
(T) 0208-898 3129.

HAREFIELD TACKLE, 2-4 High Street, Harefield, Uxbridge, MIDDLESEX, UB9 6BU **England**
Mr Adrian Gooche (Manager)
(T) 01895 822900.

HOUNSLOW ANGLING CENTRE, 265-267 Bath Road, Hounslow, MIDDLESEX, TW3 3DA **England**
Mr L Bloomfield (Partner)
(T) 0208-570 6156.

JUDDS OF HILLINGDON LTD, 3 Westbourne Parade, Uxbridge Road, Hillingdon, Uxbridge, MIDDLESEX, UB10 0NY **England**
Mr Christopher John Harrigan (Director)
(T) 0208-573 0196.

JUDDS OF HILLINGTON (RUISLIP) LTD, 524-526 Victoria Road, Ruislip, MIDDLESEX, HA4 0HD **England**
Mr C Harrigan (Proprietor)
(T) 0208-841 7194.

LONDON TACKLE REPAIRS, Horton Road, Staines, MIDDLESEX, TW19 6AE **England**
Mr A Arpino (Proprietor)
(T) 01784 491610.

P M AQUATICS, The Granaries, Theobalds Park Road, Enfield, MIDDLESEX, EN2 9BB **England**
(T) 0208-367 3751.

SHARPES RODS, Deetech House/411b Alexandra Avenue, Rayners Lane, Harrow, MIDDLESEX, HA2 9SG **England**
(T) 0208-429 4894.

TACKLE TECHNIK LTD, 25 Felbridge Avenue, Stanmore, MIDDLESEX, HA7 2BZ **England**
Mr G Elvin (Director)
(T) 0208-427 0009.

TAILS UP, 105 Bear Road, Feltham, MIDDLESEX, TW13 6SA **England**
Mr M J Rawcliffe (Proprietor)
(T) 0208-893 8000.

THAMES ANGLING, 11 Feltham Road, Ashford, MIDDLESEX, TW15 1DQ **England**
Mr M Giordano (Proprietor)
(T) 01784 243185.

WOODYS OF WEMBLEY, 565 High Road, Wembley, MIDDLESEX, HA0 2DW **England**
Mr J F Drewett (Proprietor)
(T) 0208-902 7217.

MIDLANDS (WEST)

A T CLISSET, 666 Alum Rock Road, Birmingham, MIDLANDS (WEST), B8 3NU **England**
Mr K Clissett (Proprietor)
(T) 01213 273113.

ALDRIDGE ANGLING CENTRE, 41 High Street, Aldridge, Walsall, MIDLANDS (WEST), WS9 8LX **England**
Mr D R Nicholls (Proprietor)
(T) 01922 455311.

ALLENS FISHING TACKLE, 651 Bloxwich Road, Walsall, MIDLANDS (WEST), WS3 2BQ **England**
Mr J J Allen (Director)
(T) 01922 407398.

AUSTIN CLISSETT, 1805 Pershore Road, Kings Norton, Birmingham, MIDLANDS (WEST), B30 3DN **England**
Mr A Clissett (Proprietor)
(T) 0121-459 4639.

BIRMINGHAM ANGLING CENTRE, Beech Road, Erdington, Birmingham, MIDLANDS (WEST), B23 5QN **England**
Mr E Oaks (Manager)
(T) 0121-373 6627.

BLACK COUNTRY TACKLE & BAIT SHOP, Shop 2, 51 High Street, Brockmoor, Brierley Hill, MIDLANDS (WEST), DY5 3HY **England**
Mr Mark Wardley (Proprietor)
(T) 01384 571519.

BOB TROMAN, 135 Toll End Road, Tipton, MIDLANDS (WEST), DY4 0ET **England**
Mr Bob Troman (Proprietor)
(T) 0121-556 0875.

BRITTONS OF WEDNESFIELD, 85 Lichfield Road, Wolverhampton, MIDLANDS (WEST), WV11 3HP **England**
Mr P Britton (Proprietor)
(T) 01902 722231.

CASTERS FISHING TACKLE, 109 Proffitt Avenue, Coventry, MIDLANDS (WEST), CV6 7ES **England**
Mr R Allen (Proprietor)
(T) 02476 662093.

CATMASTER TACKLE, 37 Marsh End, Birmingham, MIDLANDS (WEST), B38 9BB **England**
Mr C Bunn (Proprietor)
(T) 0121-451 1861.

CLIVE SMITH, 212 New Road, Rednal, Birmingham, MIDLANDS (WEST), B45 9JA **England**
Mr R D Haynes (Proprietor)
(T) 0121-453 5434.

CLUB 2000 FISHING TACKLE, 86 Wynall Lane, Stourbridge, MIDLANDS (WEST), DY9 9AQ **England**
Mr D Dhadwall (Proprietor)
(T) 01384 892892.

COLINS SPORT & TACKLE, 145 Salop Road, Oldbury, MIDLANDS (WEST), B68 9PT **England**
Mr Colin Brain (Proprietor)
(T) 0121-434 5884.

DINSMORES LTD, Westgate, Aldridge, Walsall, MIDLANDS (WEST), WS9 8BS **England**
Mr N May (Managing Director)
(T) 01922 456421.

DINSMORES LTD, Westgate, Aldridge, Walsall, MIDLANDS (WEST), WS9 8EX **England**
Mr N May (Managing Director)
(T) 01922 456421.

ELECTRACATCH INTERNATIONAL, 24-26 Buckley Road, Wolverhampton, MIDLANDS (WEST), WV4 4LJ **England**
(T) 01902 340625.

F C SERVICES RETAIL, 159 Heath Lane, West Bromwich, MIDLANDS (WEST), B71 2BL **England**
(T) 0121-567 5100.

FISHERMAN OF ENGLAND, 154b High Street, Bloxwich, Walsall, MIDLANDS (WEST), WS3 3JT **England**
Mrs P Cummins (Proprietor)
(T) 01922 492222.

FISHERMANS FRIEND, 31 Abbey Road, Smethwick, MIDLANDS (WEST), B67 5RA **England**
Mr A Troth (Proprietor)
(T) 0121-429 4866.

FISHERMANS KNOCKOUT, 1118 Stratford Road, Hall Green, Birmingham, MIDLANDS (WEST), B28 8AE **England**
Mr K D Mclearner (Proprietor)
(T) 0121-777 0307.

FISHING LODGE, 1770 Coventry Road, Yardley, Birmingham, MIDLANDS (WEST), B26 1PB **England**
Mrs J Robinson (Proprietor)
(T) 0121-743 0448.

FISHING LODGE, 72 East Meadway, Birmingham, MIDLANDS (WEST), B33 0AP **England**
Mr M Robinson (Proprietor)
(T) 0121-783 6177.

FLETCHER'S TACKLE, 5 Silvercourt, Walsall, MIDLANDS (WEST), WS8 6HA **England**
(T) 01543 372395.

FOSTERS OF BIRMINGHAM, 214-216 Kingstanding Road, Birmingham, MIDLANDS (WEST), B44 8JP **England**
Mr Mark Foster (Proprietor)
(T) 0121-344 3333.

FOX HOLLIES EXCHANGE, 292 Fox Hollies Road, Acocks Green, Birmingham, MIDLANDS (WEST), B27 7PT **England**
Mr B Roberts (Proprietor)
(T) 0121-764 6263.

G BEDDOW, 49 Planks Lane, Wombourne, Wolverhampton, MIDLANDS (WEST), WV5 8DX **England**
Mr Gordon Beddow (Proprietor)
(T) 01902 896432.

GORDON GRIFFITHS LTD, 1 Lifford Way, Binley Industrial Estate, Coventry, MIDLANDS (WEST), CV3 2RN **England**
Mr P Griffiths (Director)
(T) 02476 440859.

GRAYLINGS FISHING TACKLE, Oaktree Lane, Selly Oak, Birmingham, MIDLANDS (WEST), B29 6JF **England**
Mr Gary Cardhall (Proprietor)
(T) 0121-414 0580.

GREEN LANE HARDWARE & DIY, 371 Green Lane, Coventry, MIDLANDS (WEST), CV3 6EJ **England**
(T) 02476414875.

GREENWAY'S FISHING TACKLE, 1004 Chester Road, Erdington, Birmingham, MIDLANDS (WEST), B24 0LL **England**
Mr S D Greenway (Partner)
(T) 0121-373 0057.

GWEN'S, 123 High Street, Princes End, Tipton, MIDLANDS (WEST), DY4 9JE **England**
Mrs G Cook (Partner)
(T) 0121-557 3954.

HINGLEY'S ALL SPORT & HOBBIES, 164 Lower High Street, Stourbridge, MIDLANDS (WEST), DY8 1TT **England**
Mr E Hingley (Partner)
(T) 01384 395438.

J CHAPLAIN, 884 Alum Rock Road, Birmingham, MIDLANDS (WEST), B8 2TY **England**
Mr Colin Chaplain (Proprietor)
(T) 0121-327 4193.

JOHN'S FISHING TACKLE, 806 Alcester Road South, Birmingham, MIDLANDS (WEST), B14 5HH **England**
Mr J Sidebottom (Partner)
(T) 0121-430 5177.

KEN AUSTIN & SON, 2 Alfred Street, West Bromwich, MIDLANDS (WEST), B70 7PU **England**
Mr A Austin (Proprietor)
(T) 0121-553 0392.

MALCOLM STOREY, 236 Hagley Road, Halesowen, MIDLANDS (WEST), B63 4QQ **England**
Mr S Percival (Manager)
(T) 0121-550 1830.

MIDLEISURE ANGLING CENTRE, 20 Broadway, Bushbury, Wolverhampton, MIDLANDS (WEST), WV10 8EB **England**
Mr W Hartless (Partner)
(T) 01902 783491.

NEW DAWN ROD CO, 153 Station Street East, Coventry, MIDLANDS (WEST), CV6 5FR **England**
Mr M Rooker (Proprietor)
(T) 02476 689487.

NIGEL WILLIAMS, 210 Newhampton Road West, Wolverhampton, MIDLANDS (WEST), WV6 0RW **England**
Mr N Williams (Proprietor)
(T) 01902 744824.

PEREIRA AQUATICS, 552-554 Walsall Road, Great Barr, Birmingham, MIDLANDS (WEST), B42 1LR **England**
Mr G Pereira (Proprietor)
(T) 0121-358 6238.

PHOENIX ANGLING SUPPLIES, 213 Streetly Road, Birmingham, MIDLANDS (WEST), B23 7AH **England**
Mr Trevor Lapsley (Proprietor)
(T) 0121-382 3748.

RICK'S ANGLING CENTRE, 958 Bristol Road South, Northfield, Birmingham, MIDLANDS (WEST), B31 2PE **England**
Mr R Haynes (Proprietor)
(T) 0121-475 2859.

ROGER WARD, 1a Summer Road, Acocks Green, Birmingham, MIDLANDS (WEST), B27 7UT **England**
(T) 0121-706 6387.

SIMMONDS & PRIDDEY, 9 Stratford Road, Shirley, Solihull, MIDLANDS (WEST), B90 3LU **England**
Mr B Simmonds (Proprietor)
(T) 0121-744 1376.

SPORT 'N' TACKLE, 53 High Street, Bilston, MIDLANDS (WEST), WV14 0EP **England**
Mr R Wootton (Proprietor)
(T) 01902 496200.

STAY ON FISHING, 242 Station Road, Balsall Common, Coventry, MIDLANDS (WEST), CV7 7EE **England**
Mr A Macklevoy (Director)
(T) 01676 534738.

STEVENS, 5 St. Annes Road, Cradley Heath, MIDLANDS (WEST), B64 5BP **England**
Mr Andrew Stevens (Proprietor)
(T) 01384 567778.

STRETTONS, 110 Brettell Lane, Stourbridge, MIDLANDS (WEST), DY8 4BS **England**
(T) 01384 392741.

STRIKE ANGLING, Oldbury Road, Rowley Regis, MIDLANDS (WEST), B65 0QJ **England**
Mr Mark Thompson (Proprietor)
(T) 0121-561 3200.

SURECATCH ANGLING, 242 Jeffcock Road, Wolverhampton, MIDLANDS (WEST), WV3 7AH **England**
Mr M Brooks (Proprietor)
(T) 01902 335545.

TERRY EUSTACE, 378 Boldmere Road, Sutton Coldfield, MIDLANDS (WEST), B73 5EZ **England**
Mr Terry Eustace (Proprietor)
(T) 0121-377 7533.

TEX LEVER BAIT SUPPLIES, 179 Darlaston Road, Walsall, MIDLANDS (WEST), WS2 9SD **England**
Mr M Lever (Proprietor)
(T) 01922 638333.

TEX LEVER BAIT SUPPLIES, Willenhall Road, Wednesbury, MIDLANDS (WEST), WS10 8JG **England**
Mr Martin Lever (Proprietor)
(T) 01215 687975.

THOROUGHBRED CO LTD, 370 Shirley Road, Acocks Green, Birmingham, MIDLANDS (WEST), B27 7NS **England**
M. Ernest Ronald Roy Jarvis (Sole Director)
(T) 0121-706 4509.

TIM'S TACKLE, 46 Wolverhampton Street, Dudley, MIDLANDS (WEST), DY1 3AE **England**
Mr T Benton (Proprietor)
(T) 01384 234780.

TINCA OUTDOOR LTD, The Technocentre/Coventry University Technology Pk, Puma Way, Coventry, MIDLANDS (WEST), CV1 2TT **England**
Mr D Wick (Managing Director)
(T) 02476 236061.

TREVOR TONKINSON, 50 High Street, Rowley Regis, MIDLANDS (WEST), B65 0EH **England**
Mr T Tonkinson (Proprietor)
(T) 0121-559 2426.

TUSSES FISHING TACKLE, 360 Aldermans Green Road, Coventry, MIDLANDS (WEST), CV2 1NN **England**
(T) 02476 365635.

VAL'S PET FOODS, 100 Childs Avenue, Bilston, MIDLANDS (WEST), WV14 9XB **England**
Mrs V J Evans (Proprietor)
(T) 01902 677006.

W H LANE & SON, 31-35 London Road, Coventry, MIDLANDS (WEST), CV1 2JP **England**
Mr H Humphrey (Manager)
(T) 02476 223316.

WEDNESBURY ANGLING CENTRE, 44 Union Street, Wednesbury, MIDLANDS (WEST), WS10 7HB **England**
(T) 0121-505 6119.

WEST MIDLANDS ANGLING CENTRE, Unit 8 Darlaston Central Trading Estate, Wednesbury, MIDLANDS (WEST), WS10 8XB **England**
Mr G Woods (Manager)
(T) 0121-526 3696.

Z L T ANGLING PRODUCTS LTD, Star Street, Stourbridge, MIDLANDS (WEST), DY9 8TU **England**
Mr G Billingham (Director)
(T) 01384 895141.

NEWPORT

A P SCOTT & SONS, 11 Lugley Street, Newport, NEWPORT, PO30 5HD **England**
Mr W J Copeland (Proprietor)
(T) 01983 522115.

NORFOLK

ABOUT TURN WORMS, Waterlow Road, Terrington St. Clement, King's Lynn, NORFOLK, PE34 4PT **England**
Mrs J Turner (Proprietor)
(T) 01553 827337.

ADIE MARTELL, 7 Earlham West Centre, Norwich, NORFOLK, NR5 8AD **England**
Mr A Martell (Proprietor)
(T) 01603 441543.

ANGLERS 'ARMOURY', 15 Mundesley Road, North Walsham, NORFOLK, NR28 0DA **England**
Mr Simon Farrow (Partner)
(T) 01692 403369.

ANGLERS CORNER, 55 London Road, King's Lynn, NORFOLK, PE30 5QH **England**
Mr Martin Allen (Proprietor)
(T) 01553 775852.

ANGLING DIRECT, Unit 12B Folgate Road, North Walsham, NORFOLK, NR28 0AJ **England**
Mr J Hall (Manager)
(T) 0800-085 8169.

AVENUE ANGLING, 16 Denbigh Road, Norwich, NORFOLK, NR2 3AA **England**
Mr J Lambert (Proprietor)
(T) 01603 764004.

BRIGHT OUTDOOR MAN, 8 Wyndham Street, Sheringham, NORFOLK, NR26 8BA **England**
Mrs S Bright (Partner)
(T) 01263 825858.

BRUNDALL ANGLING CENTRE, Riverside Stores, Brundall, Norwich, NORFOLK, NR13 5PY **England**
(T) 01603 715289.

COUNTRY PURSUITS, 49 Market Place, North Walsham, NORFOLK, NR28 9BT **England**
Mr J Hall (Proprietor)
(T) 01692 403162.

COUNTRY PURSUITS 2, 12B Folgate Road, North Walsham, NORFOLK, NR28 0AJ **England**
Mr J Hall (Manager)
(T) 01692 500523.

DAVE DOCWRA, 79 Churchill Road, Great Yarmouth, NORFOLK, NR30 4NQ **England**
Mr D Docwra (Proprietor)
(T) 01493 850900.

DAVE'S FISHING TACKLE & PET SUPPLIES, 8 Millers Walk, Fakenham, NORFOLK, NR21 9AP **England**
Mr D Playford (Proprietor)
(T) 01328 862543.

DE NOVO LURES LTD, Denovo, Low Road, Thurlton, Norwich, NORFOLK, NR14 6RL **England**
Mr L Dinter (Managing Director)
(T) 01508 548155.

DUNHAM CARP & TENCH LAKES, Lakeside, Great Dunham, King's Lynn, NORFOLK, PE32 2LQ **England**
(T) 01760 725286.

DYBLE & WILLIAMSON, Crown Cottage, Scratby Road, Scratby, Great Yarmouth, NORFOLK, NR29 3PQ **England**
Mr R Williamson (Proprietor)
(T) 01493 731305.

EXPRESS OIL BURNER SERVICES, 6 Orange Row, Terrington St. Clement, King's Lynn, NORFOLK, PE34 4NN **England**
Mr L Marshall (Proprietor)
(T) 01553 828834.

FISHING & CAMPING HIRE, 2 Halford Road, Attleborough, NORFOLK, NR17 2HZ **England**
(T) 01953 455566.

GORLESTON TACKLE CENTRE LTD, 7 & 8 Pier Walk, Gorleston, Great Yarmouth, NORFOLK, NR31 6DA **England**
Mr D Amies (Proprietor)
(T) 01493 662448.

GREENSTED TACKLE CENTRE, 73 High Street, Gorleston, Great Yarmouth, NORFOLK, NR31 6RQ **England**
(T) 01493 602474.

HEACHAM TACKLE, 31 Kenwood Road, Heacham, King's Lynn, NORFOLK, PE31 7DD **England**
(T) 01485 570333.

HORNING FISHING TACKLE & CHANDLEY SHOP, Ferry Corner, Ferry Road, Horning, Norwich, NORFOLK, NR12 8PS **England**
Mrs A Bucanhon (Manager)
(T) 01692 631401.

J M P TACKLE, Unit 26 Haverscroft Industrial Estate, New Road, Attleborough, NORFOLK, NR17 1YE **England**
(T) 01953 455282.

J R C PRODUCTS LTD, Unit 4/Redgrave Business Centre, Gallows Hill, Redgrave, Diss, NORFOLK, IP22 1RZ **England**
Mrs L Powell (Manager)
(T) 01379 890930.

JOHN'S TACKLE DEN, 16 Bridewell Alley, Norwich, NORFOLK, NR2 1AQ **England**
Mr M Page (Managing Director)
(T) 01603 614114.

J'S TACKLE, 102 Canons Walk, Thetford, NORFOLK, IP24 3PT **England**
Mr J Laurie (Proprietor)
(T) 01842 765159.

KEV'S TACKLE, 2 Mangate Street, Swaffham, NORFOLK, PE37 7QN **England**
Mr Kevin Pitt (Proprietor)
(T) 01760 720188.

KINGFISHER GIFT SHOP, Coast Road, Walcott, Norwich, NORFOLK, NR12 0AP **England**
Mrs J Warby (Proprietor)
(T) 01692 652977.

MARINE SPORTS, 21 New Street, Cromer, NORFOLK, NR27 9HP **England**
Mr Martin Steward (Manager)
(T) 01263 513676.

MARVIC ANGLING, 476 Sprowston Road, Norwich, NORFOLK, NR3 4DY **England**
Mr D Bailey (Manager)
(T) 01603 406927.

POWNALL & SONS LTD, 74-75 Regent Road, Great Yarmouth, NORFOLK, NR30 2AJ **England**
Mr S Pownall (Proprietor)
(T) 01493 851120.

RIVERSIDE ANGLING, 12 Bishop Bridge Road, Norwich, NORFOLK, NR1 4ET **England**
Mr T Barratt (Proprietor)
(T) 01603 633317.

STOWERS, 30 Greevegate, Hunstanton, NORFOLK, PE36 6AA **England**
Mr G Stowers (Proprietor)
(T) 01485 535141.

TACKLE & TIDE, 50 King Street, Great Yarmouth, NORFOLK, NR30 2PW **England**
Mr D Adams (Partner)
(T) 01493 852221.

TACKLE BOX, 38 Tower Street, King's Lynn, NORFOLK, PE30 1EJ **England**
Mr G Baker (Proprietor)
(T) 01553 761293.

TOM BOULTON, 6 St Johns Close, Norwich, NORFOLK, NR1 2AD **England**
Mr Tom Boulton (Proprietor)
(T) 01603 626770.

WAVENEY ANGLING, 5 London Road, Harleston, NORFOLK, IP20 9BH **England**
Mr Trevor Harrowven (Proprietor)
(T) 01379 854886.

WRIGHT TACKLE, The Dixon Centre, 159 Reepham Road, Norwich, NORFOLK, NR6 5PH **England**
Mr Peter Wright (Proprietor)
(T) 01603 416680.

WROXHAM ANGLING & GIFT CENTRE, Station Road, Hoveton, Norwich, NORFOLK, NR12 8UR **England**
Mr Martin Allen (General Manager)
(T) 01603 782453.

NORTHAMPTONSHIRE

ALLANS ANGLING MART, 86 Rockingham Road, Corby, NORTHAMPTONSHIRE, NN17 1AE **England**
Mr Allan Marriott (Proprietor)
(T) 01536 202900.

ANGLING CENTRE, 85 St Leonards Road, Northampton, NORTHAMPTONSHIRE, NN4 8DN **England**
(T) 01604 764847.

AQUAFLOW FISHING LUGGAGE, 13a Victoria Road, Wellingborough, NORTHAMPTONSHIRE, NN8 1HN **England**
Mrs Donna Minett (Partner)
(T) 01933 270463.

BAIT & BITS, 26 Church Street, Rushden, NORTHAMPTONSHIRE, NN10 9YT **England**
Mr B Whiteman (Partner)
(T) 01933 353007.

BILLING AQUADROME TACKLE, Billing Aquadrome, Crow Lane, Little Billing, Northampton, NORTHAMPTONSHIRE, NN3 9DA **England**
Mr S Booth (Proprietor)
(T) 01604 414428.

BOB CHURCH & CO LTD, 16 Lorne Road, Northampton, NORTHAMPTONSHIRE, NN1 3RN **England**
Mr B Church (Managing Director)
(T) 01604 627052.

CORBY TACKLE CENTRE, 196 Studfall Avenue, Corby, NORTHAMPTONSHIRE, NN17 1LJ **England**
Mr Mark Goodsir (Proprietor)
(T) 01536 203035.

FISHY BUSINESS BIKE & HIKE, 12 Station Close Retail Park, Daventry, NORTHAMPTONSHIRE, NN11 5AG **England**
Mr Michael Stevens (Proprietor)
(T) 01327 872175.

GILDERS (NORTHAMPTON) LTD, 32 Montagu Street, Kettering, NORTHAMPTONSHIRE, NN16 8RU **England**
Mr T J Davies (Director)
(T) 01536 514509.

GILDERS (NORTHAMPTON) LTD, 250 Wellingborough Road, Northampton, NORTHAMPTONSHIRE, NN1 4EJ **England**
Mr J Davis (Director)
(T) 01604 636723.

J C ANGLING WHOLESALE, The Warehouse, Albert Road, Rushden, NORTHAMPTONSHIRE, NN10 0BU **England**
(T) 01933 413499.

M J B PRODUCTS, 55 Northumberland Road, Kettering, NORTHAMPTONSHIRE, NN15 6LN **England**
(T) 01536 417254.

R & G (CATS & DOGS) ANGLING BAITS MANUFACTURERS, 1 Grant Road, Wellingborough, NORTHAMPTONSHIRE, NN8 1ES **England**
Mr Colin Revell (Partner)
(T) 01933 443646.

RON'S TACKLE, Osprey, 5 Church Way, Wellingborough, NORTHAMPTONSHIRE, NN8 4HJ **England**
(T) 01933 226913.

SENSAS, 38 Fairway, Northampton, NORTHAMPTONSHIRE, NN2 7JZ **England**
Mr Joseph Roberts (Proprietor)
(T) 01604 712897.

SPORTSMANS LODGE, 44 Kingsthorpe Road, Northampton, NORTHAMPTONSHIRE, NN2 6EZ **England**
(T) 01604 713399.

TRINDERS TACKLE, 221 Birchfield Road East, Northampton, NORTHAMPTONSHIRE, NN3 2BZ **England**
Mr R Stafford (Proprietor)
(T) 01604 714899.

TRINDERS TACKLE, Weedon Road, Nether Heyford, Northampton, NORTHAMPTONSHIRE, NN7 3LG **England**
Mr K Solverlock (Proprietor)
(T) 01327 340002.

NORTHUMBERLAND

AMBLE ANGLING CENTRE, 4 Newburgh Street, Amble, Morpeth, NORTHUMBERLAND, NE65 0AQ **England**
Mr Robert White (Proprietor)
(T) 01665 711200.

ARKLES ANGLING, 3 Ravensworth Ter, Bedlington, NORTHUMBERLAND, NE22 7JW **England**
Mr P Arkle (Proprietor)
(T) 01670 828887.

C D FISHING TACKLE, 94B Front Street, Newbiggin-by-the-Sea, NORTHUMBERLAND, NE64 6AW **England**
Mr C Douglas (Proprietor)
(T) 01670 520133.

GREYS OF ALNWICK, Unit 2b Greensfield Estate, Willowburn Avenu, Alnwick, NORTHUMBERLAND, NE66 2DD **England**
(T) 01665 510020.

HOUSE OF HARDY LTD, Willowburn Trading Estate, Alnwick, NORTHUMBERLAND, NE66 2PF **England**
Mr R Maudflay (Managing Director)
(T) 01665 510027.

M R TACKLE, 14 Market Street, Hexham, NORTHUMBERLAND, NE46 3NU **England**
(T) 01434 606988.

MCDERMOTT'S, 112 Station Road, Ashington, NORTHUMBERLAND, NE63 8HE **England**
Mr John Laidler (Proprietor)
(T) 01670 812214.

NORMAN SPORTS INTERNATIONAL, Unit 6 I/Greensfield Court, Greensfield Industrial Estate, Alnwick, NORTHUMBERLAND, NE66 2DE **England**
Mr David Norman (Proprietor)
(T) 01665 830698.

SEABAIT LTD, Ashington, NORTHUMBERLAND, NE63 9FB **England**
Mr Peter Cowin (Managing Director)
(T) 01670 814102.

NOTTINGHAMSHIRE

ANDY'S RODS & REELS, 1 Broxtowe Avenue, Nottingham, NOTTINGHAMSHIRE, NG8 5EL **England**
(T) 0115-978 0941.

ANGLING SUPPLIES, 49 Retford Road, Worksop, NOTTINGHAMSHIRE, S80 2PU **England**
Mr D Brooks (Proprietor)
(T) 01909 482974.

BRIDGE TACKLE SHOP, 30 Derby Road, Long Eaton, Nottingham, NOTTINGHAMSHIRE, NG10 1PD **England**
(T) 0115-972 8338.

BRITISH BREADCRUMB PROCESSING CO, Wolds Farm, The Fosse, Cotgrave, Nottingham, NOTTINGHAMSHIRE, NG12 3HG **England**
Mr M Twidale (Partner)
(T) 0115-989 9060.

CARRILON UK, Maple House, North Road, Torworth, Retford, NOTTINGHAMSHIRE, DN22 8NW **England**
Mr R S Clarke (Partner)
(T) 01777 816333.

CLUMBER PETS, 1 Clumber Street, Warsop, Mansfield, NOTTINGHAMSHIRE, NG20 0LR **England**
Mr E Hill (Proprietor)
(T) 01623 842652.

COOPER PRODUCTS, 42 Main Road, Ravenshead, Nottingham, NOTTINGHAMSHIRE, NG15 9GT **England**
Mr M Cooper (Proprietor)
(T) 01623 792659.

DUKERIES FIELD SPORTS, Flat, 37 Appleton Gate, Newark, NOTTINGHAMSHIRE, NG24 1JR **England**
Mr Kenneth Jenkins (Proprietor)
(T) 01636 612630.

EAST MIDLANDS ANGLING, 213 Station Road, Shirebrook, Mansfield, NOTTINGHAMSHIRE, NG20 8AF **England**
Mr I Plant (Proprietor)
(T) 01623 744724.

ELITE ANGLING, 69 Ratcliffe Gate, Mansfield, NOTTINGHAMSHIRE, NG18 2JB **England**
Mr John Baldwin (Partner)
(T) 01623 624545.

EUROBAIT CO LTD, Private Rd 4, Colwick Industrial Estate, Nottingham, NOTTINGHAMSHIRE, NG4 2JT **England**
Mr A Phelps (Manager)
(T) 0115-987 9650.

EUROBAIT LTD, 111 Potter Street, Worksop, NOTTINGHAMSHIRE, S80 2HL **England**
Mr M Hammond (Managing Director)
(T) 01909 479688.

EXCHANGE ANGLING, 287-289 Ilkeston Road, Nottingham, NOTTINGHAMSHIRE, NG7 3FY **England**
Mr John Dowse (Proprietor)
(T) 0115-942 4941.

FOREST TOWN ANGLING, 50 Mansfield Road, Clipstone Village, Mansfield, NOTTINGHAMSHIRE, NG21 9EQ **England**
Mr G Beech (Proprietor)
(T) 01623 627422.

G D B TACKLE, 100 Bunbury Street, Nottingham, NOTTINGHAMSHIRE, NG2 2LE **England**
Mr D Pike (Proprietor)
(T) 0115-956 0096.

GATEFORD ANGLING SUPPLIES, 155 Gateford Road, Worksop, NOTTINGHAMSHIRE, S80 1UD **England**
Mr G Mawby (Proprietor)
(T) 01909 531115.

GEORDIE MAGGOT, 3 Station Street, Mansfield Woodhouse, Mansfield, NOTTINGHAMSHIRE, NG19 8AE **England**
Mr R Atherton (Proprietor)
(T) 01623 628056.

GERRY'S MAVER POLE CENTRE, Unit 14, Little Tennis Street, Nottingham, NOTTINGHAMSHIRE, NG2 4EL **England**
Mr J Hankins (Manager)
(T) 0115-841 5657.

GERRY'S OF NOTTINGHAM, 96-100 Radford Boulevard, Nottingham, NOTTINGHAMSHIRE, NG7 3BN **England**
Mr S Woodcliffe (Manager)
(T) 0115-978 1695.

GO-BAITES, Doncaster Road, Langold, Worksop, NOTTINGHAMSHIRE, S81 9RJ **England**
Mr J Goulding (Proprietor)
(T) 01909 540105.

GREAVES TACKLE, Annesley Road, Hucknall, Nottingham, NOTTINGHAMSHIRE, NG15 7DB **England**
(T) 0115-963 2079.

J & S TACKLE, 59 West Street, Arnold, Nottingham, NOTTINGHAMSHIRE, NG5 7DB **England**
Mr J Brooks (Proprietor)
(T) 0115-926 2644.

JUNCTION TACKLE, 210 Tamworth Road, Long Eaton, Nottingham, NOTTINGHAMSHIRE, NG10 3GS **England**
Mr K Fessey (Proprietor)
(T) 0115-973 6326.

KEN WARD (SPORTS SPECIALIST) LTD, 6 Carlton Road, Worksop, NOTTINGHAMSHIRE, S80 1PH **England**
Mr K Ward (Proprietor)
(T) 01909 472904.

KENWYNN PRODUCTS, 269 Carlton Road, Nottingham, NOTTINGHAMSHIRE, NG3 2NT **England**
Mrs I Hyem (Proprietor)
(T) 0115-911 8817.

LONG BENNINGTON BAIT, The Bait Factory, Valley Lane, Long Bennington, Newark, NOTTINGHAMSHIRE, NG23 5EE **England**
Mr D Holmes (Proprietor)
(T) 01400 281525.

M PRIDMORE, 378 Carlton Road, Worksop, NOTTINGHAMSHIRE, S81 7LR **England**
Mr M Pridmore (Proprietor)
(T) 01909 501258.

MANSFIELD ANGLING, 20 Byron Street, Mansfield, NOTTINGHAMSHIRE, NG18 5NX **England**
Mr C E Perry (Partner)
(T) 01623 633790.

MATCHMAN SUPPLIES, 4 Ella Road, West Bridgford, Nottingham, NOTTINGHAMSHIRE, NG2 5GW **England**
Mr T Aplin (Proprietor)
(T) 0115-981 3834.

MATCHMEN, 5 Bannerman Road, Nottingham, NOTTINGHAMSHIRE, NG6 9JA **England**
Mr R W Welch (Proprietor)
(T) 0115-927 8859.

MILL TACKLE, 85 Station Road, Langley Mill, Nottingham, NOTTINGHAMSHIRE, NG16 4DU **England**
Mr Peter Thexton (Proprietor)
(T) 01773 710679.

MONARCH BAITS, 313 Watnall Road, Hucknall, Nottingham, NOTTINGHAMSHIRE, NG15 6EP **England**
Mr Terence Dorman (Proprietor)
(T) 01572 787601.

MR B'S, 2 Mansfield Road, Creswell, Worksop, NOTTINGHAMSHIRE, S80 4AA **England**
Mr G Burton (Proprietor)
(T) 01909 721322.

MR MAGGOT MAN, 32 High Street, Warsop, Mansfield, NOTTINGHAMSHIRE, NG20 0AG **England**
Mr I Rowney (Proprietor)
(T) 01623 842521.

NETHERFIELD TACKLE CENTRE, 75 Victoria Road, Netherfield, Nottingham, NOTTINGHAMSHIRE, NG4 2NN **England**
Mr Brent Moor (Partner)
(T) 0115-987 0525.

NEWARK ANGLING CENTRE, 29 Albert Street, Newark, NOTTINGHAMSHIRE, NG24 4BJ **England**
Mr T Ratford (Proprietor)
(T) 01636 686212.

PEG 1, Unit 4 Manchester House, Church Street East, Pinxton, Nottingham, NOTTINGHAMSHIRE, NG16 6JN **England**
Mr A Payling (Proprietor)
(T) 01773 510324.

PHILS BAIT & TACKLE, 2 Market Place, Sutton-in-Ashfield, NOTTINGHAMSHIRE, NG17 1AQ **England**
Mrs Sharon Taylor (Proprietor)
(T) 01623 554654.

RAY LEACH FISHING TACKLE, 19 Boar Lane, Newark, NOTTINGHAMSHIRE, NG24 1AJ **England**
(T) 01636 674232.

RETFORD ANGLING CENTRE, Northfield Way, Retford, NOTTINGHAMSHIRE, DN22 7LR **England**
Mr I Johnstone (Manager)
(T) 01777 706168.

SECONDHAND TACKLE SUPPLIES, 3 Hazel Street, Nottingham, NOTTINGHAMSHIRE, NG6 8EA **England**
Mr R Surgay (Proprietor)
(T) 0115-927 7297.

SPARTON FISHING TACKLE, Unit 2 Fields Farm Road, Long Eaton, Nottingham, NOTTINGHAMSHIRE, NG10 3FZ **England**
Mr S Parton (Proprietor)
(T) 0115-946 3572.

STAPLEFORD ANGLING, 8 Archer Road, Stapleford, Nottingham, NOTTINGHAMSHIRE, NG9 7EP **England**
Mr C Buckingham (Proprietor)
(T) 0115-949 9889.

SUPERTACKLE, 192 Station Road, Beeston, Nottingham, NOTTINGHAMSHIRE, NG9 2AY **England**
(T) 0115-922 9669.

T C & B J CROWDEN LTD, 16 Friary Road, Newark, NOTTINGHAMSHIRE, NG24 1LE **England**
Mrs B J Crowden (Partner)
(T) 01636 702139.

TOM C SAVILLE LTD, 9 Nottingham Road, Trowell, Nottingham, NOTTINGHAMSHIRE, NG9 3PA **England**
Mr Mike Batchelor (Manager)
(T) 0115-930 8800.

USED TACKLE, 28 Baker Street, Hucknall, Nottingham, NOTTINGHAMSHIRE, NG15 7AS **England**
Mr Roger Surgay (Proprietor)
(T) 0115-963 1683.

WALKERS OF TROWELL, 9-15 Nottingham Road, Trowell, Nottingham, NOTTINGHAMSHIRE, NG9 3PA **England**
Mr D Bardens (Proprietor)
(T) 0115-930 1816.

WORLD WIDE WORMS, Mansfield Road, Clipstone Village, Mansfield, NOTTINGHAMSHIRE, NG21 9EQ **England**
(T) 01623 481426.

WORLDWIDE SUPPLIES, Hallcroft Road, Retford, NOTTINGHAMSHIRE, DN22 7RA **England**
Mr B Talbort (Proprietor)
(T) 01777 704569.

OXFORDSHIRE

BOSS DEVELOPMENTS, Unit 25-26 Monument Industrial Park, Warpsgrove Lane, Chalgrove, Oxford, OXFORDSHIRE, OX44 7RW **England**
Mr B Watts (Proprietor)
(T) 01865 891695.

CASTAWAY, 86 Warwick Road, Banbury, OXFORDSHIRE, OX16 2AJ **England**
Mr D R Eve (Proprietor)
(T) 01295 254274.

CORNBURY PARK TROUT FISHERY, Southill Lodge, Cornbury Park, Charlbury, Chipping Norton, OXFORDSHIRE, OX7 3EW **England**
Mr B D Morris (Manager)
(T) 01608 811509.

DIDCOT ANGLING CENTRE, 36 Wantage Road, Didcot, OXFORDSHIRE, OX11 0BT **England**
Mr C Turner (Proprietor)
(T) 01235 817005.

DRENNAN INTERNATIONAL LTD, 55 Randolph Street, Oxford, OXFORDSHIRE, OX4 1YA **England**
(T) 01865 790445.

DRENNAN INTERNATIONAL LTD, Bacardo Court, Temple Road, Oxford, OXFORDSHIRE, OX4 2EX **England**
Mr P Dreenan (Managing Director)
(T) 01865 748989.

FAT PHIL'S ANGLING CENTRE, 334-336 Abingdon Road, Oxford, OXFORDSHIRE, OX1 4TQ **England**
Mr P Cross (Proprietor)
(T) 01865 201020.

J & K TACKLE, 62-64 Sheep Street, Bicester, OXFORDSHIRE, OX26 6LG **England**
Mr Mark Taylor (Partner)
(T) 01869 242589.

J & K TACKLE, 8-10 Wesley Lane, Bicester, OXFORDSHIRE, OX6 7JU **England**
Mr Mark Taylor (Partner)
(T) 01869 242589.

K & M, 23 West Street, Chipping Norton, OXFORDSHIRE, OX7 5EU **England**
Mr Ken Watts (Partner)
(T) 01608 645435.

M & M WORMS, 2 Church Lane, Middle Barton, Chipping Norton, OXFORDSHIRE, OX7 7BX **England**
(T) 01608 683372.

NEW BANBURY ANGLING CENTRE, 12b South Street, Banbury, OXFORDSHIRE, OX16 3LB **England**
Mr J Garrett (Proprietor)
(T) 01295 272876.

NORTH OXFORD TACKLE, 95 Islip Road, Oxford, OXFORDSHIRE, OX2 7SP **England**
Mr S R Johnson (Proprietor)
(T) 01865 556955.

OXFORD ANGLING CENTRE, 136 Oxford Road, Cowley, Oxford, OXFORDSHIRE, OX4 2DU **England**
Mr P M Hunt (Proprietor)
(T) 01865 711410.

PREDITOR ANGLING, 6a Kidlington Centre, High Street, Kidlington, OXFORDSHIRE, OX5 2DL **England**
Mr M Filiimore (Manager)
(T) 01865 372066.

RIGHT ANGLE, Wootton Road, Abingdon, OXFORDSHIRE, OX13 6BH **England**
Mr Andrew Lawson (Proprietor)
(T) 01235 524144.

STATE FISHING TACKLE, 19 Fettiplace Road, Witney, OXFORDSHIRE, OX8 5AP **England**
Mr G State (Proprietor)
(T) 01993 702587.

TURNER'S TACKLE & BAIT, 4a Station Road, Faringdon, OXFORDSHIRE, SN7 7BN **England**
(T) 01367 241044.

WESTLAKE FLY FISHING, 78 Grove Street, Wantage, OXFORDSHIRE, OX12 7BG **England**
Mr I Hockley (Proprietor)
(T) 01235 227228.

WYCHWOOD TACKLE, The Old Brewery, Priory Lane, Burford, OXFORDSHIRE, OX18 4SG **England**
Mr Bruce Vaughan (Director)
(T) 01993 822822.

POWYS

M K SPORTS, 2 Boot Street, Welshpool, POWYS, SY21 7SA **England**
Mr M Evans (Proprietor)
(T) 01938 552202.

RUTLAND

REAL IDEAS, Glebe House, Market Overton, Oakham, RUTLAND, LE15 7PL **England**
Mr Nick Palmer (Proprietor)
(T) 01572 768082.

SHROPSHIRE

BAIT SPRAY LTD, Unit 18 Hardwicke Industrial Estate, Hardwicke Stables, Hadnall, Shrewsbury, SHROPSHIRE, SY4 4AS **England**
Mrs V Brown (Director)
(T) 01939 210782.

BAIT-SPRAY LTD, Unit 64, Atcham Industrial Estate, Upton Magna, Shrewsbury, SHROPSHIRE, SY4 4UG **England**
Mr N Brown (Managing Director)
(T) 01743 761544.

BRIDGE NORTH TACKLE, 58 Mill Street, Bridgnorth, SHROPSHIRE, WV15 5AG **England**
(T) 01746 767286.

FINBECK AGENCIES LTD, The Hollies, Chester Road, Whitchurch, SHROPSHIRE, SY13 1LZ **England**
Mrs K Griffiths (Director)
(T) 01948 665400.

HOCKLEY POT CO, Perrydene, Brownhill, Ruyton XI Towns, Shrewsbury, SHROPSHIRE, SY4 1LR **England**
Mr W E Evans (Proprietor)
(T) 01939 260357.

KINGFISHER ANGLING CENTRE, 9 New Street, Shrewsbury, SHROPSHIRE, SY3 8JN **England**
Mr P Richards (Proprietor)
(T) 01743 240602.

LUDLOW TACKLE, Bromfield Road, Ludlow, SHROPSHIRE, SY8 1DW **England**
Mr N Price (Manager)
(T) 01584 875886.

MALSTOREY ANGLING CENTRE, 5 Underhill Street, Bridgnorth, SHROPSHIRE, WV16 4BB **England**
(T) 01746 762832.

MARCHES ANGLING SUPPLIES, Red Lion Garage, Horse Market, Oswestry, SHROPSHIRE, SY11 1JS **England**
Mr T Scott (Proprietor)
(T) 01691 661111.

MENWAL DESIGNS LTD, The Kiln, Noble Street, Wem, Shrewsbury, SHROPSHIRE, SY4 5DZ **England**
Mr M K Shuker (Managing Director)
(T) 01939 232148.

NEWPORT TACKLE, 91a High Street, Newport, SHROPSHIRE, TF10 7AY **England**
Mrs J Ashcroft (Partner)
(T) 01952 820334.

PHOENIX TACKLE, Unit 1 198 Whitchurch Road, Shrewsbury, SHROPSHIRE, SY1 4EY **England**
Mr Mick Argue (Proprietor)
(T) 01743 446759.

PRESTON INNOVATIONS LTD, Unit E2, Stafford Pk 4, Telford, SHROPSHIRE, TF3 3BA **England**
Mr D Preston (Managing Director)
(T) 01952 290520.

ROD & GUN LTD, 3 High Street, Dawley, Telford, SHROPSHIRE, TF4 2ET **England**
Mr D Biddle (Proprietor)
(T) 01952 503550.

SID KNIGHT, 59a Whitburn Street, Bridgnorth, SHROPSHIRE, WV16 4QP **England**
Mr S Knight (Proprietor)
(T) 01746 765407.

SUNDORNE FISHING TACKLE, 1 Sundorne Avenue, Shrewsbury, SHROPSHIRE, SY1 4JW **England**
Mr Keith Robson (Proprietor)
(T) 01743 361804.

TELFORD ANGLING CENTRE, 15 Church Street, St. Georges, Telford, SHROPSHIRE, TF2 9JU **England**
Mr A Edwards (Proprietor)
(T) 01952 610497.

WARNERS FISHING TACKLE, Deermoss Lane, Whitchurch, SHROPSHIRE, SY13 1AH **England**
Mr K Warner (Proprietor)
(T) 01948 665076.

SOMERSET

ABBEY ANGLING & AQUATIC CENTRE, 54b High Street, Hanham, Bristol, SOMERSET, BS15 3DR **England**
Mr Steve Hicks (Proprietor)
(T) 0117-908 1130.

AVON ANGLING CENTRE, 348 Whitehall Road, Bristol, SOMERSET, BS5 7BP **England**
Mr T Rixon (Manager)
(T) 0117-951 7250.

BACON'S TACKLE BOX, 83 Lower Bristol Road, Bath, SOMERSET, BA2 3BQ **England**
Mr David Bacon (Partner)
(T) 01225 448850.

BRISTOL ANGLING CENTRE, 12-16 Doncaster Road, Bristol, SOMERSET, BS10 5PL **England**
(T) 0117-950 0201.

BRISTOL DISCOUNT FISHING TACKLE, Bell Barn Road, Bristol, SOMERSET, BS9 2DG **England**
Mr Shaun Mellor (Proprietor)
(T) 0117-968 8158.

CHARD ANGLING CENTRE, The Old Bakehouse, 2 Holyrood Street, Chard, SOMERSET, TA20 2AH **England**
Mr L J Braunton (Proprietor)
(T) 01460 63771.

CHRIS'S ANGLING CENTRE, 12 Regent Street, Burnham-on-Sea, SOMERSET, TA8 1AX **England**
Mr Chris Greenslade (Proprietor)
(T) 01278 794442.

ENTERPRISE ANGLING, 137 Taunton Road, Bridgwater, SOMERSET, TA6 6BD **England**
Mr Alex Johnston (Proprietor)
(T) 01278 428159.

ENTERPRISE ANGLING, 1 Grays Road, Taunton, SOMERSET, TA1 3BA **England**
Mr A Johnston (Proprietor)
(T) 01823 282623.

FISH & FIELD, 60 Broad Street, Chipping Sodbury, Bristol, SOMERSET, BS37 6AG **England**
Mr J Salsbury (Proprietor)
(T) 01454 314034.

FISHERMANS CORNER HARBOUR KIOSK, Quay Street, Minehead, SOMERSET, TA24 5UL **England**
Mr Steve Liddle (Proprietor)
(T) 01643 705745.

FISHING TACKLE, South Street, Montacute, SOMERSET, TA15 6XH **England**
Mr L Hann (Proprietor)
(T) 01935 822645.

FREETIME UK LTD, Unit 5C/Carey Development, Tweed Road, Clevedon, SOMERSET, BS21 6RR **England**
Mr N Bracey (Manager)
(T) 01275 343928.

FROME ANGLING CENTRE, 11 Church Street, Frome, SOMERSET, BA11 1PW **England**
Mr Tony Smith (Proprietor)
(T) 01373 467143.

HAINES ANGLING, 10 Christchurch Street West, Frome, SOMERSET, BA11 1EQ **England**
Mr C Haines (Proprietor)
(T) 01373 466406.

HAINES ANGLING, 47 Vallis Way, Frome, SOMERSET, BA11 3BA **England**
Mr C Haines (Proprietor)
(T) 01373 466406.

KNIGHTSTONE ANGLING CENTRE, Elton Road, Clevedon, SOMERSET, BS21 7RH **England**
Mr A Carpenter (Proprietor)
(T) 01275 878783.

KNIGHTSTONE ANGLING CENTRE, 8 Upper Church Road, Weston-super-Mare, SOMERSET, BS23 2DT **England**
Mr A Martin (Proprietor)
(T) 01934 419996.

M5 (WHOLESALE) ANGLING, Rivermoor House, Long Load, Langport, SOMERSET, TA10 9JX **England**
(T) 01458 241630.

MENDIP BAIT LTD, Creech Hill, Bruton, SOMERSET, BA10 0QH **England**
Mr R Banwell (Manager)
(T) 01749 812377.

MICK'S TACKLE & GUNS, 67 Princes Street, Yeovil, SOMERSET, BA20 1EE **England**
Mr M Williams (Proprietor)
(T) 01935 411087.

MIXED FISHING, Bullocks Farm, Back Lane, Kingston Seymour, Clevedon, SOMERSET, BS21 6XA **England**
Mr P T Simmons (Partner)
(T) 01934 835020.

P A MEGABAITS, 25 Nunney Road, Frome, SOMERSET, BA11 4LA **England**
Mrs J Ansteth (Proprietor)
(T) 01373 471418.

PEREGRINE, Unit 56 Haydon Industrial Estate, Radstock, Bath, SOMERSET, BA3 3RD **England**
Mr Roger Mccourtney (Manager)
(T) 01761 436900.

PLANET VIDEO & ANGLING, 19A High Street, Chard, SOMERSET, TA20 1QF **England**
Mr L Braunton (Manager)
(T) 01460 64000.

S SHIPP, 7 Victoria Street, Staple Hill, Bristol, SOMERSET, BS16 5JP **England**
Mr S Shipp (Proprietor)
(T) 0117-956 6985.

SCOTT TACKLE, 42 Soundwell Road, Bristol, SOMERSET, BS16 4QP **England**
Mr Peter Kent (Partner)
(T) 0117-956 7371.

SOMERSET ANGLING, 74 Bath Road, Bridgwater, SOMERSET, TA6 4PL **England**
Mr S Kedge (Manager)
(T) 01278 431777.

STREET ANGLING CENTRE, 160 High Street, Street, SOMERSET, BA16 0NH **England**
Mr R N Hughes (Proprietor)
(T) 01458 447830.

SUNNY HOLME ENTERPRISES, Sunny Holme, Lovington, Castle Cary, SOMERSET, BA7 7PT **England**
Mr Steve Randle (Proprietor)
(T) 01963 240542.

TACKLE SHACK, North Street, Langport, SOMERSET, TA10 9RQ **England**
Mr M Brook (Partner)
(T) 01458 253665.

TALBOTS TACKLE, 1 North Street, Bedminster, Bristol, SOMERSET, BS3 1EN **England**
(T) 01179 663701.

THATCHER'S PET & TACKLE SHOP, 18 Queen Street, Wells, SOMERSET, BA5 2DP **England**
Mrs A Miles (Partner)
(T) 01749 673513.

THYERS TACKLE, 1a Church Street, Highbridge, SOMERSET, TA9 3AE **England**
Mr C Lockier (Manager)
(T) 01278 786934.

TONY'S, 4 Wootton Road, Bristol, SOMERSET, BS4 4AL **England**
Mr T Pasley (Proprietor)
(T) 0117-977 7129.

TOPP TACKLE, 63 Station Road, Taunton, SOMERSET, TA1 1PA **England**
Mr I Topp (Proprietor)
(T) 01823 282518.

VEALS S & SON LTD, 61 Old Market Street, Bristol, SOMERSET, BS2 0EJ **England**
Mr P Hughes (Director)
(T) 0117-926 0790.

WAYNES TACKLE & DARTS, 61 Eastover, Bridgwater, SOMERSET, TA6 5AP **England**
Mr W Foran (Proprietor)
(T) 01278 429335.

WELLINGTON COUNTRY SPORTS, 24 High Street, Wellington, SOMERSET, TA21 8RA **England**
Mr Timothy James (Proprietor)
(T) 01823 662120.

WESTON ANGLING CENTRE, 25A Locking Road, Weston-super-Mare, SOMERSET, BS23 3BY **England**
(T) 01934 631140.

YEOVIL & DISTRICT ANGLING CENTRE, 27-29 Forest Hill, Yeovil, SOMERSET, BA20 2PH **England**
Mr Tony Goddard (Proprietor)
(T) 01935 476777.

STAFFORDSHIRE

ALLENS OF KINGSBURY, 7 Cardigan Place, Cannock, STAFFORDSHIRE, WS12 5AQ **England**
Mrs G Allen (Manageress)
(T) 01543 451858.

ALLENS OF KINGSBURY, Premier Angling Centre, Coventry Road, Kingsbury, Tamworth, STAFFORDSHIRE, B78 2NP **England**
(T) 01827 872451.

ANGLERS WORKSHOP, 2a Jervis Street, Stoke-on-Trent, STAFFORDSHIRE, ST1 2DX **England**
Ms Vanessa Baynes (Joint Director)
(T) 01782 214466.

BRIAN MELLOR, 30-32 Brunswick Street, Stoke-on-Trent, STAFFORDSHIRE, ST1 1DR **England**
Mr B Mellor (Partner)
(T) 01782 266742.

BURTON ANGLING SUPPLIES, 30 Borough Road, Burton-on-Trent, STAFFORDSHIRE, DE14 2DA **England**
Mr Derek Spilsbury (Proprietor)
(T) 01283 548540.

CHASE ANGLING CENTRE, 119 High Street, Chasetown, Burntwood, STAFFORDSHIRE, WS7 8XL **England**
Mr L Till (Proprietor)
(T) 01543 683308.

CHASE MATCHMAN, 9 Station Road, Cannock, STAFFORDSHIRE, WS12 4DH **England**
Mr G Bird (Proprietor)
(T) 01543 877478.

CHESTERTON PET & NET, 75 London Road, Chesterton, Newcastle, STAFFORDSHIRE, ST5 7DY **England**
Mrs A Matthews (Proprietor)
(T) 01782 562597.

COUNTRY SPORTS, 119 Lichfield Street, Tamworth, STAFFORDSHIRE, B79 7QB **England**
Mr K J Horsham (Proprietor)
(T) 01827 63456.

DOLPHIN DISCOUNT FISHING TACKLE GUNS & BOATS, The Boat Yard, Old Whieldon Road, Stoke-on-Trent, STAFFORDSHIRE, ST4 4HW **England**
(T) 01782 849390.

FISHING LODGE, 2 Barford Street, Stoke-on-Trent, STAFFORDSHIRE, ST3 2NN **England**
(T) 01782 335526.

G BATE (STAFFORD) LTD, 7 Market Square, Stafford, STAFFORDSHIRE, ST16 2JN **England**
Ms Lilian Bates (Joint Director)
(T) 01785 244191.

GILLS FISHING TACKLE & PET SHOP, 82 Watling Street, Wilnecote, Tamworth, STAFFORDSHIRE, B77 5BJ **England**
Mr Geoff Gill (Proprietor)
(T) 01827 280889.

GONE FISHING, 409 Ash Bank Road, Werrington, Stoke-on-Trent, STAFFORDSHIRE, ST9 0JP **England**
(T) 01782 302198.

HAMBRY'S, 8 Tamworth Road, Polesworth, Tamworth, STAFFORDSHIRE, B78 1JH **England**
(T) 01827 895011.

HOLT'S FISHING TACKLE, 122 Marston Road, Stafford, STAFFORDSHIRE, ST16 3BX **England**
Mr Andrew Holt (Proprietor)
(T) 01785 251073.

J E MASSEY, 60-64 High Street, Uttoxeter, STAFFORDSHIRE, ST14 7JD **England**
Mr J Massey (Proprietor)
(T) 01889 569787.

JOHN BIRKS, 293 Uttoxeter Road, Stoke-on-Trent, STAFFORDSHIRE, ST3 5LQ **England**
Mr John Birks (Proprietor)
(T) 01782 319939.

KAMP ANGLING SUPPLIES, 1 New Road, Rugeley, STAFFORDSHIRE, WS15 4AA **England**
Mr Paul Carthy (Proprietor)
(T) 01543 491228.

MULLARKEY & SONS, 184-185 Waterloo Street, Burton-on-Trent, STAFFORDSHIRE, DE14 2NH **England**
Mr D Mullarkey (Proprietor)
(T) 01283 566777.

MULLARKEY & SONS, 184-185 Waterloo Street, Burton-on-Trent, STAFFORDSHIRE, DE14 2NQ **England**
Mr D Mullarkey (Proprietor)
(T) 01283 566777.

ONE LAST CAST, Unit 6, Browning Street, Stafford, STAFFORDSHIRE, ST16 3AT **England**
Mr M Smith (Proprietor)
(T) 01785 213629.

PICKERINGS, 4-8 William Clowes Street, Stoke-on-Trent, STAFFORDSHIRE, ST6 3AP **England**
Mr D Pickering (Proprietor)
(T) 01782 814941.

PLANTY'S TACKLE, 15 Brunswick Street, Newcastle, STAFFORDSHIRE, ST5 1HF **England**
Mr J Plant (Proprietor)
(T) 01782 631344.

R & J ANGLING & PET SUPPLIES, 36 Swallow Croft, Lichfield, STAFFORDSHIRE, WS13 7HF **England**
Mr R Spilsbury (Proprietor)
(T) 01543 262014.

ROD'S FISHING TACKLE, Unit 6 Penkridge Industrial Estate, Boscomoor Lane, Penkridge, Stafford, STAFFORDSHIRE, ST19 5NU **England**
(T) 01785 715744.

ROWLEY'S FISHING SUPPLIES, 21a Carlisle Street, Stoke-on-Trent, STAFFORDSHIRE, ST3 4HA **England**
Mrs J Rowley (Partner)
(T) 01782 341035.

TACKLE EXCHANGE, Linden House, 95B Trentham Road, Stoke-on-Trent, STAFFORDSHIRE, ST3 4EG **England**
(T) 01782 599858.

TAMWORTH FISHING TACKLE, 23 Lichfield Street, Tamworth, STAFFORDSHIRE, B79 7QE **England**
Mr Kevin Lee (Partner)
(T) 01827 66701.

TAYLOR'S FISHING, 130 Northwood Park Road, Stoke-on-Trent, STAFFORDSHIRE, ST1 6QS **England**
Mrs C A Taylor (Partner)
(T) 01782 219436.

TRENTSIDE ANGLING CENTRE, 1254 Leek Road, Stoke-on-Trent, STAFFORDSHIRE, ST2 8BP **England**
(T) 01782 545493.

WALKERS ONE STOP TACKLE SHOP LTD, 69 St. Michaels Road, Stoke-on-Trent, STAFFORDSHIRE, ST6 6LE **England**
Mr T Walker (Proprietor)
(T) 01782 811919.

SUFFOLK

A & P SUPPLIES, Unit 4c1 Site 3 Ellough Industrial Estate, Ellough, Beccles, SUFFOLK, NR34 7TD **England**
Mr Adrian Dyer (Proprietor)
(T) 01502 713379.

ALDEBURGH FISHING TACKLE, 30 Crabbe Street, Aldeburgh, SUFFOLK, IP15 5BN **England**
Mr S Smalley (Proprietor)
(T) 01728 454030.

BACKONS DOZEN, 13 Waveney Road, Lowestoft, SUFFOLK, NR32 1BT **England**
Mr Kevin Backon (Proprietor)
(T) 01502 564120.

BAIT MAIT, Unit 31b Hardwick Industrial Estate, Hardwick Lane, Bury St. Edmunds, SUFFOLK, IP33 2QH **England**
Mr C Parrell (Proprietor)
(T) 01284 750889.

BREAKAWAY TACKLE DEVELOPMENT CO LTD, 376 Bramford Road, Ipswich, SUFFOLK, IP1 5AY **England**
Mr Dave Brown (Manager)
(T) 01473 741393.

CASTAWAY, 20 Undercliff Road West, Felixstowe, SUFFOLK, IP11 2AW **England**
Mr L O Harold (Proprietor)
(T) 01394 278316.

DING-ITS TACKLE DEN, 1/Jubilee Buildings, London Road, Pakefield, Lowestoft, SUFFOLK, NR33 7AF **England**
Mrs J Waters (Proprietor)
(T) 01502 519483.

GUNDRY MARINE LTD, Allerton Buildings, Battery Green Road, Lowestoft, SUFFOLK, NR32 1DH **England**
Mr David Goddard (Area Manager)
(T) 01502 568786.

HAVERHILL ANGLING, 2a Primrose Hill, Haverhill, SUFFOLK, CB9 9LS **England**
Mr G Rowe (Director)
(T) 01440 705011.

HOOKED, 127 All Saints Road, Newmarket, SUFFOLK, CB8 8ES **England**
Mr S Howard (Proprietor)
(T) 01638 661594.

I G PRODUCTS, 15a Walton Avenue, Felixstowe, SUFFOLK, IP11 3HH **England**
Mr E Granville (Proprietor)
(T) 01394 673635.

INOVATION UNLIMITED, Unit 5 Crest Land Business Pk/Bull La Industrial Estate, Bull Lane, Acton, Sudbury, SUFFOLK, CO10 0BD **England**
Mr K Johnson (Director)
(T) 01787 319101.

IPSWICH ANGLING CENTRE, 154 Felixstowe Road, Ipswich, SUFFOLK, IP3 8EF **England**
Mr Roger Oliver (Proprietor)
(T) 01473 728004.

L & T ANGLING CENTRE, 1 Carlton Road, Lowestoft, SUFFOLK, NR33 0RU **England**
Mrs L Quinn (Proprietor)
(T) 01502 539425.

LOWESTOFT ANGLING CENTRE, 191 London Road South, Lowestoft, SUFFOLK, NR33 0DR **England**
Mr L Phillips (Proprietor)
(T) 01502 573392.

N J C FISHING TACKLE, 5-6 Yacht Station, Lowestoft, SUFFOLK, NR33 9JS **England**
(T) 01502 589556.

R MARKHAM, 717 Woodbridge Road, Ipswich, SUFFOLK, IP4 4NB **England**
Mr R Markham (Proprietor)
(T) 01473 727841.

SAM HOOK LOWESTOFT LTD, 131-132 Bevan St East, Lowestoft, SUFFOLK, NR32 2AQ **England**
Mrs Gillian Avril Page (Joint Director)
(T) 01502 565821.

SAXMUNDHAM ANGLING CENTRE, Rear Of Market Place, Saxmundham, SUFFOLK, IP17 1AH **England**
Mr Brian Finbow (Proprietor)
(T) 01728 603443.

SOUTHWOLD ANGLING CENTRE, 9 Station Road, Southwold, SUFFOLK, IP18 6AX **England**
Mr Martin Smith (Proprietor)
(T) 01502 722085.

STANDARD BAIT LTD, Oak Hill, Bramfield, Halesworth, SUFFOLK, IP19 9HN **England**
Mr L S Higgins (Proprietor)
(T) 01986 872385.

SUDBURY ANGLING CENTRE, 1-2 Acton Square, Sudbury, SUFFOLK, CO10 1HG **England**
Mr G Rowe (Director)
(T) 01787 312118.

TACKLE UP, 49A St. Johns Street, Bury St. Edmunds, SUFFOLK, IP33 1SP **England**
Miss R A Nunn (Manager)
(T) 01284 755022.

TACKLE-X-CHANGE, 2 Essex Road, Lowestoft, SUFFOLK, NR32 2HH **England**
Mr P Wilson (Proprietor)
(T) 01502 508989.

TED BEAN, 175 London Road North, Lowestoft, SUFFOLK, NR32 1HG **England**
Mr J F Straw (Proprietor)
(T) 01502 565832.

UKON SUPPLIES LTD, 2 Thoroughfare, Halesworth, SUFFOLK, IP19 8AH **England**
Mrs C Higgins (Managing Director)
(T) 01986 873761.

VISCOUNT FISHING TACKLE, 207 Clapgate Lane, Ipswich, SUFFOLK, IP3 0RF **England**
Mrs Y Green (Partner)
(T) 01473 728179.

SURREY

ALBURY GAME ANGLING, The Street, Albury, Guildford, SURREY, GU5 9AG **England**
Mr P Cockwill (Proprietor)
(T) 01483 205196.

ANGEL ANGLING, 6 Trehaven Parade, Hornbeam Road, Reigate, SURREY, RH2 7LL **England**
Mr Martin Cover (Proprietor)
(T) 01737 225377.

APOLLO ANGLING CENTRE, 79 Brighton Road, Addlestone, SURREY, KT15 1PT **England**
(T) 01932 848354.

BANKSIDE, 2 Castle Parade, Ewell By Passage, Epsom, SURREY, KT17 2PR **England**
Mr R Keane (Manager)
(T) 0208-786 8432.

CARP SHOP, 2 South Parade, Horley Row, Horley, SURREY, RH6 8BH **England**
Mr P Maloney (Proprietor)
(T) 01293 407687.

CATERHAM ANGLING, 10 High Street, Caterham, SURREY, CR3 5UA **England**
Mr P Marsh (Partner)
(T) 01883 347357.

CHEAM ANGLING CENTRE, 705 London Road, Sutton, SURREY, SM3 9DL **England**
Mr R Murton (Proprietor)
(T) 0208-330 4787.

CHERTSEY BAIT WHOLESALERS, 40 Guildford Street, Chertsey, SURREY, KT16 9BE **England**
Mr A Ockendon (Partner)
(T) 01932 561499.

COULSDON ANGLING CENTRE, 232 Brighton Road, Coulsdon, SURREY, CR5 2NF **England**
Mr D Eteson (Manager)
(T) 0208-763 2458.

E VENIARD (WHOLESALE) LTD, 138 Northwood Road, Thornton Heath, SURREY, CR7 8YG **England**
Mr Peter Veniard (Managing Director)
(T) 0208-653 3565.

ESHER ANGLING CENTRE, Pond House, Weston Green, Thames Ditton, SURREY, KT7 0JX **England**
Mr A Barlow (Proprietor)
(T) 0208-398 2405.

ESSENTIAL TACKLE, 49 Dartmouth Avenue, Woking, SURREY, GU21 5PE **England**
Mrs Jody Smith (Proprietor)
(T) 01932 345414.

FINNISH FUR FLY EUROPE, 40 Buckhurst Road, Frimley Green, Camberley, SURREY, GU16 6LJ **England**
Mr Andy Stewart (Proprietor)
(T) 01252 834165.

FISHING UNLIMITED, 2-3 Hampton Ct Parade, East Molesey, SURREY, KT8 9HB **England**
Mr P Davidson (Proprietor)
(T) 0208-941 6633.

FISHING UNLIMITED, 5 Worplesdon Road, Guildford, SURREY, GU2 9RW **England**
Mr P Steer (Manager)
(T) 01483 504106.

FULLING MILL LTD, Unit 5/Holmesdale House, 46 Croydon Road, Reigate, SURREY, RH2 0NH **England**
Mr B Unwin (Managing Director)
(T) 01737 243991.

GARDNER TACKLE LTD, Collins Court, High Street, Cranleigh, SURREY, GU6 8AS **England**
Ms M Gardner (Proprietor)
(T) 01483 276446.

GARDNERS TACKLE LTD, Charters Yard, Mary Road, Guildford, SURREY, GU1 4QU **England**
Mr R Gardner (Director)
(T) 01483 276446.

GOLDSWORTH ANGLING CENTRE, 73-75 Goldsworth Road, Woking, SURREY, GU21 1LJ **England**
Mr P Sparling (Managing Director)
(T) 01483 776667.

GRAYSHOTT TACKLE, 1 Crossways Road, Grayshott, Hindhead, SURREY, GU26 6HJ **England**
Mr M N Lunn (Proprietor)
(T) 01428 606122.

GUILDFORD ANGLING CENTRE, 92-94 Haydon Place, Guildford, SURREY, GU1 4LR **England**
Mr R Marshall (Proprietor)
(T) 01483 506333.

LONGBOAT CONSULTING LTD, Meadows, Elm Corner, Ockham, Woking, SURREY, GU23 6PX **England**
Mr A Leaiper (Managing Director)
(T) 01483 223440.

P C L WHOLESALE FISHING TACKLE, 104 Overbury Cresent, New Addington, Croydon, SURREY, CR0 0LP **England**
Mr P Lamb (Proprietor)
(T) 01689 844515.

S C FULLER, 32 South Street, Dorking, SURREY, RH4 2HQ **England**
(T) 01306 882177.

SPECIALIST TACKLE LTD, 65 London Road, Croydon, SURREY, CR0 2RF **England**
Mr A Macarthy (y 00)
(T) 020 86813776.

STS ANGLING SUPPLIES, 114 Carshalton Road, Sutton, SURREY, SM1 4RL **England**
Mr S Saunders (Managing Director)
(T) 0208-770 7744.

SURBITON ANGLING CENTRE, 177 Hook Road, Surbiton, SURREY, KT6 5AR **England**
Mr Leonard White (Proprietor)
(T) 0208-391 4110.

SURREY ANGLING, 57-58 The Market, Rosehill, Sutton, SURREY, SM1 3HE **England**
Mrs B M Finch (Partner)
(T) 020 86411654.

TACKLE EXCHANGE, 95-97 Terrace Road, Walton-on-Thames, SURREY, KT12 2SG **England**
Mr Martin Schofield (Proprietor)
(T) 01932 242377.

WEYBRIDGE GUNS & TACKLE, 137 Oatlands Drive, Weybridge, SURREY, KT13 9LB **England**
(T) 01932 842675.

SUSSEX (EAST)

A R TACKLE, 8 Castle Street, Hastings, SUSSEX (EAST), TN34 3DY **England**
Mr Alan Ralph (Proprietor)
(T) 01424 422094.

ANGLERS DEN, 6 North Road, Pevensey Bay, Pevensey, SUSSEX (EAST), BN24 6AY **England**
Mr Kevin Morgan (Partner)
(T) 01323 460441.

B & P COMMERCIAL WHOLESALERS LTD, 35 Baldslow Down, St. Leonards-on-Sea, SUSSEX (EAST), TN37 7NJ **England**
(T) 01424 755472.

BATTLE TACKLE & BAIT, Unit 5 18b High Street, Battle, SUSSEX (EAST), TN33 0AE **England**
Mr A Holman (Proprietor)
(T) 01424 775566.

BLACK ROCK BAIT, 4a The Broadway, Brighton, SUSSEX (EAST), BN2 5NF **England**
Mr P Douch (Manager)
(T) 01273 622001.

BRIGHTON ANGLER, 1-2 Madeira Drive, Brighton, SUSSEX (EAST), BN2 1PS **England**
Mr J Lighton (Proprietor)
(T) 01273 671398.

CROWBOROUGH TACKLE, Croft Road, Crowborough, SUSSEX (EAST), TN6 1DL **England**
(T) 01892 669923.

CROWBOROUGH TACKLE, Whitehill Road, Crowborough, SUSSEX (EAST), TN6 1JU **England**
Mr F Russell (Manager)
(T) 01892 661145.

EASTBOURNE PIER BAIT & TACKLE SHOP, Grand Parade, Eastbourne, SUSSEX (EAST), BN21 3EL **England**
(T) 01323 648322.

FISHERMAN FRIENDS, 135 Islingword Road, Brighton, SUSSEX (EAST), BN2 2SH **England**
Mr D Sprigg (Partner)
(T) 01273 681010.

G R N TACKLE, 7 Coastguard Cottages, New Lydd Road, Camber, Rye, SUSSEX (EAST), TN31 7QT **England**
Mr G R Neilson (Proprietor)
(T) 01797 225302.

GUNDRY MARINE LTD, 30 Fishmarket, Rock-A-Nore Road, Hastings, SUSSEX (EAST), TN34 3DW **England**
Mr T Forrow (Manager)
(T) 01424 442045.

HAILSHAM BAIT & TACKLE, 9 Station Road, Hailsham, SUSSEX (EAST), BN27 2BE **England**
Mr Paul Hamper (Proprietor)
(T) 01323 449669.

HASTINGS ANGLING CENTRE, 33 The Bourne, Hastings, SUSSEX (EAST), TN34 3AY **England**
Mr W Crosby (Proprietor)
(T) 01424 432178.

HOOK LINE & SINKER, 54 Sackville Road, Bexhill-on-Sea, SUSSEX (EAST), TN39 3JE **England**
Mr Paul Naves (Proprietor)
(T) 01424 733211.

LAGOON BAIT & TACKLE, 327 Kingsway, Hove, SUSSEX (EAST), BN3 4LD **England**
Mr P Winder (Proprietor)
(T) 01273 415879.

NEWHAVEN ANGLER, 107 Fort Road, Newhaven, SUSSEX (EAST), BN9 9DA **England**
Mr G Hutchinson (Proprietor)
(T) 01273 512186.

PEACEHAVEN ANGLER, 135 South Coast Road, Peacehaven, SUSSEX (EAST), BN10 8PA **England**
Mr J Shervington (Proprietor)
(T) 01273 586000.

PERCYS, 9 Cliffe High Street, Lewes, SUSSEX (EAST), BN7 2AH **England**
Mr Derek Walter (Proprietor)
(T) 01273 473207.

POLEGATE ANGLING CENTRE, 101 Station Road, Polegate, SUSSEX (EAST), BN26 6EB **England**
Mr T Lelliott (Proprietor)
(T) 01323 486379.

S H TACKLE, 58 Bohemia Road, St. Leonards-on-Sea, SUSSEX (EAST), TN37 6RQ **England**
Mr A Thorn (Proprietor)
(T) 01424 431583.

SEA BREEZE CHARTER ANGLING, 13a Tor Road, Peacehaven, SUSSEX (EAST), BN10 7SX **England**
Mr T W Lee (Proprietor)
(T) 01273 585372.

STEVES TACKLE SHOP, 38 White Rock, Hastings, SUSSEX (EAST), TN34 1JL **England**
Mr Steve Hankinson (Proprietor)
(T) 01424 433404.

TACKLE BOX, Brighton Marina Village, Brighton, SUSSEX (EAST), BN2 5UF **England**
Mrs S E Goatcher (Proprietor)
(T) 01273 696477.

TONY'S TACKLE, 211 Seaside, Eastbourne, SUSSEX (EAST), BN22 7NP **England**
Mr Anthony Kerridge (Proprietor)
(T) 01323 739562.

TRADE SALES, The Toll House, Lower Horsebridge, Hailsham, SUSSEX (EAST), BN27 4DJ **England**
Mr Robert Baker (Proprietor)
(T) 01323 841336.

UCKFIELD ANGLING CENTRE, 212a High Street, Uckfield, SUSSEX (EAST), TN22 1RD **England**
Mr Ken Roberts (Proprietor)
(T) 01825 760300.

WADHURST ROD & LINE, 1 Wellington Place, Sparrows Green, Wadhurst, SUSSEX (EAST), TN5 6SW **England**
Mr D E Preedy (Proprietor)
(T) 01892 783231.

WYLAND ANGLING CENTRE, Wylands Farm, Powdermill Lane, Battle, SUSSEX (EAST), TN33 0SU **England**
Mr Colin Bourner (Proprietor)
(T) 01424 893394.

SUSSEX (WEST)

ANGLING SPECIALISTS, 29 Queen Street, Horsham, SUSSEX (WEST), RH13 5AA **England**
Mr C Martin (Proprietor)
(T) 01403 264644.

ARUN ANGLING CENTRE, 4 True Blue Precinct, Wick Street, Wick, Littlehampton, SUSSEX (WEST), BN17 7JN **England**
Mr T Nudds (Proprietor)
(T) 01903 718546.

ARUN ANGLING CENTRE, Roundstone Garden Centre, Roundstone By-Pass, Angmering, Littlehampton, SUSSEX (WEST), BN16 4BD **England**
(T) 01903 859315.

ASHDOWN FIELDSPORTS, Unit 2A, Wellington Town Road, East Grinstead, SUSSEX (WEST), RH19 2ES **England**
Mr Clive Nichols (Proprietor)
(T) 01342 315118.

BURGESS HILL ANGLING CENTRE LTD, 143 Lower Church Road, Burgess Hill, SUSSEX (WEST), RH15 9AA **England**
Mr David Blake (Proprietor)
(T) 01444 232287.

BURGESS HILL ANGLING CENTRE LTD, 143 Lower Church Road, Burgess Hill, SUSSEX (WEST), RH15 9AB **England**
Mr David Blake (Director)
(T) 01444 232287.

COOMBS TACKLE CENTRE, 24 West Street, Bognor Regis, SUSSEX (WEST), PO21 1XE **England**
Mr T Coombs (Proprietor)
(T) 01243 866663.

CRAWLEY ANGLING CENTRE, 2 Gossops Parade, Crawley, SUSSEX (WEST), RH11 8HH **England**
Mr D G Rann (Proprietor)
(T) 01293 536638.

CUSTOM BUILT RODS, 1c Valebridge Road, Burgess Hill, SUSSEX (WEST), RH15 0RA **England**
Mr G Dadswell (Proprietor)
(T) 01444 250930.

DELMAR ENGINEERING, 20 Church Road, Selsey, Chichester, SUSSEX (WEST), PO20 0LS **England**
Ms Carmen Vinter (Manager)
(T) 01243 605123.

JACK FROST LTD, 52-54 Ewhurst Road, Crawley, SUSSEX (WEST), RH11 7HE **England**
Mr S Muggeridge (Director)
(T) 01293 521186.

KEN DUNMAN, 2 Marine Place, Opposite Worthing Pier, Worthing, SUSSEX (WEST), BN11 3DN **England**
Mr R W Briggs (Proprietor)
(T) 01903 239802.

LANCING ANGLING CENTRE, 8 Queensway, North Road, Lancing, SUSSEX (WEST), BN15 9AY **England**
(T) 01903 522890.

LOGO SADDLERY & FISHING TACKLE, West Street, Midhurst, SUSSEX (WEST), GU29 9NQ **England**
Mr G A Oram (Proprietor)
(T) 01730 817016.

M A WICKHAM, 4 Middle Row, East Grinstead, SUSSEX (WEST), RH19 3AX **England**
Mr M Wickham (Proprietor)
(T) 01342 315073.

MICKEY'S PLACE, 4a Spencers Road, Horsham, SUSSEX (WEST), RH12 2JG **England**
Mr M Hillman (Proprietor)
(T) 01403 274877.

PREMIER ANGLING, 2 Swindon Road, Horsham, SUSSEX (WEST), RH12 2HD **England**
Mr M Newman (Proprietor)
(T) 01403 265711.

PRIME ANGLING, 74 Brighton Road, Worthing, SUSSEX (WEST), BN11 2EN **England**
Mr M Perfect (Proprietor)
(T) 01903 527050.

SELSEY FISHING SUPPLIERS, 101c High Street, Selsey, Chichester, SUSSEX (WEST), PO20 0QL **England**
Mr C Harvey (Proprietor)
(T) 01243 605289.

SHORELINE, 7 Shore Road, East Wittering, Chichester, SUSSEX (WEST), PO20 8DY **England**
Mr S Terry (Proprietor)
(T) 01243 673353.

SOUTHERN ANGLING SPECIALISTS, 2 Stockbridge Place, Stockbridge Road, Chichester, SUSSEX (WEST), PO19 2QH **England**
(T) 01243 531669.

SPORTING CHANCE, Unit 2 Sheffield House, 29 Boltro Road, Haywards Heath, SUSSEX (WEST), RH16 1BP **England**
Mr J Riczkowski (Manager)
(T) 01444 458729.

TROPICANA OF LITTLEHAMPTON, 5-6 Pier Road, Littlehampton, SUSSEX (WEST), BN17 5BA **England**
Mr M F Pearce (Proprietor)
(T) 01903 715190.

TYNE AND WEAR

ANGLERS CHOICE, 8-9 Murton Street, Sunderland, TYNE AND WEAR, SR1 2QY **England**
Mr Steve Bland (Proprietor)
(T) 01915 140000.

ANGLING LEISURE SPORT, 6-10 Bowsden Terrace, Newcastle upon Tyne, TYNE AND WEAR, NE3 1RX **England**
Mr A Rowell (Partner)
(T) 0191-213 1682.

BAIT FACTORY, 37h Bede Trading Estate, Jarrow, TYNE AND WEAR, NE32 3HG **England**
(T) 0191-483 3527.

CENTURY COMPOSITES LTD, 58-59 Hutton Close, Crowther, Washington, TYNE AND WEAR, NE38 0AH **England**
Mr S Chilcott (Director)
(T) 0191-416 8200.

CONCORD ANGLING SUPPLIES, 25 Front Street, Washington, TYNE AND WEAR, NE37 2BA **England**
Mr F Davies (Managing Director)
(T) 0191-417 1242.

FRASERS ANGLING & OUTDOORS, 15 Sandy Lane, Gateshead, TYNE AND WEAR, NE9 7YB **England**
(T) 0191-487 2451.

I D FISHING, 137 Chillingham Road, Newcastle upon Tyne, TYNE AND WEAR, NE6 5XL **England**
Mr John Bohill (Proprietor)
(T) 01912 763041.

I D FISHING, 206 Ocean Road, South Shields, TYNE AND WEAR, NE33 2JQ **England**
Mr J Bohill (Proprietor)
(T) 0191-456 3953.

JOHN ROBERTSON, 101 Percy Street, Newcastle upon Tyne, TYNE AND WEAR, NE1 7RY **England**
Mr John Robertson (Proprietor)
(T) 0191-232 2018.

JOHNS FISHING TACKLE, 10 High Street East, Wallsend, TYNE AND WEAR, NE28 8PQ **England**
Mr R Heeles (Manager)
(T) 0191-234 3142.

KINGFISHER, 27 Hylton Road, Sunderland, TYNE AND WEAR, SR4 7AF **England**
Mr David King (Proprietor)
(T) 0191-510 3543.

METRO ANGLING CENTRE, 14 Garden Walk/Yellow Quadrant, Metro Centre, Gateshead, TYNE AND WEAR, NE11 9XY **England**
(T) 0191-460 8733.

REELSPORT, 237a Victoria Road East, Hebburn, TYNE AND WEAR, NE31 1YE **England**
Mr Terry Wood (Proprietor)
(T) 0191-430 0247.

RUTHERFORDS ANGLING, 125 Roker Avenue, Sunderland, TYNE AND WEAR, SR6 0HL **England**
Mr Andrew Rutherford (Proprietor)
(T) 0191-565 4183.

STEVE'S, 2 Prudhoe Street, North Shields, TYNE AND WEAR, NE29 6RA **England**
Mr Phil Gee (Proprietor)
(T) 0191-257 9999.

TITAN, 17 Witney Way, Boldon Colliery, TYNE AND WEAR, NE35 9PE **England**
Mr A Lund (Managing Director)
(T) 0191-536 1141.

ULTIMATE FISHING SUPPLIES, 72 Derwent Street, Chopwell, Newcastle upon Tyne, TYNE AND WEAR, NE17 7HY **England**
Mr L D Hawley (Manager)
(T) 01207 560931.

W TEMPLE, 43 Ocean View, Whitley Bay, TYNE AND WEAR, NE26 1AL **England**
Mr Bill Rutherford (Proprietor)
(T) 0191-252 6017.

WALKER ANGLING CENTRE, 1200 Walker Road, Newcastle upon Tyne, TYNE AND WEAR, NE6 3JN **England**
Mrs L Gill (Partner)
(T) 0191-276 4774.

WHITING NETS, Bilton Buildings, Fish Quay, North Shields, TYNE AND WEAR, NE30 1JA **England**
Mr D Whiting (Proprietor)
(T) 0191-296 1809.

WARWICKSHIRE

ALCESTER SPORTS & TACKLE, 3a High Street, Alcester, WARWICKSHIRE, B49 5AE **England**
Mr A Stephens (Proprietor)
(T) 01789 762200.

ATTLEBOROUGH ANGLING CENTRE, 5 George Street, Attleborough, Nuneaton, WARWICKSHIRE, CV11 4LA **England**
Mr P Randell (Proprietor)
(T) 02476 343718.

BAILEYS OF WARWICK, 30 Emscote Road, Warwick, WARWICKSHIRE, CV34 4PP **England**
Mr A Cox (Partner)
(T) 01926 490636.

BANKS & BURR, 25 Claremont Road, Rugby, WARWICKSHIRE, CV21 3NA **England**
Mr C Burr (Partner)
(T) 01788 576782.

CENTRAL TACKLE, 89 King Street, Bedworth, WARWICKSHIRE, CV12 8JE **England**
(T) 02476 313235.

CRYSTAL RIVER, 2 Southam Road, Dunchurch, Rugby, WARWICKSHIRE, CV22 6NL **England**
Mr Gary Lyttle (Proprietor)
(T) 01788 815855.

DAVE JONES, 17 Evesham Road, Stratford-upon-Avon, WARWICKSHIRE, CV37 9AA **England**
Mr David Jones (Proprietor)
(T) 01789 293950.

KALIUM PRODUCTS LTD, West Court, Morton Bagot, Studley, WARWICKSHIRE, B80 7EL **England**
(T) 01527 857870.

MARTINS FISHING TACKLE, 48 Queens Road, Nuneaton, WARWICKSHIRE, CV11 5JX **England**
(T) 02476 381745.

MATCHBOX TACKLE LTD, Station Road, Alcester, WARWICKSHIRE, B49 5ET **England**
Mr J Burton (Director)
(T) 01789 766266.

NORTH FARM FISHERY, North Farm, Priors Marston, Southam, WARWICKSHIRE, CV47 7RY **England**
(T) 01327 260617.

TACKLE SELLER, 24 Russell Terrace, Leamington Spa, WARWICKSHIRE, CV31 1EZ **England**
Mr I Shirley (Partner)
(T) 01926 888834.

ULTRA FISHING TACKLE LTD, 34 Longfield Road, Leamington Spa, WARWICKSHIRE, CV31 1XB **England**
Mr Shaun Stenton (Sales Manager)
(T) 01926 424722.

V M C WATERQUEEN (UK) LTD, Unit 8/Avenue Fields Industrial Estate, Avenue Farm, Stratford-upon-Avon, WARWICKSHIRE, CV37 0HT **England**
Miss A Monnot (Managing Director)
(T) 01789 262404.

WAYLAND AUTOMATIC PRODUCTS LTD, Brickyard Lane, Studley, WARWICKSHIRE, B80 7EE **England**
Mr G Holloway (Director)
(T) 01527 857360.

WILTSHIRE

ANGLING TECHNICS, 5 Kemble Business Park, Crudwell, Malmesbury, WILTSHIRE, SN16 9SH **England**
Mr P Fry (Partner)
(T) 01666 575144.

AVON ANGLING & SPORTS CENTRE, 13 Bath Road, Melksham, WILTSHIRE, SN12 6LL **England**
Mr Stephen Clunie (Partner)
(T) 01225 702219.

CAIN ROD COMPANY-FLY FISHING CENTRE, Meadow Barn, Lower Woodford, Salisbury, WILTSHIRE, SP4 6NQ **England**
Mr M Tunley (General Manager)
(T) 01722 782602.

COTSWOLD ANGLING, Hyde Road, Swindon, WILTSHIRE, SN2 7SE **England**
Mr Gary Davies (Manager)
(T) 01793 721173.

COTSWOLD AQUARIUS, The Old Brickyard, Northend, Ashton Keynes, Swindon, WILTSHIRE, SN6 6QR **England**
Mr P J Kemp (Proprietor)
(T) 01285 869090.

DEVIZES ANGLING CENTRE, 5 Snuff Street, Devizes, WILTSHIRE, SN10 1DU **England**
Mr K B Snow (Proprietor)
(T) 01380 722350.

HINDERS PARTICLE TACKLE & BIVVY, Manor Garden Centre, Cheney Manor Industrial Estate, Swindon, WILTSHIRE, SN2 2QJ **England**
Mrs J Fothergill (Partner)
(T) 01793 333900.

HOUSE OF ANGLING, 101 Cricklade Road, Swindon, WILTSHIRE, SN2 1AB **England**
Mr M J Cottle (Manager)
(T) 01793 644748.

HOUSE OF ANGLING, 59-60 Commercial Road, Swindon, WILTSHIRE, SN1 5NX **England**
(T) 01793 693460.

KEENETS, Woodcock Industrial Estate, Woodcock Road, Warminster, WILTSHIRE, BA12 9DX **England**
Mr A Read (Managing Director)
(T) 01985 214551.

LUMINASA EUROPE LTD, 28 Woodcock Industrial Estate, Woodcock Road, Warminster, WILTSHIRE, BA12 9DX **England**
Mr A Johnston (General Manager)
(T) 01985 847111.

MELKSHAM ANGLING CENTRE, Melsham House, 27 Market Place, Melksham, WILTSHIRE, SN12 6ES **England**
Mr J Pang (Proprietor)
(T) 01225 793546.

MILL FARM FISHERIES, Kingfisher Lodge, Southcross Lane, Worton, Devizes, WILTSHIRE, SN10 5UW **England**
Mr F W Coleman (Proprietor)
(T) 01380 813138.

MUDDLERS, 25 Wooton Bassett Road, Swindon, WILTSHIRE, SN1 4NQ **England**
Mr Jim Williams (Proprietor)
(T) 01793 845730.

REIDS TACKLE, Kingsway House, Warminster Road, Wilton, Salisbury, WILTSHIRE, SP2 0AT **England**
Mr D Moody (Proprietor)
(T) 01722 743192.

RICHARDS TROUT & SALMON FLIES, 86 Manchester Road, Swindon, WILTSHIRE, SN1 2AJ **England**
Mr Richard Reddaway (Proprietor)
(T) 01793 487170.

ROB'S TACKLE, 19 New Road, Chippenham, WILTSHIRE, SN15 1HT **England**
Mr R Bullock (Proprietor)
(T) 01249 659210.

SOUTHWEST ANGLIAN SUPPLIES, Redlynch, Salisbury, WILTSHIRE, SP5 2JU **England**
Mr L Woodhouse (Proprietor)
(T) 01725 513753.

STEVE'S TACKLE, 3 Station Road, Warminster, WILTSHIRE, BA12 9BR **England**
Mr Steven Ware (Proprietor)
(T) 01985 214934.

SWINDON ANGLING CENTRE, 5 Sheppard Street, Swindon, WILTSHIRE, SN1 5DB **England**
Mr D Cleaver (Proprietor)
(T) 01793 619909.

T K TACKLE, 123a London Road, Calne, WILTSHIRE, SN11 0AQ **England**
Mr A Knowler (Proprietor)
(T) 01249 812003.

WESTS, 32 Roundstone Street, Trowbridge, WILTSHIRE, BA14 8DE **England**
Mr S Ince (Partner)
(T) 01225 755472.

WILTSHIRE ANGLING, 5 Timbrell Street, Trowbridge, WILTSHIRE, BA14 8PP **England**
Mr P Cooper (Partner)
(T) 01225 763835.

WORM BREEDERS UK, Quarry Farm/The Hyde, Purton, Swindon, WILTSHIRE, SN5 4EA **England**
Mr John Cook (Proprietor)
(T) 01793 770574.

WORM BREEDERS UK, Quarry Farm/The Hyde, Purton, Swindon, WILTSHIRE, SN5 9EA **England**
Mr John Cook (Proprietor)
(T) 01793 770574.

WORCESTERSHIRE

ALLANS FISHING TACKLE, 26-30 Malvern Road, Worcester, WORCESTERSHIRE, WR2 4LG **England**
Mr D Burford (Manager)
(T) 01905 422107.

ANGLERS STOP, 161 Rose Avenue, Worcester, WORCESTERSHIRE, WR4 9QN **England**
Mr Clifford Adams (Proprietor)
(T) 01905 619803.

B B WHOLESALE LTD, Mayfield Works, Mayfields, Redditch, WORCESTERSHIRE, B98 7DU **England**
Mr R E Bignell (Director)
(T) 01527 540484.

BAIT BOX, 122 High Street, Evesham, WORCESTERSHIRE, WR11 4EJ **England**
Mr D M Packwood (Proprietor)
(T) 01386 442955.

BEWDLEY ANGLING CENTRE, 10a Severn Side North, Bewdley, WORCESTERSHIRE, DY12 2EE **England**
Mr W Leedsley (Proprietor)
(T) 01299 402835.

BRENT, Unit 2-3/Briar Cl Business Pk, Briar Cl, Evesham, WORCESTERSHIRE, WR11 4JT **England**
Mr M Attwood (Managing Director)
(T) 01386 422288.

DES TAYLOR AGENCIES, 44 Stourport Road, Bewdley, WORCESTERSHIRE, DY12 1BL **England**
Mr Des Taylor (Proprietor)
(T) 01299 402294.

ENSIGN, 3 Stoke Road, Bromsgrove, WORCESTERSHIRE, B60 3EQ **England**
Mr R Kings (Manager)
(T) 01527 833322.

FISHERMANS FEATHERS, Hill End Farm, Station Road, Bransford, Worcester, WORCESTERSHIRE, WR6 5JJ **England**
Mr R B T Taylor (Proprietor)
(T) 01905 830157.

FISHERMANS FRIEND, Woodland View, Haye Lane, Ombersley, Droitwich, WORCESTERSHIRE, WR9 0EJ **England**
Mr T Trough (Proprietor)
(T) 01905 621521.

FISHING TACKLE SHOP, 21-23 Old Street, Upton-upon-Severn, Worcester, WORCESTERSHIRE, WR8 0HN **England**
(T) 01684 592102.

H W ALLCOCK LTD, 86 Arthur Street, Redditch, WORCESTERSHIRE, B98 8JY **England**
Mr Anthony Roger Allcock (Joint Director)
(T) 01527 526974.

KENLEY LTD, Unit 2 Briar Close Industrial Estate, Evesham, WORCESTERSHIRE, WR11 4JT **England**
Mrs M A Attwood (Managing Director)
(T) 01386 45031.

LEEDA, 16-17 Padgets Lane, Redditch, WORCESTERSHIRE, B98 0RA **England**
Mr D Adams (Chief Executive)
(T) 01527 529030.

MAL STOREY ANGLING CENTRE, 129 Sutton Road, Kidderminster, WORCESTERSHIRE, DY11 6QR **England**
Mr M Storey (Proprietor)
(T) 01562 745221.

MARK DOWNES, 32 Jersey Close, Redditch, WORCESTERSHIRE, B98 9LS **England**
(T) 01527 61833.

MARK'S, 11 Raven Street, Stourport-on-Severn, WORCESTERSHIRE, DY13 8UU **England**
Mr Mark Lewis (Proprietor)
(T) 01299 871735.

MAVER (UK) LTD, Unit 87/The Washford Industrial Estate, Heming Road, Redditch, WORCESTERSHIRE, B98 0EA **England**
Mr P J Briscoe (Managing Director)
(T) 01527 510500.

PARTRIDGE OF REDDITCH LTD, Mount Pleasant, Redditch, WORCESTERSHIRE, B97 4JE **England**
Mr Ole Bjerke (Managing Director)
(T) 01527 541380.

PENN SERVICING, 33 Farleigh Road, Pershore, WORCESTERSHIRE, WR10 1LF **England**
Mr M G Simons (Proprietor)
(T) 01386 552949.

POWELLS FISHING & SHOOTING ACCESSORIES, 28 Mount Pleasant, Redditch, WORCESTERSHIRE, B97 4JB **England**
Mr Robert Powell (Proprietor)
(T) 01527 62669.

PROFISH, Unit 4/Industrial Estate, Sanders Road, Bromsgrove, WORCESTERSHIRE, B61 7DG **England**
Mr P Muddyman (Proprietor)
(T) 01527 577881.

ROY HUINS, 138 Worcester Road, Bromsgrove, WORCESTERSHIRE, B61 7AS **England**
Mr Roy Huins (Proprietor)
(T) 01527 833445.

S R LEWIS, 2 Severn Side South, Bewdley, WORCESTERSHIRE, DY12 2DX **England**
(T) 01299 403358.

SHAKESPEARE K2 CO LTD, P O Box 1, Redditch, WORCESTERSHIRE, B98 8NQ **England**
Mr John Tomsett (Managing Director)
(T) 01527 510570.

SPORTING HEIGHTS, Clay Farm, Clows Top, Kidderminster, WORCESTERSHIRE, DY14 9NN **England**
Mrs Ella Grimmell (Proprietor)
(T) 01299 832421.

SPRITE FISH HOOKS, Arrow Road North, Redditch, WORCESTERSHIRE, B98 8NT **England**
Mr V Green (Proprietor)
(T) 01527 65164.

STAN WOOD, 140 Evesham Street, Redditch, WORCESTERSHIRE, B97 4HP **England**
Mr Stanley Wood (Proprietor)
(T) 01527 64411.

THAMES FISHING TACKLE LTD, Unit 2/Mayfield Works, Mayfields, Redditch, WORCESTERSHIRE, B98 7DU **England**
Mr Nicholas Wilkes (Director)
(T) 01527 547162.

W B CLARKE, Unit 2, Briar Cl, Evesham, WORCESTERSHIRE, WR11 4JT **England**
Mr M A Attwood (Managing Director)
(T) 01386 423350.

YORKSHIRE (NORTH)

ACOMB, 227 Hamilton Drive West, York, YORKSHIRE (NORTH), YO24 4PL **England**
Mrs L Brind (Partner)
(T) 01904 785237.

ANGLERS CORNER, 41 Huby Court, York, YORKSHIRE (NORTH), YO1 9UD **England**
Mr Nigel Baker (Proprietor)
(T) 01904 629773.

BECKWITH LINES SEA TACKLE, The Cabin, Howhill Quarry Road, Beckwithshaw, Harrogate, YORKSHIRE (NORTH), HG3 1QH **England**
(T) 01423 562762.

C SWIFT, 25 Castlegate, Malton, YORKSHIRE (NORTH), YO17 7DP **England**
Mr C Swift (Partner)
(T) 01653 694580.

CASTLE FOOT TACKLE SUPPLIES, Pier Terrace, Quay Street, Scarborough, YORKSHIRE (NORTH), YO11 1PL **England**
(T) 01723 370390.

COUNTRY PASSIONS, 63 Market Place, Market Weighton, York, YORKSHIRE (NORTH), YO43 3AJ **England**
Mrs S May (Proprietor)
(T) 01430 874142.

EDWIN ASHWORTH MARINE LTD, Kirby Mills Industrial Estate, Kirkbymoorside, York, YORKSHIRE (NORTH), YO62 6NR **England**
Mrs Caroline Ashworth (Joint Director)
(T) 01751 433039.

FIELD SPORTS, 24-26 New Street, Selby, YORKSHIRE (NORTH), YO8 4PT **England**
Mr C Shipley (Proprietor)
(T) 01757 709607.

FILEY FISHING TACKLE, 12 Hope Street, Filey, YORKSHIRE (NORTH), YO14 9DL **England**
Mr R Roberts (Partner)
(T) 01723 513732.

FISH-N-THINGS, 5 Horsefair, Bridge Street, Boroughbridge, York, YORKSHIRE (NORTH), YO51 9LF **England**
Mr J Giles (Proprietor)
(T) 01423 324776.

G B ANGLING, 119 Victoria Road, Scarborough, YORKSHIRE (NORTH), YO11 1SP **England**
(T) 01723 365000.

G B ANGLING, 56 Eastborough, Scarborough, YORKSHIRE (NORTH), YO11 1NJ **England**
Mrs P Degg (Proprietor)
(T) 01723 374017.

GONE FISHING, 16 Victoria Road, Scarborough, YORKSHIRE (NORTH), YO11 1SD **England**
Mr Barry Smith (Partner)
(T) 01723 501653.

GUIDE FLY FISHING LTD, The Vivars Industrial Centre/Vivars Way, Canal Road, Selby, YORKSHIRE (NORTH), YO8 8BE **England**
Mr C Hartley (Managing Director)
(T) 01757 210812.

HARROGATE ANGLING SUPPLIES, 61 High Street, Harrogate, YORKSHIRE (NORTH), HG2 7LQ **England**
Mr S Hill (Partner)
(T) 01423 883270.

LINSLEY BROS (ESTABLISHED 1780) LTD, 55 Tower Street, Harrogate, YORKSHIRE (NORTH), HG1 1HS **England**
Mr B C Davies (Managing Director)
(T) 01423 505677.

M H & C JOHNSON, 2 Briggate, Knaresborough, YORKSHIRE (NORTH), HG5 8BH **England**
Mr M Johnson (Partner)
(T) 01423 863065.

MITRE PETS FISHING TACKLE & AQUARIUM, 212-214 Shipton Road, York, YORKSHIRE (NORTH), YO30 5RZ **England**
Mr T Nunns (Partner)
(T) 01904 654841.

NORTHALLERTON ANGLING CENTRE, 3 East Road, Northallerton, YORKSHIRE (NORTH), DL6 1ND **England**
Mr Andy Scaise (Proprietor)
(T) 01609 779140.

ORVIS CO INC, 17 Parliament Street, Harrogate, YORKSHIRE (NORTH), HG1 2QU **England**
Mr P Moore (Manager)
(T) 01423 561354.

RICHMOND ANGLING CENTRE, 8 Temple Square, Cravengate, Richmond, YORKSHIRE (NORTH), DL10 4ED **England**
Mr S Collins (Proprietor)
(T) 01748 822989.

RIPON ANGLING CENTRE, 58-59 North Street, Ripon, YORKSHIRE (NORTH), HG4 1EN **England**
Mr B Phain (Proprietor)
(T) 01765 604666.

RODS & REELS, 67 Church Street, Whitby, YORKSHIRE (NORTH), YO22 4AS **England**
Mr T Neapby (Proprietor)
(T) 01947 825079.

SCARBOROUGH ANGLING CENTRE, 7 Market Way, Scarborough, YORKSHIRE (NORTH), YO11 1HR **England**
Mr G Collins (Proprietor)
(T) 01723 381111.

SELBY ANGLING CENTRE, 69 Brook Street, Selby, YORKSHIRE (NORTH), YO8 4AL **England**
Mr Adrian Gill (Proprietor)
(T) 01757 703471.

THIRSK ANGLERS CENTRE, 7 Sowerby Road, Sowerby, Thirsk, YORKSHIRE (NORTH), YO7 1HR **England**
Mr D Stratton (Proprietor)
(T) 01845 524684.

WATERHOUSE IRVING, 32 Lady Ediths Avenue, Scarborough, YORKSHIRE (NORTH), YO12 5RB **England**
Mr I Waterhouse (Proprietor)
(T) 01723 870272.

WHITBY ANGLING SUPPLIES, 65 Haggersgate, Whitby, YORKSHIRE (NORTH), YO21 3PP **England**
Mr E Wilson (Proprietor)
(T) 01947 603855.

WILLY WORMS, Baxter Hall, Long Drax, Selby, YORKSHIRE (NORTH), YO8 8NH **England**
Mr J A Hargreaves (Managing Director)
(T) 01757 618630.

YORK TACKLE SHOP, 13 Hull Road, York, YORKSHIRE (NORTH), YO10 3JL **England**
Mr B Bell (Partner)
(T) 01904 411210.

YORKSHIRE (SOUTH)

A T WHOLESALE, Bankwood Lane, New Rossington, Doncaster, YORKSHIRE (SOUTH), DN11 0PS **England**
Mr T Pickering (Proprietor)
(T) 01302 865425.

ALAN'S, 111 Main Street, Bramley, Rotherham, YORKSHIRE (SOUTH), S66 2SE **England**
Mr Alan Tyler (Proprietor)
(T) 01709 702454.

ARMTHORPE TIGHT LINES, 45 Doncaster Road, Armthorpe, Doncaster, YORKSHIRE (SOUTH), DN3 2BU **England**
Mr K Chapman (Proprietor)
(T) 01302 302316.

BARNSLEY ANGLING CENTRE, 48-50 Sheffield Road, Hoyland, Barnsley, YORKSHIRE (SOUTH), S74 0DQ **England**
Mr A Peel (Manager)
(T) 01226 742859.

BARRY'S OF GOOLE LTD, 35 Copley Road, Doncaster, YORKSHIRE (SOUTH), DN1 2PE **England**
Mr Ian Jepson (Manager)
(T) 01302 365930.

BENNETTS OF SHEFFIELD LTD, 1 Stanley Street, Sheffield, YORKSHIRE (SOUTH), S3 8JP **England**
Mr D Duffes (General Manager)
(T) 0114-275 6756.

BILLY CLARKE, 77-81 Alderson Road, Sheffield, YORKSHIRE (SOUTH), S2 4UB **England**
Mr B Clarke (Proprietor)
(T) 0114-255 1145.

BRITANNIA ANGLING PRODUCTS LTD, Unit 3 Mill Trading Estate, Pontefract Road, Barnsley, YORKSHIRE (SOUTH), S71 1HF **England**
Mr A Clegg (Partner)
(T) 01226 247590.

C KERFOOT, 6 Southey Green Road, Sheffield, YORKSHIRE (SOUTH), S5 8GW **England**
Mr G Kerfoot (Partner)
(T) 0114-231 3265.

CALCOTT'S, 34-38 Wicker, Sheffield, YORKSHIRE (SOUTH), S3 8JB **England**
Mr S Calcott (Proprietor)
(T) 0114-272 2817.

CARP CABIN, 300-302 Greenfield Road, Sheffield, YORKSHIRE (SOUTH), S8 7RQ **England**
Mr T Flint (Proprietor)
(T) 01142 359126.

CATCH CARP BAITS, 9 Gleneagles Rise, Swinton, Mexborough, YORKSHIRE (SOUTH), S64 8TP **England**
Mrs D Parks (Proprietor)
(T) 01709 585398.

CHAPELTOWN CATCH FISHING TACKLE, 16d Station Road, Chapeltown, Sheffield, YORKSHIRE (SOUTH), S35 2XH **England**
Mr Lawrence Woodward (Proprietor)
(T) 0114-246 6670.

COUNTRY TACKLE, 2 Hough Lane, Wombwell, Barnsley, YORKSHIRE (SOUTH), S73 0DR **England**
Mr J A Smeils (Proprietor)
(T) 01226 758899.

D J ANGLING CENTRE, 1 Wortley Road, High Green, Sheffield, YORKSHIRE (SOUTH), S35 4LQ **England**
Mr D Pearce (Proprietor)
(T) 0114-284 5176.

DAVE BELL, Unit 11/Wright Business Pk, Stevens Road, Doncaster, YORKSHIRE (SOUTH), DN4 0LT **England**
Mr D Bell (Proprietor)
(T) 01302 859989.

DAWSON'S OF HILLSBOROUGH, 70 Holme Lane, Sheffield, YORKSHIRE (SOUTH), S6 4JW **England**
Mrs E Dawson (Manager)
(T) 0114-281 2178.

DONCASTER ANGLING CENTRE, 207 Carr House Road, Doncaster, YORKSHIRE (SOUTH), DN4 5DR **England**
Mr P Burton (Proprietor)
(T) 01302 363629.

E WAIT, 625 Chesterfield Road, Sheffield, YORKSHIRE (SOUTH), S8 0RX **England**
Mr G E Wait (Proprietor)
(T) 0114-258 5133.

ECCO BAITS, 101 Mill Road, Ecclesfield, Sheffield, YORKSHIRE (SOUTH), S35 9XP **England**
Mr Vic Lister (Proprietor)
(T) 01142 578637.

FRANCOS, 148 High Street, Bentley, Doncaster, YORKSHIRE (SOUTH), DN5 0AT **England**
Mr F Bezzulo (Proprietor)
(T) 01302 874888.

G & S HAMSTEAD, 14 Guardian Centre, Rotherham, YORKSHIRE (SOUTH), S65 1DD **England**
Mr G Hamstead (Proprietor)
(T) 01709 365454.

GOLDTHORPE ANGLING CENTRE, 53 High Street, Goldthorpe, Rotherham, YORKSHIRE (SOUTH), S63 9LQ **England**
Mr Russ Fowler (Proprietor)
(T) 01709 893489.

GUNNIES TACKLE, 297 Buchanan Road, Sheffield, YORKSHIRE (SOUTH), S5 8AU **England**
Mr John Gunn (Proprietor)
(T) 0114-232 1437.

HANDSWORTH ANGLING CENTRE, 7 Hendon Street, Sheffield, YORKSHIRE (SOUTH), S13 9AX **England**
Mr Richard Thorn (Partner)
(T) 0114-269 6065.

IAN'S FISHING TACKLE SHOP, 303 Prince Of Wales Road, Sheffield, YORKSHIRE (SOUTH), S2 1FH **England**
Mr Ian Marsden (Proprietor)
(T) 0114-253 1161.

KEENETS SHEFFIELD LTD, Units 1-2, Kettlebridge Road, Sheffield, YORKSHIRE (SOUTH), S9 3AJ **England**
Mr David Strafford (Proprietor)
(T) 0114-243 4550.

KILLAMARSH ANGLING CENTRE, 36 Bridge Street, Killamarsh, Sheffield, YORKSHIRE (SOUTH), S21 1AH **England**
(T) 0114-248 2648.

LAKESIDE ANGLING CENTRE, 120 Sheffield Road, Killamarsh, Sheffield, YORKSHIRE (SOUTH), S21 1EB **England**
Mr R Platts (Proprietor)
(T) 0114-251 4936.

LUREFLASH LTD, Victoria Buildings, Victoria Street, Kilnhurst, Mexborough, YORKSHIRE (SOUTH), S64 5SQ **England**
Mr S Gross (Managing Director)
(T) 01709 580238.

M D S FISHING TACKLE, 58a Clough Street, Rotherham, YORKSHIRE (SOUTH), S61 1RJ **England**
(T) 01709 512007.

MOSBOROUGH TACKLE BOX, 38b High Street, Mosborough, Sheffield, YORKSHIRE (SOUTH), S19 5AE **England**
Mr Tony Marsden (Proprietor)
(T) 0114-251 0664.

NEILS TACKLE BOX, 640 Staniforth Road, Sheffield, YORKSHIRE (SOUTH), S9 4LP **England**
(T) 0114-244 2939.

NUTRABAITS, Units C1-C2 Canklow Meadows Industrial Estate, West Bawtry Road, Rotherham, YORKSHIRE (SOUTH), S60 2XL **England**
Mr Richard Skidmore (Proprietor)
(T) 01709 370990.

OAKLEYS, 161-163 Northfield Road, Sheffield, YORKSHIRE (SOUTH), S10 1QQ **England**
Mr David Dixon (Proprietor)
(T) 0114-268 1723.

PARKES DAVE, 28 Westgate, Rotherham, YORKSHIRE (SOUTH), S60 1AP **England**
(T) 01709 363085.

PARKGATE ANGLING CENTRE, 19 Broad Street, Parkgate, Rotherham, YORKSHIRE (SOUTH), S62 6DX **England**
Mr D Lindley (Partner)
(T) 01709 527297.

PAULS FISHING TACKLE CENTRE, Doncaster Road, Denaby Main, Doncaster, YORKSHIRE (SOUTH), DN12 4HU **England**
Mr M Bacon (Manager)
(T) 01709 862558.

PEG 31, Laughton Road, Dinnington, Sheffield, YORKSHIRE (SOUTH), S25 2PT **England**
Mr John Evason (Proprietor)
(T) 01909 562552.

PEG 31, Laughton Road, Dinnington, Sheffield, YORKSHIRE (SOUTH), S31 7PN **England**
Mr John Evason (Proprietor)
(T) 01909 562552.

PEG TWO, 27 King Street, Thorne, Doncaster, YORKSHIRE (SOUTH), DN8 5AU **England**
Mr M Turner (Proprietor)
(T) 01405 814417.

PENROSE ANGLING SYSTEMS, Unit 2a Old Waleswodd Colliery, Mansfield Road, Kiveton Park, Sheffield, YORKSHIRE (SOUTH), S26 5PQ **England**
Mr M Penrose (Partner)
(T) 01909 774555.

PETE'S FISHING TACKLE, 65 Main Street, Mexborough, YORKSHIRE (SOUTH), S64 9ND **England**
Mrs Y Nadin (Proprietor)
(T) 01709 581715.

POWERPLUS CARP PRODUCTS, Foundry Street, Parkgate, Rotherham, YORKSHIRE (SOUTH), S62 6EH **England**
Miss S Towler (Partner)
(T) 01709 527752.

R & R SPORTS, 40 High Street, Bawtry, Doncaster, YORKSHIRE (SOUTH), DN10 6JE **England**
Mrs V Squire (Partner)
(T) 01302 711130.

RAINBOW ANGLING SUPPLIES, Fulwood House, Cliffefield Road, Sheffield, YORKSHIRE (SOUTH), S8 9DH **England**
Mrs H Drabble (Partner)
(T) 0114-258 9755.

ROB'S FISHING & SHOOTING, 17 Newmarket Road, Doncaster, YORKSHIRE (SOUTH), DN4 6HP **England**
Mr R W Coates (Proprietor)
(T) 01302 537237.

ROWLEY'S FISHING TACKLE, 2 High Fishergate, Doncaster, YORKSHIRE (SOUTH), DN1 1QZ **England**
Mrs Susan Rowley (Partner)
(T) 01302 369660.

SHAMROCK ANGLING PRODUCTS, Unit V1-2/Staniforth Works, Main Street, Sheffield, YORKSHIRE (SOUTH), S12 4LB **England**
Mr L Nash (Proprietor)
(T) 0114-248 6921.

SIX AM TACKLE & BAIT, 82 Worksop Road, Swallownest, Sheffield, YORKSHIRE (SOUTH), S26 4WD **England**
Mr P J Reaney (Proprietor)
(T) 0114-287 3070.

SOUTH HIENDLEY BAIT FARM, Old Colliery Farm, Main Street, South Hiendley, Barnsley, YORKSHIRE (SOUTH), S72 9BG **England**
(T) 01226 780856.

SPECIALIST ANGLING SHEFFIELD, Avon Works, Capel Street, Sheffield, YORKSHIRE (SOUTH), S6 2HL **England**
Mr J Leary (Proprietor)
(T) 01142 854612.

STAINFORTH ANGLING CENTRE, 24 Finkle Street, Stainforth, Doncaster, YORKSHIRE (SOUTH), DN7 5AL **England**
Mr S Fullwood (Proprietor)
(T) 01302 846623.

SUPABAIT, Clifton Lane, Conisbrough, Doncaster, YORKSHIRE (SOUTH), DN12 2AL **England**
Mr D Savage (Proprietor)
(T) 01709 863341.

SWALE ANGLING CENTRE, 738 Attercliffe Road, Sheffield, YORKSHIRE (SOUTH), S9 3RQ **England**
Mrs M Oldfield (Partner)
(T) 0114-243 6218.

TACKLE BOX, 7 Doncaster Road, Barnsley, YORKSHIRE (SOUTH), S70 1TH **England**
Mrs C Mcgraw (Proprietor)
(T) 01226 247131.

TARDIS TACKLE, 4 Sicey Avenue, Sheffield, YORKSHIRE (SOUTH), S5 6NE **England**
Mr D Slatter (Proprietor)
(T) 0114-243 6655.

THORNE PET & ANGLING, 5 The Green, Thorne, Doncaster, YORKSHIRE (SOUTH), DN8 5AP **England**
Mr John Eddleston (Manager)
(T) 01405 814056.

TIGHT LINES TACKLE, Glenshiel, Birley Moor Road, Sheffield, YORKSHIRE (SOUTH), S12 4WG **England**
Mr J Shaw (Proprietor)
(T) 0114-265 8178.

TONY'S TACKLE, 10 Lidget Lane, Thurnscoe, Rotherham, YORKSHIRE (SOUTH), S63 0BU **England**
Mr A Feast (Proprietor)
(T) 01709 880065.

WATERLINE ANGLING PRODUCTS LTD, 199 Neill House, Woodbourn Road, Sheffield, YORKSHIRE (SOUTH), S9 3LR **England**
Mr R Townsend (Director)
(T) 0114-276 7722.

WICKERSLEY ANGLING CENTRE, 222 Bawtry Road, Wickersley, Rotherham, YORKSHIRE (SOUTH), S66 1AA **England**
Mr Dave Ulyett (Partner)
(T) 01709 540998.

WOMBWELL ANGLING CENTRE, 25 Barnsley Road, Wombwell, Barnsley, YORKSHIRE (SOUTH), S73 8HT **England**
Mrs L D Champion (Partner)
(T) 01226 750659.

WOODLANDS ANGLING SUPPLIES, 232 Great North Road, Woodlands, Doncaster, YORKSHIRE (SOUTH), DN6 7HR **England**
Mr D Goodfellow (Proprietor)
(T) 01302 728876.

YORKSHIRE GROUNDBAITS, Unit 4/Rutland Business Pk, 50 Rutland Road, Sheffield, YORKSHIRE (SOUTH), S3 8BD **England**
Mr A Benn (Proprietor)
(T) 0114-273 7049.

YORKSHIRE (WEST)

A J JEWSON, 28 Horton Street, Halifax, YORKSHIRE (WEST), HX1 1PU **England**
Mr Graham Walters (Proprietor)
(T) 01422 354146.

ABBAY MATCH ANGLERS, 4 Bank Street, Wakefield, YORKSHIRE (WEST), WF1 1EH **England**
Mr A Jennings (Proprietor)
(T) 01924 378878.

ABBEY MATCH ANGLERS, 38 Commercial Road, Leeds, YORKSHIRE (WEST), LS5 3AQ **England**
Mr M Stanley (Manager)
(T) 01132 744562.

ADDLEES, Station Rd Corn Mills, Station Road, South Elmsall, Pontefract, YORKSHIRE (WEST), WF9 2HP **England**
Mr I Crapnell (Proprietor)
(T) 01977 658803.

ANGLING & COUNTRY SPORT, 36 Cross Green, Otley, YORKSHIRE (WEST), LS21 1HD **England**
Mrs A Thompson (Manager)
(T) 01943 462770.

ANGLING SUPPLIES, 7 Finkle Street, Pontefract, YORKSHIRE (WEST), WF8 1HE **England**
Mr Glen Humphries (Proprietor)
(T) 01977 780377.

ANTHONY SEED, Pennine Industrial Estate, Modder Place, Armley, Leeds, YORKSHIRE (WEST), LS12 3ES **England**
Mr A Seed (Manager)
(T) 0113-231 1007.

ARMLEY ANGLING CENTRE, 14 Branch Road, Armley, Leeds, YORKSHIRE (WEST), LS12 3AQ **England**
Mr Stephen Willis (Proprietor)
(T) 0113-279 0738.

BOB'S TACKLE SHOP, 1a Chapel Lane, Garforth, Leeds, YORKSHIRE (WEST), LS25 1AG **England**
Mr Robert Snowdon (Proprietor)
(T) 0113-286 7112.

CALDER ANGLING SUPPLIES, 39a Rastrick Common, Brighouse, YORKSHIRE (WEST), HD6 3DW **England**
Mr John Gledhill (Proprietor)
(T) 01484 711063.

CASTLEFORD ANGLING SUPPLIES, 143 Lower Oxford Street, Castleford, YORKSHIRE (WEST), WF10 4AQ **England**
Mrs Y Starbuck (Proprietor)
(T) 01977 550465.

E & J COOTE, 20 Middleton Park Road, Leeds, YORKSHIRE (WEST), LS10 3ST **England**
Mr E Coote (Partner)
(T) 0113-276 0034.

ERICS ANGLING CENTRE, 401 Selby Road, Leeds, YORKSHIRE (WEST), LS15 7AY **England**
Mr E Smith (Proprietor)
(T) 0113-264 6883.

FAGINS FISHING TACKLE, 6 Bradford Road, Huddersfield, YORKSHIRE (WEST), HD1 6HY **England**
Mr A Fergusson (Proprietor)
(T) 01484 451118.

FEATHERSTONE ANGLERS, 15-17 Station Lane, Featherstone, Pontefract, YORKSHIRE (WEST), WF7 5BE **England**
Mr N Inman (Proprietor)
(T) 01977 602822.

FRED ALEXANDER, 3 The Springs, Wakefield, YORKSHIRE (WEST), WF1 1PU **England**
Mr R Gorbutt (Proprietor)
(T) 01924 373820.

GEE TEE, 13 Briggate, Silsden, Keighley, YORKSHIRE (WEST), BD20 9JS **England**
Mr G Trigg (Proprietor)
(T) 01535 655555.

GRAHAM'S, 57 Cross Bank Road, Batley, YORKSHIRE (WEST), WF17 8PN **England**
Mr G Athey (Proprietor)
(T) 01924 442040.

GUISELEY ANGLING CENTRE, 84 Otley Road, Guiseley, Leeds, YORKSHIRE (WEST), LS20 8BH **England**
Mr Colin Spencer (Proprietor)
(T) 01943 879938.

HEADINGLEY ANGLING CENTRE, 58 North Lane, Headingley, Leeds, YORKSHIRE (WEST), LS6 3HU **England**
Mr Richard Thorne (Proprietor)
(T) 0113-278 4445.

J T RODGERS, 12 Barwick Road, Leeds, YORKSHIRE (WEST), LS15 7QG **England**
Mr P Stead (Proprietor)
(T) 0113-264 1195.

K & L TACKLE, 131 Mornington Street, Keighley, YORKSHIRE (WEST), BD21 2EB **England**
Mr D Ward (Proprietor)
(T) 01535 667574.

KIRKGATE ANGLERS, 95 Kirkgate, Leeds, YORKSHIRE (WEST), LS2 7DJ **England**
Mr P Edge (Proprietor)
(T) 0113-243 4880.

KNOTTINGLEY PET & ANGLING, 4 The Arcade, Hill Top, Knottingley, YORKSHIRE (WEST), WF11 8EA **England**
Mrs A Heppinstaw (Proprietor)
(T) 01977 670687.

LOWER WHARFE ANGLING CENTRE, 236 High Street, Boston Spa, Wetherby, YORKSHIRE (WEST), LS23 6AD **England**
Mr M Hope (Proprietor)
(T) 01937 844260.

MERLIN BAIT PRODUCTS LTD, Unit 10, Langthwaite Road, South Kirkby, Pontefract, YORKSHIRE (WEST), WF9 3AP **England**
Mr J Brooks (Director)
(T) 01977 651349.

MERLIN BAIT PRODUCTS LTD, Unit 12, Lidgate Cr, South Kirkby, Pontefract, YORKSHIRE (WEST), WF9 3NS **England**
Mr I Crackell (Managing Director)
(T) 01977 651349.

MORLEY MATCH ANGLERS, 47a Queen Street, Morley, Leeds, YORKSHIRE (WEST), LS27 8EE **England**
Mr A Perkins (Proprietor)
(T) 01132 537688.

NIGEL HIRST, 727 Huddersfield Road, Dewsbury, YORKSHIRE (WEST), WF13 3LQ **England**
Mr N Hirst (Proprietor)
(T) 01924 491275.

OUTWOOD ANGLING CENTRE, 557-559 Leeds Road, Wakefield, YORKSHIRE (WEST), WF1 2JL **England**
Mr R Hope (Manager)
(T) 01924 835443.

PREMIER ANGLING CENTRE, 66-68 Station Lane, Featherstone, Pontefract, YORKSHIRE (WEST), WF7 5BB **England**
Mr Paul Chambers (Partner)
(T) 01977 706921.

R D MEDLEY, Grove Farm/Dewsbury Road, Churwell, Morley, Leeds, YORKSHIRE (WEST), LS27 8PW **England**
Mr Robert Medley (Manager)
(T) 0113-238 1301.

RICHMONDS, 71 Park Road, Bradford, YORKSHIRE (WEST), BD5 0SG **England**
Mr K Thomson (Partner)
(T) 01274 721042.

ROBERTS CHRIS, 22 Chapel Hill, Huddersfield, YORKSHIRE (WEST), HD1 3EB **England**
Mr C Roberts (Proprietor)
(T) 01484 545032.

S & B DAVISON, Pontefract Road, Crofton, Wakefield, YORKSHIRE (WEST), WF4 1LW **England**
Mr B Davison (Partner)
(T) 01924 864416.

S M F BAIT SUPPLIES, Swales Moor Road, Halifax, YORKSHIRE (WEST), HX3 6UF **England**
(T) 01422 353325.

SPENBOROUGH ANGLING CENTRE, Brook Forge, Hightown Road, Cleckheaton, YORKSHIRE (WEST), BD19 5JS **England**
Mr Andrew Halford (Proprietor)
(T) 01274 852764.

SWILLINGTON GAME FISHING, Home Farm, Wakefield Road, Swillington, Leeds, YORKSHIRE (WEST), LS26 8UA **England**
(T) 0113-287 5685.

TACKLE BOX, 22 Cross Hills, Kippax, Leeds, YORKSHIRE (WEST), LS25 7JP **England**
Mr Roy Evans (Proprietor)
(T) 0113-286 1435.

TACKLE SHOP, 58 North Road, Kirkburton, Huddersfield, YORKSHIRE (WEST), HD8 0RH **England**
Mr A Mallinson (Proprietor)
(T) 01484 606006.

WATERCRAFT PRODUCTS, 899 Harrogate Road, Bradford, YORKSHIRE (WEST), BD10 0QY **England**
Mr J Gilpen (Proprietor)
(T) 01274 620173.

WESTGATE ANGLERS, 63 Westgate, Bradford, YORKSHIRE (WEST), BD1 2RD **England**
Mr Matthew Green (Manager)
(T) 01274 729570.

WIBSEY ANGLING CENTRE, 208 High Street, Wibsey, Bradford, YORKSHIRE (WEST), BD6 1QP **England**
(T) 01274 604542.

IRELAND

COUNTY CARLOW

MA MCCULLAGH, Market Square, Muine Bheag, COUNTY CARLOW, **Ireland**
(T) 00 353 50 321 381.

COUNTY CAVAN

FLYING SPORTSMAN, Carrick Street, Kells, COUNTY CAVAN, **Ireland**
(T) 00 353 46 40 205.

JOE MULLIGAN, Main Street, Shercock, COUNTY CAVAN, **Ireland**
(T) 00 353 42 966 9184.

JOE O'LOUGHLIN, Main Street, Lisdoonvarna, COUNTY CAVAN, **Ireland**
(T) 00 353 65 707 4038.

MCM SPORTS, Main Street, Killeshandra, COUNTY CAVAN, **Ireland**
(T) 00 353 49 433 4438.

RAYMOND LLOYD, Main Street, Bailieboro, COUNTY CAVAN, **Ireland**
(T) 00 353 42 966 5032.

SPORTS WORLD, Townhall Street, Cavan, COUNTY CAVAN, **Ireland**
(T) 00 353 49 433 1812.

COUNTY CLARE

PATRICK CLEARY, Westcliffe Lodge, Spainish Port, COUNTY CLARE, **Ireland**
(T) 00 353 65 708 4037.

PATRICK CRONIN, Barrack Street, Ennis, COUNTY CLARE, **Ireland**
(T) 00 353 65 684 2055.

RIVERBANK FISHING SHOP, Main Street, Sixmilebridge, COUNTY CLARE, **Ireland**
(T) 00 353 61 369 633.

TJ'S FISHING TACKLE AND ANGLING CENTRE, Ballina, Killaloe, COUNTY CLARE, **Ireland**
(T) 00 353 61 376 009.

COUNTY CORK

BAOITE MARA TEO, Cape Clear, Skibbereen, COUNTY CORK, **Ireland**
(T) 00 353 28 39 148.

BILL COLLINS, Killinardish House, Carrigadrohid, COUNTY CORK, **Ireland**
(T) 00 353 26 48 288.

BLAST BAITS, Rushbrooke Commual Park, Rushbrooke, Cobh, COUNTY CORK, **Ireland**
(T) 00 353 21 814 880.

CB CYCLES, 18 Main Street, Kinsale, COUNTY CORK, **Ireland**
(T) 00 353 21 774 884.

CLONTACKLE, Spillers Lane, Bridge Street, Clonakilty, COUNTY CORK, **Ireland**
(T) 00 353 23 35 580.

COBH FISHING TACKLE, Sycamore House, Ballynoe, Cobh, COUNTY CORK, **Ireland**
(T) 00 353 21 812 167.

DECO'S CYCLES, 18 Main Street, Kinsale, COUNTY CORK, **Ireland**
(T) 00 353 21 477 4884.

FALLONS SPORTS SHOP, North Street, Skibbereen, COUNTY CORK, **Ireland**
(T) 00 353 28 22 264.

JEFFERSPORTS, 7 Pearse Street, Bandon, COUNTY CORK, **Ireland**
(T) 00 353 23 41 133.

MURRAY TW AND CO LIMITED, 87 Patrick Street, Cork, COUNTY CORK, **Ireland**
(T) 00 353 21 271 089.

RIVERS EDGE TACKLE, Inniscarra Road, Carrigrohane, Cork, COUNTY CORK, **Ireland**
(T) 00 353 21 487 1771.

TACKLE SHOP, Lavitts Quay, Cork, COUNTY CORK, **Ireland**
(T) 00 353 21 427 2842.

TH SPORTS LIMITED, Main Street, Midleton, COUNTY CORK, **Ireland**
(T) 00 353 21 631 800.

TOOMEY BRIAN SPORTS AND LEISURE, 18 McCurtain Street, Fermoy, COUNTY CORK, **Ireland**
(T) 00 353 25 31 101.

COUNTY DONEGAL

CHARLES BONNER, The Bridge, Dungloe, COUNTY DONEGAL, **Ireland**
(T) 00 353 75 21 163.

CHAS JOS DOHERTY, Main Street, Donegal, COUNTY DONEGAL, **Ireland**
(T) 00 353 73 21 119.

COUNTY DUBLIN

ABC FISHING TACKLE SPECIALISTS, 15 Mary's Abbey, Dublin 7, COUNTY DUBLIN, **Ireland**
(T) 00 353 87 31 525.

ANGLING AND SHOOTING CENTRE, Ballydowd, Lucan, COUNTY DUBLIN, **Ireland**
(T) 00 353 16 281 112.

BOLANDS HARDWARE, 349 Ballyfermot Road, Ballyfermont, Dublin 10, COUNTY DUBLIN, **Ireland**
(T) 00 353 16 264 777.

CATCH TACKLE, 26 Sion Hill Road, Drumcondra, Dublin 9, COUNTY DUBLIN, **Ireland**
(T) 00 353 18 376 326.

CLEERE PATRICK AND SON LIMITED, 5 Bedford Row, Dublin 2, COUNTY DUBLIN, **Ireland**
(T) 00 353 16 777 406.

CYCLE AND ARMY STORE, 38 Castlelands, Balbriggan, COUNTY DUBLIN, **Ireland**
(T) 00 353 18 413 597.

DUN LAOGHAIRE ANGLING, 129 George's Street, Dun Laoghaire, COUNTY DUBLIN, **Ireland**
(T) 00 353 12 842 462.

GAYNESTOWN, Main Street, Blanchardstown, Dublin 15, COUNTY DUBLIN, **Ireland**
(T) 00 353 18 201 127.

GLASLOCH, 9 South Circular Road, Dublin 8, COUNTY DUBLIN, **Ireland**
(T) 00 353 14 755 429.

HENRY'S TACKLE SHOP, 19 Ballybough Road, Dublin 3, COUNTY DUBLIN, **Ireland**
(T) 00 353 18 555 218.

JOE'S ANGLING, 326 Clontarf Road, Dollymount, Dublin 3, COUNTY DUBLIN, **Ireland**
(T) 00 353 18 330 312.

RORY'S FISHING TACKLE, 17a Temple Bar, Dublin 2, COUNTY DUBLIN, **Ireland**
(T) 00 353 16 772 351.

SOUTHSIDE ANGLING, 80 Clanbrssil Street, Dublin 8, COUNTY DUBLIN, **Ireland**
(T) 00 353 14 530 266.

TALLAGHT ROD AND GUN SHOP, 2 Castletymon, Tallaght, Dublin 24, COUNTY DUBLIN, **Ireland**
(T) 00 353 14 526 522.

WATTS BROS LIMITED, 18 Upper Ormond Quay, Dublin 7, COUNTY DUBLIN, **Ireland**
(T) 00 353 16 778 574.

COUNTY FERMANAGH

MULLEN PET AND SHOOTING SUPPLIES, Sligo Road, Enniskillen, COUNTY FERMANAGH, **Ireland**

COUNTY GALWAY

DUFFY'S FISHING AND SHOOTING, 5 Mainguard Street, Galway, COUNTY GALWAY, **Ireland**
(T) 00 353 91 562 367.

FREENEY'S, High Street, Galway, COUNTY GALWAY, **Ireland**
(T) 00 353 91 568 794.

KYNE ANNE, Clonbur, COUNTY GALWAY, **Ireland**
(T) 00 353 92 46 197.

TUCK THOMAS, Oughterard, COUNTY GALWAY, **Ireland**
(T) 00 353 91 552 335.

COUNTY KERRY

HALPIN JIM SHOOTING SUPPLIES LIMITED, William Street, Listowel, COUNTY KERRY, **Ireland**
(T) 00 353 68 22 392.

LANDERS LEISURE LINES, Courthouse Lane, Tralee, COUNTY KERRY, **Ireland**
(T) 00 353 66 712 6644.

LAUNE SPORTS, 34 Langford Street, Killorglin, COUNTY KERRY, **Ireland**
(T) 00 353 66 976 1404.

O'NEILLS, Plunkett Street, Killarney, COUNTY KERRY, **Ireland**
(T) 00 353 64 31 970.

TADHG O'SULLIVAN, Ferraneraigh, Caherdaniel, COUNTY KERRY, **Ireland**
(T) 00 353 66 947 5384.

COUNTY KILDARE

CONLON NOEL AND SONS, Eyre Street, Newbridge, COUNTY KILDARE, **Ireland**
(T) 00 353 45 433 311.

COUNTRYMAN ANGLING AND GAME SUPPLIES LIMITED, Pacelli Road, Naas, COUNTY KILDARE, **Ireland**
(T) 00 353 45 879 341.

GRIFFIN HAWE LIMITED, 22 Duke Street, Athy, COUNTY KILDARE, **Ireland**
(T) 00 353 50 731 221.

MA FINLAY AND SONS LIMITED, Monasterevin, COUNTY KILDARE, **Ireland**
(T) 00 353 45 525 331.

TACKLE BOX, Eyre Street, Newbridge, COUNTY KILDARE, **Ireland**
(T) 00 353 45 435 853.

COUNTY KILKENNY

HOOK LINE AND SINKER, 31 Rose Inn Street, Kilkenny, COUNTY KILKENNY, **Ireland**
(T) 00 353 56 71 699.

TOWN AND COUNTRY SPORTS SHOP, 82 High Street, Kilkenny, COUNTY KILKENNY, **Ireland**
(T) 00 353 56 24 517.

COUNTY LAOIS

HYLAND FISHING TACKLE, Main Street, Portarlington, COUNTY LAOIS, **Ireland**
(T) 00 353 50 223 456.

PORTARLINGTON AUTO PARTS, Main Street, Portarlington, COUNTY LAOIS, **Ireland**
(T) 00 353 50 223 456.

COUNTY LEITRIM

TOOMAN ANGLING AND LEISURE, Bridge Street, Carrick on Shannon, COUNTY LEITRIM, **Ireland**
(T) 00 353 78 21 872.

TOOMAN BAIT AND TACKLE, Bornacoola Dromod, Leitrim, COUNTY LEITRIM, **Ireland**
(T) 00 353 43 24 119.

COUNTY LIMERICK

BONDS TACKLE, 40 Wickham Street, Limerick, COUNTY LIMERICK, **Ireland**
(T) 00 353 61 316 809.

LIMERICK ANGLING CENTRE, 3 John Street, Limerick, COUNTY LIMERICK, **Ireland**
(T) 00 353 61 316 637.

MIKES TACKLE CENTRE, 281 Hyde Road, Limerick, COUNTY LIMERICK, **Ireland**
(T) 00 353 61 312 663.

STEVES FISHING AND SHOOTING STORES, 7 Denmark Street, Limerick, COUNTY LIMERICK, **Ireland**
(T) 00 353 61 413 484.

COUNTY LONGFORD

DENNISTON EDWARD AND CO LIMITED, Centenary Square, Longford, COUNTY LONGFORD, **Ireland**
(T) 00 353 43 46 345.

J AND B HOLMES, Main Street, Lanesboro, COUNTY LONGFORD, **Ireland**
(T) 00 353 43 21 491.

J AND M GIFT STORES LIMITED, Main Street, Edgeworthstown, COUNTY LONGFORD, **Ireland**
(T) 00 353 43 71 285.

TOOMAN ANGLING AND LEISURE, 34 Main Street, Longford, COUNTY LONGFORD, **Ireland**
(T) 00 353 43 45 151.

COUNTY LOUTH

ARDEE SPORTS COMPANY LIMITED, Pepperstown, Ardee, COUNTY LOUTH, **Ireland**
(T) 00 353 41 685 3711.

DROGHEDA ANGLING CENTRE, 2 Stockwell Close, Drogheda, COUNTY LOUTH, **Ireland**
(T) 00 353 41 984 5442.

ISLAND FISHING TACKLE AND FIREARMS, 58 Park Street, Dundalk, COUNTY LOUTH, **Ireland**
(T) 00 353 42 933 5698.

COUNTY MAYO

ERRIS AUTOPARTS AND ACCESSORIES, Belmullet, COUNTY MAYO, **Ireland**
(T) 00 353 97 82 093.

MAYO FLYCRAFT, Rathbawn Drive, Castlebar, COUNTY MAYO, **Ireland**
(T) 00 353 94 22 757.

MJ NALLEN FISHING TACKLE SHOP, Belmullet, COUNTY MAYO, **Ireland**
(T) 00 353 97 82 093.

RIDGE POOL TACKLE SHOP, Cathedral Road, Ballina, COUNTY MAYO, **Ireland**
(T) 00 353 96 72 656.

WALKIN'S FISHING TACKLE, Tone Street, Ballina, COUNTY MAYO, **Ireland**
(T) 00 353 96 22 442.

COUNTY MEATH

SPORTSDEN, Trimgate Street, Navan, COUNTY MEATH, **Ireland**
(T) 00 353 46 21 130.

COUNTY MONAGHAN

MC GRAHAM, Old Cross Square, Monaghan, COUNTY MONAGHAN, **Ireland**
(T) 00 353 47 71 453.

COUNTY OFFALY

TACKLE SHOP, Rahan, Tullamore, COUNTY OFFALY, **Ireland**
(T) 00 353 50 655 979.

COUNTY ROSCOMMON

CHRISTOPHER WYNNE, Main Street, Boyle, COUNTY ROSCOMMON, **Ireland**
(T) 00 353 79 62 456.

JOHN TRAPPER, Castlerea Road, Tulsk, COUNTY ROSCOMMON, **Ireland**
(T) 00 353 78 39 181.

COUNTY SLIGO

BARTON SMITH, Hyde Bridge, Sligo, COUNTY SLIGO, **Ireland**
(T) 00 353 71 42 356.

KINGFISHER BATES, Pier Road, Enniscrone, COUNTY SLIGO, **Ireland**
(T) 00 353 96 36 733.

COUNTY TIPPERARY

OPEN SEASON, 55 Kenyon Street, Nenagh, COUNTY TIPPERARY, **Ireland**
(T) 00 353 67 31 774.

ROBIN HOODS OUTDOOR STORE, 34-35 Croke Street, Thurles, COUNTY TIPPERARY, **Ireland**
(T) 00 353 50 424 724.

COUNTY WATERFORD

ARMY AND OUTDOOR STORES, New Street, Waterford, COUNTY WATERFORD, **Ireland**
(T) 00 353 51 857 554.

BAUMANN O AND SONS LIMITED, 6 St Mary Street, Dungarvan, COUNTY WATERFORD, **Ireland**
(T) 00 353 58 41 395.

SHOOT'N AND FISH'N, 26a Ballybricken, Waterford, COUNTY WATERFORD, **Ireland**
(T) 00 353 51 878 007.

COUNTY WESTMEATH

DAVID O'MALLEY, 33 Dominick Street, Mullingar, COUNTY WESTMEATH, **Ireland**
(T) 00 353 44 48 300.

OUTDOOR PURSUITS, 35 Dominick Street, Mullingar, COUNTY WESTMEATH, **Ireland**
(T) 00 353 44 48 306.

SAMS TACKLE, Castle Street, Mullingar, COUNTY WESTMEATH, **Ireland**
(T) 00 353 44 40 431.

STRAND FISHING TACKLE, Strand Athlone (86), COUNTY WESTMEATH, **Ireland**
(T) 00 353 90 279 277.

COUNTY WEXFORD

HAYES CYCLES, 108 Main Street South, Wexford, COUNTY WEXFORD, **Ireland**
(T) 00 353 53 22 462.

MURPHY'S FISHING TACKLE SHOP, 92 North Street, Wexford, COUNTY WEXFORD, **Ireland**
(T) 00 353 53 24 717.

COUNTY WICKLOW

NATIONAL DISABLE ANGLING FACILITY LIMITED, Redna Road, Aughrim, COUNTY WICKLOW, **Ireland**
(T) 00 353 40 236 552.

VIKING TACKLE BRAY, Unit 5 Everst Centre, Castle Street, Bray, COUNTY WICKLOW, **Ireland**
(T) 00 353 28 69 215.

NEWPORT

MCGEES COUNTRY SPORTS, Main Street, Newport, NEWPORT, **Ireland**
(T) 00 353 98 41 433.

NORTHERN IRELAND

COUNTY ANTRIM

BUSHSIDE TACKLES, 108 Main Street, Bushmills, COUNTY ANTRIM, BT57 8QD **Northern Ireland**
Mr N Blaney (Proprietor)
(T) 02820 732700.

C F BEATTIE, 39 Main Street, Ballycarry, Carrickfergus, COUNTY ANTRIM, BT38 9HH **Northern Ireland**
(T) 02893 353462.

CASAAY BAITS TACKLE, 39 Main Street, Bushmills, COUNTY ANTRIM, BT57 8QA **Northern Ireland**
Mr J Maclaughlan (Proprietor)
(T) 02890 730025.

COUNTRY SPORTS & TACKLE, 9 Rough Lane, Antrim, COUNTY ANTRIM, BT41 2QG **Northern Ireland**
Mr V Hatliss (Proprietor)
(T) 02894 467378.

FALCON, 66a Ballygomartin Road, Belfast, COUNTY ANTRIM, BT13 3NE **Northern Ireland**
Mrs J Chestnutt (Proprietor)
(T) 02890 710711.

GET HOOKED, 49 Suffolk Road, Belfast, COUNTY ANTRIM, BT11 9PB **Northern Ireland**
Mr Michael O'neil (Proprietor)
(T) 02890 623431.

GUNS & TACKLE, 9 Smithfield, Lisburn, COUNTY ANTRIM, BT28 1TH **Northern Ireland**
Mr F Johnston (Manager)
(T) 02892 677975.

J S MULLAN, 74 Main Street, Portrush, COUNTY ANTRIM, BT56 8BN **Northern Ireland**
Mr J Mullan (Proprietor)
(T) 02870 822209.

JOSEPH BRADDELL & SONS LTD, 11 North Street, Belfast, COUNTY ANTRIM, BT1 1NA **Northern Ireland**
Mr Charlie Costley (Proprietor)
(T) 02890 320525.

LARNE ANGLING CENTRE, 128 Main Street, Larne, COUNTY ANTRIM, BT40 1RG **Northern Ireland**
Mr G Bodless (Proprietor)
(T) 02828 270404.

MOYLE OUTDOOR ANGLING & LEISURE, 17 Castle Street, Ballycastle, COUNTY ANTRIM, BT54 6AS **Northern Ireland**
Mr D Mccolly (Proprietor)
(T) 02820 769521.

O'NEILL COUNTRY SPORTS, 25 Mill Street, Cushendall, Ballymena, COUNTY ANTRIM, BT44 0RR **Northern Ireland**
Mr Tom O'neill (Proprietor)
(T) 02821 772009.

OUT & ABOUT, 159a Shore Road, Newtownabbey, COUNTY ANTRIM, BT37 9SZ **Northern Ireland**
Mr M Whiteside (Proprietor)
(T) 02890 854096.

SPENCE BROS, 32 New Street, Randalstown, Antrim, COUNTY ANTRIM, BT41 3AF **Northern Ireland**
(T) 02894 472248.

T MCCUTCHEON, 114 Sandy Row, Belfast, COUNTY ANTRIM, BT12 5EX **Northern Ireland**
Mr T Mccutcheon (Proprietor)
(T) 02890 249509.

TACKLEBOX, 508a Falls Road, Belfast, COUNTY ANTRIM, BT12 6EP **Northern Ireland**
(T) 02890 600637.

TIGHT LINES, 198-200 Albertbridge Road, Belfast, COUNTY ANTRIM, BT5 4GU **Northern Ireland**
Mr Alistair Smith (Proprietor)
(T) 02890 457357.

VILLAGE TACKLE SHOP, 55a Newtownbreda Road, Belfast, COUNTY ANTRIM, BT8 7BS **Northern Ireland**
Mr Richard Johnson (Proprietor)
(T) 02890 491916.

COUNTY ARMAGH

FIRST BITE, Unit 5 Foundry Street, Portadown, Craigavon, COUNTY ARMAGH, BT63 5AB **Northern Ireland**
Mr David Trimbley (Proprietor)
(T) 02890 393361.

PREMIER ANGLING CENTRE, 17 Queen Street, Lurgan, Craigavon, COUNTY ARMAGH, BT66 8BQ **Northern Ireland**
Mr Alan Ball (Proprietor)
(T) 02838 325204.

COUNTY DOWN

COMBER ANGLING & COUNTRY PURSUITS, 23 Bridge Street, Comber, Newtownards, COUNTY DOWN, BT23 5AT **Northern Ireland**
Mr John Rowan (Proprietor)
(T) 02891 870777.

FLY BOX, 95a Burren Road, Ballynahinch, COUNTY DOWN, BT24 8LF **Northern Ireland**
(T) 02897 533311.

KILKEEL FISHING SUPPLIES, The Harbour, Kilkeel, Newry, COUNTY DOWN, BT34 4AX **Northern Ireland**
(T) 02841 769122.

MCKEES'S OF BANGOR, 59 Church Street, Bangor, COUNTY DOWN, BT20 3HX **Northern Ireland**
(T) 02891 454983.

NORTHERN IRELAND FISH PRODUCERS ORGANISATION LTD, The Harbour, Rooney Road, Kilkeel, Newry, COUNTY DOWN, BT34 4AG **Northern Ireland**
Mr R Annett (Manager)
(T) 02841769580.

TACKLE SHOP, Unit 5 Old Mill, Ballydown Road, Banbridge, COUNTY DOWN, BT32 4JB **Northern Ireland**
Mr S Dunlop (Proprietor)
(T) 02840 622226.

TRAP & TACKLE, 6 Seacliff Road, Bangor, COUNTY DOWN, BT20 5EY **Northern Ireland**
Mr John Ross (Proprietor)
(T) 02891 458515.

COUNTY FERMANAGH

ERNE TACKLE, 118 Main Street, Lisnaskea, Enniskillen, COUNTY FERMANAGH, BT92 0JD **Northern Ireland**
Mr M Emerson (Proprietor)
(T) 02867 721969.

FRANKIE MCPHILLIPS FLY-DRESSER, The Butter Market, Down Street, Enniskillen, COUNTY FERMANAGH, BT74 7DU **Northern Ireland**
Mr Frankie McPhillips (Proprietor)
(T) 02866 323047.

HOME FIELD & STREAM, 18 Church Street, Enniskillen, COUNTY FERMANAGH, BT74 7EJ **Northern Ireland**
Mr Trevor Kingston (Director)
(T) 02866 322114.

MULLEN'S PET & SHOOTING SUPPLIES, Unit 1 Sligo Road, Enniskillen, COUNTY FERMANAGH, BT74 7JY **Northern Ireland**
Mr K Mullen (Proprietor)
(T) 02866 324975.

COUNTY LONDONDERRY

ALBERT ATKINS, 71 Coleraine Road, Garvagh, Coleraine, COUNTY LONDONDERRY, BT51 5HR **Northern Ireland**
Mr A Atkins (Proprietor)
(T) 02829557691.

GREAT OUTDOORS, 21 Society Street, Coleraine, COUNTY LONDONDERRY, BT52 1LA **Northern Ireland**
Mr P Neeson (Proprietor)
(T) 02870 320701.

ROD & LINE, 1 Clarendon Street, Londonderry, COUNTY LONDONDERRY, BT48 7EP **Northern Ireland**
Mr T C Hutchman (Proprietor)
(T) 02871 262877.

SMYTHS COUNTRY SPORTS, 1 Park Street, Coleraine, COUNTY LONDONDERRY, BT52 1BD **Northern Ireland**
Mr S Smyth (Proprietor)
(T) 02870 343970.

TOM'S TACKLE SHOP, The Gate Lodge, 31 Ardlough Road, Londonderry, COUNTY LONDONDERRY, BT47 5SP **Northern Ireland**
Mr Tom Mcglinchey (Proprietor)
(T) 02871 346265.

COUNTY TYRONE

CAMPBELLS, 12 Killymore Road, Newtownstewart, Omagh, COUNTY TYRONE, BT78 4DT **Northern Ireland**
(T) 02881 661543.

CHISM FISHING TACKLE, 2 Bridge Street, Omagh, COUNTY TYRONE, BT78 1BX **Northern Ireland**
(T) 02882 244932.

DENNETT GAME SERVICES, Lisnaragh Road, Dunamanagh, Strabane, COUNTY TYRONE, BT82 0SA **Northern Ireland**
Mr A Gamble (Proprietor)
(T) 02871 398235.

DIVERS TACKLE, 5 Castle Place, Strabane, COUNTY TYRONE, BT82 8AW **Northern Ireland**
Mr William Diver (Proprietor)
(T) 02871 883021.

FIELD & STREAM, 24 Charlemont Street, Moy, Dungannon, COUNTY TYRONE, BT71 7SL **Northern Ireland**
Mr I Cowan (Proprietor)
(T) 02887 789533.

LAKEVIEW TACKLE GUNS AND ACCESSORIES, 106 Ballygawley Road, Dungannon, COUNTY TYRONE, BT70 1TA **Northern Ireland**
Mr J Mcnulty (Proprietor)
(T) 02887 761133.

N M TACKLE, 8 Fyfin Road, Victoria Bridge, Strabane, COUNTY TYRONE, BT82 9JQ **Northern Ireland**
Mr J Gough (Proprietor)
(T) 02881 659501.

SMITH & CO, 63 Market Street, Omagh, COUNTY TYRONE, BT79 0AA **Northern Ireland**
Mr J Smith (Proprietor)
(T) 02882 242534.

SCOTLAND

ABERDEENSHIRE

ALEX STRACHAN, School Street, Fraserburgh, ABERDEENSHIRE, AB43 5XY **Scotland**
(T) 01346 518449.

ANDERSON COUNTRY WEAR, 39 New Street, Rothes, Aberlour, ABERDEENSHIRE, AB38 7BQ **Scotland**
(T) 01340 831407.

ANDERSON COUNTRY WEAR, 77 High Street, Aberlour, ABERDEENSHIRE, AB38 9QB **Scotland**
Mrs A Anderson (Proprietor)
(T) 01340 871570.

ATHOLL COUNTRYWARE LTD, 8 Bridge Street, Banchory, ABERDEENSHIRE, AB31 5SX **Scotland**
(T) 01330 824319.

AVCOR FLIES, 4 Millburn Street, Aberdeen, ABERDEENSHIRE, AB11 6SS **Scotland**
Mrs Linda Craig (Partner)
(T) 01224 212490.

BALGOWNIE SPORTS SHOP (SHOOTING & FISHING) LTD, 23 Scotstown Road, Bridge of Don, Aberdeen, ABERDEENSHIRE, AB22 8HH **Scotland**
Mr I Muir (Proprietor)
(T) 01224 826232.

BANFFSHIRE FISHSELLING CO, 21 Shore Street, MacDuff, ABERDEENSHIRE, AB44 1TX **Scotland**
Mr A West (Director)
(T) 01261 832891.

BRDR MARKUSSENS, 1 Frederick Street, Inverallochy, Fraserburgh, ABERDEENSHIRE, AB43 5XX **Scotland**
Mr D Reid (Manager)
(T) 01346 583200.

C NETS, Slacks Of Braeside, Auchnagatt, Ellon, ABERDEENSHIRE, AB41 8YE **Scotland**
Mrs Carol Crutchfield (Partner)
(T) 01358 701308.

COTESI UK LTD, South Percyhorner Farm, Fraserburgh, ABERDEENSHIRE, AB43 7EH **Scotland**
(T) 01346 517723.

COUNTRYWEAR, 15 Bridge Street, Ballater, ABERDEENSHIRE, AB35 5QP **Scotland**
Mr N Clements (Proprietor)
(T) 01339 755453.

FAITHLIE TRAWL, Commerce Street, Fraserburgh, ABERDEENSHIRE, AB43 5LP **Scotland**
(T) 01346 517625.

FALCON FISHING GEAR LTD, 9 Ugie Street, Peterhead, ABERDEENSHIRE, AB42 1US **Scotland**
Mr Robbie Davidson (Director)
(T) 01779 478186.

FRASER'S FISHING TACKLE, 32 Marischal Street, Aberdeen, ABERDEENSHIRE, AB11 5AJ **Scotland**
Mr Keith Fraser (Proprietor)
(T) 01224 590221.

G K N CHEP LTD, Fraserburgh Harbour, Fraserburgh, ABERDEENSHIRE, AB43 8TL **Scotland**
(T) 01346 517335.

GENESIS NET STORE, Crook O Ness Street, MacDuff, ABERDEENSHIRE, AB44 1QS **Scotland**
Mr D Watt (Partner)
(T) 01261 833884.

J A J MUNRO, 93-95 High Street, Aberlour, ABERDEENSHIRE, AB38 9PB **Scotland**
Mr H E Mitchill (Proprietor)
(T) 01340 871428.

OCEAN FISHSELLING CO LTD, Steamboat Quay, Fraserburgh, ABERDEENSHIRE, AB43 9EE **Scotland**
Mr A Buckthorp (Manager)
(T) 01346 518461.

SEAWAY NET CO, Station Brae, MacDuff, ABERDEENSHIRE, AB44 1UL **Scotland**
(T) 01261 832877.

SHARPE'S OF ABERDEEN, Deveron Mill, Glass, Huntly, ABERDEENSHIRE, AB54 4XH **Scotland**
Mr J G Metclaffe (Chief Executive)
(T) 01466 700257.

SOMERS FISHING TACKLE, 13-15 Bon Accord Terrace, Aberdeen, ABERDEENSHIRE, AB11 6DP **Scotland**
Mr D Craik (Proprietor)
(T) 01224 210008.

TURRIFF TROPHY CENTRE, 6 Castle Street, Turriff, ABERDEENSHIRE, AB53 7BJ **Scotland**
Mr I Masson (Proprietor)
(T) 01888 562428.

TURRIFF TROPHY CENTRE, 6 Castle Street, Sunnybrae, Turriff, ABERDEENSHIRE, AB53 4BL **Scotland**
Mr I Masson (Proprietor)
(T) 01888 562428.

ANGUS

ANGLERS CHOICE, 183 High Street, Lochee, Dundee, ANGUS, DD2 3DB **Scotland**
Mr R Macgregor (Proprietor)
(T) 01382 400555.

ANGLERS CREEL, 33 Exchange Street, Dundee, ANGUS, DD1 3DJ **Scotland**
Mr I Wilson (Proprietor)
(T) 01382 205075.

ARBROATH CYCLE & TACKLE CENTRE, 274 High Street, Arbroath, ANGUS, DD11 1JE **Scotland**
Mr C Strachan (Proprietor)
(T) 01241 873467.

BROTY TACKLE SHOP, 67 King Street, Broughty Ferry, Dundee, ANGUS, DD5 1EY **Scotland**
Mr D Holden (Proprietor)
(T) 01382 480113.

GRAHAM CARROLL, 48 St. David Street, Brechin, ANGUS, DD9 6EQ **Scotland**
(T) 01356 625700.

JOHN R GOW LTD, 12 Union Street, Dundee, ANGUS, DD1 4BH **Scotland**
Mr D Masson (Director)
(T) 01382 225427.

STEVE'S FISHING TACKLE, 7 Arbroath Road, Dundee, ANGUS, DD4 6EW **Scotland**
(T) 01382 453040.

TACKLE BOX, 157 High Street, Lochee, Dundee, ANGUS, DD2 3BZ **Scotland**
(T) 01382 610490.

ARGYLL AND BUTE

ANGLERS CORNER, 114 George Street, Oban, ARGYLL AND BUTE, PA34 5NT **Scotland**
Mr A Binnie (Proprietor)
(T) 01631 566374.

ANGLERS CORNER, John Street, Oban, ARGYLL AND BUTE, PA34 5NS **Scotland**
(T) 01631 566374.

FISH FINDER, 37 Dumbarton Road, Clydebank, ARGYLL AND BUTE, G81 1UA **Scotland**
Mr J Mcewan (Proprietor)
(T) 0141-952 9295.

FYNE TACKLE, 22 Argyll Street, Lochgilphead, ARGYLL AND BUTE, PA31 8NE **Scotland**
Mr A Mcgill (Proprietor)
(T) 01546 606878.

I C PURDIE, 112 Argyle Street, Dunoon, ARGYLL AND BUTE, PA23 7NE **Scotland**
Mrs I Purdie (Proprietor)
(T) 01369 703232.

IAN GIBSON, 225 Bank Street, Alexandria, ARGYLL AND BUTE, G83 0UJ **Scotland**
Mrs A Gibson (Proprietor)
(T) 01389 752037.

KFT LTD, Baliscate, Tobermory, Isle of Mull, ARGYLL AND BUTE, PA75 6QA **Scotland**
Mr B Swinbanks (Director)
(T) 01688 302113.

KNOTLESS FISHING TACKLE, 10 Main Street, Tobermory, Isle of Mull, ARGYLL AND BUTE, PA75 6NU **Scotland**
Mr B Swinbanks (Director)
(T) 01688 302113.

LOCHSIDE BAIT & TACKLE, 112a East Princes Street, Helensburgh, ARGYLL AND BUTE, G84 7DQ **Scotland**
Mr S Flemming (Proprietor)
(T) 01436 677796.

LOMOND GAME FISHING SERVICES, The Kennels, Alexandria, ARGYLL AND BUTE, G83 8RB **Scotland**
Mr Robert Lyon (Proprietor)
(T) 01389 850652.

TACKLE & BOOKS, 7 Main Street, Tobermory, Isle of Mull, ARGYLL AND BUTE, PA75 6NU **Scotland**
Mr Duncan Swinbanks (Proprietor)
(T) 01688 302336.

AYRSHIRE (EAST)

AQUAMOTIVE CONTROL SYSTEMS LTD, Unit A Station Yard, Mauchline, AYRSHIRE (EAST), KA5 5EU **Scotland**
Mrs M Welsh (Managing Director)
(T) 01290 552694.

AYRSHIRE (NORTH)

CRAFT FISHING SHOP, 42 Main Street, Kilwinning, AYRSHIRE (NORTH), KA13 6AQ **Scotland**
Mr M Hall (Proprietor)
(T) 01294 558559.

AYRSHIRE (SOUTH)

BILKO'S STORE, 6A New Bridge Street, Ayr, AYRSHIRE (SOUTH), KA7 1JX **Scotland**
Ms Elizabeth Ross (Proprietor)
(T) 01292 280822.

GAMESPORT OF AYR, 60 Sandgate, Ayr, AYRSHIRE (SOUTH), KA7 1BX **Scotland**
Mr Alfred Coli (Proprietor)
(T) 01292 263822.

DUMFRIES AND GALLOWAY

ANGLER CRAFT, Greenbogue, Torthorwald, Dumfries, DUMFRIES AND GALLOWAY, DG1 3QG **Scotland**
Mr J Younger (Proprietor)
(T) 01387 750247.

D G GUNS & TACKLE, 19-21 Albert Street, Newton Stewart, DUMFRIES AND GALLOWAY, DG8 6EF **Scotland**
Mr Paul Stewart (Manager)
(T) 01671 403224.

ESK & BOARDERS GUIDE SERVICE, Netherknock, Bentpath, Langholm, DUMFRIES AND GALLOWAY, DG13 0PB **Scotland**
Mr K King (Proprietor)
(T) 013873 70288.

FISHING TACKLE SHOP, 132 High Street, Annan, DUMFRIES AND GALLOWAY, DG12 6DP **Scotland**
Mr S Rammell (Proprietor)
(T) 01461 204140.

FISHING TACKLE SHOP, 35 Drumlanrig Street, Thornhill, DUMFRIES AND GALLOWAY, DG3 5LJ **Scotland**
Mr S Rammell (Proprietor)
(T) 01848 331054.

GALLAWAY ANGLING CENTRE, Bladnoch, Wigtown, Newton Stewart, DUMFRIES AND GALLOWAY, DG8 9AB **Scotland**
Mr D Vincent (Proprietor)
(T) 01988 403363.

LOCKERBIE GAME FISHING SUPPLIES, 34-36 High Street, Lockerbie, DUMFRIES AND GALLOWAY, DG11 2AA **Scotland**
Mrs L Charlton (Proprietor)
(T) 01576 204695.

M MCCOWAN & SON, 50-52 King Street, Castle Douglas, DUMFRIES AND GALLOWAY, DG7 1AD **Scotland**
Miss A Cockren (Manageress)
(T) 01556 502009.

M MCCOWAN & SON, 43 High Street, Dalbeattie, DUMFRIES AND GALLOWAY, DG5 4AD **Scotland**
Mr E Mccowan (Partner)
(T) 01556 610270.

MCMILLAN DAVID, 6 Friars Vennel, Dumfries, DUMFRIES AND GALLOWAY, DG1 2RN **Scotland**
(T) 01387 252075.

FIFE

A & M TACKLE, 21 Main Street, Lochgelly, FIFE, KY5 9AG **Scotland**
Mr A Ferguson (Partner)
(T) 01592 783000.

ALADDIN'S CAVE, 259 High Street, Leslie, Glenrothes, FIFE, KY6 3AZ **Scotland**
Mr Paul Irvine (Proprietor)
(T) 01592 743347.

B R M FISHING TACKLE, St. Andrews Street, Dunfermline, FIFE, KY11 4QG **Scotland**
Mr Raymond Martin (Proprietor)
(T) 01383 621999.

DEALS ON REELS, 18 Station Road, Cowdenbeath, FIFE, KY4 9SG **Scotland**
Mr S R Baxter (Proprietor)
(T) 01383 515550.

SPIKE'S PLAICE, 273 High Street, Kirkcaldy, FIFE, KY1 1JH **Scotland**
Mrs Kate Anderson (Proprietor)
(T) 01592 597231.

WE'RE GAME, 126 St. Clair Street, Kirkcaldy, FIFE, KY1 2BZ **Scotland**
(T) 01592 654301.

GLASGOW (CITY OF)

ANGLER'S RENDEZVOUS, 18 Saltmarket, Glasgow, GLASGOW (CITY OF), G1 5LD **Scotland**
Mr Ken Mcgowan (Manager)
(T) 01415 524662.

ANGLER'S RENDEZVOUS, 18 Saltmarket, Glasgow, GLASGOW (CITY OF), G1 5LY **Scotland**
Mr Ken Mcgowan (Manager)
(T) 0141-552 4662.

BROWNSIDE ANGLING CENTRE, 324 Victoria Road, Glasgow, GLASGOW (CITY OF), G42 7RP **Scotland**
Mr J Lemarie (Partner)
(T) 0141-424 1001.

CAFARO BROS, 140 Renfield Street, Glasgow, GLASGOW (CITY OF), G2 3AU **Scotland**
Mr P Mckinley (Partner)
(T) 0141-332 6224.

CAMPBELL SPEIRS (UK) LTD, 61 Miller Street, Glasgow, GLASGOW (CITY OF), G1 1EB **Scotland**
Mr M Mcgowan (Director)
(T) 0141-221 9106.

DANNY'S DEN, 2380 Dumbarton Road, Glasgow, GLASGOW (CITY OF), G14 0QL **Scotland**
Mr Danny Garrigan (Proprietor)
(T) 0141-952 1629.

FISH TANK MANUFACTURING CO, 274 Broomloan Road, Glasgow, GLASGOW (CITY OF), G51 2JQ **Scotland**
Mr A Steven (Managing Director)
(T) 01414 011184.

GLASGOW ANGLING CENTRE, 6 Claythorn Street, Glasgow, GLASGOW (CITY OF), G40 2HP **Scotland**
(T) 0141-552 4737.

GRAY'S OF KILSYTH, 8 Market Street, Kilsyth, Glasgow, GLASGOW (CITY OF), G65 0BD **Scotland**
Mr John Gray (Proprietor)
(T) 01236 825320.

HOOKED IN SCOTLAND, 49a Main Street, Cambuslang, Glasgow, GLASGOW (CITY OF), G72 7HB **Scotland**
Mr G Mcvee (Proprietor)
(T) 0141-646 1000.

J B ANGLING CENTRE, 37 Eastside, Kirkintilloch, Glasgow, GLASGOW (CITY OF), G66 1QA **Scotland**
Mr N Foulds (Proprietor)
(T) 0141-775 0083.

LOGIES TACKLE, 427 Great Western Road, Glasgow, GLASGOW (CITY OF), G4 9JA **Scotland**
Mr Brian Pitchers (Sole Director)
(T) 01413 570100.

P D FISHING TACKLE & GUNS, 69 Main Street, Cumbernauld, Glasgow, GLASGOW (CITY OF), G67 2RT **Scotland**
Mr D Egan (Manager)
(T) 01236 735527.

TACKLE & GUNS, 920 Pollokshaws Road, Glasgow, GLASGOW (CITY OF), G41 2ET **Scotland**
Mr B Macmartin (Proprietor)
(T) 0141-632 2005.

HIGHLAND

ALLENS, Deshar Road, Boat of Garten, HIGHLAND, PH24 3BN **Scotland**
Mr Andrew Allen (Proprietor)
(T) 01479 831372.

CLAN FISHING RODS LTD, Nethy Bridge, HIGHLAND, PH25 3ED **Scotland**
Harry Jamieson (Joint Director)
(T) 01479 821676.

CRAIG WOOD, Elmbank, Rosehaugh, Avoch, HIGHLAND, IV9 8RF **Scotland**
Mr G Tanner (Proprietor)
(T) 01381 620958.

CYCLOPS CREELS, 2 Clanranald Place, Arisaig, HIGHLAND, PH39 4NN **Scotland**
Mr M Maceachen (Proprietor)
(T) 01687 450328.

DUNVEGAN SPORTS & TACKLE, Dunvegan, Isle of Skye, HIGHLAND, IV55 8WA **Scotland**
(T) 01470 521730.

GUN & TACKLE ROOM, Uiginish Lodge, Dunvegan, Isle of Skye, HIGHLAND, IV55 8ZR **Scotland**
(T) 01470 521445.

HARPERS FLY FISHING SERVICES, 57 High Street, Thurso, HIGHLAND, KW14 8AZ **Scotland**
Mrs P Brooks (Proprietor)
(T) 01847 893179.

HUGO ROSS, 56 High Street, Wick, HIGHLAND, KW1 4BP **Scotland**
(T) 01955 604200.

J GRAHAM & CO, 37-39 Castle Street, Inverness, HIGHLAND, IV2 3DU **Scotland**
Mr W Armstrong (Proprietor)
(T) 01463 233178.

NAUTILUS CONSULTANTS LTD, Crancil Brae House, Strathpeffer, HIGHLAND, IV14 9AW **Scotland**
Mr John Hambrey (Director)
(T) 01997 420086.

ROB WILSON, Rosslyn Street, Brora, HIGHLAND, KW9 6NY **Scotland**
Mr T Barker (Proprietor)
(T) 01408 621373.

SPORTS & MODEL SHOP, 66 High Street, Dingwall, HIGHLAND, IV15 9RY **Scotland**
(T) 01349 862346.

TACKLE SHOP, Dunrobin Street, Helmsdale, HIGHLAND, KW8 6JA **Scotland**
Mr Chris Gross (Proprietor)
(T) 01431 821102.

WEST-R-WELD LTD, Alness Industrial Estate, Teaninich Industrial Estate, Alness, HIGHLAND, IV17 0XS **Scotland**
Mrs Lorna Thompson (Director)
(T) 01349 882745.

ISLE OF BUTE

FISHING TACKLE, 6 Deanhood Place, Rothesay, ISLE OF BUTE, PA20 0AS **Scotland**
(T) 01700 505062.

ISLE OF ISLAY

JOHN REID, Glenegedale, Port Ellen, ISLE OF ISLAY, PA42 7AS **Scotland**
Mrs Margaret Reid (Partner)
(T) 01496 302090.

ISLE OF LEWIS

ISLAND FLIES, 23 Gravir, Gravir, Isle of Lewis, ISLE OF LEWIS, HS2 9QX **Scotland**
(T) 01851 880233.

STORNOWAY FISHERMEN'S CO-OPERATIVE LTD, 1 North Beach, Stornoway, ISLE OF LEWIS, HS1 2XP **Scotland**
Mr A Morrison (Managing Director)
(T) 01851 702563.

LANARKSHIRE (NORTH)

ANGLERS ATTIC, 55 Caledonian Road, Wishaw, LANARKSHIRE (NORTH), ML2 8AP **Scotland**
Mr Kenny Mcmillan (Proprietor)
(T) 01698 359757.

ANGLER'S DEN, 521 Main Street, Bellshill, LANARKSHIRE (NORTH), ML4 1DG **Scotland**
Mr D Mccutcheon (Proprietor)
(T) 01698 327789.

DANNY'S DEN, 3 Forrest Street, Airdrie, LANARKSHIRE (NORTH), ML6 7BA **Scotland**
Mr D Garrigan (Proprietor)
(T) 01236 750288.

MACLEOD'S FISHING TACKLE, 176 High Street, Motherwell, LANARKSHIRE (NORTH), ML1 5JQ **Scotland**
Mr R Macleod (Proprietor)
(T) 01698 860530.

ROD & GUN RACK, 145 Merry Street, Motherwell, LANARKSHIRE (NORTH), ML1 1JP **Scotland**
Mr P Polatajko (Proprietor)
(T) 01698 265777.

LANARKSHIRE (SOUTH)

AQUARIUS, 49-51 Hamilton Street, Carluke, LANARKSHIRE (SOUTH), ML8 4HA **Scotland**
(T) 01555 772773.

JAMES RITCHIE, 30 Bannatyne Street, Lanark, LANARKSHIRE (SOUTH), ML11 7JR **Scotland**
Mr J Ritchie (Proprietor)
(T) 01555 662380.

SPORTSMAN'S EMPORIUM, 68 Cadzow Street, Hamilton, LANARKSHIRE (SOUTH), ML3 6DS **Scotland**
Mr Eric Bowden (Proprietor)
(T) 01698 283903.

TORBET'S OUTDOOR LEISURE, 5 Portland Street, Troon, LANARKSHIRE (SOUTH), KA10 6AA **Scotland**
Ms Fiona Torbet (Proprietor)
(T) 01292 317464.

LOTHIAN (EAST)

CAPTAIN HOOK, 116 High Street, Dunbar, LOTHIAN (EAST), EH42 1JJ **Scotland**
Mr D Johnson (Partner)
(T) 01368 860350.

CROMWELL MARINE LTD, Cromwell Harbour, Shore Street, Dunbar, LOTHIAN (EAST), EH42 1HN **Scotland**
Mr Alan Gillespie (Sole Director)
(T) 01368 863354.

HARKESS TRAWLS, 12 Whin Pk, Cockenzie, Prestonpans, LOTHIAN (EAST), EH32 0JQ **Scotland**
Mr A Harkess (Proprietor)
(T) 01875 813696.

LOTHIAN (MID)

A & P SUPPLIES, 24 The Square, Penicuik, LOTHIAN (MID), EH26 8LN **Scotland**
(T) 01968 678700.

COUNTRY LIFE, 229 Balgreen Road, Edinburgh, LOTHIAN (MID), EH11 2RZ **Scotland**
Mr M Stewart (Manager)
(T) 0131-337 6230.

CRAFTYE FISHERMAN, 60A Inverleith Row, Edinburgh, LOTHIAN (MID), EH3 5PX **Scotland**
(T) 0131-551 1224.

DICKSON & MECNAUGHTON LTD, 21 Frederick Street, Edinburgh, LOTHIAN (MID), EH2 2NE **Scotland**
Mr Jim Newbiggey (Director)
(T) 0131-225 4218.

FARLOWS SPORTFISH LTD, 58 George Street, Edinburgh, LOTHIAN (MID), EH2 2LR **Scotland**
Mr B Cornwall (Branch Manager)
(T) 0131-225 7225.

PRIME CATCH (UK) LTD, 28-30 West Preston Street, Edinburgh, LOTHIAN (MID), EH8 9PZ **Scotland**
Mr D Aitkin (Managing Director)
(T) 0131-662 0663.

RIVERSIDE TACKLE, 67 Eskside West, Musselburgh, LOTHIAN (MID), EH21 6RA **Scotland**
Mr D Shields (Proprietor)
(T) 0131-665 3371.

TIMELESS TACKLE, 1 Blackwood Cresent, Edinburgh, LOTHIAN (MID), EH9 1QZ **Scotland**
Mr M Graham (Proprietor)
(T) 0131-667 1407.

LOTHIAN (WEST)

ANGLERS CHOICE, 19 Main Street, Bo'ness, LOTHIAN (WEST), EH51 9NQ **Scotland**
Miss P Conway (Proprietor)
(T) 01506 828926.

LINDALE LEISURE, Unit 48g Linbar House, North Bridge Street, Bathgate, LOTHIAN (WEST), EH48 4PP **Scotland**
(T) 01506 634028.

LIVELINE FISHING TACKLE, 41 West Main Street, Armadale, Bathgate, LOTHIAN (WEST), EH48 3PZ **Scotland**
Mr Jim Glesby (Proprietor)
(T) 01501 733150.

LOCHSIDE TACKLE, 22 South Street, Armadale, Bathgate, LOTHIAN (WEST), EH48 3ES **Scotland**
Mrs M Douglas (Proprietor)
(T) 01501 730559.

LOCHSIDE TACKLE & SPORTS, 254 High Street, Linlithgow, LOTHIAN (WEST), EH49 7ES **Scotland**
Mrs L Webb (Proprietor)
(T) 01506 671477.

LOTHIAN SCHOOL OF FLY FISHING, Selmmuir Loch, Mid Calder, Livingston, LOTHIAN (WEST), EH53 0JT **Scotland**
Mr G Gowland (Proprietor)
(T) 01506 882987.

MORAY

ANGLING CENTRE, Moss Street, Elgin, MORAY, IV30 1LU **Scotland**
Mr D Colhoun (Proprietor)
(T) 01343 547615.

ANGUS STUART, 60 High Street, Grantown-on-Spey, MORAY, PH26 3EH **Scotland**
Mr P Hemming (Partner)
(T) 01479 872612.

FISHING TACKLE SHOP, 97d High Street, Forres, MORAY, IV36 1AA **Scotland**
Mr Mike Grant (Proprietor)
(T) 01309 672936.

MORTIMERS, 3 High Street, Grantown-on-Spey, MORAY, PH26 3HB **Scotland**
Mr Grant Mortimer (Proprietor)
(T) 01479 872684.

SPEY PRODUCTS, 1 Pilmuir Road, Forres, MORAY, IV36 1HD **Scotland**
Mr Dave Goodsir (Proprietor)
(T) 01309 674107.

TACKLE SHOP, 188 High Street, Elgin, MORAY, IV30 1BA **Scotland**
Mrs S Sharpe (Proprietor)
(T) 01343 543129.

NORTHUMBERLAND

GAME FAIR, 12 Marygate, Berwick-upon-Tweed, NORTHUMBERLAND, TD15 1BN **Scotland**
Mr R Bell (Proprietor)
(T) 01289 305119.

ORKNEY ISLES

W S SINCLAIR, 27 John Street, Stromness, ORKNEY ISLES, KW16 3AD **Scotland**
Mr W S Sinclair (Proprietor)
(T) 01856 850469.

PERTH AND KINROSS

BALLINLUIG SMIDDY, The Old Smiddy, Ballinluig, Pitlochry, PERTH AND KINROSS, PH9 0LG **Scotland**
Mr C Ellam (Proprietor)
(T) 01796 482565.

DAVID CAMPBELL, The Square, Aberfeldy, PERTH AND KINROSS, PH15 2DD **Scotland**
Mr D Campbell (Proprietor)
(T) 01887 829545.

JAMES BAYNE FISHING TACKLE, 76 Main Street, Callander, PERTH AND KINROSS, FK17 8BD **Scotland**
(T) 01877 330218.

JAMES PHILP, 102 High Street, Kinross, PERTH AND KINROSS, KY13 8AJ **Scotland**
(T) 01577 862371.

KATE FLEMING, 26 Allan Street, Blairgowrie, PERTH AND KINROSS, PH10 6AD **Scotland**
Mrs K Walker (Proprietor)
(T) 01250 873990.

MITCHELLS OF PITLOCHRY, 23 Atholl Road, Pitlochry, PERTH AND KINROSS, PH16 5BX **Scotland**
Mr N Mitchell (Proprietor)
(T) 01796 472613.

PERTHSHIRE FIELD SPORTS, 13 Charlotte Street, Perth, PERTH AND KINROSS, PH1 5LW **Scotland**
Mr Ron Stewart (Manager)
(T) 01738 441572.

RENFREWSHIRE

A & G (LEISURE) LTD, 48 Macdowall Street, Johnstone, RENFREWSHIRE, PA5 8QL **Scotland**
Mr George Patterson (Proprietor)
(T) 01505 320397.

BRIAN PETERSON, 24 Union Street, Greenock, RENFREWSHIRE, PA16 8DD **Scotland**
Mr Brian Peterson (Proprietor)
(T) 01475 888085.

COUNTRY SPORTS, 47 Neilston Road, Paisley, RENFREWSHIRE, PA2 6LY **Scotland**
Mr C Mitchell (Partner)
(T) 0141-889 5535.

NAPIER & CRAIG LTD, 88 Clark Street, Paisley, RENFREWSHIRE, PA3 1RB **Scotland**
Mr L Renfrew (Manager)
(T) 0141-840 1349.

PENN FISHING TACKLE EUROPE, Glenlora Estate, Lochwinnoch, RENFREWSHIRE, PA12 4DN **Scotland**
Mr Alan Caulfield (Proprietor)
(T) 01505 843131.

PENN FISHING TACKLE EUROPE, Cartside Avenue, Inchinnan, Renfrew, RENFREWSHIRE, PA4 9RX **Scotland**
Mr D Caulfield (Manager)
(T) 01418 146565.

SCOTTISH BORDERS

COUNTRY SPORT SHOP, 6-8 Canongate, Jedburgh, SCOTTISH BORDERS, TD8 6AJ **Scotland**
Mr I R Sanford (Proprietor)
(T) 01835 863019.

J & A TURNBULL, 30 Bank Street, Galashiels, SCOTTISH BORDERS, TD1 1EN **Scotland**
Mr B Hardy (Proprietor)
(T) 01896 753191.

J & W STUART LTD, Eyemouth Industrial Estate, Coldingham Road, Eyemouth, SCOTTISH BORDERS, TD14 5AN **Scotland**
Mr W Hay (Proprietor)
(T) 018907 51684.

R WELSH & SON, 28 Castle Street, Duns, SCOTTISH BORDERS, TD11 3DP **Scotland**
Mr George Whiteford (Partner)
(T) 01361 883466.

TWEEDDALE TACKLE CENTRE, 1 Bridgegate, Peebles, SCOTTISH BORDERS, EH45 8RZ **Scotland**
Mr E MacDonald (Proprietor)
(T) 01721 720979.

TWEEDSIDE TACKLE, 36-38 Bridge Street, Kelso, SCOTTISH BORDERS, TD5 7JD **Scotland**
Mr T Vipond (Partner)
(T) 01573 225306.

SHETLAND ISLANDS

J J MEASURING SYSTEMS, Nordhaven, Muckle Roe, Brae, Shetland, SHETLAND ISLANDS, ZE2 9QW **Scotland**
(T) 01806 522396.

JAMES A MANSON, 88 Commercial Street, Lerwick, SHETLAND ISLANDS, ZE1 0EX **Scotland**
Mr E Manson (Proprietor)
(T) 01595 693448.

ROD & LINE, 9 Harbour Street, Lerwick, SHETLAND ISLANDS, ZE1 0LR **Scotland**
Mr J Ivens (Proprietor)
(T) 01595 695055.

WHALSAY TRAWL NETS, Hamister, Symbister, Whalsay, Shetland, SHETLAND ISLANDS, ZE2 9AE **Scotland**
Mr J Williamson (Proprietor)
(T) 01806 566526.

STIRLING

COUNTRY PURSUITS, 46 Henderson Street, Bridge of Allan, Stirling, STIRLING, FK9 4HS **Scotland**
Mr J Henderson (Partner)
(T) 01786 834495.

DENNY, 8 Broad Street, Denny, STIRLING, FK6 6DY **Scotland**
Mr J Moffat (Proprietor)
(T) 01324 820088.

HOOKED ON SCOTLAND LTD, 74 Port Street, Stirling, STIRLING, FK8 2LP **Scotland**
Mr G Nash (Director)
(T) 01786 446564.

JACK MCWATT, 50 North Main Street, Carronshore, Falkirk, STIRLING, FK2 8HL **Scotland**
Mrs Eleanor Mcwatt (Managing Director)
(T) 01324 570595.

LOCHSIDE TACKLE & SPORTS, 10 Manor Street, Falkirk, STIRLING, FK1 1NH **Scotland**
Mrs E Timmons (Proprietor)
(T) 01324 625086.

MITCHELL'S FISHING TACKLE, 13 Bannockburn Road, Stirling, STIRLING, FK7 0BP **Scotland**
Mr Alan Mitchell (Proprietor)
(T) 01786 445587.

SCRIMGEOUR W J, 28 Newmarket Street, Falkirk, STIRLING, FK1 1JQ **Scotland**
Mr W Campbell (Proprietor)
(T) 01324 624581.

TACKLE UP, 33 West Bridge Street, Falkirk, STIRLING, FK1 5RJ **Scotland**
Mr John Orr (Proprietor)
(T) 01324 617646.

WALES

BLAENAU GWENT

FASTMAIL, 39 Hill Street, Rhymney, Tredegar, BLAENAU GWENT, NP22 5JH **Wales**
Mr Mark Duggan (Proprietor)
(T) 01685 844066.

SOMETHING FISHY, 3 Honeyfield Road, Rassau, Ebbw Vale, BLAENAU GWENT, NP23 5TA **Wales**
Mr S Witney (Proprietor)
(T) 01495 304050.

CAERPHILLY

GREEN'S FISHING TACKLE, Bryn Road, Pontllanfraith, Blackwood, CAERPHILLY, NP12 2BU **Wales**
Mr H Green (Proprietor)
(T) 01495 221881.

CARMARTHENSHIRE

ANGLERS CORNER, 80 Station Road, Llanelli, CARMARTHENSHIRE, SA15 1AN **Wales**
Mr Richard Lewis (Partner)
(T) 01554 773981.

BAY FISHING TACKLE, High Street, Saundersfoot, CARMARTHENSHIRE, SA69 9EJ **Wales**
Mr D W Jones (Proprietor)
(T) 01834 813115.

CASTAWAY, 1 College Row, Cardigan, CARMARTHENSHIRE, SA43 1LL **Wales**
Mr G Smith (Manager)
(T) 01239 621856.

COLLECTIVE TACKLE PURCHASING LTD, Heol Stanllyd, Cross Hands, Llanelli, CARMARTHENSHIRE, SA14 6RB **Wales**
Mr Robert Dyer (Joint Director)
(T) 01269 845777.

FISHFINDER, 51 King Street, Carmarthen, CARMARTHENSHIRE, SA31 1BH **Wales**
Mr M J Makin (Partner)
(T) 01267 220226.

FISHING TACKLE & BAIT, Manchester House, Margaret Street, New Quay, CARMARTHENSHIRE, SA45 9QJ **Wales**
Mr P Watts (Proprietor)
(T) 01545 561382.

JONESYS TACKLE & BAIT, Willings Passage, Main Street, Pembroke, CARMARTHENSHIRE, SA71 4JS **Wales**
Mr M Jones (Proprietor)
(T) 01646 622303.

NINE OAKS FISHERY, Craigfryn, Oakford, Llanarth, CARMARTHENSHIRE, SA47 0RW **Wales**
Mrs J Steels (Partner)
(T) 01545 580482.

PEMBROKE ANGLING, 31 Meyrick Street, Pembroke Dock, CARMARTHENSHIRE, SA72 6AL **Wales**
Mr W Brunton (Proprietor)
(T) 01646 622712.

SALMONS LEAP, Salmon Leap, Cenarth, Newcastle Emlyn, CARMARTHENSHIRE, SA38 9JP **Wales**
Mrs Pat Milner (Partner)
(T) 01239 711242.

SEA STORES, 4 Brunel Quay, Neyland, Milford Haven, CARMARTHENSHIRE, SA73 1PY **Wales**
Mrs K Viles (Proprietor)
(T) 01646 601946.

TENBY ANGLING, The Market, High Street, Tenby, CARMARTHENSHIRE, SA70 7EU **Wales**
Mr W Brunton (Partner)
(T) 01834 844430.

TIGHTLINES DIRECT LTD, 72 Wind Street, Ammanford, CARMARTHENSHIRE, SA18 3DR **Wales**
Mr D R Williams (Proprietor)
(T) 01269 595858.

CEREDIGION

ABER FISHING, 3 Terrace Road, Aberystwyth, CEREDIGION, SY23 1NY **Wales**
Mrs J Edwards (Manager)
(T) 01970 611200.

CONWY

S T RUSSELL, 4 Parc Ffynnon, Llysfaen, Colwyn Bay, CONWY, LL29 8SA **Wales**
(T) 01492 516101.

TACKLE BOX, 17 Greenfield Road, Colwyn Bay, CONWY, LL29 8EL **Wales**
Mr T S Ronald (Proprietor)
(T) 01492 531104.

VICTORIA PIER ANGLING CENTRE, The Promenade, Colwyn Bay, CONWY, LL29 8HH **Wales**
Mr K Simpson (Proprietor)
(T) 01492 530663.

DENBIGHSHIRE

ALANS, Unit 5 Piazza Shopping Centre, Sussex Street, Rhyl, DENBIGHSHIRE, LL18 1SE **Wales**
Mr A Alan (Proprietor)
(T) 01745 351644.

BRIDEN BAIT, Wesley Buildins, Gronant Hill, Gronant, Prestatyn, DENBIGHSHIRE, LL19 9SR **Wales**
(T) 01745 888013.

FOXON'S TACKLE, Penrhewl, Lower Denbigh Road, St. Asaph, DENBIGHSHIRE, LL17 0ED **Wales**
Mr A Foxon (Proprietor)
(T) 01745 583583.

GEOFF'S TACKLE & BAIT, 163b Wellington Road, Rhyl, DENBIGHSHIRE, LL18 1LW **Wales**
Mr D Blazier (Manager)
(T) 01745 356236.

FLINTSHIRE

SELECTAFLY, Connah's Quay, Deeside, FLINTSHIRE, CH5 4PJ **Wales**
(T) 01244 810271.

GLAMORGAN (VALE OF)

A MILES & SON, East Lodge, Druidstone Road, Old St. Mellons, Cardiff, GLAMORGAN (VALE OF), CF3 6XE **Wales**
Mrs D E Miles (Partner)
(T) 01633 680155.

AFAN ANGLING CENTRE, Unit 37 Aberafan Centre, Port Talbot, GLAMORGAN (VALE OF), SA13 1PB **Wales**
Mrs L E Adams (Proprietor)
(T) 01639 883123.

ANGLERS SUPPLIES, 172 Penarth Road, Cardiff, GLAMORGAN (VALE OF), CF11 6NL **Wales**
Mr Steven Myles (Partner)
(T) 02920 220723.

ARTHUR BALE & SONS, 3 Frederick Street, Cardiff, GLAMORGAN (VALE OF), CF10 2DB **Wales**
Mr M Bale (Proprietor)
(T) 02920 229929.

ASPINALL'S ANGLING SUPPLIES, 36 Cross Street, Barry, GLAMORGAN (VALE OF), CF63 4LU **Wales**
Mr R Aspinall (Proprietor)
(T) 01446 742645.

BAIT FOR BITES, Youngs Boat Yard/Compass House, Baldwins Cr, Crymlyn Burrows, Swansea, GLAMORGAN (VALE OF), SA1 8QE **Wales**
Miss R Young (Proprietor)
(T) 01792 480490.

BOB'S FISHING TACKLE & BAIT, Hillside Cardiff Road, Mwyndy, Pontyclun, GLAMORGAN (VALE OF), CF72 8PN **Wales**
Mr Bob Clear (Proprietor)
(T) 01443 227267.

C WHITE, The Square, Pontlottyn, Bargoed, GLAMORGAN (VALE OF), CF81 9PF **Wales**
Mr C White (Proprietor)
(T) 01685 841245.

CLIFF HARVEY, 10 Albion Industrial Estate, Cilfynydd Road, Pontypridd, GLAMORGAN (VALE OF), CF37 4NX **Wales**
Mr Cliff Harvey (Proprietor)
(T) 01443 400766.

COUNTRY ANGLING, 3a Church Street, Gowerton, Swansea, GLAMORGAN (VALE OF), SA4 3EA **Wales**
(T) 01792 875050.

D C A MOULDS, The Maltings, East Tyndall Street, Cardiff, GLAMORGAN (VALE OF), CF24 5EA **Wales**
Mr M H Williams (Partner)
(T) 02920 489342.

ELY ANGLING SUPPLIES LTD, 572 Cowbridge Road East, Cardiff, GLAMORGAN (VALE OF), CF5 1BP **Wales**
Mr W J Ackerman (Proprietor)
(T) 02920 555133.

EWENNY ANGLING SUPPLIES, 11b Ewenny Road, Bridgend, GLAMORGAN (VALE OF), CF31 3HN **Wales**
Mrs M Roberts (Partner)
(T) 01656 662691.

FISHING WORLD LTD, 1 High Street, Tonyrefail, Porth, GLAMORGAN (VALE OF), CF39 8PG **Wales**
Mr S Williams (Manager)
(T) 01443 670218.

GARRY EVANS FISHING TACKLE, 109 Whitchurch Road, Cardiff, GLAMORGAN (VALE OF), CF14 3JQ **Wales**
(T) 02920 619828.

KEENS TACKLE, 119 Bridgend Road, Aberkenfig, Bridgend, GLAMORGAN (VALE OF), CF32 9AP **Wales**
Mr G Keen (Proprietor)
(T) 01656 722448.

M REYNOLDS, Stall 53 Neath Market, Neath, GLAMORGAN (VALE OF), SA11 1DP **Wales**
Mr M Reynolds (Proprietor)
(T) 01639 645176.

MAINWARINGS ANGLING CENTRE, 44 Vivian Road, Sketty, Swansea, GLAMORGAN (VALE OF), SA2 0UH **Wales**
Mr R E Mainwarings (Partner)
(T) 01792 202245.

MERPHYR ANGLING CENTRE, 185 High Street, Cefn Coed, Merthyr Tydfil, GLAMORGAN (VALE OF), CF48 2PG **Wales**
Mr C Jones (Proprietor)
(T) 01685 379809.

P B J SPORT & LEISURE, 33 Lewis Street, Aberdare, GLAMORGAN (VALE OF), CF44 6PY **Wales**
Mr T G Evans (Manager)
(T) 01685 884295.

PADDIWACKS, 14 New Road, Porthcawl, GLAMORGAN (VALE OF), CF36 5DN **Wales**
Mrs C Bartle (Proprietor)
(T) 01656 773773.

PORTHCAWL ANGLING CENTRE, 10 Dock Street, Porthcawl, GLAMORGAN (VALE OF), CF36 3BL **Wales**
Mr B J Audsley (Proprietor)
(T) 01656 772404.

ROGER'S TACKLE, Swansea Sea Angling Centre, Pilot House Wharf, Swansea, GLAMORGAN (VALE OF), SA1 1UN **Wales**
Mr Roger Gore (Proprietor)
(T) 01792 469999.

SPORTS ACCESSORIES & EQUIPMENT, 127 Commercial Street, Maesteg, GLAMORGAN (VALE OF), CF34 9DL **Wales**
Mr D Davis (Proprietor)
(T) 01656 733518.

SPORTSMAIL LTD, 3 Allensbank Road, Cardiff, GLAMORGAN (VALE OF), CF14 3PN **Wales**
Mr A Brodie-Smith (Director)
(T) 0870-800 3050.

STEVE'S ANGLING, 826 Newport Road, Rumney, Cardiff, GLAMORGAN (VALE OF), CF3 4LH **Wales**
Mr S Powell (Proprietor)
(T) 02920 257505.

SVENDSEN SPORTS (UK) LTD, Unit 29/Business Development Centre, Main Avenue, Treforest Industrial Estate, Pontypridd, GLAMORGAN (VALE OF), CF37 5UR **Wales**
Mr Y Sorensen (Manager)
(T) 01443 844334.

TACKLE & BAIT, 149 Windsor Road, Neath, GLAMORGAN (VALE OF), SA11 1NU **Wales**
Mr Ron Stevens (Proprietor)
(T) 01639 634148.

TACKLE & TOW BARS, 22 Stuart Terrace, Talbot Green, Pontyclun, GLAMORGAN (VALE OF), CF72 8AA **Wales**
Mr R C Summerfield (Proprietor)
(T) 01443 226611.

TAFF'S ANGLING SUPPLIES, 11 Fox Street, Treharris, GLAMORGAN (VALE OF), CF46 5HE **Wales**
Mrs J Drane (Proprietor)
(T) 01443 413500.

TONY'S TACKLE SHOP, 14 Castle Street, Caerphilly, GLAMORGAN (VALE OF), CF83 1NY **Wales**
Mr Tony Watkins (Proprietor)
(T) 02920 885409.

VALLEYS ANGLING, Unit 20, Aberaman Industrial Estate, Aberaman, Aberdare, GLAMORGAN (VALE OF), CF44 6DA **Wales**
Mr S Davies (Proprietor)
(T) 01685 882632.

WHICH TACKLE, 14 Park Cresent, Barry, GLAMORGAN (VALE OF), CF62 6HD **Wales**
Mr G Porter (Proprietor)
(T) 01446 736008.

GWYNEDD

ANGLESEY BAIT CENTRE, Gallows Point, Beaumaris, GWYNEDD, LL58 8YL **Wales**
Mr M Gilroy (Proprietor)
(T) 01248 810009.

B HAYCOCK, 8 College Green, Tywyn, GWYNEDD, LL36 9BS **Wales**
Mr B Haycock (Proprietor)
(T) 01654 710357.

BANGOR ANGLING SUPPLY STORES, 21 High Street, Bangor, GWYNEDD, LL57 1NP **Wales**
Mr Jeff Holmes (Proprietor)
(T) 01248 355518.

BARNICLE BILL'S FISHING TACKLE, Tyn Y Coed, Jubilee Road, Barmouth, GWYNEDD, LL42 1EE **Wales**
Mr J Bouncer (Proprietor)
(T) 01341 280328.

BEACHCASTER, Aber Avon, High Street, Barmouth, GWYNEDD, LL42 1DS **Wales**
Mr F Slater (Partner)
(T) 01341 281537.

D & E HUGHES, 24 Penlan Street, Pwllheli, GWYNEDD, LL53 5DE **Wales**
Mrs E Hughes (Partner)
(T) 01758 613191.

DEXTER PRODUCTS & CO, Llanerch Road, Llanfairfechan, GWYNEDD, LL33 0EB **Wales**
Mr B G Westmoreland (Managing Director)
(T) 01248 680003.

F W ROBERTS, 32 Church Street, Blaenau Ffestiniog, GWYNEDD, LL41 3HD **Wales**
Mr F W Roberts (Proprietor)
(T) 01766 830607.

FISHERMAN, High Street, Porthmadog, GWYNEDD, LL49 9LR **Wales**
Mr A Roberts (Proprietor)
(T) 01766 512464.

FISHTAILS, Link House, Bridge Street, Dolgellau, GWYNEDD, LL40 1AU **Wales**
Mr John Jones (Proprietor)
(T) 01341 421080.

LIN'S DISCOUNT, Britannia Shop, King Edward Street, Barmouth, GWYNEDD, LL42 1AD **Wales**
Miss Linda Jones (Proprietor)
(T) 01341 281667.

LLANDUDNO FISHING TACKLE, 14 Mostyn Avenue, Llandudno, GWYNEDD, LL30 1YS **Wales**
Mr M Robinson (Proprietor)
(T) 01492 878425.

MARLIN BAIT & TACKLE, Tai Newyddion, Clynnogfawr, Caernarfon, GWYNEDD, LL54 5PT **Wales**
(T) 01286 660057.

NORTH WALES ANGLING CENTRE, 72 Pool Street, Caernarfon, GWYNEDD, LL55 2AF **Wales**
Mr B Cooper (Director)
(T) 01286 677099.

PADDYS BAIT & TACKLE, North Parade, Llandudno, GWYNEDD, LL30 2LP **Wales**
Mr P Casey (Proprietor)
(T) 01492 877678.

PARC NEWYDD TROUT FISHING, Parc Newydd, Carmel, Llanerchymedd, GWYNEDD, LL71 7BT **Wales**
Mr A Gannon (Proprietor)
(T) 01248 470700.

PILOT STORES, 66 Machine Street, Amlwch, GWYNEDD, LL68 9HA **Wales**
Mr T Graham (Proprietor)
(T) 01407 831771.

STRAWSONS FISHING GEAR, Preswylfa, Bull Bay, Amlwch, GWYNEDD, LL68 9SF **Wales**
Mr M Strawson (Proprietor)
(T) 01407 831841.

ISLE OF ANGLESEY

KEN JOHNSON, Devon House, Water Street, Menai Bridge, ISLE OF ANGLESEY, LL59 5DD **Wales**
Mr Ken Johnson (Proprietor)
(T) 01248 712700.

TACKLE BAR PETS & AQUATICS, 23 William Street, Holyhead, ISLE OF ANGLESEY, LL65 1RN **Wales**
Mrs C Roberts (Proprietor)
(T) 01407 761855.

MONMOUTHSHIRE

ANTIQUE FISHING TACKLE, Rivermill House, 1 Woodside Court, Llanbadoc, Usk, MONMOUTHSHIRE, NP15 1SY **Wales**
Mrs A Ayres (Partner)
(T) 01291 672710.

CWMBRAN ANGLING, 39 Richmond Road, Pontnewydd, Cwmbran, MONMOUTHSHIRE, NP44 1EQ **Wales**
Mr S Jefferies (Proprietor)
(T) 01633 868890.

DAVE RICHARDS, 73 Church Road, Newport, MONMOUTHSHIRE, NP19 7EH **Wales**
Ms Brenda Richards (Proprietor)
(T) 01633 254910.

DAVY WOTTON, Heron House, Station Road, Sebastopol, Pontypool, MONMOUTHSHIRE, NP4 5ES **Wales**
Mr Davey Wooton (Managing Director)
(T) 01495 762911.

GARRY EVANS (NEWPORT) LTD, 29 Redland Street, Newport, MONMOUTHSHIRE, NP20 5LZ **Wales**
M. Colin Arthur Cook (Director)
(T) 01633 855086.

MONO ANGLING SUPPLIES, 109 Monnow Street, Monmouth, MONMOUTHSHIRE, NP25 3EG **Wales**
Mrs Ruth Massey (Proprietor)
(T) 01600 719056.

NEWPORT ANGLING CENTRE, 172 Chepstow Road, Newport, MONMOUTHSHIRE, NP19 8EG **Wales**
Mr A Smith (Partner)
(T) 01633 222444.

PILL ANGLING CENTRE, 160 Commercial Road, Newport, MONMOUTHSHIRE, NP20 2PJ **Wales**
Mr G Whittington (Proprietor)
(T) 01633 267211.

PONTYPOOL ANGLING CENTRE, 11 Osborne Road, Pontypool, MONMOUTHSHIRE, NP4 6NN **Wales**
Mr M R Harvey (Proprietor)
(T) 01495 764839.

RON COUSINS, 8 Cadoc Close, Caerwent, Caldicot, MONMOUTHSHIRE, NP26 4QT **Wales**
(T) 01291 420001.

SWEET'S FISHING TACKLE, 14 Porthycarne Street, Usk, MONMOUTHSHIRE, NP15 1RY **Wales**
Mrs J P Williams (Proprietor)
(T) 01291 672552.

TIME FLIES, PO Box 24, Monmouth, MONMOUTHSHIRE, NP25 5YA **Wales**
Miss S Norris (Managing Director)
(T) 01600 715457.

NEWPORT

PETERSTON TROUT LAKE, St. Brides Wentlooge, Newport, NEWPORT, NP10 8SQ **Wales**
Mr P Scrivens (Proprietor)
(T) 01633 680905.

PEMBROKESHIRE

ANGLERS CORNER (MILFORD HAVEN), 1 Pill Road, Milford Haven, PEMBROKESHIRE, SA73 2NS **Wales**
Mr M Bassett (Partner)
(T) 01646 698899.

MILFORD ANGLING SUPPLIES, The Old Customs Hse, The Docks, Milford Haven, PEMBROKESHIRE, SA73 3AA **Wales**
Mr C Roberts (Manager)
(T) 01646 692765.

POWYS

AIRFRO DISTRIBUTION LTD, Unit 6 Ffrwdgrech Industrial Estate, Ffrwdgrech Road, Brecon, POWYS, LD3 8LA **Wales**
Mr Ian Burgess (Managing Director)
(T) 01874 611633.

BRIAN'S TACKLE & BAIT SUPPLIES, Canalside, North Road, Llanymynech, POWYS, SY22 6EA **Wales**
(T) 01691 830027.

CRICKHOWELL ANGLING SUPPLIES, Riverside Business Centre, New Road, Crickhowell, POWYS, NP8 1AY **Wales**
Mr S Dziadulewicz (Proprietor)
(T) 01873 811877.

FISHTEC, Unit 6/Ffrwdgrech Industrial Estate, Ffrwdgrech Road, Brecon, POWYS, LD3 8LA **Wales**
Mr Ian Burgess (Managing Director)
(T) 01874 612600.

RHONDDA CYNON TAFF

ALAN SMITH, Main Road, Church Village, Pontypridd, RHONDDA CYNON TAFF, CF38 1RL **Wales**
Mr Alan Smith (Proprietor)
(T) 01443 218437.

CYMREIG MOULDS, 7 Ynysmaerdy Terrace, Ynysmaerdy, Pontyclun, RHONDDA CYNON TAFF, CF72 8LG **Wales**
Mr R James (Director)
(T) 01443 228471.

TAFF ANGLING SUPPLIES, 41a Elm Street, Pontypridd, RHONDDA CYNON TAFF, CF37 5DF **Wales**
Mrs J Roberts (Proprietor)
(T) 01443 406006.

SWANSEA

SHIMANO UK LTD, St Johns Court, Upper Fforest Way, Morriston, Swansea, SWANSEA, SA6 8QR **Wales**
Mr C Brew (General Manager)
(T) 01792 791571.

WREXHAM

DEGGY'S FISHING TACKLE, 2 Ruabon Road, WREXHAM, LL13 7PB **Wales**
Mrs Ann Phillips (Proprietor)
(T) 01978 351815.

MORRISONS OF WREXHAM, 38-40 Mount Street, WREXHAM, LL13 8DW **Wales**
(T) 01978 364460.

Clubs and Associations

SECTION 14

Find your nearest fishing club or association.

Listed by Country by County.

Angling Times Fishooked Directory

ENGLAND

BEDFORDSHIRE

- **AMPTHILL AND DISTRICT ANGLING FISH PRESERVATION SOCIETY**
Contact/s:
Mr R Ward (Secretary), 15 Kingfisher Rd, Flitwick, Bedford, BEDFORDSHIRE, MK45 1RA **England**

- **BEDFORD ANGLING CLUB**
Contact/s:
Mrs M E Appleton (Secretary), 18 Moriston Rd, Brickhill, Bedford, BEDFORDSHIRE, MK41 7UG **England**
(T) 01234 354708.

- **BIGGLESWADE, HITCHEN AND DISTRICT ANGLING CLUB**
Contact/s:
Mr P Currell (Secretary), 10 Popular Cl, Sandy, BEDFORDSHIRE, SG19 **England**
(T) 01767 682619.

- **BLUNHAM AND DISTRICT ANGLING CLUB**
Contact/s:
Mr G Palmer (Club Secretary), 5 Brockwell, Oakley, Bedford, BEDFORDSHIRE, MK43 7TD **England**
(T) 01234 823959.

- **BRAGGERS ANGLING CLUB**
Contact/s:
Mr J Iddon (Secretary), 16 Copthorne, Luton, BEDFORDSHIRE, LU2 8RJ **England**

- **KEMPSTON ANGLING CLUB**
Contact/s:
Mr Ken Green (Secretary), 24 The Elms, Kempston, Bedford, BEDFORDSHIRE, MK42 7JW **England**
(T) 01234 854165.

- **LEIGHTON BUZZARD AND DISTRICT WMC**
Contact/s:
Mr T Brightman (Secretary), 37 Garden Hedge, Leighton Buzzard, BEDFORDSHIRE, LU7 8EF **England**
(T) 01525 371075.

- **LEIGHTON BUZZARD ANGLING CLUB**
Contact/s:
Mr B Smalley (Secretary), 3 Isis Walk, Leighton Buzzard, BEDFORDSHIRE, LU7 3DB **England**
(T) 01525 852227.

- **LEIGHTON BUZZARD ANGLING SOCIETY**
Contact/s:
Mr H Holliday (Secretary), 54 Pebble Moor, Eddlesborough, Leighton Buzzard, BEDFORDSHIRE, LU7 8EF **England**
(T) 01525 221247.

- **LUTON AND DISTRICT ANGLING CLUB**
Contact/s:
Mr G Buss (Secretary), 1 Easthill Rd, Houghton Regis, Dunstable, BEDFORDSHIRE, LU5 5EQ **England**
(T) 01582 28114.
Mr G Buss (Secretary), 179 Tithe Farm Rd, Houghton Regis, Dunstable, BEDFORDSHIRE, LU5 5JF **England**
(T) 01582 28114.

- **SHEFFORD AND DISTRICT ANGLING ASSOCIATION**
Contact/s:
A Thomas (Secretary), 18 Stoneland Avenue, Biggleswade, BEDFORDSHIRE, SG18 0EA **England**
Mr J Leath (Secretary), 3 Ivel Cl, Shefford, BEDFORDSHIRE, SG17 5JX **England**
(T) 01462 812323.

- **VAUXHALL ANGLING CLUB**
Contact/s:
Mr Roy Poulton (Secretary), 20 Leeches Way, Cheddington, Leighton Buzzard, BEDFORDSHIRE, LU7 0SJ **England**
(T) 01296 668985.

- **VERULAM ANGLING CLUB**
Contact/s:
Mr J Trew (Secretary), 128 Benson Cl, Bramingham Wood, Luton, BEDFORDSHIRE, LU3 3QR **England**
(T) 01582 593798.

BERKSHIRE

- **ANGLERS CONSERVATION ASSOCIATION**
Contact/s:
Secretary, Shalford Dairy, Shalford Hill, Aldermaston,Reading, BERKSHIRE, RG7 4NB **England**
(T) 0118 9714770.

- **ARBORLEIGH ANGLING CLUB**
Contact/s:
Mr J Drisse (Secretary), 49 Tilehurst Rd, Reading, BERKSHIRE, RG30 2JL **England**

- **NATIONAL FEDERATION OF ANGLERS**
Contact/s:
Mr David Wright (Nfa Disability Officer, Southern Region), 3 Wantage Rd, Reading, BERKSHIRE, RG3 2SH **England**
(T) 01734 573607.

- **READING AND DISTRICT ANGLING ASSOCIATION**
Contact/s:
Mr Bill Brown-Lee (Secretary), 47 Calbourne Drive, The Orchard, Calcot,Reading, BERKSHIRE, RG3 7DB **England**
(T) 0118 9417368.
Ms Dusty Millar (Ticket Administrator), Dorstans, Hatch Lane, Brimpton Village,Reading, BERKSHIRE, RG7 4TR **England**
(T) 0118 9874882.

- **READING CIVIL SERVICE SPORTS ASSOCIATION**
Contact/s:
Mr A Byrne (Secretary), 131 Foxhays Rd, Reading, BERKSHIRE, RG2 8NN **England**
(T) 0118 9833423.

- **SOUTH LAKE ANGLING SOCIETY**
Contact/s:
Mr Williams (Secretary), 24 Duncan Rd, Woodley, Reading, BERKSHIRE, RG5 4HR **England**

BRISTOL

- **BRISTOL AND WEST OF ENGLAND FEDERATION OF ANGLERS**
Contact/s:
Mr B Williams (Secretary), 157 Whiteway Rd, BRISTOL, BS5 7RH **England**

- **BRISTOL WATER**
Contact/s:
Mr Bob Handford (Secretary), Recreations Department, Woodford Lodge, Chew Stoke,BRISTOL, BS18 8XH **England**
(T) 01275 332339.
(F) 01275 331377.

- **BRISTOL, BATH AND WILTSHIRE ANGLING ASSOCIATION**
Contact/s:
Mr Jeff Parker (Secretary), 16 Lansdown View, Kingswood, BRISTOL, BS15 4AW **England**
(T) 01179 672977.

- **KEYNSHAM ANGLING ASSOCIATION**
Contact/s:
K N Jerrom (Secretary), 21 St Georges Rd, Keynsham, BRISTOL, BS18 2HU **England**
Veals, Old Market, BRISTOL, BS **England**

- **UK FLY FISHERMAN AND TYERS FEDERATION**
Contact/s:
Secretary, Po Box 126, Patchway, BRISTOL, BS12 6TP **England**
(T) 01179 833661.
(F) 01179 833661.

BUCKINGHAMSHIRE

- **BEACON ANGLING CLUB**
Contact/s:
Mr D Bacon (Secretary), 18 The Hedgerows, Furzton, Milton Keynes, BUCKINGHAMSHIRE, MK4 1BD **England**
(T) 01908 502577.

- **BLENHEIM ANGLING SOCIETY**
Contact/s:
Mr Fred Lancaster (Secretary), Briarwood, Burtons Lane, Chalfont St Giles, BUCKINGHAMSHIRE, HP8 4BB **England**
(T) 01494 764977.

- **BUCKINGHAM AND DISTRICT ANGLING ASSOCIATION**
Contact/s:
Mrs J Begley (Secretary), 20 Vicarage Rd, Steeple Claydon, Buckingham, BUCKINGHAMSHIRE, MK18 2PU **England**
(T) 01296 730577.

- **DEANSHANGER AND STRATFORDS ANGLING ASSOCIATION**
Contact/s:
Mr T Valentine (Secretary), 34 Malletts Cl, Stony Stratford, Milton Keynes, BUCKINGHAMSHIRE, MK11 1DQ **England**

- **DYKE ANGLING CLUB**
Contact/s:
Mr A Hill (Secretary), 29 Elora Rd, Totteridge, High Wycombe, BUCKINGHAMSHIRE, HP13 7LL **England**
(T) 01494 526557.

- **MARLOW ANGLING CLUB**
Contact/s:
Mr J Woodhouse (Secretary), Conifers, Ash Rd, High Wycombe, BUCKINGHAMSHIRE, HP12 4SW **England**
(T) 01494 523988.

- **NEWPORT PAGNELL FISHING ASSOCIATION**
Contact/s:
Mr R Dorrill (Secretary), 7 Bury St, Newport Pagnell, BUCKINGHAMSHIRE, MK16 0DS **England**
(T) 01908 610639.

- **OLD WINDSOR ANGLING CLUB**
Contact/s:
Mr A Beaven (Secretary), 88 St Andrews Way, Slough, BUCKINGHAMSHIRE, SL1 5LJ **England**

- **OLNEY AND CLIFTON FISHING ASSOCIATION**
Contact/s:
Mr Kv Osborne (Secretary), 11 Gilpin Way, Olney, BUCKINGHAMSHIRE, MK46 4DN **England**
(T) 01234 713144.

- **PRESTWOOD AND DISTRICT ANGLING CLUB**
Contact/s:
Mr D Mumford (Secretary), 20 Hale Rd, Wendover, Aylesbury, BUCKINGHAMSHIRE, HP22 6NF **England**
(T) 01296 622531.

READING AND DISTRICT ANGLING ASSOCIATION
Contact/s:
D Capon (Secretary), 61 Thame Rd, Haddenham, Aylesbury, BUCKINGHAMSHIRE, HP17 8EP **England**

SALT HILL ANGLING SOCIETY
Contact/s:
Mrs Phyliss Symons (Secretary), 18 Wood Lane, Cippenham, Slough, BUCKINGHAMSHIRE, SL1 9EA **England**

WESTON UNDERWOOD ANGLING CLUB
Contact/s:
Mr D Adams (Secretary), 12 The Close, Weston Underwood, Olney, BUCKINGHAMSHIRE, MK46 5JP **England**
(T) 01234 711418.

CAMBRIDGESHIRE

AGREVO ANGLING CLUB
Contact/s:
Mr T Allison (Secretary), Agr Evo Uk Limited, Hauxton, Cambridge, CAMBRIDGESHIRE, CB2 5HU **England**
(T) 01223 870312.

ASHMIRE CARP SYNDICATE
Contact/s:
Mr Ron Middleton (Secretary), Earith, Cambridge, CAMBRIDGESHIRE, CB **England**
(T) 01487 740943.

BENWICK ANGLING CLUB
Contact/s:
Mr C Onyett (Secretary), 82 Ramsey Rd, Ramsey Forty Foot, Huntingdon, CAMBRIDGESHIRE, PE17 2XN **England**
(T) 01487 814671.

BLACKSMITH ARMS ANGLING CLUB
Contact/s:
Mr Ma Burrows (Secretary), 6 Sachwood Avenue, Emneth, Wisbech, CAMBRIDGESHIRE, PE **England**

BRAMPTON ANGLING CLUB
Contact/s:
Mr K Medlock (Secretary), 1 Staunch Hill Rd, Sawtry, Huntingdon, CAMBRIDGESHIRE, PE17 5XG **England**
(T) 01487 830984.

BRAMPTON ANGLING SOCIETY
Contact/s:
S Clark (Secretary), 89 High St, Buckden, St Neots,Huntingdon, CAMBRIDGESHIRE, PE18 9TA **England**

CAMBRIDGE ALBION ANGLING SOCIETY
Contact/s:
Mr R Gentle (Secretary), 34 Ramsden Sq, Cambridge, CAMBRIDGESHIRE, CB4 2BL **England**
(T) 01223 426711.

CAMBRIDGE FISH PRESERVATION ANGLING SOCIETY
Contact/s:
Mr Graham Tweed (Secretary), 27A Villa Rd, Impington, Cambridge, CAMBRIDGESHIRE, CB4 9NZ **England**
(T) 01223 234616.

CAMBRIDGE IZAAK WALTON SOCIETY
Contact/s:
Mr T Sawyer (Secretary), 6 Pump Lane, Hardwick, Cambridge, CAMBRIDGESHIRE, CB3 7QW **England**
(T) 01954 211531.

CAMBRIDGESHIRE AND ISLE OF ELY FEDERATION OF ANGLERS
Contact/s:
Mr Roy Page (Secretary), 1 Fen Rd, Peterborough, CAMBRIDGESHIRE, PE6 **England**

CHATTERIS WORKING MENS CLUB AND INSTITUTE
Contact/s:
Mr B Knightley (Secretary), 10 Salem Court, Chatteris, CAMBRIDGESHIRE, PE16 **England**
(T) 01354 692015.

CHERRY HINTON ANGLING CLUB
Contact/s:
Mr Hobson (Secretary), 25 Ivory Cl, Cherry Hinton, Cambridge, CAMBRIDGESHIRE, CB1 **England**

CHURCH PIT FPAS
Contact/s:
Mr T Bridgefoot (Secretary), Bluebell Cottage, Walnut Rd, Walpole St Peter,Wisbech, CAMBRIDGESHIRE, PE14 7PE **England**

COOPERS ANGLING CLUB
Contact/s:
Mr John Dickens (Secretary), 2 Witchford Rd, Ely, CAMBRIDGESHIRE, CB6 3DP **England**
(T) 01353 663398.

COTTERSTOCK ANGLING ASSOCIATION
Contact/s:
Mrs Joan Popplewell (Secretary), 40 North St, Oundle, Peterborough, CAMBRIDGESHIRE, PE8 4AL **England**
(T) 01832 273671.

DEEPING ST JAMES ANGLING CLUB
Contact/s:
Mr D Bailey (Secretary), 11 Lime Tree Avenue, Towngate West, Market Deeping,Peterborough, CAMBRIDGESHIRE, PE6 8DQ **England**
(T) 01778 346355.

ELY BEET SPORTS AND SOCIAL CLUB
Contact/s:
Mr D Dummet (Secretary), 79 West Fen Rd, Ely, CAMBRIDGESHIRE, CB6 3AA **England**
(T) 01353 664919.

FENLAND ASSOCIATION OF ANGLERS
Contact/s:
Mr Colin Clare (Secretary), 1 Mount Pleasant Rd, Wisbech, CAMBRIDGESHIRE, PE13 3NF **England**

FOURWAYS FISHING CLUB
Contact/s:
Secretary, Baston, Peterborough, CAMBRIDGESHIRE, PE **England**
(T) 01406 380473or380557.

GODMANCHESTER AFPS
Contact/s:
Mrs L Christian (Secretary), 35 Post St, Godmanchester, Huntingdon, CAMBRIDGESHIRE, PE1 **England**
(T) 01480 451260.

HISTON AND DISTRICT ANGLING CLUB
Contact/s:
Mr Colin Dodd (Secretary), 122 Rampton Rd, Willingham, Cambridge, CAMBRIDGESHIRE, CB4 **England**

HOLME AND DISTRICT ANGLING ASSOCIATION
Contact/s:
Mr K Burt (Secretary), 55 Windsor Rd, Yaxley, Peterborough, CAMBRIDGESHIRE, PE7 **England**
(T) 01733 241119.

HOUGHTON, WYTON AND HEMINGFORD ANGLING SOCIETY
Contact/s:
Mr A Wilkinson (Secretary), 22 Erica Rd, St Ives, Huntingdon, CAMBRIDGESHIRE, PE17 6AE **England**
(T) 01480 466525.

HUNTINGDON ANGLING AND FISH PRESERVATION SOCIETY
Contact/s:
Mrs A Wallis (Secretary), 8 Claytons Way, Huntingdon, CAMBRIDGESHIRE, PE18 7UT **England**
(T) 01480 458935.

LARK ENGINE ANGLING CLUB
Contact/s:
Mr A Palmer (Secretary), 13 Kingdom Avenue, Prickwillow, Ely, CAMBRIDGESHIRE, CB **England**
(T) 01353 688447.

LITTLEPORT ANGLING CLUB
Contact/s:
Mr D Yardy (Secretary), 168 High Barns, Ely, CAMBRIDGESHIRE, CB7 4RP **England**
(T) 01353 669323.

Mr John W Shelsher (Secretary), 20 New River Bank, Littleport, Ely, CAMBRIDGESHIRE, CB7 4TA **England**
(T) 01353 860787.

MANEA ANGLING CLUB
Contact/s:
Mr R Dent (Secretary), 1 Lynford Cottages, Fodder Fen, Manea,March, CAMBRIDGESHIRE, PE15 8LS **England**
(T) 01354 78411or01223315315.

MANTON ANGLING CLUB
Contact/s:
Mr G Culley (Secretary), Manton Insulations Ltd, Little End Rd, Eaton Socon,St Neots, Huntingdon, CAMBRIDGESHIRE, PE19 3JH **England**
(T) 01480 214300.

MARCH AND DISTRICT ANGLING ASSOCIATION
Contact/s:
Mr Hc Asplin (Secretary), 21 New Park, March, CAMBRIDGESHIRE, PE15 **England**
(T) 01354 52707.

MARCH ANGLING CLUB
Contact/s:
Secretary, 88A High St, March, CAMBRIDGESHIRE, PE15 9LQ **England**
(T) 01354 658747.

NENE AND WELLAND ANGLING CONSULTATIVE ASSOCIATION
Contact/s:
Mr G Bibby (Secretary), 5 Ermine Way, Sawtry, Huntingdon, CAMBRIDGESHIRE, PE28 5UQ **England**
(T) 01487 831718.

OFFORD AND BUCKDEN ANGLING SOCIETY
Contact/s:
Mr R Wood (Secretary), The Boat House, Carters Boatyard, Mill Rd,Buckden, Huntingdon, CAMBRIDGESHIRE, PE18 9RY **England**
(T) 01480 811503.

Mr John Astell (Secretary), 154 Eastrea Rd, Whittlesey, CAMBRIDGESHIRE, PE7 2AJ **England**

OFFORD AND BUCKDEN FISHING SOCIETY
Contact/s:
A Plumb (Secretary), 75 High St, Great Paxton, Huntingdon, CAMBRIDGESHIRE, PE17 4RG **England**

OUNDLE ANGLING ASSOCIATION
Contact/s:
Mr D Laxton (Secretary), 31 St Peters St, Oundle, Peterborough, CAMBRIDGESHIRE, PE8 4 **England**

OVER AND SWAVERLEY DISTRICT ANGLING SOCIETY
Contact/s:
Mr D Cook (Secretary), 588 Coldhams Lane, Cherry Hinton, Cambridge, CAMBRIDGESHIRE, CB1 3JR **England**
(T) 01954 230076.

PBI ANGLING CLUB
Contact/s:
Mr A Taylor (Secretary), 5 Greenfield Cl, Stapleford, Cambridge, CAMBRIDGESHIRE, CB2 5BT **England**
(T) 01223 843036.

PETERBOROUGH AND DISTRICT ANGLING ASSOCIATION
Contact/s:
W Yates (Secretary), 75 Lawn Avenue, Dogsthorpe, Peterborough, CAMBRIDGESHIRE, PE1 3RA **England**

PETERBOROUGH ANGLING CLUB
Contact/s:
Mr R Warr (Secretary), 24 Whitmore Court, Whittlesey, CAMBRIDGESHIRE, PE7 **England**

PYMOOR ANGLING CLUB
Contact/s:
Mr F Gilbert (Secretary), 10 Park Lane, Little Downham, Ely, CAMBRIDGESHIRE, CB6 2TF **England**
(T) 01353 699415.

RAMSEY AND DISTRICT ANGLING SOCIETY
Contact/s:
Mr P Aldred (Secretary), 9 Blackmill St, Chatteris, CAMBRIDGESHIRE, PE16 6SR **England**

RIDGEWOOD ANGLING CLUB
Contact/s:
Mr P Middleton (Secretary), 9 Abercorn Pl, Kings Hedges Rd, Cambridge, CAMBRIDGESHIRE, CB4 2UX **England**
(T) 01223 573453.

SAFFRON WALDON ANGLING CLUB
Contact/s:
Mr N Roberts (Secretary), 55 St Marys Rd, Sawston, Cambridge, CAMBRIDGESHIRE, CB2 4SP **England**
(T) 01223 836773.

SOHAM ANGLING CLUB
Contact/s:
Mr P Brooks (Secretary), 17 Fleet Cl, Littleport, Ely, CAMBRIDGESHIRE, CB6 1PG **England**
(T) 01353 862815.

SPRATTS ANGLING CLUB
Contact/s:
Mr K Wilkinson (Secretary), 9 Goodens Lane, Newton, Wisbech, CAMBRIDGESHIRE, PE13 5HQ **England**
(T) 01945 870020.
P Pearce (Secretary), Shankly Gate, High Rd, Guyhirn,Wisbech, CAMBRIDGESHIRE, PE13 4ED **England**
(T) 01945 450730.

ST IVES DISTRICT FISH PRESERVATION AND ANGLING SOCIETY
Contact/s:
Mr H Pace (Secretary), 48 Fairfields, St Ives, Huntingdon, CAMBRIDGESHIRE, PE17 4QF **England**
(T) 01480 469254.

ST NEOTS AND DISTRICT ANGLING AND FISH PRESERVATION SOCIETY
Contact/s:
Ms Diane Linger (Secretary), Skewbridge Cottage, Great Paxton, St Neots,Huntingdon, CAMBRIDGESHIRE, PE19 4RA **England**
(T) 01480 216730.

STANSTEAD ANGLING SOCIETY
Contact/s:
Mr C Hampton (Secretary), 44 New Rd, Sawston, CAMBRIDGESHIRE, CB2 4BW **England**

SUTTON ANGLING CLUB
Contact/s:
Mr T Sulman (Secretary), 105 Stretham Rd, Wilburton, Ely, CAMBRIDGESHIRE, CB6 3RY **England**
(T) 01353 649509.

WANSFORD, YARWELL, NASSINGTON AND DISTRICT ANGLING CLUB
Contact/s:
Mr Steve Longfoot (Secretary), 2 Dovecote Cl, Yarwell, Peterborough, CAMBRIDGESHIRE, PE8 6PE **England**

WARMINGTON ANGLING CLUB
Contact/s:
Mr Bailey (Secretary), 2 Buntings Lane, Warmington, Peterborough, CAMBRIDGESHIRE, PE8 6TT **England**

WATERBEACH ANGLING CLUB
Contact/s:
Mr H Reynolds (Secretary), 3 Crosskeys Court, Cottenham, Cambridge, CAMBRIDGESHIRE, CB4 4UW **England**
(T) 01954 250886.

WELNEY ANGLING CLUB
Contact/s:
Mr D Booth (Secretary), Shaneden, Bedford Bank West, Welney,Wisbech, CAMBRIDGESHIRE, PE38 **England**
(T) 01354 610247.

WHITTLESEY ANGLING ASSOCIATION
Contact/s:
Mr J Warren (Secretary), 55 Belimans Rd, Whittlesey, Peterborough, CAMBRIDGESHIRE, PE7 1TY **England**
(T) 01733 203800.

WISBECH AND DISTRICT ANGLING ASSOCIATION
Contact/s:
B Lakey (Secretary), 28 Hill St, Wisbech, CAMBRIDGESHIRE, PE13 1BA **England**

YAXLEY FARCET, HOLME AND DISTRICT ANGLING CLUB
Contact/s:
Mr Paul Marriet (Secretary), 72 Portchester Cl, Park Farm, Peterborough, CAMBRIDGESHIRE, PE2 8UP **England**

CHESHIRE

BAY MALTON ANGLING CLUB
Contact/s:
Mr Stewart Godber (Club Secretary), 38 Edenfield Rd, Mobberley, CHESHIRE, **England**
(T) 01565 872582.

CAPENHURST ANGLING CLUB
Contact/s:
Mr A T Howdon (Secretary), 24 Saughall Hey, Saughall, Chester, CHESHIRE, CH1 6EJ **England**
(T) 01244 880621.

CHESHIRE ANGLERS ASSOCIATION
Contact/s:
Mr G Brassington (Secretary), 12 Highfield Drive, Nantwich, CHESHIRE, CW5 **England**

CHESHIRE ANGLING ASSOCIATION
Contact/s:
Mr Graham Tompkinson (Secretary), 31 Wareham Drive, Crewe, CHESHIRE, CW1 3XA **England**

CHESTER ASSOCIATION OF ANGLERS
Contact/s:
Mr B W Roberts (Secretary), 23 Alpraham Cres, Upton Cross, Chester, CHESHIRE, CH2 1QX **England**

CONGLETON ANGLING SOCIETY
Contact/s:
Mr N J Bours (Secretary), 8 Norfolk Rd, Congleton, CHESHIRE, CW12 1NY **England**

ERRWOOD FLYFISHING CLUB
Contact/s:
T Speake (Treasurer), 11 Cliffmere Cl, Cheadle Hulme, CHESHIRE, SK8 **England**

HALTON JOINT ANGLERS' ASSOCIATION
Contact/s:
Mr Dave Forbes (Sceretary), 132 Edinburgh Rd, Hough Green, Widnes, CHESHIRE, WA8 8BB **England**
(T) 0151 4245594.

LAVISTER ANGLING CLUB
Contact/s:
Mr G Watkins (Secretary), Rathgillan, Lache Hall Cres, Chester, CHESHIRE, CH4 7NE **England**

LIVERPOOL ANGLING ASSOCIATION
Contact/s:
Mr Steve Owen (Secretary), British Waterways, North West Region, Navigation Rd,Northwich, CHESHIRE, CW8 1BH **England**

LYMM ANGLING CLUB
Contact/s:
Mr Neil Jupp (Club Secretary), Po Box 350, Warrington, CHESHIRE, WA4 5HZ **England**
(T) 01925 411774.

MACCLESFIELD FLYFISHERS CLUB
Contact/s:
Mr W F Williams (Secretary), 1 Westwood Drive, Brooklands, Sale, CHESHIRE, M33 3QW **England**

MACCLESFIELD WALTONIAN ANGLING SOCIETY
Contact/s:
Mr Micheal E Bowyer (Secretary), 7 Ullswater, Macclesfield, CHESHIRE, SK11 7YN **England**

MIDDLEWICH JOINT ANGLERS
Contact/s:
Mr C Bratt (Secretary), 13 Elm Rd, Middlewich, CHESHIRE, CW10 0AX **England**

NORTHERN ANGLERS ASSOCIATION
Contact/s:
Mr A G R Brown (Secretary), 10 Dale Rd, Golborne, Warrington, CHESHIRE, WA3 3PN **England**
(T) 01942 726917.

NORTHWICH ANGLING ASSOCIATION
Contact/s:
Ms J Clithero (Secretary), High Arces, Hartford, Northwich, CHESHIRE, CW8 1PP **England**

PRINCE ALBERT ANGLING SOCIETY
Contact/s:
Mr J A Turner (Secretary), 15 Pexhill Drive, Macclesfield, CHESHIRE, SK1 3LP **England**

STALYBRIDGE (FOX) ANGLING SOCIETY
Contact/s:
Mr Is Warton (Secretary), 17 Coneymead, Stalybridge, CHESHIRE, SK15 2LJ **England**

STOCKPORT DAF
Contact/s:
Mr H Ollerenshaw (Secretary), 133 Manchester Rd, Hyde, CHESHIRE, SK14 2BK **England**

UPTON ANGLING CLUB
Contact/s:
Mr Mark Williams (Secretary), 4 Cornwall Rd, Upton-By-Chester, Chester, CHESHIRE, CH2 1NP **England**

WARRINGTON ANGLING ASSOCIATION
Contact/s:
Mr Frank Lythgoe (Secretary), 52 Parker St, Warrington, CHESHIRE, WA1 1LR **England**
(T) 01928 716238.
(F) 01928 713898.

- **WINSFORD AND DISTRICT ANGLING ASSOCIATION**
Contact/s:
Mr J Stewart Bailey (Secretary), 22 Plover Avenue, Winsford, CHESHIRE, CW7 1LA **England**

CLEVELAND

- **FISHERIES OFFICE**
Contact/s:
Secretary, 103 Northgate, Hartlepool, CLEVELAND, TS24 0JX **England**
(T) 01429 860221.

- **MIDDLESBROUGH ANGLING CLUB**
Contact/s:
R Thompson (Secretary), 25 Endsleigh Drive, Acklam, Middlesbrough, CLEVELAND, TS5 4RG **England**

- **SALTBURN AND DISTRICT ANGLING ASSOCIATION**
Contact/s:
Saltburn Information Bureau, Saltburn-By-The-Sea, CLEVELAND, TS12 **England**

- **THORNABY ANGLING ASSOCIATION**
Contact/s:
Mr D Speight (Secretary), 10 Stainsby Gate, Thornaby, Stockton-on-Tees, CLEVELAND, TS17 9AQ **England**

CORNWALL

- **BODMIN ANGLING ASSOCIATION**
Contact/s:
Mr R Burrows (Secretary), 26 Meadow Pl, Bodmin, CORNWALL, PL31 1JD **England**

- **BUDE ANGLING ASSOCIATION**
Contact/s:
Mrs P Casson (Secretary), 29 West Park Rd, Bude, CORNWALL, EX23 0NA **England**

- **BUDE CANAL ANGLING ASSOCIATION**
Contact/s:
Mr R Turner (Secretary), 2 Passfields, Bude, CORNWALL, EX23 **England**

- **CAMBORNE ANGLING ASSOCIATION**
Contact/s:
C McLoughlin (Secretary), 10 Dolcoath Rd, Camborne, CORNWALL, TR14 8RW **England**

- **FALMOUTH BOAT OWNERS ASSOCIATION**
Contact/s:
Mr Peter Newman (Chairman), Custom House Quay, Falmouth, CORNWALL, TR11 **England**
(T) 01326 311434.

- **GLENVILLE FISHING CLUB**
Contact/s:
Social Club, St Dennis, St Austell, CORNWALL, PL26 **England**

- **LANHYDROCK ANGLING ASSOCIATION**
Contact/s:
National Trust Regional Office, Lanhydrock Park, Lanhydrock,Bodmin, CORNWALL, PL30 4DE **England**

- **LISKEARD AND DISTRICT ANGLING CLUB**
Contact/s:
O Gilbert (Secretary), 11 Richmond Rd, Pelnyt, Looe, CORNWALL, PL13 2NH **England**
Mr Bill Eliot (Hon Secretary), 64 Portbyhan Rd, Looe, CORNWALL, PL13 2QN **England**
(T) 01503 264173.
Secretary, Looe Tropical & Pet Supplies, The Quay, East Looe,Looe, CORNWALL, PL13 **England**
(T) 01503 263535.

- **LOSTWITHIEL FISHING ASSOCIATION**
Contact/s:
Mr J H Hooper (Secretary), 4 Reeds Park, Lostwithiel, CORNWALL, PL22 0HF **England**

- **MARAZION ANGLING CLUB**
Contact/s:
County Angler, 39 Cross St, Camborne, CORNWALL, TR14 8ES **England**

- **PADSTOW ANGLING CLUB**
Contact/s:
Social Club, Padstow, CORNWALL, PL28 **England**

- **ROCHE (ST AUSTELL) ANGLING CLUB**
Contact/s:
Marcus Watts (Secretary), Angling Ctre, 10A Victoria Pl, St Austell, CORNWALL, PL25 5PE **England**
(T) 01208 816403.
(F) 01208 816403.

- **ST COLUMB CLUB**
Contact/s:
The Red Lion, St Columb, CORNWALL, TR9 **England**

- **ST IVES FRESHWATER ANGLING SOCIETY**
Contact/s:
Dr C Franklin (Fishery Manager), Chy-Am-Meor, Westward Rd, St Ives, CORNWALL, TR26 1JX **England**
(T) 01736 798251.

- **ST MAWGAN ANGLING CLUB**
Contact/s:
Mr T J Trevenns (Secretary), Lanvean House, St Mawgan, Newquay, CORNWALL, TR8 4EY **England**

- **TRENINNICK TAVERN ANGLING CLUB**
Contact/s:
The Tavern, Newquay, CORNWALL, TR **England**

- **WADEBRIDGE ANGLING ASSOCIATION**
Contact/s:
A Gill (Secretary), Jasmine Cottage, Kelly Park, St Mabyn,Bodmin, CORNWALL, PL30 3BL **England**

COUNTY DURHAM

- **BISHOP AUCKLAND AND DISTRICT ANGLING CLUB**
Contact/s:
Mr J Winter (Secretary), 7 Royal Gr, Crook, COUNTY DURHAM, DL15 9ER **England**

- **CHESTER-LE-STREET AND DISTRICT ANGLING CLUB**
Contact/s:
Mr G Curry (Hon Secretary), 62 Newcastle Rd, Chester-Le-Street, COUNTY DURHAM, DH3 3UF **England**

- **DARLINGTON ANGLING CLUB**
Contact/s:
Mr I Ablott (Secretary), 58 Swaledale Avenue, Darlington, COUNTY DURHAM, DL3 9AL **England**

- **DARLINGTON BROWN TROUT ANGLING ASSOCIATION**
Contact/s:
Mr G Coulson (Secretary), 5 Grange Avenue, Hurworth Pl, Darlington, COUNTY DURHAM, DL **England**

- **DARLINGTON FLY FISHERS CLUB**
Contact/s:
W D Holmes (Secretary), 39 Barrett Rd, Darlington, COUNTY DURHAM, DL3 8LA **England**

- **DURHAM ANGLING ASSOCIATION**
Contact/s:
J Hope (Secretary), 16 Sandford Rd, Bridgehill, Consett, COUNTY DURHAM, DH8 **England**

- **DURHAM CITY ANGLING CLUB**
Contact/s:
Mr Mj Hall (Secretary), 21 Northumbria Pl, Stanley, COUNTY DURHAM, DH9 0UB **England**

- **FERRY HILL AND DISTRICT ANGLING CLUB**
Contact/s:
Mr Barry Hignett (Secretary), 74 Grasmere Rd, Garden Farm Estate, Chester-Le-Street, COUNTY DURHAM, DH **England**
(T) 0191 3883557.
R Staff (Secretary), 19 Opal Avenue, Chilton, Durham, COUNTY DURHAM, DH **England**

- **KIRKBY FLEETHAM ANGLING CLUB**
Contact/s:
Mr Ml Smith (Secretary), 26 Eden Gr, Newton Aycliffe, COUNTY DURHAM, DL5 7JG **England**

- **STANHOPE ANGLING ASSOCIATION**
Contact/s:
J J Lee (Secretary), 1 Eastcroft, Stanhope, Bishop Auckland, COUNTY DURHAM, DL13 2NS **England**

- **UPPER WEARDALE ANGLING ASSOCIATION**
Contact/s:
H C Lee (Secretary), 7 Westfall, Wearhead, Bishop Auckland, COUNTY DURHAM, DL13 1BP **England**
Wearhead Post Office, Upper Weardale, Bishop Auckland, COUNTY DURHAM, DL13 **England**

CUMBRIA

- **BARROW ANGLING ASSOCIATION**
Contact/s:
69 Prince St, Dalton-In-Furness, CUMBRIA, LA15 8ET **England**

- **BURNESIDE ANGLING ASSOCIATION**
Contact/s:
Mr Chris Green (Secretary), Millside, Hall Rd, Burneside,Kendal, CUMBRIA, LA9 6QE **England**
(F) 01539 818486.

- **CALDER ANGLING ASSOCIATION**
Contact/s:
Mr W Holmes (Secretary), W N Holmes, 45 Main St, Egremont, CUMBRIA, CA22 **England**
(T) 01946 820368.

- **COCKERMOUTH ANGLING ASSOCIATION**
Contact/s:
Mr Ken Simpson (Secretary), 36 High Rigg, Brigham, Cockermouth, CUMBRIA, CA13 **England**

- **CONISTON AND TORVER DISTRICT ANGLERS ASSOCIATION**
Contact/s:
J Carrol (Secretary), 8 Old Furness Rd, Coniston, CUMBRIA, LA21 8HU **England**

- **EGREMONT ANGLING ASSOCIATION**
Contact/s:
C Fisher (Secretary), 69 North Rd, Egremont, CUMBRIA, CA22 2PR **England**
(T) 01946 820855.

- **ELLEN ANGLING ASSOCIATION**
Contact/s:
Mr Dale Stephen Renac (Secretary), 10 Selby Trce, Maryport, CUMBRIA, CA15 6NF **England**
(T) 01900 813595.

- **FISHER TARN ANGLERS**
Contact/s:
A Moore, 65 Waterside, Kendal, CUMBRIA, LA **England**

- **FRESHWATER BIOLOGICAL ASSOCIATION**
Contact/s:
Secretary, The Ferry House, Far Sawrey, Ambleside, CUMBRIA, LA22 0LP
England
(T) 01539 424468.

- **GOSFORTH ANGLING CLUB**
Contact/s:
W N Holmes (Secretary), 45 Main St, Egremont, CUMBRIA, CA22 **England**

- **HAWKSHEAD ANGLING CLUB**
Contact/s:
Mr J L Locke (Secretary), Flat 1, The Croft, Hawkshead,Ambleside, CUMBRIA, LA22 0NX **England**

- **KENT (WESTMORLAND) ANGLING ASSOCIATION**
Contact/s:
Mr J Atkinson (Secretary), Town End, Natland, Kendal, CUMBRIA, LA9 7QL
England

- **KESWICK ANGLING ASSOCIATION**
Contact/s:
Mr Jd Thompson (Secretary), 15 Low Mill, Greta Side, Keswick, CUMBRIA, GA12 5LL **England**
W Ashcroft (Secretary), Spring Haven, How Lane, Portinscale,Keswick, CUMBRIA, CA12 **England**

- **KIRKBY LONSDALE AND DISTRICT ANGLING ASSOCIATION**
Contact/s:
F Mellor (Secretary), 48 Mitchelgate, Kirkby Lonsdale, Carnforth, CUMBRIA, LA6 2BE **England**

- **KIRKBY LONSDALE ANGLING ASSOCIATION**
Contact/s:
Tourist Information Ctre, 24 Main St, Kirkby Lonsdale,Carnforth, CUMBRIA, LA6 2EA **England**

- **LUNE AND WYRE FISHERY ASSOCIATION**
Contact/s:
R A Challenor (Secretary), 6 Main St, Kirkby Lonsdale, Carnforth, CUMBRIA, LA6 2AJ **England**

- **MILLOM AND DISTRICT ANGLING ASSOCIATION**
Contact/s:
Mr D J Dixon (Secretary), 1 Churchill Drive, Millom, CUMBRIA, LA18 5DD
England
(T) 01229 774241.

- **MILNTHORPE ANGLING ASSOCIATION**
Contact/s:
Kendal Sports, Stramongate, Kendal, CUMBRIA, LA **England**

- **PENRITH ANGLING ASSOCIATION**
Contact/s:
Mrs P Studholme (Secretary), 39 Brougham St, Penrith, CUMBRIA, CA11 8DH **England**

- **SEDBERGH AND DISTRICT ANGLING ASSOCIATION**
Contact/s:
Mr G Bainbridge (Secretary), El Kantara, Frostrow, Sedbergh, CUMBRIA, LA10 5JL **England**
(T) 01539 620044.

- **STAVELEY AND DISTRICT ANGLING ASSOCIATION**
Contact/s:
D & H Woof, 22 Main St, Staveley,Kendal, CUMBRIA, LA8 9LN **England**

- **TEBAY ANGLERS**
Contact/s:
Mr Harold Riley (Secretary), White Cross House, Tebay, Penrith, CUMBRIA, CA11 **England**
(T) 01539 624376.

- **ULVERSTON ANGLING ASSOCIATION**
Contact/s:
J A Baldwin (Secretary), 24 Springfield Park Rd, Ulverston, CUMBRIA, LA12 0EQ
England

- **WATH BROW AND ENNERDALE ANGLING ASSOCIATION**
Contact/s:
D F Whelan (Secretary), 11 Crossing Cl, Cleator Moor, CUMBRIA, CA25
England

- **WINDERMERE, AMBLESIDE AND DISTRICT ANGLING ASSOCIATION**
Contact/s:
Mr Chris Sodo (Hon Treasurer), Brackenthwaite House, Black Beck Wood, Storrs Park,Windermere, CUMBRIA, LA23 3LF **England**
(T) 01539 445083.

DERBYSHIRE

- **BELPER AND DISTRICT ANGLING CLUB**
Contact/s:
Mr P Smith (Secretary), 11 Lander Lane, Belper, DERBYSHIRE, DE56 **England**

- **BRETBY ANGLING CLUB**
Contact/s:
Mr K Woods (Secretary), Swadlincote, DERBYSHIRE, DE11 **England**
(T) 01283 212668.

- **CHAPELTOWN AND DISTRICT ANGLING ASSOCIATION**
Contact/s:
Mr Jim Rowlinson (Secretary), 8 Brook Rd, High Green, Sheffield, DERBYSHIRE, S30 4GG **England**
(T) 0114 2844553.

- **DERBY ANGLING ASSOCIATION**
Contact/s:
Mr R Roche (Secretary), 4 Randolphe Rd, Derby, DERBYSHIRE, DE **England**
(T) 01332 200001.

- **DERBY RAILWAY INSTITUTE ANGLING CLUB**
Contact/s:
Mr K Ottewell (Secretary), 65 Leytonstone Drive, Mackworth Estate, Derby, DERBYSHIRE, DE22 4 **England**

- **DERBYSHIRE AF**
Contact/s:
Mr Sw Clifton (Secretary), 14 Highfield Rd, Little Eaton, Derby, DERBYSHIRE, DE21 5 **England**

- **DERBYSHIRE COUNTRY ANGLING CLUB**
Contact/s:
Mr O W Handley (Secretary), Osprey House, Ogston Higham, Alfreton, DERBYSHIRE, DE55 6EL **England**

- **LONG EATON VICTORIA ANGLING SOCIETY**
Contact/s:
Mr David Kent (Secretary), 2 Edgehill Court, Fields Farm, Long Eaton, DERBYSHIRE, NG10 1PQ **England**
(T) 0115 8492854.

- **MATLOCK ANGLING CLUB**
Contact/s:
Secretary, Midland Hotel, 1 North Prde, Matlock Bath,Matlock, DERBYSHIRE, DE4 3NS **England**
(T) 01629 582630.

- **NATIONAL FEDERATION OF ANGLERS**
Contact/s:
Mr Rodney Coldron (Secretary), Halliday House, Egginton Junction, Egginton,Derby, DERBYSHIRE, DE65 6GU
England
(T) 01283 734735.
Mr David Kent (East Midlands Point Of Contact), 2 Edgehill Court, Fields Farm, Long Eaton, DERBYSHIRE, NG10 1PQ
England
(T) 0115 8492854.
Mr Roger Preston (North East Region Point Of Contact), 18 Webb Avenue, Deepcar, Sheffield, DERBYSHIRE, S30 5SX **England**
(T) 0114 2883728.

- **NCB WATERS**
Contact/s:
Mr Derek Olsop (Secretary), Heanor, DERBYSHIRE, DE75 **England**
(T) 01773 717727.

- **OLYMPIC ANGLING CLUB**
Contact/s:
P W Simpkin (Secretary), 8 Walter St, Draycott, Derby, DERBYSHIRE, DE72 3NU
England

- **PEAK FOREST ANGLING CLUB**
Contact/s:
Greenwood, Edale Rd, Hope,Hope Valley, DERBYSHIRE, S33 2RF **England**

- **PRIDE OF DERBY ANGLING ASSOCIATION**
Contact/s:
Mr Alan Miller (Secretary), 16 Mercia Drive, Willington, Derby, DERBYSHIRE, DE65 6DA **England**
(T) 01283 702701.

- **SHEFFIELD AMALGAMATED ANGLING SOCIETY**
Contact/s:
Mr A D Baynes (Secretary), Headquarters Lord Nelson, 166-168 Arundel St, Sheffield, DERBYSHIRE, S30
England

- **SWADLINCOTE ANGLING ASSOCIATION**
Contact/s:
Mrs J Kirby (Secretary), 8 Rawson Rd, Moira, Swadlincote, DERBYSHIRE, DE12 6
England
(T) 0121 3515970.

- **TRENT AND DISTRICT ANGLERS CONSULTATIVE ASSOCIATION**
Contact/s:
N Walsh (Secretary), 5 Derby Rd, Homesford, Matlock, DERBYSHIRE, DE4 5HL **England**

DEVON

- **AVON FISHING ASSOCIATION**
Contact/s:
Mr J E Coombes (Secretary), 19 Stella Rd, Preston, Paignton, DEVON, TQ3 1BH **England**

- **BARNSTAPLE AND DISTRICT ANGLING ASSOCIATION**
Contact/s:
S Toms (Secretary), 1 Maysleary Cottages, Filleigh, Barnstaple, DEVON, EX32 7TJ **England**

- **BIDEFORD AND DISTRICT ANGLING CLUB**
Contact/s:
Mrs Joan Ash (Secretary), 42 Clovelly St, Bideford, DEVON, EX39 **England**
Secretary, Honestone St, Bideford, DEVON, EX39 2DL **England**
(T) 01237 477996.

- **BRITISH RECORD (ROD- CAUGHT) FISH COMMITTEE**
Contact/s:
Mr David Rowe (Acting Secretary), National Federation Of Sea Anglers, 51A Queen St, Newton Abbot, DEVON, TQ12 2QJ **England**
(T) 01626 331330.
(F) 01626 331330.

- **CREDITON AND DISTRICT FLY FISHING CLUB**
Contact/s:
Mr Howard Thresher (Treasurer), 30 Tuckers Meadow, Crediton, DEVON, EX17 3NX **England**
(T) 01363 774926.

- **DARTMOUTH AND DISTRICT ANGLING ASSOCIATION**
Contact/s:
Mr L Berry (Chairman), Club Hq, 5 Oxford St, Dartmouth, DEVON, TQ6 **England**
Sport 'N' Fish, Fairfax Pl, Dartmouth, DEVON, TQ6 **England**

- **EXETER AND DISTRICT ANGLING ASSOCIATION**
Contact/s:
Mr Dave Cornish (Secretary), 9 Denmark Rd, Exeter, DEVON, EX1 1SL **England**

- **KENNICK FLY FISHERS ASSOCIATION**
Contact/s:
Mr Mike Boston (Secretary), 5 Shirburn Rd, Torquay, DEVON, TQ1 3JL **England**
(T) 01803 325722.

- **KINGSLAKE FISHING HOLIDAYS**
Contact/s:
Mr David Langdown (Secretary), Chilla, Beaworthy, DEVON, EX21 5JS **England**
(T) 01409 231401.
(F) 01409 231401.

- **MAFF DISTRICT FISHERIES OFFICE**
Contact/s:
Secretary, Plymouth Fisheries, Fish Quay, Sutton Harbour,Plymouth, DEVON, PL4 0LH **England**
(T) 01752 228001.

- **NATIONAL FEDERATION OF ANGLERS**
Contact/s:
Mr John Carr (Nfa Disability Officer, South West & South Wales Region), 61 Quarry Park Rd, Heavitree, Exeter, DEVON, EX2 5PD **England**
(T) 01392 76167.

- **NEWTON ABBOT FISHING ASSOCIATION**
Contact/s:
Mr David Horder (Secretary), 22 Mount Pleasant Rd, Newton Abbot, DEVON, TQ1 **England**
(T) 01626 364173.

- **PENINSULAR COARSE FISHERIES**
Contact/s:
Mr Reg England (Secretary), Leisure Services Dept, Higher Coombe Park, Lewdown,Okehampton, DEVON, EX20 4QT **England**
(T) 01837 871565.
(F) 01837 871534.

- **PLYMOUTH AND DISTRICT FRESHWATER ANGLING ASSOCIATION**
Contact/s:
Mr D L Owen (Secretary), 39 Burnett Rd, Crownhill, Plymouth, DEVON, PL6 5BH **England**
(T) 01752 705033.

- **SIMON GAWESWORTH SCHOOL OF FLY FISHING**
Contact/s:
Mr Simon Gawesworth (Secretary), 95 New St, Torrington, DEVON, EX38 8BT **England**
(T) 01805 623256.

- **SOUTH MOLTON ANGLING CLUB**
Contact/s:
I T S Binding (Secretary), 40 Parklands, South Molton, DEVON, EX34 4EW **England**

- **TAVY, WALKHAM AND PLYM FISHING CLUB**
Contact/s:
Mr John Soul (Hon Secretary), Trevenevow, Crapstone Rd, Yelverton, DEVON, PL20 6BT **England**
(T) 01822 854923.

- **TAW FISHING CLUB**
Contact/s:
Mr J D V Michie (Hon Secretary), Wheel Barton, Broadwood Kelly, Winkleigh, DEVON, EX19 8ED **England**

- **TIVERTON AND DISTRICT ANGLING CLUB**
Contact/s:
R Retallick (Secretary), 21 Alstone Rd, Canal Hill, Tiverton, DEVON, EX16 4LH **England**

- **TORBAY AMALGAMATED ANGLERS SOCIETY**
Contact/s:
Mrs C Wilden (Secretary), 100 St Marychurch Rd, Torquay, DEVON, TQ1 3HL **England**

- **UPPER TEIGN FISHING ASSOCIATION**
Contact/s:
Mr John Getliff (Secretary), 22 The Square, Chagford, Newton Abbot, DEVON, TQ13 8AB **England**

DORSET

- **BLANDFORD AND DISTRICT ANGLING CLUB**
Contact/s:
Mrs J Leslie (Secretary), 20 Fields Oak, Blandford Forum, DORSET, DT11 7PP **England**

- **DORCHESTER FISHING CLUB**
Contact/s:
Mr J Grindle (Secretary), 36 Cowleaze, Martinstown, Dorchester, DORSET, DT2 9TD **England**

- **GILLINGHAM AND DISTRICT ANGLING ASSOCIATION**
Contact/s:
Mr Paul Stone (Treasurer), The Timepiece, High St, Newbury,Gillingham, DORSET, SP8 4HZ **England**

- **RINGWOOD ANGLING CLUB**
Contact/s:
Mr Tim Bawn (Secretary), 65 Arnewood Rd, Southbourne, Bournemouth, DORSET, BH6 5DN **England**
(T) 01202 427305.

- **STURMINSTER AND HINTON ANGLING ASSOCIATION**
Contact/s:
Mr S Dimmer (Secretary), 38 Grosvenor Rd, Stalbridge, Sturminster Newton, DORSET, DT10 2PN **England**
(T) 01963 363291.

- **SWANAGE AND DISTRICT ANGLING CLUB**
Contact/s:
Peveril Slipway, Swanage, DORSET, BH19 **England**

- **WAREHAM AND DISTRICT ANGLING SOCIETY**
Contact/s:
G Elmes & Son, St John's Hill, Wareham, DORSET, BH20 **England**

- **WEYMOUTH ANGLING SOCIETY**
Contact/s:
Mr S Atkinson (Secretary), Angling Ctre, Commerical Rd, Weymouth, DORSET, DT **England**

- **WIMBORNE AND DISTRICT ANGLING CLUB**
Contact/s:
Mr B Heap (Secretary), 76 Higher Blandford Rd, Broadstone, Wimborne, DORSET, BH18 8ED **England**
(T) 01202 382123.

- **WYLYE FLY FISHING CLUB**
Contact/s:
W J P Price (Secretary), Apple Tree Cottage, Huntingford, Gillingham, DORSET, SP8 **England**

- **YEDLINGTON PISCATORIAL ANGLING ASSOCIATION**
Contact/s:
2 The Old Bakery, Beaminster, DORSET, DT8 3RU **England**

ESSEX

- **BASILDON AND DISTRICT ANGLING CLUB**
Contact/s:
Mr Sid Hibbert (Secretary), 15 Culverdown, Basildon, ESSEX, SS14 2AL **England**
(T) 01268 287798.

- **BECMAIN ANGLING CLUB**
Contact/s:
Mr Cheeseman (Secretary), 3 Meadow Rd, Rush Green, Romford, ESSEX, RM7 0LR **England**
(T) 01708 741906.

- **BILLERICAY AND DISTRICT ANGLING CLUB**
Contact/s:
Mr P Morris (Secretary), 31 Lilac Avenue, Wickford, ESSEX, SS12 0BL **England**
(T) 01268 761281.
Mr Derek Howard (Hon Treasurer), 4 Long Meadow Drive, Wickford, ESSEX, SS11 8AX **England**
(T) 01268 734468.

- **BISHOP STORTFORD AND DISTRICT ANGLING SOCIETY**
Contact/s:
Mr H Toynton (Secretary), 33 Blythwood Gardens, Stanstead, ESSEX, CM24 6HQ **England**

- **BRAINTREE AND BOCKING ANGLING SOCIETY**
Contact/s:
Mr M Hill (Secretary), 19 Gilda Trce, Raine Rd, Braintree, ESSEX, CM7 8RE **England**

- **BRUNSWICK BROTHERS ANGLING SOCIETY**
Contact/s:
Mr Terry Taylor (Secretary), 40 St Andrews Rd, Cranbrook, Ilford, ESSEX, IG1 3PF **England**

- **CHELMSFORD ANGLING ASSOCIATION**
Contact/s:
Mrs Irene Lewis (Membership Secretary), 60 Delamere Rd, Chelmsford, ESSEX, CM1 2TG **England**
(T) 01245 264832.

- **CHERPONT**
Contact/s:
Mr Lamb (Owner), 105 Brentwood Rd, Romford, ESSEX, RM1 2SB **England**
(T) 01708 761726.

- **COLCHESTER ANGLING PRESERVATION SOCIETY**
Contact/s:
Mr M K Turner (Hon Secretary), 29 Lodge Rd, Braintree, ESSEX, CM7 7JA **England**
(T) 01376 323520.

- **COLCHESTER PISCATORIAL SOCIETY**
Contact/s:
Mr R J Moore (Secretary), 66 The Willows, Colchester, ESSEX, CO2 8PX **England**
(T) 01206 766650.

COLNES ANGLING SOCIETY
Contact/s:
Mr P Emson (Secretary), 16 Station Rd, Colne Engain, Colchester, ESSEX, CO6 2ES **England**
(T) 01787 223331.

DUNMOW AND DISTRICT PISCATORIAL SOCIETY
Contact/s:
Mr D J Walker (Secretary), 17 Mill Lane, Dunmow, ESSEX, CN6 1BD **England**
(T) 01371 874348.

EAST LONDON AND WEST ESSEX (REGION 83) OF THE PIKE ANGLERS CLUB OF GREAT BRITAIN AND IRELAND
Contact/s:
Mr Geoffrey Latham (Secretary), 26 North Rd, Romford, ESSEX, RM6 6XU **England**
(T) 01812 203637.

ELM PARK HORNCHURCH AND DISTRICT ANGLING CLUB
Contact/s:
Mr R Richardson (Secretary), 67 Adelaide Gardens, Chadwell Heath, Romford, ESSEX, RM6 6SU **England**

ESSEX ANGLING CONSULTATIVE ASSOCIATION
Contact/s:
Mr Br Plummer (Secretary), Ardeens, 20 Barbara Cl, Rochford, ESSEX, SS4 1NQ **England**

ESSEX FLYFISHERS CLUB
Contact/s:
Mr J Flight (Secretary), 16 Rainsford Avenue, Chelmsford, ESSEX, CM1 2PJ **England**
(T) 01245 258485.

HALSTEAD AND HEDINGHAM ANGLING CLUB
Contact/s:
Mr P Webb (Secretary), 63 Trinity Rd, Halstead, ESSEX, CO9 1ED **England**
(T) 01787 473643.

HANNINGFIELD WATER FLY FISHING CLUB
Contact/s:
Mr K A Pettican (Secretary), 6 The Drive, Harlow, ESSEX, CM20 3QD **England**
(T) 01279 420454.

HARWICH ANGLING CLUB
Contact/s:
Mr G Shields (Secretary), 5 Gordon Way, Dovercourt, Harwich, ESSEX, CO12 3TW **England**

HAVERING ANGLING
Contact/s:
Mr Doug Law (Secretary), 95 Wood Lane, Elm Park, Hornchurch, ESSEX, RM12 **England**

HAVERING YOUTH AND JUNIOR ANGLING CLUB
Contact/s:
Mr J Norman (Secretary), 15 Edmund Rd, Rainham, ESSEX, RM13 8LS **England**
(T) 01708 522081.

KELVEDON AND DISTRICT ANGLING ASSOCIATION
Contact/s:
Mr B Pike (Secretary), 11 Keene Way, Galleywood, Chelmsford, ESSEX, CM2 8NT **England**
(T) 01245 262545.
M Murton (Secretary), 189 High St, Kelvedon, Colchester, ESSEX, CO5 **England**

LAKEVIEW ANGLING CLUB
Contact/s:
Mr D Forshaw (Secretary), 22 Constable Avenue, Clacton-on-Sea, ESSEX, CO16 8XA **England**

LAWFORD ANGLING CLUB
Contact/s:
Mr C Shaw (Secretary), 45 Briardale Avenue, Dovercourt, Harwich, ESSEX, CO12 4LH **England**
(T) 01255 506158.

MALDON ANGLING SOCIETY
Contact/s:
Mr T Lazell (Secretary), 14 Barn View Rd, Coggeshall, Colchester, ESSEX, CO6 1RF **England**
(T) 01376 563937.

MOOR HALL AND BELHUS ANGLING SOCIETY
Contact/s:
Mr M Tilbrook (Secretary), 46 Mill Rd, Aveley, South Ockendon, ESSEX, RM15 4SL **England**

PAXMANS ANGLING CLUB
Contact/s:
Secretary, E Paxman Memorial Club, Hythe Hill, Colchester, ESSEX, CO1 2ND **England**
(T) 01206 796515.

ROCHFORD ANGLING CLUB
Contact/s:
Mr L Dorey (Secretary), 231 Kents Hill Rd, Benfleet, ESSEX, SS7 5PF **England**

RURAL ANGLING SOCIETY
Contact/s:
Mr Pf Callow (Secretary), 5 Rushin Avenue, Waltham Abbey, ESSEX, EN9 3BW **England**
(T) 01712 540564.

SAWBRIDGEWORTH ANGLING SOCIETY
Contact/s:
Ms D Barns (Secretary), 10 The Crescent, Harlow, ESSEX, CM17 0HN **England**

STORT VALLEY ANGLING SOCIETY
Contact/s:
Mr Bob Groom (Secretary), 28 Park Mead, Harlow, ESSEX, CM20 1RJ **England**

THURROCK ANGLING CLUB
Contact/s:
B Cowell (Secretary), 56 Beechcroft Avenue, Linford, Standford-Le-Hope, ESSEX, SS17 0RE **England**

WHITE HART ANGLING CLUB
Contact/s:
Dennis (Secretary), 25 Dereham Rd, Barking, ESSEX, IG11 9EZ **England**

GLOUCESTERSHIRE

ABBEY LAKE ANGLING CLUB
Contact/s:
Mr Clive Barton (Secretary), 15 Rose Way, Cirencester, GLOUCESTERSHIRE, GL7 1PS **England**
(T) 01793 511333.

ENVIRONMENT AGENCY
Contact/s:
Area Manager, Lower Severn Area Office, Riversmeet House, Newtown Industrial Estate,Tewkesbury, GLOUCESTERSHIRE, GL20 8JG **England**
(T) 01684 850951.
(F) 01684 293599.

NEWPORT ANGLING ASSOCIATION
Contact/s:
Mr G H Crouch (Secretary), Greenway Cottage, Stowefield Rd, Lower Lydbrook,Lydbrook, GLOUCESTERSHIRE, GL17 **England**
(T) 01594 60048.

ROYAL FOREST OF DEAN ANGLING CLUB
Contact/s:
Mr Paul Reeds (Secretary), 20 Abbey St, Cinderford, GLOUCESTERSHIRE, GL14 2NW **England**

SOUTH CERNEY ANGLING CLUB
Contact/s:
Mr Ray Daffon (Secretary), Fishermans Rest, 21 Broadway Lane, South Cerney,Cirencester, GLOUCESTERSHIRE, GL7 5UH **England**
(T) 01285 861876.

TEWKESBURY POPULAR ANGLING ASSOCIATION
Contact/s:
R Smith (Secretary), 10 Tretawn Gardens, Newtown, Tewkesbury, GLOUCESTERSHIRE, GL20 8EF **England**

GUERNSEY

CASTAWAYS ANGLING CLUB
Contact/s:
Mr P Dunne (Secretary), Dieu Donne, La Bellieuse, St Martins, GUERNSEY, GY **England**

GUERNSEY FRESHWATER ANGLING SOCIETY
Contact/s:
Mr A Bradley (Secretary), Les Tracheries Cottage, Les Tracheries, L Islet, GUERNSEY, GY2 4CW **England**

GUERNSEY MULLET CLUB
Contact/s:
Mr M Weyson (Secretary), La Cachette, 6 Clos Des Caches, St Martins, GUERNSEY, GY4 6PL **England**

HAMPSHIRE

BASINGSTOKE CANAL ANGLING ASSOCIATION
Contact/s:
Mr Michael Wild (Secretary), 49 Wentworth Cres, Ash Vale, Aldershot, HAMPSHIRE, GU12 5LE **England**
(T) 01252 676979.
Mr R Jenkins (Secretary), 26 Tinern Cl, Basingstoke, HAMPSHIRE, RG24 9HE **England**

CHRISTCHURCH ANGLING CLUB
Contact/s:
Andrews (Secretary), 4 Marley Cl, New Milton, HAMPSHIRE, BH25 5LL **England**

EASTLEIGH AND DISTRICT ANGLING CLUB
Contact/s:
J Remington (Secretary), 121 Desborough Rd, Eastleigh, HAMPSHIRE, SO50 5NP **England**
Eastleigh Angling Ctre, 325 Market St, Eastleigh, HAMPSHIRE, SO50 **England**

FARNHAM ANGLING SOCIETY
Contact/s:
Mr Mick Borra (Secretary), The Creel, 36 Station Rd, Aldershot, HAMPSHIRE, GU11 1HT **England**
(T) 01252 320871.

FORDINGBRIDGE LAKE FARM
Contact/s:
Mr P S Birch (Secretary), Sandle Heath, Fordingbridge, HAMPSHIRE, SP6 **England**
(T) 01425 653383.
(F) 01425 653383.

HARTLEY WINTNEY ANGLING ASSOCIATION
Contact/s:
Mr Mick Cross (Secretary), 43 Marlborough View, Farnborough, HAMPSHIRE, GU14 9YA **England**

HORIZON ANGLING CLUB
Contact/s:
Mr P Bradley (Secretary), The Bungalow, 12A Petworth Rd, Milton,Portsmouth, HAMPSHIRE, PO3 6DH **England**

- **LYDE SYDICATE**
Contact/s:
Mr Wh Lyne (Secretary), 6 Cock-A-Dobby, Sandhurst, HAMPSHIRE, GU17 8LB **England**
(T) 01344 771610.

- **NATIONAL FEDERATION OF ANGLERS**
Contact/s:
Mr Ian Epps (Southern Region Point Of Contact), 62 Longmynd Drive, Fareham, HAMPSHIRE, PO14 1SS **England**
(T) 01329 285726.

- **POOLE SPECIMEN GROUP**
Contact/s:
S Bealing (Secretary), 47 Chatsworth Way, New Milton, HAMPSHIRE, BH25 5UQ **England**

- **PORTSMOUTH AND DISTRICT ANGLING SOCIETY**
Contact/s:
Mr R G Snook (Secretary), 86 Caernarvon Rd, Copnor, Portsmouth, HAMPSHIRE, PO2 7NL **England**

- **SOUTHERN ANGLERS**
Contact/s:
Mr B D Smith (Secretary), 3 Cheriton Cl, Havant, HAMPSHIRE, PO9 4PU **England**
T Irons (Secretary), 7 Nelson Cres, Horndean, Portsmouth, HAMPSHIRE, PO8 9LZ **England**

- **STRATFIELD SAYE ESTATES**
Contact/s:
Mr S Penney (Secretary), Fishery Bungalow, Strat Turgis, Hook, HAMPSHIRE, RG27 0AB **England**
(T) 01256 882694.

- **TEST AND ITCHEN ASSOCIATION**
Contact/s:
Mr Jim Glasspool (Secretary), West Haye, Itchen Abbas, Winchester, HAMPSHIRE, SO21 1AX **England**

HEREFORDSHIRE

- **GAMEFISHERS CLUB**
Contact/s:
Mr J H Andrews (Secretary), Meadow View, Dinedor, Hereford, HEREFORDSHIRE, HR2 6LQ **England**

- **HAY-ON-WYE FISHING ASSOCIATION**
Contact/s:
Mr B Wigington (Secretary), Flat 2, Pembertons, 4 High Town,Hay-on-Wye, Hereford, HEREFORDSHIRE, HR3 5AE **England**

- **HEREFORD AND DISTRICT ANGLING ASSOCIATION**
Contact/s:
Po Box 35, Hereford, HEREFORDSHIRE, HR **England**

- **ROSS-ON-WYE ANGLING CLUB**
Contact/s:
Mr T Gibson (Secretary), 10 Redwood Cl, Ross-on-Wye, HEREFORDSHIRE, HR9 5UD **England**

- **WELSH FEDERATION OF COARSE ANGLERS**
Contact/s:
Mrs A Mayers (Secretary), 6 Biddulph Rise, Tupsley, Hereford, HEREFORDSHIRE, HR1 1RA **England**

HERTFORDSHIRE

- **ABBEY CROSS ANGLING CLUB**
Contact/s:
Mr P Jordan (Secretary), 12 Burnside, Hertford, HERTFORDSHIRE, SG12 2AW **England**

- **ABBEY CROSS ANGLING SOCIETY**
Contact/s:
Mr P Rawlings (Secretary), 110 College Rd, Cheshunt, HERTFORDSHIRE, EN8 9NL **England**

- **AYLESBURY DAF**
Contact/s:
Mr John MacDonald (Secretary), Aylesbury, HERTFORDSHIRE, HP1 **England**
(T) 01296 429983.

- **BARNET AND DISTRICT ANGLING CLUB**
Contact/s:
Mr Ja Perkins (Secretary), 4 East View, Hadley Green, Barnet, HERTFORDSHIRE, EN5 5TN **England**

- **BRITISH WATERWAYS**
Contact/s:
Secretary, Brindley House, Corner Hall, Lawn Lane,Hemel Hempstead, HERTFORDSHIRE, HP3 9YT **England**
(T) 01442 235400.
(F) 01442 234932.

- **CARPENTERS PARK ANGLING CLUB**
Contact/s:
Mr C Wood (Secretary), 2 Long Pightle, Chandlers Cross, Rickmansworth, HERTFORDSHIRE, WD3 4NE **England**
(T) 01923 268618.

- **COUNTY HALL ANGLING CLUB**
Contact/s:
Mr Dc Bootle (Secretary), 3 Green Meadows, Potters Bar, HERTFORDSHIRE, EN6 1LL **England**

- **CROWN NETHERALL FISHING CLUB**
Contact/s:
Mr Anthony Johnson (Secretary), Johnson Ross Tackle, 3 Amwell St, Hoddesdon, HERTFORDSHIRE, EN11 8TP **England**
(T) 01992 462044.

- **DE HAVILLAND ANGLING SOCIETY**
Contact/s:
Mr Dave Eves (Secretary), 74 Drovers Way, Hatfield, HERTFORDSHIRE, AL10 0PX **England**

- **ETERNIT UK LIMITED ANGLING CLUB**
Contact/s:
Mr Yaxley (Secretary), Meldreth, Royston, HERTFORDSHIRE, SG8 5JX **England**

- **FLY DRESSERS GUILD**
Contact/s:
Mr Dl Mason (Secretary), 36 Hockerill, Watton-At-Stone, Hertford, HERTFORDSHIRE, SG14 3SQ **England**

- **KINGS ARMS AND CHESNUT ANGLING SOCIETY**
Contact/s:
Mr Roger Glindon (Secretary), Po Box 13, Waltham Cross, HERTFORDSHIRE, EN7 5QT **England**

- **KINGS LANGLEY ANGLING SOCIETY**
Contact/s:
Mr R Foulger (Secretary), 155-157 St Albans Rd, Watford, HERTFORDSHIRE, WD2 5BD **England**
(T) 01923 232393.

- **KINGSWEIR ANGLING CLUB**
Contact/s:
Mrs B Newton (Secretary), King's Weir, Slap Lane, Wormley, HERTFORDSHIRE, EN10 6EX **England**
(T) 01992 468394.

- **LETCHWORTH AND DISTRICT ANGLING ASSOCIATION**
Contact/s:
P N Jones (Secretary), 79 Howard Drive, Letchworth, HERTFORDSHIRE, SG6 2BU **England**

- **LONDON COLNEY ANGLING CLUB**
Contact/s:
Mr A Barrett (Secretary), 94 Roestock Lane, Colney Heath, St Albans, HERTFORDSHIRE, AL4 0QN **England**

- **PALMERS GREEN ANGLING SOCIETY**
Contact/s:
Mr Simon Maddock (Secretary), 32 Lea Forris Rd, Cheshunt, HERTFORDSHIRE, EN7 6ND **England**
(T) 01992 628992.

- **POTTERS BAR AND DISTRICT ANGLING CLUB**
Contact/s:
Mr R Clarke (Secretary), 34 St Annes Cl, Cuffley, Potters Bar, HERTFORDSHIRE, EN7 6JA **England**

- **ROYSTON AND DISTRICT ANGLING CLUB**
Contact/s:
P R Harrow (Secretary), 46 Greengage Rise, Melbourne, Royston, HERTFORDSHIRE, SG8 6DS **England**

- **SAWBRIDGEWORTH ANGLING SOCIETY**
Contact/s:
Mr Aj Vidler (Secretary), 11 The Orchards, Sawbridgeworth, HERTFORDSHIRE, CM21 9BB **England**
(T) 01279 870069.

- **SHAMLEY GREEN ANGLING SOCIETY**
Contact/s:
Mr P Swindon (Secretary), 206 Bushy Hill Drive, Merrow, Guildford, HERTFORDSHIRE, CM21 9BB **England**

- **THREE VALLEYS ANGLING CLUB**
Contact/s:
Mr T Prichard (Secretary), Three Valleys Water Plc, London Rd, Rickmansworth, HERTFORDSHIRE, WD3 1LB **England**

- **TRING ANGLERS**
Contact/s:
Mr Stuart Riddle (Secretary), Po Box 1947, Tring, HERTFORDSHIRE, HP23 5LZ **England**

- **TURNFORD ANGLING CONSORTIUM**
Contact/s:
Mr Simon Maddock (Secretary), 32 Lea Forris Rd, Cheshunt, HERTFORDSHIRE, EN7 6ND **England**
(T) 01992 628992.

- **WATFORD PISCATORS**
Contact/s:
Mr J A Dickinson (Secretary), 51 Gallows Hill, Kings Langley, HERTFORDSHIRE, WD4 8LX **England**

- **WELWYN GARDEN CITY ANGLING CLUB**
Contact/s:
Mr Dennis Jakes (Secretary), 62 Sweet Briar, Welwyn Garden City, HERTFORDSHIRE, AL7 3DY **England**

HUMBERSIDE

- **GRANT COARSE FISHERIES CONSULTANT**
Contact/s:
Secretary, 1 Oak Cottages, Rise, Hull, HUMBERSIDE, HU11 5BP **England**
(T) 01964 562074.

- **HULL AND DISTRICT ANGLING ASSOCIATION**
Contact/s:
Mr Dave Harold (Secretary), Po Box 188, Hull, HUMBERSIDE, HU9 1AN **England**
(T) 01482 809832.

- **MABLETHORPE, SUTTON AND DISTRICT ANGLING CLUB**
Contact/s:
Mr S Oxborough (Secretary), 6 Ormsby Cl, Cleethorpes, HUMBERSIDE, DN35 9PE **England**
(T) 01472 508639.

- **TETNEY LOCK ANGLING CLUB**
  Contact/s:
  Mr B Norman, The Wharf, Tetney Lock, North Coates,Grimsby, HUMBERSIDE, DN **England**
  (T) 01427 388488.
- **WITHAM AND DISTRICT JOINT ANGLERS FEDERATION**
  Contact/s:
  Mr S Oxborough (Secretary), 6 Ormsley Cl, Cleethorpes, HUMBERSIDE, DN35 9PE **England**
  (T) 01472 508639.

ISLE OF MAN

- **DOUGLAS AND DISTRICT ANGLING CLUB**
  Contact/s:
  Mr A Ashton (Secretary), 58 Laurel Avenue, Birchill, Onchan,Douglas, ISLE OF MAN, IM **England**
- **ISLE OF MAN ANGLING ASSOCIATION**
  Contact/s:
  K A Walmsley (Secretary), 13 Berkley St, Douglas, ISLE OF MAN, IM **England**
- **ISLE OF MAN FLY FISHING ANGLING ASSOCIATION**
  Contact/s:
  Mr Ray Caley (Secretary), Caley's Stores, Sulby, ISLE OF MAN, IM **England**
- **MANX GAME FISHING CLUB**
  Contact/s:
  Po Box 95, 2a Lord St, Douglas, ISLE OF MAN, IM **England**

ISLE OF WIGHT

- **BEMBRIDGE ISLE OF WIGHT ANGLING CLUB**
  Contact/s:
  Mr P Knight (Secretary), Berrylands, Heathfield Rd, Bembridge, ISLE OF WIGHT, PO35 5UW **England**
- **ISLE OF WIGHT FRESHWATER ANGLING ASSOCIATION**
  Contact/s:
  Mr Ian De Gruchy (Secretary), 66 Merrie Gardens Lake, Sandown, ISLE OF WIGHT, PO36 **England**

KENT

- **ALDERS ANGLING SOCIETY**
  Contact/s:
  Mrs Babbage (Secretary), 116 Crampton Rd, Sevenoaks, KENT, TN14 5DZ **England**
  (T) 01732 461964.
- **ASSOCIATION OF PROFESSIONAL GAME ANGLING INSTRUCTORS**
  Contact/s:
  Mr Michael Evans (Secretary), Little Saxbys Farm, Cowden, Edenbridge, KENT, TN8 7DX **England**
  (T) 01342 850765.
  (F) 01342 850926.
- **CANTERBURY AND DISTRICT ANGLING ASSOCIATION**
  Contact/s:
  R Barton (Secretary), 14 Mill Rd, Sturry, Canterbury, KENT, CT2 0AF **England**
- **DARENT VALLEY TROUT FISHERS**
  Contact/s:
  Mr D J Rees (Secretary), 21 Ramus Avenue, Farnborough, KENT, BR6 7HF **England**
- **DEAL AND INSHORE FISHERMENS ASSOCIATION**
  Contact/s:
  R Tucker (Secretary), 111 Church Lane, Deal, KENT, CT14 **England**
- **DEAL AND WALMER INSBORNE FISHING ASSOCIATION**
  Contact/s:
  Mr Ajc Robinson (Secretary), 4 Tormore Park, Deal, KENT, CT14 9UY **England**
- **FAVERSHAM ANGLING CLUB**
  Contact/s:
  Mr N Prior (Secretary), Flat 1C, St Nicholas Rd, Faversham, KENT, ME13 7PG **England**
- **HERNE BAY ANGLING ASSOCIATION**
  Contact/s:
  59 Central Prde, Herne Bay, KENT, CT6 **England**
- **HERON ANGLING SOCIETY**
  Contact/s:
  Red Shelter, Spa Esplanade, Herne Bay, KENT, CT6 **England**
- **HOLMESDALE ANGLING SOCIETY**
  Contact/s:
  S Banks (Secretary), 58 Chevening Rd, Chipstead, Sevenoaks, KENT, TN13 2SA **England**
- **LINTON ANGLING SOCIETY**
  Contact/s:
  Club Secretary, 60 Hockers Lane, Dettling, Maidstone, KENT, ME14 3JW **England**
  (T) 01622 639155.
- **MAIDSTONE VICTORY ANGLING AND MEDWAY PRESERVATION SOCIETY**
  Contact/s:
  Mr J Perkins (Secretary), 33 Hackney Rd, Maidstone, KENT, ME16 7YN **England**
- **MAIDSTONE VICTORY APS**
  Contact/s:
  King's Head, Wye, Ashford, KENT, TN25 **England**
- **OLD CENTRALS ANGLING CLUB**
  Contact/s:
  130 Grosvenor Pl, Margate, KENT, CT9 1UY **England**
- **ORPINGTON AND DISTRICT AC**
  Contact/s:
  St Marys Cray, Orpington, KENT, BR5 **England**
- **PENSHURST ANGLING SOCIETY**
  Contact/s:
  M Mills (Secretary), 3 Montgomery Rd, Tunbridge Wells, KENT, TN3 9EP **England**
- **ROTHER FISHERY ASSOCIATION**
  Contact/s:
  Mr Steve Crowley (Hon Secretary), 9 Haydens Cl, Orpington, KENT, BR5 4JE **England**
  (T) 01303 872160.
- **SOUTHWARK AND CAMBERWELL SOCIETY (SE)**
  Contact/s:
  Mr R Wilkinson (Secretary), 11 Vernon Cl, St Paul's Cray, Orpington, KENT, BR5 3AS **England**
- **TONBRIDGE AND DISTRICT ANGLING AND PRESERVATION SOCIETY**
  Contact/s:
  Mr Alex Heggie (Membership Secretary), Little Lucy's Farmhouse, Lower St, Hildenborough,Tonbridge, KENT, TN11 8PT **England**
  (T) 01732 832352.
  (F) 01732 832352.
- **WILTON FLY-FISHING CLUB**
  Contact/s:
  Dr J D McGill (Secretary), Hillside Cottages, 60 Church Rd, Sundridge,Sevenoaks, KENT, TN14 6EA **England**

LANCASHIRE

- **ACCRINGTON AND DISTRICT FISHING CLUB**
  Contact/s:
  Mr A Balderstone (Secretary), 42 Townley Avenue, Huncoat, Accrington, LANCASHIRE, BB5 6LP **England**
  (T) 01254 233517.
- **BOLTON AND DISTRICT ANGLING ASSOCIATION**
  Contact/s:
  Mr Terence A McKee (Secretary), 1 Lever Edge Lane, Great Lever, Bolton, LANCASHIRE, BL3 3BU **England**
  (T) 01204 393726.
- **CLITHEROE ANGLING ASSOCIATION**
  Contact/s:
  Mr B McNulty (Secretary), 16 Mitton Rd, Whalley, Clitheroe, LANCASHIRE, BB7 9RX **England**
- **COLNE WATER ANGLING CLUB**
  Contact/s:
  Mr Robin Varley (Hon Secretary), Keepers House, Keighley Rd, Laneshawbridge,Colne, LANCASHIRE, BB8 7EJ **England**
  (T) 01535 634426.
- **DARWEN ANGLERS ASSOCIATION**
  Contact/s:
  Mr F W Kendall (Secretary), 45 Holden Fold, Darwen, LANCASHIRE, BB3 3AU **England**
- **DARWEN LOYAL ANGLERS**
  Contact/s:
  Mr T Berry (Secretary), 5 Springvale, Garden Village, Darwen, LANCASHIRE, BB3 2HJ **England**
- **HASLINGDEN AND DISTRICT FLY FISHING CLUB**
  Contact/s:
  Mr William Monk (Membership Secretary), 6 Ryde Cl, Haslingden, Rossendale, LANCASHIRE, BB4 6QR **England**
  (T) 01706 211724.
- **KIRKBY LONSDALE AND DISTRICT ANGLING ASSOCIATION**
  Contact/s:
  Mr D E Halton (Secretary), Briglands, Wennington Rd, Wray,Lancaster, LANCASHIRE, LA2 8QH **England**
- **KIRKHAM AND DISTRICT FLY FISHERS CLUB**
  Contact/s:
  D Wardham (Secretary), 65 Longhouse Lane, Poulton-Le-Fylde, LANCASHIRE, FY6 8DE **England**
- **LONSDALE ANGLING CLUB**
  Contact/s:
  M Casseroy (Secretary), 33 Bridge St, Greaves, Lancaster, LANCASHIRE, LA1 4UL **England**
- **MARDEN STAR ANGLING SOCIETY**
  Contact/s:
  Mr Jeff Hartley (Secretary), 3 Duerden St, Nelson, LANCASHIRE, BB9 9BJ **England**
  (T) 01282 603362.
- **MINISTRY OF AGRICULTURE FISHERIES AND FOOD**
  Contact/s:
  Secretary, 26 London St, Fleetwood, LANCASHIRE, FY7 6JG **England**
  (T) 01253 873515.
- **NATIONAL FEDERATION OF ANGLERS**
  Contact/s:
  Mr Ernie Swindells (Nfa Disability Officer, North West Region), 16 School St, Little Lever, Bolton, LANCASHIRE, BL3 1NH **England**
  (T) 01204 706658.

- **NELSON ANGLING ASSOCIATION**
Contact/s:
Mr H Hargreaves (Secretary), 171 Reedley Rd, Briarfield, Nelson, LANCASHIRE, BB9 5ES **England**
- **NORTHERN ANGLERS ASSOCIATION**
Contact/s:
Mr B Davies (Secretary), 51 Brennard St, Burnley, LANCASHIRE, BB10 1SU **England**
- **RIBBLE AND WYRE FISHERIES ASSOCIATION**
Contact/s:
S A Gray (Secretary), 18 Lord St, Wigan, LANCASHIRE, WN1 2BN **England**
- **ROYAL ASHTON ANGLING CLUB**
Contact/s:
D T Dobson (Secretary), Rumworth Lodge, 1 Parkway, Westhoughton,Bolton, LANCASHIRE, BL5 **England**
- **TODMORDEN ANGLING SOCIETY**
Contact/s:
Mr R Barber (Secretary), 12 Grisedale Drive, Burnley, LANCASHIRE, BB12 8AR **England**
- **WIGAN AND DISTRICT ANGLING ASSOCIATION**
Contact/s:
Mr G Wilson (Secretary), 11 Guilford Avenue, Chorley, LANCASHIRE, PR6 8TG **England**
(T) 01257 265905.
- **WITHNELL ANGLING CLUB**
Contact/s:
Brinscall Service Station, Chorley, LANCASHIRE, PR **England**

LEICESTERSHIRE

- **ASFORDBY SOCIETY OF ANGLERS**
Contact/s:
Mrs H Birch (Secretary), Riverside Cottage, Mill Lane, Asfordby,Melton Mowbray, LEICESTERSHIRE, LE **England**
- **BROOME ANGLING SOCIETY**
Contact/s:
Mr A Smith (Secretary), 73 Farrier Lane, Leicester, LEICESTERSHIRE, LE4 0WB **England**
- **BROUGHTON AND DUNTON ANGLING CLUB**
Contact/s:
M Startin (Secretary), 23 Hill Field, Oadby, Leicester, LEICESTERSHIRE, LE2 4RW **England**
- **LEICESTER AND DISTRICT AMALGAMATED SOCIETY OF ANGLERS**
Contact/s:
R Fossey (Secretary), 431 Gleneagles Avenue, Rushley Mead, Leicester, LEICESTERSHIRE, LE4 7YL **England**
- **MARKET HARBOROUGH AND DISTRICT SOCIETY OF ANGLERS**
Contact/s:
Mr N Bale (Secretary), 27 Rainsborough Gardens, Market Harborough, LEICESTERSHIRE, LE16 9LN **England**
- **MELTON MOWBRAY SOCIETY OF ANGLERS**
Contact/s:
R M Dyer (Secretary), 36 Winster Cres, Melton Mowbray, LEICESTERSHIRE, LE1 **England**

LINCOLNSHIRE

- **ANGLERS CONSERVATION ASSOCIATION**
Contact/s:
Mrs Jane Brett (Director), 23 Castlegate, Grantham, LINCOLNSHIRE, NG31 6SW **England**
(T) 01476 561008.
(F) 01476 560900.
- **AUBURN ANGLING CLUB**
Contact/s:
Mr Tony Satchet (Secretary), The Royal Oak, Auburn, Lincoln, LINCOLNSHIRE, LN **England**
- **AVELING BARFORD ANGLING CLUB**
Contact/s:
Mr K Hall (Secretary), 7 Seventh Avenue, Alma Park, Grantham, LINCOLNSHIRE, NG **England**
- **BOSTON AND DISTRICT ANGLING ASSOCIATION**
Contact/s:
Mrs B Clifton (Secretary), Wyberton West Rd, Hatfield, Boston, LINCOLNSHIRE, PE21 7LQ **England**
(T) 01205 365406.
(F) 01205 365406.
- **DUKE OF WELLINGTON ANGLING CLUB**
Contact/s:
78 Wellington Rd, Louth, LINCOLNSHIRE, LN11 **England**
- **GRANTHAM ANGLING ASSOCIATION**
Contact/s:
Mr W L C Hutchins (Secretary), 28 Cottesmore Cl, Grantham, LINCOLNSHIRE, NG31 9JL **England**
- **HORNCASTLE ANGLING ASSOCIATION**
Contact/s:
K F Dannatt (Secretary), 95 Tennyson Gardens, Horncastle, LINCOLNSHIRE, LN9 6DF **England**
- **HORNCASTLE ANGLING SOCIETY**
Contact/s:
Mr G Alder (Secretary), The Cottage, Sandy Lane, Woodhall Spa, LINCOLNSHIRE, LN10 6UR **England**
(T) 01526 353619.
- **LINCOLN AND DISTRICT ANGLING ASSOCIATION**
Contact/s:
Mr P Robinson (Bailiff), 37 Lincoln Rd, Fenton, Marton,Lincoln, LINCOLNSHIRE, LN1 2EP **England**
Mr F Butler (Secretary), 74 Edgehill, Lincoln, LINCOLNSHIRE, LN5 9TZ **England**
(T) 01522 534174.
- **LINESGRAN SPORTS CLUB**
Contact/s:
F J Walker (Secretary), British Sugar Plc, Station Rd, Bardney,Lincoln, LINCOLNSHIRE, LN3 5UH **England**
- **LOUTH CROWN AND WOOLPACK ANGLING CLUB**
Contact/s:
Mr Rod Hutchinson (Secretary), Charles St, Louth, LINCOLNSHIRE, LN11 **England**
(T) 01507 609069.
(F) 01507 609051.
- **NETTLEHAM ANGLING CLUB**
Contact/s:
J Bremner (Secretary), 46 Fairleas, Branston, Lincoln, LINCOLNSHIRE, LN4 1NW **England**
- **NEW LEAKE ANGLING CLUB**
Contact/s:
T L Cuppleditch (Secretary), Basses Farm, Stickford Fen, Boston, LINCOLNSHIRE, PE22 8HJ **England**
- **RUSTON FISHING CLUB**
Contact/s:
Mr R Thorley (Secretary), 121 Boultham Park Rd, Lincoln, LINCOLNSHIRE, LN **England**
- **SALMON AND TROUT ASSOCIATION**
Contact/s:
Mr R Gibson-Bevan (Secretary), Little Langley, Bardney Rd, Wragby,Market Rasen, LINCOLNSHIRE, LN8 5 **England**
- **SOUTH KYME GOLF CLUB**
Contact/s:
Ec Mablethorpe (Secretary), Skinners Lane, South Kyme, Lincoln, LINCOLNSHIRE, LN4 4AE **England**
- **STAMFORD WELLAND AMALGAMATED ANGLERS ASSOCIATION**
Contact/s:
G E Bates (Secretary), 16A Austin St, Stamford, LINCOLNSHIRE, PE9 2QP **England**
- **STAMFORD WELLAND ANGLING CLUB**
Contact/s:
Mr Graham Money (Secretary), 30 Dundee Drive, Stamford, LINCOLNSHIRE, PE9 2TR **England**
(T) 01780 480209.
- **WHITE SWAN ANGLING CLUB**
Contact/s:
W Wrath, Three Trees, Newark Rd, Torksey,Lincoln, LINCOLNSHIRE, LN1 2EJ **England**
(T) 01427 718342.
- **WORKSOP AND DISTRICT ANGLING ASSOCIATION**
Contact/s:
M Tidwells (Secretary), Fen Lane, Spalding, LINCOLNSHIRE, PE **England**

LINCOLNSHIRE (NORTH)

- **GOOLE AND DISTRICT ANGLING ASSOCIATION**
Contact/s:
Mr Les Rogers (Secretary), 39 Clifton Gardens, Goole, LINCOLNSHIRE (NORTH), DN15 6AR **England**
(T) 01405 769096.
- **IRON AND STEEL ANGLING CLUB**
Contact/s:
Mr N Heaton (Secretary), 9 Anderson Rd, Scunthorpe, LINCOLNSHIRE (NORTH), DN15 **England**
- **SCUNTHORPE AND DISTRICT ANGLING ASSOCIATION**
Contact/s:
M Storey (Secretary), 74 Appleby Lane, Broughton, Brigg, LINCOLNSHIRE (NORTH), DN20 0AS **England**

LONDON (GREATER)

- **AQUACULTURE LTD**
Contact/s:
Mr Ivar Warrer - Hansen (Director), 15 Alderville Rd, Fulham, London, LONDON (GREATER), SW6 3RL **England**
(T) 020 77312885.
- **BARNES AND MORTLAKE ANGLING AND PRESERVATION SOCIETY**
Contact/s:
Mr K Dellard (Secretary), 23 Cleveland Gardens, Barnes, London, LONDON (GREATER), SW13 0AE **England**
- **BARNET AND DISTRICT ANGLING CLUB**
Contact/s:
Mr D Porter (Secretary), 72 Rivington Cres, Mill Hill, London, LONDON (GREATER), NW7 2LF **England**
(T) 020 84401303.
- **BRITISH FIELD SPORTS SOCIETY**
Contact/s:
Mr Robin Hanbury-Tenison (Secretary), 59 Kennington Rd, Lambeth, London, LONDON (GREATER), SE1 7PZ **England**
(T) 020 79284742.

- **BRITISH TROUT ASSOCIATION**
  Contact/s:
  Secretary, 10 Barley Mow Passage, Chiswick, London, LONDON (GREATER), W4 4PH **England**
  (T) 020 79946477.
  (F) 020 77423080.
- **CHERTSEY ROAD ANGLING CLUB**
  Contact/s:
  Mr Peter Goode (Secretary), 35 Fernside Avenue, Hanworth, Feltham,London, LONDON (GREATER), TW13 7BJ **England**
- **EDMONTON AND TOTTENHAM ANGLERS**
  Contact/s:
  Mr M Rhodes (Secretary), 15 Argyle, Tottenham, London, LONDON (GREATER), N17 0BE **England**
- **ENFIELD ANGLERS COUNCIL**
  Contact/s:
  Mr Ron Sears (Secretary), 37 Rowantree Rd, Enfield, London, LONDON (GREATER), EN2 8PY **England**
- **FELTHAM PISCATORIAL SOCIETY**
  Contact/s:
  Mrs V Sivyer (Secretary), 96 Raleigh Rd, Feltham, London, LONDON (GREATER), TW13 4LP **England**
  (T) 01818 909005.
- **FLYFISHERS CLUB**
  Contact/s:
  Commander N T Fuller (Secretary), 69 Brook St, Mayfair, London, LONDON (GREATER), W1Y 2ER **England**
- **GLOBE ANGLING SOCIETY**
  Contact/s:
  R Eaton (Secretary), 80 Caversham Avenue, Palmers Green, London, LONDON (GREATER), N13 4LN **England**
- **GOOD INTENT ANGLING SOCIETY**
  Contact/s:
  Mr Kg Walker (Secretary), 24 Montagu Cres, Edmonton, London, LONDON (GREATER), N18 2HA **England**
  (T) 020 82459937.
- **LEATHERHEAD DISTRICT ANGLING CLUB**
  Contact/s:
  Mr N Marchington (Secretary), 466 Crockerton Rd, London, LONDON (GREATER), SW17 5HG **England**
- **LEE ANGLERS CONSORTIUM**
  Contact/s:
  Mr Terry Mansbridge (Secretary), 7 Warren Rd, Chingford, London, LONDON (GREATER), E4 6QR **England**
  (T) 020 75240869.
  (F) 020 75240869.
  Mr Peter Green (Secretary), Po Box 19426, London, LONDON (GREATER), E4 8UZ **England**
  (T) 01279 654434.
- **LEE VALLEY REGIONAL PARK AUTHORITY**
  Contact/s:
  Mr Krizim Seltham (Angling Manager), Myddelton House, Bulls Cross, Enfield,London, LONDON (GREATER), EN2 9HG **England**
  (T) 01992 709832.
- **LEVIATHAN ANGLING CLUB**
  Contact/s:
  Mrs B Myers (Secretary), 19 Grendon Gardens, Wembley, London, LONDON (GREATER), MA9 9NE **England**
  (T) 020 89043692.
- **LEWISHAM PISCATORIALS ASSOCIATION**
  Contact/s:
  D J Head (Secretary), 75 Riverview Park, Catford, London, LONDON (GREATER), SE6 4PL **England**
- **LONDON ANGLERS ASSOCIATION**
  Contact/s:
  Mr A E Hedges (Secretary), Izaak Walton House, 2a Harvey Park Rd, Walthamstow,London, LONDON (GREATER), E17 6LJ **England**
  (T) 020 85207477.
- **MORAR DISTRICT SALMON FISHERY BOARD**
  Contact/s:
  Mr Mh Spence (Acts Operator), 2 Gray's Inn, Gray's Inn, London, LONDON (GREATER), WC1R 5JH **England**
  (T) 020 72424986.
- **NATIONAL FEDERATION OF ANGLERS**
  Contact/s:
  Mr Bill Harris (Nfa Disability Officer, London & South East Region), 22 Windsor Court, Sudbury On Thames, London, LONDON (GREATER), TW16 7RA **England**
  (T) 01932 785005.
- **RAVEN ANGLING CLUB**
  Contact/s:
  E G Mears (Secretary), 16 Broomshouse Rd, Fulham, London, LONDON (GREATER), SW6 3QX **England**
- **RED SPINNER ANGLING SOCIETY**
  Contact/s:
  Mr K Stabler (Secretary), 9 Marlborough Rd, Edmonton, London, LONDON (GREATER), N9 9PT **England**
- **SALMON AND TROUT ASSOCIATION**
  Contact/s:
  Mr C Poupard (Director), Fishmonger's Hall, London Bridge, London, LONDON (GREATER), EC4R 9EL **England**
  (T) 020 72835838.
  (F) 020 79291389.
- **SPORTS COUNCIL**
  Contact/s:
  Secretary, 16 Upper Woburn Pl, Woburn Pl, London, LONDON (GREATER), WC1H 0QP **England**
  (T) 020 73881277.
  (F) 020 73835740.
- **THAMES MEAD TOWN ANGLING CLUB**
  Contact/s:
  Mr Jeff (Secretary), 509 Abbey Rd, Abbey Wood, London, LONDON (GREATER), SE2 9HA **England**
  (T) 020 83702750.
- **TUMBLING BAY ANGLING CLUB**
  Contact/s:
  Mr I Findall (Secretary), The White Cottage, Canalside, Harefield,London, LONDON (GREATER), UB9 **England**
- **TWICKENHAM PISCATORIAL**
  Contact/s:
  Mr Del Botterill (Secretary), 59 Walnut Tree Cl, Barnes, London, LONDON (GREATER), SW13 9QP **England**
- **UXBRIDGE ROVERS ANGLING AND CONSERVATION SOCIETY**
  Contact/s:
  Mr L Dalton (Secretary), 16 Park View, Hatch End, Pinner,London, LONDON (GREATER), HA5 4LN **England**
  (T) 01814 281739.
  Po Box 253, Harrow, London, LONDON (GREATER), HA3 8XU **England**
- **UXBRIDGE ROVERS ANGLING SOCIETY**
  Contact/s:
  Mr L Dalton (Secretary), 16 Park View, Hatch End, Pinner,London, LONDON (GREATER), HA5 4LN **England**
- **WALTHAMSTOW RESERVOIR GROUP**
  Contact/s:
  Mr Chris King, Thames Water Gatehouse, 2 Forest Rd, Tottenham,London, LONDON (GREATER), N17 9NH **England**
  (T) 020 88081527.
- **WARWICK ANGLING SOCIETY**
  Contact/s:
  Mr D Meadhurst (Secretary), 54 Waverley Avenue, Chingford, London, LONDON (GREATER), E4 8HT **England**
- **WEYBRIDGE ANGLING CLUB**
  Contact/s:
  Mr H Whiting (Secretary), 79 Gaston Way, Shepperton, London, LONDON (GREATER), TW17 8EZ **England**
  (T) 01932 242978.
- **WOOLWICH DOCKYARD ANGLING CLUB**
  Contact/s:
  Mr D R Etherington (Owner), Europe Rd, Woolwich Dockyards, Woolwich,London, LONDON (GREATER), SE18 5QS **England**
  (T) 020 88557849.

MANCHESTER (GREATER)

- **ANGLING CLUB**
  Contact/s:
  Secretary, Riverside House, St Simon St, Salford,Manchester, MANCHESTER (GREATER), M3 7ET **England**
  (T) 0161 8395737.
- **DARLEY DALE FLY-FISHING CLUB**
  Contact/s:
  Mr Brian Jones (Secretary), Rose Cottage, Horsforth Lane, Greenfield,Oldham, MANCHESTER (GREATER), OL3 7HL **England**
- **DYSTELEGH FLY FISHING CLUB**
  Contact/s:
  10 Martlett Avenue, Disley, Stockport, MANCHESTER (GREATER), SK **England**
- **GRAYLING SOCIETY**
  Contact/s:
  Dr R B Broughton (Secretary), 10 Park Rd, Salford, MANCHESTER (GREATER), M6 8HN **England**
- **LEIGH AND DISTRICT ANGLING ASSOCIATION**
  Contact/s:
  Mr C Hibbs (Secretary), 417 Nabchester Rd, Leigh, MANCHESTER (GREATER), WN7 2ND **England**
- **MOSS SIDE SOCIAL ANGLING SOCIETY**
  Contact/s:
  A Jones (Secretary), 10 Purley Avenue, Northenden, Manchester, MANCHESTER (GREATER), M23 0DA **England**
- **NATIONAL FEDERATION OF ANGLERS**
  Contact/s:
  Mr David Crookall (North West Region Point Of Contact), 12 Wincombe St, Rusholme, Manchester, MANCHESTER (GREATER), M14 7PJ **England**
  (T) 0161 2559768.
- **OLD GLOSSOP ANGLING CLUB**
  Contact/s:
  Mr R North (Secretary), 1 Morpeth Cl, Ashton-under-Lyne, MANCHESTER (GREATER), OL7 9SH **England**
- **ROCHDALE WALTON ANGLING SOCIETY**
  Contact/s:
  Mr R Pealin (Secretary), 723 Whitworth Rd, Rochdale, MANCHESTER (GREATER), OL12 0TF **England**
- **SADDLEWORTH AND DISTRICT ANGLING SOCIETY**
  Contact/s:
  Mr John Cox (Secretary), 3 Rhodes Avenue, Uppermill, Saddleworth,Oldham, MANCHESTER (GREATER), OL3 6ED **England**

MERSEYSIDE

- **ASSOCIATION OF WIRRAL ANGLING CLUBS**
  Contact/s:
  Mr S Ross (Secretary), 17 Greenville Rd, Bebington, Wirral, MERSEYSIDE, CH63 **England**
  Mr D Billing (Chairman), 2 Patterdale Rd, Bebington, Wirral, MERSEYSIDE, CH63 **England**
- **KIRKDALE ANGLING ASSOCIATION**
  Contact/s:
  Mr Ac Hoer (Secretary), 61 Baythorne Rd, Liverpool, MERSEYSIDE, L4 9TJ **England**
- **LIVERPOOL AND DISTRICT ANGLING ASSOCIATION**
  Contact/s:
  Mr James Browne (Secretary), 33 Eleanor Rd, Bootle, Liverpool, MERSEYSIDE, L20 6BP **England**
- **MAGHULL AND LYDIATE ANGLING CLUB**
  Contact/s:
  Mr J Johnson (Secretary), 97 Liverpool Road (North), Maghull, Liverpool, MERSEYSIDE, L31 2HG **England**
- **ST HELENS ANGLING ASSOCIATION**
  Contact/s:
  Mrs Leslie Bromilow (Secretary), 4 Bassenthwaite Avenue, Moss Bank, St Helens, MERSEYSIDE, WA11 7AB **England**
- **WIRRAL GAME FISHING CLUB**
  Contact/s:
  Mr D Jones (Secretary), 31 Meadway, Upton, Wirral, MERSEYSIDE, L49 6JQ **England**
  (T) 0151 6777506.

MIDLANDS (WEST)

- **ASSOCIATION OF STILLWATER GAME FISHERY MANAGERS**
  Contact/s:
  Lord C H Guernsey (Secretary), Packington Fisheries, Meriden, Coventry, MIDLANDS (WEST), CV7 78R **England**
  (T) 01676 522754.
  (F) 01676 523399.
- **BARNT GREEN FISHING CLUB**
  Contact/s:
  Mrs J Lunt (Secretary), Square Cottage, Cherry Hill Drive, Barnt Green,Birmingham, MIDLANDS (WEST), B45 8JY **England**
- **BIRMINGHAM ANGLERS ASSOCIATION**
  Contact/s:
  J Williams (Secretary), 100 Icknield Port Rd, Rotton Park, Birmingham, MIDLANDS (WEST), B16 0AP **England**
- **COVENTRY AND DISTRICT ANGLING ASSOCIATION**
  Contact/s:
  Mr A J Hyde (Secretary), 1 Oak Tree Avenue, Green Lane, Coventry, MIDLANDS (WEST), CV3 6DG **England**
  (T) 024 76418893.
- **ENVIRONMENT AGENCY**
  Contact/s:
  Area Manager, Sapphire East, 550 Streetsbrook Rd, Solihull, MIDLANDS (WEST), B91 1QT **England**
  (T) 0121 7112324.
  (F) 0121 7115824.
- **LAMB ANGLING CLUB**
  Contact/s:
  Mr Terry D Brindle (Secretary), 247A Clarence Rd, Four Oaks, Sutton Coldfield, MIDLANDS (WEST), B74 4LP **England**
- **NATIONAL FEDERATION OF ANGLERS**
  Contact/s:
  Mr Ken Aske (West Midlands Region Point Of Contact), 18A Bushmore Rd, Hall Green, Birmingham, MIDLANDS (WEST), B28 9QX **England**
  (T) 0121 7778369.
- **PHOENIX ANGLING CLUB**
  Contact/s:
  Mr J A Mobley (Secretary), 155 Greenhill Rd, Halesowen, MIDLANDS (WEST), B62 8EZ **England**
- **SUTTON COLDFIELD ANGLING SOCIETY**
  Contact/s:
  Mr D Jones (Secretary), Bricklyn House, Wishaw, Sutton Coldfield, MIDLANDS (WEST), B76 9 **England**
- **SWAN ANGLING CLUB**
  Contact/s:
  Mr J Stanhope (Secretary), 4 High Rd, Lane Head, Willenhall, MIDLANDS (WEST), WV12 4JQ **England**
  (T) 01902 630110.

NORFOLK

- **AYLSHAMAND DISTRICT ANGLING CLUB**
  Contact/s:
  Mr Mk Turner (Secretary), 17 Town Lane, Aylsham, Norwich, NORFOLK, NR11 6HH **England**
  (T) 01263 732433.
- **BRANDON AND DISTRICT ANGLING CLUB**
  Contact/s:
  Mr P Cooper (Secretary), 16 High St, Feltwell, Thetford, NORFOLK, IP26 4AF **England**
  (T) 01843 828448.
- **DEREHAM AND DISTRICT ANGLING CLUB**
  Contact/s:
  Mr David Appleby (Secretary), 6 Rump Cl, Swanton Morley, Dereham, NORFOLK, NR20 4NH **England**
  (T) 01362 637591.
  S R Allison (Secretary), Pound Cottage, Cemetery Rd, Dereham, NORFOLK, NR19 2ET **England**
- **DISS AND DISTRICT ANGLING CLUB**
  Contact/s:
  Mr Dave Gladwell (Secretary), 5 Martin Rd, Diss, NORFOLK, IP22 3HR **England**
  (T) 01379 652980.
  Mr K Rodwell (Secretary), 5 Tayler Rd, Diss, NORFOLK, IP22 3BB **England**
  (T) 01379 644304.
  P Allen (Secretary), 4 Gaye Cres, Eye, NORFOLK, IP21 **England**
- **FAKENHAM ANGLING CLUB**
  Contact/s:
  Mr G Twite (Secretary), 16 Back St, Hempton, Fakenham, NORFOLK, NR21 7LR **England**
  (T) 01328 863054.
- **GREAT YARMOUTH AND NORFOLK COUNTY ANGLING ASSOCIATION**
  Contact/s:
  Mr Keith Ford (Secretary), 2 Parana Cl, Sprowston, Norwich, NORFOLK, NR7 8BG **England**
  (T) 01603 483923.
- **KINGS LYNN ANGLING ASSOCIATION**
  Contact/s:
  Mr Mick Grief (Secretary), 67 Peckover Way, South Woonton, King's Lynn, NORFOLK, PE30 3UE **England**
  (T) 01553 671545.
- **MARTHAM AND DISTRICT ANGLING CLUB**
  Contact/s:
  Mr Ian Bradford (Secretary), 15 Repps Rd, Martham, Great Yarmouth, NORFOLK, NR29 4TJ **England**
- **NATIONAL FEDERATION OF ANGLERS**
  Contact/s:
  Mr Robert Burning (Nfa Disability Officer, Eastern Region), 3 Waterside, King's Lynn, NORFOLK, PE30 2NA **England**
  (T) 01553 661122.
- **NORFOLK AND SUFFOLK FLYFISHERS CLUB**
  Contact/s:
  E A Fenn (Secretary), Crickmore Farm House, White Horse Common, North Walsham, NORFOLK, NR28 9NG **England**
  (T) 01692 403185.
- **NORFOLK ANGLERS CONSERVATION ASSOCIATION**
  Contact/s:
  Mr M Hitchens (Secretary), Woodside House, 5 The Meadows, Aylsham,Norwich, NORFOLK, NR11 6HP **England**
  (T) 01263 732752.
- **NORWICH AND DISTRICT ANGLERS ASSOCIATION**
  Contact/s:
  Mr C Wigg (Secretary), 3 Coppice Avenue, Norwich, NORFOLK, NR6 5RB **England**
- **SALMON AND TROUT ASSOCIATION**
  Contact/s:
  Mr L D Temple-Richards (Secretary), Vale Farm, Stibbard, Fakenham, NORFOLK, NR21 0EQ **England**
  (T) 01328 78217.
  Secretary, Hockley's, 36 Prince Of Wales Rd, Norwich, NORFOLK, NR1 1LH **England**
  (T) 01606 620551.
- **THETFORD AND BRECKLAND ANGLING CLUB**
  Contact/s:
  Mr Sj Armes (Secretary), Kings Croft, Shropham Rd, Great Hockham,Thetford, NORFOLK, IP24 1NJ **England**
  (T) 01953 498686.
- **WHITTINGTON ANGLING CLUB**
  Contact/s:
  Mr M Mycock (Secretary), 4 Furlong Rd, Stoke Ferry, King's Lynn, NORFOLK, PE33 9SU **England**
  (T) 01366 500250.
- **WISSINGTON ANGLING CLUB**
  Contact/s:
  Mr R Preston (Secretary), Bsc Plc, Wissington, Stoke Ferry,King's Lynn, NORFOLK, PE **England**
  (T) 01366 66364.
- **WROXHAM AND DISTRICT ANGLING ASSOCIATION**
  Contact/s:
  Mr R Westgate (Club Secretary), 31 The Paddocks, Old Catton, Norwich, NORFOLK, NR6 7HF **England**
  (T) 01603 401062.
  (F) 01603 897122.
- **WYMONDHAM AND DISTRICT ANGLING CLUB**
  Contact/s:
  Mr T Binks (Secretary), 25 Rosemary Rd, Sprowston, Norwich, NORFOLK, NR **England**
  (T) 01603 405341.

NORTHAMPTONSHIRE

- **CASTLE ANGLING ASSOCIATION**
Contact/s:
Mr Terry Rodhouse (Secretary), 12 Somerville Rd, Daventry, NORTHAMPTONSHIRE, NN11 4RT **England**
(T) 01327 705692.

- **EARLS BARTON ANGLING CLUB**
Contact/s:
Mr P Tipler (Secretary), 70 Station Rd, Earls Barton, Northampton, NORTHAMPTONSHIRE, NN6 0NT **England**
(T) 01604 812433.

- **EASTFIELD ANGLING ASSOCIATION**
Contact/s:
J Ford (Secretary), 3 Newby Court, Eastfield, Wellingborough, NORTHAMPTONSHIRE, NN8 **England**

- **GLEBE ANGLING CLUB**
Contact/s:
C Broom (Secretary), 2 Crockett Cl, Links View Estate, Northampton, NORTHAMPTONSHIRE, NN **England**

- **KETTERING AND THRAPSTON ANGLING ASSOCIATION**
Contact/s:
Mr Lr Garret (Secretary), 10 Naseby Rd, Kettering, NORTHAMPTONSHIRE, NN14 **England**

- **LONG BUCKBY ANGLING CLUB**
Contact/s:
Mr M Hill (Secretary), 33 South Cl, Long Buckby, Northampton, NORTHAMPTONSHIRE, NN6 7PX **England**

- **NORTHAMPTON BRITANNIA ANGLING CLUB**
Contact/s:
Mr G H Richmond (Secretary), 34 Ilex Cl, Hardingstone, Northampton, NORTHAMPTONSHIRE, NN4 6SD **England**
C W Gray (Secretary), 61 Bouverie Walk, Northampton, NORTHAMPTONSHIRE, NN1 5SN **England**

- **NORTHAMPTON NENE ANGLING CLUB**
Contact/s:
Mrs P Walsh (Secretary), 363 Kettering Rd, Northampton, NORTHAMPTONSHIRE, NN3 6QT **England**
(T) 01604 492652.

- **PAC**
Contact/s:
Mr P Stewart (Secretary), Hillcrest, Pury End, Towcester, NORTHAMPTONSHIRE, NN12 7NX **England**
(T) 01954 230076.

- **RUSHDEN AND HIGHAM FERRERS AND IRCHESTER ANGLING ASSOCIATION**
Contact/s:
Mr A Ireson (Chairman), 26 Church St, Rushden, NORTHAMPTONSHIRE, NN10 **England**

- **RUSHDEN, HIGHAM FERRERS AND IRCHESTER ANGLING ASSOCIATION**
Contact/s:
Mr D Perkins (Secretary), 31 Mountfield Rd, Irthlingborough, Wellingborough, NORTHAMPTONSHIRE, NN9 5 **England**
(T) 01933 651400.

- **TOWCESTER AND DISTRICT ANGLING ASSOCIATION**
Contact/s:
Mr C Walden (Secretary), 5 Towcester Rd, Silverstone, Towcester, NORTHAMPTONSHIRE, NN12 8UB **England**
(T) 01327 858299.

- **TOWCESTER AND DISTRICT ANGLING CLUB**
Contact/s:
Mr Pannet (Secretary), 30 Bickerstaff Rd, Towcester, NORTHAMPTONSHIRE, NN12 **England**

- **WELLINGBOROUGH AND DISTRICT NENE ANGLING CLUB**
Contact/s:
Mr Richard Blenkharn (Secretary), 66 Redland Drive, Kingsthorpe, Northampton, NORTHAMPTONSHIRE, NN10 8TU **England**
(T) 01604 847106.

NORTHUMBERLAND

- **ALN ANGLING ASSOCIATION**
Contact/s:
Mr L Jobson (Secretary), Tower Showrooms, Alnwick, NORTHUMBERLAND, NE66 **England**

- **ANGLO-SCOTTISH FISH PRODUCERS ORGANISATION**
Contact/s:
Mr David Harriot (Chief Executive), 12 Castlegate, Berwick-upon-Tweed, NORTHUMBERLAND, TD15 1JT **England**
(T) 01289 306873.

- **BEDLINGTON AND BLAGDON ANGLING ASSOCIATION**
Contact/s:
Mr S Symons (Secretary), 8 Moorland Drive, Bedlington, NORTHUMBERLAND, NE22 7HB **England**

- **BERWICK AND DISTRICT ANGLING CLUB**
Contact/s:
Mr D Cowan (Secretary), 129 Etal Rd, Tweedmouth, Berwick-upon-Tweed, NORTHUMBERLAND, TD15 **England**

- **BERWICK SALMON CO**
Contact/s:
Secretary, 1 Main St, Spittal, Berwick-upon-Tweed, NORTHUMBERLAND, TD15 1QY **England**
(T) 01289 307474.

- **CHATTON ANGLING ASSOCIATION**
Contact/s:
Mr J Douglas (Secretary), 10 Church Hill, Chatton, Alnwick, NORTHUMBERLAND, NE66 **England**

- **COQUET ANGLING CLUB**
Contact/s:
Mr J Engles (Secretary), 80 Castle Trce, Ashington, NORTHUMBERLAND, NE63 **England**

- **HALTWHISTLE AND DISTRICT ANGLING ASSOCIATION**
Contact/s:
Mr Chris Wilson (Secretary), Melkridge House, Melkridge, Haltwhistle, NORTHUMBERLAND, NE49 0LT **England**

- **ROTHBURY AND THROPTON ANGLING CLUB**
Contact/s:
Mr Colin Bell (Treasurer), 1 Silverdale Cottages, Snitter, Morpeth, NORTHUMBERLAND, NE65 7EL **England**
(T) 01669 621083.
J Ball (Secretary), Gimmerknowle, Rothbury, Morpeth, NORTHUMBERLAND, NE65 **England**

- **THROPTON AND ROTHBURY ANGLING CLUB**
Contact/s:
C Bell (Secretary), Morpeth Tackle Shop, Morpeth, NORTHUMBERLAND, NE **England**
(T) 01669 621083.

- **TWEED COMMISSIONERS**
Contact/s:
Secretary, Dry, Berwick-upon-Tweed, NORTHUMBERLAND, TD15 2NF **England**
(T) 01289 330630.

- **WANSBECK ANGLING ASSOCIATION**
Contact/s:
Mr Peter Wigham (Secretary), School House, Chantry School, Mitford Rd,Morpeth, NORTHUMBERLAND, NE61 1RQ **England**
(T) 01670 511480.

NOTTINGHAMSHIRE

- **BOTTESFORD ANGLING ASSOCIATION**
Contact/s:
Bottesford, Nottingham, NOTTINGHAMSHIRE, NG13 **England**

- **COLLINGHAM ANGLING ASSOCIATION**
Contact/s:
Mrs J Wilson (Secretary), 93 Braemar Rd, Collingham, Newark, NOTTINGHAMSHIRE, NG23 7PN **England**
(T) 01636 892700.

- **EARL MANVERS ANGLING ASSOCIATION**
Contact/s:
Mr G R Dennis (Secretary), 11 First Avenue, Carlton, Nottingham, NOTTINGHAMSHIRE, NG **England**
(T) 0115 9879994.

- **EASTWOOD ANGLERS**
Contact/s:
Mr I Robinson, 9 Wilson Rd, Eastwood, Nottingham, NOTTINGHAMSHIRE, NG **England**

- **ENVIRONMENT AGENCY**
Contact/s:
Trentside Offices, Scarrington Rd, West Bridgford,Nottingham, NOTTINGHAMSHIRE, NG2 5FA **England**

- **GRAFTON ANGLING ASSOCIATION**
Contact/s:
Mr Gd Williams (Secretary), 9 Edward St, Worksop, NOTTINGHAMSHIRE, S80 1QP **England**

- **MANSFIELD AND DISTRICT ANGLING ASSOCIATION**
Contact/s:
A Quick (Secretary), 158 Huthwaite Rd, Sutton-In-Ashfield, NOTTINGHAMSHIRE, NG17 2GX **England**

- **MIDLAND ANGLING SOCIETY**
Contact/s:
Mr Jack Bradbury (Secretary), 19 Ethel Avenue, Lindby, Hucknall,Nottingham, NOTTINGHAMSHIRE, NG14 8DB **England**
(T) 0115 9634487.

- **NATIONAL FEDERATION OF ANGLERS**
Contact/s:
Mr Bill Turner (Nfa Disability Officer, East Midlands Region), 3a Beckhampton Rd, Bestwood Park Estate, Nottingham, NOTTINGHAMSHIRE, NG5 5SP **England**
(T) 01559 204103.

- **NEWARK AND DISTRICT PISCATORIAL FEDERATION**
Contact/s:
Mr Garland (Secretary), 58 Riverside Rd, Newark, NOTTINGHAMSHIRE, NG24 4RJ **England**
(T) 01636 702962.

● **NOTTINGHAM AND DISTRICT FEDERATION OF ANGLING SOCIETIES**
Contact/s:
Mr W Belshaw (Secretary), 17 Spring Green, Clifton Estate, Nottingham, NOTTINGHAMSHIRE, NG **England**

● **NOTTINGHAM ANGLING ASSOCIATION**
Contact/s:
Mr I Foulds (Secretary), 95 Ilkeston Rd, Nottingham, NOTTINGHAMSHIRE, NG7 3HA **England**

● **NOTTINGHAM PISCATORIAL SOCIETY**
Contact/s:
Mr P F Olko (Secretary), 63 Forest Rd, Annesley Woodhouse, Kirkby-In-Ashfield,Nottingham, NOTTINGHAMSHIRE, NG17 9HA **England**

● **NOTTINGHAM WALTONIANS**
Contact/s:
C P Scott (Secretary), 58 Lorimer Avenue, Gedling, Nottingham, NOTTINGHAMSHIRE, NG4 4WA **England**

● **PARKSIDE FISHING CLUB**
Contact/s:
Mr D Fallows (Secretary), 27 Woodstock Avenue, Radford, Nottingham, NOTTINGHAMSHIRE, NG7 5QP **England**
(T) 0115 9787350.

● **RALIEGH ANGLING CLUB**
Contact/s:
Mr E Mantle (Secretary), 32 Colin Broughton Court, St Albans Rd, Bulwell,Nottingham, NOTTINGHAMSHIRE, NG6 9JL **England**
(T) 0115 9273486.

● **RANSOM HOFFMAN POLLARD ANGLING CLUB**
Contact/s:
G Fletcher (Secretary), Rhp Bearings Ltd, Po Box 18, Northern Rd,Newark, NOTTINGHAMSHIRE, NG **England**

● **RETFORD AND DISTRICT ANGLING ASSOCIATION**
Contact/s:
Mr Harrold Wells (Secretary), 31 Ainsdale Green, Ordsall, Retford, NOTTINGHAMSHIRE, DN22 7NQ **England**
(T) 01777 702227.

● **SHEFFIELD PISCATORIAL SOCIETY**
Contact/s:
Mr Anderson (Secretary), Farm House, Retford, NOTTINGHAMSHIRE, DN22 **England**

● **TAYLOR W H**
Contact/s:
Mrs J Richardson (Secretary), 93 Wigman Rd, Bilborough, Nottingham, NOTTINGHAMSHIRE, NG8 4PA **England**

● **WORKSOP AND DISTRICT AMALGAMATED ANGLERS ASSOCIATION**
Contact/s:
D Brown (Secretary), 4 Dove Cl, Worksop, NOTTINGHAMSHIRE, S81 7LG **England**

● **WORTHINGTON SIMPSON ANGLING CLUB**
Contact/s:
Mr Gvh Pickering (Secretary), 31 Wilfred Avenue, Balderton, Newark, NOTTINGHAMSHIRE, NG24 3DS **England**

OXFORDSHIRE

● **BANBURY AND DISTRICT ANGLING ASSOCIATION**
Contact/s:
Mr Geoff Bradbeer (Secretary), 7 Bentley Cl, Banbury, OXFORDSHIRE, OX16 7PB **England**
(T) 01295 268047.

● **BENSON ANGLING CLUB**
Contact/s:
Mr Julian Humm (Secretary), Rainbow Cottage, Oxford, OXFORDSHIRE, OX44 7TZ **England**
(T) 01235 464099.

● **BICESTER ROYAL PIONEER CORPS ANGLING**
Contact/s:
Mr Tony Hoodles (Secretary), 15 Rookery Way, Bicester, OXFORDSHIRE, OX6 8LQ **England**

● **BURFORD ANGLING CLUB**
Contact/s:
Mr Dave Cohen (Secretary), 117 High St, Burford, OXFORDSHIRE, OX18 4RG **England**
(T) 01993 822136.
J Swallow (Secretary), 8 Meadow End, Fulford, Burford, OXFORDSHIRE, OX18 **England**

● **CLANFIELD ANGLING CLUB**
Contact/s:
Mr Doug Foreshaw (Secretary), 117 Farmers Cl, Witney, OXFORDSHIRE, OX8 6NR **England**

● **DORCHESTER ANGLING CLUB**
Contact/s:
Mr Mj Marriott (Secretary), 14 Shadwell Rd, Berinsfield, Wallingford, OXFORDSHIRE, OX10 7PN **England**

● **EYNSHAM AND DISTRICT ANGLING CLUB**
Contact/s:
Mr M Cross (Secretary), 29 Witney Rd, Eynsham, Witney, OXFORDSHIRE, OX8 1PH **England**

● **FARMOOR FLY FISHING CLUB**
Contact/s:
Mr Wr Ward (Secretary), 17 Perrott Cl, Witney, OXFORDSHIRE, OX8 6RU **England**

● **JOLLY ANGLERS ANGLING SOCIETY**
Contact/s:
Ms Pam Biggs (Secretary), 16 Radnor Rd, Wallingford, OXFORDSHIRE, OX10 **England**

● **MARSTON ANGLING CLUB**
Contact/s:
Mr N Brown (Secretary), 26 Kelburne Rd, Cowley, Oxford, OXFORDSHIRE, OX4 3SJ **England**

● **NORTH OXFORD ANGLING SOCIETY**
Contact/s:
Mr Andrew Crisp (Secretary), 4 Groves St, Summertown, Oxford, OXFORDSHIRE, OX3 7JT **England**
(T) 01865 554800.
Mr L Ballard (Secretary), 70 Blackbird Leys Rd, Cowley, Oxford, OXFORDSHIRE, OX4 5HR **England**

● **OXFORD AND ABINGDON ANGLING PRESERVATION**
Contact/s:
Mr Martin Room (Secretary), 136 Oxford Rd, Cowley, OXFORDSHIRE, OX4 2DU **England**
(T) 01865 711410.

● **OXFORD AND DISTRICT ANGLERS ASSOCIATION**
Contact/s:
Mr J Rayner (Secretary), 16 Cotmore Gardens, Thame, OXFORDSHIRE, OX9 3LZ **England**
(T) 01844 214383.

● **THAMES WATER UTILITIES**
Contact/s:
Mr Steven Symonds (Secretary), Farmoor Trout Fishery, Cumnor Rd, Farmoor,Oxford, OXFORDSHIRE, OX2 9NS **England**
(T) 01865 863033.

● **UPPER THAMES FISHERIES CONSULTATIVE ASSOCIATION**
Contact/s:
R Knowles (Secretary), 360 Banbury Rd, Oxford, OXFORDSHIRE, OX2 7PP **England**

● **WARBOROUGH AND SHILLINGFORD ANGLING CLUB**
Contact/s:
Mr R Hall (Secretary), 67 St Nicholas Rd, Wallingford, OXFORDSHIRE, OX10 8HX **England**

RUTLAND

● **SOUTH WITHAM ANGLING CLUB**
Contact/s:
R Bradley (Secretary), 24 Thistleton Rd, Market Overton, Oakham, RUTLAND, LE15 **England**

● **UPPINGHAM AND DISTRICT ANGLING ASSOCIATION**
Contact/s:
Mr David Johnson (Secretary), 20 Wheatley Avenue, Uppingham, Oakham, RUTLAND, LE15 9FN **England**
(T) 01572 821128.

SHROPSHIRE

● **AIR-FLUID HYDRAULIC ANGLING CLUB**
Contact/s:
Paint & Tool Stores, Wellington, Telford, SHROPSHIRE, TF **England**

● **DAWLEY ANGLING SOCIETY**
Contact/s:
Mrs Ellen Rogers (Secretary), 68 Coronation St, Madeley, Telford, SHROPSHIRE, TF7 5EH **England**

● **ENVIRONMENT AGENCY**
Contact/s:
Manager, Upper Severn Area Office, Hafren House, Welshpool Rd,Shrewsbury, SHROPSHIRE, SY3 8BB **England**
(T) 01743 272828.
(F) 01743 272138.

● **LUDLOW ANGLING CLUB**
Contact/s:
Mr D Bastin (Chairman), 96 Greenacres, Ludlow, SHROPSHIRE, SY8 1LZ **England**
(T) 01584 873577.

● **NATIONAL FEDERATION OF ANGLERS**
Contact/s:
Mr Malcolm Kelly (Nfa Disability Officer, West Midlands Region), 14 Sycamore Cl, Wellington, Telford, SHROPSHIRE, TF1 3NH **England**
(T) 01952 244272.

● **OSWESTRY ANGLING CLUB**
Contact/s:
Mr L Allen (Secretary), 30 Brookfields, Weston Rhyn, Oswestry, SHROPSHIRE, SY10 **England**

● **PLOWDEN FISHING CLUB**
Contact/s:
Mr S J Finnegan (Membership Secretary), The Old School, Brimfield, Ludlow, SHROPSHIRE, SY8 4NZ **England**

● **SHROPSHIRE ANGLERS FEDERATION**
Contact/s:
Mr Ian Moorhouse (Secretary), 22 Pendle Way, Washford Park, Shrewsbury, SHROPSHIRE, SY3 9QN **England**

- **TELFORD ANGLING ASSOCIATION**
Contact/s:
Mr Stan Harris (Secretary), 73 Burnside, Brookside, Telford, SHROPSHIRE, TF3 1DA **England**

SOMERSET

- **AVON AND TRIBUTARIES ANGLING ASSOCIATION**
Contact/s:
Mr J G L Lewis (Secretary), Chapel Cottage, Clarendon Rd, Widcombe Hill,Bath, SOMERSET, BA2 4NJ **England**
- **BATHAMPTON ANGLING ASSOCIATION**
Contact/s:
D Crookes (Secretary), 25 Otago Trce, Larkhall, Bath, SOMERSET, BA1 6SX **England**
Hunstrete Park Lake, Pensford, Bristol, SOMERSET, BS39 **England**
- **BRIDGWATER ANGLING ASSOCIATION**
Contact/s:
Mrs Carol Howe (Secretary), 3 Cedar Cl, Bridgwater, SOMERSET, TA6 5DP **England**
- **CHEDDAR ANGLING ASSOCIATION**
Contact/s:
Mr At Lane (Secretary), Po Box 1183, Cheddar, SOMERSET, BS27 3LT **England**
- **CLEVEDON AND DISTRICT ANGLING CLUB**
Contact/s:
Mr R F Newton (Hon Treasurer), 13 Tennyson Avenue, Clevedon, SOMERSET, BS21 7UQ **England**
(T) 01275 856107.
- **CLEVEDON DISTRICT FRESHWATER ANGLING CLUB**
Contact/s:
Mr D Harper (Secretary), 5 Kingsley Rd, Clevedon, SOMERSET, BS21 6NT **England**
- **FROME AND DISTRICT ANGLING ASSOCIATION**
Contact/s:
Mr R J Lee (Secretary), Marvic, Keyford Trce, Frome, SOMERSET, BA11 1JL **England**
- **KNOWLE (BRISTOL) ANGLING ASSOCIATION**
Contact/s:
Mr Keith Caddick (Secretary), 35 Wyndham Cres, Broomhill, Bristol, SOMERSET, BS4 4SX **England**
(T) 01798 57974.
- **NATIONAL FEDERATION OF ANGLERS**
Contact/s:
Mr Colin Scull (South West and South Wales Region Point Of Contact), 20 Parkfield Cres, Taunton, SOMERSET, TA1 4RZ **England**
(T) 01823 275493.
- **NORTH SOMERSET ASSOCIATION OF ANGLERS**
Contact/s:
Mr R F Newton (Hon Treasurer), 64 Clevedon Rd, Tickenham, Clevedon, SOMERSET, BS21 6RD **England**
(T) 01275 856107.
- **TAUNTON ANGLING ASSOCIATION**
Contact/s:
Mr Mike Hewitson (Secretary), 56 Parkfield Rd, Taunton, SOMERSET, TA1 4SE **England**
(T) 01823 271194.
- **TAUNTON FLYFISHING CLUB**
Contact/s:
Mr J Greene (Secretary), 2 Old Vicarage, Bradford On Tone, Taunton, SOMERSET, TA4 1HG **England**
- **WELLINGTON ANGLING ASSOCIATION**
Contact/s:
M Cave (Secretary), 60 Sylvan Rd, Wellington, SOMERSET, TA21 8EH **England**
- **WESSEX FEDERATION OF ANGLING CLUBS**
Contact/s:
Mr J J Mathrick (Secretary), Perham Farmhouse, Wick, Langport, SOMERSET, TA10 0NN **England**
- **WESTON-SUPER-MARE AND DISTRICT ANGLING ASSOCIATION**
Contact/s:
K Tucker (Secretary), 26 Coniston Cres, Weston-Super-Mare, SOMERSET, BS23 3RX **England**
- **WIMBLEBALL FLY FISHERS CLUB**
Contact/s:
Mr A D Ridgway (Membership Secretary), 12 Gaunts Rd, Bridgwater, SOMERSET, TA6 4SF **England**
- **WINDMILL ANGLING CLUB**
Contact/s:
Mr G F Miller (Secretary), 22 Benedict St, Glastonbury, SOMERSET, BA6 **England**

STAFFORDSHIRE

- **ALREWAS ANGLING CLUB**
Contact/s:
Mr T Turner (Secretary), Unit 5, Cosfield Rd, Lichfield, STAFFORDSHIRE, WS **England**
Mr J Mitchell (Secretary), 4 Benson View, Tamworth, STAFFORDSHIRE, B7 **England**
(T) 01827 53787.
- **BURTON-ON-TRENT MUTUAL ANGLERS ASSOCIATION**
Contact/s:
D J Clark (Secretary), 7 Denton Rise, Burton-on-Trent, STAFFORDSHIRE, DE13 0AQ **England**
(T) 01283 544734.
- **DOSTHILL COSMOPOLITAN ANGLING CLUB**
Contact/s:
Secretary, High St, Dosthill, Tamworth, STAFFORDSHIRE, B7 **England**
(T) 01827 286908.
- **FENTON AND DISTRICT ANGLING SOCIETY**
Contact/s:
Mr C Yates (Secretary), The Puzzels, 5 Gatley Gr, Meir Park,Stoke-on-Trent, STAFFORDSHIRE, ST3 7SH **England**
- **HANLEY ANGLING SOCIETY**
Contact/s:
Mr R Connell (Secretary), 17 Central Drive, Blurton, Stoke-on-Trent, STAFFORDSHIRE, ST3 2 **England**
- **HAZELDINE ANGLING ASSOCIATION**
Contact/s:
Warren Farm, Amington, Tamworth, STAFFORDSHIRE, B77 **England**
- **IZAAK WALTON (STAFFORD) ANGLING ASSOCIATION**
Contact/s:
Mr Colin Pearson (Secretary), Club Office, Gailey Lea Lane, Penkridge,Stafford, STAFFORDSHIRE, ST19 **England**
(T) 01785 715848.
- **KANAIRD DISTRICT SALMON FISHERY BOARD**
Contact/s:
Mr J Bramell (Acts Operator), Drummond Rd, Astonfields Industrial Estate, Stafford, STAFFORDSHIRE, ST16 3HJ **England**
- **LEEK AND MOORLANDS ANGLING CLUB**
Contact/s:
Mr Roy Birch-Machin (Secretary), 53 Novi Lane, Leek, STAFFORDSHIRE, ST13 6NX **England**
- **LEEK AND MOORLANDS FISHING CLUB**
Contact/s:
H Emery (Secretary), 8 Gladstone St, Leek, STAFFORDSHIRE, ST13 5EP **England**
- **PHOENIX ANGLING CLUB**
Contact/s:
Mr S Baylay (Secretary), 73 Masterson St, Fenton, Stoke-on-Trent, STAFFORDSHIRE, ST4 4PE **England**
(T) 01782 413823.
- **POTTERIES ANGLING SOCIETY**
Contact/s:
Mr D Heath (Secretary), 180 Broadway, Meir Heath, Stoke-on-Trent, STAFFORDSHIRE, ST3 5SR **England**
(T) 01782 332605.
- **SHUTTINGTON AND ALVECOTE ANGLING CLUB**
Contact/s:
M H Taylor (Secretary), 39 Alvecote Cottages, Alvecote, Tamworth, STAFFORDSHIRE, B79 0DJ **England**
- **STOKE CITY AND DISTRICT ANGLERS ASSOCIATION**
Contact/s:
Peter Johansen (Secretary), 31 East Cres, Sneyd Green, Stoke-on-Trent, STAFFORDSHIRE, ST10 6ES **England**
(T) 01782 214840.
- **STOKE ON TRENT ANGLING SOCIETY**
Contact/s:
Mr A Perkins (Secretary), Muirhearlich, Fowlers Lane, Light Oaks,Stoke-on-Trent, STAFFORDSHIRE, ST2 7NB **England**
- **STONE AND DISTRICT ANGLING SOCIETY**
Contact/s:
A Kenny (Secretary), 24 Albert Avenue, Stone, STAFFORDSHIRE, ST15 **England**
(T) 01785 819035.
- **UTTOXETER ANGLING ASSOCIATION**
Contact/s:
I E Davies (Secretary), Three Oaks, Hollington Lane, Stramshall,Uttoxeter, STAFFORDSHIRE, ST14 5AJ **England**
- **VICTORIA AND BIDDULPH ANGLING SOCIETY**
Contact/s:
Mr Phillip R Moston (Secretary), 4 Stile Cl, Brown Lees, Biddulph,Stoke-on-Trent, STAFFORDSHIRE, ST8 6NL **England**
- **VICTORIA ANGLING CLUB**
Contact/s:
Mr John Rowley (Secretary), 98 Franklin Rd, Penkhull, Stoke-on-Trent, STAFFORDSHIRE, ST4 5DS **England**
- **WHITE EAGLE ANGLERS**
Contact/s:
Mr R A M Skelton (Secretary), 339B Stone Rd, Stafford, STAFFORDSHIRE, ST16 1LB **England**

SUFFOLK

- **BECCLES ANGLING CLUB**
Contact/s:
Mr Arthur Crane (Secretary), 27 Rigbourne Hill, Beccles, SUFFOLK, NR34 9JG **England**
(T) 01502 716716.

BUNGAY CHERRY TREE ANGLING ASSOCIATION
Contact/s:
Mr Ian Gosling (Hon Secretary), 37 St Marys Trce, Waveney, Bungay, SUFFOLK, NR35 1DN **England**
(T) 01986 892982.

BURY ST EDMUNDS ANGLING ASSOCIATION
Contact/s:
Mr J Easdon (Secretary), 11 Fiske Cl, Bury St Edmunds, SUFFOLK, IP32 7LX **England**

CORNARDS ANGLING CLUB
Contact/s:
Mr P Franklin (Secretary), 48 Queens Rd, Great Cornard, Sudbury, SUFFOLK, CO10 0HQ **England**
(T) 01787 373766.

FRAMLINGHAM AND DISTRICT ANGLING CLUB
Contact/s:
Mr Dave Smith (Secretary), 11 Lark Rise, Martlesham Village, Martelsham,Ipswich, SUFFOLK, IP5 7SA **England**
(T) 01473 623228.

GIPPING ANGLING PRESERVATION SOCIETY
Contact/s:
Mr George Alderson (Secretary), 19 Clover Cl, Chantry, Ipswich, SUFFOLK, IP2 0PW **England**
(T) 01473 602828.

GIPPING VALLEY ANGLING CLUB
Contact/s:
Mr J North (Secretary), 17 Foxglove Avenue, Needham Market, Ipswich, SUFFOLK, IP6 8 **England**
(T) 01449 720414.
I Lawrence (Secretary), 30 Lincoln Gardens, Claydon, Ipswich, SUFFOLK, IP **England**

GREAT CORNARD ANGLING CLUB
Contact/s:
Mr P Franklin (Secretary), 48 Queensway, Great Cornard, Sudbury, SUFFOLK, CO10 0 **England**

HADLEIGH AND DISTRICT ANGLING SOCIETY
Contact/s:
Mr D Warner (Secretary), 5 Churchill Avenue, Hadleigh, Ipswich, SUFFOLK, IP7 6BT **England**
(T) 01473 828368.

HARLESTON, WORTWELL AND DISTRICT ANGLING CLUB
Contact/s:
Mr P Brown (Secretary), 15 Pine Cl, Harleston, SUFFOLK, IP20 9DZ **England**
(T) 01379 853505.

HAVERHILL ANGLING CLUB
Contact/s:
Mr T Langley (Secretary), 30 Parkside, Haverhill, SUFFOLK, CB9 8NG **England**
(T) 01440 7045921.
Mr D White (Secretary), 33 Bute Court, Haverhill, SUFFOLK, CB9 8LP **England**
(T) 01440 763057.

ISLEHAM ANGLING SOCIETY
Contact/s:
Mr A W F Mayes (Secretary), 88 Churchill Avenue, Newmarket, SUFFOLK, CB8 **England**
(T) 01638 662665.

LAKENHEATH ANGLING CLUB
Contact/s:
Mr R Powell (Secretary), 12 Compass Cl, Lakenheath, SUFFOLK, IP27 9AL **England**
(T) 01842 860060.

LARK ANGLING PRESERVATION SOCIETY
Contact/s:
Mr E T West (Secretary), 8 Arrowhead Drive, Lakenheath, SUFFOLK, IP27 9JN **England**

LONG MELFORD AND DISTRICT ANGLING ASSOCIATION
Contact/s:
Mr N Mealham (Secretary), 6 Springfield Trce, East St, Sudbury, SUFFOLK, CO10 6TS **England**
(T) 01787 377139.

MILDENHALL ANGLING CLUB
Contact/s:
Mr P Lyes (Secretary), 10 Church Walk, Bury St Edmunds, SUFFOLK, IP28 7 **England**
(T) 01638 715895.
M Hampshire (Secretary), 63 Downing Cl, Mildenhall, Bury St Edmunds, SUFFOLK, IP28 7PB **England**

NATIONAL FEDERATION OF ANGLERS
Contact/s:
Mr Derek King (Nfa Eastern Region Point Of Contact), 20 Manderville Rd, Bury St Edmunds, SUFFOLK, IP33 2JB **England**
(T) 01284 753176.

NORFOLK AND SUFFOLK FLY FISHING CLUB
Contact/s:
Mr D Armes (Chairman), Tuddenham, Bury St Edmunds, SUFFOLK, IP **England**
(T) 01603 423169.

SAXMUNDHAM ANGLING CLUB
Contact/s:
Mr A Firman (Secretary), 48 Barhams Way, Wickham Market, Woodbridge, SUFFOLK, IP13 0SR **England**
(T) 01728 747787.

SOUTHWOLD AND DISTRICT FAPS
Contact/s:
Mr J Purdy (Secretary), 37 High St, Southwold, SUFFOLK, IP18 6AB **England**
(T) 01502 724250.

SUDBURY AND DISTRICT ANGLING ASSOCIATION
Contact/s:
Mr Trevor Fairless (Secretary), 39 Pot Kiln Rd, Great Cornard, Sudbury, SUFFOLK, CO10 0DG **England**
(T) 01787 312536.

SUFFOLK COUNTY AMALGAMATED ANGLING ASSOCIATION
Contact/s:
Mr G W Howard (Secretary), 4 Merryfield Rd, Lowestoft, SUFFOLK, NR33 7HB **England**
(T) 01502 574024.

WOODBRIDGE AND DISTRICT ANGLING CLUB
Contact/s:
Mr D N Abbott (Secretary), 17 Prospect Pl, Leiston, SUFFOLK, IP16 4AL **England**
(T) 01728 832781.

SURREY

BROMLEY AND DISTRICT ANGLING SOCIETY
Contact/s:
Mr M Sale (Secretary), 13A Charlesfield Rd, Horley Rd, Horley, SURREY, RH6 8BJ **England**

CENTRAL ASSOCIATION OF LONDON AND PROVINCIAL ANGLING CLUBS (CALPAC)
Contact/s:
A J Jenkinson (Secretary), 68 Taynton Drive, Merstham, Redhill, SURREY, RH1 3PT **England**

DORKING AND DISTRICT ANGLING ASSOCIATION
Contact/s:
P Knight (Secretary), Stone Cottage, Ridgeway Rd, Dorking, SURREY, RH4 3EY **England**

DUNSFOLD FLY FISHERS
Contact/s:
Mr P Barker (Secretary), Hunterswood Farm, Dunsfold, Godalming, SURREY, GU8 4NP **England**
(T) 01483 200477.

EDENBRIDGE ANGLING CLUB
Contact/s:
Mr Fishlock (Secretary), 3 Locks Meadow, Dormansland, Lingfield, SURREY, RH7 6P **England**

EFFINGHAM FLY FISHERS
Contact/s:
Mr Skinner (Owner), Highway Farm, Horsley Rd, Cobham, SURREY, KT11 3JZ **England**
(T) 01932 862410.

EPSOM ANGLING SOCIETY
Contact/s:
Mr G Taylor (Secretary), 59 Reynolds Avenue, Chessington, SURREY, KT9 2LQ **England**
(T) 01372 226106.

FARNBOROUGH AND DISTRICT ANGLING SOCIETY
Contact/s:
Mr David Rance (Secretary), Orchard Bungalow, Henley Park, Normandy,Guildford, SURREY, GU3 2AB **England**
(T) 01483 234054.

GODALMING ANGLING SOCIETY
Contact/s:
Mr Mr Richardson (Secretary), 87 Summers Rd, Farncombe, Godalming, SURREY, GU7 3BE **England**
(T) 01483 422791.
Secretary, Flat 1, 5 Peperharow Rd, Godalming, SURREY, GU7 2PH **England**
(T) 01483 429537.

GREYSHOTT ANGLING CLUB
Contact/s:
Greyshott Tackle, Crossway Rd, Greyshott,Hindhead, SURREY, GU26 **England**

HORLEY PISCATORIAL SOCIETY
Contact/s:
Mr J Davis (Secretary), 32 Lechford Rd, Horley, SURREY, RH6 7NB **England**

LEISURE SPORT ANGLING
Contact/s:
Secretary, Thorpe Park, Staines Rd, Chertsey, SURREY, KT16 8PN **England**
(T) 01932 569393.

MERCERS PARK ANGLING
Contact/s:
Secretary, The Aqua Sports Company, Nufield Rd, Merstham, SURREY, RH1 4SU **England**
(T) 01737 644288.

PEPER HAROW PARK FLYFISHERS CLUB
Contact/s:
Mr Charles Stuart (Secretary), 6 Lynch Rd, Farnham, SURREY, GU9 8BZ **England**

PETERSFIELD AND DISTRICT ANGLING CLUB
Contact/s:
Mr Ash Girdler (Secretary), 3 Chase Plain Cottages, Portsmouth Rd, Hindhead, SURREY, GU26 6BZ **England**
(T) 01428 607768.

PORTSMOUTH SERVICES FLY FISHING ASSOCIATION
Contact/s:
Captain F Hefford Obe, Dsc, Afc, Rn (Retired) (Secretary), 20 Stoatley Rise, Haslemere, SURREY, GU27 1AF **England**

RUDGWICK ANGLING SOCIETY
Contact/s:
Mr C Wood (Secretary), 16 Waldy Rise, Cranleigh, SURREY, GU6 7DF **England**
(T) 01483 275978.
Mr Robbie Gaiger (Secretary), 32 Glebe Rd, Cranleigh, SURREY, GU6 7AS **England**
(T) 01483 275944.

RUNNYMEDE ANGLING ASSOCIATION
Contact/s:
Mr S Currier (Secretary), 16 Brookside, Chertsey, SURREY, KT16 9ES **England**
(T) 01932 561733.

SUNMEAD ANGLING SOCIETY
Contact/s:
Mr P Tanner (Secretary), 24 Ryebrook Rd, Leatherhead, SURREY, KT22 7QG **England**

WEY NAVIGATION ANGLING AMALGAMATION
Contact/s:
Village Hall, Byfleet, SURREY, KT14 **England**

WEY VALLEY FISHERIES CONSERVATIVE ASSOCIATION
Contact/s:
Mr Mark Hatcher (Secretary), 30 Ainsdale Way, Goldsworth, Woking, SURREY, GU21 3PP **England**

WEYBRIDGE ANGLING CLUB
Contact/s:
Mrs M Colclough (Secretary), 137 Oatlands Drive, Oatlands Village, Weybridge, SURREY, KT13 9LB **England**

WOKING AND DISTRICT ANGLING ASSOCIATION
Contact/s:
Mr T Pilott (Secretary), 71 Albert Drive, Sheerwater, Woking, SURREY, GU21 5PB **England**
(T) 01483 714880.

SUSSEX (EAST)

CLIVE VALE ANGLING CLUB
Contact/s:
Mr J Greenhalf (Secretary), 33 Hollington Park Rd, St Leonards-on-Sea, SUSSEX (EAST), TN38 0SE **England**
(T) 01424 719703or438987.

COMPLEAT ANGLER FISHING CLUB
Contact/s:
Mr T Lelliott (Secretary), Polegate Angling Ctre, 101 Polegate Rd, Polegate, SUSSEX (EAST), BN26 6EB **England**

EASTBOURNE ANGLING ASSOCIATION
Contact/s:
Mrs Szott (Secretary), Club House, Royal Prde, Eastbourne, SUSSEX (EAST), BN22 7AA **England**
(T) 01323 723442.

HAILSHAM ANGLING ASSOCIATION
Contact/s:
M G Richardson (Secretary), 64 Grange Cl, Horam, Heathfield, SUSSEX (EAST), TN21 0EF **England**
(T) 01435 812854.

HASTINGS AND ST LEONARDS ANGLING ASSOCIATION
Contact/s:
Competition Secretary, Marine Prde, Hastings, SUSSEX (EAST), TN34 3AG **England**
(T) 01424 430120or431923.

HASTINGS FLY FISHERS' CLUB DARWELL
Contact/s:
Mr D Davey (Secretary), Darwell Reservoir, Battle, SUSSEX (EAST), TN32 5LB **England**
(T) 01580 880407.

HASTINGS FLYFISHERS CLUB LTD
Contact/s:
Mr Donald Tack (Secretary), 23 Wealden Way, Little Common, Bexhill-on-Sea, SUSSEX (EAST), TN39 4NZ **England**
(T) 01424 843957.

HASTINGS, BEXHILL AND DISTRICT FRESHWATER ANGLING ASSOCIATION
Contact/s:
Mr Peter Maclean (Hon Secretary), 37 Colliers Rd, Hastings, SUSSEX (EAST), TN34 3JR **England**
(T) 01424 715218.
Mr T Barton (Secretary), 51 Helen's Park Rd, Hastings, SUSSEX (EAST), TN34 **England**

MINISTRY OF AGRICULTURE FISHERIES AND FOOD
Contact/s:
Mr Angus Radford (Secretary), Fishmarket, Rock-A-Nore Rd, Hastings, SUSSEX (EAST), TN34 3DW **England**
(T) 01424 424109.

NATIONAL FEDERATION OF ANGLERS
Contact/s:
Mr Alan Bates (Nfa London and South East Region Point Of Contact), "analan", Sandy Cross Lane, Heathfield, SUSSEX (EAST), TN21 8QN **England**
(T) 01435 863981.

NORTHIAM ANGLING CLUB
Contact/s:
Mr D Stone (Secretary), 21 South Undercliffe, Rye, SUSSEX (EAST), TN31 7HN **England**
(T) 01797 224952.

RUEL DISTRICT SALMON FISHERY BOARD
Contact/s:
Mr J Ferguson (Acts Operator), 6 The Strand, Rye, SUSSEX (EAST), TN31 7DB **England**

RYE AND DISTRICT ANGLING SOCIETY
Contact/s:
Mr Derek Willis (Secretary), 79 Udimore Rd, Rye, SUSSEX (EAST), TN31 7EA **England**
(T) 01797 224049.

SALMON AND TROUT ASSOCIATION (EAST SUSSEX)
Contact/s:
Mr Bob Thomson (Secretary), 87 Tongdean Lane, Brighton, SUSSEX (EAST), BN1 5JE **England**
(T) 01273 507832.

SHOREHAM ANGLING CLUB
Contact/s:
A Smith (Secretary), 11 St Richards Rd, Portslade, Brighton, SUSSEX (EAST), BN41 1PA **England**

VICTORIA ANGLING CLUB
Contact/s:
Black Rabbit, Offham, Lewes, SUSSEX (EAST), BN7 **England**

WALTON ON THAMES ANGLING SOCIETY
Contact/s:
Mr Reg Perry (Membership Secretary), 9 Upper Cl, Forest Row, SUSSEX (EAST), RH18 5DS **England**
(T) 020 89419016.

SUSSEX (WEST)

BILLINGHURST ANGLING SOCIETY
Contact/s:
Mr J Hitchin (Secretary), 12 West Lark Lake, Goring-By-Sea, Worthing, SUSSEX (WEST), BN **England**

CHICHESTER AND DISTRICT ANGLING SOCIETY
Contact/s:
Mrs Luffham (Secretary), 3 Birdham Cl, Bognor Regis, SUSSEX (WEST), PO21 **England**

CHICHESTER CANAL SOCIETY
Contact/s:
Mr Edward Hill (Secretary), 9 Marden Avenue, Chichester, SUSSEX (WEST), PO19 2QZ **England**

FISHERIES OFFICE
Contact/s:
Secretary, Martlett House, St Johns St, Chichester, SUSSEX (WEST), PO19 1UY **England**
(T) 01243 539087.

HAYWARDS HEATH AND DISTRICT ANGLING SOCIETY
Contact/s:
Mr J Kenward (Secretary), 60 Franklyn Rd, Haywards Heath, SUSSEX (WEST), RH16 4DH **England**
(T) 01444 452572.

HENFIELD AND DISTRICT ANGLING SOCIETY
Contact/s:
Mrs L Smith (Secretary), 7 Wantley Hill Estate, Henfield, SUSSEX (WEST), BN5 9JR **England**

LITTLEHAMPTON AND DISTRICT ANGLING CLUB
Contact/s:
Mrs Anne Francis (Secretary), 15 Hide Gardens, Littlehampton, SUSSEX (WEST), BN16 3NP **England**

OUSE ANGLING PRESERVATION SOCIETY
Contact/s:
E W McLening (Secretary), Old Barn Cottage, Peak Lane, Littlehampton, SUSSEX (WEST), BN16 1RN **England**

PETWORTH ANGLING CLUB
Contact/s:
Mr R Haenaire (Secretary), 25 Station Rd, Petworth, SUSSEX (WEST), GU28 0EX **England**

ROTHER ANGLING CLUB
Contact/s:
Mr C Boxall (Treasurer), Innisfree, Ashfield Rd, Midhurst, SUSSEX (WEST), GU29 9JX **England**
(T) 01730 813885.

ROYAL TUNBRIDGE WELLS ANGLING SOCIETY
Contact/s:
R Carr (Secretary), 17 Kennedy Avenue, East Grinstead, SUSSEX (WEST), RH19 2DF **England**
(T) 01342 324718.

RUDGWICK ANGLING SOCIETY
Contact/s:
Holmhurst, Church St, Rudgwick,Horsham, SUSSEX (WEST), RH12 3ET **England**

SELSEY ANGLING AND TOPE CLUB
Contact/s:
Mr Mike Bell (Secretary), 166 Littlefield Cl, Selsey, Chichester, SUSSEX (WEST), PO20 **England**

WORTHING AND DISTRICT PISCATORIAL SOCIETY
Contact/s:
Jane Kirby (Secretary), 22 Middle Mead, Steyning, SUSSEX (WEST), BN44 3RG **England**

TYNE AND WEAR

- **DERWENT VALLEY ANGLING ASSOCIATION**
Contact/s:
Po Box 12, Blaydon-on-Tyne, TYNE AND WEAR, NE21 5TQ **England**
- **ENVIRONMENT AGENCY**
Contact/s:
Area Manager, Northumbria Area Office, Tyneside House, Skinnerburn Rd,Newcastle Business Park, Newcastle Upon Tyne, TYNE AND WEAR, NE4 7AR **England**
(T) 0191 2034000.
(F) 0191 2034004.
- **NORTHUMBRIAN ANGLERS FEDERATION**
Contact/s:
Mr P A Hall (Secretary), 3a Ridley Pl, Newcastle Upon Tyne, TYNE AND WEAR, NE1 8LF **England**
- **WESTWATER ANGLING**
Contact/s:
3 Crossways, East Boldon, TYNE AND WEAR, NE **England**
- **YARM ANGLING ASSOCIATION**
Contact/s:
Mr M Dresser (Secretary), 4 Blenavon Court, Yarm, TYNE AND WEAR, TS15 **England**
(T) 01642 786444.

WARWICKSHIRE

- **ALVESTON VILLAGE ASSOCIATION ANGLING CLUB**
Contact/s:
M A Pitcher (Secretary), 6 Ferry Lane, Alveston, Stratford-upon-Avon, WARWICKSHIRE, CV37 7QX **England**
- **ANGLING FOUNDATION**
Contact/s:
Secretary, Stoneleigh Park Pavilion, National Agriculture Ctre, Stoneleigh Park,Kenilworth, WARWICKSHIRE, CV8 1JQ **England**
(T) 024 76414999.
(F) 024 76414990.
- **ANGLING TRADE ASSOCIATION**
Contact/s:
Secretary, Stoneleigh Park Pavilion, National Agriculture Ctre, Stoneleigh Park,Kenilworth, WARWICKSHIRE, CV8 1JQ **England**
(T) 024 76414999.
(F) 024 76414990.
- **ROYAL LEAMINGTON SPA ANGLING ASSOCIATION**
Contact/s:
E G Archer (Secretary), 9 Southway, Leamington Spa, WARWICKSHIRE, CV31 2PG **England**
- **STRATFORD-UPON-AVON ANGLING ASSOCIATION**
Contact/s:
A Bruce (Secretary), 42 Cherry Orchard, Stratford-upon-Avon, WARWICKSHIRE, CV37 9AP **England**
Mr A Bruce (Secretary), Lower Lodge Farm, Bishopton Lane, Stratford-upon-Avon, WARWICKSHIRE, CV37 0RJ **England**

WILTSHIRE

- **AVON ANGLING CLUB**
Contact/s:
Mr R Edwards (Secretary), 56 Addison Rd, Melksham, WILTSHIRE, SN12 8DR **England**
(T) 01225 705036.
- **BRADFORD-ON-AVON ANGLING ASSOCIATION**
Contact/s:
Mr S Keates (Secretary), 12 Bear Cl, Bradford-on-Avon, WILTSHIRE, BA15 **England**
- **CALNE ANGLING ASSOCIATION**
Contact/s:
Ms J M Knowler (Secretary), 123A London Rd, Calne, WILTSHIRE, SN11 0AQ **England**
- **CHIPPENHAM ANGLING CLUB**
Contact/s:
Mr J Duffield (Secretary), 95 Malmesbury Rd, Chippenham, WILTSHIRE, SN15 1PY **England**
- **DEVIZES ANGLING ASSOCIATION**
Contact/s:
T Fell (Secretary), 21 Cornwall Cresent, Devizes, WILTSHIRE, SN10 5HG **England**
- **HIGHWORTH ANGLING CLUB**
Contact/s:
Mr N Holder (Secretary), 166 Beechcroft Rd, Upper Stratton, Swindon, WILTSHIRE, SN2 6QE **England**
(T) 01739 820694.
- **HUNGERFORD CANAL ANGLING ASSOCIATION**
Contact/s:
Mrs Lj Keen (Secretary), 8 Kandahar, Aldbourne, Marlborough, WILTSHIRE, SN8 2EE **England**
- **ISIS ANGLING CLUB**
Contact/s:
Newleaze Farm, Calne, WILTSHIRE, SN11 **England**
- **LAWN AND DISTRICT ANGLING CLUB**
Contact/s:
Mr Campbell (Secretary), 72 Rodbourne Rd, Swindon, WILTSHIRE, SN2 1DH **England**
- **LIDEN JUNIOR ANGLING CLUB**
Contact/s:
Mr Dave Cleaver (Secretary), Swindon Angling Ctre, 5 Sheppard St, Swindon, WILTSHIRE, SN1 5DP **England**
(T) 01793 619909.
- **LOWER MILL ESTATE ANGLING CLUB**
Contact/s:
Mr Steve Rowley (Secretary), Goldenlands Cottage, 177 Collingborune Rd, Burbage,Marlborough, WILTSHIRE, SN8 3RU **England**
(T) 01793 562163.
- **MARLBOROUGH AND DISTRICT ANGLING ASSOCIATION**
Contact/s:
Mr M Ellis (Secretary), 'Failte', Elcot Cl, Marlborough, WILTSHIRE, SN8 2BB **England**
- **MELKSHAM AND DISTRICT ANGLING ASSOCIATION**
Contact/s:
D Branton (Secretary), 16 Ingram Rd, Melksham, WILTSHIRE, SN12 **England**
- **PEATMOOR ANGLING CLUB**
Contact/s:
Mr Pete Sarahs (Secretary), 3 Holly Cl, Swindon, WILTSHIRE, SN2 1HX **England**
(T) 01793 551320.
- **PLAUMS PIT ANGLING CLUB**
Contact/s:
Mr Tony Aisbitt (Secretary), 32 Windermere, Liden, Swindon, WILTSHIRE, SN3 6JZ **England**
(T) 01793 541740.
- **RAYCHEM ANGLING CLUB**
Contact/s:
Mr M Bowsher (Secretary), 5 Nevis Cl, Sparcells, Swindon, WILTSHIRE, SN5 9FP **England**
(T) 01793 876865.
- **SALISBURY AND DISTRICT ANGLING CLUB**
Contact/s:
Mr Ron Hillier (Secretary), 29 New Zealand Avenue, Salisbury, WILTSHIRE, SP2 7JX **England**
(T) 01722 321164.
- **SERVICES DRY FLY FISHING ASSOCIATION**
Contact/s:
Mr D A N C Miers (Secretary), Hq Spta, Bulford Camp, Salisbury, WILTSHIRE, SP4 9PA **England**
- **SERVICES DRY FLY FISHING ASSOCIATION (SALISBURY PLAIN)**
Contact/s:
Mr Cd Taylor (Secretary), G2 Regional Headquarters, 3rd (United Kingdom) Division, Picton Barracks,Bulford Camp, Salisbury, WILTSHIRE, SP4 9NY **England**
- **SWINDON GOLDEN CARP ANGLING ASSOCIATION**
Contact/s:
Mr E Bizley (Secretary), 8 Glenwood Cl, Swindon, WILTSHIRE, SN1 4EB **England**
(T) 01793 693268.
- **TISBURY ANGLING CLUB**
Contact/s:
Mr B Ricketts (Secretary), 26 St Martins Cl, Barford St Martins, Salisbury, WILTSHIRE, SP3 4AX **England**
(T) 01722 744786.
Mr Ej Stevens (Treasurer), Ravenscroft Fovant, Salisbury, WILTSHIRE, SP3 5JW **England**
- **WROUGHTON ANGLING CLUB**
Contact/s:
Mr Martin Drury (Secretary), 20 St Johns Rd, Wroughton, Swindon, WILTSHIRE, SN4 9ED **England**

WORCESTERSHIRE

- **DROITWICH AND DISTRICT ANGLING ASSOCIATION**
Contact/s:
Talbot Hotel, High St, Droitwich, WORCESTERSHIRE, WR9 **England**
- **EVESHAM AND DISTRICT ANGLING ASSOCIATION**
Contact/s:
C Leeming (Secretary), 44 Coronation St, Evesham, WORCESTERSHIRE, WR11 5BD **England**
- **KIDDERMINSTER AND DISTRICT ANGLING ASSOCIATION**
Contact/s:
M Millinchip (Secretary), 246 Marpol Lane, Kidderminster, WORCESTERSHIRE, DY11 5DD **England**
- **NATIONAL COARSE FISHERIES CENTRE**
Contact/s:
Mr Phil Hickley (Head Of Centre), Arthur Drive, Hoo Farm Industrial Estate, Worcester Rd,Kidderminster, WORCESTERSHIRE, DY11 7RA **England**
(T) 01562 68975.
(F) 01562 69477.
- **SEVEN STARS ANGLING CLUB**
Contact/s:
The Seven Stars, Birchfield Rd, Headless Cross,Redditch, WORCESTERSHIRE, B97 **England**
- **TENBURY FISHING ASSOCIATION**
Contact/s:
Mrs L M Rickett (Secretary), The Post House, Berrington Rd, Tenbury Wells, WORCESTERSHIRE, WR15 8EN **England**

- **WARWICKSHIRE AVON**
Contact/s:
Mr John Davis (Water Allocation Officer), Crown Meadows, Evesham, WORCESTERSHIRE, **England**
(T) 01386 41273.
(F) 01386 41273.
- **WORCESTER AND DISTRICT UNITED ANGLING ASSOCIATION**
Contact/s:
Mr John Wells (Chairman), Poplar Cottage, Poplar Rd, Worcester, WORCESTERSHIRE, WR6 6YF **England**
(T) 01886 888459.

YORKSHIRE (NORTH)

- **ALLIANCE FISH WHITBY**
Contact/s:
Secretary, 12 Fish Market, Whitby, YORKSHIRE (NORTH), YO21 1AU **England**
(T) 01947 820324.
- **BLACK OX ANGLING CLUB**
Contact/s:
5 Lascelles Lane, Northallerton, YORKSHIRE (NORTH), DL **England**
- **BOROUGHBRIDGE AND DISTRICT ANGLING CLUB**
Contact/s:
Secretary, Boroughbridge Post Office, Horsefair, Boroughbridge,York, YORKSHIRE (NORTH), YO51 9AA **England**
(T) 01423 322560.
(F) 01423 324578.
- **BRADFORD NO1 ANGLING ASSOCIATION**
Contact/s:
Buck Inn, Maunby, Thirsk, YORKSHIRE (NORTH), YO7 **England**
- **DANBY ANGLING CLUB**
Contact/s:
Mr F Farrow (Secretary), 11 Dale End, Danby, Whitby, YORKSHIRE (NORTH), YO21 2JF **England**
- **ENVIRONMENT AGENCY**
Contact/s:
Area Manager, Dales Area Office, Coverdale House, Amy Johnson Way,Clifton Way, York, YORKSHIRE (NORTH), YO3 4UZ **England**
(T) 01904 692296.
(F) 01904 693748.
- **ESK FISHERY ASSOCIATION**
Contact/s:
Rosedene, Priory Park, Grosmont,Whitby, YORKSHIRE (NORTH), YO2 **England**
- **FILEY BOAT ANGLING CLUB**
Contact/s:
Mr H Cammish (Secretary), 11 Ravine Top, Filey, YORKSHIRE (NORTH), YO14 9HA **England**
- **FILEY BRIGG ANGLING SOCIETY**
Contact/s:
K C Carpenter (Secretary), 18 Ash Gr, Filey, YORKSHIRE (NORTH), YO14 9LZ **England**
Mrs K Marshall (Secretary), 87 Scarborough Rd, Filey, YORKSHIRE (NORTH), YO14 9NQ **England**
- **GOATHLAND FISHING CLUB**
Contact/s:
P Skelton (Secretary), Spring Hill, Darnholm, Goathland,Whitby, YORKSHIRE (NORTH), YO2 **England**
- **HARROGATE AND CLARO CONSERVATIVE ANGLING ASSOCIATION**
Contact/s:
Mr M G Cooke (Secretary), 1 Kirkham Rd, Bilton, Harrogate, YORKSHIRE (NORTH), HG1 4EL **England**
- **HARROGATE ANGLING ASSOCIATION**
Contact/s:
Aykroyd, Skip Bridge Filling Station, Green Hammerton,York, YORKSHIRE (NORTH), YO26 **England**
- **HAWES AND HIGH ABBOTSIDE ANGLING ASSOCIATION**
Contact/s:
Mr G Phillips (Secretary), Holmlands, Appersett, Hawes, YORKSHIRE (NORTH), DL8 3LN **England**
Lowis Country Wear, Hawes, YORKSHIRE (NORTH), DL8 **England**
- **HELPERBY AND BRAFFERTON ANGLING CLUB**
Contact/s:
Mr F Marrison (Hon Secretary), Gardeners Cottage, York Rd, Helperby,York, YORKSHIRE (NORTH), YO6 2PJ **England**
(T) 01423 360632.
- **HOWDEN AND DISTRICT ANGLING CLUB**
Contact/s:
Mr Mike Redman (Secretary), 2 Meadowfield, Breighton Rd, Bubwith,Selby, YORKSHIRE (NORTH), YO8 7DZ **England**
(T) 01757 288891.
- **HUTTONS AMBO ANGLING CLUB**
Contact/s:
Mr Paul Thompson (Secretary), Firby Hall, Firby, Bedale, YORKSHIRE (NORTH), YO6 7LH **England**
- **KIRKBY FLEETHAM ANGLING CLUB**
Contact/s:
S Schofield (Secretary), 1 Colstan Rd, Northallerton, YORKSHIRE (NORTH), DL6 1AZ **England**
- **KNARESBOROUGH PISCATORIALS**
Contact/s:
Mr P Davies (Secretary), 26 Kendal Rd, Harrogate, YORKSHIRE (NORTH), HG1 4SH **England**
- **LANCASHIRE FLY-FISHING ASSOCIATION**
Contact/s:
J Winnard (Secretary), Manor House, Grunsagill, Tosside,Skipton, YORKSHIRE (NORTH), BD23 **England**
- **MALTON AND NORTON ANGLING CLUB**
Contact/s:
Mr M Foggins (Secretary), 123 Wellram Rd, Norton, Malton, YORKSHIRE (NORTH), YO17 **England**
Mr C Swift (Secretary), 25 Castlegate, Malton, YORKSHIRE (NORTH), YO17 7DP **England**
(T) 01653 694580.
- **MASHAM ANGLING CLUB**
Contact/s:
Mr A R Proud (River Keeper), Park St, Masham, Ripon, YORKSHIRE (NORTH), HG4 **England**
(T) 01765 689361.
- **NIDDERDALE ANGLING CLUB**
Contact/s:
Mr T Harpham (Secretary), Po Box 7, Pateley Bridge, Harrogate, YORKSHIRE (NORTH), HG3 5XB **England**
(T) 01423 711960.
- **NORTHALLERTON ANGLING CLUB**
Contact/s:
Mrs Grainger (Secretary), Morton On Swale, Northallerton, YORKSHIRE (NORTH), DL7 **England**
- **RIPON ANGLING CLUB**
Contact/s:
Mr John Jackson (Secretary), 43 College Rd, Ripon, YORKSHIRE (NORTH), HG4 2HE **England**
(T) 01653 693606.
- **RIPON FLY FISHERS**
Contact/s:
Mr C Clarke (Secretary), 9 Moorside Avenue, Ripon, YORKSHIRE (NORTH), HG4 1TA **England**
- **RIPON PISCATORIAL ASSOCIATION**
Contact/s:
S Looney (Secretary), Cornerstones, 2 Hellwath Gr, Redwell Heath,Ripon, YORKSHIRE (NORTH), HG4 2JT **England**
- **SCARBOROUGH MERE ANGLING CLUB**
Contact/s:
Mr D Pratt (Secretary), Seamer Rd, Scarborough, YORKSHIRE (NORTH), YO13 **England**
(T) 01723 585155.
- **SEVEN ANGLING CLUB**
Contact/s:
Mrs B J Stansfield (Secretary), Sun Seven, Sinnington, York, YORKSHIRE (NORTH), YO6 6RZ **England**
- **SKIPTON ANGLING ASSOCIATION**
Contact/s:
R Noble (Secretary), 3 Uplands, Skipton, YORKSHIRE (NORTH), BD23 1BJ **England**
- **TADCASTER ANGLING AND PRESERVATION ASSOCIATION**
Contact/s:
Mr A Emmett (Secretary), 3 Ingleby Drive, Tadcaster, YORKSHIRE (NORTH), LS24 8HW **England**
- **THIRSK ANGLING CLUB**
Contact/s:
Mr Derek Stratton (President), Thirsk Anglers Ctre, 7 Sowerby Rd, Town End,Thirsk, YORKSHIRE (NORTH), YO7 1HR **England**
(T) 01845 524684.
(F) 01845 525549.
- **THORNTON DALE FISHERIES**
Contact/s:
Secretary, 2 Pickering Rd, Thornton Dale, Pickering, YORKSHIRE (NORTH), YO18 7LG **England**
(T) 01751 474502.
- **WENSLEYDALE ANGLING ASSOCIATION**
Contact/s:
Mrs Pa Thorpe (Secretary), Grange Farm, High Birstwith, Harrogate, YORKSHIRE (NORTH), HG3 2ST **England**
Mr Scarr (Secretary), Cravenholme Farm, Bainbridge, Leyburn, YORKSHIRE (NORTH), DL8 3EG **England**
Village Shop, Bainbridge, Leyburn, YORKSHIRE (NORTH), DL8 **England**
Secretary, Worton, Leyburn, YORKSHIRE (NORTH), DL8 **England**
(T) 01380 860328.
- **YORK AND DISTRICT ANGLING ASSOCIATION**
Contact/s:
Mr John Lane (Secretary), 39 Lowfields Drive, Acomb, York, YORKSHIRE (NORTH), YO2 3DQ **England**
(T) 01904 783178.
- **YORK ANGLING ASSOCIATION**
Contact/s:
Melbourne Arms, Melbourne, York, YORKSHIRE (NORTH), YO42 **England**

YORKSHIRE (SOUTH)

- **BARNSLEY AND DISTRICT AMALGAMATED ANGLERS SOCIETY**
Contact/s:
Mr Tony Eaton (Secretary), 60 Walton St, Gawber, Barnsley, YORKSHIRE (SOUTH), S75 2PD **England**
(T) 01226 203090.

- **DONCASTER AND DISTRICT ANGLING ASSOCIATION**
Contact/s:
Mr Maurice Tate (Secretary), 28 Holmescarr Rd, New Rossington, Doncaster, YORKSHIRE (SOUTH), DN11 0QF **England**
(T) 01302 865482.
Mr W Sams (Secretary), 28 Pipering Lane, Scawthorpe, Doncaster, YORKSHIRE (SOUTH), DN5 9NY **England**
D T Ward (Secretary), 9 Cemetery Rd, Hatfield, Doncaster, YORKSHIRE (SOUTH), DN7 6LT **England**
- **NATIONAL FEDERATION OF ANGLERS**
Contact/s:
Mr Harold Howarth (Nfa Disability Officer, North East Region), 4 Scarborough Rd, Wickersley, Rotherham, YORKSHIRE (SOUTH), S66 0HS **England**
(T) 01709 545997.
- **SHEFFIELD AND DISTRICT ANGLERS ASSOCIATION**
Contact/s:
Mr F E Turner (Secretary), 142-144 Princess St, Sheffield, YORKSHIRE (SOUTH), S4 7UW **England**
- **THORNE AND DISTRICT ANGLING CLUB**
Contact/s:
Mr Derek Burke (Secretary), Bali-Hai, North Eastern Rd, Thorne,Doncaster, YORKSHIRE (SOUTH), DN12 **England**
(T) 01405 812088.
- **WALTONIANS ANGLING CLUB**
Contact/s:
Mr J Rose (Secretary), 35-47 North Church St, Sheffield, YORKSHIRE (SOUTH), S1 2DH **England**
(T) 0114 2752888.
(F) 0114 2730108.
- **WHITE HORSE ANGLING CLUB**
Contact/s:
Mr Peter Rumble (Secretary), 21 St Thomas' Cl, Warmsworth, Doncaster, YORKSHIRE (SOUTH), DN4 9LG **England**

YORKSHIRE (WEST)

- **ADDINGHAM ANGLING ASSOCIATION**
Contact/s:
Mr H Sutherland (Secretary), 51 Moor Park Drive, Addingham, Ilkley, YORKSHIRE (WEST), LS29 0PU **England**
(T) 01943 830331.
- **ALLERTON BYWATER ANGLING CLUB**
Contact/s:
Allerton Bywater, Castleford, YORKSHIRE (WEST), **England**
(T) 01977 559022.
- **APPLETREEWICK BARDEN AND BURNSALL ANGLING CLUB**
Contact/s:
Mr J G H Mackrell (Secretary), Mouldgreave, Oxenhope, Keighley, YORKSHIRE (WEST), BD22 9RT **England**
- **BOLTON BROW FISHERIES**
Contact/s:
Secretary, 113 Bolton Brow, Sowerby Bridge, YORKSHIRE (WEST), HX6 2BD **England**
(T) 01422 839069.
- **BOSTON SPA ANGLING CLUB**
Contact/s:
Mr A Waddington (Secretary), 17 The Village, Thorp Arch, Wetherby, YORKSHIRE (WEST), LS23 7AR **England**
(T) 01937 842664.
- **BRADFORD CITY ANGLING ASSOCIATION**
Contact/s:
Post Office, Cononley, Keighley, YORKSHIRE (WEST), BD20 **England**
- **BRADFORD NO1 ANGLING ASSOCIATION**
Contact/s:
D B Arnett (Secretary), 49 Templars Way, Bradford, YORKSHIRE (WEST), BD8 0LW **England**
Mr F Gibson (Secretary), 60 Brow Lane, Shibden, Halifax, YORKSHIRE (WEST), HX3 7UT **England**
- **BRADFORD WALTONIANS ANGLING ASSOCIATION**
Contact/s:
H J B Swarbrick (Secretary), 43 Hawksworth Drive, Menston, Ilkley, YORKSHIRE (WEST), LS29 6HP **England**
- **BRIGHOUSE ANGLING ASSOCIATION**
Contact/s:
Mr D Noble (Secretary), 1a Church Lane, Brighouse, YORKSHIRE (WEST), HD6 1AT **England**
(T) 01484 717034.
- **DEAN CLOUGH AND RYBURN ANGLING SOCIETY**
Contact/s:
Mr T Hooson (Secretary), 4 Chester Trce, Boothtown, Halifax, YORKSHIRE (WEST), HX3 6LT **England**
- **ENVIRONMENT AGENCY**
Contact/s:
Area Manager, Ridings Area Office, Phoenix House, Global Avenue,Leeds, YORKSHIRE (WEST), LS11 8PG **England**
(T) 0113 2440191or2314834.
(F) 0113 2134609.
- **HALIFAX AND DISTRICT ANGLING ASSOCIATION**
Contact/s:
Mr Tim Worsnop (Secretary), 45 Upper Green Lane, Hove Edge, Brighouse, YORKSHIRE (WEST), HD6 **England**
(T) 01484 713397.
- **HARROGATE ANGLING ASSOCIATION**
Contact/s:
W Walker (Secretary), 22 Mercia Way, Leeds, YORKSHIRE (WEST), LS15 8UA **England**
- **HOLME VALLEY PISCATORIAL ASSOCIATION**
Contact/s:
Mr Ir McCullie (Membership Secretary), 199 Bourne View Rd, Netherton, Huddersfield, YORKSHIRE (WEST), HD4 7JS **England**
P Budd (Secretary), 39 Derwent Rd, Honley, Huddersfield, YORKSHIRE (WEST), HD7 2EL **England**
- **IDLE AND THACKLEY ANGLING ASSOCIATION**
Contact/s:
Mr Charles Taylor Hardaker (Secretary), 24 Park Avenue, Thackley, Bradford, YORKSHIRE (WEST), BD2 4LP **England**
- **KEIGHLEY ANGLING CLUB**
Contact/s:
Mr Dennis Freeman (Secretary), 62 Eelholme View St, Beechcliffe, Keighley, YORKSHIRE (WEST), BD20 6AY **England**
Willis Walker Sports Shop, 109 Cavendish St, Keighley, YORKSHIRE (WEST), BD2 **England**
- **LEEDS AND DISTRICT ANGLING ASSOCIATION**
Contact/s:
Mr Derek Taylor (Secretary), 75 Stoney Rock Lane, Beckett St, Leeds, YORKSHIRE (WEST), LS29 7TB **England**
(T) 0113 2482373.
- **MARSDEN STAR ANGLING CLUB**
Contact/s:
D H G Brown (Secretary), 36 Western Avenue, Riddlesden, Keighley, YORKSHIRE (WEST), BD20 5DJ **England**
- **OTLEY ANGLING CLUB**
Contact/s:
Mr Tim Windross (Secretary), 43 Newall Carr Rd, Otley, YORKSHIRE (WEST), LS21 2AF **England**
(T) 01943 466041.
- **SALTAIRE ANGLING ASSOCIATION**
Contact/s:
Mr W M Troman (Ticket Secretary), Saltaire, YORKSHIRE (WEST), **England**
(T) 01274 583088.
- **SLAITHWAITE AND DISTRICT ANGLING CLUB**
Contact/s:
Mr Sk Martin (Secretary), 1 Weldon Drive, Outlane, Huddersfield, YORKSHIRE (WEST), HD3 3FZ **England**
Mr D Rushforth (Secretary), 122 Longwood Gate, Longwood, Huddersfield, YORKSHIRE (WEST), HD3 4US **England**
(T) 01484 651028.
- **UNITY ANGLING CLUB**
Contact/s:
Mr E K Mann (Club Secretary), 19 Busfield St, Bradford, YORKSHIRE (WEST), BD4 7QX **England**
(T) 01274 720072.
- **WETHERBY AND DISTRICT ANGLING CLUB**
Contact/s:
Mr Pete Broxham (Club Secretary), 1 Eel Mires Garth, Wetherby, YORKSHIRE (WEST), LS22 7TQ **England**
(T) 01937 585764.
- **WHEATSHEAF ANGLING CLUB**
Contact/s:
Mr Robert Howgate (Secretary), 4 Sprigfield Rd, Sherburn In Elmet, Leeds, YORKSHIRE (WEST), LS25 6BD **England**
(T) 01977 684772.

IRELAND

COUNTY CARLOW

- **BARROW ANGLERS**
Contact/s:
Mr E Moore (Secretary), Chaplestown, Carlow, COUNTY CARLOW, **Ireland**
- **TULLOW TROUT AND SALMON ANGLERS**
Contact/s:
Mr Richard Burgess (Secretary), The Lodge, Tullow, COUNTY CARLOW, **Ireland**

COUNTY CAVAN

- **CAVAN ANGLERS**
Contact/s:
Ms Brendan Coulter (Secretary), Blaiwith, Ceighan, COUNTY CAVAN, **Ireland**
- **KILLESHANDRA ANGLERS CLUB**
Contact/s:
Mr Sean McMahon (Secretary), Main St, Killeshandra, COUNTY CAVAN, **Ireland**
- **KILLESHANDRA ANGLING CLUB**
Contact/s:
Mr Jim Murphy (Secretary), Coragh, Killeshandra, COUNTY CAVAN, **Ireland**
- **LOUGH SHEELIN TROUT PROTECTION ASSOCIATION**
Contact/s:
Mr Paddy Lyons (Secretary), Drumbee, Kilnaleck, COUNTY CAVAN, **Ireland**
- **VIRGINIA ANGLING CLUB**
Contact/s:
Mr Raymond Lloyd (Secretary), Main St, Bailieborough, COUNTY CAVAN, **Ireland**

- **VIRGINIA COARSE ANGLING CLUB**
  Contact/s:
  Mr Pat McCabe (Secretary), Rahardrum, Virginia, COUNTY CAVAN, **Ireland**
  (T) 042 9694352or498547649.

COUNTY CLARE

- **ST COLMANS ANGLING CLUB**
  Contact/s:
  Corofin, COUNTY CLARE, **Ireland**
- **WEST CLARE ANGLERS ASSOCIATION**
  Contact/s:
  Mr Francis Meaney (Secretary), Ennis Rd, Kilrush, COUNTY CLARE, **Ireland**

COUNTY CORK

- **BALLYHOOLY TROUT ANGLERS**
  Contact/s:
  Mr Jim Ahern (Secretary), Ashgrove, Ballyhooly, COUNTY CORK, **Ireland**
- **CAPPOQUIN SALMON AND TROUT ANGLING CLUB**
  Contact/s:
  Mr Jeremy Nicholson (Secretary), Littlebridge Inches, Cappoquin, COUNTY CORK, **Ireland**
- **CASTLELYONS TROUT ANGLERS**
  Contact/s:
  Mr P O'Dwyer (Secretary), Glenarousk, Castlelyon, COUNTY CORK, **Ireland**
- **CORK SALMON ANGLERS**
  Contact/s:
  Mr J Buckley (Secretary), Raheen House, Carrigrohane, COUNTY CORK, **Ireland**
- **CORK TROUT ANGLERS ASSOCIATION**
  Contact/s:
  Mr Joseph Cahill (Secretary), 5 Golden Villa, Commons Rd, Cork, COUNTY CORK, **Ireland**
- **CORK TROUT ANGLING ASSOCIATION**
  Contact/s:
  Mr Ja O Connell (Secretary), 87 Patrick St, Cork, COUNTY CORK, **Ireland**
- **FERMOY AND DISTRICT TROUT ANGLING ASSOCIATION**
  Contact/s:
  Mr M Fanning (Secretary), 41 Saint Mary's Trce, Fermoy, COUNTY CORK, **Ireland**
- **FERMOY SALMON ANGLERS**
  Contact/s:
  Mr E Glendon (Secretary), 21 Connaught Pl, Wellington Rd, Fermoy, COUNTY CORK, **Ireland**
- **GLENGARIFF ANGLING ASSOCIATION**
  Contact/s:
  Mr Patrick Power (Secretary), Reenmeen, Glengariff, COUNTY CORK, **Ireland**
- **RIVER ILEN ANGLING CLUB**
  Contact/s:
  A Taylor (Secretary), Cois Abhann, Coolnagarrane, Skibbereen, COUNTY CORK, **Ireland**
- **SOUTH WESTERN REGIONAL FISHERIES BOARD**
  Contact/s:
  Angling Officer, 1 Nevilles Trce, Masseytown, Macroom, COUNTY CORK, **Ireland**
  (T) 026 41221.
  (F) 026 41223.

COUNTY DONEGAL

- **BALLYBOFEY AND STRANORLAR ANGLING ASSOCIATION**
  Contact/s:
  D McCollum (Secretary), Edenmore, Ballybofey, Lifford, COUNTY DONEGAL, **Ireland**
- **BUNCRANA ANGLERS ASSOCIATION**
  Contact/s:
  Secretary, Buncrana, COUNTY DONEGAL, **Ireland**
  (T) 077 63733.
- **CULDAFF ANGLING ASSOCIATION**
  Contact/s:
  C/O Faulkner's, Main St, Culdaff, COUNTY DONEGAL, **Ireland**
- **DEELE ANGLING CLUB**
  Contact/s:
  Mr Billy Vance (Secretary), Convoy, Lifford, COUNTY DONEGAL, **Ireland**
- **LETTERKENNY AND DISTRICT ANGLERS ASSOCIATION**
  Contact/s:
  Mr Gerry McNulty (Secretary), 50 Port Rd, Letterkenny, COUNTY DONEGAL, **Ireland**
- **NORTHERN REGIONAL FISHERIES BOARD**
  Contact/s:
  Angling Officer, Station Rd, Ballyshannon, COUNTY DONEGAL, **Ireland**
  (T) 072 51435.
  (F) 072 51816.
- **ROSSES ANGLERS ASSOCIATION**
  Contact/s:
  Mr John Ward (Secretary), Donegal, COUNTY DONEGAL, **Ireland**
  (T) 073 31114.
- **SILABH LIÁG ANGLERS ASSOCIATION**
  Contact/s:
  Mr Frank O'Donnell (Secretary), Carrick Lower, Carrick, COUNTY DONEGAL, **Ireland**

COUNTY DUBLIN

- **BORD FÁILTE (IRISH TOURIST BOARD)**
  Contact/s:
  Manager, Baggot Street Bridge, Dublin, COUNTY DUBLIN, DUBLIN 2 **Ireland**
  (T) 01 765871.
- **CENTRAL FISHERIES BOARD**
  Contact/s:
  Manager, Balnagowan House, Mobhi Boreen, Glasnevin,Dublin, COUNTY DUBLIN, DUBLIN 9 **Ireland**
  (T) 003792067/8.
  (F) 01360060.
- **CHAPELIZOD ANGLERS CLUB**
  Contact/s:
  Mr John McMahon (Secretary), 40 Main St, Chapelizod, Dublin, COUNTY DUBLIN, DUBLIN 20 **Ireland**
- **CHAPELIZOD ANGLING CLUB**
  Contact/s:
  Mr Paul Deverox (Secretary), 23 Liffey Trce, Chapelizod, COUNTY DUBLIN, **Ireland**
- **DEPARTMENT OF TOURISM, FISHERIES AND FORESTRY**
  Contact/s:
  Secretary, Leeson Lane, Leeson St, Dublin, COUNTY DUBLIN, DUBLIN 2 **Ireland**
  (T) 01 210111.
- **EASTERN REGIONAL FISHERIES BOARD**
  Contact/s:
  Angling Officer, Balnagowan House, Mobhi Boreen, Glasnevin, COUNTY DUBLIN, DUBLIN 9 **Ireland**
  (T) 01 2787022.
- **IRISH SPECIMEN FISH COMMITTEE**
  Contact/s:
  Secretary, Mohbi Boreen, Glasnevin, Dublin, COUNTY DUBLIN, DUBLIN 9 **Ireland**
  (T) 01 8379206.
- **ROSSIN AND SLANE ANGLERS**
  Contact/s:
  Mr Ray Foster (Secretary), 181 Foxfield Gr, Raheny, COUNTY DUBLIN, **Ireland**

COUNTY GALWAY

- **CARRAROE ANGLING CLUB**
  Contact/s:
  Carraroe, COUNTY GALWAY, **Ireland**
- **CLONBUR ANGLING CLUB**
  Contact/s:
  Mr Edward Lynch (Secretary), Clonbur, COUNTY GALWAY, **Ireland**
- **COROFIN ANGLERS ASSOCIATION**
  Contact/s:
  Mr Ned Cusack (Secretary), Gortchalla, Moycullen, COUNTY GALWAY, **Ireland**
- **HEADFORD AND CORRIB ANGLERS ASSOCIATION**
  Contact/s:
  Mr Michael Walshe (Secretary), Parks Ower, Ower Post Office, Ower, COUNTY GALWAY, **Ireland**
- **TUAM DISTRICT ANGLERS**
  Contact/s:
  Mr Sonny Martyn (Secretary), Esso Station, Galway Rd, Tuam, COUNTY GALWAY, **Ireland**
- **WESTERN REGIONAL FISHERIES BOARD**
  Contact/s:
  Mr Danny Goldrick (Angling Officer), The Weir Lodge, Earls Island, Galway, COUNTY GALWAY, **Ireland**
  (T) 091 563118.
  (F) 091 566335.

COUNTY KERRY

- **KENMARE TROUT ANGLERS CLUB**
  Contact/s:
  Mr John O'Hara (Secretary), 21 Main St, Kenmare, COUNTY KERRY, **Ireland**
- **NORTH KERRY ANGLERS ASSOCIATION**
  Contact/s:
  Mr Jim Horgan (Secretary), 6 The Square, Listowel, COUNTY KERRY, **Ireland**

COUNTY KILDARE

- **ATHY ANGLERS**
  Contact/s:
  J Shaughnessy (Secretary), Athy Library, Athy, COUNTY KILDARE, **Ireland**
- **CLANE ANGLING ASSOCIATION**
  Contact/s:
  Mr A McDonald (Secretary), Downstown Lodge Stud, Maynooth, COUNTY KILDARE, **Ireland**
- **GREESE ANGLERS**
  Contact/s:
  Mr P Leigh (Secretary), Woodhill, Narraghmore, Ballitore, COUNTY KILDARE, **Ireland**

COUNTY KILKENNY

- **FRESHFORD ANGLERS**
  Contact/s:
  Mr Pearce (Secretary), Doherty, Freshford, COUNTY KILKENNY, **Ireland**
- **INISTIOGE ANGLERS CLUB**
  Contact/s:
  Mr Bill Doherty (Secretary), High St, Inistioge, COUNTY KILKENNY, **Ireland**
  (T) 056 58571.

- **KILKENNY ANGLERS ASSOCIATION**
Contact/s:
Mr Edward Stack (Secretary), Garda Station, Kilkenny, COUNTY KILKENNY, **Ireland**

- **THOMASTOWN ANGLERS**
Contact/s:
P Heafey (Secretary), Castel Avenue, Thomastown, COUNTY KILKENNY, **Ireland**

COUNTY LAOIS

- **ABBEYLEIX ANGLERS**
Contact/s:
M O'Brien (Secretary), Ballyruan, Portlaoise, COUNTY LAOIS, **Ireland**

- **DURROW ANGLING CLUB**
Contact/s:
Mr Micheal Walsh (Secretary), 18 Erkindale Drive, Durrow, COUNTY LAOIS, **Ireland**

- **MONASTEREVIN ANGLING CLUB**
Contact/s:
Mr P Moran (Secretary), Rathangan Rd, Monasterevin, COUNTY LAOIS, **Ireland**

- **MOUNTMELLICK ANGLERS**
Contact/s:
B Lynch (Secretary), 5 Wolfe Tone Rd, Mountmellick, COUNTY LAOIS, **Ireland**

- **PORTARLINGTON ANGLING CLUB**
Contact/s:
Ms Patsy Farrell (Secretary), White Hart Lane, Kilmalogue, Portarlington, COUNTY LAOIS, **Ireland**

- **RATHDOWNEY ANGLERS ASSOCIATION**
Contact/s:
Mr Timothy Barry (Secretary), Publican Sq, Rathdowney, COUNTY LAOIS, **Ireland**

- **RATHDOWNEY ANGLING ASSOCIATION**
Contact/s:
M White (Secretary), Mooreville, Rathdowney, COUNTY LAOIS, **Ireland**

COUNTY LEITRIM

- **DUFF ANGLING SYNDICATE**
Contact/s:
Mr John Fahey (Secretary), Kinlough, COUNTY LEITRIM, **Ireland**

- **KINLOUGH AND DISTRICT ANGLERS ASSOCIATION**
Contact/s:
Secretary, Edenville, Kinlough, COUNTY LEITRIM, **Ireland**
(T) 072 41166.

COUNTY LIMERICK

- **ABBEYFEALE ANGLING ASSOCIATION**
Contact/s:
Mr Pat O'Callaghan (Secretary), Ballybehy, Abbeyfeale, COUNTY LIMERICK, **Ireland**

- **SHANNON REGIONAL FISHERIES BOARD**
Contact/s:
Angling Officer, Thomond Weir, Limerick, COUNTY LIMERICK, **Ireland**
(T) 061 455171.
(F) 061 326533.

COUNTY LOUTH

- **DROGHEDA AND DISTRICT ANGLING CLUB**
Contact/s:
Mr John Murphy (Secretary), 39 Annville Cres, Drogheda, COUNTY LOUTH, **Ireland**

- **DUNDALK AND DISTRICT SALMON ANGLERS ASSOCIATION**
Contact/s:
Mr Patrick Wehrly (Secretary), Island Fishing Tackle, 58 Park St, Dundalk, COUNTY LOUTH, **Ireland**
Mr Neil O'Neill (Secretary), Mullaharlin Rd, Heynestown, Dundalk, COUNTY LOUTH, **Ireland**

- **SLANE ROSSIN AND DISTRICT ANGLERS CLUB**
Contact/s:
Mr Ray Foster (Secretary), 8 Laurence Rd, Drogheda, COUNTY LOUTH, **Ireland**
(T) 01 8315406.

- **VILLAGE ANGLERS**
Contact/s:
Mr Arthur Campbell (Secretary), Monvallet, Louth, Dundalk, COUNTY LOUTH, **Ireland**

COUNTY MAYO

- **FOXFORD SALMON ANGLING ASSOCIATION**
Contact/s:
Mr Micheal Tiernan (Secretary), Riverside, Foxford, COUNTY MAYO, **Ireland**

- **NEWPORT ANGLING CLUB**
Contact/s:
Mr Ciaran Moran (Secretary), Moynish House, Mulranny, COUNTY MAYO, **Ireland**

- **NORTH WESTERN REGIONAL FISHERIES BOARD**
Contact/s:
Mr John Burke (Angling Officer), Ardnaree House, Abbey St, Ballina, COUNTY MAYO, **Ireland**
(T) 096 22788.
(F) 096 70543.

COUNTY MEATH

- **KELLS ANGLERS**
Contact/s:
Mr John Flynn (Secretary), Old School House, Kells, COUNTY MEATH, **Ireland**

COUNTY MONAGHAN

- **CORKEERAN AND DROMORE TROUT AND COARSE ANGLING ASSOCIATION**
Contact/s:
Mr Talbot Duffy (Secretary), 4 Lake View, Ballybay, COUNTY MONAGHAN, **Ireland**

COUNTY OFFALY

- **EDENDERRY COARSE ANGLING CLUB**
Contact/s:
Mr Pauric Kelly (Hon Secretary), 48 Murphy St, Edenderry, COUNTY OFFALY, **Ireland**

- **SHANNONBRIDGE ANGLERS ASSOCIATION**
Contact/s:
Mr Dermot Killeen (Secretary), Shannonbridge, COUNTY OFFALY, **Ireland**

- **TULLAMORE COARSE FISHING CLUB**
Contact/s:
Mr Pat Gorman (Secretary), Tullamore, COUNTY OFFALY, **Ireland**

COUNTY ROSCOMMON

- **BALLAGHADERREN ANGLING CLUB**
Contact/s:
Mr Jas Cogan (Secretary), Kilcolman Rd, Ballaghaderren, COUNTY ROSCOMMON, **Ireland**
(T) 090 760077.

- **BOYLE AND DISTRICT ANGLING CLUB**
Contact/s:
Mrs L Conroy (Secretary), Deerpark, Boyle, COUNTY ROSCOMMON, **Ireland**

- **LOUGH ARROW FISH PRESERVATION SOCIETY**
Contact/s:
Mr J Hargadon (Secretary), Annaghloy, Boyle, COUNTY ROSCOMMON, **Ireland**
(T) 079 66050.

COUNTY SLIGO

- **LOUGH ARROW AND DISTRICT ANGLING CLUB**
Contact/s:
Ms Muriel Frazer (Secretary), Ballindoon, Riverstown, COUNTY SLIGO, **Ireland**

COUNTY TIPPERARY

- **ARDFINNAN ANGLERS**
Contact/s:
Mr John Maher (Secretary), Green View, Ardfinnan, Clonmel, COUNTY TIPPERARY, **Ireland**

- **CAHIR AND DISTRICT ANGLING CLUB**
Contact/s:
Mr Tom Butler (Secretary), Railway View, Cahir Abbey, COUNTY TIPPERARY, **Ireland**
Mr W O'Donnell (Secretary), Cahir Abbey Upr, COUNTY TIPPERARY, **Ireland**

- **CARRICK- ON-SUIR ANGLING CLUB**
Contact/s:
Mr N Power (Secretary), Tinhalla, Carrick-on-Suir, COUNTY TIPPERARY, **Ireland**

- **CASHEL, TIPPERARY AND GOLDEN ANGLING CLUB**
Contact/s:
Mr James Doyle (Secretary), 2 Moor Lane, Cashel, COUNTY TIPPERARY, **Ireland**

- **CLODIAGH ANGLING ASSOCIATION**
Contact/s:
Mr Timmy Delaney (Secretary), Rathmoyle, Borrisoleigh, COUNTY TIPPERARY, **Ireland**

- **CLONMEL ANGLERS**
Contact/s:
Mr John Carroll (Secretary), 3 Dr Croke Pl, Clonmel, COUNTY TIPPERARY, **Ireland**

- **CLONMEL SALMON AND TROUT ANGLERS**
Contact/s:
Mr John Kavanagh (Secretary), West Gate, Clonmel, COUNTY TIPPERARY, **Ireland**

- **DENDRUM AND DISTRICT ANGLERS**
Contact/s:
Sean Breen, Garryduff West, Dundrum, COUNTY TIPPERARY, **Ireland**

- **DUNDRUM AND DISTRICT ANGLERS**
Contact/s:
Mr Sean Breen (Secretary), Garrduff West, Dundrum, COUNTY TIPPERARY, **Ireland**

- **MOUNTRATH AND DISTRICT ANGLING CLUB**
Contact/s:
Mr Tom Wakins (Secretary), 6 Fintan Trce, Mountrath, COUNTY TIPPERARY, **Ireland**

- **ORMOND ANGLING ASSOCIATION**
Contact/s:
Mr Joe O'Donoghue (Secretary), Cameron, Gortlandroe, Nenagh, COUNTY TIPPERARY, **Ireland**

● **SOUTHERN REGIONAL FISHERIES BOARD COMMISSION**
Contact/s:
Mr Colmen Kelliher (Angling Officer), Anglesea St, Clonmel, COUNTY TIPPERARY, **Ireland**
(T) 052 23624.
(F) 052 23971.

● **TAR TROUT ANGLING ASSOCIATION**
Contact/s:
Mr Tony O'Brien (Secretary), 27 Fr Sheedy Trce, Clogheen, COUNTY TIPPERARY, **Ireland**

● **THURLES, HOLLYCROSS, BALLYCAMAS ANGLERS**
Contact/s:
Mr Jimmy Purcell (Secretary), Rathcannon, Holycross, Thurles, COUNTY TIPPERARY, **Ireland**

COUNTY WATERFORD

● **BALLYDUFF TROUT FLY ANGLING ASSOCIATION**
Contact/s:
Mr Eamon Bolger (Secretary), Post Office, Ballyduff, COUNTY WATERFORD, **Ireland**

● **LISMORE ANGLERS CLUB**
Contact/s:
Hogans Printers, Lismore, COUNTY WATERFORD, **Ireland**

● **LISMORE SALMON ANGLERS**
Contact/s:
Mr B Hogan (Secretary), Main St, Lismore, COUNTY WATERFORD, **Ireland**

● **LISMORE TROUT ANGLERS**
Contact/s:
Main St, Lismore, COUNTY WATERFORD, **Ireland**

● **TALLOW AND DISTRICT ANGLERS CLUB**
Contact/s:
Mr Alan Sivyer (Secretary), Bridge View Bar, Tallow Birdge, Tallow, COUNTY WATERFORD, **Ireland**
(T) 01784 240013.

● **TRAMORE ANGLERS**
Contact/s:
J Cashin (Secretary), 33 Rockinham, Ferrybank, Waterford, COUNTY WATERFORD, **Ireland**

COUNTY WESTMEATH

● **LOUGH OWEL TROUT PRESERVATION ASSOCIATION**
Contact/s:
Mr S McKeown (Secretary), Irishtown, Mullingar, COUNTY WESTMEATH, **Ireland**

COUNTY WEXFORD

● **BANNOW BAY ANGLERS**
Contact/s:
Mr J Whitty (Secretary), Wellington Bridge, COUNTY WEXFORD, **Ireland**

NORTHERN IRELAND

COUNTY ANTRIM

● **ANTRIM AND DISTRICT ANGLING ASSOCIATION**
Contact/s:
Mr T Wilson (Secretary), 6 Alder Park, Greystone Rd, Antrim, COUNTY ANTRIM, BT41 **Northern Ireland**
Mr B McNeill (Secretary), 41 Derry Rd, Newtownabbey, COUNTY ANTRIM, BT36 7UF **Northern Ireland**

● **BALLYMONEY AND DISTRICT ANGLING CLUB**
Contact/s:
Mr J McKay (Secretary), 15 Pharis Rd, Ballymoney, COUNTY ANTRIM, BT53 **Northern Ireland**

● **BALLYNURE ANGLING CLUB**
Contact/s:
Mr John Arneill (Secretary), 17 Collinview Drive, Ballyclare, COUNTY ANTRIM, BT39 9PQ **Northern Ireland**

● **BELFAST ANGLERS ASSOCIATION**
Contact/s:
Mr John A Collinson (Secretary), 7 Hawthorne Drive, Belfast, COUNTY ANTRIM, BT4 2HG **Northern Ireland**

● **CLADY AND DISTRICT ANGLING CLUB**
Contact/s:
Mr H Doherty (Secretary), 95 Clady Rd, Portglenone, Ballymena, COUNTY ANTRIM, BT44 8LB **Northern Ireland**

● **DROMORE ANGLING CLUB**
Contact/s:
Mr R Russell (Secretary), 49 Ravenscroft Avenue, Belfast, COUNTY ANTRIM, BT5 5BB **Northern Ireland**

● **GALGORM AND DISTRICT ANGLING CLUB**
Contact/s:
Mr N Anderson (Secretary), 56 Ballykennedy Rd, Gracehill, Ballymena, COUNTY ANTRIM, BT42 **Northern Ireland**

● **GLENRAVEL AND CLOGH ANGLING CLUB**
Contact/s:
Mr D Anderson (Secretary), 6 Old Cushendun Rd, Newtown Crommelin, Ballymena, COUNTY ANTRIM, BT43 **Northern Ireland**

● **GLENS ANGLING CLUB**
Contact/s:
Mr J McKillop (Secretary), 30 Coast Rd, Cushendall, Ballymena, COUNTY ANTRIM, BT44 0RX **Northern Ireland**

● **GRACEHILL, GALGORM AND DISTRICT ANGLING CLUB**
Contact/s:
Mr Norman Anderson (Secretary), 50 Ballykennedy Rd, Gracehill, Ballymena, COUNTY ANTRIM, BT42 8NP **Northern Ireland**

● **GREENISLAND ANGLING CLUB**
Contact/s:
Mr W Hinton (Secretary), 18 Glenkeen Drive, Greenisland, Carrickfergus, COUNTY ANTRIM, BT38 8XG **Northern Ireland**

● **IRISH LADIES FLYFISHING ASSOCIATION**
Contact/s:
Ms Susan Brown (Chairman), Chairman's Office, C/O Ulster Bank Group, 11-16 Donegal Street East,Belfast, COUNTY ANTRIM, BT1 5UB **Northern Ireland**
(T) 028 90275503.

● **KELLS AND CONNOR ANGLING CLUB**
Contact/s:
Mr N Wilson (Secretary), 35 Temlemoyle Kells, Ballymena, COUNTY ANTRIM, BT4 **Northern Ireland**

● **KINGS ROAD GAME ANGLING CLUB**
Contact/s:
8 Kirn Park, Dundonald, Belfast, COUNTY ANTRIM, BT5 7GA **Northern Ireland**

● **LISBURN AND DISTRICT ANGLING CLUB**
Contact/s:
Mr D Croot (Secretary), 109 Benson St, Lisburn, COUNTY ANTRIM, BT28 2AF **Northern Ireland**

● **MAINE ANGLING CLUB**
Contact/s:
Mr Eddie Hopkins (Secretary), 5 Lenaghan Avenue, Belfast, COUNTY ANTRIM, BT8 7JF **Northern Ireland**

● **MID-ANTRIM ANGLING CLUB**
Contact/s:
Mr R Topping (Secretary), 24 Cameron Park, Ballymena, COUNTY ANTRIM, BT42 1QJ **Northern Ireland**

● **RANDALSTOWN ANGLING CLUB**
Contact/s:
Mr R Magee (Secretary), 67 Muckamore Garden Village, Antrim, COUNTY ANTRIM, BT41 1NB **Northern Ireland**

COUNTY ARMAGH

● **ARMAGH ANGLING CLUB**
Contact/s:
Armagh Colour Copy Shop, Dobbin Ctre, Armagh, COUNTY ARMAGH, BT60 **Northern Ireland**

● **GILFORD ANGLING CLUB**
Contact/s:
Mr M Magee (Secretary), Station Rd, Scarva, Craigavon, COUNTY ARMAGH, BT63 **Northern Ireland**

COUNTY DOWN

● **ARDS FLY FISHING CLUB**
Contact/s:
Mr James Crothers (Secretary), Lough Cowey Fishery, Lough Cowey Rd, Portaferry,Newtownards, COUNTY DOWN, BT22 1PJ **Northern Ireland**

● **BANBRIDGE ANGLING CLUB**
Contact/s:
Mr J Curran (Secretary), 2 Ballydown Rd, Banbridge, COUNTY DOWN, BT32 4JB **Northern Ireland**

● **CASTLEWELLAND AND ANNSBOROUGH ANGLING CLUB**
Contact/s:
Mr S P Harrison (Secretary), Garden Cottage, Forest Park, Castlewellan, COUNTY DOWN, BT31 **Northern Ireland**

● **DUNDALK AND DISTRICT BROWN TROUT ANGLERS ASSOCIATION**
Contact/s:
Mr J Clarke (Secretary), 3 Mill Rd, Folkhill, COUNTY DOWN, BT35 9SJ **Northern Ireland**

● **DUNDONALD ANGLING CLUB**
Contact/s:
Mr Peter Grahame (Secretary), 13 Cherryhill Drive, Dundonald, Belfast, COUNTY DOWN, BT16 OJG **Northern Ireland**

● **HOLYWOOD FLY FISHING CLUB**
Contact/s:
Mr Cf Kyle (Secretary), 2 Seymour Park, Crawfordsburn Rd, Bangor, COUNTY DOWN, BT19 1BW **Northern Ireland**

● **HOLYWOOD FLYDRSSERS GUILD**
Contact/s:
Mr Aj Kennedy (Secretary), 6 Demesne Park, Holywood, COUNTY DOWN, BT18 9NE **Northern Ireland**

● **KILKEEN ANGLING CLUB**
Contact/s:
Mr A Kilgore (Secretary), 4 Mill St, Annalong, Newry, COUNTY DOWN, BT34 **Northern Ireland**

● **MAINE ANGLING CLUB**
Contact/s:
Mr Bill McCartney (Secretary), 7 Demesne Manor, Holywood, COUNTY DOWN, BT18 9NW **Northern Ireland**

● **NEWRY AND DISTRICT ANGLING CLUB**
Contact/s:
Mr D Kidd (Secretary), 8 Cloneden, Dallan Rd, Warrenpoint,Newry, COUNTY DOWN, BT34 3PJ **Northern Ireland**

NORTHERN IRELAND CARP ANGLERS SOCIETY
Contact/s:
Mr Gary Webb (Society Chairman), 2 Balmoral Dale, Bangor, COUNTY DOWN, BT19 7XJ **Northern Ireland**
(T) 028 91275648.

RATHFRILAND AND DISTRICT ANGLING ASSOCIATION
Contact/s:
Mr D A Crory (Secretary), 5 Castlewellan Rd, Rathfriland, Newry, COUNTY DOWN, BT34 **Northern Ireland**

SHIMNA ANGLING CLUB
Contact/s:
Mr P Mornin (Secretary), 84 Bryansford Rd, Newcastle, COUNTY DOWN, BT33 0LE **Northern Ireland**

WARRENPOINT, ROSTREVOR AND DISTRICT ANGLING CLUB
Contact/s:
Mr John O'Crey (Secretary), Springfield Rd, Warrenpoint, Newry, COUNTY DOWN, BT34 **Northern Ireland**

COUNTY LONDONDERRY

AGIVEYANGLING ASSOCIATION
Contact/s:
Mr Jp McCusker (Secretary), 27 Drumeil Rd, Aghadowey, Coleraine, COUNTY LONDONDERRY, BT51 4BB **Northern Ireland**

COLERAINE ANGLING CLUB
Contact/s:
Mr B Liddell (Secretary), 53 Seapark, Castlerock, Coleraine, COUNTY LONDONDERRY, BT51 4TH **Northern Ireland**

FOYLE FISHERIES COMMISSION
Contact/s:
Angling Officer, 8 Victoria Rd, Derry, COUNTY LONDONDERRY, BT47 2AB **Northern Ireland**
(T) 028 71342100.
(F) 028 71342720.

KILREA AND DISTRICT ANGLING CLUB
Contact/s:
Mr J Templeton (Secretary), Main St, Garvagh, Coleraine, COUNTY LONDONDERRY, BT51 **Northern Ireland**
Mr David Laughlin (Secretary), Bann Rd, Kilrea, COUNTY LONDONDERRY, BT51 5RX **Northern Ireland**

MOYOLA ANGLING ASSOCIATION
Contact/s:
Mr Tom Maguire (Angling Development Officer), 3 Craigmore Rd, Maghera, COUNTY LONDONDERRY, BT46 5AL **Northern Ireland**
(T) 028 79642793.
(F) 028 79642793.

RIVER FAUGHAN ANGLERS
Contact/s:
Mr Lf Thompson (Secretary), 17 Rockport Park, Londonderry, COUNTY LONDONDERRY, BT47 1JH **Northern Ireland**

ROE ANGLERS
Contact/s:
R Douglas And Son, 6 Irish Green St, Limavady, COUNTY LONDONDERRY, BT49 9AD **Northern Ireland**

COUNTY TYRONE

BLUE CIRCLE ANGLING CLUB
Contact/s:
Mr N Hutchinson (Secretary), Blue Circle, 29 Sandholes Rd, Cookstown, COUNTY TYRONE, BT80 9AP **Northern Ireland**

BRITISH LEGION ANGLING CLUB
Contact/s:
Mrs C McFetridge (Secretary), British Legion, Burn Rd, Cookstown, COUNTY TYRONE, BT80 **Northern Ireland**
(T) 028 21761251.

BURN DENNET ANGLING ASSOCIATION
Contact/s:
Mr W O'Neill (Secretary), Carrickatane Rd, Dunamanagh, Strabane, COUNTY TYRONE, BT82 **Northern Ireland**

CASTLEDERG ANGLING ASSOCIATION
Contact/s:
Mr V McCormick (Grocer), 5 John St, Castlederg, COUNTY TYRONE, BT81 **Northern Ireland**

CASTLEDREG ANGLING CLUB
Contact/s:
Mr Rr Harron (Secretary), 36 Ferguson Cres, Castlederg, COUNTY TYRONE, BT81 7AG **Northern Ireland**

CLOGHER ANGLING CLUB
Contact/s:
Mr Seamus McGirr (Secretary), 2 Richmond Drive, Clogher, COUNTY TYRONE, BT76 0AM **Northern Ireland**
(T) 028 85548293or85548279.

DERG ANGLING CLUB
Contact/s:
Secretary, 50 Main St, Newtownstewart, Omagh, COUNTY TYRONE, BT78 **Northern Ireland**

FINN ANGLING CLUB
Contact/s:
Mr Francis Curran (Secretary), 1 Derry Rd, Strabane, COUNTY TYRONE, BT82 8DT **Northern Ireland**

GAFF ANGLING CLUB
Contact/s:
Campbell's Mourne Valley Tackle, 50 Main St, Newtownstewart,Omagh, COUNTY TYRONE, BT78 **Northern Ireland**

GLEBE ANGLING CLUB
Contact/s:
Mr William Cochrane (Secretary), 87 Mourne Park, Newtownstewart, COUNTY TYRONE, BT78 4BN **Northern Ireland**
(T) 028 81661469.
(F) 028 81661469.

KILDRESS ANGLING CLUB
Contact/s:
Mr Edgar Thom (Secretary), 3a Killycurrage Rd, Cookstown, COUNTY TYRONE, BT80 **Northern Ireland**

KINGSBRIDGE ANGLING CLUB
Contact/s:
Mr Stanley Aspinall (Secretary), The Dunleath Bar, Church St, Cookstown, COUNTY TYRONE, BT80 **Northern Ireland**
(T) 028 86765905.

MID-ULSTER ANGLING CLUB
Contact/s:
Mr D Boner (Secretary), 57 Molesworth Rd, Cookstown, COUNTY TYRONE, BT80 8NU **Northern Ireland**

MOY ANGLING CLUB
Contact/s:
Mr D Tomney (Secretary), 10 The Square, Moy, Dungannon, COUNTY TYRONE, BT71 7SG **Northern Ireland**

OMAGH ANGLING ASSOCIATION
Contact/s:
Mr C A Anderson (Secretary), 64 Market St, Omagh, COUNTY TYRONE, BT78 1EN **Northern Ireland**

SION MILLS ANGLING CLUB
Contact/s:
Mr Eddie McCrea (Secretary), 35 Main St, Sion Mills, Strabane, COUNTY TYRONE, BT82 **Northern Ireland**

TULLYLAGAN ANGLING CLUB
Contact/s:
Mr Jim Warnock (Secretary), 133 Dungannon Rd, Cookstown, COUNTY TYRONE, BT80 9BD **Northern Ireland**

SCOTLAND

ABERDEEN (CITY OF)

DEE (ADERDEEN) DISTRICT SALMON FISHERY BOARD
Contact/s:
Mr George Alpine (Acts Operator), Messrs Paul And Williamson Solicitors, Investment House, 6 Union Row,Aberdeen, ABERDEEN (CITY OF), AB9 8DQ **Scotland**
(T) 01224 621621.

DON DISTRICT BOARD
Contact/s:
Mr George Alpine (Acts Operator), Messrs Paul And Williamson Solicitors, Investment House, Aberdeen, ABERDEEN (CITY OF), AB9 8DQ **Scotland**
(T) 01224 621621.

DON DISTRICT SALMON FISHERY BOARD
Contact/s:
Mr Jim Kerr (Superintendent), 28 Sclattie Park, Bucksburn, Aberdeen, ABERDEEN (CITY OF), AB2 9QR **Scotland**
(T) 01224 712989.

ABERDEENSHIRE

BALLATER ANGLING ASSOCIATION
Contact/s:
Mr M Holroyd (Secretary), Golf Rd, Ballater, ABERDEENSHIRE, AB35 **Scotland**

DEVERON DISTRICT SALMON FISHERY BOARD
Contact/s:
Mr John Christie (Acts Operator), Murdoch, Mcmath And Mitchell Solicitors, 27-29 Duke St, Huntly, ABERDEENSHIRE, AB54 5DP **Scotland**
(T) 01466 792291.

FYVIE ANGLING ASSOCIATION
Contact/s:
Mr J D Pirie (Secretary), Prenton, South Rd, Oldmeldrum,Inverurie, ABERDEENSHIRE, AB51 0AB **Scotland**

HADDO HOUSE ANGLING ASSOCIATION
Contact/s:
Mr J French (Secretary), Kirktown, Methlick, Ellon, ABERDEENSHIRE, AB41 **Scotland**

NORTH EAST OF SCOTLAND FISHERMANS ORGANISATION
Contact/s:
Mr R D Gilland (Chief Executive), 75 Broad St, Peterhead, ABERDEENSHIRE, AB42 6JL **Scotland**
(T) 01779 479149.

UGIE DISTRICT SALMON FISHERY BOARD
Contact/s:
Mr B Milton (Acts Operator), Masson And Glennie Solicitors, Broad House, Broad St,Peterhead, ABERDEENSHIRE, AB42 6JA **Scotland**
(T) 01779 74271.

YTHAN DISTRICT SALMON FISHERY BOARD
Contact/s:
Mr M Andrew (Acts Operator), Estate Office, Mains Of Haddo, Tarves,Ellon, ABERDEENSHIRE, AB41 0LD **Scotland**
(T) 01651 851664.

ANGUS

AGRICULTURE AND FISHERIES DEPT THE SCOTTISH OFFICE
Contact/s:
Secretary, 58 High St, Arbroath, ANGUS, DD11 1AW **Scotland**
(T) 01307 462191.
(F) 01307 462686.

BRECHIN ANGLING CLUB
Contact/s:
Mr W Balfour (Secretary), 9 Cookston Cres, Brechin, ANGUS, DD9 6BP **Scotland**

ESK DISTRICT SALMON FISHERY BOARD
Contact/s:
Mr John Scott (Acts Operator), Scott Alexander, 113 High St, Montrose, ANGUS, DD10 8QR **Scotland**
(T) 01674 671477.

INVER DISTRICT SALMON FISHERY BOARD
Contact/s:
Mr Dl Laird (Acts Operator), Thornton Oliver Ws, Solicitors And Estate Agents, 53 East High St,Forfar, ANGUS, DD8 2EL **Scotland**
(T) 01764 655277.

KIRKAIG DISTRICT SALMON FISHERY BOARD
Contact/s:
Mr Dl Laird (Acts Operator), Thornton Oliver Ws, Solicitors And Estate Agents, 53 East High St,Forfar, ANGUS, DD8 2EL **Scotland**
(T) 01764 655277.

MONIKIE ANGLING CLUB
Contact/s:
Mr I Smith (Secretary), 6 Collier St, Carnoustie, ANGUS, DD7 7AJ **Scotland**

STRATHMORE ANGLING IMPROVEMENT ASSOCIATION
Contact/s:
Mrs M C Milne (Secretary), 1 West Park Gardens, Dundee, ANGUS, DD2 1NY **Scotland**

ARGYLL AND BUTE

AWE DISTRICT SALMON FISHERY BOARD
Contact/s:
Mr Tc McNair (Acts Operator), Messrs Macarthur, Stewart And Co Solicitors, Boswell House, Argyll Sq,Oban, ARGYLL AND BUTE, PA34 4BD **Scotland**
(T) 01631 562215.

CARRADALE ANGLING CLUB
Contact/s:
Mr Donald Paterson (Secretary), 21 Tormhor, Campbeltown, ARGYLL AND BUTE, PA28 6SD **Scotland**

DALMALLY ANGLING CLUB
Contact/s:
Mr I MacIntyre (Secretary), Glenview, Dalmally, ARGYLL AND BUTE, PA33 **Scotland**

DUNOON AND DISTRICT ANGLING CLUB
Contact/s:
Mr A H Young (Hon Secretary), Ashgrove, 28 Royal Cres, Dunoon, ARGYLL AND BUTE, PA23 7AH **Scotland**
(T) 01369 705732or703232.

EACHAIG DISTRICT SALMON FISHERY BOARD
Contact/s:
Mr Robert Teasdale (Acts Operator), Quarry Cottage, Rashfield, Dunoon, ARGYLL AND BUTE, PA23 8QT **Scotland**
(T) 01369 840510.

ISLE OF BUTE TROUT CO
Contact/s:
Mr James Poole (Secretary), Lochly Beside, Rothesay, ARGYLL AND BUTE, PA20 9PA **Scotland**
(T) 01700 504871.
(F) 01700 504871.

KINTYRE FISH PROTECTION AND ANGLING CLUB
Contact/s:
Mr MacMillan (Secretary), Banbreck, Kilberran Rd, Campbeltown, ARGYLL AND BUTE, PA28 **Scotland**

KYLES OF BUTE ANGLING CLUB
Contact/s:
Mr Allen Richardson (Secretary), Allt Beag, Tighnabruaich, ARGYLL AND BUTE, PA21 2BE **Scotland**

LAGGAN AND SORN DISTRICT SALMON FISHERY BOARD
Contact/s:
Mr Rig Ferguson (Acts Operator), Messrs Stewart, Balfour And Sutherland, 2 Castlehill, Campbeltown, ARGYLL AND BUTE, PA28 6AW **Scotland**
(T) 01586 552871.

LIGHTHOUSE OF SCOTLAND
Contact/s:
Mr William Somerville (Managing Director), Ardkinglas, Cairndow, ARGYLL AND BUTE, PA26 8BH **Scotland**
(T) 01499 600212.

LOCH FYNE DISTRICT SALMON FISHERY BOARD
Contact/s:
Mr Robert MacPherson (Acts Operator), Messrs Stewart And Bennet Solicitors, 82 Argyll St, Dunoon, ARGYLL AND BUTE, PA23 7NE **Scotland**
(T) 01369 702885.

LOCHGILPHEAD AND DISTRICT ANGLING CLUB
Contact/s:
Mr D MacDougall (Secretary), 23 High Bank Park, Lochgilphead, ARGYLL AND BUTE, PA31 8NL **Scotland**
Mr Archie MacGilp (Secretary), Suilven, Manse Brae, Lochgilphead, ARGYLL AND BUTE, PA31 8QZ **Scotland**
(T) 01546 606878.

OBAN AND LORN ANGLING CLUB
Contact/s:
Mr Paul Hampson (Secretary), Gylen, Morven Hill, Oban, ARGYLL AND BUTE, PA34 **Scotland**

SCOTTISH FISHERIES PROTECTION AGENCY
Contact/s:
Secretary, Old Quay, Campbeltown, ARGYLL AND BUTE, PA28 6ED **Scotland**
(T) 01586 552251.

TOBERMORY ANGLING CLUB
Contact/s:
Mr Wg Anderson (Secretary), Carna, 7 West St, Tobermory, ARGYLL AND BUTE, PA75 6QJ **Scotland**
Mrs Olive Brown (Secretary), Stronsaule, Tobermory, ARGYLL AND BUTE, PA75 6PR **Scotland**

AYRSHIRE (EAST)

MUIRKIRK ANGLING ASSOCIATION
Contact/s:
Mr J Timmins (Secretary), 38 Hareshaw Cres, Muirkirk, Cumnock, AYRSHIRE (EAST), KA18 3PY **Scotland**
(T) 01290 661114.

AYRSHIRE (NORTH)

IORSA (ARRAN) DISTRICT SALMON FISHERY BOARD
Contact/s:
Mr Jw Perkins (Acts Operator), Ramera, Sannox, Brodick, AYRSHIRE (NORTH), KA27 **Scotland**
(T) 01770 810671.

AYRSHIRE (SOUTH)

AYR DISTRICT SALMON FISHERY BOARD
Contact/s:
Mr Fm Watson (Acts Operator), Dw Shaw And Company, 34A Sandgate, Ayr, AYRSHIRE (SOUTH), KA7 1BG **Scotland**
(T) 01292 265033.

DOON DISTRICT SALMON FISHERY BOARD
Contact/s:
Mr Am Thomson, 23 Wellington Sq, Ayr, AYRSHIRE (SOUTH), KA7 2HG **Scotland**
(T) 01292 266900.

GIRVAN DISTRICT SALMON FISHERY BOARD
Contact/s:
Mr Sb Sheddon (Acts Operator), Messrs Smith And Valentine, Solicitors And Estate Agents, 16 Hamilton St,Girvan, AYRSHIRE (SOUTH), KA26 9EY **Scotland**
(T) 01465 713476.

KILMAURS ANGLING CLUB
Contact/s:
Mr Colin Ritchie (Secretary), 48 Hillmoss, Kilmaurs, Kilmarnock, AYRSHIRE (SOUTH), KA3 **Scotland**

SCOTTISH FISHERIES PROTECTION AGENCY
Contact/s:
Secretary, Russell House, King St, Ayr, AYRSHIRE (SOUTH), KA8 0BE **Scotland**
(T) 01292 610177.

STINCHAR DISTRICT SALMON FISHERY BOARD
Contact/s:
Mrs A McGinnis (Acts Operator), 6 The Avenue, Barr, Girvan, AYRSHIRE (SOUTH), KA26 9TX **Scotland**

CLACKMANNANSHIRE

DEVON ANGLING ASSOCIATION
Contact/s:
Mr R Breingan (Secretary), 33 Redwell Pl, Alloa, CLACKMANNANSHIRE, FK10 2BT **Scotland**

COUNTY KILKENNY

INISTIOGE ANGLERS CLUB
Contact/s:
Mr John O Donnell (Treasurer), Castle Inn, Inistioge, COUNTY KILKENNY, **Scotland**
(T) 056 58483.

DUMFRIES AND GALLOWAY

ANNAN DISTRICT SALMON FISHERY BOARD
Contact/s:
Ms Cak Rafferty (Acts Operator), Messrs Mcjerrow And Stevenson, 55 High St, Lockerbie, DUMFRIES AND GALLOWAY, DG11 2JJ **Scotland**
(T) 01576 202123.

BLADNOCH DISTRICT SALMON FISHERY BOARD
Contact/s:
Mr Peter Murray (Acts Operator), Messrs A B And A Matthews Solicitors, Bank Of Scotland Buildings, Newton Stewart, DUMFRIES AND GALLOWAY, DG8 6EG **Scotland**
(T) 01671 404100.

- **CASTLE DOUGLAS AND DISTRICT ANGLING ASSOCIATION**
Contact/s:
Mr Stanley Kaye (Secretary), 2 Cairnsmore Rd, Castle Douglas, DUMFRIES AND GALLOWAY, DG7 1BN **Scotland**
(T) 01556 502695.

- **CREE DISTRICT SALMON FISHERY BOARD**
Contact/s:
Mr Peter Murray (Acts Operator), Messrs A B And A Matthews Solicitors, Bank Of Scotland Buildings, Newton Stewart, DUMFRIES AND GALLOWAY, DG8 6EG **Scotland**
(T) 01671 404100.

- **DALBEATTIE ANGLING ASSOCIATION**
Contact/s:
Mr John Moran (Secretary), 12 Church Cres, Dalbeattie, DUMFRIES AND GALLOWAY, DG5 4BA **Scotland**
(T) 01556 610026.

- **DALRY ANGLING ASSOCIATION**
Contact/s:
Mr N Harvey (Secretary), Dalry Post Office, St John's Town Of Dalry, Castle Douglas, DUMFRIES AND GALLOWAY, DG7 3UW **Scotland**
Mr N Harvey (Secretary), Lochside Cottage, Balmaclellan, Castle Douglas, DUMFRIES AND GALLOWAY, DG7 3QA **Scotland**

- **DEE (KIRKCUDBRIGHTSHIRE) DISTRICT SALMON FISHERY BOARD**
Contact/s:
Mr Gs Scott (Acts Operator), Messrs Gillespie, Gifford And Brown, 27 St Cuthbert St, Kirkcudbright, DUMFRIES AND GALLOWAY, DG6 4DJ **Scotland**
(T) 01557 330539.

- **ESK AND LIDDLE FISHERIES ASSOCIATION**
Contact/s:
Mr G L Lewis (Secretary), Langholm, DUMFRIES AND GALLOWAY, DG13 **Scotland**
(T) 01387 380202.
(F) 01387 381103.

- **FLEET (KIRKCUDBRIGHTSHIRE) DISTRICT SALMON FISHERY BOARD**
Contact/s:
Mr Cr Graves (Acts Operator), Pinnacle, Gatehouse Of Fleet, Castle Douglas, DUMFRIES AND GALLOWAY, DG7 2HH **Scotland**
(T) 01557 814610.

- **GATEHOUSE AND KIRKCUDBRIGHT ANGLING ASSOCIATION**
Contact/s:
Mr Eric Farrer (Secretary), 32 Boreland Rd, Kirkcudbright, DUMFRIES AND GALLOWAY, DG6 4JB **Scotland**

- **LAUDERDALE ANGLING ASSOCIATION**
Contact/s:
Mr Donald Milligan (Secretary), The Torts, Portling, Dalbeattie, DUMFRIES AND GALLOWAY, DG5 4PZ **Scotland**

- **LUCE DISTRICT SALMON FISHERY BOARD**
Contact/s:
Mr Ea Fleming-Smith (Acts Operator), Stair Estates Office, Rephad, Stranraer, DUMFRIES AND GALLOWAY, DG9 8BX **Scotland**
(T) 01776 702024.

- **NEW ABBEY FISHING ASSOCIATION**
Contact/s:
Mr Ian Cooper (Secretary), West Shambellie, New Abbey, Dumfries, DUMFRIES AND GALLOWAY, DG2 8HG **Scotland**
(T) 01387 850280.

- **NEW GALLOWAY ANGLING ASSOCIATION**
Contact/s:
Mr Allan Cairnie (Secretary), 4 Carsons Knowe, New Galloway, Castle Douglas, DUMFRIES AND GALLOWAY, DG7 3RY **Scotland**

- **NEWTON STEWART ANGLING ASSOCIATION**
Contact/s:
Mr Bertie Marr (Secretary), 1 St Coans Pl, Newton Stewart, DUMFRIES AND GALLOWAY, DG8 **Scotland**

- **NITH DISTRICT SALMON FISHERY BOARD**
Contact/s:
Mr R Styles (Acts Operator), Walker And Sharp Solicitors, 37 George St, Dumfries, DUMFRIES AND GALLOWAY, DG1 1EB **Scotland**
(T) 01387 267222.

- **STRANRAER AND DISTRICT ANGLING ASSOCIATION**
Contact/s:
Mr D Pride (Secretary), Almar View, Ochtrelure, Stranraer, DUMFRIES AND GALLOWAY, DG9 8RR **Scotland**

- **UPPER ANNANDALE ANGLING ASSOCIATION**
Contact/s:
Mr A Dickson (Secretary), Braehead, Woodfoot, Beattock,Moffat, DUMFRIES AND GALLOWAY, DG10 9PL **Scotland**

EDINBURGH (CITY OF)

- **CENTRAL SCOTLAND ANGLERS ASSOCIATION**
Contact/s:
Mr Kevin Burns (Secretary), 53 Fernside Cres, Edinburgh, EDINBURGH (CITY OF), EH17 7HS **Scotland**

- **ESK VALLEY ANGLING IMPROVEMENT ASSOCIATION**
Contact/s:
Mr Kevin Burns (Secretary), 53 Fernside Cres, Edinburgh, EDINBURGH (CITY OF), EH **Scotland**

- **KINLOCH DISTRICT SALMON FISHERY BOARD**
Contact/s:
Mr A Sykes (Acts Operator), Messrs Brodies Ws, 15 Atholl Cres, Edinburgh, EDINBURGH (CITY OF), EH3 8HA **Scotland**
(T) 0131 2284111.

- **LOCH INCHARD DISTRICT SALMON FISHERY BOARD**
Contact/s:
Mr Jc Drysdale (Acts Operator), Anderson Strathern Ws, 48 Castle St, Edinburgh, EDINBURGH (CITY OF), EH2 3LX **Scotland**
(T) 0131 2202345.

- **SCOTTISH ANGLERS NATIONAL ASSOCIATION**
Contact/s:
Ms Helen M Bull (Administrator), Caledonia House, South Gyle, Edinburgh, EDINBURGH (CITY OF), EH12 9DQ **Scotland**
(T) 0131 3398808.
(F) 0131 3177202.

- **SCOTTISH FISHERIES PROTECTION AGENCY STORE**
Contact/s:
Secretary, Unit 2 6B Tower St, Leith, Edinburgh, EDINBURGH (CITY OF), EH6 7BY **Scotland**
(T) 0131 5543755.

FALKIRK

- **BIOMAR**
Contact/s:
Mr Guy Mace (Managing Director), North Farm Rd, Grangemouth Docks, Grangemouth,FALKIRK, FK3 9AB **Scotland**
(T) 01324 665585.

FIFE

- **DUNFERMLINE ARTISAN ANGLING CLUB**
Contact/s:
Mr Wb Stewart (Secretary), 13 Foresters Lea Cross, Dunfermline, FIFE, KY12 7TE **Scotland**

- **ST ANDREWS ANGLING CLUB**
Contact/s:
Mr Peter F Malcolm (Secretary), 54 St Nicholas St, St Andrews, FIFE, KY16 8BQ **Scotland**

GLASGOW (CITY OF)

- **INTERNATIONAL FLY FISHING ASSOCIATION**
Contact/s:
Mr Ian Campbell (Secretary/Treasurer), 2 Golf View, Bearsden, Glasgow, GLASGOW (CITY OF), G61 4HJ **Scotland**

- **LEVEN DISTRICT SALMON FISHERY BOARD**
Contact/s:
Mr Alister Sutherland (Acts Operator), Burness Ws Solicitors, 242 West George St, Glasgow, GLASGOW (CITY OF), G2 4QY **Scotland**
(T) 0141 2484933.

- **LOCH SHEIL DISTRICT SALMON FISHERY BOARD**
Contact/s:
Mr Et Cameron (Acts Operator), Robertson Paul, 95 Bothwell St, Glasgow, GLASGOW (CITY OF), G2 7JH **Scotland**
(T) 0141 2041231.

- **PIKE ANGLERS ALLIANCE FOR SCOTLAND**
Contact/s:
Mr Billy Noon (Membership Secretary), 445 Royston Rd, Germiston, GLASGOW (CITY OF), G21 2DE **Scotland**

HIGHLAND

- **ACHNASHEEN ANGLING CLUB**
Contact/s:
Ledgowan Lodge Hotel, Achnasheen, HIGHLAND, IV22 2EJ **Scotland**

- **ALNESS DISTRICT SALMON FISHERY BOARD**
Contact/s:
Mr Jhs Stewart (Acts Operator), 57 Culduthel Rd, Inverness, HIGHLAND, IV1 1HQ **Scotland**
(T) 01463 714477.

- **ASSYNT ANGLING CLUB**
Contact/s:
Mr S Taylor (Secretary), 17 Kirk Rd, Lochinver, Lairg, HIGHLAND, IV27 4LM **Scotland**

- **BADENOCH ANGLING ASSOCIATION**
Contact/s:
Mr Sandy Bennett (Secretary), 113 High St, Kingussie, HIGHLAND, PH21 **Scotland**

- **BEAULY ANGLING CLUB**
Contact/s:
Mr J Morrison (Secretary), Mo-Dhachaidh, Windhill, Beauly, HIGHLAND, IV4 7AS **Scotland**
Mr Hugh Galbraith (Secretary), Braedown Cottage, Belmaduthy, Munlochy, HIGHLAND, IV8 8PF **Scotland**

BEAULY DISTRICT SALMON FISHERY BOARD
Contact/s:
Mr J Wotherspoon (Acts Operator), Macandrew And Jenkins Ws, Solicitors And Estate Agents, 5 Drummond St,Inverness, HIGHLAND, IV1 1QF **Scotland**
(T) 01463 233001.

BROOM DISTRICT SALMON FISHERY BOARD
Contact/s:
Mr Gc Muirden (Acts Operator), Ross And Arnot Solictors, Po Box 8, Mansfield House,Dingwall, HIGHLAND, IV15 9HJ **Scotland**
(T) 01349 862214.

BRORA DISTRICT SALMON FISHERY BOARD
Contact/s:
Mr Cj Whealing (Acts Operator), Sutherland Estates Office, Duke St, Golspie, HIGHLAND, KW10 6RR **Scotland**
(T) 01408 633268.

CAITHNESS DIATRICT SALMON FISHERY BOARD
Contact/s:
Mr P Blackwood (Acts Operator), Estates Office, Thurso East, Thurso, HIGHLAND, KW14 8HW **Scotland**
(T) 01847 893134.

CONON DISTRICT SALMON FISHERY BOARD
Contact/s:
Mr Miles Larby (Acts Operator), Ckd Finlayson Huges, 45 Church St, Inverness, HIGHLAND, IV1 1DR **Scotland**
(T) 01463 224707.
(F) 01436 243234.

CROWE AND SHIEL (LOCH DUICH) SALMON FISHERY BOARD
Contact/s:
Lord Burton (Acts Operator/Chairman), Dochfour Estate Office, Dochgarroch, Inverness, HIGHLAND, IV3 6JP **Scotland**

EVANTON ANGLING CLUB
Contact/s:
Mr Pf Cumberlege (Secretary), Balavoulin, Evanton, Dingwall, HIGHLAND, IV16 9XW **Scotland**

EWE DISTRICT SALMON FISHERY BOARD
Contact/s:
Mr Gc Muirden (Acts Operator), Ross And Arnot Solictors, Po Box 8, Mansfield House,Dingwall, HIGHLAND, IV15 9HJ **Scotland**
(T) 01349 862214.

FEDERATION OF HIGHLAND ANGLING CLUBS
Contact/s:
Mr W Brown (Secretary), Coruisk, Strathpeffer, HIGHLAND, IV14 9BD **Scotland**

GAIRLOCH ANGLING CLUB
Contact/s:
Mrs L Mackenzie (Secretary), 4 Strath, Gairloch, HIGHLAND, IV21 2BX **Scotland**

GRUDIE OR DIONARD DISTRICT SALMON FISHERY BOARD
Contact/s:
Mr A Mackenzie (Acts Operator), Redwood, 19 Culduthel Rd, Inverness, HIGHLAND, IV2 4AA **Scotland**
(T) 01463 235353.

GRUINARD DISTRICT SALMON FISHERY BOARD
Contact/s:
Mr Gc Muirden (Acts Operator), Ross And Arnot Solictors, Po Box 8, Mansfield House,Dingwall, HIGHLAND, IV15 9HJ **Scotland**
(T) 01349 862214.

HALLADALE DISTRICT SALMON FISHERY BOARD
Contact/s:
Mr Gd Robertson (Acts Operator), 29 Traill St, Thurso, HIGHLAND, KW14 8EQ **Scotland**
(T) 01847 893247.

HARLOSH SALMON
Contact/s:
Mr Neil Campbell (Director), 5 Dunanellerich, Dunvegan, HIGHLAND, IV55 8ZH **Scotland**
(T) 01470 521483.

HELMSDALE DISTRICT SALMON FISHERY BOARD
Contact/s:
Mr N Wright (Acts Operator), Arthur And Carmicheal, Cathedral Sq, Dornoch, HIGHLAND, IV25 **Scotland**
(T) 01862 810202.

HOPE AND POLLA DISTRICT SALMON FISHERY BOARD
Contact/s:
Mr Gc Muirden (Acts Operator), Ross And Arnot Solictors, Po Box 8, Mansfield House,Dingwall, HIGHLAND, IV15 9HJ **Scotland**
(T) 01349 862214.

INVERNESS ANGLING CLUB
Contact/s:
Mr K MacDonald (Secretary), 30 Swanston Avenue, Inverness, HIGHLAND, IV3 6QW **Scotland**

KINLOCHEWE ANGLING ASSOCIATION
Contact/s:
Mr S Condon (Secretary), Glendocherty Craft Shop, Achnasheen, HIGHLAND, IV22 2PA **Scotland**

KYLE OF SUTHERLAND DISTRICT SALMON FISHERY BOARD
Contact/s:
Mr J Mason (Acts Operator), Bell Ingram Limited, Estates Office, Bonar Bridge,Ardgay, HIGHLAND, IV24 3EA **Scotland**

LAIRG ANGLING CLUB
Contact/s:
Mr Jm Ross (Secretary), St Murie, Church Hill Rd, Lairg, HIGHLAND, IV27 4BL **Scotland**

LAXFORD DISTRICT SALMON FISHERY BOARD
Contact/s:
Mr Ar Whitefield (Acts Operator), The Estate Office, Achfary, Lairg,Lairg, HIGHLAND, IV27 4PQ **Scotland**
(T) 01971 500221.

LOCHY DISTRICT SALMON FISHERY BOARD
Contact/s:
Mr D MacPhee (Acts Operator), Messrs Arthur, Stewart And Co Solicitors, St Marys House, Gordon Sq,Fort William, HIGHLAND, PH33 6DY **Scotland**
(T) 01397 701000.

NAIRN ANGLING ASSOCIATION
Contact/s:
Mr G Young (Secretary), Earlseat Cottage, Moyness, Nairn,Inverness, HIGHLAND, IV12 5LB **Scotland**

NAIRN DISTRICT SALMON FISHERY BOARD
Contact/s:
Mr Emb Larby (Acts Operator), Finlayson Hughes, 45 Church St, Inverness, HIGHLAND, IV4 1DR **Scotland**

NAVER AND BORGIE DISTRICT SALMON FISHERY BOARD
Contact/s:
Mr N Wright (Acts Operator), Arthur And Carmicheal, Catherdral Sq, Dornoch,Dornoch, HIGHLAND, IV25 3SW **Scotland**

NESS DISTRICT SALMON FISHERY BOARD
Contact/s:
Mr F Kelly (Acts Operator), Messrs Anderson, Shaw And Gilbert, York House, 20 Church St,Inverness, HIGHLAND, IV1 1ED **Scotland**
(T) 01463 236123.

PORTREE ANGLING ASSOCIATION
Contact/s:
Mr Neil Cameron (Secretary), Hillcroft, Treaslane, Portree, HIGHLAND, IV51 9NX **Scotland**

SCOTTISH FISHERIES PROTECTION AGENCY
Contact/s:
Secretary, Culag Sq, Lochinver, Lairg, HIGHLAND, IV27 4LE **Scotland**
(T) 01571 844486.
Secretary, Estate Office, Portree, HIGHLAND, IV51 9DH **Scotland**
(T) 01478 612038.
Secretary, The Old Chapel, The Harbour, Scrabster,Thurso, HIGHLAND, KW14 7UL **Scotland**
(T) 01847 895074.
Secretary, West Shore St, Ullapool, HIGHLAND, IV26 2UB **Scotland**
(T) 01854 612704.

SKYE DISTRICT SALMON FISHERY BOARD
Contact/s:
Mr P Butler (Acts Operator), Mile End House, Glen Hinnisdal, Snizort,Portree, HIGHLAND, IV51 9UX **Scotland**
(T) 01470 42331.

THURSO ANGLING ASSOCIATION
Contact/s:
Horndean, Glengolly, Thurso, HIGHLAND, KW14 7XP **Scotland**

ULLAPOOL ANGLING CLUB
Contact/s:
Mr D Taggart (Secretary), 37 Morefield Pl, Ullapool, HIGHLAND, IV26 2TS **Scotland**

INVERCLYDE

GREENOCK AND DISTRICT ANGLING CLUB
Contact/s:
Secretary, Fairlie Moor, Dalry Moor Rd, Fairly,Greenock, INVERCLYDE, PA **Scotland**
(T) 01850 162543.
Mr John Weir (Secretary), Haylie And Largs, Greenock, INVERCLYDE, PA **Scotland**
(T) 01475 676005.
Secretary, Pine Wood, Kilmacolm, Greenock, INVERCLYDE, PA **Scotland**
(T) 01589 033403.
Mr Billy McFern (Secretary), Houston Rd, Lawfield, Kilmacolm, INVERCLYDE, PA13 **Scotland**
(T) 01505 874182.

ISLE OF UIST (NORTH)

MULLANAGEARAN DISTRICT SALMON FISHERY BOARD
Contact/s:
Estate Office, Lochmaddy, ISLE OF UIST (NORTH), PA82 5AA **Scotland**

LANARKSHIRE (NORTH)

- **AIRDRIE AND DISTRICT ANGLING CLUB**
Contact/s:
Mr J Potter (Secretary), 12 Sharp Avenue, Coatbridge, LANARKSHIRE (NORTH), ML5 5RP **Scotland**

- **MONKLANDS DISTRICT COARSE ANGLING CLUB**
Contact/s:
Mr John McShane (Secretary), 5 Crinian Cres, Townhead, Coatbridge, LANARKSHIRE (NORTH), ML5 2LG **Scotland**

- **UNITED CLYDE ANGLING PROTECTIVE ASSOCIATION**
Contact/s:
Mr Joseph Quigley (Secretary), 39 Hillfoot Avenue, Branchalwood, Wishaw, LANARKSHIRE (NORTH), ML2 8TR **Scotland**

LANARKSHIRE (SOUTH)

- **AVON ANGLING CLUB**
Contact/s:
Mr P Brooks (Secretary), 3 The Neuk, Stonehouse, LANARKSHIRE (SOUTH), ML9 3HP **Scotland**

- **KILBRYDE ANGLING CLUB**
Contact/s:
Mr John Cooper (Secretary), 65 Carlisle Rd, Crawford, Biggar, LANARKSHIRE (SOUTH), ML12 6TP **Scotland**

- **LAMINGTON AND DISTRICT ANGLING IMPROVEMENT ASSOCIATION**
Contact/s:
Mr B Dexter (Secretary), Red Lees, 18 Boghall Park, Biggar, LANARKSHIRE (SOUTH), ML12 6EY **Scotland**

LOTHIAN (EAST)

- **EAST LOTHIAN ANGLING ASSOCIATION**
Contact/s:
Mr John Crombie (Secretary), 10 St Lawrence, Haddington, LOTHIAN (EAST), EH41 **Scotland**
(T) 01620 822058.

- **LAUDERDALE ANGLING ASSOCIATION**
Contact/s:
Mr Donald Milligan (Secretary), Gifford Cottage, Main St, Gifford,Haddington, LOTHIAN (EAST), EH41 4QH **Scotland**

- **MUSSELBURGH AND DISTRICT ANGLING ASSOCIATION**
Contact/s:
Mr George Brooks (Secretary), 29 Eskside West, Musselburgh, LOTHIAN (EAST), EH21 6PP **Scotland**
Mr James W Dickson (Secretary), 3 Haddington Rd, Musselburgh, LOTHIAN (EAST), EH21 7PT **Scotland**

- **NORTH BERWICK ANGLING CLUB**
Contact/s:
Mr Norman M Morrison (Secretary), Kidlaw Farm, Gifford, Haddington, LOTHIAN (EAST), EH39 4JW **Scotland**

LOTHIAN (WEST)

- **CRAMOND ANGLING CLUB**
Contact/s:
Mr Craig Campbell (Secretary), 2 Canmore St, South Queensferry, LOTHIAN (WEST), EH30 9ND **Scotland**

- **RIVER ALMOND ANGLING ASSOCIATION**
Contact/s:
Mr H Meikle (Secretary), 23 Glen Trce, Deans, Livingston, LOTHIAN (WEST), EH54 8BU **Scotland**

MORAY

- **ELGIN AND DISTRICT ANGLING ASSOCIATION**
Contact/s:
Mr W E Mulholland (Secretary), 9 Conon Cres, Elgin, MORAY, IV30 1SZ **Scotland**

- **FINDHORN DISTRICT SALMON FISHERY BOARD**
Contact/s:
Sir William Gordon Cumming (Acts Operator), Altyre House, Altyre, Forres, MORAY, IV36 2SH **Scotland**

- **LOSSIE DISTRICT SALMON FISHERY BOARD**
Contact/s:
Mr Andrew McCartan (Acts Operator), Mccartan Solicitors, 145 High St, Forres, MORAY, IV36 1DX **Scotland**

- **SPEY DISTRICT SALMON FISHERY BOARD**
Contact/s:
Mr C Whittle (Acts Operator), Messrs R And R Urquhart, 121 High St, Forres, MORAY, IV36 0AB **Scotland**
(T) 01309 72216.

ORKNEY ISLES

- **LOCH SHIN GAME OF SCOTLAND**
Contact/s:
Secretary, Rendall, Tingwall, Orkney, ORKNEY ISLES, KW17 2HB **Scotland**
(T) 01856 751499.

- **ORKNEY TROUT FISHING ASSOCIATION**
Contact/s:
Mr James Purvis (Secretary), 3 Maitland Pl, Finstown, ORKNEY ISLES, KW17 2EQ **Scotland**
Mr Malcolm A Russell (Secretary), Caolica, Heddle Rd, Finstown,Orkney, ORKNEY ISLES, KW17 **Scotland**

PERTH AND KINROSS

- **ABERFELDY ANGLING CLUB**
Contact/s:
Mr G MacDougall (Secretary), 60 Moness Cres, Aberfeldy, PERTH AND KINROSS, PH15 2DN **Scotland**

- **AGRICULTURE AND FISHERIES DEPT THE SCOTTISH OFFICE**
Contact/s:
Mr Mike Miles (Officer In Charge), Cromwell Park, Almondbank, Perth, PERTH AND KINROSS, PH1 3LW **Scotland**
(T) 01738 583361.

- **ATLANTIC SALMON TRUST**
Contact/s:
Mr D J Mackenzie (Director), Moulin, Pitlochry, PERTH AND KINROSS, PH16 5JQ **Scotland**

- **BLAIRGOWRIE, RATTRAY AND DISTRICT ANGLING ASSOCIATION**
Contact/s:
Mr Walter Matthew (Secretary), 9 Mitchell Sq, Blairgowrie, PERTH AND KINROSS, PH10 6HR **Scotland**

- **CRIEFF ANGLING CLUB**
Contact/s:
Mr Percy Wilson (Secretary), Tulliallan, Duchlage Rd, Crieff, PERTH AND KINROSS, PH7 3BN **Scotland**

- **DUNKELD AND BIRNAM ANGLING ASSOCIATION**
Contact/s:
Mr Archie Steele (Secretary), 21 Willowbank, Birnam, Dunkeld, PERTH AND KINROSS, PH8 **Scotland**
(T) 01350 727428.

Mr K L Scott (Secretary), Mandaya, Highfield Pl, Bankfoot,Perth, PERTH AND KINROSS, PH1 4AX **Scotland**

- **FORTH DISTRICT SALMON FISHERY BOARD**
Contact/s:
Mr T Mackenzie (Acts Operator), 12 Charles St, Dunblane, PERTH AND KINROSS, FK15 9BY **Scotland**
(T) 01786 825544.

- **HAMILTON FGA**
Contact/s:
Secretary, Kindrochet Byre, Dunira, Crieff, PERTH AND KINROSS, PH6 2JZ **Scotland**
(T) 01764 685337.

- **KEITHICK ANGLING CLUB**
Contact/s:
Mr John Carrick (Secretary), Athole Arms, Coupar Angus, Blairgowrie, PERTH AND KINROSS, PH13 **Scotland**

- **LOCH RANNOCH CONSERVATION ANGLING ASSOCIATION**
Contact/s:
Mr Em Beattie (Secretary), 2 Schiehallion Pl, Kinloch Rannoch, Pitlochry, PERTH AND KINROSS, PH16 5PT **Scotland**

- **PERTH AND DISTRICT ANGLERS ASSOCIATION**
Contact/s:
Mr G D Nicholls (Secretary), 30 Wallace Cres, Perth, PERTH AND KINROSS, PH1 2RF **Scotland**

- **RANNOCHAND DISTRICT ANGLING CLUB**
Contact/s:
Mr John Brown (Secretary), The Square, Pitlochry, PERTH AND KINROSS, PH16 5PN **Scotland**

- **ST FILLANS AND LOCH EARN ANGLING ASSOCIATION**
Contact/s:
Mr Grant Mackay (Secretary), 37 Alligan Cres, Crieff, PERTH AND KINROSS, PH7 3JT **Scotland**
Mrs W Henry (Secretary), Tullichettle Lodge, Comrie, Crieff, PERTH AND KINROSS, PH6 2HU **Scotland**

- **STANLEY AND DISTRICT ANGLING CLUB**
Contact/s:
Mr S Grant (Secretary), 7 Murray Pl, Stanley, PERTH AND KINROSS, PH1 4LX **Scotland**

- **TAY DISTRICT SALMON FISHERY BOARD**
Contact/s:
Mr R Blake (Acts Operator), Messrs Condies Solicitors, 2 Tay St, Perth, PERTH AND KINROSS, PH1 5LJ **Scotland**
(T) 01738 440088.

RENFREWSHIRE

- **GOIL ANGLING CLUB**
Contact/s:
Mr Ian Given (Secretary), Bonnyrigg, 25 Churchill Drive, Bishopton, RENFREWSHIRE, PA7 5HB **Scotland**

SCOTTISH BORDERS

- **EARLSTON ANGLING ASSOCIATION**
Contact/s:
Mr C T Austin (Secretary), 23 Summerfield, Earlston, SCOTTISH BORDERS, TD4 6DP **Scotland**
Mr Dg Stafford (Secretary), 36 Queensway, Earlston, SCOTTISH BORDERS, TD4 **Scotland**

- **EYE WATER ANGLING CLUB**
Contact/s:
Mr William Gillie (Secretary), 2 Tod's Court, Eyemouth, SCOTTISH BORDERS, TD14 5HW **Scotland**

- **GALASHIELS ANGLING ASSOCIATION**
Contact/s:
Mr S Grzybowski (Secretary), 3 St. Andrews St, Galashiels, SCOTTISH BORDERS, TD1 1EA **Scotland**

- **GORDON FISHING CLUB**
Contact/s:
Mr J Fairgrieve (Secretary), Burnbrae, Eden Rd, Gordon, SCOTTISH BORDERS, TD3 6UU **Scotland**

- **GREENLAW ANGLING ASSOCIATION**
Contact/s:
Mr T Waldie (Secretary), 26 East High St, Greenlaw, Duns, SCOTTISH BORDERS, TD10 6UF **Scotland**

- **HAWICK ANGLING CLUB**
Contact/s:
Mr Eric Stewart (Secretary/Treasurer), 5 Sandbed, Hawick, SCOTTISH BORDERS, TD9 0HE **Scotland**
(T) 01450 373771.

- **JEDFOREST ANGLING ASSOCIATION**
Contact/s:
Mr J Tait (Secretary), 9 Boundaries, Jedburgh, SCOTTISH BORDERS, TD8 6EX **Scotland**

- **KELSO ANGLING ASSOCIATION**
Contact/s:
Mr Euan M Robson (Secretary), Elmbank, 33 Tweedside Park, Kelso, SCOTTISH BORDERS, TD5 7RF **Scotland**

- **MELROSE AND DISTRICT ANGLING ASSOCIATION**
Contact/s:
Mr T McLeish (Secretary), Planetree Cottage, Newstead, Melrose, SCOTTISH BORDERS, TD6 **Scotland**

- **MOREBATTLE ANGLING CLUB**
Contact/s:
Mr Dy Gray (Secretary), 17 Mainsfield Avenue, Morebattle, Kelso, SCOTTISH BORDERS, TD5 8QW **Scotland**

- **ST MARYS LOCH ANGLING CLUB**
Contact/s:
Mr Neil MacIntyre (Secretary), Whincroft, 8 Rosetta Rd, Peebles, SCOTTISH BORDERS, EH45 8JU **Scotland**

- **TWEED DISTRICT SALMON FISHERY BOARD**
Contact/s:
Mrs J Nicol (Acts Operator), River Tweed Commissioners, North Court, Drygrange Steading,Melrose, SCOTTISH BORDERS, TD6 9DJ **Scotland**
(T) 01896 848294.

- **TWEED FOUNDATION**
Contact/s:
Drygrange, Steading, Melrose, SCOTTISH BORDERS, TD6 9DJ **Scotland**
(T) 01898 48271.

SHETLAND ISLANDS

- **SCOTTISH FISHERIES PROTECTION AGENCY**
Contact/s:
Secretary, Albert Buildings, Lerwick, SHETLAND ISLANDS, ZE1 0LL **Scotland**
(T) 01595 692007.

- **SHETLAND ANGLERS ASSOCIATION**
Contact/s:
Mr Andrew Miller (Secretary), 3 Gladstone Trce, Lerwick, SHETLAND ISLANDS, ZE1 0EG **Scotland**
(T) 01595 695903.

- **SHETLAND ANGLING ASSOCIATION**
Contact/s:
Mr Alec Miller (Secretary), 55 Burgh Rd, Lerwick, SHETLAND ISLANDS, ZE1 0HJ **Scotland**
(T) 01595 695903.
(F) 01595 696568.

- **THOMPSON BROS SALMON**
Contact/s:
Secretary, Basta Voe, Yell, Mid Yell,Shetland, SHETLAND ISLANDS, ZE2 9DB **Scotland**
(T) 01957 744305.

WESTERN ISLES

- **EAST LEWIS DISTRICT SALMON FISHERY BOARD**
Contact/s:
Mr George MacDonald (Acts Operator), Estate Office, North Uist Estate, Lochmaddy, WESTERN ISLES, HS6 5AA **Scotland**
(T) 01876 500428.

- **HARRIS DISTRICT SALMON FISHERY BOARD**
Contact/s:
Mr Ga MacDonald (Acts Operator), The Estate Office, Lochmaddy, WESTERN ISLES, HS6 5AA **Scotland**
(T) 01876 500428.

- **NORTH UIST ANGLING CLUB**
Contact/s:
Mr P Harding (Secretary), Claddach Kyles, Lochmaddy, WESTERN ISLES, HS6 5EW **Scotland**
Mr Albert Thompson (Secretary), Sea Swallow Cottage, Lochmaddy, WESTERN ISLES, HS6 5AA **Scotland**

- **SIDINISH SALMON**
Contact/s:
Mr Alastair D MacLellan (Director), 5 Locheport, Lochmaddy, WESTERN ISLES, HS6 **Scotland**
(T) 01876 580311.

- **SOVAL ANGLING ASSOCIATION**
Contact/s:
Mr Edward Young (Secretary), Stile Park, Willowglen Rd, Stornoway, WESTERN ISLES, HS1 2EW **Scotland**

- **STORNOWAY ANGLING ASSOCIATION**
Contact/s:
Mr H Fraser (Secretary), 5 Laxdale, Stornoway, WESTERN ISLES, HS1 **Scotland**

- **WESTERN ISLES FISHERIES TRUST**
Contact/s:
Mr Mark Bilsby (Secretary), Creed Lodge, Stornoway, WESTERN ISLES, HS2 9JN **Scotland**
(T) 01851 701526.

WALES

BLAENAU GWENT

- **CWMCELYN ANGLING CLUB**
Contact/s:
Mr P Hunt (Secretary), East Pentwyn Farm, Blaina, Abertillery, BLAENAU GWENT, NP3 3HX **Wales**

- **EBBW VALE WELFARE ANGLING CLUB**
Contact/s:
Mr R Satterley (Secretary), 8 Pen-Y-Lan, Ebbw Vale, BLAENAU GWENT, NP3 5LS **Wales**

- **RHYMNEY AND DISITRCT ANGLING SOCIETY**
Contact/s:
Mr J Pugh (Secretary), 12 Castle Field, Rhymney, Tredegar, BLAENAU GWENT, NP25 **Wales**

BRIDGEND

- **LLYNFI VALLEY ANGLING ASSOCIATION**
Contact/s:
Mr Philip Davies (Secretary), 15 Turberville St, Maesteg, BRIDGEND, CF34 0LP **Wales**
Mr G Thomas (Secretary), 39 Darren Veiw, Llangynwyd, Maesteg, BRIDGEND, CF34 9SG **Wales**

- **OGMORE ANGLING ASSOCIATION**
Contact/s:
Mr W A Protheroe (Secretary), Henllan, Coychurch Rd, Pencoed,BRIDGEND, CF35 5LY **Wales**
(T) 01656 861139.

- **OGWR BOROUGH ANGLING ASSOCIATION**
Contact/s:
Mr T J Hughes (Secretary), 20 Hoel Glannant, Bettws, BRIDGEND, CF32 8SP **Wales**

- **PENCOEDAND DISTRICT ANGLING CLUB**
Contact/s:
Mr Gm Gwilliam (Secretary), 5 Velindre Rd, Pencoed, BRIDGEND, CF31 **Wales**

CARDIFF

- **BIRCHGROVE (CARDIFF) ANGLING ASSOCIATION**
Contact/s:
Mr J S Wilmot (Hon Secretary), 4 Clydesmuir Rd, Tremorfa, CARDIFF, CF24 2QA **Wales**
(T) 029 20460697.

- **BUTE ANGLING SOCIETY**
Contact/s:
Mr Sg Allen (Secretary), 37 Aberporth Rd, Gabalfa, CARDIFF, CF14 2RX **Wales**

CARMARTHENSHIRE

- **ABERGWILI ANGLING CLUB**
Contact/s:
Mr Eric Thomas (Secretary), 60 Abergwili Rd, Carmarthen, CARMARTHENSHIRE, SA31 2HH **Wales**
(T) 01267 231115.

- **AMMANFORD AND DISTRICT ANGLING CLUB**
Contact/s:
Mr Ron Woodland (Secretary), 2 Pontarddulais Rd, Llangennech, Llanelli, CARMARTHENSHIRE, SA14 8YF **Wales**
(T) 01554 820477.

- **CARMARTHEN AMATEUR ANGLING ASSOCIATION**
Contact/s:
Mr Ron Ratti (Secretary), Rhydal Mount, The Parade, Carmarthen, CARMARTHENSHIRE, SA31 3PS **Wales**
(T) 01267 221422.

- **CARMARTHEN AND DISTRICT ANGLING CLUB**
Contact/s:
Mr Herbert Evans (Secretary), 25 Maple Cres, Carmarthen, CARMARTHENSHIRE, SA31 3PS **Wales**

- **CLWB GODRE R MYNYDD DU**
Contact/s:
Secretary, 203 Cwmamman Rd, Glanamman, Ammanford, CARMARTHENSHIRE, SA18 1EJ **Wales**
(T) 01269 825497.

- **CROSS HANDS AND DISTRICT ANGLING ASSOCIATION**
Contact/s:
Pat Kieran (Secretary), 48 Waterloo Rd, Penygroes, Llanelli, CARMARTHENSHIRE, SA14 7NS **Wales**

Mr L R Thomas (Secretary), 71 Caeglas, Cross Hands, Llanelli, CARMARTHENSHIRE, SA **Wales**

- **FELINDRE ANGLING CLUB**
Contact/s:
Mr M Randall (Secretary), 77 Water St, Kidwelly, CARMARTHENSHIRE, SA17 **Wales**
- **GWAUN-CAE-GURWEN ANGLING ASSOCIATION**
Contact/s:
Mr P E Edwards (Secretary), 32 Heol Cae, Gurwen, Gwaun-Cae-Gurwen,Ammanford, CARMARTHENSHIRE, SA18 **Wales**
- **LLANDEILO ANGLING ASSOCIATION**
Contact/s:
Mr Robert James (Information Officer), 28A Rhomaen St, Llandeilo, CARMARTHENSHIRE, SA19 **Wales**
(T) 01558 822248.
- **LLANDOVERY ANGLING ASSOCIATION**
Contact/s:
Mr Mick Davies (Secretary), Cwmrhudden Lodge, Llangadog, Llandovery, CARMARTHENSHIRE, SA20 0DX **Wales**
(T) 01550 720633.
- **LLANDYBIE ANGLING ASSOCIATION**
Contact/s:
Mr R Jones (Secretary), 9 Margaret Rd, Llandybie, Ammanford, CARMARTHENSHIRE, SA18 3YB **Wales**
- **LLANELLI ANGLING ASSOCIATION**
Contact/s:
Mr David Watkins (Hon Secretary), 60 Llwyn Hendy, Llanelli, CARMARTHENSHIRE, SA **Wales**
(T) 01554 774859.
- **LLANGADOG ANGLING ASSOCIATION**
Contact/s:
Hafan Las, Llangadog, CARMARTHENSHIRE, SA19 **Wales**
- **LLANGENNECH ANGLING CLUB**
Contact/s:
Mr D A Owen (Secretary), 99 Hendre Rd, Llangennech, Llanelli, CARMARTHENSHIRE, SA14 8TH **Wales**
- **LLANYBYDDER ANGLING ASSOCIATION**
Contact/s:
Mr William Wilkins (Secretary), Maes-Y-Fedw, Llanybydder, CARMARTHENSHIRE, SA40 9UG **Wales**
- **NEW QUAY ANGLING CLUB**
Contact/s:
Mr H Davies (Secretary), Min-Yr-Afon, Abergorlech, Carmarthen, CARMARTHENSHIRE, SA32 7SN **Wales**
- **TEIFI TROUT ASSOCIATION**
Contact/s:
Mr W Bishop (Secretary), Greenacres, Pentrecagal, Newcastle Emlyn, CARMARTHENSHIRE, SA38 9HT **Wales**
- **WHITLAND ANGLING ASSOCIATION**
Contact/s:
Mr Peter Hunt (Treasurer), White House Mill, Lampeter Velfrey, Whitland, CARMARTHENSHIRE, SA34 0RB **Wales**
(T) 01834 831304.

CEREDIGION

- **ABERAERON ANGLING CLUB**
Contact/s:
Mr Nigel D Davies (Secretary), Wenallt, 16 Belle Vue Trce, Aberaeron, CEREDIGION, SA46 0HB **Wales**
- **ABERAERON TOWN ANGLING CLUB**
Contact/s:
Mr D S Rees (Secretary), 10 North Rd, Aberaeron, CEREDIGION, SA46 0JF **Wales**
- **ABERYSTWYTH ANGLING ASSOCIATION LIMITED**
Contact/s:
Mr Peredur Eklund (Hon Secretary), 42 Erwgoch, Waunfawr, Aberystwyth, CEREDIGION, SY23 3AZ **Wales**
(T) 01970 623021.
- **CARMARTHEN FISHERMENS FEDERATION**
Contact/s:
Mr Garth Roberts (Secretary), Talrhyn, Tresaith Rd, Cardigan, CEREDIGION, SA43 2EB **Wales**
- **CYMDEITHAS PYSGOTA TALYBONT ANGLING ASSOCIATION**
Contact/s:
Mr Ithel Jones (Hon Secretary), Wern, Talybont, CEREDIGION, SY24 5ER **Wales**
(T) 01970 832363.
- **CYMDEITHAS PYSGOTA TREGARON ANGLING ASSOCIATION**
Contact/s:
Mr Aled Davis (Secretary), 4 Brennig Trce, Tregaron, CEREDIGION, SY25 6HA **Wales**
(T) 01974 298146.
- **LLANDYSUL ANGLING ASSOCIATION**
Contact/s:
Mr Artie Jones (Secretary), Glas-Y-Dorlan, Llyn-Y-Fran Rd, Llandysul, CEREDIGION, SA44 4JW **Wales**
- **LLANILAR ANGLING ASSOCIATION**
Contact/s:
Mr John Astill (Secretary), Dryslwyn, Llanafan, Aberystwyth, CEREDIGION, SY23 4AX **Wales**
- **PYSGOTWYR MAESNANT**
Contact/s:
Mr Dp Higgins (Secretary), 90 Maesceinion, Waunfawr, Aberystwyth, CEREDIGION, SY23 3QQ **Wales**
- **TEIFI TROUT ASSOCIATION**
Contact/s:
Mr Mike Evans (Membership Secretary), Llysycoed, Llandygwydd, Llechryd,Cardigan, CEREDIGION, SA43 **Wales**
- **TRAWSCOED ANGLING CLUB**
Contact/s:
Mr C Evans (Secretary), A D A S, Trawscoed, Aberystwyth, CEREDIGION, SY23 **Wales**
- **TREGARON ANGLING ASSOCIATION**
Contact/s:
Mr M J Morgan Obe (Hon Secretary), Swyn Teifi, Pontrhydfendigaid, Aberystwyth, CEREDIGION, SY25 6EF **Wales**
(T) 01974 831316.
(F) 01974 831316.

CONWY

- **BETWS-Y-COED ANGLING CLUB**
Contact/s:
Mr Melfyn Hughes (Secretary), Cae Garw, Betws-Y-Coed, CONWY, LL24 0BY **Wales**
- **CONWAY VALLEY FISHERIES ASSOCIATION**
Contact/s:
Mr Gareth Hughes (Secretary), Golygfa'r Graig, Betws Rd, Llanrwst, CONWY, LL26 **Wales**
- **DOLGARROG FISHING CLUB**
Contact/s:
Mr Peter Jones (Secretary), 12 Hillside Cottages, Dolgarrog, CONWY, LL32 **Wales**
- **DOLWYDDELAN FISHING ASSOCIATION**
Contact/s:
Mr D E Foster (Secretary), Post Office, Dolwyddelan, CONWY, LL25 0NJ **Wales**
- **LLANRWST ANGLING CLUB**
Contact/s:
Mr David Hughes (Secretary), 36 Station Rd, Llanrwst, CONWY, LL26 0AD **Wales**

DENBIGHSHIRE

- **CEIRIOG FLY FISHERS**
Contact/s:
Mr Alan Hudson (Secretary), Kingfisher, 96 Crogen, Lodgevale Park,Chirk, Wrexham, DENBIGHSHIRE, LL14 5BJ **Wales**
- **CERRIG-Y-DRUDION ANGLING ASSOCIATION**
Contact/s:
Mr Wm Roberts (Secretary), 4 Cae Lwydd, Cerrig-Y-Drudion, Corwen, DENBIGHSHIRE, LL21 9 **Wales**
- **CORWEN AND DISTRICT ANGLING CLUB**
Contact/s:
Mr Gordon Smith (Secretary), Llais-Yr-Afon, Bontuchel, Ruthin, DENBIGHSHIRE, LL15 2BE **Wales**
(T) 01824 7196091.
- **DENBIGH AND CLWYD ANGLING CLUB**
Contact/s:
Mr C P Harness (Membership Secretary), 8 Llwyn Menlli, Ruthin, DENBIGHSHIRE, LL15 1RG **Wales**
(T) 01824 705208.
- **HOLYWELL ANGLERS**
Contact/s:
Mr B Brushett (Secretary), 27 Long Ceiriog, Prestatyn, DENBIGHSHIRE, LL19 **Wales**
- **LLANGOLLEN ANGLING ASSOCIATION**
Contact/s:
Mr W N Elbourn (Secretary), Bwthyn Bach, 2 Green Lane, Llangollen, DENBIGHSHIRE, LL20 8TB **Wales**
- **MAELOR ANGLING ASSOCIATION**
Contact/s:
Mr Ken Bathers (Chairman), Sunnyside, Hill St, Cefn Mawr,Wrexham, DENBIGHSHIRE, LL14 3AY **Wales**
(T) 01978 820608.
- **NEWBRIDGE ANGLING ASSOCIATION**
Contact/s:
Mr Kerry Clutton (Hon Secretary), 28 Worsley Avenue, Johnstown, Wrexham, DENBIGHSHIRE, LL14 2TD **Wales**
(T) 01978 840377.
- **NORTH WALES ANGLING ASSOCIATION**
Contact/s:
Mr Paul M Litson (Secretary), Penmaes Villa, High St, Dyserth,Rhyl, DENBIGHSHIRE, LL18 6AA **Wales**
- **RHOSTYLLEN ANGLING CLUB**
Contact/s:
Mr J R Williams (Secretary), 57 West Gr, Rhostyllen, Wrexham, DENBIGHSHIRE, LL14 4NB **Wales**
(T) 01978 842017.
- **RHYL AND DISTRICT ANGLING ASSOCIATION**
Contact/s:
Mr Martin Fowell (Secretary), Bon Amie, 28 Ffordd Tanrallt, Meliden,Prestatyn, DENBIGHSHIRE, LL19 8PS **Wales**
(T) 01745 854390.
- **ST ASAPH ANGLING ASSOCIATION**
Contact/s:
Mr W J P Staines (Hon Secretary), Delamere, Coed Esgob Lane, St Asaph, DENBIGHSHIRE, LL17 0LH **Wales**
(T) 01745 583926.

FLINTSHIRE

- **ALLTAMI ANGLING CLUB**
  Contact/s:
  Mr A Price (Secretary), 69 Circular Drive, Ewloe, Connahs Quay, FLINTSHIRE, CH5 3 **Wales**
- **BUCKLEY ANGLING ASSOCIATION**
  Contact/s:
  Mr R W Jones (Secretary), Cresta, 35 Bryn Awelon, Mold, FLINTSHIRE, CH7 1LT **Wales**
- **CILCAIN FLY FISHING ASSOCIATION**
  Contact/s:
  Mr Ae Williams (Treasurer), Gwynfryn, Caerwys Hill, Caerwys,Mold, FLINTSHIRE, CH7 **Wales**
- **CONNAHS QUAY AND DISTRICT ANGLING CLUB**
  Contact/s:
  Mr Paul Roberts (Secretary), 118 Wepre Park, Connahs Quay, FLINTSHIRE, CH5 4HW **Wales**
- **DEE ANGLERS ASSOCIATION**
  Contact/s:
  Mr A Hogg (Hon Secretary), 6 Llwynon Cl, Bryn-Y-Baal, Mold, FLINTSHIRE, CH7 6TN **Wales**
  (T) 01352 754745.
- **GREENFIELD VALLEY ANGLING CLUB**
  Contact/s:
  Mr Helen Brockley (Operation Manager), Basingwork House, Greenfield Valley Heritage Park, Greenfield,Holywell, FLINTSHIRE, CH8 7BQ **Wales**
  (T) 01352 714172.
- **MOLD FLY FISHERS**
  Contact/s:
  Mr At Allcock (Secretary), 3 Highfield Avenue, Mynydd Isa, Mold, FLINTSHIRE, CH7 6XY **Wales**
- **MOLD KINGFISHERS ANGLING CLUB**
  Contact/s:
  Mr Rw Ambrose (Secretary), 25 Pinewood Avenue, Connahs Quay, FLINTSHIRE, CH5 4 **Wales**
- **MOLD TROUT ANGLERS**
  Contact/s:
  Mr Alun Powell (Secretary), Makuti, Sunny Ridge, Mold, FLINTSHIRE, CH7 1RU **Wales**
  (T) 01352 752468.
- **PEN Y FFRITH FLY FISHING CENTRE**
  Contact/s:
  Ms Wendy Minshull (Secretary), Llandegla Rd, Llanarmon Yn Lal, Mold, FLINTSHIRE, CH7 4QX **Wales**
  (T) 01824 780501.
- **WREXHAM AND DISTRICT ANGLING ASSOCIATION**
  Contact/s:
  Mr J E Tattum (Secretary), Llys Athro, King St, Leeswood,Mold, FLINTSHIRE, CH7 4SB **Wales**

GLAMORGAN (VALE OF)

- **GLAMORGAN ANGLERS CLUB**
  Contact/s:
  Mr John Taylor (Hon Secretary), 23 Adenfield Way, Rhoose, Barry, GLAMORGAN (VALE OF), CF62 3EA **Wales**
  (T) 01446 711216.
- **GLYNNEATH AND DISTRICT ANGLING ASSOCIATION**
  Contact/s:
  Mr Gareth Evans (Secretary), 21 Godfrey Avenue, Glynneath, Neath, GLAMORGAN (VALE OF), SA11 5HF **Wales**
- **NEATH AND DULAIS ANGLING ASSOCIATION**
  Contact/s:
  Mr Ivor Jones (Secretary), 5 Bryndulais Row, Seven Sisters, Neath, GLAMORGAN (VALE OF), SA10 9EB **Wales**
- **PYRDDIN ANGLING SOCIETY**
  Contact/s:
  Mr Robert Browning (Secretary), 91 Main Rd, Duffryn Cellwen, Neath, GLAMORGAN (VALE OF), SA10 9LG **Wales**
- **SKEWEN ANGLING CLUB**
  Contact/s:
  Mr Mike Doyle (Secretary), 58 The Highlands, Skewen, Neath, GLAMORGAN (VALE OF), SA10 6PD **Wales**
- **TAWE AND TRIBUTARIES ANGLING ASSOCIATION**
  Contact/s:
  Mr Michael Matthews (Secretary), 32 Farm Rd, Briton Ferry, Neath, GLAMORGAN (VALE OF), SA11 2TA **Wales**

GWYNEDD

- **ARTRO AND TALSARNAU FISHING ASSOCIATION**
  Contact/s:
  Mr B Powell (Secretary), 3 Glandwr, Llanbedr, GWYNEDD, LL45 2PB **Wales**
- **BALA AND DISTRICT ANGLING ASSOCIATION**
  Contact/s:
  Mr David Gumbley (Secretary), Llwyn Ffynnon, 17 Mawnog Fach, Bala, GWYNEDD, LL23 7YY **Wales**
- **BANGOR CITY ANGLING CLUB**
  Contact/s:
  Mrs Pat Thomas (Secretary), 21 Lon-Y-Glyder, Bangor, GWYNEDD, LL57 **Wales**
- **CAMBRIAN ANGLING ASSOCIATION**
  Contact/s:
  Mrs M Wilson (Secretary), Blaenau Ffestiniog, GWYNEDD, LL41 **Wales**
  (T) 01766 831676.
- **CRICCIETH, LLANYSTUMDWY AND DISTRICT ANGLING ASSOCIATION**
  Contact/s:
  Mr Gordon Hamilton (Secretary), Morawel, Llanystumdwy, Criccieth, GWYNEDD, LL52 0SF **Wales**
- **DWYRYD ANGLERS**
  Contact/s:
  Mr Gareth Ffestin Price (Secretary), Hafan, Ffordd Peniel, Ffestiniog, GWYNEDD, LL41 4LP **Wales**
- **ESTIMANER ANGLING ASSOCIATION**
  Contact/s:
  Mr John Baxter (Secretary), 11 Tan Y Fedw, Abergynolwyn, Tywyn, GWYNEDD, LL36 9YU **Wales**
- **GLASLYN ANGLING ASSOCIATION**
  Contact/s:
  Mr J Daniel Hughes (Secretary), Berthlwyd, Penrhyndeudraeth, GWYNEDD, LL48 6RL **Wales**
  Mr Alan Pritchard (Secretary), Dolafon, Maes-Y-Garth, Minffordd,Penrhyndeudraeth, GWYNEDD, LL48 6EE **Wales**
- **OGWEN VALLEY ANGLING ASSOCIATION**
  Contact/s:
  Mr Bryn Evans (Secretary), 31 Erw Las, Bethesda, Bangor, GWYNEDD, LL57 **Wales**
  Mr Bryn Evans (Secretary), Tan-Y-Coed, Bron Afon, Llanllechid,Bangor, GWYNEDD, LL57 3LW **Wales**
- **PRYSOR ANGLING ASSOCIATION**
  Contact/s:
  Mr Idwal Wyn Williams (Secretary), 8 Pantcelyn, Blaunau Ffestiniog, GWYNEDD, LL41 4UH **Wales**
  (T) 01766 540435.
  (F) 01766 540435.
- **PWLLHELI AND DISTRICT ANGLING ASSOCIATION**
  Contact/s:
  Mr Rg Jones (Secretary), 18 Lleyn St, Pwllheli, GWYNEDD, LL53 5SL **Wales**
- **SEIONT, GWYRFAI AND LLYFNI ANGLING SOCIETY**
  Contact/s:
  Mr Hp Hughes (Secretary), Llugwy, Ystad Eryri, Bethel,Caernarfon, GWYNEDD, LL55 1BX **Wales**

ISLE OF ANGLESEY

- **CEFNI ANGLING ASSOCIATION**
  Contact/s:
  Mr Gr Williams (Secretary), Tyn Lon, Pentre Berw, Gaerwen, ISLE OF ANGLESEY, LL60 6 **Wales**
- **WYGYR FISHING ASSOCIATION**
  Contact/s:
  Mr J M Fraser (Treasurer), Crug Mor Farm, Rhydwyn, Llanfaethlu,Holyhead, ISLE OF ANGLESEY, LL65 **Wales**

MERTHYR TYDFIL

- **MERTHYR TYDFIL ANGLING ASSOCIATION**
  Contact/s:
  Mr Nigel Morgan (Secretary), 20 James St, Twynyrodyn, MERTHYR TYDFIL, CF47 **Wales**
  (T) 01685 377848.

MONMOUTHSHIRE

- **CWMCELYN ANGLING CLUB**
  Contact/s:
  Mr T Dee (Secretary), Boat House, Llanfoist, Abergavenny, MONMOUTHSHIRE, NP7 **Wales**
  (T) 01495 312289.
- **GILWERNAND DISTRICT ANGLING CLUB**
  Contact/s:
  Mr Hr Lewis (Secretary), 27 Brynglas, Gilwern, Abergavenny, MONMOUTHSHIRE, NP7 0BP **Wales**
- **MONMOUTH AND DISTRICT ANGLING ASSOCIATION**
  Contact/s:
  E Holloway (Secretary), The Lodge, Osbaston Rd, Monmouth, MONMOUTHSHIRE, NP25 **Wales**
- **WENTWOOD RESERVOIR FLY FISHING ASSOCIATION**
  Contact/s:
  Mr Dgp Jones (Secretary), 123 Castle Lea, Caldicot, MONMOUTHSHIRE, NP26 **Wales**

NEATH PORT TALBOT

- **AFAN VALLEY ANGLING CLUB**
  Contact/s:
  Mr M Reynolds (Secretary), 8 Newlands, Baglan, Port Talbot, NEATH PORT TALBOT, SA13 **Wales**

NEWPORT

- **GWENT AVENGERS**
  Contact/s:
  Mr R Dalling (Secretary), 3 The Spinney, Malpas Park, NEWPORT, NP20 **Wales**
- **ISCA ANGLING CLUB**
  Contact/s:
  Mr P Facey (Secretary), 357 Pilton Vale, NEWPORT, NP19 6LU **Wales**

- **ISLWYN DISTRICT ASSOCIATION**
Contact/s:
Mrs J Meller (Secretary), 7 Penllwyn St, Cwmfelinfach, NEWPORT, NP1 7HE **Wales**

- **NEVERN ANGLING ASSOCIATION**
Contact/s:
Mr Nica Prichard (Hon Secretary), Spring Gardens, Parrog Rd, NEWPORT, SA42 0RL **Wales**
(T) 01239 820671.

- **NEWPORT (GWENT) ANGLING ASSOCIATION**
Contact/s:
P Climo (Secretary), 2 Darwin Drive, NEWPORT, NP20 6FS **Wales**

- **NEWPORT ANGLING ASSOCIATION**
Contact/s:
Mr L J Clarke (Secretary), 14 Allt-Yr-Yn Avenue, NEWPORT, NP19 5DB **Wales**

- **NEWPORT DSA**
Contact/s:
Mr Joe Guscott (Secretary), 51 Monnow Walk, Bettws Estate, NEWPORT, NP19 6SS **Wales**
Mr Joe Crowley (Chairman), 55 Moore Crest, NEWPORT, NP20 **Wales**

- **NEWPORT RESERVOIR FLY FISHING ASSOCIATION**
Contact/s:
Mr Jack Stone (Secretary), 13 Hawke Cl, Royal Oak, NEWPORT, NP19 9GJ **Wales**
Mr Wgc Jones (Secretary), 74 Greenfield, Newbridge, NEWPORT, NP19 4QZ **Wales**

- **PONTYPOOL ANGLING ASSOCIATION**
Contact/s:
Mr Bj Jones (Secretary), 79 Robertson Way, Woodlands, Malpas,NEWPORT, NP19 6QQ **Wales**

PEMBROKESHIRE

- **LLYS-Y-FRAN ANGLING CLUB**
Contact/s:
Mr Peter J Eaton (Secretary), 18 Mount Pleasant Way, Milford Haven, PEMBROKESHIRE, SA73 1AB **Wales**

- **PEMBROKE AND DISTRICT ANGLING CLUB**
Contact/s:
Mrs T Lustig (Secretary), 10 Deer Park, Stackpole, Pembroke, PEMBROKESHIRE, SA71 5DD **Wales**

- **PEMBROKESHIRE ANGLERS ASSOCIATION**
Contact/s:
Mr Tony Summers (Chairman), 72 City Rd, Haverfordwest, PEMBROKESHIRE, SA61 2RR **Wales**
(T) 01437 763216.

- **PEMBROKESHIRE FLY FISHERS**
Contact/s:
Mrs Oliver (Secretary), Red House, Llawhaden, Narberth, PEMBROKESHIRE, SA67 **Wales**

- **PICTON WATERS ANGLING CLUB**
Contact/s:
Mr I Richards (Secretary), North Pines, Wiston, Haverfordwest, PEMBROKESHIRE, SA62 4PS **Wales**

- **RIDGEWAY ANGLING CLUB**
Contact/s:
Mr R Martin (Secretary), Hillcroft, Bethlehem, Cardigan Rd,Haverfordwest, PEMBROKESHIRE, SA **Wales**

- **TENBY AND DISTRICT ANGLING CLUB**
Contact/s:
Mr Bird (Secretary), Primrose Villa, Narbeth Rd, Tenby, PEMBROKESHIRE, SA70 **Wales**

POWYS

- **BRECON ANGLING SOCIETY**
Contact/s:
Mr Dd Harris (Secretary), 66 Coryton Cl, Brecon, POWYS, LD3 9HP **Wales**

- **CAERSWS ANGLING CLUB**
Contact/s:
Mr David Corfield (Club Secretary), Bucks Hotel, Main St, Caersws, POWYS, SY17 5EL **Wales**
(T) 01686 688717.

- **CAERSWS ANGLING SOCIETY**
Contact/s:
Mr R Davies (Secretary), 1 Broneirion Cottages, Llandinam, POWYS, SY17 5 **Wales**

- **CORRIS AND DISTRICT ANGLING ASSOCIATION**
Contact/s:
Mr Jeremy Thomas (Secretary), Foamation Products, Era Works, Ceinws,Machynlleth, POWYS, SY20 9HA **Wales**

- **CRICKHOWELL ANGLING CLUB**
Contact/s:
Mr Tom Probert (Secretary), Crickhowell, POWYS, NP8 **Wales**

- **ELAN VALLEY ANGLING CLUB**
Contact/s:
Mr Noel Hughes (Secretary), 25 Brynheulog, Rhayader, POWYS, LD6 5EF **Wales**

- **GROE PARK AND IFON ANGLING CLUB**
Contact/s:
Mr H G Lloyd (Secretary), Dolrhedyn, 15 Irfon Rd, Builth Wells, POWYS, LD2 3DE **Wales**

- **LLANBRYNMAIR AND DISTRICT ANGLING CLUB**
Contact/s:
Mr M Jones (Secretary), Craig-Y-Gronfa, Mallwyd, Machynlleth, POWYS, SY20 **Wales**

- **LLANDRINDOD WELLS ANGLING ASSOCIATION**
Contact/s:
Mr B D Price (Secretary), The Cedars, Llanyre, Llandrindod Wells, POWYS, LD1 6DY **Wales**

- **LLANGYNIDR SERVICE STATION ANGLING CLUB**
Contact/s:
Mr Tb Williams (Secretary), Llangynidr Service Station, Llangynidr, Crickhowell, POWYS, NP8 1LU **Wales**

- **LLANIDLOES AND DISTRICT ANGLING ASSOCIATION**
Contact/s:
Mr J Dallas Davis (Secretary), Dresden House, Great Oak St, Llanidloes, POWYS, SY18 6BU **Wales**
(T) 01686 412644.

- **MONTGOMERYSHIRE ANGLING ASSOCIATION**
Contact/s:
Mr P Hulme (Secretary), 306 Heol-Y-Coleg, Vaynor Estate, Newtown, POWYS, SY16 1RA **Wales**

- **MONTGOMERYSHIRE ANGLING ASSOCIATION (INC. LLANFAIR CAEREINION FISHING CLUB, WELSHPOOL ANGLING CLUB)**
Contact/s:
Mr Lionel Whitley (Secretary), 18 Adelaide Drive, Welshpool, POWYS, SY21 **Wales**

- **NEW DOVERY FISHERY ASSOCIATION (1929)**
Contact/s:
Mr Ian Reece (Club Secretary), Leeds House, 20 Maengwyn St, Machynlleth, POWYS, SY20 8DT **Wales**
(T) 01970 615563.

- **PENLLWYN LODGES ANGLING CLUB**
Contact/s:
Mr Derek Thomas Field (Secretary), Penllwyn, Garthmyl, Montgomery, POWYS, SY15 6SB **Wales**

- **RHAYADER ANGLING ASSOCIATION**
Contact/s:
G H Roberts (Secretary), Belmullet, Rhayader, POWYS, LD6 5BY **Wales**

- **SEVERNSIDE AND NEWTOWN ANGLING CLUB**
Contact/s:
Mr Micheal John Thomas (Secretary), 253 Measyrhandir, Newtown, POWYS, SY16 1LB **Wales**
Mr Steve Potts (Secretary), 902 Falcon Court, Newtown, POWYS, SY16 1LQ **Wales**
(T) 01686 624871.

- **SEVERNSIDE ANGLING CLUB**
Contact/s:
Mr H Rodway (Secretary), Fairview, Bryn Gardens, Newtown, POWYS, SY16 1NP **Wales**

- **UPPER TANAT FISHING CLUB**
Contact/s:
Mr Rr Hall (Secretary), Melynoig, Llansantffraid, POWYS, SY22 6AX **Wales**

RHONDDA CYNON TAFF

- **GLYNCORNEL ANGLING ASSOCIATION**
Contact/s:
Mr John M Evans (Secretary), 126 Ystrad Rd, Ystrad, Pentre, RHONDDA CYNON TAFF, CF41 7PS **Wales**

- **KINGFISHERS ANGLING CLUB**
Contact/s:
Mr M Howells (Secretary), 97 Bwllfa Rd, Cwmdas, Aberdare, RHONDDA CYNON TAFF, CF44 **Wales**

- **MAERDY AND FERNDALE ANGLING CLUB**
Contact/s:
Mr Terry Pain (Secretary), 16 Highfield, Ferndale, RHONDDA CYNON TAFF, CF43 4TA **Wales**

SWANSEA

- **BRYNMILLAND DISTRICT ANGLING CLUB**
Contact/s:
Mr C Tonner (Secretary), 14 Notts Gardens, Uplands, SWANSEA, SA2 0RU **Wales**

- **CWMLLYNFELL FLY FISHING CLUB**
Contact/s:
Mr D Lloyd (Secretary), 73 Bryn Rd, Bryn Villas, Cwmllynfell,SWANSEA, SA9 2 **Wales**

- **LLANGYFELACH AND DISTRICT ANGLING ASSOCIATION**
Contact/s:
Mr R L Griffiths (Secretary), Cefn Cottage, Cilibion, Llanrhidian,SWANSEA, SA3 1ED **Wales**
(T) 01792 391048.

- **PONTARDAWE AND DISTRICT ANGLING ASSOCIATION**
Contact/s:
Mr R H Lockyer (Secretary), 8 Bwllfa Rd, Ynystawe, SWANSEA, SA6 5AL **Wales**
(T) 01792 844014.

TAWE DISABLED FISHERS ASSOCIATION
Contact/s:
Mr R W Hale (Secretary), Willow Bank, Ilston, SWANSEA, SA2 7LD **Wales**
(T) 01792 842920.

TORFAEN

CWMBRAN ANGLING ASSOCIATION
Contact/s:
Mr P M Gulliford (Secretary), 305 Llantarnam Rd, Cwmbran, TORFAEN, NP44 3BJ **Wales**

PONTYPOOL ANGLING ASSOCIATION
Contact/s:
Mr M R Harvey (Secretary), 11 Osbourne Rd, Pontypool, TORFAEN, NP4 6NN **Wales**
(T) 01495 764839.

WREXHAM

BANGOR-ON-DEE SALMON ANGLING ASSOCIATION
Contact/s:
Mr P Edwards (Secretary), 13 Ludlow Rd, Bangor-on-Dee, WREXHAM, LL13 0JG **Wales**

BRADLEY ANGLING CLUB
Contact/s:
Secretary, 6 Yorke Avenue, Marchwiel, WREXHAM, LL1 **Wales**
(T) 01978 262317.

BRYN-Y-PYS ANGLING ASSOCIATION
Contact/s:
Mrs Ann Phillips (Hon Secretary), 2 Ruabon Rd, WREXHAM, LL13 7PB **Wales**
(T) 01978 351815.

CAERGWRIE ANGLING CLUB
Contact/s:
Mrs E Lewis (Secretary), Bronwlfa, Hawarden Rd, Caergwrie,WREXHAM, LL12 9BB **Wales**

GRIFFIN ANGLING CLUB
Contact/s:
Mr A Pickles (Secretary), Green Pastures, Pont-Y-Capel, Gresford,WREXHAM, LL11 **Wales**

HOLT AND FARNDON ANGLING ASSOCIATION
Contact/s:
Mr R Williams (Secretary), 4 The Cross, Holt, WREXHAM, LL1 **Wales**

LLAY ANGLING ASSOCIATION
Contact/s:
Mr John Preston (Secretary), 20 Mold Road Estate, Gwersylls, WREXHAM, LL11 4AA **Wales**

PONCIAU ANGLING SOCIETY
Contact/s:
Mr Dk Valentine (Secretary), Bryn-Yr-Owen, Ponciau, WREXHAM, LL11 **Wales**

ROSSETT AND GRESFORD FLY FISHERS
Contact/s:
Mr Brain Harper (Secretary), 7 Hawthorn Rd, Marford, WREXHAM, LL12 8XJ **Wales**

Fishery Update Form

Fishery Name

Fishery Address

County / Postcode /

Contact Name for fishing

Telephone / Fax /

Fishing Type ☐ Coarse ☐ Game ☐ Both

Name of Water e.g. River Thames

Fish Species available List specimen weights

Adult Day Ticket price £ **Junior Day Ticket price** £

Is Fishery listed in Fishooked ☐ Yes ☐ No

Your Name

Your Address

Your Telephone / Fax /

Your Email

Please send a more detailed questionnaire to this Fishery ASAP to ensure their details are accurately shown in Fishooked

Return this form to:
Freepost
HCC Publishing
Meaford Power Station
Meaford, Stone
Staffs, ST15 0UU. UK

Fax: 01782 371166